# 2019

# UNITRADE SPECIALIZED CATALOGUE OF CANADIAN STAMPS

**NEW BRUNSWICK • NOVA SCOTIA • PRINCE EDWARD ISLAND**
**BRITISH COLUMBIA and VANCOUVER ISLAND • NEWFOUNDLAND**

**EDITOR:** D. Robin Harris FRPSC, OTB Lifetime Achievement Award

**EDITORIAL ASSOCIATES**

Leopold Beaudet FRPSC (Admirals), Christopher W. Carmichael (pricing)
Andrew Chung FRPSC (FDC, CP items, Reply Coupons)
Robert Cooperman (pricing), Roy Houtby (pricing), John Jamieson FRPSC (pricing)
Ian Kimmerly (pricing), Gary Lyon (pricing), Robert Lemire OTB (stationery)
Hank Narbonne FRPSC, OTB (covers, FDC), Lyse Rousseau (Fondation de la faune du Québec)
Ray Simrak (Semi-Official), Ralph E. Trimble FRPSC (re-entries)
E.S.J. van Dam (Wildlife Habitat, Prisoner of War, Semi-Official), Dr. James Watt, Mirko Zatka (pricing)

Special thanks to Pascal LeBlond, Manager, Philatelic Collections, Library and Archives Canada

**Illustration Credits**

Terry Averbeck, Leopold Beaudet FRPSC, W.G. Burden, Chris W. Carmichael, Ben Cohen, Earle Covert OTB, Bruce Craw
Ron DeWitt, Eastern Auctions Ltd., D. Robin Harris FRPSC, John Jamieson FRPSC, Walter Krasowski, Robert Lemire OTB
Gary Lyon, David Marasco, North Main Stamp Company, Steve Oltean, Bill Pawluk OTB, Rick Penko FRPSC
Terry Rhoades, Lyse Rousseau, Saskatoon Stamp Centre, Sebastien Simard, Spink Shreves Galleries, Irv Singer
Brian Skinner, Ray Simrak, Paul Smith, Michael Smith, Ralph E. Trimble FRPSC, Gordon Turnbull
Bob Vogel, Frank von Hausen, Dr. James Watt, Clarence Wigmore, Mirko Zatka

Designed and prepared in Canada

Cover design by Steven Dobbing

ISBN-10: 1-894763-65-3
ISBN-13: 978-1-894763-65-3

Printed in China

Suggested Retail Price
$52.95

**THE UNITRADE PRESS**

TORONTO, CANADA M6L 2C4

# CONTENTS


**INTRODUCTION** .......... **13**

Item Numbering / 13
Understanding the Listings / 14
Catalogue Value / 16
Condition Grading; Cancellations / 17
"Gems" / 18
Stamp Formats / 20
Perforation / 21
Self-adhesive Die Cutting / 22
Gum; Tagging / 23
Paper / 25
Constant Plate Varieties / 26
Errors, Freaks and Oddities; Double-Printed Stamps / 27
Precancels / 28
Selected Philatelic Terms / 29
Selected Postal Rates; On-Line Resources / 30

**PROVINCE OF CANADA** .......... **39**

**DOMINION OF CANADA** .......... **47**

Complete Booklets / 565
Semi-Postal / 591
Air Mail / 595
Air Mail Special Delivery / 597
Air Post Semi-Official / 598
Private Commercial Airlines / 600
Columbia SCADTA Consular Overprints / 610
Computer Vended Postage / 611
Special Delivery / 613
Registration / 615
Postage Due / 616
War Tax / 620
Perforated Official / 622
Overprinted Official / 624
Officially Sealed / 630
Prisoner of War Free Franks / 630
Picture Postage™ / 631
"Stick 'n Tic" Labels / 633
United Nations stamps in Canadian denominations / 633
Reply Coupons / 634
Uncut Press Sheets / 636
Canada Post Souvenir Articles / 642
Annual Collections / 643
Semi-Annual and Quarterly Packs / 644
Thematic Collections / 647
Special Event Covers / 651
Stamp Sponsorship Products (1990–1993) / 655
Federal Wildlife Habitat Conservation / 657
Quebec Wildlife Habitat Conservation / 659

**FOUR-RING NUMERAL CANCELS** .......... **662**

**TWO-RING NUMERAL CANCELS** .......... **662**

**SQUARED CIRCLE POSTMARKS** .......... **664**

**NATIONAL CHRISTMAS SEALS** .......... **669**

**POSTAL STATIONERY – CANADA** .......... **677**

Province of Canada and
Dominion of Canada Envelopes / 677
Special Order Envelopes / 685
Election Envelopes / 686
Regular and Special Order Letter Sheets / 686
Post Bands and Wrappers / 686
Air Letters / 688
Postal Cards / 690
Special Order Postal Cards / 703
Letter Cards / 704

**COLONIAL ISSUES** .......... **706**

British Columbia and Vancouver Island / 706
British Columbia Numeral Cancels / 707
New Brunswick / 708
New Brunswick Plate Proofs / 709
New Brunswick Numeral Cancels / 710
Nova Scotia / 711
Nova Scotia Plate Proofs / 712
Prince Edward Island / 713

**NEWFOUNDLAND** .......... **715**

Plate Proofs / 738
Air Mail / 740
Postage Due / 743
Officially Sealed / 743
Watermarks / 743
Complete Booklets / 745

Postal Stationery – Newfoundland / 745

Envelopes; Post Bands / 745
Reply Letter Card; Postal Cards / 745
Formular Registered Envelopes / 747
Formular Aerogrammes / 747

Reply Coupons – Newfoundland / 747

**TOPICAL LISTING** .......... **748**

**DEFINITIVE STAMP IDENTIFIER** .......... **753**

**NUMBER CHANGES/ADDITIONS** .......... **767**

**INDEX TO ADVERTISERS** .......... **767**

**SYMBOLS AND ABBREVIATIONS** .......... **768**

# WORLD

## 17 Worldwide in Packets

| Country | Quantity | Price |
|---|---|---|
| **J** | | |
| Jamaica | 100 | 31.95$ |
| Japan | 200 | 11.95$ |
| Japan | 500 | 44.95$ |
| Japan | 1000 | 149.95$ |
| Japan prefectures | 100 | 24.95$ |
| Japan prefectures | 200 | 39.95$ |
| Jersey | 100 | 19.95$ |
| Jordan | 50 | 10.95$ |
| **K** | | |
| Katanga | 25 | 9.95$ |
| Kenya - Ouganda - Tanzania | 300 | 44.95$ |
| Kenya only | 100 | 39.95$ |
| Kiribati | 50 | 16.95$ |
| Koweit | 50 | 20.95$ |
| Korea North | 500 | 33.95$ |
| Korea South | 100 | 16.95$ |
| Kirgyzstan | 50 | 9.95$ |
| **L** | | |
| Laos | 300 | 18.95$ |
| Latvia (1918-1940) | 25 | 9.95$ |
| Latvia (all periods) | 50 | 14.95$ |
| Lebanon | 100 | 14.95$ |
| Leeward Islands | 25 | 15.95$ |
| Lesotho | 100 | 29.95$ |
| Liberia | 100 | 15.95$ |
| Libya | 100 | 24.95$ |
| Liechtenstein | 50 | 16.95$ |
| Liechtenstein | 200 | 89.95$ |
| Lithuania | 50 | 16.95$ |
| Lubjana | 50 | 69.95$ |
| Luxembourg | 200 | 24.95$ |

**All Different**
**Ask for complete listing**

## 18 World Special Mint-NH / Complete Set
**($1 US = 1$ CDN)**

| | No. | Descr. | Value |
|---|---|---|---|
| Albania | 1320 | Painting | 3.75$ |
| Australia | 932-39 | Fossil | 5.95$ |
| Azerbarjan | 426-31 | Music | 2.05$ |
| Belgium | 1305-07 | Technology | 4.70$ |
| Bolivia | 418-22, C-212-16 | Refugees | 7.80$ |
| Brunei | 246-49 | King | 2.50$ |
| Bulgaria | 3766-74 | Fish | 15.75$ |
| Burundi | 589-600 (12/13) | Animals | 187.50$ |
| Cambodia | 1426-30 | Mushroom | 5.00$ |
| Chili | 978-79 | Ship | 2.85$ |
| China | B-10a (4) | Kids painting | 1.50$ |
| Germany | B-344-47 | Celebrities | 37.50$ |

**SPECIAL**
**All 12 sets for 139.95$**

## 19 Worldwide by Topics

| Topic | Quantity | Price |
|---|---|---|
| **T** | | |
| Three Dimensional | 30 | 10.95$ |
| Trains | 100 | 5.95$ |
| Trains | 500 | 54.95$ |
| Transportation | 100 | 4.95$ |
| Transportation | 500 | 24.95$ |
| Transportation (Canada) | 25 | 3.95$ |
| Trees | 25 | 3.95$ |
| Triangles | 50 | 5.95$ |
| Turtles | 25 | 4.95$ |
| **U** | | |
| UNICEF | 25 | 6.95$ |
| Uniforms | 50 | 6.95$ |
| **V** | | |
| Vegetables | 50 | 4.95$ |
| Volleyball | 25 | 6.95$ |
| **W** | | |
| War | 50 | 4.95$ |
| Wrestling | 50 | 16.95$ |
| WWF | 25 | 4.95$ |

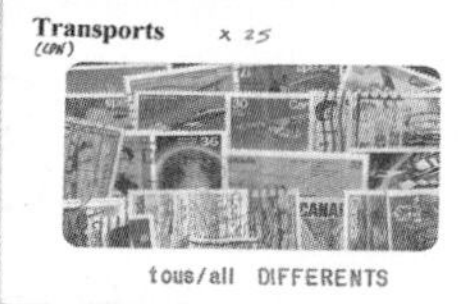


## 20 Commonwealth VICTORIA PERIOD "Great Deal"

Value $500 US
Up to 50 different!
**Only 124.95$ CDN**
**75% discount + !!!**

## 21 Worldwide
**(Mint, under face value!!!)**

a) United States 100$ for 89.95$
b) United Nations 100$ for 89.95$
c) Great Britain 100$ for 89.95$
d) France 100$ for 89.95$
e) Japan 100$ for 89.95$
f) All 5 (a-e) less 40% face value

**299.95$!!!**

## 22 Worldwide: All Different

a) 1,000 for 14.95$
b) 2,000 for 39.95$
c) 5,000 for 99.95$
d) 10,000 for 249.95$
e) 20,000 for 699.95$
f) 30,000 for 999.95$
g) 60,000 for 3499.95$

## 23 Canadian Silver 5¢ Coin
*(smaller than the 10¢)*
**x 12 different**

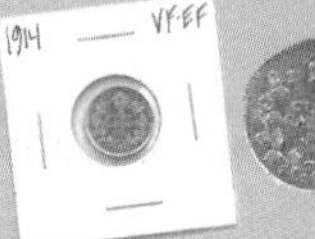


**Catalogue value: 120$**
**SPECIAL 69.95$**

## 24 Worldwide
FDC and Postal Stationary

**a) 100 for 29.95$**
**b) 200 for 69.95$**
**All Different**

**GREAT BARGAIN!**

## 25 Worldwide Coins - Super Sale!

**a) 1 lb: 14.95$**
**b) 5 lbs: 49.95$**

Extra shipping charge: 8.95$

## 26 Worldwide Paper Money

**a) 50 for 39.95$**
**b) 100 for 99.95$**
**All Different**

## NEW
**World Wantlist Service**
**INDICATE:**
1-Topical or Country and catalogue number
2-Catalogue Value
3-Indicate your limit $ payment order
Less 50% (Scott International)
No Change Rate ! ($1.00US=.50¢ CDN)
**No taxes, no shipping charge !**

# PROMO TPM
## Delivery in Canada ! Free taxes and shipping* !

- REFERENCE VALUE: UNITRADE SPECIALIZED OR SCOTT INTERNATIONAL
- BENEFIT FROM OUR NUMEROUS SPECIAL DISCOUNTS ANYTIME YOU WANT
- WITH YOUR ORDER, YOU WILL RECEIVE OUR FREE 56 PAGE CATALOGUE, OR YOU CAN ORDER IT FOR 4.95$
- REFUNDABLE WITH YOUR FIRST ORDER (AUSSI DISPONIBLE EN FRANÇAIS SUR DEMANDE)
- YOUR SATISFACTION IS GUARANTEED, OTHERWISE WE WILL OFFER YOU A REPLACEMENT OR A CREDIT
- WE HAVE MOST OF THE STAMPS YOU ARE LOOKING FOR IN STOCK. TAKE ADVANTAGE OF OUR REGULAR DISCOUNTS IF IN QUEBEC, VISIT OUR STORE AT FLEUR DE LYS SHOPPING CENTER
- nh=never hinged (original gum, without fault)
- $ before amount=US value (Scott International catalogue)
- Additional Shipping; USA = 7.50$ INTL. = 10.95$

* Excluding no. 2, 5, 12 and 25

**Online catalogue: boutique-tpm.com**

## SEND YOUR ORDER TO:

**TPM, C.P. 9693, Succ. Ste-Foy,**
**Quebec, QC, G1V 4C2**
**Phone: (418) 524-7894 (ask for JP)**
**Fax: (418) 524-0092**
**info@boutique-tpm.com**

**RUSH PAYMENT = RUSH DELIVERY**

MONEY ORDER CHECKS 2 WEEKS+

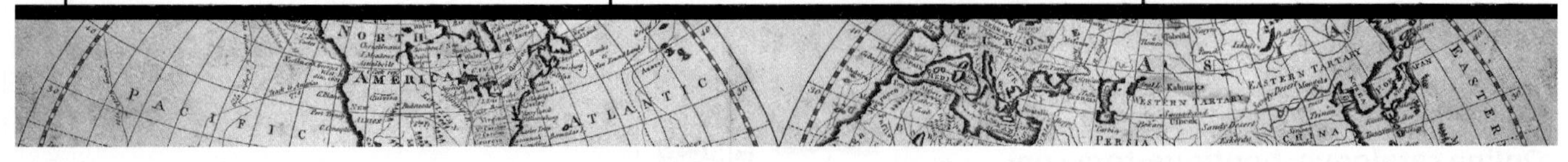

# INTRODUCTION

**Dear Unitrade Catalogue User:**

Thank you for your interest in this catalogue. A lot of effort by a number of people has been undertaken to provide the listings, information, and pricing details found within these pages.

This is the fourteenth edition I have now had the privilege to edit. I believe that each new catalogue over the last 14 years has improved upon its predecessors.

We continue to make improvements throughout the entire catalogue; some are more subtle to spot.

In addition, we continue to add the latest Canada Post new issues, update images with better scans when they become available, and correct minor typographical mistakes, some of which have been around for far too long.

Is the Unitrade specialized catalogue *specialized*?

This catalogue is specialized in the sense that it lists the major varieties that have been reported to the editors for Canada/BNA stamps. A simplified catalogue would likely list just the basic design. We list major colour varieties, perforation changes, errors, and many constant plate varieties including significant/major re-entries.

Requests are received quite often to add this variety or that variety which is not yet in the catalogue. Please remember that it would be impossible to list varieties that are quite variant in nature, such as perforation shifts, colour shifts and tagging shifts – these are certainly collectible but outside the scope of this catalogue. Non-constant plate varieties cannot be listed, such as freaks and oddities (see page 27). If the catalogue were to list these kinds of varieties the book would be several times larger than it already is, and would most likely confuse the beginning collector. It would be great to list all known constant plate varieties (including re-entries), but some of these are quite minute (some might call them flyspecks).

It is true that there are many, many more varieties that exist that are not specifically listed in the Unitrade catalogue. We encourage you to build up your philatelic library with the many specialized reference works that are available for all aspects of Canadian philately. These works will most often provide additional information about your collecting specialty.

With that said, I do encourage you to report a new variety you have found; please send an e-mail (and scan?) directly to myself, at the e-mail address noted below.

I thank all of those who passed along their thoughts, questions, and concerns about last year's catalogue — all were very much appreciated. I encourage you to continue to e-mail me directly with your thoughts on how we can improve this catalogue (please *do not mail stamps* without first contacting me!).

Please enjoy this catalogue and your time collecting stamps.

D. Robin Harris FRPSC
OTB Lifetime Achievement Award
Unitrade Editor
unitrade@adminware.ca

## Item Numbering

It is essential for every collector to identify each item in a collection by some unique number or notation which will be understood readily by dealers and other collectors. The Scott numbering system has been used in Canada for nearly a century and has become the most widely accepted means of identifying BNA stamps. Because most of the items in this catalogue are listed according to the Scott system, a brief explanation of the Scott method of numbering is included here.

Scott allocates a different number to each new stamp issued, identifying obvious varieties by lower case alphabetical notation (a, b, c, etc.) following each number. To group all stamps of a definitive series together, Scott reserves a block of numbers for the series, and begins numbering the commemorative issues of the new rate with the first number following the reserved block. When the definitive series does not require as many numbers as the reserved block, the balance of the numbered block is not used and there will be a gap in the numbering. At this time the following numbers are not used for the regular issues: 6, 48, 49, 121, 185–189, 307–308, 344, 346, 545–548, 551, 602–603, 706, 722, 728, 731, 788, 793–796, 798–799, 801–805, 807–812, 931, 949, 1085–1089, 1242, 1377, 1379–1387, 1390–1393, 1397–1398, 1599, 1701–1707, 1978 and 2007. When the definitive series requires more numbers than the reserved block, upper case alphabetical notations are used—the latest being 2710A — to avoid renumbering all of the following commemorative stamp issues.

With the exception of booklet singles (see next paragraph), all varieties appearing in this catalogue which are not listed in *Scott's Standard Catalogue of Postage Stamps* are identified by lower case Roman numerals (i, ii, iii, etc.) and are listed in order of variety type, not necessarily in numerical order.

Those booklet singles which are not listed in *Scott's Standard Catalogue of Postage Stamps* are numbered with a lower case "s" as a sub-variety of the respective booklet pane, as in 1627as.

The numbering of i, ii, iii, etc. and s (for booklet singles) are assigned by Unitrade with approval of Scott Publishing Co. These numbers are ***not*** assigned by Scott Publishing Co.

This catalogue usually lists more varieties than the standard catalogue and confusion can sometimes arise when collectors try to determine which Roman numeral variety pertains to which Scott variety. The Standard catalogue, for instance, lists the 6¢ black from the Centennial series as number 460, followed by eleven varieties (a-h, p, cp and fp). To simplify the listings, this catalogue will sometimes consider the Scott sub-number as if it were a full number, listing the varieties for each separately. Using the same stamp (No. 460) as an example, all varieties pertaining to the untagged sheet stamp are listed under the number 460, while varieties of the tagged sheet stamp are listed under number 460p. All varieties pertaining to booklet panes of the same stamp are listed under the sub-number of the booklet pane containing the variety.

It should be noted that Scott does not reserve alphabetical notations, other than a lower-case 'p' (tagged stamp), and allocates a, b, c, etc. sequentially as each variety is identified. Hence 460a is the number for a booklet pane, 523a is a strip of 5 different stamps and 535a represents an imperforate pair.

Untagged errors have been assigned numbers T1, T2, etc.

## Understanding the Listings

Identifying an item in your collection by a unique catalogue number is an important process of every stamp collector.

A "typical" listing from this catalogue is shown on the next page. Following are detailed explanations of each of the highlighted items in the listing.

❶ **Scott/Unitrade number** — Scott Publishing Co. allocates a different number to each new stamp issued. Although Scott usually lists stamps in chronological order by date of issue, when a set of stamps is issued over a period of time the stamps within that set are kept together without regard to date of issue. This follows the normal collecting approach of keeping stamps in their natural sets.

When a set of stamps is known to be issued over a period of time, a group of consecutive catalogue numbers is reserved for the stamps in that set, as issued. If that group of numbers proves to be too few, capital-letter suffixes are added to the numbers to create enough catalogue numbers to cover all items in the set. Scott uses a suffix letter, e.g., "A", "b," etc., only once. If there is a Scott 723A in a set, there will not be a Scott 723a also. [Recent Canadian definitive stamps, however, have been assigned in chronological order.]

There are times when the block of numbers is too large for the set, leaving some numbers unused. Such gaps in the sequence also occur when the editors move an item elsewhere in the catalogue or remove it from the listings entirely. Scott does not attempt to account for every possible number, but rather it does attempt to assure that each stamp is assigned its own number.

Scott numbers designating regular postage normally are only numerals. Scott numbers for other types of stamps, e.g., air post, special delivery, and so on, will have a prefix of either a capital letter or a combination of numerals and capital letters.

❷ **Minor number** — Scott assigns a small-letter suffix for a variety of the "normal". Examples include colour variations or perforation differences.

All varieties appearing in this catalogue which are not listed in Scott's Standard Catalogue of Postage Stamps are identified by lower case Roman numerals (i, ii, iii, etc.). They are listed in order of variety *type*, not necessarily in numerical order.

❸ **Denomination and colour** — the denomination is the value printed on the stamp (generally known as the *face value*), which is — unless otherwise stated — the cost of the stamp at the time of issue.

The colour or other description provides information to solidify identification of the stamp. Historically, when stamps normally were printed in a single colour, only the colour appeared here. Modern printing techniques allow for "multicolour" stamps. The colour of the paper is noted in italic type when the paper used is not white.

❹ **Basic stamp information** — introducing each stamp issue, this section normally includes the stamp's "name", designer (and engraver and illustrator if known), method of printing (with number of colours for the stamp/se-tenant issue, not including 'tagging'), pane layout size, printer, date of issue, tagging, paper type, and perforation. Dates of issue are as precise as Unitrade is able to confirm, either year only, month and date, or month, day and year.

In stamp sets issued over more than one date, the year or span of years will be in bold type above the first catalogue number. Individual stamps in the set will have a date-of-issue appearing in italics.

❺ **Date of issue** — as precisely as Unitrade is able to confirm, either year only, month and date, or month, day and year. In some cases, the earliest known use (EKU) is given. All dates, especially where no official date of issue has been given, are subject to change as new information is obtained. Many cases are known of inadvertent sale and use of stamps prior to dates of issue announced by postal officials. These are not listed here.

❻ **Changes in basic stamp or set** — bold or other type is used to show any change in the basic data between stamps within a set of stamps (e.g. perforation, printer, or paper type) or even within a single stamp's listing.

❼ **Catalogue values** — the catalogue values are in Canadian dollars and are based on the column heading. Early issues include various grades ranging from Very Good (VG), Fine (F) to Very Fine (VF). Modern issues are for Fine or Very Fine condition. Mint (★ or NH) and Used (⊙) prices are provided. Modern issues have a column for plate or inscription blocks (PB). A final column is provided for on cover (🖂) or First Day Covers (FDC).

❽ **Other varieties** — these include shades, plate varieties, re-entries, fluorescent paper varieties, errors, multiples, plate number blocks (early issues), coil line pairs, coil gutter strips of four, etc.

❾ **Footnote** — where other important details about the stamps can be found. If known, the quantity of stamps printed (or distributed) is provided.

❿ **Variety illustrations** — close-up detailed pictures of constant plate varieties are presented. Illustrations of missing colours and other selected errors or varieties are provided.

## MEDIUM-VALUE STREET DEFINITIVES
## 1977–1982

723
Prairie Street Scene

723C
Ontario Street Scene

724
Row Houses

725
Maritime Street Scene

Scott number ❶

Basic stamp information ❹

Designer: Tom Bjarnason. Engraved by Arthur Ponting.

Engraved (1 colour) and Photogravure (3 colours), pane of 50
British American Bank Note Company

**Tagged, GT2** **Perf 13.3**

| | | NH–VF | ⊙F | PB | FDC |
|---|---|---|---|---|---|
| **723** | **50¢ multicoloured**, *Jul 6, 1978* | 1.50 | .25 | 7.50 | 2.10 |
| **T1** | untagged (error) | | 40.00 | | |
| **i** | dot above 5 (pos. 5) | 10.00 | 7.50 | 20.00 | |

Qty: BABN: 8,650,000

Minor number ❷

Date of issue ❺

Engraved (1 colour) and Lithography (3 colours), pane of 50
Canadian Bank Note Company

Changes in basic stamp or set ❻

| | | NH–VF | ⊙F | PB | FDC |
|---|---|---|---|---|---|
| **723A** | **50¢ multicoloured**, plates 2, 3, *Dec 13, 1978* | 1.25 | .25 | 6.25 | |
| **b** | "ghost town" variety, brown inscriptions omitted (150 known) | 3,000.00 | — | 12,500.00* | |
| **ii** | complete doubling of brown inscriptions | 1,000.00† | | | |
| **iii** | "dented bumper" (pos. 6–10) | 5.00 | 3.50 | 6.25 | |
| **iv** | "black sweater" (pos. 22) | 7.50 | 5.00 | | |

Qty: CBN: 85,250,000

Catalogue values ❼

Denomination, colour ❸

Other varieties ❽

Variety 723A shows "©1978" on the license plate of the car at the LR corner.
* Blank corner block of 4.
† Value for full doubling of inscriptions, poles and wires; both impressions of equal strength. Kiss prints showing portions of CANADA 50 shifted below the regular impression are valued at $100.00 to $300.00 depending on strength of second impression.

Footnote(s) ❾

723i

Variety illustrations ❿

723Ab

723Aiii

723Aiv

Introduction

## Catalogue Value

One reason why you are likely to be using this catalogue is to determine the value of a stamp you currently own or are about to purchase.

The Unitrade catalogue provides retail values; that is, an amount you might expect to pay for a stamp in a particular grade with no faults. Where possible, the value listed for any given stamp is a reference that reflects recent actual dealer selling prices for that item.

All prices listed in this catalogue are in Canadian dollars. Pricing is arranged in multiple columns for easy reference (such as mint and used) by grade, covers/first day covers and plate blocks.

The prices in this catalogue are based on a number of factors including input from collectors, dealers and auction results. Although no catalogue can be 100% accurate as so many conditions affect the buying and selling of stamps, our pricing committee has endeavoured to put together the most accurate retail prices possible.

Use this catalogue as a guide for buying and selling. The actual price you pay for a stamp may be higher or lower than the catalogue value because of many factors. These include the source of your purchase, the amount of supply on hand by that particular source, your specific demand for an item, auctions that do not allow for the direct inspection of material by both parties, and most importantly, condition.

The best available material will almost always sell for more than the catalogue value; stamps that are damaged or with faults (even minor in nature) will sell for considerably less than catalogue value. You may also buy an item less expensively at public auction because of little interest in that item at that time or because it is part of a larger lot.

Where items are listed without prices, or without prices in some columns, the variety is known to exist but a value has not been established. Dashes in price columns indicate that the variety does not exist (or is not likely to exist) in that condition.

Although some items may be listed for less, it should be noted that a collector will probably have to pay a minimum of 20¢ for any single stamp. This is necessary because of the labour costs involved in single-purchase transactions. The relative value of the item as listed in this catalogue should prevail when a number of items are purchased at one time.

### 1870 to 1948 – Never-Hinged Pricing Factor (NH%)

A percentage factor (NH%) is shown for mint stamps. This figure is the percentage of the price for a mint stamp in very fine condition (★VF) to be added to that price if the stamp has never been hinged. To determine the final price for a mint stamp in the next lower grade (★F), divide the NH% factor by 2 and add this percentage to the price shown. This process is continued for all mint grades.

THUS a VF NH ½¢ Jubilee (#50) = $140 + 200% = $420.00
..... a F NH ½¢ Jubilee (#50) = $70 + 1/2 of 200% = 100% = $140.00
AND a F-VF NH ½¢ Jubilee (#50) = $420 + $140 = $560 / 2 = $280.00

### From 1949

Never-hinged mint stamps in very fine condition are listed in the NH–VF column. All hinged VF and NH-F are worth 50% of the listed NH-VF value.

The prices shown in the NH-VF column for **self-adhesive** stamps are for stamps *on* the original backing paper, *as issued* (i.e. undisturbed).

### Modern Used

The price shown for used stamps is for those cancelled with "in period" cancellations. Used stamps with circular date cancels or sock-on-the-nose cancels command a premium. Commercially used souvenir sheets, cancelled in period with circular date cancels are very scarce and may sell for more than the mint price.

Be aware that at least one source has been creating used souvenir sheets and se-tenant multiples by using an out-of-period cancelling device and offering these for sale.

### Plate Block Pricing

When valuing HINGED plate blocks it is a good idea to check the sum of the values of the singles in the block or strip, as often this total is *greater* than the value listed for the block. This situation often arises where a block has, say, 3 VF stamps and 3 Fine stamps with two of each unhinged. As a block it only "appears" as a fine block BUT if it was split the 3 VF stamps would be worth MORE than the list price for a hinged block. These situations are always considerably subjective and to list every possible grade/hinging combination would result in a dozen additional listings for every plate block which is just not possible within the scope of this catalogue.

### Precancel Pricing

Precancels are priced for the most common type in the conditions listed. Many precancels are much rarer and prices should be checked against a specialized precancel catalogue: *The Standard Canada Precancel Catalogue 7th Edition* (D. Marasco, B. Field, 2015), illustrated ar right.

Note that precancels on cover are seldom tied to the cover (i.e. no postmark). Prices shown are for a sound copy with no additional markings or cancellations. When a stamp is precancelled it is considered cancelled.

### Stamps on Cover

On cover prices shown for numbers 1–140 are for proper use of a *single* stamp on cover. The value of multiples of these on cover can vary considerably. For some issues (Nos. 34, 50, 66, 74 for example) multiples on cover are relatively common; for other issues, multiples on cover can demand several times the prices shown for single usage. Because there is no firm pattern in evaluating multiples on cover, collectors are advised to consult with several reputable dealers to determine the value for such items.

### First Day Cover (FDC)

FDC prices are shown from number 141. Unless otherwise noted, the price represents a single stamp on cover, cancelled by the post office on the first day of issue.

In 1949 Canada Post established a First Day Cover service in Ottawa, using a slogan cancel "First Day of Issue". A bilingual version of the cancel was introduced in 1951. Several private cachet makers have offered FDCs since 1949.

Canada Post began issuing Official First Day Covers in April of 1971.

*The New Specialized Catalogue of Canada Post Official First Day Covers Fourth Edition,* Andrew Chung and R.F. Narbonne, 2015

| | |
|---|---|
| 1927–1931 | FDC prices are for addressed covers. Cacheted covers will command a premium. |
| 1932–1948 | FDC prices are for addressed cachet covers. |
| 1949–1971 | FDC prices are for the most common unaddressed cachet covers of the stamp. |

### Varieties and Re-entries

Where varieties or re-entries are listed, the price is given for the variety on the most common paper or shade. A note has been added to some early listings to indicate that the variety or re-entry does exist or is likely to exist on the other (scarcer) listed papers or shades, and would then command a premium over the listed value.

Many of the *major* re-entries for any particular issue are illustrated, thanks to Ralph E. Trimble's website: www.re-entries.com. For those interested in re-entries we encourage you to visit this site to see additional varieties that exist.

## Condition Grading

Grading is a subjective evaluation when appraising a stamp and even seasoned experts may disagree on individual points. The overall quality is extremely important when grading early issues. Choice copies with large margins and no hidden flaws command much higher prices than those indicated. Conversely, attractive "very fine appearing" examples with thins or corner creases, no matter how minor these may be, sell for reduced prices.

Condition is by far the most important item when pricing your collection. A quick glance at an individual stamp is not sufficient. One must make a concerted effort to study the stamp in detail, both front and back, for any thins or creases, identify the centering, and check all perforations (if any) for any "short" perfs. This all takes time but is required to get an accurate grading of a stamp. A cursory glance at a stamp may suggest that it is VF (very fine), but under closer examination it may actually have a grade of F (fine) or perhaps even be damaged.

**Describing a stamp correctly**, for sale or inventory purposes, includes grading (centering), state of the gum (if mint) and any faults, no matter how small or trivial.

> **CAUTION**
>
> Many early stamps (numbers 1–50 in particular) have been repaired to enhance their values. When purchasing early stamps it is important to know your dealer well. Certificates of authenticity can be obtained from several third-party sources.

**VERY GOOD** stamps have designs that are quite off centre, with the perforations cutting the design on at least one side. The gum may be slightly disturbed, and the stamp may not have all of its original freshness. If used, the cancellation may be medium to heavy and indistinct.

**FINE** stamps have designs that are quite off centre, with the perforations on one or two sides very close to the design but not quite touching it. There is white space between the perforations and the design that is minimal but evident to the unaided eye. Imperforate stamps may have small margins, and earlier issues may show the design just touching one edge of the stamp design. Very early perforated issues normally will have the perforations slightly cutting into the design. Used stamps may have heavier than usual cancellations.

**VERY FINE** stamps will be just slightly off centre on one or two sides, but the design will be well clear of the edge. The stamp will present a nice, balanced appearance. Imperforate stamps will be well centred within normal-sized margins. *However, certain early issues may be printed in such a way that the perforations may touch the design on one or more sides. Where this is the case, a boxed note will be found defining the centring and margins of the stamps being valued.* Used stamps will have light or otherwise neat cancellations.

**EXTREMELY FINE** stamps (not illustrated) are close to being perfectly centred. Imperforate stamps will have even margins that are slightly larger than normal. Even the earliest perforated issues will have perforations clear of the design on all sides.

**VERY FINE**

**FINE**

**VERY GOOD**

Examples shown are computer-manipulated images made from single digitized master illustrations.

## Cancellations

Modern day used material is becoming tougher and tougher to come by, particularly due to the recently introduced Privacy laws. Couple this with the advent of mechanized cancelling devices and a collector has a very tough time finding nicely cancelled stamps.

The prices in this catalogue for modern-era used stamps (about 1950 and on) are for Fine copies. This is for a typical in-period cancellation. Heavy or smudged cancels detract from a stamp and result in much lower prices. On the other hand, lightly cancelled circular date stamp (CDS) or sock-on-the nose (SOTN) cancels, particularly on those stamps used from the 1990's and on, are very difficult to find and will command premiums.

Slogan

POCON-style

Ink jet (lined and text)

SOTN (smudged)

CDS

Introduction

## "Gems"

Over the past several years most of the price changes that have been recorded in the Unitrade catalogue have been to the better grade material — the mint and used VF columns.

This particular material continues to be popular with collectors (and investors?).

There was much discussion by many people to incorporate an XF (extra fine) pricing column to the "classic" issues because of the recent popularity of high-end grade stamps. Unfortunately, some of this material is seldom seen and difficult to price.

As such, we illustrate here a **small** sampling of specific material that has sold over the past year at exceptional prices.

Remember:

* on any given day, quality will command high prices
* the most important factor of any stamp is condition, condition, condition
* use these images as a guide to show what high grade material looks like
* you may not be willing to pay more than catalogue value ... and that is fine.

**Eastern Auctions Ltd. sale November 3–4, 2017, lot #429**
Unitrade for Used = $1,500.
Sold for $3,500 + 15% = $4,025.00

**429 ⊙ 1, 1851 3p Red on Handmade Laid Paper, Imperforate**, An extraordinary used single with large margins, prominent laid lines and socked-on-nose concentric rings cancellation in RED - a rare coloured cancellation on any of Canada's Pence issues and especially desirable centrally struck on the 3p Laid Paper. A Superb stamp in all respects, VF+

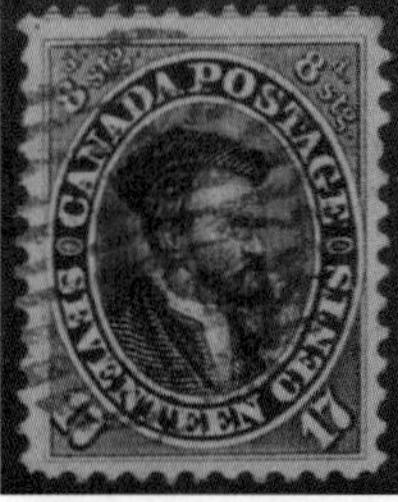

**Sparks Auctions Sale #27, May 29, 2018, Lot #58**
Unitrade for Used = $300.
Sold for $425 + 15% = $488.75

**58 #19 1859 17c blue Cartier**, used with grid cancel and exceptionally large margins all around (well clear of frameline on each side, and showing part of the adjoining stamp at top), a lovely and extremely fine stamp. A great stamp for the connoisseur.

**Eastern Auctions Ltd. sale November 3–4, 2017, lot #575**
Unitrade for Mint NH = $2,400.
Sold for $5,000 + 15% = $5,750.00

**575 ★ 45a, 1890-1891 10¢ Dull Rose (Ottawa Printing), Perf 12** A phenomenal mint single with lovely pastel-like colour associated with early Ottawa printings, clear impression and precisely centered with eye-arresting and unusually large margins, small portion of imprint (Boggs Type V), full unblemished original gum, never hinged. A record setting stamp displaying the finest attributes anyone can hope for, XF NH GEM; 1990 and 2014 Greene Foundation certs.

**Sparks Auctions Sale #26, January 30, 2018, Lot #202**
Unitrade for Mint NH = $1,200.
Sold for $2,600 + 15% = $2,990.00

**202 #58 1897 15c steel blue Jubilee**, mint never hinged, fresh and extremely fine. Accompanied by a 2017 Greene Foundation certificate. A gorgeous stamp.

**Sparks Auctions Sale #25, September 26, 2017, Lot #86**
Unitrade for Mint NH = $240.
Sold for $400 + 15% = $460.00

**86 #75 1898 1c grey green Queen Victoria Numeral**, mint never hinged, with four large and balanced margins, fresh and extremely fine. Accompanied by a 2017 Greene Foundation certificate. A lovely stamp.

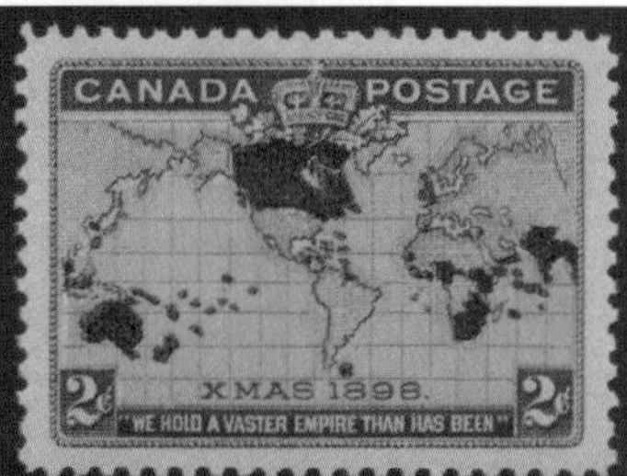


**Sparks Auctions Sale #26, January 30, 2018, Lot #261**
Unitrade for Mint NH = $180.
Sold for $375 + 15% = $431.25

**261 #86 1898 2c blue Map**, mint never hinged, with bright colour and large even margins, extremely fine.

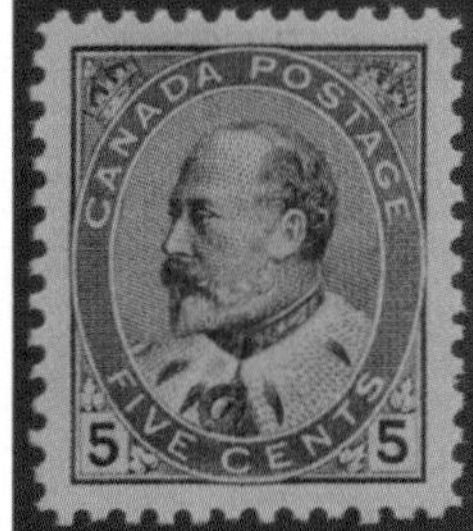


**Sparks Auctions Sale #26, January 30, 2018, Lot #272**
Unitrade for Used = $1,400.
Sold for $2,800 + 15% = $3,220.00

**272 #91 1903 5c blue King Edward VII**, mint never hinged and fresh, perfectly centered among four large margins, extremely fine. Accompanied by a 2016 Philatelic Foundation certificate grading it as "XF-S 95." A truly remarkable stamp, for the connoisseur.

**Eastern Auctions Ltd. sale February 24, 2018, lot #1022**
Unitrade for Mint NH = $150.
Sold for $400 + 15% = $460.00

**1022 ★ 97, 1908 1¢ Green**
Superb mint with precise centering amidst very large margins, post office fresh with immaculate original gum, XF NH GEM

**Eastern Auctions Ltd. sale February 23, 2018, lot #358**
Unitrade for Mint NH = $120.
Sold for $475 + 15% = $546.25

**358 ★ 1¢ Pale Green** Very well centered mint in a distinctive shade of green, lovely impression and full original gum, XF NH (Unitrade 104 shade)

**Eastern Auctions Ltd. sale February 23, 2018, lot #379**
Unitrade for Mint NH = $120.
Sold for $800 + 15% = $920.00

**379 ★ 2¢ Red** An exceptional mint example, precisely centered with large even margins, radiant colour on fresh paper and with full original gum; a superb stamp, XF NH GEM (Unitrade 106vii)

**Eastern Auctions Ltd. sale February 23, 2018, lot #392**
Unitrade for Mint NH = $180.
Sold for $475 + 15% = $546.25

**392 ★ 3¢ Yellow Brown (Wet Printing)** Extremely well centered mint example of this distinctive shade with characteristic full white original gum, XF NH (Unitrade 108b)

**Sparks Auctions Sale #26, January 30, 2018, Lot #304**
Unitrade for Mint NH = $240.
Sold for $550 + 15% = $632.50

**304 #110 1922 4c olive bistre Admiral, Wet Printing**, mint never hinged, very nicely centered and extremely fine. Accompanied by a 2015 Philatelic Foundation certificate grading it as "XF 90". A lovely and fresh stamp.

**Eastern Auctions Ltd. sale February 23, 2018, lot #452**
Unitrade for Mint NH = $180.
Sold for $500 + 15% = $575.00

**452 ★ 8¢ Blue** A premium mint example, well-balanced large margins and full original gum; a great stamp, XF NH GEM (Unitrade 115)

**Eastern Auctions Ltd. sale November 3–4, 2017, lot #753**
Unitrade for Mint NH = $1,600.
Sold for $3,500 + 15% = $4,025.00

**753 ★ 122b, 1923 $1 Deep Orange (Wet Printing)** An impressive mint example of this sought-after early printing, superior centering and fresh, deep colour with intact perforations and full unblemished original gum. A challenging early printing to find in such nice quality - only a small percentage of the One dollar Admiral is found on the wet printing, XF NH

**Sparks Auctions Sale #27, May 29, 2018, Lot #326**
Unitrade for Mint NH = $120.
Sold for $230 + 15% = $264.50

**326 #MR4 1916 2c + 1c brown Admiral War Tax**, Die II, mint never hinged, with large and even margins, bright fresh colour and extremely fine. Accompanied by a 2018 Greene Foundation certificate. A very nice stamp.

**Eastern Auctions Ltd. sale February 23, 2018, lot #565**
Unitrade for Mint NH = $240.
Sold for $425 + 15% = $488.75

**565 ★ 2¢+1¢ Carmine, Die I, Perf 12x8** An outstanding mint example surrounded by enormous margins, very well centered with intact perforations, bright colour and with full pristine original gum; an absolute gem, XF NH JUMBO (Unitrade MR5)

**Eastern Auctions Ltd. sale February 24, 2018, lot #714**
Unitrade for Mint NH = $300.
Sold for $750 + 15% = $862.50

**714 ★ 8, 1863 9p Violet, Perf 11½-12**
A superb mint example of this difficult stamp, surrounded by huge boardwalk margins, brilliant colour, showing characteristic brown original gum, never hinged. One would need to search a very long time to find a stamp in similar quality; a great stamp in all respects, XF NH Jumbo

**Sparks Auctions Sale #27, May 29, 2018, Lot #687**
Unitrade for Mint NH = $1,200.
Sold for $3,600 + 15% = $4,140.00

**687 #24a 1870 2c green Codfish** on Thin Yellowish Paper, mint never hinged, quite fresh and very fine. The two cent printed on thin paper is rarely seen in this exceptional quality.

**Sparks Auctions Sale #27, May 29, 2018, Lot #707**
Unitrade for Mint NH = $2,500.
Sold for $5,800 + 15% = $6,670.00

**707 #53 1880 5c pale blue Harp Seal**, mint with full original gum, never hinged. A fresh and extremely fine stamp, accompanied by a 1995 Greene Foundation certificate. A lovely stamp and quite possibly one of the finest examples in existence.

## Stamp Formats

Canadian stamps have been printed in various formats.

### Sheets/Panes

A printer's sheet of stamps will typically consist of multiple panes of stamps. The printed sheet of 400 or 600 subjects (or some other number depending upon the size of a stamp) is separated into post office panes of 50 or 100 stamps (or some other number). From the early 1900's until the mid 1950's, almost every small-size stamp was printed in sheets of 400 subjects that were divided into four post office panes of 100.

Post office pane of 50

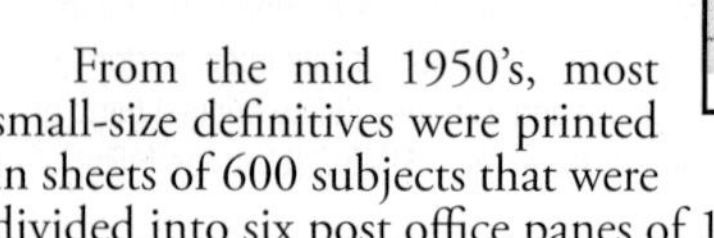

From the mid 1950's, most small-size definitives were printed in sheets of 600 subjects that were divided into six post office panes of 100.

### Plate Number and Inscription Blocks

Prior to 1958, most Canadian stamps were printed in sheets of 200 or 400 with an inscription, usually the printer's name and a plate number, printed on the selvedge at each of the four corners. The sheets were cut into equal panes, with only one inscription block (plate block) per pane, before delivery to the post offices.

In 1957, to reduce the number of broken panes in post office stock (because of collectors purchasing only the plate blocks), post office officials began ordering all panes trimmed to eliminate all inscription blocks before delivery to the post offices. This decision was quickly reversed because of pressure from the philatelic community, but not before the first two commemorative issues of 1958 and several definitive printings had been trimmed. As a compromise, it was decided that only panes sold through the Philatelic Service of the post office would include inscription sheets and "field stock" shipped to regular postal outlets would not. Trimmed panes were also issued for most Winnipeg tagged stamps and the issues with General tagging prior to 1973. Starting in the 1990's, the practise of shipping "field stock" panes (ie. panes with inscriptions removed) was abandoned.

Stamp sheets printed entirely by lithography do not use plate numbers and philatelic panes usually bear an inscription comprised of the names of the printer and designer. These inscribed corner blocks are called inscription blocks rather than plate blocks.

All plate blocks are now listed with the stamp, although the plate blocks for multi-stamp definitive issues and some commemorative issues are placed together at the end of each issue. Plate blocks for numbers 274 to 329 are listed in fine, never-hinged condition and those from number 330 on are priced in very fine, never-hinged condition.

### Coil Stamps

Postage stamps in rolls or "coils" issued before 1967 were intended for use in vending and affixing machines. Early rolls were constructed by joining part- perforate sheets of stamps end to end to form a large roll. This roll was then slit between the columns and rewound into single-column rolls of 500 for vending machines. Paste-up pairs then occurred wherever the bottom of one sheet was pasted over or under the top of the sheet following. More recently, coil stamps were printed on rotary presses which print from two identical curved plates fastened to opposite halves of the rotary cylinder. On coils of the Arch Issue (178–183) and the Medallion issue (205–207) a line of colour appears between the end stamps of the two plates because ink would build up in the recesses between the two plates. The resulting "line pairs" are sought by coil specialists and are listed herein. On later issues the plates met more smoothly, eliminating the line pairs. In a perfect situation, the distance between the final stamp image on one plate and the first stamp image on the other plate will be exactly the same as the gap between any other pair of stamp images on either plate. All images on the two plates will also be in perfect alignment with the direction of rotation of the cylinder. Misalignment in either direction results in either "jump strips" or "wide and narrow spacing strips" both of which are popular with collectors.

Line pair

Jump strip of 4

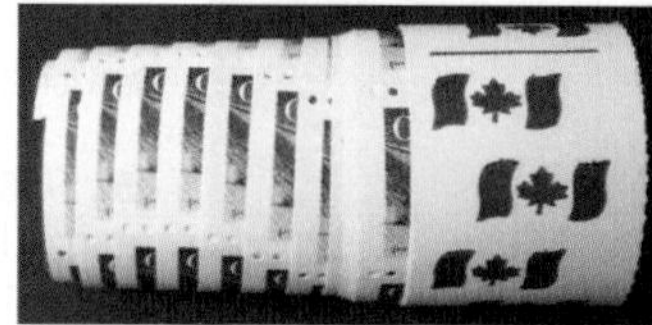

In 1969 CBN Company began producing coils of 100, which remained the norm until December 2000. Rather than plates of 100 (10 x 10) the newer presses used plates of 250 (10 x 25) for producing coil stamps. The stamps were printed on a continuous web of paper, tagged, rouletted between the 10 columns and passed through a machine which perforated between 13 rows of stamps, across 10 columns, with each strike. The stamps were cut after every hundredth row, rolled and sealed in post office tubes containing 10 breakaway coils of 100 in each tube. Operating at approximately 12 tubes a minute the coil stamps were produced almost completely without visual inspection. Imperforate and double-perforated coil stamps were a regular occurrence and are explained as follows.

The harrow-type perforator lifted after each strike and the web moved forward ready for the following strike. Imperfs occurred when the perforating bed failed to strike and the web moved forward for the next strike, leaving 12 gutters imperforate between the stamps. It may also happened that the web could "stall" and remain almost stationary while the perforator struck twice. It should be noted that both the imperforate and the double perforated varieties will occur in each of the ten coils in the post office tube.

Mention should also be made of the part perforate blocks of four of coil stamps sometimes offered for sale. As stated above, the post office tube will contain a "stick" of 10 coils of 100 stamps each, which have been rouletted between to permit the postal clerk to snap off a coil of 100 stamps at a time. By purchasing multiple coils at one time (without being snapped apart) and unrolling them together, it is sometimes possible to find blocks of stamps with no visible rouletting between but separated by perforations in the opposite direction. Coil pairs with any trace of rouletting (score line) between are common, commanding little or no premium. Pairs exhibiting no sign of rouletting whatever command a premium and are listed where known.

Since December 2000, the perforated coil stamps have been replaced by rolls of 100 (or 50) self-adhesive stamps.

This catalogue lists coils in a variety of collectible ways, depending upon the issue. Pairs, both mint and used, are the most popular form of collecting coils. Coils prior to 1969 are also collected as paste-up pairs: two stamps joined together having an extra piece of paper on the back, used for repairs and to maintain a fixed number in the continuous roll. Line pairs which bear a colour line down the perforations exist for coils printed by British American Bank Note (BABN) in the 1930s. Self-adhesive rolls include a "gutter" at some interval (such as 10 or 23 stamps). These gutters are collected in strips of 4 with the gutter in the middle.

### Miniature Panes

Canada Post introduced miniature panes in cello-paqs for the 2¢ and 5¢ Wilding definitives in 1961. They were also issued for the Cameo series, early Centennials and the 3¢ Christmas stamps from 1964 to 1967. The cello-paqs of miniature panes were discontinued when the larger booklets were introduced in 1968. Since then, several commemorative issues (1972 Earth Sciences, 1979 Flags, etc.) have been produced in miniature panes only, and include commemorative inscriptions on the selvedge. The earlier cello-paqs bore no inscriptions.

Most panes issued today are in panes of 16, 20 or 25 stamps with descriptive text on the selvedge and 'internal' gutters. In recent years, Canada Post has become very innovative in their stamp pane arrangements.

### Complete Booklets

Booklets are comprised of cardboard covers containing one or more small panes of stamps, and are designed for sale in vending machines as well as over the counter. Prior to 1968, booklets were held together by stitching or staples which passed through the selvedge of the panes. BABN assumed production of booklets in 1968 and produces booklets with panes glued to the cover along the selvedge edge.

Stapled and stitched booklet

Information pertaining to complete booklets can be found in the "Complete Booklets" section of the catalogue. In this edition, complete booklets are also listed in the general issue listings for Canada.

**Booklet Panes and Singles**

All booklet panes and single booklet pane stamps, including those which differ from the similar sheet stamps only by the number of edges perforated, are now listed in the main body of the catalogue. To facilitate the identification of the stamps occurring in a booklet pane, a reduced illustration of the pane appears as near as possible to its description. Prices for *used* complete panes are for panes *without* the selvedge that attached the pane to the booklet cover.

## Perforation

Perforation was introduced on Canadian stamps in 1858, just prior to the issue of the first decimal stamps. A perforation gauge measures the number of holes in every 2 cm. Stamps which are perforated equally on all four sides can be referred to as "Perf. 13.0", or "Perf. 13.0 x 13.0". When the perforations are unequal, the perforation is listed as "Perf. 13.0 x 13.5", with the first number indicating the top and bottom, the second the sides. Perforation measurement, as listed in this catalogue, has been rounded to the nearest tenth for all non-line perforated stamps. On Canadian stamps, three types of perforations exist.

### Line Perforation

By this method sheets are perforated in one direction at a time, usually by passing them between two cylinders around one of which are rows of pins with corresponding holes around the other. As the sheet passes between them, parallel rows of perforations are made between the stamps. The sheets are then passed through a similar arrangement, but in the opposite direction. When the cross perforations are made, two overlapping holes are usually discernible at the corners of the stamps because the horizontal and vertical perforations do not intersect perfectly. Canadian stamps were line perforated until 1968 when British American Bank Note Company (BABN) introduced comb perforation.

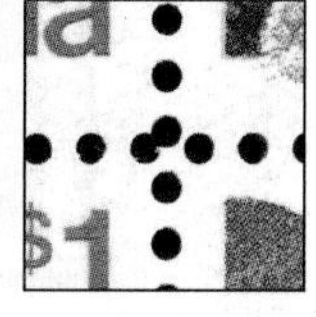

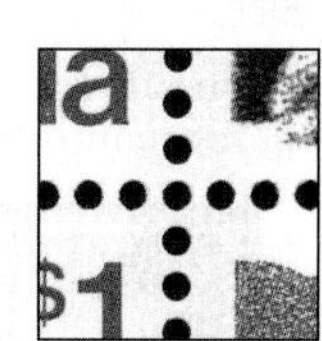

Top: line perf
Bottom: comb

### Comb Perforation

A comb perforator will perforate a pattern similar to a hair comb with wide spaced teeth. The long row of perforations (usually across a full sheet of stamps) is termed the "line" and the shorter rows resembling the teeth of a comb are termed legs. Each strike of the comb perforator results in a line of perforations between two complete rows of stamps and perforations between each of the stamps in one of the rows. After the first strike the sheet of stamps is moved the distance required for a row of stamps and the process is repeated. Multiple comb perforators are used to simplify the process even further.

### Harrow Perforation

Although multiple comb perforators can be similar, harrow perforators are designed to perforate a complete sheet or pane with each strike. The Canadian coil perforation errors which produce strips of twelve imperforate or double-perforated stamps are probably the result of a harrow perforator missing a strike or the paper failing to move forward between strikes.

### Rouletting

Some of the early stamps of Newfoundland were rouletted.

Some modern Canadian self-adhesive coils have rouletting on the backing paper to facilitate the separation of individual stamps. Many self-adhesive booklets include rouletting through the middle of the pane to allow for the folding of the booklet into a more convenient size.

## Self-adhesive Die Cutting

The advent of self-adhesive stamps has introduced a new form of stamp separation: die cutting. This die cutting can be either straight, simulated "perfs", or a combination of the two.

Stamps with simulated "perfs" are referred to as *serpentine die cut*, and straight die cutting as simply *die cut*. This latter form can take virtually any shape imaginable.

Die cut

Die cut "perf"

Serpentine *and* Die cut

In 2004, Canada Post issued a fully perforated self-adhesive pair of stamps (and again in 2005, 2008 and 2009).

Fully perforated self-adhesive

Serpentine die cutting has introduced a new requirement for identifying varieties on certain stamp issues: *peaks* and *valleys*. In particular, the medium-value Wildlife definitives of 2000–2001 and the medium-value Trades definitives of 2002–2003 have different die cutting between the coils and booklets.

### Lowe-Martin Coils

Lowe-Martin, a security printer in Ottawa, ON, began printing self-adhesive coils in 2004 (80¢ and $1.40 Leaf, Sc. 2054 and 2055). Since then, they have printed over sixty different designs. As of mid-June 2010, the designs printed in rolls of 50 or 100 stamps (and now 300 and 500 stamps) have produced over 6,500 unique different specimens to collect. Why so many different?

The stamps are printed and die cut from one long continuous web. The printing press used by Lowe-Martin to print their coil stamps was illustrated on page 3 of Canada Post's October-December 2004 *Details* magazine. It shows the printed and die cut $1.40 Leaf stamps coming off the end of the press. It is clear from this image that the stamps are printed in 10 columns across the continuous web roll of paper with a gutter every 10 rows. The issued rolls of 50 (or 100) stamps available at post offices across the country confirms this gutter every 10 stamps.

The die cuts are produced from "die cutting mats". The mats make the peak and valley configurations, and are *pressed* into rather than *cutting through* the stamps. The mats have nothing to do with the cutting of the web into individual coil rolls of 50/100. "Slitter wheels" cut the web into the actual coil strips, and have no relation to the die cuts.

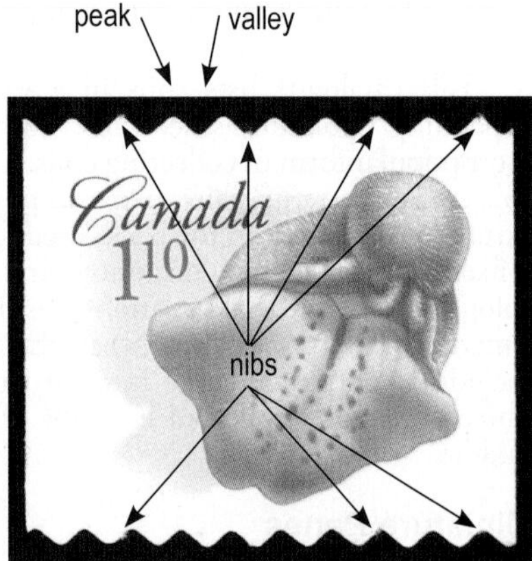


The full die cutting mat consists of very sharp, thin pieces of metal that are bent in an inconsistent manner along their length that resembles the peaks and valleys illustrated above. It is the lack of perfect repeatability of the bends in the wavy die cutting metal strips during manufacture that results in a unique signature, like individual fingerprints, on each and every stamp in a 10x10 die cutting mat matrix.

Careful examination and study of the die cutting on the issued rolls shows that the pattern repeats every 10 stamps, or after every gutter. Thus, the full die cutting mat is 10 stamps across by 10 stamps along the web of paper.

Since the first Leaf coils were printed by Lowe-Martin in 2004, thirteen different die cutting mats of 10x10 stamps each have been identified — all but one of these have been fully plated. Most die cutting mats were used on more than one design. A new die cutting mat has appeared about every 5 or 6 months. In two cases, the die cutting mat has been *inverted* in relation to itself to print other stamps. In at least one other case, a previously used and "discarded" die cutting mat has been re-employed for a short time.

Purchasing, and studying mint sets of 10 strips (or full rolls) from a post office-fresh box is the easiest way to get a full 10x10 die cutting mat pattern ... and then produce a chart that can be used for plating purposes. Be forewarned that it is possible to have a box of 10 rolls which has a duplicate roll(s).

The single Flower coil stamps supplied in the 2005–2008 Quarterly packs (Quarter 1 in all cases) are specially cut stamps, in that they are die cut entirely through the stamp and backing paper. In order for this to happen a different die cutting mat was prepared. As such, the die cutting measurements found on the single stamps supplied in these Quarterly packs are different from any of the corresponding stamps issued in rolls of 50 (or 100).

There are only 36 different stamps (6 columns by 6 rows each) that comprise the die cutting mat for Quarterly pack singles. The first three Flower series (2005, 2006, 2007) all share the same pattern. The 2008 Flower series uses the same 6x6 die cutting mat but it was *inverted* in relation to that used on the previous stamps.

As you study all of the Lowe-Martin produced coil stamps you will find that the die cutting is very, very inconsistent. This is true from one row to the next (i.e. the top of a stamp can measure noticeably different from the bottom of the stamp), from one stamp to another, and even across the same stamp.

With this very inconsistent nature, measurements should be taken from the middle of the first peak at the upper *left* of the stamp to the right most peak at the upper *right* of the stamp.

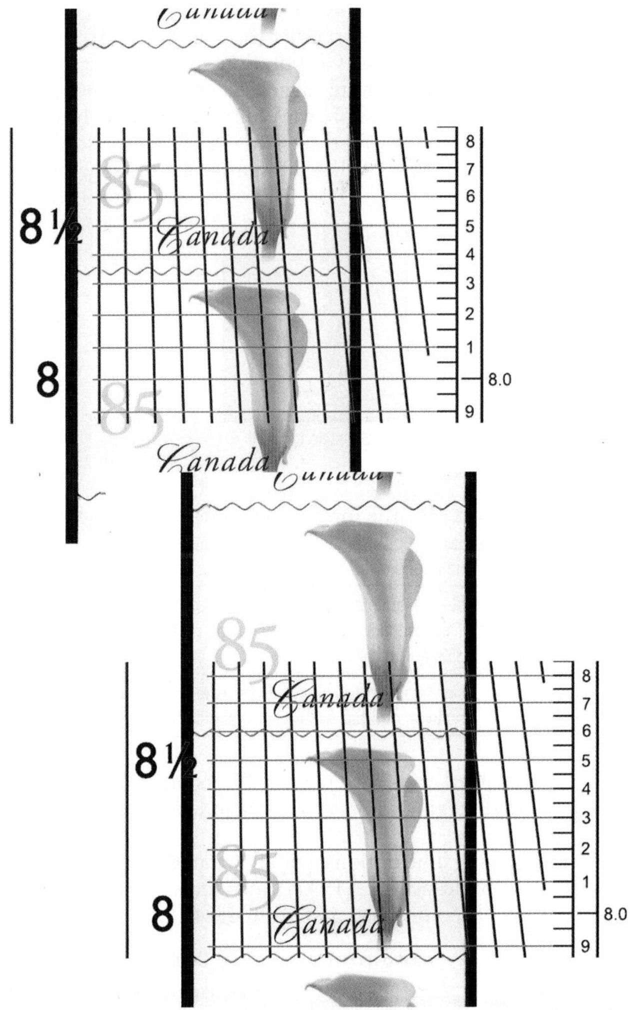


Illustrated above are measurements taken of the *same* stamp showing the variable "perforation" measurements across the top. The measurement in the top illustration ('perf' 8.35) shows the correct method of 'perfing' the stamp (i.e. from the left-most peak to the right-most peak). Notice that the peaks do not align with the perforation gauge through the middle of the stamp due to the inconsistent nature of the die cutting. The bottom illustration measures from the left edge until the peaks 'widen', giving a false measurement (for the entire stamp) of 8.60.

The listings for the affected issues in this catalogue include notes about the number of die cutting mats found for the different issues but the thousands of unique stamps are not individually identified (an impossible task in a catalogue of this size).

## Gum

The existence of differing types of gum on modern Canadian issues is not listed in this catalogue, with the exception of 1967 Centennial definitives, although collectors should be aware of the differences.

With the exception of the 1966 Highway Safety stamp (Sc 447) and the 1967 Centennial commemorative (Sc 453) stamps (which had Davac gum), all Canadian stamps issued prior to 1971 had dextrine gum, which appears yellowish in colour with a shiny appearance.

PVA gum (polyvinyl alcohol) was first introduced on late printings of the 1967–73 Centennial definitives and this is the only issue for which two types of gum exist. Early PVA gum has a matte appearance and lacks any shine. However, in recent years the gum's appearance has taken on a more shiny effect, though not nearly as pronounced as that exhibited by the earlier dextrine gum. A transparent, colourless gum was introduced in the spring of 2010.

## Tagging

Phosphorescent tagging of Canadian stamps was introduced on January 13, 1962 to facilitate the use of automatic facer-cancelling equipment being installed at Winnipeg. The 1¢ through 5¢ values of the Queen Elizabeth (Wilding portrait) definitives were overprinted with phosphorescent material which glows when exposed to ultraviolet light, retaining an after-glow for a few seconds once the light is removed. Although the Winnipeg area was flooded with tagged issues, the detection system was not fully operational before this issue was replaced by the 1962–63 Cameo definitives.

### Winnipeg Tagging

The varieties of Winnipeg tagging listed are identified by the following notations:

| | |
|---|---|
| W1B | Winnipeg 1-Bar tagging, a single tagging bar along one edge of the stamp. |
| W2B | Winnipeg 2-Bar tagging, a tagging bar along two opposite edges of the stamp. |
| WCB | Winnipeg Centre-Bar tagging, a single tagging bar through the middle portion of the stamp. |

These bars can be different widths on printings of the same value.

### General Tagging

Winnipeg tagging was used until 1972 when it was replaced with General (or Ottawa) tagging which is fluorescent rather than phosphorescent. The phosphor compound OP2, produced by General Electric (U.S.), was found suitable for application by lithographic presses but a practical gravure ink for applying the tagging could not be developed at the time. A second General Electric phosphor compound, OP4 was used by BABN until it was found to be migratory. When OP4 tagging migrates onto other stamps it produces "apparent" tagging errors (extra bars, etc.). The affected stamps are not varieties, but are, in fact, damaged stamps. OP4 fluoresces yellow under ultra-violet light and can be controlled somewhat by isolating the stamps in mounts or envelopes of acetate, glassine or polyethylene. OP4 was used on all copies of 560p and 561p, on some of numbers 544p–s, and 594–598. Extensive testing finally produced an acceptable gravure ink using the OP2 compound.

Canadian stamp issues since 1973 have been overprinted with the General OP2 tagging (GT) which is more noticeable to the naked eye and, although it glows more brightly under ultraviolet light, retains no after-glow.

The following definitions describe the appearance of General Tagging bars listed in this catalogue:

| | |
|---|---|
| UN | Untagged; Canada Post has left low- and high-value definitives untagged since 1988. |
| GT2 | General Tagging on two opposite edges only. |
| GT3 | General Tagging on two opposite edges, and one parallel bar through the middle of the stamp. |
| GT4 | General Tagging along all edges of stamp. |
| GTX | Special General Tagging for the "Greet-More" Christmas stamps (1987–1991) appears along all sides of the illustration plus four vertical bars to the left of the illustration. During the years 1992–1995 there is tagging on all white areas except within the illustration. |

Various styles of general tagging have appeared due to either testing purposes or printing requirements (the following images were taken with an ultraviolet light source). They are numbered in the order of their appearance.

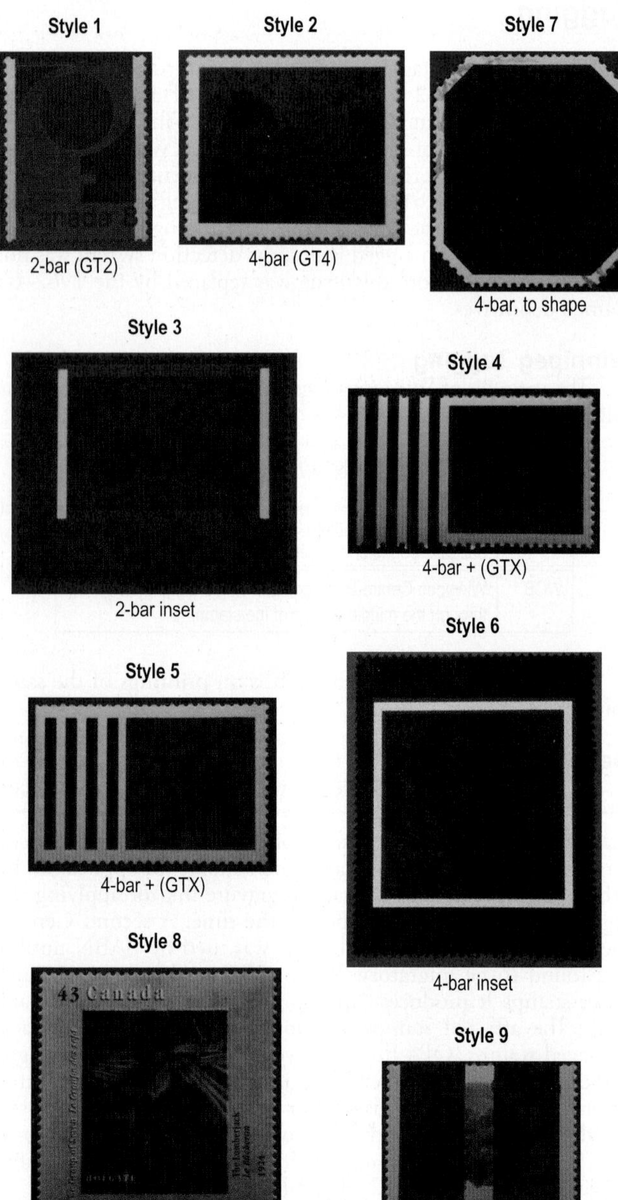

2-bar (GT2)
4-bar (GT4)
4-bar, to shape
2-bar inset
4-bar + (GTX)
4-bar + (GTX)
4-bar inset
all-over (FCP)
3-bar (GT3)

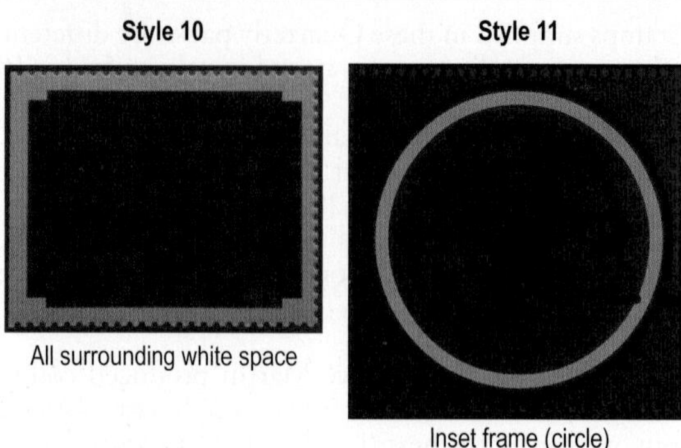

All surrounding white space
Inset frame (circle)

In many cases, there are instances where the tagging has been "indented", or removed, to allow for an extension of the underlying design. For example, the circle in Style 11 above is notched at the right side to allow for the hockey stick design.

## USA-style Tagging

In 1998, two Canadian stamps (Sc. 1696 and 1699) were printed by Avery Dennison Corporation in the United States. In both cases the stamps were tagged using USA-style taggant. This is only visible with a short wave ultraviolet light. It glows a yellow-green colour. Viewing these two stamps with a long wave ultraviolet light will suggest that the stamps are untagged (ie. no tagging will show).

USA-style taggant

### Tagging errors

Tagging errors take the form of one of the following:

| | |
|---|---|
| Missing | untagged error |
| Extra | double, triple or more applications of the tagging. This also includes a variety having normal tagging plus an overall tag wash. |
| Shifted | significant shifts will give 1-bar (where there should be two), or 3-bar (where there should be 4) |

Only untagged and extra tagging errors are included in the listings. Shifted tagging errors are *not* included at this time.

The following illustrations are all from the 48¢ Flag over Canada Post building (Sc. 1931) and show several types of tagging errors. The normal tagging is 4-sided (GT4, Style 2).

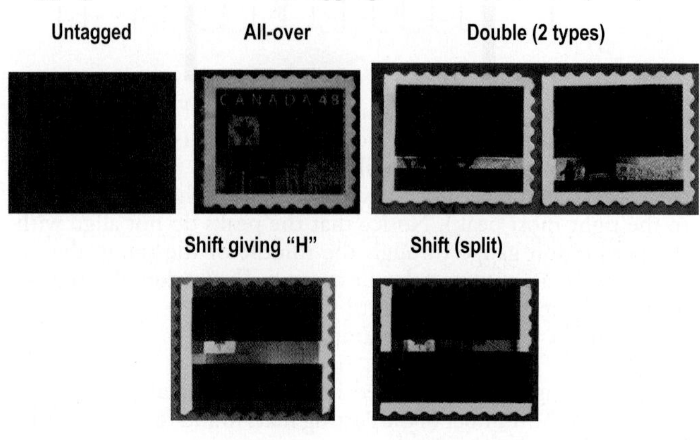

## Paper

Many stamps have been printed on papers with a discernable grain pattern. Philatelists refer to this as the weave of the paper. A sheet of stamps printed with the stamp design running vertically along the grain is said to be printed on "vertical wove" paper. If printed with the design running vertically across the grain, the stamps are said to be printed on "horizontal wove" paper.

Early issues were printed on dampened paper and shrinkage across the grain occurred as the paper dried. A new process was introduced in 1922 to print stamps on dry, pre-gummed paper which does not shrink. The Admiral issue of King George V was printed from 1911 to 1928, with earlier printings on dampened paper (wet printing) and later printings on dry paper (dry printing). The wet printings were usually made with the stamp design running vertically along the grain and copies are noticeably narrower than those from dry printings because the dampened paper shrank slightly as it dried.

The term "squat printing" was coined within the philatelic community to describe early "wet" printings made with the stamp design running vertically across the grain, resulting in stamps which are noticeably shorter than other copies printed on dry paper.

Certain values of the "Arch" or "Leaf" issue (1930) and the "Medallion" issue (1932) were produced using two different types of printing press. "Flat Press" printings were produced on a press which momentarily holds the paper motionless while impressing the image onto the paper using an inked, flat plate. The resulting sheet of stamps will measure the same as the original engraving in both directions.

When the same engraving is used to produce plates for a rotary press, the situation changes. Plates on a rotary press must be curved to fit around one-half of the rotating drum, or cylinder, used by these presses. As the plates are bent into their final semicircular form the design is stretched in the direction of the bend. The press transfers the image from the rotating cylinder onto the moving paper. "Rotary Press" copies are slightly taller than those printed by Flat press method.

Stamp sheets printed on rotary presses have a tendency to curl, and are passed through a series of rollers to correct this. The rollers cause a slight alteration of the gum, leaving it smooth but with slight bends or ridges, approximately 5½ mm apart, across the sheet.

### Paper Types

**Coated paper** The coating on coated stamp paper can be marked easily using a 1-cent coin and if done carefully, the mark can be erased without seriously damaging the stamp.

**India paper** is a thin, transparent paper often used for making plate and die proofs.

**Laid paper** shows alternate light and dark lines when held up to a light. Seen on early issues, up to 1868 (up to Sc # 33).

**Ribbed Paper** has an uneven corrugated surface from being passed between ridged rollers.

**Wove paper** has an even, smooth surface of uniform texture. When held to a light the slight weave-like pattern of the grain can be seen.

### Paper Fluorescence

With the use of an ultraviolet light in modern philately, paper fluorescence is an attribute often used to distinguish between varieties. The following notations are used to describe the appearance of a stamp when exposed to ultraviolet light.

| | |
|---|---|
| NF | no fluorescence (coated non-fluorescent paper)<br>paper appears extremely dull or "dead" |
| DF | dull fluorescence (uncoated non-fluorescent paper) |
| LF | low fluorescence |
| F | fluorescent paper |
| MF | medium fluorescence |
| HF | high fluorescence |
| HB | hibrite paper |
| SF | speckled fluorescence (or "flecked") |

Fluorescent paper varieties are listed where a significant and noticeable difference can be seen in a particular issue. Be aware that soaking a stamp can affect its fluorescence level. Other chemical additives (and prolonged exposure to sunlight?) can also affect the fluorescence of stamp. Flecked fibers (identified as "/fl") will make a stamp's fluorescence appear brighter.

Some stamps may have different fluorescence on the front versus the back of the stamp. In this case the variety listings will show "LF/DF", where the first entry refers to the front of the stamp and the second entry refers to the back of the stamp.

The following table provides a reference comparison between the various paper manufacturers (see next page for a discussion) and known stamps that exist with only one paper fluorescence.

| | Fluorescence | | | | | | |
|---|---|---|---|---|---|---|---|
| Paper | NF/ Dead | Dull | LF | F | MF | HF | HB |
| pre Abitibi-Price | 505 | 400 | | | | 485 | 497 |
| Abitibi-Price | 899 | 884 | 726 | | 633 | 664 | 640 |
| Harrison* | 1334-37 | 1038 | | — | | — | |
| Clark ‡ | 1015 | | 1029 | | | | |
| Rolland | 1111–12 | 1146 | 925b | — | — | — | — |
| Peterborough ‡ | 1251 | | — | | 1738 | 1639 | 1814 |
| Slater ‡ | | 1154 | | | | | |
| Coated Papers (TRC) ‡ | 1589 | | | | | | |

Fluorescence as seen on back of stamp, except for pre-Abitibi paper with gum arabic adhesive, where fluorescence is measured on front.

* All Harrison NF / Dull back paper is NF / Dead on the front.

‡ All Slater, Clark, Coated (TRC), and Peterborough (surface coated only) papers are NF / Dead on the front.

Blank cells indicate no such paper used / known.
Cells with — indicate no unique stamp (only on this paper) is known.
NF and DEAD paper are deemed to be the same.

Table prepared by Mirko Zatka of Zatka Philately, Calgary, AB.
**A Raytech LS-4 lamp (longwave) was used as the standard for determining the most recent fluorescence levels. Different ultraviolet lamps can give varying readings.**

### Paper Manufacturers

In 1983, following Abitibi Paper's decision to cease manufacturing stamp paper, Canada Post's primary printing suppliers began using stamp papers manufactured in Great Britain and some definitive values can be found on four discernably different stamp papers. Canadian stamps are now printed on papers from a number of manufacturers, both domestic and foreign. Most of these manufacturers produce paper literally indistinguishable from the others and for that reason the name of the stamp paper manufacturer is of no more consequence than the name of the tree from which its paper was made.

Probably because of many requests for more information on types of paper, Canada Post now identifies the paper manufacturer both in its literature and by placing the company's first initial in the inscription blocks of sheets, panes, etc. Because the manufacturer is now known, collectors attempt to add examples from each paper company wherever possible. Some paper companies use gum, the colour of which is singular among these manufacturers, making it possible to identify the paper mill in this way. The only other way to identify the paper company is to collect stamps with all, or part of the inscription block attached—showing the letter which identifies the paper manufacturer. Many now collect inscription blocks or inscription pairs instead of singles for this reason.

It should also be noted that Coated Papers is the name of a paper company. Paper mills may produce both coated and uncoated papers.

**Paper Manufacturers**

| Initials | Company | Gum colour (mint stamp) | Paper appearance (used) | First seen |
|---|---|---|---|---|
| APP | Abitibi-Price | clear | | |
| HP | Harrison | blue-green tinge; paper curls | back of stamp has horizontal "lines" when viewed against a darker background | Aug 1983 |
| CLP | Clark | clear | | Dec 1983 |
| RP | Rolland | white; slight paper curl | | Aug 1985 |
| PP | Peterborough Paper Converters | greyish; very shiny | very smooth, white, crispy | Feb 1988 |
| SP | Slater | light cream colour | looks like a mixture of "pulp" and has a darker tone (beige); slightly darker than CPP | Feb 1988 |
| CPP | Coated Papers Ltd | slight blue-green tinge | textured or "indented" appearance | Dec 1990 |
| TRC | Tullis Russel Coatings | same paper as CPP; name changed [transparent gum starting in May 2010] | | Jan 1998 |
| SR | Spicer | | | Dec 2007 |
| WCP | Wausau Coated Products | | [fabric] | Feb 2015 |

## Constant Plate Varieties

Collectors have always been fascinated with the study of plate varieties. Those that appear on the same position on the plate over a significant portion of the printing of a stamp and are thus constant, are of the most importance as they give the collector the opportunity to "plate" a stamp's position. A constant plate variety includes a re-entry, scratch, excess material or the lack of detail.

Many of the recognized constant plate varieties that have been reported to the editors are listed, and in most cases, illustrated.

Flaws are classified according to their frequency of occurrence on the plate:

| Classification | Frequency |
|---|---|
| Die flaw | Occurs on every stamp of the plate |
| Primary flaw | Occurs on several consecutive stamps in a pane, typically on all the stamps in one row or column, on every pane in the sheet |
| Secondary flaw | Occurs on one stamp on several consecutive panes in the sheet, typically on all of them |
| Tertiary flaw | Typically occurs on just one stamp on the entire plate |

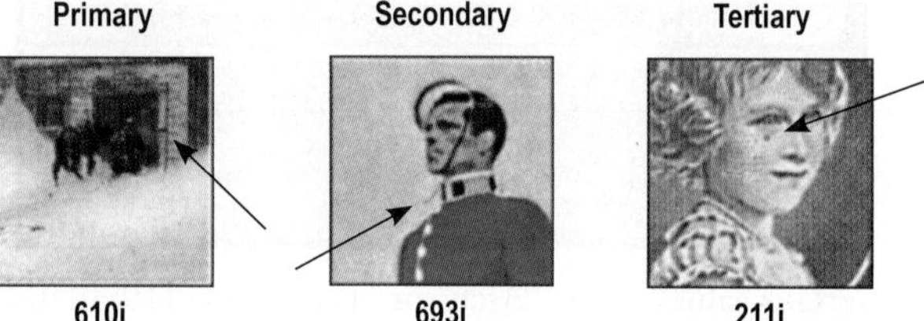
Primary 610i — Secondary 693i — Tertiary 211i

Constant flaws are identified by their location on the sheet/pane. This can be done in a couple of ways: Row/Column or position number. The latter method requires knowing the pane layout arrangement and counting to the stamp in question, starting with the first stamp on the pane.

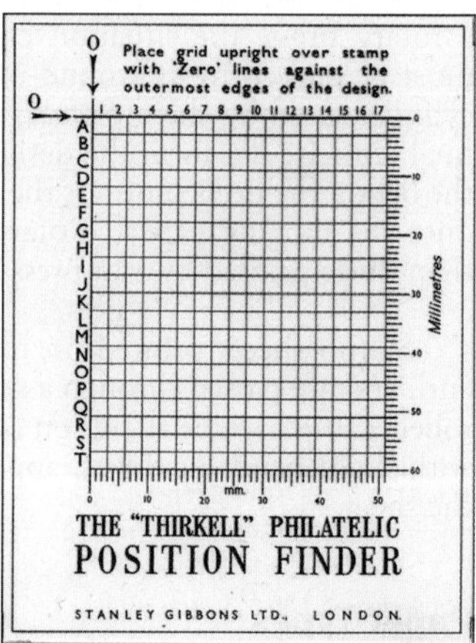


A stamp collector's tool, *The "Thirkell" Philatelic Position Finder* has been developed by Stanley Gibbons Ltd. of London England to aid in identifying the position of the flaw on a single stamp. The gauge uses a grid, numbered from 1–17 across and A–T down; each grid is 3mm square. As an example of its use, the "dented bumper" constant plate variety found on the 50¢ Prairie Town definitive printed by CBN (Sc. 723A) is located at "I10". It is anticipated that a future edition of this catalogue will include this variety positioning information.

When checking used stamps for a constant variety, be mindful of cancellations and foreign particles that may interfere with, or confuse, your searching.

## Errors, Freaks and Oddities

An error is a stamp released to the public that contains some sort of major mistake in the design or production of the stamp. This can include:

- imperforate
- missing colour
- printed on the gum side
- printed in the wrong colour
- centre or frame inverted
- untagged (when it should be tagged, since this is a missing colour)

A freak is an abnormal, usually non-repetitive occurrence in the production of stamps. Most paper folds, overinking, ink smears, and perforation/colour shifts are freaks.

With the rare exception of a couple of colour shifts that were listed many years ago, we do not list perforation, colour, or tagging shifts in this catalogue. We certainly recognize that there is strong collector interest in these sorts of varieties. The problem is ... at what point does one list such a variety? After a 1mm shift? 2.45mm shift? and so on? The degree to which a shift exists will determine its ultimate value. Obviously, the larger the shift, the more dramatic the variety becomes, and the more demand one might expect of such an item.

Here are some examples of perforation, colour shifts, and other oddities, and an estimated range of value one might expect of such an item. Although only modern definitives are illustrated, these types of varieties can occur on any stamp. A similar variety on an older stamp or higher-denominated stamp or commemorative stamp could result in different pricing.

**Perforation shifts**

$20–$30 $50–$60 $125–$150 $100–$125

**Colour shifts**

$80–$100 $50–$75 $150–$200

**Offset on gum side**

$75–$125

**Paper crease**

$75–$100

**Under inked**

$30–$40

**Fold-over**

$10,000–$12,500

**Repellex**

$1,500–$2,000

## Double-Printed Stamps

Early printing presses were constructed to print only one colour at a time. To add an additional colour it was necessary to use a second press, or to wash the ink from the press, change the plate and load the fountain with a different colour of ink. Modern high-speed presses consist of several "stations," each with its own plates and ink fountains, capable of adding an additional colour to the paper. These presses can be either sheet or web fed—a web press prints on a continuous roll of paper— with each colour added as the paper moves continuously through the system.

One of the most important facets of quality control for multi-colour printing is the proper registration of the colours. To describe the process, let's consider an early one-colour press. As the press prints the first colour, samples are pulled and reserved as "run-up" sheets. To adjust the registration of the second colour plate, a run-up sheet is printed and carefully checked for registration. Adjustments are made to the positioning of the second plate, the make-ready and ink coverage, etc. are checked and the process is repeated—using the same run-up sheet so that the progress of these adjustments can be monitored. Once all adjustments have been completed the press is put into production and usually a signed copy is placed into the job docket as proof of the quality of the print run. Any other run-up sheets are then considered printer's waste. This process would be repeated for each additional colour.

While a modern multi-station press is printing, the sheet or web moves continuously, at high speeds, through each of the stations. It is difficult to conceive of a single colour being printed in multiples during this process. Whenever a press is shut down, or shuts down automatically, for whatever reason, several checks must be made to ensure that the approved set-up is continuing. Any paper caught or otherwise affected by the paper jam, dry fountain, broken web, damaged blanket or plate, etc. is systematically delegated to the garbage bin. In recent years quite a few pieces of printer's waste have reached the philatelic market. Many of these have been bought and sold at high prices.

## Precancels

| Style | Bars per stamp | Time period | Scott #'s |
|---|---|---|---|
| A | 2 | 1888–97 | 34–53 |
| B | 3 to 5 | 1888–97 | 34–43 |
| C | 5 to 6 | 1888–97 | 35–46 |
| D | 5½ | 1888–97 | 35–44 |
| E | 7 | 1888–97 | 34–44 |
| F | 7½ | 1888–97 | 35–41 |
| G | 7½ to 8 | 1888–97 | 35–44 |
| H | 8½ | 1888–97 | 34–44 |
| I | 10 | 1888–98 | 29–85 |
| J | 11 | 1888–97 | 30–46 |
| K | 2 | 1888–97 | 35 |
| L | 3 | 1888–97 | 35–41 |
| M | 4 | 1888–97 | 35–41 |
| N | 5 | 1888–97 | 35 |
| R | 3 | 1888–97 | 29–46 |
| S | 3 | 1888–97 | 30–47 |
| T | 3 | 1888–03 | 29–94 |
| U | 3 | 1888–03 | 29–93 |
| V | 3 pairs | 1911–67 | 105–468 |
| W | 3 pairs | 1928–35 | 149–219 |
| X | 3 pairs | 1935–72 | 217–460 |
| Y | 2 pairs | 1973–77 | 586–787 |

The study of precancels can be a specialization in its own right. This catalogue lists only the most common variety for any given stamp. In many cases, the same stamp can come precancelled with different **Bar** types and/or **Town** types. In other cases, various varieties such as inverts, doubles, triples, etc. can be found. Adding all of these types and varieties to this catalogue would make it unwieldy. The listing here will show that a particular stamp can be found in precancelled form. We refer you to *The Standard Canada Precancel Catalogue* for even more specialized information and where you will find over 300 major bar type listings and nearly 1,650 major town/city listings (over 4,000 different varieties are identified).

**Bar Types**

Style A

Style B

Style C

Style D

Style E

Style F

Style G

Style H

Style I

Style J

Style K

Style L

Style M

Style N

Style R

Style S

Style T

Style U

Style V

Style W

Style X

Style Y

Style Y (red overprint)

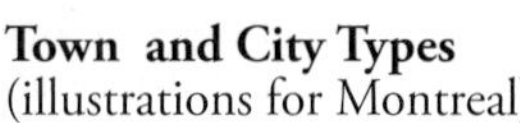

**Town and City Types**
(illustrations for Montreal)

58 towns/cities have used at least one style of precancel with its name and province indicated. Most of the towns have used one or two different styles. Others have used many more (Montreal with 10; Toronto with 15).

Style 1 for one town or city may not necessarily be the same Style 1 for another.

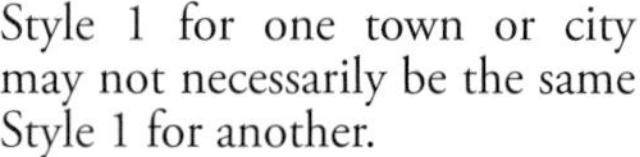

THIS CATALOGUE LISTS A SINGLE PRECANCEL WITH A PRICE OF THE LOWEST VALUE VARIETY; THE NUMBER OF STYLES FOUND ON THE GIVEN STAMP IS NOTED.

Style 1

Style 2

Style 3

Style 4

Style 5

Style 6

Style 7

Style 8

Style 9

Style 10

## Selected Philatelic Terms

**Barcode**: a Universal Product Code (UPC) image applied to a booklet cover or in the margin (selvedge) of a pane of stamps which is scanned at the time of purchase to aid in an inventory control computer program.

Canada Post began using UPC barcodes on its products in December 1989 — on a 39¢ Flag over Clouds booklet of 10 (BK112). The first stamp sheet in Canada to have a UPC barcode imprinted on the pane was the 47¢ Royal Canadian Legion issued on November 11, 2001 (Sc # 1926). To date, there is no definitive pattern as to the placement or orientation of the barcode on the pane.

**Bisect**: a stamp cut into two parts (diagonally, vertically, or horizontally), each part paying postage of half the face value of the complete stamp.

**Blind perforations**: impressions made for perforations but not fully removed. Not to be confused with imperforate stamps. These are considered freaks, not errors, and do not command a premium.

**Cachet**: text or drawing applied to a First Day Cover envelope describing the new stamp(s).

**Cello-Paq**: a miniature pane (either 1 or 2 panes) of stamps enclosed in a sealed, clear plastic wrapper. Introduced in 1961 with the Wilding definitives. Cello-paqs appeared in the Wilding, Cameo, and Centennial definitive series. In addition, several Christmas issues, starting in 1964, have appeared in this format.

**Commemorative**: a stamp issued, usually for a limited period of time, to mark a particular event or anniversary, as distinct from a definitive.

**Counterfeit:** a stamp, cover or cancel created to deceive postal authorities.

**Definitive**: the 'common' stamps, intended for normal everyday postal use, issued in large quantities and available (typically) for several years.

**Denomination**: the face value of stamp, indicated either with a numeral or a letter (the latter being non-denominated).

**Die & Plate Proofs**: impressions taken from an approved die or plate, in which the design and colour are the same as the stamps issued to the public.

**Die cut**: the separation method used around self adhesive stamps. This can be straight, curved, simulated perforations, serpentine or any other unique shape.

**Fake:** a stamp, cover or cancel altered to appeal to the collector.

**Forgery:** the process of making, adapting, or imitating stamp items with the intent to deceive. There are two type of forgeries: counterfeits and fakes.

**Hairlines**: fine lines across the face of a stamp caused by plate cracks.

**Imperforate**: stamps without perforations, intended to be separated using scissors. It is recommended that imperforate varieties of normally perforated stamps be collected in pairs to verify their authenticity.

**Perfin**: acronym for Perforated Initials. Stamps with punched holes in either a letter or design form indicating the company of usage.

**Phosphor**: 'invisible' ink (tagging) applied to the front of the stamp in vertical bars (one, two, or three have been used on Canadian stamps) or around all four sides of the stamp that, when exposed to ultraviolet light, activates a sorting and canceling machine.

Canada issued its first phosphor tagged stamps in 1962 in readiness for the installation of a British-made letter-facing machine in Winnipeg, Manitoba.

**Plate block**: four or more stamps to which are attached the marginal paper bearing the printing plate or cylinder number inscription.

**Plating**: term used to describe the collecting of stamps according to their position on the sheet; in many issues, this can be determined by close study of the design. When stamps representing a complete sheet have thus been assembled, it is said to be a 'reconstructed sheet'.

**Quarterly pack**: collection of stamps issued by Canada Post for a specified quarter of the year (Jan-Mar, Apr-Jun, Jul-Sep, or Oct-Dec) and sold at face value in a sealed envelope.

Certain stamp varieties have only appeared in these quarterly packs or annual collections.

**Re-entry**: early plates showed wear quickly and images were often sharpened by rocking the transfer roll over the original impression. The slightest variation in registration would cause a doubling of parts of the design. These double images are called re-entries.

A 'fresh entry' involves the (incomplete) removal of a faulty entry from the plate, which is then replaced by a new, or "fresh" entry being transferred into the smoothed 'cleaned' area where the faulty entry once existed.

A "misplaced" entry is a major re-entry wherein the details of the errant entry are at least half a millimeter or more away from where they should be found on the design. The best Canadian example of a misplaced entry is the Ten Cents Decimal Issue, Scott #16/17, "Double Epaulettes" variety, where the errant entry is misplaced by a full half a stamp. (Other examples include the 2c SQ latent entries, several Edwards, and a handful of wonderful 1c Numerals.)

**Se-tenant**: joined together, referring to an unseparated pair, strip or block of stamps differing in design, denomination or overprint.

**Tête-bêche**: a pair of stamps in which one stamp is upside down in relation to the other.

**Traffic lights**: a series of coloured dots (or small images) included with the plate inscription in the selvedge of booklets, panes or gutters of coils that indicate each of the colours used to print the stamp.

First used in Canada in June 1986. More recent issues have seen the use of small images relevant to the topic being commemorated, rather than "traffic lights".

**Trial Colour Die and Plate Proofs**: similar impressions to die and plate proofs but not in the colour of issue.

**Wet and Dry Printings**: early Canadian stamps were printed on dampened paper. Shrinkage across the grain would occur as the paper dried. Beginning in 1922 a new process was used to print stamps on dry, pregummed paper. These did not shrink, resulting in stamps half a millimetre wider than previous.

## Selected Postal Rates

Throughout the catalogue we list selected postal rates to give the collector an idea of why certain stamp values exist. Here is a summarized listing of selected postal rates (surface for Canada and USA), for the lowest weight classification (eg. 0–1oz/0–30g).

| Date | Canada | to USA | International |
|---|---|---|---|
| Jul 1, 1859 | 5¢ | | (see chart to right) |
| Apr 1, 1868 | 3¢ | 6¢ | |
| May 8, 1889 | 3¢ | 3¢ | |
| Jan 1, 1899 | 2¢ | 2¢ | |
| Apr 15, 1915 | 3¢ | 3¢ | |
| Jul 1, 1926 | 2¢ | 2¢ | |
| Jul 1, 1931 | 3¢ | 3¢ | |
| Apr 1, 1943 | 4¢ | 4¢ | |
| Apr 1, 1954 | 5¢ | 5¢ | |
| Nov 1, 1968 | 6¢ | 6¢ | |
| Jul 1, 1971 | 7¢ | 7¢ | 15¢ |
| Jan 1, 1972 | 8¢ | 8¢ | |
| Jan 1, 1976 | | | 20¢ |
| Mar 1, 1976 | | 10¢ | |
| Sep 1, 1976 | 10¢ | | |
| Jan 1, 1977 | | | 25¢ |
| Mar 1, 1977 | 12¢ | 12¢ | |
| Apr 1, 1978 | 14¢ | 14¢ | 30¢ |
| Apr 1, 1979 | 17¢ | 17¢ | 35¢ |
| Jan 1, 1982 | 30¢ | 35¢ | 60¢ |
| Jan 15, 1983 | | 37¢ | 64¢ |
| Feb 15, 1983 | 32¢ | | |
| Jun 24, 1985 | 34¢ | 39¢ | 68¢ |
| Apr 1, 1987 | 36¢ | 42¢ | 72¢ |
| Jan 1, 1988 | 37¢ | 43¢ | 74¢ |
| Jan 1, 1989 | 38¢ | 44¢ | 76¢ |
| Jan 1, 1990 | 39¢ | 45¢ | 78¢ |
| Jan 1, 1991 | 40¢ | 46¢ | 80¢ |
| Jan 1, 1992 | 42¢ | 48¢ | 84¢ |
| Jan 1, 1993 | 43¢ | 49¢ | 86¢ |
| Mar 1, 1994 | | 50¢ | 88¢ |
| Aug 1, 1995 | 45¢ | 52¢ | 90¢ |
| Jan 1, 1999 | 46¢ | 55¢ | 95¢ |
| Jan 1, 2001 | 47¢ | 60¢ | $1.05 |
| Jan 14, 2002 | 48¢ | 65¢ | $1.25 |
| Jan 12, 2004 | 49¢ | 80¢ | $1.40 |
| Jan 17, 2005 | 50¢ | 85¢ | $1.45 |
| Jan 16, 2006 | 51¢ | 89¢ | $1.49 |
| Jan 16, 2007 | 52¢ | 93¢ | $1.55 |
| Jan 14, 2008 | 52¢ | 96¢ | $1.60 |
| Jan 12, 2009 | 54¢ | 98¢ | $1.65 |
| Jan 11, 2010 | 57¢ | $1.00 | $1.70 |
| Jan 17, 2011 | 59¢ | $1.03 | $1.75 |
| Jan 16, 2012 | 61¢ | $1.05 | $1.80 |
| Jan 14, 2013 | 63¢ | $1.10 | $1.85 |
| Mar 31, 2014 | 85¢ | $1.20 | $2.50 |
| *Jan 2019* | *90¢* | | |

| | International | |
|---|---|---|
| Date | See list below* | Other Countries |
| Jan 1, 1892 | | 5¢/½ oz |
| Dec 25, 1898 | 2¢/½ oz | |
| 1907 (per oz) | 2¢ | 5¢ |
| Apr 15, 1915 | 3¢ | |
| Oct 1, 1921 | 4¢ | 10¢ |
| Oct 1, 1925 | | 8¢ |
| Jul 1, 1926 | 2¢ (Mexico) 3¢ (others) | |
| Dec 24, 1928 | 2¢ | |
| Jul 1, 1930 | | 5¢ |
| Jul 1, 1931 | 3¢ | |
| Apr 1, 1943 | 4¢ | |
| Apr 1, 1954 | 5¢ | 6¢ |
| Jan 1, 1966 | | 10¢ |
| Nov 1, 1968 | 6¢ | 12¢ |

* Great Britain and British Empire/Commonwealth, Republic of Ireland, West Indies, Mexico (1905), France (May 1929), Central and South America (Dec 1929), Spain (Mar 1932).

The basic postal rate and period of use, starting with the 5¢ domestic postal rate in 1954, is noted at the bottom of each page. Beginning with the 30¢ rate in 1982, the basic domestic, USA, and International rates are all noted at the bottom of the listing pages throughout this catalogue.

## The Canadian Postal Archives

Much of the technical data for the stamp listings found in this catalogue has been gathered from the Library and Archives Canada website: **http://www.collectionscanada.gc.ca/postal-archives**

In addition to offering an overview of the philatelic collections preserved by Library and Archives Canada, the *Canadian Postal Archives* site allows visitors to find information about every postage stamp issued by Canada and British North America since 1851. The site includes search engines that are linked to the Philatelic Library's catalogue database, to a database relating to post offices, and to a database on Canadian stamps. The latter provides access to thousands of digitized documents. (as of this writing [summer 2018], the stamp details have been disabled!)

## Other On-line Resources

The world wide web is an ever-changing resource for philatelists. We would encourage you to use your favourite search engine to find information on-line.

The Editor maintains an extensive website of Canadian philatelic information: **www.adminware.ca**. Included on this site is an up-to-date, searchable tagging database of all reported tagging errors. In addition, an errata to this catalogue is also available (something we wish did not have to exist!).

## National Philatelic Societies

National philatelic societies that may be of interest to the Canadian collector:

*The Royal Philatelic Society of Canada* **www.rpsc.org**

*The British North America Philatelic Society* **www.bnaps.org**

*Canadian Philatelic Society of Great Britain* **www.canadianpsgb.org.uk**

*The Canadian Forces Philatelic Society* **www.cfps-web.com**

*Postal History Society of Canada* **www.postalhistorycanada.org**

*Société Philatelique de Québec* **www.s-p-q.org**

*Société d'Histoire Postale du Québec* **www.shpq.org**

# UNITRADE ASSOCIATES

## UA Harris Canada 2 volume Album Set

* Album up to 2010...............$93.95/ set
* Harris Pages 2011 to 2017......$40.95

***Discount break down is as follows:***
****Note there is 3 albums sets per case***

| | | |
|---|---|---|
| ***3 Units*** | - | ***40%*** |
| ***6 Units*** | - | ***45%*** |
| ***9 Units*** | - | ***50%*** |
| ***12 Units*** | - | ***55%*** |

## NEW EDITIONS AVAILABLE

**Unirade Postage Stamp Indentifier**
**$12.95 EACH**

**THE STANDARD CANADA PRECANCEL CATALOGUE 7TH EDITION**
**$18.95 EACH**

**Form 102**
**Dealer Window Card**

These cards are made of white bristol with crystal-clear pockets to hold stamps. Card size is 4¼ x 2¾" with a pocket size of 3½ x 2". Space for entering prices of stamps.

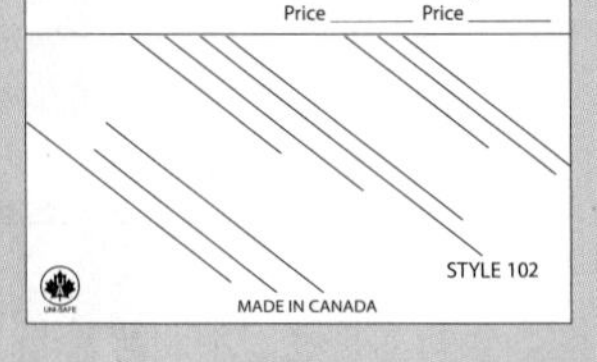


| | | |
|---|---|---|
| Form 102 | Box of 1,000 | 51.95 |
| | Pkg of 100 | 5.50 |

***Lets organize better by colour...***

**NEW COLOURED F102 CARDS;**

| | | |
|---|---|---|
| Form 102 | Box of 1,000 | $56.95 |
| | Pkg of 100 | $6.00 |

**BLUE**
**CHERRY**
**GREEN**

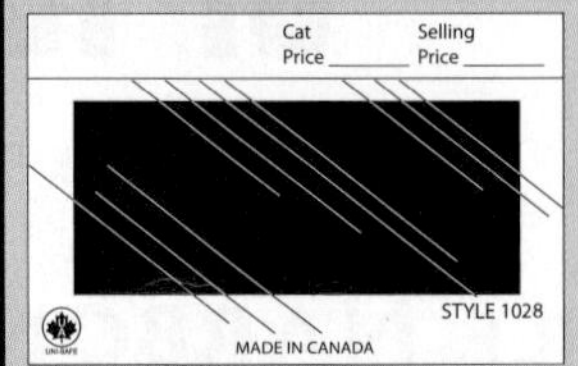


**Form 102B**
**Dealer Window Card**

102B window cards are the same size as #102 and also have the same size pocket. The difference is that they have a black patch printed behind the pocket. This patch makes the perforations easy to see.

| | | |
|---|---|---|
| Form 102B | Box of 1,000 | 51.95 |
| | Pkg of 100 | 5.50 |

**UNITRADE ASSOCIATES**

99 FLORAL PARKWAY, TORONTO, ONTARIO, M6L 2C4
PHONE: 416.242.5900 FAX: 416. 242.6115
EMAIL: unitrade@rogers.com
WEBSITE: www.unitradeassoc.com

# GLASSINE ENVELOPE PRICES 2018 * NEW*

| ORDER # | REF. # | SIZE | per 1,000 | per 100 |
|---|---|---|---|---|
| W101 | No. 1 | 1-3/4 X 2-7/8" | $69.95 | $7.95 |
| W103 | No. 2 | 2-5/16 X 3-5/8" | $78.50 | $8.95 |
| W104 | No. 3 | 2-1/2 X 4-1/4" | $81.95 | $9.50 |
| W105 | No. 4 | 3-1/4 X 4-7/8" | $92.95 | $10.95 |
| W106 | No. 4-1/2 | 3-1/8 X 5-1/16" | $93.95 | $11.50 |
| W107 | No. 5 | 3-1/2 X 6" | $125.95 | $14.95 |
| W108 | No. 6 | 3-3/4 X 6-3/4" | $141.95 | $16.95 |
| W109 | No. 7 | 4-1/8 X 6-1/4" | $146.95 | $17.95 |
| W110 | No. 8 | 4-1/2 X 6-5/8" | $158.95 | $19.95 |
| W112 | No. 10 | 4-1/8 X 9-1/2" | $263.95 | $31.95 |
| W113 | No. 11 | 4 1/2 X 10-1/4" | $279.95 | $33.50 |
| W114 | No. 12 | 9-1/2 X 11" | $399.95 | $47.95 |

**UNITRADE ASSOCIATES**
99 FLORAL PARKWAY, TORONTO, ONTARIO, M6L 2C4
PHONE: 416.242.5900 FAX: 416. 242.6115
EMAIL: unitrade@rogers.com
WEBSITE: www.unitradeassoc.com

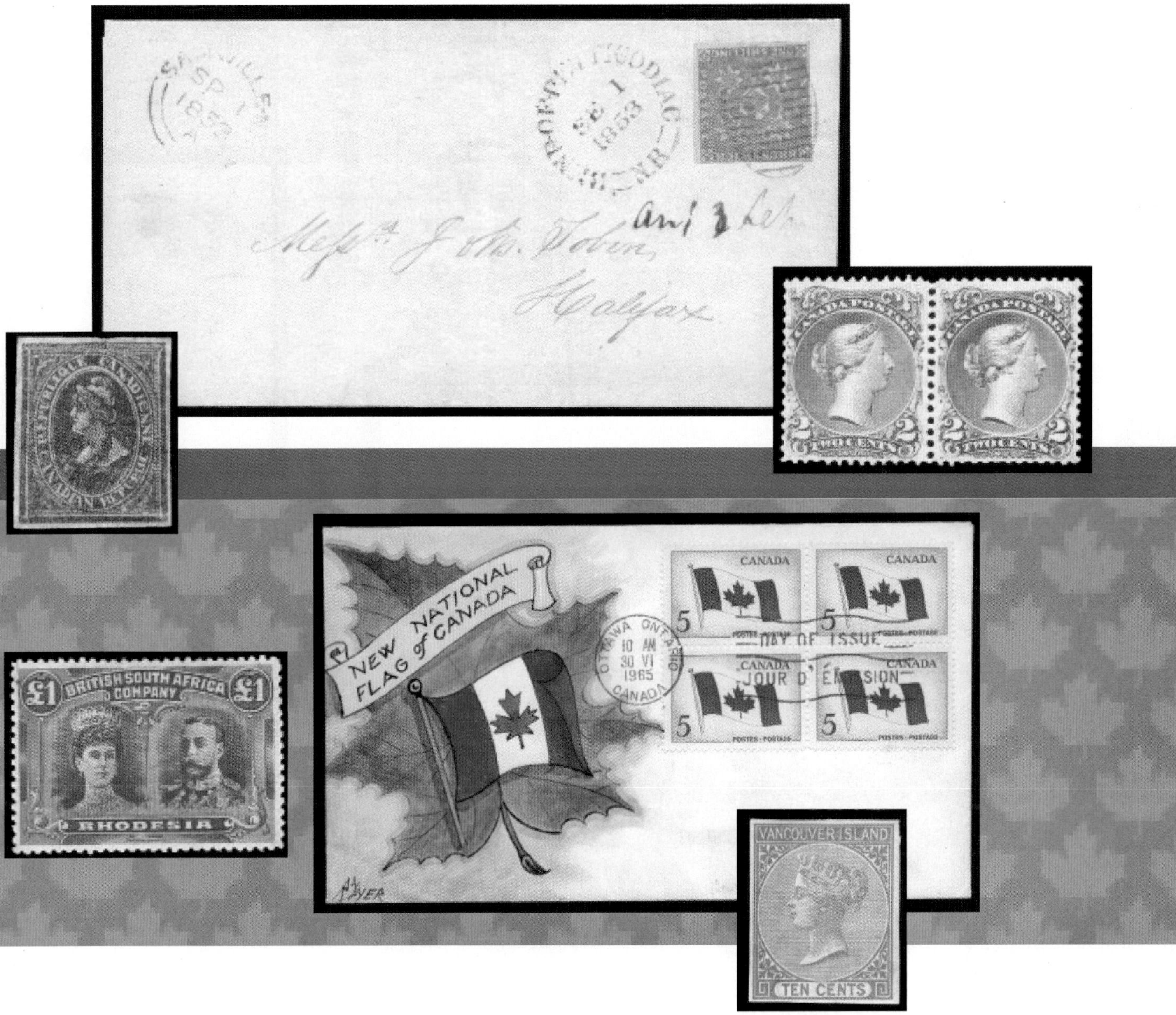

# PROVINCE OF CANADA

## PENCE ISSUE

1 Beaver — 2 HRH Prince Albert — 3 Queen Victoria

**Rates:** Apr 6/1851 — Inland letters to Canada, Nova Scotia, New Brunswick, Cape Breton and Prince Edward Island: 3d per ½ oz.

Drop letter†: ½d per letter

Letters to USA (except California and Oregon): 6d per ½ oz.

Letters to California and Oregon: 9d per ½ oz.

† Drop letter: letters deposited (dropped) at a post office for delivery at that post office or by a letter carrier of that post office.

Designer: 3d: Sandford Fleming; other values by the printers.
Portraits: 6d: HRH Prince Albert, the Prince Consort: drawing by William Drummond, Esq, engraved by W. H. Egleton, stamp portrait vignette engraving by Alfred Jones; 12d: Her Majesty, Queen Victoria, reproduced from a full-length painting by Alfred Edward Chalon, engraved by Alfred Jones.

Rawdon, Wright, Hatch and Edson of New York
Engraved: 3d (one plate of 200 subjects cut into two panes of 100); 6d & 12d (one plate of 200 subjects)

**1851** — **Laid Paper (3d: horizontal; 6d & 12d: vertical)** — **Imperforate**

Mint copies (★) with original gum, add 100% (should have certs for OG copies)

| | | ★VF | ★F | ★VG | ⊙VF | ⊙F | ⊙VG | ✉ |
|---|---|---|---|---|---|---|---|---|
| **1** | **3d red**, *Apr 23, 1851* | 60,000 | 30,000 | 10,000 | 1,600 | 800.00 | 400.00 | 2,500 |
| **a** | orange red (vermilion) | 60,000 | 30,000 | 10,000 | 1,600 | 800.00 | 400.00 | 2,500 |
| **ii** | major re-entry (pos. 34, pane A) | | | | 3,000 | 1,500.00 | 900.00 | 4,000 |
| **iii** | major re-entry (pos. 47, pane A) | | | | 3,000 | 1,500.00 | 900.00 | 4,000 |
| **iv** | minor re-entries, (numerous) | | | | 1,800† | 900.00† | 550.00† | |
| **v** | major re-entry (pos. 80, pane A) | | | | | | | |
| **vi** | major re-entry (pos. 61, pane B) ** | | | | | | | |

Qty ordered: 250,000
ERD is May 1, 1851. Two covers mailed on this date recorded.
Position 34 re-entry shows doubling of lines below REE PENC and below bottom 3s.
Position 47 re-entry shows more extensive doubling EE PEN, above and below POS, in and below ANADA THR and in all four numerals.
** Other major re-entries exist on pane B at positions **42** (doubling is found in almost all of the lettering, but is particularly clear in and above POSTAGE; distinctive doubling of the vertical inner frameline in the lower left corner), **53** (the 'VR' re-entry, due to the markings in both of those letters; shows doubling in both of the left 3's, the UL corner of the frame, in and above the letters of CANADA, and in THREE PENCE), and **65** (extensive re-entry, with doubling in virtually all of the lettering, including VR, the white ovals, and all four 3's).
† Values are for most common shade or paper.

| | | ★VF | ★F | ★VG | ⊙VF | ⊙F | ⊙VG | ✉ |
|---|---|---|---|---|---|---|---|---|
| **2** | **6d slate violet** | 60,000 | 30,000 | 10,000 | 2,000 | 1,000 | 500.00 | 3,000 |
| **a** | diagonal half used as 3d on cover | | | | | | | 40,000 |
| **b** | greyish purple, *May 17, 1851* (brown purple) | 60,000 | 30,000 | 10,000 | 2,400 | 1,200 | 500.00 | 3,500 |

Qty ordered: 100,000

| | | ★VF | ★F | ★VG | ⊙VF | ⊙F | ⊙VG | ✉ |
|---|---|---|---|---|---|---|---|---|
| **3** | **12d black**, *Jun 14, 1851* | 150,000 | 90,000 | 30,000 | 180,000 | 80,000 | 25,000 | 250,000 |

Qty ordered: 50,000. Issued: 1,450

Multiples of the laid papers are extremely rare: only 2 blocks of 4 are known of the 3d Beaver; only 5 mint pairs and 3 used pairs are known of the 12d Queen Victoria. On some copies the laid lines are almost invisible.

1ii
Tripling of the LL 3, doubling of the LR 3, and lines of doubling in and below 'EE PENCE.'

1iii
Distinctive doubling in and below 'EE PEN' and the bottoms of three of the 3's.

1v
Sharp doubling in most lettering, both left 3's, with a horizontal line touching the top of the upper left 3.

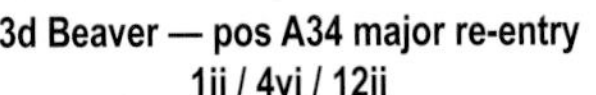

**3d Beaver — pos A34 major re-entry**
**1ii / 4vi / 12ii**

**3d Beaver — pos A47 major re-entry**
**1iii / 4vii / 12iii**

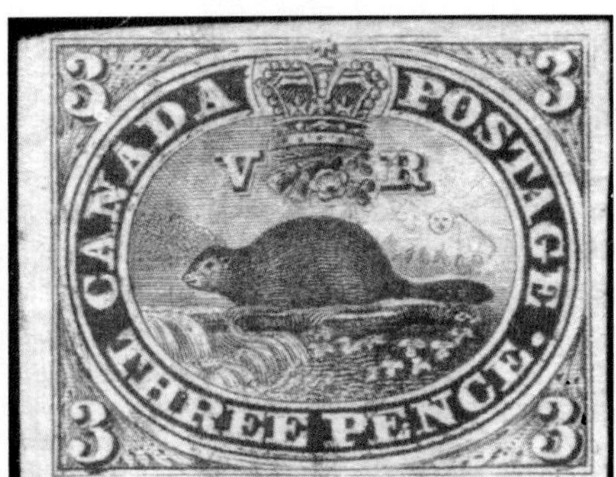

**3d Beaver — pos B61 major re-entry**
**1vi / 4xii / 12vii**

4
Beaver

5
HRH Prince Albert

7
Jacques Cartier

8
Queen Victoria

9
Queen Victoria

10
HRH Prince Albert

**Rates:** ½d: prepaid postage on newspapers in Canada; drop letter

7½d: prepaid postage to Newfoundland and British West Indies, via Halifax. Sterling rate also shown.

10d: closed mail via US by British Packet (per ½ oz.). Sterling rate also shown.

Registration of domestic letters (effective May 1/55): 1d.

Designer: 3d: Sandford Fleming; 10d: sketch by William Henry Griffin, Deputy Postmaster-General of Canada, painting by François Riss. ½d: sketch by Griffin, based on a medal by William Wyon.

Rawdon, Wright, Hatch and Edson of New York
Engraved, one plate of 120 subjects (½d, 7½ and 10d)

**1852–1857** **Wove Paper** **Imperforate**

Mint copies (★) with original gum, add 100%

| | | ★VF | ★F | ★VG | ⊙VF | ⊙F | ⊙VG | ✉ |
|---|---|---|---|---|---|---|---|---|
| **4** | **3d red**, medium wove, *Apr 17, 1852* | 2,000.00 | 1,250.00 | 500.00 | 300.00 | 150.00 | 75.00 | 300.00 |
| a | brown red, *1853* | 2,100.00 | 1,300.00 | 550.00 | 350.00 | 175.00 | 100.00 | 300.00 |
| b | diagonal half used as 1½d on cover | | | | | | | 40,000.00 |
| c | ribbed, soft wove paper | 6,000.00 | 3,000.00 | 1,500.00 | 800.00 | 400.00 | 200.00 | 900.00 |
| d | thin paper, orange red | 2,000.00 | 1,000.00 | 500.00 | 300.00 | 150.00 | 100.00 | 300.00 |
| i | deep red | 2,200.00 | 1,200.00 | 500.00 | 350.00 | 175.00 | 75.00 | 350.00 |
| ii | orange red | 2,000.00 | 1,100.00 | 500.00 | 350.00 | 175.00 | 75.00 | 350.00 |
| iii | ribbed, hard wove paper | 4,000.00 | 2,000.00 | 1,000.00 | 850.00 | 500.00 | 200.00 | 800.00 |
| iv | thin oily paper, orange red | 2,500.00 | 1,250.00 | 600.00 | 350.00 | 250.00 | 125.00 | 450.00 |
| v | thick hard paper, deep red | 3,000.00 | 1,500.00 | 750.00 | 600.00 | 400.00 | 200.00 | 600.00 |
| vi | major re-entry (pos. 34, pane A) | 6,000.00† | 2,500.00† | 1,250.00† | 1,200.00† | 600.00† | 300.00† | 1,350.00† |
| vii | major re-entry (pos. 47, pane A) | 7,000.00† | 3,000.00† | 1,500.00† | 1,300.00† | 650.00† | 325.00† | 1,800.00† |
| viii | minor re-entry, (numerous) | | 1,500.00† | 750.00† | 450.00† | 250.00† | 100.00† | 400.00 |
| ix | cracked plate LR (pos. 31) | 4,000.00† | 2,000.00† | | 1,000.00† | 450.00† | 250.00† | 750.00 |
| x | stitch watermark* | 6,000.00† | 2,500.00† | | 1,000.00† | 500.00† | 300.00† | — |
| xi | scarlet vermilion, thin paper | 2,500.00 | 1,250.00 | 600.00 | 350.00 | 250.00 | 125.00 | 450.00 |
| xii | major re-entry (pos. 61, pane B) ** | | 2,500.00† | 1,250.00† | 1,200.00† | 600.00† | 300.00† | 1,250.00† |
| xiii | major re-entry (pos. 80, pane A) | | | | 1,200.00† | 600.00† | 300.00† | |

Qty ordered: 2,850,000

The 3d is known perf. 14 (probably 1855) and rouletted (c. 1855-57). Both are unofficial "experimental" perfs. Covers are known from "Ontario Foundry co., Machinists, Kingston", probable makers of the perforating machine(s) used. Ribbed paper varieties: 4c is a thick whiter paper showing strong horizontal ribbing; 4iii is a thinner paper with fainter, more closely spaced ribbing. Re-entries are described following No. 1.

* The "stitch watermark" (4x) exists on several shades and papers.

** See note after No. 1; re-entries are described following No. 1.

The editors have seen it on 4, 4a, 4d, 4i, 4ii, 4iv, 4ix and 4xi.

**4xii**
Pos. 61: Doubling of almost all lettering, all four 3's, and horizontal framelines at upper and lower centre

| | | ★VF | ★F | ★VG | ⊙VF | ⊙F | ⊙VG | ✉ |
|---|---|---|---|---|---|---|---|---|
| **5** | **6d slate grey**, *Mar 1855* | 35,000.00 | 15,000.00 | 7,500.00 | 1,600.00 | 800.00 | 400.00 | 2,000.00 |
| a | brownish grey | 45,000.00 | 20,000.00 | 10,000.00 | 2,400.00 | 1,200.00 | 600.00 | 2,500.00 |
| b | greenish grey | 35,000.00 | 15,000.00 | 7,500.00 | 1,600.00 | 800.00 | 400.00 | 2,000.00 |
| c | diagonal half used as 3d on cover | | | | | | | 25,000.00 |
| d | thick hard paper (grey violet) | 45,000.00 | 20,000.00 | 10,000.00 | 4,000.00 | 2,000.00 | 750.00 | 2,500.00 |
| i | stitch watermark | — | — | — | 5,000.00 | — | — | — |

Qty ordered: 250,000 (includes Scott # 5 and 10)

No. 6 is not assigned.

**7ii**
Heavy line through the bottom of CANADA

| | | ★VF | ★F | ★VG | ⊙VF | ⊙F | ⊙VG | ✉ |
|---|---|---|---|---|---|---|---|---|
| **7** | **10d blue** on thin, crisp, transparent paper, *Jan 1855* | 16,000.00 | 8,000.00 | 2,500.00 | 2,400.00 | 1,200.00 | 500.00 | 3,000.00 |
| a | thick, white, opaque paper | 14,000.00 | 7,000.00 | 2,500.00 | 3,000.00 | 1,500.00 | 550.00 | 3,500.00 |
| i | dull blue | 14,000.00 | 7,000.00 | 2,500.00 | 2,500.00 | 1,250.00 | 500.00 | 3,000.00 |
| ii | major re-entry (pos. 29) | | 7,500.00† | | 3,000.00† | 1,750.00† | 950.00† | 4,800.00 |
| iii | strong re-entry (pos. 1) | | | | 3,000.00† | 1,750.00† | 950.00† | 4,500.00 |
| iv | strong re-entry (pos. 53) | | | | 4,000.00† | 2,000.00† | 1,000.00† | 4,500.00 |
| v | strong re-entry (pos. 90) | | | | 2,750.00† | 1,350.00† | 750.00† | 4,000.00 |
| vi | stitch watermark | — | — | — | — | 3,000.00 | — | — |

Qty ordered: 172,200

Numerous other re-entries exist.

Variety 7ii: top frame line and upper left "8 Stg." strongly doubled; a line through lower part of ANAD of CANADA and ENCE of PENCE; with traces of doubling in many other places. Variety 7iii is similar but shows no doubling of the oval above CANADA. Variety 7iv shows doubling of design, particularly the top of NCE in PENCE. Variety 7v shows doubling of left frameline, left portion of bottom frameline and bottom of CANADA.

† Values are for most common shade or paper.

**7iii**
Distinctive line in the bottom of ANAD

**7iv**

| OG +100% | | ★VF | ★F | ★VG | ⊙VF | ⊙F | ⊙VG | ✉ |
|---|---|---|---|---|---|---|---|---|
| **8** | **½d rose**, *Aug 1, 1857* | 1,400.00 | 700.00 | 350.00 | 1,000.00 | 500.00 | 250.00 | 1,100.00 |
| a | horizontally ribbed paper | 13,500.00 | 7,000.00 | 3,000.00 | 3,500.00 | 1,500.00 | 900.00 | 3,500.00 |
| b | vertically ribbed paper | 15,000.00 | 8,000.00 | 3,000.00 | 5,000.00 | 2,750.00 | 1,350.00 | 6,000.00 |
| i | lilac rose shade | 1,500.00 | 750.00 | 350.00 | 1,100.00 | 550.00 | 300.00 | 1,200.00 |
| ii | major re-entry (pos. 120) | 4,000.00† | 2,500.00† | 1,250.00† | 2,500.00† | 1,250.00† | 700.00† | 3,000.00† |
| iii | vertical stitch watermark | | | | 1,750.00† | 1,000.00† | 600.00† | |
| iv | horizontal stitch watermark | | | | | 1,750.00† | | |

Qty ordered: 2,600,000

Major re-entries also exist on positions 22, 42, 46, 58, 60, 70, 72, 84 and 96.
Strong re-entries exist on positions 10 and 102.

8ii
Doubling of the enitre design, particularly in most of the lettering (especially notable in HALF), all four sets of framelines, with a diagonal plate scratch through the upper left corner frame.

| | | ★VF | ★F | ★VG | ⊙VF | ⊙F | ⊙VG | ✉ |
|---|---|---|---|---|---|---|---|---|
| **9** | **7½d green**, *Jun 2, 1857** | 12,000.00 | 6,000.00 | 2,500.00 | 5,000.00 | 2,000.00 | 750.00 | 6,000.00 |
| a | deep green | 15,000.00 | 7,500.00 | 3,000.00 | 6,000.00 | 2,500.00 | 900.00 | 6,250.00 |
| ii | major re-entry (pos. 7) | | 7,500.00† | 3,750.00† | 6,000.00† | 3,750.00† | 1,500.00† | 6,400.00† |
| iii | stitch watermark | — | — | — | 15,000.00† | 6,000.00† | 3,000.00† | |
| iv | misplaced entry, UL and UR spandrels and upper margin (pos. 47 and 83) | — | — | — | 10,000.00 | 5,000.00 | 3,500.00 | — |

Qty ordered: 100,080

Re-entry shows line through X PEN and traces of doubling in STERLING and CANA, etc.
† Values are for most common shade or paper.
* a cover in an August 2009 Vance Auctions Ltd. auction had a May 2, 1857 date.

9ii
Doubling in all of the lettering, the corner numerals, and the portrait itself.

| | | ★VF | ★F | ★VG | ⊙VF | ⊙F | ⊙VG | ✉ |
|---|---|---|---|---|---|---|---|---|
| **10** | **6d reddish purple** on very thick fibrous soft paper, *1857* | 40,000.00 | 18,000.00 | 6,000.00 | 9,000.00 | 4,000.00 | 1,500.00 | 10,000.00 |
| a | half used as 3d on cover | | | | | | | 30,000.00 |

9iv (pos. 47)

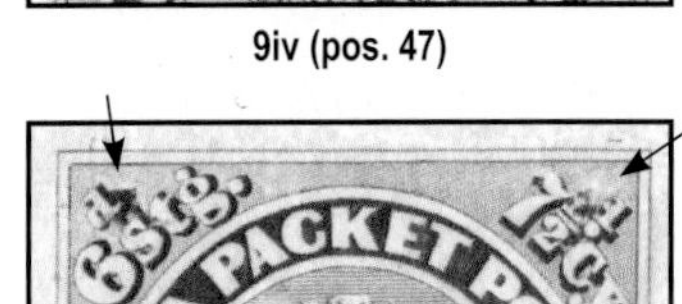

9iv (pos. 83)

11
Queen Victoria

12
Beaver

13
HRH Prince Albert

**1858–1859** **Engraved, Wove Paper** **Perf 11¾**

Well-centred VF copies of this issue (Canada's first perforated stamps) are extremely rare and seldom offered for sale. VG is the average quality for the perforated pence (11–13). Perfs. almost always cut into the outer framelines of the designs because of the very narrow margins between stamps. Ribbed paper varieties are known on the ½d and 3d values. Both are RARE.

Mint copies (★) with original gum, add 150%

| | | ★VF | ★F | ★VG | ⊙VF | ⊙F | ⊙VG | ✉ |
|---|---|---|---|---|---|---|---|---|
| **11** | **½d rose**, *Dec 1858* | 6,000.00 | 2,000.00 | 1,000.00 | 2,500.00 | 1,000.00 | 500.00 | 3,000.00 |
| i | lilac rose | 6,000.00 | 2,000.00 | 1,000.00 | 2,500.00 | 1,000.00 | 500.00 | 3,000.00 |
| ii | major re-entry, pos. 100* | 9,000.00 | 3,000.00 | 1,200.00 | 4,000.00 | 3,000.00 | 1,500.00 | |

Qty ordered: 850,000

Major re-entries also exist on positions 18, 34, 38, 48, 50, 60, 70 and 80.
Strong re-entries exist on positions 8 and 84.
* This is the same re-entry as position 120 on the imperf. sheet (as 8ii). Two vertical columns were removed from the original 120 character plate (12 x 10) used for the imperforate issue resulting in the loss of the first two columns from the sheet. The last position on the perforated sheet is position 100 (10 x 10) and is the same as position 120 on the imperforate sheet. It was apparently necessary to remove two columns so the sheet would fit the perforator.

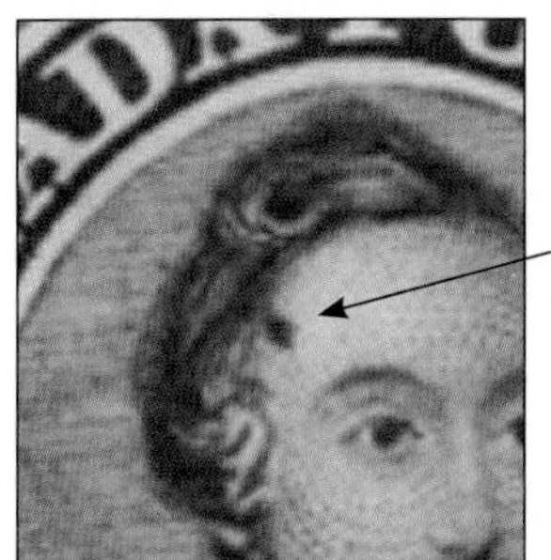
13ii

| | | ★VF | ★F | ★VG | ⊙VF | ⊙F | ⊙VG | ✉ |
|---|---|---|---|---|---|---|---|---|
| **12** | **3d red**, *Jan 1859* | 25,000.00 | 12,000.00 | 5,000.00 | 1,600.00 | 600.00 | 300.00 | 1,750.00 |
| i | brown red | 25,000.00 | 12,000.00 | 5,000.00 | 1,600.00 | 600.00 | 300.00 | 1,750.00 |
| ii | major re-entry (pos. 34, pane A) | | | | | 1,200.00† | 750.00† | 2,250.00† |
| iii | major re-entry (pos. 47, pane A) | | | | | 1,500.00† | 950.00† | 2,250.00† |
| iv | minor re-entries (numerous) | | | | | 750.00† | 450.00† | 2,000.00† |
| v | stitch watermark | — | 30,000.00 | — | — | 1,500.00 | — | — |
| vi | major re-entry (pos. 80, pane A) | | | | | 1,500.00† | 750.00† | |
| vii | major re-entry (pos. 61, pane B) ** | | | | | | | |

Qty ordered: 450,000

** See note after No. 1; re-entries are described following No. 1.

| | | ★VF | ★F | ★VG | ⊙VF | ⊙F | ⊙VG | ✉ |
|---|---|---|---|---|---|---|---|---|
| **13** | **6d brown violet**, *Jan 1859* | 30,000.00 | 10,000.00 | 4,000.00 | 10,000.00 | 5,000.00 | 2,500.00 | 9,000.00 |
| a | grey violet | 30,000.00 | 10,000.00 | 4,000.00 | 10,000.00 | 5,000.00 | 2,500.00 | 9,000.00 |
| b | diagonal half used as 3d on cover | | | | | | | 30,000.00 |
| i | stitch watermark | — | 20,000.00 | — | — | — | 8,000.00 | — |
| ii | burr on forehead (pos. 43) | | 25,000.00 | | | | | |

Qty ordered: 70,000

† Prices are for most common shade or paper.

*Canada's Pence Era The Pence Stamps and the Canadian mail 1851–1859*, George B. Arfken, Arthur W. Leggett, Charles G. Firby, Allan L. Steinhart, 1997.

## PROVINCE OF CANADA PLATE PROOFS — PENCE ISSUES

This section lists Proofs (P), Trial Colour Proofs (TC) and Specimen Overprint proofs. A specimen overprint is indicated by its orientation in parentheses, followed by the overprint colour.

(V) = vertical specimen overprint (H) = horizontal specimen overprint (D) = diagonal specimen overprint

Prices are for single copies in VF condition. A premium should be added for blocks with marginal inscription. All Province of Canada proofs are on India paper and were originally mounted on card. SPECIMEN overprints are always in capital letters.

### 1851–64 Three Pence

| | | |
|---|---|---|
| **1P** | red (1857) | 350.00 |
| **1TC** | red, (H) carmine | 500.00 |
| **i** | brown red, (H) green black | 300.00 |
| **ii** | black | 400.00 |
| **iii** | as ii, (H) carmine | 400.00 |
| **iv** | as ii, (D) carmine | 700.00 |
| **v** | as ii, (H) orange | 300.00 |
| **vi** | orange yellow (1864) | 350.00 |

### Six Pence

| | | |
|---|---|---|
| **2TC** | red lilac (1857) | 300.00 |
| **i** | red purple (1857) | 325.00 |
| **ii** | orange yellow (1864) | 450.00 |
| **iii** | grey | 1,500.00 |
| **iv** | as iii, (D) carmine | 900.00 |
| **v** | as iii, (V) orange | 300.00 |
| **vi** | as iii, (V) green | 375.00 |
| **vii** | dark grey, (V) carmine | 300.00 |
| **viii** | greenish grey, (V) carmine | 300.00 |
| **ix** | black, (V) carmine | 350.00 |
| **x** | as ix, (V) orange | 375.00 |
| **xi** | grey blue, (V) carmine | 350.00 |
| **xii** | lilac, (V) carmine | 325.00 |
| **xiii** | as xii, (V) orange | 300.00 |
| **xiv** | blue, no specimen | 3,500.00 |
| **xv** | as i, with ‘burr on forehead’ | 2,000.00 |

### Twelve Pence

| | | |
|---|---|---|
| **3P** | black | 6,000.00 |
| **i** | black, (V) carmine | 2,500.00 |
| **ii** | as i, (D) carmine | 5,000.00 |
| **iii** | as i, (V) green | 6,500.00 |
| **3TC** | “scar” die proof, any colour* | 9,000.00 |
| **i** | with 16TCiii, any colour* | *25,000.00* |

### 1854. Ten Pence

| | | |
|---|---|---|
| **7P** | blue (shades) | 300.00 |
| **i** | blue, (V) carmine | 300.00 |
| **7TC** | black | 750.00 |
| **i** | black, (V) carmine | 1,000.00 |
| **ii** | as i, (D) carmine | 1,000.00 |
| **iii** | orange yellow (1864) | 400.00 |
| **7P & 8P** | Composite** | 12,000.00 |

### 1857–1864. Half Pence

| | | |
|---|---|---|
| **8P** | rose | 350.00 |
| **i** | rose, (V) green black | 300.00 |
| **8TC** | deep rose (1858) | 300.00 |
| **i** | orange yellow (1864) | 400.00 |
| **ii** | black (V) carmine | 300.00 |
| **iii** | brown, (V) carmine | 300.00 |
| **iv** | black w/o specimen, gummed | 1,000.00 |

### Seven and One-Half Pence

| | | |
|---|---|---|
| **9P** | green | 350.00 |
| **9TC** | black | 1,200.00 |
| **i** | black, (V) carmine | 500.00 |
| **ii** | as i, (D) carmine | 1,000.00 |
| **iii** | orange yellow (1864) | 550.00 |

* From composite die proofs with 16TCiii (10¢ of 1859) with a “scar” in CE of PENCE. All are rare. Black, brown, vermilion, green & slate blue are known. 10 cents (16TCiii, any shade, from the composite: $2,500.

** 10d and ½d with gutter between, from the trade sample sheets. Several colours exist. Single examples of either value, any shade, $1,000 for VF.

1TCi 2TCv 2TCvii 3Pi 3Piii

7Pi 8Pi 8TC 8TCi 8TCiii

9P 9TC 9TCi

3TCi

## FIRST CENTS ISSUE

14
Queen Victoria

15
Beaver



**Rates:** Jul 1/1859 — Surface letter, each ½ oz. prepaid: 5¢

Surface letter, each ½ oz. unpaid: 7¢

Drop letter: 1¢ per letter

16
HRH Prince Albert

17
HRH Prince Albert

18
Queen Victoria

19
Jacques Cartier

20
Queen Victoria

Designer: 2¢: Based on a sketch by William Henry Griffin, based on a medal by William Wyon.

American Bank Note Company, New York
Engraved, sheets of 100

**1859–1864** **Wove Paper** **Perf 11¾, 12 x 11¾, 12**

This is the first issue of Canada that was regularly perforated. Because gutters between the stamps are very narrow and the spacing of the perforation did not precisely match the spacing of the stamp designs, the issue is generally very poorly centered. On Fine centered stamps, the perfs will touch or be very close to the outer framelines. Stamps with perforations clear of the design on all sides and reasonably well centered are very scarce and can be considered as VF copies. Beware of regumming on this issue—certificates of authenticity are recommended.

**Outstanding SUPERB QUALITY examples with jumbo borders will sell for well above the very fine prices listed. These rarely change hands.**

Mint copies (★) with original gum, add 150%. NH with OG (cert. required) add 300%.

| | | ★VF | ★F | ★VG | ⊙VF | ⊙F | ⊙VG | ✉ |
|---|---|---|---|---|---|---|---|---|
| **14** | **1¢ rose**, perf 12, *Jul 1, 1859* | 600.00 | 300.00 | 100.00 | 120.00 | 40.00 | 20.00 | 75.00 |
| **a** | rose, imperf. pair, no gum, (100 stamps) | 9,000.00 | 4,000.00 | 2,500.00 | — | — | — | — |
| **b** | deep rose, perf. 11¾ | 800.00 | 500.00 | 200.00 | 200.00 | 70.00 | 30.00 | 125.00 |
| **ii** | very thick paper | 1,500.00 | 900.00 | 300.00 | 500.00 | 200.00 | 100.00 | |
| **iii** | very thin paper | 1,500.00 | 900.00 | 300.00 | 500.00 | 200.00 | 100.00 | |
| **iv** | "Q" flaw (pos. 38) | — | 2,500.00 | 1,250.00 | 2,000.00 | 1,000.00 | 500.00 | 1,800.00 |
| **v** | "E" flaw (pos. 34) | 2,500.00 | 1,000.00 | 400.00 | 400.00 | 150.00 | 75.00 | 350.00 |
| **vi** | "C" flaw (pos. 37) | 2,500.00 | 1,000.00 | 400.00 | 400.00 | 150.00 | 75.00 | 235.00 |
| **vii** | imprint copy, any position | 800.00 | 400.00 | 200.00 | 150.00 | 60.00 | 30.00 | 125.00 |
| **viii** | 1¢ rose, perf 12 x 11¾ | 500.00 | 250.00 | 80.00 | 125.00 | 40.00 | 20.00 | 110.00 |
| **ix** | stitch watermark | — | 1,500.00 | — | — | 1,000.00 | — | 1,000.00 |
| **x** | major re-entry (pos. 58) | | | | | | | |
| **xi** | major misplaced entry (pos. 28) | | | | | | | |

No. 14 exists with three perforations: 1) printing orders 1–10 (8,000,000 stamps) perf. 11¾ x 11¾; 2) orders 11–19 (7,500,000 stamps) perf. 12 x 11¾; 3) orders 20–26 (12,000,000 stamps) perf. 12 x 12.

No. 14 exists on laid paper (7 recorded). Last recorded auction sale was Harmers New York sale of the Carey Fox collection @ US$825 in 1968. Value "used": *$2,500.00*

**"Q" flaw**: flaw in oval below O of ONE plus line in cross-hatching and weak entry of cross-hatching at LL corner. Three states exist as the lines below O and N varied in length as the flaw wore. Prices are for strong flaw.

**"E" flaw**: a line in the bottom of the E in CENT.

**"C" flaw**: dot in C of CENT and line below C through the white oval to the bottom margin.

Imprint copy: should show "erican Bank Note Co. New Yo" portion of the imprint at top, bottom or either side.

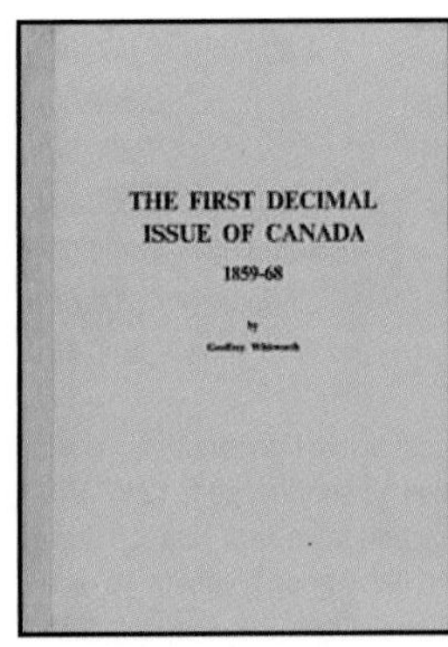

*The First Decimal Issue of Canada*, Geoffrey Whitworth, 1966.

*The Five Cents Beaver Stamp of Canada*, Geoffrey Whitworth,. 1985.

**14iv**

**14v**

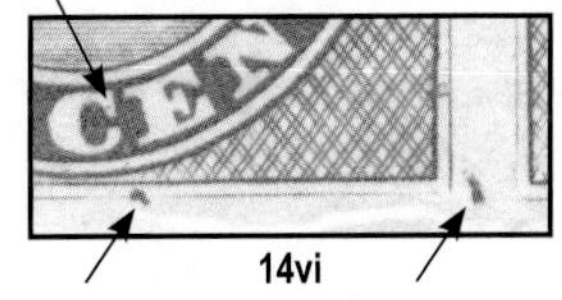
**14vi**

**14x**

Marks are found in the white oval above CANA, in POST and ONE CE, and the white band to the upper left of the O of ONE. The framelines are also doubled at the LL, LR, and left centre.

**14xi**

Bottom and lower right margins and AGE and ONE.

15ix 15viii

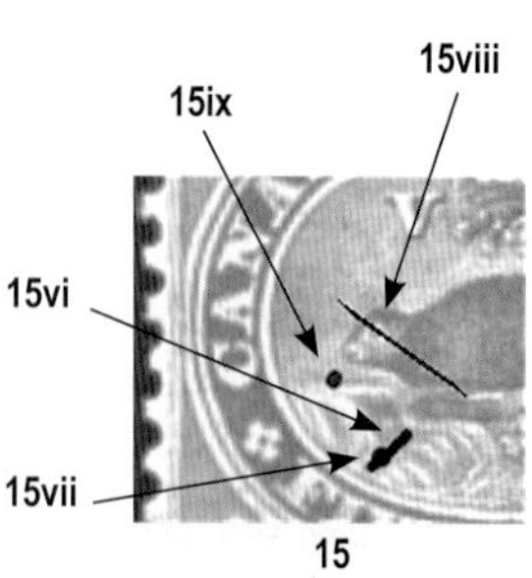

15

15v

The entire design is strongly doubled to the left, with the left side particularly heavy; virtually all of the lettering, all four 5's, the crown at top-centre, the head of the beaver, the sun in the sky, oval bands, and left and right framelines are sharply doubled. This re-entry did not occur until the tenth of the eleven states of this plate.

| No. | | | ★VF | ★F | ★VG | ⊙VF | ⊙F | ⊙VG | ✉ |
|---|---|---|---|---|---|---|---|---|---|
| 15 | | **5¢ vermilion,** *Jul 1859* | 800.00 | 400.00 | 100.00 | 50.00 | 20.00 | 10.00 | 35.00 |
| | a | vermilion, imperf. pair, no gum, (100 stamps)* | 27,500.00 | 13,500.00 | | — | — | — | — |
| | b | diagonal half used as 2½¢ on cover | | | | | | | 12,000.00 |
| | c | brick red (brownish orange red) perf. 11¾, 1st printing | 850.00 | 450.00 | 200.00 | 60.00 | 25.00 | 10.00 | 50.00 |
| | ii | orange red | 750.00 | 350.00 | 100.00 | 50.00 | 15.00 | 7.50 | 35.00 |
| | iii | very thick paper | 1,800.00† | 900.00† | 450.00† | 300.00† | 150.00† | 90.00† | |
| | iv | very thin paper | 3,000.00† | 1,800.00† | 900.00† | 450.00† | 300.00† | 150.00† | |
| | v | major re-entry (pos. 28) | 3,000.00† | 1,500.00† | 750.00† | 1,000.00† | 500.00† | 250.00† | 1,100.00† |
| | vi | "log in waterfall" (pos. 50) | | 2,000.00† | 1,000.00† | 1,250.00† | 650.00† | 300.00† | 1,300.00† |
| | vii | "rock in waterfall" variety (pos. 53) | | 1,350.00† | 750.00† | 750.00† | 300.00† | 150.00† | 950.00† |
| | viii | "split beaver" (pos. 90) | | 750.00† | 375.00† | 750.00† | 300.00† | 150.00† | 700.00† |
| | ix | "leaping fish" variety (pos. 54) | | 750.00† | 375.00† | 750.00† | 300.00† | 125.00† | 600.00† |
| | x | imprint copy | | 450.00† | 150.00† | 100.00† | 35.00† | 17.50† | 60.00† |
| | xi | ribbed paper | | | | | | | |

Numerous re-entries and minor plate flaws exist. The plate of 100 was retouched or re-entered 10 times, resulting in up to 11 recognizable states of each plate position. Thus potentially 1,100 identifiably different stamps. Only the more prominent and well-known flaws are listed. No. 15b was used with 10¢ for 12½¢ rate. The "very thick paper" (15iii) measures .0042 to .0045 inches thick.

* Only 2 blocks and 2 pairs of 15a are known. Several "singles" have been seen by the editors but margins are nearly always a bit too close to prove they are/were imperforate as there are numerous jumbos around that could be trimmed to make it look like imperforate. All need certificates.

† Prices are for most common shade or paper.

Qty: There were 31 printings of No. 15, producing 39,100,000 stamps.

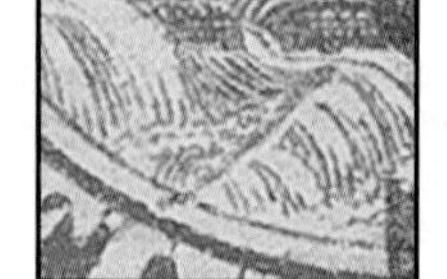
15vi

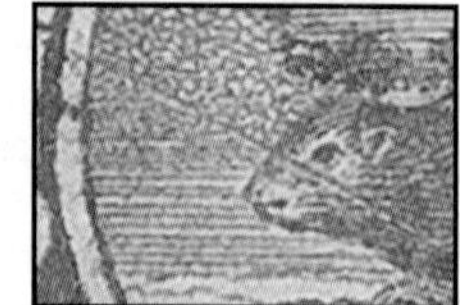
15viii

| No. | | | ★VF | ★F | ★VG | ⊙VF | ⊙F | ⊙VG | ✉ |
|---|---|---|---|---|---|---|---|---|---|
| 16 | | **10¢ black brown**, perf. 11¾ first printing, very deep shade | 20,000.00 | 8,000.00 | 4,000.00 | 8,500.00 | 3,500.00 | 1,250.00 | 7,500.00 |
| | a | half used as 5¢ on cover | | | | | | | 18,000.00 |
| | i | chocolate brown, perf. 11¾ 1st printing | 20,000.00 | 8,000.00 | 4,000.00 | 8,500.00 | 3,500.00 | 1,250.00 | 7,500.00 |
| | ii | major re-entry (pos. 29 and 51)* | | | | | 4,500.00 | 1,600.00 | |
| | iii | "string of pearls" (pos. 3)* | | | | | 5,000.00 | 2,000.00 | |
| | iv | "double epaulette" (pos. 61)* | | | | | 5,000.00 | 2,000.00 | |

* Black brown or chocolate brown.

Numbers 16 and 16i must be perf. 11¾ on all edges, 1,000 sheets of the first printing were printed in chocolate brown or black brown.

ERD for 10¢ is a No. 16i (chocolate brown) on cover, July 1, 1859.

17iv

17v

17iii (pos. 29)

17v

| No. | | | ★VF | ★F | ★VG | ⊙VF | ⊙F | ⊙VG | ✉ |
|---|---|---|---|---|---|---|---|---|---|
| 17 | | **10¢ red lilac**, perf. 12, last printing | 1,600.00 | 800.00 | 250.00 | 240.00 | 80.00 | 40.00 | 200.00 |
| | a | violet, perf 12 | 2,000.00 | 1,000.00 | 300.00 | 300.00 | 100.00 | 50.00 | 225.00 |
| | b | brown (and shades), perf. 11¾ , 12 x 11¾ | 1,600.00 | 800.00 | 250.00 | 200.00 | 60.00 | 30.00 | 200.00 |
| | c | red lilac, imperf. pair, no gum, (100 stamps) | 25,000.00 | 15,500.00 | | — | — | — | — |
| | ci | as "c", with "string of pearls" | 30,000.00 | 16,500.00 | | — | — | — | — |
| | d | diagonal half used as 5¢ on cover | | | | | | | 10,000.00 |
| | e | deep red purple, perf. 11¾ , 2nd ptg. | 4,000.00 | 2,500.00 | 1,200.00 | 1,200.00 | 500.00 | 225.00 | 1,250.00 |
| | ii | very thick paper (later printings) | | 3,600.00 | 1,800.00 | 750.00 | 350.00 | 150.00 | |
| | iii | major re-entry (pos. 29 and 51) | | 1,600.00 | 800.00 | 500.00 | 250.00 | 125.00 | 600.00† |
| | iv | "string of pearls" (pos. 3)* | 4,000.00† | 2,200.00† | 1,500.00† | 1,000.00† | 500.00† | 250.00† | 1,000.00† |
| | v | "double epaulette" (pos. 61)* | 4,000.00† | 2,200.00† | 1,500.00† | 1,000.00† | 500.00† | 250.00† | 1,100.00† |
| | vi | "C" flaw | 2,500.00† | 1,200.00† | 600.00† | 300.00† | 175.00† | 75.00† | 350.00† |
| | vii | imprint copy | | 650.00† | 300.00† | 200.00† | 80.00† | 50.00† | 250.00† |
| | viii | stitch watermark | | | | 1,750.00† | 950.00† | 600.00† | |

There were 26 printings of No. 17 and 3 distinct perforations: 1) nine printings (1,500,000 stamps) in 21 shades, perf. 11¾; 2) eight printings (1,500,000 stamps) in 16 shades, perf. 12 x 11¾; 3) nine printings (2,700,000 stamps) in 24 shades, perf. 12.

* These varieties occur on all printings and shades of Nos. 16 and 17. To determine the value on 16 or 16i, add the value for the variety in the same grade on 17 to the basic price given for 16 or 16i. The "C" flaw occurs on the 9th and 10th vertical columns and is due to a repair during the preparation of Order 17. The flaw appears on the later printings (perf. 12) and only rarely on perf. 12 x 11¾ because Order 17 was the final order to use this perf. and only 2,000 sheets were printed. Position 29 shows slight doubling at top and bottom. Position 51 shows stronger doubling, but only at the bottom.

† Prices are for most common shade or paper.

| No. | | ★VF | ★F | ★VG | ⊙VF | ⊙F | ⊙VG | ✉ |
|---|---|---|---|---|---|---|---|---|
| **18** | **12½¢ yellow green** (ERD *Jul 13,1859*) | 1,250.00 | 600.00 | 200.00 | 220.00 | 80.00 | 30.00 | 250.00 |
| a | blue green, perf 11¾ | 1,500.00 | 750.00 | 300.00 | 200.00 | 70.00 | 30.00 | 250.00 |
| b | blue green, imperf. pair, no gum, (100 stamps) | 10,000.00 | 4,000.00 | 2,750.00 | — | — | — | — |
| i | olive green | 1,350.00 | 600.00 | 275.00 | 220.00 | 80.00 | 30.00 | 250.00 |
| ii | green | 1,350.00 | 600.00 | 250.00 | 220.00 | 80.00 | 30.00 | 250.00 |
| iii | very thick paper | 3,000.00 | 1,600.00 | | 300.00 | 175.00 | 125.00 | |
| iv | major re-entry (pos. 94) | 3,000.00† | 1,800.00† | 650.00† | 900.00† | 300.00† | 175.00† | 600.00† |
| v | imprint copy | | 650.00† | 300.00† | 250.00† | 100.00† | 45.00† | 320.00† |
| vi | stitch watermark | — | — | — | — | 2,000.00 | 750.00 | — |
| vii | major re-entry (pos. 61 & 62) | 3,000.00† | 1,800.00† | 650.00† | 600.00† | 300.00† | 175.00† | 600.00† |

No. 18 exists with 3 perforations: 1) printing orders 1–8, perf. 11¾ (1,100,000); 2) orders 9–14, perf. 12 x 11¾ (1,200,000); 3) orders 15–19, perf. 12 (1,200,000). Position 61 re-entry shows lines in N of PENCE and doubling of oval over PACKET. Position 94 re-entry shows distinctive line in E of PENCE plus doubling of oval over and in POSTAGE.
† Prices are for most common shade or paper.

18iv

18vii

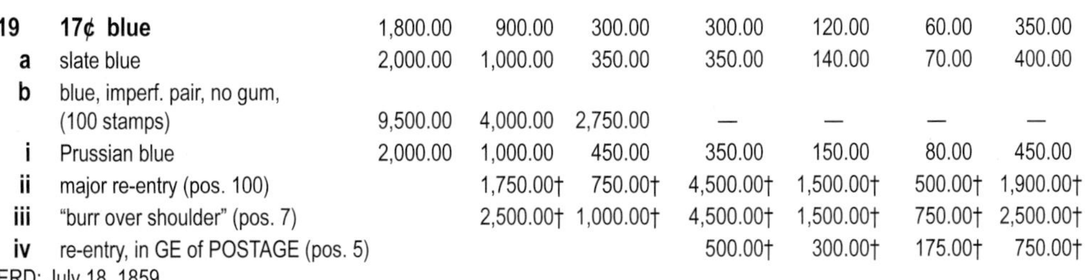

| No. | | ★VF | ★F | ★VG | ⊙VF | ⊙F | ⊙VG | ✉ |
|---|---|---|---|---|---|---|---|---|
| **19** | **17¢ blue** | 1,800.00 | 900.00 | 300.00 | 300.00 | 120.00 | 60.00 | 350.00 |
| a | slate blue | 2,000.00 | 1,000.00 | 350.00 | 350.00 | 140.00 | 70.00 | 400.00 |
| b | blue, imperf. pair, no gum, (100 stamps) | 9,500.00 | 4,000.00 | 2,750.00 | — | — | — | — |
| i | Prussian blue | 2,000.00 | 1,000.00 | 450.00 | 350.00 | 150.00 | 80.00 | 450.00 |
| ii | major re-entry (pos. 100) | | 1,750.00† | 750.00† | 4,500.00† | 1,500.00† | 500.00† | 1,900.00† |
| iii | "burr over shoulder" (pos. 7) | | 2,500.00† | 1,000.00† | 4,500.00† | 1,500.00† | 750.00† | 2,500.00† |
| iv | re-entry, in GE of POSTAGE (pos. 5) | | | | 500.00† | 300.00† | 175.00† | 750.00† |

ERD: July 18, 1859.
No. 19 exists with 3 perforations: 1) five orders (more than 200,000 stamps) perf. 11¾; 2) three orders (more than 100,000 stamps) perf. 12 x 11¾; 3) five orders (250,000 stamps) perf. 12. The major re-entry shows strong doubling of the left frame line, the inner frame line at upper right, and the letters TS of CENTS and TAG of POSTAGE. The Prussian blue shade is found in Order 2, perf. 11¾ and in Order 7, perf. 12 x 11¾ .
XF NH at least two exist, value $12,500.
† Prices are for most common shade or paper.

19ii

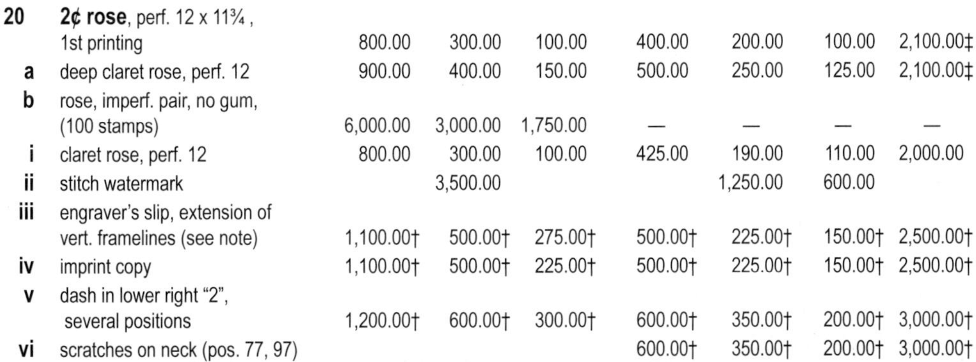

| No. | | ★VF | ★F | ★VG | ⊙VF | ⊙F | ⊙VG | ✉ |
|---|---|---|---|---|---|---|---|---|
| **20** | **2¢ rose**, perf. 12 x 11¾ , 1st printing | 800.00 | 300.00 | 100.00 | 400.00 | 200.00 | 100.00 | 2,100.00‡ |
| a | deep claret rose, perf. 12 | 900.00 | 400.00 | 150.00 | 500.00 | 250.00 | 125.00 | 2,100.00‡ |
| b | rose, imperf. pair, no gum, (100 stamps) | 6,000.00 | 3,000.00 | 1,750.00 | — | — | — | — |
| i | claret rose, perf. 12 | 800.00 | 300.00 | 100.00 | 425.00 | 190.00 | 110.00 | 2,000.00 |
| ii | stitch watermark | | 3,500.00 | | | 1,250.00 | 600.00 | |
| iii | engraver's slip, extension of vert. framelines (see note) | 1,100.00† | 500.00† | 275.00† | 500.00† | 225.00† | 150.00† | 2,500.00† |
| iv | imprint copy | 1,100.00† | 500.00† | 225.00† | 500.00† | 225.00† | 150.00† | 2,500.00† |
| v | dash in lower right "2", several positions | 1,200.00† | 600.00† | 300.00† | 600.00† | 350.00† | 200.00† | 3,000.00† |
| vi | scratches on neck (pos. 77, 97) | | | | 600.00† | 350.00† | 200.00† | 3,000.00† |

No. 20 exists with 2 perforations: 1) printing order 1 (200,000 stamps) perf. 12 x 11¾; 2) orders 2–8 (665,000 stamps) perf. 12. There is only one unused example of the "stitch watermark" variety recorded. The engraver's slip occurs on more than 20 positions in a sheet of 100, at any one of the four corners, the LL corner being the most common. Position 61 is the best example.
† Prices are for most common shade, perforation or paper.
‡ Price is for single usage, soldier's letter, double drop letter, drop letter with additional 1¢ for ferriage fee.

19iv

20v

Queen Victoria — Cents

## PROVINCE OF CANADA PLATE PROOFS — CENTS ISSUES

This section lists Proofs (P), Trial Colour Proofs (TC) and Specimen Overprint proofs. A specimen overprint is indicated by its orientation in parentheses, followed by the overprint colour.

(V) = vertical specimen overprint (H) = horizontal specimen overprint (D) = diagonal specimen overprint

Prices are for single copies in VF condition. A premium should be added for blocks with marginal inscription (premium of 25% over the sum of the singles in the imprint block). All Province of Canada proofs are on India paper and were originally mounted on card. SPECIMEN overprints are always in capital letters.

### 1859–67 One Cent

| | | |
|---|---|---|
| **14P** | rose/deep rose (shades) | 250.00 |
| **i** | rose, (V) black | 250.00 |
| **ii** | as i, (D) black | 500.00 |
| **14TC** | pale rose | 250.00 |
| **i** | black | 400.00 |
| **ii** | orange yellow (1864) | 350.00 |
| **iii** | claret (1864) | 275.00 |

### Five Cents

| | | |
|---|---|---|
| **15P** | vermilion (1867) | 300.00 |
| **15TC** | orange vermilion | 250.00 |
| **i** | orange brownish-red | 250.00 |
| **ii** | brown red | 275.00 |
| **iii** | as ii, (D) carmine | 350.00 |
| **iv** | as ii, (H) black | 250.00 |
| **v** | as ii, (H) black "SPECInEN" (1 known) | *3,750.00* |
| **vi** | as ii, (D) black | 1,800.00 |
| **vii** | black | 800.00 |
| **viii** | orange yellow (1864) | 600.00 |

### Ten Cent

| | | |
|---|---|---|
| **16P** | black brown | 500.00 |
| **i** | black brown, (V) carmine | 450.00 |
| **ii** | as i, (D) carmine | 600.00 |
| **16TC** | black | 400.00 |
| **i** | black, (D) carmine | 450.00 |
| **ii** | orange yellow (1864) | 450.00 |
| **iii** | from composite die proofs (with the 12d) any colour | 3,000.00 |
| **17TC** | lilac | 250.00 |
| **i** | brownish purple (1864) | 275.00 |

### Twelve and One-Half Cents

Three types of specimen overprints occur on a sheet of 100:

Type A - 20 mm long, thin letters, 50 on sheet from columns 1, 2, 3, 4 and 6.

Type B - 20 mm long, thick letters, 40 on sheet from columns 7, 8, 9 and 10.

Type C - 21.5 mm long, medium letters, 10 on sheet from column 5, no period after SPECIMEN.

Multiples with se-tenant specimen types are worth a premium: 2 types + 25%, 3 types + 100%.

| | | |
|---|---|---|
| **18P** | yellow green | 350.00 |
| **i** | yellow green (V) carmine | 300.00 |
| **ii** | as i, (V) black | 350.00 |
| **iii** | as i, (D) black | 450.00 |
| **18TC** | blue green (1864) | 300.00 |
| **i** | blue | 400.00 |
| **ii** | blue, (V) carmine, Type A, 50 exist | 400.00 |
| **iii** | as ii, Type B, 40 exist | 500.00 |
| **iv** | as ii, Type C, 10 exist | 4,000.00 |
| **v** | black, (V) carmine, Type A, 50 exist | 600.00 |
| **vi** | as v, Type B, 40 exist | 700.00 |
| **vii** | as v, Type C, 10 exist | 4,000.00 |
| **viii** | orange yellow (1864) | 450.00 |
| **ix** | black | 650.00 |

### Seventeen Cent

| | | |
|---|---|---|
| **19P** | blue | 350.00 |
| **i** | blue, (V) carmine | 300.00 |
| **ii** | as i, (D) carmine | 650.00 |
| **19TC** | pale blue (1867) | 300.00 |
| **i** | black | 550.00 |
| **ii** | orange yellow (1864) | 450.00 |

### 1864 Two Cent

| | | |
|---|---|---|
| **20TC** | dark rose | 300.00 |
| **i** | claret | 350.00 |
| **ii** | green | 400.00 |
| **iii** | dark rose, red | 550.00 |

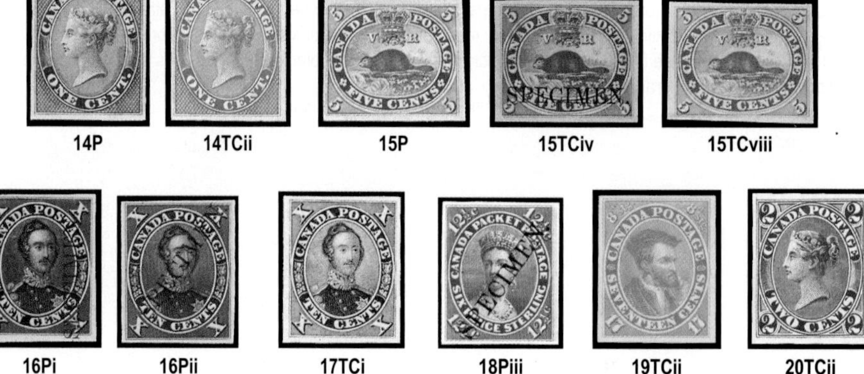

14P 14TCii 15P 15TCiv 15TCviii

16Pi 16Pii 17TCi 18Piii 19TCii 20TCii

# DOMINION OF CANADA

## LARGE QUEEN ISSUE

21 22 23 24 25

26 27 28 29 30

**Rates:**

Domestic: 3¢ per ½ oz.
USA: 6¢
Red River: 6¢
British Columbia and Vancouver Island: 10¢
Great Britain and Newfoundland: 12½¢
Great Britain via New York: 15¢
Transient newspapers: 2¢
Printed matter: 1¢
Single periodicals: ½¢
Drop letters: 1¢ per ½ oz. (posted for delivery at same office)
Registration: 2¢ (letters); 5¢ (parcels)

21ii

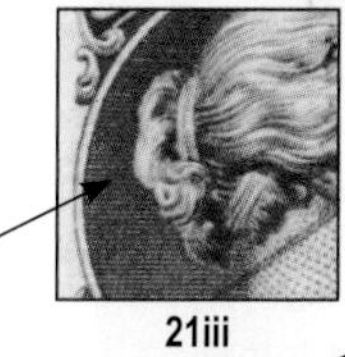

21iii

21iv

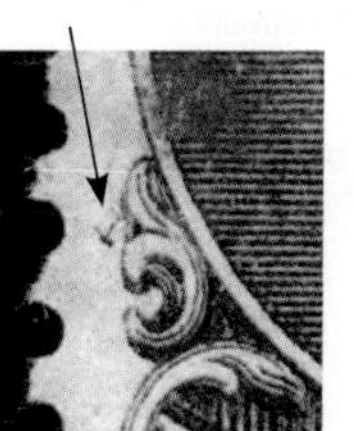

21v



Based on an engraving by Charles Henry Jeens. Portrait engraved by Alfred Jones. Lettering and frame engraved by Henry Earle Sr.
British American Bank Note Company at Montreal and Ottawa

**1868–1876** **Engraved** **Perf 12**

Regummed copies are frequently encountered on this issue. Also, there are very few copies of the Large Queen Issue with original gum which have never been hinged [OG–NH] except for examples of the ½¢ and the common shades of the 15¢ values. Certificates of authenticity are recommended for all OGNH copies, and all the more expensive values with original gum.

Plate proofs on card in the colour of issue exist for each value, Nos. 21–22, 24–28 $750, No. 29 $1,000.

Mint copies (★) with original gum, add 100%. NH with OG (cert. required) add 300% (½¢ at 200%).

| | | ★VF | ★F | ★VG | ⊙VF | ⊙F | ⊙VG | ✉ |
|---|---|---|---|---|---|---|---|---|
| **21** | **½¢ black**, *Apr 1, 1868* | 125.00 | 60.00 | 30.00 | 100.00 | 40.00 | 20.00 | 1,200.00‡ |
| a | perf. 11½ x 12, *1873* | 180.00 | 90.00 | 40.00 | 125.00 | 50.00 | 22.50 | 1,200.00‡ |
| b | watermarked (Bothwell) paper | | 32,000.00 | 22,000.00 | | 15,000.00 | 10,000.00 | |
| vii | Bothwell paper | 1,250.00 | 600.00 | 240.00 | 400.00 | 200.00 | 100.00 | — |
| c | thin paper | 180.00 | 90.00 | 45.00 | 100.00 | 60.00 | 25.00 | 1,200.00‡ |
| i | thicker paper | 250.00 | 150.00 | 90.00 | 250.00 | 150.00 | 90.00 | 1,200.00‡ |
| ii | line above P of POSTAGE | 250.00 | 125.00 | 50.00 | 150.00 | 90.00 | 37.50 | 1,300.00‡ |
| iii | white area on bun of hair | 200.00 | 100.00 | 45.00 | 125.00 | 75.00 | 37.50 | 1,200.00‡ |
| iv | "spur" in scroll left of H | 200.00 | 100.00 | 45.00 | 125.00 | 75.00 | 37.50 | 1,300.00‡ |
| v | "H" spur (pos. 4) | 500.00 | 300.00 | 125.00 | 500.00 | 250.00 | 100.00 | 1,350.00‡ |
| vi | grey black shade | 125.00 | 60.00 | 30.00 | 100.00 | 40.00 | 20.00 | 1,200.00‡ |
| viii | vert. stitch watermark | — | — | — | 4,000.00 | 2,000.00 | — | — |
| ix | re-entry in UL corner (pos 1, pos 11) | | | | | | | |

Qty: 6,700,000

No. 21iii (chignon variety), occurs on positions 33, 43, 53, 63 and 73. Position 63 is the strongest and position 73 the weakest. No. 21v is the true spur variety from position 4 only; 21iv is a smaller single line from the left scroll on positions 1, 11 and all of columns 2–4 except position 4 [which is the "H" spur (21v)]. A total of 31 positions on the sheet, two of which also show the Chignon variety (positions 33 and 43). These two positions command a premium over the other 29 positions. No. 21i is a higher opacity paper than the "soft white blotting paper". Bothwell paper is watermarked on part of the sheet (See illustration below No. 33), singles without the watermark (21vii) are identified by the distinct vertical weave of the paper.
‡ Single usage only.

21ix (pos. 1)

21ix (pos. 11)

**1870 to 1948 — Never-Hinged Pricing Factor (NH%)**

A percentage factor (NH%) is shown for mint stamps. This figure is the percentage of the price for a mint stamp in very fine condition (★VF) to be added to that price if the stamp has never been hinged. To determine the final price for a mint stamp in the next lower grade (★F), divide the NH% factor by 2 and add this percentage to the price shown. This process is continued for all mint grades.

*The Large Queen Stamps of Canada and Their Use, 2nd Edition*, H.E. and H.W. Duckworth, 2008.

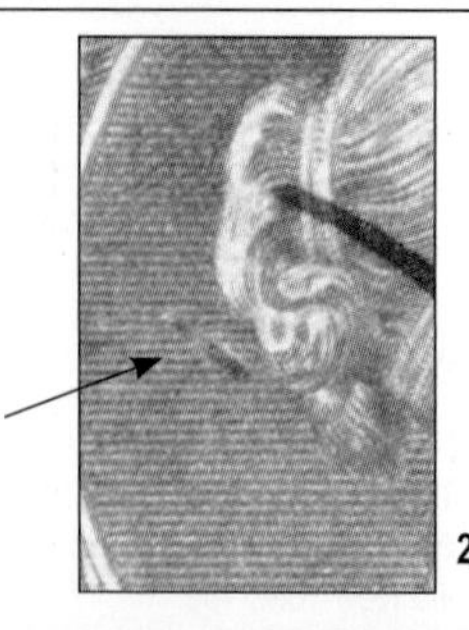
22iii

| No. | | ★VF | ★F | ★VG | ⊙VF | ⊙F | ⊙VG | ✉ |
|---|---|---|---|---|---|---|---|---|
| 22 | **1¢ brown red**, *Apr 1, 1868* | 1,000.00 | 400.00 | 200.00 | 200.00 | 80.00 | 30.00 | 135.00 |
| a | watermarked (Bothwell) paper | 4,000.00 | 2,000.00 | 1,000.00 | 700.00 | 300.00 | 125.00 | — |
| ii | Bothwell paper | 1,400.00 | 600.00 | 300.00 | 250.00 | 100.00 | 50.00 | — |
| b | thin paper | 1,200.00 | 500.00 | 250.00 | 200.00 | 80.00 | 30.00 | 135.00 |
| i | thick soft white (blotting) paper † | 2,000.00 | 1,200.00 | 600.00 | 750.00 | 300.00 | 150.00 | — |
| iii | burr to left of head variety | | | | | 350.00 | | |

Qty: 4,610,000

† Duckworth paper 8, no grain, soft, white paper, is not particularly thick but appears so because of its high opacity.

24v
Doubling in CANADA POSTAGE, particularly a strong line in the back of the 'D.'

| No. | | ★VF | ★F | ★VG | ⊙VF | ⊙F | ⊙VG | ✉ |
|---|---|---|---|---|---|---|---|---|
| 23 | **1¢ yellow orange**, ERD: *Jan 28, 1869* | 2,000.00 | 800.00 | 400.00 | 250.00 | 100.00 | 40.00 | 150.00 |
| a | deep orange (first printing) | 3,000.00 | 1,000.00 | 450.00 | 400.00 | 160.00 | 60.00 | 150.00 |
| i | yellow (last printing) | 2,250.00 | 850.00 | 500.00 | 300.00 | 120.00 | 50.00 | 200.00 |
| ii | vert. stitch watermark | — | — | — | — | 1,000.00 | — | — |
| iii | thin paper (Duckwork paper 9) | | | | | 500.00 | | |

Qty: 4,990,000

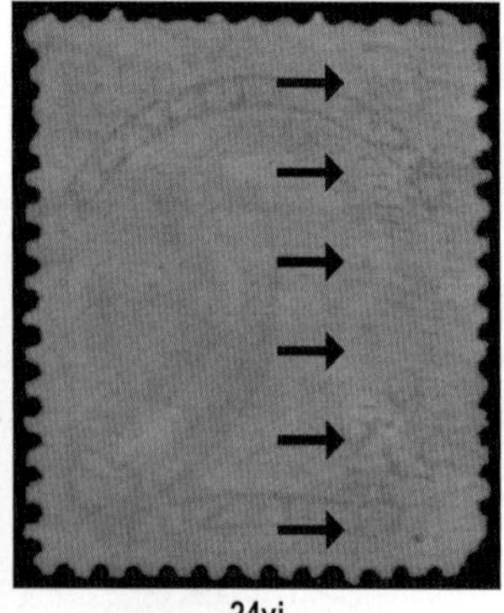
24vi
Vertical stitch watermark

| No. | | ★VF | ★F | ★VG | ⊙VF | ⊙F | ⊙VG | ✉ |
|---|---|---|---|---|---|---|---|---|
| 24 | **2¢ green**, *Apr 1, 1868* | 1,400.00 | 600.00 | 250.00 | 130.00 | 50.00 | 20.00 | 250.00† |
| a | watermarked (Bothwell) paper | 4,000.00 | 2,000.00 | 1,000.00 | 550.00 | 250.00 | 125.00 | |
| iv | Bothwell paper | 1,500.00 | 700.00 | 300.00 | 175.00 | 75.00 | 37.50 | — |
| b | thin paper, deep green | 1,400.00 | 600.00 | 300.00 | 130.00 | 50.00 | 27.50 | 300.00 |
| c | diagonal half used as 1¢ on cover | | | | | | | 6,500.00 |
| i | emerald green | 2,000.00 | 800.00 | 250.00 | 150.00 | 75.00 | 37.50 | 275.00 |
| ii | blue green | 1,600.00 | 600.00 | 225.00 | 140.00 | 60.00 | 25.00 | 250.00 |
| iii | soft white (blotting) paper | 3,000.00 | 1,500.00 | 750.00 | 350.00 | 150.00 | 75.00 | |
| v | major re-entry (pos. 7) | | 3,000.00 | 1,500.00 | 800.00 | 375.00 | 150.00 | 750.00 |
| vi | vert. stitch watermark* | — | 4,000.00 | — | — | 1,000.00 | 500.00 | — |
| vii | "needle nose" variety | | | | 1,200.00 | 600.00 | 300.00 | |
| viii | "spur" in left outer frame line (two states known) | | | | 1,000.00 | 500.00 | 300.00 | |

Qty: 10,300,000

† Single usage only

* 3 used copies recorded, two with faults.

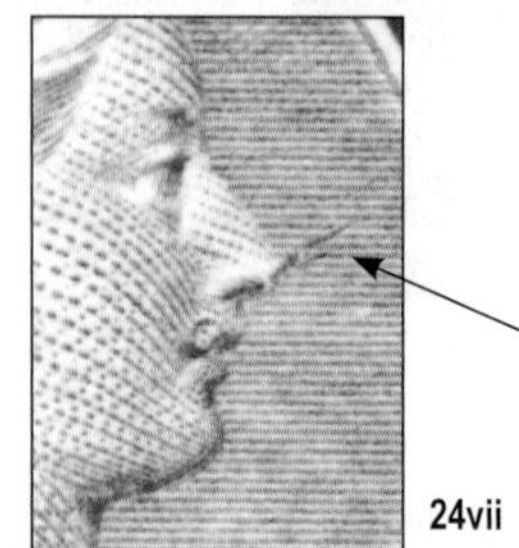
24vii

| No. | | ★VF | ★F | ★VG | ⊙VF | ⊙F | ⊙VG | ✉ |
|---|---|---|---|---|---|---|---|---|
| 25 | **3¢ red**, *Apr 1, 1868* | 2,500.00 | 1,000.00 | 500.00 | 50.00 | 20.00 | 10.00 | 25.00 |
| a | watermarked (Bothwell) paper | 6,000.00 | 4,000.00 | 1,200.00 | 600.00 | 250.00 | 125.00 | |
| viii | Bothwell paper | 2,750.00 | 1,100.00 | 550.00 | 200.00 | 80.00 | 50.00 | — |
| b | thin paper | 2,750.00 | 1,100.00 | 550.00 | 75.00 | 30.00 | 15.00 | 25.00 |
| i | orange red | 2,500.00 | 1,000.00 | 500.00 | 50.00 | 20.00 | 10.00 | 25.00 |
| ii | rose red | 2,500.00 | 1,000.00 | 500.00 | 50.00 | 20.00 | 10.00 | 25.00 |
| iii | thick soft white (blotting) paper | 5,000.00 | 2,750.00 | 1,350.00 | 600.00 | 300.00 | 150.00 | |
| iv | "Goatee" variety | | | | 2,500.00 | 1,000.00 | 500.00 | 1,700.00 |
| v | cracked plate variety (at least 3 different are known) | | | | 1,250.00 | 600.00 | 300.00 | 900.00 |
| vi | vert. stitch watermark | — | — | — | — | 600.00 | — | — |
| vii | "shaving nick" variety | | | | 1,800.00 | 900.00 | 450.00 | |

Qty: 22,000,000

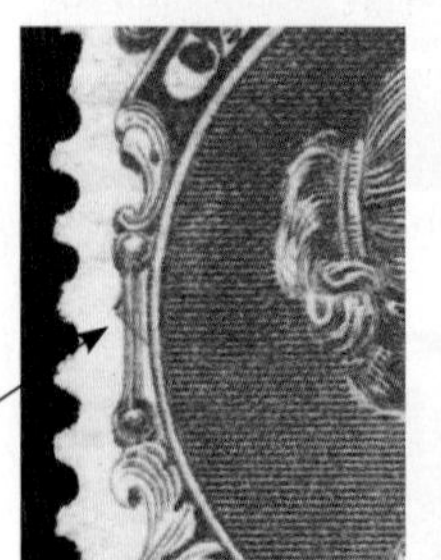
24viii
(2 states)

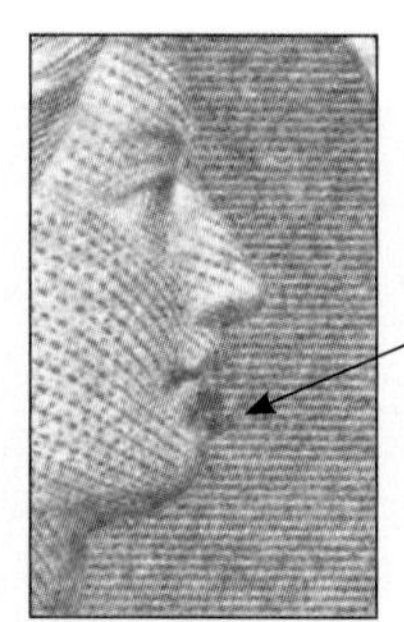
25iv

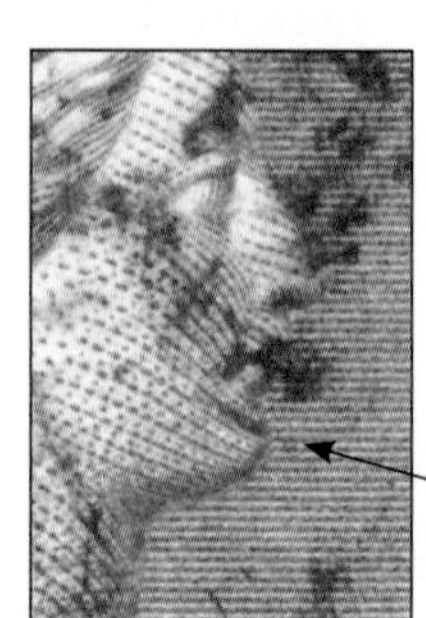
25vii

25v (thru NTS)

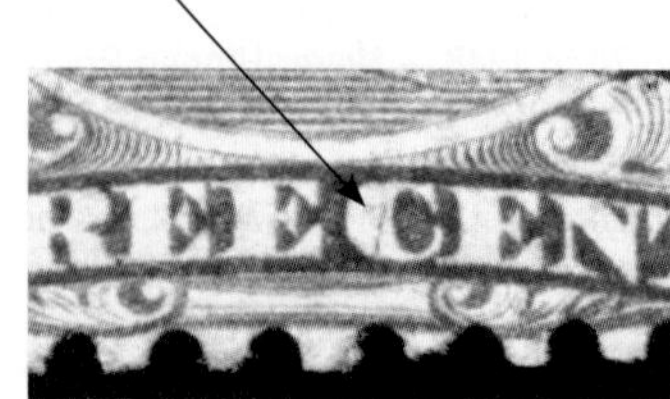
25v (thru C)

| No. | | Description | ★VF | ★F | ★VG | ⊙VF | ⊙F | ⊙VG | ✉ |
|---|---|---|---|---|---|---|---|---|---|
| **26** | | **5¢ olive green**, vert. mesh, perf. 11½ x 12, *Oct 1, 1875* | 2,500.00 | 800.00 | 450.00 | 270.00 | 130.00 | 55.00 | 225.00 |
| | a | perf. 12 x 12 | | 8,000.00 | 4,000.00 | 1,250.00 | 750.00 | 450.00 | 900.00 |
| | b | imperf. pair (unique) | — | *32,500.00* | — | — | — | — | — |
| | i | deep olive green | 2,500.00 | 800.00 | 450.00 | 300.00 | 140.00 | 60.00 | 225.00 |
| | iv | olive green, perf. 11¾ x 12 | 2,500.00 | 800.00 | 450.00 | 270.00 | 130.00 | 55.00 | 225.00 |
| | v | horiz. mesh, perf. 11½ x 12 | | 4,000.00 | 2,500.00 | 1,250.00 | 750.00 | 450.00 | |

The perf. variety on the 5¢ (26a) must measure at least 12.1 on the perf. gauge and should be the same perf. on all edges. A perf. 11¾ x 12 variety (26iv) is often mistaken for the rare perf. 12 variety. Approximately 33% are perf. 11½ x 12, 60% are perf. 11¾ x 12 and only 6% are perf. 12 (12.1 x 12.1). Examples of 26a should have a certificate from a competent authority.

**27iii (pos. 93)**
Doubling of 'S' of POSTAGE; doubling of scroll in upper right; doubling of lower frameline below SIX CENTS; and doubling of inner frameline to the right of the right '6'.

| No. | | Description | ★VF | ★F | ★VG | ⊙VF | ⊙F | ⊙VG | ✉ |
|---|---|---|---|---|---|---|---|---|---|
| **27** | | **6¢ dark brown**, *Apr 1, 1868* | 2,500.00 | 1,200.00 | 425.00 | 200.00 | 60.00 | 30.00 | 125.00 |
| | a | yellow brown | 2,200.00 | 800.00 | 400.00 | 160.00 | 60.00 | 30.00 | 125.00 |
| | b | watermarked (Bothwell) paper | | 15,000.00 | 5,000.00 | 3,500.00 | 1,500.00 | 750.00 | — |
| | vi | Bothwell paper | — | — | — | 325.00 | 150.00 | 90.00 | — |
| | c | thin paper | | 2,000.00 | 900.00 | 200.00 | 80.00 | 40.00 | 125.00 |
| | d | diagonal half used as 3¢ on cover | | | | | | | 4,000.00 |
| | e | vertical half used as 3¢ on cover | | | | | | | |
| | f | black brown, thin paper | 3,500.00 | 1,250.00 | 600.00 | 325.00 | 125.00 | 50.00 | 125.00 |
| | ii | soft white (blotting) paper | 4,000.00 | 2,000.00 | 800.00 | 1,250.00 | 500.00 | 200.00 | |
| | iii | major re-entry (pos. 93 or 95) | | 6,500.00 | | 750.00 | 400.00 | 250.00 | 700.00 |
| | iv | partial double print at right | — | — | — | — | *25,000.00* | *10,000.00* | *20,000.00* |
| | v | brown (shade between 27 & 27a) | 2,200.00 | 900.00 | 400.00 | 200.00 | 60.00 | 30.00 | 125.00 |
| | vii | vert. stitch watermark | — | — | — | — | 1,500.00 | 750.00 | — |
| | viii | horiz. stitch watermark | — | — | — | — | 1,750.00 | — | — |

Qty: 9,400,000

Re-entry (27iii): pos. 93 shows doubling lines in S of Postage; pos. 95 shows doubling of UL and UR corners.
Nos. 24iii, 25iii and 27ii are Duckworth paper 8. Only 4 copies of 27iv are known. All are off centre.
The 6¢ re-entry (27iii) shows doubling at UR corner.
Plate 1 copies show "dot" below scroll at lower left; Plate 2 copies show "dot" under S of SIX.

**27iv**

**28ii (at right)**

**28ii (at left)**

| No. | | Description | ★VF | ★F | ★VG | ⊙VF | ⊙F | ⊙VG | ✉ |
|---|---|---|---|---|---|---|---|---|---|
| **28** | | **12½¢ blue**, *Apr 1, 1868* | 1,400.00 | 600.00 | 250.00 | 160.00 | 60.00 | 25.00 | 225.00 |
| | a | watermarked (Bothwell) paper | 6,000.00 | 2,500.00 | 900.00 | 600.00 | 300.00 | 150.00 | — |
| | v | Bothwell paper | 1,800.00 | 700.00 | 300.00 | 250.00 | 125.00 | 50.00 | — |
| | b | thin paper, deep blue | 1,350.00 | 500.00 | 250.00 | 200.00 | 75.00 | 35.00 | 225.00 |
| | c | horiz. pair, imperf. vert. | | | | *— May not exist —* | | | |
| | d | vert. pair, imperf. horiz.* | — | — | — | — | *20,000.00* | — | — |
| | i | milky blue | 1,500.00 | 600.00 | 250.00 | 180.00 | 60.00 | 25.00 | 225.00 |
| | ii | no outer frameline at value tablet | 1,750.00 | 800.00 | 300.00 | 300.00 | 150.00 | 90.00 | 275.00 |
| | iii | soft white, almost blotting paper (Duckworth paper 8) | | 2,000.00 | 1,000.00 | | 600.00 | 300.00 | |
| | iv | "balloon flaw" variety | | 2,000.00 | 1,000.00 | 1,000.00 | 500.00 | 250.00 | |
| | vi | horiz. stitch watermark | | | | | 1,500.00 | 750.00 | |

Qty: 1,940,000

* 28d is known only in vertical strip of 6 (3 pairs).

**28iv**

**NH% Premium**
Full "NH premium" only applies to stamps with pristine original gum in the state it left the printer – no gum disturbance at all. NH stamps with any disturbance will USUALLY sell for the listed "OG" price or perhaps a little more if the disturbance is very minor.

**Cover Prices**
Cover prices are for "fine" condition. VF condition covers and covers with interesting postal markings or attractive Advertising covers will sell for more ... sometimes much more.

29ii

29iii
Has a blurred 'kiss print' type of appearance

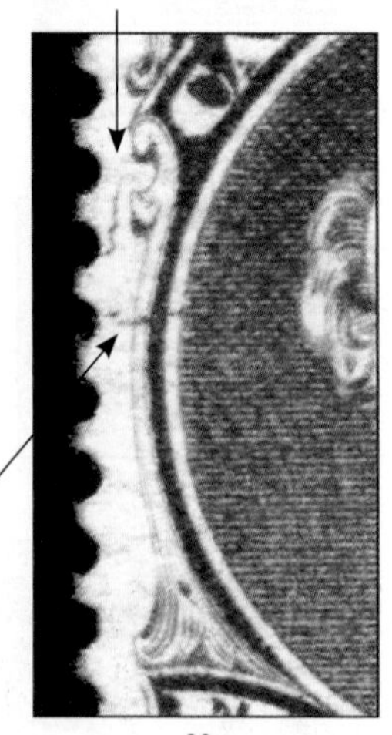

30v

30vi

29vi/30viii
(pos. 9)

29vi/30viii
(pos. 81 and 91)

**Colour shades of 15¢ Large Queen**

29 29b 30 30b 30e

| | | ★VF | ★F | ★VG | ⊙VF | ⊙F | ⊙VG | ✉ |
|---|---|---|---|---|---|---|---|---|
| **29** | **15¢ grey violet** | 120.00 | 40.00 | 20.00 | 80.00 | 30.00 | 15.00 | 600.00 |
| a | perf. 11½ x 12, greyish purple, *1874* | 2,500.00 | 1,000.00 | 400.00 | 700.00 | 200.00 | 100.00 | 1,500.00 |
| b | red lilac ‡ | 1,200.00 | 600.00 | 350.00 | 150.00 | 80.00 | 50.00 | 1,500.00 |
| c | watermarked "Bothwell" * | 7,500.00 | 4,000.00 | 2,500.00 | 1,500.00 | 750.00 | 350.00 | — |
| v | Bothwell paper | 2,000.00† | 1,000.00† | 750.00† | 300.00† | 150.00† | 90.00† | — |
| d | brown purple, imperf. pair, with OG (NH add 100%) (400 stamps) | 1,600.00 | 800.00 | 400.00 | — | — | — | — |
| e | thin paper, red lilac | 900.00 | 500.00 | 325.00 | 175.00 | 90.00 | 60.00 | 750.00 |
| i | purple (shades) | 125.00 | 60.00 | 30.00 | 75.00 | 25.00 | 15.00 | 600.00 |
| ii | "Pawnbroker" variety (pos. 10) | 1,000.00† | 600.00† | 300.00† | 450.00† | 225.00† | 125.00† | 1,100.00† |
| iii | major re-entry, reddish purple (pos. 1) | | 2,000.00† | | 2,500.00† | 1,250.00† | | 2,000.00† |
| iv | cracked plate (pos. 65) | — | 900.00 | 450.00 | — | 500.00 | 300.00 | |
| vi | other plate cracks/scratches (pos. 9, 81, 91) | | 900.00 | 450.00 | — | 500.00 | 300.00 | |
| vii | imprint copy, any position | 2,000.00 | 1,000.00 | 750.00 | 450.00 | 250.00 | 125.00 | |
| xx | No. 29, precancelled [5 styles] | — | — | — | — | 200.00† | 150.00† | 350.00† |

Qty: 2,370,000

* A variety of 29c known as "perf. 11½ x 12, watermarked" is really perf. 11.8 x 12. It is scarce and worth a premium over variety 29c.

‡ ERD on cover is 03/23/68 (No. 29b). A poor cover dated 03/22/68 was also reported. ERD for single, used: 03/02/68 (2 known).

† Prices are for most common shade, perforation or paper.

| | | ★VF | ★F | ★VG | ⊙VF | ⊙F | ⊙VG | ✉ |
|---|---|---|---|---|---|---|---|---|
| **30** | **15¢ grey** (many shades) | 120.00 | 40.00 | 20.00 | 80.00 | 30.00 | 15.00 | 600.00 |
| a | perf. 11½ x 12, greenish grey, *1873* | 2,500.00 | 1,000.00 | 400.00 | 700.00 | 200.00 | 80.00 | 1,500.00 |
| b | blue grey, *1875* | 150.00 | 75.00 | 40.00 | 100.00 | 40.00 | 20.00 | 600.00 |
| c | very thick paper, deep violet | 6,000.00 | 3,500.00 | 1,750.00 | 2,000.00 | 1,000.00 | 450.00 | 3,000.00 |
| d | script watermark, perf. 11½ x 12 greenish grey, *1876* | 30,000.00 | 15,000.00 | 8,000.00 | 10,000.00 | 4,000.00 | 2,000.00 | |
| vii | Pirie paper, without watermark | 6,000.00 | 3,000.00 | 1,600.00 | 1,700.00 | 800.00 | 400.00 | |
| e | deep blue | 2,500.00 | 1,000.00 | 500.00 | 600.00 | 250.00 | 125.00 | 750.00 |
| i | slate grey | 150.00 | 60.00 | 35.00 | 100.00 | 40.00 | 20.00 | 600.00 |
| iii | "Pawnbroker" variety (pos. 10)* | 1,250.00† | 750.00† | 350.00† | 600.00 | 300.00† | 150.00† | 1,200.00† |
| iv | greenish grey, perf. 12, *1873* | 2,000.00 | 1,000.00 | 500.00 | 150.00 | 75.00 | 45.00 | |
| v | cracked plate (pos. 65) | 2,200.00 | 900.00 | 450.00 | 1,100.00 | 500.00 | 300.00 | |
| viii | other plate cracks/scratches (pos. 9, 81, 91) | | 900.00 | 450.00 | — | 500.00 | 300.00 | |
| vi | "balloon flaw" | — | 900.00 | 450.00 | — | 500.00 | 300.00 | |
| ix | imprint copy, any position | | 2,000.00 | 1,000.00 | 750.00 | 450.00 | 250.00 | |
| xx | No. 30, precancelled [3 styles] | — | — | — | — | 300.00† | 250.00† | 450.00† |
| xxa | No. 30b, precancelled [3 styles] | — | — | — | — | 250.00† | 200.00† | 400.00† |

* The "Pawnbroker" variety shows three dots to the right of "15" and occurs on all printings, 29ii and 30iii indicate the value of the variety only and this should be added to the listed value of the shade or printing (i.e. the pawnbroker variety on a mint VF copy of 30b would be valued at $150 + $1,250 = $1,400. In mint Fine it would be $75 + $750 = $825.)

† Prices are for most common shade, perforation or paper.

The 15¢ re-entry (29iii) shows doubling of CANADA P, FIFTE and in left "15".

The watermark reads: "E & G. BOTHWELL CLUTHA MILLS" on two lines, except for the 15¢ script watermark which reads: "Alexr. Pirie & Sons" in script. Each stamp shows only a portion of the watermark (usually parts of only one or two letters). Examples of No. 30d should have certificates of authenticity.

29vii

30ix

| 1868 | | Engraved, Laid Paper | | | | | Perf 12 |
|---|---|---|---|---|---|---|---|
| Mint copies (★) with original gum, add 50% | | | | | | | |
| | | ★F | ★VG | ⊙VF | ⊙F | ⊙VG | ✉ |
| **31** | **1¢ brown red** (22) | 30,000.00 | 10,000.00 | 10,000.00 | 4,000.00 | 1,500.00 | 10,000.00 |
| **32** | **2¢ green** (3 known, all used) (24) | — | — | — | *350,000.00* | *125,000.00* | |
| **33** | **3¢ bright red** (25) | 25,000.00 | 8,500.00 | 2,500.00 | 1,000.00 | 400.00 | 2,500.00 |

Only three copies of the 2¢ green on laid paper have been recorded to date; all used. Fewer than 10 unused copies of each of the 1¢ and 3¢ laid paper are recorded. Unused examples of Nos. 31 and 33 should have certificates of authenticity from a recognized expert committee.

'Large Queens' vs. 'Small Queens'
(designs at actual size)

½ cent

1–10 cent

The "E. & G. Bothwell, Clutha Mills" watermark appears on some paper used for all values in the "Large Queens" issue except 5¢

"Alexr. Pirie & Sons" script watermark used on 15¢ Large Queen

| Large Queen cross-reference (by Duckworth paper types) | | | | | | | | | | | | | | |
|---|---|---|---|---|---|---|---|---|---|---|---|---|---|---|
| Paper** | 1 | 2 | 3 | 4 | 5 | 6 | 7 | 8 | 9 | 9b | 10 | 1875 | 1876 | 1880 |
| description | thin | thin | wove | stout | laid | Bothwell | course ivory | soft white | soft white | thin | stout wove | SQ paper | Script watermark | carton paper |
| mesh | vert. | horiz. | horiz. | horiz. | vert. | vert. | vert. | none | horiz. or vert. | horiz. | horiz. | horiz or vert. | horiz. | vert. |
| ½¢ black | | 21c | 21 / 21vi | | | 21a / 21b / 21vii | | 21i | | | 21 / 21a | | | |
| 1¢ brown red | 22b | | 22 | 22 | 31 | 22a / 22ii | x | 22i | x | x | | | | |
| 1¢ yellow orange | | | | | | | | | x | x | 23 / 23a / 23i | | | |
| 2¢ green | 24b | | 24 | 24 | 32 | 24a / 24iv | x | 24iii | | | 24 / 24i | | | |
| 3¢ red | 25b | x | 25 | 25 | 33 | 25a / 25viii | | 25iii | | | | | | |
| 5¢ olive green | | | | | | | | | | | | 26 / 26a / 26i / 26iv / 26v | | |
| 6¢ dark brown (pl 1) | | 27c / 27f | 27 / 27v | 27 | | 27b / 27vi | x | 27ii | x | x | 27 / 27a | | | |
| 6¢ brown (pl 2) | | | | | | | | 27ii | x | x | 27a | | | |
| 12½¢ blue | | 28b | 28 | | | 28a / 28v | x | 28iii | | | 28 / 28i | | | |
| 15¢ grey violet | | 29e | 29b | | | 29c / 29v | x | | | | 29 | | | |
| 15¢ grey | | | 30 | | | | | | | | 30 | | 30d / 30vii | 30c |

x variety exists but not yet assigned a catalogue number

** A more detailed paper study is underway at the time of writing that may result in additional entries to this chart.

## SMALL QUEEN ISSUE

34 35 36
37 38 39 40

Due to its lengthy period of usage and the many printings which occurred both in Montreal and Ottawa, the "Small Queen" issue is one of the most difficult to classify. The gum on the perf. 11½ x 12 printings is always dull and generally blotchy or streaky. Earlier printings, first in Ottawa and then in Montreal, have a much finer paper stock than the later Ottawa printings which were rather coarse.

Cover prices are for "fine". Very fine covers worth 50% to 100% more. "NH" means "pristine" original gum for full premium gum; creases and wrinkles reduce the percentage.

**Plate Proofs**
Plate Proofs of all values exist. Value as singles: $600.00; Imprint blocks of 4: $4,000.00

Based on an engraving by Charles Henry Jeens. Portrait engraved by Alfred Jones. Lettering and frame engraved by Henry Earle Sr.

British American Bank Note Company

**1870–1893** **Engraved, Wove paper** **Perf 12**

Mint copies (★) beware of regumming on this issue

| | | NH% | ★VF | ★F | ★VG | ⊙VF | ⊙F | ✉ |
|---|---|---|---|---|---|---|---|---|
| **34** | **½¢ black**, *1882* | 150 | 30.00 | 10.00 | 3.00 | 12.00 | 6.00 | 300.00* |
| a | imperf. pair, with and without gum (400 stamps) | 150 | 800.00 | 450.00 | 300.00 | — | — | — |
| b | horiz. pair, imperf. between | 150 | 1,500.00 | 750.00 | 450.00 | — | — | — |
| i | grey black | 150 | 30.00 | 10.00 | 3.00 | 12.00 | 6.00 | 300.00* |
| ii | thick white paper | 150 | 70.00 | 30.00 | 7.50 | 25.00 | 12.50 | — |
| iii | gutter pair | 150 | 400.00 | 250.00 | 175.00 | — | — | 1,800.00† |
| iv | major re-entry (pos. 49, right pane) | 150 | 250.00 | 120.00 | 40.00 | 200.00 | 80.00 | 160.00§ |
| v | vert. pair, imperf. between ¤ | | | 3,000.00 | | | | |
| vi | major re-entry (pos. 1R98 ‡) | 150 | 150.00 | 75.00 | 37.50 | 150.00 | 75.00 | 160.00§ |
| vii | major re-entry (pos. 1R10, 1R96) | | 250.00 | 120.00 | 40.00 | 200.00 | 80.00 | |
| xx | No. 34, precancelled [10 styles] | — | — | — | — | 75.00 | 50.00 | |

Many, many minor re-entries exist, due to several states of the plate.

* No. 34 (½¢ black): Cover price is for proper single usage on cover to pay circular rate. Multiples on cover are quite common. Price for multiples on cover: $20 plus appropriate used single value for each stamp on the cover. (See also Nos. 66 and 74.)

† No. 34iii, three pairs, one block of six, one strip of five, and a damaged block of four are known on cover.

§ Price for a copy on cover in multiple; any cover with single stamp franking $500.00.

¤ Three pairs known.

‡ 1R98 = Plate 1 Right, position 98.

**34iv**
Entire design is doubled, including radial lines to UR and LL of portrait oval, four lines of engraved dots on neck appear as solid lines.

**34vi**
Entire design doubled, including radial lines around bottom of portrait from 3:00 to 7:00.

**34vii (pos. 10)**
Entire design doubled, including strong doubling in POSTAGE, CENT and UR corner, and faintly in radial lines below portrait.

See also Registration issues (F1–F3)

*Constant Plate Varieties of the Canada Small Queens*, Hans Reiche and Mike Sendbuehler, 1991.

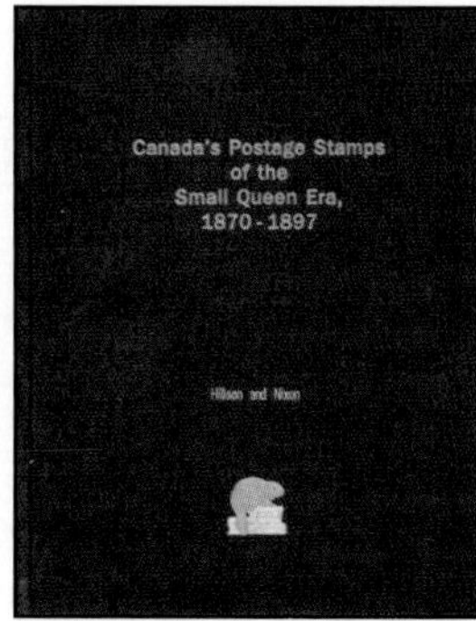


*Canada's Postage Stamps of the Small Queen Era, 1870–1897*, John Hillson and Ted Nixon, 2008.

35viii

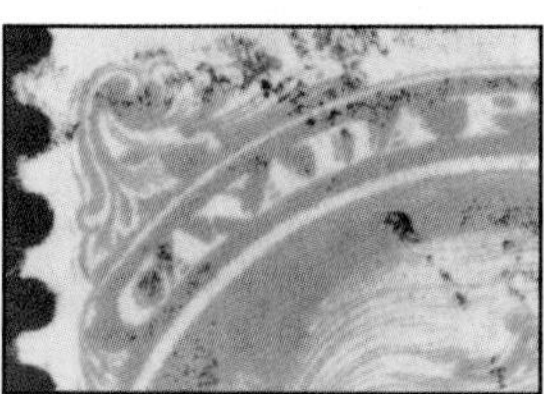
35x

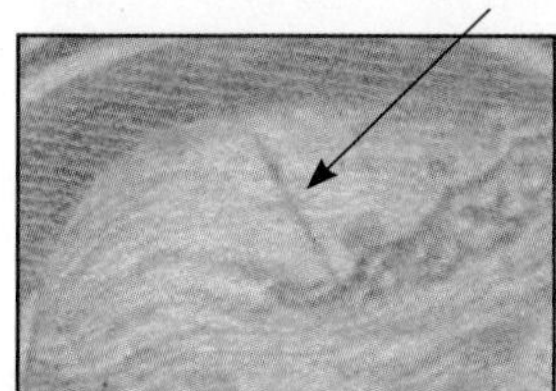
35xi

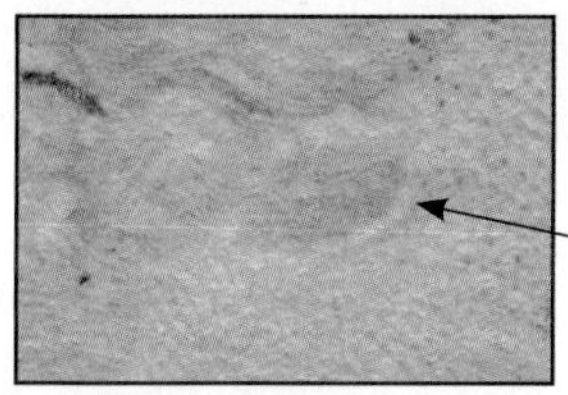
35xii

| | | NH% | ★VF | ★F | ★VG | ⊙VF | ⊙F | ✉ |
|---|---|---|---|---|---|---|---|---|
| **35** | **1¢ yellow** (Ottawa) | 200 | 60.00 | 20.00 | 10.00 | 1.50 | .50 | 12.00 |
| a | orange (Montreal), *1873–74* | 200 | 400.00 | 150.00 | 50.00 | 15.00 | 7.00 | 25.00 |
| b | imperf. pair, lemon yellow, all shades (800 stamps) | 150 | 600.00 | 400.00 | 300.00 | — | — | — |
| c | diagonal half used as ½¢ on circular | | | | | | | 6,000.00 |
| d | orange, perf. 11½ x 12 (Montreal) | 200 | 600.00 | 200.00 | 75.00 | 25.00 | 10.00 | 75.00 |
| i | yellow (Montreal) | 200 | 100.00 | 30.00 | 15.00 | 3.00 | 1.25 | 12.00 |
| ii | orange (Ottawa) | 200 | 300.00 | 100.00 | 60.00 | 20.00 | 6.50 | 15.00 |
| iii | lemon yellow, perf. 11½ x 12 | 200 | 600.00 | 200.00 | 75.00 | 20.00 | 10.00 | 40.00 |
| iv | red orange, *Mar 1870*** | 200 | 750.00 | 250.00 | 60.00 | 60.00 | 20.00 | 60.00 |
| v | deep red orange (Montreal), *1873–74* | 200 | 500.00 | 150.00 | 50.00 | 60.00 | 20.00 | 60.00 |
| vi | deep orange, perf. 11½ x 12 (Montreal) | 200 | 750.00 | 250.00 | 100.00 | 40.00 | 15.00 | 30.00 |
| vii | yellow, perf. 11½ x 12 | 200 | 600.00 | 200.00 | 75.00 | 20.00 | 10.00 | 17.50 |
| viii | "strand of hair" variety (Plate C, right pane, pos. 13 and 26†) | 200 | 1,200.00 | 600.00 | 300.00 | 600.00 | 300.00 | 825.00 |
| ix | yellow orange on thick paper* | 200 | 2,500.00 | 1,200.00 | — | 400.00 | 200.00 | — |
| x | major re-entry, CANADA POSTAGE and ONE, UL and LL | | | | | | | 300.00 |
| xi | diagonal line in hair variety | 200 | 1,200.00 | 500.00 | 250.00 | 1,000.00 | 400.00 | 1,200.00 |
| xii | blob under ear variety | 200 | 1,500.00 | 600.00 | 300.00 | 750.00 | 300.00 | 1,000.00 |
| xxi | 35i, precancelled [18 styles] | — | — | — | — | 2.00 | .75 | |

** ERD for 35iv is Mar 10, 1870.
Numerous other re-entries exist.
* Thick soft (blotting) paper. Examples usually display hairiness (paper fibres) in perf. holes, with all or part of perf. disc remaining.
† Position 26 also has a major re-entry of all letters and numerals.

36iv

36viii

| | | NH% | ★VF | ★F | ★VG | ⊙VF | ⊙F | ✉ |
|---|---|---|---|---|---|---|---|---|
| **36** | **2¢ green** (Montreal), *Feb 1872* | 200 | 100.00 | 40.00 | 20.00 | 3.00 | 1.00 | 15.00 |
| a | imperf. pair, deep green (Montreal) † | 150 | 900.00 | 600.00 | 400.00 | — | — | — |
| b | diagonal half used as 1¢ on cover‡ | | | | | | | 3,000.00 |
| c | vertical half used as 1¢ on cover‡ | | | | | | | 3,000.00 |
| d | blue green (Montreal) | 200 | 140.00 | 60.00 | 30.00 | 6.00 | 3.00 | 14.00 |
| e | perf. 11½ x 12, deep green | 200 | 1,000.00 | 300.00 | 100.00 | 30.00 | 14.00 | 30.00 |
| f | double impression | | 7,500.00 | | | | 5,000.00 | |
| i | green (Ottawa) | 200 | 100.00 | 40.00 | 20.00 | 2.50 | 1.00 | 14.00 |
| ii | blue green (Ottawa) | 200 | 150.00 | 60.00 | 30.00 | 4.00 | 2.00 | 14.00 |
| iii | imperf. pair, deep green, yellowish paper (Ottawa)† | 150 | 900.00 | 600.00 | 400.00 | — | — | — |
| iv | latent re-entry, horiz. lines in LR margin | 100 | — | 1,500.00 | — | 650.00 | 400.00 | 800.00 |
| v | as iii, on white paper | 150 | 900.00 | 600.00 | 400.00 | — | — | — |
| vi | major re-entry, both 2s and CENTS show strong doubling, pos. 97 (Montreal) | 200 | 1,500.00 | 500.00 | 300.00 | 500.00 | 150.00 | 400.00 |
| vii | blue green, imperf. at top margin (10 exist) | 100 | — | 3,500.00 | — | — | — | — |
| viii | latent entry (pos. 188) (Ottawa) horiz. lines in UL margin | 100 | — | 1,500.00 | — | 650.00 | 400.00 | 800.00 |
| ix | horizontal stitch watermark | | | | | 450.00 | 300.00 | |
| x | vertical stitch watermark | | | | | 450.00 | 300.00 | |
| xx | No. 36, precancelled [11 styles] | — | — | — | — | 25.00 | 20.00 | 30.00 |
| xxa | No. 36d, precancelled [5 styles] | — | — | — | — | 100.00 | 75.00 | 125.00 |

There are numerous re-entries, some major.
† All imperf. pairs (Montreal and Ottawa printings) including all shades, 600 stamps.
‡ Copies postmarked "Halifax" are a private speculation.

36vi

36f

| No. | | NH% | ★VF | ★F | ★VG | ⊙VF | ⊙F | ✉ |
|---|---|---|---|---|---|---|---|---|
| 37 | **3¢ orange red** (Montreal), ERD: *Mar 1, 1873* | 200 | 250.00 | 60.00 | 30.00 | 2.00 | 1.25 | 12.00 |
| a | rose (Ottawa), *1870* | 200 | 750.00 | 300.00 | 125.00 | 20.00 | 7.50 | 20.00 |
| b | copper or Indian red, *1870* | 200 | 2,500.00 | 1,000.00 | 600.00 | 80.00 | 40.00 | 75.00 |
| c | dull red (*1872*) | 200 | 250.00 | 60.00 | 30.00 | 4.00 | 2.00 | 12.00 |
| d | copper or Indian red, perf. 12½ (*Jan 17, 1870*) ERD: *Jan 13,1870* | 200 | 15,000.00 | 6,000.00 | 3,000.00 | 1,750.00 | 900.00 | 1,800.00‡ |
| e | red, perf. 11½ x 12 | 200 | 800.00 | 200.00 | 90.00 | 15.00 | 7.50 | 15.00 |
| i | dark rose on thick paper* | 200 | 6,000.00 | 4,000.00 | | 250.00 | 100.00 | 400.00 |
| ii | dull red, perf. 11½ x 12 | 200 | 800.00 | 200.00 | 90.00 | 15.00 | 7.50 | 15.00 |
| iii | orange red, perf. 11½ x 12 | 200 | 800.00 | 200.00 | 90.00 | 15.00 | 7.50 | 15.00 |
| iv | rose, kiss print †, one used example known, with faults | — | — | — | — | — | 4,000.00 | — |
| v | as 37b, vertical stitch watermark | | | | | — | 700.00 | |
| vi | as 37, vertical stitch watermark | | | | | — | 500.00 | |
| xx | No. 37ii, precancelled [1 style] | — | — | — | — | 200.00 | 150.00 | 175.00 |

There are numerous re-entries, some major.
* See note following No. 35.
‡ cover postmarked other than St. John – $2,100.
† Not constant; considered a freak.

37iv

| No. | | NH% | ★VF | ★F | ★VG | ⊙VF | ⊙F | ✉ |
|---|---|---|---|---|---|---|---|---|
| 38 | **5¢ slate green** (Montreal) *Feb 1, 1876* | 200 | 1,000.00 | 300.00 | 175.00 | 35.00 | 15.00 | 60.00 |
| a | slate green, perf. 11½ x 12 | 200 | 1,500.00 | 500.00 | 250.00 | 60.00 | 25.00 | 75.00 |
| i | deep olive green | 200 | 1,200.00 | 300.00 | 175.00 | 35.00 | 15.00 | 50.00 |
| iv | "Feather in hair" variety (pos. 60) | 200 | 2,500.00 | 1,250.00 | 700.00 | 2,000.00 | 600.00 | 2,500.00 |
| xx | No. 38, precancelled [3 styles] | — | — | — | — | 200.00 | 125.00 | 150.00 |

38iv

| No. | | NH% | ★VF | ★F | ★VG | ⊙VF | ⊙F | ✉ |
|---|---|---|---|---|---|---|---|---|
| 39 | **6¢ yellow brown**, *Jan 1872* | 200 | 800.00 | 250.00 | 125.00 | 35.00 | 15.00 | 45.00 |
| a | diagonal half used as 3¢ on cover | | | | | | | *5,000.00* |
| b | yellow brown, perf. 11½ x 12 | 200 | 1,200.00 | 500.00 | 250.00 | 75.00 | 25.00 | 60.00 |
| v | yellow brown, perf. 12 x 11½ | | | | | *3,000.00* | *1,500.00* | |
| c | dark yellow brown, imperf. pair, w/o gum (Montreal), *1888*, one strip of 3 known, unique | — | *4,500.00* | — | — | — | — | — |
| d | brown, *1875* | 200 | 900.00 | 300.00 | 150.00 | 35.00 | 15.00 | 45.00 |
| ii | major re-entry (pos. 67), heavy line through CANADA POSTAGE and line below design | 200 | 1,200.00 | 500.00 | 250.00 | 250.00 | 100.00 | 500.00 |
| iii | semi-major re-entry, complete lower frameline doubled | | | | | | | |
| iv | neck flaw | 200 | 1,600.00 | 800.00 | 400.00 | 750.00 | 250.00 | 775.00 |
| xx | No. 39, precancelled [7 styles] | — | — | — | — | 175.00 | 100.00 | 125.00 |

Numerous other re-entries, some major.

39ii

39iii

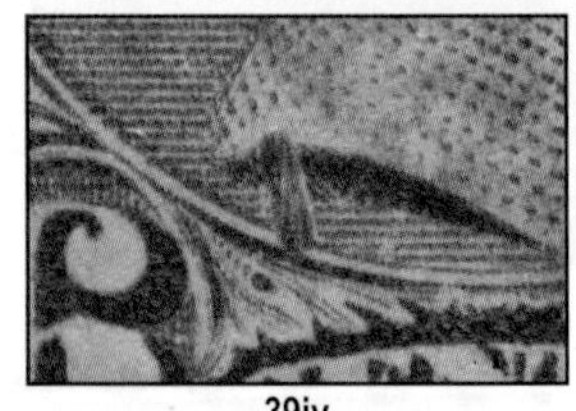
39iv

| No. | | NH% | ★VF | ★F | ★VG | ⊙VF | ⊙F | ✉ |
|---|---|---|---|---|---|---|---|---|
| 40 | **10¢ dull rose lilac**, *1877* | 300 | 1,700.00 | 500.00 | 150.00 | 120.00 | 50.00 | 500.00 |
| a | magenta, *1880* | 300 | 1,750.00 | 500.00 | 175.00 | 120.00 | 50.00 | 500.00 |
| b | deep lilac rose | 300 | 1,750.00 | 500.00 | 150.00 | 120.00 | 50.00 | 500.00 |
| c | dull rose lilac, perf. 11½ x 12 | 300 | 2,400.00 | 800.00 | 400.00 | 350.00 | 150.00 | 600.00 |
| d | magenta, perf. 11½ x 12 | 300 | 2,400.00 | 800.00 | 400.00 | 350.00 | 150.00 | 600.00 |
| e | pale milky rose lilac, perf. 11½ x 12, *Nov 1874* | 300 | 4,000.00 | 1,500.00 | 750.00 | 900.00 | 400.00 | 1,500.00 |
| i | light rose lilac | 300 | 1,750.00 | 500.00 | 150.00 | 100.00 | 40.00 | 500.00 |
| ii | re-entry of top frameline (pos. 89) | 300 | 2,000.00 | 600.00 | 350.00 | 750.00 | 375.00 | 1,200.00 |
| iii | gash in right "1" (pos 85) | 300 | 2,000.00 | 700.00 | 350.00 | 750.00 | 375.00 | 1,200.00 |

40ii

**Small Queen Identification Table**

| | | Ottawa (1870–1873) | Montreal (1873– ) | Montreal ( –1888) | Montreal (1888–1889) | Ottawa (1889–1897) |
|---|---|---|---|---|---|---|
| | paper | high quality wove | high quality wove | appears closer to newsprint | | poor quality – more white |
| ½¢ | plate | | | new in 1882 | | continued |
| | colour | | | black to grey-black | | black |
| | perf, reg | | | 12 x 12 | none | 12 x 12 |
| | Kiusalas | | | 66 | printed | 65 |
| | pos dot | | | top centre | | top centre |
| | Unitrade # | | | 34 | | |
| 1¢ | plate | new | continued | new in 1886 | continued | new in 1888 |
| | colour | red-orange to orange | orange | yellow | bright yellow | bright yellow |
| | perf, reg | 12 x 12 | 11½ x 12 | 12 x 12 | 12 x 12¼ | 12 x 12 |
| | Kiusalas | 66 | 68 x 66 | 66 | 66 x 64 | 65 |
| | pos dot | lower left except left column | lower left except left column | 3 or 9 o'clock on medallion rim | continued | none |
| | Unitrade # | 35a | 35d | 35 | | |
| 2¢ | plate | new | continued | new in 1886 | continued | new |
| | colour | emerald green | deep green | green | blue-green | green |
| | perf, reg | 12 x 12 | 11½ x 12 | 12 x 12 | 12 x 12¼ | 12 x 12 |
| | Kiusalas | 66 | 68 x 66 | 66 | 66 x 64 | 65 |
| | pos dot | lower left except left column | lower left except left column | 3 or 9 o'clock on medallion rim | continued | none |
| | Unitrade # | 36i | 36e | 36 | 36d | |
| 3¢ | plate | new | continued | new in 1886 | continued | new |
| | colour | copper red to rose-red | orange red | vermilion-red | rose carmine | bright vermilion |
| | perf, reg | 12 x 12 or (rare) 12½ x 12½ | 11½ x 12 | 12 x 12 | 12 x 12¼ | 12 x 12 |
| | Kiusalas | 66 or (rare) 63 | 68 x 66 | 66 | 66 x 64 | 65 |
| | pos dot | lower left except left column | lower left except left column | 3 or 9 o'clock on medallion rim | continued | none |
| | Unitrade # | 37b or (rare) 37d | 37e | 37 | 41a | 41 |
| 5¢ | plate | | new in 1876 | new in 1886 | continued | new |
| | colour | | olive green | slate green | slate green | pearl grey |
| | perf, reg | | 11½ x 12 | 12 x 12 | 12 x 12¼ | 12 x 12 |
| | Kiusalas | | 68 x 66 | 66 | 66 x 64 | 65 |
| | pos dot | | lower left except left column | 3 or 9 o'clock on medallion rim | continued | none |
| | Unitrade # | | 38a | 38 | | 42 |
| 6¢ | plate | new | continued | continued | | continued |
| | colour | yellow-brown | yellow-brown | yellow-brown | | chestnut or chocolate |
| | perf, reg | 12 x 12 | 11½ x 12 | 12 x 12 | none | 12 x 12 |
| | Kiusalas | 66 | 68 x 66 | 66 | printed | 65 |
| | pos dot | lower left except left column | lower left except left column | lower left except left column | | continued |
| | Unitrade # | 39 | 39b | 39d | | 43/a |
| 8¢ | plate | | | | | new |
| | colour | | | | | slate |
| | perf, reg | | | | | 12 x 12 |
| | Kiusalas | | | | | 65 |
| | pos dot | | | | | none |
| | Unitrade # | | | | | 44/a/b |
| 10¢ | plate | | new | continued | | continued |
| | colour | | pale lilac | lilac-pink | | orange-pink |
| | perf, reg | | 11½ x 12 | 12 x 12 | none | 12 x 12 |
| | Kiusalas | | 68 x 66 | 66 | printed | 65 |
| | pos dot | | lower left except left column | lower left except left column | | continued |
| | Unitrade # | | 40c/d/e | 40a/b | | 45/a/b |

Two perforation measurements are presented: the "reg"ular perforation gauge (metric measurement in perfs per 2cm) and the Kiusalas gauge (imperial gauge showing distance between perforation holes measured in 1000th's of an inch). The chart at right compares the Stanley Gibbons Instanta gauge measurements to the Kiusalas gauge.

**Perforation gauge comparison between the Kiusalas gauge, the old (slightly yellow) Instanta gauge, and the new Instanta gauge**

| Kiusalas gauge | Old Instanta | New Instanta |
|---|---|---|
| 63 | 12.5 | 12.58 |
| 64 | 12.3 | 12.38 |
| 65 | 12.1 | 12.18 |
| 66 | 11.9 | 12.01 |
| 67 | 11.7 | 11.81 |
| 68 | 11.5 | 11.63 |

Small Queen identification table courtesy Garfield Portch; perforation gauge table courtesy DGL Philatelics.

**Hereafter, covers with commercial illustrations, unusual postal markings, mixed values or franking (registered), are valued much higher if used in period.**

**Covers with postmarks out of period are considered philatelic and have little value.**

41

42

43

44

45

46

47

20¢ and 50¢: Based on a photograph by Hills & Saunders

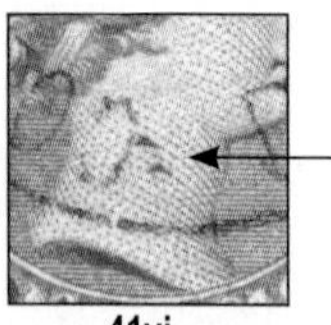
41vi

42ii

42ii; unique plate strip of 4

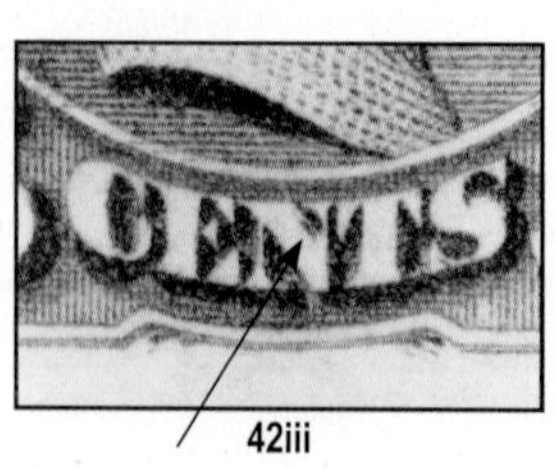
42iii

42iv

**1888–1897** **Ottawa Printings** **Perf 12**

| | | | NH% | ★VF | ★F | ★VG | ⊙VF | ⊙F | ✉ |
|---|---|---|---|---|---|---|---|---|---|
| **41** | | **3¢ bright vermilion**, *1888* | 200 | 90.00 | 30.00 | 10.00 | 1.00 | .30 | 6.00 |
| | **a** | rose carmine, perf. 12 x 12.25 (Montreal), *Autumn 1888* | 200 | 750.00 | 300.00 | 150.00 | 22.00 | 8.00 | 25.00 |
| | **b** | imperf. pair, orange (*1891*), rose vermilion shade, with and without gum† | 150 | 600.00 | 300.00 | 200.00 | | | |
| | **i** | deep rose carmine (Montreal) | 200 | 850.00 | 400.00 | 175.00 | 40.00 | 15.00 | 40.00 |
| | **ii** | imperf. pair, orange verm., *1885–86*† | 150 | 600.00 | 300.00 | 200.00 | | | |
| | **iv** | imperf. pair, brownish vermilion on thinner paper (*late 1896*) w/o gum † | — | 500.00 | 350.00 | | — | — | — |
| | **v** | imperf. pair, vermilion on coarse white paper (*1895*) w/o gum † | — | 750.00 | 450.00 | | — | — | — |
| | **vi** | "Vampire bite" variety, two triangular marks on queen's neck | — | 600.00 | 300.00 | 200.00 | 300.00 | 150.00 | 400.00 |
| | **vii** | major re-entry, LL corner & cents | | | | | | | |
| | **xx** | orange vermilion, precancelled [13 styles] | — | — | — | — | 20.00 | 15.00 | 25.00 |
| | **ixx** | as "i", precancelled [1 style] | — | — | — | — | | 150.00 | |

Numerous other re-entries, some major
† Varieties 41b, 41ii, 41iv and 41v total 1,000 stamps.

| | | | NH% | ★VF | ★F | ★VG | ⊙VF | ⊙F | ✉ |
|---|---|---|---|---|---|---|---|---|---|
| **42** | | **5¢ grey** | 200 | 300.00 | 80.00 | 20.00 | 7.00 | 3.00 | 45.00 |
| | **a** | imperf. pair, grey (Ottawa, *1891*), with and without gum † | 150 | *900.00* | 450.00 | 300.00 | — | — | — |
| | **i** | imperf. pair, brownish grey, (Ottawa, *1895*) with gum † | 150 | *900.00* | 450.00 | 300.00 | — | — | — |
| | **ii** | kiss print at bottom ‡ | 150 | — | *10,000.00* | *8,000.00* | — | *2,500.00* | |
| | **iii** | major re-entry, doubling throughout lower portion of design including portrait oval and 5 CENTS 5 (pos. 196 of 200, plate 1) | 150 | | 200.00 | 100.00 | | 50.00 | 200.00 |
| | **iv** | major re-entry, doubling of CANADA POSTAGE and below E in oval | | | | | | | |
| | **v** | major re-entry, doubling of CANADA POSTAGE, UL & LL corners | | | | | | | |
| | **vi** | chignon (white area on bun) | | | | | 80.00 | 50.00 | 150.00 |
| | **xx** | No. 42, precancelled [7 styles] | — | — | — | — | 50.00 | 30.00 | 75.00 |

‡ Not constant; considered a freak. All known copies are poorly centered. Unique plate strip of 4, $70,000.
† Total quantity for varieties 42a and 42i (with and without gum): 600 (300 pairs) with gum and 200 (100 pairs) without gum.

| | | NH% | ★VF | ★F | ★VG | ⊙VF | ⊙F | ✉ |
|---|---|---|---|---|---|---|---|---|
| **43** | **6¢ red brown** | 300 | 300.00 | 75.00 | 30.00 | 15.00 | 8.00 | 50.00 |
| a | chocolate (*1890*) | 300 | 800.00 | 300.00 | 100.00 | 50.00 | 20.00 | 100.00 |
| b | imperf. pair, red brown, with and without gum (*1895*) ‡ | 150 | 750.00 | 500.00 | 350.00 | | | |
| c | 5¢ on 6¢ major re-entry* (pos. B25) | 200 | — | 5,000.00 | 2,500.00 | 7,500.00 | 3,000.00 | |
| i | chestnut (*1890*) | 200 | 350.00 | 100.00 | 35.00 | 20.00 | 10.00 | 50.00 |
| ii | major re-entry (pos. A24) | 200 | 500.00 | 250.00 | 125.00 | 150.00 | 75.00 | 500.00 |
| iv | minor re-entry (numerous) | 200 | 400.00† | 100.00† | 40.00† | 30.00† | 20.00† | 70.00 |
| v | major re-entries (pos. B87, C7 & C81) | 200 | 800.00 | 500.00 | 250.00 | 250.00 | 150.00 | 550.00 |
| vi | imperf. pair, chocolate shade, on greyish paper (*1891*) w/o gum ‡ | — | 1,250.00 | 700.00 | 450.00 | — | — | |
| vii | "hairball" variety (pos. B97) | | | 1,000.00 | 500.00 | 1,000.00 | 500.00 | |
| xx | No. 43, precancelled [7 styles] | — | — | — | — | 50.00 | 30.00 | 75.00 |
| xxa | No. 43a, precancelled [2 styles] | — | — | — | — | 75.00 | 50.00 | 100.00 |

* Re-entry is found on 3 positions. Only pos. B25 has been identified. Lesser 5¢ on 6¢ re-entries are known at A11, A20 and A21: values $1,000 for F*, $400 for VG*, $500 for F Used and $250 for VG Used. A great many re-entries exist on this stamp.
† Prices are for most common shade or paper.
‡ Total quantity for varieties 43b and 43vi (with and without gum) 600 stamps.

43c

43ii

Doubling overall, particularly in CANADA POS, CEN, and below the bottom of the design on the left.

43v (pos. B87)

All three majors show significant doubling of the bottoms of the stamps, resulting in a very mangled look to the word CENTS. The doubling is so strong, they almost appear to be double prints. The distinction between the three is difficult to describe in words, as they are all very similar. Comparison to identified copies is recommended.

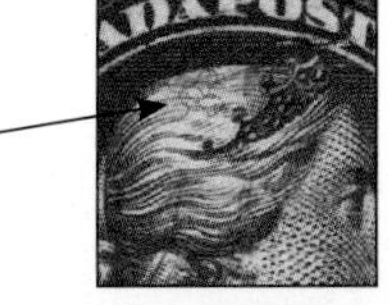
43vii

| | | NH% | ★VF | ★F | ★VG | ⊙VF | ⊙F | ✉ |
|---|---|---|---|---|---|---|---|---|
| **44** | **8¢ violet black** | 300 | 350.00 | 80.00 | 35.00 | 10.00 | 5.00 | 30.00 |
| a | blue grey (*Aug 1, 1893*) | 300 | 550.00 | 150.00 | 75.00 | 12.00 | 6.00 | 30.00 |
| b | slate | 300 | 400.00 | 100.00 | 50.00 | 10.00 | 5.00 | 30.00 |
| c | grey | 300 | 400.00 | 100.00 | 50.00 | 10.00 | 5.00 | 30.00 |
| d | imperf. pair, blue grey, with gum (*1895*) ‡ | 150 | 1,000.00 | 500.00 | 300.00 | — | — | — |
| i | imperf. pair, violet black, without gum (*1897*) ‡ | — | 1,250.00 | 650.00 | 400.00 | — | — | — |
| ii | major re-entry, doubling of oval and top of CENTS | 200 | 650.00 | 250.00 | 100.00 | 150.00 | 60.00 | 400.00 |
| xx | No. 44, precancelled [11 styles] | — | — | — | — | 75.00 | 50.00 | 200.00 |
| xxi | No. 44b, precancelled | — | — | — | — | — | 150.00 | |

‡ Estimated total, with and without gum, 800 stamps.

44ii

| | | NH% | ★VF | ★F | ★VG | ⊙VF | ⊙F | ✉ |
|---|---|---|---|---|---|---|---|---|
| **45** | **10¢ brown red**, *1897* | 200 | 900.00 | 300.00 | 90.00 | 80.00 | 40.00 | 250.00 |
| a | dull rose | 200 | 800.00 | 250.00 | 90.00 | 70.00 | 30.00 | 250.00 |
| vi | dull rose, thin paper | | | | | | | |
| b | pink | 200 | 900.00 | 300.00 | 90.00 | 80.00 | 40.00 | 250.00 |
| c | imperf. pair, brown red, with brownish yellow gum, *1897*† | 150 | 750.00 | 450.00 | 275.00 | — | — | — |
| i | imperf. pair, rose carmine, with and w/o gum, *1891*† | 150 | 750.00 | 450.00 | 275.00 | — | — | — |
| ii | imperf. pair rose pink, with and w/o gum, *1896*† | 150 | 750.00 | 450.00 | 275.00 | — | — | — |
| iii | re-entry of top frameline (3 lines instead of 2) (pos. 89) | 200 | | 500.00 | 150.00 | | 150.00 | 300.00 |
| iv | gash in right "1" (pos. 88) | 200 | 1,250.00 | 500.00 | 150.00 | 250.00 | 125.00 | 450.00 |
| v | pitted right "0" (pos. 21) | 200 | 1,250.00 | 500.00 | 150.00 | 250.00 | 125.00 | 450.00 |
| xx | No. 45, precancelled [5 styles] | — | — | — | — | 75.00 | 50.00 | 300.00* |
| xxa | No. 45a, precancelled [6 styles] | — | — | — | — | 75.00 | 50.00 | 300.00 |

Using the Stanley Gibbons Colour Key: 45c is Venetian red; 45i is pale lake brown; 45ii is dull scarlet.
† Estimated total, with and without gum, 1,000 stamps.
* On cover, without postal cancellation.

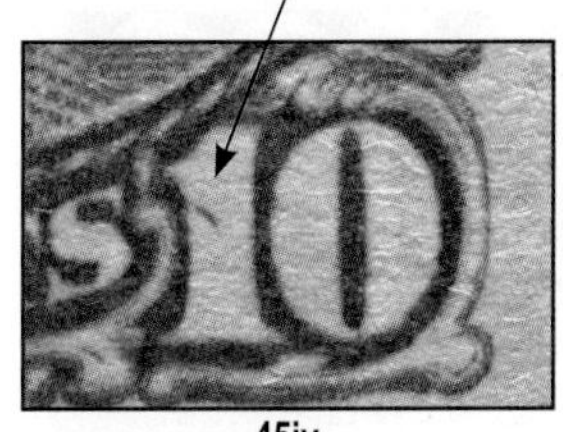
45iv

45v

| | | NH% | ★VF | ★F | ★VG | ⊙VF | ⊙F | ✉ |
|---|---|---|---|---|---|---|---|---|
| **46** | **20¢ vermilion,** *Feb 15, 1893* | 300 | 600.00 | 200.00 | 100.00 | 150.00 | 50.00 | 1,200.00‡ |
| a | imperf. pair, brown orange * | 200 | 1,800.00 | 1,100.00 | 900.00 | — | — | — |
| i | brown orange shade | 300 | 750.00 | 250.00 | 125.00 | 175.00 | 75.00 | 1,200.00 |
| xx | No. 46, precancelled [7 styles] | | | | | 200.00 | 150.00 | 200.00† |

Qty: 525,200
† $1,200.00 if tied to cover by postmark.

| | | NH% | ★VF | ★F | ★VG | ⊙VF | ⊙F | ✉ |
|---|---|---|---|---|---|---|---|---|
| **47** | **50¢ deep blue**, *Feb 15, 1893* | 300 | 600.00 | 200.00 | 100.00 | 90.00 | 30.00 | 1,200.00‡ |
| a | imperf. pair, deep violet blue * | 200 | 1,800.00 | 1,100.00 | 900.00 | — | — | — |
| i | re-entry (pos. 6)† | 300 | 1,200.00 | 400.00 | 200.00 | 200.00 | 100.00 | 1,500.00‡ |
| ii | vertical stitch watermark | | | | | | 500.00 | |
| xx | No. 47, precancelled [5 styles] | | | | | 50.00 | 25.00 | 300.00 |

Qty: 530,200
The gum on these later Ottawa printings appears bright and shiny, often with a yellowish tint.
* The estimated total for varieties 46a and 47a is 200 stamps (100 pairs).
† Most stamps in the top row exhibit similar doublings of the top frameline.
‡ Single usage only.

Nos. 48 and 49 are not assigned.

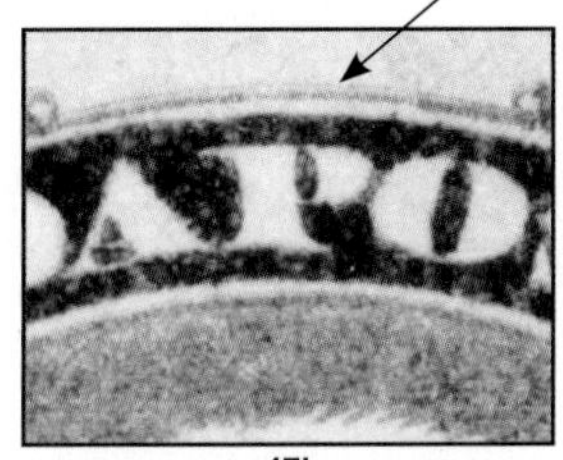
47i

## DIAMOND JUBILEE ISSUE

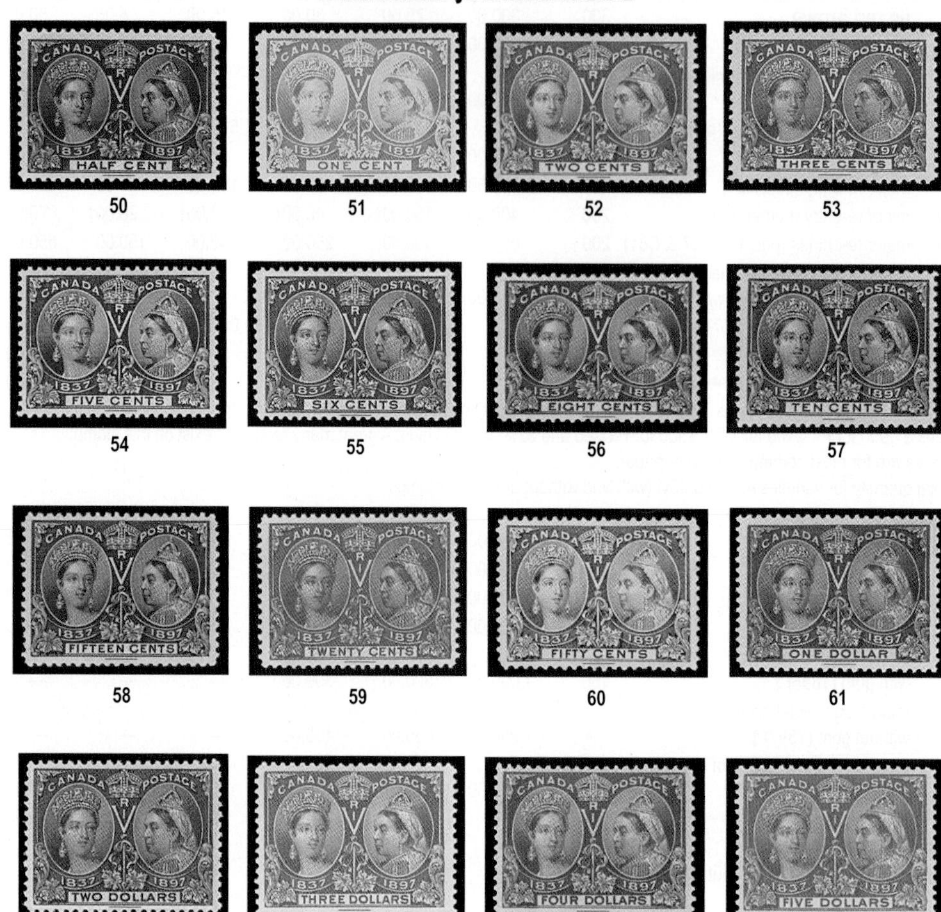

50 51 52 53
54 55 56 57
58 59 60 61
62 63 64 65

**Rates:**

Domestic: 3¢ per oz.
Local: 2¢ per oz.
USA: 3¢ per oz.
Registration: 5¢

Plate Proofs:
All plate proofs for this issue are mounted on cardboard. Quantities in parentheses are previously known quantities in private hands plus the quantities offered at the American Bank Note Company archives sale in 1990.

SPECIMEN overprints were applied to an unknown quantity of the seven higher values in this issue for distribution to foreign postal administrations as samples of Canada's postage stamps. Never hinged examples of SPECIMENS are rare—add 150%. The low values (#50 to #58) also exist with Specimen overprints; value $500 each.

The American Bank Note Company archives sale at Christies in 1990 included more than 300 complete sets of Jubilee proofs, plus additional quantities of values.

51ii

Designer: Lyndwode Charles Pereira and Peleg Franklin Brownell.
Portraits: Young Queen: Alfred Edward Chalon; Old Queen: Alexander Bassano.
American Bank Note Company, Panes of 100 (½¢–8¢); Panes of 50 (10¢–$5)

**1897, Jun 19** **Engraved** **Perf 12**

| | | | NH% | ★VF | ★F | ★VG | ⊙VF | ⊙F | ✉ |
|---|---|---|---|---|---|---|---|---|---|
| **50** | | **½¢ black** | 200 | 140.00 | 70.00 | 40.00 | 140.00 | 70.00 | 650.00‡ |
| | P | Plate proof (1,750) | — | 90.00 | 50.00 | 25.00 | — | — | — |

Qty: 150,000
‡ Single usage on cover with postal cancellation.
Numerous re-entries exist.

51iii

| | | | NH% | ★VF | ★F | ★VG | ⊙VF | ⊙F | ✉ |
|---|---|---|---|---|---|---|---|---|---|
| **51** | | **1¢ orange** | 200 | 40.00 | 10.00 | 3.50 | 12.50 | 4.00 | 30.00 |
| | i | yellow orange | 200 | 40.00 | 10.00 | 3.50 | 12.50 | 4.00 | 30.00 |
| | ii | re-entry in POSTAGE (pos. 82) | | | | | | | |
| | iii | re-entry in DA and PO | | | | | | | |
| | iv | re-entry in A and POSTA and crown | | | | | | | |
| | v | bisected, on cover | | | | | | | *6,000.00* |
| | xx | No. 51, precancelled [3 styles] | — | — | — | — | 25.00 | 15.00 | 25.00 |
| | P | Plate proof (2,000) | — | 65.00 | 30.00 | 15.00 | — | — | — |

Qty: 8,000,000

51iv

| | | NH% | ★VF | ★F | ★VG | ⊙VF | ⊙F | ✉ |
|---|---|---|---|---|---|---|---|---|
| **52** | **2¢ green** | 200 | 50.00 | 12.00 | 4.50 | 20.00 | 9.50 | 35.00 |
| i | deep green | 200 | 50.00 | 15.00 | 4.50 | 20.00 | 9.50 | 35.00 |
| xx | No. 52, precancelled [1 style] | — | — | — | — | 250.00 | 100.00 | 200.00† |
| P | Plate proof (1,850) | — | 65.00 | 30.00 | 15.00 | — | — | — |

Qty: 2,500,000
† On cover, without postal cancellation.

| | | NH% | ★VF | ★F | ★VG | ⊙VF | ⊙F | ✉ |
|---|---|---|---|---|---|---|---|---|
| **53** | **3¢ bright rose** | 200 | 40.00 | 10.00 | 2.00 | 4.00 | 1.75 | 15.00 |
| i | rose | 200 | 40.00 | 10.00 | 2.00 | 4.00 | 1.75 | 15.00 |
| ii | imperf bottom margin (2 known) | — | — | 2,500.00 | — | — | 1,000.00 | — |
| xx | No. 53, precancelled [2 styles] | — | — | — | — | 30.00 | 25.00 | 30.00† |
| P | Plate proof (3,000) | — | 50.00 | 25.00 | 12.50 | — | — | — |

Qty: 20,000,000
Numerous re-entries exist, mainly in crown.

| | | NH% | ★VF | ★F | ★VG | ⊙VF | ⊙F | ✉ |
|---|---|---|---|---|---|---|---|---|
| **54** | **5¢ deep blue** | 200 | 100.00 | 30.00 | 10.00 | 60.00 | 20.00 | 150.00 |
| i | slate blue | 200 | 100.00 | 30.00 | 10.00 | 60.00 | 20.00 | 150.00 |
| ii | re-entry in portrait oval and CENTS (pl. 10, pos. 10) | | | | | | | |
| xx | No. 54, precancelled [1 style] | — | — | — | — | — | 250.00 | 300.00† |
| P | Plate proof (1,700)* | — | 90.00 | 50.00 | 25.00 | — | — | — |

Qty: 750,000
* Three shades of Plate proofs are known: blue, deep blue and slate blue, all valued the same.

| | | NH% | ★VF | ★F | ★VG | ⊙VF | ⊙F | ✉ |
|---|---|---|---|---|---|---|---|---|
| **55** | **6¢ yellow brown** | 200 | 300.00 | 150.00 | 60.00 | 250.00 | 125.00 | 500.00‡ |
| i | re-entry in POSTAGE | 200 | 900.00 | 450.00 | 150.00 | 750.00 | 375.00 | |
| P | Plate proof (600) | — | 350.00 | 200.00 | 75.00 | — | — | — |
| Pi | Plate proof with re-entry in POSTAGE | — | 750.00 | 450.00 | | | | |

Qty: 75,000

| | | NH% | ★VF | ★F | ★VG | ⊙VF | ⊙F | ✉ |
|---|---|---|---|---|---|---|---|---|
| **56** | **8¢ dark violet** | 200 | 200.00 | 60.00 | 20.00 | 100.00 | 30.00 | 300.00‡ |
| i | misplaced entry in UL corner (pos. 3) | | | | | | | |
| ii | re-entry in crown (pos. 11) | | | | | | | |
| xx | No. 56, precancelled [1 style] | — | — | — | — | — | 300.00 | 375.00 |
| P | Plate proof (1,150) | — | 140.00 | 75.00 | 35.00 | — | — | — |

Qty: 200,000

| | | NH% | ★VF | ★F | ★VG | ⊙VF | ⊙F | ✉ |
|---|---|---|---|---|---|---|---|---|
| **57** | **10¢ brown violet** | 200 | 250.00 | 75.00 | 30.00 | 160.00 | 60.00 | 375.00‡ |
| i | major re-entry (pos. 5) | 200 | 500.00 | 250.00 | 75.00 | 300.00 | 150.00 | 600.00 |
| ii | major re-entry in CANADA POSTAGE, R & V, upper right margin (pos. 46) | 200 | 300.00 | 125.00 | 60.00 | 250.00 | 125.00 | 475.00 |
| iii | re-entry in P and oval (pos. 3) | 200 | 300.00 | 125.00 | 60.00 | 250.00 | 125.00 | 475.00 |
| xx | No. 57, precancelled [1 style] | | | | | | 200.00 | 350.00† |
| P | Plate proof (550) | — | 350.00 | 200.00 | 75.00 | — | — | — |

Qty: 150,000

| | | NH% | ★VF | ★F | ★VG | ⊙VF | ⊙F | ✉ |
|---|---|---|---|---|---|---|---|---|
| **58** | **15¢ steel blue** | 200 | 400.00 | 150.00 | 75.00 | 250.00 | 120.00 | 600.00‡ |
| xx | No. 58, precancelled [2 styles] | — | — | — | — | — | 250.00 | 350.00† |
| P | Plate proof (600) | — | 350.00 | 200.00 | 75.00 | — | — | — |

Qty: 100,000

| | | NH% | ★VF | ★F | ★VG | ⊙VF | ⊙F | ✉ |
|---|---|---|---|---|---|---|---|---|
| **59** | **20¢ vermilion** | 200 | 400.00 | 150.00 | 80.00 | 250.00 | 115.00 | 600.00‡ |
| i | deep vermilion | 200 | 450.00 | 150.00 | 90.00 | 300.00 | 150.00 | 600.00‡ |
| ii | W-E variety, (Pl. 21, pos. 15)* | 200 | 900.00 | 400.00 | 200.00 | 600.00 | 300.00 | 1,000.00‡ |
| iii | re-entry in crown and P of POSTAGE (pos. 2) | 200 | 750.00 | 300.00 | 150.00 | — | 250.00 | — |
| iv | re-entry in P and crown (pos. 8) | 200 | 900.00 | 400.00 | 200.00 | 600.00 | 300.00 | |
| v | re-entry in POS and crown (pos. 37) | 200 | 900.00 | 400.00 | 200.00 | 600.00 | 300.00 | |
| xx | No. 59, precancelled [1 style] | — | — | — | — | — | 250.00 | 750.00† |
| | SPECIMEN overprint | 200 | 600.00 | 300.00 | 150.00 | — | — | — |
| P | Plate proof (850) | — | 375.00 | 200.00 | 100.00 | — | — | — |

Qty: 100,000
* The W-E variety (59ii) shows a line between the W and E of TWENTY.
† On cover, without postal cancellation.
‡ Single usage.

54ii

56i

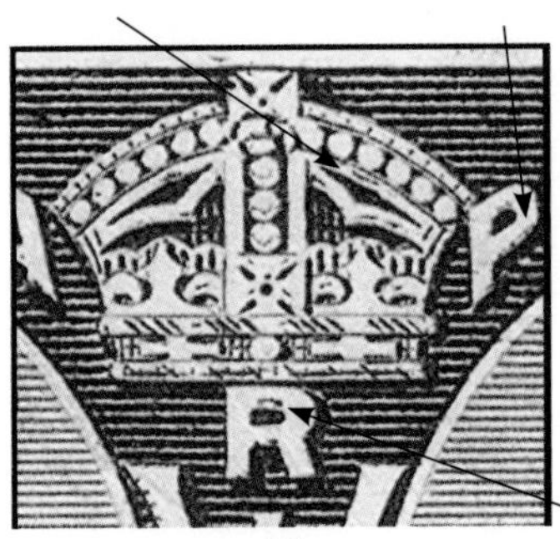
57i

57ii

57iii

59ii

59iii

| No. | | NH% | ★VF | ★F | ★VG | ⊙VF | ⊙F | ✉ |
|---|---|---|---|---|---|---|---|---|
| **60** | **50¢ ultramarine** | 200 | 500.00 | 150.00 | 55.00 | 250.00 | 115.00 | 600.00‡ |
| i | deep ultramarine | 200 | 600.00 | 175.00 | 75.00 | 275.00 | 150.00 | 600.00‡ |
| ii | pale blue ("powder blue" shade) | 200 | 850.00 | 350.00 | 125.00 | 350.00 | 175.00 | |
| xx | No. 60, precancelled [1 style] | — | — | — | — | — | 250.00 | 750.00† |
| | SPECIMEN overprint | 200 | 600.00 | 300.00 | 150.00 | — | — | — |
| P | Plate proof (800) | — | 375.00 | 200.00 | 100.00 | — | — | — |

Qty: 100,000
† On cover, without postal cancellation.
‡ Single usage.

| No. | | NH% | ★VF | ★F | ★VG | ⊙VF | ⊙F | ✉ |
|---|---|---|---|---|---|---|---|---|
| **61** | **$1 lake** | 200 | 1,200.00 | 600.00 | 375.00 | 1,000.00 | 600.00 | 1,750.00¶ |
| xx | No. 61, precancelled [1 style] | | | | | 550.00 | 300.00 | |
| | SPECIMEN overprint | 200 | 800.00 | 400.00 | 200.00 | — | — | — |
| P | Plate proof (400) | — | 1,500.00 | 750.00 | 500.00 | — | — | — |

Qty: 24,900
Used blocks of the $1 value are very rare.

| No. | | NH% | ★VF | ★F | ★VG | ⊙VF | ⊙F | ✉ |
|---|---|---|---|---|---|---|---|---|
| **62** | **$2 dark purple** | 200 | 2,000.00 | 1,200.00 | 600.00 | 800.00 | 400.00 | 2,000.00¶ |
| xx | No. 62, precancelled [1 style] | — | — | — | — | 550.00 | 300.00 | |
| | SPECIMEN overprint | 200 | 800.00 | 400.00 | 250.00 | — | — | — |
| P | Plate proof (750) | — | 800.00 | 400.00 | 250.00 | — | — | — |

Qty: 25,000
Used blocks of the $2 value are almost always from parcels, cancelled with a roller, and are scarce.
Used $2 with CDS cancel (1897–1907) are rare—add 50%.

63i

| No. | | NH% | ★VF | ★F | ★VG | ⊙VF | ⊙F | ✉ |
|---|---|---|---|---|---|---|---|---|
| **63** | **$3 yellow bistre** | 200 | 2,000.00 | 1,200.00 | 600.00 | 1,600.00 | 800.00 | 2,750.00¶ |
| i | re-entry in POSTA and mark in the left slant of the large central V (pos. 19) | 200 | 3,000.00 | 1,800.00 | | 2,000.00 | 1,000.00 | |
| | SPECIMEN overprint | 200 | 800.00 | 400.00 | 250.00 | — | — | — |
| P | Plate proof (750) | — | 800.00 | 400.00 | 250.00 | — | — | — |

Qty: 13,500

| No. | | NH% | ★VF | ★F | ★VG | ⊙VF | ⊙F | ✉ |
|---|---|---|---|---|---|---|---|---|
| **64** | **$4 purple** | 200 | 2,000.00 | 1,200.00 | 600.00 | 1,600.00 | 800.00 | 2,750.00¶ |
| | SPECIMEN overprint | 200 | 800.00 | 400.00 | 250.00 | — | — | — |
| P | Plate proof (650) | — | 800.00 | 400.00 | 250.00 | — | — | — |

Qty: 14,500

65i

65ii

| No. | | NH% | ★VF | ★F | ★VG | ⊙VF | ⊙F | ✉ |
|---|---|---|---|---|---|---|---|---|
| **65** | **$5 olive green** | 200 | 2,000.00 | 1,200.00 | 600.00 | 1,600.00 | 800.00 | 2,750.00¶ |
| | SPECIMEN overprint | 200 | 800.00 | 400.00 | 250.00 | — | — | — |
| i | re-entry in ADA PO and IR of VRI (pos. 11) | | | | | | | |
| ii | re-entry in P and T (pos. 10) | | | | | | | |
| P | Plate proof (800) | — | 800.00 | 400.00 | 250.00 | — | — | — |

Qty: 16,500

| Set | NH% | ★VF | ★F | ★VG | ⊙VF | ⊙F | ✉ |
|---|---|---|---|---|---|---|---|
| **Nos. 50–65** (16) Complete set | 200 | 11,615.00 | 6,267.00 | 3,165.00 | 8,036.50 | 4,120.25 | |
| **Nos. 50–60** (11) Short set | 200 | 2,415.00 | 867.00 | 390.00 | 1,486.50 | 670.25 | |
| **Nos. 50P–65P** (16 Plate proofs) set | — | 7,000.00 | 3,610.00 | 2,052.50 | — | — | — |
| **Nos. 50P–60P** (11 Plate proofs) Short set | — | 2,300.00 | 1,260.00 | 552.50 | — | — | — |
| **Nos. 59–65** (7 SPECIMEN overprint) set | 200 | 5,200.00 | 2,600.00 | 1,500.00 | — | — | — |

Nos. 61 to 65 ($1 to $5) in XF NH condition command very large premiums — copies of 63 to 65 ($3 to $5) were selling up to $14,000 at auction over the past couple of years.

Issued to commemorate the 60th anniversary of the reign of Queen Victoria.
The dollar values used, with roller or smudge cancellations, sell for nearly 50% below the listed prices. Used blocks of the three highest values ($3–$5) exist with magenta Winnipeg cancels recording payment for bulk mailing of Winnipeg Free Press newspapers. Block value is 4 x used single prices.
Imprint pairs, imprint strips of three, or imprint blocks of four or six of the Jubilee Issue are all scarce. Value approximately double that of the same number of singles.

¶ On cover prices (for fine stamps on individual covers) of $1–$5 are for "philatelic" origin, dated 1897.

## QUEEN VICTORIA "MAPLE LEAF" ISSUE

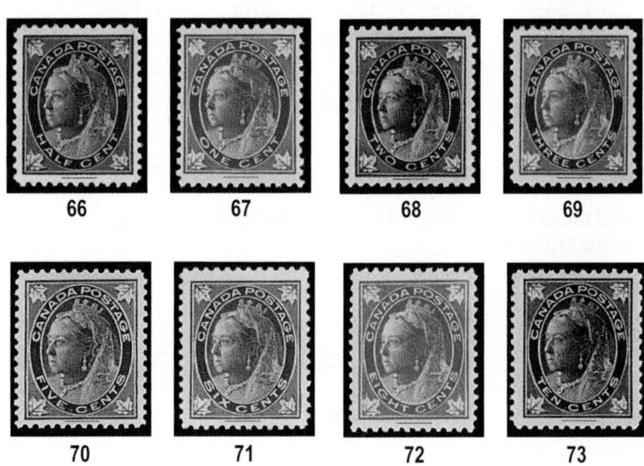

66 67 68 69

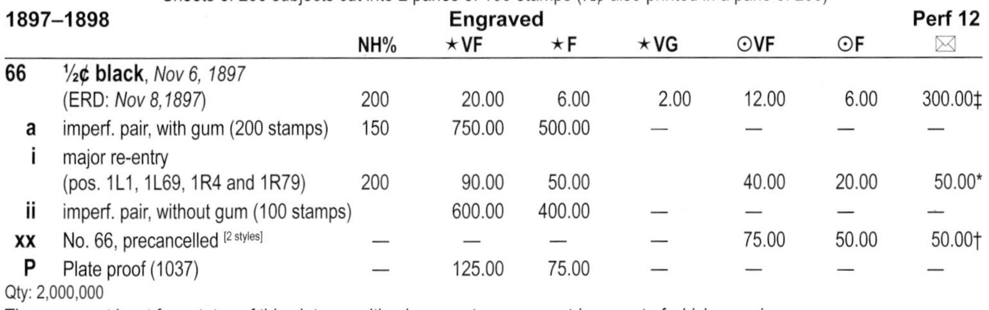

70 71 72 73

**Rates:**

Domestic: 3¢ per oz.
Local: 2¢ per oz.
USA: 3¢ per oz.
Registration: 5¢

Plate Proofs:
Only a few plate proofs of this issue were known prior to the American Bank Note Company archives sale in New York in 1990. The quantity shown in parentheses were sold at this sale and are now in private hands. Approximately 10% of the proofs sold at the archive sale were defective. All proofs are on India paper, on card, in the colour of issue.

**66i (pos 1R79)**
Doubling overall in most of lettering, particularly distinctive in HALF CE; the left vertical frame; the bottom frameline, and inside the bottom frameline.

Portrait: photograph taken by W. & D. Downey. Portrait engraved by Charles Skinner.
American Bank Note Company, Ottawa.
Sheets of 200 subjects cut into 2 panes of 100 stamps (½¢ also printed in a pane of 200)

**1897–1898** **Engraved** **Perf 12**

| | | NH% | ★VF | ★F | ★VG | ⊙VF | ⊙F | ✉ |
|---|---|---|---|---|---|---|---|---|
| **66** | **½¢ black**, *Nov 6, 1897* (ERD: *Nov 8, 1897*) | 200 | 20.00 | 6.00 | 2.00 | 12.00 | 6.00 | 300.00‡ |
| **a** | imperf. pair, with gum (200 stamps) | 150 | 750.00 | 500.00 | — | — | — | — |
| **i** | major re-entry (pos. 1L1, 1L69, 1R4 and 1R79) | 200 | 90.00 | 50.00 | | 40.00 | 20.00 | 50.00* |
| **ii** | imperf. pair, without gum (100 stamps) | | 600.00 | 400.00 | — | — | — | — |
| **xx** | No. 66, precancelled [2 styles] | — | — | — | — | 75.00 | 50.00 | 50.00† |
| **P** | Plate proof (1037) | — | 125.00 | 75.00 | — | — | — | — |

Qty: 2,000,000
There were at least four states of this plate, resulting in a great many re-entries, most of which are minor.
* Single usage $400.00.
† Single usage $300.00.
‡ Single usage only. See note following No. 34.

**66i (pos 1L69)**
Doubling overall in most of lettering, particularly distinctive in STAGE, HAL, and N of CENT; the right vertical frame is doubled out in the right margin, while there is doubling inside the left vertical frame to the lower right.

| | | NH% | ★VF | ★F | ★VG | ⊙VF | ⊙F | ✉ |
|---|---|---|---|---|---|---|---|---|
| **67** | **1¢ blue green**, *Dec 1, 1897* | 200 | 70.00 | 20.00 | 4.00 | 2.50 | .75 | 10.00 |
| **a** | imperf. pair with gum † | 150 | 750.00 | 500.00 | — | — | — | — |
| **i** | imperf. pair without gum † | — | 600.00 | 400.00 | — | — | — | — |
| **ii** | major re-entry in CANADA | 200 | 250.00 | 75.00 | | 30.00 | 17.50 | 70.00 |
| **xx** | No. 67, precancelled [2 styles] | — | — | — | — | 2.00 | .30 | 5.00 |
| **P** | Plate proof (471) | — | 165.00 | 75.00 | — | — | — | — |

Qty: 34,000,000
† Estimated total, with and without gum, 400 stamps, probably 100 pairs each.

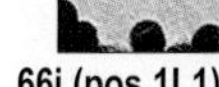

**66i (pos 1L1)**
Doubling overall in most lettering, particularly distinctive in POSTAGE and HAF; the left outer frameline shows sharp doubling in the top left corner, and fainter doubling in the outer lower left margin.

| | | NH% | ★VF | ★F | ★VG | ⊙VF | ⊙F | ✉ |
|---|---|---|---|---|---|---|---|---|
| **68** | **2¢ purple**, *Dec 4, 1897* | 200 | 80.00 | 20.00 | 4.50 | 3.00 | 1.20 | 15.00* |
| **a** | imperf. pair, with gum † | 150 | 750.00 | 500.00 | — | — | — | — |
| **i** | imperf. pair, without gum † | — | 600.00 | 400.00 | — | — | — | — |
| **ii** | major re-entry (pos. 1L2) | 200 | 200.00 | 80.00 | | 35.00 | 17.50 | 65.00 |
| **iii** | misplaced entry (pos. 1L1, 1L7, 1L11 and 1L21) | | 150.00 | 50.00 | | 30.00 | 15.00 | |
| **xx** | No. 68, precancelled [1 style] | — | — | — | — | 20.00 | 10.00 | 30.00 |
| **P** | Plate proof, deep purple (667) | — | 100.00 | 60.00 | — | — | — | — |
| **Pi** | Plate proof, dull purple (included above) | — | 100.00 | 60.00 | — | — | — | — |

Qty: 12,000,000
68iii are misplaced entries with evidence throughout the design (which also exist on the Plate proofs); 68ii is a major re-entry in POSTAGE and LR corner.
* used prior to Sep 2, 1898.
† Estimated total, with and without gum, 400 stamps.

**67ii**

69ii

| No. | | NH% | ★VF | ★F | ★VG | ⊙VF | ⊙F | ✉ |
|---|---|---|---|---|---|---|---|---|
| 69 | **3¢ carmine** (ERD: *Jan 4, 1898*) | 200 | 130.00 | 40.00 | 10.00 | 2.50 | .50 | 10.00 |
| a | imperf. pair (200 stamps) | 150 | 1,200.00 | 800.00 | — | — | — | — |
| i | imperf. left margin (fewer than 10 exist)* | | — | 1,500.00 | — | — | — | — |
| ii | major re-entry in CANADA | 200 | 200.00 | 60.00 | | 35.00 | 17.50 | 50.00 |
| xx | No. 69, precancelled [1 style] | — | — | — | — | 10.00 | 5.00 | 25.00 |
| P | Plate proof (713) | — | 125.00 | 75.00 | — | — | — | — |

Qty: 44,000,000

* The editors have only recorded two examples although it is thought that ten "should" exist.

For 2¢ on 3¢ surcharge issue, see Scott # 87.

70ii

| No. | | NH% | ★VF | ★F | ★VG | ⊙VF | ⊙F | ✉ |
|---|---|---|---|---|---|---|---|---|
| 70 | **5¢ dark blue**, *on bluish paper, Dec 10,1897* | 200 | 250.00 | 65.00 | 20.00 | 14.00 | 6.00 | 60.00 |
| a | imperf. pair, slate blue on horiz. wove paper (200 stamps) | 150 | 800.00 | 500.00 | — | — | — | — |
| i | imperf. pair w/o gum, bright blue on horiz. wove paper (200 stamps) | — | 600.00 | 400.00 | — | — | — | — |
| ii | "guide dot" and plate scratch at LL (pos. 1L91) | 200 | 1,200.00 | 600.00 | 250.00 | 600.00 | 300.00 | 900.00 |
| xx | No. 70, precancelled [2 styles] | — | — | — | — | 20.00 | 12.50 | 40.00 |
| P | Plate proof (300) | — | 300.00 | 150.00 | — | — | — | — |

Qty: 3,500,000

Numerous re-entries exist, some major.

71i

71ii

| No. | | NH% | ★VF | ★F | ★VG | ⊙VF | ⊙F | ✉ |
|---|---|---|---|---|---|---|---|---|
| 71 | **6¢ brown**, *Nov 22, 1897* | 200 | 200.00 | 55.00 | 20.00 | 60.00 | 20.00 | 750.00‡ |
| a | imperf. pair (200 stamps) | 150 | 1,000.00 | 600.00 | | — | — | — |
| i | engraver's slip at bottom, later corrected (pos. 14, left pane) | 200 | 1,200.00 | 600.00 | 250.00 | 600.00 | 300.00 | 925.00‡ |
| ii | misplaced entry (pos. 72) | 200 | 1,000.00 | 500.00 | 250.00 | 600.00 | 300.00 | 900.00‡ |
| xx | No. 71, precancelled [1 style] | — | — | — | — | 40.00 | 25.00 | 500.00† |
| P | Plate proof (619) | — | 225.00 | 125.00 | — | — | — | — |

Qty: 500,000

72v

| No. | | NH% | ★VF | ★F | ★VG | ⊙VF | ⊙F | ✉ |
|---|---|---|---|---|---|---|---|---|
| 72 | **8¢ orange**, vertical wove, *Dec 15,1897* | 200 | 500.00 | 150.00 | 35.00 | 30.00 | 7.50 | 75.00 |
| a | imperf. pair, horiz. wove** | 150 | 1,000.00 | 600.00 | | — | — | — |
| i | imperf. pair, vert. wove, brownish orange, ** | 150 | 1,000.00 | 600.00 | | — | — | — |
| ii | orange, horizontal wove paper | 200 | 500.00 | 150.00 | 35.00 | 25.00 | 7.50 | 65.00 |
| iii | brownish orange shade | 200 | 500.00 | 150.00 | 35.00 | 30.00 | 7.50 | 65.00 |
| iv | Thin paper, strong vert. weave, white gum | 200 | 500.00 | 150.00 | 50.00 | 35.00 | 15.00 | — |
| v | re-entry in CANA | | | | | | | |
| xx | No. 72, precancelled [1 style] | — | — | — | — | 150.00 | 90.00 | 125.00† |
| P | Plate proof (171) | — | 600.00 | 250.00 | — | — | — | — |

Qty: 1,400,000

73iii

| No. | | NH% | ★VF | ★F | ★VG | ⊙VF | ⊙F | ✉ |
|---|---|---|---|---|---|---|---|---|
| 73 | **10¢ brown violet**, vertical wove, *Dec 27, 1897* | 200 | 800.00 | 200.00 | 60.00 | 150.00 | 60.00 | 1,000.00‡ |
| a | reddish brown violet, imperf. pair, horiz. wove paper ** | 150 | 1,000.00 | 600.00 | | — | — | — |
| i | brown violet, imperf. pair, vert. wove paper ** | 150 | 1,000.00 | 600.00 | | — | — | — |
| ii | brown violet, horizontal wove paper | 200 | 800.00 | 300.00 | 90.00 | 225.00 | 90.00 | |
| iii | re-entry in CAN | | | | | | | |
| xx | No. 73, precancelled [style] | — | — | — | — | 100.00 | 50.00 | 880.00† |
| P | Plate proof (235) | — | 500.00 | 200.00 | — | — | — | — |

Qty: 300,000

| | | NH% | ★VF | ★F | ★VG | ⊙VF | ⊙F | ✉ |
|---|---|---|---|---|---|---|---|---|
| **Nos. 66–73** | (8) Set | 200 | 2,050.00 | 555.00 | 153.50 | 271.50 | 100.95 | |
| **Nos. 66P–73P** | Set of 8 plate proofs | — | 2,000.00 | 1,000.00 | — | — | — | — |

The 1¢ (67a), 2¢ (68a) and 5¢ (70a) imperfs. were issued both with and without gum. Shades vary noticeably.

** Quantities of the 8¢ and 10¢ imperf. pairs: 72a – 100 stamps (50 pairs), 72i – 200 stamps (100 pairs), 73a – 200 stamps (100 pairs) and 73i – 100 stamps (50 pairs).

† On cover, without postal cancellation.

‡ Single usage only.

Imprint pairs, imprint strips of three, or imprint blocks of four or more (need 8-10 for full imprints on some) of the "Maple Leaf" Issue are all scarce. Value approximately 50% more than the sum of the individual value of the singles in the imprint piece.

## QUEEN VICTORIA "NUMERAL" ISSUE

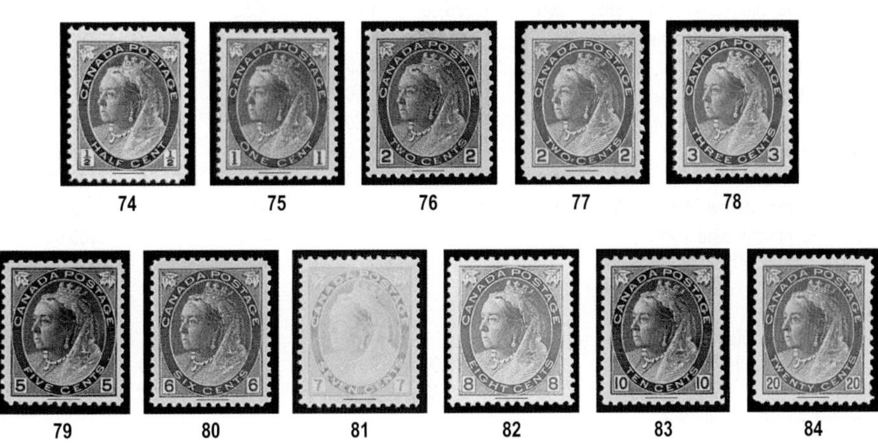
74 75 76 77 78
79 80 81 82 83 84

**Rates:**

Domestic: 3¢ per oz.
Local: 2¢ per oz.
Postcard: 1¢
Printed matter: 1¢ per 4 oz.
USA: 3¢ per oz.
Registration: 5¢
Special delivery: 10¢ (from Jul 1/98)



Plate Proofs:
All proofs are on India paper, on card, in colour of issue. Quantities shown are from the ABN archives sale. Essays exist of the 4¢, 15¢ and 50¢ values, which were never regularly issued. Very few die proofs of these exist in black and in proposed colours of issue. Value $4,000–$5,000 depending on the size of the proof.

Portrait: photograph taken by W. & D. Downey. Portrait engraved by Charles Skinner.
American Bank Note Company, Ottawa.
Sheets of 200 subjects cut into 2 panes of 100 stamps

**1898–1902** **Engraved** **Perf 12**

| | | NH% | ★VF | ★F | ★VG | ⊙VF | ⊙F | ✉ |
|---|---|---|---|---|---|---|---|---|
| **74** | **½¢ black**, *Sep 6, 1898* | 200 | 20.00 | 5.00 | .60 | 4.00 | 1.25 | 300.00‡ |
| a | imperf. pair, with gum* | 150 | 700.00 | 400.00 | — | | | |
| i | grey | 200 | 30.00 | 6.00 | .60 | 4.00 | 1.25 | 300.00‡ |
| ii | major re-entry (pos. 18, Pl. 1 R) | 200 | 150.00 | 75.00 | 50.00 | 90.00 | 50.00 | 350.00‡ |
| iii | imperf. gutter strip of 4 (without gum)* | — | *4,000.00* | *2,000.00* | | — | — | — |
| iv | imperf. pair, horiz. wove paper (without gum)* | — | 500.00 | 300.00 | | — | — | — |
| v | Imperf pair, vert. wove, (without gum) | — | 500.00 | 300.00 | | — | — | — |
| vi | horizontal stitch watermark | | | | | | 350.00 | |
| xx | No. 74, precancelled [5 styles] | — | — | — | — | — | 20.00 | 300.00‡ |
| P | Plate proof (537) | — | 200.00 | — | — | — | — | — |

Qty: 6,800,000
* The ½¢ imperf. (74a) was issued both with and without gum. There were 597 stamps in full and part sheets, without gum, from the ABNC archives auction in 1990. Prior to this, Jephcott & Gates reported 400 known (200 with gum and 200 without) making a total of 200 (100 pairs) with gum and 797 (398 pairs) without gum.
‡ Single usage only. See note following No. 34.
Numerous other re-entries exist.

74ii

| | | NH% | ★VF | ★F | ★VG | ⊙VF | ⊙F | ✉ |
|---|---|---|---|---|---|---|---|---|
| **75** | **1¢ grey green**, *Jun 17, 1898* | 200 | 80.00 | 15.00 | 4.00 | 1.00 | .20 | 5.00 |
| a | deep green, imperf. pair, with gum, vertical wove paper (200 stamps) | 150 | 1,600.00 | 800.00 | | — | — | — |
| i | green | 200 | 75.00 | 15.00 | 4.00 | 1.00 | .20 | 5.00 |
| ii | blue green | 200 | 80.00 | 20.00 | 6.00 | 1.50 | .30 | 5.00 |
| iii | major re-entry in '1's | 200 | 200.00 | 125.00 | 75.00 | 100.00 | 50.00 | 90.00 |
| iv | major re-entry at top | 200 | 200.00 | 125.00 | 75.00 | 100.00 | 50.00 | 90.00 |
| v | on thick paper | 200 | 200.00 | 100.00 | 40.00 | | | — |
| vi | paler green, imperf. pair on vertical wove paper (without gum) † | — | 900.00 | 600.00 | | — | — | — |
| vii | "10¢ on 1¢ numeral", pos. 1R82* | | | | | 500.00 | 250.00 | |
| viii | major misplaced entry, UR corner in LR numeral box | | | | | 500.00 | 250.00 | |
| ix | major misplaced entry, UR corner 4.3 mm too low in margin** | | | | | | 250.00 | |
| x | horizontal stitch watermark | | | | | | 350.00 | |
| xx | No. 75, precancelled [3 styles] | — | — | — | — | 1.00 | .20 | 5.00 |
| P | Plate proof (520) | — | 200.00 | — | — | — | — | — |

Qty: 313,900,000
Numerous other re-entries and misplaced entries exist.
* A narrow band of details from the 10¢ design appears across the 1¢ stamp 6 mm above the bottom frameline.
** Also known 1 mm too low.
† A total of 600 imperf stamps on wove paper (75vi, plates 5 & 6) were sold at the ABNC archives auction in 1990, all without gum.

75iii

75vii

75viii

76iv

| No. | | NH% | ★VF | ★F | ★VG | ⊙VF | ⊙F | ✉ |
|---|---|---|---|---|---|---|---|---|
| **76** | **2¢ purple**, Die I (ERD: *Sep 2, 1898*) | 200 | 75.00 | 15.00 | 4.50 | 1.00 | .20 | 5.00 |
| a | violet, on somewhat yellowish, thick paper, *Jun 1899* | 200 | 250.00 | 100.00 | 45.00 | 20.00 | 7.50 | 30.00 |
| i | violet, Die I | 200 | 75.00 | 15.00 | 7.00 | 1.00 | .20 | 5.00 |
| ii | reddish purple, Die I | 200 | 85.00 | 20.00 | 7.50 | 1.50 | .25 | 5.00 |
| iii | re-entry (pos. 1L5) | 200 | 400.00 | 200.00 | | 75.00 | 40.00 | 100.00 |
| iv | "C-flaw" (pos. 2L14) | 200 | 500.00 | 250.00 | | 200.00 | 120.00 | |
| xx | No. 76, precancelled [2 styles] | — | — | — | — | 4.00 | 3.00 | 8.00 |
| xxa | No. 76a, precancelled [1 style] | — | — | — | — | | 100.00 | |

Qty: total, all shades: 72,021,200

**TWO CENT FRAMELINE VARIETIES:**

**Die I**
Four very thin lines

**Die II**
One thick line between two thin lines

77v
1.5mm misplaced entry

| No. | | NH% | ★VF | ★F | ★VG | ⊙VF | ⊙F | ✉ |
|---|---|---|---|---|---|---|---|---|
| **77** | **2¢ carmine**, Die I (ERD: *Aug 22, 1899*) | 200 | 90.00 | 20.00 | 6.50 | 1.00 | .20 | 5.00 |
| a | Die II | 200 | 120.00 | 30.00 | 7.00 | 1.50 | .30 | 5.00 |
| c | imperf. pair, Die I, with gum (300 stamps) ‡ | 150 | 800.00 | 400.00 | — | — | — | — |
| d | imperf. pair, Die II, without gum † | — | 1,500.00 | 750.00 | — | — | — | — |
| i | imperf. gutter strip of 4, without gum, Die I (10 strips) ‡ | — | *4,000.00* | *2,000.00* | — | — | — | — |
| iv | imperf. pair, Die I, vertical wove paper, without gum (160 stamps) ‡ | — | 500.00 | 350.00 | — | — | — | — |
| v | major re-entry, "hook on 2" | | 250.00 | 125.00 | 75.00 | 75.00 | 45.00 | 100.00 |
| vi | horizontal stitch watermark | | | | | | 350.00 | |
| xx | No. 77, precancelled [2 styles] | — | — | — | — | 1.25 | 1.00 | 5.00 |
| xxa | No. 77a, precancelled [2 styles] | — | — | — | — | .75 | .50 | 5.00 |
| P | Plate proof (551) | — | 200.00 | — | — | — | — | — |

Qty: 619,000,000

There are numerous re-entries, some major.

† There were 500 imperf. stamps, without gum (77d) sold at the ABNC archive sale in 1990. These were Die II, from plates 15 and 16. Prior to the 1990 sale there were only a few pairs known of Die II, imperf.

‡ The 2¢, Die I imperf. was issued both with (77c) and without gum (77i and 77iv). Shades vary somewhat.

77b

| No. | | NH% | ★VF | ★F | ★VG | ⊙VF | ⊙F | ✉ |
|---|---|---|---|---|---|---|---|---|
| 77b | booklet pane of 6 x 2¢ carmine, Die II (77bs), *Jun 11, 1900*, (BK1) | 100 | 2,000.00 | 1,000.00 | 400.00 | | | |
| bs | single (Die II) with straight edge, from 77b | 100 | 100.00 | 65.00 | 35.00 | 25.00 | 13.00 | 20.00 |
| e | 2 panes, tête-bêche (77b), imperf., without gum, 1 inverted, (no more than 12 exist)† | — | *25,000.00* | *12,500.00* | *7,500.00* | — | — | |
| ei | imperf. tête-bêche pair, without gum, (4 pairs likely exist) | — | *4,000.00* | *3,000.00* | — | — | — | — |
| BK1 | 2 panes of 77b in cover (100,167) $4,500. | | | | | | | |

† The booklet panes of 6 were printed in sheets of 4 columns, 7 panes per column, with the second and fourth columns inverted. This resulted in 14 tête-bêche panes (77e) possible from each sheet. At least two tête-bêche panes (77e) have been cut into tête-bêche imperf. pairs (77ei) and Die II imperf. pairs (77d); three or more panes are defective with significant thin spots—value $7,500.

78i

| No. | | NH% | ★VF | ★F | ★VG | ⊙VF | ⊙F | ✉ |
|---|---|---|---|---|---|---|---|---|
| **78** | **3¢ carmine**, *Jun 17, 1898* | 200 | 140.00 | 40.00 | 10.00 | 2.00 | .50 | 5.00 |
| i | major re-entry in LL corner | | | | | | | 75.00 |
| xx | No. 78, precancelled [2 styles] | — | — | — | — | 4.00 | 2.50 | 5.00 |
| P | Plate proof (459) | — | 200.00 | — | — | — | — | — |

Qty: 51,287,600

Numerous other re-entries exist, some major

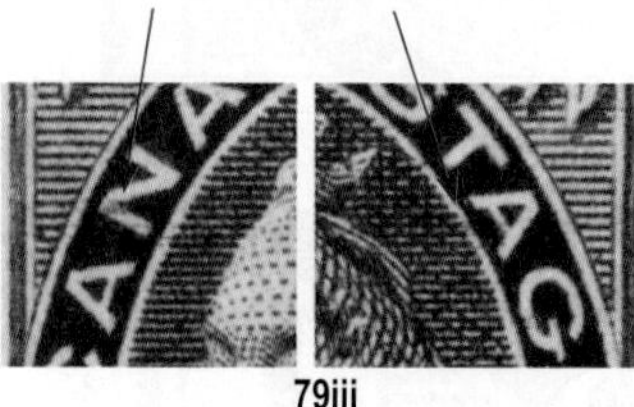

79iii

| No. | | NH% | ★VF | ★F | ★VG | ⊙VF | ⊙F | ✉ |
|---|---|---|---|---|---|---|---|---|
| **79** | **5¢ blue**, *bluish paper, Jul 3, 1899* | 200 | 300.00 | 100.00 | 40.00 | 4.00 | 1.00 | 60.00 |
| a | imperf. pair, whiter paper, with gum (200 stamps) | 150 | 1,500.00 | 750.00 | | — | — | — |
| b | whiter paper | 200 | 350.00 | 150.00 | 40.00 | 4.00 | 1.00 | 60.00 |
| ii | imperf. pair, on bluish, horizontal wove paper, without gum † | — | 900.00 | 600.00 | | — | — | — |
| iii | foreign entry of different numeral value* | | | | | | | |
| xx | No. 79, precancelled [2 styles] | | | | | 17.50 | 15.00 | 50.00 |
| P | Plate proof (496) | — | 200.00 | — | — | — | — | — |

Qty: 22,070,000

Numerous re-entries exist in and around CANADA, some major.

* In a thin band across the stamp, the entry shows through the N of CANADA and the A of POSTAGE, pos. 1R22.

† There were 597 imperf. stamps from Plate 1, without gum, sold at the ABNC auction in 1990.

Queen Victoria — Jub/Leaf/Numeral

| | | NH% | ★VF | ★F | ★VG | ⊙VF | ⊙F | ✉ |
|---|---|---|---|---|---|---|---|---|
| **80** | **6¢ brown**, *Aug 27, 1898* | 200 | 300.00 | 100.00 | 50.00 | 80.00 | 30.00 | 750.00‡ |
| a | imperf. pair, with gum (200 stamps) | 150 | 1,500.00 | 750.00 | | — | — | — |
| xx | No. 80, precancelled [1 style] | — | — | — | — | 30.00 | 20.00 | 600.00‡ |
| P | Plate proof (197) | — | 850.00 | — | — | — | — | — |

Qty: 560,000
‡ Single usage only.
There were no 6¢ stamps (No. 80) offered imperforate on stamp paper in the ABNC archives sale in 1990.

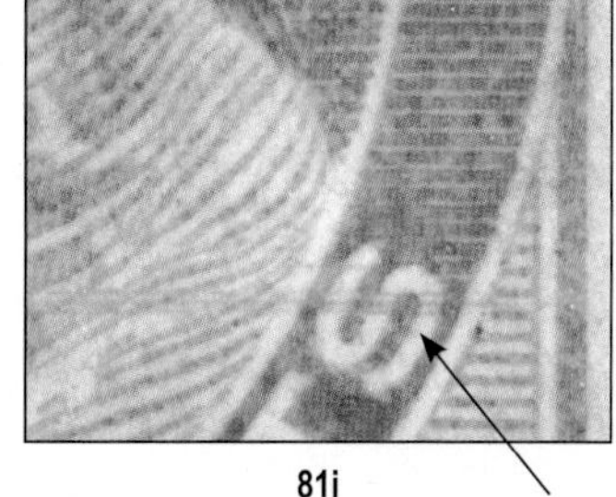
81i

| | | NH% | ★VF | ★F | ★VG | ⊙VF | ⊙F | ✉ |
|---|---|---|---|---|---|---|---|---|
| **81** | **7¢ olive yellow**, *Dec 23, 1902* (ERD *Dec 29, 1902*) | 200 | 250.00 | 75.00 | 25.00 | 30.00 | 15.00 | 125.00‡ |
| a | imperf. pair, without gum (200 stamps) | — | 800.00 | 400.00 | | — | — | — |
| i | major misplaced entry across S of SEVEN and S of CENTS, and necklace and veil (3 types: low [pos. 63], mid [pos. 53], high) | | | | | | | |
| ii | major re-entry in C and E (pos. 77) | | | | | | | |
| xx | No. 81, precancelled [2 styles] | — | — | — | — | 25.00 | 15.00 | 50.00† |
| P | Plate proof (537) | — | 225.00 | — | — | — | — | — |

Qty: 1,515,000
‡ Usage before July 1903.

81ii

| | | NH% | ★VF | ★F | ★VG | ⊙VF | ⊙F | ✉ |
|---|---|---|---|---|---|---|---|---|
| **82** | **8¢ orange**, vertical wove paper *Sep 24,1898* | 200 | 600.00 | 200.00 | 50.00 | 40.00 | 15.00 | 175.00‡ |
| a | brown orange, imperf. pair, with gum (200 stamps) | 150 | 1,500.00 | 750.00 | | — | — | — |
| i | brownish orange (*Feb 1899*) | 200 | 600.00 | 200.00 | 50.00 | 35.00 | 15.00 | 175.00‡ |
| ii | orange, on vertical wove paper, imperf. pair, without gum § | — | 900.00 | 600.00 | — | — | — | — |
| xx | No. 82, precancelled [2 styles] | — | — | — | — | 40.00 | 20.00 | 70.00† |
| P | Plate proof (487) | — | 225.00 | — | — | — | — | — |

Qty: all shades, papers: 893,800
‡ Single usage, 24 Sept.–31 Dec. 1898.
§ There were 592 imperf. stamps without gum, from Plate 1, sold at the ABNC auction in 1990.

| | | NH% | ★VF | ★F | ★VG | ⊙VF | ⊙F | ✉ |
|---|---|---|---|---|---|---|---|---|
| **83** | **10¢ brown violet**, *Nov 5,1898* | 200 | 750.00 | 200.00 | 75.00 | 40.00 | 20.00 | 850.00‡ |
| a | deep brown violet, imperf. pair, with gum (200 stamps) | 150 | 1,500.00 | 750.00 | | — | — | — |
| i | deep brown violet | 200 | 750.00 | 200.00 | 75.00 | 40.00 | 20.00 | 850.00‡ |
| ii | brown violet, imperf. pair, without gum § | — | 1,250.00 | 800.00 | — | — | — | — |
| iii | re-entry in and below CANADA | | | | | | | |
| xx | No. 83, precancelled [2 styles] | — | — | — | — | 30.00 | 25.00 | 600.00† |
| P | Plate proof (237) | — | 850.00 | — | — | — | — | — |

Qty: 2,725,000
‡ Single usage only.
§ There were 300 imperf. stamps without gum, from Plate 1, sold at the ABNC auction in 1990.

84i

| | | NH% | ★VF | ★F | ★VG | ⊙VF | ⊙F | ✉ |
|---|---|---|---|---|---|---|---|---|
| **84** | **20¢ olive green**, *Dec 24, 1900* | 200 | 1,000.00 | 300.00 | 125.00 | 160.00 | 80.00 | 1,750.00‡ |
| a | imperf. pair, horizontal wove paper, without gum (100 stamps) | — | 8,000.00 | 4,000.00 | — | — | — | — |
| i | engraver's slip (pos. 2) | 200 | 1,500.00 | 700.00 | 375.00 | 600.00 | 375.00 | 1,800.00‡ |
| xx | No. 84 precancelled [1 style] | — | — | — | — | 300.00 | 200.00 | 1,200.00† |
| P | Plate proof (229) | — | 850.00 | — | — | — | — | — |

Qty: 540,000
Only one sheet of 100 of the 20¢ imperf. (84a) was issued. This was badly mishandled, resulting in almost all pairs having creases.
‡ Single usage only.
† On cover, without postal cancellation.

| | NH% | ★VF | ★F | ★VG | ⊙VF | ⊙F |
|---|---|---|---|---|---|---|
| **Nos. 74–84** (11) Set | 200 | 3,605.00 | 1,070.00 | 386.10 | 351.50 | 163.35 |
| **Nos. 74P–84P** Set of 10 plate proofs | | 4,000.00 | | | | |

Imprint pairs, imprint strips of three, or imprint blocks of four or more (need 8-10 for full imprints on some) of the "Numeral" Issue are all scarce. Value approximately 50% more than the sum of the individual value of the singles in the imprint piece.

**‡ Single usage only.**
Covers with commercial illustrations, unusual postal markings, **mixed** values or franking (registered), are valued much higher if used in period. Covers with postmarks out of period are considered philatelic and have little value.

## IMPERIAL PENNY POSTAGE

85
Lavender

85i
Grey

86
Blue

86b
Deep blue

Designer: Warren L. Green. Based on a map by George Robert Parkin. Picture engraved by Charles Skinner.
American Bank Note Company, Ottawa.
Engraved (black) and Typographed (2 colours)

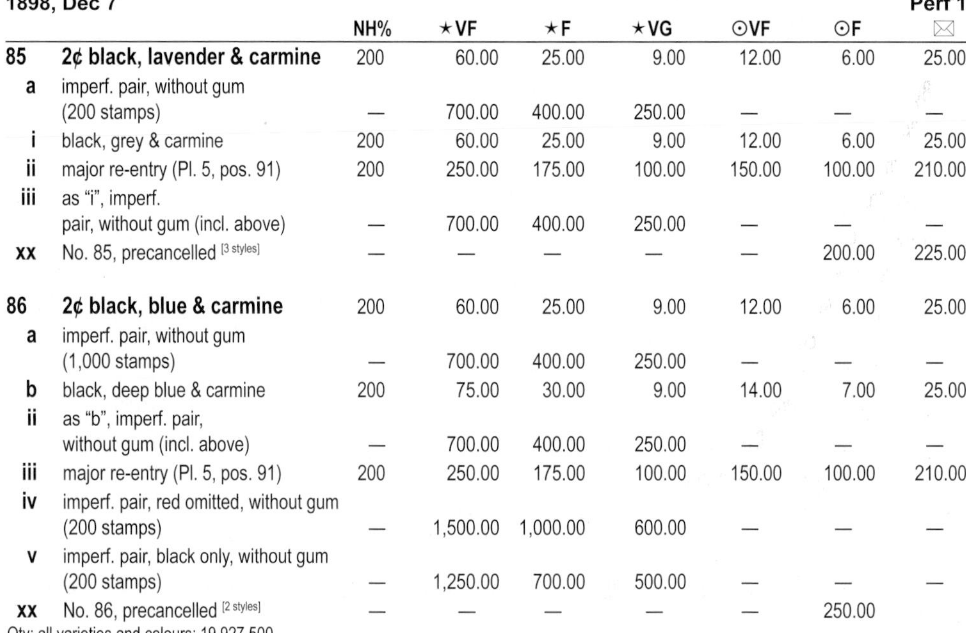

85ii, 86iii

**1898, Dec 7** **Perf 12**

| | | NH% | ★VF | ★F | ★VG | ⊙VF | ⊙F | ✉ |
|---|---|---|---|---|---|---|---|---|
| **85** | **2¢ black, lavender & carmine** | 200 | 60.00 | 25.00 | 9.00 | 12.00 | 6.00 | 25.00 |
| a | imperf. pair, without gum (200 stamps) | — | 700.00 | 400.00 | 250.00 | — | — | — |
| i | black, grey & carmine | 200 | 60.00 | 25.00 | 9.00 | 12.00 | 6.00 | 25.00 |
| ii | major re-entry (Pl. 5, pos. 91) | 200 | 250.00 | 175.00 | 100.00 | 150.00 | 100.00 | 210.00 |
| iii | as "i", imperf. pair, without gum (incl. above) | — | 700.00 | 400.00 | 250.00 | — | — | — |
| xx | No. 85, precancelled [3 styles] | — | — | — | — | — | 200.00 | 225.00 |
| **86** | **2¢ black, blue & carmine** | 200 | 60.00 | 25.00 | 9.00 | 12.00 | 6.00 | 25.00 |
| a | imperf. pair, without gum (1,000 stamps) | — | 700.00 | 400.00 | 250.00 | — | — | — |
| b | black, deep blue & carmine | 200 | 75.00 | 30.00 | 9.00 | 14.00 | 7.00 | 25.00 |
| ii | as "b", imperf. pair, without gum (incl. above) | — | 700.00 | 400.00 | 250.00 | — | — | — |
| iii | major re-entry (Pl. 5, pos. 91) | 200 | 250.00 | 175.00 | 100.00 | 150.00 | 100.00 | 210.00 |
| iv | imperf. pair, red omitted, without gum (200 stamps) | — | 1,500.00 | 1,000.00 | 600.00 | — | — | — |
| v | imperf. pair, black only, without gum (200 stamps) | — | 1,250.00 | 700.00 | 500.00 | — | — | — |
| xx | No. 86, precancelled [2 styles] | — | — | — | — | — | 250.00 | |

Qty: all varieties and colours: 19,927,500

Many retouches, re-entries and varieties of the "red" plate (islands & colonies) exist. These have been identified in a book on the map stamp by W. Bradley. The major re-entry (Pl. 5, pos. 91) shows real doubling in CANADA POSTAGE, especially in CANADA and also in the left value tablet. Other major re-entries exist at: Pl. 1, pos. 3 (in CANADA POSTAGE, left cable and both 2's); Pl. 1, Pos. 89 (in CANADA POSTAGE and overall); Pl. 2, Pos. 7 (marks above crown and XMAS); Pl. 2, Pos. 84 (in and above 'STAGE'); Pl. 3, Pos. 47 (on left side including '2'); Pl. 5, Pos. 29 (entire black plate doubled). Numerous other re-entries exist on the black plate. This stamp also has the retouched base.

No. 85 covers dated the first day of issue (12/07/98) are very rare with perhaps 10 recorded; value $2,500. The Official First Day was Christmas, December 25, 1898; value $900.00. One recorded cover dated December 2, 1898 has subsequently been proven to be a fake. The ERD for No. 86 is December 17, 1898.

Blocks of 4 with Plate number are scarce as the sheets were often folded and split down the middle of columns 5 and 6, thus splitting the plate number. Plate #5 is rare.
**NH +150%**

| Blocks of 4 with | ★VF | ★F |
|---|---|---|
| "1" | 300.00 | 150.00 |
| "2" | 300.00 | 150.00 |
| "3" | 300.00 | 150.00 |
| "4" | not issued | |
| "5" | 600.00 | 300.00 |

Imperforate Plate blocks of 4 of 85a, 85iii, 86a, 86ii: $3,000 each.

There are 4 distinct shades of the Map imperfs – lavender, grey, pale blue and deep blue; 600 pairs are thought to exist. The so-called muddy water variety is a colour changeling caused by oxidation and is NOT a printing variety.

Imprint pairs, imprint strips of three, or imprint blocks of four or more (need 8-10 for full imprints on some) of these stamps are all scarce. Value approximately 50% more than the sum of the individual value of the singles in the imprint piece.

Perforated centreline (cross) blocks from positions 45-46/55-56 are very rare. Value $1,000 for common shades. IMPERFORATE centreline (cross) blocks from positions 45-46/55-56 are seen occasionally as those who cut up the Imperforate sheets were careful to save this centre block. 12 Imperf centreline blocks are thought to possibly exist. Value IMPERF $4,000 in any shade.

Centreline (cross) blocks

## PROVISIONAL ISSUES

87

88

**Rates:**
Effective Jan 1, 1899:

Domestic: 2¢ per oz.
USA: 2¢ per oz.

(this is a decrease of 1¢)

**1899** — **Engraved and Electrotype (surcharge)** — **Perf 12**

| | | NH% | ★VF | ★F | ★VG | ⊙VF | ⊙F | ✉ |
|---|---|---|---|---|---|---|---|---|
| 87 | **2¢ on 3¢ carmine** (No. 69) | | | | | | | |
| | (ERD: *Aug 10, 1899*) | 200 | 30.00 | 10.00 | 4.00 | 10.00 | 4.50 | 9.00 |
| i | narrow spacing strip of 3* | 200 | 120.00 | 40.00 | 30.00 | 60.00 | 40.00 | — |
| ii | narrow spacing pair* | 200 | 70.00 | 30.00 | 15.00 | 30.00 | 20.00 | — |
| iii | inverted surcharge† | | | *1,000.00* | | | | |
| xx | No. 87, precancelled [1 style] | | | | | 80.00 | 50.00 | 100.00 |

Qty: 1,375,000

| | | NH% | ★VF | ★F | ★VG | ⊙VF | ⊙F | ✉ |
|---|---|---|---|---|---|---|---|---|
| 88 | **2¢ on 3¢ carmine** (No. 78) | | | | | | | |
| | (ERD: *Jul 28, 1899*) | 200 | 50.00 | 20.00 | 4.50 | 7.50 | 3.75 | 9.00 |
| i | narrow spacing strip of 3* | 200 | 200.00 | 60.00 | 30.00 | 60.00 | 45.00 | — |
| ii | narrow spacing pair* | 200 | 100.00 | 40.00 | 15.00 | 30.00 | 20.00 | — |
| iii | inverted surcharge† | | | *1,000.00* | | | | |
| xx | No. 88, precancelled [1 style] | | | | | 50.00 | 40.00 | 75.00 |

† Most inverted overprints on the above are thought to be forgeries. Certificates of authenticity are highly recommended.
* Regular spacing measures 7.0 mm; narrow spacing measures 4.0 mm.
Qty: 2,745,000

88iii

## PORT HOOD PROVISIONALS

**1899, Jan 5** — **Engraved** — **Perf 12**

| | | NH% | ★VF | ★F | ★VG | ⊙VF | ⊙F | ✉ |
|---|---|---|---|---|---|---|---|---|
| 88B | **1¢ on one-third of 3¢ carmine** | | | | | | | |
| | (No. 78), on cover | — | — | *20,000.00* | — | — | *5,000.00* | *12,000.00* |
| 88C | **2¢ on two-thirds of 3¢ carmine** | | | | | | | |
| | (No. 78), on cover | — | — | *20,000.00* | — | — | *5,000.00** | *10,000.00* |

* One example of a single tied on piece has been reported.
The above were prepared and used at Port Hood, Nova Scotia, without official authorization. Covers seen by editors are all dated January 4th or January 5th, 1899. All stamps and covers require an expertising certificate.

Queen Victoria — Jub/Leaf/Numeral

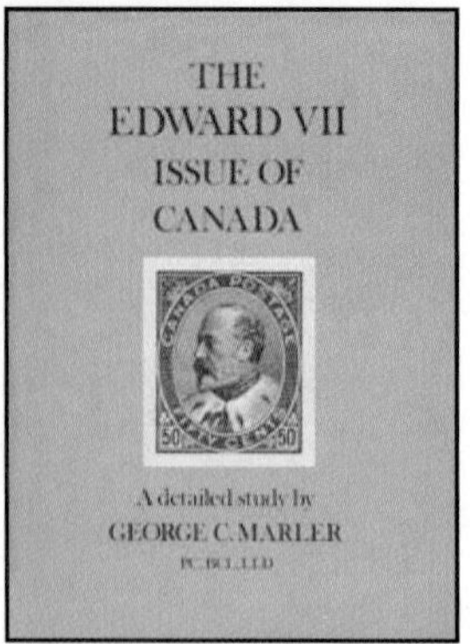

*The Edward VII Issue of Canada,*
George C. Marler, 1975

**Rates:**

Domestic: 2¢ per oz.
Local: 2¢ per oz.
Postcard: 1¢
Printed matter: 1¢ per 4 oz.
USA: 2¢ per oz.
Registration: 5¢
Special delivery: 10¢



## KING EDWARD VII

89 90 91

92 93 94 95

Designer: Prince of Wales and J.A. Tilleard. Vignette engraved by Charles Skinner.
American Bank Note Company, Ottawa.
Sheets of 200 subjects cut into 2 panes of 100 stamps
(some plates of the 1¢ and 2¢ were 400 subjects in 4 panes of 100 stamps)

| 1903–1908 | | | | Engraved | | | | | Perf 12 |
|---|---|---|---|---|---|---|---|---|---|
| | | | NH% | ★VF | ★F | ★VG | ⊙VF | ⊙F | ✉ |
| **89** | | **1¢ green**, *Jul 1, 1903* | 250 | 80.00 | 20.00 | 5.00 | .50 | .20 | 4.00 |
| | **a** | imperf. pair, without gum (400 stamps) | — | 900.00 | 625.00 | 400.00 | — | — | — |
| | **i** | deep green | 250 | 90.00 | 20.00 | 6.00 | .50 | .20 | 4.00 |
| | **ii** | grey green | 250 | 90.00 | 20.00 | 8.00 | 1.00 | .20 | 4.00 |
| | **iii** | blue green | 250 | 90.00 | 20.00 | 10.00 | 1.00 | .20 | 4.00 |
| | **iv** | "hairlines" | 250 | 120.00 | 40.00 | 25.00 | 10.00 | 5.00 | 7.50 |
| | **v** | yellow green | 250 | 120.00 | 40.00 | 10.00 | .50 | .20 | 4.00 |
| | **vi** | major re-entry in CANADA POSTAGE, ONE CENT and right numeral box | | | | | | | 75.00 |
| | **vii** | "SPECIMEN" overprint | — | 200.00 | 125.00 | — | — | — | |
| | **xx** | No. 89, precancelled [41 styles] | — | — | — | — | 1.00 | .25 | 5.00 |

Qty: 1,470,000,000
There are numerous other re-entries, some major.

89vi

| | | | NH% | ★VF | ★F | ★VG | ⊙VF | ⊙F | ✉ |
|---|---|---|---|---|---|---|---|---|---|
| **90** | | **2¢ carmine**, Type II, wet printing, *Jul 1, 1903* | 250 | 100.00 | 20.00 | 4.50 | .50 | .20 | 4.00 |
| | **A** | imperf. pair, Pl. 13 & 14, with gum, Type II, the only imperf. issued to public (100,000)* | 100 | 50.00 | 30.00 | 10.00 | 50.00 | 30.00 | 60.00 |
| | **i** | rose carmine, Type II, wet printing | 250 | 120.00 | 30.00 | 4.50 | .50 | .20 | 4.00 |
| | **ii** | hairlines, Type II, wet printing | 250 | 125.00 | 45.00 | 25.00 | 10.00 | 5.00 | 10.00 |
| | **c** | imperf. pair, Type I, Plates 1 and 2, without gum (400 stamps) | — | 1,100.00 | 800.00 | 600.00 | — | — | — |
| | **iv** | imperf. pair, Pl. 43, red line | 50 | 300.00 | 200.00 | 100.00 | — | — | — |
| | **v** | imperf. pair, Pl. 31 & 32, black line | 50 | 300.00 | 200.00 | 100.00 | — | — | — |
| | **vi** | as iv and v imperf. gutter strip of 4 | 50 | 2,500.00 | 2,000.00 | | — | — | — |
| | **e** | 2¢ carmine, Type I, wet printing | 250 | 200.00 | 60.00 | 10.00 | 2.50 | 1.00 | 5.00 |
| | **f** | vertical pair, imperf. horiz. (4 pairs known, all faulty) | — | — | *5,000.00* | — | — | — | — |
| | **ix** | major misplaced entry (pos. 86UL93) | | | | | | | |
| | **x** | stitch watermark | — | — | — | — | — | 300.00 | — |
| | **xi** | "SPECIMEN" overprint | — | 200.00 | 125.00 | — | — | — | |
| | **xii** | 2¢ carmine, Type II, dry printing† (17.8 to 18.5 mm in width) | | | | | | | |
| | **xx** | No. 90, precancelled [28 styles] | — | — | — | — | 1.25 | 1.00 | 5.00 |

Qty: 2,287,300,000
Numerous re-entries and misplaced entries exist, some major.
* Number 90A, imperf. plate block of 8, Plate 13 or 14; VF with light hinge 350.00, NH-VF 650.00.
Type I imperfs. can be distinguished by the characteristic breaks in the right tip of the top shading line at the upper left. The issued imperfs. from plates 13 and 14 were gummed and show strong unbroken lines in the upper left corner.

† Marler found 200 dry printed stamps among 30,000 copies he examined. Besides the larger width, the stamps showed an unusual clarity in impression. According to Marler, the dry printings come from plates 13 to 16, 31, and 32.

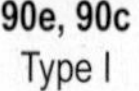

**90e, 90c**
Type I

**90, 90A, 90i**
Type II

**90f**

**90ix**
Misplaced entry 2.5mm lower than it should be, showing in cape, centre tie, 'T' and leaf above left numeral box

| | | NH% | ★VF | ★F | ★VG | ⊙VF | ⊙F | ✉ |
|---|---|---|---|---|---|---|---|---|
| **90b** | booklet pane of 6 x 2¢ carmine (90bs), *Jul 1, 1903* (BK2) | 100 | 2,000.00 | 1,000.00 | 400.00 | | 1,500.00 | |
| bs | single with straight edge, from 90b | 100 | 75.00 | 60.00 | 30.00 | 10.00 | 6.00 | 10.00 |
| d | 2 panes, tête-bêche (90b), imperf., without gum, 1 inverted, (14 exist) | — | *30,000.00* | *12,000.00* | | — | — | — |

**BK2** 2 panes of 90b in cover (883,333) $4,750.

The booklet panes of six were printed in sheets of 168 comprised of 14 tête-bêche panes of 12.

90b

| | | NH% | ★VF | ★F | ★VG | ⊙VF | ⊙F | ✉ |
|---|---|---|---|---|---|---|---|---|
| **91** | **5¢ blue**, *on bluish paper, Jul 1, 1903* | 250 | 400.00 | 120.00 | 30.00 | 8.00 | 2.00 | 50.00 |
| a | imperf. pair, without gum (200 stamps) | — | 1,500.00 | 950.00 | 625.00 | | | |
| b | blue on whiter paper | 250 | 400.00 | 120.00 | 30.00 | 10.00 | 3.00 | 60.00 |
| i | indigo on bluish paper | 250 | 400.00 | 120.00 | 30.00 | 10.00 | 3.00 | 60.00 |
| iii | major re-entry (pos. 3R89) | 250 | 600.00 | 250.00 | 90.00 | 125.00 | 75.00 | 150.00 |
| iv | major re-entry in "ADA POS" and top margin (pos. 4L27) | | | | | | | |
| v | "portcullis" retouch between A and P and major re-entry (pos. 4L28) | | | | | | | |
| vi | major misplaced entry: '5' in upper left crown (pos. 3R79) | | | | | | | |
| vii | "SPECIMEN" overprint | 250 | 200.00 | 125.00 | — | — | — | |
| xx | No. 91, precancelled [24 styles] | — | — | — | — | 5.00 | 2.00 | 75.00 |

Qty: 66,210,000 (all shades)

There are numerous other re-entries, some major.

91iii

Doubling overall; CANADA POSTAGE, FIVE CENTS; particularly strong in CENTS and LR 5..

91iv

| | | NH% | ★VF | ★F | ★VG | ⊙VF | ⊙F | ✉ |
|---|---|---|---|---|---|---|---|---|
| **92** | **7¢ olive bistre**, *Jul 1, 1903* | 250 | 500.00 | 160.00 | 20.00 | 9.00 | 3.00 | 35.00 |
| a | imperf. pair, without gum (400 stamps) | — | 1,000.00 | 625.00 | 400.00 | — | — | — |
| i | greenish bistre | 250 | 600.00 | 200.00 | 20.00 | 9.00 | 3.00 | 35.00 |
| ii | yellow olive | 250 | 500.00 | 160.00 | 20.00 | 9.00 | 3.00 | 35.00 |
| iii | straw | 200 | 400.00 | 120.00 | 50.00 | 50.00 | 20.00 | |
| iv | major re-entry (pos. 1L48) | | | | | | | |
| v | "SPECIMEN" overprint | — | 200.00 | 125.00 | — | — | — | |
| xx | No. 92, precancelled [9 styles] | — | — | — | — | 10.00 | 7.50 | 50.00 |

Qty: 25,305,000 (all shades)

There are numerous re-entries, some major (including pos. 1R12 and pos. 1R82).

91v

Heavy lines between A and P.

| | | NH% | ★VF | ★F | ★VG | ⊙VF | ⊙F | ✉ |
|---|---|---|---|---|---|---|---|---|
| **93** | **10¢ brown lilac,** *Jul 1, 1903* | 250 | 800.00 | 200.00 | 45.00 | 20.00* | 6.00 | 500.00‡ |
| a | imperf. pair, without gum (200 stamps) | — | 1,500.00 | 950.00 | 700.00 | — | — | — |
| i | dull lilac | 250 | 800.00 | 200.00 | 45.00 | 20.00* | 6.00 | 500.00‡ |
| ii | "SPECIMEN" overprint | — | 200.00 | 125.00 | — | — | — | |
| xx | No. 93, precancelled [6 styles] | — | — | — | — | 15.00 | 7.50 | 400.00† |

Qty: 15,080,000 (all shades)

* VF well centred copies with light, legible contemporary CDS cancels are rare and command a premium of 100%.

† On cover, without postal cancellation ($450 with any postmark).

Numerous re-entries exist in the vertical lines of numeral boxes.

91vi

| | | NH% | ★VF | ★F | ★VG | ⊙VF | ⊙F | ✉ |
|---|---|---|---|---|---|---|---|---|
| **94** | **20¢ olive green**, *Sep 27, 1904* | 250 | 1,250.00 | 400.00 | 200.00 | 60.00* | 25.00 | 700.00‡ |
| i | deep olive green | 250 | 1,350.00 | 450.00 | 200.00 | 70.00* | 25.00 | 700.00‡ |
| ii | "SPECIMEN" overprint | — | 500.00 | 250.00 | — | — | — | |
| xx | No. 94, precancelled [5 styles] | — | — | — | — | 40.00 | 12.50 | 500.00† |

Qty: 3,150,000

† On cover, without postal cancellation ($550 with any postmark).

| | | NH% | ★VF | ★F | ★VG | ⊙VF | ⊙F | ✉ |
|---|---|---|---|---|---|---|---|---|
| **95** | **50¢ purple**, *ERD: Oct 6, 1908* | 250 | 1,500.00 | 400.00 | 200.00 | 200.00* | 60.00 | 2,000.00‡ |
| i | deep purple | 250 | 1,500.00 | 500.00 | 250.00 | 250.00* | 70.00 | 2,000.00‡ |
| xx | No. 95, precancelled [2 styles] | — | — | — | — | 150.00 | 50.00 | 1,800.00† |

Qty: 500,000

* VF well centred copies with light legible contemporary CDS cancels are rare and command a premium of at least 50%.

† On cover, without postal cancellation ($2000 with any postmark).

‡ Single usage only.

92iv

| | NH% | ★VF | ★F | ★VG | ⊙VF | ⊙F |
|---|---|---|---|---|---|---|
| **Nos. 89–95** (7) Set | 250 | 4,630.00 | 1,320.00 | 504.50 | 298.00 | 96.40 |

Imprint pairs, imprint strips of three, or imprint blocks of four or more (need 8-10 for full imprints on some) of the King Edward VII Issue are all scarce. Value approximately 50% more than the sum of the individual value of the singles in the imprint piece.

## KING EDWARD VII EXPERIMENTAL COILS

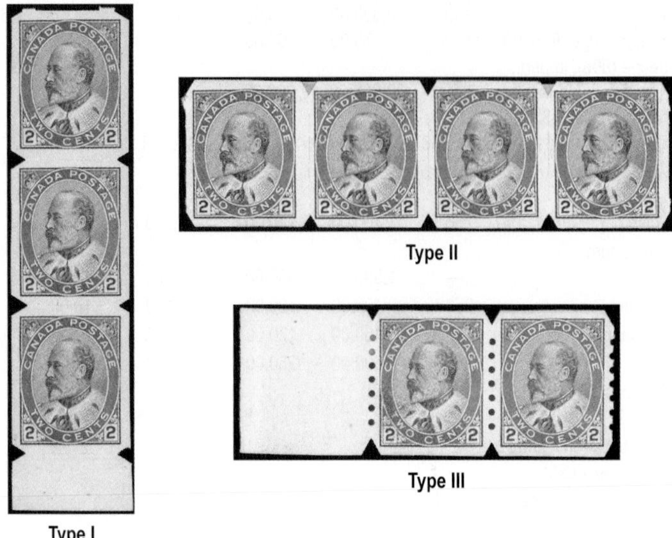

Type I

Type II

Type III

Certificate of authenticity recommended

Fine examples with perforations clear of design and undamaged – add 50%

| | | NH% | ★VG | ★VG |
|---|---|---|---|---|
| **89xxx** | **1¢ green**, vertical strip of 4, Ottawa roller cancel | 100 | 350.00 | paste-up strip: 750.00 |
| i | vertical strip of 4, Ottawa precancel | 100 | 400.00 | paste-up strip: 1,000.00 |
| ii | vertical strip of 4, Ottawa roller cancel "1" | 100 | 400.00 | paste-up strip: 1,000.00 |
| **90xxx** | **2¢, carmine**, vertical strip of 4, Ottawa roller cancel "1" | 100 | 400.00 | paste-up strip: 700.00 |
| i | vertical strip of 4, Ottawa precancel | 100 | 450.00 | paste-up strip: 750.00 |
| ii | vertical strip of 4, Ottawa roller cancel "14" | 100 | 400.00 | paste-up strip: 700.00 |
| iii | vertical imperf. pair, vending machine roulette, Type I | 100 | (F-VF)2,750.00 | |
| iv | horiz. imperf. pair, vending machine roulette, Type II | 100 | (F-VF)3,000.00 | |
| v | horiz. imperf. pair, vend. mach. notched & perf., Type III | 100 | (F-VF)2,750.00 | |

89xxxi 89xxxii

90xxx

90xxxi

90xxxii

## QUEBEC TERCENTENARY ISSUE

**96**
Prince & Princess of Wales

**97**
Cartier & Champlain

**98**
King Edward VII and Queen Alexandra

**99**
Champlain's Habitation

**100**
Montcalm & Wolfe

**101**
Quebec in 1700

**102**
Champlain's Departure

**103**
Cartier's Arrival

**Rates:**

Domestic: 2¢ per oz.
Local: 2¢ per oz.
(1¢ per oz. from Aug 8/08)
Postcard: 1¢
Printed matter: 1¢ per 4 oz.
USA: 2¢ per oz.
Registration: 5¢
Special delivery: 10¢



Designer: José Antonio Machado.
Vignette engravers: ½¢: Edward Gunn. 1¢: Robert Savage. 2¢, 5¢, 15¢, 20¢: Elie Timothée Loizeaux. 7¢, 10¢: Charles Skinner.

PLATE BLOCKS OF 4
Plate blocks of 4 are from the top margins of all values, and from the bottom margins of Plates 3 and 4 of the 1¢ and 2¢ values. Values are for fine centering on lightly hinged plate blocks.

Stamps of this issue in XF condition sell at much more than VF.

American Bank Note Company, Ottawa. Sheets of 100 stamps

**1908, Jul 16** — **Engraved** — **Perf 12**

| | | | NH% | ★VF | ★F | ⊙VF | ⊙F | ✉ |
|---|---|---|---|---|---|---|---|---|
| **96** | | **½¢ black brown** | 200 | 15.00 | 5.00 | 7.00 | 3.00 | 375.00‡ |
| | a | imperf. pair, with gum | 150 | 1,000.00 | 600.00 | — | — | — |
| | i | major re-entry (pos. 44) | 200 | 60.00 | 30.00 | 60.00 | 30.00 | 425.00 |
| | | 96i, in block with 3 normal | 200 | 90.00 | 45.00 | 90.00 | 45.00 | — |
| | ai | as 'a', major re-entry (pos. 44) [unique] | — | *10,000.00* | | — | — | — |
| | ii | imperf. pair, without gum | — | 1,000.00 | 600.00 | — | — | — |
| | iii | minor re-entry in EN (pos. 50) | 200 | 45.00 | 25.00 | 30.00 | 20.00 | 400.00 |
| | | plate blocks: (plate 1) | 200 | 80.00 | 40.00 | | | |
| | iv | as 'ii', major re-entry (pos. 44) [unique] | — | *10,000.00* | | — | — | — |

Qty: 2,000,000
‡ Single usage only, multiples on cover are common.

| | | | NH% | ★VF | ★F | ⊙VF | ⊙F | ✉ |
|---|---|---|---|---|---|---|---|---|
| **97** | | **1¢ green** | 200 | 50.00 | 15.00 | 8.00 | 4.00 | 10.00† |
| | a | imperf. pair, with gum | 150 | 1,000.00 | 600.00 | — | — | — |
| | i | hairlines in margins | 200 | 60.00 | 20.00 | 20.00 | 10.00 | 20.00 |
| | ii | imperf. pair, without gum | | 1,000.00 | 600.00 | — | — | — |
| | iii | major re-entry in "1908", right "1" and "BEC" | 200 | 200.00 | 75.00 | 125.00 | 60.00 | 150.00 |
| | | 97iii, in block with 3 normal | 200 | 350.00 | 120.00 | 90.00 | 50.00 | — |
| | | plate blocks: (plates 1, 2, 3, 4) | 200 | 250.00 | 120.00 | | | |
| | | 97i (bottom plate 3, 4) | 200 | 300.00 | 150.00 | | | |
| | | 97i hairlines (plate 2) | 200 | 350.00 | 150.00 | | 120.00 | |

Qty: 22,530,000
† $5 on postcard.
Several re-entries are known, some major.

**96i**
Horizontal lines in CANADA, HAL, 08 of 1608, and left 1/2; bottom frameline retouched (tripled).

**97iii**

| | | NH% | ★VF | ★F | ⊙VF | ⊙F | ✉ |
|---|---|---|---|---|---|---|---|
| **98** | **2¢ carmine** | 200 | 70.00 | 15.00 | 6.00 | 2.00 | 10.00 |
| a | imperf. pair, with gum | 150 | 1,000.00 | 600.00 | — | — | — |
| i | hairlines in margins | 200 | 200.00 | 100.00 | 75.00 | 35.00 | 100.00 |
| ii | imperf. pair, without gum | — | 1,000.00 | 600.00 | — | — | — |
| | plate blocks, plates 1, 2, 3, 4 | 200 | 200.00 | 100.00 | | | |
| | (bottom, plate 3) | 200 | 250.00 | 125.00 | | | |
| | inverted imprint (bottom, plate 4) | 200 | 300.00 | 150.00 | | | |
| | 98i hairlines, plate 2 | 200 | 600.00 | 300.00 | | | |
| Qty: 35,100,000 | | | | | | | |
| **99** | **5¢ blue** | 200 | 150.00 | 45.00 | 100.00 | 35.00 | 200.00† |
| a | imperf. pair, with gum | 150 | 1,000.00 | 600.00 | — | — | — |
| ii | imperf. pair, without gum | — | 1,000.00 | 600.00 | — | — | — |
| | plate blocks: (plate 1) | 200 | 600.00 | 300.00 | | | |
| | (plate 2) | 200 | | 2,500.00 | | | |
| Qty: 1,200,000 | | | | | | | |
| **100** | **7¢ olive green** | 200 | 250.00 | 80.00 | 150.00 | 50.00 | 200.00† |
| a | imperf. pair, with gum | 150 | 1,000.00 | 600.00 | — | — | — |
| i | imperf. pair, without gum | — | 1,000.00 | 600.00 | — | — | — |
| | plate blocks, plate 1 | 200 | 1,500.00 | 750.00 | | | |
| Qty: 700,000 | | | | | | | |
| **101** | **10¢ violet** | 200 | 300.00 | 100.00 | 200.00 | 80.00 | 500.00† |
| a | imperf. pair, with gum | 150 | 1,000.00 | 600.00 | — | — | — |
| i | imperf. pair, without gum | — | 1,000.00 | 600.00 | — | — | — |
| | plate blocks: (plate 1) | 200 | 1,800.00 | 900.00 | | | |
| Qty: 500,000 | | | | | | | |
| **102** | **15¢ orange** | 200 | 350.00 | 120.00 | 250.00 | 100.00 | 700.00† |
| a | imperf. pair, with gum | 150 | 1,000.00 | 600.00 | — | — | — |
| i | imperf. pair, without gum | — | 1,000.00 | 600.00 | — | — | — |
| | Plate blocks (plate 1) | 200 | 2,000.00 | 1,000.00 | | | |
| Qty: 300,000 | | | | | | | |
| **103** | **20¢ brown** | 200 | 400.00 | 150.00 | 300.00 | 120.00 | 900.00† |
| a | imperf. pair, with gum | 150 | 1,000.00 | 600.00 | — | — | — |
| i | major re-entry (pos. 41) | 200 | 800.00 | 500.00 | 650.00 | 400.00 | 1,250.00† |
| ii | imperf. pair, without gum | — | 1,000.00 | 600.00 | — | — | — |
| | Plate blocks (plate 1) | 200 | 2,400.00 | 1,200.00 | | | |
| Qty: 304,200 | | | | | | | |

† Commercial usage in time period.

| | NH% | ★VF | ★F | ⊙VF | ⊙F | ✉ |
|---|---|---|---|---|---|---|
| **Nos. 96–103** Set of 8 | 200 | 1,585.00 | 530.00 | 1,021.00 | 394.00 | — |
| **Nos. 96a–103a** Set of 8 imperf. pairs with original gum | 150 | 8,000.00 | 4,800.00 | — | — | — |
| **Nos. 96ii–103ii** Set of 8 imperf. pairs without gum | — | 8,000.00 | 4,800.00 | — | — | — |

Issued to commemorate the 300th anniversary of the founding of Quebec by Champlain in 1608.

The Quebec Tercentenary stamps were issued imperforate, both with and without gum. The so-called first printings were without gum, and in deeper shades. Only 100 pairs of each value are thought to have been issued, 50 with gum and 50 without gum.

**103i**

UR corner of design is strongly doubled; 1908, 20 and scroll, inner right vertical lines and outer right frame.

Imprint pairs, imprint strips of three, or imprint blocks of four or more (need 8-10 for full imprints on some) of the Quebec Tercentenary Issue are all scarce. Value approximately 50% more than the sum of the individual value of the singles in the imprint piece.

**NH% Premium**

Full "NH premium" only applies to stamps with pristine original gum in the state it left the printer – no gum disturbance at all. NH stamps with any disturbance will USUALLY sell for the listed "OG" price or perhaps a little more if the disturbance is very minor.

**Cover Prices**

Cover prices are for "fine" condition. VF condition covers and covers with interesting postal markings or attractive Advertising covers will sell for more ... sometimes much more.

## KING GEORGE V "ADMIRAL" ISSUE

See also War Tax issues (MR1–MR7)

Designer: central vignette is a composite portrait with the head taken from a photograph by W. & D. Downey and the chest and uniform from a photograph by W. Barnett. Vignette engraved by Robert Savage.

*The Admiral Issue of Canada*, George C. Marler, 1982.

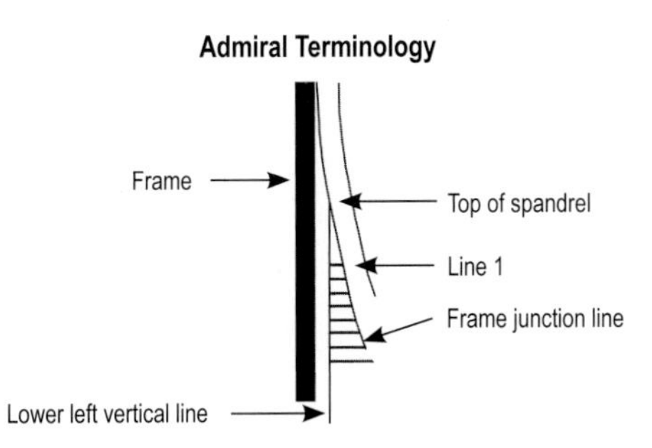


This is a spandrel

## "ADMIRALS" AT A GLANCE

| Format: | Sheet | | | | | Coil | | | | Booklet pane |
|---|---|---|---|---|---|---|---|---|---|---|
| Perforation: | 12 Wet | 12 Dry | 12x8 | Imperf | Surcharge 2¢ on 3¢ | 8 horiz | 8 vert | 12 horiz | Part imperf | 12 |
| 1¢ green | 104 | | | | | 123 | 125 | 131 | | 104a |
| 1¢ yellow | 105 | 105d* | | 136 | | | 126* | | 126a | 105a, 105b |
| 2¢ carmine | 106 | | | | 139*, 140 | 124 | 127 | 132 | | 106a |
| 2¢ green | 107 | 107e | | 137 | | | 128 | 133 | 128a | 107b, 107c |
| 3¢ brown | 108 | 108c | | | | | 129 | 134 | | 108a |
| 3¢ carmine | | 109* | 184 | 138 | | | 130* | | 130a | 109a |
| 4¢ olive bistre | 110 | 110d | | | | | | | | |
| 5¢ blue | 111 | | | | | | | | | |
| 5¢ violet | 112 | 112c | | | | | | | | |
| 7¢ yellow ochre | 113 | | | | | | | | | |
| 7¢ red brown | 114b | 114 | | | | | | | | |
| 8¢ blue | | 115 | | | | | | | | |
| 10¢ plum | 116 | | | | | | | | | |
| 10¢ blue | 117 | 117a | | | | | | | | |
| 10¢ bistre brown | | 118 | | | | | | | | |
| 20¢ olive green | 119b | 119 | | | | | | | | |
| 50¢ black brown | 120a | 120 | | | | | | | | |
| $1 orange | 122b | 122 | | | | | | | | |
| **War tax:** | | | | | | | | | | |
| 1¢ green | MR1 | | | | | | | | | |
| 2¢ carmine | MR2 | | | | | | | | | |
| 2¢+1¢ carmine | MR3* | | MR5 | | | | MR6 | | | |
| 2¢+1¢ brown | MR4* | | | | | | MR7* | | | |

* 2 dies

**Width of design (dry vs. wet), generally speaking**

[Image at 200%]

Initial printings were by the "wet" printing method, in which the paper was moist during printing and the gum was applied after the paper had dried. After December 26, 1922, a "dry" printing method was employed in which the printing was performed on dried, gummed sheets. Stamps from each printing can be distinguished, as the "wet" method led to the shrinking of the stamps after printing, across the grain of the paper, to such an extent that the stamps appear squat or narrow depending on whether the stamps were printed on horizontal or vertical wove paper. On gummed copies the design appears embossed in the gum on the "dry" printings.

Many re-entries exist on Admiral stamps, but only a few of the major ones are actually listed in the catalogue.

Four types of plate layout were used to produce post office sheets:

Type A - 200 subjects divided by a vertical gutter into two panes of 100 subjects each (10x10).
Type B - 400 subjects divided by a vertical and horizontal gutters into four panes of 100 subjects each (10x10).
Type C - 200 subjects arranged in 10 rows of 20 subjects, a guide arrow being placed at the top and bottom to indicate the 10th and 11th row division.
Type D - 400 subjects arranged in 20 rows of 20 subjects, with guide arrows at the top, bottom and sides to indicate the division between both the vertical and horizontal 10th and 11th rows. Also known without guide arrows.

Individual stamps from the pane edges of layouts Type C and D result in straight edged stamps: stamps from Type C panes may have one straight edge while stamps from pane type D may have a straight edge on one side *and* the bottom or top.

American Bank Note Company of Ottawa (became the Canadian Bank Note Company in 1923)

**1911–1925** **Engraved** **Perf 12**

| | | NH% | ★VF | ★F | ⊙VF | ⊙F | ✉ |
|---|---|---|---|---|---|---|---|
| **104** | **1¢ dark green**, *Dec 22, 1911* | 200 | 40.00 | 10.00 | .25 | .20 | 3.00† |
| b | blue green, *1911–13* | 200 | 60.00 | 15.00 | .25 | .20 | 3.00† |
| c | deep blue green, *1913–14* | 300 | 90.00 | 20.00 | .25 | .20 | 3.00† |
| e | yellow green, *1915–19* | 200 | 40.00 | 10.00 | .25 | .20 | 3.00† |
| ii | dark yellow green, *1920* | 200 | 50.00 | 10.00 | .25 | .20 | 3.00† |
| v | green on greyish paper, *1915* | 200 | 150.00 | 75.00 | 25.00 | 15.00 | |
| vi | green on thick paper | 200 | 120.00 | 60.00 | 25.00 | 15.00 | |
| vii | blue green, major re-entry (Pl. 12 LR, pos. 35) | | | 10,000.00* | 2,500.00 | 1,500.00 | 3,500.00‡ |
| viii | deep blue green, hairlines | 200 | 70.00 | 35.00 | 10.00 | 7.50 | 15.00 |
| ix | grey green, Pl. 9 | 200 | 100.00 | 50.00 | 25.00 | 15.00 | |
| x | thin paper | 200 | 250.00 | 100.00 | 50.00 | 35.00 | |
| xi | stitch watermark | | | | 200.00 | 100.00 | |
| xii | "Shilling mark" | | | | | | |
| xx | No. 104, precancelled [71 styles] | — | — | — | — | .20 | 5.00 |
| xxi | as 104vii (major re-entry), precancelled | — | — | — | — | *5,000.00* | |

Qty: 3,218,000,000

† Price on postcard; on cover price $3.

* the unique mint example, in a F–VF block of four, sold at auction in early 2013 for $7,848.75.

‡ On postcard or cover.

**104vii**

Spectacular doubling of LR corner framelines, leaves and 1; ONE CENT; TAG; LL corner, including numeral box lines and 1.

**104xii**

**104a**

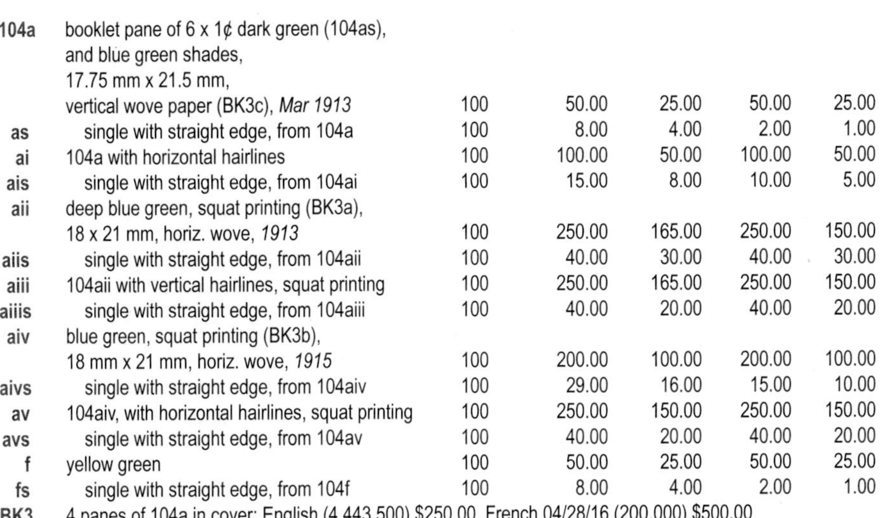

| | | NH% | ★VF | ★F | ⊙VF | ⊙F |
|---|---|---|---|---|---|---|
| 104a | booklet pane of 6 x 1¢ dark green (104as), and blue green shades, 17.75 mm x 21.5 mm, vertical wove paper (BK3c), *Mar 1913* | 100 | 50.00 | 25.00 | 50.00 | 25.00 |
| as | single with straight edge, from 104a | 100 | 8.00 | 4.00 | 2.00 | 1.00 |
| ai | 104a with horizontal hairlines | 100 | 100.00 | 50.00 | 100.00 | 50.00 |
| ais | single with straight edge, from 104ai | 100 | 15.00 | 8.00 | 10.00 | 5.00 |
| aii | deep blue green, squat printing (BK3a), 18 x 21 mm, horiz. wove, *1913* | 100 | 250.00 | 165.00 | 250.00 | 150.00 |
| aiis | single with straight edge, from 104aii | 100 | 40.00 | 30.00 | 40.00 | 30.00 |
| aiii | 104aii with vertical hairlines, squat printing | 100 | 250.00 | 165.00 | 250.00 | 150.00 |
| aiiis | single with straight edge, from 104aiii | 100 | 40.00 | 20.00 | 40.00 | 20.00 |
| aiv | blue green, squat printing (BK3b), 18 mm x 21 mm, horiz. wove, *1915* | 100 | 200.00 | 100.00 | 200.00 | 100.00 |
| aivs | single with straight edge, from 104aiv | 100 | 29.00 | 16.00 | 15.00 | 10.00 |
| av | 104aiv, with horizontal hairlines, squat printing | 100 | 250.00 | 150.00 | 250.00 | 150.00 |
| avs | single with straight edge, from 104av | 100 | 40.00 | 20.00 | 40.00 | 20.00 |
| f | yellow green | 100 | 50.00 | 25.00 | 50.00 | 25.00 |
| fs | single with straight edge, from 104f | 100 | 8.00 | 4.00 | 2.00 | 1.00 |
| BK3 | 4 panes of 104a in cover; English (4,443,500) $250.00, French 04/28/16 (200,000) $500.00 | | | | | |

**Die I**

- Bottom of numeral (1) is straight.
- CENT on second line above base of design.

**Die II**

- Numerals (1) have more pronounced serifs.
- CENT on first line above base of design.

| | | NH% | ★VF | ★F | ⊙VF | ⊙F | ✉ |
|---|---|---|---|---|---|---|---|
| **105** | **1¢ orange yellow**, wet printing, Die I, *Jun 7, 1922* | 200 | 40.00 | 10.00 | .25 | .20 | 3.00 |
| d | orange yellow, dry printing, Die II, *1924–25* | 200 | 30.00 | 6.00 | .25 | .20 | 3.00 |
| e | lemon yellow, wet printing, Die I | 200 | 60.00 | 25.00 | 10.00 | 5.00 | |
| f | yellow, dry printing, Die I (plates 186-7 only) | 200 | 50.00 | 20.00 | 1.00 | .50 | |
| i | yellow, wet printing, Die I | 200 | 40.00 | 10.00 | .25 | .20 | 3.00 |
| iv | pale yellow, dry printing, Die II, *1924–25* | 200 | 50.00 | 10.00 | .25 | .20 | 3.00 |
| v | pyramid guide, block of 4 | 200 | | 300.00 | | | |
| xx | No. 105, precancelled [66 styles] | — | — | — | — | .20 | 5.00 |
| xxa | No. 105d, precancelled [58 styles] | — | — | — | — | .20 | 5.00 |

Nos. 105, 105e and 105i (Die I, wet printing) are from plates 169–182 ONLY. Nos. 105d and 105iv (Die II, dry printing) are from plates 183–185 and 188–199. No. 105f (Die I, dry printing) is from plates 186–187 ONLY.

Qty: 1,278,000,000

105a

105ai

105b

106xv

106xv (pos. 137LL77)

106a

106aiv

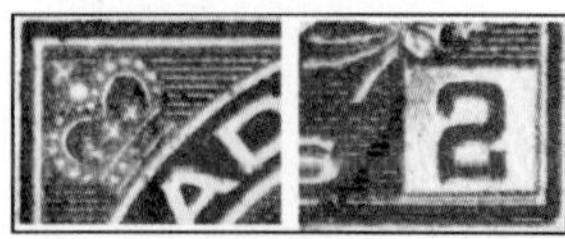
107vii

| | | NH% | ★VF | ★F | ⊙VF | ⊙F | ✉ |
|---|---|---|---|---|---|---|---|
| 105a | booklet pane of 4 x 1¢ yellow (105as) + 2 labels (BK9, 10), *Jul 1922* | 100 | 80.00 | 40.00 | 80.00 | 40.00 | |
| as | single with straight edge, from 105a or 105b | 100 | 15.00 | 12.00 | 4.00 | 2.00 | |
| ai | 105a with pyramid guidelines on tab | 100 | 3,500.00 | 2,500.00 | | | |
| 105b | booklet pane of 6 x 1¢ yellow (105aii) (BK4), *Dec 1922* | 100 | 90.00 | 45.00 | 90.00 | 45.00 | |
| c | 2 panes tête-bêche (105b), imperf., without gum, 1 inverted (7 known) | — | *22,500.00* | — | — | — | |
| BK4 | 4 panes of 105b in cover; English (981,225) $500.00, French (163,750) $700.00. | | | | | | |
| **106** | **2¢ carmine**, *1917–22* | 200 | 40.00 | 10.00 | .25 | .20 | 3.00† |
| b | pink, *1911–12* | 200 | 200.00 | 100.00 | 25.00 | 12.50 | 25.00 |
| c | rose carmine, *1914* | 200 | 40.00 | 10.00 | .25 | .20 | 3.00 |
| ii | deep rose red, *Dec 22, 1911* | 200 | 50.00 | 10.00 | .25 | .20 | 3.00 |
| iii | dark carmine, *1920* | 200 | 40.00 | 10.00 | .50 | .20 | 3.00 |
| iv | orange red, *1915–16* | 200 | 60.00 | 12.00 | .50 | .20 | 3.00 |
| v | deep red | 200 | 40.00 | 10.00 | .50 | .20 | 3.00 |
| vii | red, *1917–18* | 200 | 40.00 | 10.00 | .25 | .20 | 3.00 |
| ix | deep rose red, hairlines, *1912* | 200 | 100.00 | 25.00 | 10.00 | 4.00 | 20.00 |
| x | stitch watermark | | | | 200.00 | 100.00 | |
| xv | major re-entry* | | | | | | |
| xx | No. 106, precancelled [53 styles] | — | — | — | — | .25 | 5.00 |

Qty: 3,043,000,000

† Price on postcard; on cover price $3.

* Numerous major re-entries exist (2 are illustrated at left).

| | | NH% | ★VF | ★F | ⊙VF | ⊙F | ✉ |
|---|---|---|---|---|---|---|---|
| 106a | booklet pane of 6 x 2¢ carmine (106as), vert. wove paper (BK5c–f) | 100 | 60.00 | 35.00 | 60.00 | 40.00 | |
| as | single with straight edge, from 106a | 100 | 10.00 | 5.00 | 3.00 | 2.00 | |
| ai | 106aiii or 106av with vertical hairlines | 100 | 80.00 | 50.00 | 80.00 | 50.00 | |
| ais | single with straight edge, from 106ai | 100 | 10.50 | 6.50 | 4.00 | 2.50 | |
| aii | 106a with horizontal hairlines | 100 | 85.00 | 55.00 | 85.00 | 55.00 | |
| aiis | single with straight edge, from 106aii | 100 | 12.00 | 8.00 | 5.25 | 4.00 | |
| aiii | as 106a, squat printing (BK5b), 2 shades, 18 mm x 21 mm, *Jan 1912* | 100 | 350.00 | 200.00 | 350.00 | 240.00 | |
| aiiis | single with straight edge, from 106aiii | 100 | 52.00 | 31.00 | 20.00 | 13.00 | |
| aiv | 106a, OTTAWA-TOP on tab† | 100 | 6,500.00 | 4,500.00 | | | |
| av | 106a on horiz. wove paper (BK5a), 17.7 mm x 21.5 mm *1912–15* | 100 | 350.00 | 200.00 | 350.00 | 210.00 | |
| avs | single with straight edge, from 106av | 100 | 50.00 | 35.00 | 50.00 | 35.00 | |
| BK5 | 2 panes of 106a in cover; English (9,139,000) $125.00, French 04/–/16 (168,000) $225.00 | | | | | | |

† Variety 106aiv comes only from plates 15 and 16. Two different positions exist. Both are extremely rare and both show only a tiny portion of the OTTAWA TOP imprint.

| | | NH% | ★VF | ★F | ⊙VF | ⊙F | ✉ |
|---|---|---|---|---|---|---|---|
| **107** | **2¢ yellow green**, wet printing, *Apr 5, 1922* | 200 | 45.00 | 10.00 | .25 | .20 | 3.00 |
| a | deep green, thin paper, wet printing, *1924* | 200 | 30.00 | 6.00 | 3.50 | 2.00 | 3.00 |
| e | green, dry printing, *1923* | 200 | 30.00 | 6.00 | .25 | .20 | 3.00 |
| i | deep green, wet printing | 200 | 40.00 | 6.00 | .25 | .20 | 3.00 |
| ii | green, wet printing | 200 | 45.00 | 10.00 | .25 | .20 | 3.00 |
| iii | pyramid guide, block of 4 | 200 | 1,000.00 | 400.00 | | | |
| iv | yellow green, dry printing, *1923–25* | 200 | 30.00 | 6.00 | .25 | .20 | 3.50 |
| vi | R-Gauge, block of 4 | 200 | | 500.00 | | | |
| vii | major re-entry, UL and LR corners (pos. 161LL69) | 200 | | 300.00 | | | |
| xx | No. 107, precancelled [62 styles] | — | — | — | — | .25 | 10.00 |
| xxa | No. 107a, precancelled [28 styles] | — | — | — | — | 10.00 | |

Qty: 2,229,000,000

Tête-bêche booklet panes (105c, 107d, 109b)

| | | NH% | ★VF | ★F | ⊙VF | ⊙F | ✉ |
|---|---|---|---|---|---|---|---|
| **107b** | booklet pane of 4 x 2¢ yellow green (107bs) + 2 labels (BK9, 10), *Jul 1922* | 100 | 100.00 | 60.00 | 110.00 | 65.00 | — |
| **bs** | single with straight edge, from 107b or 107c | 100 | 30.00 | 12.00 | 4.50 | 2.00 | |
| **bi** | 107b with pyramid guidelines on tab | 100 | 4,200.00 | 3,000.00 | — | — | — |

107b

107bi

| | | NH% | ★VF | ★F | ⊙VF | ⊙F | ✉ |
|---|---|---|---|---|---|---|---|
| **107c** | booklet pane of 6 x 2¢ yellow green (107bs), wet printing (BK6), *Dec 1922* | 100 | 450.00 | 300.00 | 450.00 | 300.00 | — |
| **d** | 2 panes tête-bêche (107c), imperf., 1 inverted, 9 recorded, all hinged | — | *22,500.00* | — | — | — | |
| **di** | imperf. tête-bêche pair from 107d | 100 | 6,000.00 | | — | — | |
| **f** | 107c, dry printing | 100 | 450.00 | 300.00 | 450.00 | 300.00 | |
| **fs** | single with straight edge, from 107f | 100 | 30.00 | 12.00 | 4.50 | 2.00 | |

**BK6** 2 panes 107c in cover; English (5,123,425) $1,100.00; French (431,325) $1,300.00

All known tête-bêche panes (107d) are hinged. Two tête-bêche pairs (107di) are known from one cut pane 107d, both are NH.

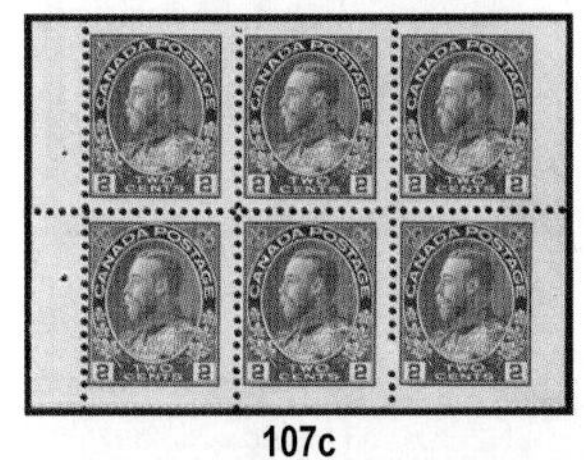
107c

| | | NH% | ★VF | ★F | ⊙VF | ⊙F | ✉ |
|---|---|---|---|---|---|---|---|
| **108** | **3¢ brown**, wet printing, *Aug 6, 1918* | 200 | 40.00 | 10.00 | .50 | .20 | 3.00 |
| **b** | yellow brown, wet printing | 200 | 60.00 | 20.00 | .50 | .20 | 3.00 |
| **c** | brown, dry printing, *1923* | 200 | 40.00 | 10.00 | .50 | .20 | 3.00 |
| **ii** | dark brown, wet printing | 200 | 50.00 | 10.00 | .50 | .20 | 3.00 |
| **iv** | pyramid guide, block of 4 | 200 | 1,200.00 | 600.00 | | | |
| **xx** | No. 108, precancelled [48 styles] | — | — | — | — | 1.50 | 10.00 |

Qty: 2,044,000,000

| | | NH% | ★VF | ★F | ⊙VF | ⊙F | ✉ |
|---|---|---|---|---|---|---|---|
| **108a** | booklet pane of 4 x 3¢ brown (108as) + 2 labels (BK7, 9) | 100 | 120.00 | 75.00 | 120.00 | 72.00 | |
| **as** | single with straight edge, from 108a | 100 | 20.00 | 8.00 | 15.00 | 5.00 | |

**BK7** 2 panes of 108a in cover; English 03/–/22? (1,600,000) $750.00, French late 1922? (200,000) $2,000.00

**BK9** 1 pane each of 105a, 107b, 108a in cover, English 07/–/22? (600,000) $650.00, French 12/–/22 (75,000) $1,300.00

108a

**Die I**

- Space between stems at left is filled in with colour.
- Bottom line of vignette does not touch the heavy diagonal stroke at right.
- 3 white dashes above second E of THREE are aligned with E.

**Die II**

- Stem nearest oval ends with white blob and has four short white lines parallel to middle stem.
- Bottom horizontal line of vignette touches the heavy diagonal stroke at right.
- White dashes above second E of THREE are not aligned with E.

109iv

| | | NH% | ★VF | ★F | ⊙VF | ⊙F | ✉ |
|---|---|---|---|---|---|---|---|
| **109** | **3¢ carmine**, Die I, *Dec 18, 1923* | 200 | 30.00 | 10.00 | .25 | .20 | 3.00 |
| **c** | carmine, Die II, *1924* | 200 | 70.00 | 25.00 | 1.00 | .25 | 5.00 |
| **ci** | as "c", double paper (in strip of 3) | 200 | | 900.00 | | | |
| **d** | rose carmine, Die I, *1923* | 200 | 40.00 | 20.00 | 5.00 | 2.50 | 15.00 |
| **iii** | pyramid guide, block of 4 | 200 | 200.00 | 150.00 | | | |
| **iv** | R-gauge, block of 4 | 200 | 200.00 | 150.00 | | | |
| **xx** | No. 109, precancelled [57 styles] | — | — | — | — | .25 | 10.00 |
| **xxa** | No. 109c, precancelled [20 styles] | — | — | — | — | .75 | |

Qty: 1,092,000,000

For perf. 12x8, see Sc. 184.

| | | NH% | ★VF | ★F | ⊙VF | ⊙F | ✉ |
|---|---|---|---|---|---|---|---|
| **109a** | booklet pane of 4 x 3¢ carmine (109as) + 2 labels (BK8, 10) | 100 | 100.00 | 50.00 | 108.00 | 72.00 | |
| **as** | single with straight edge, from 109a | 100 | 15.00 | 7.50 | 5.00 | 2.50 | |
| **b** | 2 panes tête-bêche (109a), imperf., without gum, 1 inverted (7 known) | — | *22,500.00* | — | — | — | |

**BK8** 2 panes of 109a in cover; English 12/–/23 (3,027,000) $450.00, French 5/–/24 (168,000) $900.00

**BK10** 1 pane each 105a, 107b, 109a in cover; English 12/–/23 (1,791,000) $500.00, French 12/–/23 (86,000) $1,250.00

109a

King George V — Admiral

111ii

111iv

111v

112

112c

(112x Essay)
6¢ unissued value

113v (pos. 1L72)

113v (pos. 1L72)

113v (pos. 1L73)

| | | NH% | ★VF | ★F | ⊙VF | ⊙F | ✉ |
|---|---|---|---|---|---|---|---|
| **110** | **4¢ olive bistre**, *Jul 7, 1922* | 200 | 80.00 | 30.00 | 6.00 | 2.00 | 35.00‡ |
| a | imperf. pair (100 stamps) | 100 | 3,000.00 | 2,000.00 | — | — | — |
| b | olive yellow, wet printing | 200 | 90.00 | 30.00 | 6.00 | 2.00 | 25.00‡ |
| c | golden yellow, wet printing | 200 | 220.00 | 80.00 | 15.00 | 6.00 | 35.00‡ |
| d | yellow ochre, dry printing, Plates 5–7, *1925* | 200 | 70.00 | 25.00 | 6.00 | 2.00 | 25.00‡ |
| iv | pyramid guide, block of 4 | 200 | 1,200.00 | 600.00 | | | |
| xx | No. 110, precancelled [30 styles] | — | — | — | — | 1.00 | 45.00‡ |

Qty: 75,900,000
‡ Single usage only.

| | | NH% | ★VF | ★F | ⊙VF | ⊙F | ✉ |
|---|---|---|---|---|---|---|---|
| **111** | **5¢ dark blue**, *Apr 1914* | 200 | 300.00 | 70.00 | 3.00 | 1.00 | 50.00‡ |
| a | indigo, 1st printing , *Jan 17, 1912* | 300 | 500.00 | 140.00 | 4.00 | 1.00 | 50.00‡ |
| b | grey blue (ERD: *Feb 15, 1912*) | 200 | 350.00 | 80.00 | 3.00 | 1.00 | 50.00‡ |
| i | hairlines | — | — | — | 25.00 | | |
| ii | major re-entry (pos. 8UL5) (strong doubling throughout CANADA POSTAGE; retouches found on the vertical inner frames) | | | | 1,250.00 | 750.00 | |
| iii | retouched vert. line in upper right spandrel | 200 | 300.00 | 125.00 | 75.00 | 50.00 | |
| iv | major re-entry in C of CANADA and E of POSTAGE | | 1,000.00 | 500.00 | | 450.00 | |
| v | major re-entry (odd markings in the 'T' of POSTAGE and in the white oval below it) | | | | 750.00 | 450.00 | |
| xx | No. 111, precancelled [33 styles] | — | — | — | — | 1.00 | 75.00‡ |

Qty: 198,000,000
‡ Single usage only.
The common dark blue shades (No. 111) are from after April, 1914.

| | | NH% | ★VF | ★F | ⊙VF | ⊙F | ✉ |
|---|---|---|---|---|---|---|---|
| **112** | **5¢ violet**, wet printing, *Feb 2, 1922* | 200 | 60.00 | 20.00 | 1.50 | .50 | 50.00‡ |
| a | thin paper, wet printing, *1924* | 200 | 50.00 | 15.00 | 10.00 | 5.00 | 50.00‡ |
| b | imperf. pair (100 stamps) | 100 | 3,000.00 | 2,000.00 | — | — | — |
| c | re-drawn vert. line in upper right spandrel, dry printing, pl. 23–25, *1925* | 200 | 70.00 | 25.00 | 2.00 | 1.50 | 50.00‡ |
| i | grey violet, wet printing | 200 | 65.00 | 20.00 | 2.00 | 1.00 | 50.00‡ |
| ii | rose violet, wet printing | 200 | 60.00 | 20.00 | 2.00 | 1.00 | 50.00‡ |
| iii | retouched vert. line in upper right spandrel, wet printing, *1924* | 200 | 120.00 | 40.00 | 2.00 | 1.50 | 50.00‡ |
| v | pyramid guide*, block of 4 | 200 | 1,200.00 | 600.00 | | | |
| vi | R-gauge, block of 4 | 200 | — | 600.00 | | | |
| xx | No. 112, precancelled [47 styles] | — | — | — | — | .25 | 60.00‡ |
| xxa | No. 112a, precancelled [22 styles] | — | — | — | — | 5.00 | 60.00‡ |

Qty: 185,650,000
‡ Single usage only.
* Pyramid guide exists on both regular and thin paper (112a). Values are the same.

A 6¢ "unissued" value exists as a die essay (12 known in carmine). Value $4,500.00

| | | NH% | ★VF | ★F | ⊙VF | ⊙F | ✉ |
|---|---|---|---|---|---|---|---|
| **113** | **7¢ yellow ochre**, wet printing, *1916* | 200 | 80.00 | 30.00 | 5.00 | 1.75 | 20.00 |
| a | olive bistre, *1913* | 200 | 120.00 | 40.00 | 5.00 | 1.75 | 20.00 |
| b | straw, 1st printing, *Jan 12,1912* | 300 | 350.00 | 120.00 | 20.00 | 6.00 | 60.00 |
| c | sage green, *1914* | 300 | 750.00 | 250.00 | 40.00 | 15.00 | 75.00 |
| iii | retouched vert. line in upper right spandrel | 200 | 200.00 | 80.00 | 50.00 | 17.50 | 60.00 |
| iv | greenish yellow, *1915–16* | 200 | 400.00 | 150.00 | 20.00 | 10.00 | 50.00 |
| v | major re-entry (pos. 1L72, 1L73) | | | | 800.00 | 500.00 | |
| xx | No. 113, precancelled [33 styles] | — | — | — | — | 1.00 | 50.00‡ |

Qty: 103,200,000

| | | NH% | ★VF | ★F | ⊙VF | ⊙F | ✉ |
|---|---|---|---|---|---|---|---|
| 114 | **7¢ red brown**, dry printing | 200 | 35.00 | 12.00 | 15.00 | 6.00 | 55.00‡ |
| a | imperf. pair (100 stamps) | 100 | 3,000.00 | 2,000.00 | — | — | — |
| b | red brown, wet printing, *Dec 12, 1924* | 200 | 45.00 | 15.00 | 20.00 | 10.00 | 55.00‡ |
| ii | pale red brown, dry printing | 200 | 100.00 | 70.00 | 25.00 | 12.50 | 65.00‡ |
| iii | thin paper, dry printing | 200 | 300.00 | 125.00 | 50.00 | 20.00 | 85.00‡ |
| iv | diagonal line in V of SEVEN (Pl. 7)* | 200 | 150.00 | 50.00 | 25.00 | 12.00 | 75.00 |
| v | diagonal line in N of CENTS (Pl. 8)* | 200 | 150.00 | 50.00 | 25.00 | 12.00 | 75.00 |
| xx | No. 114, precancelled [23 styles] | — | — | — | — | 7.50 | 75.00‡ |
| xxa | No. 114iii, precancelled [2 styles] | — | — | — | — | 100.00 | |

Qty: 16,280,000

Varieties 114iv and 114v exist on both wet and dry printings, the values are the same.

‡ Single usage only.

* The flaw consists of a hairline (the illustration to right has been enhanced), and varies from stamp to stamp.

114iv
(Enhanced)

114v

| | | NH% | ★VF | ★F | ⊙VF | ⊙F | ✉ |
|---|---|---|---|---|---|---|---|
| 115 | **8¢ blue**, dry printing (only), *Sep 1, 1925* | 200 | 60.00 | 20.00 | 15.00 | 6.00 | 70.00‡ |
| a | imperf. pair (100 stamps) | 100 | 3,000.00 | 2,000.00 | — | — | — |
| i | light blue | 200 | 70.00 | 22.00 | 15.00 | 6.00 | 70.00‡ |
| xx | No. 115, precancelled [10 styles] | — | — | — | — | 7.50 | 75.00‡ |

Qty: 25,350,000

‡ Single usage only.

| | | NH% | ★VF | ★F | ⊙VF | ⊙F | ✉ |
|---|---|---|---|---|---|---|---|
| 116 | **10¢ plum** (brown purple), wet printing, *Jan 12, 1912* | 200 | 400.00 | 120.00 | 6.00 | 1.00 | 70.00‡ |
| a | reddish purple, 1st printing | 300 | 450.00 | 150.00 | 6.00 | 1.00 | 70.00‡ |
| i | retouched vert. line in upper left or upper right spandrel, various | 200 | 450.00 | 150.00 | 25.00 | 10.00 | |
| xx | No. 116, precancelled [23 styles] | — | — | — | — | 1.00 | 75.00‡ |

Qty: 148,800,000

‡ Single usage only.

| | | NH% | ★VF | ★F | ⊙VF | ⊙F | ✉ |
|---|---|---|---|---|---|---|---|
| 117 | **10¢ blue**, wet printing, *Feb 20, 1922* | 200 | 80.00 | 30.00 | 3.00 | 1.00 | 40.00‡ |
| a | blue, dry printing | 200 | 70.00 | 30.00 | 3.00 | 1.00 | 40.00‡ |
| ii | light blue, wet printing | 200 | 80.00 | 30.00 | 3.00 | 1.00 | 40.00‡ |
| iii | light blue, dry printing | 200 | 70.00 | 30.00 | 3.00 | 1.00 | 40.00‡ |
| iv | pyramid guide, block of 4 | 200 | 3,000.00 | 2,000.00 | | | |
| v | R-gauge, block of 4 | 200 | | 3,000.00 | | | |
| vi | horizontal wove paper** | — | — | — | 200.00 | 80.00 | |
| xx | No. 117, precancelled [37 styles] | — | — | — | — | .50 | 75.00‡ |

Qty: 128,382,000

‡ Single usage only.

** On non-precancelled stamp; value on precancel $100 (used VF), $50 (used F).

| | | NH% | ★VF | ★F | ⊙VF | ⊙F | ✉ |
|---|---|---|---|---|---|---|---|
| 118 | **10¢ bistre brown**, dry printing | 200 | 60.00 | 25.00 | 3.00 | 1.00 | 40.00‡ |
| a | imperf. pair (100 stamps) | 100 | 3,000.00 | 2,000.00 | — | — | — |
| b | yellow brown, dry printing, *Aug 1, 1925* | 200 | 80.00 | 30.00 | 3.00 | 1.00 | 40.00‡ |
| xx | No. 118, precancelled [39 styles] | — | — | — | — | .50 | 75.00‡ |

Qty: 89,713,000

‡ Single usage only.

| | | NH% | ★VF | ★F | ⊙VF | ⊙F | ✉ |
|---|---|---|---|---|---|---|---|
| 119 | **20¢ olive green**, dry printing, *1925* | 200 | 160.00 | 60.00 | 3.00 | 1.00 | 250.00‡ |
| a | imperf. pair (100 stamps) | 100 | 3,000.00 | 2,000.00 | — | — | — |
| b | sage green, wet printing | 200 | 350.00 | 140.00 | 9.00 | 3.00 | 250.00‡ |
| c | dark olive green, wet printing, *1912* | 200 | 220.00 | 90.00 | 3.00 | 1.25 | 250.00‡ |
| d | grey green, wet printing, *Jan 23, 1912* | 300 | 300.00 | 120.00 | 7.50 | 3.00 | 250.00‡ |
| iv | retouched vert. line in upper right spandrel, dry printing | 200 | 180.00 | 70.00 | 3.00 | 1.00 | 250.00‡ |
| xx | No. 119, precancelled [34 styles] | — | — | — | — | 1.00 | 250.00‡ |

Qty: 95,416,000

‡ Single usage only.

King George V — Admiral

| | | NH% | ★VF | ★F | ⊙VF | ⊙F | ⊠ |
|---|---|---|---|---|---|---|---|
| **120** | **50¢ black brown**, re-engraved, dry printing (Pl. 4), *1925* | 200 | 130.00 | 50.00 | 5.00 | 2.00 | 400.00‡ |
| a | black, wet printing, *Jan 26, 1912* | 300 | 550.00 | 160.00 | 15.00 | 5.00 | |
| b | imperf. pair, re-engraved, dry printing, Pl. 4 (100 stamps)* | 100 | 4,000.00 | 2,500.00 | — | — | — |
| i | silver black, wet printing, *1917* | 300 | 500.00 | 150.00 | 15.00 | 5.00 | |
| ii | brown black, wet printing, *1923* | 200 | 350.00 | 120.00 | 10.00 | 3.00 | |
| iii | cracked plate | — | — | — | 60.00 | | |
| xx | No. 120, precancelled [15 styles] | — | — | — | — | 4.00 | 370.00‡ |
| xxa | No. 120a, precancelled [17 styles] | — | — | — | — | 3.00 | 370.00‡ |

Qty: 11,070,000

The wet printings are plates 1–3; varieties 120a, 120i and 120ii are plates 1, 2 and 3. Plate 4 was re-engraved.
"R-Gauge" and pyramid lines exist on plate 3 of the 50¢ value.

No. 121 is not assigned.

| | | NH% | ★VF | ★F | ⊙VF | ⊙F | ⊠ |
|---|---|---|---|---|---|---|---|
| **122** | **$1 orange**, dry printing, *1925* | 200 | 150.00 | 70.00 | 15.00 | 7.00 | 550.00‡ |
| a | imperf. pair (100 stamps)* | 100 | 3,000.00 | 2,000.00 | — | — | — |
| b | deep orange, wet printing, *Jul 22, 1923* | 300 | 400.00 | 160.00 | 20.00 | 8.00 | 550.00‡ |
| iii | pyramid guide, block of 4 | 200 | 1,750.00 | 1,000.00 | | 600.00 | |
| iv | brown orange, dry printing | 200 | 250.00 | 100.00 | 20.00 | 8.00 | 550.00‡ |
| v | R-gauge, block of 4 | 200 | — | 1,000.00 | — | 600.00 | |
| xx | No. 122, precancelled [12 styles] | — | — | — | — | 10.00 | 500.00‡ |

Qty: 2,600,000

*Due to serious mishandling of the imperf. sheets, an estimated 10–15 pairs each of the 50¢ and $1 are quite seriously creased, leaving 35–40 sound pairs of each. Unhinged pairs are very rare for all Admiral imperforates.
‡ Single usage only. Proper commercial rate in time period.
Bulk mailing tags and receipts are valued much less.

| | NH% | ★VF | ★F | ⊙VF | ⊙F |
|---|---|---|---|---|---|
| **Nos 104–122** Set of 18 | 200 | 1,750.00 | 500.00 | 82.25 | 31.20 |
| **Nos. 110a–122a** Set of 8 imperf. pairs | 100 | 25,000.00 | 16,500.00 | — | — |

Imprint pairs, imprint strips of three, or imprint blocks of four or more (need 8-10 for full imprints on some) of the Admiral Issue are all scarce. Value approximately 50% more than the sum of the individual value of the singles in the imprint piece.

## "ADMIRAL" EXPERIMENTAL COIL STAMPS

| | | NH% | ★VF | ★F |
|---|---|---|---|---|
| **106x** | **2¢ deep rose red**. strip of 4, backstamp Type A over paste-up, *May 11, 1915* | 100 | 500.00 | 300.00 |
| xi | strip of 4, backstamp Type B over paste-up | 100 | 1,500.00 | 900.00 |
| xii | strip of 4, backstamp Type C over paste-up† | 100 | | 5,000.00 |
| xiii | strip of 4, back signed JNS‡ | 100 | | 125.00 |
| xiv | strip of 4, backstamp Type D over paste-up* | 100 | | 1,750.00 |

* Type D shows POSTAGE STAMP BRANCH in circle with date stamp MAY 11 and "1915" in manuscript.
† Only a few Type C are known. All are in generally poor condition.
‡ Initials are for "Jim N. Sissons".

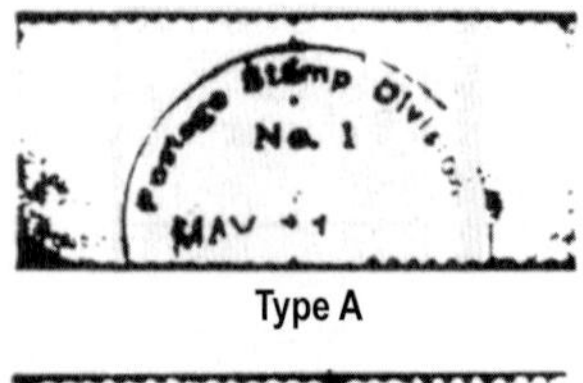

Type A

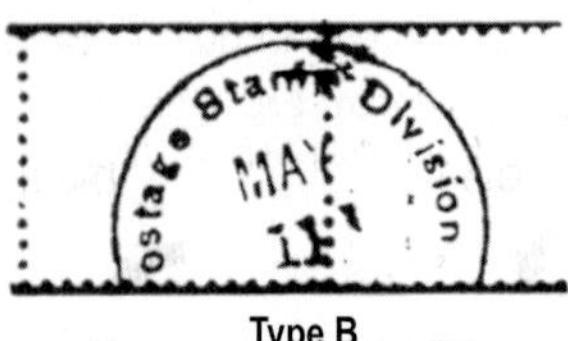

Type B

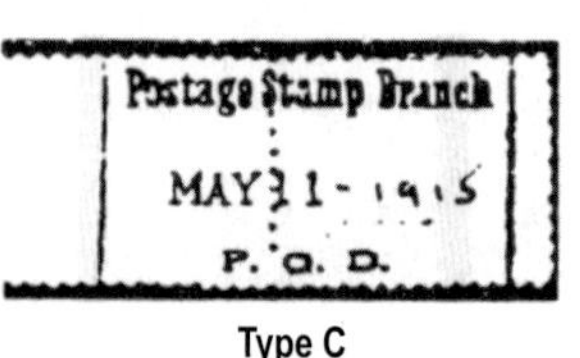

Type C

106x

106xii

106xiii

## KING GEORGE V "ADMIRAL" COIL STAMPS

123

124

| 1913 | | Engraved NH% | ★VF | ★F | ⊙VF | Perf 8 Horizontal ⊙F | ✉ |
|---|---|---|---|---|---|---|---|
| **123** | **1¢ dark green** (104), *Feb 13, 1913* | 200 | 150.00 | 60.00 | 100.00 | 40.00 | 90.00 |
| | pair | 200 | 300.00 | 120.00 | 250.00 | 100.00 | 150.00 |
| | strip of 4 | 200 | 600.00 | 240.00 | 500.00 | 250.00 | |
| i | paste-up pair | 200 | 400.00 | 150.00 | 300.00 | 100.00 | 250.00 |
| **124** | **2¢ carmine** (106), *Feb 15, 1913* | 200 | 150.00 | 60.00 | 100.00 | 40.00 | 100.00 |
| | pair | 200 | 300.00 | 120.00 | 300.00 | 150.00 | 250.00‡ |
| | strip of 4 | 200 | 600.00 | 240.00 | 600.00 | 300.00 | |
| i | paste-up pair | 200 | 400.00 | 150.00 | 400.00 | 150.00 | 350.00‡ |

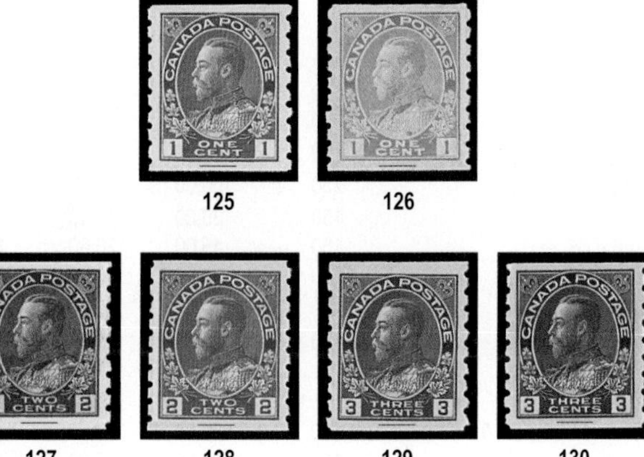
125 126

127 128 129 130

| 1912–1924 | | Engraved NH% | ★VF | ★F | ⊙VF | Perf 8 Vertical ⊙F | ✉ |
|---|---|---|---|---|---|---|---|
| **125** | **1¢ green** (104), *Oct 1912* | 150 | 40.00 | 12.00 | 3.00 | .75 | 8.00 |
| | green, pair | 150 | 80.00 | 24.00 | 7.50 | 2.00 | 15.00‡ |
| | green, strip of 4 | 150 | 160.00 | 48.00 | 25.00 | 10.00 | |
| i | green, paste-up pair | 150 | 100.00 | 25.00 | 40.00 | 20.00 | 40.00 |
| ii | blue green | 150 | 50.00 | 15.00 | 3.50 | 1.25 | 8.00 |
| | blue green, pair | 150 | 100.00 | 30.00 | 9.00 | 3.00 | 15.00‡ |
| | blue green, strip of 4 | 150 | 200.00 | 60.00 | 35.00 | 15.00 | |
| iii | blue green, paste-up pair | 150 | 125.00 | 30.00 | 50.00 | 25.00 | 45.00 |
| iv | yellow green | 150 | 40.00 | 12.00 | 3.00 | .75 | 8.00 |
| | yellow green, pair | 150 | 80.00 | 24.00 | 7.50 | 2.00 | 15.00‡ |
| | yellow green, strip of 4 | 150 | 160.00 | 48.00 | 25.00 | 10.00 | |
| v | yellow green, paste-up pair | 150 | 100.00 | 25.00 | 40.00 | 20.00 | 40.00‡ |
| vi | major re-entry in "1"s (only one known)* | — | — | — | — | *4,500.00* | — |

* This is the same re-entry type as 104vii. It is damaged.

| | | NH% | ★VF | ★F | ⊙VF | ⊙F | ⊠ |
|---|---|---|---|---|---|---|---|
| **126** | **1¢ orange yellow** Die II, dry printing (105), *1923* | 150 | 15.00 | 7.50 | 10.00 | 5.00 | 10.00 |
| | orange yellow Die II, dry printing, pair | 150 | 32.00 | 15.00 | 25.00 | 12.50 | 24.00‡ |
| | orange yellow Die II, dry printing, strip of 4 | 150 | 64.00 | 30.00 | 60.00 | 30.00 | |
| i | orange yellow Die II, dry printing, paste-up pair | 150 | 50.00 | 20.00 | 40.00 | 20.00 | 40.00‡ |
| b | orange yellow, Die I, dry printing (Pl. 10) | 150 | 40.00 | 20.00 | 15.00 | 7.50 | 20.00 |
| | orange yellow, Die I, dry (Pl. 10), pair | 150 | 90.00 | 40.00 | 35.00 | 15.00 | 35.00‡ |
| | orange yellow, Die I, dry (Pl. 10), strip of 4 | 150 | 180.00 | 80.00 | 80.00 | 40.00 | |
| v | orange yellow, Die I, dry (Pl. 10), paste-up pair | 150 | 110.00 | 55.00 | 50.00 | 25.00 | 50.00‡ |
| d | yellow, Die I, wet printing | 150 | 15.00 | 7.50 | 10.00 | 5.00 | 10.00 |
| | yellow, Die I, wet printing, pair | 150 | 32.00 | 15.00 | 25.00 | 12.50 | 25.00‡ |
| | yellow, Die I, wet printing, strip of 4 | 150 | 64.00 | 30.00 | 60.00 | 30.00 | |
| iii | yellow, Die I, wet printing, paste-up pair | 150 | 50.00 | 20.00 | 40.00 | 20.00 | 40.00‡ |
| xx | No 126, precancelled [1 style] | | | | | 1.00 | 5.00 |
| xxa | No 126d, precancelled [1 style] | | | | | 2.50 | |

127iv

| | | NH% | ★VF | ★F | ⊙VF | ⊙F | ⊠ |
|---|---|---|---|---|---|---|---|
| **127** | **2¢ carmine**, wet printing (106), *Oct 1912* | 150 | 60.00 | 15.00 | 3.00 | .60 | 8.00 |
| | carmine, pair | 150 | 120.00 | 30.00 | 10.00 | 5.00 | 30.00‡ |
| | carmine, strip of 4 | 150 | 240.00 | 60.00 | 40.00 | 20.00 | |
| i | carmine, paste-up pair | 150 | 150.00 | 40.00 | 50.00 | 30.00 | 45.00‡ |
| ii | rose red | 150 | 60.00 | 20.00 | 3.00 | .75 | 8.00 |
| | rose red, pair | 150 | 120.00 | 40.00 | 10.00 | 5.00 | 30.00‡ |
| | rose red, strip of 4 | 150 | 240.00 | 80.00 | 40.00 | 20.00 | |
| iii | rose red, paste-up pair | 150 | 150.00 | 45.00 | 50.00 | 30.00 | 45.00‡ |
| iv | major re-entry (pos. 5LL34)* | | | | | | |

* Sharp doubling above the upper frameline, above the 'AN' of CANADA, in and below the 'T' of TWO and 'C' of CENTS, and particularly in the lower left '2'.

‡ Single usage only. Proper commercial rate in time period.

| | | NH% | ★VF | ★F | ⊙VF | ⊙F | ⊠ |
|---|---|---|---|---|---|---|---|
| **128** | **2¢ green**, wet printing (107), *1922* | 150 | 40.00 | 10.00 | 1.50 | .50 | 8.00 |
| | wet printing, pair | 150 | 80.00 | 20.00 | 5.00 | 2.00 | 30.00‡ |
| | wet printing, strip of 4 | 150 | 160.00 | 40.00 | 20.00 | 7.50 | |
| i | wet printing, paste-up pair | 150 | 100.00 | 30.00 | 25.00 | 15.00 | 35.00‡ |
| ii | dry printing | 150 | 20.00 | 10.00 | 1.50 | .50 | 8.00 |
| | dry printing, pair | 150 | 45.00 | 20.00 | 5.00 | 2.00 | 35.00‡ |
| | dry printing, strip of 4 | 150 | 90.00 | 40.00 | 20.00 | 7.50 | |
| iii | dry printing, paste-up pair | 150 | 50.00 | 30.00 | 25.00 | 15.00 | 35.00‡ |
| iv | hairlines (dry) | 150 | 50.00 | 25.00 | 10.00 | | |

129iv

| | | NH% | ★VF | ★F | ⊙VF | ⊙F | ⊠ |
|---|---|---|---|---|---|---|---|
| **129** | **3¢ brown**, wet printing (108), *1918* | 150 | 50.00 | 7.50 | 2.00 | .50 | 8.00 |
| | brown, pair | 150 | 100.00 | 15.00 | 6.00 | 3.00 | 40.00‡ |
| | brown, strip of 4 | 150 | 200.00 | 30.00 | 25.00 | 10.00 | |
| i | brown, paste-up pair | 150 | 125.00 | 35.00 | 30.00 | 15.00 | 45.00‡ |
| ii | yellow brown | 150 | 50.00 | 7.50 | 2.00 | .50 | 8.00 |
| | yellow brown, pair | 150 | 100.00 | 15.00 | 6.00 | 3.00 | 45.00‡ |
| | yellow brown, strip of 4 | 150 | 200.00 | 30.00 | 25.00 | 10.00 | |
| iii | yellow brown, paste-up pair | 150 | 125.00 | 35.00 | 30.00 | 15.00 | 45.00‡ |
| iv | major re-entry (pos. 8UR34) (strong doubling in CANA and STAG at top) | | | | | 1,000.00 | |

| | | NH% | ★VF | ★F | ⊙VF | ⊙F | ⊠ |
|---|---|---|---|---|---|---|---|
| **130** | **3¢ carmine**, Die I, wet printing (109), *1924* | 150 | 100.00 | 50.00 | 12.50 | 5.25 | 22.00 |
| | Die I, wet printing, pair | 150 | 200.00 | 100.00 | 60.00 | 30.00 | 65.00‡ |
| | Die I, wet printing, strip of 4 | 150 | 400.00 | 200.00 | 200.00 | 100.00 | |
| i | Die I, wet printing, paste-up pair | 150 | 250.00 | 125.00 | 120.00 | 60.00 | 100.00‡ |
| b | carmine, Die II, dry printing | 150 | 125.00 | 60.00 | 15.00 | 7.00 | 22.00 |
| | Die II, dry printing, pair | 150 | 250.00 | 120.00 | 75.00 | 45.00 | 60.00‡ |
| | Die II, dry printing, strip of 4 | 150 | 500.00 | 240.00 | 225.00 | 135.00 | |
| iii | Die II, dry printing, paste-up pair | 150 | 300.00 | 150.00 | 150.00 | 100.00 | 120.00‡ |

‡ Single pair only (non-philatelic franking).

| | NH% | ★VF | ★F | ⊙VF | ⊙F |
|---|---|---|---|---|---|
| **Nos. 125–130** Set of 6 | 150 | 305.00 | 102.00 | 32.00 | 12.60 |
| **Nos. 125–130** Set of 6 pairs | 150 | 612.00 | 204.00 | 113.50 | 54.50 |
| **Nos. 125i–130i** Set of 6 paste-up pairs | 150 | 775.00 | 275.00 | 305.00 | 160.00 |

## PART PERFORATE COILS (SHEET FORM)

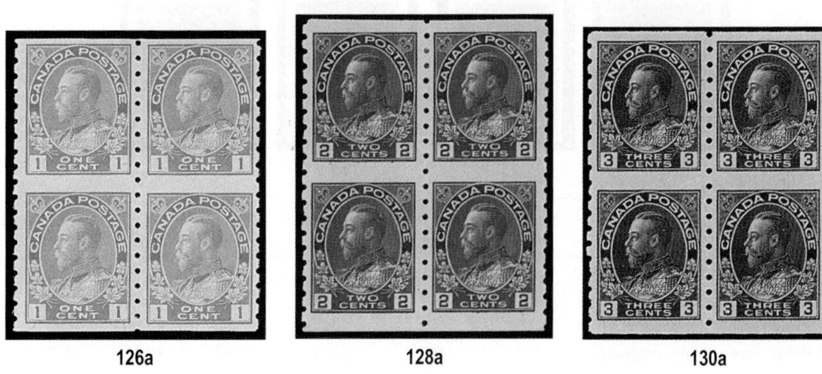

126a 128a 130a

| 1924 | | Engraved | | | | Perf 8 Vertical | |
|---|---|---|---|---|---|---|---|
| | | NH% | ★VF | ★F | ⊙VF | ⊙F | ✉ |
| **126a** | **1¢ yellow**, 2nd (dry) printing, Die II, block of 4 (105) | 50 | 80.00 | 40.00 | 75.00 | 40.00 | 80.00† |
| | vertical pair, imperf. horizontally (50,000 issued to public) | 50 | 40.00 | 20.00 | 37.50 | 20.00 | 40.00† |
| c | 1st (wet) printing, Die I (126b), block of 4 | 150 | 1,000.00 | 400.00 | | | |
| | as "c", vertical pair, imperf. horizontally (2,200 stamps issued by favour) | 150 | 500.00 | 200.00 | | | |
| ii | as "c", gutter block of 4 | 100 | *10,000.00* | 5,000.00 | — | — | — |
| **128a** | **2¢ green**, 2nd (dry) printing, block of 4 (107) | 50 | 80.00 | 40.00 | 75.00 | 40.00 | 80.00† |
| | vertical pair, imperf. horizontally (50,000 issued to public) | 50 | 40.00 | 20.00 | 37.50 | 20.00 | 40.00† |
| i | 1st (wet) printing, block of 4 | 150 | 1,000.00 | 400.00 | | | |
| | vertical pair, imperf. horizontally (2,200 stamps issued by favour) | 150 | 500.00 | 200.00 | | | |
| ii | as "i", gutter block of 4 | 100 | *10,000.00* | 5,000.00 | — | — | — |
| **130a** | **3¢ carmine**, Die I, wet printing, block of 4 (109)* | 150 | 1,500.00 | 850.00 | | | |
| | vertical pair, imperf. horizontally (2,200 stamps issued by favour) | 150 | 500.00 | 200.00 | | | 600.00† |
| i | as above, gutter block of 4 | 100 | *10,000.00* | 5,000.00 | — | — | — |
| ii | R-gauge, block of 4 | 100 | 4,500.00 | 2,000.00 | | | |

130aii

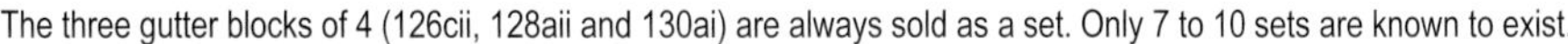

The three gutter blocks of 4 (126cii, 128aii and 130ai) are always sold as a set. Only 7 to 10 sets are known to exist.
† Value shown is for commercially-used pair on cover (non first flight). First flight – half of value shown.
*Genuine examples of 130a have smooth gum. Dry printing examples with strong embossing on gum side are fakes, made by adding vertical perfs to the issued imperforates (#138). Certificates of authenticity are recommended.

### MACDONALD CARTIER ESSAYS

Unissued Macdonald Cartier large die essays (two different 10¢ designs) are known in private hands. These are on India paper die sunk on cards (86 x 75mm and 147–154 x 124–127mm sizes are known) – examples shown have been cropped. The 7¢ and 50¢ values are known in different colours. The 50¢ is the key value and much scarcer than the others. Price: $1,500–4,000 each.

131 132 133 134

131iv

131vii

| 1915–1924 | | Engraved NH% | ★VF | ★F | ⊙VF | ⊙F | Perf 12 Horizontal ✉ |
|---|---|---|---|---|---|---|---|
| **131** | **1¢ dark green**, wet printing (104) | 150 | 10.00 | 5.00 | 8.00 | 4.00 | 12.00† |
| | dark green, wet printing, pair | 150 | 20.00 | 10.00 | 20.00 | 10.00 | 30.00‡ |
| | dark green, wet printing, strip of 4 | 150 | 40.00 | 20.00 | 40.00 | 20.00 | |
| i | dark green, wet printing, paste-up pair | 150 | 25.00 | 17.50 | 30.00 | 15.00 | 35.00‡ |
| ii | blue green | 150 | 27.50 | 15.00 | 15.00 | 8.00 | 30.00‡ |
| | blue green, pair | 150 | 55.00 | 30.00 | 40.00 | 20.00 | 40.00‡ |
| | blue green, strip of 4 | 150 | 110.00 | 60.00 | 100.00 | 50.00 | |
| iii | blue green, paste-up pair | 150 | 65.00 | 40.00 | 60.00 | 30.00 | 40.00‡ |
| iv | experimental Toronto coil, 2 large holes in perfs., *Jul 1918* | 150 | 100.00 | 40.00 | 110.00 | 40.00 | 200.00 |
| | experimental Toronto coil, pair | 150 | 200.00 | 80.00 | 220.00 | 80.00 | 300.00 |
| | experimental Toronto coil, strip of 4 | 150 | 400.00 | 160.00 | 450.00 | 180.00 | |
| v | experimental Toronto coil, paste-up pair | 150 | 250.00 | 100.00 | | | |
| vi | as "v", top margin imprint under paste-up | 150 | 450.00 | 300.00 | — | — | |
| vii | "Shilling mark" | 150 | 350.00 | 200.00 | 200.00 | | |
| viii | gripper coil* | | | | | | 25.00 |
| | as "viii", pair | | | | | | 40.00 |

† Price on cover is $20; $12 is for postcard.

| | | NH% | ★VF | ★F | ⊙VF | ⊙F | ✉ |
|---|---|---|---|---|---|---|---|
| **132** | **2¢ carmine** (106) | 150 | 60.00 | 15.00 | 12.00 | 6.00 | 15.00† |
| | carmine, pair | 150 | 120.00 | 30.00 | 40.00 | 17.50 | 45.00‡ |
| | carmine, strip of 4 | 150 | 240.00 | 60.00 | 100.00 | 45.00 | |
| i | carmine, paste-up pair | 150 | 140.00 | 40.00 | 60.00 | 30.00 | 75.00‡ |
| ii | as "i", top margin imprint under paste-up | | | | | | |
| iii | 2¢ rose carmine | 150 | 75.00 | 15.00 | 12.00 | 6.00 | 15.00 |
| | rose carmine, pair | 150 | 150.00 | 30.00 | 40.00 | 20.00 | 40.00‡ |
| | rose carmine, strip of 4 | 150 | 300.00 | 60.00 | 100.00 | 50.00 | |
| iv | rose carmine, paste-up pair | 150 | 150.00 | 40.00 | 60.00 | 30.00 | 50.00‡ |
| v | gripper coil* | | | | | | 25.00 |
| | as "v", pair | | | | | | 40.00 |

† Price on cover is $20; $15 is for postcard.

| | | NH% | ★VF | ★F | ⊙VF | ⊙F | ✉ |
|---|---|---|---|---|---|---|---|
| **133** | **2¢ yellow green**, wet printing (107), *1924* | 150 | 120.00 | 60.00 | 100.00 | 50.00 | 125.00 |
| | pair | 150 | 250.00 | 125.00 | 200.00 | 100.00 | 300.00‡ |
| | strip of 4 | 150 | 500.00 | 250.00 | 400.00 | 200.00 | |
| i | paste-up pair | 150 | 300.00 | 150.00 | 250.00 | 150.00 | 400.00‡ |
| ii | transfer roll flaw in "N" of "CENTS" | — | 300.00 | 150.00 | 150.00 | — | 250.00 |
| **134** | **3¢ brown** (108), *1921* | 150 | 20.00 | 6.00 | 8.00 | 4.00 | 15.00 |
| | pair | 150 | 40.00 | 12.00 | 20.00 | 10.00 | 45.00‡ |
| | strip of 4 | 150 | 80.00 | 24.00 | 60.00 | 30.00 | |
| i | paste-up pair | 150 | 60.00 | 20.00 | 30.00 | 15.00 | 75.00‡ |
| **Nos. 131–134** Set of 4 | | 150 | 210.00 | 86.00 | 128.00 | 64.00 | |
| **Nos. 131–134** Set of 4 pairs | | 150 | 430.00 | 177.00 | 280.00 | 137.50 | |
| **Nos. 131i–134i** Set of 4 paste-up pairs | | 150 | 525.00 | 227.50 | 370.00 | 210.00 | |

Varieties 131vi and 132ii occurred when sheets were pasted up to make coils, with the top imprint margin covered by the bottom stamp from another sheet. Approximately 1 in 5 paste-up pairs should show traces of the top margin imprint, OTTAW or "A No. 2", under the tab. 132ii is also known to exist with traces of the imprint "- No - 1" under the tab.

‡ Single pair only (Non-philatelic franking).

* One pair of pin holes, usually at the top; the pin holes were produced by the coil dispensing machine (gripper).

## 50TH ANNIVERSARY OF CONFEDERATION

135
*Fathers of Confederation*, by Robert Harris

Based on a painting by Robert Harris. Engraved by Edwin H. Gunn.

American Bank Note Company, Ottawa

**1917, Sep 15** **Engraved** **Perf 12**

| | | NH% | ★VF | ★F | ⊙VF | ⊙F | ✉ |
|---|---|---|---|---|---|---|---|
| **135** | **3¢ brown** | 200 | 70.00 | 20.00 | 3.00 | .50 | 11.00 |
| a | imperf. pair (w/o gum) (200 pairs recorded)* | — | 800.00 | 500.00 | — | — | — |
| i | dark brown | 200 | 80.00 | 24.00 | 4.00 | 1.00 | 11.00 |
| | plate blocks, plate 1–2 | | | ? | | | |
| | plate blocks of 6, plate 3 | | | 200.00 | | | |
| | plate blocks of 6, plate 4–6 | | | 150.00 | | | |
| | plate blocks of 6, plate 7–9 | | | 175.00 | | | |
| | plate blocks of 6, plate 10–12 | | | 200.00 | | | |

Qty: 98,650,000

Plate blocks of 6 are required to show both the plate number and order number. Only bottom plate blocks exist.

* Imperforate bottom plate blocks recorded from plates 7 and 8. LL and LR of each plate number exist. All four are unique plate number and position blocks of 10. Value: $6,000 each.

Issued to commemorate the 50th anniversary of Confederation, the design features a painting of the Fathers of Confederation. First day covers exist, value $400. Used blocks dated in period are scarce; value $100.00.

## KING GEORGE V "ADMIRAL" IMPERFORATE ISSUES

136

137

138

**1924** **Engraved** **Imperforate**

| | | NH% | ★VF | ★F | ⊙VF | ⊙F | ✉ |
|---|---|---|---|---|---|---|---|
| **136** | **1¢ yellow** (105), *Oct 6, 1924* | 100 | 50.00 | 35.00 | 50.00 | 35.00 | 50.00 |
| | pair | 100 | 100.00 | 70.00 | 100.00 | 70.00 | 100.00* |
| | plate blocks, plates 179, 180 (strip of 4) | 100 | 300.00 | 200.00 | — | — | — |
| | plates 179, 180 (block of 8) | 100 | 500.00 | 350.00 | — | — | — |

Qty: 25,000 pairs

Need a block of 10 (or strip of 5) to show full imprint on Pl. 180.

| | | NH% | ★VF | ★F | ⊙VF | ⊙F | ✉ |
|---|---|---|---|---|---|---|---|
| **137** | **2¢ green** (107), *Oct 6, 1924* | 100 | 50.00 | 35.00 | 50.00 | 35.00 | 50.00 |
| | pair | 100 | 100.00 | 70.00 | 100.00 | 70.00 | 100.00* |
| | plate blocks, plates 188, 189 (strip of 4) | 100 | 300.00 | 200.00 | — | — | — |
| | plates 188, 189 (block of 8) | 100 | 500.00 | 350.00 | — | — | — |

Qty: 25,000 pairs

| | | NH% | ★VF | ★F | ⊙VF | ⊙F | ✉ |
|---|---|---|---|---|---|---|---|
| **138** | **3¢ carmine**, Die I (109), *Jan 23, 1924* | 100 | 25.00 | 17.50 | 25.00 | 17.50 | 25.00 |
| | pair | 100 | 50.00 | 35.00 | 50.00 | 35.00 | 50.00* |
| i | pyramid guide, block of 4 | 100 | 300.00 | 200.00 | | | |
| ii | R-gauge, block of 4 | 100 | 300.00 | 200.00 | 300.00 | 200.00 | |
| | Plate blocks, plates 126–128† (strip of 4) | 100 | 300.00 | 250.00 | — | — | — |
| | plates 126–128 (block of 8) | 100 | 750.00 | 350.00 | — | — | — |
| | plates 129–131‡ (block of 8) | 100 | 3,000.00 | 1,500.00 | — | — | — |

Qty: 50,000 pairs

* Value shown is for pair on cover.

† The imprint is above the lathework in the bottom margin.

‡ Imprint is in the top margin. These were not issued regularly; probably no more than 8 plate imprint pieces are thought to exist, all are imperf. and most are VF.

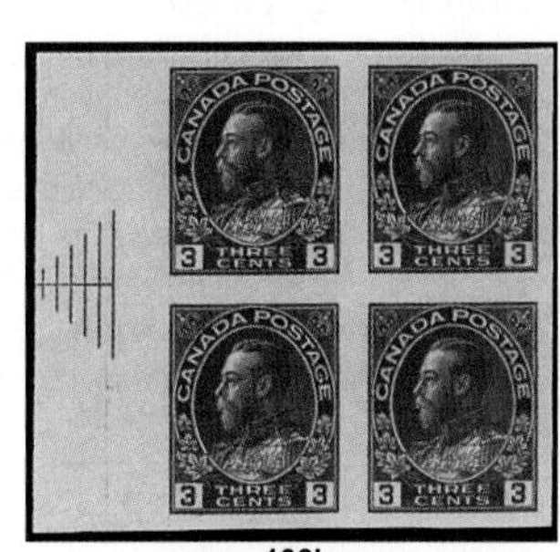

138i

138ii

King George V — Admiral

## KING GEORGE V "ADMIRAL" PROVISIONALS

139

140

139v

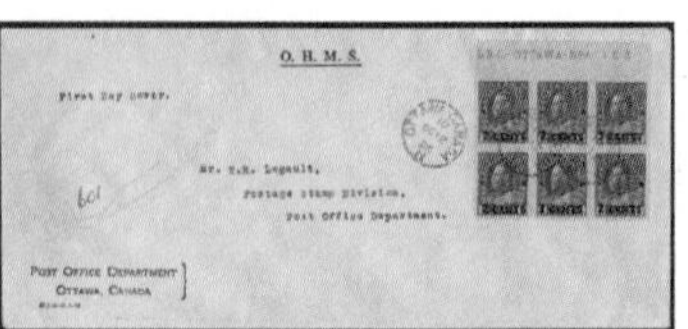
139c, plate #163, unique FDC

**1926** Engraved Perf 12

| | | NH% | ★VF | ★F | ⊙VF | ⊙F | ✉ |
|---|---|---|---|---|---|---|---|
| **139** | **2¢ on 3¢ carmine**, Die I*, *Oct 12, 1926* | 150 | 80.00 | 40.00 | 80.00 | 40.00 | 100.00† |
| a | pair, one without surcharge | 100 | 1,000.00 | 600.00 | — | — | — |
| b | double surcharge | 100 | 400.00 | 200.00 | — | — | — |
| c | Die II*, *Oct 12, 1926* | 150 | 1,200.00 | 600.00 | | | |
| i | surcharge badly slanted or shifted‡ | 100 | 180.00 | 90.00 | — | — | — |
| iii | pyramid guide, block of 4, Die I | 100 | 1,000.00 | 400.00 | | | |
| iv | as 139i, pyramid guide, block of 4 | 100 | 1,500.00 | 900.00 | | | |
| v | essay, vertical pair, one large overprint, one small § | 100 | 1,250.00 | 900.00 | | | |
| | 139 plate blocks, plates 115–117 (block of 8) | 100 | 750.00 | 500.00 | | | |
| | 139c plate blocks, plates 162–163 (block of 8) | | | | | | *12,500.00*** |
| | 139i plate blocks, plates 115, 116 (block of 8) | 100 | 1,500.00 | 1,000.00 | | | |

Qty: 50,000

* See No. 109 for explanation of dies.

‡ No. 139i is known in R-gauge block, value $1000 in VF condition.

§ Also exists with black and orange surcharges.

** Price for unique imprint block of 6 (plate 163) on FDC.

| | | NH% | ★VF | ★F | ⊙VF | ⊙F | ✉ |
|---|---|---|---|---|---|---|---|
| **140** | **2¢ on 3¢ carmine**, *Oct 16, 1926* | 150 | 40.00 | 20.00 | 40.00 | 20.00 | 70.00† |
| a | double surcharge | 100 | 350.00 | 200.00 | — | — | — |
| b | triple surcharge | 100 | 350.00 | 200.00 | — | — | — |
| c | double surcharge, one inverted | 100 | 550.00 | 300.00 | — | — | — |
| ii | pyramid guide, block of 4 | 100 | 600.00 | 250.00 | | | |
| iii | shifted two-line surcharge | 100 | 200.00 | 100.00 | | | |
| | plate blocks, plates 115–117 (block of 8) | 100 | 450.00 | 300.00 | | | *2,250.00*** |

Qty: 103,600

† Value shown is for commercially-used cover. First flight covers are half the values shown.

** Price for imprint blocks of 6 on FDC.

## "ADMIRAL" LATHEWORK

Late in 1916 the manufacturers introduced the practice of engraving an engine-turned pattern called "lathework" on the bottom margin of the plates. The first lathework appeared on plates 31 and 32 of the 1T¢ brown War Tax issue (MR4), which was engraved on November 25, 1916.

Ten different lathework types are known: A, B, B–INV, C, C–INV, D, D–INV, D1, D1–INV, and E–SPECIAL (one example known, used, submitted by R.F. Narbonne). All issues are wet printing unless indicated otherwise. Type D and D1 consist of partly overlapping bands of lathework taken from a design that is wider than either type. Because the bands overlap, the two types share common design elements. Because the overlap is partial, each type shows part of the overall lathework design that is unique to that type. In addition, type D1 has a horizontal line above and below the lathework similar to type B and C. The line below is normally cut off the issued panes.

Values are for lightly-hinged Fine singles and Fine blocks of 4 with light hinge on top pair (bottom pair NH) with lathework in the strength most commonly found on that issue. On some issues, only a trace of lathework can be found, while full lathework is common on others. The Strength column lists the percentage of lathework most commonly found on the issue, followed by a ratio of higher-strength impressions (which command a premium) known to exist.

For VF examples add 100%, for NH add 100% (for NH–VF add 200%). Very strong or complete lathework impressions command a premium. A blank space in a price column indicates that the type exists, or should exist, but insufficient information is available to establish a price. "Used" lathework is generally worth 80% of the mint values. Values for common precancels with lathework are the same as listed for the same stamp without precancel. For VF add 50%.

For type B lathework in particular, the lathework was laid down on the plate in strips that were shorter than the width of the plate. In many cases, there is an overlap of several millimeters between the end of one strip and the beginning of the next. The lathework appears doubled in the area where the strips overlap. This overlap is listed as "lathework doubled" in the listings that follow.

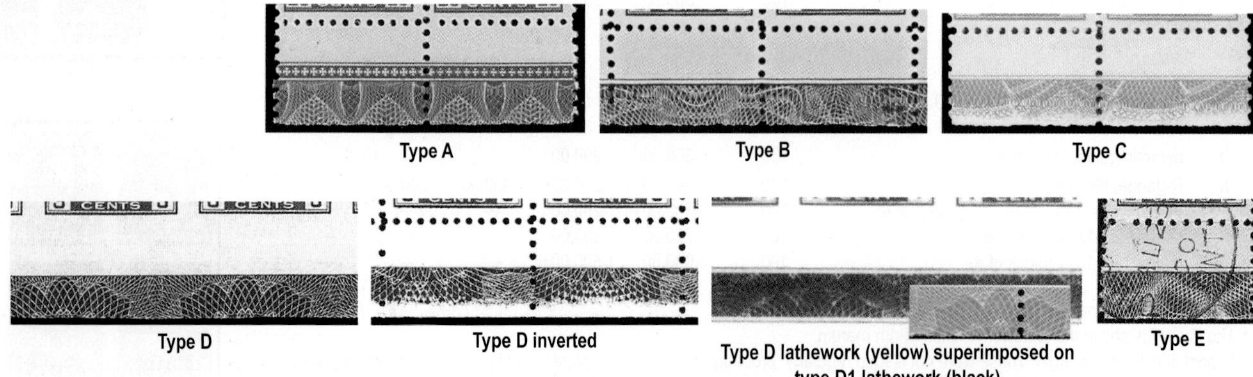
Type A | Type B | Type C

Type D | Type D inverted | Type D lathework (yellow) superimposed on type D1 lathework (black) | Type E

[Type D1 lathework strip is reproduced from George C. Marler, *The Admiral Issue of Canada*, p. 57]

## "ADMIRAL" LATHEWORK

Note: "precancelled" lathework blocks and singles are known. All are worth at least the value listed for the normals. Examples with "rare" precancels are valued much higher.

| VF+100%, NH+100% | | Type | Strength | Single | Block |
|---|---|---|---|---|---|
| **104** | **1¢ green** | B | Full | 60.00 | 150.00 |
| | | B Double | Strong/Full | 200.00 | 600.00 |
| | | C | Full | 400.00 | 1,000.00 |
| **105** | **1¢ yellow**, wet printing, Die I, from plate 150 | B | One mint single known | | |
| | wet printing, Die I | C | 80% (1 in 5, Full) | 60.00 | 200.00 |
| | wet printing, Die I, from plates 177, 181, 182 | D | Full | 50.00 | 150.00 |
| | wet printing, Die I | D–INV | 80% | 100.00 | 250.00 |
| | wet printing, Die I | D1 | 60% (80% known) | 300.00 | 750.00 |
| **f** | dry printing, Die I (plates 186, 187 only) | D | 80% (100% known) | 200.00 | 600.00 |
| **106** | **2¢ carmine** | B | Full | 60.00 | 150.00 |
| | lathework doubled | B | | 200.00 | 500.00 |
| | from plates 145, 146, 159 | C | Full | 500.00 | 1,200.00 |
| | from plate 160 only | C–INV | Full | 2,000.00 | 4,500.00 |
| **107** | **2¢ green**, wet printing, plate 159, 161, 162 | C | 80% | 150.00 | 500.00 |
| | from plate 160 only | C–INV | 90% | 3,000.00 | — |
| | | D | 80% | 100.00 | 225.00 |
| | | D–INV | 40% | 100.00 | 250.00 |
| | from plate 166 only | D1-INV | | 2,000.00 | 4,500.00 |
| **e** | dry printing, plate 169, 170, 188, 193, 194 | D | 100% | 1,000.00 | 2,500.00 |

Dry printings are known from plate 168. Since plate 168 has Type D inverted lathework, dry printings of this lathework should exist although to date no examples have been reported.

| VF+100%, NH+100% | | Type | Strength | Single | Block |
|---|---|---|---|---|---|
| **107a** | **2¢ green**, thin paper | D | 20% | 150.00 | 450.00 |
| | | D–INV | 40% | 250.00 | 750.00 |
| **108** | **3¢ brown** | B | | 75.00 | 225.00 |
| | lathework doubled | "B" | | 200.00 | 400.00 |
| | plate no. under lathework | "B" | | | |
| | | B–INV | — | 2,500.00 | 5,500.00 |
| | | C | 40% | 200.00 | 750.00 |
| | | C–INV | — | 3,500.00 | 7,500.00 |
| | wet printing | D | 60% | 150.00 | 400.00 |
| | wet printing | D–INV | 80% | 150.00 | 450.00 |
| | dry printing | D | Full | 250.00 | 750.00 |
| | SPECIAL LATHEWORK | E | One used single | 10,000.00 | — |
| **109** | **3¢ carmine**, dry printing | D | Full | 50.00 | 150.00 |
| | as above, with plate 125, 126, 127 or 128 above lathework, plate strip of 4 | D | Full | 250.00 | (8)350.00 |
| **110** | **4¢ olive yellow** | D | 80% (1 in 10, Full) | 150.00 | 450.00 |
| | | D–INV | 40% (1 in 20, Full) | 200.00 | 600.00 |
| **c** | golden yellow | D–INV | | | |
| **112** | **5¢ violet** | D | 60% | 120.00 | 350.00 |
| | | D–INV | Full | 400.00 | 900.00 |
| **iii** | retouched frameline, wet printing | D | | 150.00 | 500.00 |
| **112a** | **5¢ violet**, thin paper | D–INV | 40% | 150.00 | 500.00 |
| **113** | **7¢ yellow ochre** | B | Full | 150.00 | 500.00 |
| **iii** | redrawn frameline | B | 80% | 250.00 | 900.00 |
| **114** | **7¢ red brown**, wet printing | D | 40% | 60.00 | 200.00 |
| | dry printing | D | 40% (1 in 20, Full) | 40.00 | 150.00 |
| | dry printing | D | Full | 125.00 | 400.00 |
| | dry printing, thin paper | D | 40% | 450.00 | 1,200.00 |
| **116** | **10¢ plum** | A | 80% | 800.00 | 2,400.00 |
| | as above, with plate number under lathework | A | | 1,250.00 | 3,000.00 |
| | | B | Full | 2,000.00 | 4,500.00 |
| | | C | 80% | 1,250.00 | 3,000.00 |

| | | Type | Strength | Single | Block |
|---|---|---|---|---|---|
| 117 | **10¢ blue**, wet printing | D | 40% (1 in 10, 80%) | 300.00 | 750.00 |
| | wet printing | D | 80% to Full | 800.00 | 2,000.00 |
| | dry printing | D | 40% | 200.00 | 500.00 |
| | wet printing | D–INV | 40% | | |
| 118 | **10¢ bistre brown** | D | Full | 2,500.00 | 6,500.00 |
| 119 | **20¢ olive green** | A | Full | 300.00 | 900.00 |
| | lathework doubled | A | Full | 1,000.00 | 2,500.00 |
| | plate no. under lathework | A | 40% | 350.00 | 1,000.00 |
| | wet printing | D | 80% | 350.00 | 1,000.00 |
| | dry printing | D | Full | 350.00 | 1,250.00 |
| 120ii | **50¢ brown black**, wet printing | D | 20% | 3,000.00 | 7,500.00 |
| | Full lathework on 50¢ is rare | D | 80% to Full | 6,000.00 | 14,000.00 |
| 122 | **$1 orange**, dry printing | D | Full | 300.00 | 750.00 |
| b | wet printing | D | 60% | 500.00 | 1,200.00 |

### IMPERFORATE HORIZONTALLY

(pairs from part perforate coil sheets)

| | | Type | Strength | Single | Block |
|---|---|---|---|---|---|
| 126c | **1¢ yellow**, wet printing | B | Full | 800.00 | 1,750.00 |
| 128ai | **2¢ green**, wet printing | D | 20% | 800.00 | 1,750.00 |
| 130a | **3¢ carmine**, wet printing | D | Trace | 800.00 | 1,750.00 |

### IMPERFORATE ISSUES

(Imperf. values are for VF stamps; NH + 50%)

| | | Type | Strength | Single | Block |
|---|---|---|---|---|---|
| 136 | **1¢ yellow**, wet printing, from plate 150 | B | 40% | 400.00 | 1,500.00 |
| | wet printing, from plates 175 or 176 | D1* | | | |
| | wet printing, from plates 179–180 | D–INV | 40% | 350.00 | 1,000.00 |

* The existence of the D1 lathework on the 1c Yellow imperf has been questioned.

| | | Type | Strength | Single | Block |
|---|---|---|---|---|---|
| 138 | **3¢ carmine**, dry printing | D | Full | 40.00 | 150.00 |
| | as above, with plate #126, 127 or 128 above lathework, plate strip of 4 | D | Full | 300.00 | (8)750.00 |

### PROVISIONAL ISSUES

| | | Type | Strength | Single | Block |
|---|---|---|---|---|---|
| 139 | **2¢ on 3¢** (1 line surcharge), dry printing | D | — | 750.00 | 2,000.00 |
| | shifted surcharge, dry printing | D | Full | 1,000.00 | 3,000.00 |
| 140 | **2¢ on 3¢** (2 line surcharge)† | | | — unknown — | |

† Marler reports that the overprinting was done on panes of 100, not sheets of 400. Although the one-line overprint was applied to panes from all four positions of the sheet, it appears that the two-line overprint was limited to UL and UR panes. If so, the two-line overprint does not exist with lathework.

### WAR TAX STAMPS

| | | Type | Strength | Single | Block |
|---|---|---|---|---|---|
| MR1 | **1¢ green** | B | Full | 60.00 | 200.00 |
| MR2 | **2¢ carmine** | B | Full | 80.00 | 250.00 |
| MR4 | **2¢ + 1¢ brown** | A | Full | 80.00 | 250.00 |
| | plate no. under lathework | A | 40% | 150.00 | 450.00 |
| | Double lathework, plate 35 LR, position 94 | A | | 500.00 | 1,000.00 |
| | | B | Full | 80.00 | 250.00 |
| | | B–INV | 80% | 2,000.00 | 4,500.00 |
| | Double lathework | B-INV | 80% | 2,500.00 | 5,500.00 |

### POSTAGE DUE ISSUES

| | | Type | Strength | Single | Block |
|---|---|---|---|---|---|
| J2 | **2¢ violet** | A | Full | 1,250.00 | 3,500.00 |
| | 2¢ violet (regular paper) | D * | Full | 2,500.00 | 6,000.00 |
| J2a | thin paper | D | Full | 800.00 | 2,000.00 |

* The editors know of only four examples of 2¢ violet postage due on regular paper with Lathework D.

Used examples of postage due lathework are worth half of the above prices.

## 60TH ANNIVERSARY OF CONFEDERATION

141
Sir John A. Macdonald

142
*Fathers of Confederation,*
by Robert Harris

143
Parliament Buildings

144
Sir Wilfrid Laurier

145
Map of Canada 1867–1927

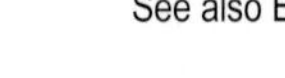

See also E3

Designer: Herman Herbert Schwartz. 1¢: Based on a photograph by William James Topley, portrait engraved by Edwin H. Gunn. 2¢: Based on a painting by Robert Harris, picture engraved by Edwin H. Gunn. 3¢: Picture engraved by Harold Osborn. 5¢: Portrait engraved by Edwin H. Gunn. 12¢: Portrait engraved by Edwin H. Gunn.

Canadian Bank Note Company, Limited

**1927, Jun 29** — **Engraved** — **Perf 12**

| No. | | | NH% | ★VF | ★F | ⊙VF | ⊙F | FDC |
|---|---|---|---|---|---|---|---|---|
| **141** | | **1¢ orange** | 100 | 4.00 | 2.00 | 2.00 | .75 | 150.00 |
| | a | imperf. pair, est. 250 pairs | 50 | 160.00 | 140.00 | — | — | — |
| | b | horiz. pair, imperf. vert, est. 250 pairs | 50 | 160.00 | 140.00 | — | — | — |
| | c | vert. pair, imperf. horiz., est. 250 pairs | 50 | 160.00 | 140.00 | — | — | — |
| | xx | No. 141, precancelled [4 styles] | — | — | — | — | .50 | |
| | | plate blocks, plates A1, A2*, (block of 8) | 100 | 60.00 | 35.00 | | | |
| | | plate A3*, (block of 8) | 100 | 65.00 | 40.00 | | | |
| | | plates A4–A6*, (block of 8) | 100 | 70.00 | 45.00 | | | |
| Qty: 148,034,000 | | | | | | | | |
| **142** | | **2¢ green** | 100 | 3.00 | 1.50 | .25 | .20 | 150.00 |
| | a | imperf. pair, est. 250 pairs | 50 | 160.00 | 140.00 | — | — | — |
| | b | horiz. pair, imperf. vert., est. 250 pairs | 50 | 160.00 | 140.00 | — | — | — |
| | c | vert. pair, imperf. horiz., est. 250 pairs | 50 | 160.00 | 140.00 | — | — | — |
| | | plate blocks, plates A1, 3L, 6, 8L, 10, 7R, 13, 15, 11R*, (block of 6) | 100 | 30.00 | 20.00 | | | |
| | | plates 2, 3R, 4, 5, 7L, 8R, 9, 11L*, (block of 4) | 100 | 60.00 | 40.00 | | | |
| | | plates 12, 14*, (block of 6) | 100 | 60.00 | 40.00 | | | |
| Qty: 333,757,000 | | | | | | | | |
| **143** | | **3¢ brown carmine** | 100 | 12.00 | 6.00 | 9.00 | 4.50 | 150.00 |
| | a | imperf. pair, est. 250 pairs | 50 | 160.00 | 140.00 | — | — | — |
| | b | horiz. pair, imperf. vert., est. 250 pairs | 50 | 160.00 | 140.00 | — | — | — |
| | c | vert. pair, imperf. horiz., est. 250 pairs | 50 | 160.00 | 140.00 | — | — | — |
| | i | imperf. between stamp and right margin | | | *2,400.00* | | | |
| | | plate blocks, plate A1*, (block of 4) | 100 | 100.00 | 60.00 | | | |
| | | plate A2*, (block of 6) | 100 | 150.00 | 90.00 | | | |
| | | plate A3*, (block of 6) | 100 | 120.00 | 75.00 | | | |
| Qty: 15,431,000 | | | | | | | | |
| **144** | | **5¢ violet** | 100 | 6.00 | 3.00 | 5.00 | 2.50 | 150.00 |
| | a | imperf. pair, est. 250 pairs | 50 | 160.00 | 140.00 | — | — | — |
| | b | horiz. pair, imperf. vert., est. 250 pairs | 50 | 160.00 | 140.00 | — | — | — |
| | c | vert. pair, imperf. horiz., est. 250 pairs | 50 | 160.00 | 140.00 | — | — | — |
| | | plate blocks, plates A1–A3*, (block of 8) | 100 | 80.00 | 50.00 | | | |
| Qty: 26,627,000 | | | | | | | | |

**Rates:**

Domestic: 2¢ per oz.
Local: 2¢ per oz. (0–1 oz.)
3¢ per oz. (1–2 oz.)
Postcard: 2¢
Printed matter: 1¢ per 4 oz.
USA: 2¢ per oz.
UK: 3¢ per oz.
Non-UK: 8¢ per oz.
Registration: 10¢
Special delivery: 20¢

143i

| | | NH% | ★VF | ★F | ⊙VF | ⊙F | FDC |
|---|---|---|---|---|---|---|---|
| **145** | **12¢ dark blue** | 100 | 35.00 | 15.00 | 9.00 | 4.50 | 200.00 |
| a | imperf. pair, est. 250 pairs | 50 | 160.00 | 140.00 | — | — | — |
| b | horiz. pair, imperf. vert., est. 250 pairs | 50 | 160.00 | 140.00 | — | — | — |
| c | vert. pair, imperf. horiz., est. 250 pairs | 50 | 160.00 | 140.00 | — | — | — |
| iii | imperf. at right between stamp and margin, (10 recorded) | 50 | 1,500.00 | 1,000.00 | — | — | — |
| | plate blocks, plates A1, A2*, (block of 6) | 100 | 250.00 | 150.00 | | | |

Qty: 7,492,000
Examples of 145 exist with hairlines.

| | NH% | ★VF | ★F | ⊙VF | ⊙F | FDC |
|---|---|---|---|---|---|---|
| **Nos. 141–145** Set of 5 | 100 | 60.00 | 27.50 | 25.25 | 12.45 | 750.00† |
| **Nos. 141a–145a** Set of 5 imperf. pairs | 50 | 800.00 | 700.00 | | | (on 1 FDC) |
| **Nos. 141b–145b** Set of 5 horiz. pairs, imperf. vert. | 50 | 800.00 | 700.00 | | | |
| **Nos. 141c–145c** Set of 5 vert. pairs, imperf. horiz. | 50 | 800.00 | 700.00 | | | |

There were 500 stamps (250 pairs) of each of the imperforate and part-imperforate varieties on the Confederation and Historical issues (141–148) recorded by early researchers Jephcott and Gates.
* Values shown are for lightly hinged plate blocks. Plate blocks with ALL stamps VF and NH are very scarce. Imperforate and part-imperforate plate blocks exist. All are very rare (5–10 of any value are known, depending on the sheet layout). Most are from different plates and positions and are valued at the sum of the pairs in the block plus 60%.
† FDC of 141–145 and E3 (set of 6 on one cover) value $1,000.00

Issued to commemorate the 60th anniversary of the Dominion of Canada. See also No. E3.

## HISTORICAL ISSUE

**146**
Thomas D'Arcy McGee

**147**
Laurier & Macdonald

**148**
Baldwin & Lafontaine

5¢: Based on a photograph by William James Topley, portrait engraved by Elie Timothée Loizeaux. 12¢: Portraits engraved by Edwin H. Gunn. 20¢: Based on a photograph by William Notman and a painting by Théophile Hamel, portrait engraved by William F. Ford.

Canadian Bank Note Company, Limited

**1927, Jun 29** **Engraved** **Perf 12**

| | | NH% | ★VF | ★F | ⊙VF | ⊙F | FDC |
|---|---|---|---|---|---|---|---|
| **146** | **5¢ violet** | 100 | 6.00 | 3.00 | 5.00 | 2.50 | 150.00 |
| i | double paper, in vert. pair | | | 400.00 | | | |
| a | imperf. pair, est. 250 pairs | 50 | 160.00 | 140.00 | — | — | — |
| b | horiz. pair, imperf. vert., est. 250 pairs | 50 | 160.00 | 140.00 | — | — | — |
| c | vert. pair, imperf. horiz., est. 250 pairs | 50 | 160.00 | 140.00 | — | — | — |
| | plate blocks, plates UL A1, A2*, (block of 10) | 100 | 90.00 | 60.00 | | | |
| | plates UR A1, A2*, (block of 8) | 100 | 75.00 | 50.00 | | | |

Qty: 20,349,000

| | | NH% | ★VF | ★F | ⊙VF | ⊙F | FDC |
|---|---|---|---|---|---|---|---|
| **147** | **12¢ green** | 100 | 15.00 | 7.50 | 8.00 | 3.75 | 200.00 |
| a | imperf. pair, est. 250 pairs | 50 | 160.00 | 140.00 | — | — | — |
| b | horiz. pair, imperf. vert., est. 250 pairs | 50 | 160.00 | 140.00 | — | — | — |
| c | vert. pair, imperf. horiz., est. 250 pairs | 50 | 160.00 | 140.00 | — | — | — |
| | plate blocks, plates A1, A2*, (block of 6) | 100 | 135.00 | 90.00 | | | |

Qty: 5,273,000

| | | NH% | ★VF | ★F | ⊙VF | ⊙F | FDC |
|---|---|---|---|---|---|---|---|
| **148** | **20¢ brown carmine** | 100 | 45.00 | 15.00 | 10.00 | 5.50 | 200.00 |
| a | imperf. pair, est. 250 pairs | 50 | 160.00 | 140.00 | — | — | — |
| b | horiz. pair, imperf. vert., est. 250 pairs | 50 | 160.00 | 140.00 | — | — | — |
| c | vert. pair, imperf. horiz., est. 250 pairs | 50 | 160.00 | 140.00 | — | — | — |
| | plate blocks, plates A1, A2*, (block of 6) | 100 | 262.00 | 175.00 | | | |
| | plates UR A2*, (block of 4) | 100 | 182.50 | 125.00 | | | |

Qty: 7,632,000

| | NH% | ★VF | ★F | ⊙VF | ⊙F | FDC |
|---|---|---|---|---|---|---|
| **Nos. 146–148** (3) Set | 100 | 66.00 | 25.50 | 23.00 | 11.75 | 750.00† |
| **Nos. 146a–148a** Set of 3 imperf. pairs | 50 | 480.00 | 420.00 | | | |
| **Nos. 146b–148b** Set of 3 horiz. pairs, imperf. vert. | 50 | 480.00 | 420.00 | | | |
| **Nos. 146c–148c** Set of 3 vert. pairs, imperf. horiz. | 50 | 480.00 | 420.00 | | | |

This set was intended for release in 1926 but was held back and released the same day as the Confederation set.
* Values shown are for lightly hinged plate blocks. Plate blocks with ALL stamps VF and NH are very scarce. Imperforate and part-imperforate plate blocks exist. All are very rare (5–10 of any value are known, depending on the sheet layout). Most are from different plates and positions and are valued at the sum of the pairs in the block plus 60%.
† set of 3 on same FDC.

## KING GEORGE V "SCROLL" ISSUE

149 150

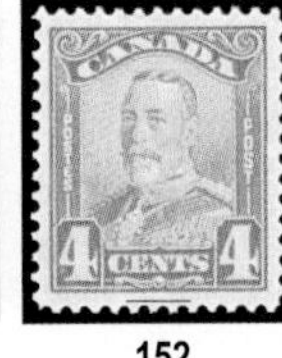
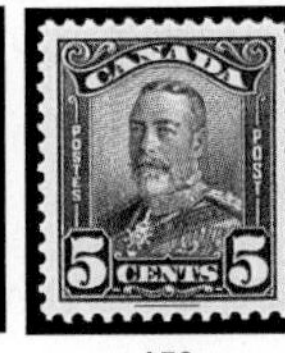

151 152 153 154

**Rates:**

Domestic: 2¢ per oz.
Local: 2¢ per oz. (0–1 oz.)
3¢ per oz. (1–2 oz.)
Postcard: 2¢
Printed matter: 1¢ per 4 oz.
USA: 2¢ per oz.
UK: 2¢ per oz.
Non-UK: 8¢ per oz.
Airmail: 5¢ (from Aug 24/28)
Registration: 10¢
Special delivery: 20¢

155
Mount Hurd, BC

156
Quebec Bridge

157
Harvesting Wheat

158
*Bluenose*

159
Parliament Building

See also C1

### PLATE PROOFS FOR KING GEORGE V "SCROLL" ISSUE

Plate proofs of all values are on horizontally ribbed India paper peculiar to this issue which has not appeared on the market before. Some of the 1, 2, 4 and 8¢ values are also on vertically ribbed India paper. All proof sheets were without gum. None of the "issued" stamps were issued on this paper. A set of singles of these proofs, $2,500, pairs $5,000. Short set 1¢ to 8¢, $800, pairs $1,600.

The number of proofs of these stamps offered at the ABNC archives sale in 1990 ranged from 1200 (600 pairs) of the 1¢ to 200 (100 pairs) of the 50¢ Bluenose.

Imperforate and part-perforate plate blocks exist on gummed "Stamp" paper. All are very rare (5–10 of any value are known, depending on sheet format). Most are from different plates and positions. Valued at sum of the Imperforate or part imperforate pairs in block, plus 60%. Thus a "VF hinged" imperforate plate block of 6 of the the 50¢ Bluenose would be valued as 3 imperforate pairs of #158a at $1,000.00 = $3,000.00 + 60% = $4,800.00. If the block is NH then the 50% NH Premium would apply and the catalogue value would jump to $7,200.00. A plate block of 6 that is hinged only on the margin would catalogue $4,500 as 3 VF NH Imperforate pairs but should have a significant premium for the imprint even if hinged on that top margin, and would sell for something between $4,500 and $7,200. I would want around $6,000+ for such a block as all Imperforate or Part Imperforate Plate blocks are incredibly RARE.

Designer: Herman Herbert Schwartz.
Engraver: 1¢–10¢, $1: Robert Savage; 12¢–20¢: Silas Robert Allen; 50¢: Harold Osborn.

Canadian Bank Note Company, Limited

| **1928–1929** | | **Engraved** NH% | ★VF | ★F | ⊙VF | ⊙F | **Perf 12** FDC |
|---|---|---|---|---|---|---|---|
| **149** | **1¢ orange**, *Oct 29, 1928* | 100 | 5.00 | 2.00 | .50 | .20 | 375.00 |
| **b** | imperf. pair, est. 250 pairs | 50 | 125.00 | 100.00 | — | — | — |
| **d** | horiz. pair, imperf. vert., est. 250 pairs | 50 | 150.00 | 125.00 | — | — | — |
| **e** | vert. pair, imperf. horiz., est. 250 pairs | 50 | 150.00 | 125.00 | — | — | — |
| **xx** | No. 149, precancelled [54 styles] | — | — | — | — | .20 | 5.00* |
| | plate blocks, plates A1–A3, (block of 8) | 100 | 60.00 | 28.00 | | | |
| | plates A4–A6, (block of 8) | 100 | 375.00 | 250.00 | | | |

Qty: 278,652,000
* Any cover.

**Known "Scroll" imprint plate blocks on FDC:**

| | | |
|---|---|---|
| **149** | Block of 12, plates 1, 2, 3 | $1,500.00 |
| **150** | Block of 6, plates 1, 2, 3 | $1,500.00 |
| **151** | Block of 4, plates 1, 2, 3 | $1,500.00 |
| **152** | Block of 4, plates 1, 2, 3 | $1,500.00 |
| **153** | Block of 4, plates 1, 2, 3 | $1,500.00 |
| **155** | Block of 4, plate 1 | $1,500.00 |

149a

| | | NH% | ★VF | ★F | ⊙VF | ⊙F | FDC |
|---|---|---|---|---|---|---|---|
| 149a | booklet pane of 6 x 1¢ orange (149as) | | | | | | |
| | (BK11, 13), *Oct 25, 1928* | 50 | 45.00 | 30.00 | 30.00 | 20.00 | |
| as | single with straight edge, from 149a | 50 | 5.00 | 3.00 | 3.00 | 1.50 | |
| c | 2 panes tête-bêche (149a), imperf., 1 inverted, | | | | | | |
| | (narrow 4.5 mm vert. gutter between panes) | 50 | 1,350.00 | 1,200.00 | — | — | |
| cii | imperf. tête-bêche block of 4 (right pair inverted) | | | | | | |
| | (narrow 4.5 mm vert. gutter, 3.0 mm horiz. gutter) | 50 | 750.00 | 600.00 | — | — | |
| ciii | as ii with 4.5 mm vert. and 4.5 mm horiz. gutters | 50 | 1,000.00 | 800.00 | — | — | |
| civ | imperf. tête-bêche block of 4 (right pair inverted) | | | | | | |
| | (wide 17.0 mm vert. gutter, 3.0 mm horiz. gutter) | 50 | 1,000.00 | 800.00 | — | — | |
| cv | as iv with 17.0 mm vert. and 4.5 mm horiz. gutters | 50 | 1,250.00 | 1,000.00 | — | — | |
| cvi | imperf. horiz. tête-bêche pair, | | | | | | |
| | with narrow vertical gutter (4.5 mm) | 50 | 375.00 | 300.00 | — | — | |
| cvii | imperf. horiz. tête-bêche pair, | | | | | | |
| | with wide vertical gutter (17.0 mm) | 50 | 500.00 | 400.00 | — | — | |

BK11 4 panes of 149a in cover; English (99,575) $200.00 French (16,375) $500.00

Qty: 149a: 616,000

| | | NH% | ★VF | ★F | ⊙VF | ⊙F | FDC |
|---|---|---|---|---|---|---|---|
| **150** | **2¢ green**, *Oct 17, 1928* | 100 | 3.00 | 1.10 | .25 | .20 | 375.00† |
| **b** | imperf. pair, est. 250 pairs | 50 | 125.00 | 100.00 | — | — | — |
| **d** | horiz. pair, imperf. vert., est. 250 pairs | 50 | 150.00 | 125.00 | — | — | — |
| **e** | vert. pair, imperf. horiz., est. 250 pairs | 50 | 150.00 | 125.00 | — | — | — |
| **xx** | No. 150, precancelled [35 styles] | — | — | — | — | .40 | 3.00* |
| | plate blocks, plates A1–A4, (block of 8) | 100 | 40.00 | 19.00 | | | |
| | plates A5, A6, (block of 8) | 100 | 30.00 | 14.00 | | | |
| | plates A7–A9, (block of 8) | 100 | 40.00 | 19.00 | | | |
| | plate A10, (block of 8) | 100 | 30.00 | 12.00 | | | |
| | plates A11, (block of 8) | 100 | 80.00 | 50.00 | | | |

Qty: 1,311,000,000

* Any cover.

† Although October 17, 1928 is widely recognized as the first day of issue, the editors are aware of four "predated" October 16, 1928 covers, two originating from Edmonton, Alberta and two from Winnipeg, Manitoba. Value: $500.

## IMPERFORATE TETE-BECHE BOOKLET PANES AND BLOCKS OF 4

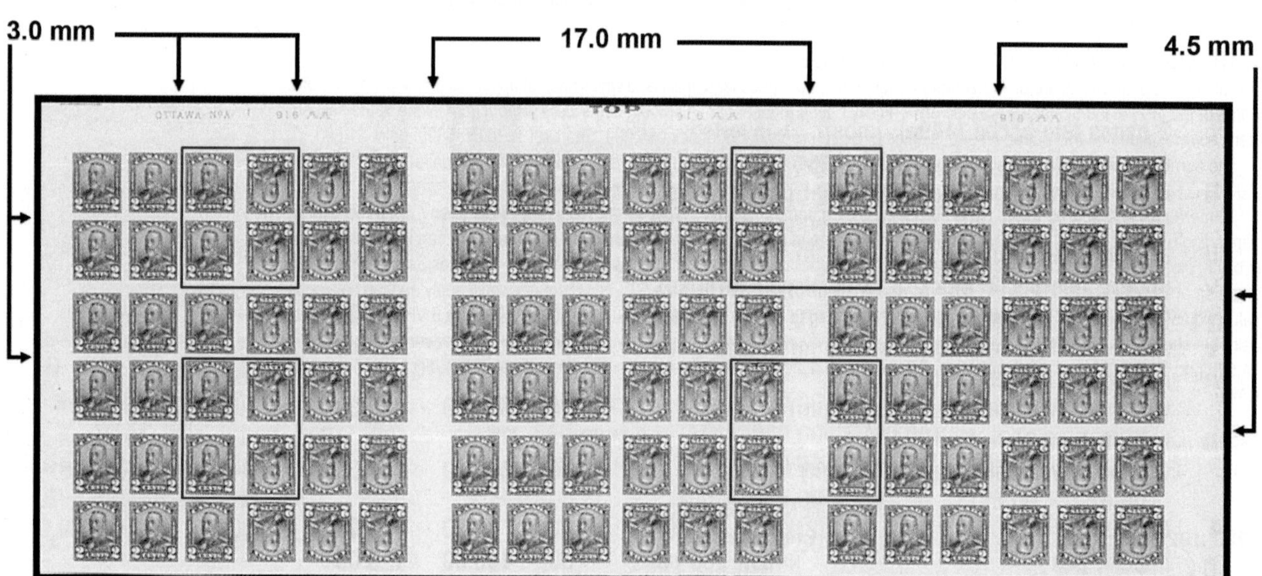


**Nos. 149a, 150a and 153a** [booklet panes of 6 (3 x 2)] were printed in sheets of 360 stamps arranged in 6 vertical columns of 10 booklet panes each. Alternate columns are inverted (tête-bêche), resulting in 3 vertical columns of tête-bêche pairs of booklet panes. Within each tête-bêche column the booklet panes are separated by 4.5 mm vertical and horizontal gutters. The vertical gutter between each of the three tête-bêche columns is 17.0 mm and the left and right sheet margins are a similar width. The space between individual stamps on a booklet pane of six is 3.0 mm (vertically and horizontally). Imperf. sheets of the 3 values have been cut to produce the imperf. tête-bêche booklet panes (149ai. 150ai and 153ai) and the 4 different tête-bêche blocks of 4 are indicated by solid red lines in the illustration above. Sheets have also been cut into horiz. imperf. tête-bêche pairs, with the right stamp inverted.

Only 3 of the 10 rows of booklet panes are illustrated above.

The imperf. tête-bêche booklet panes and the 4 types of imperf tête-bêche blocks of 4 shown in the diagram, and the imperf. tête-bêche pairs are each collected in sets of the three different values (1¢, 2¢ and 5¢). The value for each set of three values is 3 x the value listed for one value.

It is estimated that 150 imperf. tête-bêche pairs of booklet panes existed from 5 complete sheets of 360 stamps. At least 2 of the original sheets were cut creatively into the various blocks and pairs listed. Perhaps 50 sets of imperf. tête-bêche pairs of booklet panes remain intact today.

| | | NH% | ★VF | ★F | ⊙VF | ⊙F | FDC |
|---|---|---|---|---|---|---|---|
| 150a | booklet pane of 6 x 2¢ green (150as) | | | | | | |
| | (BK12, 13), *Oct 16, 1928* | 50 | 45.00 | 30.00 | 30.00 | 20.00 | |
| as | single with straight edge, from 150a | 50 | 5.00 | 3.00 | 3.00 | 1.50 | |
| ai | 150a with horizontal hairlines to left of UL stamp | 50 | | 100.00 | | | |
| c | 2 panes tête-bêche (150a), imperf., 1 inverted, | | | | | | |
| | (4.5 mm vert. gutter between panes) | 50 | 1,350.00 | 1,200.00 | — | — | |
| cii | imperf. tête-bêche block of 4 (right pair inverted) | | | | | | |
| | (4.5 mm vert. gutter, 3.0 mm horiz. gutter) | 50 | 750.00 | 600.00 | — | — | |
| ciii | as ii with 4.5 mm vert. and 4.5 mm horiz. gutters | 50 | 1,000.00 | 800.00 | — | — | |
| civ | imperf. tête-bêche block of 4 (right pair inverted) | | | | | | |
| | (17.0 mm vert. gutter, 3.0 mm horiz. gutter) | 50 | 1,000.00 | 800.00 | — | — | |
| cv | as iv with 17.0 mm vert. and 4.5 mm horiz. gutters | 50 | 1,250.00 | 1,000.00 | — | — | |
| cvi | imperf. horiz. tête-bêche pair, | | | | | | |
| | with 4.5 mm vert. gutter | 50 | 375.00 | 300.00 | — | — | |
| cvii | imperf. horiz. tête-bêche pair, | | | | | | |
| | with 17.0 mm vert. gutter | 50 | 500.00 | 400.00 | — | — | |

BK12 2 panes of 150a in cover; English (4,160,000) $125.00, French (328,825) $300.00

Qty: 150a: 9,079,000

150a

| | | NH% | ★VF | ★F | ⊙VF | ⊙F | FDC |
|---|---|---|---|---|---|---|---|
| **151** | **3¢ dark carmine**, *Dec 12, 1928* | 100 | 40.00 | 15.00 | 17.50 | 9.00 | 500.00 |
| **a** | imperf. pair, est. 250 pairs | 50 | 150.00 | 125.00 | — | — | — |
| **b** | horiz. pair, imperf. vert., est. 250 pairs | 50 | 150.00 | 125.00 | — | — | — |
| **c** | vert. pair, imperf. horiz., est. 250 pairs | 50 | 150.00 | 125.00 | — | — | — |
| **xx** | No. 151, precancelled [1 style] | — | — | — | — | 150.00 | 200.00* |
| | plate blocks, plates A1, (block of 6) | 100 | 300.00 | 200.00 | | | |
| | plate blocks, plates A2, (block of 8) | 100 | 300.00 | 200.00 | | | |
| | plate A3, (block of 8) | 100 | 427.50 | 285.00 | | | |

Qty: 11,000,000

* Any cover.

There were 500 stamps (250 pairs each) of the imperforate and part-imperforate varieties recorded by early researchers Jephcott and Gates. There are perhaps 40–50 more imperf. pairs of the 1¢, 3¢ and 5¢ values from the imperf. booklet pane sheets of these values.

| | | NH% | ★VF | ★F | ⊙VF | ⊙F | FDC |
|---|---|---|---|---|---|---|---|
| **152** | **4¢ bistre**, *Aug 16, 1929* | 100 | 35.00 | 12.00 | 7.50 | 4.00 | 625.00 |
| **a** | imperf. pair, est. 250 pairs | 50 | 150.00 | 125.00 | — | — | — |
| **b** | horiz. pair, imperf. vert., est. 250 pairs | 50 | 150.00 | 125.00 | — | — | — |
| **c** | vert. pair, imperf. horiz., est. 250 pairs | 50 | 150.00 | 125.00 | — | — | — |
| | plate blocks, plate A1, (block of 8) | 100 | 350.00 | 150.00 | | | |

Qty: 10,020,000

| | | NH% | ★VF | ★F | ⊙VF | ⊙F | FDC |
|---|---|---|---|---|---|---|---|
| **153** | **5¢ deep violet**, *Dec 12, 1928* | 100 | 25.00 | 8.00 | 4.00 | 2.00 | 500.00 |
| **b** | imperf. pair, est. 250 pairs | 50 | 150.00 | 125.00 | — | — | — |
| **d** | horiz. pair, imperf. vert., est. 250 pairs | 50 | 150.00 | 125.00 | — | — | — |
| **e** | vert. pair, imperf. horiz., est. 250 pairs | 50 | 150.00 | 125.00 | — | — | — |
| **xx** | No. 153, precancelled [1 style] | — | — | — | — | 100.00 | |
| | plate blocks, plates A1–A3, (block of 8) | 100 | 200.00 | 80.00 | | | |

Qty: 21,422,000

153a

| | | NH% | ★VF | ★F | ⊙VF | ⊙F | FDC |
|---|---|---|---|---|---|---|---|
| 153a | booklet pane of 6 x 5¢ violet (153as) | | | | | | |
| | (BK13), *Jan 6, 1929* | 50 | 350.00 | 200.00 | 350.00 | 200.00 | |
| as | single with straight edge, from 153a | 50 | 35.00 | 25.00 | 25.00 | 20.00 | |
| c | 2 panes tête-bêche (153a), imperf., 1 inverted, | | | | | | |
| | (narrow 4.5 mm vert. gutter between panes) | 50 | 1,350.00 | 1,200.00 | — | — | |
| cii | imperf. tête-bêche block of 4 (right pair inverted) | | | | | | |
| | (narrow 4.5 mm vert. gutter, 3.0 mm horiz. gutter) | 50 | 750.00 | 600.00 | — | — | |
| ciii | as ii with 4.5 mm vert. and 4.5 mm horiz. gutters | 50 | 1,000.00 | 800.00 | — | — | |
| civ | imperf. tête-bêche block of 4 (right pair inverted) | | | | | | |
| | (wide 17.0 mm vert. gutter, 3.0 mm horiz. gutter) | 50 | 1,000.00 | 800.00 | — | — | |
| cv | as iv with 17.0 mm vert. and 4.5 mm horiz. gutters | 50 | 1,250.00 | 1,000.00 | — | — | |
| cvi | imperf. horiz. tête-bêche pair, | | | | | | |
| | with narrow vertical gutter (4.5 mm) | 50 | 375.00 | 300.00 | — | — | |
| cvii | imperf. horiz. tête-bêche pair, | | | | | | |
| | with wide vertical gutter (17.0 mm) | 50 | 500.00 | 400.00 | — | — | |

BK13 3 panes of 149a, 2 panes 150a, and 1 pane of 153a in cover (50,650) $800.00*

* Value shown is with plain manila cover. With handstamp on cover $5,000.00; with "1928" in centre of handstamp $3,850.00

| | | NH% | ★VF | ★F | ⊙VF | ⊙F | FDC |
|---|---|---|---|---|---|---|---|
| **154** | **8¢ blue**, *Dec 21, 1928* | 100 | 25.00 | 10.00 | 12.00 | 6.00 | 625.00 |
| a | imperf. pair, est. 250 pairs | 50 | 150.00 | 125.00 | — | — | — |
| b | horiz. pair, imperf. vert., est. 250 pairs | 50 | 150.00 | 125.00 | — | — | — |
| c | vert. pair, imperf. horiz., est. 250 pairs | 50 | 150.00 | 125.00 | — | — | — |
| | plate blocks, plates A1 UR, (block of 6) | 100 | 225.00 | 150.00 | | | |
| | plate blocks, plates A1–A3, (block of 8) | 100 | 225.00 | 150.00 | | | |
| Qty: 12,100,000 | | | | | | | |
| **155** | **10¢ green**, *Dec 5, 1928* | 100 | 30.00 | 12.00 | 4.00 | 2.00 | 750.00 |
| a | imperf. pair, est. 250 pairs | 50 | 250.00 | 175.00 | — | — | — |
| b | horiz. pair, imperf. vert., est. 250 pairs | 50 | 250.00 | 175.00 | — | — | — |
| c | vert. pair, imperf. horiz., est. 250 pairs | 50 | 250.00 | 175.00 | — | — | — |
| | plate blocks, plate A1, (block of 6) | 100 | 275.00 | 175.00 | | | |
| | plates A2, A3, (block of 6) | 100 | 250.00 | 150.00 | | | |
| Qty: 36,077,000 | | | | | | | |
| **156** | **12¢ grey**, *Jan 8, 1929* | 100 | 70.00 | 20.00 | 12.00 | 6.00 | 750.00 |
| a | imperf. pair, est. 250 pairs | 50 | 250.00 | 175.00 | — | — | — |
| b | horiz. pair, imperf. vert., est. 250 pairs | 50 | 250.00 | 175.00 | — | — | — |
| c | vert. pair, imperf. horiz., est. 250 pairs | 50 | 250.00 | 175.00 | — | — | — |
| | plate blocks, plate A1, A2 (block of 6) | 100 | 500.00 | 200.00 | | | |
| Qty: 4,300,000 | | | | | | | |
| **157** | **20¢ dark carmine**, *Jan 8, 1929* | 100 | 100.00 | 30.00 | 16.00 | 8.00 | 800.00 |
| a | imperf. pair, est. 250 pairs | 50 | 250.00 | 175.00 | — | — | — |
| b | horiz. pair, imperf. vert., est. 250 pairs | 50 | 250.00 | 175.00 | — | — | — |
| c | vert. pair, imperf. horiz., est. 250 pairs | 50 | 250.00 | 175.00 | — | — | — |
| | plate blocks, plates A1–A3, (block of 6) | 100 | 750.00 | 250.00 | | | |
| Qty: 7,009,000 | | | | | | | |
| **158** | **50¢ dark blue**, *Jan 8, 1929* | 100 | 350.00 | 200.00 | 100.00 | 50.00 | 7,500.00‡ |
| a | imperf. pair, est. 250 pairs | 50 | 1,000.00 | 800.00 | — | — | — |
| b | horiz. pair, imperf. vert., est. 250 pairs | 50 | 1,000.00 | 800.00 | — | — | — |
| c | vert. pair, imperf. horiz., est. 250 pairs | 50 | 1,000.00 | 800.00 | — | — | — |
| iii | "man on the mast" variety (pos. 58) | 100 | 3,000.00 | 1,500.00 | 2,000.00 | 1,000.00 | 3,000.00† |
| iv | as iii, in imperf. pair | 50 | 12,000.00 | | | | |
| v | as iii, horiz. pair, imperf. between | 50 | 12,000.00 | | | | |
| | plate blocks: | | | | | | |
| | plates A2 UL, UR, A3 UR, (block of 4) | 100 | 2,000.00 | 1,000.00 | | | |
| | plate A3 UL, (block of 6) | 100 | 3,000.00 | 2,000.00 | | | |

158iii

Qty: 1,045,000
See also 913, 1228 and 1738.
† Single on cover, not FDC.

| | | NH% | ★VF | ★F | ⊙VF | ⊙F | FDC |
|---|---|---|---|---|---|---|---|
| **159** | **$1 olive green**, *Jan 8, 1929* | 100 | 450.00 | 250.00 | 120.00 | 60.00 | 5,000.00‡ |
| a | imperf. pair, est. 250 pairs | 50 | 900.00 | 700.00 | — | — | — |
| b | horiz. pair, imperf. vert., est. 250 pairs | 50 | 900.00 | 700.00 | — | — | — |
| c | vert. pair, imperf. horiz., est. 250 pairs | 50 | 900.00 | 700.00 | — | — | — |
| iii | bronze green shade | 100 | 500.00 | 325.00 | 125.00 | 75.00 | |
| | plate blocks, plate A1, (block of 6) | 100 | 4,000.00 | 2,500.00 | | | |

Qty: 561,000
‡ Bulk payment receipts worth $300.

| | NH% | ★VF | ★F | ⊙VF | ⊙F | FDC |
|---|---|---|---|---|---|---|
| **Nos. 149–159** Set of 11 | 100 | 1,100.00 | 546.10 | 293.70 | 147.40 | |
| **Nos. 149b–159a** Set of 11 imperf. pairs | 50 | 3,475.00 | 2,700.00 | — | — | — |
| **Nos. 149d–159b** Set of 11 horiz. pairs, imperf. vert. | 50 | 3,550.00 | 2,775.00 | — | — | — |
| **Nos. 149e–159c** Set of 11 vert. pairs, imperf. horiz. | 50 | 3,550.00 | 2,775.00 | — | — | — |

## KING GEORGE V "SCROLL" ISSUE COIL STAMPS

160

161

| 1929 | | Engraved NH% | ★VF | ★F | ⊙VF | Perf 8 Vertical ⊙F | ✉ |
|---|---|---|---|---|---|---|---|
| **160** | **1¢ orange** (149) | 100 | 60.00 | 20.00 | 30.00 | 15.00 | 20.00 |
| | pair | 100 | 120.00 | 40.00 | 75.00 | 32.50 | 50.00 |
| | strip of 4 | 100 | 240.00 | 80.00 | 200.00 | 80.00 | |
| i | paste-up pair | 100 | 150.00 | 60.00 | 100.00 | 50.00 | 75.00 |
| **xx** | No. 160, precancelled [2 styles] | 100 | 35.00 | 15.00 | 30.00 | 2.00 | 20.00 |

Qty: Total: 10,000,000. 160 (not precancelled): 1,485,000, 160xx (precancelled): 8,515,000

160i

| | | NH% | ★VF | ★F | ⊙VF | ⊙F | ✉ |
|---|---|---|---|---|---|---|---|
| **161** | **2¢ green** (150) | 100 | 60.00 | 20.00 | 5.00 | 2.00 | 10.00† |
| | pair | 100 | 120.00 | 40.00 | 15.00 | 5.00 | 30.00† |
| | strip of 4 | 100 | 240.00 | 80.00 | 50.00 | 20.00 | |
| i | paste-up pair | 100 | 150.00 | 60.00 | 50.00 | 30.00 | 50.00 |

Qty: 83,259,000

161i

Most of No. 160 were precancelled. Prices shown (except 160xx) are for NON-PRECANCELS.
Values shown for Nos. 160 and 161 (singles and pairs) are for any cover, not FDC.
† First Flight covers are half the value shown, or more if scarce flight.

King George V — Arch

## KING GEORGE V "ARCH/LEAF" ISSUE

162

163

164

165

166

167

168

169

170

171

172

173
Library of Parliament

174
Quebec Citadel

175
Harvesting Wheat

176
Grand Pré, NS
Acadian Memorial Church

177
Mt. Edith Cavell, AB

**Rates:**

Domestic: 2¢ per oz.
Local: 2¢ per oz. (0–1 oz.)
3¢ per oz. (1–2 oz.)
Postcard: 2¢
Printed matter: 1¢ per 4 oz.
USA: 2¢ per oz.
UK: 2¢ per oz.
Non-UK: 8¢ per oz. (5¢ per oz. from Jul 1/30)
Airmail: 5¢ (from Aug 24/28)
Registration: 10¢
Special delivery: 20¢

1¢ War tax imposed effective Jul 1, 1931
Domestic: 3¢ (0–1 oz.)
2¢ each additional oz.
USA: 3¢ per oz.

See also C2

Designer: Herman Herbert Schwartz. Portrait engraver: 1¢-8¢: Carl Theodore Arlt.

British American Bank Note Company

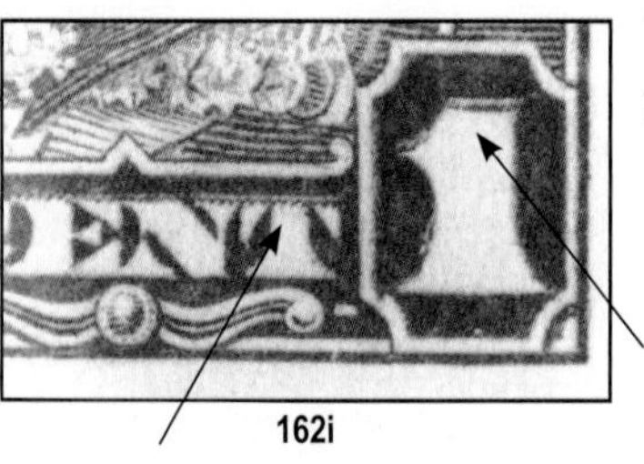

162i

| 1930–1931 | Engraved | NH% | ★VF | ★F | ⊙VF | ⊙F | Perf 11 FDC |
|---|---|---|---|---|---|---|---|
| **162** | **1¢ orange**, *Jul 17, 1930* | 100 | 2.00 | .75 | 1.00 | .40 | 300.00 |
| i | major re-entry in right "1" (pos. 96, Pl. 2 UL) | 100 | 80.00 | 30.00 | 50.00 | 20.00 | 60.00† |
| | 162i in block with 3 normal | 100 | 90.00 | 35.00 | 75.00 | 35.00 | |
| ii | imperf. pair (w/o gum) only 1 strip of 3 known ‡ | — | *9,500.00* | — | — | — | — |
| xx | No. 162, precancelled [35 styles] | — | — | — | — | .20 | 5.00 |
| | plate blocks | 100 | 12.00 | 6.00 | | | |
| | plate 1, reversed 1, centre UL | 100 | 12.00 | 6.00 | | | |
| | plate 2, reversed 2, centre UL | 100 | 12.00 | 6.00 | | | |

Qty: 74,900,000

‡ Probably printer's waste.

**The Two dies of the 1¢ green**

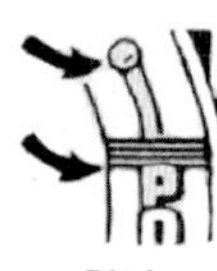

Die I

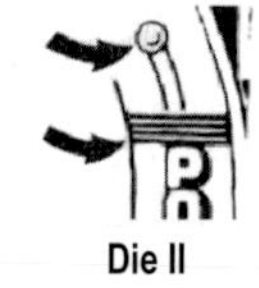

Die II

**Die I** Three thick coloured lines and one thin line above P

**Die II** Four thick coloured lines. Curved line in ball is longer than in Die I

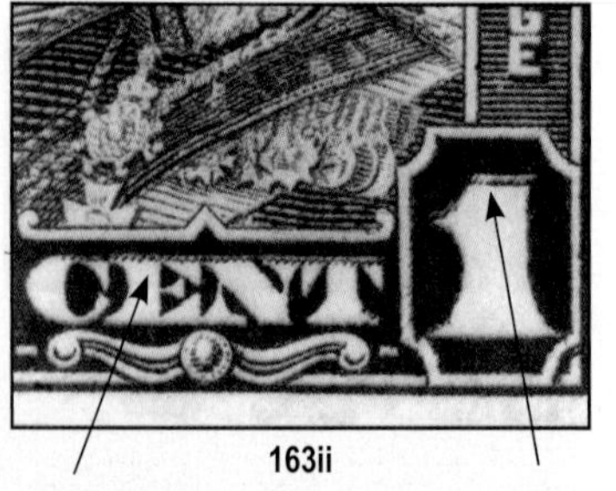

163ii

163iii



| | | NH% | ★VF | ★F | ⊙VF | ⊙F | FDC |
|---|---|---|---|---|---|---|---|
| **163** | **1¢ deep green**, Die II | 100 | 3.00 | 1.25 | .30 | .20 | 3.00† |
| d | imperf. pair, Die II, (est. 50 pairs) | 100 | 2,000.00 | 1,500.00 | — | — | — |
| xx | No. 163, Die II, precancelled [45 styles] | — | — | — | — | .25 | 5.00† |
| | plate blocks, plate 5, all blocks | 100 | 15.00 | 6.00 | | | |
| | plate 6, UL, LR | 100 | 20.00 | 10.00 | | | |
| | plate 6, UR | 100 | 24.00 | 12.00 | | | |
| | plate 6, LL | 100 | 120.00 | 60.00 | | | |
| | plate 7, UL | 100 | 20.00 | 10.00 | | | |
| | plate 7, UR, LL, LR | 100 | 24.00 | 12.00 | | | |
| | plate 8, UL | 100 | 28.00 | 14.00 | | | |
| | plate blocks, plate 8, UR, LL | 100 | 120.00 | 60.00 | | | |
| | plate 8, LR | 100 | 40.00 | 20.00 | | | |
| b | Die I, *Dec 6, 1930* | 100 | 3.00 | 1.25 | .30 | .20 | 300.00 |
| ii | major re-entry in right "1" (pos. 96, Pl. 2 UL), Die I | 100 | 80.00 | 30.00 | 50.00 | 20.00 | 60.00† |
| | 163ii in block with 3 normal | 100 | 90.00 | 35.00 | 75.00 | 35.00 | |
| iii | retouch to major re-entry (163ii) | | | | | | |
| xxi | No. 163b, Die I, precancelled [52 styles] | — | — | — | — | .25 | 5.00† |
| | plate blocks, plates 1, 2, all corners | 100 | 15.00 | 6.00 | | | |
| | plate 1, reversed 1, centre UL | 100 | 15.00 | 6.00 | | | |
| | plate 2, reversed 2, centre UL | 100 | 15.00 | 6.00 | | | |

Qty: 423,000,000

† Commercial cover.

163a

163c

163cii

| | | NH% | ★VF | ★F | ⊙VF | ⊙F |
|---|---|---|---|---|---|---|
| 163a | booklet pane of 4 x 1¢ deep green (163as) + 2 labels (BK19), *Nov 13, 1931* | 50 | 150.00 | 100.00 | 125.00 | 90.00 |
| as | single (Die II) with straight edge, from 163a | 50 | 5.00 | 3.00 | 4.00 | 2.00 |
| ai | 163a, with tab inscribed PLATE | 50 | 175.00 | 125.00 | 150.00 | 110.00 |
| aii | 163a, with tab inscribed NO. 1 | 50 | 175.00 | 125.00 | 150.00 | 110.00 |
| 163c | booklet pane of 6 x 1¢ (163cs), (BK14), *Jul 21, 1931* | 50 | 30.00 | 20.00 | 25.00 | 20.00 |
| cs | single (Die I) with straight edge, from 163c | 50 | 5.00 | 3.00 | 4.00 | 2.00 |
| ci | 163c, with tab inscribed PLATE | 50 | 100.00 | 75.00 | 75.00 | 50.00 |
| cii | 163c, with tab inscribed NO. 4 | 50 | 140.00 | 85.00 | 75.00 | 50.00 |

BK14 4 panes of 163c in cover; English (115,000) $250.00, French (10,000) $450.00

**NH% Premium**

Full "NH premium" only applies to stamps with pristine original gum in the state it left the printer – no gum disturbance at all. NH stamps with any disturbance will USUALLY sell for the listed "OG" price or perhaps a little more if the disturbance is very minor.

**Cover Prices**

Cover prices are for "fine" condition. VF condition covers and covers with interesting postal markings or attractive Advertising covers will sell for more ... sometimes much more.

**The Two dies of the 2¢**

**Die I (plates 1–6)**
The top of the letter P encloses a tiny dot of colour.

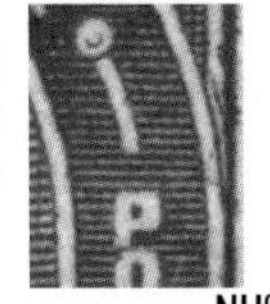

**Die II (plates 7–10)**
The top of the P encloses a larger spot of colour than in Die I. The P appears almost like a D. The curved line in the ball is longer than in Die I.

| | | NH% | ★VF | ★F | ⊙VF | ⊙F | FDC |
|---|---|---|---|---|---|---|---|
| **164** | **2¢ dull green**, Die I, *Jun 6, 1930* | 100 | 2.50 | 1.00 | .30 | .20 | 300.00 |
| i | imperf. pair (w/o gum) (Only 3 pairs known)‡ | — | *12,000.00* | — | — | — | — |
| ii | major re-entry in CANADA and CENTS (Pl. 3 UR, pos. 15) | | | | | | |
| xx | No. 164, precancelled [10 styles] | — | — | — | — | 2.00 | — |
| | plate blocks | 100 | 13.50 | 6.50 | | | |
| | plate 1, reversed 1, centre UL* | 100 | 80.00 | 40.00 | | | |
| | plate 2, reversed 2, centre UL | 100 | 80.00 | 40.00 | | | |
| | plate 3, UL, LL | 100 | 40.00 | 20.00 | | | |
| | plate 3, UR | 100 | 32.00 | 16.00 | | | |
| | plate 3, LR | 100 | 13.50 | 6.50 | | | |
| | plate 3, reversed 3, centre UL | 100 | 80.00 | 40.00 | | | |
| | plate 4, UL, UR | 100 | 120.00 | 60.00 | | | |
| | plate 4, LL | 100 | 40.00 | 20.00 | | | |
| | plate 4, LR | 100 | 13.50 | 6.50 | | | |
| | plate 4, reversed 4, centre UL | 100 | 80.00 | 40.00 | | | |
| | plate 5, LL | 100 | 100.00 | 50.00 | | | |
| | plate 5, centre UL with symbol left of PLATE | 100 | 35.00 | 20.00 | | | |
| | plate 5, centre LL, UR, LR | 100 | 15.00 | 7.50 | | | |
| | plate 6, LL | 100 | 150.00 | 75.00 | | | |
| | plate 6, centre UL with symbol left of PLATE | 100 | 35.00 | 20.00 | | | |
| | plate 6, centre LL, UR, LR | 100 | 20.00 | 10.00 | | | |

* reversed '1' appears alongside row 6, letter 'C' alongside row 7
Centre imprints are 6mm from adjacent stamps; corner imprints only 5mm
Qty: 319,000,000

164a

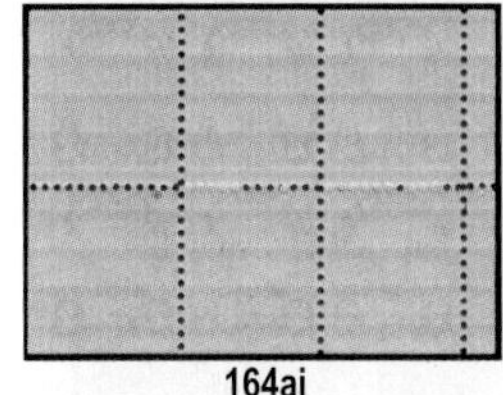

164ai

164aii

164aiii

| | | NH% | ★VF | ★F | ⊙VF | ⊙F |
|---|---|---|---|---|---|---|
| 164a | booklet pane of 6 x 2¢ dull green (164as), flat press (BK15), *Jun 17, 1930* | 50 | 45.00 | 30.00 | 45.00 | 30.00 |
| as | single (flat press) with straight edge, from 164a | 50 | 6.00 | 4.00 | 6.00 | 3.00 |
| ai | 164a, rotary press (BK15c) | 50 | 200.00 | 140.00 | 200.00 | 140.00 |
| ais | single (rotary press) with straight edge, from 164ai | 50 | 25.00 | 15.00 | 25.00 | 15.00 |
| aii | pane, with tab inscribed PLATE | 50 | 200.00 | 140.00 | 205.00 | 140.00 |
| aiii | pane with perforations at right only | 50 | 400.00 | 275.00 | 400.00 | 275.00 |
| aiv | pane with perforations at left and right | 50 | 600.00 | 400.00 | 500.00 | 300.00 |
| av | pane, with tab inscribed NO. 4 | 50 | 400.00 | 260.00 | 400.00 | 260.00 |
| avi | pane, with tab inscribed NO. 5 | 50 | 400.00 | 260.00 | 400.00 | 260.00 |
| avii | pane with perforations at left only | 50 | 400.00 | 275.00 | 400.00 | 260.00 |
| aviii | pane, with tab inscribed 1 (reversed) | 50 | 750.00 | 500.00 | 750.00 | 500.00 |
| aix | pane, with tab inscribed with partial 3 (inverted) | 50 | 750.00 | 500.00 | 750.00 | 500.00 |

**BK15** 2 panes of 164a in cover; English (1,016,000) $250.00, French (111,000) $500.00

NOTE: The PLATE and NO. inscriptions on the tabs of some booklet panes are poorly inked showing partially to completely albino impressions.

| | | NH% | ★VF | ★F | ⊙VF | ⊙F | FDC |
|---|---|---|---|---|---|---|---|
| **165** | **2¢ deep red**, Die I, *Nov 17, 1930* | 100 | 2.50 | 1.00 | .35 | .20 | 300.00 |
| ii | major re-entry in CANADA and CENTS (Pl. 3 UR, pos. 15) | | | | | | |
| xx | No, 165, Die I, precancelled [16 styles] | — | — | — | — | 1.00 | 3.00† |
| | plate 3 UL | 100 | 40.00 | 20.00 | | | |
| | plate 3 UR, LL | 100 | 20.00 | 10.00 | | | |
| | plate 3 LR | 100 | 13.50 | 6.50 | | | |
| | plate 3, reversed 3 centre UL | 100 | 15.00 | 7.50 | | | |
| | plate 4 UL | 100 | 20.00 | 10.00 | | | |
| | plate 4 UR, LL, LR | 100 | 13.50 | 6.50 | | | |
| | plate 4, reversed 4 centre UL | 100 | 15.00 | 7.50 | | | |
| | plate 5 UL | 100 | 13.50 | 6.50 | | | |
| | plate 5 UR, LR | 100 | 20.00 | 10.00 | | | |
| | plate 5 LL | 100 | 15.00 | 7.50 | | | |
| | plate 5 centre UL with symbol left of PLATE | 100 | 30.00 | 15.00 | | | |
| | plate 5 centre LL, UR, LR | 100 | 15.00 | 7.50 | | | |
| | plate 6 UL, LL | 100 | 13.50 | 6.50 | | | |
| | plate 6 UR, LR | 100 | 15.00 | 7.50 | | | |
| | plate 6 centre UL with symbol left of PLATE | 100 | 35.00 | 20.00 | | | |
| | plate 6 centre LL, UR, LR | 100 | 15.00 | 7.50 | | | |

Centre imprints are 6mm from adjacent stamps; corner imprints only 5mm
Qty: 431,000,000
† Commercial cover ‡ Probably printer's waste

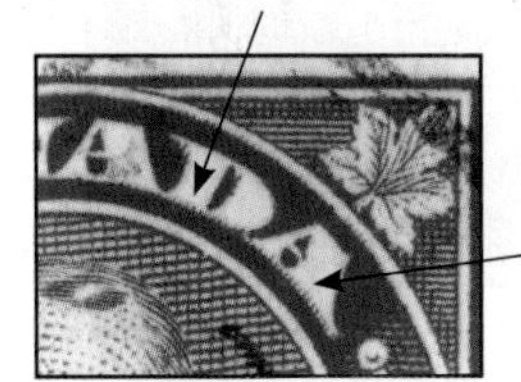

164ii/165ii

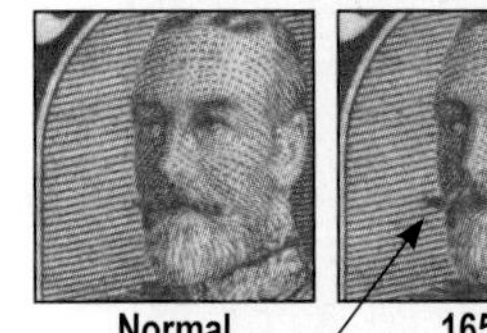

Normal 165ai

King George V — Arch

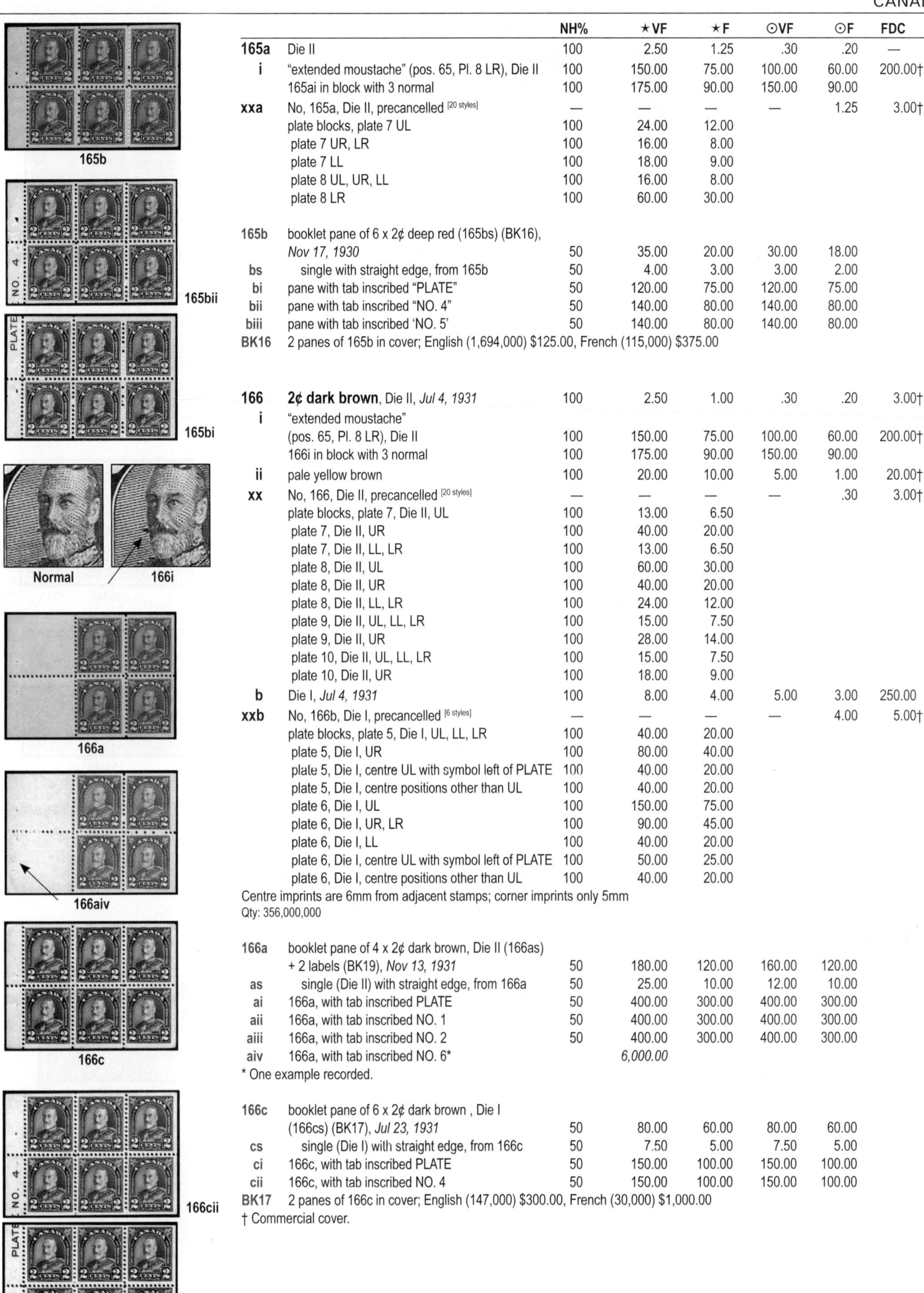

165b

165bii

165bi

Normal 166i

166a

166aiv

166c

166cii

166ci

King George V — Arch

| | | NH% | ★VF | ★F | ⊙VF | ⊙F | FDC |
|---|---|---|---|---|---|---|---|
| **165a** | Die II | 100 | 2.50 | 1.25 | .30 | .20 | — |
| i | "extended moustache" (pos. 65, Pl. 8 LR), Die II | 100 | 150.00 | 75.00 | 100.00 | 60.00 | 200.00† |
| | 165ai in block with 3 normal | 100 | 175.00 | 90.00 | 150.00 | 90.00 | |
| **xxa** | No, 165a, Die II, precancelled [20 styles] | — | — | — | — | 1.25 | 3.00† |
| | plate blocks, plate 7 UL | 100 | 24.00 | 12.00 | | | |
| | plate 7 UR, LR | 100 | 16.00 | 8.00 | | | |
| | plate 7 LL | 100 | 18.00 | 9.00 | | | |
| | plate 8 UL, UR, LL | 100 | 16.00 | 8.00 | | | |
| | plate 8 LR | 100 | 60.00 | 30.00 | | | |
| **165b** | booklet pane of 6 x 2¢ deep red (165bs) (BK16), *Nov 17, 1930* | 50 | 35.00 | 20.00 | 30.00 | 18.00 | |
| bs | single with straight edge, from 165b | 50 | 4.00 | 3.00 | 3.00 | 2.00 | |
| bi | pane with tab inscribed "PLATE" | 50 | 120.00 | 75.00 | 120.00 | 75.00 | |
| bii | pane with tab inscribed "NO. 4" | 50 | 140.00 | 80.00 | 140.00 | 80.00 | |
| biii | pane with tab inscribed 'NO. 5' | 50 | 140.00 | 80.00 | 140.00 | 80.00 | |
| **BK16** | 2 panes of 165b in cover; English (1,694,000) $125.00, French (115,000) $375.00 | | | | | | |
| **166** | **2¢ dark brown**, Die II, *Jul 4, 1931* | 100 | 2.50 | 1.00 | .30 | .20 | 3.00† |
| i | "extended moustache" (pos. 65, Pl. 8 LR), Die II | 100 | 150.00 | 75.00 | 100.00 | 60.00 | 200.00† |
| | 166i in block with 3 normal | 100 | 175.00 | 90.00 | 150.00 | 90.00 | |
| ii | pale yellow brown | 100 | 20.00 | 10.00 | 5.00 | 1.00 | 20.00† |
| **xx** | No, 166, Die II, precancelled [20 styles] | — | — | — | — | .30 | 3.00† |
| | plate blocks, plate 7, Die II, UL | 100 | 13.00 | 6.50 | | | |
| | plate 7, Die II, UR | 100 | 40.00 | 20.00 | | | |
| | plate 7, Die II, LL, LR | 100 | 13.00 | 6.50 | | | |
| | plate 8, Die II, UL | 100 | 60.00 | 30.00 | | | |
| | plate 8, Die II, UR | 100 | 40.00 | 20.00 | | | |
| | plate 8, Die II, LL, LR | 100 | 24.00 | 12.00 | | | |
| | plate 9, Die II, UL, LL, LR | 100 | 15.00 | 7.50 | | | |
| | plate 9, Die II, UR | 100 | 28.00 | 14.00 | | | |
| | plate 10, Die II, UL, LL, LR | 100 | 15.00 | 7.50 | | | |
| | plate 10, Die II, UR | 100 | 18.00 | 9.00 | | | |
| b | Die I, *Jul 4, 1931* | 100 | 8.00 | 4.00 | 5.00 | 3.00 | 250.00 |
| **xxb** | No, 166b, Die I, precancelled [6 styles] | — | — | — | — | 4.00 | 5.00† |
| | plate blocks, plate 5, Die I, UL, LL, LR | 100 | 40.00 | 20.00 | | | |
| | plate 5, Die I, UR | 100 | 80.00 | 40.00 | | | |
| | plate 5, Die I, centre UL with symbol left of PLATE | 100 | 40.00 | 20.00 | | | |
| | plate 5, Die I, centre positions other than UL | 100 | 40.00 | 20.00 | | | |
| | plate 6, Die I, UL | 100 | 150.00 | 75.00 | | | |
| | plate 6, Die I, UR, LR | 100 | 90.00 | 45.00 | | | |
| | plate 6, Die I, LL | 100 | 40.00 | 20.00 | | | |
| | plate 6, Die I, centre UL with symbol left of PLATE | 100 | 50.00 | 25.00 | | | |
| | plate 6, Die I, centre positions other than UL | 100 | 40.00 | 20.00 | | | |

Centre imprints are 6mm from adjacent stamps; corner imprints only 5mm

Qty: 356,000,000

| | | NH% | ★VF | ★F | ⊙VF | ⊙F | FDC |
|---|---|---|---|---|---|---|---|
| **166a** | booklet pane of 4 x 2¢ dark brown, Die II (166as) + 2 labels (BK19), *Nov 13, 1931* | 50 | 180.00 | 120.00 | 160.00 | 120.00 | |
| as | single (Die II) with straight edge, from 166a | 50 | 25.00 | 10.00 | 12.00 | 10.00 | |
| ai | 166a, with tab inscribed PLATE | 50 | 400.00 | 300.00 | 400.00 | 300.00 | |
| aii | 166a, with tab inscribed NO. 1 | 50 | 400.00 | 300.00 | 400.00 | 300.00 | |
| aiii | 166a, with tab inscribed NO. 2 | 50 | 400.00 | 300.00 | 400.00 | 300.00 | |
| aiv | 166a, with tab inscribed NO. 6* | | *6,000.00* | | | | |

* One example recorded.

| | | NH% | ★VF | ★F | ⊙VF | ⊙F | FDC |
|---|---|---|---|---|---|---|---|
| **166c** | booklet pane of 6 x 2¢ dark brown , Die I (166cs) (BK17), *Jul 23, 1931* | 50 | 80.00 | 60.00 | 80.00 | 60.00 | |
| cs | single (Die I) with straight edge, from 166c | 50 | 7.50 | 5.00 | 7.50 | 5.00 | |
| ci | 166c, with tab inscribed PLATE | 50 | 150.00 | 100.00 | 150.00 | 100.00 | |
| cii | 166c, with tab inscribed NO. 4 | 50 | 150.00 | 100.00 | 150.00 | 100.00 | |
| **BK17** | 2 panes of 166c in cover; English (147,000) $300.00, French (30,000) $1,000.00 | | | | | | |

† Commercial cover.

| | | NH% | ★VF | ★F | ⊙VF | ⊙F | FDC |
|---|---|---|---|---|---|---|---|
| **167** | **3¢ deep red**, *Jul 13, 1931* | 100 | 4.00 | 1.75 | .30 | .20 | 350.00 |
| **xx** | No, 167, precancelled [3 styles] | — | — | — | — | .50 | 3.00† |
| | plate blocks, plate 1, all blocks | 100 | 25.00 | 12.00 | | | |
| | plate 2, UL | 100 | 100.00 | 50.00 | | | |
| | plate 2, UR | 100 | 25.00 | 12.00 | | | |
| | plate 2, LL, LR | 100 | 130.00 | 65.00 | | | |
| | plate 3, UL, UR | 100 | 130.00 | 65.00 | | | |
| | plate 3, LL | 100 | 30.00 | 15.00 | | | |
| | plate 3, LR | 100 | 30.00 | 15.00 | | | |
| | plate 4, all blocks | 100 | 25.00 | 12.00 | | | |
| | plate 5, all blocks | 100 | 30.00 | 15.00 | | | |

Qty: 492,000,000

| | | NH% | ★VF | ★F | ⊙VF | ⊙F | FDC |
|---|---|---|---|---|---|---|---|
| **167a** | booklet pane of 4 x 3¢ deep red (167as) + 2 labels (BK18, 19), *Jul 13, 1931* | 50 | 55.00 | 35.00 | 45.00 | 35.00 | |
| as | single with straight edge, from 167a | 50 | 5.00 | 3.00 | 2.50 | 2.00 | |
| ai | pane with tab inscribed PLATE | 50 | 185.00 | 125.00 | 185.00 | 125.00 | |
| aii | pane with tab inscribed NO. 1 | 50 | 225.00 | 165.00 | 225.00 | 165.00 | |
| aiii | pane with tab inscribed NO. 2 | 50 | 225.00 | 165.00 | 225.00 | 165.00 | |

**BK18** 2 panes of 167a in cover; English (3,444,000) $150.00, French (250,000) $250.00

**BK19** 1 pane each of 163a, 166a, 167a in cover; English 11/13/31 (302,000) $600.00; French 11/13/31 (20,000) $1,200.00

167a

| | | NH% | ★VF | ★F | ⊙VF | ⊙F | FDC |
|---|---|---|---|---|---|---|---|
| **168** | **4¢ yellow bistre**, *Nov 5, 1930* | 100 | 25.00 | 7.50 | 10.00 | 4.00 | 350.00 |
| | plate blocks, plate 1, all corners | 100 | 125.00 | 50.00 | | | |
| | plate 1, reversed/inverted 1 at centre UL | 100 | 125.00 | 50.00 | | | |
| | plate 1, centre left or right (block of 8) | 100 | 200.00 | 90.00 | | | |
| | plate 2, UL, UR | 100 | 100.00 | 45.00 | | | |
| | plate 2, LL | 100 | 110.00 | 50.00 | | | |
| | plate 2, LR | 100 | 200.00 | 90.00 | | | |
| | plate 2, centre left or right | 100 | 110.00 | 50.00 | | | |

Qty: 11,100,000

Centre imprints are 6mm from adjacent stamps; corner imprints only 5mm.

| | | NH% | ★VF | ★F | ⊙VF | ⊙F | FDC |
|---|---|---|---|---|---|---|---|
| **169** | **5¢ dull violet**, rotary press, *Jun 18, 1930* | 100 | 10.00 | 4.00 | 7.00 | 3.00 | 325.00* |
| | plate blocks, plate 1, rotary press, UL, UR, LL | 100 | 50.00 | 25.00 | | | |
| | plate 1, rotary press, LR | 100 | 60.00 | 30.00 | | | |
| | plate 1, rotary press, reversed 1, centre UL | 100 | 180.00 | 90.00 | | | |
| | plate 2, rotary press, UL, UR | 100 | 60.00 | 30.00 | | | |
| | plate 2, rotary press, LL, LR | 100 | 100.00 | 50.00 | | | |
| | plate 2, rotary press, reversed 2, centre UL | 100 | 180.00 | 90.00 | | | |
| a | dull violet, flat plate printing | 100 | 15.00 | 6.00 | 7.00 | 3.00 | 350.00 |
| | plate blocks, plate 3, flat press, UL, UR, LR | 100 | 60.00 | 30.00 | | | |
| | plate 3, flat press, LL | 100 | 100.00 | 50.00 | | | |

Qty: 10,300,000

* Commercial cover $25.

| | | NH% | ★VF | ★F | ⊙VF | ⊙F | FDC |
|---|---|---|---|---|---|---|---|
| **170** | **5¢ dull blue**, *Nov 13, 1930* | 100 | 12.00 | 3.00 | 2.00 | .30 | 350.00 |
| | plate blocks, plate 3, UL, UR, LL | 100 | 50.00 | 20.00 | | | |
| | plate 3, LR | 100 | 75.00 | 30.00 | | | |
| i | milky blue | 100 | 40.00 | 15.00 | 3.00 | .50 | 18.00† |
| | plate 3, milky blue colour, UL, UR, LL | 100 | 160.00 | 60.00 | | | |
| | plate 3, milky blue colour, LR | 100 | 200.00 | 75.00 | | | |
| **xx** | No, 170, precancelled [2 styles] | — | — | — | — | 40.00 | |

Qty: 45,500,000

| | | NH% | ★VF | ★F | ⊙VF | ⊙F | FDC |
|---|---|---|---|---|---|---|---|
| **171** | **8¢ dark blue**, *Aug 13, 1930* | 100 | 40.00 | 15.00 | 18.00 | 7.50 | 400.00 |
| | plate blocks, plate 1, UL, UR | 100 | 180.00 | 90.00 | | | |

Qty: 888,000

No. 171, plate 1 was printed in sheets of 100 with UL and UR imprints but no lower imprints.

† Commercial cover.

| | | NH% | ★VF | ★F | ⊙VF | ⊙F | FDC |
|---|---|---|---|---|---|---|---|
| **172** | **8¢ red orange**, *Nov 5, 1930* | 100 | 12.00 | 4.00 | 7.50 | 3.50 | 400.00 |
| | plate blocks, plate 1, UL, UR | 100 | 70.00 | 35.00 | | | |
| | plate 2, UR | 100 | 70.00 | 35.00 | | | |
| | plate 3, UL | 100 | 90.00 | 45.00 | | | |
| | plate 3, UR, LL, LR | 100 | 70.00 | 35.00 | | | |

Qty: 5,912,000

No. 172, Plate 1 was printed in sheets of 100 with UL and UR imprints — but no lower imprints.

No. 172, Plate 2 was printed in sheets of 100 with an UR imprint only.

No. 172, Plate 3 was printed in sheets of 400 with imprints at the four corners, and cut into panes of 100 for sale to the public, each pane of 100 having only one imprint block.

Normal

173i

| | | NH% | ★VF | ★F | ⊙VF | ⊙F | FDC |
|---|---|---|---|---|---|---|---|
| **173** | **10¢ olive green**, *Sep 15, 1930* | 100 | 15.00 | 8.00 | 1.75 | .75 | 400.00 |
| **a** | imperf. pair, est. 50 pairs | 100 | 2,000.00 | 1,500.00 | — | — | — |
| **i** | "missing spire" | 100 | 60.00 | 30.00 | 35.00 | 20.00 | 35.00* |
| | "missing spire" in block of 4 with 3 normal stamps | 100 | 125.00 | 60.00 | 50.00 | 30.00 | 75.00* |
| **ii** | "broken spire" | 100 | 40.00 | 20.00 | 25.00 | 15.00 | 25.00* |
| | "broken spire" in block of 4 with 3 normal stamps | 100 | 100.00 | 50.00 | 40.00 | 20.00 | 50.00* |
| **iii** | double paper, in block | | 750.00 | 400.00 | | | |
| | plate blocks, plate 1, UL, UR, LR | 100 | 100.00 | 45.00 | | | |
| | plate 1, LL | 100 | 150.00 | 75.00 | | | |

Qty: 21,100,000

* Any cover.

A heavy numeral '1' can be found in the left margin just below the UL pane.

| | | NH% | ★VF | ★F | ⊙VF | ⊙F | FDC |
|---|---|---|---|---|---|---|---|
| **174** | **12¢ grey black**, *Dec 4, 1930* | 100 | 50.00 | 15.00 | 9.00 | 4.50 | 700.00 |
| **a** | imperf. pair, 75 pairs | 100 | 1,250.00 | | — | — | — |
| | plate blocks, plate 1, all blocks | 100 | 250.00 | 90.00 | | | |

Qty: 6,975,000

An additional column of perforations is occasionally found in the vertical margin of the 12¢, 20¢, and 50¢ values.

| | | NH% | ★VF | ★F | ⊙VF | ⊙F | FDC |
|---|---|---|---|---|---|---|---|
| **175** | **20¢ brown red**, *Dec 4, 1930* | 100 | 70.00 | 25.00 | 2.00 | .35 | 700.00 |
| **a** | imperf. pair, 75 pairs | 100 | 1,250.00 | | — | — | — |
| | plate blocks, plate 1, all blocks | 100 | 350.00 | 150.00 | | | |

Qty: 21,000,000

| | | NH% | ★VF | ★F | ⊙VF | ⊙F | FDC |
|---|---|---|---|---|---|---|---|
| **176** | **50¢ dull blue shade**, *Dec 4, 1930* | 100 | 300.00 | 150.00 | 20.00 | 10.00 | 1,600.00‡ |
| **a** | imperf. pair, 75 pairs | 100 | 1,250.00 | | — | — | — |
| **i** | pale blue shade | 100 | 300.00 | 150.00 | 20.00 | 10.00 | 1,500.00‡ |
| | plate blocks, plate 1, UL, UR | 100 | 1,800.00 | 900.00 | | | |
| | plate 1, LL, LR | 100 | 2,000.00 | 1,000.00 | | | |
| | plate 1, centre left or right | 100 | 1,500.00 | 800.00 | | | |

Qty: 2,811,000

Centre imprints are 3mm from adjacent stamps; corner imprints 5mm.

| | | NH% | ★VF | ★F | ⊙VF | ⊙F | FDC |
|---|---|---|---|---|---|---|---|
| **177** | **$1 dark olive green**, *Dec 4, 1930* | 100 | 300.00 | 150.00 | 40.00 | 20.00 | 1,600.00‡ |
| **a** | imperf. pair, 75 pairs | 100 | 1,250.00 | | — | — | — |
| | plate blocks, plate 1, UL, UR | 100 | 2,000.00 | 1,000.00 | | | |

Qty: 606,000

‡ Bulk payment receipts worth $200.

| | | NH% | ★VF | ★F | ⊙VF | ⊙F | FDC |
|---|---|---|---|---|---|---|---|
| **Nos. 162–177** (16) Set | | 100 | 850.00 | 387.75 | 119.80 | 55.30 | |

## KING GEORGE V "ARCH/LEAF" ISSUE COIL STAMPS

178 179 180 181 182 183

**1930–1931** **Engraved** **Perf 8½ vertical**

| | | NH% | ★VF | ★F | ⊙VF | ⊙F | ✉ |
|---|---|---|---|---|---|---|---|
| **178** | **1¢ orange** (162), *Sep 18, 1930* | 100 | 20.00 | 10.00 | 13.50 | 8.00 | 12.00* |
| | pair | 100 | 40.00 | 20.00 | 30.00 | 17.00 | 30.00* |
| | strip of 4 | 100 | 80.00 | 40.00 | 75.00 | 35.00 | |
| i | line pair | 100 | 70.00 | 35.00 | 35.00 | 25.00 | 40.00* |
| **xx** | No. 178, precancelled [1 style] | 100 | 12.00 | 6.00 | 3.00 | 1.50 | 6.00* |
| Qty: 2,000,000; precancelled: 4,350,000 | | | | | | | |
| **179** | **1¢ deep green** (163), *Feb 4, 1931* | 100 | 12.00 | 6.00 | 7.50 | 4.00 | 10.00 |
| | pair | 100 | 24.00 | 12.00 | 20.00 | 9.00 | 22.00* |
| | strip of 4 | 100 | 50.00 | 25.00 | 45.00 | 20.00 | 50.00* |
| i | line pair | 100 | 40.00 | 20.00 | 30.00 | 15.00 | 28.00 |
| **xx** | No. 179, precancelled [2 styles] | 100 | 6.00 | 3.00 | 1.00 | .50 | 5.00 |
| Qty: 16,427,000; precancelled: 11,130,000 | | | | | | | |
| **180** | **2¢ dull green** (164), *Jun 27, 1930* | 100 | 8.00 | 4.00 | 4.00 | 2.50 | 10.00 |
| | pair | 100 | 16.00 | 8.00 | 10.00 | 5.00 | 22.00* |
| | strip of 4 | 100 | 32.00 | 16.00 | 30.00 | 15.00 | 50.00 |
| i | line pair | 100 | 30.00 | 15.00 | 17.50 | 12.00 | 24.00 |
| ii | "Cockeyed King", single | 100 | 70.00 | 45.00 | 60.00 | 40.00 | 60.00 |
| iii | 180ii, in line pair with normal** | 100 | 100.00 | 50.00 | 90.00 | 45.00 | 90.00 |
| | 180ii, in line strip of 4, with 3 normal** | 100 | 125.00 | 65.00 | 125.00 | 60.00 | |
| Qty: 20,000,000 | | | | | | | |
| **181** | **2¢ deep red** (165), *Nov 19, 1930* | 100 | 35.00 | 17.50 | 3.50 | 2.00 | 10.00 |
| | pair | 100 | 70.00 | 35.00 | 8.00 | 4.50 | 22.00 |
| | strip of 4 | 100 | 140.00 | 70.00 | 30.00 | 15.00 | 40.00* |
| i | line pair | 100 | 100.00 | 50.00 | 20.00 | 10.00 | 24.00† |
| ii | "Cockeyed King", single | 100 | 80.00 | 50.00 | 70.00 | 50.00 | 70.00† |
| iii | 181ii, in line pair with normal** | 100 | 120.00 | 60.00 | 100.00 | 60.00 | 100.00† |
| | 181ii, in line strip of 4, with 3 normal** | 100 | 200.00 | 100.00 | 125.00 | 75.00 | |
| Qty: 24,880,000 | | | | | | | |
| **182** | **2¢ dark brown** (166), *Jul 4, 1931* | 100 | 20.00 | 10.00 | 1.00 | .50 | 10.00 |
| | pair | 100 | 40.00 | 20.00 | 3.00 | 1.25 | 24.00† |
| | strip of 4 | 100 | 80.00 | 40.00 | 10.00 | 5.00 | 40.00* |
| i | line pair | 100 | 50.00 | 25.00 | 8.00 | 5.00 | 30.00 |
| ii | "Cockeyed King", single | 100 | 75.00 | 50.00 | 60.00 | 50.00 | 60.00 |
| iii | 182ii, in line pair with normal** | 100 | 110.00 | 65.00 | 90.00 | 60.00 | 90.00 |
| | 182ii, in line strip of 4, with 3 normal** | 100 | 145.00 | 90.00 | 125.00 | 75.00 | |
| Qty: 25,255,000 | | | | | | | |
| **183** | **3¢ deep red** (167), *Jul 13, 1931* | 100 | 25.00 | 12.50 | 1.00 | .50 | 9.00 |
| | pair | 100 | 50.00 | 25.00 | 2.50 | 1.00 | 30.00† |
| | strip of 4 | 100 | 100.00 | 50.00 | 10.00 | 4.00 | 40.00 |
| i | line pair | 100 | 80.00 | 40.00 | 10.00 | 5.00 | 38.00† |
| Qty: 37,190,000 | | | | | | | |
| **Nos. 178-183** (6) Set | | 100 | 120.00 | 60.00 | 30.50 | 17.50 | |

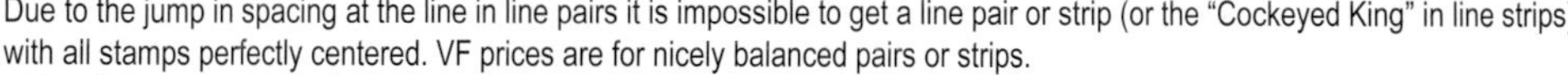

Due to the jump in spacing at the line in line pairs it is impossible to get a line pair or strip (or the "Cockeyed King" in line strips) with all stamps perfectly centered. VF prices are for nicely balanced pairs or strips.

* First flight covers are half of values shown, unless on scarce flight.

** The "Cockeyed King" variety occurs to the left of the line in line pairs and line strips of four.

† Commercial cover.

178i

180ii 180

180iii

**Start or End Strips**
2 stamps + 2 blank tabs
NH: +100%

| Sc# | ★VF | ★F |
|---|---|---|
| 178 | 120.00 | 100.00 |
| 179 | 100.00 | 60.00 |
| 180 | 100.00 | 60.00 |
| 181 | 200.00 | 100.00 |
| 182 | 125.00 | 75.00 |
| 183 | 150.00 | 90.00 |

Starts and ends come with up to 11 blank tabs. Full strips with 4 stamps plus full tabs are 3 times listed price.

**Paste-up repair pairs** exist for all values. Price 4x a normal pair.

184

190

191

## KING GEORGE V "ADMIRAL" PROVISIONAL

Canadian Bank Note Company, Limited

**1931, Jun 24** **Engraved** **Perf 12x8**

| | | NH% | ★VF | ★F | ⊙VF | ⊙F | FDC |
|---|---|---|---|---|---|---|---|
| **184** | **3¢ carmine** | 200 | 12.00 | 4.00 | 6.00 | 2.50 | 900.00 |
| | plate blocks, plates A13–A15, UL, UR , block of 8 | 100 | 120.00 | 60.00 | | | |

Qty: 10,000,000

All perf 12x8 3¢ carmine stamps (184) are Die II. For perf. 12, see Sc. 109.

Nos. 185–189 are not assigned.

## GEORGE-ÉTIENNE CARTIER

Based on a photograph by William Notman.

British American Bank Note Company

**1931, Sep 30** **Engraved, panes of 100** **Perf 11**

| | | NH% | ★VF | ★F | ⊙VF | ⊙F | FDC |
|---|---|---|---|---|---|---|---|
| **190** | **10¢ dark green** | 200 | 20.00 | 8.00 | .25 | .20 | 900.00 |
| a | imperf. pair, 150 pairs | 100 | 650.00 | 400.00 | | | |
| | plate blocks, plate 1, all blocks, blocks of 4 | 100 | 100.00 | 50.00 | | | |
| | plates 2, 3, UR, LR, blocks of 4 | 100 | 350.00 | 175.00 | | | |

Qty: 64,300,000

This stamp was issued as a definitive to replace the 10¢ Library of Parliament in the 'Leaf' or 'Arch' issue.



## KING GEORGE V "ARCH/LEAF" PROVISIONAL

**1932, Jun 21** **Engraved** **Perf 11**

| | | NH% | ★VF | ★F | ⊙VF | ⊙F | FDC |
|---|---|---|---|---|---|---|---|
| **191** | **3¢ on 2¢ deep red**, Die II | 50 | 2.00 | 1.00 | .25 | .20 | 25.00 |
| i | "extended moustache" variety, | | | | | | |
| | Die II (Pl. 8 LR, pos. 65) | 100 | 150.00 | 75.00 | 100.00 | 60.00 | 125.00† |
| | 191i, in block of 4 with 3 normal | 100 | 175.00 | 90.00 | 150.00 | 90.00 | — |
| | plates 7, 8, Die II, all blocks | 50 | 10.00 | 5.00 | | | |
| ii | shifted surcharge* | 50 | 150.00 | 100.00 | | | — |
| iii | period after '3' (UR, pos. 87), Die II | 50 | 60.00 | 35.00 | | | |
| a | Die I | 50 | 4.00 | 2.00 | 2.50 | 1.25 | 500.00** |
| ai | top bar at right bent down (LR, pos. 54) | 50 | | | | | |
| aii | shifted surcharge* | 50 | 150.00 | 100.00 | | | — |
| | plate blocks, plate 3, Die I, UL | 50 | 80.00 | 40.00 | | | |
| | plate 3, Die I, UR, LL | 50 | 20.00 | 10.00 | | | |
| | plate 3, Die I, LR | 50 | 30.00 | 15.00 | | | |
| | plate 3, Die I, reversed 3, centre UL | 50 | 30.00 | 15.00 | | | |
| | plate 4, Die I, UL | 50 | 50.00 | 25.00 | | | |
| | plate 4, Die I, UR, LR | 50 | 40.00 | 20.00 | | | |
| | plate 4, Die I, LL | 50 | 20.00 | 10.00 | | | |
| | plate 4, Die I, reversed 4, centre UL | 50 | 30.00 | 15.00 | | | |
| | plate 5, Die I, UL | 50 | 65.00 | 32.50 | | | |
| | plate 5, Die I, UR, LL | 50 | 20.00 | 10.00 | | | |
| | plate 5, Die I, LR | 50 | 20.00 | 10.00 | | | |
| | plate 5, Die I, centre UL with symbol left of PLATE | 50 | 30.00 | 15.00 | | | |
| | plate 5, Die I, centre positions other than UL | 50 | 20.00 | 10.00 | | | |
| | plate 6, Die I, UL | 50 | 200.00 | 100.00 | | | |
| | plate 6, Die I, UR | 50 | 20.00 | 10.00 | | | |
| | plate 6, Die I, LL, LR | 50 | 50.00 | 25.00 | | | |
| | plate 6, Die I, centre UL with symbol left of PLATE | 50 | 30.00 | 15.00 | | | |
| | plate 6, Die I, centre positions other than UL | 50 | 25.00 | 12.50 | | | |

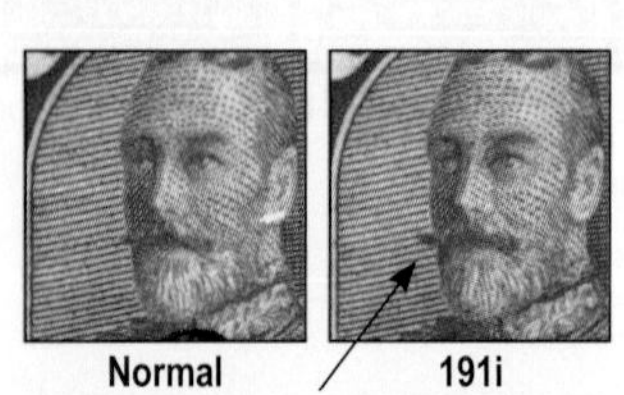
Normal 191i

191iii

191ai

191ii / 191aii

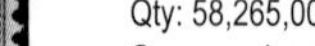

Qty: 58,265,000

See number 165 for description of dies.

* The position of the shifted surcharge varies from the middle to the top of the stamp.

** ERD: commercial cover from Woodstock, Ont. Nov 2/32. No Die 1 stamps were cancelled on June 21, 1932, the official release date for the 3 cent surcharge.

† Commercial cover.

## IMPERIAL ECONOMIC CONFERENCE

192
King George V

193
Prince of Wales

194
Britannia

See also C4

3¢: Based on a sculpture by Edgar Bertram Mackennal. 5¢: Based on a photograph by C. Vandyk.
British American Bank Note Company

| 1932, Jul 12 | | Engraved NH% | ★VF | ★F | ⊙VF | ⊙F | Perf 11 FDC |
|---|---|---|---|---|---|---|---|
| 192 | **3¢ deep red** | 100 | 2.00 | .75 | .25 | .20 | 12.00 |
| i | broken E (Pl. 2 LR, pos. 87) | 100 | 80.00 | 35.00 | 50.00 | 25.00 | 60.00‡ |
| | 192i in block of 4 with 3 normal | 100 | 120.00 | 40.00 | 60.00 | 30.00 | |
| | 192i in Pl. 2 LR, block of 8 | 100 | 150.00 | 60.00 | 100.00 | 60.00 | |
| | plates 1, 2, all blocks | 100 | 8.00 | 4.50 | | | |

Qty: 100,700,000
‡ Any cover, not FDC.

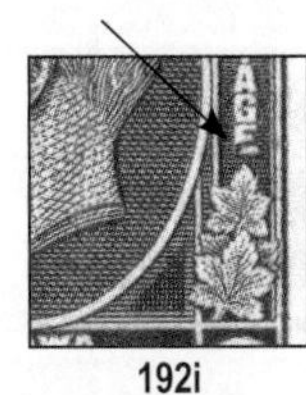
192i

| | | NH% | ★VF | ★F | ⊙VF | ⊙F | FDC |
|---|---|---|---|---|---|---|---|
| 193 | **5¢ dull blue** | 100 | 10.00 | 5.00 | 4.00 | 2.00 | 16.00 |
| | plate blocks, plate 1, UL | 100 | 75.00 | 50.00 | | | |
| | plate 1, UR, LL, LR | 100 | 70.00 | 35.00 | | | |

Qty: 8,300,000

| | | NH% | ★VF | ★F | ⊙VF | ⊙F | FDC |
|---|---|---|---|---|---|---|---|
| 194 | **13¢ deep green** | 100 | 14.00 | 6.00 | 9.00 | 4.50 | 30.00 |
| | plate blocks, plates 1, 2, UL, UR | 100 | 120.00 | 60.00 | | | |

Qty: 2,000,000

| | | NH% | ★VF | ★F | ⊙VF | ⊙F | FDC |
|---|---|---|---|---|---|---|---|
| **Nos. 192–194** (3) Set | | 100 | 26.00 | 11.75 | 13.25 | 6.70 | 45.00 |

Plate block values are for FINE centred, lightly hinged plate blocks of 4.

Issued to commemorate the Imperial Economic Conference held in Ottawa. See also No. C4.



## KING GEORGE V "MEDALLION" ISSUE

195 196 197 198
199 200 201
Quebec Citadel

**Rates:**

Domestic: 3¢ per oz.
Local: 2¢ per oz. (0–1 oz.)
3¢ per oz. (1–2 oz.)
Postcard: 2¢
Printed matter: 1¢ per 4 oz.
USA: 3¢ per oz.
UK: 3¢ per oz.
Non-UK: 5¢ per oz.
Airmail: 6¢ (from Aug 24/28)
Registration: 10¢
Special delivery: 20¢

1¢–8¢: Based on a sculpture by Edgar Bertram Mackennal.
British American Bank Note Company

195a

195b

195bi

195biii

196a

196b

196bi

**1932, Dec 1** — **Engraved** — **Perf 11**

| No. | Description | NH% | ★VF | ★F | ⊙VF | ⊙F | FDC |
|---|---|---|---|---|---|---|---|
| **195** | **1¢ dark green**, rotary press, wet printing | 100 | 2.00 | .75 | .25 | .20 | 20.00 |
| c | imperf. pair, rotary press, 150 pairs | 100 | 350.00 | 200.00 | — | — | — |
| xx | No. 195, precancelled [70 styles] | — | — | — | — | .20 | 3.00‡ |
| | plate blocks, rotary press, plates 1–3, all blocks | 100 | 9.00 | 6.00 | | | |
| | plate 4, UL, LL, LR | 100 | 10.00 | 5.00 | | | |
| | plate 4, UR | 100 | 18.00 | 12.00 | | | |
| | plates 5, 6, all blocks | 100 | 10.00 | 5.00 | | | |
| d | rotary press, dry printing | 100 | 6.00 | 2.00 | .25 | .20 | |
| | plate blocks, flat press, plates 1–3, all blocks | 100 | 25.00 | 10.00 | | | |

Qty: 527,450,000

Unused examples of 195 will show gum ridges about 5mm apart. The gum on No. 195d is flat.

| No. | Description | NH% | ★VF | ★F | ⊙VF | ⊙F | FDC |
|---|---|---|---|---|---|---|---|
| 195a | booklet pane of 4 x 1¢ (195as) + 2 labels (BK23), *Sep 19, 1933* | 100 | 125.00 | 70.00 | 120.00 | 70.00 | |
| as | single with straight edge, from 195a or 195b | 50 | 7.00 | 4.00 | 1.50 | .75 | |
| ai | 195a, tab inscribed PLATE | 100 | 200.00 | 110.00 | 180.00 | 110.00 | |
| aii | 195a, tab inscribed NO. 1 | 100 | 200.00 | 110.00 | 180.00 | 110.00 | |
| 195b | booklet pane of 6 x 1¢ (195as) (BK20), *Dec 28, 1933* | 100 | 75.00 | 35.00 | 65.00 | 35.00 | |
| bi | 195b, tab inscribed PLATE | 100 | 150.00 | 90.00 | 125.00 | 90.00 | |
| biii | 195b, tab inscribed NO. 2 | 100 | 150.00 | 90.00 | 125.00 | 90.00 | |

BK20 4 panes of 195b in cover; English (27,087) $325.00, French 3/26/34 (15,461) $520.00

‡ Any cover, not FDC

| No. | Description | NH% | ★VF | ★F | ⊙VF | ⊙F | FDC |
|---|---|---|---|---|---|---|---|
| **196** | **2¢ black brown** | 100 | 2.00 | .90 | .25 | .20 | 20.00 |
| c | imperf. pair, 150 pairs | 100 | 350.00 | 200.00 | — | — | — |
| xx | No. 196, precancelled [29 styles] | — | — | — | — | .25 | 3.00‡ |
| | plate blocks, plates 1–3, all blocks | 100 | 10.00 | 5.00 | | | |

Qty: 514,300,000

| No. | Description | NH% | ★VF | ★F | ⊙VF | ⊙F | FDC |
|---|---|---|---|---|---|---|---|
| 196a | booklet pane of 4 x 2¢ (196as) + 2 labels (BK23), *Sep 19, 1933* | 100 | 160.00 | 100.00 | 150.00 | 100.00 | |
| as | single with straight edge, from 196a or 196b | 50 | 7.00 | 4.00 | 1.50 | .75 | |
| ai | 196a, with tab inscribed PLATE | 100 | 275.00 | 150.00 | 250.00 | 150.00 | |
| aii | 196a, with tab inscribed NO. 1 | 100 | 275.00 | 150.00 | 250.00 | 150.00 | |
| 196b | booklet pane of 6 x 2¢ (196as) (BK21), *Sep 7, 1933* | 100 | 120.00 | 75.00 | 100.00 | 75.00 | |
| bi | 196b, tab inscribed PLATE | 100 | 200.00 | 125.00 | 200.00 | 125.00 | |
| bii | 196b, tab inscribed NO. 1 * | | | | | | |
| biii | 196b, tab inscribed NO. 2 | 100 | 225.00 | 125.00 | 200.00 | 125.00 | |

BK21 2 panes of 196b in cover; English (103,000) $500.00, French (10,284) $1,000.00

* Confirmation of this item is requested.

**Die I**
Top point of 3 even with line

**Die II**
Top point of 3 above line

| No. | Description | NH% | ★VF | ★F | ⊙VF | ⊙F | FDC |
|---|---|---|---|---|---|---|---|
| **197** | **3¢ deep red**, Die I | 100 | 2.00 | 1.25 | .25 | .20 | 2.00† |
| b | imperf. pair, Die I, rotary, 150 pairs | 100 | 350.00 | 200.00 | — | — | — |
| xx | No. 197, Die I, precancelled [2 styles] | — | — | — | — | 15.00 | 20.00‡ |
| | plates blocks, plates 1, 2, Die I, all blocks | 100 | 20.00 | 10.00 | | | |
| c | Die II | 100 | 2.00 | 1.25 | .25 | .20 | 20.00 |
| e | deep brown red, imperf., flat press, Die II* | 50 | *5,000.00* | | | | |
| xxc | No. 197c, Die II, precancelled [7 styles] | — | — | — | — | .50 | 3.00‡ |
| | plates blocks, plate 3, Die II, UL | 100 | 20.00 | 10.00 | | | |
| | plate 3, Die II, UR, LL, LR | 100 | 15.00 | 7.50 | | | |
| | plate 4, Die II, all blocks | 100 | 20.00 | 10.00 | | | |
| | plate 5, Die II, all blocks | 100 | 20.00 | 10.00 | | | |
| | plate 6, Die II, all blocks | 100 | 15.00 | 7.50 | | | |
| | plates 7, 8, Die II, all blocks | 100 | 225.00 | 150.00 | | | |
| | blocks, plates 9, 10, Die II, all blocks | 100 | 12.00 | 6.00 | | | |
| | blocks, plates 11, 12, Die II, UL, LL | 100 | 20.00 | 10.00 | | | |
| | blocks, plates 11, 12, Die II, UR | 100 | 70.00 | 35.00 | | | |
| | blocks, plates 11, 12, Die II, LR | 100 | 18.00 | 9.00 | | | |

Qty: 1,162,700,000

* Only one block of four is known. † Commercial cover. ‡ Any cover, not FDC.

| | | NH% | ★VF | ★F | ⊙VF | ⊙F | FDC |
|---|---|---|---|---|---|---|---|
| 197d | booklet pane of 4 x 3¢ (197ds) + 2 labels, Die II (BK22) | 100 | 60.00 | 35.00 | 50.00 | 35.00 | |
| ds | single (Die II) with straight edge, from 197d | 50 | 5.00 | 3.50 | 1.00 | .75 | |
| di | 197d, tab inscribed PLATE | 100 | 150.00 | 90.00 | 125.00 | 90.00 | |
| dii | 197d, tab inscribed NO. 1 | 100 | 160.00 | 100.00 | 140.00 | 100.00 | |
| diii | 197d, tab inscribed NO. 2 | 100 | 160.00 | 100.00 | 140.00 | 100.00 | |

BK22 2 panes of 197d in cover; English 11/13/33 (2,424,000) $170.00, French 8/22/33 (216,000) $300.00
BK23 1 pane each of 195a, 196a, 197d in cover; English (125,000) $350.00, French 12/05/33 (40,292) $500.00
Gum shades vary from white to brown.

197d

197dii

| | | NH% | ★VF | ★F | ⊙VF | ⊙F | FDC |
|---|---|---|---|---|---|---|---|
| **198** | **4¢ ochre** | 100 | 75.00 | 35.00 | 9.00 | 4.50 | 30.00† |
| a | imperf. pair, 150 pairs | 100 | 350.00 | 200.00 | — | — | — |
| i | brownish ochre shade | 100 | 80.00 | 37.50 | 10.00 | 5.00 | 35.00† |
| | plate blocks, plates 1, 2, UL, LL | 100 | 400.00 | 175.00 | | | |
| | blank corner block, UR, LR | 100 | 400.00 | 175.00 | | | |

Qty: 7,017,000
† Single commercial usage $40.

| | | NH% | ★VF | ★F | ⊙VF | ⊙F | FDC |
|---|---|---|---|---|---|---|---|
| **199** | **5¢ dark blue** | 100 | 18.50 | 6.00 | .75 | .20 | 30.00 |
| a | horiz. pair, imperf. vert., 50 pairs exist | 75 | 2,000.00 | 1,250.00 | — | — | — |
| b | imperf. pair, 150 pairs | 100 | 350.00 | 200.00 | — | — | — |
| i | major re-entry (Pl. 1 UL, pos. 10) | 100 | 75.00 | 50.00 | 60.00 | 40.00 | 60.00‡ |
| | 199i, in block with 3 normal | 100 | 150.00 | 100.00 | 100.00 | 70.00 | |
| iii | retouched major re-entry (Pl. 1 UL, pos. 10) | 100 | 75.00 | 50.00 | 60.00 | 40.00 | 60.00‡ |
| ii | "blue nose" re-entry (Pl. 2 UL, pos. 79) | 100 | 75.00 | 50.00 | 50.00 | 30.00 | 50.00‡ |
| | 199ii, in block with 3 normal | 100 | 150.00 | 100.00 | 90.00 | 60.00 | |
| iv | retouched "blue nose" re-entry (Pl. 2 UL, pos. 79) | 100 | 75.00 | 50.00 | 50.00 | 30.00 | 50.00‡ |
| xx | No. 199, precancelled [1 style] | — | — | — | — | 50.00 | |
| | plate blocks, plates 1, 2, UL, LL | 100 | 100.00 | 45.00 | | | |
| | blank corner block, UR, LR | 100 | 90.00 | 40.00 | | | |

Qty: 54,500,000
‡ Any cover, not FDC.
Both re-entries (199i, 199ii) were retouched (199iii, 199iv) to remove these varieties, but elements remain that allow identification.

199i

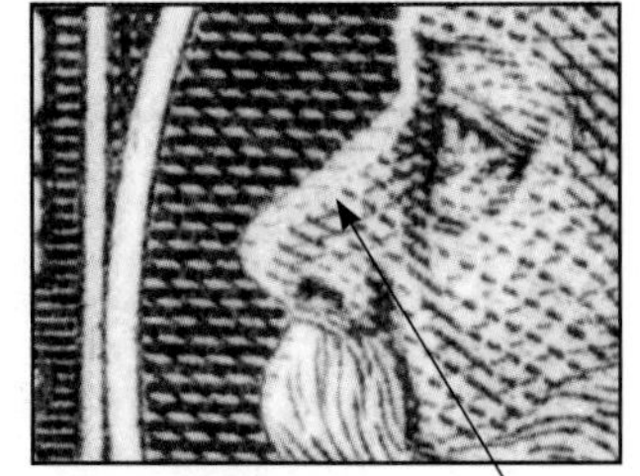
199ii
Shift results in a doubling of the horizontal lines on the King's nose

| | | NH% | ★VF | ★F | ⊙VF | ⊙F | FDC |
|---|---|---|---|---|---|---|---|
| **200** | **8¢ red orange** | 100 | 50.00 | 25.00 | 5.00 | 3.00 | 35.00† |
| a | imperf. pair, 150 pairs | 100 | 350.00 | 200.00 | — | — | — |
| | plate blocks, plates 1, 2, UR, LR | 100 | 350.00 | 125.00 | | | |
| | blank corner block, UL, LL | 100 | 350.00 | 125.00 | | | |

Qty: 4,465,000
† Price shown is for FDC; value for a commercial cover, used in period, single usage $100.00.

| | | NH% | ★VF | ★F | ⊙VF | ⊙F | FDC |
|---|---|---|---|---|---|---|---|
| **201** | **13¢ dull violet** | 100 | 60.00 | 30.00 | 5.00 | 2.50 | 45.00 |
| a | imperf. pair, 100 pairs | 75 | 1,000.00 | 700.00 | — | — | — |
| i | red violet | 100 | 80.00 | 35.00 | 6.00 | 3.00 | 45.00 |
| | plate blocks, plates 1, 2, UL, UR | 100 | 325.00 | 150.00 | | | |
| | blank corner block, UR, LR | 100 | 300.00 | 120.00 | | | |

Qty: 5,017,000

| | NH% | ★VF | ★F | ⊙VF | ⊙F | FDC |
|---|---|---|---|---|---|---|
| **Nos. 195–201** (7) Set | 100 | 200.00 | 98.85 | 20.30 | 10.80 | 50.00* |
| **Nos. 195c–200a** Set of 6 imperf. pairs | 100 | 2,100.00 | 1,200.00 | — | — | — |
| **Nos. 195c–200a** Set of 6 imperf. plate blocks of 4 ** | | 9,000.00 | | | | |

* Value shown is for large (#10) envelope. Value on small (#8) envelope is $65.00.
** 3 sets of VF LH recorded by editors.

202
Parliament Buildings

203
Harvesting Wheat Overprint

## UPU MEETING

202i

British American Bank Note Company

1933, May 18 — Engraved — Perf 11

| | | NH% | ★VF | ★F | ⊙VF | ⊙F | FDC |
|---|---|---|---|---|---|---|---|
| **202** | **5¢ dark blue** | 100 | 16.00 | 6.00 | 4.50 | 2.50 | 35.00 |
| a | imperf. pair, 75 pairs | 100 | 800.00 | — | — | — | — |
| | plate blocks, plates 1, 2, UL, UR | 100 | 75.00 | 50.00 | | | |
| | blank corner blocks from plates 1, 2, LL, LR* | 100 | 75.00 | 35.00 | | | |
| i | "line in 5" variety (pos. 20) | 100 | 30.00 | 20.00 | 20.00 | 12.50 | |
| | as "i", Plate 1, UR plate block | 100 | 100.00 | 75.00 | | | |

Qty: 5,100,000

* Printed in sheets of 100 with imprints at UL and UR only, lower corners are blank.

Imperf plate block (3 known): 202a XF LH/NH $3,800.; 202ai UR $4,000.

Issued to commemorate the Universal Postal Union Executive Committee meeting in Ottawa.

## GRAIN EXHIBITION

203i

British American Bank Note Company

1933, Jul 24 — Engraved — Perf 11

| | | NH% | ★VF | ★F | ⊙VF | ⊙F | FDC |
|---|---|---|---|---|---|---|---|
| **203** | **20¢ brown red** | 100 | 60.00 | 25.00 | 20.00 | 10.00 | 75.00 |
| a | imperf. pair, 75 pairs† | 100 | 800.00 | — | — | — | — |
| i | broken X variety (pos. 19) | 100 | 150.00 | 75.00 | 80.00 | 40.00 | 100.00 |
| | 203i, in block with 3 normal | 100 | 350.00 | 175.00 | 250.00 | 150.00 | |
| ii | as i, imperf. pair (3 known, 2 are NH) | 100 | *10,000.00* | — | — | — | — |
| | plate blocks, plate 1, all blocks | 100 | 300.00 | 200.00 | | | |
| | plate 1, broken X, UR vert. block of 8 | 100 | 600.00 | 400.00 | | | |

Qty: 1,560,000

† Three imperf. pairs exist with variety 203i (broken X) on one stamp.

Printed in sheets of 200 and cut into 4 panes of 50 (1 imprint/pane).

Imperf plate block (3 known): LR XF NH $6,000.

Issued to commemorate the World's Grain Exhibition and Conference, Regina.

## ROYAL WILLIAM

204
Royal William

Designed and engraved by Bruce Hay. Based on a painting by Stephan D. Skillet.

British American Bank Note Company

1933, Aug 17 — Engraved — Perf 11

| | | NH% | ★VF | ★F | ⊙VF | ⊙F | FDC |
|---|---|---|---|---|---|---|---|
| **204** | **5¢ dark blue** | 100 | 16.00 | 6.00 | 4.50 | 2.50 | 35.00 |
| a | imperf. pair, 75 pairs | 100 | 800.00 | — | — | — | — |
| | plate blocks, plates 1, 2, UL, UR | 100 | 75.00 | 50.00 | | | |
| | corner blocks, plate 1, 2, LL, LR* | 100 | 75.00 | 35.00 | | | |

Qty: 4,854,000

* Printed in sheets of 100 with imprints at UL and UR only, lower corners are blank.

Imperf plate block (3 known): XF LH/NH $3,800.; UR no gum $2,000.

Issued to commemorate the 100th anniversary of the trans-Atlantic crossing of the Royal William entirely by steam.

## KING GEORGE V "MEDALLION" COIL STAMPS

205

206

207

| 1933 | | Engraved NH% | ★VF | ★F | ⊙VF | Perf 8½ vertical ⊙F | FDC |
|---|---|---|---|---|---|---|---|
| 205 | **1¢ dark green** (195), *Nov 3, 1933* | 75 | 20.00 | 12.00 | 4.00 | 2.00 | 10.00* |
| | pair | 75 | 40.00 | 24.00 | 8.00 | 4.00 | 20.00*† |
| | strip of 4 | 75 | 80.00 | 48.00 | 25.00 | 12.50 | 40.00*† |
| i | line pair | 75 | 50.00 | 30.00 | 10.00 | 6.00 | 24.00* |
| xx | No. 205, precancelled [2 styles] | 75 | 12.00 | 7.00 | 1.50 | .40 | 5.00 |
| Qty: 13,573,000 | | | | | | | |
| 206 | **2¢ black brown** (196), *Aug 15, 1933* | 75 | 25.00 | 14.00 | 1.50 | .75 | 12.00* |
| | pair | 75 | 50.00 | 28.00 | 3.00 | 1.50 | 25.00*† |
| | strip of 4 | 75 | 100.00 | 56.00 | 10.00 | 5.00 | 50.00*† |
| i | line pair | 75 | 60.00 | 40.00 | 7.50 | 4.50 | 30.00* |
| Qty: 19,265,000 | | | | | | | |
| 207 | **3¢ deep red** (197), *Aug 16, 1933* | 75 | 25.00 | 12.00 | .50 | .30 | 10.00* |
| | pair | 75 | 50.00 | 24.00 | 1.50 | .75 | 25.00*† |
| | strip of 4 | 75 | 100.00 | 48.00 | 6.00 | 3.00 | 60.00*† |
| i | line pair | 75 | 60.00 | 35.00 | 4.00 | 2.00 | 30.00*† |
| Qty: 28,310,000 | | | | | | | |

* Value shown is for any cover, not FDC.
† First flight covers are one third of value shown.

| **Nos. 205–207** (3) Set | 75 | 70.00 | 40.00 | 6.00 | 3.05 |
|---|---|---|---|---|---|

**Start or End Strips**
2 stamps + 2 blank tabs
NH: +75%

| Sc# | ★VF | ★F |
|---|---|---|
| 205 | 150.00 | 100.00 |
| 206 | 200.00 | 120.00 |
| 207 | 150.00 | 100.00 |

These starts and ends are scarce; full strips are rare and worth much more.

207i

## JACQUES CARTIER

208
Jacques Cartier

Designer: George Arthur Gundersen. Picture engraved by Bruce Hay.
British American Bank Note Company

| 1934, Jul 1 | | Engraved NH% | ★VF | ★F | ⊙VF | ⊙F | Perf 11 FDC |
|---|---|---|---|---|---|---|---|
| 208 | **3¢ blue** | 100 | 6.00 | 3.00 | 2.00 | 1.00 | 25.00 |
| a | imperf. pair, 125 pairs | 100 | 800.00 | — | — | — | — |
| i | 'burr on shoulder' (Pl. 2 R, pos. 2) | 100 | 150.00 | 75.00 | 90.00 | 60.00 | 175.00* |
| | 208i, in block with 3 normal | 100 | 200.00 | 100.00 | 160.00 | 110.00 | |
| | 208i, in wide gutter block of 8 (UR stamp)† | 100 | 1,000.00 | 700.00 | — | — | |
| | 208i, in wide gutter strip of 4 (right stamp) | 100 | 600.00 | 400.00 | — | — | |
| ii | 'scarface' (Pl. 2 R, pos. 97) | 100 | 150.00 | 75.00 | 90.00 | 60.00 | 175.00* |
| | 208ii, in block with 3 normal | 100 | 200.00 | 100.00 | 160.00 | 110.00 | |
| | 208ii, Pl. 2 LR, in block of 8 with 7 normal | 100 | 300.00 | 175.00 | — | — | |
| iii | 'hairline from hand' (Pl. 1 R, pos. 89) | 100 | 150.00 | 75.00 | 50.00 | 35.00 | 75.00* |
| | 208iii, Pl. 1 LR, in block of 4 with 3 normal | 100 | 175.00 | 100.00 | | | |
| iv | wide gutter strip of 4 | 100 | 400.00 | 300.00 | | | |
| | plate blocks, plates 1, 2, all blocks | 100 | 40.00 | 20.00 | | | |

Qty: 12,370,000
† The burr variety exists in the wide gutter top margin strip of four (or block of eight) from Plate 2 (not from Plate 1). Approximately 20–25 examples should exist.
* Price shown is for single on any cover, not FDC. 208i or 208ii on FDC, value $1,500.
The wide gutter at the centre of the printer's sheet of 200 was intended to provide space to guillotine the sheet into 2 panes of 100. Later it was decided to simply perforate this gutter. Approximately 50 wide gutter sheets were sold intact.
Imperf plate block (5 recorded): $4,000.
Issued to commemorate the 400th anniversary of Jacques Cartier's first voyage of discovery to Canada.

208i

208ii

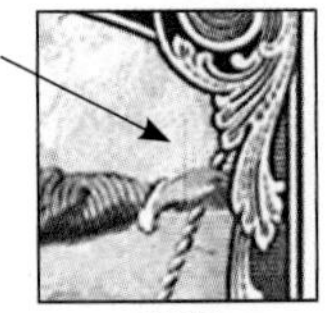
208iii

209
Loyalists Statue

210
New Brunswick Seal

## LOYALISTS

Designer: Robert Bruce McCracken. Based on a sculpture by Sydney March.

British American Bank Note Company

**1934, Jul 1** **Engraved** **Perf 11**

| | | NH% | ★VF | ★F | ⊙VF | ⊙F | FDC |
|---|---|---|---|---|---|---|---|
| **209** | **10¢ olive green** | 100 | 40.00 | 20.00 | 10.00 | 6.00 | 25.00 |
| a | imperf. pair, 50 pairs | 75 | 2,000.00 | 1,350.00 | — | — | — |
| | plate blocks, plate 1, UL, UR, LR | 100 | 240.00 | 120.00 | | | |
| | plate 1, LL | 100 | 300.00 | 150.00 | | | |

Qty: 3,000,000

Imperf. plate blocks (2 thought to exist): LR VF NH $9,500.; LL XF XLH/NH $8,000.
Issued for the 150th anniversary of the arrival of the United Empire Loyalists following the American Revolution.

## NEW BRUNSWICK

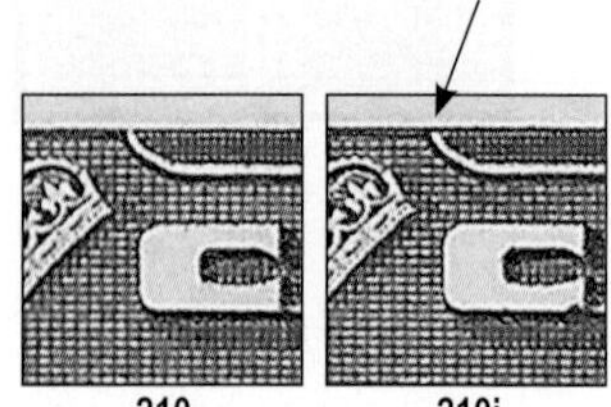
210 210i

British American Bank Note Company

**1934, Aug 16** **Engraved** **Perf 11**

| | | NH% | ★VF | ★F | ⊙VF | ⊙F | FDC |
|---|---|---|---|---|---|---|---|
| **210** | **2¢ red brown** | 100 | 4.00 | 2.00 | 3.00 | 1.00 | 15.00 |
| i | "closed frameline" variety* | 100 | 6.00 | 3.00 | 5.00 | 2.50 | 30.00 |
| a | imperf. pair, 45 pairs | 75 | 850.00 | 750.00 | — | — | — |
| aii | as i, imperf. pair, 35 pairs (right margin pair) | 75 | 1,750.00 | 1,200.00 | — | — | — |
| | plate blocks, plate 1, 2, UL | 100 | 25.00 | 10.00 | | | |
| | (210/i) plate 1, 2, UR | 100 | 30.00 | 20.00 | | | |
| | (210) LL blank corner block | 100 | 25.00 | 10.00 | | | |
| | (210/i) LR blank corner block | 100 | 30.00 | 20.00 | | | |

Qty: 5,050,000

* The closed frameline variety occurs on all stamps in the far right-hand column. All UR imprint blocks include two examples of the closed frameline.
Imperf. plate blocks: 210a Pl. 1 UL XF NH $5,000.; 210aii Pl. 1 UR XF NH $9,500.

Issued to commemorate the 150th anniversary of the founding of New Brunswick.

King George V — Medallion

**Rates:**

Domestic: 3¢ per oz.
Local: 2¢ per oz. (0–1 oz.)
3¢ per oz. (1–2 oz.)
Postcard: 2¢
Printed matter: 1¢ per 4 oz.
USA: 3¢ per oz.
UK: 3¢ per oz.
Non-UK: 5¢ per oz.
Airmail: 6¢ (from Aug 24/28)
Registration: 10¢
Special delivery: 20¢

## KING GEORGE V SILVER JUBILEE

211
Princess Elizabeth

212
Duke of York

213
King George V and Queen Mary

214
Prince of Wales

215
Windsor Castle

216
Royal Yacht Britannia

Canadian Bank Note Company, Limited

**1935, May 4** **Engraved** **Perf 12**

| | | NH% | ★VF | ★F | ⊙VF | ⊙F | FDC |
|---|---|---|---|---|---|---|---|
| **211** | **1¢ green** | 50 | 1.00 | .50 | .45 | .25 | 8.00 |
| **a** | imperf. pair, 100 pairs | 50 | 400.00 | 200.00 | — | — | — |
| **i** | "weeping princess" (Pl. 1 UR, pos. 21) | 50 | 175.00 | 100.00 | 120.00 | 70.00 | 400.00* |
| | 211i in block with 3 normals | 50 | 200.00 | 125.00 | 160.00 | 120.00 | |
| | 211i in UL corner block of 6 | 50 | 225.00 | 150.00 | 180.00 | 135.00 | |
| **xx** | No. 211, precancelled [1 style] | | — | — | — | 12.50 | |
| | plate blocks, plate 1, UL, LL, block of 8 | 50 | 13.50 | 9.00 | | | |
| | plate 1, UR (block of 8), LR (block of 6) | 50 | 15.00 | 10.00 | | | |
| | plate 2, UL, LL, block of 6 | 50 | 13.50 | 9.00 | | | |
| | plate 2, UR, block of 6 | 50 | 15.00 | 10.00 | | | |
| | plate 2, LR, block of 6 | 50 | 22.50 | 15.00 | | | |
| | Plate proof (800) | | 75.00 | | | | |

Qty: 30,500,000

No. 211i exists in top margin imprint blocks of 30 or more with plate 1, UR imprint, proving the position of the variety, valued at $400.00 for F–VF NH.

211i

| | | NH% | ★VF | ★F | ⊙VF | ⊙F | FDC |
|---|---|---|---|---|---|---|---|
| **212** | **2¢ brown** | 50 | 1.00 | .50 | .30 | .20 | 8.00 |
| **a** | imperf. pair, 100 pairs | 50 | 400.00 | 200.00 | — | — | — |
| **xx** | No. 212, precancelled [1 style] | | — | — | — | 20.00 | |
| | plate blocks, plate 1, UL, LR, block of 6 | 50 | 12.00 | 8.00 | | | |
| | plate 1, UR, block of 6 | 50 | 15.00 | 10.00 | | | |
| | plate 1, LL, block of 6 | 50 | 18.00 | 12.00 | | | |
| | plate 2, UL, block of 6 | 50 | 15.00 | 10.00 | | | |
| | plate 2, UR, block of 6 | 50 | 26.25 | 17.50 | | | |
| | plate 2, LL, block of 6 | 50 | 18.00 | 12.00 | | | |
| | plate 2, LR, block of 6 | 50 | 11.25 | 7.50 | | | |
| | Plate proof (800) | | 75.00 | | | | |

Qty: 31,000,000

| | | NH% | ★VF | ★F | ⊙VF | ⊙F | FDC |
|---|---|---|---|---|---|---|---|
| **213** | **3¢ carmine** | 50 | 3.00 | 1.50 | .25 | .20 | 8.00 |
| **a** | imperf. pair, 130 pairs | 50 | 400.00 | 200.00 | — | — | — |
| **i** | imperf. gutter block of 8, 10 exist | 50 | *3,500.00* | — | | | |
| | plate blocks, plate 1, UL, LL, LR, block of 6 | 50 | 27.00 | 18.00 | | | |
| | plate 1, UR, block of 6 | 50 | 67.50 | 45.00 | | | |
| | plate 1, LL, hairlines in margin, block of 6 | 50 | 45.00 | 30.00 | | | |
| | plate 2, UL, LL, LR, block of 6 | 50 | 45.00 | 30.00 | | | |
| | plate 2, UR, block of 6 | 50 | 60.00 | 40.00 | | | |
| | plate 3, UL, UR, block of 6 | 50 | 75.00 | 50.00 | | | |
| | plate 3, LL, block of 6 | 50 | 48.00 | 32.00 | | | |
| | plate 3, LR, block of 6 | 50 | 150.00 | 100.00 | | | |
| | Plate proof (400) | | 175.00 | | | | |

Qty: 60,425,000

| | | NH% | ★VF | ★F | ⊙VF | ⊙F | FDC |
|---|---|---|---|---|---|---|---|
| **214** | **5¢ blue** | 50 | 6.00 | 3.00 | 4.00 | 2.00 | 20.00 |
| **a** | imperf. pair, 100 pairs | 50 | 400.00 | 200.00 | — | — | — |
| | plate blocks, plate 1, UL, LL, block of 6 | 50 | 75.00 | 50.00 | | | |
| | plate 1, UR, block of 6 | 50 | 135.00 | 90.00 | | | |
| | plate 1, LR, block of 6 | 50 | 90.00 | 60.00 | | | |
| | plate 2, UL, LL, LR, block of 6 | 50 | 90.00 | 60.00 | | | |
| | plate 2, UR, block of 6 | 50 | 150.00 | 100.00 | | | |
| | Plate proof (800) | | 75.00 | | | | |

Qty: 3,025,000

| | | NH% | ★VF | ★F | ⊙VF | ⊙F | FDC |
|---|---|---|---|---|---|---|---|
| **215** | **10¢ green** | 50 | 12.00 | 6.00 | 4.00 | 2.00 | 25.00 |
| **a** | imperf. pair, 130 pairs | 50 | 400.00 | 200.00 | — | — | — |
| **i** | imperf. gutter block of 8, 10 exist | 50 | *3,500.00* | — | | | |
| | plate 1, UL, LL, LR, block of 6 | 50 | 90.00 | 60.00 | | | |
| | plate 1, UR, block of 6 | 50 | 112.50 | 75.00 | | | |
| | plate 2, UL, LL, LR, block of 6 | 50 | 90.00 | 60.00 | | | |
| | plate 2, UR, block of 6 | 50 | 150.00 | 100.00 | | | |
| | Plate proof (400) | | 175.00 | | | | |

Qty: 3,125,000

**SILVER JUBILEE ISSUE**
**PLATE PROOFS**

All proofs are on India paper, on card.

Two complete printer's sheets of each value were offered at the ABNC archives sale in 1990.

The 1¢, 2¢ and 5¢ sheets are each divided into 4 panes of 100 by a vertical and horizontal gutter through the middle of the sheet. Total 800 stamps of each value.

The 3¢ and 10¢ sheets are similarly divided into 4 panes of 50, separated by gutters. Total 400 stamps of each value.

The 13¢ sheets are divided into 2 panes of 100 by a horizontal gutter through the middle of the sheets. Total 400 stamps of the 13¢ value. There were no imprint blocks as most or all had been trimmed by the printer.

**Gutter Blocks of 8**

| | Vert. | Qty. | Horiz. | Qty. |
|---|---|---|---|---|
| **211** | 1,200.00 | (16) | 1,200.00 | (16) |
| **212** | 1,200.00 | (16) | 1,200.00 | (16) |
| **213** | 1,200.00 | (16) | 2,000.00 | ( 4) |
| **214** | 1,200.00 | (16) | 1,200.00 | (16) |
| **215** | 1,200.00 | (16) | 2,000.00 | ( 4) |
| **216** | DOES NOT EXIST | | 1,500.00 | (10) |
| **211–215** | 6,000.00 | | | |
| **211–216** | | | 9,100.00 | |

211P–215P Set of 5 cross gutter blocks (with vert. and horiz. gutters). Two sets of 5 exist, $17,500.00

Nos. 213P, 215P and 216P in vertical strips of 4 with wide horizontal gutter between top and bottom pairs, value $1,250.00 each. Four strips exist for each value, other than in the blocks listed above.

216i

| | | NH% | ★VF | ★F | ⊙VF | ⊙F | FDC |
|---|---|---|---|---|---|---|---|
| **216** | **13¢ dark blue** | 50 | 13.00 | 6.00 | 9.00 | 5.00 | 35.00 |
| i | 'shilling mark' (Pl. 1 UR, pos. 78) | 100 | 675.00 | 400.00 | 500.00 | 300.00 | 475.00* |
| | in block with 3 normals | 50 | 850.00 | 600.00 | 650.00 | 500.00 | 500.00 |
| b | imperf. pair, 150 pairs | 50 | 400.00 | 200.00 | — | — | — |
| bi | imperf. pair, one with 'shilling mark' (Pl. 1 UR, pos. 78) | | *8,000.00* | | | | |
| | plate blocks, plate 1, UL, UR, LL, block of 6 | 50 | 120.00 | 80.00 | | | |
| | plate 1, LR, block of 6 | 50 | 150.00 | 100.00 | | | |
| | plate 1, LL, block of 10‡ | 50 | 202.50 | 135.00 | | | |
| | plate 2, UL, UR, block of 6 | 50 | 120.00 | 80.00 | | | |
| | plate 2, LL, block of 6† | 50 | 135.00† | 90.00† | | | |
| | plate 2, LL, block of 10† | 50 | 202.50† | 135.00† | | | |
| | plate 2, LR , block of 10† | 50 | 300.00† | 175.00† | | | |
| | Plate proof (400) | | 175.00 | | | | |

Qty: 1,100,000

† Plate block of ten needed to show full imprint. ‡ block of 10 showing additional imprint adjacent to bottom left block of 4

* Value shown is for any cover, not FDC.

Two imperf. plate blocks of 6 might still exist for 211a, 212a & 214a, value (NH-VF) $2,750.

Six imperf. plate blocks of 6 might still exist for 213a, 215a & 216a, value (NH-VF) $2,000.

| | NH% | ★VF | ★F | ⊙VF | ⊙F | FDC |
|---|---|---|---|---|---|---|
| **Nos. 211–216** (6) Set | 50 | 36.00 | 17.50 | 18.00 | 9.60 | 60.00 |
| **Nos. 211a–216a** Set of 6 imperf. pairs | 50 | 2,400.00 | 1,200.00 | — | — | — |
| **Nos. 211–216** (6 Plate proofs) Set | | 750.00 | | | | |

Issued to commemorate the 25th anniversary of the accession to the throne of King George V.

## KING GEORGE V PICTORIAL ISSUE

**Rates:**

Domestic: 3¢ per oz.
Local: 2¢ per oz. (0–1 oz.)
3¢ per oz. (1–2 oz.)
Postcard: 2¢
Printed matter: 1¢ per 4 oz.
USA: 3¢ per oz.
UK: 3¢ per oz.
Non-UK: 5¢ per oz.
Airmail: 6¢ (from Aug 24/28)
Registration: 10¢
Special delivery: 20¢

217 218 219

220 221 222

First issue with *hidden date* ('1935', to right of maple leaf)

223
RCMP

224
Charlottetown

See also C5

225
Niagara Falls

226
Parliament, Victoria, BC

227
Champlain Statue

Designer: Herman Herbert Schwartz.
13¢: Based on a photograph by G.P. Roberts. $1: Based on a sculpture by Paul-Romain Chevré.

Canadian Bank Note Company, Limited

**1935, Jun 1** — **Engraved** — **Perf 12**

| No. | Description | NH% | ★VF | ★F | ⊙VF | ⊙F | FDC |
|---|---|---|---|---|---|---|---|
| **217** | **1¢ green** | 50 | .50 | .25 | .25 | .20 | 7.00 |
| c | imperf. pair, 150 pairs | 50 | 300.00 | 150.00 | — | — | — |
| xx | No. 217, precancelled [84 styles] | — | — | — | — | .20 | 3.00† |
| | plate blocks, plate 1, 2, all blocks, blocks of 6* | 50 | 8.00 | 4.00 | | | |
| | plate 3, centre blocks of 8, blocks of 8 | 50 | 10.00 | 5.00 | | | |
| | Plate proof (800) | | 100.00 | | | | |

Qty: 355,494,000

217a

| No. | Description | NH% | ★VF | ★F | ⊙VF | ⊙F | FDC |
|---|---|---|---|---|---|---|---|
| 217a | booklet pane of 4 x 1¢ (217as) + 2 labels (BK27), *Jul 22, 1935* | 50 | 100.00 | 60.00 | 100.00 | 60.00 | |
| as | single with straight edge, from 217a or 217b | 50 | 5.00 | 3.00 | 1.00 | .75 | |
| 217b | booklet pane of 6 x 1¢ (217as) (BK24), *Aug 19, 1935* | 50 | 70.00 | 50.00 | 70.00 | 50.00 | |

BK24 4 panes of 217b in cover; English (102,000) $175.00, French 10/18/35 (11,400) $350.00

217b

* For corner blocks of 10, add 50%. LL corner blocks of 4 exist with imprint in LL margin. Values are the same as the blocks of 6 above.

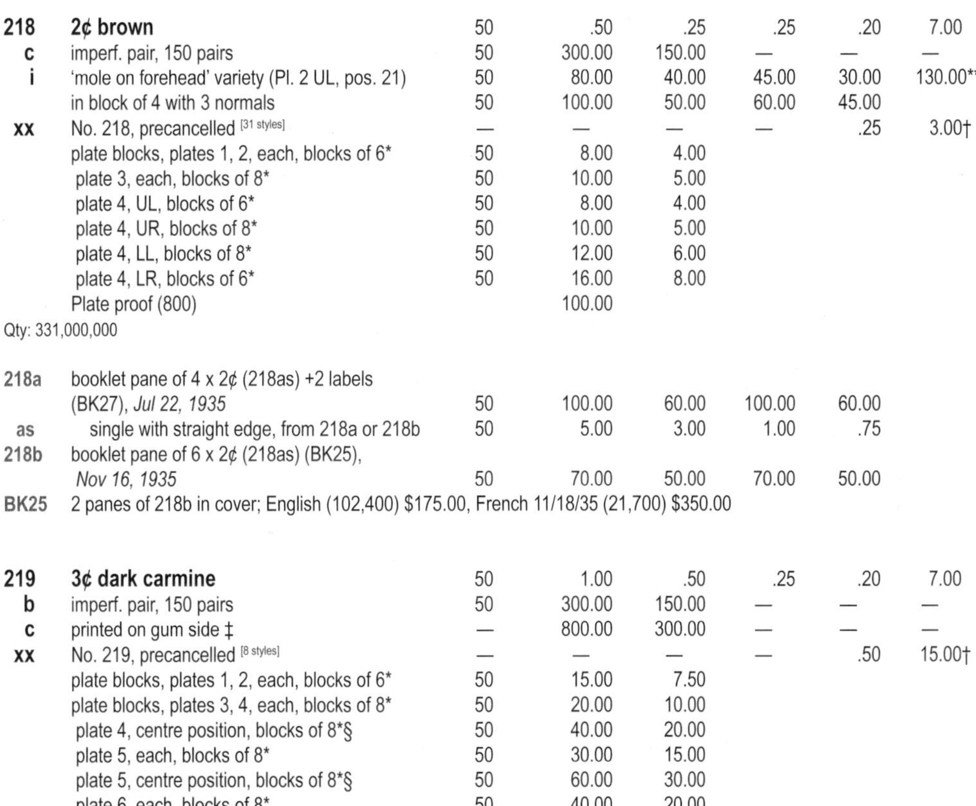

| No. | Description | NH% | ★VF | ★F | ⊙VF | ⊙F | FDC |
|---|---|---|---|---|---|---|---|
| **218** | **2¢ brown** | 50 | .50 | .25 | .25 | .20 | 7.00 |
| c | imperf. pair, 150 pairs | 50 | 300.00 | 150.00 | — | — | — |
| i | 'mole on forehead' variety (Pl. 2 UL, pos. 21) | 50 | 80.00 | 40.00 | 45.00 | 30.00 | 130.00** |
| | in block of 4 with 3 normals | 50 | 100.00 | 50.00 | 60.00 | 45.00 | |
| xx | No. 218, precancelled [31 styles] | — | — | — | — | .25 | 3.00† |
| | plate blocks, plates 1, 2, each, blocks of 6* | 50 | 8.00 | 4.00 | | | |
| | plate 3, each, blocks of 8* | 50 | 10.00 | 5.00 | | | |
| | plate 4, UL, blocks of 6* | 50 | 8.00 | 4.00 | | | |
| | plate 4, UR, blocks of 8* | 50 | 10.00 | 5.00 | | | |
| | plate 4, LL, blocks of 8* | 50 | 12.00 | 6.00 | | | |
| | plate 4, LR, blocks of 6* | 50 | 16.00 | 8.00 | | | |
| | Plate proof (800) | | 100.00 | | | | |

Qty: 331,000,000

218i

| No. | Description | NH% | ★VF | ★F | ⊙VF | ⊙F | FDC |
|---|---|---|---|---|---|---|---|
| 218a | booklet pane of 4 x 2¢ (218as) +2 labels (BK27), *Jul 22, 1935* | 50 | 100.00 | 60.00 | 100.00 | 60.00 | |
| as | single with straight edge, from 218a or 218b | 50 | 5.00 | 3.00 | 1.00 | .75 | |
| 218b | booklet pane of 6 x 2¢ (218as) (BK25), *Nov 16, 1935* | 50 | 70.00 | 50.00 | 70.00 | 50.00 | |

BK25 2 panes of 218b in cover; English (102,400) $175.00, French 11/18/35 (21,700) $350.00

218a

218b

| No. | Description | NH% | ★VF | ★F | ⊙VF | ⊙F | FDC |
|---|---|---|---|---|---|---|---|
| **219** | **3¢ dark carmine** | 50 | 1.00 | .50 | .25 | .20 | 7.00 |
| b | imperf. pair, 150 pairs | 50 | 300.00 | 150.00 | — | — | — |
| c | printed on gum side ‡ | — | 800.00 | 300.00 | — | — | — |
| xx | No. 219, precancelled [8 styles] | — | — | — | — | .50 | 15.00† |
| | plate blocks, plates 1, 2, each, blocks of 6* | 50 | 15.00 | 7.50 | | | |
| | plate blocks, plates 3, 4, each, blocks of 8* | 50 | 20.00 | 10.00 | | | |
| | plate 4, centre position, blocks of 8*§ | 50 | 40.00 | 20.00 | | | |
| | plate 5, each, blocks of 8* | 50 | 30.00 | 15.00 | | | |
| | plate 5, centre position, blocks of 8*§ | 50 | 60.00 | 30.00 | | | |
| | plate 6, each, blocks of 8* | 50 | 40.00 | 20.00 | | | |
| | plate 6, centre position, blocks of 8*§ | 50 | 80.00 | 40.00 | | | |
| | plates 7, 8, each, blocks of 8* | 50 | 20.00 | 10.00 | | | |
| | plates 7, 8, centre positions, blocks of 8*§ | 50 | 40.00 | 20.00 | | | |
| | Plate proof (800) | | 100.00 | | | | |

Qty: 701,490,000

| No. | Description | NH% | ★VF | ★F | ⊙VF | ⊙F | FDC |
|---|---|---|---|---|---|---|---|
| 219a | booklet pane of 4 x 3¢ (219as) + 2 labels (BK26, 27) | 50 | 60.00 | 40.00 | 60.00 | 40.00 | |
| as | single with straight edge, from 219a | 50 | 6.00 | 4.00 | .75 | .60 | |

BK26 2 panes of 219a in cover; English 08/08/35 (2,350,000) $140.00, French (06/01/35) (301,000) $300.00
BK27 1 pane each of 217a, 218a, 219a in cover; English 07/22/35 (370M) $300.00, French 09/01/35 (27,600) $400.00

219a

Gum shades vary from white to brown.
* For corner blocks of 10, add 50%. LL corner blocks of 4 exist with imprint in LL margin. Values are the same as the blocks of 6 above.
** Value shown is for any cover, not FDC.
† Commercial cover
‡ Two hundred recorded, most are off centre; VF examples are rare.
§ Centre plate positions, Upper and Lower, exist in plate strip of 20, $100.00, any plate number.

| No. | | NH% | ★VF | ★F | ⊙VF | ⊙F | FDC |
|---|---|---|---|---|---|---|---|
| **220** | **4¢ yellow** | 50 | 4.00 | 2.00 | .75 | .45 | 10.00† |
| a | imperf. pair, 150 pairs | 50 | 300.00 | 150.00 | — | — | — |
| | plate blocks, plate 1, each, blocks of 6* | 50 | 70.00 | 35.00 | | | |
| | Plate proof (800) | | 100.00 | | | | |

Qty: 7,037,000
† Commercial cover $20.00.

| No. | | NH% | ★VF | ★F | ⊙VF | ⊙F | FDC |
|---|---|---|---|---|---|---|---|
| **221** | **5¢ blue** | 50 | 5.00 | 2.00 | .50 | .20 | 10.00 |
| a | horiz. pair, imperf. vert., 150 pairs | 50 | 300.00 | 200.00 | — | — | — |
| b | imperf. pair, 150 pairs | 50 | 300.00 | 150.00 | — | — | — |
| i | paste-up double paper (1 UL block of 6 known) | — | | 1,000.00 | | | |
| xx | No. 221, precancelled [2 styles] | — | — | — | — | 20.00 | 50.00† |
| | plate blocks, plates 1, 2, each, blocks of 6* | 50 | 70.00 | 35.00 | | | |
| | Plate proof (800) | | 100.00 | | | | |

Qty: 41,045,000
† Value shown is for any cover, not FDC.

223ii

| No. | | NH% | ★VF | ★F | ⊙VF | ⊙F | FDC |
|---|---|---|---|---|---|---|---|
| **222** | **8¢ deep orange** | 50 | 4.00 | 2.00 | 3.00 | 1.50 | 15.00† |
| a | imperf. pair, 150 pairs | 50 | 300.00 | 150.00 | — | — | — |
| | plate blocks, plate 1, each, blocks of 6* | 50 | 70.00 | 35.00 | | | |
| | Plate proof (800) | | 100.00 | | | | |

Qty: 3,066,000
† Commercial cover in period, single usage $100.00.
* For corner blocks of 10, add 50%. LL corner blocks of 4 exist with imprint in LL margin. Values are the same as the blocks of 6 above.

223iv

223v

| No. | | NH% | ★VF | ★F | ⊙VF | ⊙F | FDC |
|---|---|---|---|---|---|---|---|
| **223** | **10¢ carmine rose** | 50 | 12.50 | 6.25 | .25 | .20 | 15.00 |
| a | imperf. pair, 150 pairs | 50 | 400.00 | 200.00 | — | — | — |
| i | deep rose shade | 50 | 12.50 | 6.25 | .25 | .20 | 25.00 |
| ii | "broken leg" variety (pos. 48) | 50 | 3,000.00 | 2,250.00 | 2,250.00 | 1,600.00 | *4,000.00*† |
| | "broken leg" variety in block of 4 with 3 normals | 50 | 3,500.00 | 2,500.00 | — | — | — |
| iii | imperf. gutter block of 8 | 50 | *2,500.00* | | — | — | — |
| iv | "bird cage" variety (Pl. 1, pos. 48, UL) | 50 | 500.00 | 350.00 | 375.00 | 250.00 | |
| v | re-entry of R.C.M.P. and vertical lines to the left | | | | | | |
| | plate blocks, plates 1, 2, each, blocks of 6* | 50 | 100.00 | 50.00 | | | |
| | Plate proof (400) | | 200.00 | | | | |

Qty: 4,086,000
Certificates of authenticity are recommended for copies of the "broken leg" variety.

224ii

| No. | | NH% | ★VF | ★F | ⊙VF | ⊙F | FDC |
|---|---|---|---|---|---|---|---|
| **224** | **13¢ violet** | 50 | 12.50 | 6.25 | 1.00 | .60 | 30.00 |
| a | imperf. pair, 150 pairs | 50 | 400.00 | 200.00 | — | — | — |
| i | imperf. gutter block of 8 | 50 | *2,500.00* | — | — | — | — |
| ii | strong re-entry in scroll below POSTES | | | | | | |
| iii | re-entry in scroll below POSTES and doubling of the upper half of the left frameline | | | | | | |
| iv | vertical scratch in N of CANADA (Pl. 1, LR, pos. 46) | | | | | | |
| | plate blocks, plates 1, 2, each, blocks of 6* | 50 | 90.00 | 60.00 | | | |
| | Plate proof (400) | | 200.00 | | | | |

Qty: 8,035,000

224iv

| No. | | NH% | ★VF | ★F | ⊙VF | ⊙F | FDC |
|---|---|---|---|---|---|---|---|
| **225** | **20¢ olive green** | 50 | 20.00 | 12.50 | 1.00 | .50 | 35.00 |
| a | imperf. pair, 150 pairs | 50 | 400.00 | 200.00 | — | — | — |
| i | deep olive green shade | 50 | 25.00 | 12.50 | 1.00 | .50 | 25.00‡ |
| ii | imperf. gutter block of 8 | 50 | *3,000.00*§ | — | — | — | — |
| iii | strong re-entry of left side, including POSTES (1UR35) | | | | | | |
| | plate blocks, plates 1, 2, each, blocks of 6* | 50 | 250.00 | 125.00 | | | |
| | Plate proof (400) | | 200.00 | | | | |

Qty: 13,513,000
§ The 20¢ gutter block is rarer than the other 4 as at least one block was cut into pairs.
‡ Commercial cover.

226i

| No. | | NH% | ★VF | ★F | ⊙VF | ⊙F | FDC |
|---|---|---|---|---|---|---|---|
| **226** | **50¢ dull violet** | 50 | 35.00 | 20.00 | 8.00 | 4.00 | 75.00 |
| a | imperf. pair, 150 pairs | 50 | 400.00 | 200.00 | — | — | — |
| i | major re-entry in CANADA (Pl. 1 LR, pos. 25) | 50 | 150.00 | 100.00 | 100.00 | 60.00 | 140.00† |
| | 226i, in block with 3 normal | 50 | 275.00 | 175.00 | 250.00 | 150.00 | — |
| ii | imperf. gutter block of 8 | 50 | *2,500.00* | | — | — | — |
| iii | minor re-entry; doubling of left side | | | | | | |
| | plate blocks, plate 1, each, blocks of 6* | 50 | 320.00 | 160.00 | | | |
| | Plate proof (400) | | 200.00 | | | | |

Qty: 2,416,000

| | | NH% | ★VF | ★F | ⊙VF | ⊙F | FDC |
|---|---|---|---|---|---|---|---|
| 227 | **$1 blue** | 50 | 80.00 | 45.00 | 15.00 | 9.00 | 200.00 |
| a | imperf. pair, 150 pairs | 50 | 500.00 | 250.00 | — | — | — |
| i | pale blue shade | 50 | 90.00 | 45.00 | 15.00 | 9.00 | 120.00† |
| ii | imperf. gutter block of 8 | 50 | *2,500.00* | | — | — | — |
| | plate blocks, plate 1, each, blocks of 6* | 50 | 600.00 | 300.00 | | | |
| | 227i, plate 1, each, blocks of 6* | 50 | 700.00 | 350.00 | | | |
| | Plate proof (400) | | 200.00 | | | | |

Qty: 818,000

* For corner blocks of 10, add 50%.

† Value shown is for any cover, not FDC. Single usage, proper time period, $500.00. Bulk payment receipts are valued much less.

| | NH% | ★VF | ★F | ⊙VF | ⊙F | FDC |
|---|---|---|---|---|---|---|
| **Nos. 217–227** (11) Set | 50 | 175.00 | 97.45 | 35.05 | 17.05 | 250.00 |
| **Nos. 217c–227a** Set of 11 imperf. pairs | 50 | 3,900.00 | 1,950.00 | — | — | — |
| **Nos. 217–227** (11 Plate proofs) Set | | 1,800.00 | | | | |

Probably fewer than 6 sets of gutter blocks (223iii–227ii) exist today.

**1935 PICTORIAL ISSUE**
**IMPERFORATE PLATE BLOCKS**

**217c–222a**: Three imperf. plate blocks of 8 can exist for each value. NH-VF – *$2,500* each.

**223a–227a**: Six imperf. plate blocks of 6 can exist for each value. NH-VF – *$2,000* each.

**PLATE PROOFS**

All proofs are on India paper, on card.

Two complete printer's sheets of each were offered at the American Bank Note Company Archives sale.

All proof sheets are divided into 4 panes by horizontal and vertical gutters through the middle of the sheets. Total 800 stamps each of the 1¢ through 8¢ values and 400 stamps each of the 10¢ through $1 values. Two sets of cross gutter blocks exist from these sheets.

## KING GEORGE V PICTORIAL COIL STAMPS

228

229

230

| 1935 | | Engraved | | | | Perf 8 vertical | |
|---|---|---|---|---|---|---|---|
| | | NH% | ★VF | ★F | ⊙VF | ⊙F | ✉ |
| 228 | **1¢ green** (217), *Nov 5, 1935* | 50 | 20.00 | 15.00 | 4.00 | 2.00 | 10.00† |
| | pair | 50 | 40.00 | 30.00 | 8.00 | 4.00 | 14.00† |
| | strip of 4 | 50 | 80.00 | 60.00 | 30.00 | 15.00 | |
| i | jump strip of 4 | 50 | 100.00 | 65.00 | 40.00 | 25.00 | — |
| ii | "narrow 1" variety | 50 | 75.00 | 45.00 | 45.00 | 30.00 | 60.00 |
| | 228ii in pair with normal | 50 | 95.00 | 60.00 | 60.00 | 40.00 | 70.00 |
| iii | 228ii in jump strip of 4, with 3 normal | 50 | 150.00 | 90.00 | 75.00 | 50.00 | — |
| iv | repair paste-up pair | 50 | 80.00 | 50.00 | — | — | — |
| xx | No. 228, precancelled [1 style] | 50 | 10.00 | 7.50 | 3.00 | .40 | 3.00 |
| | start or end strip of 4 with full strip of 10 tabs* | 50 | 200.00 | 125.00 | | | |

Qty: 9,625,000

Normal

228ii

| | | NH% | ★VF | ★F | ⊙VF | ⊙F | ✉ |
|---|---|---|---|---|---|---|---|
| 229 | **2¢ brown** (218), *Oct 14, 1935* | 50 | 25.00 | 15.00 | 1.25 | .75 | 12.00† |
| | pair | 50 | 50.00 | 30.00 | 3.00 | 1.50 | 24.00† |
| | strip of 4 | 50 | 100.00 | 60.00 | 12.00 | 6.00 | |
| i | jump strip of 4 | 50 | 120.00 | 65.00 | 35.00 | 25.00 | — |
| ii | "damaged 2" variety | 50 | 120.00 | 60.00 | 70.00 | 50.00 | 75.00 |
| | 229ii in pair, with normal | 50 | 150.00 | 75.00 | 80.00 | 60.00 | 100.00 |
| | 229ii in strip of 4, with 3 normal | 50 | 250.00 | 125.00 | 100.00 | 80.00 | — |
| iii | repair paste-up pair | 50 | 80.00 | 50.00 | — | — | — |
| | start or end strip of 4 with full strip of 10 tabs* | 50 | 200.00 | 125.00 | | | |

Qty: 13,500,000

| | | NH% | ★VF | ★F | ⊙VF | ⊙F | ✉ |
|---|---|---|---|---|---|---|---|
| 230 | **3¢ dark carmine** (219), *Jul 20, 1935* | 50 | 20.00 | 12.00 | .75 | .30 | 10.00† |
| | pair | 50 | 40.00 | 24.00 | 3.00 | 1.50 | 22.00† |
| | strip of 4 | 50 | 80.00 | 48.00 | 10.00 | 5.00 | |
| i | jump strip of 4 | 50 | 100.00 | 65.00 | 37.50 | 25.00 | — |
| ii | repair paste-up pair | 50 | 120.00 | 75.00 | — | — | — |
| | start or end strip of 4 with full strip of 10 tabs* | 50 | 200.00 | 125.00 | | | |

Qty: 25,080,000

| | NH% | ★VF | ★F | ⊙VF | ⊙F | ✉ |
|---|---|---|---|---|---|---|
| **Nos. 228–230** (3) Set | 50 | 65.00 | 42.00 | 6.00 | 3.05 | — |

* Strips with fewer stamps or fewer tabs will have less value.

† Commercial usage.

## KING GEORGE VI MUFTI ISSUE

**Rates:**

Domestic: 3¢ per oz.
Local: 2¢ per oz. (0–1 oz.)
3¢ per oz. (1–2 oz.)
Postcard: 2¢
Printed matter: 1¢ per 4 oz.
USA: 3¢ per oz.
UK: 3¢ per oz.
Non-UK: 5¢ per oz.
Airmail: 6¢ (from Aug 24/28)
Registration: 10¢
Special delivery: 20¢

231

232

233

234

235

236

Designer: Herman Herbert Schwartz. Based on a photograph by Bertram Park. Portrait engraved by William F. Ford.

Canadian Bank Note Company, Limited

**1937, Apr 1** — **Engraved** — **Perf 12**

| | | NH% | ★VF | ★F | ⊙VF | ⊙F | FDC |
|---|---|---|---|---|---|---|---|
| **231** | **1¢ green** | 50 | .50 | .35 | .25 | .20 | 7.50 |
| c | imperf. pair, 100 pairs | 50 | 400.00 | 200.00 | — | — | — |
| xx | No. 231, precancelled [41 styles] | — | — | — | — | .20 | 3.00 |

Qty: 1,394,000,000

**No. 231 (1¢) Plate Blocks (NH +50%)**

| Plate No. | Location | ★VF | ★F | Plate No. | Location | ★VF | ★F |
|---|---|---|---|---|---|---|---|
| 1 | all | 3.75 | 2.50 | 8 | UL, UR | 6.75 | 4.50 |
| 2 | all | 3.75 | 2.50 | | LL, LR | 3.75 | 2.50 |
| 3 | all | 4.50 | 3.00 | 8 | LL or LR, cracked plate | | |
| | UL cracked plate | 40.00 | 15.00 | | block of 8 | 40.00 | 17.50 |
| 4 | UL, LL | 13.50 | 9.00 | 9 | UL | 67.50 | 45.00 |
| | UR | 22.50 | 15.00 | | UR | 11.25 | 7.50 |
| | LR | 11.25 | 7.50 | | LL | 30.00 | 20.00 |
| 5 | all | 3.75 | 2.50 | | LR | 33.00 | 22.00 |
| 6 | all | 3.75 | 2.50 | 10 | UL, UR | 225.00 | 150.00 |
| 7 | UL, LL | 9.00 | 6.00 | | LL | 240.00 | 160.00 |
| | UR | 13.50 | 9.00 | | LR | 262.50 | 175.00 |
| | LR | 11.25 | 7.50 | 11 | UL | 112.50 | 75.00 |
| | LL cracked plate | 30.00 | 20.00 | | UR | 150.00 | 110.00 |
| | | | | | LL | 225.00 | 150.00 |
| | | | | | LR | 300.00 | 200.00 |

231a

231b

| | | NH% | ★VF | ★F | ⊙VF | ⊙F | FDC |
|---|---|---|---|---|---|---|---|
| 231a | booklet pane of 4 x 1¢ (231as) + 2 labels (BK31), *Apr 14, 1937* | 50 | 25.00 | 17.50 | 30.00 | 20.00 | |
| as | single with straight edge, from 231a or 231b | 50 | 1.00 | .75 | .50 | .30 | |
| b | booklet pane of 6 x 1¢ (231as) (BK28), *May 18, 1937* | 50 | 10.00 | 7.00 | 28.00 | 20.00 | |

BK28 4 panes of 231b in cover; English 05/18/37 (296,334) $55.00, French 10/14/38 (51,500) $100.00

| | | NH% | ★VF | ★F | ⊙VF | ⊙F | FDC |
|---|---|---|---|---|---|---|---|
| **232** | **2¢ brown** | 50 | 1.00 | .50 | .25 | .20 | 7.50 |
| c | imperf. pair, 100 pairs | 50 | 400.00 | 200.00 | — | — | — |
| i | pale yellow brown shade | 50 | 3.50 | 2.50 | — | — | 5.00† |
| xx | No. 232, precancelled [25 styles] | — | — | — | — | .20 | 3.00 |

Qty: 1,163,000,000
† Commercial cover.

**No. 232 (2¢) Plate Blocks (NH +50%)**

| Plate No./Location | | ★VF | ★F | Plate No./Location | | ★VF | ★F |
|---|---|---|---|---|---|---|---|
| 1–5 | all | 4.50 | 3.00 | 9, 10 Lower Centre | | | |
| 5 | UL, UR, cracked plate | 26.25 | 17.50 | | block of 20 | 187.50 | 125.00 |
| 6 | all | 11.25 | 7.50 | | block of 8 | 150.00 | 100.00 |
| 7 | UL | 52.50 | 35.00 | | strip of 4 | 112.50 | 75.00 |
| | UR, LL | 37.50 | 25.00 | 10 | UL | 112.50 | 75.00 |
| | LR | 45.00 | 30.00 | | UR | 25.00 | 20.00 |
| 8 | all | 4.50 | 3.00 | | LL | 75.00 | 60.00 |
| 9 | UL | 112.50 | 75.00 | | LR | 67.50 | 45.00 |
| | UR | 30.00 | 20.00 | 11 | all | 5.25 | 3.50 |
| | LL | 90.00 | 60.00 | 12 | UL, UR | 11.25 | 7.50 |
| | LR | 67.50 | 45.00 | | LL LR | 22.50 | 15.00 |
| 9, 10 Upper Centre | | | | 13 | all | 6.75 | 4.50 |
| | block of 20 | 187.50 | 125.00 | 14 | UL | 30.00 | 20.00 |
| | block of 8 | 150.00 | 100.00 | | UR | 22.50 | 15.00 |
| | strip of 4 | 112.50 | 75.00 | | LL, LR | 27.00 | 18.00 |

232a

| | | NH% | ★VF | ★F | ⊙VF | ⊙F | FDC |
|---|---|---|---|---|---|---|---|
| 232a | booklet pane of 4 x 2¢ (232as) + 2 labels (BK31), *May 14, 1937* | 50 | 25.00 | 17.50 | 30.00 | 25.00 | |
| as | single with straight edge, from 232a or 232b | 50 | 1.50 | 1.00 | .75 | .60 | |
| b | booklet pane of 6 x 2¢ (232as) (BK29), *May 3,1937* | 50 | 15.00 | 12.00 | 20.00 | 15.00 | |
| BK29 | 2 panes of 232b in cover; English 05/03/38 (196,900) $60.00, French 03/03/39 (42,000) $100.00 | | | | | | |

232b

| | | NH% | ★VF | ★F | ⊙VF | ⊙F | FDC |
|---|---|---|---|---|---|---|---|
| **233** | **3¢ carmine** | 50 | 1.00 | .65 | .25 | .20 | 7.50 |
| **b** | imperf. pair, 150 pairs | 50 | 400.00 | 200.00 | — | — | — |
| **i** | "crease on collar" variety (Pl. 2 UR, pos. 85) | 50 | 100.00 | 40.00 | 45.00 | 35.00 | 160.00† |
| | 233i in block of 4 with 3 normals | 50 | 150.00 | 60.00 | 60.00 | 45.00 | 160.00† |
| **ii** | "cracked ear" variety (Pl. 3 UR, pos. 18) | 50 | 100.00 | 40.00 | 45.00 | 35.00 | 150.00† |
| | 233i in block of 4 with 3 normals | 50 | 150.00 | 60.00 | 60.00 | 45.00 | 150.00† |
| **xx** | No. 233, precancelled [16 styles] | — | — | — | — | .30 | |

Qty: 2,634,000,000

An imperf. pair with 'crease on collar' variety was reported in May 2016; likely unique, $15,000.00.

233i

| | NH% | ★VF | ★F | ⊙VF | ⊙F | FDC |
|---|---|---|---|---|---|---|
| **Combination FDC (1¢–3¢)** | — | — | — | — | — | 10.00 |

233ii

**No. 233 (3¢) Plate Blocks (NH +50%)**

| Plate No./Location | | ★VF | ★F | Plate No./Location | | ★VF | ★F |
|---|---|---|---|---|---|---|---|
| 1 | all | 6.00 | 4.00 | 14 | UL | 15.00 | 10.00 |
| 2 | all | 5.60 | 3.75 | | UR, LL, LR | 11.25 | 7.50 |
| | UR cracked | 45.00 | 30.00 | 15 | UL, LL | 7.50 | 5.00 |
| 3 | UL | 37.50 | 25.00 | | UR, LR | 9.00 | 6.00 |
| | UR | 22.50 | 15.00 | 16 | UL, UR | 15.00 | 10.00 |
| | LL, LR | 30.00 | 20.00 | | LL | 22.50 | 15.00 |
| 4, 5 | UL, UR | 15.00 | 10.00 | | LR | 30.00 | 20.00 |
| | LL, LR | 9.00 | 6.00 | 17 | UL, UR, LL | 6.00 | 4.00 |
| 6 | UL, UR, LL | 11.25 | 7.50 | | LR | 15.00 | 10.00 |
| | LR | 9.00 | 6.00 | 18 | UL, UR | 30.00 | 20.00 |
| 7 | all | 6.00 | 4.00 | | LL, LR | 37.50 | 25.00 |
| 8 | all | 7.50 | 5.00 | 19 | UL, UR, LR | 30.00 | 20.00 |
| 9, 10 | all | 5.60 | 3.75 | | LL | 22.50 | 15.00 |
| 11 | all | 6.00 | 4.00 | 20 | UL | 150.00 | 100.00 |
| 12 | UL | 22.50 | 15.00 | | UR, LL, LR | 112.50 | 75.00 |
| | UR,LL | 18.00 | 12.00 | 21 | UL, UR | 67.50 | 45.00 |
| | LR | 225.00 | 150.00 | | LL, LR | 30.00 | 20.00 |
| 12, 13 Upper Centre | | | | 22 | UL, UR | 37.50 | 25.00 |
| | block of 20 | 225.00 | 150.00 | | LL | 18.00 | 12.00 |
| | block of 8 | 150.00 | 100.00 | | LR | 22.50 | 15.00 |
| | strip of 4 | 112.50 | 75.00 | 23 | UL | 30.00 | 20.00 |
| 12, 13 Lower Centre | | | | | UR | 60.00 | 40.00 |
| | block of 20 | 180.00 | 120.00 | | LL | 12.00 | 8.00 |
| | block of 8 | 135.00 | 90.00 | | LR | 11.25 | 7.50 |
| | strip of 4 | 101.25 | 67.50 | | | | |
| 13 | UL | 75.00 | 50.00 | | | | |
| | UR | 22.50 | 15.00 | | | | |
| | LL | 52.50 | 35.00 | | | | |
| | LR | 187.50 | 125.00 | | | | |

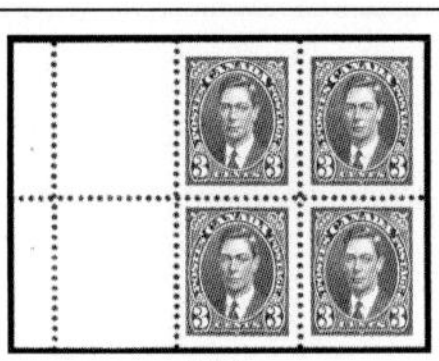
233a

| | | NH% | ★VF | ★F | ⊙VF | ⊙F | FDC |
|---|---|---|---|---|---|---|---|
| 233a | booklet pane of 4 x 3¢ (233as) + 2 labels (BK30, 31), *Apr 14, 1937* | 50 | 10.00 | 7.50 | 17.50 | 15.00 | |
| as | single with straight edge, from 233a | 50 | 1.50 | 1.00 | .25 | .20 | |
| BK30 | 2 panes of 233a in cover; English 04/27/37 (13,455,000) $25.00, French 04/23/37 (1,595,474) $40.00 | | | | | | |
| BK31 | 1 pane each of 231a, 232a, 233a in cover; English 04/14/37 (1,703,640) $65.00, French 01/04/38 (227,474) $140.00 | | | | | | |

Gum shades vary from white to brown.
† Commercial cover.

| | | NH% | ★VF | ★F | ⊙VF | ⊙F | FDC |
|---|---|---|---|---|---|---|---|
| **234** | **4¢ yellow**, *May 10, 1937* | 50 | 4.00 | 2.50 | .25 | .20 | 10.00 |
| a | imperf. pair, 100 pairs | 50 | 400.00 | 200.00 | — | — | — |
| | plate blocks, plate 1, all blocks | 50 | 30.00 | 15.00 | | | |

Qty: 24,074,000

| | | NH% | ★VF | ★F | ⊙VF | ⊙F | FDC |
|---|---|---|---|---|---|---|---|
| **235** | **5¢ blue**, *May 10, 1937* | 50 | 6.00 | 4.00 | .25 | .20 | 10.00 |
| a | imperf. pair, 100 pairs | 50 | 400.00 | 200.00 | — | — | — |
| xx | No. 235, precancelled [1 style] | — | — | — | — | 10.00 | 50.00 |
| | plate blocks, plate 1, all blocks | 50 | 30.00 | 15.00 | | | |
| | plate 2, all blocks | 50 | 30.00 | 20.00 | | | |
| | plate 2, LL, cracked plate | 50 | 52.50 | 35.00 | | | |
| | plate 3, all blocks | 50 | 150.00 | 100.00 | | | |

Qty: 133,000,000

| | | NH% | ★VF | ★F | ⊙VF | ⊙F | FDC |
|---|---|---|---|---|---|---|---|
| **236** | **8¢ orange**, *May 10, 1937* | 50 | 4.00 | 2.50 | .60 | .35 | 10.00† |
| a | imperf. pair, 100 pairs | 50 | 400.00 | 200.00 | — | — | — |
| | combination FDC (4¢–8¢) | — | — | — | — | — | 20.00 |
| | plate blocks, plate 1, all blocks | 50 | 30.00 | 15.00 | | | |

Qty: 14,035,000
† Commercial cover in period, single usage $100.00.

| | NH% | ★VF | ★F | ⊙VF | ⊙F | FDC |
|---|---|---|---|---|---|---|
| **Nos. 231–236** (6) Set | 50 | 16.65 | 10.50 | 1.65 | 1.35 | — |
| **Nos. 231c–236a** (6) Set of imperf. pairs (100 sets) | 50 | 2,400.00 | 1,200.00 | — | — | — |

## KING GEORGE VI, MUFTI ISSUE
## IMPERFORATE PLATE BLOCKS

Nos. 231c–236a Two imperforate plate blocks are thought to exist for each value.
$2,000 each (NH-VF). Set of 6, $12,000.
One extra imperf. plate block of the 3¢ has been seen, indicating the existence of a third sheet of 100 of the 3¢. Value: $2,000.

### EDWARD VIII

Unissued Edward VIII (abdicated) large die essays (in rose red and green) are known in private hands. These are on India die sunk on large card (155x230mm – example shown below has been cropped). Price: $9,500.

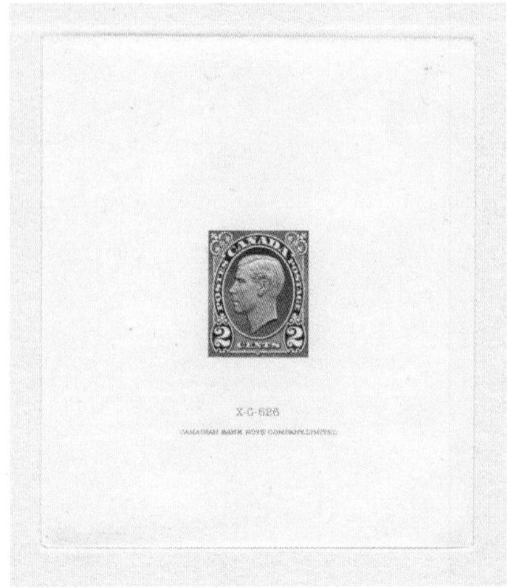

## KING GEORGE VI CORONATION

237
King George VI & Queen Elizabeth

Based on a photograph by Peter North and Bertram Park. Portraits engraved by William F. Ford.
Canadian Bank Note Company, Limited

| 1937, May 10 | | Engraved NH% | ★VF | ★F | ⊙VF | ⊙F | Perf 12 FDC |
|---|---|---|---|---|---|---|---|
| 237 | **3¢ carmine** | 25 | .50 | .20 | .25 | .20 | 10.00 |
| a | imperf. pair 75 pairs | 50 | 800.00 | 400.00 | — | — | — |
| | plate blocks, plates 1–4, LL, UL, UR | 30 | 4.00 | 2.00 | | | |
| | plates 1–4, LR | 30 | 6.00 | 3.00 | | | |
| | 237a imperf. plate block $3,600. (NH-VF). Only 3 exist. | | | | | | |

Qty: 51,400,000

## KING GEORGE VI COIL STAMPS

238

239

240

| 1937 | | Engraved NH% | ★VF | ★F | ⊙VF | ⊙F | Perf 8 vertical FDC |
|---|---|---|---|---|---|---|---|
| 238 | **1¢ green** (231), *Jun 15, 1937* | 50 | 4.00 | 2.00 | 1.50 | .75 | 20.00† |
| | pair | 50 | 8.00 | 4.00 | 3.00 | 1.50 | 12.00 |
| | strip of 4 | 50 | 16.00 | 8.00 | 9.00 | 4.50 | 26.00 |
| i | jump strip of 4 | 50 | 24.00 | 15.00 | 15.00 | 8.00 | — |
| | repair paste-up pair | 50 | | 60.00 | — | — | |
| xx | No. 238, precancelled [1 style] | 50 | 2.50 | 1.50 | .50 | .25 | 3.00 |
| | as 'xx', repair paste-up pair | 50 | | 80.00 | — | — | |

Qty: 23,022,000

| | | | | | | | |
|---|---|---|---|---|---|---|---|
| 239 | **2¢ brown** (232), *Jun 18, 1937* | 50 | 7.50 | 3.50 | .50 | .25 | 25.00† |
| | pair | 50 | 15.00 | 7.00 | 2.00 | 1.00 | 18.00 |
| | strip of 4 | 50 | 30.00 | 14.00 | 5.00 | 2.50 | 40.00 |
| i | jump strip of 4 | 50 | 40.00 | 15.00 | 15.00 | 10.00 | — |
| | repair paste-up pair | 50 | | 80.00 | — | — | |

Qty: 34,565,000

| | | | | | | | |
|---|---|---|---|---|---|---|---|
| 240 | **3¢ carmine** (233), *Apr 15, 1937* | 50 | 12.50 | 5.00 | .25 | .20 | 20.00† |
| | pair | 50 | 25.00 | 10.00 | 1.00 | .40 | 17.00* |
| | strip of 4 | 50 | 50.00 | 20.00 | 4.00 | 2.00 | 40.00* |
| i | jump strip of 4 | 50 | 60.00 | 27.00 | 10.00 | 5.00 | — |
| | repair paste-up pair | 50 | | 90.00 | — | — | |

Qty: 57,827,000

| | | | | | | | |
|---|---|---|---|---|---|---|---|
| **Nos. 238–240** (3) Set | | 50 | 24.00 | 10.50 | 2.25 | 1.20 | — |

† FDC or commercial cover.
* Commercial cover.

**Start or End Strips**
2 stamps + 2 blank tabs
NH: +50%

| Sc# | ★VF | ★F |
|---|---|---|
| 238 | 25.00 | 20.00 |
| 239 | 40.00 | 30.00 |
| 240 | 80.00 | 60.00 |

Full strips are scarce and worth much more.

## 1938 PICTORIAL ISSUE

241
Memorial Chamber

242
Halifax Harbour

See also C6

243
Fort Garry Gate, Winnipeg

244
Vancouver Harbour

245
Château de Ramezay, Montreal

Designer: Herman Herbert Schwartz.

Canadian Bank Note Company, Limited

**1938** **Engraved** **Perf 12**

| | | | NH% | ★VF | ★F | ⊙VF | ⊙F | FDC |
|---|---|---|---|---|---|---|---|---|
| **241** | | **10¢ dark carmine**, *Jul 28, 1938* | 50 | 15.00 | 6.00 | .25 | .20 | 300.00 |
| | | plate blocks, plates 1, 2, all blocks | 50 | 75.00 | 35.00 | | | |
| | **a** | carmine rose, *Jun 15, 1938* | 50 | 12.00 | 6.00 | .25 | .20 | 30.00 |
| | | plate blocks, plates 1, 2, all blocks | 50 | 52.50 | 35.00 | | | |
| | **b** | imperf. pair, dark carmine, 75 pairs | 50 | 750.00 | 500.00 | — | — | — |
| | **c** | imperf. pair, carmine rose, 75 pairs | 50 | 750.00 | 500.00 | — | — | — |

Qty: 241: 54,019,000; 241a: 10,187,000

| | | | NH% | ★VF | ★F | ⊙VF | ⊙F | FDC |
|---|---|---|---|---|---|---|---|---|
| **242** | | **13¢ deep blue**, *Nov 15, 1938* | 50 | 20.00 | 6.00 | .75 | .35 | 30.00 |
| | **a** | imperf. pair, 75 pairs | 50 | 750.00 | 500.00 | — | — | — |
| | | plate blocks, plate 1, all blocks | 50 | 100.00 | 50.00 | | | |

Qty: 13,028,000

| | | | NH% | ★VF | ★F | ⊙VF | ⊙F | FDC |
|---|---|---|---|---|---|---|---|---|
| **243** | | **20¢ red brown**, *Jun 15, 1938* | 50 | 25.00 | 10.00 | .60 | .25 | 35.00 |
| | **a** | imperf. pair, 75 pairs | 50 | 750.00 | 500.00 | — | — | — |
| | | plate blocks, plate 1, UL, LL, LR | 50 | 150.00 | 100.00 | | | |
| | | plate 1, UR | 50 | 155.00 | 110.00 | | | |
| | | plate 2, UL, LL, LR | 50 | 150.00 | 100.00 | | | |
| | | plate 2, UR | 50 | 180.00 | 120.00 | | | |

Qty: 30,499,000

| | | | NH% | ★VF | ★F | ⊙VF | ⊙F | FDC |
|---|---|---|---|---|---|---|---|---|
| **244** | | **50¢ green**, *Jun 15, 1938* | 50 | 50.00 | 20.00 | 7.50 | 4.00 | 75.00 |
| | **a** | imperf. pair, 75 pairs | 50 | 750.00 | 500.00 | — | — | — |
| | | plate blocks, plate 1, UL | 50 | 262.50 | 175.00 | | | |
| | | plate 1, UR, LL | 50 | 300.00 | 200.00 | | | |
| | | plate 1, LR | 50 | 375.00 | 250.00 | | | |

Qty: 4,924,000

245a

| | | | NH% | ★VF | ★F | ⊙VF | ⊙F | FDC |
|---|---|---|---|---|---|---|---|---|
| **245** | | **$1 dull violet**, *Jun 15, 1938* | 50 | 100.00 | 50.00 | 10.00 | 5.00 | 150.00† |
| | **a** | vertical pair, imperf. horiz. error | 50 | *6,000.00* | *4,000.00* | — | — | — |
| | **b** | imperf. pair, 75 pairs | 50 | 1,000.00 | 700.00 | — | — | — |
| | | plate blocks, plate 1, all blocks | 50 | 600.00 | 400.00 | | | |
| | **i** | aniline violet | 50 | 150.00 | 60.00 | 10.00 | 5.00 | 150.00† |
| | | 245i, plate blocks, plate 1, all blocks | 50 | 750.00 | 500.00 | | | |

Qty: 2,210,000

No. 245a: The sheet was cut in two by the discoverers, 12 pairs, one plate block of 6, 6 strips of 3 and 2 wide margin singles exist.

† Single usage, proper time frame, $500.00. Bulk payment receipts are valued much less.

| | NH% | ★VF | ★F | ⊙VF | ⊙F | FDC |
|---|---|---|---|---|---|---|
| **Nos. 241–245** (5) Set | 50 | 210.00 | 92.00 | 19.00 | 9.80 | 180.00 |
| **Nos. 241b–245b** Set, 6 imperf. pairs, with both shades of 10¢ | 50 | 4,750.00 | 3,200.00 | — | — | — |

### 1938 PICTORIAL ISSUE
### IMPERFORATE PLATE BLOCKS

Nos. 241b–245b: three exist for each value; 241b–244a (NH-VF) $2,700 each.
No. 245b (NH-VF) $3,600 each
No. 245a (imperf. horizontally) UR plate block of 6 (2 x 3) is unique, $25,000.

### PLATE PROOFS

All proofs are on India paper, on card. There were no plate proofs of the 13¢ value. See also C6.
Two complete printer's sheets of 200 stamps each of the 10¢, 20¢, 50¢ and $1 values were offered at the ABNC archives sale. Each sheet is divided into 4 panes of 50 by horizontal and vertical gutters through the middle of the sheet. These sheets have been cut up and sets of the 4 values offered as follows: singles $600, pairs $1,200, blocks (4) $2,400, gutter blocks (8) $6,000. and cross gutter blocks (16) $15,000. Plate blocks of 4 (two from each corner exist) set of 4 $5,000.

## ROYAL VISIT

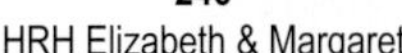
246
HRH Elizabeth & Margaret

247
National Memorial, Ottawa

248
George VI & Queen Elizabeth

This issue is the first to have combined two separate engraved plates, one for the frame and a separate one to print the black of the heads and the monument. Thus each stamp has a combination plate number, 1–1, 1–2, 1–3, etc. There are 176 "possible" plate number combinations on these three values although 11 of these have not, as yet, been reported. There are 13 such combinations that have been reported with only a few examples known.

Designer: Herman Herbert Schwartz. 1¢: Based on photographs by Marcus Adams. 2¢: Based on a sculpture designed by Vernon March. 3¢: Based on photographs by Dorothy Wilding.

Canadian Bank Note Company, Limited

**1939, May 15** — **Engraved** — **Perf 12**

| | | NH% | ★VF | ★F | ⊙VF | ⊙F | FDC |
|---|---|---|---|---|---|---|---|
| **246** | **1¢ green & black** | 50 | .50 | .25 | .25 | .20 | 5.00 |
| a | imperf. pair, 100 pairs | 50 | 700.00 | | — | — | — |

Qty: 50,043,000

**No. 246 (1¢) Plate Blocks (NH +50%)**

| Plate No. | Location | ★VF | ★F | Plate No. | Location | ★VF | ★F |
|---|---|---|---|---|---|---|---|
| 1-1 | UL, UR | 9.00 | 6.00 | 3-3 | UL | 10.50 | 7.00 |
| | LL, LR | 10.50 | 7.00 | | UR | 15.00 | 10.00 |
| 1-2 | UL, UR | 7.50 | 5.00 | | LL | 18.00 | 12.00 |
| | LL, LR | 9.00 | 6.00 | | LR | 30.00 | 20.00 |
| 1-3 | UL, UR | 1,600.00 | 1,000.00 | 3-4 | UL, UR | 30.00 | 20.00 |
| | LL | 1,200.00 | 750.00 | | LL, LR | 37.50 | 25.00 |
| 1-4 | UL, LL, LR | 1,600.00 | 1,000.00 | 4-1, 4-2 | all blocks | 3.00 | 2.00 |
| 2-1, 2-2 | LL, LR | 6.00 | 4.00 | 4-3 | UL | 15.00 | 10.00 |
| | UL, UR | 7.50 | 5.00 | | UR, LL | 60.00 | 40.00 |
| 2-3 | UL, LL, LR | 1,600.00 | 1,000.00 | | LR | 105.00 | 70.00 |
| 2-4 | UL | 900.00 | 500.00 | 4-4 | UL | 15.00 | 10.00 |
| | UR, LL | 1,600.00 | 1,000.00 | | UR | 45.00 | 30.00 |
| 3-1, 3-2 | all blocks | 3.00 | 2.00 | | LL | 30.00 | 20.00 |
| | | | | | LR | 32.50 | 25.00 |
| | | | | 5-1, 5-2 | all blocks | 22.50 | 15.00 |

| | | NH% | ★VF | ★F | ⊙VF | ⊙F | FDC |
|---|---|---|---|---|---|---|---|
| **247** | **2¢ brown & black** | 50 | .50 | .30 | .25 | .20 | 5.00 |
| a | imperf. pair, 100 pairs | 50 | 700.00 | | — | — | — |
| i | re-entry on lower steps, pos. 17, Pl. 2-2 LL | 50 | 30.00 | 20.00 | 10.00 | 5.00 | |
| | plate blocks, plates 1-1, 1-2, all blocks | 50 | 3.00 | 2.00 | | | |
| | plates 2-1, 2-2, all blocks | 50 | 3.00 | 2.00 | | | |
| | plate 3-1, all blocks | 50 | 15.00 | 10.00 | | | |
| | plate 3-2, all blocks | 50 | 18.00 | 12.00 | | | |

Qty: 50,244,000

| | | NH% | ★VF | ★F | ⊙VF | ⊙F | FDC |
|---|---|---|---|---|---|---|---|
| **248** | **3¢ dark carmine & black** | 50 | .50 | .30 | .25 | .20 | 5.00 |
| a | imperf. pair, 100 pairs | 50 | 700.00 | | — | — | — |
| | combination FDC | — | — | — | — | — | 10.00 |

Qty: 100,000,000

| | NH% | ★VF | ★F | ⊙VF | ⊙F | FDC |
|---|---|---|---|---|---|---|
| **Nos. 246–248** (3) Set | 50 | 1.50 | .70 | .60 | .60 | — |
| **Nos. 246a–248a** Set of 3 imperf. Pairs | 50 | 2,100.00 | | | | |

**No. 248 (3¢) Plate Blocks (NH +50%)**

| Plate No. | Location | ★VF | ★F | Plate No. | Location | ★VF | ★F |
|---|---|---|---|---|---|---|---|
| 1-1 | UL | 52.50 | 35.00 | 3-3 | UL | 90.00 | 60.00 |
| | UR | 45.00 | 30.00 | | UR | 67.50 | 45.00 |
| | LL | 15.00 | 10.00 | | LL | 60.00 | 40.00 |
| | LR | 37.50 | 25.00 | | LR | 105.00 | 70.00 |
| 1-2 | all blocks | 3.00 | 2.00 | 3-4 | all blocks | 4.50 | 3.00 |
| 1-3 | UL, LR | 90.00 | 60.00 | 4-1 | UL, LR | 18.00 | 12.00 |
| | UR | 52.50 | 35.00 | | UR | 120.00 | 80.00 |
| | LL | 45.00 | 30.00 | | LL | 52.50 | 35.00 |
| 1-4 | all blocks | 3.00 | 2.00 | 4-2 | all blocks | 4.50 | 3.00 |
| 2-1 | UL, LR | 22.50 | 15.00 | 4-3 | UL | 37.50 | 25.00 |
| | UR | 90.00 | 60.00 | | UR, LL | 60.00 | 40.00 |
| | LL | 12.00 | 8.00 | | LR | 15.00 | 10.00 |
| 2-2 | all blocks | 4.50 | 3.00 | 4-4 | all blocks | 4.50 | 3.00 |
| 2-3 | UL | 15.00 | 10.00 | 5-1 | Probably does not exist. | | |
| | UR | 22.50 | 15.00 | 5-2 | UL, UR | 135.00 | 90.00 |
| | LL | 30.00 | 20.00 | | LL | 105.00 | 70.00 |
| | LR | 18.00 | 12.00 | | LR | 180.00 | 120.00 |
| 2-4 | all blocks | 4.50 | 3.00 | 5-3 | UL | 2,000.00 | 1,250.00 |
| 3-1 | UL | 67.50 | 45.00 | | LL | 2,500.00 | 1,500.00 |
| | UR | 22.50 | 15.00 | 5-4 | UL | 105.00 | 70.00 |
| | LL, LR | 37.50 | 25.00 | | UR | 135.00 | 90.00 |
| 3-2 | all blocks | 4.50 | 3.00 | | LL | 225.00 | 150.00 |
| | | | | | LR | 180.00 | 120.00 |

Four imperforate plate blocks of each of 246a–248a are known:

246a 1¢ imperf: Plate 4-2 UL, 2-1 UR, 2-1 LL, 1-1 LR
247a 2¢ imperf: Plate 2-2 UR, 2-2 LR, 1-2 LL, 2-2 LL
248a 3¢ imperf: Plate 2-3 LR, 2-1 UL, 2-2 LL, 4-3 LL

## KING GEORGE VI WAR ISSUE

249 250 251 252

253 Grain Elevators · 254 · 255 · 256 Farm Scene



Designer: Herman Herbert Schwartz. George VI image based on a photograph by Hugh Cecil Saunders.

For **O.H.M.S.** overprints see:
1¢ green (249): see O1
2¢ brown (250): see O2
3¢ rose violet (252): see O3
4¢ dark carmine (254): see O4

Canadian Bank Note Company, Limited

**1942–1943** **Engraved** **Perf 12**

| | | NH% | ★VF | ★F | ⊙VF | ⊙F | FDC |
|---|---|---|---|---|---|---|---|
| **249** | **1¢ green**, *Jul 1, 1942* | 50 | .50 | .25 | .25 | .20 | 5.00 |
| **d** | imperf. pair, 150 pairs | 50 | 400.00 | — | — | — | — |
| **i** | vert. pair with full horiz. gutter pair (unique) | — | — | *8,000.00* | — | — | — |
| **xx** | No. 249, precancelled [30 styles] | — | — | — | — | .20 | 3.00 |

Qty: 2,543,000,000

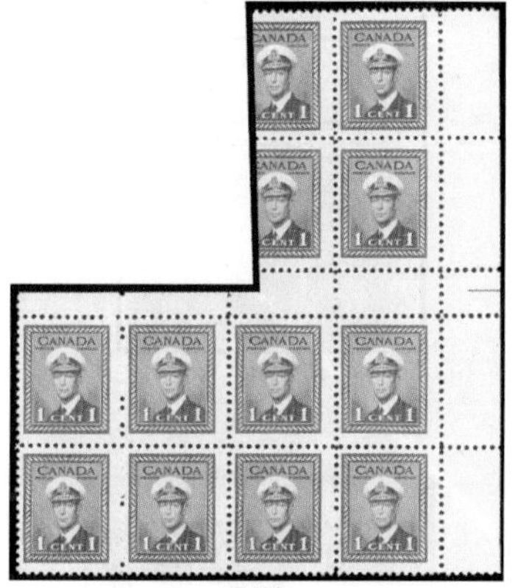

249i

**No. 249 (1¢) Plate Blocks (NH +50%)**

| Plate No. | Location | ★VF | ★F |
|---|---|---|---|
| 1 | all blocks | 5.25 | 3.50 |
| 2 | all blocks | 4.50 | 3.00 |
| 3 | all blocks | 3.75 | 2.50 |
| 4 | UL | 15.00 | 10.00 |
| | UR | 4.50 | 3.00 |
| | LL | 6.00 | 4.00 |
| | LR | 18.00 | 12.00 |
| 5 | UL | 4.50 | 3.00 |
| | UR | 6.00 | 4.00 |
| | LL | 3.75 | 2.50 |
| | LR | 7.50 | 5.00 |
| 6 | UL, UR | 4.50 | 3.00 |
| | LL, LR | 3.75 | 2.50 |
| 7 | UL, LL, LR | 3.75 | 2.50 |
| | UR | 6.00 | 4.00 |
| 8 | UL | 10.50 | 7.00 |
| | UR | 18.00 | 12.00 |
| | LL, LR | 11.25 | 7.50 |
| 9 | UL | 75.00 | 50.00 |
| | UR | 30.00 | 20.00 |
| | LL | 26.25 | 17.50 |
| | LR | 45.00 | 30.00 |
| 10 | UL, LL | 22.50 | 15.00 |
| | UR, LR | 27.00 | 18.00 |
| 11 | UL, UR | 22.50 | 15.00 |
| | LL | 10.50 | 7.00 |
| | LR | 6.00 | 4.00 |
| 12 | UL | 15.00 | 10.00 |
| | UR | 22.50 | 15.00 |
| | LL | 7.50 | 5.00 |
| | LR | 9.00 | 6.00 |
| 13 | UL, LL, LR | 15.00 | 10.00 |
| | UR | 18.00 | 12.00 |
| 14 | UR, UL | 15.00 | 10.00 |
| | LL | 7.50 | 5.00 |
| | LR | 18.00 | 12.00 |
| 15, 16 | all blocks | 3.75 | 2.50 |
| 16 | LL, cracked plate | 50.00 | 30.00 |
| 17 | UL | 13.50 | 9.00 |
| | UR | 9.00 | 6.00 |
| | LL | 7.50 | 5.00 |
| | LR | 18.00 | 12.00 |
| 18 | UL | 10.50 | 7.00 |
| | UR | 15.00 | 10.00 |
| | LL | 7.50 | 5.00 |
| | LR | 18.00 | 12.00 |
| 18 | LL, cracked plate | 50.00 | 30.00 |
| 19 | all blocks | 3.75 | 2.50 |
| 20 | UL | 4.50 | 3.00 |
| | UR, LL, LR | 3.75 | 2.50 |
| 20 | LL, cracked plate | 50.00 | 30.00 |
| 21 | all blocks | 3.75 | 2.50 |
| 21 | LL, cracked plate | 50.00 | 30.00 |
| 22 | all blocks | 3.75 | 2.50 |
| 23 | UL | 12.00 | 8.00 |
| | UR | 15.00 | 10.00 |
| | LL | 4.50 | 3.00 |
| | LR | 40.00 | 25.00 |
| 23 | LL, cracked plate, (block of 20) | 150.00 | 90.00 |
| 24–27 | all blocks | 3.75 | 2.50 |
| 28 | UL, LL, LR | 3.75 | 2.50 |
| | UR | 6.00 | 4.00 |
| 29 | UL | 10.50 | 7.00 |
| | UR, LL, LR | 3.75 | 2.50 |
| 30, 31 | all blocks | 3.75 | 2.50 |
| 32 | UL, LR | 10.50 | 7.00 |
| | UR | 15.00 | 10.00 |
| | LL | 12.00 | 8.00 |

249a

249b

249c

| | | NH% | ★VF | ★F | ⊙VF | ⊙F | FDC |
|---|---|---|---|---|---|---|---|
| 249a | booklet pane of 4 x 1¢ (249as) + 2 labels (BK37), *Sep 14, 1942* | 50 | 5.00 | 4.00 | 5.00 | 4.00 | |
| as | single with straight edge, from 249a or 249b | 50 | 1.00 | .75 | .30 | .20 | |
| b | booklet pane of 6 x 1¢ (249as) (BK32), *Nov 24, 1942* | 50 | 7.00 | 5.00 | 7.00 | 5.00 | |
| c | booklet pane of 3 x 1¢ (249cs), perf. 12 vert. (BK38), *Sep 1, 1943* | 50 | 3.50 | 2.75 | 7.00 | 5.00 | |
| cs | single from 249c* | 50 | 1.00 | .75 | 1.00 | .75 | |

BK32 4 panes 249b in cover; English 11/24/42 (699,000) $28.00, French 02/16/43 (145,000) $45.00, bilingual 01/08/46 (99,000) $48.00

* Straight edge at top and bottom.

| | | NH% | ★VF | ★F | ⊙VF | ⊙F | FDC |
|---|---|---|---|---|---|---|---|
| **250** | **2¢ brown**, *Jul 1, 1942* | 50 | .65 | .50 | .25 | .20 | 5.00 |
| **c** | imperf. pair, 150 pairs | 50 | 400.00 | — | — | — | — |
| **d** | vertical strip of 3, imperf. horiz. showing some blind perfs | 50 | — | *1,500.00* | — | — | — |
| **xx** | No. 250, precancelled [17 styles] | — | — | — | — | .20 | 3.00 |
| | plate blocks, plates 1, 2, all blocks | 50 | 4.50 | 3.00 | | | |
| | plate 3, UL | 50 | 9.00 | 6.00 | | | |
| | plate 3, UR, LR | 50 | 5.25 | 3.50 | | | |
| | plate 3, LL | 50 | 7.50 | 5.00 | | | |
| | plates 4–6, all blocks | 50 | 4.50 | 3.00 | | | |

Qty: 471,000,000

Ten vertical strips of three of 250d exist. Nine show faint traces of blind perfs. Only one is totally imperf. and is the middle strip of three in a block of nine. Value *$8,000.*

250a

250b

| | | NH% | ★VF | ★F | ⊙VF | ⊙F | FDC |
|---|---|---|---|---|---|---|---|
| 250a | booklet pane of 4 x 2¢ (250as) + 2 labels (BK37), *Sep 14, 1942* | 50 | 9.25 | 7.50 | 9.25 | 7.50 | |
| as | single with straight edge, from 250a or 250b | 50 | 2.00 | 1.50 | 1.00 | .75 | |
| b | booklet pane of 6 x 2¢ (250as) (BK33), *Oct 6, 1942* | 50 | 14.00 | 12.50 | 15.00 | 12.50 | |

BK33 2 panes of 250b in cover; English 10/06/42 (75,000) $45.00; French 04/06/43 (10,000) $90.00

| | | NH% | ★VF | ★F | ⊙VF | ⊙F | FDC |
|---|---|---|---|---|---|---|---|
| **251** | **3¢ dark carmine**, *Jul 1, 1942* | 50 | 1.00 | .40 | .25 | .20 | 5.00 |
| **b** | imperf. pair, 150 pairs | 50 | 400.00 | — | — | — | — |
| **xx** | No. 251, precancelled [6 styles] | — | — | — | — | 4.00 | 25.00 |

Qty: 606,000,000

250d

**No. 251 (3¢ dark carmine) Plate Blocks (NH +50%)**

| Plate No. | Location | ★VF | ★F |
|---|---|---|---|
| 1 | UL | 6.00 | 4.00 |
| | UR | 5.25 | 3.50 |
| | LL, LR | 5.00 | 3.25 |
| 2 | UL, UR, LL | 5.00 | 3.25 |
| | LR | 5.25 | 3.50 |
| 3 | UL, UR, LL | 13.50 | 9.00 |
| | LR | 10.50 | 7.00 |
| 4 | UL, LL | 5.00 | 3.25 |
| | UR | 15.00 | 10.00 |
| | LR | 9.00 | 6.00 |
| 5 | UL | 10.50 | 7.00 |
| | UR | 7.50 | 5.00 |
| | LL, LR | 5.00 | 3.25 |
| | LL strip of 20 cracked | 150.00 | 90.00 |
| 6 | UL, UR | 22.50 | 15.00 |
| | LL | 6.75 | 4.50 |
| | LR | 7.50 | 5.00 |
| 7 | UL, UR | 7.50 | 5.00 |
| | LL, LR | 6.00 | 4.00 |
| 8 | UL, LL | 45.00 | 30.00 |
| | UR | 45.00 | 30.00 |
| | LR | 15.00 | 10.00 |
| 9 | UL | 37.50 | 25.00 |
| | UR | 105.00 | 70.00 |
| | LL | 22.50 | 15.00 |
| | LR | 15.00 | 10.00 |
| 10 | UL | 15.00 | 10.00 |
| | UR, LL | 11.25 | 7.50 |
| | LR | 9.00 | 6.00 |

251a

| | | NH% | ★VF | ★F | ⊙VF | ⊙F | FDC |
|---|---|---|---|---|---|---|---|
| 251a | booklet pane of 4 x 3¢ (251as) + 2 labels (BK34, 37), *Aug 20, 1942* | 50 | 5.75 | 5.00 | 7.00 | 5.00 | |
| as | single with straight edge, from 251a | 50 | 1.25 | 1.00 | .40 | .30 | |

BK34 2 panes of 251a in cover; English 08/20/42 (4,650,000) $14.00, French 08/29/42 (560,000) $18.00

BK37 1 pane each of 249a, 250a, 251a in cover; English 09/14/42 (700,000) $30.00, French 09/12/42 (102,000) $60.00

| | | NH% | ★VF | ★F | ⊙VF | ⊙F | FDC |
|---|---|---|---|---|---|---|---|
| **252** | **3¢ rose violet**, *Jun 30, 1943* | 50 | .85 | .65 | .25 | .20 | 40.00 |
| d | imperf. pair, 150 pairs | 50 | 400.00 | — | — | — | — |
| i | horiz. pair with full vert. gutter between, 20 pairs exist | 50 | *3,500.00* | *2,000.00* | — | — | — |
| xx | No. 252, precancelled [11 styles] | | | | — | .30 | 5.00 |

Qty: 2,118,000,000

No. 252i exists in a plate strip of 22 (11 x 2) – *$6,000.*

252i

**No. 252 (3¢ rose violet) Plate Blocks (NH +50%)**

| Plate No./Location | | ★VF | ★F | Plate No./Location | | ★VF | ★F |
|---|---|---|---|---|---|---|---|
| 6 | UL, UR | 337.50 | 225.00 | 18 | all blocks | 90.00 | 60.00 |
| | LL, LR | 300.00 | 200.00 | | LL, cracked plate | 150.00 | 100.00 |
| 7 | UL | 45.00 | 30.00 | 19 | all blocks | 5.00 | 3.25 |
| | UR, LR | 30.00 | 20.00 | | LL, cracked plate | 150.00 | 100.00 |
| | LL | 22.50 | 15.00 | 20 | all blocks | 7.50 | 5.00 |
| 10 | UL | 45.00 | 30.00 | | LL, cracked plate | 55.00 | 35.00 |
| | UR, LR | 30.00 | 20.00 | 21 | all blocks | 5.00 | 3.25 |
| | LL | 22.50 | 15.00 | 22 | UL | 75.00 | 50.00 |
| | LL cracked plate | 110.00 | 70.00 | | UR | 30.00 | 20.00 |
| 11 | UL, LL, LR | 5.00 | 3.25 | | LL, LR | 6.00 | 4.00 |
| | UR | 9.00 | 6.00 | 23 | all blocks | 5.00 | 3.25 |
| 12 | all blocks | 5.00 | 3.25 | 24 | UL, UR | 15.00 | 10.00 |
| | UL cracked plate | 50.00 | 30.00 | | LL, LR | 6.00 | 4.00 |
| | LL cracked plate | 55.00 | 35.00 | 25 | UL, LL, LR | 5.00 | 3.25 |
| 13 | UL, LL, LR | 5.00 | 3.25 | | UR | 5.25 | 3.50 |
| | UR | 5.25 | 3.50 | 26 | all blocks | 7.50 | 5.00 |
| 14 | UL | 10.50 | 7.00 | 27 | UL, UR, LL | 5.00 | 3.25 |
| | UR | 15.00 | 10.00 | | LR | 6.00 | 4.00 |
| | LL | 9.00 | 6.00 | 28 | all blocks | 7.50 | 5.00 |
| | LR | 18.00 | 12.00 | | UL, cracked plate | 50.00 | 30.00 |
| 15 | all blocks | 5.00 | 3.25 | 29, 30 | UL, UR | 5.00 | 3.25 |
| 16 | UL, LL, LR | 5.00 | 3.25 | | LL, LR | 6.00 | 4.00 |
| | UR | 5.25 | 3.50 | 31 | all blocks | 4.50 | 3.00 |
| 17 | UL, UR | 100.00 | 65.00 | 32–34 | UL, LL, LR | 5.00 | 3.25 |
| | LL, LR | 90.00 | 55.00 | | UR | 6.00 | 4.00 |

| | | NH% | ★VF | ★F | ⊙VF | ⊙F | FDC |
|---|---|---|---|---|---|---|---|
| 252a | booklet pane of 4 x 3¢ (252as) + 2 labels (BK35), *Aug 28, 1943* | 50 | 4.50 | 3.75 | 6.00 | 5.00 | |
| as | single with straight edge, from 252a or 252c | 50 | 1.00 | .75 | .50 | .35 | |
| b | booklet pane of 3 x 3¢ (252bs), perf. 12 vert. (BK38), *Sep 1, 1943* | 50 | 4.25 | 3.50 | 5.95 | 4.00 | |
| bs | single with straight edge, from 252b* | 50 | 1.25 | 1.00 | 1.50 | 1.00 | |
| c | booklet pane of 6 x 3¢ (252as) (BK39), *Dec 1, 1947* | 50 | 6.00 | 3.75 | 6.00 | 5.00 | |

BK35 2 panes of 252a in cover, English 08/28/43 (1,201,000) $7.50, French 09/07/43 (61,000) $24.00, bilingual 01/08/46 (407,000) $20.00

* Straight edge at top and bottom.

252a

252b

252c

| | | NH% | ★VF | ★F | ⊙VF | ⊙F | FDC |
|---|---|---|---|---|---|---|---|
| **253** | **4¢ greenish black**, *Jul 1, 1942* | 50 | 2.00 | 1.25 | .75 | .60 | 10.00† |
| a | imperf. pair, 150 pairs | 50 | 400.00 | — | — | — | — |
| | plate blocks, plate 1, UL, UR | 50 | 18.00 | 12.00 | | | |
| | plate 1, LL, LR | 50 | 15.00 | 10.00 | | | |

Qty: 7,900,000

† Any cover. Commercial cover $12.00.

| | | NH% | ★VF | ★F | ⊙VF | ⊙F | FDC |
|---|---|---|---|---|---|---|---|
| **254** | **4¢ dark carmine**, *Apr 9, 1943* | 50 | 1.00 | .40 | .25 | .20 | * |
| **c** | imperf. pair, 150 pairs | 50 | 400.00 | — | — | — | — |
| **xx** | No. 254, precancelled [1 style] | — | — | — | — | 15.00 | |

Qty: 3,149,000,000

* First issued at the Calgary main post office at 10:30 a.m. on April 9, 1943. There was no official first day in Ottawa. Covers dated April 9, 1943 are valued at $100.00.

**No. 254 (4¢) Plate Blocks (NH +50%)**

| Plate No. | Location | ★VF | ★F |
|---|---|---|---|
| 1 | UL, UR | 7.50 | 5.00 |
| | LL | 5.00 | 3.25 |
| | LR | 5.25 | 3.50 |
| 2 | all blocks | 5.00 | 3.25 |
| 3 | UL | 15.00 | 10.00 |
| | UR | 5.25 | 3.50 |
| | LL | 4.50 | 3.00 |
| | LR | 9.00 | 6.00 |
| 4 | UL, UR | 22.50 | 15.00 |
| | LL | 5.25 | 3.50 |
| | LR | 12.00 | 8.00 |
| 5 | all blocks | 5.00 | 3.25 |
| 6 | UL, UR, LL | 5.00 | 3.25 |
| | LR | 6.00 | 4.00 |
| 7 | UL | 10.50 | 7.00 |
| | UR | 30.00 | 20.00 |
| | LL | 9.00 | 6.00 |
| | LR | 45.00 | 30.00 |
| 8 | UL | 15.00 | 10.00 |
| | UR | 105.00 | 70.00 |
| | LL | 13.50 | 9.00 |
| | LR | 52.50 | 35.00 |
| 9 | UL | 26.25 | 17.50 |
| | UR | 97.50 | 65.00 |
| | LL | 12.00 | 8.00 |
| | LR | 37.50 | 25.00 |
| 10 | UL, LR | 37.50 | 25.00 |
| | UR | 90.00 | 60.00 |
| | LL | 9.00 | 6.00 |
| 11 | UL, UR | 26.25 | 17.50 |
| | LL | 15.00 | 10.00 |
| | LR | 37.50 | 25.00 |
| 12 | UL, UR | 12.00 | 8.00 |
| | LL, LR | 6.00 | 4.00 |
| 13 | UL | 22.50 | 15.00 |
| | UR, LL | 7.50 | 5.00 |
| | LR | 11.25 | 7.50 |
| 14 | UL | 18.00 | 12.00 |
| | UR, LL | 30.00 | 20.00 |
| | LR | 60.00 | 40.00 |
| 15 | UL, LR | 22.50 | 15.00 |
| | UR | 37.50 | 25.00 |
| | LL | 18.00 | 12.00 |
| 16 | UL | 52.50 | 35.00 |
| | UR | 60.00 | 40.00 |
| | LL | 45.00 | 30.00 |
| | LR | 75.00 | 50.00 |
| 17 | UL, LL | 22.50 | 15.00 |
| | UR | 37.50 | 25.00 |
| | LR | 90.00 | 60.00 |
| 18 | UL, UR, LR | 24.00 | 16.00 |
| | LL | 22.50 | 15.00 |
| 19 | UL | 18.00 | 12.00 |
| | UR | 15.00 | 10.00 |
| | LL | 13.50 | 9.00 |
| | LR | 30.00 | 20.00 |
| 20 | UL | 18.00 | 12.00 |
| | UR | 12.00 | 8.00 |
| | LL | 9.00 | 6.00 |
| | LR | 22.50 | 15.00 |
| 21 | UL, UR, LR | 22.50 | 15.00 |
| | LL | 15.00 | 10.00 |
| 22 | UL, LL | 15.00 | 10.00 |
| | UR | 22.50 | 15.00 |
| | LR | 18.00 | 12.00 |
| 23 | UL | 30.00 | 20.00 |
| | UR, LL, LR | 37.50 | 25.00 |
| 24 | UL, UR | 60.00 | 40.00 |
| | LL | 105.00 | 70.00 |
| | LR | 90.00 | 60.00 |
| 25 | UL, UR | 30.00 | 20.00 |
| | LL | 24.00 | 16.00 |
| | LR | 35.00 | 25.00 |
| | LL, cracked plate | 60.00 | 35.00 |
| 26 | UL | 5.25 | 3.50 |
| | UR | 6.00 | 4.00 |
| | LL | 5.00 | 3.25 |
| | LR | 9.00 | 6.00 |
| | LL, cracked plate | 50.00 | 30.00 |
| 27 | UL | 30.00 | 20.00 |
| | UR, LL | 15.00 | 10.00 |
| | LR | 22.50 | 15.00 |
| 28 | UL, UR, LR | 22.50 | 15.00 |
| | LL | 18.00 | 12.00 |
| 29 | Plate not used | | |
| 30 | UL, UR, LR | 22.50 | 15.00 |
| | LL | 18.00 | 12.00 |
| | LL, cracked plate | 60.00 | 35.00 |
| 31 | all blocks | 5.00 | 3.25 |
| | LL, cracked plate | 50.00 | 30.00 |
| | LR, cracked plate | 35.00 | 25.00 |
| 32 | all blocks | 4.90 | 3.25 |
| | LL, cracked plate | 50.00 | 30.00 |
| 33 | UL | 37.50 | 25.00 |
| | UR | 30.00 | 20.00 |
| | LL | 15.00 | 10.00 |
| | LR | 22.50 | 15.00 |
| 34 | UL | 30.00 | 20.00 |
| | UR, LL | 18.00 | 12.00 |
| | LR | 7.50 | 5.00 |
| 35 | UL | 105.00 | 70.00 |
| | UR, LL, LR | 22.50 | 15.00 |
| | LL, cracked plate | 55.00 | 35.00 |
| 36 | UL | 12.00 | 8.00 |
| | UR | 15.00 | 10.00 |
| | LL | 13.50 | 9.00 |
| | LR | 10.50 | 7.00 |
| 37 | all blocks | 5.00 | 3.25 |
| 38 | UL | 5.00 | 3.25 |
| | UR, LR | 9.00 | 6.00 |
| | LL | 6.00 | 4.00 |
| 39 | all blocks | 5.00 | 3.25 |
| 40 | UL | 5.00 | 3.25 |
| | UR, LL | 6.00 | 4.00 |
| | LR | 6.75 | 4.50 |
| 41 | UL | 7.50 | 5.00 |
| | UR | 5.25 | 3.50 |
| | LL, LR | 5.00 | 3.25 |
| 42, 43 | all blocks | 5.00 | 3.25 |
| 44 | UL | 52.50 | 35.00 |
| | UR | 22.50 | 15.00 |
| | LL | 15.00 | 10.00 |
| | LR | 30.00 | 20.00 |
| 45 | UL | 5.25 | 3.50 |
| | UR, LL, LR | 5.00 | 3.25 |
| | UL, cracked plate | 50.00 | 30.00 |
| 46 | UL | 12.00 | 8.00 |
| | UR | 5.25 | 3.50 |
| | LL | 5.00 | 3.25 |
| | LR | 16.50 | 11.00 |
| 47–50 | all blocks | 5.00 | 3.25 |
| 48 | UL, cracked plate | 50.00 | 35.00 |

| | | NH% | ★VF | ★F | ⊙VF | ⊙F | FDC |
|---|---|---|---|---|---|---|---|
| 254a | booklet pane of 6 x 4¢ (254as) (BK36), *May 3, 1943* | 50 | 7.00 | 6.00 | 14.00 | 12.00 | |
| as | single with straight edge, from 254a or 254ai | 50 | 1.00 | .75 | .50 | .35 | |
| ai | as 254a, with larger tab (from gift booklet) (BK39) | 50 | 10.00 | 8.00 | 12.50 | 10.00 | |
| b | booklet pane of 3 x 4¢ (254bs), perf. 12 vert. (BK38), *Sep 1, 1943* | 50 | 4.25 | 3.50 | 6.00 | 5.00 | |
| bs | single with straight edge, from 254b* | 50 | 1.25 | 1.00 | 1.75 | 1.00 | |

**BK36** 1 pane 254a in cover; English 05/03/43 (24,114,000) $8.75, French 05/12/43 (1,789,000) $12.00, bilingual 01/08/46 (3,001,000) $15.00

**BK38** 1 pane each 249c, 252b and 254b in cover; English 09/01/43 (5,464,000) $15.00, French 09/18/43 (496,000) $25.00, bilingual 01/23/46 (992,000) $22.00.

**BK39** 1 pane each 252c, 254ai, 2 panes C9a (Air Mail), 2 panes Air Mail stickers in cover; English 12/01/47 (404,500) $40.00, French 12/01/47 (100,000) $48.00

* Straight edge at top and bottom.

254a

254b

| | | NH% | ★VF | ★F | ⊙VF | ⊙F | FDC |
|---|---|---|---|---|---|---|---|
| **255** | **5¢ deep blue**, *Jul 1, 1942* | 50 | 2.00 | 1.00 | .25 | .20 | 15.00 |
| a | imperf. pair, 150 pairs | 50 | 400.00 | — | — | — | — |
| xx | No. 255, precancelled [1 style] | — | — | — | — | 4.00 | 5.00 |
| | plate blocks, plates 1–4, all blocks | 50 | 13.50 | 9.00 | | | |

Qty: 174,000,000

| | | NH% | ★VF | ★F | ⊙VF | ⊙F | FDC |
|---|---|---|---|---|---|---|---|
| **256** | **8¢ red brown**, *Jul 1, 1942* | 50 | 2.50 | 1.50 | .75 | .50 | 20.00† |
| a | imperf. pair, 150 pairs | 50 | 400.00 | — | — | — | — |
| | plate blocks, plate 1, all blocks | 50 | 20.00 | 12.50 | | | |
| | plate 1, LL block of 6 (2 x 3) | 50 | 52.50 | 35.00 | | | |

Qty: 22,979,000

† Any cover.

King George VI — War

257
Parliament Buildings

258
Ram Tank, Canadian Army

259
Ram Tank, Canadian Army

260
Corvette

261
Munitions Factory

262
Tribal Class Destroyer, Royal Canadian Navy

See also C7, C8

| | | NH% | ★VF | ★F | ⊙VF | ⊙F | FDC |
|---|---|---|---|---|---|---|---|
| **257** | **10¢ brown**, *Jul 1, 1942* | 50 | 8.00 | 3.50 | .25 | .20 | 15.00 |
| a | imperf. pair, 75 pairs | 50 | 600.00 | — | — | — | — |
| i | imperf. at right margin, 10 may exist | 50 | 1,500.00 | | | | |
| | as "i", plate block of 4, plate 3, LR (unique, NH) | — | | *6,000.00* | | | |

Qty: 157,680,577

**No. 257 (10¢) Plate Blocks (NH +50%)**

| Plate No. | Location | ★VF | ★F | Plate No. | Location | ★VF | ★F |
|---|---|---|---|---|---|---|---|
| 1 | all blocks | 50.00 | 32.50 | 5 | UL | 135.00 | 90.00 |
| 2, 3 | all blocks | 50.00 | 30.00 | | UR, LL | 112.50 | 75.00 |
| 3 | UL cracked | 250.00 | 150.00 | | LR | 150.00 | 100.00 |
| 4 | UL, LR | 187.50 | 125.00 | 6 | all blocks | 50.00 | 30.00 |
| | UR | 262.50 | 175.00 | | | | |
| | LL | 112.50 | 75.00 | | | | |

257i

| | | NH% | ★VF | ★F | ⊙VF | ⊙F | FDC |
|---|---|---|---|---|---|---|---|
| **258** | **13¢ dull green**, *Jul 1, 1942* | 50 | 8.00 | 5.00 | 5.50 | 4.00 | 15.00 |
| a | imperf. pair, 50 pairs | 50 | 600.00 | — | — | — | — |
| | plate blocks, plate 1, all blocks | 50 | 60.00 | 40.00 | | | |

Qty: 4,000,000

| | | NH% | ★VF | ★F | ⊙VF | ⊙F | FDC |
|---|---|---|---|---|---|---|---|
| **259** | **14¢ dull green**, *Apr 16, 1943* | 50 | 12.00 | 6.00 | .50 | .30 | 40.00 |
| a | imperf. pair, 75 pairs | 50 | 600.00 | — | — | — | — |
| i | "hairlines" variety (Pl. 1 LL, pos. 46) | 50 | 40.00 | 30.00 | 20.00 | 15.00 | 40.00 |
| | 259i, in LL block of 4, with 3 normal | 50 | 90.00 | 60.00 | 60.00 | 40.00 | |
| | plate blocks, plate 1, all blocks | 50 | 67.50 | 45.00 | | | |

Qty: 14,878,673

First issued at the Edmonton main post office at 8:00 a.m. on April 16, 1943. There was no official first day in Ottawa. First Day covers exist in combination with C8 and CE2 which were issued the same day. These are rare – $250.

| | | NH% | ★VF | ★F | ⊙VF | ⊙F | FDC |
|---|---|---|---|---|---|---|---|
| **260** | **20¢ chocolate**, *Jul 1, 1942* | 50 | 15.00 | 8.50 | .30 | .25 | 25.00 |
| a | imperf. pair, 75 pairs | 50 | 600.00 | — | — | — | — |
| | plate blocks, plates 1, 2, all blocks | 50 | 75.00 | 50.00 | | | |

Qty: 62,028,166

| | | NH% | ★VF | ★F | ⊙VF | ⊙F | FDC |
|---|---|---|---|---|---|---|---|
| **261** | **50¢ violet**, *Jul 1, 1942* | 50 | 40.00 | 30.00 | 2.75 | 2.25 | 50.00 |
| a | imperf. pair, 75 pairs | 50 | 600.00 | — | — | — | — |
| | plate blocks, plate 1, all blocks | 50 | 240.00 | 180.00 | | | |

Qty: 16,486,515

| | | NH% | ★VF | ★F | ⊙VF | ⊙F | FDC |
|---|---|---|---|---|---|---|---|
| **262** | **$1 deep blue**, *Jul 1, 1942* | 50 | 80.00 | 70.00 | 11.00 | 8.00 | 150.00† |
| a | imperf. pair, 75 pairs | 50 | 800.00 | — | — | — | — |
| | plate blocks, plate 1, all blocks | 50 | 500.00 | 300.00 | | | |

Qty: 6,195,600

† Single usage $250.00. Bulk payment receipts are worth less.

| | NH% | ★VF | ★F | ⊙VF | ⊙F | FDC |
|---|---|---|---|---|---|---|
| **Nos. 249–262** (14) Set | 50 | 171.00 | 128.70 | 22.95 | 17.30 | 400.00 |
| **Nos. 249d–262a** (14) Set of imperf. pairs | 50 | 7,000.00 | — | — | — | — |

## KING GEORGE VI WAR ISSUE COIL STAMPS

263

264

265

266

267

| 1942–1943 | | Engraved NH% | ★VF | ★F | ⊙VF | Perf 8 vertical ⊙F | ✉ |
|---|---|---|---|---|---|---|---|
| **263** | **1¢ green** (249), *Feb 9, 1943* | 50 | 2.00 | 1.00 | .75 | .45 | 8.00† |
| | pair | 50 | 4.00 | 2.00 | 2.00 | 1.00 | 10.00† |
| | strip of 4 | 50 | 8.00 | 4.00 | 5.00 | 3.00 | 20.00† |
| i | jump strip of 4 | 50 | 10.00 | 5.00 | 7.50 | 5.00 | — |
| | repair paste-up pair | 50 | 30.00 | 20.00 | — | — | — |
| xx | No. 263, precancelled [1 style] | — | — | — | — | .50 | |
| Qty: 26,000,000 | | | | | | | |
| **264** | **2¢ brown** (250), *Nov 24, 1942* | 50 | 3.00 | 1.50 | 1.50 | 1.00 | 9.00† |
| | pair | 50 | 6.00 | 3.00 | 3.50 | 2.50 | 15.00† |
| | strip of 4 | 50 | 12.00 | 6.00 | 10.00 | 5.00 | 30.00† |
| i | jump strip of 4 | 50 | 15.00 | 7.50 | 11.00 | 7.50 | — |
| | repair paste-up pair | 50 | 45.00 | 30.00 | — | — | — |
| Qty: 8,465,000 | | | | | | | |
| **265** | **3¢ dark carmine** (251), *Sep 23, 1942* | 50 | 3.00 | 1.50 | 1.50 | 1.00 | 8.00† |
| | pair | 50 | 6.00 | 3.00 | 3.50 | 2.50 | 18.00† |
| | strip of 4 | 50 | 12.00 | 6.00 | 10.00 | 5.00 | 37.50† |
| i | jump strip of 4 | 50 | 15.00 | 7.50 | 11.00 | 7.50 | — |
| | repair paste-up pair | 50 | 45.00 | 30.00 | — | — | — |
| Qty: 9,975,000 | | | | | | | |
| **266** | **3¢ rose violet** (252), *Aug 19, 1943* | 50 | 6.00 | 2.50 | .50 | .25 | 8.00† |
| | pair | 50 | 12.00 | 5.00 | 2.50 | 1.50 | 18.00† |
| | strip of 4 | 50 | 24.00 | 10.00 | 10.00 | 5.00 | 37.50† |
| i | jump strip of 4 | 50 | 30.00 | 12.50 | 15.00 | 10.00 | — |
| | repair paste-up pair | 50 | 80.00 | 50.00 | — | — | — |
| Qty: 45,990,000 | | | | | | | |
| **267** | **4¢ dark carmine** (254), May 13, 1943 | 50 | 8.00 | 4.00 | .40 | .20 | 8.00† |
| | pair | 50 | 16.00 | 8.00 | 5.00 | 2.50 | 30.00† |
| | strip of 4 | 50 | 32.00 | 16.00 | 15.00 | 7.50 | 60.00† |
| i | jump strip of 4 | 50 | 40.00 | 20.00 | 25.00 | 15.00 | — |
| | repair paste-up pair | 50 | 140.00 | 70.00 | — | — | — |
| Qty: 47,590,000 | | | | | | | |
| **Nos. 263-267** (5) Set | | 50 | 22.00 | 10.50 | 4.65 | 2.90 | — |

† Commercial cover. FDC's are scarce; value any cover $100.00 each.

For perf 9½ vertical coils of the same design, see 278–281.

**Start or End Strips**
2 stamps + 2 blank tabs
NH: +50%

| Sc# | ★VF | ★F |
|---|---|---|
| 263 | 22.50 | 15.00 |
| 264 | 35.00 | 22.50 |
| 265 | 35.00 | 22.50 |
| 266 | 60.00 | 37.50 |
| 267 | 100.00 | 60.00 |

Full strips of 4 stamps with full tabs (10) are 3 times listed price.

More than two stamps add catalogue value of extra stamps.

## KING GEORGE VI PEACE ISSUE

268
Eastern Farm Scene

269
Great Bear Lake, NWT

270
Hydroelectric Station, Quebec

271
Combine Harvesting

272
Logging, BC

273
Train Ferry, PEI
*Q.S.M.V. Abegweit*

See also C9

Designer: Herman Herbert Schwartz
Engravers: 8¢: Warrell Hauck; 10¢, 20¢, $1: Silas Robert Allen; 14¢: Arthur C. Vogel; 50¢: Joseph Keller

Canadian Bank Note Company, Limited

**1946, Sep 16** **Engraved** **Perf 12**

| NH +50% | | ★VF | ★F | ⊙VF | ⊙F | FDC |
|---|---|---|---|---|---|---|
| **268** | **8¢ red brown** | 3.00 | 1.25 | 1.00 | .50 | 7.00† |
| | plate blocks, plates 1, 2, all blocks | 12.75 | 8.50 | | | |
| Qty: 15,100,000 | | | | | | |
| † Commerical cover $15.00. | | | | | | |
| **269** | **10¢ olive** | 4.50 | 2.00 | .25 | .20 | 7.00 |
| | plate blocks, plates 1, 2, all blocks | 15.75 | 10.50 | | | |
| Qty: 118,250,000 | | | | | | |
| **270** | **14¢ black brown** | 5.50 | 3.25 | .30 | .20 | 15.00 |
| i | thin ribbed paper* | | 200.00 | | | |
| ii | imperf at right margin | | *2,500.00* | | | |
| | plate blocks, plate 1, all blocks | 26.25 | 17.50 | | | |
| Qty: 21,900,000 | | | | | | |
| * One imprint block is known of the thin paper variety, value $1,000.00 | | | | | | |
| **271** | **20¢ slate black** | 7.00 | 3.50 | .25 | .20 | 20.00 |
| | plate blocks, plates 1, 2, all blocks | 30.00 | 20.00 | | | |
| Qty: 84,350,000 | | | | | | |
| **272** | **50¢ dark blue green** | 20.00 | 10.00 | 3.00 | 1.50 | 35.00* |
| | plate blocks, plate 1, all blocks | 150.00 | 75.00 | | | |
| Qty: 13,970,000 | | | | | | |
| * Commercial cover $50.00. | | | | | | |

| NH +50% | | ★VF | ★F | ⊙VF | ⊙F | FDC |
|---|---|---|---|---|---|---|
| **273** | **$1 red violet** | 45.00 | 25.00 | 5.00 | 2.75 | 55.00* |
| | combination FDC | | | | | 70.00 |
| | plate blocks, plate 1, all blocks | 300.00 | 150.00 | | | |
| Qty: 15,375,000 | | | | | | |
| * Commercial cover $70.00; bulk payment receipts are worth much less. | | | | | | |
| **Nos. 268–273** (6) Set | | 85.00 | 45.00 | 9.75 | 5.35 | — |

270ii

For **O.H.M.S.** overprints see:
10¢: see O6
14¢: see O7
20¢: see O8
50¢: see O9
$1: see O10

For **G** overprints see:
10¢: see O21
14¢: see O22
20¢: see O23
$1: see O25

## ALEXANDER GRAHAM BELL

274
Bell and winged figure of Fame

Designer: Herman Herbert Schwartz. Engraver: Silas Robert Allen.

Canadian Bank Note Company, Limited

**1947, Mar 3** **Engraved** **Perf 12**

| NH +25% | | ★VF | ★F | ⊙VF | ⊙F | FDC |
|---|---|---|---|---|---|---|
| **274** | **4¢ deep blue** | .30 | .20 | .25 | .20 | 3.00 |
| | plate blocks, plates 1, 2 (NH-VF) $2.00 each | | | | | |
| Qty: 25,050,000 | | | | | | |

Issued to mark the 100th anniversary of the birth of Alexander Graham Bell, inventor of the telephone.

## CONFEDERATION

275
Canadian Citizenship

Designer: Alan Brookman Beddoe. Modeled by Herman Herbert Schwartz. Engraver: Silas Robert Allen.

Canadian Bank Note Company, Limited

**1947, Jul 1** **Engraved** **Perf 12**

| NH +25% | | ★VF | ★F | ⊙VF | ⊙F | FDC |
|---|---|---|---|---|---|---|
| **275** | **4¢ deep blue** | .30 | .20 | .25 | .20 | 3.00 |
| | plate blocks, plates 1, 2 (NH-VF) $2.00 each | | | | | |
| Qty: 25,100,000 | | | | | | |

Issued on the occasion of the 80th anniversary of Confederation and to mark the advent of Canadian Citizenship.

## ROYAL WEDDING

276
Princess Elizabeth

Designer: Herman Herbert Schwartz. Based on a photograph by Dorothy Wilding. Engraver: William F. Ford.

Canadian Bank Note Company, Limited

**1948, Feb 16** **Engraved** **Perf 12**

| NH +25% | | ★VF | ★F | ⊙VF | ⊙F | FDC |
|---|---|---|---|---|---|---|
| **276** | **4¢ deep blue** | .25 | .20 | .25 | .20 | 3.00 |
| | plate blocks, plates 1, 2 (NH-VF) $2.00 each | | | | | |

Qty: 50,010,000

Issued to commemorate the marriage of Princess Elizabeth to Philip Mountbatten on 20 November 1947.

## RESPONSIBLE GOVERNMENT

277
Parliament Buildings

Designer: Herman Herbert Schwartz. Engraver: Silas Robert Allen.

Canadian Bank Note Company, Limited

**1948, Oct 1** **Engraved** **Perf 12**

| NH +25% | | ★VF | ★F | ⊙VF | ⊙F | FDC |
|---|---|---|---|---|---|---|
| **277** | **4¢ grey** | .25 | .20 | .25 | .20 | 3.00 |
| | plate blocks, plates 1, 2 (NH-VF) $1.50 each | | | | | |

Qty: 50,300,000

Issued to mark the 100th anniversary of Responsible Government in Canada.

## KING GEORGE VI WAR ISSUE COIL STAMPS

278

279

280

281

**1948** **Engraved** **Perf 9½ vertical**

| NH +50% | | ★VF | ★F | ⊙VF | ⊙F | ✉ |
|---|---|---|---|---|---|---|
| **278** | **1¢ green** (249), *Jul 13, 1948* | 6.00 | 3.00 | 3.00 | 1.75 | 11.00† |
| | pair | 12.00 | 6.00 | 8.50 | 4.00 | 16.00† |
| | strip of 4 | 24.00 | 12.00 | 18.00 | 12.00 | 35.00† |
| i | jump strip of 4 | 35.00 | 17.50 | 25.00 | 17.50 | |
| | repair paste-up pair | 75.00 | 30.00 | — | — | — |
| xx | No. 278, precancelled [1 style] | 3.50 | 1.50 | 1.50 | 1.00 | 3.00 |
| **279** | **2¢ brown** (250), *Oct 1, 1948* | 20.00 | 10.00 | 13.00 | 7.50 | 15.00† |
| | pair | 40.00 | 20.00 | 27.50 | 16.00 | 28.00† |
| | strip of 4 | 80.00 | 40.00 | 56.00 | 35.00 | 60.00† |
| i | jump strip of 4 | 120.00 | 60.00 | 75.00 | 50.00 | |
| | repair paste-up pair | 120.00 | 90.00 | — | — | — |

| NH +50% | | ★VF | ★F | ⊙VF | ⊙F | ✉ |
|---|---|---|---|---|---|---|
| **280** | **3¢ rose violet** (252), *Jul 2, 1948* | 14.00 | 6.00 | 3.00 | 2.50 | 14.00† |
| | pair | 28.00 | 12.00 | 11.00 | 7.50 | 24.00† |
| | strip of 4 | 56.00 | 24.00 | 25.00 | 17.50 | 60.00† |
| i | jump strip of 4 | 90.00 | 40.00 | 45.00 | 30.00 | |
| | repair paste-up pair | 80.00 | 52.50 | — | — | — |

An "imperf at bottom" of 280 has been reported (illustrated below).

| | | ★VF | ★F | ⊙VF | ⊙F | ✉ |
|---|---|---|---|---|---|---|
| **281** | **4¢ dark carmine** (254), *Jul 22, 1948* | 20.00 | 8.50 | 3.50 | 3.00 | 14.00† |
| | pair | 40.00 | 17.00 | 9.00 | 7.50 | 26.00† |
| | strip of 4 | 80.00 | 34.00 | 30.00 | 20.00 | 60.00† |
| i | jump strip of 4 | 120.00 | 50.00 | 50.00 | 35.00 | |
| | repair paste-up pair | 150.00 | 75.00 | — | — | — |
| **Nos. 278–281** | (4) Set | 60.00 | 27.50 | 22.50 | 14.75 | |

† Commercial cover. FDC's are scarce; value any cover $100.00 each.

For perf 8 vertical coils of the same design, see 263–267.

280
Imperf at bottom

**Start or End Strips**
2 stamps + 2 blank tabs; NH: +50%

| Sc# | ★VF | ★F |
|---|---|---|
| 278 | 50.00 | 30.00 |
| 279 | 100.00 | 60.00 |
| 280 | 75.00 | 50.00 |
| 281 | 100.00 | 60.00 |

Full strips of 4 stamps with full tabs (10) are 3 times listed price.

## NEWFOUNDLAND

282
Cabot's ship *Matthew*

Designer: Herman Herbert Schwartz. Based on a model by Herbert Ernest Maunder. Engraver: Silas Robert Allen.

Canadian Bank Note Company, Limited

**1949, Apr 1** **Engraved** **Perf 12**

| | | NH–VF | ★F | ⊙F | FDC |
|---|---|---|---|---|---|
| **282** | **4¢ deep green** | .30 | .20 | .20 | 3.00 |
| | plate blocks, plates 1, 2 (NH-VF) $1.50 each | | | | |

Qty: 50,850,000

Issued on the occasion of Newfoundland's entry into Confederation as Canada's 10th province.

## HALIFAX BICENTENARY

283
Founding of Halifax

Designer: Herman Herbert Schwartz. Based on a painting by Charles William Jefferys. Engraver: Silas Robert Allen.

Canadian Bank Note Company, Limited

**1949, Jun 21** **Engraved** **Perf 12**

| | | NH–VF | ★F | ⊙F | FDC |
|---|---|---|---|---|---|
| **283** | **4¢ purple** | .30 | .20 | .20 | 3.00 |
| | plate blocks, plates 1, 2 (NH-VF) $1.50 each | | | | |

Qty: 25,450,000

## KING GEORGE VI WITH "POSTES-POSTAGE"

284

285

286

287

288

For **O.H.M.S.** overprints see numbers O12–O15A.
For **G** overprints see numbers O16–O20.

Designer: Herman Herbert Schwartz. Based on a photograph by Dorothy Wilding. Portrait engraved by John Hay.

Canadian Bank Note Company, Limited

| **1949** | **Engraved** | | | | | **Perf 12** |
|---|---|---|---|---|---|---|
| | | NH–VF | ★F | ⊙VF | ⊙F | FDC |
| **284** | **1¢ green**, *Nov 15, 1949* | .30 | .20 | .25 | .20 | 8.00 |
| **xx** | No. 284, precancelled [23 styles] | — | — | — | .20 | 2.00 |

Qty: 803,000,000

| No. 284 (1¢) Plate Blocks (NH +25%) | | | | | | | |
|---|---|---|---|---|---|---|---|
| Plate No./Location | | ★VF | ★F | Plate No./Location | | ★VF | ★F |
| 1, 2 | all blocks | 1.10 | .90 | 6 | all blocks | 1.90 | 1.50 |
| 3 | never used | | | 7 | UL, UR | 8.75 | 7.00 |
| 4 | all blocks | 7.50 | 6.00 | | LL, LR | 10.00 | 8.00 |
| 5 | all blocks | 1.25 | 1.00 | 8, 9 | all blocks | 1.55 | 1.25 |
| | UL, cracked plate | 50.00 | 25.00 | | | | |

| | | NH–VF | ★F | ⊙VF | ⊙F | FDC |
|---|---|---|---|---|---|---|
| **284a** | booklet pane of 3 x 1¢ (284as), (BK43, 44), *May 18, 1950* | 1.00 | .50 | 4.00 | 3.50 | |
| **as** | single with straight edge, from 284a | .50 | .25 | 1.00 | .50 | |
| **285** | **2¢ sepia**, *Nov 15, 1949* | .40 | .20 | .25 | .20 | 8.00 |
| **xx** | No. 285, precancelled [13 styles] | — | — | — | .20 | 2.00 |

Qty: 202,000,000

| No. 285 (2¢) Plate Blocks (NH +25%) | | | | | | | |
|---|---|---|---|---|---|---|---|
| Plate No./Location | | ★VF | ★F | Plate No./Location | | ★VF | ★F |
| 1 | all blocks | 1.90 | 1.50 | 3 | UL, LL, LR | 2.50 | 2.00 |
| 2 | UL, LL | 2.50 | 2.00 | | UR | 3.75 | 3.00 |
| | UR, LR | 1.90 | 1.50 | 4 | all blocks | 15.00 | 12.00 |

| | | NH–VF | ★F | ⊙VF | ⊙F | FDC |
|---|---|---|---|---|---|---|
| **286** | **3¢ rose violet**, *Nov 15, 1949* | .50 | .25 | .25 | .20 | 8.00 |
| **xx** | No. 286, precancelled [5 styles] | — | — | — | .25 | 2.00 |

Qty: 1,357,000,000

| No. 286 (3¢) Plate Blocks (NH +25%) | | | | | | | |
|---|---|---|---|---|---|---|---|
| Plate No./Location | | ★VF | ★F | Plate No./Location | | ★VF | ★F |
| 1 | all blocks | 2.05 | 1.65 | 7 | all blocks | 2.05 | 1.65 |
| 2 | UL, LL | 2.05 | 1.65 | 8 | all blocks | 1.90 | 1.50 |
| | UR | 2.50 | 2.00 | 9 | all blocks | 10.00 | 8.00 |
| | LR | 2.20 | 1.75 | | LL, cracked plate | 50.00 | 30.00 |
| 3, 4 | all blocks | 1.90 | 1.50 | | LR, cracked plate* | 50.00 | 30.00 |
| 4 | UL, cracked plate | 50.00 | 25.00 | 10, 11 | all blocks | 2.05 | 1.65 |
| | UR, cracked plate | 50.00 | 30.00 | | LR, cracked plate | 50.00 | 25.00 |
| 5 | UL, UR | 3.75 | 3.00 | 12–14 | all blocks | 2.05 | 1.65 |
| | LL, LR | 3.10 | 2.50 | *No 286: plates 9, 11, LR, cracked plate in strip of 20—crack visible under left 6 stamps but not under plate block, VF$150.00; F$100.00. | | | |
| 6 | UL | 3.10 | 2.50 | | | | |
| | UR, LL, LR | 2.20 | 1.75 | | | | |

| | | NH–VF | ★F | ⊙VF | ⊙F | FDC |
|---|---|---|---|---|---|---|
| **286a** | booklet pane of 3 x 3¢ (286as), (BK43, 44), *May 18, 1950* | 3.50 | 3.00 | 10.00 | 8.00 | |
| **as** | single with straight edge, from 286a* | 1.00 | .75 | .75 | .50 | |
| **b** | booklet pane of 4 x 3¢ (286bs) + 2 labels (BK40), *Apr 12, 1950* | 4.50 | 4.00 | 5.00 | 4.00 | |
| **bs** | single with straight edge, from 286b | 1.00 | .75 | .50 | .30 | |

**BK40** 2 panes of 286b in cover; English 04/12/50 (825,000) $9.00, bilingual 05/18/50 (202,000) $13.00

* Straight edge at top and bottom.

284a

286a

286b

| | | NH–VF | ★F | ⊙VF | ⊙F | FDC |
|---|---|---|---|---|---|---|
| **287** | **4¢ dark carmine**, *Nov 15, 1949* | .80 | .40 | .30 | .20 | 8.00 |

Qty: 710,000,000

| No. 287 (4¢) Plate Blocks (NH +25%) | | | | | | | |
|---|---|---|---|---|---|---|---|
| Plate No./Location | | ★VF | ★F | Plate No./Location | | ★VF | ★F |
| 1, 2 | all blocks | 3.45 | 2.75 | 8 | all blocks | 3.15 | 2.50 |
| 3 | all blocks | 3.75 | 3.00 | 9 | all blocks | 3.75 | 3.00 |
| 4 | all blocks | 3.10 | 2.50 | | UL, cracked plate | 50.00 | 30.00 |
| 5 | UL | 75.00 | 60.00 | 10 | all blocks | 3.75 | 3.00 |
| | UR, LL, LR | 25.00 | 20.00 | 11 | UL, LL, LR | 25.00 | 20.00 |
| 6 | all blocks | 3.10 | 2.50 | | UR | 75.00 | 60.00 |
| | LL, cracked plate | 50.00 | 30.00 | | | | |
| 7 | UL, LL, LR | 4.40 | 3.50 | | | | |
| | UR | 5.60 | 4.50 | | | | |

| | | NH–VF | ★F | ⊙VF | ⊙F | FDC |
|---|---|---|---|---|---|---|
| **287a** | booklet pane of 3 x 4¢ (287as), (BK43), *May 18, 1950* | 17.50 | 14.00 | 17.50 | 14.00 | |
| **as** | single with straight edge, from 287a* | 5.00 | 2.00 | 5.00 | 4.00 | |
| **b** | booklet pane of 6 x 4¢ (287bs) (BK41a), *May 5, 1950* | 25.00 | 20.00 | 25.00 | 20.00 | |
| **bs** | single with straight edge, from 287b | 2.50 | 2.25 | 2.50 | 2.25 | |
| **bi** | as b, stitched (BK41c) | 90.00 | 50.00 | 75.00 | 60.00 | |

**BK41** 1 pane 287b in cover; English 05/05/50 (4,500,000) $30.00, bilingual 05/10/50 (1,203,000) $50.00

**BK43** 1 pane each 284a, 286a, 287a in cover; English 05/18/50 (914,500) $28.00, bilingual 05/18/50 (332,950) $40.00

* Straight edge at top and bottom.

287a

287b

| | | NH–VF | ★F | ⊙VF | ⊙F | FDC |
|---|---|---|---|---|---|---|
| **288** | **5¢ deep blue**, *Nov 15, 1949* | 1.75 | 1.00 | 1.00 | .20 | 8.00 |
| | plate blocks, plates 1–3, all blocks | 8.45 | 6.75 | | | |

Qty: 95,000,000

| | | NH–VF | ★F | ⊙VF | ⊙F | FDC |
|---|---|---|---|---|---|---|
| **Nos. 284–288** | (5) Set | 3.75 | 2.05 | 2.05 | 1.00 | 15.00† |

Although issued first, this is really the "revised" set with the inscription POSTES-POSTAGE designating Canada as a bilingual country.

† Combination FDC

## KING GEORGE VI — "POSTES-POSTAGE" OMITTED

289

290

291

292

293

**1950, Jan 19** | **Engraved** | **Perf 12**

| No. | | Description | NH–VF | ★F | ⊙VF | ⊙F | FDC |
|---|---|---|---|---|---|---|---|
| **289** | | **1¢ green** | .30 | .20 | .25 | .20 | 100.00 |
| | | plate blocks, plates 1, 2, all blocks | 1.50 | 1.00 | | | |
| Qty: 84,000,000 | | | | | | | |
| **290** | | **2¢ sepia** | .50 | .20 | .25 | .20 | 100.00 |
| | | plate blocks, plates 1, 2, all blocks | 3.75 | 3.00 | | | |
| Qty: 10,200,000 | | | | | | | |
| **291** | | **3¢ rose violet** | .50 | .25 | .25 | .20 | 100.00 |
| | | plate blocks, plates 1, 2, all blocks | 2.50 | 1.35 | | | |
| Qty: 101,300,000 | | | | | | | |
| **292** | | **4¢ dark carmine** | .50 | .35 | .25 | .20 | 100.00 |
| | | plate blocks, plates 1, 2, all blocks | 2.50 | 1.75 | | | |
| Qty: 101,100,000 | | | | | | | |
| **293** | | **5¢ deep blue** | 2.00 | 1.00 | 1.50 | 1.25 | 100.00 |
| | | plate blocks, plates 1, 2, UR | 10.00 | 7.00 | | | |
| | | plates 1, 2, UL, LL, LR | 9.50 | 6.00 | | | |
| Qty: 5,000,000 | | | | | | | |
| **Nos. 289-293** (5) Set | | | 3.50 | 2.00 | 2.50 | 2.05 | 275.00* |

* Combination FDC

## OIL WELLS

294

Designer: Herman Herbert Schwartz. Engraver: Silas Robert Allen.
Canadian Bank Note Company, Limited

**1950, Mar 1** | **Engraved** | **Perf 12**

| No. | | Description | NH–VF | ★F | ⊙F | FDC |
|---|---|---|---|---|---|---|
| **294** | | **50¢ dull green** | 12.00 | 6.00 | 1.75 | 40.00 |
| | | plate blocks, plate 1, all blocks 60.00 | | | | |
| | i | imperf. top margin (in pair with normal) | *3,500.00* | — | — | — |
| | | 294i in plate block (unique) – *$10,000.00* | | | | |
| Qty: 10,150,000 | | | | | | |

For **O.H.M.S.** overprint see number O11. For **G** overprint see number O24.

294i

## KING GEORGE VI — "POSTES-POSTAGE" OMITTED
## 1949 COIL STAMPS

295

296

**1949, Dec 23** | **Engraved** | **Perf 9½ vertical**

| No. | | Description | NH–VF | ★F | ⊙F | ✉ |
|---|---|---|---|---|---|---|
| **295** | | **1¢ green** (289) | 1.00 | .45 | .40 | 10.00† |
| | | pair | 2.00 | .85 | .80 | 12.00† |
| | | strip of 4 | 4.00 | 1.60 | 2.00 | 22.50 |
| | i | jump strip of 4 | 6.00 | 4.00 | 4.00 | 40.00 |
| | | repair paste-up pair | 40.00 | 28.00 | | |
| | xx | No. 295, precancelled [1 style] | 3.00 | 2.00 | 2.00 | 2.00 |
| | xxi | precancelled, jump strip of 4 | 20.00 | 12.00 | — | — |
| Qty: 2,660,000 | | | | | | |
| **296** | | **3¢ rose violet** (291) | 1.50 | .80 | .75 | 11.00† |
| | | pair | 3.00 | 1.60 | 1.50 | 16.00† |
| | | strip of 4 | 6.00 | 3.20 | 3.20 | 22.50† |
| | i | jump strip of 4 | 7.50 | 5.00 | 5.00 | 40.00† |
| | | repair paste-up pair | 50.00 | 35.00 | | |
| Qty: 3,085,000 | | | | | | |

Jump strips are always "at least" a little off centre due to spacing variation and jump (slightly out of alignment) at the jump. Similarly, repair paste-ups are a bit off centre. FDC's are scarce; value any cover $100.00 each.

**Start or End Strips**
2 stamps + 2 blank tabs

| Sc# | NH-VF | ★F |
|---|---|---|
| 295 | 25.00 | 12.50 |
| 296 | 30.00 | 15.00 |

Full strips of 4 stamps with full tabs (10) are 3 times listed price.

## KING GEORGE VI WITH "POSTES-POSTAGE"
## 1950 COIL STAMPS

297

298

299

300

**1950** | **Engraved** | **Perf 9½ vertical**

| No. | | Description | NH–VF | ★F | ⊙F | ✉ |
|---|---|---|---|---|---|---|
| **297** | | **1¢ green** (284), *May 18, 1950* | .60 | .40 | .30 | 9.00† |
| | | pair | 1.20 | .80 | .70 | 11.00† |
| | | strip of 4 | 2.40 | 1.60 | 1.60 | 20.00† |
| | i | jump strip of 4 | 3.50 | 2.50 | 2.50 | 30.00† |
| | | repair paste-up pair | 60.00 | 35.00 | — | |
| | xx | No. 297, precancelled [1 style] | 2.00 | 1.00 | .25 | 2.00 |
| | xxi | precancelled, jump strip of 4 | 20.00 | 12.00 | — | — |
| Qty: 8,675,000 | | | | | | |
| **298** | | **2¢ sepia** (285), *May 18, 1950* | 5.00 | 2.50 | 2.00 | 10.00† |
| | | pair | 10.00 | 5.00 | 4.00 | 18.00† |
| | | strip of 4 | 20.00 | 11.00 | 10.00 | 35.00† |
| | i | lower left corner flaw | 8.00 | 5.00 | 4.00 | 18.00† |
| | ii | jump strip of 4 | 25.00 | 13.00 | 12.50 | — |
| | iii | jump strip of 4 with lower left corner flaw | 30.00 | 18.00 | 17.50 | — |
| | xx | No. 298, precancelled [1 style] | 3.00 | 2.00 | .50 | 2.00 |
| | | repair paste-up pair | 60.00 | 35.00 | — | |
| Qty: 3,195,000 | | | | | | |

| | | NH–VF | ★F | ⊙F | ✉ |
|---|---|---|---|---|---|
| **299** | **3¢ rose violet** (286), *May 18, 1950* | 3.00 | 1.25 | .25 | 7.00† |
| | pair | 6.00 | 3.50 | .60 | 14.00† |
| | strip of 4 | 12.00 | 7.00 | 2.50 | 40.00† |
| i | jump strip of 4 | 15.00 | 9.00 | 6.00 | — |
| | repair paste-up pair | 40.00 | 28.00 | — | |

Qty: 26,256,000

| | | NH–VF | ★F | ⊙F | ✉ |
|---|---|---|---|---|---|
| **300** | **4¢ dark carmine** (287), *Apr 20, 1950* | 25.00 | 15.00 | 1.00 | 17.00† |
| | pair | 50.00 | 30.00 | 3.00 | 42.00† |
| | strip of 4 | 100.00 | 60.00 | 10.00 | 100.00† |
| i | jump strip of 4 | 110.00 | 70.00 | 25.00 | — |
| | repair paste-up pair | 200.00 | 150.00 | — | |

Qty: 10,980,000

† Price is for correct postal usage in time period, commercial cover.
FDC's are scarce; value any cover $100.00 each.

**Start or End Strips**
2 stamps + 2 blank tabs

| Sc# | NH-VF | ★F |
|---|---|---|
| 297 | 20.00 | 12.50 |
| 298 | 50.00 | 25.00 |
| 299 | 30.00 | 20.00 |
| 300 | 150.00 | 100.00 |

Full strips of 4 stamps with full tabs (10) are 3 times listed price.

**PLEASE NOTE**
**Hereafter, unless noted otherwise:**
Mint stamps are valued as NH-VF (Never Hinged-Very Fine).
All hinged VF and NH-F copies are worth 50% of the listed values.
Plate block values are for mint NH–VF plate or inscription blocks of four.
1947–1971 FDC values are for the most common unaddressed cachet covers of the period.

## FUR RESOURCES

301
Drying Skins

Designer: Herman Herbert Schwartz and National Film Board.
Engraved (1 colour), Plates of 200 subjects in four panes of 50
Canadian Bank Note Company

**1950, Oct 2** **Perf 12**

| | | NH–VF | ⊙F | FDC |
|---|---|---|---|---|
| **301** | **10¢ black brown** | 1.40 | .20 | 7.00 |
| | plate blocks, plates 1, 2, all blocks | 7.50 | | |

Qty: 115,000,000

For **G** overprint see number O26.
Indian encampment near James Bay with an Indian women drying beaver pelts on stretchers.

## 1951

## FISHING RESOURCES

302
Fisherman

Designer: Fairbairn Art Studios of Ottawa in consultation with the Federal Department of Fisheries.
Engraved (1 colour), Plates of 200 subjects in four panes of 50
Canadian Bank Note Company

**1951, Feb 1** **Perf 12**

| | | NH–VF | ⊙F | FDC |
|---|---|---|---|---|
| **302** | **$1 bright ultramarine** | 60.00 | 15.00 | 90.00 |
| | plate blocks, plate 1, all blocks | 300.00 | | |

Qty: 4,460,000

For **G** overprint see number O27.
Typical fisherman hauling his net into an open boat. A fish net border shows sixteen varieties of fishery products.

| **Rates:** | Domestic Registry fee | Third class: 2¢ |
|---|---|---|
| Apr 2/51 | ≤$25: 10¢ | |
| | > $25, ≤$50: 20¢ | |
| | > $50, ≤$75: 30¢ | |
| | > $75, ≤$100: 40¢ | |

## PRIME MINISTERS

303
Sir Robert Borden

304
William Lyon Mackenzie King

Designer: Herman Herbert Schwartz
Borden: from a photograph by William James Topley.
King: from a Yousuf Karsh of Ottawa photograph.
Engraved (1 colour), Plates of 400 subjects in four panes of 100
Canadian Bank Note Company

**1951, Jun 25** **Perf 12**

| | | NH–VF | ⊙F | FDC |
|---|---|---|---|---|
| **303** | **3¢ turquoise green** | .35 | .20 | 3.00 |
| | plate blocks, plates 1, 2, all blocks | 2.15 | | |

Qty: 50,800,000

Sir Robert Borden was Conservative/Unionist Prime Minister from 1911 to 1920. Born 1854, died 1937. There is an error of design: it is improper to use initials with the title "Sir". His title requires all given names be used.

| | | NH–VF | ⊙F | FDC |
|---|---|---|---|---|
| **304** | **4¢ rose pink** | .40 | .20 | 3.00 |
| | plate blocks, plates 1, 2, all blocks | 2.20 | | |

Qty: 49,953,000

Mackenzie King was Canada's Prime Minister from 1921 to 1926, 1926 to 1930 and 1935 to 1948. Born 1874, died 1950.
See also 318–319, 349–350, 357–358.

## KING GEORGE VI "POSTES-POSTAGE
### 1951 new colours

305

306

Engraved (1 colour), Plates of 400 subjects in four panes of 100
Canadian Bank Note Company

| 1951, Jul 25 | | | | Perf 12 |
|---|---|---|---|---|
| | | NH–VF | ⊙F | FDC |
| **305** | **2¢ olive green** | .25 | .20 | 3.00† |
| xx | No. 305, precancelled [11 styles] | — | .20 | 2.00† |

Qty: 653,000,000

For **G** overprint see number O28.

| | | NH–VF | ⊙F | FDC |
|---|---|---|---|---|
| **306** | **4¢ orange vermillion** | .45 | .20 | 3.00† |

Qty: 791,000,000

For **G** overprint see number O29.

† Commercial cover. FDC's are scarce; value any cover $75.00 each.

| No. 305 (2¢) Plate Blocks (NH +25%) | | | |
|---|---|---|---|
| Plate No./Location | | ★VF | ★F |
| 3 | all blocks | 1.25 | 1.00 |
| 4 | all blocks | 6.25 | 5.00 |
| 5 | all blocks | 1.25 | 1.00 |
| 6 | all blocks | 1.90 | 1.50 |
| 7 | all blocks | 1.25 | 1.00 |
| 8 | all blocks | 2.50 | 2.00 |

| No. 306 (4¢) Plate Blocks (NH +25%) | | | |
|---|---|---|---|
| Plate No./Location | | ★VF | ★F |
| 6 | UL | 125.00 | 75.00 |
| | UR | 100.00 | 60.00 |
| | LL ‡ | 200.00 | 125.00 |
| | LR | 175.00 | 100.00 |
| 11 | all blocks | 2.50 | 2.00 |
| 12, 13 | all blocks | 1.90 | 1.50 |
| 14, 15 | all blocks | 2.50 | 2.00 |
| 16 | never used | | |
| 17, 18 | all blocks | 1.90 | 1.50 |

‡ all have hairlines in left selvedge.

| | | | |
|---|---|---|---|
| **306a** | booklet pane of 3 x 4¢ orange (306as) (BK44), *Oct 25, 1951* | 7.50 | 4.00 |
| as | single with straight edge, from 306a* | 1.00 | .75 |
| b | booklet pane of 6 x 4¢ orange (306bs) (BK42a), *Jun 2, 1951* | 7.00 | 7.00 |
| bs | single with straight edge, from 306b | 1.00 | .50 |
| bi | as b, stitched (BK42b) | 14.00 | 10.00 |

Qty: 306a: 1,196,000; 306b: 6,898,000

**BK42** 1 pane 306b in cover; English 01/02/51 (5,300,125) $9.00; bilingual 01/02/51 (1,579,300) $13.00; stitched BK42b $18.00

**BK44** 1 pane each 284a, 286a, 306a, in cover; English 10/25/51 (991,700) $17.50, bilingual 07/09/52 (204,875) $30.00

* Straight edge at top and bottom.

306a

306b

Nos. 307–308 are not assigned.

## KING GEORGE VI "POSTES-POSTAGE 1951 COIL STAMPS

309

310

| 1951 | | | | Perf 9½ vertical |
|---|---|---|---|---|
| | | NH–VF | ⊙F | ✉ |
| **309** | **2¢ olive green** (305), *Oct 9, 1951* | 2.00 | .85 | 10.00† |
| | pair | 4.00 | 2.00 | 16.00† |
| | strip of 4 | 8.00 | 6.00 | 22.00† |
| i | "lower left corner flaw" | 12.00 | 5.00 | 14.00† |
| | corner flaw, jump strip of 4 | 20.00 | 15.00 | 30.00† |
| ii | jump strip of 4 | 15.00 | 7.50 | — |
| | repair paste-up | 60.00 | 36.00 | |
| | start or end strips of 2 stamps & 2 blank tabs | 20.00 | 12.50 | |
| xx | No. 309, precancelled [1 style] | 2.50 | .25 | 3.00 |
| xxi | precancelled, jump strip of 4 | 18.50 | — | |

Qty: 7,332,000

† Commercial cover.

| | | NH–VF | ⊙F | ✉ |
|---|---|---|---|---|
| **310** | **4¢ orange vermillion** (306), *Nov 27, 1951* | 4.00 | 1.00 | 11.00† |
| | pair | 8.00 | 2.25 | 25.00† |
| | strip of 4 | 16.00 | 10.00 | 50.00† |
| i | jump strip of 4 | 20.00 | 12.00 | — |
| | repair paste-up | 100.00 | 100.00 | |
| | start or end strips of 2 stamps & 2 blank tabs | 40.00 | 25.00 | |

Qty: 9,645,000

† Commercial cover.

309–310: FDC's are scarce; value any cover $75.00 each.

Full start or end strips of 4 and full tabs (10) are 3 times the listed price.

## STAMP CENTENARY

311
Trains of 1851 and 1951

312
Steamships of 1851 and 1951

313
Stagecoach and Plane

314
"Three penny Beaver"

Designer: Herman Herbert Schwartz.

Engraved (1 colour)
4¢–7¢: Plates of 200 subjects in four panes of 50
15¢: Plates of 400 subjects in four panes of 100
Canadian Bank Note Company

| 1951, Sep 24 | | | | Perf 12 |
|---|---|---|---|---|
| | | NH–VF | ⊙F | FDC |
| **311** | **4¢ dark grey** | .85 | .20 | 5.00 |
| | plate blocks, plates 1, 2, all blocks | 3.75 | | |
| Qty: 49,750,000 | | | | |
| **312** | **5¢ purple** | 2.75 | 2.00 | 5.00 |
| | plate blocks, plates 1, 2, UR, LL | 15.00 | | |
| | plates 1, 2, UL, LR | 12.50 | | |
| Qty: 5,050,000 | | | | |
| **313** | **7¢ deep blue** | 1.65 | .45 | 5.00 |
| | plate blocks, plates 1, 2, all blocks | 7.50 | | |
| Qty: 19,900,000 | | | | |
| **314** | **15¢ bright red** | 1.80 | .40 | 5.00 |
| | plate blocks, plate 1, all blocks | 8.75 | | |
| Qty: 54,035,000 | | | | |
| **Nos. 311–314** (4) Set | | 7.05 | 3.05 | |
| **Nos. 311–314 (4) combination FDC** | | | | **10.00** |

Issued to commemorate the 100th anniversary of the Canadian postal administration on the occasion of CAPEX, Canada's first international philatelic exhibition.

## ROYAL VISIT

**315**
Duchess and Duke of Edinburgh

Designer: Herman Herbert Schwartz. Based on photographs by Sterling Henry Nahum.
Engraved (1 colour), Plates of 200 subjects in four panes of 50
Canadian Bank Note Company

**1951, Oct 26** **Perf 12**

| | | NH–VF | ⊙F | FDC |
|---|---|---|---|---|
| **315** | **4¢ violet** | .30 | .20 | 3.00 |
| | plate blocks, plate 1, all blocks | 2.80 | | |
| | plate 1, UL, cracked plate, pos. 2 (in selvedge) | 50.00 | | |
| | plates 2, 3, all blocks | 1.55 | | |

Qty: 50,300,000

Marked the occasion of the visit of Their Royal Highnesses, The Princess Elizabeth and The Duke of Edinburgh to Canada.

**316**, Cracked plate in upper selvedge

# 1952

## FORESTRY PRODUCTS

**316**
Paper Mill

Designer: Allan L. Pollock. Picture engraved by Joseph Keller.
Engraved (1 colour), Plates of 200 subjects in four panes of 50
Canadian Bank Note Company

**1952, Apr 1** **Perf 12**

| | | NH–VF | ⊙F | FDC |
|---|---|---|---|---|
| **316** | **20¢ grey** | 2.25 | .25 | 8.50 |
| | plate blocks, plates 1, 2, all blocks | 12.50 | | |

Qty: 104,975,000

For **G** overprint see number O30.

## RED CROSS CONFERENCE

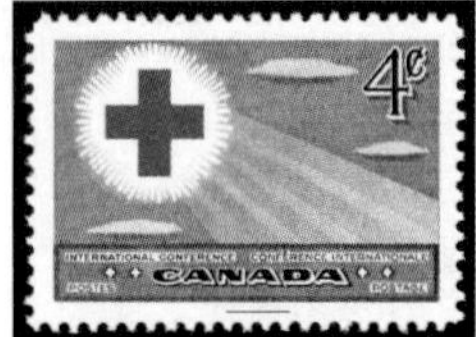


**317**
Red Cross Symbol

Designer: Herman Herbert Schwartz from an illustration supplied by the Canadian Red Cross.
Engraved (1 colour) and Lithography (1 colour),
Plates of 200 subjects in four panes of 50
Canadian Bank Note Company

**1952, Jul 26** **Perf 12**

| | | NH–VF | ⊙F | FDC |
|---|---|---|---|---|
| **317** | **4¢ blue and red** | .30 | .20 | 3.00 |
| | plate blocks, plates 1, 2, all blocks | 1.75 | | |

Qty: 50,000,000

This was the first Canadian stamp produced by engraving and lithography.

## PRIME MINISTERS

**318** Sir John Abbott
**319** Alexander Mackenzie

Designer: Herman Herbert Schwartz. Engraver: Silas Robert Allen.
Engraved (1 colour), Plates of 400 subjects in four panes of 100
Canadian Bank Note Company

**1952, Nov 3** **Perf 12**

| | | NH–VF | ⊙F | FDC |
|---|---|---|---|---|
| **318** | **3¢ rose lilac** | .30 | .20 | 3.00 |
| | plate blocks, plates 1, 2, UL | 1.90 | | |
| | plates 1, 2, UR, LL, LR | 1.55 | | |

Qty: 50,365,000

Sir John Joseph Caldwell Abbott was Conservative Prime Minister from 1891 to 1892. Born 1821, died 1893.

| | | NH–VF | ⊙F | FDC |
|---|---|---|---|---|
| **319** | **4¢ orange vermilion** | .35 | .20 | 3.00 |
| | plate blocks, plates 1, 2, UL | 1.90 | | |
| | plates 1, 2, UR, LL, LR | 1.55 | | |

Qty: 50,868,000

Alexander Mackenzie was the first Liberal Party Prime Minister, serving from 1873 to 1878. Born 1822, died 1892.
See also 303–304, 349–350, 357–358.

## WILDLIFE

**320**
Canada Goose

Designer: Emanuel Otto Hahn. Modeled by Herman Herbert Schwartz. Picture engraved by Silas Robert Allen.
Engraved (1 colour), Plates of 200 subjects in four panes of 50
Canadian Bank Note Company

**1952, Nov 3** **Perf 12**

| | | NH–VF | ⊙F | FDC |
|---|---|---|---|---|
| **320** | **7¢ blue** | .55 | .20 | 8.50 |
| | plate blocks, plates 1, 2, all blocks | 2.80 | | |

Qty: 161,820,000

For **G** overprint see number O31.
This value had been used prior to the institution of all-up mail in Canada for Airmail. The airmail rate to the United States remained, however, so that while the stamp is not officially an Airmail stamp the subject, the Canada Goose, does symbolize flight.

## 1953

### TOTEM POLE

321
Pacific Coast Totem Pole

Designer: Emanuel Otto Hahn. Picture engraved by Silas Robert Allen.
Engraved (1 colour), Plates of 200 subjects in four panes of 50
Canadian Bank Note Company

**1953, Feb 2** — Perf 12

| | | NH–VF | ⊙F | FDC |
|---|---|---|---|---|
| **321** | **$1 grey** | 8.00 | 1.20 | 45.00† |
| | plate blocks, plates 1, 2, all blocks | 50.00 | | |

Qty: 27,865,000
† Commercial single usage $75.00. Bulk payment receipt worth less.

For **G** overprint see number O32.
Features an Indian House and Totem Pole from the Pacific Coast.

### WILDLIFE

322
Polar Bear

323
Moose

324
Bighorn Sheep

Designer: 2¢: John Alexander Crosby; 3¢ and 4¢: Emanuel Otto Hahn. All pictures engraved by Silas Robert Allen.
Engraved (1 colour), Plates of 400 subjects in four panes of 100
Canadian Bank Note Company

**1953, Apr 1** — Perf 12

| | | NH–VF | ⊙F | FDC |
|---|---|---|---|---|
| **322** | **2¢ blue** | .25 | .20 | 3.00 |
| | plate blocks, plates 1, 2, all blocks | 1.55 | | |
| Qty: 50,900,000 | | | | |
| **323** | **3¢ brown** | .30 | .20 | 3.00 |
| | plate blocks, plates 1, 2, UL | 3.10 | | |
| | plates 1, 2, UR, LL, LR | 1.70 | | |
| Qty: 51,100,000 | | | | |
| **324** | **4¢ slate** | .35 | .20 | 3.00 |
| | plate blocks, plates 1, 2, UL | 3.10 | | |
| | plates 1, 2, UR, LL, LR | 1.85 | | |
| Qty: 50,100,000 | | | | |

**Nos. 322–324 (3) combination FDC** — **5.00**

### QUEEN ELIZABETH II – KARSH PORTRAIT

325

326

327

328

329

For **G** overprints see numbers O33–O37.

Designer: Herman Herbert Schwartz. Based on a photograph by Yousuf Karsh.
Engraved (1 colour), Plates of 400 subjects in four panes of 100
Canadian Bank Note Company

**1953, May 1** — Perf 12

| | | NH–VF | ⊙F | FDC |
|---|---|---|---|---|
| **325** | **1¢ violet brown** | .25 | .20 | 8.00 |
| | plate blocks, plates 1, 2, all blocks | .90 | | |
| | plate 3, UL, UR | 1.20 | | |
| | plate 3, LL, LR | 1.80 | | |
| Qty: 169,000,000 | | | | |
| 325a | booklet pane of 3 x 1¢ violet brown (325as) (BK47), *Aug 12, 1953* | 2.00 | 2.00 | |
| as | single with straight edge, from 325a* | .80 | .60 | |

* Straight edge at top and bottom.

| | | NH–VF | ⊙F | FDC |
|---|---|---|---|---|
| **326** | **2¢ green** | .25 | .20 | 8.00 |
| | plate blocks, plate 1, UL, UR, LL | 1.20 | | |
| | plate 1, LR | 1.50 | | |
| | plate 2, UL, UR, LL | 1.20 | | |
| | plate 2, LR | 1.50 | | |
| | plate 3, UL | 1.50 | | |
| | plate 3, UR, LL, LR | 1.20 | | |
| | plate 4, all blocks | 1.20 | | |
| | plate 5, UL, LL, LR | 1.20 | | |
| | plate 5, UR | 1.80 | | |
| | plate 6, all blocks | 14.40 | | |
| **xx** | No. 326, precancelled [1 style] | 5.00 | .20 | 4.00† |
| Qty: 338,000,000 | | | | |

† Commercial cover.

| | | NH–VF | ⊙F | FDC |
|---|---|---|---|---|
| **327** | **3¢ carmine rose** | .25 | .20 | 8.00 |
| | plate blocks, plates 1–3, all blocks | 1.50 | | |
| | plate 4, UL | 12.00 | | |
| | plate 4, UR | 9.00 | | |
| | plate 4, LL, LR | 6.00 | | |
| **xx** | No. 327, precancelled [1 style] | 4.00 | 2.00 | 3.50† |
| Qty: 332,000,000 | | | | |

† Commercial cover.

| | | NH–VF | ⊙F |
|---|---|---|---|
| 327a | booklet pane of 3 x 3¢ carmine rose (327as) (BK47), *Aug 12, 1953* | 2.50 | 2.00 |
| as | single with straight edge, from 327a* | .90 | .60 |
| b | booklet pane of 4 x 3¢ carmine rose (327bs) + 2 labels (BK46), *Jul 17, 1953* | 1.75 | 2.50 |
| bs | single with straight edge, from 327b | .75 | .30 |
| BK46 | 2 panes 327b, in cover; English 07/17/53 (200,000) $4.00; bilingual 10/20/53 (50,000) $6.00 | | |

* Straight edge at top and bottom.

QE II — Karsh

QE II — Karsh

| | | NH–VF | ⊙F | FDC |
|---|---|---|---|---|
| **328** | **4¢ violet** | .35 | .20 | 8.00 |
| i | imperf. top margin single | *1,500.00* | | |
| | plate blocks, plate 1, all blocks | 2.10 | | |
| | plates 2, 3, all blocks | 3.30 | | |
| | plates 4, 5, all blocks | 2.10 | | |
| | plate 6, all blocks | 2.90 | | |
| | pl. 6, with variety 328i | *5,000.00* | | |
| **xx** | No. 328, precancelled [4 styles] | 6.00 | 1.25 | 5.00† |

Qty: 406,000,000
† Commercial cover.

| | | | |
|---|---|---|---|
| 328a | booklet pane of 3 x 4¢ violet (328as) (BK47), *Aug 12, 1953* | 2.50 | 2.00 |
| as | single with straight edge, from 328a* | 1.00 | .60 |
| b | booklet pane of 6 x 4¢ violet (328bs) (BK45), *Jul 6, 1953* | 2.00 | 2.00 |
| bs | single with straight edge, from 328b | .80 | .50 |

BK45 1 pane 328b in cover; English 07/06/53 (2,502,000) $2.50, bilingual 08/19/53 (700,275) $2.50
BK47 1 pane each 325a, 327a, 328a, in cover; English 08/12/53 (305,550) $12.00, bilingual 08/12/53 (154,050) $20.00
* Straight edge at top and bottom.

| | | | | |
|---|---|---|---|---|
| **329** | **5¢ ultramarine** | .45 | .20 | 8.00 |
| | plate blocks, plates 1, 2, all blocks | 3.30 | | |
| | plate 3, all blocks | 3.60 | | |
| **xx** | No. 329, precancelled [3 styles] | 8.00 | .75 | 6.00† |
| **xxi** | precancelled '0700' vertical pair, imperf between, 2 pairs known, due to perf. shift. | *5,000.00* | | |
| **xxii** | precancelled '0700', imperf. between top of stamp and margin. From same block as 329xxi | 500.00 | | |

Qty: 109,000,000
† Commercial cover.

| | | | |
|---|---|---|---|
| **Nos. 325–329** (5) Set | 1.45 | 1.00 | 14.00† |

† Combination FDC.
*Die proofs of this issue exist in various shades – value $1,500.00*
*"PROGRESSIVE" die proofs with no denomination exist in various shades – value $1,500.00*

325a

327a

327b

328a

328b

328i

Source of 329xxi and 329xxii

## QUEEN ELIZABETH II CORONATION

330
Queen Elizabeth II

Designer: Emanuel Otto Hahn. Based on a photograph by Yousuf Karsh. Portrait engraved by Silas Robert Allen.

Engraved (1 colour), Plates of 400 subjects in four panes of 100
Canadian Bank Note Company

**1953, Jun 1** — **Perf 12**

| | | NH–VF | ⊙F | FDC |
|---|---|---|---|---|
| **330** | **4¢ violet** | .25 | .20 | 3.00 |
| | plate blocks, plate 1, UL, LL, LR | 6.00 | | |
| | plate 1, UR | 12.00 | | |
| | plates 2, 3, all blocks | 1.50 | | |
| | plate 4, UL, LL, LR | 3.00 | | |
| | plate 4, UR | 12.00 | | |

Qty: 100,127,000

Issued to commemorate the coronation of Queen Elizabeth II on June 2, 1953.

## QUEEN ELIZABETH II – KARSH PORTRAIT COIL STAMPS

331

332

333

**1953** — **Perf 9½ vertical**

| | | NH–VF | ⊙F | ✉ |
|---|---|---|---|---|
| **331** | **2¢ green** (326), *Jul 30, 1953* | 2.00 | 1.25 | 15.00‡ |
| | pair | 4.00 | 2.50 | 26.00‡ |
| | strip of 4 | 8.00 | 6.00 | 40.00‡ |
| i | jump strip of 4 | 10.00 | 7.50 | 50.00‡ |
| ii | as i, with cutting guidelines | 75.00* | | |
| **xx** | No. 331, precancelled [1 style] | 4.00 | .30 | 5.00 |
| | start or end strips of 4 | 60.00† | | |
| | repair paste-up strips of 4 | 40.00* | | |

Qty: 5,000,000

| | | NH–VF | ⊙F | ✉ |
|---|---|---|---|---|
| **332** | **3¢ carmine rose** (327), *Jul 27, 1953* | 2.00 | 1.25 | 20.00‡ |
| | pair | 4.00 | 2.50 | 34.00‡ |
| | strip of 4 | 8.00 | 6.00 | 50.00‡ |
| i | jump strip of 4 | 10.00 | 7.50 | 60.00‡ |
| ii | as i, with cutting guidelines | 75.00* | | |
| | start or end strips of 4 | 60.00† | | |
| | repair paste-up strips of 4 | 40.00* | | |

Qty: 5,500,000

| | | NH–VF | ⊙F | ✉ |
|---|---|---|---|---|
| **333** | **4¢ violet** (328), *Sep 3, 1953* | 4.50 | 2.00 | 20.00‡ |
| | pair | 9.00 | 4.00 | 34.00‡ |
| | strip of 4 | 18.00 | 9.00 | 60.00‡ |
| i | jump strip of 4 | 20.00 | 15.00 | 80.00‡ |
| ii | as i, with cutting guidelines | 90.00* | | |
| | start or end strips of 4 | 120.00† | | |
| | repair paste-up strips of 4 | 75.00* | | |

Qty: 4,960,000

* Jump strips and repair paste-up strips cannot have VF centring and still show the cutting guideline.
† Values are for coil starter strips of 4 plus 10 blank labels (shaded in the colour of the stamps) and for end strips of 4 plus 10 unprinted labels. Shorter strips sell for much less.
‡ Non-philatelic single usage 1953–September 1954 (alone on cover without other stamps).
331–333: FDC's are scarce; value any cover $50.00 each.

## TEXTILE INDUSTRY

334

Designer: Alan L. Pollock. Picture engraved by Joseph Keller.
Engraved (1 colour), Plates of 200 subjects in four panes of 50
Canadian Bank Note Company

**1953, Nov 2** — **Perf 12**

| | | NH–VF | ⊙F | FDC |
|---|---|---|---|---|
| **334** | **50¢ light green** | 4.00 | .30 | 13.00 |
| i | high fluorescent paper | 200.00 | 15.00 | |
| ii | left vertical frame line retouched with engraver's slip along left edge of design at bottom (pos. 41, LL pane)* | 60.00 | 25.00 | |
| iii | bottom frame line retouched with engraver's slip from below last A in CANADA to the T of POSTAGE (pos. 47, LL pane)* | 60.00 | 25.00 | |
| iv | speckled fluorescence | 10.00 | .50 | |
| v | re-entry, strongest in LR corner (pos. 40, UL pane) | | | |
| | plate blocks, plate 1, all blocks | 30.00 | | |
| | plate 1, LL, varieties 334ii, 334iii* | 140.00 | | |
| | plate 2, all blocks | 36.00 | | |
| | variety 334i, plate block of 4 | 1,250.00 | | |
| | variety 334iv, plate block of 4 | 40.00 | | |

Qty: 63,075,000

* Varieties 334ii and 334iii occur together on the same plate block, plate 1, LL.
For **G** overprint see number O38.

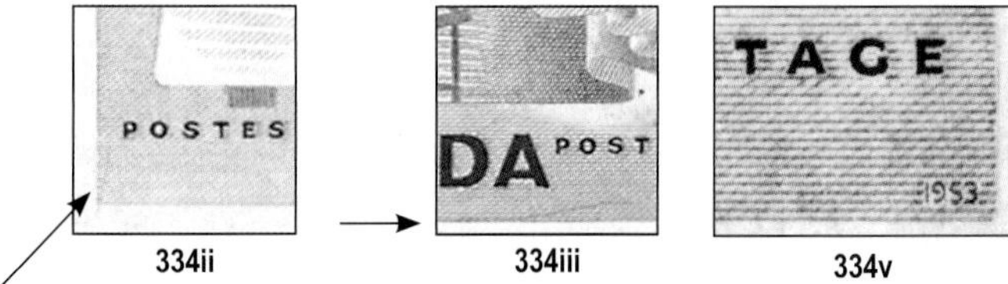


334ii 334iii 334v

## 1954

| **Rates:** | Domestic: 5¢ (0–1 oz), 8¢ (1–2 oz) |
|---|---|
| Effective: | Local: 4¢ (0–1 oz); 6¢ (1–2 oz) |
| Apr 1, 1954– | Postcard: 4¢ |
| Oct 31, 1968 | Printed matter: 2¢ |
| | USA: 5¢ |
| | Registration: 20¢ |
| | Special delivery: 10¢ |

## WILDLIFE

335 Walrus — 336 Beaver

Designer: Emanuel Otto Hahn. Modeled by Herman Herbert Schwartz. Picture engraved by Silas Robert Allen.
Engraved (1 colour), Plates of 400 subjects in four panes of 100
Canadian Bank Note Company

**1954, Apr 1** — **Perf 12**

| | | NH–VF | ⊙F | FDC |
|---|---|---|---|---|
| **335** | **4¢ grey** | .40 | .20 | 3.00 |
| | plate blocks, plates 1, 2, UL | 3.00 | | |
| | all others | 2.40 | | |

Qty: 50,630,000

| | | NH–VF | ⊙F | FDC |
|---|---|---|---|---|
| **336** | **5¢ ultramarine** | .45 | .20 | 3.00 |
| | plate blocks, plates 1, 2, all blocks | 2.40 | | |
| 336a | booklet pane of 5 x 5¢ Beaver (336as) + label (BK48a) | 2.50 | 2.00 | 20.00 |
| as | single with straight edge, from 336a | .45 | .35 | — |
| ai | as "a", stitched (BK48b) | 4.00 | 3.00 | — |
| BK48a | 1 pane 336a in bilingual cover (2,004,000) $3.00 | | | |

This was the first Canadian commemorative stamp to be issued in booklet format.

336a

## QUEEN ELIZABETH II – WILDING PORTRAIT

337 338 339

340 341 342

For **G** overprints (1¢, 2¢, 4¢, 5¢) see numbers O40–O44.

Definitive Series Historical Notes:

- phosphor tagging introduced
- miniature panes introduced
- separate English and Bilingual booklets no longer issued

Designer: Herman Herbert Schwartz. Based on a photograph by Dorothy Wilding. Portrait engraved by Silas Robert Allen.

Engraved (1 colour)
Plates of 400 subjects in four panes of 100 (ribbed horiz.)
Plates of 600 subjects in six panes of 100 (ribbed vert.)
Canadian Bank Note Company

**1954, Jun 10** **Perf 12**

| | | NH–VF | ⊙F | PB | FDC |
|---|---|---|---|---|---|
| **337** | **1¢ violet brown**, | | | | |
| | Ribbed (horiz), plates 1–8n, 9 | .25 | .20 | | 5.00 |
| ii | F | 10.00 | 1.50 | 50.00 | — |
| v | Ribbed (vert), plates 11, 12 | .30 | .20 | | |
| vi | Ribbed (vert), SF | 3.00 | .75 | 15.00 | |
| p | tagged, W2B, *Jan 13, 1962* | 1.75 | 1.25 | 9.00† | 3.00* |
| iii | W2B, F | 10.00 | 5.00 | 50.00 | — |
| iv | W2B, HB | 20.00 | 10.00 | 125.00 | — |
| xx | No. 337, precancelled, Ribbed (horiz) | 1.25 | .75 | 6.25 | 2.00 |
| xxi | No. 337v, precancelled, Ribbed (vert) | 1.75 | 1.00 | 8.75 | |

Qty: 1,041,000,000; W2B: 8,200,000
† Blank corner block of 4.
* With Winnipeg cancel; Ottawa *day of issue* cancel $3.00; Commercial cover $7.00.

| | | NH–VF | ⊙F |
|---|---|---|---|
| 337a | booklet pane of 5 x 1¢ violet brown (337as) + label (BK51), *Jan 1, 1956* | 1.50 | 1.50 |
| as | single with straight edge, from 337a | .30 | .20 |
| ai | pane with cutting guideline | 5.00 | 4.50 |
| aii | LF pane | 50.00 | 25.00 |
| aiis | single with straight edge, from 337aii | 10.00 | 4.00 |
| aiii | HB pane | 100.00 | 70.00 |
| aiiis | single with straight edge, from 337aiii | 20.00 | 10.00 |
| aiv | MF pane | 50.00 | 25.00 |
| aivs | single with straight edge, from 337aiv | 10.00 | 4.00 |

**No. 337 (1¢) Plate Blocks**

| Plate No. | Location | NH–VF | Plate No. | Location | NH–VF |
|---|---|---|---|---|---|
| 1, 2 | all blocks | 1.25 | 7 | all blocks | 10.80 |
| 3 | UL, UR | 1.80 | 8 | all blocks | 30.00 |
| | LL, LR | 1.25 | 8n | all blocks | 12.00 |
| 4 | all blocks | 1.25 | 9 | all blocks | 3.60 |
| 5 | UL, LR | 7.20 | 10 | no insc. | |
| | UR, LL | 6.00 | 11, 12 | all blocks | 4.20 |
| 6 | all blocks | 1.25 | | | |
| | | | All 337 imprint blocks | | 311.70 |

| | | NH–VF | ⊙F | PB | FDC |
|---|---|---|---|---|---|
| **338** | **2¢ green**, Ribbed (horiz), plates 1–9 | .25 | .20 | | 5.00 |
| iv | NF, Ribbed (vert), plates 11–20 | .20 | .20 | | |
| ii | F, Ribbed (vert) (incl. pl. 13, 14) | 5.00 | .75 | 25.00 | — |
| iii | HF, Ribbed (vert) (incl. pl. 13, 14) | 60.00 | 5.00 | 300.00 | — |
| v | SF, Ribbed (vert) | 3.00 | .50 | 15.00 | |
| p | tagged, W2B, Ribbed (vert), *Jan 13/62* | 1.75 | 1.25 | 8.75† | 3.00* |
| xx | No. 338, precancelled, Ribbed (horiz) | 1.00 | .50 | 5.00 | 2.00 |
| xxi | No. 338iv, precancelled, NF, Ribbed (vert) | 1.25 | .75 | 6.25 | |
| xxii | No. 338v, precancelled, SF, Ribbed (vert) | 5.00 | 2.50 | 25.00 | |
| xxiii | HF, Ribbed (vert), precancelled | 75.00 | 10.00 | 375.00 | |

Qty: 4,186,000,000; W2B: 29,595,000
† Blank corner block of 4.
* With Winnipeg cancel; Ottawa *day of issue* cancel $3.00; Commercial cover $8.00.

| | | NH–VF | ⊙F |
|---|---|---|---|
| 338a | miniature pane of 25 (5x5) | 5.00 | 5.00 |
| as | single with straight edge, from 338a | .20 | .20 |
| ai | Cello paq containing 2 panes of 25 | 11.00 | — |
| b | vert. pair, imperf. between (a block of 10 exists) | | |

Miniature panes were introduced in 1961 in cello paqs.
Two types exist: Type I has instructions at the sides; Type II has instructions at the top and bottom.

**No. 338 (2¢) Plate Blocks**

| Plate No. | Location | NH–VF | Plate No. | Location | NH–VF |
|---|---|---|---|---|---|
| 1, 2 | all blocks | 1.25 | 9 | UL, UR | 24.00 |
| 3 | UL, LL, LR | 1.25 | | LL, LR | 18.00 |
| | UR | 1.80 | 9n | UL, UR | 7.20 |
| 4, 5 | all blocks | 1.25 | | LL, LR | 4.80 |
| 6 | UL, LL, LR | 2.40 | 10 | no insc. | |
| | UR | 12.00 | 11, 12 | all blocks | 12.00 |
| 7 | all blocks | 1.40 | 13 | all blocks | 4.80 |
| 7n | all blocks | 1.25 | 14, 15 | all blocks | 2.40 |
| 8 | all blocks | 1.40 | 16 | all blocks | 3.60 |
| 8n | all blocks | 1.25 | 17, 18 | all blocks | 1.80 |
| | | | 19, 20 | all blocks | 2.40 |
| All 338 imprint blocks | | 356.35 | | | |

| | | NH–VF | ⊙F | PB | FDC |
|---|---|---|---|---|---|
| **339** | **3¢ carmine rose** | .25 | .20 | | 5.00 |
| ii | F | 5.00 | .50 | 25.00 | — |
| iii | HB | 25.00 | 3.00 | 135.00 | — |
| iv | SF | 1.50 | 1.00 | 8.75 | |
| a | horiz. pair, imperf. vert. (50 pairs exist) | 2,000.00 | — | *9,500.00†* | — |
| | plate blocks, plates 1, 2, UL | | | 1.80 | |
| | plates 1, 2, UR, LL, LR | | | 1.50 | |
| p | tagged, W2B, *Jan 13, 1962* | 1.75 | 1.25 | | 3.00* |
| | 339p, plates 1, 2, all blocks | | | 10.50 | |
| | 339p, blank corner blocks | | | 9.00 | |
| xx | No. 339, precancelled | — | .50 | 3.75 | 5.00 |

Qty: 233,755,000; W2B: 11,695,000
† Unique, Plate 2 LR.
* With Winnipeg cancel; Ottawa *day of issue* cancel $3.00; Commercial cover, single usage $10.00

| | | NH–VF | ⊙F | PB | FDC |
|---|---|---|---|---|---|
| **340** | **4¢ violet**, Ribbed (horiz), plates 1–12n | .30 | .20 | | 8.00 |
| i | NF, Ribbed (vert), plates 15–19 | .35 | .20 | | |
| ii | F, Ribbed (vert) | 15.00 | 3.00 | 75.00 | — |
| iii | HB, Ribbed (vert) | 30.00 | 5.00 | 125.00 | — |
| v | SF, Ribbed (vert) (incl. pl. 17) | 2.00 | 1.50 | 10.00 | |
| iv | gutter pair (2 known, from one major foldover error)‡ | *4,000.00* | — | — | — |
| p | tagged, WCB, *Jan 13, 1962* | 5.00 | 4.50 | 25.00† | 3.00* |
| xx | No. 340, precancelled, Ribbed (horiz) | 2.50 | 1.50 | 10.00 | 2.00 |
| xxi | No. 340ii precancelled, Ribbed (vert) | 2.50 | 1.50 | 10.00 | |

Qty: 3,008,000,000; WCB: 37,345,000
‡ This piece is still together. Value $8,000 (2 x $4,000)
† Blank corner block of 4.
* With Winnipeg cancel; Ottawa *day of issue* cancel $3.00.

| | | NH–VF | ⊙F |
|---|---|---|---|
| 340a | booklet pane of 5 x 4¢ violet (340as) + label, PL (BK51), *Jan 1, 1956* | 2.00 | 2.00 |
| as | single with straight edge, from 340a or 340b | .40 | .25 |
| ai | pane with cutting guideline | 15.00 | 15.00 |
| aii | MF pane | 50.00 | 35.00 |
| aiis | single with straight edge, from 340 aii | 10.00 | 7.00 |
| aiii | HB pane | 150.00 | 90.00 |
| aiiis | single with straight edge, from 340aiii | 35.00 | 15.00 |
| b | booklet pane of 6 x 4¢ violet (340as) (BK50), *Jul 7, 1955* | 4.00 | 4.00 |
| bi | LF pane | 30.00 | 25.00 |
| BK50 | 1 pane 340b in bilingual cover (301,825) $4.50 | | |
| BK51 | 1 pane each 337a, 340a, in bilingual cover 01/01/56 $4.00 | | |

| No. 340 (4¢) Plate Blocks | | | | | |
|---|---|---|---|---|---|
| **Plate No./Location** | | **NH–VF** | **Plate No./Location** | | **NH–VF** |
| 1, 2 | all blocks | 1.50 | 10 | all blocks | 1.80 |
| 3 | UL, LL, LR | 1.80 | 10n | all blocks | 1.50 |
| | UR | 2.40 | 11,12 | all blocks | 14.40 |
| 4 | all blocks | 12.00 | 12n | all blocks | 6.00 |
| 5-7 | all blocks | 1.50 | 13, 14 | no insc. | |
| 8 | UL, UR, LL | 1.80 | 15, 16 | all blocks | 7.20 |
| | LR | 4.80 | 17 | all blocks | 3.60 |
| 9 | all blocks | 2.40 | 18 | all blocks | 6.00 |
| | | | 19 | all blocks | 3.60 |
| All 340 imprint blocks | | 339.60 | | | |

| | | NH–VF | ⊙F | PB | FDC |
|---|---|---|---|---|---|
| **341** | **5¢ bright blue**, Ribbed (horiz), plates 1–13, *Apr 1, 1954* | .30 | .20 | | 5.00 |
| c | horiz. pair, imperf. vert. (approx. 6 pairs exist) | *7,500.00* | — | | — |
| v | plate block, imperf. at left margin‡ | — | — | *6,000.00* | — |
| | single, imperf. at left margin‡ | 900.00 | — | | — |
| i | NF, Ribbed (vert), plates 15–19 | .35 | .20 | | |
| ii | F, Ribbed (vert) | 30.00 | 3.00 | 150.00 | — |
| iv | SF, Ribbed (vert) | 3.00 | 2.50 | 15.00 | |
| iii | gutter pair (ribbed vert) | *6,750.00* | — | | — |
| vi | minor re-entry, UL frameline | | | | |
| p | tagged, W2B, Ribbed (vert), *Jan 13/62* | 5.50 | 3.00 | 27.50† | 3.00* |
| xx | No. 341, precancelled, Ribbed (horiz) | 2.50 | 1.50 | 12.50 | 2.00 |
| xxi | No. 341i, precancelled, Ribbed (vert) | 2.50 | 1.50 | 12.50 | |

Qty: 3,630,000,000; W2B: 32,095,000

‡ Six singles are known without gum and creased in margin. One plate 11, LL block with gum, LH and one left margin block of 6 (3x2), NH are known. With original gum add 50%.

† Blank corner block of 4.

* With Winnipeg cancel; Ottawa *day of issue* cancel $3.00. Commercial cover $8.00.

Wilding plate blocks:

Plate inscriptions appear in one corner of the post office pane. Until the fall of 1957, the lower left pane included an order number in the left selvedge. Some panes have narrow selvedge (the order number was trimmed off; indicated as "n" in the charts). Imprints were discontinued (i.e. trimmed before distribution to post offices) from November 1957 to May 1958 (these include 1¢ Pl 10, 2¢ Pl 10, 4¢ Pl 13–14, and 5¢ Pl 14). Plate blocks from these plates do not exist. Subsequent imprints had the inscription placed very close to the edge of the pane.

| | | NH–VF | ⊙F |
|---|---|---|---|
| 341a | booklet pane of 5 x 5¢ bright blue (341as) + label (BK49), *Jul 14, 1954* | 1.50 | 1.50 |
| as | single with straight edge, from 341a | .30 | .20 |
| ai | LF pane | 32.50 | 25.00 |
| ais | single with straight edge, from 341ai | 4.00 | 1.50 |
| aii | HB pane | 100.00 | 75.00 |
| aiis | single with straight edge, from 341aii | 20.00 | 15.00 |
| aiii | as a, stitched pane (BK49b) | 6.00 | 6.00 |
| aiv | MF pane | 25.00 | 18.00 |
| aivs | single with straight edge, from 341aiv | 6.00 | 4.00 |
| BK49 | 1 pane 341a in bilingual cover (77,298,000) $2.75 | | |
| 341b | miniature pane of 20 (5x4) | 9.00 | 9.00 |
| bs | single with straight edge, from 341b | .30 | .20 |
| bi | Cello paq containing 1 pane of 20 | 11.00 | — |

Miniature panes were introduced in 1961 in cello paqs.

Two types exist: Type I has instructions at the sides; Type II has instructions at the top and bottom.

| No. 341 (5¢) Plate Blocks | | | | | |
|---|---|---|---|---|---|
| **Plate No./Location** | | **NH–VF** | **Plate No./Location** | | **NH–VF** |
| 1–3 | all blocks | 2.10 | 8 | all blocks | 2.40 |
| 4 | UL, LL, LR | 2.40 | 9 | UL, UR, LR | 2.40 |
| | UR | 3.00 | | LL | 3.00 |
| 5 | all blocks | 2.10 | 10–12 | all blocks | 2.10 |
| 6 | UL, LL, LR | 2.10 | 13 | UL, UR, LL | 3.60 |
| | UR | 3.60 | | LR | 6.00 |
| 7 | UL | 3.00 | 14 | no insc. | |
| | UR, LL, LR | 2.40 | 15–17 | all blocks | 6.00 |
| | | | 18–19 | all blocks | 3.60 |
| All 341 imprint blocks | | 226.50 | | | |

| | | NH–VF | ⊙F | PB | FDC |
|---|---|---|---|---|---|
| **342** | **6¢ orange** | .65 | .25 | 3.50† | 8.00* |

Qty: 50,000,000

† Plates 1, 2.

* Commercial single usage in time period only: local delivery letter $35.00; transatlantic delivery letter $100.00.

337ai

341vi

338ai

**1¢–6¢ Wilding**

| | Sheet | | | | Booklet | Miniature pane | Precancel | | Official | | Coil | Coil: Precancel |
|---|---|---|---|---|---|---|---|---|---|---|---|---|
| | Ribbed | | Tag: 2-bar | Tag: 1-bar | | | Ribbed | | Ribbed | | | |
| | Horiz | Vert | | | | | Horiz | Vert | Horiz | Vert | | |
| 1¢ brown | 337 (Pl 1–9) | 337v (Pl 11–12) | 337p | | 337a | | 337xx | 337xxi | O40 | O40iii | | |
| 2¢ green | 338 (Pl 1–9) | 338ii (Pl 11–20) | 338p | | | 338a | 338xx | 338xxi | O41 | O41ii | 345 | 345xx |
| 3¢ carmine | 339 (Pl 1–2) | | 339p (Pl 1–2) | | | | 339xx | | | | | |
| 4¢ violet | 340 (Pl 1–12n) | 340i (Pl 15–19) | | 340p | 340a | | 340xx | 340xxi | O43 | O43i | 347 | |
| 5¢ blue | 341 (Pl 1–13) | 341i (Pl 15–19) | 341p | | 341a | 341b | 341xx | 341xxi | O44 | O44ii | 348 | |
| 6¢ orange | 342 | | | | | | | | | | | |

338b

340a

340b

341a

341b

343
Gannet

Designer: Laurence Hyde. Picture engraved by Silas Robert Allen.
Engraved (1 colour)
Plates of 400 subjects in four panes of 100 (ribbed horiz.)
Plates of 600 subjects in six panes of 100 (ribbed vert.)
Canadian Bank Note Company

| 1954, Apr 1 | | Perf 12 | | |
|---|---|---|---|---|
| | | NH–VF | ⊙F | FDC |
| 343 | **15¢ grey**, Ribbed (horiz), plates 1–3 | 2.00 | .25 | 7.50 |
| i | block, imperf. at right margin (5 blocks recorded) | *4,000.00* | — | |
| | plate blocks, plates 1, 2, all blocks | 10.00 | | |
| | plate 2n, all blocks | 10.00 | | |
| | plate 3, all blocks | 20.00 | | |
| ii | Ribbed (vert), plate 4 | 2.50 | .50 | |
| | plate 4, all blocks | 14.00 | | |

Qty: 262,100,000

| | | | | |
|---|---|---|---|---|
| **Nos. 337–343** | (7) Set | 3.70 | 1.40 | 9.00† |
| **Nos 337p–341p** | (5) Set | 15.75 | 11.25 | 10.00‡ |

† Combination FDC consists of 1¢, 2¢, 3¢, 4¢ and 6¢ only (Jun 10/54).
‡ Combination FDC

343i

No. 344 is not assigned.

## QUEEN ELIZABETH II – WILDING PORTRAIT COIL STAMPS

345

347

348

| 1954 | | Perf 9½ vertical | | |
|---|---|---|---|---|
| | | NH–VF | ⊙F | ✉ |
| 345 | **2¢ green** (338), *Sep 9, 1954* | .75 | .25 | 5.00 |
| | pair | 1.50 | .65 | 9.00 |
| | strip of 4 | 3.00 | 2.00 | |
| i | jump strip of 4 | 5.00* | 3.00* | — |
| iii | "damaged E" variety | 9.00 | 3.00 | 5.00 |
| | 345iii, in jump strip of 4 with 3 normal | 15.00* | 15.00* | — |
| iv | 2¢ green, F | 10.00 | 5.00 | — |
| | F, pair | 20.00 | 12.00 | — |
| | F, strip of 4 | 40.00 | 30.00 | — |
| v | F, jump strip of 4 | 50.00* | 40.00* | — |
| vi | F, "damaged E" variety | 50.00 | 20.00 | — |
| | 345vi, in jump strip of 4 with 3 normal | 75.00 | 30.00* | — |
| xx | No. 345, precancelled | 1.00 | 1.00 | 2.00 |
| | No. 345, start or end strip of 4 | 36.00† | | |
| | No. 345iv, start or end strip of 4 | 180.00† | | |
| | No. 345, repair paste-up strip of 4 | 40.00* | | |
| | No. 345iv, repair paste-up strip of 4 | 200.00* | | |

Qty: 24,400,000
A used precancelled has been reported on HF paper.
No. 346 is not assigned.

| | | | | |
|---|---|---|---|---|
| 347 | **4¢ violet** (340), *Aug 23, 1954* | 2.00 | .30 | 9.00 |
| | pair | 4.00 | 1.00 | 14.00 |
| | strip of 4 | 8.00 | 3.00 | |
| i | jump strip of 4 | 12.00* | 5.00* | — |
| ii | HB | 30.00 | 5.00 | 20.00 |
| | HB, pair | 60.00 | 15.00 | 30.00 |
| | HB, strip of 4 | 120.00 | 40.00 | — |
| iii | HB, jump strip of 4 | 150.00* | 50.00* | — |
| iv | "damaged E" variety | 15.00 | 5.00 | — |
| | 347iv, in jump strip of 4 with 3 normal | 25.00* | 25.00* | — |
| v | HB, "damaged E" variety | 60.00 | 15.00 | |
| | 347v, in jump strip of 4 with 3 normal | 150.00* | 60.00* | — |
| | No. 347, start or end strip of 4 | 55.00† | | |
| | No. 347ii, start or end strip of 4 | 300.00† | | |
| | No. 347, repair paste-up strip of 4 | 48.00* | | |
| | No. 347ii, repair paste-up strip of 4 | 240.00* | | |

Qty: 39,445,000

| | | | | |
|---|---|---|---|---|
| 348 | **5¢ bright blue** (341), *Jul 6, 1954* | 3.00 | .25 | 6.00 |
| | pair | 6.00 | .65 | 18.00 |
| | strip of 4 | 12.00 | 3.00 | |
| i | jump strip of 4 | 15.00* | 6.00* | — |
| ii | "damaged E" variety | 15.00 | 5.00 | 7.00 |
| | 348ii, in jump strip of 4 with 3 normal | 25.00* | 15.00* | — |
| | No. 348, start or end strip of 4 | 72.00† | | |
| | No. 348, repair paste-up strip of 4 | 55.00* | | |

Qty: 52,745,000
No. 348 also exists on LF paper.

| | | | | |
|---|---|---|---|---|
| **Nos. 345-348** | (3) Set | 5.75 | .80 | — |

"Damaged E" variety occurs to the right of the jump in jump strips of four.
CUTTING GUIDELINES exist and may exist on all listed varieties. Generally these are off centre to allow the variety to show on the margin edge. Price for F NH Jump Strip showing the CUTTING GUIDELINE on the most common paper are: 2¢ $60.00, 2¢ Precancel $100.00, 4¢ $60.00, 5¢ $75.00
* Jump strips and repair paste-up strips cannot have true VF centring due to variations in the spacing at the jump or paste-up.
† Values are for coil starter strips of 4 plus 10 blank labels (shaded in the colour of the stamps) and for end strips of 4 plus 10 unprinted labels. Shorter strips sell for much less.
345–348: FDC's are scarce; value any cover $50.00 each.

## PRIME MINISTERS

349
Sir John Thompson

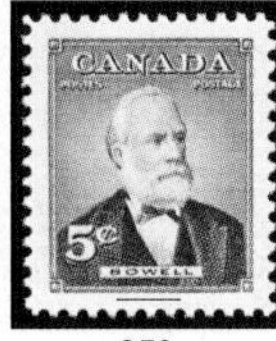
350
Sir Mackenzie Bowell

Designer: Herman Herbert Schwartz. Portrait engraved by Silas Robert Allen.
4¢: Based on a photograph by William James Topley.

Engraved (1 colour), Plates of 400 subjects in four panes of 100
Canadian Bank Note Company

**1954, Nov 1** **Perf 12**

| | | NH–VF | ⊙F | FDC |
|---|---|---|---|---|
| **349** | **4¢ violet** | .45 | .20 | 3.00 |
| | plate blocks, plates 1, 2, all blocks | 2.40 | | |

Qty: 50,500,000

| | | NH–VF | ⊙F | FDC |
|---|---|---|---|---|
| **350** | **5¢ bright blue** | .45 | .20 | 3.00 |
| | plate blocks, plates 1, 2, all blocks | 2.40 | | |

Qty: 50,800,000

Sir John Sparrow David Thompson, Prime Minister from 1892 until his death in 1894 and Sir Mackenzie Bowell from 1894 to 1896.
See also 303–304, 318–319, 357–358.

## 1955

### ESKIMO HUNTER

351
Inuk and Kayak

Designer: Thomas Harold Beament.

Engraved (1 colour), Plates of 200 subjects in four panes of 50
Canadian Bank Note Company

**1955, Feb 21** **Perf 12**

| | | NH–VF | ⊙F | FDC |
|---|---|---|---|---|
| **351** | **10¢ violet brown** | .55 | .20 | 6.00 |
| | plate blocks, plates 1–4, all blocks | 2.75 | | |
| | plate blocks, plate 5, all blocks | 4.80 | | |

Qty: 313,525,000

For **G** overprint see number O39.

### WILDLIFE

352
Musk Ox

353
Whooping Crane

4¢: Designer: Emanuel Otto Hahn. Modeled by Herman Herbert Schwartz. Picture engraved by Silas Robert Allen.
5¢: Dr. William Rowan, F.R.C.S., Professor of Zoology, University of Alberta. Picture engraved by Silas Robert Allen.

Engraved (1 colour), Plates of 400 subjects in four panes of 100
Canadian Bank Note Company

**1955, Apr 4** **Perf 12**

| | | NH–VF | ⊙F | FDC |
|---|---|---|---|---|
| **352** | **4¢ purple** | .45 | .20 | 3.00 |
| | plate blocks, plates 1, 2, all blocks | 2.40 | | |

Qty: 51,200,000

Engraved (1 colour), Plates of 200 subjects in four panes of 50

| | | NH–VF | ⊙F | FDC |
|---|---|---|---|---|
| **353** | **5¢ blue** | .50 | .20 | 3.00 |
| | plate blocks, plates 1, 2 | 2.50 | | |
| i | plate 1, UL, plate crack, left margin | 18.00 | | |

Qty: 50,950,000

### UNITED NATIONS – ICAO

354
Dove

Designer: Walter Lohse. Engraved by Silas Robert Allen. Background engraved by Yves Baril.

Engraved (1 colour), Plates of 200 subjects in four panes of 50
Canadian Bank Note Company

**1955, Jun 1** **Perf 12**

| | | NH–VF | ⊙F | FDC |
|---|---|---|---|---|
| **354** | **5¢ light blue** | .55 | .20 | 3.00 |
| | plate blocks, all blocks | 2.75 | | |

Qty: 25,000,000

Issued to commemorate the 10th anniversary of the founding of the International Civil Aviation Organization, the only U.N. agency based in Canada.
See also 1528.

### ALBERTA & SASKATCHEWAN

355
Wheat and Oil

Designer: Laurence Hyde. Picture engraved by Yves Baril. Lettering engraved by John F. Mash.

Engraved (1 colour), Plates of 200 subjects in four panes of 50
Canadian Bank Note Company

**1955, Jun 30** **Perf 12**

| | | NH–VF | ⊙F | FDC |
|---|---|---|---|---|
| **355** | **5¢ ultramarine** | .55 | .20 | 3.00 |
| | plate blocks, plates 1, 2, all blocks | 2.75 | | |

Qty: 25,200,000

Issued to commemorate the 50th anniversary of the creation of the provinces of Alberta and Saskatchewan.

## BOY SCOUTS

356
World Jamboree

Designer: Laurence Hyde. Modeled by Herman Herbert Schwartz. Picture engraved by Silas Robert Allen. Globes engraved by Yves Baril.

Engraved (2 colours), Plates of 200 subjects in four panes of 50
Canadian Bank Note Company

**1955, Aug 20** **Perf 12**

| | | NH–VF | ⊙F | FDC |
|---|---|---|---|---|
| **356** | **5¢ green and orange brown** | .55 | .20 | 3.00 |
| | plate blocks, plates 1–1 and 2–1 | 2.75 | | |

Qty: 51,350,000

Issued on the occasion of the 1955 World Jamboree held at Niagara-on-the-Lake, Ontario.

## PRIME MINISTERS

357
Richard Bennett

358
Sir Charles Tupper

Designer: Herman Herbert Schwartz.

Engraved (1 colour), Plates of 400 subjects in four panes of 100
Canadian Bank Note Company

**1955, Nov 8** **Perf 12**

| | | NH–VF | ⊙F | FDC |
|---|---|---|---|---|
| **357** | **4¢ violet** | .50 | .20 | 3.00 |
| | plate blocks, plates 1, 2, all blocks | 2.50 | | |

Qty: 49,855,000

| | | NH–VF | ⊙F | FDC |
|---|---|---|---|---|
| **358** | **5¢ ultramarine** | .50 | .20 | 3.00 |
| | plate blocks, plates 1, 2, all blocks | 2.50 | | |

Qty: 50,480,000

Richard B. Bennett was Prime Minister during the Depression, 1930–1935, and Sir Charles Tupper was Prime Minister for only three months in 1896.
See also 303–304, 318–319, 349–350.

# 1956

## HOCKEY

359
Hockey Players

Designer: James Simpkins. Picture engraved by Silas Robert Allen.

Engraved (1 colour), Plates of 200 subjects in four panes of 50
Canadian Bank Note Company

**1956, Jan 23** **Perf 12**

| | | NH–VF | ⊙F | FDC |
|---|---|---|---|---|
| **359** | **5¢ ultramarine** | .50 | .20 | 3.00 |
| | plate blocks, all blocks | 2.50 | | |

Qty: 30,000,000

Issued to honor a sport which many consider the National Sport of Canada.

## WILDLIFE

360
Caribou

361
Mountain Goat

Designer: Emanuel Otto Hahn. Picture engraved by Silas Robert Allen.

Engraved (1 colour), Plates of 400 subjects in four panes of 100
Canadian Bank Note Company

**1956, Apr 12** **Perf 12**

| | | NH–VF | ⊙F | FDC |
|---|---|---|---|---|
| **360** | **4¢ deep violet** | .55 | .20 | 3.00 |
| | plate blocks, plates 1, 2, UL | 3.60 | | |
| | all others | 2.75 | | |

Qty: 50,900,000

| | | NH–VF | ⊙F | FDC |
|---|---|---|---|---|
| **361** | **5¢ ultramarine** | .55 | .20 | 3.00 |
| | plate blocks, plates 1, 2, all blocks | 2.75 | | |

Qty: 51,100,000

## INDUSTRY

362
Paper Industry

363
Chemical Industry

Designer: 20¢: Alfred Joseph Casson. Picture engraved by Silas Robert Allen.
25¢: Alan L. Pollock. Modeled by Herman Herbert Schwartz.

Engraved (1 colour), Plates of 200 subjects in four panes of 50
Canadian Bank Note Company

**1956, Jun 7** **Perf 12**

| | | NH–VF | ⊙F | FDC |
|---|---|---|---|---|
| **362** | **20¢ green**, Ribbed (horiz), plates 1–3 | 2.00 | .20 | 9.00 |
| | plate blocks, plates 1, 2n, all blocks* | 12.00 | | |
| | plate 2, UL, LL | 12.00 | | |
| | plate 2, UR, LR | 13.80 | | |
| | plate 3, all blocks | 18.00 | | |
| i | Ribbed (vert), plate 4 | 2.50 | .25 | |
| | plate 4, all blocks | 12.00 | | |

* Plates come with wide and narrow (n) selvedge.
For **G** overprint see number O45.

| | | NH–VF | ⊙F | FDC |
|---|---|---|---|---|
| **363** | **25¢ red** | 2.25 | .20 | 10.00 |
| | plate blocks, plate 1, all blocks | 13.50 | | |
| | plate 2, all blocks | 15.00 | | |

## PREVENT FIRES

**364**
House on Fire

Designer: Arthur Donald Price. Modeled by Herman Herbert Schwartz. Picture engraved by Silas Robert Allen.

Engraved (2 colours), Plates of 400 subjects in four panes of 100
Canadian Bank Note Company

**1956, Oct 9** **Perf 12**

| | | NH–VF | ⊙F | FDC |
|---|---|---|---|---|
| **364** | **5¢ grey and red** | .45 | .20 | 3.00 |
| | plate blocks, plate 1, all blocks | 2.30 | | |

Qty: 50,750,000

# 1957

## RECREATION SPORTS

**365** Fishing — **366** Swimming

**367** Hunting — **368** Skiing

Designer: Laurence Hyde. Fishing & skiing pictures engraved by Silas Robert Allen. Swimming & hunting pictures engraved by Yves Baril.

Engraved (1 colour), Plates of 200 subjects in four panes of 50
Canadian Bank Note Company

**1957, Mar 7** **Perf 12**

| | | NH–VF | ⊙F | FDC |
|---|---|---|---|---|
| **365** | **5¢ blue** | .55 | .30 | 6.00 |
| i | identical pair | 3.00 | 3.00 | 12.00 |
| **366** | **5¢ blue** | .55 | .30 | 6.00 |
| **367** | **5¢ blue** | .55 | .30 | 6.00 |
| **368** | **5¢ blue** | .55 | .30 | 6.00 |
| a | se-tenant block of 4 (365–368) | 2.60 | 1.50 | 10.00 |
| i | identical pair | 3.00 | 3.00 | 12.00 |
| | plate blocks, plates 1–2, all blocks | 3.30 | | |

Qty: 50,200,000

Canada's first issue with se-tenant designs. The pane had an interesting layout of the four different stamps that resulted in dozens of different se-tenant combinations.

UL pane of 50 — UR pane of 50

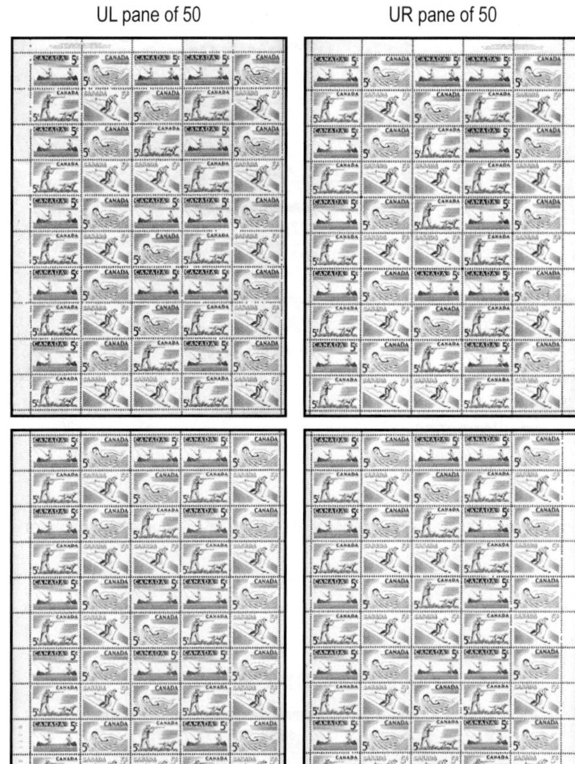

LL pane of 50 — LR pane of 50

## WILDLIFE

**369**
Loon

Designer: Laurence Hyde. Picture and lettering engraved by John F. Mash.

Engraved (1 colour), Plates of 400 subjects in four panes of 100
Canadian Bank Note Company

**1957, Apr 10** **Perf 12**

| | | NH–VF | ⊙F | FDC |
|---|---|---|---|---|
| **369** | **5¢ black** | .45 | .20 | 3.00 |
| i | "dot on water" (plate 1, pos. 1) | 3.50 | 2.50 | 15.00* |
| | plate blocks, plate 1, UL, 369i in position 1 | 5.40 | | |
| | all others | 2.30 | | |

Qty: 51,000,000
* Any cover.

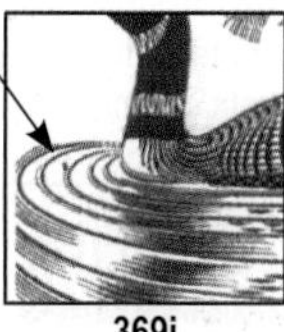

**369i**

## DAVID THOMPSON

370
Thompson and Map

Designer: George Arthur Gundersen. Picture engraved by Yves Baril.
Engraved (1 colour), Plates of 200 subjects in four panes of 50
Canadian Bank Note Company

**1957, Jun 5** **Perf 12**

| | | NH–VF | ⊙F | FDC |
|---|---|---|---|---|
| 370 | **5¢ ultramarine** | .45 | .20 | 3.00 |
| | plate blocks, all blocks | 2.30 | | |

Qty: 29,350,000

Issued on the 100th anniversary of the death of David Thompson, explorer and geographer.

## UPU CONGRESS

371
Parliament Buildings

372
Posthorn and Globe

Designer: Carl Mangold. Picture engraved by Yves Baril.
Engraved (1 colour), Plates of 400 subjects in four panes of 100
Canadian Bank Note Company

**1957, Aug 14** **Perf 12**

| | | NH–VF | ⊙F | FDC |
|---|---|---|---|---|
| 371 | **5¢ dark blue** | .45 | .20 | 3.00 |
| | plate blocks, plates 1, 2, all blocks | 2.30 | | |

Qty: 74,700,000

Engraved (1 colour), Plates of 200 subjects in four panes of 50

| | | | | |
|---|---|---|---|---|
| 372 | **15¢ dark blue** | 3.00 | 2.50 | 6.00 |
| | plate blocks, all blocks | 15.00 | | |

Qty: 7,000,000

**Nos. 371, 372** (2) combination FDC 8.00
Issued on the occasion of the 14th Universal Postal Union Congress, Ottawa.

**Values for FDCs from No. 373 to No. 534 are for unaddressed covers with Artcraft, Rosecraft cachets. Other cachets command a premium**

## MINING

373
Miner with drill

Designer: Alfred Joseph Casson. Picture engraved by Yves Baril. Based on a photograph by George Hunter.
Engraved (1 colour), Plates of 400 subjects in four panes of 100
Canadian Bank Note Company

**1957, Sep 5** **Perf 12**

| | | NH–VF | ⊙F | FDC |
|---|---|---|---|---|
| 373 | **5¢ black** | .40 | .20 | 3.00 |
| i | imperf. top margin single (10 exist) | *1,750.00* | | |
| | plate blocks, all blocks | 2.10 | | |
| | containing variety 373i, unique | *5,000.00* | | |

Qty: 25,600,000

Issued to publicize Canada's mining industry and the 6th Commonwealth Mining and Metallurgical Congress.

373i

## ROYAL VISIT

374
Queen Elizabeth II & Prince Philip

Based on photographs by Yousuf Karsh. Portraits engraved by Yves Baril.
Engraved (1 colour), Plates of 400 subjects in four panes of 100
Canadian Bank Note Company

**1957, Oct 10** **Perf 12**

| | | NH–VF | ⊙F | FDC |
|---|---|---|---|---|
| 374 | **5¢ black** | .40 | .20 | 3.00 |
| | plate blocks, plates 1, 2, all blocks | 2.10 | | |

Qty: 51,260,000

Issued to commemorate the first Royal Visit of Queen Elizabeth II as reigning monarch.

**Plate / Inscription blocks**

During this era, a printed sheet of stamps contained four post office panes. Each pane included a plate numbered inscription in just one corner of the pane, as is illustrated on the previous page. Thus, there are 4 plate positions that are collected: upper left (UL), upper right (UR), lower left (LL), and lower right (LR).

As plate block collecting became popular, collectors would make frequent trips to several post offices on a stamp's day of issue, removing and purchasing just 4 stamps from each pane. This created a nuisance for the postal clerks who were left with partial panes and an accounting headache.

From November 1957 to April 1958, stamp panes had the plate inscriptions removed (or not printed at all). This affected Scott numbers 375–376 and 337–341. An outcry by collectors resulted in the plate inscriptions returning.

## 1958

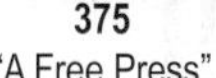

375
"A Free Press"

376
Microscope

### NEWSPAPER INDUSTRY

Designer: Alan L. Pollock

Engraved (1 colour), , Plates of 200 subjects in four panes of 50
Canadian Bank Note Company

**1958, Jan 22** **Perf 12**

| | | NH–VF | ⊙F | FDC |
|---|---|---|---|---|
| **375** | **5¢ black** | .45 | .20 | 3.00 |
| | blank corner blocks | 4.20 | | |

Qty: 15,300,000

### INTERNATIONAL GEOPHYSICAL YEAR

Designer: Alan L. Pollock.

Engraved (1 colour), Plates of 400 subjects in four panes of 100
Canadian Bank Note Company

**1958, Mar 5** **Perf 12**

| | | NH–VF | ⊙F | FDC |
|---|---|---|---|---|
| **376** | **5¢ blue** | .45 | .20 | 3.00 |
| | blank corner blocks | 4.20 | | |

Qty: 25,200,000

377
Miner Panning Gold

378
La Vérendrye Statue

### BRITISH COLUMBIA CENTENNIAL

Designer: Jack Kenneth Harman. Picture engraved by Yves Baril.

Engraved (1 colour), Plates of 200 subjects in four panes of 50
Canadian Bank Note Company

**1958, May 8** **Perf 12**

| | | NH–VF | ⊙F | PB | FDC |
|---|---|---|---|---|---|
| **377** | **5¢ bluish green** | .45 | .20 | 3.90 | 3.00 |

Qty: 20,350,000

Issued to commemorate the 100th anniversary of the founding of the Province of British Columbia.

### LA VÉRENDRYE

Designer: Gerald Mathew Trottier. Picture engraved by Yves Baril. Based on a sculpture by Jean-Émile Brunet.

Engraved (1 colour), Plates of 200 subjects in four panes of 50
Canadian Bank Note Company

**1958, Jun 4** **Perf 12**

| | | NH–VF | ⊙F | PB | FDC |
|---|---|---|---|---|---|
| **378** | **5¢ bright ultramarine** | .45 | .20 | 3.00 | 3.00 |

Qty: 20,320,000

Pierre Gaultier de Varenne, Sieur de la Vérendrye, was an 18th century French explorer of Western Canada.

379
Champlain

380
Nurse

### FOUNDING OF QUEBEC

Designer: Gerald Mathew Trottier. Picture engraved by Yves Baril. Lettering engraved by Gordon Mash.

Engraved (2 colours), Plates of 200 subjects in four panes of 50
Canadian Bank Note Company

**1958, Jun 26** **Perf 12**

| | | NH–VF | ⊙F | PB | FDC |
|---|---|---|---|---|---|
| **379** | **5¢ dark green and bistre brown** | .45 | .20 | 6.00 | 3.00 |

Qty: 19,910,000

Issued to commemorate the 350th anniversary of the founding of Quebec by Champlain in 1608.

### HEALTH

Designer: Gerald Mathew Trottier. Portrait and picture engraved by Yves Baril. Lettering engraved by John F. Mash.

Engraved (1 colour), Plates of 400 subjects in four panes of 100
Canadian Bank Note Company

**1958, Jul 30** **Perf 12**

| | | NH–VF | ⊙F | PB | FDC |
|---|---|---|---|---|---|
| **380** | **5¢ rose lilac** | .45 | .20 | 3.00 | 3.00 |

Qty: 24,600,000

This was the first Canadian postage stamp purposely designed with a living model as the featured symbol of the theme the stamps express.

381
Oil Lamp and Refinery

382
Mace and Speakers Chair

### OIL INDUSTRY

Designer: Alan L. Pollock. Picture and lettering engraved by Donald J. Mitchell.

Engraved (2 colours), Plates of 400 subjects in four panes of 100
Canadian Bank Note Company

**1958, Sep 10** **Perf 12**

| | | NH–VF | ⊙F | PB | FDC |
|---|---|---|---|---|---|
| **381** | **5¢ olive and red** | .45 | .20 | 3.00 | 3.00 |

Qty: 24,660,000

Issued to commemorate the 100th anniversary of Canada's petroleum industry.

### FIRST ELECTED ASSEMBLY

Designer: Gerald Mathew Trottier and Carl Dair. Picture engraved by Yves Baril. Lettering engraved by John F. Mash.

Engraved (1 colour), Plates of 200 subjects in four panes of 50
Canadian Bank Note Company

**1958, Oct 2** **Perf 12**

| | | NH–VF | ⊙F | PB | FDC |
|---|---|---|---|---|---|
| **382** | **5¢ slate blue** | .45 | .20 | 3.00 | 3.00 |

Qty: 25,360,000

Issued to commemorate the 200th anniversary of the first elected Assembly in Nova Scotia.

## 1959

383
Sliver Dart and Jet Planes

384
Globe

### FIRST FLIGHT IN CANADA

Designer: Harvey Thomas Prosser. Picture engraved by Yves Baril. Lettering engraved by Donald J. Mitchell.

Engraved (2 colours), Plates of 200 subjects in four panes of 50
Canadian Bank Note Company

**1959, Feb 23** **Perf 12**

| | | NH–VF | ⊙F | PB | FDC |
|---|---|---|---|---|---|
| **383** | **5¢ blue and black** | .45 | .20 | 3.00 | 3.00 |

Qty: 29,760,000

Issued to commemorate the 50th anniversary of the first flight in Canada, J.A. McCurdy's *Silver Dart* at Baddeck, N.S.

### NATO

Designer: Ephrum Philip Weiss. Picture engraved by Yves Baril. Lettering engraved by Donald J. Mitchell.

Engraved (1 colour), Plates of 400 subjects in four panes of 100
Canadian Bank Note Company

**1959, Apr 2** **Perf 12**

| | | NH–VF | ⊙F | PB | FDC |
|---|---|---|---|---|---|
| **384** | **5¢ violet blue** | .45 | .20 | 3.00 | 3.00 |

Qty: 32,760,000

Issued on the occasion of the 10th anniversary of the North Atlantic Treaty Organization.

### COUNTRY WOMEN

385
Woman and Tree

Designer: Helen Roberta Fitzgerald. Picture and lettering engraved by Donald J. Mitchell.

Engraved (2 colours), Plates of 400 subjects in four panes of 100
Canadian Bank Note Company

**1959, May 13** **Perf 12**

| | | NH–VF | ⊙F | PB | FDC |
|---|---|---|---|---|---|
| **385** | **5¢ apple green and black** | .45 | .20 | 3.00 | 3.00 |

Qty: 32,200,000

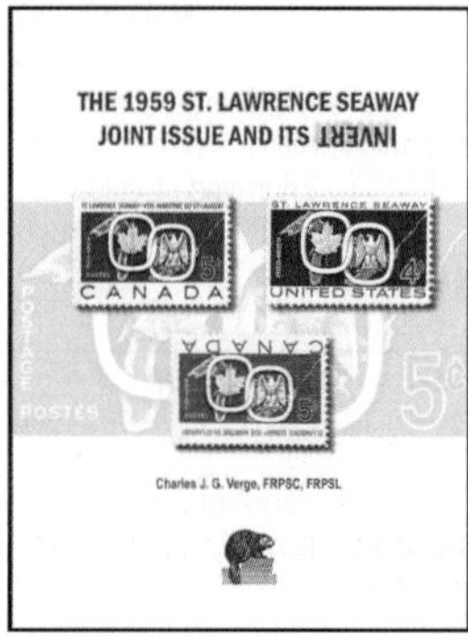


*The 1959 St. Lawrence Seaway Joint Issue and Its Invert*, Charles J.G. Verge, FRPSC, FRPSL, 2009.

### ROYAL VISIT

386
Queen Elizabeth II

Designer: Harvey Thomas Prosser. Based on a painting by Pietro Annigoni. Portrait engraved by Yves Baril. Lettering engraved by John F. Mash.

Engraved (1 colour), Plates of 300 subjects in six panes of 50
Canadian Bank Note Company

**1959, Jun 18** **Perf 12**

| | | NH–VF | ⊙F | PB | FDC |
|---|---|---|---|---|---|
| **386** | **5¢ dark carmine** | .45 | .20 | | 3.00 |
| | plate blocks, plates 1, 2, all blocks | | | 3.00 | |

Qty: 40,360,000

Issued on the occasion of Queen Elizabeth's visit to Canada to open the St. Lawrence Seaway.

### ST. LAWRENCE SEAWAY

387
Seaway and National Emblems

Designer: A.L. Pollock and Gerald Trottier of Canada; William H. Buckley, Arnold J. Copeland, and Ervine Metzl of the United States. Picture engraved by Yves Baril. Lettering engraved by Donald J. Mitchell.

Engraved (2 colours), Plates of 200 subjects in four panes of 50
Canadian Bank Note Company

**1959, Jun 26** **Perf 12**

| | | NH–VF | ⊙F | PB | FDC |
|---|---|---|---|---|---|
| **387** | **5¢ red and blue** | .45 | .20 | 6.00 | 3.00 |
| **a** | inverted text (approx. 400) | 12,500.‡ | 10,000.00 | | 25,000.* |
| **i** | red double-printed (kiss print) | 2,500.† | 1,350.00† | | *3,000.*† |

Qty: 49,110,000

Issued on the occasion of the opening of the St. Lawrence Seaway. The U.S. issued a similar design 4¢ stamp. The price for the inverted text in the FDC column is for a single stamp on any cover.

* The editors have recorded sixteen covers or cards with the Seaway invert properly used.
† Certificate of authenticity required. The second impression varies from very weak to quite strong. One single on cover recorded.
‡ Value shown is for NH-VF with no faults or fingerprints. Many Seaway Inverts display minor imperfections due to mishandling by the non-collecting "public" who found them in 1959.

**387a**
Inverted text

Joint issue with United States
**Scott # 1131**

## PLAINS OF ABRAHAM

388
National Emblems

Designer: Ephrum Philip Weiss. Picture engraved by Yves Baril. Lettering engraved by Donald J. Mitchell.

Engraved (2 colours), Plates of 300 subjects in six panes of 50
Canadian Bank Note Company

**1959, Sep 10** **Perf 12**

| | NH–VF | ⊙F | PB | FDC |
|---|---|---|---|---|
| **388 5¢ crimson rose and dark green** | .45 | .20 | 3.00 | 3.00 |

Qty: 29,240,000

Issued to commemorate the 200th anniversary of the Battle of the Plains of Abraham, the outcome of which gave Canada to the British.

## 1960

**First Day Cover values, post 1960, are for cacheted, unaddressed covers. Uncacheted and addressed covers sell for much less.**

## GIRL GUIDES

389
Girl Guide Emblem

Designer: Helen Roberta Fitzgerald. Picture and lettering engraved by John F. Mash.

Engraved (2 colours), Plates of 400 subjects in four panes of 100
Canadian Bank Note Company

**1960, Apr 20** **Perf 12**

| | NH–VF | ⊙F | PB | FDC |
|---|---|---|---|---|
| **389 5¢ brown orange and ultramarine** | .45 | .20 | 2.40 | 2.00 |

Qty: 31,360,000

Issued to honour the Canadian Girl Guides Association on its 50th anniversary.

## BATTLE OF LONG SAULT

390
Dollard des Ormeaux

Designer: Ephrum Philip Weiss. Picture engraved by Yves Baril. Lettering engraved by Donald J. Mitchell.

Engraved (2 colours), Plates of 400 subjects in four panes of 100
Canadian Bank Note Company

**1960, May 19** **Perf 12**

| | NH–VF | ⊙F | PB | FDC |
|---|---|---|---|---|
| **390 5¢ ultramarine and bistre brown** | .45 | .20 | 2.40 | 2.00 |

Qty: 30,960,000

Issued to commemorate the 300th anniversary of the Battle of Long Sault which saved Montreal from Indian attack.

## 1961

391
Surveying Crew

392
Pauline Johnson

## NORTHERN DEVELOPMENT

Designer: Bernard James Reddie. Picture engraved by Yves Baril. Lettering engraved by Gordon Mash.

Engraved (2 colours), Plates of 200 subjects in four panes of 50
Canadian Bank Note Company

**1961, Feb 8** **Perf 12**

| | NH–VF | ⊙F | PB | FDC |
|---|---|---|---|---|
| **391 5¢ green and vermilion** | .45 | .20 | 2.40 | 2.00 |

Qty: 30,055,000

## PAULINE JOHNSON

Designer: Bernard James Reddie. Portrait and picture engraved by Yves Baril.Lettering engraved by Gordon Mash.

Engraved (2 colours), Plates of 400 subjects in four panes of 100
Canadian Bank Note Company

**1961, Mar 10** **Perf 12**

| | NH–VF | ⊙F | PB | FDC |
|---|---|---|---|---|
| **392 5¢ green and red** | .45 | .20 | 2.40 | 2.00 |

Qty: 35,450,000

2 vertical imperforate pairs, one missing red as well, have been seen by the editors.

Issued on the 100th anniversary of the birth of E. Pauline Johnson, Mohawk princess and poet.

393
Arthur Meighen

394
Power Plant

## PRIME MINISTER

Designer: Harvey Thomas Prosser. Portrait engraved by Yves Baril. Lettering engraved by Donald J. Mitchell.

Engraved (1 colour), Plates of 400 subjects in four panes of 100
Canadian Bank Note Company

**1961, Apr 19** **Perf 12**

| | NH–VF | ⊙F | PB | FDC |
|---|---|---|---|---|
| **393 5¢ ultramarine** | .45 | .20 | 2.40 | 2.00 |

Qty: 30,960,000

Issued to honour Arthur Meighen, Prime Minister of Canada, 1920–1921 and 1926.

## COLOMBO PLAN

Designer: Bernard James Reddie. Picture engraved by Yves Baril. Lettering engraved by Donald J. Mitchell.

Engraved (2 colours), Plates of 300 subjects in six panes of 50
Canadian Bank Note Company

**1961, Jun 28** **Perf 12**

| | NH–VF | ⊙F | PB | FDC |
|---|---|---|---|---|
| **394 5¢ light red brown and blue** | .45 | .20 | 2.40 | 2.00 |

Qty: 32,010,000

Issued for the 10th anniversary of the Colombo Plan, which assists developing nations.

## RESOURCES FOR TOMORROW

395
Hands and Cogwheel

Designer: Alan L. Pollock. Engraved by Donald J. Mitchell. Background engraved by Yves Baril. Lettering engraved by Gordon Mash. Modeled by Harvey Thomas Prosser.

Engraved (2 colours), Plates of 300 subjects in six panes of 50
Canadian Bank Note Company

**1961, Oct 12** **Perf 12**

| | | NH–VF | ⊙F | PB | FDC |
|---|---|---|---|---|---|
| **395** | **5¢ brown and blue green** | .45 | .20 | 2.40 | 2.00 |

Qty: 36,160,000

## 1962

## EDUCATION

396
Students

Designer: Helen Roberta Fitzgerald. Picture engraved by Yves Baril. Lettering engraved by Donald J. Mitchell.

Engraved (2 colours), Plates of 400 subjects in four panes of 100
Canadian Bank Note Company

**1962, Feb 28** **Perf 12**

| | | NH–VF | ⊙F | PB | FDC |
|---|---|---|---|---|---|
| **396** | **5¢ black and light red brown** | .45 | .20 | 2.40 | 2.00 |
| i | missing black at UR incl. denomination (unique corner fold error) | *3,000* | | | |

Qty: 33,260,000

## RED RIVER SETTLEMENT

397
Lord Selkirk

Designer: Phillips-Gutkin & Associates. Portrait engraved by Allan Alexander Carswell. Picture engraved by Yves Baril. Lettering engraved by Gordon Mash.

Engraved (2 colours), Plates of 300 subjects in six panes of 50
Canadian Bank Note Company

**1962, May 3** **Perf 12**

| | | NH–VF | ⊙F | PB | FDC |
|---|---|---|---|---|---|
| **397** | **5¢ light green and violet brown**, dull | .45 | .20 | 2.40 | 2.00 |
| i | F | 1.50 | .25 | 9.00 | — |
| ii | HB | 9.00 | 3.00 | 48.00 | — |
| iii | HF | 7.00 | 2.00 | 35.00 | — |

Qty: 25,910,000

Issued to commemorate the 150th anniversary of the Red River Settlement in Manitoba. The hibrite paper is not as bright as that found on the "Centennials" but is much brighter than fluorescent.

## JEAN TALON

398
Talon and Colonists

Designer: Ephrum Philip Weiss. Picture engraved by Yves Baril. Lettering engraved by Donald J. Mitchell.

Engraved (1 colour), Plates of 400 subjects in four panes of 100
Canadian Bank Note Company

**1962, Jun 13** **Perf 12**

| | | NH–VF | ⊙F | PB | FDC |
|---|---|---|---|---|---|
| **398** | **5¢ dark blue** | .45 | .20 | 2.40 | 2.00 |
| i | missing value and 'POS' (unique) | *2,000.00* | | | |

Qty: 31,920,000

396i 398i

## VICTORIA CENTENARY

399
1860 B.C. stamp

Designer: Helen Roberta Fitzgerald. Portrait and picture engraved by Yves Baril. Lettering engraved by Donald J. Mitchell.

Engraved (2 colours), Plates of 300 subjects in six panes of 50
Canadian Bank Note Company

**1962, Aug 22** **Perf 12**

| | | NH–VF | ⊙F | PB | FDC |
|---|---|---|---|---|---|
| **399** | **5¢ black and rose**, dull | .45 | .20 | 2.40 | 2.00 |
| i | F | 2.00 | .50 | 12.00 | — |
| ii | HB | 125.00 | 10.00 | 1,200.00* | — |
| iii | MF | 25.00 | 3.00 | 150.00* | — |

Qty: 35,170,000

* Two HB plate blocks recorded to date. Blank corner block of 4 value $900.00.

The hibrite paper is not as bright as that found on the "Centennials" but is much brighter than fluorescent.

**CBN Perforating**

In middle to late 1962 Canadian Bank Note Company (CBN) changed their perforation equipment from a gauge of 11.95 to a gauge of 11.85.

This change affected some of the then current low- and medium-value Wilding definitives (including 320, 321, 334, 338, 340, 343, 351, 362, 363, 411), at least one commemorative (399), low-value Cameo definitives (401a, 402a, 404a, 405a, 405b, 405p), low-value Centennial booklet (458a), and a couple of postage due stamps (J15–J20). Other issues may also have similar varieties.

## TRANS-CANADA HIGHWAY

**400**
Provincial Coats-of-Arms

Designer: Alan L. Pollock. Picture engraved by Yves Baril. Lettering engraved by Donald J. Mitchell.

Engraved (2 colours), Plates of 300 subjects in six panes of 50
Canadian Bank Note Company

**1962, Aug 31** **Perf 12**

| | | NH–VF | ⊙F | PB | FDC |
|---|---|---|---|---|---|
| **400** | **5¢ brown orange and black** | .45 | .20 | 2.40 | 2.00 |

Qty: 25,570,000

## QUEEN ELIZABETH II – CAMEO ISSUE

**401**
Crystals (mining industry)

**402**
Tree (forestry)

**403**
Fishing industry

**404**
Tower (electricity)

**405**
Wheat (agriculture)

For **G** overprints (1¢, 2¢, 4¢, 5¢) see numbers O46–O49.

Definitive Series Historical Notes:

- first horizontal format low-value definitive set
- last Official stamps issued

Designer: Ernst Roch. Portrait engraved by Yves Baril. Lettering and symbol engraved by Donald J. Mitchell.

Engraved (1 colour), Plates of 600 subjects in six panes of 100
Canadian Bank Note Company

**1962–1963** **Perf 12**

| | | NH–VF | ⊙F | PB | FDC |
|---|---|---|---|---|---|
| **401** | **1¢ brown**, *Feb 4, 1963* | .25 | .20 | 1.25 | 3.00 |
| | plate blocks, plates 1–3, all blocks | | | 1.25 | |
| **xx** | No. 401, precancelled | .50 | .25 | — | 5.00 |
| | precancelled warning strips of 20 | | | 40.00 | |
| **p** | tagged, W2B, *May 15, 1963* | .25 | .20 | 1.25* | 25.00 |
| **ii** | W2B, F | 5.00 | .50 | 20.00* | |
| **iii** | 401p, wide & narrow tag bars in margin pair | 1.20 | 1.20 | 3.00* | |

* Blank corner block of 4.
Qty (all 1¢): 478,556,000

| | | NH–VF | ⊙F | PB | FDC |
|---|---|---|---|---|---|
| 401a | booklet pane of 5 x 1¢ brown (401as) + label, NF (BK53), *Feb 4, 1963* | 4.00 | 3.00 | | 17.50 |
| as | single with straight edge, from 401a | .85 | .60 | | |
| ai | LF pane | 20.00 | 15.00 | | |
| ais | single with straight edge, from 401ai | 5.00 | 3.00 | | |

| | | NH–VF | ⊙F | PB | FDC |
|---|---|---|---|---|---|
| **402** | **2¢ green**, *May 2, 1963* | .25 | .20 | 4.50 | 3.00 |
| | plate blocks, plates 1, 2, all blocks | | | 4.50 | |
| | plates 3, 4, all blocks | | | 6.50 | |
| **xx** | No. 402, precancelled | .50 | .50 | — | 5.00 |
| | precancelled warning strips of 20 | | | 56.00 | |
| **p** | tagged, W2B, *May 15, 1963* | .25 | .20 | 4.00* | 25.00 |
| **ii** | 402p, wide & narrow tag bars in margin pair | 1.50 | 1.50 | 7.00* | |

* Blank corner block of 4.
Qty (all 2¢): 440,000,000

| | | NH–VF | ⊙F | PB | FDC |
|---|---|---|---|---|---|
| 402a | Miniature pane of 25 (5x5) | 10.00 | 10.00 | | |
| as | single with straight edge, from 402a | .40 | .25 | | |
| ai | Cello paq containing 2 panes of 402a | 25.00 | | | |

| | | NH–VF | ⊙F | PB | FDC |
|---|---|---|---|---|---|
| **403** | **3¢ purple**, *May 2, 1963* | .25 | .20 | 1.25 | 3.00 |
| **ii** | dark purple | .25 | .20 | 1.25 | |
| | plate blocks, plates 1, 2, all blocks | | | 1.25 | |
| | plates 3, all blocks | | | 1.50 | |
| **xx** | No. 403, precancelled | .50 | .25 | — | 5.00 |
| | precancelled warning strips of 20 | | | 40.00 | |
| **p** | tagged, W2B, *May 15, 1963* | .30 | .20 | 1.50* | 25.00 |
| **iv** | W2B, F | 5.00 | .50 | 20.00* | |
| **v** | 403p with wide & narrow tag bars in margin pair | 2.50 | 2.50 | 7.50* | |
| **vi** | 3¢ dark purple, W2B | 5.00 | 3.00 | 27.50* | |
| **vii** | 403pvi with wide & narrow tag bars in margin pair | 15.00 | 15.00 | 40.00* | |
| **viii** | 3¢ dark purple, W2B, F | 5.00 | 3.00 | 27.50* | |
| **ix** | 403pviii with wide & narrow tag bars in margin pair | 15.00 | 15.00 | 40.00* | |

* Blank corner block of 4.
Qty (all 3¢): 585,778,000

| | | NH–VF | ⊙F | PB | FDC |
|---|---|---|---|---|---|
| **404** | **4¢ carmine**, *Feb 4, 1963* | .25 | .20 | 1.45 | 3.00 |
| **ii** | F | 5.00 | 1.00 | 20.00 | |
| | plate blocks, plates 1, 2, all blocks | | | 1.45 | |
| | plate 3, all blocks | | | 5.00 | |
| | plates 4, 5, all blocks | | | 1.45 | |
| **xx** | No. 404, precancelled | .50 | .25 | — | 5.00 |
| | precancelled warning strips of 20 | | | 40.00 | |
| **p** | tagged, WCB (4 mm), *Feb 1963* | 1.00 | .60 | 7.50* | 25.00 |
| **iii** | tagged, WCB (8 mm), *Aug 1964* | 5.00 | 4.00 | 22.50* | |
| **iv** | WCB (8 mm), F | 9.00 | 7.00 | 40.00* | |
| **v** | Wpg. split bar pair (5 x 9mm bars/pane), *Apr 1964* † | 3.00 | 3.00 | 12.00* | |
| **vi** | Wpg. split bar pair (6 x 8mm bars/pane), *Dec 1964* † | 2.00 | 2.00 | 15.00* | |
| **vii** | wide & narrow tag bars in margin strip of 3 | 8.00 | 8.00 | 20.00* | |
| **viii** | as 'vi', F | 10.00 | 10.00 | 40.00* | |
| **ix** | as 'vii', F | 25.00 | 25.00 | 60.00* | |
| **x** | Wpg. split bar pair (5 x 8mm bars/pane), *Mar 1965* † | 2.00 | 2.00 | 8.00* | |
| **xi** | tagged, W1B at left | 1.00 | .75 | | |
| **xii** | tagged, W1B (left or right), F | 5.00 | 5.00 | | |
| **xiii** | tagged, W1B at right | 1.00 | .75 | | |

* Blank corner block of 4.
† A "split bar pair" is tagged as illustrated here:
Qty (all 4¢): 1,452,000,000

**404v/vi/x**
Split bar pair

| | | NH–VF | ⊙F | PB | FDC |
|---|---|---|---|---|---|
| 404a | booklet pane of 5 x 4¢ carmine (404as) + label (BK53), *Feb 4, 1963* | 4.00 | 3.00 | | 17.50 |
| as | single with straight edge, from 404a | .85 | .25 | | |
| ai | LF pane | 20.00 | 15.00 | | |
| ais | single with straight edge, from 404ai | 4.00 | 3.00 | | |
| BK53 | 1 pane each 401a, 404a in bilingual cover $9.00 | | | | |
| 404b | Miniature pane of 25 (5 x 5) | 15.00 | 15.00 | | |
| bs | single with straight edge, from 404b | .50 | .30 | | |
| bii | Cello paq containing 1 pane of 404b | 20.00 | | | |
| bi | F pane | 500.00 | | | |
| bis | single with straight edge, from 404bi | 15.00 | | | |
| biii | Cello paq containing 1 pane of 404bi | 600.00 | | | |
| **405** | **5¢ violet blue**, *Oct 3, 1962* | .30 | .20 | 1.75 | 3.00 |
| d | vert. pair, imperf. horizontally | *6,000.00* | 850.00 | — | — |
| | plate blocks, plates 1, 2, all blocks | | | 1.75 | |
| | plate 3, all blocks | | | 2.50 | |
| xx | No. 405, precancelled | .50 | .50 | — | 5.00 |
| | precancelled warning strips of 20 | | | 40.00 | |
| p | tagged, W2B, *Feb 1963* | .60 | .30 | 2.50* | |
| i | 405p with wide & narrow tag bars in margin pair | 3.00 | 3.00 | 8.00* | |

* Blank corner block of 4.

Qty (all 5¢): 1,489,000,000

Used examples of 405d usually show faint traces of blind perfs. All used examples are cancelled "Gonor, MB."

| | | NH–VF | ⊙F | PB | FDC |
|---|---|---|---|---|---|
| 405a | booklet pane of 5 x 5¢ violet blue (405as) + label (BK52), *Oct 3, 1962* | 4.00 | 4.00 | | 22.50 |
| as | single with straight edge, from 405a | .85 | .25 | | |
| ai | LF pane | 24.00 | 18.00 | | |
| ais | single with straight edge, from 405ai | 5.00 | 4.00 | | |
| BK52 | 1 pane 405a in bilingual cover $5.00 | | | | |
| 405b | Miniature pane of 20 (4 x 5) | 18.00 | 18.00 | | |
| bs | single with straight edge, from 405b | .75 | .60 | | |
| bi | Cello paq containing 1 pane of 405b | 25.00 | | | |
| c | imperf. horizontal pair* | *6,750.00* | | | |
| q | tagged, mini pane of 20, W2B | 55.00 | 55.00 | | |
| qs | single with straight edge, from 405q | 2.50 | 2.00 | | 10.00† |
| qi | Cello paq containing 1 pane of 405q | 75.00 | | | |

* Eight pairs and one block of four are known. All from one imperf. pane of 20, cut up by K.Bileski in 1962.

† Commercial use.

| | NH–VF | ⊙F | PB | FDC |
|---|---|---|---|---|
| **Nos. 401–405** (5) Set | 1.30 | 1.00 | | 8.00* |
| **Nos. 401p–405p** (5) Set | 2.40 | 1.60 | | 75.00* |

* Combination FDC

**4¢ Cameo Tagging**

The 4¢ Cameo was tagged with only one bar to help aid the sorting equipment differentiate between local letters (4¢ rate) versus out-of-town letters (5¢ rate). Five different styles were used.

*4mm vert bars down centre of stamp (10 bars across pane) [Feb 63–Apr 64]*

*9–10mm vert bars down alternate perfs (5 bars across pane) [Apr 64 (1–4 weeks)]*

*8mm vert bars down centre of stamp (10 bars across pane) [Aug 64–Nov 64 ]*

*8mm vert bars down alternate perfs (6 bars across pane) [Dec 64– ]*

*8mm vert bars down alternate perfs (5 bars across pane) [Mar 65– ]*

401a

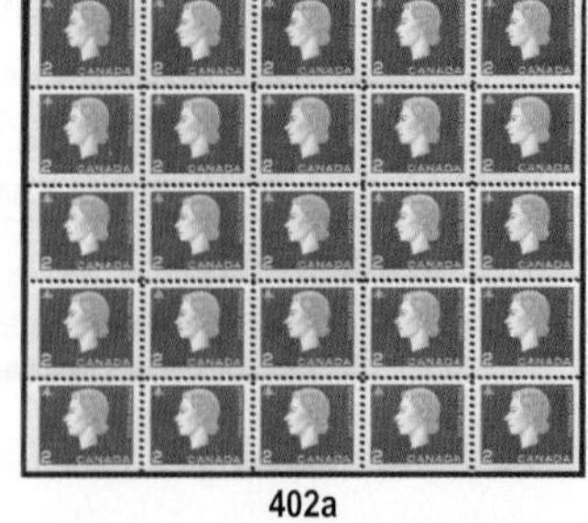
402a

404a

404bii

405a

405bi

405d

## CAMEO ISSUE – COIL STAMPS

406

407

408

409

| 1962–1963 | Rolls of 500 | NH–VF | NH–F | ⊙VF | ⊙F | ✉ |
|---|---|---|---|---|---|---|
| | | | | Perf 9½ horizontal | | |
| **406** | **2¢ green** (402), *May 2, 1963* | 6.50 | 4.25 | 3.00 | 2.00 | 10.00 |
| | pair | 13.00 | 8.50 | 7.00 | 4.00 | 18.00* |
| | strip of 4 | 26.00 | 17.00 | 14.00 | 8.00 | |
| i | jump strip of 4 | 40.00 | 24.00 | 25.00 | 12.00 | |
| ii | 406i with cutting guideline † | 90.00 | 60.00 | — | — | |
| xx | No. 406, precancelled | 6.50 | 4.25 | 3.50 | 2.50 | 7.00 |
| | start or end strip of 4 + 10 tabs ‡ | 90.00 | 50.00 | | | |
| | repair paste-up pair | | 80.00 | | | |

| | | NH–VF | NH-F | ⊙VF | ⊙F | ✉ |
|---|---|---|---|---|---|---|
| **407** | **3¢ purple** (403), *May 2, 1963* | 4.50 | 3.00 | 2.25 | 1.50 | 15.00 |
| | pair | 9.00 | 6.00 | 5.50 | 3.00 | 28.00* |
| | strip of 4 | 18.00 | 12.00 | 11.00 | 6.00 | |
| i | jump strip of 4 | 27.00 | 17.50 | 17.50 | 10.00 | |
| ii | 407i with cutting guideline † | 75.00 | 50.00 | — | — | |
| xx | No. 407, precancelled | 4.50 | 3.00 | 2.25 | 1.50 | 7.00 |
| | start or end strip of 4 + 10 tabs ‡ | 75.00 | 50.00 | | | |
| | repair paste-up pair | | 60.00 | | | |
| **408** | **4¢ carmine** (404), *Apr 4, 1963* | 6.50 | 4.25 | 3.00 | 2.00 | 14.00 |
| | pair | 13.00 | 8.50 | 7.00 | 3.00 | 26.00* |
| | strip of 4 | 26.00 | 17.00 | 14.00 | 6.00 | |
| a | vertical pair, imperf. horiz** | — | *24,000.00* | — | — | |
| i | jump strip of 4 | 40.00 | 24.00 | 25.00 | 10.00 | |
| iii | 408i with cutting guideline † | 90.00 | 60.00 | — | — | |
| | start or end strip of 4 + 10 tabs ‡ | 90.00 | 50.00 | | | |
| | repair paste-up pair | | 80.00 | | | |
| **409** | **5¢ violet blue** (405), *Oct 3, 1962* | 6.50 | 4.25 | 1.25 | .75 | 9.00 |
| | pair | 13.00 | 8.50 | 3.00 | 1.75 | 20.00* |
| | strip of 4 | 26.00 | 17.00 | 6.00 | 3.50 | |
| i | jump strip of 4 | 40.00 | 24.00 | 17.50 | 10.00 | |
| ii | 409i with cutting guideline † | 90.00 | 60.00 | — | — | |
| | start or end strip of 4 + 10 tabs ‡ | 90.00 | 50.00 | | | |
| | repair paste-up pair | | 80.00 | | | |
| **Nos. 406-409** | (4) Set | 24.00 | 15.75 | 9.50 | 6.25 | |

FDC's are not common; value on any cover $50.00 each.

* For non-philatelic usage, 1963–February 8, 1967.
These coil stamps seldom appear in well centred condition, especially jump strips of 4.
† Strips must be off centre to show the cutting guidelines. VF values are for strips which are well centred vertically, although off centre horizontally. Shorter Start or End Strips sell for much less.
‡ The first few tabs on starter strip will be "thinned" where the roll was sealed closed at end tabs.
** 408a–Only 2 genuine imperf pairs have been recorded. Both are poorly centred. Dangerous fakes have been seen and are well centred. A certificate of authenticity is mandatory for this item.

## 1963

### CASIMIR GZOWSKI

410
Sir Casimir Gzowski

Designer: Ephrum Philip Weiss. Portrait and picture engraved by Yves Baril. Lettering engraved by Donald J. Mitchell.

Engraved (1 colour), Plates of 400 subjects in four panes of 100
Canadian Bank Note Company

**1963, Mar 5** **Perf 12**

| | | NH–VF | ⊙F | PB | FDC |
|---|---|---|---|---|---|
| **410** | **5¢ rose lilac** | .40 | .20 | 2.00 | 2.00 |

Qty: 27,820,000

Issued to mark the 150th anniversary of the birth of Sir Casimir Gzowski, engineer, soldier and educator.

### CANADIAN EXPORTS

411
Crane and Map

Designer: Alan L. Pollock. Picture engraved by Yves Baril. Lettering engraved by Donald J. Mitchell.

Engraved (1 colour), Plates of 200 subjects in four panes of 50
Canadian Bank Note Company

**1963, Jun 14** **Perf 12**

| | | NH–VF | ⊙F | PB | FDC |
|---|---|---|---|---|---|
| **411** | **$1 rose carmine**, dull | 12.00 | 3.00 | 90.00 | 12.00‡ |
| i | LF | 50.00 | 6.00 | 250.00 | |

Qty: 19,360,000
‡ Single usage. Commercial use on cover: $70.00. Bulk payment receipt worth much less.

412
Sir Martin Frobisher

413
Postrider and Map

### MARTIN FROBISHER

Designer: Ephrum Philip Weiss. Based on a painting by Cornelis Ketel. Portrait and picture engraved by Yves Baril. Lettering engraved by Donald J. Mitchell.

Engraved (1 colour), Plates of 400 subjects in four panes of 100
Canadian Bank Note Company

**1963, Aug 21** **Perf 12**

| | | NH–VF | ⊙F | PB | FDC |
|---|---|---|---|---|---|
| **412** | **5¢ ultramarine** | .40 | .20 | 2.00 | 2.25 |

Qty: 27,020,000

Sir Martin Frobisher (1535–1594) was an Arctic explorer and discoverer of Frobisher Bay.

### POSTAL SERVICE

Designer: Bernard James Reddie. Picture engraved by Yves Baril. Lettering engraved by Allan Alexander Carswell.

Engraved (2 colours), Plates of 300 subjects in six panes of 50
Canadian Bank Note Company

**1963, Sep 25** **Perf 12**

| | | NH–VF | ⊙F | PB | FDC |
|---|---|---|---|---|---|
| **413** | **5¢ green and red brown** | .40 | .20 | 2.00 | 2.00 |

Qty: 27,860,000

Issued to commemorate the 200th anniversary of regular postal service between Quebec, Trois-Rivieres and Montreal.

**MINT PRICING PREMIUMS**

Mint stamps from 301 to date are valued as NH-VF (Never Hinged-Very Fine). All hinged VF and NH-F copies are worth 50% of the listed values. Plate block (PB) values are for mint NH–VF plate or inscription blocks of four.

**USED, VF/XF (with in-period, circular date cancel) PRICING PREMIUM**

Single stamps with light or circular date cancels will sell for more than catalogue value (perhaps even more than a mint copy). From *1981 to 1991* single stamps from se-tenant blocks of 4 or larger will be priced at 50% or more above the fine price. From *1992* to date single stamps from se-tenant blocks of 4 or larger plus se-tenant booklet panes and souvenir sheets will be priced at 100% or more above the fine price. From *1997* to date all other stamps will be priced at 50% or more above the fine price.

## 1963–1964 DEFINITIVES

414
Jet Plane, Ottawa

415
Canada Goose

Designer: Harvey Thomas Prosser. Picture engraved by Yves Baril. Lettering engraved by Gordon Mash.

Engraved (1 colour), Plates of 400 subjects in four panes of 100
Canadian Bank Note Company

**1964, Mar 11** **Perf 12**

| | | NH–VF | ⊙F | PB | FDC |
|---|---|---|---|---|---|
| **414** | **7¢ blue** | .70 | .60 | 3.00 | 2.00† |

Qty: 26,420,000
† Commercial cover in time period $15.
For 8¢ on 7¢ surcharge, see 430. For 8¢ value, see 436.

Designer: Angus Henry Shortt. Typographed by Paul Arthur. Picture engraved by Yves Baril. Lettering engraved by Donald J. Mitchell.

Engraved (1 colour), Plates of 300 subjects in six panes of 50

**1963, Oct 30** **Perf 12**

| | | NH–VF | ⊙F | PB | FDC |
|---|---|---|---|---|---|
| **415** | **15¢ ultramarine** | 2.50 | .25 | | 3.00† |
| | plate blocks, plates 1, 2, all blocks | | | 12.50 | |

Qty: 106,260,000
† Single usage, commercial $10.

## WORLD PEACE

416
"Pacem in Terris"

Designer: Harvey Thomas Prosser. Picture engraved by Allan Alexander Carswell.
Engraved (1 colour) and offset (2 colours), Plates of 400 subjects in four panes of 100
Canadian Bank Note Company

**1964, Apr 8** **Perf 12**

| | | NH–VF | ⊙F | PB | FDC |
|---|---|---|---|---|---|
| **416** | **5¢ greenish blue, Prussian blue, and ochre** | .40 | .20 | 2.00 | 2.00 |

Qty: 28,870,000

## FLORAL EMBLEMS AND COATS OF ARMS OF THE PROVINCES AND TERRITORIES

417
Maple Leaf Unity

418
Ontario

419
Quebec

420
Nova Scotia

421
New Brunswick

422
Manitoba

423
British Columbia

424
Prince Edward Island

425
Saskatchewan

426
Alberta

427
Newfoundland

428
Yukon

429
Northwest Territories

429A
Canada

Designer: Harvey Thomas Prosser. Picture engraved by Yves Baril (418–423, 427, 429A: Maple Leaf); Allan Alexander Carswell (424–426, 428–429A). Lettering engraved by Gordon Mash (418–421, 427–429); Donald J. Mitchell (422–423).

417 and 429A: Engraved (2 colours)
418–429: Engraved (1 colour) and offset (2 colours)
Plates of 300 subjects in six panes of 50; Canadian Bank Note Company

**1964–1966** **Perf 12**

| | | NH–VF | ⊙F | PB | FDC |
|---|---|---|---|---|---|
| **417** | **5¢ light blue and dark carmine**, dull | | | | |
| | Maple Leaf Unity, *May 14, 1964* | .35 | .20 | 1.75 | 2.00 |
| i | F | 2.00 | .50 | 10.00 | |
| | Qty: 36,870,000 | | | | |
| **418** | **5¢ red brown, buff and green**, dull | | | | |
| | White trillium, *Jun 30, 1964* | .35 | .20 | 1.75 | 2.00 |
| i | F | 2.00 | .50 | 10.00 | |
| | Qty: 19,360,000 | | | | |
| **419** | **5¢ green, yellow and orange**, dull | | | | |
| | White garden lily, *Jun 30, 1964* | .35 | .20 | 1.75 | 2.00 |
| i | F | 2.00 | .50 | 10.00 | |
| | Qty: 19,710,000 | | | | |
| **420** | **5¢ blue, pink and green**, dull | | | | |
| | Mayflower, *Feb 3, 1965* | .35 | .20 | 1.75 | 2.00 |
| i | F | 2.00 | .50 | 10.00 | |
| | Qty: 18,360,000 | | | | |
| **421** | **5¢ carmine, green and violet**, dull | | | | |
| | Purple violet, *Feb 3, 1965* | .35 | .20 | 1.75 | 2.00 |
| i | F | 2.00 | .50 | 10.00 | |
| ii | double-print of purple flower | 500.00 | 300.00 | | |
| | Qty: 18,760,000 | | | | |
| **422** | **5¢ red brown, lilac and dull green**, dull | | | | |
| | Prairie crocus, *Apr 28, 1965* | .35 | .20 | 3.00 | 2.00 |
| i | F | 2.00 | .50 | 10.00 | |
| ii | "dot on crocus" (pos. 48) | 5.00 | 5.00 | | 7.50 |
| iii | as 422ii, F | 25.00 | 15.00 | — | |
| iv | double print of purple flowers* | 500.00 | | | |
| | Qty: 15,820,000 | | | | |
| **423** | **5¢ lilac, green and bistre**, dull | | | | |
| | Dogwood, *Apr 28, 1965* | .35 | .20 | 1.75 | 2.00 |
| i | F | 2.00 | .50 | 10.00 | |
| | Qty: 17,360,000 | | | | |

| | | NH–VF | ⊙F | PB | FDC |
|---|---|---|---|---|---|
| **424** | **5¢ violet, green and deep rose**, dull Lady's Slipper, *Jul 21, 1965* | .35 | .20 | 1.75 | 2.00 |
| i | F | 2.00 | .50 | 10.00 | |
| ii | "green leaf pollen" (pos. 37) | 5.00 | 4.00 | | 7.50 |

Qty: 26,510,000

| | | NH–VF | ⊙F | PB | FDC |
|---|---|---|---|---|---|
| **425** | **5¢ sepia, orange and green**, dull Prairie lily, *Jan 19, 1966* | .35 | .20 | 1.75 | 2.00 |
| i | F | 2.00 | .50 | 10.00 | |
| ii | "broken leaf" (pos. 9) | 40.00 | 25.00 | 60.00† | 50.00 |
| iii | "green pollen" (pos. 25) | 5.00 | 4.00 | | 7.50 |
| iv | "stem pollen flaw" (pos. 30) | 5.00 | 4.00 | | 7.50 |

Qty: 15,310,000

† Blank corner block of 4.

| | | NH–VF | ⊙F | PB | FDC |
|---|---|---|---|---|---|
| **426** | **5¢ dull green, yellow and carmine**, dull Wild rose *Jan 19, 1966* | .35 | .20 | 1.75 | 2.00 |
| i | F | 2.00 | .50 | 10.00 | |

Qty: 16,160,000

| | | NH–VF | ⊙F | PB | FDC |
|---|---|---|---|---|---|
| **427** | **5¢ black, green and carmine**, dull Pitcher plant, *Feb 23, 1966* | .35 | .20 | 3.00 | 2.00 |
| i | "broken stamen" [4 types] (pos. 13, 37, 39 or 41) | 5.00 | 4.00 | 5.00 | 5.00 |
| ii | red double-printed* | 600.00 | 300.00 | 2,750.00§ | — |
| iii | F | 2.00 | .50 | 10.00 | |
| iv | as 427i, F | 7.50 | 5.00 | | |

Qty: 25,660,000

* No. 422ii and 427ii must show two distinct impressions with clear separation. Copies with a weak second image sell for less.

§ The lower left plate block, red double-printed (427ii) with "broken stamen" variety (427i) at pos. 41: $3,000.00. Three plate blocks reported.

| | | NH–VF | ⊙F | PB | FDC |
|---|---|---|---|---|---|
| **428** | **5¢ dark blue, rose and green**, dull Fireweed, *Mar 23, 1966* | .35 | .20 | 1.75 | 2.00 |
| i | F | 2.00 | .50 | 10.00 | |
| ii | "dropping flower blossom" (pos. 30) | 5.00 | 4.00 | | 7.50 |

Qty: 15,110,000

| | | NH–VF | ⊙F | PB | FDC |
|---|---|---|---|---|---|
| **429** | **5¢ olive, yellow and green**, dull Mountain Avens, *Mar 23, 1966* | .35 | .20 | 1.75 | 2.00 |
| i | F | 2.00 | .50 | 10.00 | — |
| ii | "little bee in flower" (pos. 29) | 5.00 | 4.00 | | 7.50 |

Qty: 15,010,000

| | | NH–VF | ⊙F | PB | FDC |
|---|---|---|---|---|---|
| **429A** | **5¢ dark blue and deep red**, dull Maple Leaf, *Jun 30, 1966* | .35 | .20 | 1.75 | 2.00 |
| i | deformed leaf variety | 10.00 | 5.00 | 50.00 | 15.00 |
| ii | F | 2.00 | .50 | 10.00 | |

Qty: 25,410,000

| | | NH–VF | ⊙F | PB | FDC |
|---|---|---|---|---|---|
| **Nos. 417–429A** (14) Set | | 4.90 | 2.80 | | — |

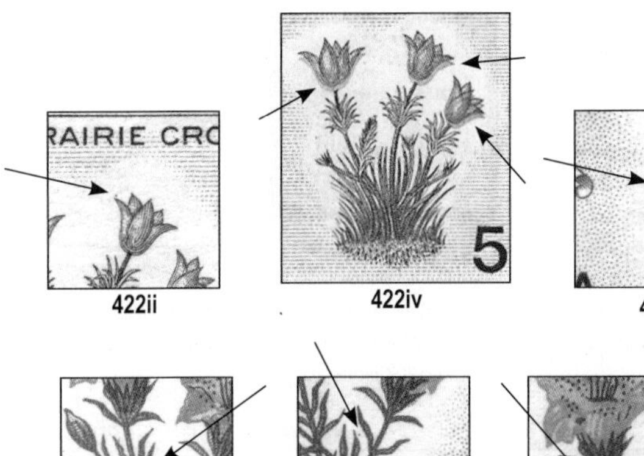

422ii 422iv 424ii

425ii 425iii 425iv

421ii

429Ai

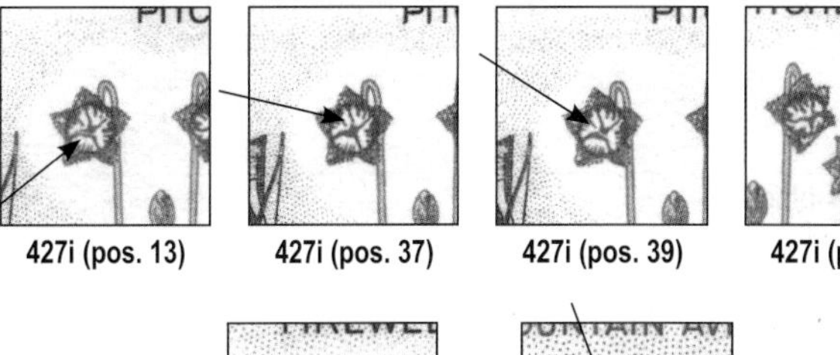

427i (pos. 13) 427i (pos. 37) 427i (pos. 39) 427i (pos. 41)

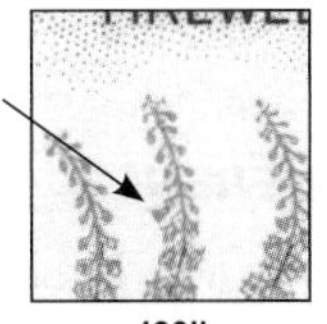

428ii

429ii

**Rates:**

| Effective: | |
|---|---|
| Jul 15, 1964– Oct 31, 1968 | USA: 8¢ (0–1 oz.), 14¢ (1–2 oz.) |

## JET SURCHARGE

430
Jet Plane, Ottawa

Designer: Harvey Prosser. Engraver: Yves Baril; lettering engraved by Gordon Mash.
Engraved (1 colour), Plates of 400 subjects in four panes of 100
Canadian Bank Note Company

**1964, Jul 15** **Perf 12**

| | | NH–VF | ⊙F | PB | FDC |
|---|---|---|---|---|---|
| **430** | **8¢ on 7¢ blue** (414) | .60 | .50 | 3.00* | 3.00 |
| a | pair, one without surcharge (unique) | *15,000.00* | | | |
| b | single with surcharge inverted on gum side (unique) | *5,000.00* | | | |

Qty: 15,510,000

* Blank corner block of 4.

For non-surcharged stamp (7¢), see 414. For 8¢ value see 436.

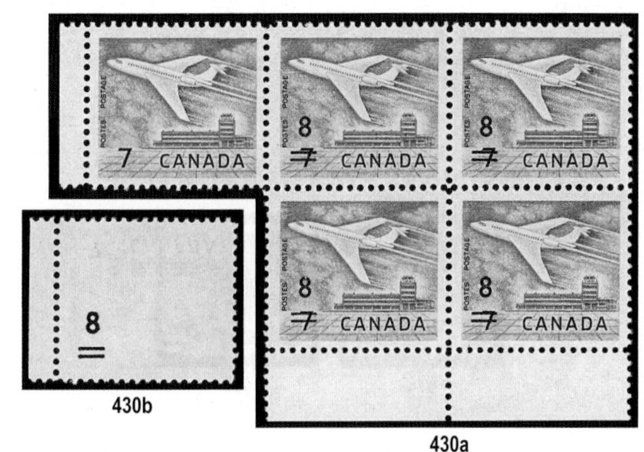

430b 430a

QE II — Cameo (1960's)

431
Confederation Memorial

432
Quill and Maple Leaf

## CHARLOTTETOWN CONFERENCE

Designer: Harvey Prosser. Engraver: Yves Baril; lettering engraved by Donald J. Mitchell
Engraved (1 colour), Plates of 300 subjects in six panes of 50
Canadian Bank Note Company

**1964, Jul 29** **Perf 12**

| | | NH–VF | ⊙F | PB | FDC |
|---|---|---|---|---|---|
| **431** | **5¢ black** | .40 | .20 | 2.00 | 2.00 |

Qty: 29,310,000

Issued for the centenary of the Charlottetown Conference which led to Canadian Confederation in 1867.

## QUEBEC CONFERENCE

Designer: Philip Weiss. Engraver: Yves Baril; lettering engraved by Donald J. Mitchell
Engraved (2 colours), Plates of 300 subjects in six panes of 50
Canadian Bank Note Company

**1964, Sep 9** **Perf 12**

| | | NH–VF | ⊙F | PB | FDC |
|---|---|---|---|---|---|
| **432** | **5¢ dark brown and rose** | .35 | .20 | 1.75 | 2.00 |

Qty: 28,510,000

Issued for the 100th anniversary of the Quebec Conference which led to Canadian Confederation in 1867.

## ROYAL VISIT

433
Queen Elizabeth II

Designer: Harvey Prosser. Based on a photography by Anthony Buckley. Engraver: Yves Baril; lettering engraved by Donald J. Mitchell
Engraved (1 colour), Plates of 300 subjects in six panes of 50
Canadian Bank Note Company

**1964, Oct 5** **Perf 12**

| | | NH–VF | ⊙F | PB | FDC |
|---|---|---|---|---|---|
| **433** | **5¢ claret** | .35 | .20 | 1.75 | 2.00 |

Qty: 38,410,000

Issued for Queen Elizabeth's visit to Canada marking the centenaries of the Charlottetown and Quebec conferences.

## CHRISTMAS – STAR OF BETHLEHEM

434

435

Designer: Harvey Prosser. Engraver: Allan Carswell; lettering engraved by Gordon Mash
Engraved (1 colour), Plates of 600 subjects in six panes of 100
Canadian Bank Note Company

**1964, Oct 14** **Perf 12**

| | | NH–VF | ⊙F | PB | FDC |
|---|---|---|---|---|---|
| **434** | **3¢ red**, dull | .25 | .20 | | 2.00 |
| | plate blocks, plates 1, 2, all blocks | | | 1.25 | |
| i | F | 1.00 | .25 | 5.00 | |
| a | No. 434, miniature pane of 25 | 10.00 | 10.00 | | 15.00† |
| as | single with straight edge, from 434a | .50 | .25 | | |
| aii | No. 434i, miniature pane of 25 | 30.00 | 30.00 | | 35.00† |
| aiis | single with straight edge, from 434aii | 1.50 | .75 | | |

Qty: 247,200,000

| | | NH–VF | ⊙F | PB | FDC |
|---|---|---|---|---|---|
| **434p** | tagged, W2B, dull | 1.00 | .50 | 5.00* | 2.50‡ |
| **pii** | 434p, wide & narrow tag bars in margin pair, dull | 4.50 | 4.50 | 10.50* | |
| **piii** | W2B, F | 1.50 | 1.00 | 7.50* | |
| **piv** | 434piii, wide & narrow tag bars in margin pair, F | 6.50 | 6.50 | 15.00* | |
| q | No. 434p, miniature pane of 25, dull | 15.00 | 15.00 | | 20.00† |
| qs | single with straight edge, from 434q | .75 | .50 | | |
| qv | No. 434piii, miniature pane of 25, F | 30.00 | 30.00 | | 35.00† |
| qvs | single with straight edge, from 434qv | 1.50 | .75 | | |

Qty: 10,400,000

‡ With Winnipeg cancel; Ottawa *day of issue* cancel $7.50. Commercial use on cover: $8.00.
The miniature panes of 25 were issued in cello-paqs of 2 panes. Value 2½x pane.

| | | NH–VF | ⊙F | PB | FDC |
|---|---|---|---|---|---|
| **435** | **5¢ blue**, dull | .35 | .20 | | 2.00 |
| | plate blocks, plate 1, all blocks | | | 3.50 | |
| | plate 2, all blocks | | | 1.80 | |
| i | F | 1.00 | .25 | 5.00 | |

Qty: 96,320,000

| | | NH–VF | ⊙F | PB | FDC |
|---|---|---|---|---|---|
| **435p** | tagged, W2B, dull | 1.50 | .50 | 12.50* | 3.00‡ |
| **pii** | 435p, wide & narrow tag bars in margin pair | 13.00 | 13.00 | 30.00* | |
| **piii** | 5¢ blue, W2B, F | 2.50 | 2.50 | 15.00* | |
| **piv** | 435piii, wide & narrow tag bars in margin pair | 17.50 | 17.50 | 40.00* | |

Qty: 6,200,000

* Blank corner block of 4.
† Price shown is for First Day Cancel, not on cover.
‡ With Winnipeg cancel; Ottawa *day of issue* cancel $10.00. Commercial use on cover: $8.00.
Miniature panes were sold in Cello Paqs containing two panes of 25 (434a or 434q).

434a

## JET DEFINITIVE

436
Jet Plane, Ottawa

Designer: Harvey Prosser. Engraver: Yves Baril; lettering engraved by Gordon Mash.
Engraved (1 colour), Plates of 400 subjects in four panes of 100
Canadian Bank Note Company

**1964, Nov 18** **Perf 12**

| | | NH–VF | ⊙F | PB | FDC |
|---|---|---|---|---|---|
| **436** | **8¢ blue**, SF | .55 | .30 | 2.75 | 3.00 |
| i | LF | 1.00 | .50 | 5.00 | |

Qty: 41,920,000

For 7¢ value see 414, for 8¢ on 7¢ surcharge see 430.

## 1965

437
Maple Leaf and ICY Symbol

438
Grenfell and Ship

### INTERNATIONAL CO-OPERATION YEAR

Designer: Harvey Prosser. Engraver: Yves Baril; lettering engraved by Donald J. Mitchell.
Engraved (1 colour), Plates of 300 subjects in six panes of 50
Canadian Bank Note Company

**1965, Mar 3** **Perf 12**

| | | NH–VF | ⊙F | PB | FDC |
|---|---|---|---|---|---|
| **437** | **5¢ slate green** | .35 | .20 | 1.75 | 2.00 |

Qty: 26,660,000

### SIR WILFRED GRENFELL

Designer: Harvey Prosser. Engraver: Yves Baril; lettering engraved by Gordon Mash.
Engraved (1 colour), Plates of 300 subjects in six panes of 50
Canadian Bank Note Company

**1965, Jun 9** **Perf 12**

| | | NH–VF | ⊙F | PB | FDC |
|---|---|---|---|---|---|
| **438** | **5¢ Prussian blue** | .35 | .20 | 1.75 | 2.00 |

Qty: 26,610,000

Birth centenary of Sir Wilfred Grenfell, author and missionary.

439

440
Churchill

### CANADIAN FLAG

Designer: Harvey Prosser. Engraver: Allan Carswell; lettering engraved by Gordon Mash.
Engraved (2 colour), Plates of 300 subjects in six panes of 50
Canadian Bank Note Company

**1965, Jun 30** **Perf 12**

| | | NH–VF | ⊙F | PB | FDC |
|---|---|---|---|---|---|
| **439** | **5¢ blue and red**, dull | .35 | .20 | 1.75 | 2.00 |
| i | F | 2.00 | .50 | 10.00 | |

Qty: 37,360,000

For non-denominated postal card of same design, see UX131 and UX145.
Canada's national flag was adopted in 1965.

### SIR WINSTON CHURCHILL

Designer: Phillip Weiss, based on the famous "Roaring Lion" portrait by Yousuf Karsh.
Duo-tone Lithography, Plates of 400 subjects in four panes of 100
Canadian Bank Note Company

**1965, Aug 12** **Perf 12**

| | | NH–VF | ⊙F | PB | FDC |
|---|---|---|---|---|---|
| **440** | **5¢ brown** | .35 | .20 | 1.75 | 2.00 |

Qty: 35,000,000

First Canadian stamp printed by this method.
Issued in memory of Sir Winston Churchill (1874–1965).

441
Peace Tower

442
Parliament Buildings (rear view)

### INTER-PARLIAMENTARY UNION

Designer: Philips-Gutkin & Associates, Winnipeg. Engraver: Allan Carswell; lettering engraved by Gordon Mash.
Engraved (1 colour), Plates of 400 subjects in four panes of 100
Canadian Bank Note Company

**1965, Sep 8** **Perf 12**

| | | NH–VF | ⊙F | PB | FDC |
|---|---|---|---|---|---|
| **441** | **5¢ slate green** | .35 | .20 | 1.75 | 2.00 |

Qty: 16,820,000

Meeting of the Inter-Parliamentary Union, Ottawa.

### NATIONAL CAPITAL

Designer: Gerald Trottier. Engraver: Yves Baril; lettering engraved by Gordon Mash.
Engraved (1 colour), Plates of 300 subjects in six panes of 50
Canadian Bank Note Company

**1965, Sep 8** **Perf 12**

| | | NH–VF | ⊙F | PB | FDC |
|---|---|---|---|---|---|
| **442** | **5¢ brown** | .35 | .20 | 1.75 | 2.00 |

Qty: 14,810,000

Centenary of the final selection of Ottawa as the national capital.

### CHRISTMAS – GIFTS FROM THE WISE MEN

443

444

Designer: Helen Roberta Fitzgerald. Picture engraved by Yves Baril. Lettering engraved by Donald J. Mitchell.
Engraved (1 colour), Plates of 400 subjects in four panes of 100
Canadian Bank Note Company

**1965, Oct 13** **Perf 12**

| | | NH–VF | ⊙F | PB | FDC |
|---|---|---|---|---|---|
| **443** | **3¢ olive** | .25 | .20 | | 2.00 |
| | plate blocks, plates 1, 2, all blocks | | | 1.25 | |
| a | No. 443, miniature pane of 25 (5x5) | 8.50 | 8.00 | | 10.00† |
| as | single with straight edge, from 443a | .50 | .25 | | |
| p | tagged, W2B | .35 | .20 | 2.00* | 2.50‡ |
| q | No. 443p, miniature pane of 25 | 12.00 | 11.00 | | 15.00† |
| qs | single with straight edge, from 443q | 1.00 | .50 | | |

Qty: 208,320,000; Tagged: 7,700,000

‡ With Winnipeg cancel; Ottawa *day of issue* cancel $7.50. Commercial use on cover: $5.00.

| | | NH–VF | ⊙F | PB | FDC |
|---|---|---|---|---|---|
| **444** | **5¢ violet blue** | .30 | .20 | | 2.00 |
| | plate blocks, plates 1, all blocks | | | 3.50 | |
| | plates 2, all blocks | | | 1.75 | |
| p | tagged, W2B | .45 | .35 | 2.50* | 3.00‡ |

Qty: 92,920,000; Tagged: 4,000,000

* Blank corner block of 4.
† Value shown is for First Day cancel, not on cover.
‡ With Winnipeg cancel; Ottawa *day of issue* cancel $10.00. Commercial use on cover: $5.00.
Miniature panes were sold in Cello Paqs containing two panes of 25 (443a or 443q).

443a

## 1966

445
Satellite over Canada

446
Cavelier de La Salle

### ALOUETTE II

Designer: Harvey Thomas Prosser. Picture engraved by Yves Baril. Lettering engraved by Donald J. Mitchell.

Engraved (1 colour), Plates of 400 subjects in four panes of 100
Canadian Bank Note Company

**1966, Jan 5** **Perf 12**

| | | NH–VF | ⊙F | PB | FDC |
|---|---|---|---|---|---|
| **445** | **5¢ dark violet blue** | .35 | .20 | 1.75 | 2.00 |

Qty: 26,370,000

Issued to commemorate the launching of Alouette II in California, November 28, 1965.

### DE LA SALLE

Designer: Leendert Verhoeven. Portrait and picture engraved by Yves Baril. Lettering engraved by Donald J. Mitchell.

Engraved (1 colour), Plates of 300 subjects in six panes of 50
Canadian Bank Note Company

**1966, Apr 13** **Perf 12**

| | | NH–VF | ⊙F | PB | FDC |
|---|---|---|---|---|---|
| **446** | **5¢ blue green** | .35 | .20 | 1.75 | 2.00 |
| i | cracked plate variety, (vertical line through right inscription) | 25.00 | 15.00 | 30.00 | — |

Qty: 25,160,000

Tercentenary of the arrival in Canada of René Robert Cavelier, Sieur de la Salle.

447
Traffic Signs

448
Canadian delegation

### HIGHWAY SAFETY

Designer: Helen Roberta Fitzgerald. Picture engraved by Yves Baril. Lettering engraved by Donald J. Mitchell.

Engraved (1 colour) and offset (2 colours), Plates of 400 subjects in four panes of 100
Canadian Bank Note Company

**1966, May 2** **Davac gum** **Perf 12**

| | | NH–VF | ⊙F | PB | FDC |
|---|---|---|---|---|---|
| **447** | **5¢ black, blue and yellow** | .35 | .20 | 1.75 | 2.00 |

Qty: 27,220,000

This stamp was issued with Davac gum, clear and tasteless.

### LONDON CONFERENCE

Designer: Paul Aleksander Pedersen. Picture engraved by Yves Baril. Lettering engraved by Donald J. Mitchell.

Engraved (1 colour), Plates of 300 subjects in six panes of 50
Canadian Bank Note Company

**1966, May 26** **Perf 12**

| | | NH–VF | ⊙F | PB | FDC |
|---|---|---|---|---|---|
| **448** | **5¢ brown** | .35 | .20 | 1.75 | 2.00 |

Qty: 25,130,000

Centenary of the final conference leading to Canadian Confederation in 1867. Features the House of Common on the River Thames, London, England and a group of delegates.

449
Atomic Reactor

450
Parliamentary Library

### ATOMIC RESEARCH

Designer: Alan L. Pollock. Picture engraved by Yves Baril. Lettering engraved by Donald J. Mitchell.

Engraved (1 colour), Plates of 300 subjects in six panes of 50
Canadian Bank Note Company

**1966, Jul 27** **Perf 12**

| | | NH–VF | ⊙F | PB | FDC |
|---|---|---|---|---|---|
| **449** | **5¢ deep ultramarine** | .35 | .20 | 1.75 | 2.00 |

Qty: 25,360,000

### C.P.A. CONFERENCE

Designer: Paul Aleksander Pedersen. Picture engraved by Allan Alexander Carswell. Lettering engraved by Donald J. Mitchell.

Engraved (1 colour), Plates of 600 subjects in six panes of 100
Canadian Bank Note Company

**1966, Sep 8** **Perf 12**

| | | NH–VF | ⊙F | PB | FDC |
|---|---|---|---|---|---|
| **450** | **5¢ plum** | .35 | .20 | 1.75 | 2.00 |

Qty: 27,320,000

Issued on the occasion of the 12th General Conference of the Commonwealth Parliamentary Association.

### CHRISTMAS – PRAYING HANDS

451

452

Designer: Geoffrey Holloway. Picture engraved by Yves Baril. Lettering engraved by Gordon Mash. Based on a drawing by Albrecht Dürer. Modeled by Harvey Thomas Prosser

Engraved (1 colour), Plates of 600 subjects in six panes of 100
Canadian Bank Note Company

**1966, Oct 12** **Perf 12**

| | | NH–VF | ⊙F | PB | FDC |
|---|---|---|---|---|---|
| **451** | **3¢ carmine rose** | .30 | .20 | | 2.00 |
| | plate blocks, plate 1, all blocks | | | 1.75 | |
| | plates 2, 3, all blocks | | | 1.50 | |
| **a** | miniature pane of 25 (5x5) | 5.00 | 5.00 | | 8.00† |
| **as** | single with straight edge, from 451a | .50 | .25 | | |
| **p** | tagged, W2B | .30 | .20 | 1.75* | 2.50‡ |
| **q** | No. 451p, miniature pane of 25 | 6.50 | 6.50 | | 10.00† |
| **qs** | single with straight edge, from 451q | .50 | .25 | | |

Qty: 164,680,000; Tagged: 8,700,000

‡ With Winnipeg cancel; Ottawa *day of issue* cancel $7.50. Commercial use on cover: $7.00.

| | | NH–VF | ⊙F | PB | FDC |
|---|---|---|---|---|---|
| **452** | **5¢ orange** | .30 | .20 | | 2.00 |
| | plate blocks, plate 1, all blocks | | | 3.50 | |
| | plates 2, 3, all blocks | | | 1.50 | |
| **p** | tagged, W2B | .60 | .40 | 3.00* | 3.00‡ |

Qty: 83,380,000; Tagged: 3,900,000

* Blank corner block of 4.

† Value shown is for First Day cancel, not on cover.

‡ With Winnipeg cancel; Ottawa *day of issue* cancel $10.00. Commercial use on cover: $7.00.

Miniature panes were sold in Cello Paqs containing two panes of 25 (451a or 451q).

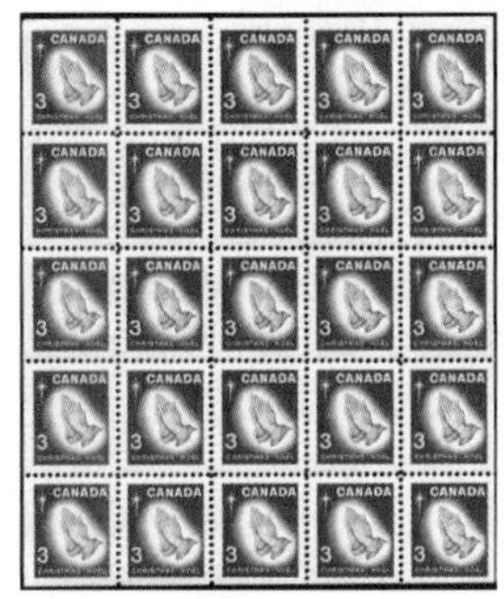

451a

## 1967

## CENTENNIAL OF CONFEDERATION

453
Flag and planet earth

Designer: Leendert Verhoeven. Picture engraved by Allan Alexander Carswell. Flag engraved by Yves Baril. Lettering engraved by Donald J. Mitchell. Modeled by Harvey Thomas Prosser.

Engraved (2 colours), Plates of 300 subjects in six panes of 50
Canadian Bank Note Company

**1967, Jan 11** **Davac gum** **Perf 12**

| | | NH–VF | ⊙F | PB | FDC |
|---|---|---|---|---|---|
| **453** | **5¢ blue and red** | .35 | .20 | | 2.00 |
| | plate blocks, plates 1, 2, all blocks | | | 1.75 | |
| **p** | tagged, W2B | .55 | .40 | 2.75* | 3.00‡ |

Qty: 105,100,000

* Blank corner block of 4.

‡ With Winnipeg cancel; Ottawa *day of issue* cancel $10.00. Commercial use on cover: $6.00.

Issued to mark the 100th anniversary of Canadian Confederation.

## 1967–1973
## CENTENNIAL DEFINITIVES – LOW VALUES

454 Northern Lights — 455 Pacific Totem

456 Prairies

457 Seaway

458 Fishing Village

459 Transportation

460 Transportation

543 Transportation

544 Library of Parliament

**Papers:** The initial printings were on plain paper. Beginning in 1968, different papers with varying degrees of whiteness were used. The brightest on the scale is known as "hibrite" (HB), with other degrees known as 'high fluorescent' (HF) and 'fluorescent' (F). It is difficult to distinguish between these paper types without the use of a long wave ultra-violet lamp.

**Gums:** Two types exist – dextrine, a shiny gum on the original printings which was later replaced by PVA, an almost invisible matte gum.

**Printers:** Canadian Bank Note Company (CBN) printed all the perf. 12 x 12 varieties, sheets and booklet panes, and the coils, British American Bank Note Company (BABN) printed the sheets and booklet panes either perf. 10 x 10 or perf. 12½ x 12.

**General (Ottawa) Tagging:** The original Ottawa tagging (OP4 variety) used on stamps until October 1972 migrates onto or through other stamps, booklet covers and album pages. It can generally be contained in acetate mounts, but it might still leak or penetrate.

Designer: Harvey Thomas Prosser. Portrait and picture engraved by Yves Baril. Lettering engraved by Gordon Mash. Based on a photograph by Anthony Buckley.

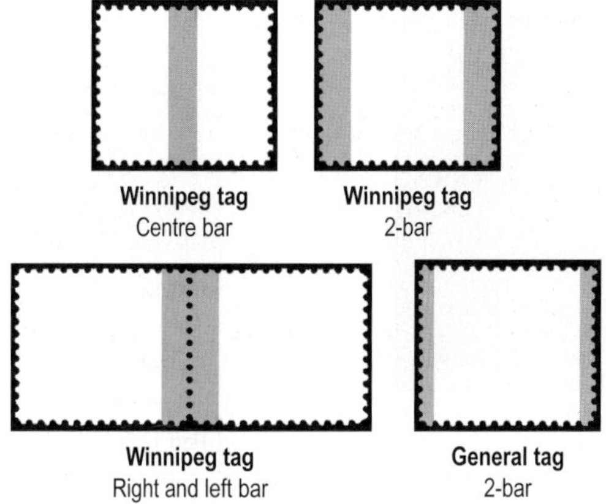

**Winnipeg tag** Centre bar — **Winnipeg tag** 2-bar — **Winnipeg tag** Right and left bar — **General tag** 2-bar

### 1¢ brown (Northern Lights)

Engraved (1 colour), Plates of 600 subjects in six panes of 100
Canadian Bank Note Company

| | | | | Perf 12 | |
|---|---|---|---|---|---|
| | | NH–VF | ⊙F | PB | FDC |
| **454** | **1¢ brown**, DF, DEX, *Feb 8, 1967* | .25 | .20 | | 2.00 |
| | plate blocks, plates 1, 2, all blocks | | | 1.25 | |
| | plate 3, all blocks | | | 5.00 | |
| | plate 4, all blocks | | | 7.50 | |
| **f** | printed on gum side | 1,500.00 | — | | — |
| **i** | NF/fl, DEX, *1968* | .75 | .20 | 5.00 | — |
| **ii** | HB, DEX, *Jun 1971* | 1.00 | .25 | 7.00* | — |
| **iii** | LF, PVA, *Dec 1971* | .25 | .20 | 2.75 | — |
| | plate blocks, plate 5, all blocks | | | 2.75 | |
| **xx** | No. 454, precancelled, DF, DEX | .25 | .20 | 15.00† | 3.00 |
| **xxi** | No. 454iii, precancelled, LF, PVA | .50 | .20 | 25.00† | 3.00 |

† Warning strip of 20.

| | | | | | |
|---|---|---|---|---|---|
| **454p** | tagged, W2B, 8mm bar, DF, DEX, *Feb 8, 1967* | .35 | .25 | 2.00* | 5.00‡ |
| **pi** | tagged, WCB, 4 mm bar, DF, DEX, *Dec 1968* | .30 | .20 | 2.50* | — |
| **piv** | WCB, 4 mm bar, LF, PVA, *Jan 1972* | .25 | .20 | 1.50* | — |
| **pii** | WCB, 4 mm bar, HB, DEX, *Oct 1971* | 7.50 | 1.00 | 50.00* | — |
| **piii** | tagged, GT2, LF, PVA, *Nov 1971* | .25 | .20 | 1.50* | — |

* Blank corner block of 4.

‡ With Winnipeg cancel; Ottawa *day of issue* cancel $15.00. Commercial use on cover: $5.00.

454a

454b

454c

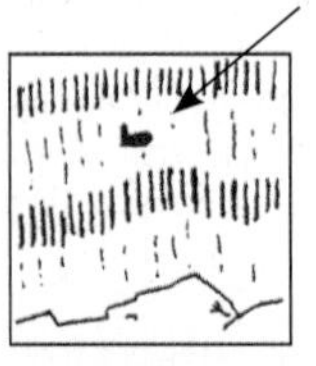
454eix

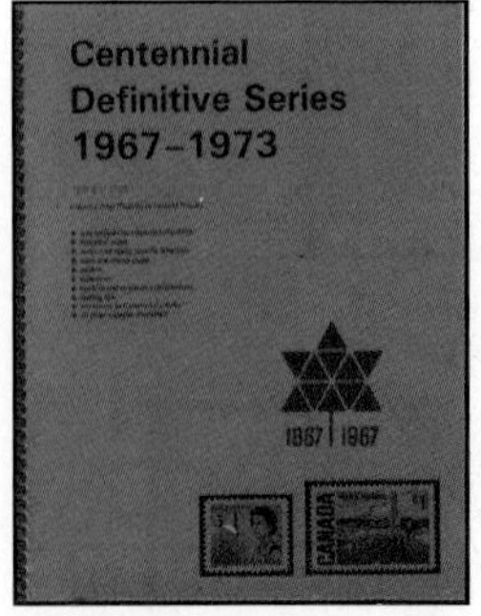

*Centennial Definitive Series 1967–1973*
D. Robin Harris, Centennial Stamp Production
by Leopold Beaudet, 2000

### 1¢ Booklets

Canadian Bank Note Company

| | | Perf 12 | |
|---|---|---|---|
| | | NH–VF | ⊙F |
| **454a** | booklet pane of 5 x 1¢ brown (454as) + label (BK54), NF, DEX, *Feb 1967* | .50 | .40 |
| **as** | single with straight edge, from 454a | .25 | .20 |
| **ai** | LF, DEX, *1967* | 5.00 | 4.00 |
| **ais** | single with straight edge, from 454ai | 1.25 | 1.00 |
| **aii** | DF, DEX | 1.00 | 1.00 |
| **aiis** | single with straight edge, from 454aii | .30 | .25 |
| **aiii** | DF/fl, DEX | 8.00 | 6.00 |
| **aiiis** | single with straight edge, from 454aiii | 1.75 | .75 |

British American Bank Note Company

| | | Perf. 10.0 | |
|---|---|---|---|
| **454b** | booklet pane of 5 + label, DF, DEX, 1 x 1¢ brown (454d) + 4 x 6¢ orange (459viii) + label (BK59a), *Oct 1968* | 4.00 | 3.00 |
| **bi** | LF, DEX | 10.00 | 8.00 |
| **bii** | HB, DEX (BK59c) | 25.00 | 20.00 |
| **biii** | fluorescent ink on 6¢ orange | 50.00 | 40.00 |
| **BK59** | pane 454b in bilingual cover (21,604,000) $5.00 | | |
| **454c** | booklet pane of 10, DF, DEX, 5 x 1¢ brown (454d) + 5 x 4¢ carmine rose (457ds) (BK56), *Sep 1968* | 2.00 | 2.00 |
| **ci** | NF/fl, DEX | 7.50 | 7.50 |
| **BK56** | pane 454c in bilingual cover (1,464,000) $2.50 | | |
| **454d** | 1¢ brown, DF, DEX, single with straight edge, from 454b or 454c | .25 | .20 |
| **di** | LF, DEX, from 454bi | 2.50 | 1.25 |
| **dii** | HB, DEX, from 454bii | 9.50 | 2.00 |
| **diii** | NF/fl, DEX, from 454ci | 1.75 | 1.75 |

British American Bank Note Company

| | | Perf. 12.5x12.0 | |
|---|---|---|---|
| **454e** | 1¢ brown, DF, DEX, single with straight edge, from 543b | .25 | .20 |
| **ei** | DF, PVA, from 543a | 2.50 | .35 |
| **eii** | LF, PVA, from 543ai or 544ai | .25 | .20 |
| **eiii** | MF, PVA, from 543aii or 544aii | .25 | .20 |
| **eiv** | DF, PVA, from 544a or 544b | .25 | .20 |
| **ev** | LF, PVA, from 544c, ribbed vert. | .25 | .20 |
| **evi** | MF, PVA, from 544ci, ribbed vert. | .25 | .20 |
| **evii** | HF, PVA, from 544aiii | .30 | .20 |
| **eviii** | HB, PVA, from 544aiv | .30 | .20 |
| **eix** | "Airplane in sky"* (544a) | 5.00 | 2.50 |

* exists on several fluorescent paper types; most common version is priced.

| | | | |
|---|---|---|---|
| **454ep** | 1¢ brown, OP4, DF, PVA, single with straight edge, from 544r | .30 | .20 |
| **epi** | OP4, LF, PVA, from 544q | .40 | .20 |
| **epii** | OP4, MF, PVA, from 544qi | 1.00 | .20 |
| **epiii** | OP4, HF, PVA, from 544qii | 1.00 | .30 |
| **epvii** | OP4, MF, PVA, from 544s, ribbed vert. | .30 | .20 |
| **epiv** | OP2, NF, PVA, from 544qiii | 4.00 | 3.00 |
| **epv** | OP2, MF, PVA, from 544qiv | .25 | .20 |
| **epvi** | OP2, HF, PVA, from 544qv | .30 | .20 |
| **epviii** | OP2, DF, PVA, from 544qvi | .30 | .20 |

| 1¢ brown (Northern Lights) | | | | | | | | | |
|---|---|---|---|---|---|---|---|---|---|
| Tagging: | Untagged | | Winnipeg tagged | | | General | | Precancel | |
| | | | 2-bar | Centre | | OP4 | OP2 | | |
| Gum: | Dex | PVA | Dex | Dex | PVA | PVA | PVA | Dex | PVA |
| Perf 12 | 454 (pl 1–4) | 454iii (pl 5) | 454p | 454pi | 454piv | | 454piii | 454xx | 454xxi |
| Perf 10.0 | 454d (BK56, 59) | | | | | | | | |
| Perf 12.5x12.0 | 454e (BK67) | 454ei (BK66) | | | | 454ep (BK70b) | 454epiv (BK69) | | |

### 2¢ green (Pacific Totem Pole)

Engraved (1 colour), Plates of 600 subjects in six panes of 100
Canadian Bank Note Company

Perf 12

| | | NH–VF | ⊙F | PB | FDC |
|---|---|---|---|---|---|
| **455** | **2¢ green**, DF, DEX, plates 1, 2, *Feb 8, 1967* | .25 | .20 | 1.25 | 2.00 |
| i | LF, PVA, *Mar 1972* | .25 | .20 | 7.50 | — |
| ii | LF/fl, PVA, plates 1,2, *Mar 1972* | .25 | .20 | 12.50 | — |
| iii | LF, PVA, ribbed horiz. (plate 1, 2) | 1.00 | .30 | 15.00 | — |
| **xx** | No. 455, precancelled, DF, DEX | 45.00 | 25.00 | 1,250.00† | 50.00‡ |

† Warning strip of 20. ‡ Single usage, alone on cover.

| | | NH–VF | ⊙F | PB | FDC |
|---|---|---|---|---|---|
| **455p** | tagged, W2B, DF, DEX, *Feb 8, 1967* | .30 | .20 | 3.00* | 5.00‡ |
| **pi** | tagged, WCB, DF, DEX, *Dec 1968* | .25 | .20 | 2.00* | — |
| **pii** | WCB, LF/fl, PVA, *Mar 1972* | .50 | .25 | 4.50* | — |
| **pvi** | WCB, LF/fl, PVA, ribbed horiz. | .50 | .25 | 4.50* | — |
| **piii** | tagged, GT2, HF/fl, PVA, *Dec 1972* | .25 | .20 | 1.50* | — |
| **piv** | GT2, LF/fl, PVA, *Dec 1972* | .50 | .20 | 3.00* | — |
| **pv** | GT2, LF/fl, PVA, ribbed horiz. | 1.00 | .30 | 6.00* | — |

* Blank corner block of 4.
‡ With Winnipeg cancel; Ottawa *day of issue* cancel $15.00. Commercial use on cover: $6.00.

### 2¢ Booklets

Canadian Bank Note Company

Perf 12

| | | NH–VF | ⊙F |
|---|---|---|---|
| 455a | booklet pane of 8, glazed HB, 4 x 2¢ green (455x) + 4 x 3¢ purple (456x), gutter between (OPAL) (BK63a), *Oct 26, 1970* | 2.00 | 2.00 |
| x | single with straight edge, glazed HB, from 455a | .40 | .25 |
| ai | pane with cross perfs. | 300.00 | |
| **BK63** | pane 455a in bilingual cover (2,200,000) $2.50 | | |

This booklet was dispensed from vending machines for 25¢ (a premium of 5¢ over the face value of the stamps). The machines were made by the Opal Manufacturing Co. Limited, thus the name given to this booklet by stamp collectors.

| 2¢ green (Pacific Totem Pole) | | | | | | | |
|---|---|---|---|---|---|---|---|
| Tag: | Untagged | | Winnipeg tagged | | | General | Precancel |
| | | | 2-bar | Centre | | OP2 | |
| Gum: | Dex | PVA | Dex | Dex | PVA | PVA | Dex |
| Perf 12 | 455 (Pl 1–2) | 455i (Pl 1–2) | 455p | 455pi | 455pii | 455piii | 455xx |

455a

455ai

Totem pole "eyes"
4 eyes closed top left eye open 4 eyes open

33 different types of open and closed eyes have been identified.

### 3¢ dull purple (Prairies)

Engraved (1 colour), Plates of 600 subjects in six panes of 100
Canadian Bank Note Company

Perf 12

| | | NH–VF | ⊙F | PB | FDC |
|---|---|---|---|---|---|
| **456** | **3¢ dull purple**, DF, DEX, *Feb 8, 1967* | .25 | .20 | | 2.00 |
| | plate blocks, plate 1, all blocks | | | 2.50 | |
| | plate 2, all blocks | | | 2.75 | |
| i | NF, DEX, *1967* | .50 | .20 | 7.50 | — |
| ii | creamy paper, LF, DEX, *1967* | .75 | .25 | 8.00 | — |
| **xx** | No. 456, precancelled, DF, DEX | .50 | .35 | 20.00† | 3.00 |
| **xxi** | No. 456i, precancelled, NF, DEX | 1.00 | .25 | 35.00† | 3.00 |
| **xxii** | No. 456ii, precancelled, LF, DEX | 1.00 | .25 | 50.00† | 3.00 |
| **456p** | tagged, W2B, DF, DEX, *Feb 8, 1967* | .25 | .20 | 4.75* | 5.00‡ |
| **pi** | W2B, red violet, DEX, *1967* | 1.50 | .25 | 10.00* | — |
| **pii** | W2B, NF, DEX, *1967* | 1.50 | .50 | 9.00* | — |
| **pxx** | No. 456p, precancelled, PVA, tagged GT2** | 3.00 | .50 | 70.00† | 3.00 |

† Warning strip of 20.
** No. 456pxx is the only way the 3¢ exists with General (GT2) tagging.
* Blank corner block of 4.
‡ With Winnipeg cancel; Ottawa *day of issue* cancel $15.00. Commercial use on cover: $8.00.

### 3¢ Booklets

Canadian Bank Note Company

Perf 12

| | | NH–VF | ⊙F |
|---|---|---|---|
| 456x | single with straight edge, glazed HB, from 455a, *Oct 26, 1970* | .40 | .25 |

British American Bank Note Company

Perf. 12.5x12.0

| | | | |
|---|---|---|---|
| 456a | 3¢ dull purple, DF, DEX, single with straight edge, from 543b, *Jun 30, 1971* | 1.00 | .40 |
| ai | DF, PVA, from 543a | 6.00 | .40 |
| aii | LF, PVA, from 543ai | 3.50 | .40 |
| aiii | MF, PVA, from 543aii | 5.00 | .75 |

| 3¢ dull purple (Prairies) | | | | | |
|---|---|---|---|---|---|
| Tagging: | Untagged | | Winnipeg tagged | Precancel | |
| | | | 2-bar | Untagged | General |
| Gum: | Dex | PVA | Dex | Dex | Dex |
| Perf 12 | 456 | | 456p | 456xx | 456pxx |
| Perf 12.5x12.0 | 456a | 456ai | | | |
| Perf 9½ horiz | 466 | | | 466xx | |

**3¢ Rate:** Third class (0–2 oz.): Jul 15, 1964–Oct 31, 1968

Definitive Series Historical Notes:

- general tagging introduced
- "integral" booklets introduced (pane glued to cover)
- comb-perfed stamps seen for first time
- stamp sizes go metric

### 4¢ carmine rose (Seaway)

Engraved (1 colour), Plates of 600 subjects in six panes of 100
Canadian Bank Note Company

Perf 12

| | | NH–VF | ⊙F | PB | FDC |
|---|---|---|---|---|---|
| **457** | **4¢ carmine rose**, DF, DEX, *Feb 8, 1967* | .25 | .20 | | 2.00 |
| | plate blocks, plates 1, 2, all blocks | | | 2.50 | |
| | plate blocks, plate 3, all blocks (DEX) | | | 5.00 | |
| **i** | NF, DEX, *1967* | .50 | .20 | 5.00 | — |
| **ii** | LF, DEX, 1968 | .50 | .20 | 5.00 | — |
| **iii** | creamy MF, DEX, 1968 | 1.00 | .20 | 5.00 | — |
| **iv** | LF, PVA, *May 1972* | .45 | .20 | | — |
| | plate blocks, plate 3, all blocks (PVA) | | | 5.00 | |
| **xx** | No. 457, precancelled, DF, DEX | .35 | .25 | 15.00† | 3.00 |
| **xxi** | No. 457ii, precancelled, LF, DEX | 4.00 | 2.00 | 150.00† | 3.00 |

† Warning strip of 20.

| | | NH–VF | ⊙F | PB | FDC |
|---|---|---|---|---|---|
| **457p** | tagged, W1B at left or right DF, DEX, *Feb 8, 1967* | .75 | .25 | 5.00* | 5.00‡ |
| **pv** | NF, DEX, W1B at left or right, *Feb 8, 1967* | .75 | .25 | 5.00* | 5.00‡ |
| **pi** | tagged, WCB, DF, DEX, *Mar 1969* | .50 | .20 | 4.00* | — |
| **pii** | WCB, LF, PVA, *May 1972* | .50 | .25 | 3.50* | — |
| **piii** | WCB, MF, PVA, *1972* | 5.00 | 1.25 | 35.00* | — |
| **piv** | tagged, GT2, MF, PVA, *Apr 1973* | .25 | .20 | 2.00* | — |

* Blank corner block of 4.

‡ With Winnipeg cancel; Ottawa *day of issue* cancel $15.00. Commercial use on cover: $5.00.

### 4¢ Booklets

Canadian Bank Note Company

Perf 12

| | | NH–VF | ⊙F |
|---|---|---|---|
| **457a** | booklet pane of 5 x 4¢ carmine rose (457as) + label, NF, DEX (BK54), *Feb 1967* | 1.50 | 1.50 |
| **as** | single with straight edge, from 457a | .30 | .20 |
| **ai** | DF, DEX | 2.50 | 2.50 |
| **ais** | single with straight edge, from 457ai | .50 | .20 |
| **aii** | DF/fl, DEX | 8.00 | 6.50 |
| **aiis** | single with straight edge, from 457aii | 1.75 | 1.00 |
| **aiii** | MF, DEX | 8.00 | 6.50 |
| **aiiis** | single with straight edge, from 457aiii | 1.75 | 1.00 |
| **BK54** | 1 pane each 454a, 457a in bilingual cover (24,093,000) $2.50 | | |
| **457b** | Miniature pane of 25 (5 x 5), DF, DEX, *Feb 8, 1967* | 32.50 | 25.00 |
| **bs** | single with straight edge, from 457b | 1.00 | .75 |
| **bi** | Miniature pane of 25 (5 x 5), NF, DEX | 100.00 | 75.00 |
| **bis** | single with straight edge, from 457bi | 6.00 | 4.00 |

British American Bank Note Company

Perf. 10.0

| | | NH–VF | ⊙F |
|---|---|---|---|
| **457c** | booklet pane of 25 x 4¢ carmine rose (457cs and 457d) + 2 labels, NF (BK57), *Jan 1968* | 10.00 | 8.50 |
| **cs** | single with straight edge (at bottom), from 457c | 2.50 | .20 |
| **ci** | NF/fl, DEX | 15.00 | 2.50 |
| **cis** | single with straight edge (at bottom only), from 457ci | 4.00 | .25 |
| **BK57** | pane 457c in bilingual cover (645,000) $12.50 | | |
| **457d** | 4¢ carmine rose, NF, DEX, from 457c, perf all around single | .75 | .20 |
| **dis** | single perf all around, NF/fl, DEX, from 457ci | .80 | .50 |
| **ds** | single with straight edge (at side or side & bottom), DF, from 454c | .30 | .20 |
| **dsi** | single with straight edge (at side or side & bottom), NF/fl, from 454ci | .90 | .50 |

Miniature panes (457b) were sold in Cello Paqs containing one pane of 25.

| 4¢ carmine rose (Seaway) | | | | | | | |
|---|---|---|---|---|---|---|---|
| Tagging: | Untagged | | Winnipeg tagged | | | General | Precancel |
| | | | Centre | | Left/ Right | OP2 | |
| Gum: | Dex | PVA | Dex | PVA | PVA | PVA | Dex |
| Perf 12 | 457 (Pl 1–3) | 457iv (Pl 3) | 457pi | 457pii | 457p | 457piv | 457xx |
| Perf 10.0 | 457d | | | | | | |
| Perf 9½ horiz | 467 | | | | | | |

**4¢ Rate:** Local First-class (0–1 oz.): Apr 1, 1954–Oct 31, 1968
Postcard (each): Apr 1, 1954–Oct 31, 1968

457a

457b

457c

## 5¢ blue (Fishing Village)

Engraved (1 colour), Plates of 600 subjects in six panes of 100
Canadian Bank Note Company

Perf 12

| | | NH–VF | ⊙F | PB | FDC |
|---|---|---|---|---|---|
| **458** | **5¢ blue**, DF, DEX, *Feb 8, 1967* | .25 | .20 | | 2.00 |
| | plate blocks, plates 1, 2, all blocks | | | 2.00 | |
| | plates 3, 4, all blocks | | | 2.25 | |
| | plate 5, all blocks | | | 2.75 | |
| **vi** | as 458, vertical line through '5' (pl. 3, pos. 11) | 10.00 | 7.50 | 15.00 (UL) | |
| **i** | NF, DEX, *1967* | .50 | .20 | 5.00 | — |
| **ii** | LF, DEX, *1967* | .50 | .20 | 2.50 | — |
| **iii** | HB, DEX, *Dec 1971* | .40 | .20 | 3.50* | — |
| **iv** | LF/fl, PVA, *Dec 1971* | .25 | .20 | 2.50 | — |
| **v** | LF, PVA, *1972* | .50 | .20 | 5.00 | — |
| | plate blocks, plate 6, all blocks | | | 2.50 | |
| **xx** | No. 458, precancelled, DF, DEX | 1.50 | .25 | 55.00† | 3.00 |
| **xxi** | No. 458iii, precancelled, HB, DEX | .50 | .20 | 25.00† | 3.00 |
| **xxii** | No. 458v, precancelled, LF, PVA | 1.00 | .20 | 40.00† | 3.00 |

† Warning strip of 20.

| | | NH–VF | ⊙F | PB | FDC |
|---|---|---|---|---|---|
| **458p** | tagged, W2B, DF, DEX, *Feb 8, 1967* | .75 | .25 | 4.50* | 5.00‡ |
| **piv** | as 458p, vertical line through '5' (pl. 3, pos. 11) | 25.00 | 15.00 | 40.00* | |
| **pi** | tagged, WCB, DF, DEX, *Dec 1968* | .50 | .20 | 4.00* | — |
| **pii** | WCB, HB, DEX, *Dec 1971* | .60 | .20 | 5.00* | — |
| **piii** | WCB, LF/fl, PVA, *Apr 1972* | .50 | .25 | 3.50* | — |

* Blank corner block of 4.

‡ With Winnipeg cancel; Ottawa *day of issue* cancel $15.00. Commercial use on cover: $10.00.

| 5¢ blue (Fishing Village) | | | | | | | |
|---|---|---|---|---|---|---|---|
| Tagging: | Untagged | | Winnipeg tagged | | | Precancel | |
| | | | 2-bar | Centre | | | |
| Gum: | Dex | PVA | Dex | Dex | PVA | Dex | PVA |
| Perf 12 | 458 (Pl 1–5) | 458iv (Pl 6) | 458p | 458pi | 458piii | 458xx | 458xxii |
| Perf 10.0 | 458d | | | | | | |
| Perf 9½ horiz | 468 | | | | | 468xx | |

**5¢ Rate:** Domestic First-class (0–1 oz.): Apr 1, 1954–Oct 31, 1968
Third class: Nov 1, 1968–Jun 30, 1971

**458vi, 458piv**

**458di**

## 5¢ Booklets

Canadian Bank Note Company

Perf 12

| | | NH–VF | ⊙F |
|---|---|---|---|
| **458a** | booklet pane of 5 x 5¢ (458as) + label, NF, DEX (BK55) *Mar 1967* | 7.00 | 7.00 |
| **as** | single with straight edge, from 458a | .50 | .20 |
| **ai** | LF/fl, DEX | 15.00 | 20.00 |
| **ais** | single with straight edge, from 458ai | 3.00 | 4.50 |
| **aii** | DF, DEX | 7.00 | 7.00 |
| **aiis** | single with straight edge, from 458aii | .50 | .20 |
| **aiii** | MF, DEX | 25.00 | 25.00 |
| **aiiis** | single with straight edge, from 458aiii | 5.00 | 3.00 |
| **BK55** | pane 458a in bilingual cover (14,002,000) $8.00 | | |
| **458b** | Miniature pane of 20 (4 x 5), DF, DEX, *Feb 8, 1967* | 40.00 | 35.00 |
| **bs** | single with straight edge, from 458b | 3.25 | 1.00 |
| **bi** | Miniature pane of 20 (4 x 5), NF, DEX | 125.00 | |
| **bis** | single with straight edge, from 458bi | 15.00 | |
| **458bp** | Miniature pane of 20 (4 x 5), tagged W2B | 75.00 | 65.00 |
| **bps** | single with straight edge, from 458bp | 5.00 | 2.50 |

British American Bank Note Company

Perf. 10.0

| | | NH–VF | ⊙F |
|---|---|---|---|
| **458c** | booklet pane of 20 x 5¢ blue (458d), DF, DEX (BK58), *Aug 1968* | 10.00 | 10.00 |
| **458d** | single with straight edge, DF, DEX from 458c | .75 | .25 |
| **di** | single with "extended lobster trap" | 1.00 | .40 |
| **BK58** | pane 458c in bilingual cover (1,724,000) $10.50 | | |

Miniature panes (458b and 458bp) were sold in Cello Paqs containing one pane of 20.

**458a**

**458b**

**458c**

**BOOKLET SINGLES**

You may pay a premium for certain mint singles removed from booklet panes as a dealer may need to break apart an entire pane.

### 6¢ orange (Transportation)

Engraved (1 colour), Plates of 600 subjects in six panes of 100
British American Bank Note Company

All 6¢ orange stamps are DEX gum

| | | NH–VF | ⊙F | PB (Perf 10.0) | FDC |
|---|---|---|---|---|---|
| **459** | **6¢ orange**, NF, plates 1, 2 *Nov 1, 1968* | .35 | .20 | 5.00 | 10.00 |
| i | LF/fl, plates 1, 2, *1969* | 1.50 | .20 | 8.00 | — |
| ii | DF, fluorescent ink, *Nov 1, 1968* | 50.00 | 5.00 | 250.00 | 30.00‡ |
| iii | doubled 'C' in CANADA (pos. 10) | 50.00 | 40.00 | | |
| **xx** | No. 459, precancelled§, DF | 2.50 | .50 | 80.00† | 3.00 |

† Warning strip of 20.
§ The orange ink was printed after (i.e. over top of) the black precancel lines.

| | | NH–VF | ⊙F | PB | FDC |
|---|---|---|---|---|---|
| **459p** | tagged, W2B, DF, *Nov 1, 1968* | 1.00 | .40 | 5.00† | 3.00‡ |

† Blank corner block of 4.
‡ With Winnipeg cancel; Ottawa *day of issue* cancel (in combination with the 5c Christmas issue of 1968) $7.50.

### 6¢ orange Booklets

British American Bank Note Company

Perf 10.0

| | | NH–VF | ⊙F |
|---|---|---|---|
| 459v | single with straight edge, LF, from 454bi | 2.50 | .75 |
| vi | single with straight edge, HB, from 454bii (BK59c) | 5.00 | 4.00 |
| vii | single with straight edge, with fluorescent ink, from 454biii | 10.00 | 8.00 |
| viii | single with straight edge, DF, from 454b (BK59a) | .90 | .75 |
| 459a | booklet pane of 25 x 6¢ orange (459 and 459as) + 2 labels, NF (BK60), *Nov 1968* | 10.00 | 10.00 |
| as | single with straight edge (at bottom), from 459a | 3.00 | .75 |
| ai | LF/fl | 15.00 | 2.50 |
| ais | single with straight edge (at bottom), from 459ai | 3.00 | .75 |
| BK60 | pane 459a in bilingual cover 01/–/69 (2,660,000) $10.50 | | |

### 6¢ orange (Transportation)

Engraved (1 colour), pane of 100
British American Bank Note Company

| | | NH–VF | ⊙F | PB (Perf 12.5 x 12.0) | FDC |
|---|---|---|---|---|---|
| **459b** | DF, plate 3, *Mar 1969* | .35 | .20 | 4.25 | — |
| **biii** | NF, *1969* | 1.50 | .20 | 15.00 | — |
| **biv** | HB, *Dec 1969* | 35.00 | 4.00 | 180.00* | — |
| **bv** | LF/fl | 3.00 | .50 | | |
| **459bp** | tagged, W2B, DF, *Apr 1969* | 1.00 | .50 | 5.00* | 5.00‡ |
| **bpi** | W2B, LF, *1969* | 20.00 | 2.50 | 100.00* | — |
| **bpii** | W2B, HB, *Dec 1969* | 2,000.00 | 500.00 | *10,000.00** | — |

Only used copies of 459bpii, with legible Winnipeg cancel were known before 1987. Fewer than 100 mint and 100 used copies are known. Beware of faked mint copies of this variety.
* Blank corner block of 4.
‡ Commercial use on cover.

| 6¢ orange (Transportation) | | | |
|---|---|---|---|
| Tagging: | Untagged | Winnipeg tagged | Precancel |
| | | 2-bar | |
| Gum: | Dex | Dex | Dex |
| Perf 10.0 | 459 | 459p | 459xx |
| Perf 12.5 x 12.0 | 459b | 459bp | |
| Perf 10 horiz | 468A | | |

**6¢ Rate:** Domestic First-class (0–1 oz.): Nov 1, 1968–Jun 30, 1971
Postcard (each): Nov 1, 1968–Aug 31, 1976

459a

BK60b
Label-stamp-label error

459iii

Nearly 100 constant plate varieties (most are minor) are recorded on the 6¢ orange design.

**MINT PRICING PREMIUMS**

Mint stamps from 301 to date are valued as NH-VF (Never Hinged-Very Fine). All hinged VF and NH-F copies are worth 50% of the listed values. Plate block (PB) values are for mint NH–VF plate or inscription blocks of four.

**USED, VF/XF (with in-period, circular date cancel) PRICING PREMIUM**

Single stamps with light or circular date cancels will sell for more than catalogue value (perhaps even more than a mint copy). From *1981 to 1991* single stamps from se-tenant blocks of 4 or larger will be priced at 50% or more above the fine price. From *1992* to date single stamps from se-tenant blocks of 4 or larger plus se-tenant booklet panes and souvenir sheets will be priced at 100% or more above the fine price. From *1997* to date all other stamps will be priced at 50% or more above the fine price.

### 6¢ black (Transportation)

Dies I and II were used by BABN (perf. 12.5 x 12.0). Die Ia is similar to Die II, but was only used by CBN (perf. 12).

Die I

Die II

Die Ia

Engraved (1 colour), Plates of 600 subjects in six panes of 100
British American Bank Note Company

| Die I | | Perf 12.5 x 12.0 | | | |
|---|---|---|---|---|---|
| | | NH–VF | ⊙F | PB | FDC |
| **460** | **6¢ black**, Die I, DF, DEX, plates 1, 2, *Jan 7, 1970* | .25 | .20 | 3.00 | 2.00 |
| | plate 3, all blocks, *Apr 1, 1970* | | | 3.00 | |
| i | Die I, LF/fl, DEX, *1970* | 1.00 | .20 | 7.50 | — |
| ii | Die I, HB, white DEX, *Jan 7, 1970* | 20.00 | 3.50 | 90.00* | — |
| **460p** | tagged, W2B, Die I, DF, DEX, *Jan 7, 1970* | .35 | .20 | 6.50* | 3.00‡ |
| pi | W2B, Die I, LF/fl, DEX, *1970* | 1.00 | .20 | 7.50* | — |

* Blank corner block of 4.

‡ With Winnipeg cancel; Ottawa *day of issue* cancel $7.50. Commercial use on cover $5.00.

### 6¢ black Die I Booklets

British American Bank Note Company

| | | Perf 12.5 x 12.0 | |
|---|---|---|---|
| | | NH–VF | ⊙F |
| 460b | booklet pane of 25 x 6¢ black (460 and 460bs) + 2 labels, DEX (BK64), *Dec, 1970* | 20.00 | 17.50 |
| bs | single with straight edge, from 460b, DEX | 4.00 | .20 |
| BK64 | pane 460b in bilingual cover (14,070,000) $22.50 | | |

| | | Perf 10.0 | |
|---|---|---|---|
| | | NH–VF | ⊙F |
| 460a | booklet pane of 25 x 6¢ black (460g) + 2 labels (BK61), NF, DEX, *Jan 1970* | 15.00 | 9.00 |
| ai | LF, DEX | 17.50 | 17.50 |
| aii | MF, DEX | 30.00 | 25.00 |
| aiii | HB, DEX | 4,500.00 | *4,500.00†* |
| BK61 | pane 460a in bilingual cover (4,070,000) $15.00 | | |

† One used pane recorded.

| | | | |
|---|---|---|---|
| 460g | 6¢ black, Die I, NF, DEX, single, from 460a | 2.00 | .40 |
| i | LF, DEX, from 460ai | 2.25 | .50 |
| ii | MF, DEX, from 460aii | 2.50 | .85 |
| iii | HB, DEX, from 460aiii | 200.00 | 60.00 |

460a

460b

460d

460e

### 6¢ black (Transportation)

British American Bank Note Company

| Die II | | Perf 12.5 x 12.0 | | | |
|---|---|---|---|---|---|
| | | NH–VF | ⊙F | PB | FDC |
| **460c** | **6¢ black**, Die II, DF, DEX, plate 4, *Apr 1970* | .30 | .20 | 3.00 | — |
| iv | as 460c, slight doubling on "6" | 75.00 | 35.00 | | |
| xx | No. 460c, precancelled§ | 3.00 | 1.50 | 65.00† | 3.00 |

† Warning strip of 20.

§ The black ink (engraved) was printed after (i.e. over top of) the black precancel lines.

| | | | | | |
|---|---|---|---|---|---|
| **460cp** | Die II, tagged, WCB, DEX, *Aug 1971* | .55 | .50 | 4.50* | — |

* Blank corner block of 4.

### 6¢ black Die II Booklets

British American Bank Note Company

| | | Perf 12.5 x 12.0 | |
|---|---|---|---|
| | | NH–VF | ⊙F |
| 460cpx | 6¢ black, Die II, tagged, OP4, DF, PVA, single with straight edge, from 544r, *Dec 30, 1971* | 2.50 | .20 |
| cpxi | OP4, LF, PVA, from 544q | 1.00 | .25 |
| cpxii | OP4, MF, PVA, from 544s, ribbed vert. | 2.00 | .30 |
| cpxiii | OP4, MF, PVA, from 544qi | 2.00 | .20 |
| cpxiv | OP4, HF, PVA, from 544qii | 2.00 | .20 |
| cpxv | OP2, NF, PVA, from 544qiii | 12.00 | 4.00 |
| cpxvi | OP2, MF, PVA, from 544qiv | .50 | .20 |
| cpxvii | OP2, HF, PVA, from 544qv | 1.00 | .20 |
| cpxviii | OP2, DF, PVA, from 544qvi | 1.25 | .20 |
| 460cx | 6¢ black, Die II, DF, PVA, single with straight edge, from 544a or 544b | 1.50 | .20 |
| cxi | LF, PVA, from 544c, ribbed, vert. | 1.25 | .20 |
| cxii | MF, PVA, from 544ci, ribbed, vert. | 1.25 | .20 |
| cxiii | LF, PVA, from 544ai | 1.25 | .20 |
| cxiv | MF, PVA, from 544aii | 1.25 | .20 |
| cxv | HF, PVA, from 544aiii | 1.25 | .20 |
| cxvi | HB, PVA, from 544aiv | 1.25 | .20 |
| 460d | booklet pane of 4 x 6¢ black (460ds), DEX (BK65a), *Nov 1970* | 4.50 | 4.00 |
| ds | single (DEX gum) with straight edge, from 460d | 1.10 | .20 |
| di | DF, PVA (BK65b) | 4.00 | 3.50 |
| dis | single (PVA gum) with straight edge, from 460di | 1.00 | .20 |
| BK65 | pane 460d in bilingual cover 05/–/70 (15,840,000) $5.00 | | |

| | | Perf 10.0 | |
|---|---|---|---|
| | | NH–VF | ⊙F |
| 460e | booklet pane of 4 x 6¢ black (460h), DF, DEX (BK62), *May 1970* | 14.00 | 8.00 |
| BK62 | pane 460e in bilingual cover (15,840,000) $15.00 | | |
| 460h | 6¢ black, Die II, DF, DEX, single with one or two straight edges, from 460e | 2.50 | .80 |

### 6¢ black (Transportation)

Canadian Bank Note Company

| Die Ia | | Perf 12 | | | |
|---|---|---|---|---|---|
| | (all PVA gum) | NH–VF | ⊙F | PB | FDC |
| **460f** | **6¢ black**, Die Ia, LF, ribbed horiz. plates 1, 2, *Jan 1972* | .50 | .20 | 3.00 | — |
| fi | Die Ia, printed on gum side | 25.00 | — | 125.00* | — |
| xxi | No. 460f, precancelled, *Feb 1972* | 2.50 | 1.00 | 65.00† | 3.00 |
| **460fp** | Die Ia, tagged, WCB, LF, ribbed horiz., *Jan 1972* | .35 | .20 | 3.25* | — |
| fpi | Die Ia, tagged GT2 (4mm), NF, *Jan 1972* | .65 | .25 | 4.00* | — |
| fpii | Die Ia, GT2 (4mm), LF/fl, *Jan 1972* | 1.25 | .50 | 8.00* | — |
| fpiii | Die Ia, GT2 (4mm), HF | 2.50 | 1.00 | 15.00* | — |
| fpiv | Die Ia, GT2 (3mm), LF, ribbed horiz., *Dec 1972* | .50 | .20 | 3.00* | — |
| fpv | Die Ia, GT2 (3mm), DF | 1.00 | .25 | 6.00* | — |
| fpvi | Die Ia, GT2 (3mm), MF, ribbed horiz. | 2.00 | .50 | 12.00* | — |

... (precancel on next page)

| | (all PVA gum) | NH–VF | ⊙F | PB | FDC |
|---|---|---|---|---|---|
| **fpxx** | No. 460fpiv, precancelled, GT2, LF, ribbed horiz., *Dec 1972* | 1.50 | .25 | 50.00† | 3.00 |
| **fpxxi** | precancelled, GT2, F, ribbed horiz. | 2.00 | .25 | 75.00† | |
| **fpxxii** | precancelled, GT2, MF, ribbed horiz. | 5.00 | 1.00 | 150.00† | |

† Warning strip of 20.
* Blank corner block of 4.

| **6¢ black (Transportation)** | | | | | | | | | | |
|---|---|---|---|---|---|---|---|---|---|---|
| Tagging: | | Untagged | | Winnipeg tagged | | | General | Precancel | | |
| | | | | 2-bar | Centre | | OP2 | | | OP2 |
| Gum: | | Dex | PVA | Dex | Dex | PVA | PVA | Dex | PVA | PVA |
| Perf 12.5 x 12.0 | Die I | 460 (Pl 1–3) | | 460p | | | | | | |
| | Die II | 460c (Pl 3–4) | | | 460cp | | | 460cxx | | |
| Perf 10.0 | Die I | 460g (BK61) | | | | | | | | |
| | Die II | 460h (BK62) | | | | | | | | |
| Perf 12 | Die Ia | | 460f (Pl 1–2) | | | 460fp | 460fpi | | 460fxxi | 460fpxx |
| Perf 10 horiz | Die II | 468B | | | | | | | | |

**6¢ Rate:** Domestic First-class (0–1 oz.): Nov 1, 1968–Jun 30, 1971
Postcard (each): Nov 1, 1968–Aug 31, 1976

### 7¢ slate green (Transportation)

Engraved (1 colour), Plates of 600 subjects in six panes of 100
British American Bank Note Company

| | Perf 12.5 x 12.0 | NH–VF | ⊙F | PB | FDC |
|---|---|---|---|---|---|
| **543** | **7¢ slate green**, DF, DEX, *Jun 30,1971* | .45 | .20 | | 2.00 |
| | plate blocks, plate 1, all blocks | | | 8.00 | |
| | plate 2, all blocks | | | 4.50 | |
| **543p** | tagged, W2B, DF, DEX, *Jun 30, 1971* | .75 | .25 | 5.50* | 3.00‡ |
| **pi** | coarse-vertically ribbed paper | 5.00 | 1.00 | 35.00* | |

* Blank corner block of 4.
‡ With Winnipeg cancel; Ottawa *day of issue* cancel $7.50.

### 7¢ green Booklets

British American Bank Note Company

| | Perf 12.5 x 12.0 | NH–VF | ⊙F |
|---|---|---|---|
| 543a | booklet pane of 5 + label, 1 x 1¢ (454ei) + 1 x 3¢ (456ai) + 3 x 7¢ (543x), DF, PVA (BK66, 68), *Jun 30, 1971* | 9.50 | 6.00 |
| ai | LF, PVA | 5.50 | 3.50 |
| aii | MF, PVA | 7.50 | 5.00 |
| BK66 | pane 543a in bilingual cover (8,660,000) $6.00 | | |
| BK68 | 2 panes 543a in bilingual cover 08/–/71 $20.00 | | |
| 543x | 7¢ green, DF, PVA, single with straight edge, from 543a | 1.00 | .20 |
| xi | LF, PVA, from 543ai | .75 | .20 |
| xii | MF, PVA, from 543aii | .85 | .20 |
| 543b | booklet pane of 20, 4 x 1¢ (454e) + 4 x 3¢ (456a) + 12 x 7¢ (543bs), DF, DEX (BK67), *Jun 30, 1971* | 10.00 | 8.00 |
| bs | single 7¢ with straight edge, DF, DEX, from 543b | .75 | .20 |
| BK67 | pane 543b in bilingual cover (468,000) $12.50 | | |

543a

543b

| **7¢ slate green (Transportation)** | | | |
|---|---|---|---|
| Tagging: | Untagged | | Winnipeg tagged |
| | | | 2-bar |
| Gum: | Dex | PVA | Dex |
| Perf 12.5 x 12.0 | 543 (Pl 1–2) | 543x (BK66) | 543p |
| Perf 10 horiz | 549 | | |

**7¢ Rate:** Domestic First-class (0–1 oz.): Jul 1, 1971–Dec 31, 1971
USA First-class (0–1 oz.): Jul 1, 1971–Dec 31, 1971

Some 86 constant cylinder flaws have been recorded on the 7¢ value.

## 8¢ slate (Library of Parliament)

Engraved (1 colour), Plates of 600 subjects in six panes of 100
British American Bank Note Company

Perf 12.5 x 12.0

| | | NH–VF | ⊙F | PB | FDC |
|---|---|---|---|---|---|
| **544** | **8¢ slate**, DF, DEX, *Dec 30, 1971* | .30 | .20 | | 2.00 |
| | plate blocks, plates 1, 2, all blocks | | | 3.50 | |
| | plate 3, all blocks | | | 4.00 | |
| **i** | LF/fl, DEX, Pl. 2, *Feb 1972* | .50 | .20 | 4.00 | — |
| **ii** | LF, PVA, Pl. 4, *May 1972* | .30 | .20 | 4.50 | — |
| **iii** | HF, PVA, *Nov 1972* | 9.00 | 2.00 | 40.00 | — |
| **iv** | "Extra Spire", LF, PVA, Pl. 4 | *150.00* | *100.00* | | |
| **544p** | tagged, W2B, NF, DEX, *Dec 30, 1971* | .40 | .20 | 2.50* | 3.00‡ |
| **pii** | W2B, LF, PVA, *Jul 1972* | .65 | .20 | 4.50* | — |
| **piii** | W2B, HF, PVA, *Nov 1972* | 9.50 | 3.50 | 47.50* | — |
| **pix** | "Extra Spire", W2B, LF, PVA | *200.00* | *150.00* | | |
| **pi** | GT2 (OP4), NF, DEX, *Dec 30, 1971* | .30 | .20 | 2.50* | 3.00 |
| **pxix** | GT2 (OP4), HF/fl, PVA | 3.00 | 2.00 | 15.00* | — |
| **piv** | GT2 (OP2), HF, PVA, Pl. 7, *Jul 1973* | 1.00 | .25 | 5.00 | — |
| **pv** | GT2 (OP2), LF/fl, PVA, Pl. 5 & 6, *Apr 73* | .75 | .20 | 7.00 | — |
| **pvii** | GT2 (OP2), HF, PVA, ribbed vert., *1973* | 3.50 | .50 | 25.00* | — |
| **pviii** | scratch on forehead variety, LF, PVA, GT2 | 25.00 | 7.50 | 125.00 | 30.00 |

Plate 1 is ribbed vert.; Plates 2 and 4 exist ribbed vert. and smooth; Plate 3 is smooth.

* Blank corner block of 4.

‡ With Winnipeg cancel; Ottawa *day of issue* cancel $7.50.

**Normal**

**544iv, 544pix**

Over 75 constant cylinder varieties have been recorded on the 8¢ Library of Parliament design.

**8¢ Rate:** Domestic First-class (0–1 oz.): Jan 1, 1972–Aug 31, 1976

**544a**
**544q (tag)**

**544b**
**544r (tag)**

**544c**
**544s (tag)**

## 8¢ slate Booklets

British American Bank Note Company

Perf 12.5 x 12.0

| | | NH–VF | ⊙F |
|---|---|---|---|
| **544a** | booklet pane of 6, 3 x 1¢ (454eiv) + 1 x 6¢ black, Die II (460cx) + 2 x 8¢ (544x), DF, PVA (BK69), *Dec 30, 1971* | 5.00 | 2.50 |
| **ai** | LF, PVA | 3.00 | 2.00 |
| **aii** | MF, PVA | 2.00 | 1.00 |
| **aiii** | HF, PVA | 2.50 | 1.50 |
| **aiv** | HB, PVA | 2.00 | 1.00 |
| **BK69** | pane 544a in bilingual cover (7,200,000) $2.50 | | |
| **544b** | booklet pane of 18, 6 x 1¢ (454eiv) + 1 x 6¢ Die II (460cx) + 11 x 8¢ (544x), DF, PVA (BK70a), *Dec 30, 1971* | 6.50 | 3.50 |
| **BK70** | pane 544b in bilingual cover $5.00 | | |
| **544c** | booklet pane of 10, 4 x 1¢ (454ev) + 1 x 6¢ Die II (460cxi) + 5 x 8¢ (544xi), LF, PVA, ribbed, vert. (BK71a), *Aug '72* | 3.00 | 4.00 |
| **ci** | MF, PVA, ribbed, vert. | 2.50 | 3.00 |
| **BK71** | pane 544c in bilingual cover $3.00 | | |
| **544px** | 8¢ slate, tagged, OP4, DF, PVA, single with straight edge, from 544r | .30 | .20 |
| **pxi** | OP4, LF, PVA, from 544q | .25 | .20 |
| **pxii** | OP4, MF, PVA, from 544s, ribbed vert. | .30 | .20 |
| **pxiii** | OP4, MF, PVA, from 544qi | .35 | .20 |
| **pxiv** | OP4, HF, PVA, from 544qii | .40 | .20 |
| **pxv** | OP2, NF, PVA, from 544qiii | 3.00 | 2.00 |
| **pxvi** | OP2, MF, PVA, from 544qiv | .25 | .20 |
| **pxvii** | OP2, HF, PVA, from 544qv | .30 | .20 |
| **pxviii** | OP2, DF, PVA, from 544qvi | .50 | .20 |
| **544q** | booklet pane of 6, 3 x 1¢ (454epi) + 1 x 6¢ black, Die II (460cpxi) + 2 x 8¢ (544pxi) OP4 (4mm), LF (BK69ei), *Dec 30, 1971* | 2.00 | 1.00 |
| **qi** | OP4 (4mm), MF, PVA | 3.00 | 1.00 |
| **qii** | OP4 (4mm), HF, PVA | 3.00 | 2.00 |
| **544qiii** | booklet pane of 6, 3 x 1¢ (454epiv) + 1 x 6¢ black, Die II (460cpxv) + 2 x 8¢ (544pxv) OP2 (3mm), NF (BK69k), *Dec 30, 1971* | 18.00 | 11.00 |
| **qiv** | OP2 (3mm), MF, PVA, | 1.00 | .60 |
| **qv** | OP2 (3mm), HF, PVA | 1.50 | .75 |
| **qvi** | OP2 (3mm), DF, PVA | 2.00 | 1.50 |
| **544r** | booklet pane of 18, 6 x 1¢ (454ep) + 1 x 6¢ black, Die II (460cpx) + 11 x 8¢ (544px) OP4 (4mm) (BK70b), DF | 4.00 | 4.50 |
| **544s** | booklet pane of 10, 4 x 1¢ (454epvii) + 1 x 6¢ black, Die II (460cpxii) + 5 x 8¢ (544pxii) OP4 (3mm) (BK71d), MF, ribbed vert. | 3.00 | 3.50 |
| **544x** | 8¢ slate, DF, PVA, single with straight edge, from 544a or 544b | .75 | .20 |
| **xi** | LF, PVA, from 544c, ribbed, vert. | .25 | .20 |
| **xii** | MF, PVA, from 544ci, ribbed, vert. | .25 | .20 |
| **xiii** | LF, PVA, from 544ai | .75 | .20 |
| **xiv** | MF, PVA, from 544aii | .25 | .20 |
| **xv** | HF, PVA, from 544aiii | .75 | .20 |
| **xvii** | HB, PVA, from 544aiv | .50 | .20 |

**8¢ slate (Library of Parliament)**

| Tagging: | Untagged | | Winnipeg tagged | | General | | |
|---|---|---|---|---|---|---|---|
| | | | 2-bar | | OP4 | | OP2 |
| Gum: | Dex | PVA | Dex | PVA | Dex | PVA | PVA |
| Perf 12.5 x 12.0 | 544 (Pl 1–3) | 544ii (Pl 4) | 544p | 544pii | 544pi | ? (sheet) 544px (BK70b) | 544piv (Pl 5–7) |
| Perf 10 horiz | | 550 | | | | | 550p |

## 1967–1973
## CENTENNIAL DEFINITIVES – HIGH VALUES

461
*Alaska Highway*, by A.Y. Jackson

462
*Jack Pine*, by Tom Thomson

463
*Greenland Mountains*, by Lawren Harris

464
*The Ferry, Quebec*, by J.W. Morrice

465
*Solemn Land*, by J.E.H. MacDonald

465A
*Summer's Stores*, by John Ensor

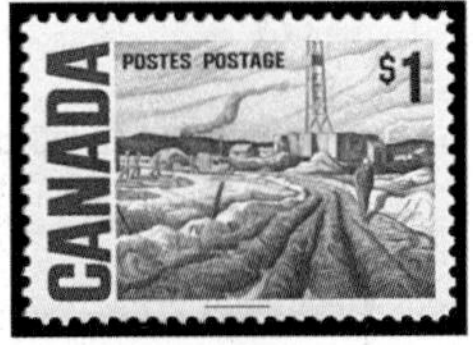

465B
*Edmonton Oil Field*, by H.G. Glyde

Engraved (1 colour), Plates of 300 subjects in six panes of 50
Canadian Bank Note Company



Perf 12

| | | NH–VF | ⊙F | PB | FDC |
|---|---|---|---|---|---|
| **461** | **8¢ violet brown,** | | | | |
| | DF, DEX, plates 1, 2, *Feb 8, 1967* | .35 | .20 | 5.00 | 4.00 |
| i | NF/fl, DEX, *1968* | 2.50 | .25 | 12.50 | — |
| ii | HB, DEX, *Jul 1971* | 35.00 | 2.00 | 175.00* | — |
| iii | "Plastic Flow" variety, doubling of "8" | 125.00 | 60.00 | 300.00† | |
| iv | NF | 5.00 | 1.00 | 25.00 | |

† The variety appears on 2 stamps in blank corner block of 4.

| | | NH–VF | ⊙F | PB | FDC |
|---|---|---|---|---|---|
| **462** | **10¢ olive green,** | | | | |
| | DF, DEX, plates 1, 2, *Feb 8, 1967* | .35 | .20 | 2.75 | 4.00‡ |
| i | NF, DEX, *1967* | 1.75 | .25 | 8.75 | — |
| ii | NF/fl, DEX, *1968* | 2.00 | .25 | 10.00 | — |
| iii | HB, spotty white gum, *Dec 1971* | 7.00 | .45 | 65.00* | — |
| iv | MF, PVA, plate 3, *Mar 1971* | 1.25 | .50 | 6.50 | — |
| v | LF, PVA, plate 3, *1973* | 2.00 | .65 | 10.00 | — |

‡ Commercial single use on cover: $15.00.

| | | NH–VF | ⊙F | PB | FDC |
|---|---|---|---|---|---|
| **462p** | 10¢ olive green, tagged, W2B, DF, DEX, *Dec 9, 1969* | 1.25 | .50 | 7.50* | — |
| pi | W2B, HB, spotty white gum, *Jan 1972* | 2.00 | 1.00 | 10.00* | — |
| piv | W2B, LF, PVA, *Nov 1972* | 6.00 | 3.50 | 32.50* | — |
| pii | tagged GT2, HB, spotty white gum, *Jan 1972* | 6.00 | 1.25 | 35.00* | — |
| piii | GT2, LF, PVA, *Feb 1972* | 1.00 | .35 | 5.00* | — |

| | | NH–VF | ⊙F | PB | FDC |
|---|---|---|---|---|---|
| **463** | **15¢ dull purple,** | | | | |
| | DF, DEX, plates 1, 2, *Feb 8, 1967* | .60 | .20 | 4.50 | 4.00‡ |
| i | LF, DEX, *1967* | 1.25 | .20 | 6.25 | — |
| ii | HB, DEX, *Mar 1971* | 20.00 | .35 | 100.00* | — |
| vi | as 463, "Plastic Flow" variety† | 125.00 | 50.00 | 300.00* | |
| vii | as 463ii (HB), "Plastic Flow" variety† | 200.00 | 75.00 | 500.00* | |
| iii | F, PVA, plate 3, *Mar 1972* | 1.00 | .25 | 6.00 | — |
| iv | DF, PVA, *1972* | 20.00 | 2.00 | 100.00 | — |
| v | LF, PVA, *1972* | 20.00 | 2.00 | 100.00 | — |
| viii | as "v", on vert. ribbed paper | 30.00 | | 150.00 | |

† doubling of "15". Corner block price is based on 2 stamps with flaw; not all stamps may show the doubling.
‡ Commercial single use on cover: $20.00.

| | | NH–VF | ⊙F | PB | FDC |
|---|---|---|---|---|---|
| **463p** | 15¢ dull purple, DF, DEX, tagged W2B, *Dec 9, 1969* | 1.25 | .50 | 7.50* | —‡ |
| pii | W2B, DF, PVA, *Mar 1972* | 1.50 | .35 | 7.50* | — |
| piii | W2B, LF, PVA, *Mar 1972* | 1.50 | .35 | 7.50* | — |
| pv | W2B, "Plastic Flow" variety, LF, PVA | 125.00 | 50.00 | 300.00* | |
| pvi | W2B, "Plastic Flow" variety, DF, PVA | 125.00 | 50.00 | 300.00* | |
| pvii | W2B, "Plastic Flow" variety, DF, Dex | 100.00 | 50.00 | 300.00* | |
| pi | GT2, DF, PVA, *Feb 1972* | 1.25 | .25 | 6.00* | — |
| piv | GT2, LF, PVA, *Feb 1972* | 1.25 | .25 | 6.00* | — |
| pviii | GT2, "Plastic Flow" variety, DF, PVA | 100.00 | 50.00 | 300.00* | — |

‡ Commercial single use on cover: $30.00.

| | | NH–VF | ⊙F | PB | FDC |
|---|---|---|---|---|---|
| **464** | **20¢ dark blue,** | | | | |
| | DF, DEX, plates 1, 2, *Feb 8, 1967* | .75 | .20 | 4.50 | 5.00‡ |
| i | NF, DEX, *1967* | 3.50 | .25 | 15.00 | — |
| ii | HB, DEX, *Aug 1971* | 20.00 | .65 | 100.00* | — |
| iii | LF, PVA, plate 2, *May 1972* | 1.50 | .20 | 18.00 | — |

‡ Commercial single use on cover: $20.00.

| | | NH–VF | ⊙F | PB | FDC |
|---|---|---|---|---|---|
| **464p** | 20¢ dark blue, DF, DEX, tagged, W2B, *Dec 9, 1969* | 2.00 | .75 | 12.00* | — |
| pi | W2B, LF, PVA, *May 1972* | 2.00 | .70 | 15.00* | — |

| | | NH–VF | ⊙F | PB | FDC |
|---|---|---|---|---|---|
| **465** | **25¢ slate green,** | | | | |
| | DF, DEX, plates 1, 2, *Feb 8, 1967* | 2.00 | .20 | | 5.00‡ |
| | plate blocks, plate 1, all blocks | | | 10.00 | |
| | plate 2, all blocks | | | 11.00 | |
| i | NF, DEX, plates 1, 2, *1967* | 5.00 | .25 | 24.00 | |
| ii | HB, DEX, *Oct 1971* | 25.00 | .25 | 125.00* | — |
| iii | as 465ii (HB), "Plastic Flow" variety | 300.00 | 100.00 | | |

‡ Commercial single use on cover: $20.00.

| | | NH–VF | ⊙F | PB | FDC |
|---|---|---|---|---|---|
| **465p** | 25¢ slate green, DF, DEX, tagged, W2B, *Dec 9, 1969* | 10.00 | 3.50 | 50.00* | — |
| pi | W2B, HB, DEX, *Dec 1971* | 50.00 | 4.50 | 250.00* | — |

| | | NH–VF | ⊙F | PB | FDC |
|---|---|---|---|---|---|
| **465A** | **50¢ brown orange,** | | | | |
| | DF, DEX, plate 1, *Feb 8, 1967* | 5.00 | .20 | 25.00 | 8.00‡ |
| i | NF, DEX, plate 1, *1967* | 17.50 | .75 | 85.00 | — |
| ii | LF, DEX, plate 1, *1967* | 8.50 | .25 | 42.50 | — |
| iii | HB, DEX, *Mar 1971* | 25.00 | .50 | 125.00* | — |
| iv | LF, PVA, plate 2, *Dec 1971* | 7.50 | .20 | 37.50 | — |

‡ Commercial single use on cover: $20.00.

| | | NH–VF | ⊙F | PB | FDC |
|---|---|---|---|---|---|
| **465B** | **$1 carmine rose,** | | | | |
| | DF, DEX, plate 1, *Feb 8, 1967* | 8.00 | 1.00 | 40.00 | 12.00‡ |
| i | NF, DEX, plate 1, *1967* | 25.00 | 2.00 | 125.00 | — |
| v | LF, DEX, plate 1 | 15.00 | 2.00 | 75.00 | — |
| ii | HB, DEX, *Mar 1971* | 50.00 | 4.50 | 250.00* | — |
| iii | LF, PVA, plate 2, *Dec 1971* | 12.50 | 1.50 | 62.50 | — |
| iv | MF, PVA, plate 2, *Dec 1971* | 25.00 | 2.50 | 125.00 | — |

* Blank corner block of 4.
‡ Commercial single use on cover: $35.00.

## 1967–1973
## CENTENNIAL DEFINITIVES – COIL STAMPS

466

467

468

468A

468B

549

550

**1967, Feb 8** **Rolls of 500** **Perf 9½ horiz**

| | | NH–VF | ⊙F | ✉ |
|---|---|---|---|---|
| **466** | **3¢ dull purple**, DF, DEX (456) | 5.00 | 1.25 | 7.00 |
| | cutting guideline, strip of 4* | 50.00 | | |
| ii | jump strip of 4* | 45.00 | | |
| | start or end strip of 4** | 90.00 | | |
| i | LF/fl, DEX | 4.50 | 1.50 | |
| | as 'i', cutting guideline, strip of 4* | 75.00 | | |
| iii | as 'i', jump strip of 4* | 42.00 | | |
| | as 'i', start or end strip of 4** | 100.00 | | |
| xx | No. 466, precancelled | 3.50 | 1.00 | |
| xxi | as 'xx', jump strip of 4* | 30.00 | | |
| | as 466 or '466xx', repair paste-up pair* | 100.00 | | |
| | as 'xx', start or end strip of 4** | 500.00 | | |
| **467** | **4¢ carmine rose**, DF, DEX (457) | 1.50 | .75 | 10.00 |
| | cutting guideline, strip of 4* | 50.00 | | |
| ii | jump strip of 4* | 15.00 | | |
| | repair paste-up pair* | 50.00 | | |
| | start or end strip of 4** | 50.00 | | |
| i | LF, DEX | 1.75 | .90 | |
| | as 'i', cutting guideline, strip of 4* | 75.00 | | |
| iii | as 'i', jump strip of 4* | 17.50 | | |
| | as 'i', repair paste-up pair* | 100.00 | | |
| | as 'i', start or end strip of 4** | 75.00 | | |
| **468** | **5¢ blue**, DF, DEX (458) | 3.00 | 1.00 | 10.00 |
| | cutting guideline, strip of 4* | 50.00 | | |
| ii | jump strip of 4* | 28.00 | | |
| | start or end strip of 4** | 80.00 | | |
| i | LF/fl, DEX | 4.50 | 1.25 | |
| | as 'i', cutting guideline, strip of 4* | 75.00 | | |
| iii | as 'i', jump strip of 4* | 42.00 | | |
| | as 'i', start or end strip of 4** | 90.00 | | |
| xx | No. 468, precancelled | 3.50 | 1.00 | |
| xxi | as 'xx', jump strip of 4* | 30.00 | | |
| | as 468 or '468xx', repair paste-up pair* | 150.00 | | |
| | as 'xx', start or end strip of 4** | 500.00 | | |

* Jump strips are always "at least" a little off centre due to spacing variation and jump (slightly out of alignment) at the jump. Similarly, repair paste-ups are a bit off centre.
** Start or end strip of 4 with full strip of 10 tabs. Shorter strips sell for less: 2 stamps plus 2 tabs at half list of full strip.

Beginning at No. 468A, most coils exist double perforated. Please read COIL STAMPS in the introduction.

**1969–1973** **Rolls of 100** **Perf 10 horiz**

| | | NH–VF | ⊙F | ✉ |
|---|---|---|---|---|
| **468A** | **6¢ orange**, DF, DEX (459), *Jan 1969* | .60 | .20 | 3.00 |
| c | imperf. pair, DF, DEX | 400.00 | | |
| i | HB, DEX, *Dec 1969* | 9.00 | .50 | |
| ii | imperf. pair, HB, DEX | 4,000.00 | | |
| iv | gutter strip of 4 (17 mm printing jump between)* | *7,500.00* | | |

* Fewer than 10 exist.

| | | NH–VF | ⊙F | ✉ |
|---|---|---|---|---|
| **468B** | **6¢ black**, HB, DEX (460f), *Aug 1970* | .50 | .20 | 3.00 |
| d | imperf. pair | 3,500.00 | | |

No. 468Bd exists with printer's "felt pen" rejection marking, $1,500.00.

| | | NH–VF | ⊙F | ✉ |
|---|---|---|---|---|
| **549** | **7¢ emerald green**, HB, DEX (543), *Jun 30, 1971* | .50 | .20 | 8.00 |
| a | imperf. pair, DEX | 1,500.00 | | |
| **550** | **8¢ slate**, F, PVA (544), *Dec 30, 1971* | .40 | .20 | 1.00 |
| a | imperf. pair, PVA | 750.00 | | |
| i | DF, PVA | 2.00 | .50 | |
| ii | DF, PVA, ribbed horiz. | 10.00 | 2.50 | |
| p | tagged, GT2, F, PVA, *Dec 30, 1971* | .30 | .20 | |
| q | GT2, imperf. pair, PVA | 1,400.00 | | |
| pii | GT2, HF, PVA, *Dec 30, 1971* | 2.00 | .25 | |
| piii | GT2, imperf. pair, HF, PVA | 1,600.00 | | |
| piv | GT2, MF, PVA | 1.50 | .50 | |
| pv | GT2, DF, PVA | 2.50 | .60 | |
| pvi | GT2, LF/fl, PVA | 7.00 | 1.50 | |

Wide and narrow spacing strips of four (with or without jumps) exist on Centennial coils, value 5 times a strip of four; the 7¢ spacing varieties are much scarcer (value is 10 times a strip). Jumps (usually small) also exist on the 6¢ through 8¢ coils.

Coil pairs or larger multiples are priced in proportion.

### CBN "Test coil"

Printed in 1967 by Canadian Bank Note Co. to use with 6¢ orange coils to display the new dispensers. Misperfs exist.

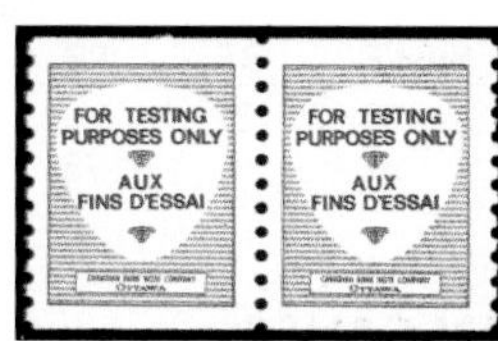

Perforated single (dex gum*): $30.00, pair $60.00
Imperforate pair: $70.00
468A (4–6 stamps) with 9 or more test coils attached: $500.00

* also exists with PVA gum (very rare).

**First Day Cover values, post 1960, are for cacheted, unaddressed covers. Uncacheted and addressed covers sell for much less.**

**469**
*Katimavik*, Canadian Pavilion

**470**
Woman and Ballot Box

## EXPO '67

Designer: Harvey Thomas Prosser. Picture engraved by Allan Alexander Carswell. Lettering engraved by Donald J. Mitchell.

Engraved (2 colours), Plates of 300 subjects in panes of 50
Canadian Bank Note Company

**1967, Apr 28** **Perf 12**

| | | NH–VF | ⊙F | PB | FDC |
|---|---|---|---|---|---|
| **469** | **5¢ blue and red** | .35 | .20 | | 2.00 |
| | plate blocks, plates 1, 2, all blocks | | | 1.75 | |

Qty: 42,360,000

Issued on opening day of Canada's World Fair held in honour of Centennial Year.

## VOTES FOR WOMEN

Designer: Helen Roberta Fitzgerald.

Lithography, Plates of 400 subjects in panes of 100
Canadian Bank Note Company

**1967, May 24** **Perf 12**

| | | NH–VF | ⊙F | PB | FDC |
|---|---|---|---|---|---|
| **470** | **5¢ black and rose lilac** | .35 | .20 | 1.75 | 2.00 |

Qty: 25,780,000

Issued on the 50th anniversary of Women's Suffrage in Canada.

**471**
Queen Elizabeth II and Centennial Symbol

**472**
Runner

## ROYAL VISIT

Designer: Harvey Thomas Prosser. Based on a photograph by Anthony Buckley. Portrait and picture engraved by Yves Baril.

Engraved (2 colours), Plates of 400 subjects in panes of 100
Canadian Bank Note Company

**1967, Jun 30** **Perf 12**

| | | NH–VF | ⊙F | PB | FDC |
|---|---|---|---|---|---|
| **471** | **5¢ deep orange and purple** | .35 | .20 | | 2.00 |
| | plate blocks, plates 1, 2, all blocks | | | 1.75 | |

Qty: 28,530,000

## PAN-AMERICAN GAMES

Designer: Paul Aleksander Pedersen. Picture engraved by Allan Alexander Carswell. Lettering engraved by Gordon Mash.

Engraved (1 colour), Plates of 300 subjects in panes of 50
Canadian Bank Note Company

**1967, Jul 19** **Perf 12**

| | | NH–VF | ⊙F | PB | FDC |
|---|---|---|---|---|---|
| **472** | **5¢ red** | .35 | .20 | | 2.00 |
| | plate blocks, plates 1, 2, all blocks | | | 1.75 | |

Qty: 28,060,000

The Fifth Pan-American Games, held in Winnipeg, July 22 to August 7.

## CANADIAN PRESS

**473**
Globe

Designer: William McLauchlan. Picture engraved by Allan Alexander Carswell.

Engraved (1 colour), Plates of 300 subjects in panes of 50
Canadian Bank Note Company

**1967, Aug 31** **Perf 12**

| | | NH–VF | ⊙F | PB | FDC |
|---|---|---|---|---|---|
| **473** | **5¢ deep ultramarine**, dull | .35 | .20 | | 2.00 |
| | plate blocks, plates 1, 2, all blocks | | | 1.75 | |
| i | F | 1.00 | .50 | 5.00 | |
| ii | NF | 2.00 | .50 | 10.00 | |

Qty: 27,460,000

Issued for the 50th anniversary of the Canadian Press.

## GEORGES VANIER

**474**
Governor-General Vanier

Designer: Harvey Thomas Prosser. Based on a photograph by Yousuf Karsh. Portrait engraved by Yves Baril. Lettering engraved by Donald J. Mitchell.

Engraved (1 colour) and Lithography, Plates of 300 subjects in panes of 50
Canadian Bank Note Company

**1967, Sep 15** **Perf 12**

| | | NH–VF | ⊙F | PB | FDC |
|---|---|---|---|---|---|
| **474** | **5¢ black**, dull | .40 | .20 | 2.00 | 2.00 |
| i | F | 4.00 | 1.00 | 20.00 | |

Qty: 25,460,000

Issued in memory of Georges P. Vanier (1888–1967). Governor-General of Canada, 1959–1967.
This was the first commemorative stamp issued in the new metric sizes.

## TORONTO CENTENARY

**475**
View of Modern Toronto

Designer: Harvey Thomas Prosser. Picture engraved by Yves Baril. Lettering engraved by Donald J. Mitchell.

Engraved (2 colours), Plates of 300 subjects in panes of 50
Canadian Bank Note Company

**1967, Sep 28** **Perf 12**

| | | NH–VF | ⊙F | PB | FDC |
|---|---|---|---|---|---|
| **475** | **5¢ slate green and salmon pink**, dull | .35 | .20 | | 2.00 |
| | plate blocks, plates 1, 2, all blocks | | | 1.75 | |
| i | F | 1.00 | .50 | | |
| | 475i, plate blocks, plates 1, 2, all blocks | | | 5.00 | |

Qty: 27,690,000

Centenary of Toronto as the capital of Ontario.

## CHRISTMAS – CHILDREN CAROLLING

476

477

Designer: George Sarras Fanais. Engraved by Yves Baril.
Engraved (1 colour), Plates of 600 subjects in six panes of 100
Canadian Bank Note Company

**1967, Oct 11** Perf 12

| | | NH–VF | ⊙F | PB | FDC |
|---|---|---|---|---|---|
| **476** | **3¢ carmine**, dull | .25 | .20 | | 2.00 |
| | plate blocks, plates 1, 2, all blocks | | | 1.25 | |
| i | No. 476, F | 1.00 | .50 | 5.00 | — |
| ii | No. 476, HF | 2.00 | 1.00 | 10.00 | — |
| a | No. 476, miniature pane of 25 (5 x 5) | 4.50 | 4.50 | — | 8.00† |
| as | single with straight edge, from 476a | .50 | .25 | | |
| ai | No. 476i, miniature pane of 25, F | 20.00 | 20.00 | — | 25.00† |
| ais | single with straight edge, from 476ai | 1.50 | .75 | | |
| aii | No. 476ii, miniature pane of 25, HF | 50.00 | 50.00 | — | 60.00† |
| aiis | single with straight edge, from 476aii | 3.00 | 1.50 | | |
| p | tagged, W2B | .30 | .20 | 1.50* | 2.50‡ |
| q | No. 476p, miniature pane of 25 (5 x 5), W2B | 6.00 | 6.00 | — | 10.00† |
| qs | single with straight edge, from 476q | .50 | .25 | | |

Qty: 183,820,000; Tagged: 8,500,000

| | | NH–VF | ⊙F | PB | FDC |
|---|---|---|---|---|---|
| **477** | **5¢ green**, dull | .25 | .20 | | 2.00 |
| | plate blocks, plate 1, all blocks | | | 1.50 | |
| | plate 2, all blocks | | | 1.25 | |
| i | F | 2.00 | .50 | 10.00 | |
| p | tagged, W2B | .40 | .30 | 2.00* | 3.00‡ |

Qty: 89,720,000; Tagged: 3,800,000
* Blank corner block of 4.
† Value shown is for First Day cancel on full pane, not on cover.
‡ With Winnipeg cancel; Ottawa *day of issue* cancel $7.50 (3¢) / $10.00 (5¢).
Commercial use on cover: $7.00.
Miniature panes were sold in Cello Paqs containing two panes of 25 (476a or 476q).

# 1968

## WILDLIFE

478
Gray Jays

Designer: Martin Glen Loates.
Lithography, pane of 50
Canadian Bank Note Company

**1968, Feb 15** Perf 12

| | | NH–VF | ⊙F | PB | FDC |
|---|---|---|---|---|---|
| **478** | **5¢ green, black and red** | .65 | .20 | 5.50 | 2.00 |
| i | "pine cone seed" variety (pos. 47) | 35.00 | 25.00 | 50.00* | 40.00† |

Qty: 24,300,000
* Block of 8.
† Any cover.
A "missing red colour resulting in Gray Jay's mouth being white instead of red" has been reported (one copy); value $750; Must have certificate.

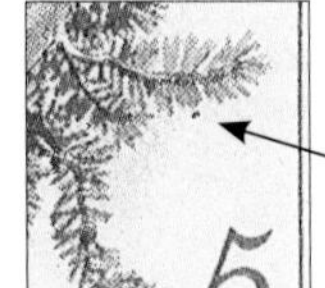
478i

479
Weather map and instruments

480
Narwhal

## METEOROLOGY

Designer: George Sarras Fanais. Modeled by Harvey Thomas Prosser.
Lithography, pane of 50
British American Bank Note Company

**1968, Mar 13** Perf 11

| | | NH–VF | ⊙F | PB | FDC |
|---|---|---|---|---|---|
| **479** | **5¢ dark and light blue, yellow, red**, dull | .35 | .20 | 1.75 | 2.00 |
| i | HB | 2.50 | .35 | 12.50 | 3.00 |
| ii | HB, "red over blue" variety ‡ | 20.00 | 10.00 | 90.00* | — |
| iii | "red over blue variety", dull paper | 10.00 | 5.00 | 40.00* | |

Qty: 24,600,000
‡ Red edge of dish appears to be printed on top of blue weather vane.
* Blank corner block of 4. Plate blocks of 479iii have been reported.

Bicentenary of the first meteorological readings in Canada.

## WILDLIFE

Designer: John Alexander Crosby.
Lithography, pane of 50
British American Bank Note Company

**1968, Apr 10** Perf 11

| | | NH–VF | ⊙F | PB | FDC |
|---|---|---|---|---|---|
| **480** | **5¢ multicoloured**, MF | .35 | .20 | 1.75 | 2.00 |
| i | dull | 2.50 | 1.00 | 12.50 | 3.00 |
| ii | F | 2.00 | .75 | 10.00 | |

Qty: 24,150,000

Several strips of 3, badly misperforated, exist in black only. All have gum disturbance and some are creased: value $500–$1,500 depending on condition. These are "printer's waste".

Blue shades on the Narwhal are caused by exposure to light. They are not legitimate colour varieties.

## UNITED NATIONS INTERNATIONAL HYDROLOGICAL DECADE

481
Rain Gauge

Designer: Imre von Mosdossy.
Lithography, pane of 50
British American Bank Note Company

**1968, May 8** Perf 11

| | | NH–VF | ⊙F | PB | FDC |
|---|---|---|---|---|---|
| **481** | **5¢ multicoloured**, dull | .35 | .20 | 1.75 | 2.00 |
| i | HB | 3.00 | .50 | 15.00 | 3.00 |
| ii | "sunspot" variety (pos. 27) (small brown dot in sun at UL) | 10.00 | — | — | — |

Qty: 24,000,000

Issued to underline Canada's participation in the International Hydrological Decade sponsored by UNESCO.

## 1668 VOYAGE OF THE NONSUCH

482
Nonsuch

Designer: George Sarras Fanais. Picture engraved by George Arthur Gundersen.
Engraved (1 colour) and Photogravure, pane of 50
British American Bank Note Company

**1968, Jun 5** **Perf 10.0**

| | | NH–VF | ⊙F | PB | FDC |
|---|---|---|---|---|---|
| **482** | **5¢ dark blue and multicoloured** | .35 | .20 | 1.75 | 2.00 |

Qty: 24,560,000

Issued to mark the 300th anniversary of the voyage of the Nonsuch.

Canada's first comb-perforated commemorative. The so-called "pink waves" variety is the result of a colour shift.

483
Lacrosse players

484
George Brown, "Globe" and Legislature

## LACROSSE

Designer: James E. Aldridge.
Engraved (1 colour) and Photogravure, pane of 50
British American Bank Note Company

**1968, Jul 3** **Perf 10.0**

| | | NH–VF | ⊙F | PB | FDC |
|---|---|---|---|---|---|
| **483** | **5¢ yellow, black and red** | .35 | .20 | 1.75 | 2.00 |
| i | kiss print, doubling of red | 50.00 | | | |

Qty: 24,560,000

The Indian game of Lacrosse is Canada's national sport.

## GEORGE BROWN

Designer: Nickolay Sabolotny.
Engraved (1 colour) and Photogravure, pane of 50
British American Bank Note Company

**1968, Aug 21** **Perf 10.0**

| | | NH–VF | ⊙F | PB | FDC |
|---|---|---|---|---|---|
| **484** | **5¢ multicoloured** | .35 | .20 | 1.75 | 2.00 |

Qty: 24,000,000

Issued to honour journalist and politician George Brown (1818–1880) on the 150th anniversary of his birth.

**BABN Printings (1968–1970)**

The BABN "experimented" with their stamp printing during this time period. One part of this was the introduction of "perf 10" commemorative stamps (Sc. 482, 483, 484, and 490). This is a very coarse perforation. Specimens of these stamps, with ***sound*** perforations all around, will command a premium.

Most of the BABN issues in this time period will result in a stamp that can have one or two straight edges. Panes produced with inscriptions (philatelic stock) will have one side of the pane without selvedge (i.e. a straight edged stamp); panes produced without inscriptions (field stock) will have a straight edge on three sides of the pane.

485
Bourassa and Le Devoir

486
Canadian Vimy Memorial, near Arras, France

## HENRI BOURASSA

Designer: Harvey Thomas Prosser. Engraved by Yves Baril.
Engraved (1 colour) and Lithography, pane of 100
Canadian Bank Note Company

**1968, Sep 4** **Perf 12**

| | | NH–VF | ⊙F | PB | FDC |
|---|---|---|---|---|---|
| **485** | **5¢ vermilion, buff and black,** HF paper | .35 | .20 | 1.75 | 2.00 |

Qty: 24,350,000

Issued to honour Henri Bourassa (1868–1952), founder of Le Devoir and Quebec nationalist.

## ARMISTICE

Designer: Harvey Thomas Prosser. Picture engraved by Yves Baril. Lettering engraved by Gordon Mash. Based on a sculpture by Walter Seymour Allward.
Engraved (1 colour), pane of 50
Canadian Bank Note Company

**1968, Oct 15** **Perf 12**

| | | NH–VF | ⊙F | PB | FDC |
|---|---|---|---|---|---|
| **486** | **15¢ slate** | 2.75 | 1.75 | 13.75 | 3.00† |

Qty: 18,250,000
† Single Trans-Atlantic on cover $10.

Issued to mark the 50th anniversary of Armistice ending World War I.

## JOHN McCRAE

487
John McCrae and poem

Designer: Imre von Mosdossy.
Engraved (1 colour) and Lithography, pane of 50
Canadian Bank Note Company

**1968, Oct 15** **Perf 12**

| | | NH–VF | ⊙F | PB | FDC |
|---|---|---|---|---|---|
| **487** | **5¢ multicoloured** | .35 | .20 | 1.75 | 2.00 |
| i | stroke in A of CANADA, on all stamps from the first column of all panes (most also have a dot in the top of the "A") | 3.50 | 2.50 | 10.00 | 6.00 |

Qty: 24,000,000

Many minor printing varieties exist for this stamp. Values $2–$10 in most cases. "McCRAB" variety (deformed E appears as B) $50.00.

Issued on the 50th anniversary of the death of Lt. Col. John McCrae (1872–1918), author of *In Flanders Fields*.

487i

| Rates: | Domestic: 6¢ (0–1 oz), 10¢ (1–2 oz) | single usage: |
|---|---|---|
| Nov 1, 1968 – | 3rd class (0–2 oz): 5¢ | USA air 10¢: 10.00 |
| Jun 30, 1971 | USA: 6¢ (0–1 oz), 10¢ (1–2 oz) | |
| | International (surface): 6¢/12¢ (0–1 oz), 10¢/19¢ (1–2 oz) | International air 10¢: $20.00 |
| | Registration: 50¢ for $50; 75¢ for $100 | 15¢: $15.00 |
| | Special delivery: 40¢ | 25¢: $25.00 |

## CHRISTMAS – INUIT SOAPSTONE CARVING

**488**
Eskimo Family

**489**
Mother and infant

Designer: Harvey Thomas Prosser. Based on a sculpture by Mary Irqiquq Sorusiluk. Based on a photograph by George Swinton.

Photogravure (2 colours), panes of 100
Canadian Bank Note Company

**1968, Nov 1** **Perf 12**

| | | NH–VF | ⊙F | PB | FDC |
|---|---|---|---|---|---|
| **488** | **5¢ bright blue and black** | .25 | .20 | 1.25 | 2.00 |
| **p** | tagged, WCB, *Nov 15, 1968* | .30 | .25 | 1.50* | 2.50‡ |

Qty: 151,700,000; Tagged: 5,900,000

| | | | | | |
|---|---|---|---|---|---|
| a | booklet pane of 10 x 5¢ (488as), (5 x 2) selvedge at left (BK72a) | 4.00 | 4.00 | — | 15.00† |
| ai | as "a", selvedge at right (BK72b) | 4.00 | 4.00 | — | 15.00† |
| as | single with straight edge, from 488a or 488ai | .45 | .20 | — | — |
| q | booklet pane of 10 x 5¢ (488qs), (5 x 2), tagged WCB, selvedge at left (BK72c), *Nov 15, 1968* | 5.00 | 5.00 | — | 16.00† |
| qi | as "q", selvedge at right (BK72d) | 5.00 | 5.00 | — | 16.00† |
| qs | single with straight edge, from 488q or 488qi | .75 | .60 | — | — |

BK72 2 panes 488a in bilingual cover 11/15/68 (3,448,000) $9.00

† Price shown is for a used pane with First Day of Issue cancel, not on cover.

| | | | | | |
|---|---|---|---|---|---|
| **489** | **6¢ deep bistre and black,** *Nov 15, 1968* | .30 | .20 | 1.50 | 2.00 |
| **p** | tagged, W2B, *Nov 15, 1968* | .35 | .25 | 1.75* | 3.00‡ |

Qty: 71,000,000; Tagged: 3,000,000

* Blank corner block of 4.

‡ With Winnipeg cancel; Ottawa *day of issue* cancel $7.50 (5¢) / $7.50 (6¢).
Commercial use on cover: $6.00.

488a 488ai

## 1969

## CURLERS

**490**
Curlers on rink

Designer: David Eales.

Engraved (1 colour) and Photogravure, pane of 50
British American Bank Note Company

**1969, Jan 15** **Perf 10.0**

| | | NH–VF | ⊙F | PB | FDC |
|---|---|---|---|---|---|
| **490** | **6¢ black, bright blue and carmine**, F | .25 | .20 | 1.60 | 2.00 |
| i | dull | 3.00 | 1.00 | 15.00 | 3.00 |

Qty: 25,200,000

## VINCENT MASSEY

**491**
Vincent Massey

Designer: Imre von Mosdossy. Engraved by Yves Baril.

Engraved (1 colour) and Lithography, pane of 50
Canadian Bank Note Company

**1969, Feb 20** **Perf 12**

| | | NH–VF | ⊙F | PB | FDC |
|---|---|---|---|---|---|
| **491** | **6¢ yellow olive and dark brown** | .30 | .20 | 1.50 | 2.00 |

Qty: 25,100,000

Issued in memory of Vincent Massey (1887–1967), first Canadian-born Governor General (1952–1959).

## SUZOR-CÔTÉ

**492**
Return from the Harvest Field

Based on a painting by Marc-Aurèle de Foy Suzor-Côté.

Photogravure (4 colours), Plates of 200 subjects in four panes of 50
Canadian Bank Note Company

**1969, Mar 14** **Perf 12**

| | | NH–VF | ⊙F | PB | FDC |
|---|---|---|---|---|---|
| **492** | **50¢ multicoloured** | 5.00 | 3.50 | 25.00 | 6.00* |
| i | "line from knee" variety (pos. 41 [D]) | 25.00 | 12.00 | 50.00† | 12.00 |
| ii | 'bird in sky' variety (pos. 36 [D]) | 25.00 | 12.00 | | 12.00 |
| iii | 'low moon' variety (pos. 5 [A]) | 25.00 | 12.00 | 50.00‡ | 12.00 |

Qty: 6,300,000

* Registered cover with 5¢ stamp $10.

† Value listed is for LL plate block containing variety 492i.

‡ Value listed is for UR plate block containing variety 492iii.

Plate Proofs: i) TC (Trial Colour) yellow, ii) TC magenta, iii) TC cyan (blue), iv) brown inscriptions, v) orange (yellow + magenta), vi) complete painting with cyan added, vii) finished proof with inscriptions added. Set of 7 proofs $1,500.00. Individual proof singles from broken sets $200 each. The finished state $400 each. Pairs pro-rata. Set of 7 corner blocks of 4 $7,500.00.

492i

492ii

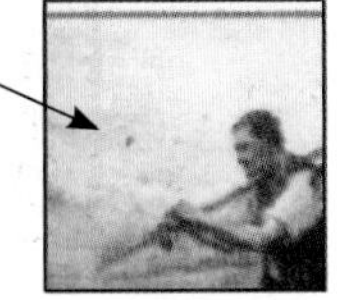

492iii

QE II — 1960's

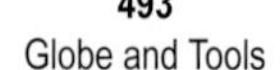

493
Globe and Tools

494
Vickers Vimy over Atlantic

## I.L.O.

Designer: Julien Hébert. Picture engraved by George Arthur Gundersen.
Engraved (1 colour), pane of 50
British American Bank Note Company

**1969, May 21** **Perf 12.0x12.5**

| | | NH–VF | ⊙F | PB | FDC |
|---|---|---|---|---|---|
| 493 | **6¢ dark olive green**, HB | .35 | .20 | 1.75 | 2.00 |
| i | dull | 2.50 | 1.00 | 12.50 | 3.00 |

Qty: 30,700,000

Issued to mark the 50th anniversary of the International Labour Organization.

## ALCOCK-BROWN FLIGHT

Designer: Robert William Bradford. Engraved by Charles Gordon Yorke.
Engraved (1 colour) and Photogravure, pane of 50
British American Bank Note Company

**1969, Jun 13** **Perf 12.0x12.5**

| | | NH–VF | ⊙F | PB | FDC |
|---|---|---|---|---|---|
| 494 | **15¢ red brown, yellow green and light ultramarine**, dull | 2.50 | 2.00 | 12.50 | 3.00 |
| i | F | 10.00 | 5.00 | 50.00 | 5.00 |

Qty: 15,170,000

## SIR WILLIAM OSLER

495
Sir William Osler

Designer: George Sarras Fanais. Based on a sketch by John Singer Sargent. Engraved by Charles Gordon Yorke.
Engraved (1 colour) and Photogravure, pane of 50
British American Bank Note Company

**1969, Jun 23** **Perf 12.5x12.0**

| | | NH–VF | ⊙F | PB | FDC |
|---|---|---|---|---|---|
| 495 | **6¢ dark blue and light red brown**, dull | .35 | .20 | 1.75 | 2.00 |
| i | HB | 2.25 | 1.00 | 11.25 | 3.00 |
| ii | horiz. gutter pair, partial imperf. | *2,000.00* | | | |

Qty: 36,060,000

Issued on the 50th anniversary of the death of the noted physician, Sir William Osler.

495ii

## BIRDS

496
White Throated Sparrow

497
Ipswich Sparrow

498
Hermit Thrush

Designer: Martin Glen Loates.
Lithography (4 colours), panes of 50
Canadian Bank Note Company

**1969, Jul 23** **Perf 12**

| | | NH–VF | ⊙F | PB | FDC |
|---|---|---|---|---|---|
| 496 | **6¢ multicoloured** | .50 | .20 | 2.50 | 2.00 |
| i | "flycatcher" variety (pos. 41) | 40.00 | 30.00 | 60.00 | 75.00 |

Qty: 36,350,000

| | | NH–VF | ⊙F | PB | FDC |
|---|---|---|---|---|---|
| 497 | **10¢ ultramarine and multicoloured** | 1.00 | .60 | 5.00 | 2.00‡ |
| i | "extra leaf" variety (pos. 41) | 5.00 | 4.00 | 20.00 | 10.00 |

Qty: 12,950,000
‡ Commercial use on cover: $10.00.

| | | NH–VF | ⊙F | PB | FDC |
|---|---|---|---|---|---|
| 498 | **25¢ black and multicoloured** | 2.50 | 2.25 | 12.50 | 3.00‡ |

Qty: 6,700,000
‡ Commercial use on cover: $20.00.

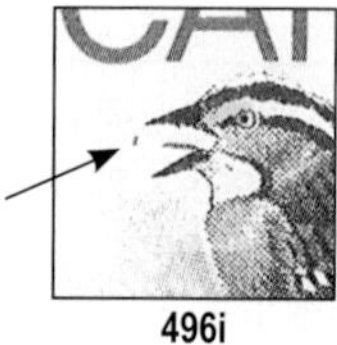

496i

497i

## CHARLOTTETOWN BICENTENNIAL

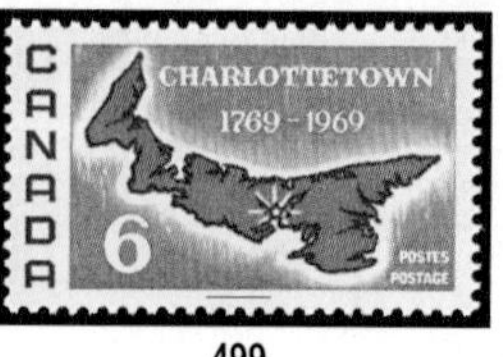

499
Map of Prince Edward Island

Designer: Lloyd Fitzgerald.
Engraved (1 colour) and Photogravure (2 colours), pane of 50
British American Bank Note Company

**1969, Aug 15** **Perf 12.0x12.5**

| | | NH–VF | ⊙F | PB | FDC |
|---|---|---|---|---|---|
| 499 | **6¢ ultramarine, orange brown and black**, HB | .35 | .20 | 1.75 | 2.00 |
| i | dull | 2.00 | 1.00 | 10.00 | 3.00 |

Qty: 16,400,000

Issued for the 200th anniversary of Charlottetown as capital of P.E.I.

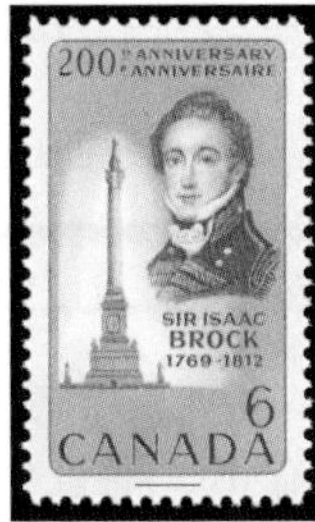

500
Flags of Summer and Winter Games

501
Brock and Monument

## CANADA GAMES

Designer: Carleton McDiarmid. Picture engraved by Yves Baril. Lettering engraved by Donald J. Mitchell.

Engraved (1 colour) and Lithography (3 colours), pane of 50
Canadian Bank Note Company

**1969, Aug 15** **Perf 12**

| | | NH–VF | ⊙F | PB | FDC |
|---|---|---|---|---|---|
| **500** | **6¢ ultramarine, bright green and red** | .30 | .20 | 1.50 | 2.00 |

Qty: 24,250,000

## SIR ISAAC BROCK

Designer: Imre von Mosdossy. Engraved by Yves Baril.

Engraved (1 colour) and Lithography (2 colours), pane of 50
Canadian Bank Note Company

**1969, Sep 12** **Perf 12**

| | | NH–VF | ⊙F | PB | FDC |
|---|---|---|---|---|---|
| **501** | **6¢ yellow brown, brown and pale salmon** | .30 | .20 | 1.50 | 2.00 |

Qty: 35,100,000

Issued on the 200th anniversary of the birth of Sir Isaac Brock, military leader in Upper Canada, killed at the Battle of Queenston Heights.

## CHRISTMAS – CHILDREN PRAYING

502 503

Designer: Designed by Rapid Grip and Batten Limited.

Lithography (4 colours), Plates of 400 subjects in panes of 100
Canadian Bank Note Company

**1969, Oct 8** **Perf 12**

| | | NH–VF | ⊙F | PB | FDC |
|---|---|---|---|---|---|
| **502** | **5¢ blue and multicoloured** | .25 | .20 | 1.25 | 2.00 |
| **i** | black arc by chin (pos. 5) | 10.00 *EP* | 4.00 | | |
| **ii** | black reverse offset on gum side | 150.00 | | 800.00¤ | |
| **p** | tagged, WCB | .35 | .20 | 1.75 | 2.50‡ |
| **pi** | as "p", black arc by chin (pos. 5) | 15.00 *EP* | 5.00 | | |

Qty: 170,500,000; Tagged: 7,750,000
¤ Blank corner block of 4.

| | | NH–VF | ⊙F | PB | FDC |
|---|---|---|---|---|---|
| a | booklet pane of 10 x 5¢ (502as), selvedge at left (5 x 2) (BK73a) | 4.00 | 4.00 | — | 15.00* |
| ai | as "a", selvedge at right (BK73b) | 4.00 | 4.00 | — | 15.00* |
| as | single with straight edge, from 502a or 502ai | .45 | .40 | — | — |
| aii | as "a", w/black arc by chin (pos. 5) | 25.00 | — | — | — |
| asi | black arc by chin (pos. 5), single from 502aii** | 20.00 | 7.50 | — | — |
| q | booklet pane of 10 x 5¢ (502qs), selvedge at left (5 x 2), WCB (BK73c) | 5.00 | 5.00 | — | 20.00* |
| qi | as "a", selvedge at right (BK73d) | 5.00 | 5.00 | — | 20.00* |
| qs | single with straight edge, from 502q or 502qi | .75 | .50 | — | — |
| qii | as "q", w/black arc by chin (pos. 5) | 30.00 | — | — | — |
| qsi | black arc by chin (pos. 5), single from 502qii** | 25.00 | 10.00 | — | — |

**BK73** 2 panes 502a in bilingual cover $9.00
* Price shown is for a used pane with First Day of Issue cancel, not on cover.
** single stamp with variety from booklet pane has straight edge at top and right.

| | | NH–VF | ⊙F | PB | FDC |
|---|---|---|---|---|---|
| **503** | **6¢ red and multicoloured** | .25 | .20 | 1.25 | 2.00 |
| **i** | "accent" above O in NOEL (pos. 39) | 15.00 *EP* | 5.00 | | |
| **a** | black omitted (400 copies known§) | 2,500.00 | 2,250.00 | 12,500.00* | 4,000* |
| **p** | tagged, W2B | .30 | .25 | 2.00 | 3.00‡ |
| **pi** | as 503p, "accent" above O in NOEL | 20.00 | 6.00 | | 15.00† |

Qty: 99,950,000; Tagged: 3,000,000
§ 204 copies are in the Library and Archives Canada including a full pane of 100.
* For blank corner block and ordinary cover (not FDC) 6 or 7 known.
† Price is for usage on any cover, not FDC.
‡ With Winnipeg cancel; Ottawa *day of issue* cancel $7.50 (5¢) / $7.50 (6¢).
Commercial use on cover: $6.00.

Plate Proofs: Both values, one on either side of two-sided proof, $250.00
Gutter block of 8 of these proofs $2,500.00
Gutter block of 8 with plate imprint $3,500.00

502i, 502pi, 502asi, 502qsi

502a

502ai

502ii

503a

503i

## STEPHEN LEACOCK

504
Leacock and Mariposa

Designer: George Sarras Fanais. Based on a photograph by Yousuf Karsh. Portrait engraved by George Arthur Gundersen.

Engraved (1 colour) and Photogravure (3 colours), pane of 50
British American Bank Note Company

**1969, Nov 12** **Perf 12.0x12.5**

| | | NH–VF | ⊙F | PB | FDC |
|---|---|---|---|---|---|
| **504** | **6¢ multicoloured** | .35 | .20 | 1.75 | 2.00 |

Qty: 35,500,000

Issued to mark the birth centenary of Stephen Leacock, humourist, historian and economist.

## 1970

### MANITOBA CENTENNIAL

505
"Crossroads of Canada"

Designer: Kenneth Campbell Lochhead.

Lithography (3 colours), pane of 50
Canadian Bank Note Company

**1970, Jan 27** **Perf 12**

| | | NH–VF | ⊙F | PB | FDC |
|---|---|---|---|---|---|
| **505** | **6¢ violet blue and multicoloured** | .30 | .20 | 1.50 | 2.00 |
| p | tagged, W2B | .40 | .20 | 2.00* | 3.00‡ |

Qty: 27,075,000; Tagged: 9,900,000

* Blank corner block of 4.

‡ With Winnipeg cancel; Ottawa *day of issue* cancel $7.50. Commercial use on cover: $5.00.

Issued to mark the centenary of the Province of Manitoba.

### NORTHWEST TERRITORIES CENTENNIAL

506
Enchanted Owl, by Kenojuak

Designer: Norman E. Hallendy and Sharon Van Raalte. Based on a stonecut print by Kenojuak Ashevak.

Engraved (2 colours), pane of 100
Canadian Bank Note Company

**1970, Jan 27** **Perf 12**

| | | NH–VF | ⊙F | PB | FDC |
|---|---|---|---|---|---|
| **506** | **6¢ dark red and black** | .30 | .20 | 1.50 | 2.00 |

Qty: 27,600,000

Issued to mark the centenary of the Northwest Territories.

### UNITED NATIONS BIOLOGICAL PROGRAMME

507
Interior of a Leaf

Designer: Israel Charney.

Engraved (1 colour) and Photogravure (2 colours), pane of 50
British American Bank Note Company

**1970, Feb 18** **Perf 12.0x12.5**

| | | NH–VF | ⊙F | PB | FDC |
|---|---|---|---|---|---|
| **507** | **6¢ green, light orange and blue** | .30 | .20 | 1.50 | 2.00 |

Qty: 34,155,000

Canada's participation in the International Biological Programme, 1967–1972.

### EXPO '70

508 Expo '67 and Expo '70 Emblems — 509 Dogwood (British Columbia)

510 White Garden Lily (Quebec) — 511 White Trillium (Ontario)

Designer: Edward R.C. Bethune.

Lithography, pane of 50
Canadian Bank Note Company

**1970, Mar 18** **Perf 12**

| | | NH–VF | ⊙F | PB | FDC |
|---|---|---|---|---|---|
| **508** | **25¢ red emblem** | 3.00 | 3.00 | | 3.00† |
| i | identical pair | 6.50 | 6.50 | | 8.50 |
| p | tagged, W2B | 3.50 | 3.50 | | 5.00‡ |
| ii | W2B, identical pair | 7.50 | 7.50 | | |
| **509** | **25¢ violet emblem** | 3.00 | 3.00 | | 3.00† |
| i | identical strip of 3 | 10.00 | 10.00 | | 12.00 |
| p | tagged, W2B | 3.50 | 3.50 | | 5.00‡ |
| ii | W2B, identical strip of 3 | 11.00 | 11.00 | | |
| **510** | **25¢ green emblem** | 3.00 | 3.00 | | 3.00† |
| p | tagged, W2B | 3.50 | 3.50 | | 5.00‡ |
| **511** | **25¢ blue emblem** | 3.00 | 3.00 | | 3.00† |
| i | identical strip of 3 | 10.00 | 10.00 | | 12.00 |
| p | tagged, W2B | 3.50 | 3.50 | | 5.00‡ |
| ii | W2B, identical strip of 3 | 11.00 | 11.00 | | |
| **511a** | se-tenant block of 4 (508–511) | 12.50 | 12.50 | 15.00 | 15.00 |
| b | W2B, se-tenant block (508p–511p) | 15.00 | 15.00 | 17.50* | 13.50§ |

Qty: 2,548,000 (#508), 2,184,000 (each of #509–511); Tagged: 532,000 (#508p), 456,000 (each of #509p–511p)

* Blank corner block of 4.

† Commercial use on cover: $8.00.

‡ With Winnipeg cancel; Ottawa *day of issue* cancel $15.00. Commercial use on cover: $12.00.

§ With Winnipeg cancel; Ottawa *day of issue* cancel $40.00.

Issued to mark Expo '70 in Osaka, Japan, in se-tenant sheets of 50, with various combinations possible.

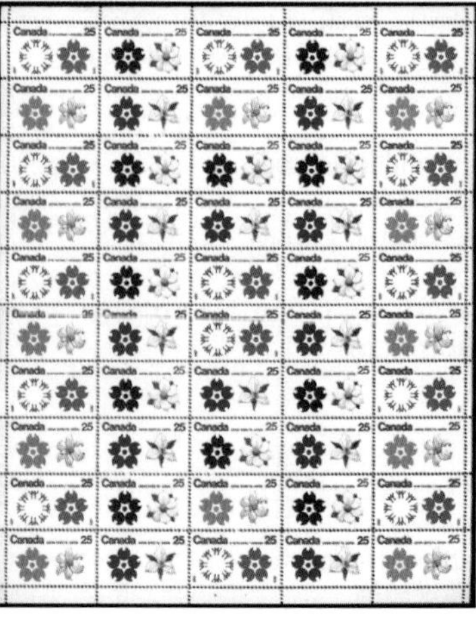

508–511
Full pane of 50

## HENRY KELSEY

**512**
Henry Kelsey

Designer: Dennis Eugene Norman Burton. Engraved by George Arthur Gundersen.
Engraved (1 colour) and Photogravure (3 colours), pane of 50
British American Bank Note Company

**1970, Apr 15** **Perf 12.0x12.5**

| | | NH–VF | ⊙F | PB | FDC |
|---|---|---|---|---|---|
| **512** | **6¢ multicoloured** | .30 | .20 | 1.50 | 2.00 |

Qty: 36,450,000

Issued to mark the 300th birth anniversary of western explorer, Henry Kelsey.

## UNITED NATIONS

**513**
Energy Unification

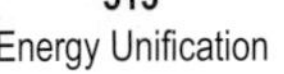

**514**
Energy Unification

Designer: Brian Fisher.
Lithography (2 colours), panes of 50
British American Bank Note Company

**1970, May 13** **Perf 11**

| | | NH–VF | ⊙F | PB | FDC |
|---|---|---|---|---|---|
| **513** | **10¢ blue**, dull | 1.00 | .80 | 5.00 | 2.00 |
| i | F | 4.00 | 3.20 | 20.00 | |
| p | tagged, W2B | 1.25 | 1.25 | 6.25* | 3.50† |
| ii | F, W2B | 2.00 | 2.00 | 10.00* | |

Qty: 12,200,000; Tagged: 700,000
† With Winnipeg cancel; Ottawa *day of issue* cancel $10.00. Commercial use on cover: $8.00.

| | | NH–VF | ⊙F | PB | FDC |
|---|---|---|---|---|---|
| **514** | **15¢ lilac and dark red**, dull | 1.50 | 1.00 | 7.50 | 2.00 |
| i | F | 4.00 | 3.00 | 20.00 | |
| p | tagged, W2B | 2.00 | 2.00 | 15.00* | 4.00‡ |
| ii | F, W2B | 5.00 | 5.00 | 25.00* | |

Qty: 11,800,000; Tagged: 700,000
* Blank corner block of 4.
‡ With Winnipeg cancel; Ottawa *day of issue* cancel $12.50. Commercial use on cover: $12.00.

Issued to mark the 25th anniversary of the United Nations.

**515**
Louis Riel

**516**
Carved Inscription

## LOUIS RIEL

Designer: Reinhard Derreth. Based on a photograph by William James Topley.
Photogravure (2 colours), pane of 50
British American Bank Note Company

**1970, Jun 19** **Perf 12.5x12.0**

| | | NH–VF | ⊙F | PB | FDC |
|---|---|---|---|---|---|
| **515** | **6¢ red and bright blue** | .30 | .20 | 1.50 | 2.00 |

Qty: 37,000,000

Issued to honour Louis Riel (1844–1885), Métis leader of the Red River and Northwest Rebellions, who was hanged as a traitor by the Canadian Government.

## SIR ALEXANDER MACKENZIE

Designer: Eiko Emori and Harvey Thomas Prosser. Designed and engraved by Yves Baril.
Engraved (1 colour), pane of 50
Canadian Bank Note Company

**1970, Jun 25** **Perf 12**

| | | NH–VF | ⊙F | PB | FDC |
|---|---|---|---|---|---|
| **516** | **6¢ brown** | .30 | .20 | 1.50 | 2.00 |

Qty: 35,500,000

Issued to mark the 150th anniversary of the death of Sir Alexander Mackenzie, first white man to cross the Canadian prairies and reach the Pacific coast.

**517**
Mowat and Parliament Buildings

**518**
*Isles of Spruce*, by Arthur Lismer

## SIR OLIVER MOWAT

Designer: Ernst Roch. Portrait engraved by George Arthur Gundersen.
Engraved (1 colour) and Photogravure (1 colour), pane of 50
British American Bank Note Company

**1970, Aug 12** **Perf 12.0x12.5**

| | | NH–VF | ⊙F | PB | FDC |
|---|---|---|---|---|---|
| **517** | **6¢ red and black** | .30 | .20 | 1.50 | 2.00 |

Qty: 35,200,000

Issued to mark the 150th anniversary of the birth of Sir Oliver Mowat, a Father of Confederation.

## GROUP OF SEVEN

Based on a painting by Arthur Lismer.
Lithography (5 colours), pane of 50
Ashton Potter Limited

**1970, Sep 18** **Perf 11**

| | | NH–VF | ⊙F | PB | FDC |
|---|---|---|---|---|---|
| **518** | **6¢ multicoloured** | .30 | .20 | 1.50 | 2.00 |
| i | "fire in bush" variety (pos. 42) | 5.00 *EP* | 3.50 | 6.00 | 5.00 |

Qty: 36,203,000

One pane (now split up), with diagonally shifted horizontal perforations, results in a couple of stamps with nearly missing inscriptions, leaving a wide white margin at bottom.

Issued to mark the 50th anniversary of the "Group of Seven," Canadian landscape artists.

**518i**

## CHRISTMAS

519
Santa Claus

520
Horse-drawn sleigh

521
Nativity

522
Children skiing

523
Snowmen and Christmas Tree

524
Christ Child

525
Children and Christmas Tree

526
Toy Store

527
Santa Claus

528
Church

529
Christ Child

530
Snowmobile and Trees

Designer: All the 1970 Christmas stamps were designed by Canadian school children.
Lithography (4 colours), panes of 100
Canadian Bank Note Company

**1970, Oct 7** Perf 12

| | | NH–VF | ⊙F | PB | FDC |
|---|---|---|---|---|---|
| **519** | **5¢ multicoloured** | .40 | .20 | | 2.00 |
| p | tagged, WCB | .45 | .20 | | 2.50‡ |

Designed by: Anthony Martin, Marius, MB (age 5)

| | | NH–VF | ⊙F | PB | FDC |
|---|---|---|---|---|---|
| **520** | **5¢ multicoloured** | .40 | .20 | | 2.00 |
| p | tagged, WCB | .45 | .20 | | 2.50‡ |

Designed by: Donna Niskala, Macrorie, SK (age 9)

| | | NH–VF | ⊙F | PB | FDC |
|---|---|---|---|---|---|
| **521** | **5¢ multicoloured** | .40 | .20 | | 2.00 |
| p | tagged, WCB | .45 | .20 | | 2.50‡ |

Designed by: Lisa Wilson, Kamloops, BC (age 8)

| | | NH–VF | ⊙F | PB | FDC |
|---|---|---|---|---|---|
| **522** | **5¢ multicoloured** | .40 | .20 | — | 2.00 |
| i | centre block of 4 (with 522iii) | 40.00 | 40.00 | — | 50.00 |
| ii | centre block of 4 (no 522iii) | 80.00 | 80.00 | — | 50.00 |
| iii | dot between 'M' and 'A' in CHRISTMAS (pos. 56) | 25.00 | 20.00 | | 20.00 |
| iv | diagonal slash in '5' (pos. 88) | 5.00 | 2.00 | | |
| p | tagged, WCB | .45 | .20 | — | 2.50‡ |
| pi | centre block of 4, WCB | 200.00 | 200.00 | — | 200.00 |
| pii | as "iii", WCB | 50.00 | 25.00 | | 30.00 |
| piii | as "iv", WCB | 5.00 | 2.00 | | |

Designed by: Dwayne Durham, Fort Erie, ON (age 7)

Nos. 522iii and 522pii occur on the LR stamp in centre block of 4. Most untagged centre blocks (5 out of 6 panes) show this variety.

522iii/pii

522iv/piii

523b (portion)

| | | NH–VF | ⊙F | PB | FDC |
|---|---|---|---|---|---|
| **523** | **5¢ multicoloured** | .40 | .20 | — | 2.00 |
| i | top of last 'S' of CHRISTMAS flat (pos. 80) | 5.00 | 2.00 | | |
| ii | red spot on cheek of snowman (pos. 54) | 5.00 | 2.00 | | |
| iii | blue "thread" on snowman (pos. 98) | 4.00 | 2.00 | | |
| p | tagged, WCB | .45 | .20 | — | 2.50‡ |
| pi | as "i", WCB | 7.50 | 2.50 | | |
| pii | as "ii", WCB | 7.50 | 2.50 | | |
| piii | as "iii", WCB | 7.50 | 3.50 | | |
| a | se-tenant strip of 5 (519–523) | 4.00 | 3.00 | — | 7.50 |
| | se-tenant block of 10 | 8.00 | 6.00 | 10.00 | 12.50 |
| b | 523a with black triple printed, 20 strips known | 750.00 | — | — | — |
| ap | se-tenant strip of 5, WCB (519p–523p) | 5.00 | 4.00 | — | 8.50§ |
| | se-tenant block of 10, WCB | 10.00 | 8.00 | 12.00* | 20.00 |

Designed by: Manon Lecompte, Laprairie, QC (age 9)
5¢ Qty: 46,560,000 of each design; Tagged: 2,600,000 of each design
§ With Winnipeg cancel; Ottawa *day of issue* cancel $25.00.

523i/pi

523ii/pii

523iii/piii

| | | NH–VF | ⊙F | PB | FDC |
|---|---|---|---|---|---|
| **524** | **6¢ multicoloured** | .50 | .20 | — | 2.00 |
| p | tagged, W2B | .55 | .20 | — | 3.00‡ |

Designed by: Janet Mckinney, Saint John, NB (age 8)

| | | NH–VF | ⊙F | PB | FDC |
|---|---|---|---|---|---|
| **525** | **6¢ multicoloured** | .50 | .20 | — | 2.00 |
| i | centre block of 4* | 40.00 | 40.00 | — | 50.00 |
| ii | scratch through window (pos. 45) | 5.00 | 2.00 | | |
| p | tagged, W2B | .55 | .20 | — | 3.00‡ |
| pi | centre block of 4, W2B* | 200.00 | 200.00 | — | 200.00 |
| pii | as "ii," W2B | 7.50 | 2.50 | | |

Designed by: Jean Pomperleau, St. Paul, AB (age 8)

* 525i exists with and without 525ii, 525pi exists with and without 525pii; add 50% for block with*out* the variety (much scarcer).

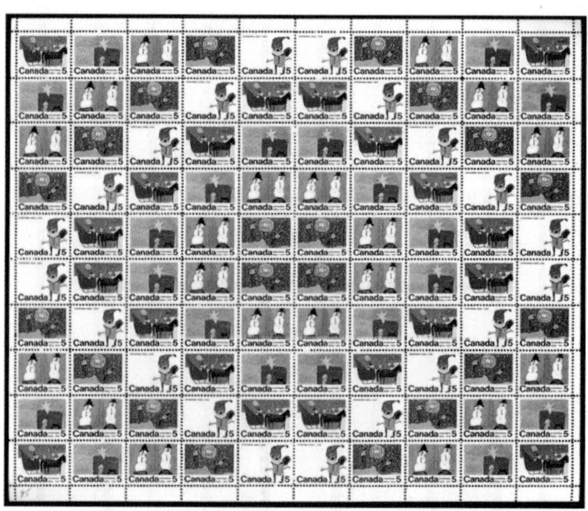
**519–523 full pane**

The 5¢ and 6¢ panes of 100 are arranged to produce 20 strips (523a or 528a). The middle two horizontal and vertical rows contain two vertical and two horizontal identical pairs of four of the designs with an identical block of four of the fifth design (522 or 525) at the centre of the pane.

| | | NH–VF | ⊙F | PB | FDC |
|---|---|---|---|---|---|
| **526** | **6¢ multicoloured** | .50 | .20 | — | 2.00 |
| p | tagged, W2B | .55 | .20 | — | 3.00‡ |

Designed by: Nancy Whatley, Armdale, NS (age 10)

| | | NH–VF | ⊙F | PB | FDC |
|---|---|---|---|---|---|
| **527** | **6¢ multicoloured** | .50 | .20 | — | 2.00 |
| p | tagged, W2B | .55 | .20 | — | 3.00‡ |

Designed by: Eugene Battacharya, St. John's, NF (age 7)

| | | NH–VF | ⊙F | PB | FDC |
|---|---|---|---|---|---|
| **528** | **6¢ multicoloured** | .50 | .20 | — | 2.00 |
| i | "flaming window" (pos. 17) | 5.00 | 2.00 | | |
| p | tagged, W2B | .55 | .20 | — | 3.00‡ |
| pi | as "i," W2B | 7.50 | 2.50 | | |
| a | se-tenant strip of 5 (524–528) | 4.50 | 3.50 | — | 7.50 |
| | se-tenant block of 10 | 9.00 | 7.00 | 10.00 | 12.50 |
| ap | se-tenant strip of 5, W2B (524p–528p) | 6.00 | 4.00 | — | 10.00§ |
| | se-tenant block of 10, W2B | 12.00 | 8.00 | 15.00* | 20.00 |

Designed by: Joseph MacMillan, Summerville, PEI (age 12)
6¢ Qty: 28,380,000 of each design; Tagged: 1,800,000 of each design

Horizontal and vertical identical pairs exist of each 5¢ and 6¢ stamp: value is 5 times the single price.

‡ With Winnipeg cancel; Ottawa *day of issue* cancel $7.50. Commercial use on cover: $5.00.

§ With Winnipeg cancel; Ottawa *day of issue* cancel $25.00.

525ii/pii

528i/pi

Lithography (4 colours), panes of 50

| | | NH–VF | ⊙F | PB | FDC |
|---|---|---|---|---|---|
| **529** | **10¢ multicoloured** | .60 | .50 | 3.00 | 3.00 |
| p | tagged, W2B | .70 | .60 | 3.50* | 3.50‡ |

Designed by: Corrine Fortier, St. Leon, MB (age 10)
Qty: 26,675,000; Tagged: 2,050,000

‡ With Winnipeg cancel; Ottawa *day of issue* cancel $10.00. Commercial use on cover: $13.00.

| | | NH–VF | ⊙F | PB | FDC |
|---|---|---|---|---|---|
| **530** | **15¢ multicoloured** | 1.25 | 1.25 | 6.25 | 4.00 |
| p | tagged, W2B | 1.50 | 1.50 | 7.50* | 4.00‡ |

Designed by: Janis Dojcak, Flin Flon, MB (age 10)
Qty: 20,000,000; Tagged: 2,000,000

‡ With Winnipeg cancel; Ottawa *day of issue* cancel $12.50. Commercial use on cover: $16.00.

| | NH–VF | ⊙F | PB | FDC |
|---|---|---|---|---|
| **Nos. 519–530** (12) Set | 6.35 | 3.25 | 29.25 | 15.00 |
| **Nos. 519p–530p** (12) Set | 7.20 | 3.60 | 38.00* | 25.00 |

* Blank corner block of 4.

All the 1970 Christmas stamps were designed by Canadian school children.
The prices shown for untagged set of 12 plate blocks and tagged set of 12 blank corner blocks are for blocks of 10 of the 5¢ and 6¢ values and blocks of 4 of the 10¢ and 15¢ values (total 28 stamps per set).

## SIR DONALD ALEXANDER SMITH

531

Based on a medallion by Dora de Pédery-Hunt.

Lithography (3 colours), panes of 100
Canadian Bank Note Company

**1970, Nov 4** **Perf 12**

| | | NH–VF | ⊙F | PB | FDC |
|---|---|---|---|---|---|
| **531** | **6¢ dark green, yellow and black** | .30 | .20 | 1.50 | 2.00 |

Qty: 35,400,000

Issued to mark the 150th birth anniversary of Sir Donald Alexander Smith, prime builder of the Canadian Pacific Railroad.

# 1971

## EMILY CARR

532
*Big Raven*, by Emily Carr

Designer: William Rueter.

Lithography (4 colours), panes of 50
Canadian Bank Note Company

**1971, Feb 12** **Perf 12**

| | | NH–VF | ⊙F | PB | FDC |
|---|---|---|---|---|---|
| **532** | **6¢ multicoloured** | .30 | .20 | 1.50 | 2.00 |
| i | "The Seven Sisters" (pos. 39) | 5.00 | 2.50 | 7.50 | |
| ii | "blue throat" (pos. 36) | 5.00 | 2.50 | | |

Qty: 27,250,000

Issued to mark the 100th birth anniversary of Emily Carr, painter and writer.

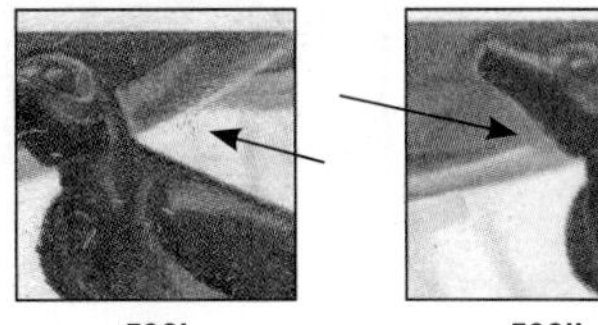
532i 532ii

533
Laboratory Equipment

534
Atom splitting

## DISCOVERY OF INSULIN

Designer: Ray Webber.

Lithography (4 colours), pane of 50
British American Bank Note Company

**1971, Mar 3** **Perf 11**

| | | NH–VF | ⊙F | PB | FDC |
|---|---|---|---|---|---|
| **533** | **6¢ multicoloured** | .30 | .20 | 1.50 | 2.00 |

Qty: 24,200,000

Issued to mark the 50th anniversary of the discovery of insulin by Drs. F.G. Banting and C.H. Best at the University of Toronto.

## ERNEST RUTHERFORD

Designer: Ray Webber.

Lithography (3 colours), pane of 50
British American Bank Note Company

**1971, Mar 24** **Perf 11**

| | | NH–VF | ⊙F | PB | FDC |
|---|---|---|---|---|---|
| **534** | **6¢ red, orange and black**, HB front | .30 | .20 | 1.50 | 2.00 |
| i | "missing atom" variety, "black" colour missing | *2,000.00* | — | — | — |
| ii | F front | 3.00 | .50 | 15.00 | |

Qty: 24,950,000

Issued on the 100th anniversary of the birth of Sir Ernest Rutherford, nuclear physicist.

**PLEASE NOTE**
**From No. 535 on, FDCs with cachets other than Canada Post command a premium.**

## MAPLE LEAVES IN FOUR SEASONS

535 Spring | 536 Summer

537 Autumn | 538 Winter

Designer: Alma Duncan.

Lithography (5 colours), panes of 50
Ashton-Potter Limited

**1971** **Perf 10.8x11.0**

| | | NH–VF | ⊙F | PB | FDC |
|---|---|---|---|---|---|
| **535** | **6¢ multicoloured**, *Apr 14, 1971* | .40 | .20 | 2.00 | 1.30 |
| i | "hook on 6" (pos. 15) | 13.00 *EP* | 6.00 | | 25.00 |
| ii | "green frog on leaf" (col. 5)* | 3.00 *EP* | .50 | | 10.00 |
| a | imperf. pair (75 pairs reported) | 1,200.00 | | 2,500.00† | |

Qty: 27,280,000

* Variety 535ii appears on every stamp in column 5 (pos. 5, 15, 25, 35, 45). Variety 535i and 535ii appear together on the same stamp.
† Value shown is for blank corner block. Plate blocks do not exist imperf.

| | | NH–VF | ⊙F | PB | FDC |
|---|---|---|---|---|---|
| **536** | **6¢ multicoloured**, *Jun 16, 1971* | .40 | .20 | 2.00 | 1.30 |

Qty: 26,440,000

| | | NH–VF | ⊙F | PB | FDC |
|---|---|---|---|---|---|
| **537** | **7¢ multicoloured**, LF, *Sep 3, 1971* | .40 | .20 | 2.00 | 1.35 |
| i | "grey" (inscriptions) missing | 4,000.00† | | | |
| ii | HB | 20.00 | | | |

Qty: 26,550,000

† Many counterfeits of 537i exist. Must have certificate of authenticity.

| | | NH–VF | ⊙F | PB | FDC |
|---|---|---|---|---|---|
| **538** | **7¢ multicoloured**, *Nov 19, 1971* | .40 | .20 | 2.00 | 1.35 |
| i | "double paper" in horiz. strip of 5 | 750.00 | | 1,500.00† | |
| ii | "snow bug" (pos. 49) | 5.00 *EP* | 2.50 | 7.50 | |

Qty: 26,000,000

† Value shown is for blank corner block of 10.

Nos. 535–538 all exist with vertical perforations through the top and bottom selvedge. Nos. 535–536 also exist with imperf. top selvedge. Nos. 537–538 also exist with imperf. top (scarce) and imperf. bottom (common) selvedge.

535i

535ii

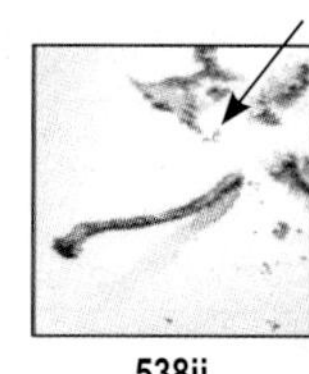

538ii

537i

## L.J. PAPINEAU

539
Louis Joseph Papineau

Designer: Laurent Marquart. Based on a drawing by Robert Auchmuty Sproule. Portrait engraved by George Arthur Gundersen.

Engraved (1 colour) and Photogravure (3 colours), pane of 50
British American Bank Note Company

**1971, May 7** **Perf 12.5x12.0**

| | | NH–VF | ⊙F | PB | FDC |
|---|---|---|---|---|---|
| **539** | **6¢ multicoloured**, dull/dull | .30 | .20 | 1.50 | 2.00 |
| i | "ghost" print, red doubled on "Canada 6", etc. | 50.00† | | | |
| ii | F/MF | 3.50 | — | 17.00 | |

Qty: 13,900,000

† Value shown is for strong (separate) second impression. Weak kiss prints showing only a shadow are worth approximately $10.00

Issued to mark the 100th anniversary of the death of Louis Joseph Papineau, French Canadian political reformist.

## SAMUEL HEARNE

540
Copper Mine River

Designer: Laurent Marquart. Engraved by Charles Gordon Yorke

Engraved (1 colour) and Photogravure (2 colours), pane of 50
British American Bank Note Company

**1971, May 7** **Perf 12.0x12.5**

| | | NH–VF | ⊙F | PB | FDC |
|---|---|---|---|---|---|
| **540** | **6¢ buff, red and brown** | .30 | .20 | 1.50 | 2.00 |
| i | "ghost" print, red doubled on "Samuel Hearne 1745-1792" | 40.00† | | | |
| ii | scratch beside south spoke (pos. 1/long; pos. 41) | 10.00 | 7.50 | | |

Qty: 14,300,000

† Value shown is for strong (separate) second impression. Weak kiss prints showing only a shadow are worth approximately $5.00

Issued for the bicentenary of Hearne's expedition to the Copper Mine River.

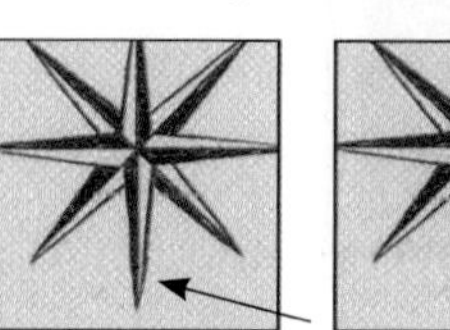

Short line (pos. 41)

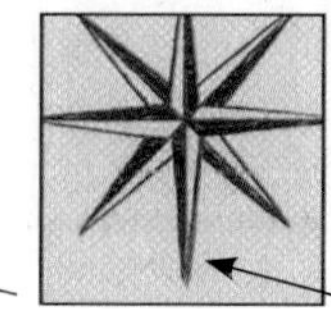

Medium line (pos. xx)

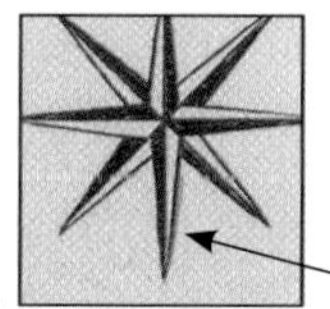

Long line (pos. 1)

## RADIO CANADA INTERNATIONAL

541
Maple Leaves

Designer: Burton Kramer.

Lithography (4 colours), pane of 50
Canadian Bank Note Company

**1971, Jun 1** **Perf 12**

| | | NH–VF | ⊙F | PB | FDC |
|---|---|---|---|---|---|
| **541** | **15¢ black, red orange and yellow** | 2.50 | 1.50 | 12.50 | 3.00 |
| **p** | tagged, W2B | 3.50 | 3.00 | 17.50* | 4.00‡ |
| **pi** | "bug on leaf", W2B | 150.00 | 110.00 | — | 150.00 |
| | 541pi, on centre stamp of block of 9 | 200.00 | 150.00 | — | 200.00 |

Qty: 9,825,000
* Blank corner block of 4.
‡ With Winnipeg cancel; Ottawa *day of issue* cancel $12.50. Commercial use on cover: $16.00.
Some Winnipeg tagged stamps exist that are wider (42mm) or narrower (38mm) than the normal (40mm) stamps due to a shift in the perforating wheel between the 4th and 5th columns on some panes.

Issued to mark the inauguration of new transmitters for Radio Canada International.

541pi

Variety 541pi is not "truly" constant and will likely be removed in a future edition.

## CENSUS

542
Computer Tape and Reels

Designer: Hans Kleefeld.

Lithography (3 colours), pane of 100
Canadian Bank Note Company

**1971, Jun 1** **Perf 12**

| | | NH–VF | ⊙F | PB | FDC |
|---|---|---|---|---|---|
| **542** | **6¢ black, ultramarine and red** | .30 | .20 | 1.50 | 2.00 |

Qty: 25,200,000

Issued to mark the centenary of Canada's first national census.

**For Nos. 543, 544, 549 and 550, see the Centennial definitives (Nos. 454–468B).**

Nos. 545–548 and 551 are not assigned.

| **Rates:** | Domestic: 7¢ (0–1 oz), 12¢ (1–2 oz) |
|---|---|
| Jul 1, 1971 – | 3rd class (0–2 oz): 6¢ |
| Dec 31, 1971 | USA: 7¢ (0–1 oz), 12¢ (1–2 oz) |
| | International: 15¢ (0–1 oz), 30¢ (1–2 oz) |
| | Registration: 50¢ for $50; 75¢ for $100 |
| | Special delivery: 40¢ |

*single usage:* USA air 10¢: 10.00 | International 15¢: $15.00

552
Stylized 'BC'

553
*Indian Encampment on Lake Huron*

## BRITISH COLUMBIA CENTENNIAL

Designer: Edward R.C. Bethune.

Lithography (4 colours), pane of 50
Canadian Bank Note Company

**1971, Jul 20** **Perf 12**

| | | NH–VF | ⊙F | PB | FDC |
|---|---|---|---|---|---|
| **552** | **7¢ multicoloured** | .30 | .20 | 1.50 | 1.35 |
| i | extra accent between "ER" (col. 2) | 1.50 | .50 | | |
| ii | dot under B of "BRITANNIQUE" (col. 3) | 1.50 | .50 | | |
| iii | dot between "BR" of "BRITISH" (pos. 35) | 5.00 | 2.50 | | |

Qty: 30,000,000

Issued to mark the 100th anniversary of British Columbia's entry into confederation.

552i 552ii 552iii

## PAUL KANE

Designer: William Rueter.

Lithography (4 colours), pane of 50
British American Bank Note Company

**1971, Aug 11** **Perf 12.5**

| | | NH–VF | ⊙F | PB | FDC |
|---|---|---|---|---|---|
| **553** | **7¢ multicoloured** | .55 | .20 | 4.00† | 1.35 |
| i | "stroke on teepee" variety | 1.50 *EP* | .50 | 5.00‡ | 5.00 |
| ii | "sun behind clouds" (pos. 29) | 7.50 | 5.00 | | |
| iii | "burr over shoulder" (pos. 9) | 7.50 | 5.00 | 10.00 | |

Qty: 25,200,000
† UR & LR imprint blocks.
‡ UL & LL imprint blocks. Variety 553i occurs on every stamp in left margin column.

Issued to mark the 100th anniversary of painter Paul Kane's death.

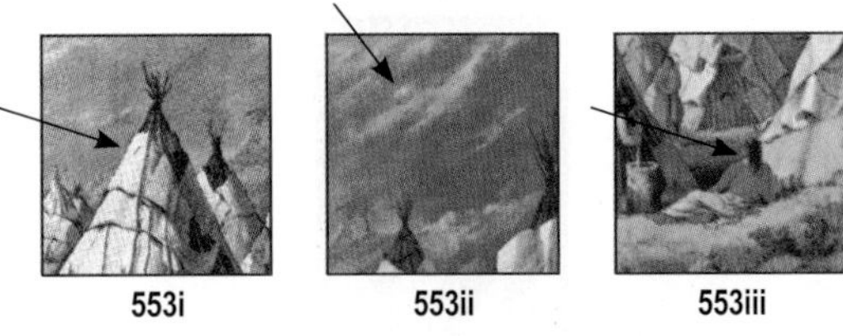

553i 553ii 553iii

## CHRISTMAS – SNOWFLAKES

554 555 556 557

Designer: Lisl Levinsohn.

Engraved (1 colour), panes of 100
Canadian Bank Note Company

**1971, Oct 6** Perf 12

| | | NH–VF | ⊙F | PB | FDC |
|---|---|---|---|---|---|
| 554 | **6¢ dark blue**, HB | .25 | .20 | | 1.30 |
| | plate blocks, plates 1, 2, all blocks | | | 1.25 | |
| i | dull | 1.00 | .50 | 5.00 | 2.00 |
| a | all colour omitted (from foldover) | *2,500.00* | | | |
| b | printed on gummed side (from foldover) | *1,500.00* | | | |
| p | tagged, WCB, HB | .35 | .20 | 1.75* | 3.00‡ |
| ii | dull, WCB | 1.50 | 1.00 | 7.50* | 3.00 |

Qty: 168,800,000; Tagged: 7,000,000

| | | NH–VF | ⊙F | PB | FDC |
|---|---|---|---|---|---|
| 555 | **7¢ bright green** | .30 | .20 | | 1.35 |
| | plate blocks, plates 1, 2, all blocks | | | 1.50 | |
| p | tagged, W2B | .45 | .20 | 2.25* | 3.00‡ |

Qty: 108,500,000; Tagged: 6,000,000

‡ With Winnipeg cancel; Ottawa *day of issue* cancel $7.50 (6¢) / $7.50 (7¢).

Engraved and Lithography, panes of 50

| | | NH–VF | ⊙F | PB | FDC |
|---|---|---|---|---|---|
| 556 | **10¢ deep carmine and silver** | .50 | .45 | 2.50 | 1.50 |
| i | ribbed, horiz. | 5.00 | 2.00 | 30.00 | |
| p | tagged, W2B | .60 | .50 | 3.00* | 3.50‡ |
| pi | tagged, W2B, ribbed, horiz. | 7.50 | 3.50 | 50.00* | |

Qty: 11,100,000; Tagged: 1,200,000

| | | NH–VF | ⊙F | PB | FDC |
|---|---|---|---|---|---|
| 557 | **15¢ light ultramarine, deep carmine, and silver** | 1.00 | 1.00 | 5.00 | 1.75† |
| i | ribbed, horiz. | 7.00 | 3.00 | 45.00 | |
| p | tagged, W2B | 1.25 | 1.25 | 6.25* | 4.00‡ |
| pi | tagged, W2B, ribbed, horiz. | 10.00 | 5.00 | 65.00* | |

Qty: 17,825,000; Tagged: 1,200,000

**Nos. 554–557 (4) Combination FDC** **20.00**

* Blank corner block of 4.
† Commercial use on cover: $10.
‡ With Winnipeg cancel; Ottawa *day of issue* cancel $10.00 (10¢) / $12.50 (15¢).
Commercial use on cover: 556p – $10.00; 557p – $15.00.

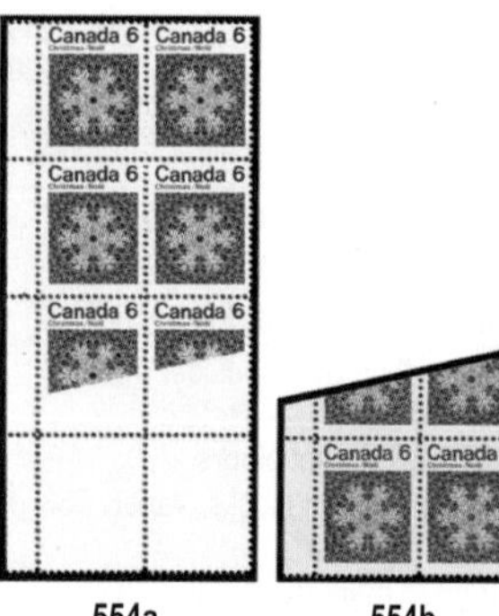


554a 554b

## PIERRE LAPORTE

558
Pierre Laporte

Designed and engraved by George Arthur Gundersen. Based on a photograph by Michel Giroux.

Engraved (1 colour), pane of 50
British American Bank Note Company

**1971, Oct 20** Perf 12.5x12.0

| | | NH–VF | ⊙F | PB | FDC |
|---|---|---|---|---|---|
| 558 | **7¢ black**, F | .35 | .20 | 3.25 | 1.35 |
| i | dull | 4.00 | .75 | 20.00 | |

Qty: 22,790,000

Issued in memory of Pierre Laporte, Quebec Minister of Labour, on the 1st anniversary of his murder by terrorists and on the 50th anniversary of his birth.

# 1972

**Rates:** Jan 1, 1972 – Aug 31, 1976
Domestic: 8¢ (0–1 oz), 14¢ (1–2 oz)
3rd class (0–2 oz): 6¢
USA: 8¢ (0–1 oz) [to 10¢ on Mar 1/72], 20¢ (1–2 oz)
International: 15¢ (0–1 oz), 30¢ (1–2 oz) [from Jul 1/71]

559
Figure Skaters

560
Heart

## FIGURE SKATING

Designer: Design Workshop.

Lithography (1 colour), pane of 50
Canadian Bank Note Company

**1972, Mar 1** Perf 12

| | | NH–VF | ⊙F | PB | FDC |
|---|---|---|---|---|---|
| 559 | **8¢ deep red lilac** | .35 | .20 | 1.75 | .85 |

Qty: 25,300,000

Issued for the World Figure Skating Championships, held in Calgary in 1972.

## UNITED NATIONS WORLD HEALTH DAY

Designer: Joyce Wieland.

Engraved (1 colour), pane of 50
British American Bank Note Company

**1972, Apr 7** Perf 12.0x12.5

| | | NH–VF | ⊙F | PB | FDC |
|---|---|---|---|---|---|
| 560 | **8¢ red**, F | .45 | .20 | 2.25 | .85 |
| i | dull | 2.00 | 1.75 | 10.00 | 1.75 |
| p | tagged, GT2 (OP4†), F | .75 | .45 | 3.75* | 1.75 |
| ii | tagged, GT2 (OP4†), dull | 2.00 | 1.75 | 10.00* | 2.75 |

Qty: 23,400,000; Tagged: 5,200,000

† The Ottawa tagging is migrating and may leach onto other stamps that contact it.
* Blank corner block of 4.

## FRONTENAC

561
Frontenac

Designer: Laurent Marquart. Based on a sculpture by Louis-Philippe Hébert. Based on a map by Jean-Baptiste Louis Franquelin.

Engraved (1 colour) and Photogravure (2 colours), pane of 50
British American Bank Note Company

**1972, May 17** Perf 12.0x12.5

| | | NH–VF | ⊙F | PB | FDC |
|---|---|---|---|---|---|
| 561 | **8¢ red brown and multicoloured**, dull | .35 | .20 | 1.75 | .85 |
| i | F | .35 | .20 | 1.75 | 1.25 |
| p | tagged, GT2 (OP4†), dull | 1.00 | 1.00 | 7.50* | 1.75 |
| ii | tagged, GT2 (OP4†), F | 1.00 | 1.00 | 7.50* | 1.50 |

Qty: 22,700,000; Tagged: 5,400,000

† The Ottawa tagging is migrating and may leach onto other stamps that contact it.
* Blank corner block of 4.

Issued to mark the 300th anniversary of Louis de Buade, Count of Frontenac, as Governor of New France.

## PLAINS INDIANS

562 *Buffalo Chase* 563 Plains artifacts

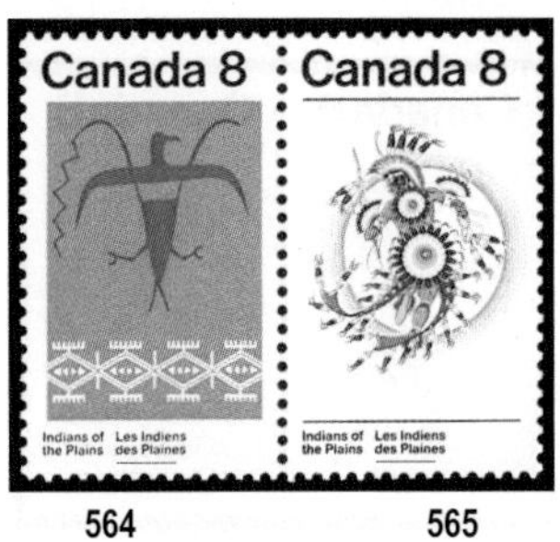

564 Assiniboine Thunderbird 565 Sun Dance Costume

Designer: Georges Beaupré. Buffalo Chase: based on a print by George Catlin. Artifacts: based on a photograph by Ray Webber. Thunderbird and Costume: Picture engraved by George Arthur Gundersen.

Lithography (4 colours), panes of 50
Ashton-Potter Limited

**1972, Jul 6** **Perf 12.2x12.6**

| | | NH–VF | ⊙F | PB | FDC |
|---|---|---|---|---|---|
| **562** | **8¢ multicoloured** | .50 | .20 | | .85 |
| i | short "n" in "Plains"† | 2.00 *EP* | 1.00 | | 2.00 |
| p | tagged, GT2 | .75 | .40 | | 1.75 |
| pi | tagged, GT2, short "n" in "Plains"† | 3.00 *EP* | 2.00 | | 4.00 |
| **563** | **8¢ multicoloured** | .50 | .20 | | .85 |
| i | short "n" in "Plains"† | 2.00 *EP* | 1.00 | | 2.00 |
| p | tagged, GT2 | .75 | .40 | | 1.75 |
| pi | tagged, GT2, short "n" in "Plains"† | 3.00 *EP* | 2.00 | | 4.00 |
| a | se-tenant pair (562, 563) | 1.10 | .40 | 2.50 | 1.25 |
| ai | as "a", black double printed | 100.00 | | | |
| b | se-tenant pair, GT2 (562p, 563p) | 1.70 | 1.00 | 3.75* | 2.50 |

Qty: 15,000,000 of each (562 and 563)

† 562i and 563i occur together in the top row only of all UL and UR corner blocks of 4, including inscription blocks. Value for block $7.50.

Engraved (1 colour) and Photogravure (3 colours), panes of 50
British American Bank Note Company

**1972, Oct 4** **Perf 12.5x12.0**

| | | NH–VF | ⊙F | PB | FDC |
|---|---|---|---|---|---|
| **564** | **8¢ multicoloured**, ribbed, NF | .50 | .20 | | .85 |
| i | smooth MF paper | 5.00 | .50 | | |
| ii | ribbed, LF paper | 5.00 | 1.00 | | |
| iii | smooth DF/LF paper | 2.00 | .75 | | |
| p | tagged, GT2, ribbed, NF | .75 | .40 | | 1.75 |
| pii | tagged, GT2, smooth MF paper | 10.00 | | | |
| **565** | **8¢ multicoloured**, ribbed, NF | .50 | .20 | | .85 |
| i | smooth MF paper | 5.00 | .50 | | |
| ii | ribbed, LF paper | 5.00 | 1.00 | | |
| iii | smooth DF/LF paper | 2.00 | .75 | | |
| p | tagged, GT2, ribbed, NF | .75 | .40 | | 1.75 |
| pii | tagged, GT2, smooth MF paper | 10.00 | | | |
| a | se-tenant pair (564, 565) | 1.10 | .40 | 2.50 | 1.25 |
| ai | se-tenant pair (564i, 565i) | 10.00 | | 50.00 | |
| aii | se-tenant pair (564ii, 565ii) | 10.00 | | 25.00 | |
| aiii | se-tenant pair (564iii, 565iii) | 4.00 | | 10.00 | |
| b | se-tenant pair, GT2 (564p, 565p) | 1.70 | 1.00 | 3.75* | 2.50 |
| bi | se-tenant pair, GT2 (564pii, 565pii) | 20.00 | | | |

Qty: 14,175,000 of each (564 and 565)

* Blank corner block of 4.

## ALGONKIAN INDIANS

566 Algonkian Artifacts 567 *Micmac Indians*

568 Thunderbird and Belt 569 Algonkian Couple

Designer: Georges Beaupré. Artifacts: based on a photograph by Ray Webber. Couple: based on a painting by Lewis Parker. Thunderbird and Couple: Picture engraved by George Arthur Gundersen.

Lithography (4 colours), panes of 50
British American Bank Note Company

**1973, Feb 21** **Tagged, GT2** **Perf 12.2x12.0**

| | | NH–VF | ⊙F | PB | FDC |
|---|---|---|---|---|---|
| **566** | **8¢ multicoloured**, HB/dull | .50 | .20 | | .85 |
| i | F/HB | 3.50 | | | |
| ii | HB/HB | .50 | .20 | | |
| T1 | untagged (error) | 100.00 | 50.00 | | |
| **567** | **8¢ multicoloured**, HB/dull | .50 | .20 | | .85 |
| i | F/HB | 3.50 | | | |
| ii | HB/HB | .50 | .20 | | |
| T1 | untagged (error) | 100.00 | 50.00 | | |
| a | se-tenant pair, HB/dull (566, 567) | 1.10 | .80 | 2.50 | 1.25 |
| ai | se-tenant pair, F/HB (566i, 567i) | 7.25 | 3.00 | 17.50 | |
| aii | se-tenant pair, HB/HB (566ii, 567ii) | 1.10 | .80 | 2.50 | |
| aT1 | as "a", se-tenant pair, untagged (error) | 200.00 | | 500.00* | |
| aiT1 | as "ai", se-tenant pair, F/HB, untagged (error) | 200.00 | | | 200.00‡ |

Qty: 13,700,000 of each (566 and 567)

* Blank corner block of 4.

‡ one FDC has been reported.

Engraved (2 colour) and Photogravure (3 colours), panes of 50

**1973, Nov 28** **Tagged, GT2** **Perf 12.5x12.0**

| | | NH–VF | ⊙F | PB | FDC |
|---|---|---|---|---|---|
| **568** | **8¢ multicoloured** , dull | .40 | .20 | | .85 |
| i | transparent HB | 3.50 | 1.00 | | |
| **569** | **8¢ multicoloured**, dull | .40 | .20 | | .85 |
| i | transparent HB | 3.50 | 1.00 | | |
| ii | "red dot above elbow" variety (pos. 28) | 6.50 | 3.75 | 20.00† | 5.00‡ |
| iii | as 569ii, transparent HB | 12.50 | 5.00 | 35.00† | |
| a | se-tenant pair (568, 569) | .90 | .80 | 2.25 | 1.25 |
| ai | se-tenant pair (568i, 569i) | 7.25 | 2.50 | 17.50 | |

Qty: 13,700,000 of each (568 and 569)

† Value shown is for position block of 9.

‡ Any cover.

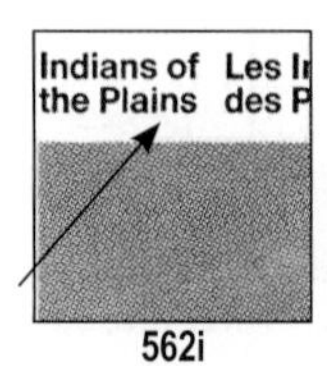


562i

563i

569ii

## PACIFIC COAST INDIANS

570
*The Inside of a Nootka Sound House*

571
Pacific Coast Artifacts

572
Chief and Blanket

573
Kwakiutl House Thunderbird

Designer: Georges Beaupré. Artifacts: based on a photograph by Ray Webber. Nootka Sound: based on a drawing by John Webber. Chief: based on a painting by Lewis Parker. Thunderbird and Chief: Picture engraved by George Arthur Gundersen.

Lithography (4 colours), panes of 50
Ashton-Potter Limited

| **1974, Jan 16** | **Tagged, GT2** | | | **Perf 12.2x12.6** | |
|---|---|---|---|---|---|
| | | NH–VF | ⊙F | PB | FDC |
| **570** | **8¢ multicoloured**, F back | .40 | .20 | | .85 |
| i | HF back | 2.00 | .50 | | |
| T1 | untagged (error) | | 100.00 | | |
| **571** | **8¢ multicoloured**, F back | .40 | .20 | | .85 |
| i | HF back | 2.00 | .50 | | |
| T1 | untagged (error) | | 100.00 | | |
| a | se-tenant pair, F back (570, 571) | .90 | .60 | 2.00 | 1.25 |
| ai | se-tenant pair, HF back (570i, 571i) | 4.00 | 1.00 | 9.00 | |
| aT1 | se-tenant pair, untagged (error) | 200.00 | | | |

Qty: 14,542,000 of each (570 and 571)

Engraved (2 colour) and Photogravure (2 colours), panes of 50
British American Bank Note Company

| **1974, Feb 22** | **Tagged, GT2** | | | **Perf 12.5x12.0** | |
|---|---|---|---|---|---|
| **572** | **8¢ multicoloured**, dull | .40 | .20 | | .85 |
| i | HB, white gum | 2.75 | | | |
| ii | "missing bird on totem" variety (pos. 28)† | 200.00 | 150.00 | — | 250.00‡ |
| | 572ii, in block of 4 (572ii, 573(2), 572) | 225.00 | — | — | 250.00‡ |
| | 572ii, in UR or LR blank corner block of 9 with 8 normal | — | — | 250.00* | |
| **573** | **8¢ multicoloured**, dull | .40 | .20 | | .85 |
| i | HB, white gum | 2.75 | | | |
| a | se-tenant pair (572, 573) | .90 | .60 | 2.00 | 1.25 |
| ai | se-tenant pair (572i, 573i) | 5.70 | | 13.75 | |

Qty: 13,450,000 of each (572 and 573)

† 5 types exist, with varying amounts of bird and totem pole missing.

‡ Any cover.

* Blank corner block of 9. Plate blocks containing variety 572ii do not exist.

572 (normal)

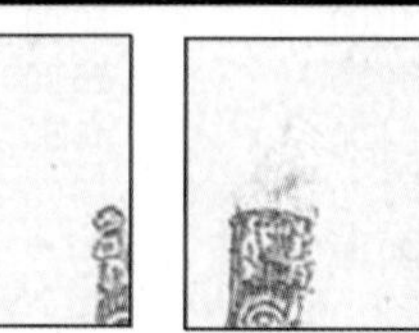

572ii (five stages)

## SUBARCTIC INDIANS

574
Montagnais-Naskapi Artifacts

575
*Dance of the Kutcha-Kutchin*

576
Kutchin Ceremonial Costume

577
Ojibwa Thunderbird

Designer: Georges Beaupré. Artifacts: based on a photograph by Ray Webber. Dance: based on a drawing by Alexander Hunter Murray. Costume: based on a painting by Lewis Parker.

Lithography (4 colours), panes of 50
Canadian Bank Note Company

| **1975, Apr 4** | **Tagged, GT2** | | | **Perf 13.3** | |
|---|---|---|---|---|---|
| | | NH–VF | ⊙F | PB | FDC |
| **574** | **8¢ multicoloured**, MF back | .30 | .20 | | .85 |
| i | HF back | 2.00 | .50 | | |
| **575** | **8¢ multicoloured**, MF back | .30 | .20 | | .85 |
| i | HF back | 2.00 | .50 | | |
| a | se-tenant pair, MF back (574, 575) | .70 | .60 | 1.50 | 1.25 |
| aii | se-tenant pair, HF back (574i, 575i) | 4.00 | 1.00 | 9.00 | |
| aiii | horiz. pair, imperf. between | 1,250.00 | | 3,000.00* | |
| ai | se-tenant pair, triple perforations | 500.00 | — | 1,200.00* | |

Qty: 14,000,000 of each (574 and 575)

* Blank corner block of 6.

Lithography (4 colours) and Embossed (#577), panes of 50
Ashton-Potter Limited

| | **Tagged, GT2** | | | **Perf 12.5** | |
|---|---|---|---|---|---|
| **576** | **8¢ multicoloured** | .30 | .20 | | .85 |
| T1 | untagged (error) | 175.00 | 125.00 | | |
| **577** | **8¢ multicoloured** | .30 | .20 | | .85 |
| T1 | untagged (error) | 175.00 | 125.00 | | |
| a | se-tenant pair (576, 577) | .70 | .60 | 1.50 | 1.25 |
| aT1 | se-tenant pair, untagged (error) | 350.00 | 250.00 | 850.00* | |

Qty: 15,565,000 of each (576 and 577)

* Blank corner block of 4.

575aiii

## IROQUOIAN INDIANS

578 Cornhusk Mask and Artifacts — 579 *Iroquoian Encampment*

580 Iroquoian Thunderbird — 581 Iroquoian Couple

Designer: Georges Beaupré. Artifacts: based on a photograph by Ray Webber. Encampment: based on a drawing by George Heriot. Couple: based on a painting by Lewis Parker.

Lithography (6 colours), panes of 50
Ashton-Potter Limited

**1976, Sep 17** **Tagged, GT2** **Perf 13.3**

| | | NH–VF | ⊙F | PB | FDC |
|---|---|---|---|---|---|
| **578** | **10¢ multicoloured** | .30 | .20 | | .90 |
| i | DF/LF paper | 3.00 | .75 | | |
| **579** | **10¢ multicoloured** | .30 | .20 | | .90 |
| i | "missing medallion" variety (on centre Indian's shoulder) | 2.00 *EP* | 1.00 | 5.00 | 2.50 |
| ii | DF/LF paper | 3.00 | .75 | | |
| a | se-tenant pair (578, 579) | .70 | .60 | 1.50 | 1.40 |
| ai | se-tenant pair (578i, 579ii) | 6.00 | | | |

Qty: 10,362,500 of each (578 and 579)

Lithography (6 colours) and Embossed (#580), panes of 50

**Tagged, GT2** **Perf 12.5**

| | | NH–VF | ⊙F | PB | FDC |
|---|---|---|---|---|---|
| **580** | **10¢ multicoloured**, DF | .30 | .20 | | .90 |
| i | LF | 3.00 | 1.00 | | |
| **581** | **10¢ multicoloured**, DF | .30 | .20 | | .90 |
| i | "extra feather" (pos. 15), DF | 5.00 | 2.50 | | |
| ii | red dot above roof line, DF | 3.50 | 1.25 | | |
| iii | LF | 3.00 | 1.00 | | |
| a | se-tenant pair, DF (580, 581) | .70 | .60 | 1.50 | 1.40 |
| ai | se-tenant pair, LF (580i, 581iii) | 6.00 | 3.00 | 15.00 | |

Qty: 10,350,000 of each (580 and 581)

LF varieties of 581i and 581ii are 3x DF price.

579

579i

581i

581ii

**Indians of Canada**

All sets were issued checkerwise in panes of 50 stamps. Nos. 566–581 exist with non-migratory General tagging only.

## EARTH SCIENCES

582 Geology: Geological Fault

583 Geography: Aerial View

584 Photogrammetry: Aerial Map Photography

585 Cartography: Contour Lines

Designer: Fritz Gottschalk.

Lithography, sheets of 128 subjects in eight panes of 16
Ashton-Potter Limited

**1972, Aug 2** **Perf 12**

| | | NH–VF | ⊙F | PB | FDC‡ |
|---|---|---|---|---|---|
| **582** | **15¢ multicoloured** | 2.00 | 1.50 | | 3.50 |
| p | tagged, GT2 | 2.75 | 2.00 | | 7.00 |
| **583** | **15¢ multicoloured** | 2.00 | 1.50 | | 3.50 |
| p | tagged, GT2 | 2.75 | 2.00 | | 7.00 |
| **584** | **15¢ multicoloured** | 2.00 | 1.50 | | 3.50 |
| p | tagged, GT2 | 2.75 | 2.00 | | 7.00 |
| **585** | **15¢ multicoloured** | 2.00 | 1.50 | | 3.50 |
| p | tagged, GT2 | 2.75 | 2.00 | | 7.00 |
| a | se-tenant block of 4 (582–585) | 8.00 | 7.00 | 12.50 | 12.00 |
| | miniature pane of 16† (4 x 4) | 35.00 | 30.00 | | |
| b | se-tenant block of 4, GT2 (582p–585p) | 11.00 | 15.00 | 17.50* | 18.00 |
| | miniature pane of 16, GT2 (4 x 4) | 40.00 | 36.00 | | |

Qty: 4,400,000 of each

* Blank corner block of 4.

† Four different philatelic panes exist depending upon the position of the corner inscription.

‡ 582–585 commercial single usage $12; 582p–585p commercial single usage $18.

Interpanneau gutter pairs exist. Eight pairs have been reported; the editors have seen five, all of which have minor defects. Value $1,500.00; sound pairs $2,000 each.

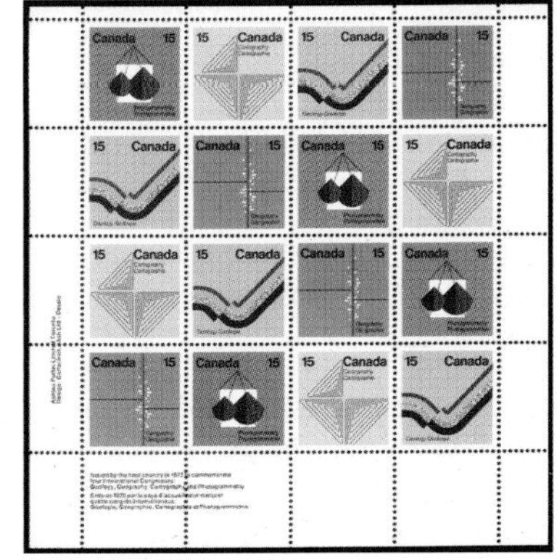

582–585
Full pane of 16 (lower left inscription)

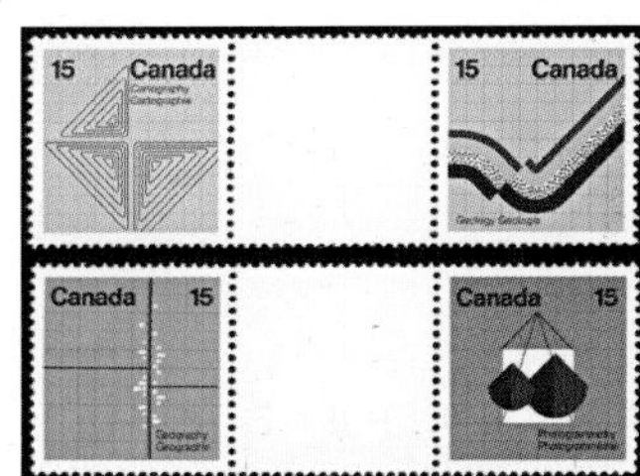


Interpanneau gutter pairs

## CARICATURE DEFINITIVES
### 1973–1976

586 Sir John A. Macdonald | 587 Sir Wilfrid Laurier | 588 Sir Robert Borden

589 William Lyon Mackenzie King | 590 Richard B. Bennett | 591 Lester B. Pearson | 592 Louis St. Laurent

593 Queen Elizabeth II | 593A Queen Elizabeth II

Designer: David Annesley. Typography and lettering: Ken Rodmell.

Engraved (1 colour), panes of 100
Canadian Bank Note Company

**1973, Oct 17** **Tagged, GT2** **Perf 12.0x12.5**

| | | NH–VF | ⊙F | PB | FDC |
|---|---|---|---|---|---|
| **586** | **1¢ orange**, LF | .25 | .20 | .75 | .80† |
| d | printed on gummed side | 1,250.00 | — | *6,500.00‡* | — |
| i | NF | .35 | .20 | 1.50* | |
| ii | DF | .25 | .20 | .75 | |
| iii | DF, ribbed, horiz. | .35 | .20 | 1.50 | |
| iv | HF | 10.00 | 1.00 | 75.00* | |
| T1 | untagged (error), NF | 50.00 | 25.00 | | |
| T2 | untagged (error), DF | 50.00 | — | | |
| xx | No. 586, precancelled, DF | .25 | .20 | 7.50** | 2.00 |
| xxi | No. 586, precancelled, LF | .75 | .20 | 20.00** | |
| xxii | No. 586, precancelled, DF/LF, ribbed, horiz. | .40 | .20 | 12.00** | |
| xxiii | No. 586, precancelled, NF | 1.25 | .30 | 40.00** | |

† Block of 6.
* Blank corner block of 4. ‡ 2 blank corner blocks have been seen by the editors.
** Warning strip of 20.

Overprinted copies of 586xx (and varieties) have been used extensively by various stamp shows for promotional/fund raising efforts.

| Caricatures | | | | | | |
|---|---|---|---|---|---|---|
| Format | Sheet | | | Bklt | Pre | Coil |
| Printer | CBN | BABN | | BABN | CBN | CBN |
| Perf | 12x12½ | 12x12½ | 13x13½ | 12x12½ | 12x12½ | 10 vert |
| 1¢ Macdonald | 586 (1) | | | 586as | 586xx | |
| 2¢ Laurier | 587 (1–2) | | | 587viii | | |
| 3¢ Borden | 588 (1) | | | | 588xx | |
| 4¢ King | 589 (1) | | | | | |
| 5¢ Bennett | 590 (1) | | | | 590xx | |
| 6¢ Pearson | 591 (1–3) | | | 591vii | 591xx | |
| 7¢ St. Laurent | 592iii (2) | 592 (1) | | | | |
| 8¢ QE II | 593vii (7–8) | 593 (1–5) | 593b (6) | 593xxi | 593xx | 604 |
| 10¢ QE II | | | 593A (1–2) | 593Ac | | 605 |

| | | NH–VF | ⊙F |
|---|---|---|---|
| **586a** | booklet pane of 6, 3 x 1¢ (586as) + 1 x 6¢ (591vii) + 2 x 8¢ (593), BABN (BK74a), DF, *Apr 10, 1974* | 1.75 | 1.50 |
| as | single 1¢ with straight edge, from 586a, 586b, 586c | .25 | .20 |
| ai | as 586a, HF (BK74b) | 1.75 | 1.50 |
| ais | single 1¢ with straight edge, from 586ai, HF | .25 | .20 |
| aiii | as 586a, re-entry in 'age' of 'Postage' on 6¢ value (BK74k) | 25.00 | |
| aiv | as 586a, LF (BK74l) | 1.75 | 1.50 |
| aivs | single 1¢ with straight edge, from 586aiv, LF | .25 | .20 |
| av | as 586a, DF, ribbed, horiz. (BK74g) | 9.00 | 7.50 |
| avs | single 1¢ with straight edge, from 586av, DF, ribbed | 1.00 | .75 |
| **586b** | booklet pane of 18, 6 x 1¢ (586as) + 1 x 6¢ (591vii) + 11 x 8¢ (593), BABN (BK75), *Jan 17, 1975* | 2.00 | 2.00 |
| **586c** | booklet pane of 10, 2 x 1¢ (586as) + 4 x 2¢ (587viii) + 4 x 10¢ (593Ac), BABN (BK76), *Sep 1, 1976* | 1.75 | 1.50 |
| **BK74** | Pane 586a in bilingual cover $2.00* | | |
| **BK75** | Pane 586b in bilingual cover $2.50 | | |
| **BK76** | Pane 586c in bilingual cover $2.00* | | |

* 10 different cover designs.

"Missing 1" and "broken 1" varieties exist from the booklet (BK74); these are generally collected as full panes/booklets. See the booklet section for listings.

586a

586c

586b

| | | NH–VF | ⊙F | PB | FDC |
|---|---|---|---|---|---|
| **587** | **2¢ green**, MF/LF (plates 1–2) | .25 | .20 | .75 | .85‡ |
| i | NF | .25 | .20 | .75 | |
| ii | DF/NF | .35 | .20 | 1.50 | |
| iii | DF | .35 | .20 | 1.50 | |
| iv | DF/LF | .35 | .20 | 1.50* | |
| v | DF, ribbed, horiz. | .25 | .20 | .75 | |
| vi | HF | .50 | .20 | 4.00 | |
| xi | LF/MF | .50 | .20 | 3.50 | |
| ix | DF/F | .50 | .20 | 3.50* | |
| x | DF/LF, ribbed, vertically | 2.50 | .75 | 15.00 | |
| vii | imperf. bottom half of stamp & margin, block of 4 | 800.00 | — | 950.00* | — |
| T1 | untagged (error), DF | 75.00 | 40.00 | | |
| T2 | untagged (error), LF | 75.00 | 40.00 | | |
| **587viii** | single 2¢ with straight edge, from 586c | .25 | .20 | — | |

‡ Block of 4. * Blank corner block of 4.

| | | NH–VF | ⊙F | PB | FDC |
|---|---|---|---|---|---|
| **588** | **3¢ brown**, LF | .25 | .20 | .75 | .80† |
| i | NF | .35 | .20 | 12.00 | |
| ii | DF/LF | .50 | .20 | 4.00* | |
| iii | DF | .50 | .20 | 4.00* | |
| T1 | untagged (error), LF | 60.00 | 35.00 | | |
| T2 | untagged (error), NF | 60.00 | 35.00 | | |
| xx | No. 588, precancelled, LF | .25 | .20 | 7.50** | 2.00 |
| xxi | No. 588, precancelled, NF | 3.50 | 3.50 | 125.00** | |

† Pair.
* Blank corner block of 4.
** Warning strip of 20.

| | | NH–VF | ⊙F | PB | FDC |
|---|---|---|---|---|---|
| **589** | **4¢ black**, LF | .25 | .20 | .75 | .85† |
| i | NF | 2.00 | .45 | 10.00 | |
| ii | NF, ribbed, horiz. | 2.50 | .50 | 15.00* | |
| iii | DF | .50 | .20 | 4.00 | |
| iv | DF/LF | .50 | .20 | 4.00 | |
| v | DF/LF, ribbed, horiz. | .35 | .20 | 2.00 | |
| vi | DF/HF, ribbed, horiz. | .35 | .20 | 2.00 | |
| vii | HF | 1.00 | .30 | 6.00 | |
| T1 | untagged (error), NF | 50.00 | 35.00 | 250.00* | |

† Pair.

| | | | | | |
|---|---|---|---|---|---|
| **590** | **5¢ lilac**, LF | .25 | .20 | 1.00 | .90 |
| i | NF | .35 | .20 | 2.00 | |
| ii | DF | .30 | .20 | 1.75 | |
| iii | MF | 5.00 | 1.35 | 40.00* | |
| T1 | untagged (error), LF | 50.00 | — | 250.00 | |
| xx | No. 590, precancelled, LF | .25 | .20 | 7.50** | 2.00 |
| xxi | printed on gummed side ‡ | 1,250.00 | — | | |

** Warning strip of 20. ‡ one single reported

| | | | | | |
|---|---|---|---|---|---|
| **591** | **6¢ dark red**, NF (plates 1–3) | .25 | .20 | 1.00 | .80 |
| a | printed on gummed side | 250.00 | — | 1,200.00* | |
| i | DF | .25 | .20 | 1.25 | |
| ii | DF, ribbed, horiz. | .35 | .20 | 2.00 | |
| iii | LF | .25 | .20 | 1.25 | |
| iv | MF | 1.00 | .30 | 6.00* | |
| v | DF/LF, ribbed, horiz. | .35 | .20 | 2.00 | |
| vi | imperf. bottom half of stamp & margin, block of 4 | 800.00 | — | 950.00* | |
| T1 | untagged (error), DF | 60.00 | 35.00 | | |
| T2 | untagged (error), MF | | 35.00 | | |
| xx | No. 591, precancelled, MF | .25 | .20 | 7.50** | 2.00 |
| xxi | No. 591, precancelled, DF, ribbed, horiz. | .50 | .25 | 20.00** | |
| xxii | No. 591, precancel, DF/LF, ribbed, horiz. | .50 | .25 | 15.00** | |
| xxiii | No. 591, precancelled, HF | 2.00 | .50 | 60.00** | |
| 591vii | single 6¢ with straight edge, from 586a or 586b, DF | .25 | .20 | | — |
| viii | as vii, re-entry on "age" of "Postage" | 15.00 | 5.00 | | |
| ix | single 6¢ with straight edge, ribbed, horiz. from 586av | 2.50 | 1.50 | | |
| x | single 6¢ with s/e, LF from 586aiv | .25 | .20 | | |
| xi | single 6¢ with s/e, HF from 586ai | .25 | .20 | | |

* Blank corner block of 4.
** Warning strip of 20.

postage

591viii

| | | | | | |
|---|---|---|---|---|---|
| **592** | **7¢ dark brown**, BABN, DF, *Apr 8, 1974* (Plate 1) | .25 | .20 | 1.25 | .80 |
| T4 | untagged (error), DF | 100.00 | 50.00 | | |
| ii | MF | 7.50 | 2.00 | 40.00 | |
| iii | CBN (Plate 2), NF, *Jan 1977* | .25 | .20 | 1.25 | |

BABN

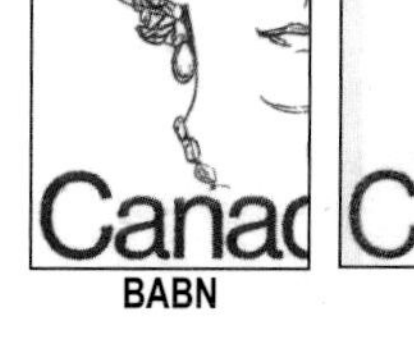

CBN

BABN CBN

The BABN printings of the 7¢ and 8¢ values appear to have a rougher surfaced paper and the tagging appears blotchy (ie. no solid).

The CBN printings have a smooth, "shinier" paper, the colour seems to have the appearance of being "toned down", and the tagging is "solid". From the back of the stamp, the 'Canada 7'/ 'Canada 8' appears "embossed."

British American Bank Note Company

**1973, Oct 17** **Tagged, GT2** **Perf 12.0x12.5**

| | | NH–VF | ⊙F | PB | FDC |
|---|---|---|---|---|---|
| **593** | **8¢ Royal blue**, NF | .25 | .20 | 1.50 | .85 |
| i | DF | .30 | .20 | 2.00 | |
| ii | DF, ribbed, horiz. | .35 | .20 | 2.50 | |
| iii | LF | .30 | .20 | 2.00 | |
| iv | LF, ribbed, horiz. | .35 | .20 | 2.50 | |
| v | MF/LF | .30 | .20 | 2.00 | |
| vi | MF | .30 | .20 | 2.00 | |
| ix | HF | .30 | .20 | 2.00 | |
| x | "weeping queen" variety, (pos. 13 or 20) | 25.00 | | | 30.00‡ |
| xi | "tear on side of nose" variety (pos. 52) | 25.00 | | | 30.00‡ |
| xii | "spur on 8" variety | 3.00 | | | |
| xv | "dot by Queen's ear" variety (pos. 44) | 15.00 | | | |
| xvi | "earring" variety, (pos. 13) | 15.00 | | 25.00(6)* | 25.00‡ |
| xiii | imperf. bottom half of stamp & margin, block of 4 | 800.00 | — | 950.00* | |
| xiv | LR corner block of 15, imperf. at bottom and right | | | 1,250.00† | |
| T1 | untagged (error), DF | 50.00 | 20.00 | | |
| T2 | untagged (error), LF | 50.00 | 20.00 | | |
| T3 | untagged (error), MF | 50.00 | 20.00 | | |
| T5 | untagged (error), HF | 50.00 | 20.00 | | |
| | Canadian Bank Note (Dec 1976) | | | | |
| vii | CBN, milky blue, plates 7, NF | 2.00 | .35 | 12.00 | — |
| viii | CBN, milky blue, plates 7, 8, DF | .80 | .25 | 4.50 | |
| xx | No. 593, precancelled | .25 | .20 | 7.50** | 2.00 |

** Warning strip of 20. * Blank corner block. ‡ Any cover.
† 593xiv exists untagged: block of 15: $1,500.00; block of 8: $1,200.00. Two of each known.

| | | | | | |
|---|---|---|---|---|---|
| 593xxi | single 8¢ with straight edge, from 586a or 586b | .25 | .20 | | — |
| xxii | single 8¢ with straight edge, ribbed, horiz. from 586av | 1.50 | 1.00 | | |
| xxiii | single 8¢ with s/e, LF from 586aiv | .25 | .20 | | |
| xxiv | single 8¢ with s/e, HF from 586ai | .25 | .20 | | |

**Perf 13.0x13.3**

| | | | | | |
|---|---|---|---|---|---|
| **593b** | No. 593, plate 6 printing, BABN, NF, *Nov 1976* | 1.00 | .20 | 5.00 | — |
| bi | DF | 2.00 | .30 | 10.00 | |

**Nos. 586–591, 593 (7) combination FDC** **1.70**

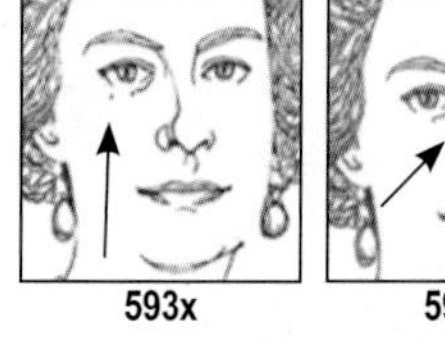
593x

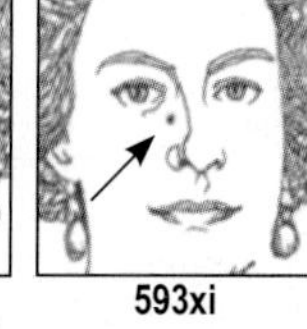
593xi

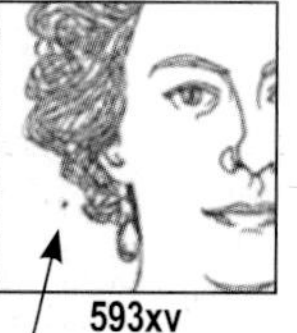
593xv

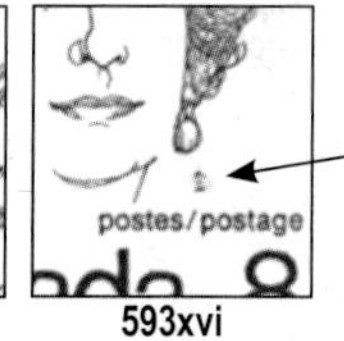

593xvi

| 8¢ Caricature paper fluorescence by plate # | NF | DF | LF | MF | MF/LF | HF |
|---|---|---|---|---|---|---|
| 1 | | | | | | x |
| 1 (ribbed) | | x | | | | |
| 2 | | | | | | |
| 2 (ribbed) | | x | x | | | |
| 3 | | x | | | | |
| 4 | | | | x | x | |
| 5 | | x | x | | | |
| 6 | x | x | | | | |
| 7 | x | x | | | | |
| 8 | | x | | | | |

British American Bank Note Company

| 1976, Sep 1 | Tagged, GT2 | | | Perf 13.0x13.3 | |
|---|---|---|---|---|---|
| **593A** | **10¢ dark carmine**, NF (Plates 1–2) | .30 | .20 | 1.50 | .90 |
| Ai | DF | .35 | .20 | 2.00 | |
| Aii | LF | .30 | .20 | 1.75 | |
| Aiii | MF | .50 | .20 | 3.50 | |
| Aiv | HB | 5.00 | 1.00 | 25.00* | |
| AT1 | untagged (error), NF | | 50.00 | | |
| AT2 | untagged (error), LF | | 50.00 | | |
| AT3 | untagged (error), HF | | 50.00 | | |

* Blank corner block of 4.

| 1976, Sep 1 | Tagged, GT2 | | | Perf 12.0x12.5 |
|---|---|---|---|---|
| 593Ac | single 10¢ with straight edge, from 586c | .50 | .20 | — |

## LANDSCAPE DEFINITIVES 1972–1977

594 Forest 595 Mountain Sheep

596 Prairies 597 Polar Bears 598 Seashore

The five medium-value Landscape definitives were all tagged with two vertical bars (down the vertical perforations). The 10¢–25¢ exist with either Winnipeg or Ottawa (General) tagging.

The General tagging (all values) exists in two formats: OP4 and OP2. The former migrates across the stamps (and onto other stamps that they come into contact with). When OP4 tagging migrates onto other stamps it produces "apparent" tagging errors (extra bars, etc.). The affected stamps are not varieties, but are, in fact, damaged stamps. OP4 can be controlled somewhat by isolating the stamps in mounts or envelopes of acetate, glassine or polyethylene. Over the years, OP4 tagging has migrated to the point that individual stamps may appear to be untagged (i.e. faded). Untagged errors should have a certificate of authenticity. OP2 tagging is stable and does not migrate.

Designer: Reinhard Derreth. Photographers: John de Visser (10¢), Harry Rowed (15¢), Chris Lund (20¢), Ted Grant (25¢), Fred Ruggles (50¢).

Engraved (1 colour) and Photogravure, panes of 100

British American Bank Note Company

**1972, Sep 8** **Perf 12.5x12.0**

Type I

Type II

Types I and II of No. 594 differ in impression and colour. Type I has distinct crosshatching in background of "C" in "Canada". In Type II this area appears solidly inked.

| | | NH–VF | ⊙F | PB | FDC |
|---|---|---|---|---|---|
| | **Type I** | | | | |
| **594** | **10¢ multicoloured**, (Plate 1), tagged, OP4, NF, ribbed, vert. | 1.50 | .20 | 7.00 | .90 |
| i | tagged, OP2 (3 mm), LF | .50 | .20 | 2.50 | |
| ii | OP2 (3 mm), DF, ribbed, vert. | .40 | .20 | 2.50 | |
| iii | tagged, W2B, DF, ribbed, vert. | 1.50 | .35 | 7.50* | 3.50‡ |
| iv | W2B, DF | 10.00 | 6.00 | 60.00* | |
| T1 | untagged (error), DF | — | 60.00 | | |
| | **Type II** Plate 2, OP2 (4mm) tagging | | | | |
| v | DF, *Jun 1974* | 1.10 | .40 | 5.50 | |
| vi | LF | .75 | .25 | 5.00* | |
| vii | LF, ribbed, vert. | 3.00 | .30 | 20.00 | |
| viii | MF | 2.00 | .60 | 10.00 | |
| ix | HB (front only) | 1.00 | .30 | 6.00 | |
| x | F | 4.00 | | 25.00 | |
| | **Type II** Plate 3, OP2 (4mm) tagging | | | **Perf 13.3** | |
| **594a** | DF/DF, *Feb 1976* | .40 | .20 | 2.00 | |
| ai | DF/NF | 1.00 | .30 | 5.00 | |
| aii | DF/LF | 1.00 | .30 | 5.00 | |
| aiii | LF/DF | 1.50 | .50 | 10.00* | |
| T2 | untagged (error) | — | 60.00 | | |

* Blank corner block of 4.

‡ With Winnipeg cancel; Ottawa *day of issue* cancel $10.00. Commercial use on cover: $10.00.

The Landscape issue covered a period of significant paper changes, many of which were only available in field stock (no plate blocks). These were often not identified by collectors during the time of availability, making them harder to find later and thus commanding premium prices.

Paper is "smooth" unless otherwise indicated.

**Landscapes**

| Type | Type I | | | | | | | Type II | | | |
|---|---|---|---|---|---|---|---|---|---|---|---|
| Perf | 12.5x12.0 | | | | | | | 12.5x12.0 | | | 13.3 |
| Tagging: | Winnipeg | | OP4 | OP2 (3mm) | | OP2 (4mm) | | OP2 (4mm) | | | |
| Texture | | Ribbed | Ribbed | | Ribbed | | Ribbed | | Ribbed | HB | |
| 10¢ Forest | 594iv | 594iii | 594 (Pl 1) | 594i (Pl 1) | 594ii (Pl 1) | | | 594v (Pl 2) | 594vii | 594ix | 594a (Pl 3) |
| 15¢ Sheep | | 595iii | 595 (Pl 1) | 595i (Pl 1) | 595ii (Pl 1) | | | 595iv | | 595vi | 595a (Pl 2) |
| 20¢ Prairie | | 596vii | 596 (Pl 1) | 596iii | 596i (Pl 1) | 596iv | 596v | | | | 596a (Pl 3) |
| 25¢ Bears | | 597iii | 597 (Pl 1) | 597i (Pl 1) | 597ii (Pl 1) | | | 597iv | | | 597a (Pl 3) |
| 50¢ Seashore | | | 598 (Pl 1) | 598i (Pl 1) | 598ii (Pl 1) | | | 598iii | | | 598a (Pl 2) |

**1972, Sep 8** — Perf 12.5x12.0

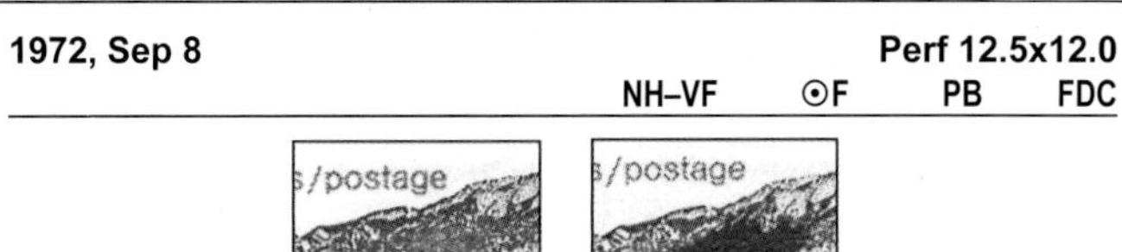


Type I Type II

Types I and II of No. 595 differ as follows: the trees (blue colour) on the hillside show clear detail on Type I, while on Type II the trees are a solid colour.

| | | NH–VF | ⊙F | PB | FDC |
|---|---|---|---|---|---|
| | **Type I** | | | | |
| **595** | **15¢ multicoloured**, (Plate 1) tagged, OP4, NF, ribbed, vert. | .75 | .20 | 4.00 | 1.10 |
| **i** | tagged, OP2 (3 mm), DF | 2.00 | .25 | 14.00 | |
| **ii** | OP2 (3 mm), DF, ribbed, vert. | .50 | .20 | 2.50 | |
| **xii** | “scratch in mountain” (pos. 10) | 10.00 | 5.00 | 20.00* | |
| **xv** | brown soil in ‘a’ of ‘Canada’ (pos. 94)§ | | | | |
| **iii** | tagged, W2B, NF, ribbed, vert. | 2.00 | 1.25 | 10.00* | 4.00‡ |
| **xi** | W2B, LF, ribbed, vert. | 10.00 | 1.50 | 60.00* | |
| **xvi** | brown soil in ‘a’ of ‘Canada’ (pos. 94)§ | | | | |
| | **Type II** OP2 (4mm) tagging | | | | |
| **iv** | NF, *Mar 1975* | 5.00 | .75 | 35.00* | |
| **v** | LF | 2.00 | .20 | 12.00* | |
| **vi** | HB (front only) | 85.00 | 15.00 | 500.00* | |
| **vii** | “blue tail” variety† | 5.00 | .75 | 25.00 | |
| **viii** | “raised rump” variety† | 5.00 | .75 | 25.00 | |
| **ix** | “double headed sheep” variety† | 10.00 | | 50.00 | |
| **x** | as 595ix, HB | 150.00 | | 900.00* | |
| **xiii** | “scratch in mountain” (pos. 10) | 15.00 | 10.00 | 30.00* | |
| **xiv** | as 595xiii, HB | | | | |
| **xvii** | brown soil in ‘a’ of ‘Canada’ (pos. 94)§ | | | | |

**Type II** — Perf 13.3

Plate 2, OP2 (4mm) tagging

| | | NH–VF | ⊙F | PB | FDC |
|---|---|---|---|---|---|
| **595a** | LF/F, *Feb 1976* | .75 | .20 | 5.00 | |
| **ai** | “blue tail” variety† | 4.00 | .75 | 20.00 | |
| **aii** | “raised rump” variety† | 4.00 | .75 | 20.00 | |
| **aiii** | DF | 2.50 | .25 | 13.00 | |
| **aiv** | DF/LF | 2.50 | .25 | 13.00 | |
| **av** | DF/MF | 1.25 | .25 | 7.00 | |
| **avi** | brown soil in ‘a’ of ‘Canada’ (pos. 94)§ | | | | |

* Blank corner block of 4.
† Caused by colour shift, cheapest paper flrsc.
‡ With Winnipeg cancel; Ottawa *day of issue* cancel $12.50. Commercial use on cover: $10.00.
§ Exists on all printings.

(These four varieties are caused by colour shifts. As a result, the listings may be removed in the future.)

595xii/xiii

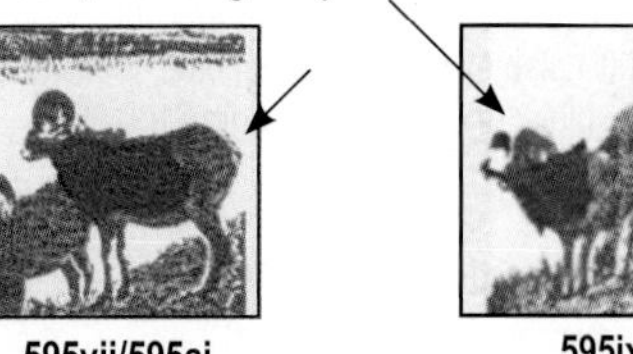

595vii/595ai 595ix

595xv/595xvi/ 595xvii/595avi

595viii/595aii

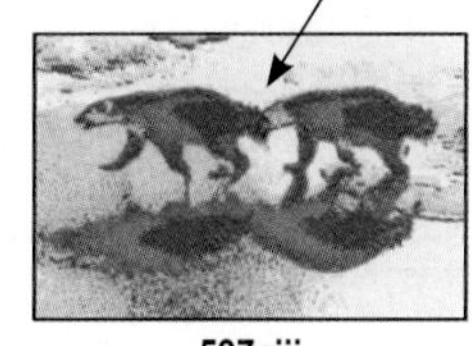

597aiii

**1972, Sep 8** — Perf 12.5x12.0

| | | NH–VF | ⊙F | PB | FDC |
|---|---|---|---|---|---|
| **596** | **20¢ multicoloured**, (Plate 1) tagged, OP4, DF, ribbed, vert. | .75 | .20 | 4.00 | 1.20 |
| **i** | tagged, OP2 (3 mm) DF, ribbed, vert. | 1.00 | .20 | 5.00 | |
| **ii** | OP2 (3 mm) DF, horiz. ribbed | 7.00 | 1.00 | 35.00 | |
| **iii** | OP2 (3 mm) DF | 2.50 | .60 | 15.00 | |
| **xiii** | OP2 (3 mm) LF, ribbed, vert. | 10.00 | | 50.00 | |
| **iv** | tagged, OP2 (4 mm) DF, *Oct 1973* | 1.50 | .25 | 8.00 | |
| **v** | OP2 (4 mm) DF, ribbed, vert. | 8.00 | 1.25 | 50.00* | |
| **vi** | OP2 (4 mm) MF | 5.00 | 1.25 | 30.00 | |
| **x** | OP2 (4 mm) HF | 125.00 | 10.00 | 600.00* | — |
| **vii** | tagged, W2B, DF, ribbed, vert. | 2.50 | 1.10 | 15.00* | 4.00‡ |
| **xi** | W2B, DF, horiz. ribbed | 8.00 | 1.50 | 40.00* | |
| **xii** | W2B, LF/DF, ribbed, vert. | 5.00 | 1.00 | 35.00* | |
| **viii** | Repellex variety, purple partly missing in pair | 250.00 | — | | — |
| **ix** | double paper, repair paste-up in horiz. pair (10 known) | 500.00 | — | | — |

Plate 2 was not issued.

Perf 13.3

Plate 3, OP2 (4mm) tagging

| | | NH–VF | ⊙F | PB | FDC |
|---|---|---|---|---|---|
| **596a** | NF, *Jan 1976* | 2.00 | .50 | 12.00 | |
| **ai** | DF/LF | .75 | .25 | 4.00 | |
| **aii** | LF/F | 1.75 | .35 | 10.00 | |
| **aiii** | MF | 4.00 | .75 | 20.00 | |

* Blank corner block of 4.
‡ With Winnipeg cancel; Ottawa *day of issue* cancel $12.50. Commercial use on cover: $10.00.

**1972, Sep 8** — Perf 12.5x12.0

Type I

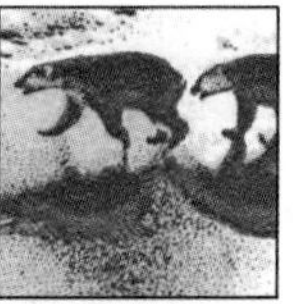

Type II

On No. 597 the bears’ shadows are evenly shaded on Type I and have a solid central area on Type II.

| | | NH–VF | ⊙F | PB | FDC |
|---|---|---|---|---|---|
| | **Type I** | | | | |
| **597** | **25¢ multicoloured**, (Plate 1) tagged, OP4, NF, ribbed, vert. | .75 | .20 | 4.00 | 1.35 |
| **i** | tagged, OP2 (3 mm), DF, horiz. ribbed | 3.50 | .90 | 25.00 | |
| **vi** | OP2 (3 mm), LF | 10.00 | 2.00 | 50.00 | |
| **vii** | OP2 (3 mm), LF, ribbed, vert. | 10.00 | 2.00 | 50.00 | |
| **ii** | OP2 (3 mm), DF, ribbed, vert. | 1.00 | .25 | 5.00 | |
| **iii** | tagged, W2B, ribbed, vert. | 2.50 | 1.25 | 12.50* | 5.00‡ |
| **T1** | untagged (error), NF | — | 60.00 | | |
| **T2** | untagged (error), LF | — | 60.00 | | |

Plate 2 was not issued.

| | | NH–VF | ⊙F | PB | FDC |
|---|---|---|---|---|---|
| | **Type II** OP2 (4mm) tagging | | | | |
| **iv** | NF, *Nov 1974* | 5.00 | 1.50 | 35.00* | |
| **v** | LF/F | 5.50 | .90 | 35.00* | |

**Type II** — Perf 13.3

Plate 3, OP2 (4mm) tagging

| | | NH–VF | ⊙F | PB | FDC |
|---|---|---|---|---|---|
| **597a** | DF/LF, *May 1976* | .90 | .20 | 4.50 | |
| **ai** | NF/DF | 2.00 | .35 | 10.00 | |
| **aii** | DF/MF | 1.50 | .30 | 8.00 | |
| **aiii** | “Siamese twins” variety (2 bears joined) (caused by colour shift) | 10.00 | 2.00 | 50.00 | |

* Blank corner block of 4.
‡ With Winnipeg cancel; Ottawa *day of issue* cancel $15.00. Commercial use on cover: $12.00.

| | 1972, Sep 8 | | | Perf 12.5x12.0 | |
|---|---|---|---|---|---|
| | | NH–VF | ⊙F | PB | FDC |

Type I

Type II

Type II of No. 598 has darker shading and a deeper tone for the dark blue areas of the photogravure impression.

**Type I**

| | | NH–VF | ⊙F | PB | FDC |
|---|---|---|---|---|---|
| **598** | **50¢ multicoloured**, (Plate 1) | | | | |
| | tagged, OP4, NF, ribbed, vert. | 1.50 | .20 | 7.00 | 2.10 |
| i | tagged, OP2 (3 mm), DF | 10.00 | 4.00 | 60.00 | |
| ii | OP2 (3 mm), DF, ribbed, vert. | 2.00 | .30 | 10.00 | |
| v | OP2 (3 mm), LF, ribbed, vert. | 7.50 | .50 | 50.00 | |
| vi | OP2 (3 mm), F | 10.00 | | 60.00 | |
| T1 | untagged (error), LF | 100.00 | 60.00 | | |

**Type II**

Plate 1, OP2 (4mm) tagging

| | | NH–VF | ⊙F | PB | FDC |
|---|---|---|---|---|---|
| iii | LF, *Aug 1974* | 2.50 | .20 | 50.00 | |
| iv | "broken C" variety | 7.50 | 4.00 | | |

**Type II** **Perf 13.3**

Plate 2, OP2 (4mm) tagging

| | | NH–VF | ⊙F | PB | FDC |
|---|---|---|---|---|---|
| **598a** | DF, *Feb 1976* | 2.50 | .20 | 13.00 | |
| ai | DF/LF (speckled paper) | 2.50 | .20 | 13.00 | |
| aii | LF/F (w/flrsc fibers) | 8.00 | .50 | 45.00* | |
| aiii | LF/MF | 10.00 | .75 | 60.00* | |
| aiv | DF/LF (non-speckled paper) | 2.50 | .20 | 13.00 | |

* Blank corner block of 4.

Six minor constant plate varieties have been reported on the 50¢ value: four are found on the Type I printings and two on the Type II printings.

**Nos. 594–598 (5) combination FDC** **4.90**



**MINT PRICING PREMIUMS**

Mint stamps from 301 to date are valued as NH-VF (Never Hinged-Very Fine). All hinged VF and NH-F copies are worth 50% of the listed values. Plate block (PB) values are for mint NH–VF plate or inscription blocks of four.

**USED, VF/XF (with in-period, circular date cancel) PRICING PREMIUM**

Single stamps with light or circular date cancels will sell for more than catalogue value (perhaps even more than a mint copy). From *1981 to 1991* single stamps from se-tenant blocks of 4 or larger will be priced at 50% or more above the fine price. From *1992* to date single stamps from se-tenant blocks of 4 or larger plus se-tenant booklet panes and souvenir sheets will be priced at 100% or more above the fine price. From *1997* to date all other stamps will be priced at 50% or more above the fine price.

## LANDSCAPE DEFINITIVES 1972–1977

599, 600
Vancouver
No. 599 has been redrawn from the original No. 600.

601
Quebec

600

599/599a

Designer: Reinhard Derreth.

Engraved (1 colour) and Photogravure (2 colours) , panes of 50
British American Bank Note Company

| | 1973, Oct 24 | Tagged, GT2 | | Perf 12.5x12.0 | |
|---|---|---|---|---|---|
| | | NH–VF | ⊙F | PB | FDC |
| **599** | **$1 multicoloured**, (Plate 2), DF | 3.50 | .75 | 17.50 | 15.00† |
| i | HB (front only) | 7.50 | 2.50 | 32.50* | |
| ii | NF | 5.00 | 1.00 | 25.00 | |
| iii | LF | 3.50 | .75 | 17.50 | |

† Any cover, single usage.

**Perf 13.3**

| | | NH–VF | ⊙F | PB | FDC |
|---|---|---|---|---|---|
| **599a** | Revised perforation, NF, *Jul 1977* | 3.50 | .50 | 17.50 | — |
| ai | DF | 3.50 | .50 | 17.50 | |
| aii | NF/LF | 3.50 | .50 | 17.50 | |
| aiii | DF/LF | 3.50 | .50 | 17.50 | |
| aiv | MF | 5.00 | .75 | 35.00* | |

* Blank corner block of 4.

Engraved (1 colour) and Lithography (4 colours)
Sheets of 200 subjects in four panes of 50
British American Bank Note Company (engraving) and
Ashton-Potter Limited (lithography)

| | 1972, Mar 17 | Untagged | | Perf 11 | |
|---|---|---|---|---|---|
| | | NH–VF | ⊙F | PB | FDC |
| **600** | **$1 multicoloured**, (Plate 1), DF | 8.00 | 2.50 | 35.00 | 6.00‡ |
| i | DF, ribbed, horiz. | 10.00 | 3.00 | 50.00 | 7.50 |
| ii | short $ flaw (pos. 21, 23, 24) | 15.00 *EP* | 5.00 | | 25.00 |
| iii | as "ii", ribbed, horiz. | 25.00 *EP* | 7.50 | | 30.00 |
| iv | short $ flaw and dot after "Postes" (pos. 22)† | 25.00 *EP* | 10.00 | | 50.00 |
| v | as "iv", ribbed, horiz. | 50.00 *EP* | 15.00 | | 60.00 |

‡ Commercial cover, single usage $70.00.
† No. 600iv also exists without dot after "Postes" (pos. 22); price shown is for positional block of 4 from left margin $100.00.

| | | NH–VF | ⊙F | PB | FDC |
|---|---|---|---|---|---|
| **601** | **$2 multicoloured**, (Plate 1) | 6.00 | 3.50 | 30.00 | 9.00 |
| i | missing '$2' (42 recorded) | *4,500.00‡* | | | |
| | plate 2, *Mar 28, 1978* § | — | — | 27.50 | |
| ii | "airplane in sky", (Pl 2, pos. 2) | 25.00 | 20.00 | 95.00 | |

‡ No. 601i should have a certificate of authenticity; one commercial cover known.
§ Singles from plate 2 cannot be differentiated from plate 1 singles.

**Nos. 600, 601 (2) Combination FDC** **75.00**
**Nos. 600ii, 601 (2) Combination FDC** **100.00**

600ii

600iv

601ii

601i

Nos. 602–603 are not assigned.

## CARICATURE DEFINITIVES – COIL STAMPS 1974–1976

604
Queen Elizabeth II

605
Queen Elizabeth II

Rolls of 100
Canadian Bank Note Company
**Tagged, GT2** — **Perf 10 vert**

| | | NH–VF | ⊙F |
|---|---|---|---|
| **604** | **8¢ Royal blue**, LF (593), *Apr 10, 1974* | .30 | .20 |
| | LF, jump strip of 4 | 8.00 | |
| a | LF, imperf. horiz. pair | 200.00 | — |
| i | HB | 1.00 | .20 |
| | HB, jump strip of 4 | 12.00 | |
| iii | HB, imperf. horiz. pair | 250.00 | — |
| iv | DF | 1.00 | .20 |
| | DF, jump strip of 4 | 12.00 | |
| v | DF, imperf. horiz. pair | 275.00 | — |
| vi | vertical pair, imperf. horizontally, with no trace of scoreline between, DF | 35.00 | 25.00 |
| vii | vertical pair, imperf. horizontally, with no trace of scoreline between, HB | 50.00 | |
| viii | HF | 3.00 | .50 |
| | HF, jump strip of 4 | 22.00 | |
| ix | MF | 3.00 | .50 |
| | MF, jump strip of 4 | 22.00 | |
| T1 | untagged (error), HF | | 60.00 |
| T5 | untagged (error), DF | | 60.00 |
| **605** | **10¢ dark carmine**, DF (593A), *Sep 1, 1976* | .40 | .20 |
| a | imperf. horiz. pair | 225.00 | — |
| ii | DF, wide spacing strip of 4 | 5.00 | 1.50 |
| iii | NF | 1.00 | .20 |
| iv | NF, wide spacing strip of 4 | 12.00 | 3.00 |
| v | vertical pair, imperf. horizontally, with no trace of scoreline between | 50.00 | |
| vi | HB | 35.00 | 25.00 |
| | HB, jump strip of 4 | 300.00 | |
| vii | HB, wide spacing strip of 4 | 300.00 | |
| T1 | untagged (error), NF | | 50.00 |

Coil pairs or larger multiples are priced in proportion.

**Image sizes**

**From this point on, stamp images are 75% actual size; booklet pane and souvenir sheet images are 25%.**

## CHRISTMAS – CANDLES

606

607

608

609

Designer: Ray Webber.

Lithography (4 colours), panes of 100
Ashton-Potter Limited

**1972, Nov 1** — **Perf 12.5x12.0**

| | | NH–VF | ⊙F | PB | FDC |
|---|---|---|---|---|---|
| **606** | **6¢ red and multicoloured** | .25 | .20 | 1.25 | .80 |
| p | tagged, WCB | .40 | .30 | 2.00* | 3.00§ |
| pi | tagged, GT2 | .35 | .20 | 1.75* | 1.60§ |
| | Qty: 127,839,000 | | | | |
| **607** | **8¢ violet blue and multicoloured** | .30 | .20 | 1.50 | .85 |
| ii | pale blue, repellex error, missing red† | 500.00 | | | |
| p | tagged, W2B | .45 | .35 | 2.25* | 3.00§ |
| pi | tagged, GT2 | .40 | .25 | 2.00* | 1.75§ |
| | Qty: 80,025,000 | | | | |

Panes of 50

**Perf 11.0x10.8**

| | | NH–VF | ⊙F | PB | FDC |
|---|---|---|---|---|---|
| **608** | **10¢ green and multicoloured** | .60 | .50 | 3.00 | 1.20 |
| ii | missing yellow, in vert. strip of 4‡ | 2,500.00 | | | |
| p | tagged, W2B | .85 | .70 | 4.25* | 3.50§ |
| pi | tagged, GT2 | .80 | .60 | 4.00* | 2.40§ |
| | Qty: 11,400,000 | | | | |
| **609** | **15¢ yellow bistre and multicoloured** | 1.00 | 1.00 | 5.00 | 1.40§ |
| p | tagged, W2B | 1.60 | 1.40 | 8.00* | 4.00§ |
| pi | tagged, GT2 | 1.40 | 1.25 | 7.00* | 2.80§ |
| | Qty: 16,688,000 | | | | |

| | |
|---|---|
| **Nos. 606–609 (4) combination FDC** | **2.95** |
| **Nos. 606p–609p (4) combination FDC** | **5.90** |
| **Nos. 606i–609i (4) combination FDC** | **5.90** |

† No. 607ii is missing red colour in flames and background. Copies showing only part of colour sell for less.
‡ No. 608ii is a repellex error. Middle 2 stamps in strip of 4 are blue instead of green. Five such strips of 4 are known.
* Blank corner block of 4.
§ Commercial use on cover: 609: $10.00; 606p–607p: $5.00; 608p–609p: $12.00.
W2B: With Winnipeg cancel; Ottawa *day of issue* cancel $7.50 (6¢, 8¢) / $10.00 (10¢) / $12.50 (15¢).

Nos. 606–609 all exist with imperf. left selvedge (philatelic stock with inscriptions). All field stock has perforated selvedge. The Winnipeg tagged stamps exist with imperf. left selvedge; the 10¢ and 15¢ values also exist with perforated left selvedge. The General tagged stamps all exist with imperf. left selvedge.

## CORNELIUS KRIEGHOFF

610
*The Blacksmith's Shop*

Designer: William Rueter. Based on a painting by Cornelius Krieghoff.
Lithography (4 colours), Plates of 200 subjects in four panes of 50
Inscription reads: British American Bank Note Company
but printed by Saults & Pollard Ltd. of Winnipeg, an affiliate of BABN

**1972, Nov 29** **Perf 12.5**

| | | NH–VF | ⊙F | PB | FDC |
|---|---|---|---|---|---|
| **610** | **8¢ multicoloured** | .40 | .20 | | .85 |
| i | "broken door frame on shed" variety* | 1.75 *EP* | 1.50 | | 2.50 |
| ii | "extra log in snow" variety (pos. 39) | 5.00 | 2.00 | | 20.00 |
| iii | "extended 1" variety (pos. 14) | 5.00 | 2.00 | | |
| iv | "icicle on roof" variety (pos. 45) | 5.00 | 2.00 | | |
| v | "branch below sleigh" variety (pos. 50) | 5.00 | 2.00 | | |
| | No. 610, inscription blocks of 4, UL, LL | | | 3.00 | |
| | No. 610 (2) & 610i (2), inscription blocks, UR, LR | | | 7.50 | |
| | No. 610 (3), 610i (2) & 610ii (1), inscription block of 6, LR | | | 20.00 | |
| p | tagged, GT2 | .45 | .20 | | 1.75 |
| pi | GT2, "broken door frame on shed"* | 2.00 *EP* | 1.75 | | 5.00 |
| pii | GT2, "log in snow" variety (pos. 39) | 6.00 | 3.00 | | 20.00 |
| piii | GT2, "extended 1" variety (pos. 14) | 6.00 | 3.00 | | |
| piv | GT2, "icicle on roof" variety (pos. 45) | 6.00 | 3.00 | | |
| pv | GT2, "branch below sleigh" (pos. 50) | 6.00 | 3.00 | | |
| | No. 610p, blank corner blocks of 4, UL, LL | | | 3.25 | |
| | No. 610p (2) & 610pi (2), blank corner blocks, UR, LR | | | 10.00 | |
| | No. 610p (3), 610pi (2) & 610pii (1), blank corner block of 6, LR | | | 20.00 | |

Qty: 29,600,000; Tagged: not known.

* Varieties 610i and 610pi occur on all stamps from the 4th column of all sheets. All other varieties only occur on only one of the four panes from the full printing sheet. This issue exists on paper with a fluorescent face but a plain or dull reverse side. Premium 50%.

At least 24 constant varieties have been reported on this stamp.

The plate inscription in all four corners incorrectly spells "Krieghoff" as "Kreighoff".

## 1973

## BISHOP LAVAL

611
Bishop Laval

Designer: Gerry Lorange and Michael Fog. Based on a painting by Claude François.
Lithography, pane of 50
Ashton-Potter Limited

**1973, Jan 31** **Tagged, GT2** **Perf 10.8x11.0**

| | | NH–VF | ⊙F | PB | FDC |
|---|---|---|---|---|---|
| **611** | **8¢ silver, ultramarine and gold** | .30 | .20 | 1.50 | .85 |
| T1 | untagged (error) | 100.00 | 60.00 | | |

Qty: 25,490,000

One example on cover, of the silver double printed (Canada 8) has been reported; value $1,000.00.

Issued for the 350th birth anniversary of Francois-Xavier de Montmorency-Laval de Montigny (1623–1708), first Bishop of Quebec.

Timeline:
**1973, Feb 21** 8¢ Algonkian Indians (566–567)

## R.C.M.P. CENTENARY

612
Commissioner G.A. French and Map

613
Spectrograph

614
R.C.M.P. Musical Ride

Designer: Michel Dallaire and Jean Morin.
Lithography (3 colours), pane of 50
Ashton-Potter Limited

**1973, Mar 9** **Tagged, GT2** **Perf 11.0x10.8**

| | | NH–VF | ⊙F | PB | FDC |
|---|---|---|---|---|---|
| **612** | **8¢ dark brown, orange, and red** | .30 | .20 | 1.50 | .85 |
| T1 | untagged (error) | 100.00 | 75.00 | | |

Qty: 29,000,000

Lithography (5 colours), pane of 50

| | | NH–VF | ⊙F | PB | FDC |
|---|---|---|---|---|---|
| **613** | **10¢ dark blue and multicoloured** | .50 | .45 | 2.50 | 1.20 |

Qty: 13,200,000

Lithography (4 colours), pane of 50

| | | NH-VF | ⊙F | PB | FDC |
|---|---|---|---|---|---|
| **614** | **15¢ yellow green and multicoloured** | 1.00 | .85 | 5.00 | 1.40 |
| a | imperf. pair | 600.00* | | 1,500.00 | |
| T1 | untagged (error) | 100.00 | 60.00 | 500.00 | |

Qty: 13,200,000

**Nos. 612–614 (3) combination FDC** **1.85**

* Many imperf. pairs have wrinkles and small faults due to improper handling. Value $300. A few imprint blocks are known to exist. Other imperf. vert. pair examples exist that are double printed on one stamp (value $900 for pair). A "10¢ on 15¢" variety also exists on one stamp in vertical pair (value $1,000 for pair).

Issued to commemorate the 100th anniversary of the Royal Canadian Mounted Police.

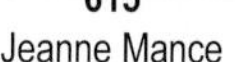

615
Jeanne Mance

616
Joseph Howe

## JEANNE MANCE

Designer: Raymond Bellemare. Based on a painting by L. Dugardin.

Lithography (4 colours), pane of 50
Ashton-Potter Limited

**1973, Apr 18** **Tagged, GT2** **Perf 11.0x10.8**

| | | NH-VF | ⊙F | PB | FDC |
|---|---|---|---|---|---|
| **615** | **8¢ multicoloured** | .30 | .20 | 1.50 | .85 |
| a | printed on gum side | 1,000.00 | | 4,500.00* | |
| T1 | untagged (error) | 100.00 | 95.00 | | |

Qty: 24,312,000

* Blank corner block of 4 (LL and LR known). 24 examples of this error known from a sheet discovered in Edmonton.

Issued to mark the 300th anniversary of the death of Jeanne Mance, first secular nurse in Canada.

## JOSEPH HOWE

Designer: Allan Robb Fleming.

Lithography (2 colours), pane of 50
Ashton-Potter Limited

**1973, May 16** **Tagged, GT2** **Perf 10.8x11.0**

| | | NH-VF | ⊙F | PB | FDC |
|---|---|---|---|---|---|
| **616** | **8¢ gold and black** | .30 | .20 | 1.50 | .85 |
| T1 | untagged (error) | 100.00 | 75.00 | 500.00 | |

Qty: 26,190,000

Issued to honour Joseph Howe (1804–1873), journalist, poet, orator, politician, and Lieutenant-Governor of Nova Scotia.

617
*Mist Fantasy, Northland*

618
Oak Trees on Shore

## J.E.H. MacDONALD

Designer: William Rueter. Based on a painting by James Edward Hervey MacDonald.

Lithography (4 colours), pane of 50
Ashton-Potter Limited

**1973, Jun 8** **Tagged, GT2** **Perf 12.6x12.5**

| | | NH-VF | ⊙F | PB | FDC |
|---|---|---|---|---|---|
| **617** | **15¢ multicoloured** | .85 | .75 | 4.25 | 1.40 |
| T1 | untagged (error) | 125.00 | | | |

Qty: 13,200,000

Issued to honour painter James E.H. MacDonald (1873–1932) on the 100th anniversary of his birth.

## PRINCE EDWARD ISLAND CENTENNIAL

Designer: Anthony Mann.

Engraved (1 colour) and Photogravure (1 colour), pane of 50
British American Bank Note Company

**1973, Jun 22** **Tagged, GT2** **Perf 12.0x12.5**

| | | NH-VF | ⊙F | PB | FDC |
|---|---|---|---|---|---|
| **618** | **8¢ orange and red brown** | .30 | .20 | 1.50 | .85 |
| T1 | untagged (error) | 100.00 | 75.00 | | |

Qty: 26,300,000

Issued to mark the 100th anniversary of P.E.I.'s entry into Confederation.

## SCOTTISH SETTLERS

619
Scottish Settlers and "Hector"

Designer: Peter Swan.

Lithography (4 colours), pane of 50
Ashton-Potter Limited

**1973, Jul 20** **Tagged, GT2** **Perf 12.3x12.7**

| | | NH-VF | ⊙F | PB | FDC |
|---|---|---|---|---|---|
| **619** | **8¢ multicoloured** | .30 | .20 | 1.50 | .85 |
| i | yellow paper (150–200 exist) | 275.00 | 150.00 | 1,250.00* | |
| T1 | untagged (error) | 125.00 | | | |

Qty: 27,487,000

* Blank (non-inscription) corner block of 4. No inscription blocks exist.

Issued for the bicentenary of the arrival of Scottish Settlers at Pictou, N.S.

## ROYAL VISIT

620
Queen Elizabeth II

621
Queen Elizabeth II

Designer: Allan Robb Fleming; designed and engraved by George Arthur Gundersen. Based on a photograph by Anthony Buckley.

Engraved (2 colour) and Photogravure (2 colours), panes of 25
British American Bank Note Company

**1973, Aug 2** **Tagged, GT2** **Perf 12.0x12.5**

| | | NH–VF | ⊙F | PB | FDC |
|---|---|---|---|---|---|
| **620** | **8¢ silver and multicoloured**, dull | .30 | .20 | 1.50 | .85 |
| i | HB | 7.50 | 1.50 | 37.50 | |
| ii | F | 1.00 | .35 | 5.00 | |

Qty: 27,500,000

| | | NH–VF | ⊙F | PB | FDC |
|---|---|---|---|---|---|
| **621** | **15¢ gold and multicoloured**, dull | .90 | .85 | 4.50 | 1.40† |
| i | "bronze" (brighter gold) shade | 2.00 | 1.45 | 10.00 | |
| ii | F | 2.00 | 1.00 | 10.00 | |
| iii | MF | 3.50 | 1.25 | 15.00 | |
| T1 | untagged (error) | 75.00 | 40.00 | 400.00* | 75.00 |

Qty: 14,300,000

† Commercial use $10.

* Price is for inscription block of 4; blank corner block of 4 value is $350.00

**Nos. 620, 621 (2) combination FDC** **1.50**

Issued to mark the visit of Queen Elizabeth to open the Commonwealth Heads of Government meeting in Ottawa.

**622**
Nellie McClung

**623**
"COJO" Symbol

**624**
"COJO" Symbol

## NELLIE McCLUNG

Designer: Stephen Mennie.

Lithography (4 colours), pane of 50
Ashton-Potter Limited

**1973, Aug 29** **Tagged, GT2** **Perf 10.8x11.0**

| | | NH–VF | ⊙F | PB | FDC |
|---|---|---|---|---|---|
| **622** | **8¢ multicoloured** | .30 | .20 | 1.50 | .85 |
| T1 | untagged (error) | 125.00 | | | |

Qty: 24,330,000

Issued to honour women's suffrage leader Nellie McClung (1873–1951) on the 100th anniversary of her birth.

## 1976 OLYMPIC GAMES

Designer: Alois Matanovic.

Lithography (5 colours), panes of 50
Ashton-Potter Limited

**1973, Sep 20** **Tagged, GT2** **Perf 12.0x12.5**

| | | NH–VF | ⊙F | PB | FDC |
|---|---|---|---|---|---|
| **623** | **8¢ silver and multicoloured** | .25 | .20 | 1.25 | .85 |
| T1 | untagged (error) | 125.00 | | | |
| **624** | **15¢ gold and multicoloured**, HF | .85 | .75 | 4.25 | 1.40† |
| i | HB | 5.00 | 1.00 | 25.00 | |
| T1 | untagged (error) | 150.00 | | | |

Qty: 8¢: 22,000,000; 15¢: 11,000,000

† Commercial use: $10.

**Nos. 623, 624 (2) combination FDC** **1.50**

First in a series of 35 stamps promoting the 21st Olympiad in Montreal in 1976. "COJO" stands for Comité Organisateur des Jeux Olympiques. See also 629–632, 644–647, 656–657, 664–666, 681–688, B1–B12.

Definitive Timeline:
1973, Oct 17 1¢–6¢ low-value Caricatures (586–591)
8¢ QEII Caricature (593)

## CHRISTMAS

**625**
Ice Skate

**626**
Dove

**627**
Santa Claus

**628**
Shepherd and Star

Designer: Arnaud Maggs.

Lithography (4 colours), panes of 100
Ashton-Potter Limited

**1973, Nov 7** **Tagged, GT2** **Perf 12.5x12.0**

| | | NH–VF | ⊙F | PB | FDC |
|---|---|---|---|---|---|
| **625** | **6¢ multicoloured** | .25 | .20 | 1.25 | .80 |
| a | black double printed | 150.00 | | | |
| ii | imperf. right side of stamp & margin, block of 4 | 900.00 | | | |
| T1 | untagged (error) | 75.00 | 50.00 | 375.00 | 100.00 |

Qty: 140,300,000

| | | NH–VF | ⊙F | PB | FDC |
|---|---|---|---|---|---|
| **626** | **8¢ multicoloured** | .25 | .20 | 1.25 | .85 |
| i | "extra feather" variety (pos. 4) | 7.50 | 5.00 | | |
| T1 | untagged (error) | 75.00 | | | |

Qty: 112,900,000

Lithography (4 colours), pane of 50

**Perf 10.8x11.0**

| | | NH–VF | ⊙F | PB | FDC |
|---|---|---|---|---|---|
| **627** | **10¢ multicoloured** | .40 | .40 | 2.00 | 1.20 |
| T1 | untagged (error) | — | 75.00 | | |

Qty: 11,755,000

Lithography (5 colours), pane of 50

| | | NH–VF | ⊙F | PB | FDC |
|---|---|---|---|---|---|
| **628** | **15¢ multicoloured** | .85 | .85 | 4.25 | 1.40 |
| T1 | untagged (error) | — | 100.00 | | |
| i | missing green & part of tagging, only one "used" single known | — | *7,000.00* | — | — |

Qty: 17,050,000

**Nos. 625–628 (4) combination FDC** **2.10**

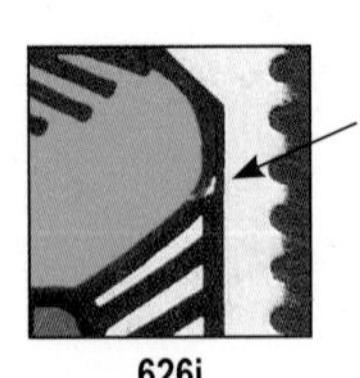

**626i**

**628i**

Timeline:
1973, Nov 28 8¢ Algonkian Indians (568–569)

QE II — 1970's

## 1974

Timeline:
1974, Jan 16 8¢ Pacific Coast Indians (570–571)

Timeline:
1974, Feb 22 8¢ Pacific Coast Indians (572–573)

### "KEEP FIT" SUMMER SPORTS

629 Swimming — 630 Jogging

631 Cycling — 632 Hiking

Designer: David Hunter. Engraved by Donald J. Mitchell.
Engraved (1 colour), pane of 50
Canadian Bank Note Company

**1974, Mar 22** — **Tagged, GT2** — **Perf 12**

| | | NH–VF | ⊙F | PB | FDC |
|---|---|---|---|---|---|
| 629 | **8¢ dark blue**, dull | .50 | .20 | | .85 |
| i | HB | .75 | .30 | | |
| T1 | untagged (error), HB | 75.00 | | | |
| 630 | **8¢ dark blue**, dull | .50 | .20 | | .85 |
| i | HB | .75 | .30 | | |
| T1 | untagged (error), HB | 75.00 | | | |
| 631 | **8¢ dark blue**, dull | .50 | .20 | | .85 |
| i | HB | .75 | .30 | | |
| T1 | untagged (error), HB | 75.00 | | | |
| 632 | **8¢ dark blue**, dull | .50 | .20 | | .85 |
| i | HB | .75 | .30 | | |
| T1 | untagged (error), HB | 75.00 | | | |
| a | se-tenant block of 4 (629–632) | 2.20 | 1.00 | 2.50 | 1.80 |
| ai | se-tenant block of 4, HB (629i–632i) | 3.20 | 1.30 | 3.75 | |
| aT1 | se-tenant block, untagged (error), HB | 300.00 | | | |

Qty: 629/631/632: 13,969,200 of each; 630: 15,133,300

The stamps are designed so that the "COJO" symbol can be seen when the stamps are held at an oblique angle.
See also 623–624, 644–647, 656–657, 664–666, 681–688, B1–B12.

Definitive Timeline:
1974, Apr 8 7¢ low-value Caricature (592)

Timeline:
1974, Apr 17 8¢+2¢, 10¢+5¢, 15¢+5¢ Olympic Symbols, semi-postals (B1–B3)

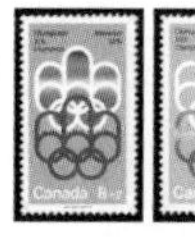

### WINNIPEG CENTENNIAL

633
Portage and Main

Designer: Jack R. MacDonald. Photo of Portage & Main (1872) by James Penrose (1845–1918).
Lithography (4 colours) and Embossing, pane of 50
Ashton-Potter Limited

**1974, May 3** — **Tagged, GT2** — **Perf 12.3x12.7**

| | | NH–VF | ⊙F | PB | FDC |
|---|---|---|---|---|---|
| 633 | **8¢ multicoloured**, 3mm bar tag | .30 | .20 | 1.50 | .85 |
| i | 3.75mm bar tagging | 3.00 | 2.00 | 15.00* | |
| T1 | untagged (error) | 150.00 | 100.00 | 750.00* | |

Qty: 28,320,000
* Blank corner block of 4.

Issued to mark the centenary of Winnipeg's incorporation as a city.

### LETTER CARRIER SERVICE

634 635
636 637
638 639

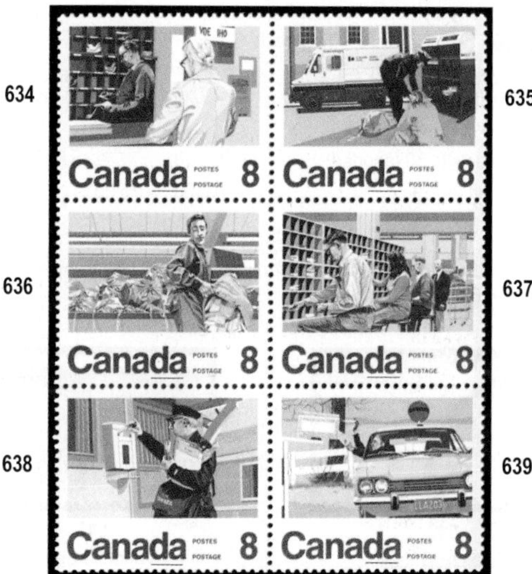

Designer: Stephen Mennie
Lithography (4 colours), pane of 50
Ashton-Potter Limited

**1974, Jun 11** — **Tagged, GT2** — **Perf 13.3**

| | | NH–VF | ⊙F | PB | FDC |
|---|---|---|---|---|---|
| 634 | **8¢ Postmaster** | .50 | .45 | | .85 |
| T1 | untagged (error) | 100.00 | | | |
| 635 | **8¢ Mail courier** | .50 | .45 | | .85 |
| T1 | untagged (error) | 100.00 | | | |
| 636 | **8¢ Mail handler** | .50 | .45 | | .85 |
| T1 | untagged (error) | 100.00 | | | |
| 637 | **8¢ Postal clerks** (sorting) | .50 | .45 | | .85 |
| T1 | untagged (error) | 100.00 | | | |
| 638 | **8¢ Letter carrier** | .50 | .45 | | .85 |
| T1 | untagged (error) | 100.00 | | | |
| 639 | **8¢ Rural mail courier** | .50 | .45 | | .85 |
| T1 | untagged (error) | 100.00 | | | |
| a | se-tenant block of 6, (634–639) | 5.00 | 5.00 | 6.00 | 2.40 |
| aT1 | se-tenant block of 6, untagged (error) | 600.00 | | | |

Qty: 634–637/639: 5,263,200 of each; 638: 6,579,000.

Issued to mark the 100th anniversary of letter carrier service in Canada.

640
Agricultural Education

641
Telephones

## AGRICULTURAL COLLEGE

Designer: Allan J. McAllister, Mary Brett, and Patrick George Cowley-Brown.
Lithography (6 colours), pane of 50
Ashton-Potter Limited

**1974, Jul 12** **Tagged, GT2** **Perf 12.7x12.3**

| | | NH–VF | ⊙F | PB | FDC |
|---|---|---|---|---|---|
| **640** | **8¢ multicoloured** | .30 | .20 | 1.50 | .85 |

Qty: 24,072,000

Issued to mark the centenary of the Ontario Agricultural College.

## TELEPHONE CENTENARY

Designer: Ray Webber.
Lithography (4 colours), pane of 50
Ashton-Potter Limited

**1974, Jul 26** **Tagged, GT2** **Perf 12.5**

| | | NH–VF | ⊙F | PB | FDC |
|---|---|---|---|---|---|
| **641** | **8¢ multicoloured** | .30 | .20 | 1.50 | .85 |
| a | imperf. pair, and untagged (two sheets of 50 reported) | 2,000.00 | | 5,000.00 | |
| T1 | untagged (error) | 100.00 | 75.00 | | |

Qty: 28,470,000

Issued to mark the centenary of the invention of the telephone by Alexander Graham Bell at Brantford, Ontario.

642
Bicycle Wheel

643
Mennonite Settlers

## CYCLING

Designer: Robert Burns of Burns & Cooper.
Engraved (1 colour) and Photogravure, pane of 50
British American Bank Note Company

**1974, Aug 7** **Tagged, GT2** **Perf 12.0x12.5**

| | | NH–VF | ⊙F | PB | FDC |
|---|---|---|---|---|---|
| **642** | **8¢ black, red and silver**, dull | .30 | .20 | 1.50 | .85 |
| i | hibrite paper | .60 | .30 | 3.00 | |
| ii | LF paper | 2.00 | | 10.00 | |
| T1 | untagged (error) | — | 150.00 | | |

Qty: 27,400,000

Issued on the occasion of the World Cycling Championships, Montreal.

## MENNONITE SETTLERS CENTENARY

Designer: Will Davies.
Lithography (4 colours), pane of 50
Ashton-Potter Limited

**1974, Aug 28** **Tagged, GT2** **Perf 12.5**

| | | NH–VF | ⊙F | PB | FDC |
|---|---|---|---|---|---|
| **643** | **8¢ multicoloured** | .30 | .20 | 1.50 | .85 |
| T1 | untagged (error) | 100.00 | 95.00 | | |

Qty: 28,700,000

Issued to mark the centenary of the arrival of Mennonite settlers in Manitoba.

## "KEEP FIT" WINTER SPORTS

644 Snowshoeing — 645 Skiing

646 Skating — 647 Curling

Designer: Hunter, Straker, Templeton Limited.
Engraved (1 colour), pane of 50
Canadian Bank Note Company

**1974, Sep 23** **Tagged, GT2** **Perf 13.3**

| | | NH–VF | ⊙F | PB | FDC |
|---|---|---|---|---|---|
| **644** | **8¢ red** | .50 | .20 | — | .85 |
| i | HB | 5.00 | 1.00 | | |
| T1 | untagged (error) | 125.00 | 100.00 | | |
| **645** | **8¢ red** | .50 | .20 | — | .85 |
| i | HB | 5.00 | 1.00 | | |
| T1 | untagged (error) | 125.00 | 100.00 | | |
| **646** | **8¢ red** | .50 | .20 | — | .85 |
| i | HB | 5.00 | 1.00 | | |
| T1 | untagged (error) | 125.00 | 100.00 | | |
| **647** | **8¢ red** | .50 | .20 | — | .85 |
| i | HB | 5.00 | 1.00 | | |
| T1 | untagged (error) | 125.00 | 100.00 | | |
| a | se-tenant block of 4 (644–647) | 2.20 | 1.00 | 2.50 | 1.80 |
| ai | as 'a' (block of 4), HB | 20.00 | | 25.00 | |
| aT1 | se-tenant block of 4, untagged (error) | 500.00 | | 600.00*† | |
| b | block or strip of 4 different, printed on gum side | 5,000.00§ | — | 6,000.00* | — |

Qty: 644/646: 15,496,000 of each; 645/647: 14,304,000 of each

* Blank corner block of 4.

§ Only one sheet reported. It was split up wrong, ruining several blocks/strips of 4 "different". Block or strip of 4 that are not all different valued at 50% of listed price.

† Just a few untagged (error) inscription blocks have been reported.

This issue exists on dull and on low fluorescent (LF) paper (same value).
The stamps are designed so that the "COJO" symbol can be seen when the stamps are held at an oblique angle.
See also 623–624, 629–632, 656–657, 664–666, 681–688, B1–B12.

## UNIVERSAL POSTAL UNION CENTENARY

648
Mercury and Winged Horses

649
Mercury and Winged Horses

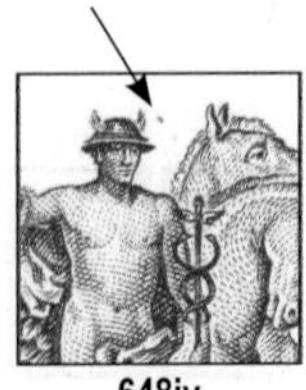

648iv

648v

648vi

Designer and engraver: George Arthur Gundersen.

Engraved (1 colour) and Photogravure (2 colours), panes of 50
British American Bank Note Company

**1974, Oct 9** **Tagged, GT2** **Perf 12.0x12.5**

| | | NH–VF | ⊙F | PB | FDC |
|---|---|---|---|---|---|
| **648** | **8¢ violet, red and blue**, DF, ribbed horiz. | .30 | .20 | 1.50 | .85 |
| i | red streak (vertical hairline) | 5.00 | 3.00 | 25.00 | |
| ii | ghost print ('Canada 8' doubled) | 5.00 | 3.00 | 25.00 | |
| iv | red dot to right of head (pos. 5) | 7.00 | 3.50 | | |
| v | red dot between 'Ca' of 'Canada' | 7.00 | 3.50 | | |
| vi | red line (dots) below 'Union 1874-' | 7.00 | 3.50 | | |
| iii | F, smooth | 2.00 | | 10.00 | |
| vii | DF, smooth | 5.00 | 1.00 | 25.00 | |
| T1 | untagged (error) | — | 125.00 | | |

Qty: 27,500,000

| | | NH–VF | ⊙F | PB | FDC |
|---|---|---|---|---|---|
| **649** | **15¢ violet, red and blue**, LF, ribbed, horiz. | 1.25 | 1.00 | 6.25 | 1.10† |
| i | HB, smooth | 15.00 | 5.00 | 75.00 | |
| ii | LF, smooth | 5.00 | 1.50 | 25.00 | |

Qty: 14,300,000

† Commercial use: $10.

**Nos. 648, 649 (2) combination FDC** **1.50**

Issued to mark the 100th anniversary of the Universal Postal Union.

## CHRISTMAS

650
*Nativity,*
by Jean Paul Lemieux

651
*Skaters at Hull,*
by Henri Masson

652
*The Ice Cone,*
by Robert C. Todd

653
*Laurentian Village,*
by Clarence A. Gagnon

Designer: Wallis & Matanovic.

Paintings: 6¢: by Jean Paul Lemieux; 8¢: painting by Henri Masson; 10¢: by Robert Clow Todd; 15¢: by Clarence Alphonse Gagnon.

Lithography (4 colours), panes of 50
Ashton-Potter Limited

**1974, Nov 1** **Tagged, GT2** **Perf 13.3**

| | | NH–VF | ⊙F | PB | FDC |
|---|---|---|---|---|---|
| **650** | **6¢ multicoloured**, HB | .25 | .20 | 1.25 | .80 |
| ii | red tear on blue skirt (pos. 46) | 40.00 *EP* | 35.00 | 50.00 | 40.00† |
| i | DF | 7.00 | 1.00 | 35.00 | |
| T1 | untagged (error) | | 100.00 | | |

Qty: 133,490,000

† Value is for plate block on FDC.

| | | NH–VF | ⊙F | PB | FDC |
|---|---|---|---|---|---|
| **651** | **8¢ multicoloured**, HB on back | .25 | .20 | 1.20 | .85 |
| ii | 'Ma' of 'Masson' joined (pos. 6) | 25.00 | 15.00 | | |
| i | MF on back | 2.00 | | 10.00 | |
| T1 | untagged (error) | | 100.00 | | |

Qty: 106,120,000

| | | NH–VF | ⊙F | PB | FDC |
|---|---|---|---|---|---|
| **652** | **10¢ multicoloured** | .50 | .40 | 2.50 | .90 |

Qty: 14,377,000

| | | NH–VF | ⊙F | PB | FDC |
|---|---|---|---|---|---|
| **653** | **15¢ multicoloured** | .85 | .75 | 4.55 | 1.10 |

Qty: 20,360,000

**Nos. 650–653 (4) combination FDC** **2.10**

There are many shades on this set (650–653), particularly on the 10¢. These are interesting, but of little added value.

650ii

CHRISTMAS
NOËL
Henri Masson

651ii

## GUGLIELMO MARCONI

654
Marconi and Signal Hill

Designer: John Bernard Boyle.

Lithography (4 colours), pane of 50
Ashton-Potter Limited

**1974, Nov 15** **Tagged, GT2** **Perf 13.3**

| | | NH–VF | ⊙F | PB | FDC |
|---|---|---|---|---|---|
| **654** | **8¢ multicoloured** | .30 | .20 | 1.50 | .85 |
| T1 | untagged (error) | 100.00 | 75.00 | | |

Qty: 31,185,000

Issued to mark the 100th anniversary of the birth of Guglielmo Marconi (1874–1937), inventor of the wireless.

## WILLIAM HAMILTON MERRITT

655
Merritt and Welland Canal

Designer: William Rueter. Based on a painting by Robert Reginald Whale.
Based on a wood engraving by Frederick Boley Schell Hogan.

Engraved (BABN, 1 colour) and Lithography (CBN, 5 colours), pane of 50
Canadian Bank Note Company *and* British American Bank Note Company

**1974, Nov 29** **Tagged, GT2** **Perf 13.0x13.4**

| | | NH–VF | ⊙F | PB | FDC |
|---|---|---|---|---|---|
| **655** | **8¢ multicoloured**, DF | .30 | .20 | 1.50 | .85 |
| i | LF | 4.00 | 1.00 | 20.00 | |

Qty: 31,200,000

Minor colour shifts result in "hair over barn" variety, value $2.

To mark the 150th anniversary of the construction of the Welland Canal between Lakes Ontario and Erie, a project conceived and supervised by William Hamilton Merritt (1793–1862).

## 1975

Timeline:
1975, Feb 5 8¢+2¢, 10¢+5¢, 15¢+5¢ Water Sports, semi-postals (B4–B6)

### OLYMPIC SCULPTURES

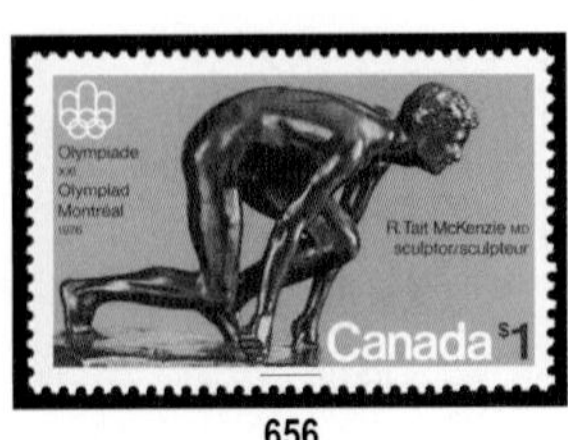

656
*The Sprinter*, by Robert Tait McKenzie

657
*The Plunger*,
by Robert Tait McKenzie

Designer: Allan Robb Fleming.
Based on sculptures by Robert Tait McKenzie and photographs by Eberhard Otto.
Lithography (6 colours) and Embossed, panes of 8
Ashton-Potter Limited

| 1975, Mar 14 | Tagged, GT2 | | | Perf 12.5x12.0 | |
|---|---|---|---|---|---|
| | | NH–VF | ⊙F | PB | FDC |
| 656 | **$1 multicoloured**, MF | 3.00 | 3.00 | 15.00 | 3.60 |
| | miniature pane of 8† (2 x 4) | 30.00 | | | |
| i | dull paper‡ | 6.50 | 4.50 | 30.00* | |
| | dull paper, pane of 8† (2 x 4) | 60.00 | | | |

Qty: 10,336,000

| | | | | Perf 12.0x12.5 | |
|---|---|---|---|---|---|
| 657 | **$2 multicoloured**, MF | 6.00 | 6.00 | 30.00 | 6.60 |
| | miniature pane of 8† (4 x 2) | 60.00 | | | |
| i | dull paper‡ | 15.00 | 10.00 | 75.00* | |
| | dull paper, pane of 8† (4 x 2) | 120.00 | | | |

Qty: 10,320,000
‡ Dull paper varieties are on non-philatelic stock, without plate blocks.
* Blank corner block of 4.

**Nos. 656, 657 (2) combination FDC** 12.50

† Four different philatelic panes exist depending upon the position of the corner inscription.

Issued to publicize the 21st Olympic Games and to honour Canadian sculptor, Robert Tait McKenzie, MD (1867–1938).
See also 623–624, 629–632, 644–647, 664–666, 681–688, B1–B12.

Timeline:
1975, Apr 4 8¢ Subarctic Indians (574–577)

### CANADIAN AUTHORS

658 Lucy Maud Montgomery
659 Louis Hémon

Designer: 658: Peter Swan; 659: Hal Wallis.
658: Typographed by Bernard N.J. Reilander. 659: Based on an illustration by Clarence Alphonse Gagnon.
Lithography (5 colours), pane of 50
Ashton-Potter Limited

| 1975, May 15 | Tagged, GT2 | | | Perf 13.3 | |
|---|---|---|---|---|---|
| | | NH–VF | ⊙F | PB | FDC |
| 658 | **8¢ blue and multicoloured** | .30 | .20 | | .85 |
| T1 | untagged (error) | 150.00 | 100.00 | | |
| 659 | **8¢ brown and multicoloured** | .30 | .20 | | .85 |
| i | "light in window" variety (pos. 22) | 20.00 | 10.00 | | |
| T1 | untagged (error) | 150.00 | 100.00 | | |
| a | se-tenant pair (658, 659) | .70 | .40 | 1.50 | 1.25 |
| ai | as 'a', double print of 'Canada 8' on 658 | 500.00 | | 1,200.00 | |

Qty: 13,550,000 of each

For non-denominated postal card of Anne of Green Gables design, see UX132.
Issued to honour Canadian authors Lucy Maud Montgomery (1874–1942) and Louis Hémon (1880–1913).

659i

### CANADIAN PERSONALITIES

660
Marguerite Bourgeoys

661
Alphonse Desjardins

Designer: 660: Jacques Roy; Based on a painting by Elmina Lachance. 661: Design & Communication.
Lithography (4 colours), panes of 50
Ashton-Potter Limited

| 1975, May 30 | Tagged, GT2 | | | Perf 12.6x12.2 | |
|---|---|---|---|---|---|
| | | NH–VF | ⊙F | PB | FDC |
| 660 | **8¢ multicoloured**, DF, ribbed, horiz. | .30 | .20 | 1.50 | .85 |
| i | "red thumb" variety (pos. 11), DF, ribbed, horiz. | 7.50 | 3.75 | 10.00 | 7.50 |
| iii | "white eye" variety (pos. 11), DF, ribbed, horiz. | 10.00 | 5.00 | 12.50 | |
| ii | F, smooth | 2.00 | .30 | 9.00 | |
| iv | as "i", F, smooth | 20.00 | 10.00 | 25.00 | |
| v | NF, smooth | 3.00 | .50 | 15.00 | |
| vi | as "i", NF, smooth | 20.00 | 5.00 | 50.00 | |
| T1 | untagged (error)* | 100.00 | | | |

Qty: 13,400,000
* All copies have tag residue inside perf holes from perf pins.

| | | | | | |
|---|---|---|---|---|---|
| 661 | **8¢ multicoloured**, NF, smooth | .30 | .20 | 1.50 | .85 |
| i | F, smooth | 3.50 | .50 | 16.00 | |
| ii | DF, ribbed, horiz. | 3.00 | .50 | 14.00 | |

Qty: 15,500,000

Marguerite Bourgeoys (1620–1700) founded the first girls' school in New France, the Congrégation de Notre Dame in Montreal. Alphonse Desjardins (1854–1920) was a journalist and founder of the first credit union in North America.

660i/iv/vi

662 Dr. Samuel Chown — 663 Dr. John Cook

Designer: William Southern. Engraved by George Arthur Gundersen.
Engraved (1 colour) and Photogravure (2 colours), panes of 50
British American Bank Note Company

| 1975, May 30 | Tagged, GT2 | | | Perf 12.0x12.5 | |
|---|---|---|---|---|---|
| | | NH–VF | ⊙F | PB | FDC |
| **662** | **8¢ dark brown, yellow and buff,** dull | .30 | .25 | | .85 |
| i | F | 2.50 | .50 | | |
| **663** | **8¢ dark brown, yellow and buff,** dull | .30 | .25 | | .85 |
| i | F | 2.50 | .50 | | |
| a | se-tenant pair, dull (662, 663) | .70 | .60 | 1.50 | 1.25 |
| ai | double paper (block of 4)† | 1,000.00 | | | |
| aii | se-tenant pair, F | 6.50 | | 13.00 | |

Qty: 8,050,000 of each
† 5 blocks exist from one pane of 50.

Dr. Samuel Chown (1853–1933), a Methodist minister and one of the founders of the United Church of Canada; and Dr. John Cook (1805–1892), first Moderator of the Presbyterian Church in Canada.

## TRACK AND FIELD SPORTS

664 Pole Vault

665 Marathon

666 Hurdles

Designer: Peter Swan.
Lithography (5 colours), panes of 50
Ashton-Potter Limited

| 1975, Jun 11 | Tagged, GT2 | | | Perf 12.0x12.5 | |
|---|---|---|---|---|---|
| | | NH–VF | ⊙F | PB | FDC |
| **664** | **20¢ dark blue and multicoloured** | .85 | .70 | 4.25 | 1.20 |

Qty: 15,400,000

| | | NH–VF | ⊙F | PB | FDC |
|---|---|---|---|---|---|
| **665** | **25¢ maroon and multicoloured** | 1.00 | .80 | 5.00 | 1.35 |
| T1 | untagged (error) | 100.00 | 75.00 | | |

Qty: 13,200,000

| | | NH–VF | ⊙F | PB | FDC |
|---|---|---|---|---|---|
| **666** | **50¢ green and multicoloured,** HB | 2.00 | 1.50 | 10.00 | 2.10 |
| i | NF cream paper | 5.00 | 2.50 | 25.00* | |

Qty: 13,200,000

* Plate blocks of No. 666i are rare. Price shown is for blank corner block of 4. Plate inscription blocks $50.00.
Note: The 25¢ (665) with bluish lettering in 'Canada 25' etc. is a change in colour caused by exposure to sunlight (ultra violet) and no premium value.

**Nos. 664–666 (3) combination FDC** **4.00**

See also 623, 624, 629–632, 644–647, 656–657, 681–688, B1–B12.

## CALGARY CENTENNIAL

667
Calgary Stampede

Designer: Bernard N.J. Reilander. Based on a photograph by Walter Petrigo.
Lithography (4 colours), panes of 50
Ashton-Potter Limited

| 1975, Jul 3 | Tagged, GT2 | | | Perf 12.0x12.5 | |
|---|---|---|---|---|---|
| | | NH–VF | ⊙F | PB | FDC |
| **667** | **8¢ grey and multicoloured** | .30 | .20 | 1.50 | .85 |
| i | blue dot on "n" of "Canada" † | 3.00 *EP* | 1.50 | 15.00 | 2.50 |
| ii | "fly beside mane" (4 stamps in row 2) | 3.00 | 1.50 | * | |
| T1 | untagged (error) | 200.00 | 150.00 | | |

Qty: 25,900,000
† Also called the "bird nest" variety.
* Plate block: UL $10.00, UR $7.50.

Issued for the 100th anniversary of the founding of Calgary.

667i

667ii

## UNITED NATIONS INTERNATIONAL WOMEN'S YEAR

668
Female Symbol

Designer: Susan McPhee.
Engraved (1 colour) and Photogravure (2 colours), pane of 100
British American Bank Note Company

| 1975, Jul 14 | Tagged, GT2 | | | Perf 13.3 | |
|---|---|---|---|---|---|
| | | NH–VF | ⊙F | PB | FDC |
| **668** | **8¢ deep yellow, grey and black,** F | .30 | .20 | 1.50 | .85 |
| i | dull | 2.50 | .50 | 15.00 | |
| T1 | untagged (error) | 100.00 | 95.00 | | |

Qty: 32,500,000

Timeline:
**1975, Aug 6** 8¢+2¢, 10¢+5¢, 15¢+5¢ Combat Sports, semi-postals (B7–B9)

## SUPREME COURT CENTENARY

**669**
*Justice*, by Allward

Designer: Allan Robb Fleming. Based on a sculpture by Walter Seymour Allward.
Lithography (5 colours), pane of 50
Ashton-Potter Limited

| **1975, Sep 2** | **Tagged, GT2** | | | **Perf 12.5** | |
|---|---|---|---|---|---|
| | | **NH–VF** | **⊙F** | **PB** | **FDC** |
| **669** | **8¢ multicoloured** | .30 | .20 | 1.50 | .85 |
| **T1** | untagged (error) | 80.00 | 50.00 | | |
| | Strong kiss prints of black inscriptions exist, showing "double black" | 125.00 | | 600.00* | |

Qty: 27,747,000
* Blank corner block of 4.

Issued to mark the 100th anniversary of the Supreme Court of Canada.

## COASTAL VESSELS

**670** Wm. D. Lawrence — **672** Neptune

**671** Beaver — **673** Quadra

Designer: Tom Bjarnason. Engraved by Charles Gordon Yorke.
Engraved (3 colours) and Photogravure (3 colours), pane of 50
British American Bank Note Company

| **1975, Sep 24** | **Tagged, GT2** | | | **Perf 12.9x13.3** | |
|---|---|---|---|---|---|
| | | **NH–VF** | **⊙F** | **PB** | **FDC** |
| **670** | **8¢ light brown**, LF | .50 | .50 | | .85 |
| **i** | dull | .75 | .75 | | |
| **ii** | HB | 4.50 | 4.50 | | |
| **iii** | 'water line' plate scratch (pos. 12,14), dull | 5.00 | | | |
| **iv** | 'water line' plate scratch (pos. 12,14), HB | 12.00 | | | |
| **T1** | untagged (error) | 100.00 | | | |
| **671** | **8¢ dull yellow green**, LF | .50 | .50 | | .85 |
| **i** | dull | .75 | .75 | | |
| **ii** | HB | 4.50 | 4.50 | | |
| **T1** | untagged (error) | 100.00 | | | |
| **672** | **8¢ grey-green**, LF | .50 | .50 | — | .85 |
| **i** | dull | .75 | .75 | | |
| **ii** | HB | 4.50 | 4.50 | | |
| **iii** | 'water line' plate scratch (pos. 11,13), dull | 5.00 | | | |
| **iv** | 'water line' plate scratch (pos. 11,13), HB | 12.00 | | | |
| **T1** | untagged (error) | 100.00 | | | |
| **673** | **8¢ yellow brown**, LF | .50 | .50 | — | .85 |
| **i** | dull | .75 | .75 | | |
| **ii** | HB | 4.50 | 4.50 | | |
| **T1** | untagged (error) | 100.00 | | | |

| | | **NH–VF** | **⊙F** | **PB** | **FDC** |
|---|---|---|---|---|---|
| **a** | se-tenant block of 4, LF (670–673) | 2.25 | 2.25 | 3.00 | 1.80 |
| **ai** | se-tenant block of 4, dull paper (670i–673i) | 3.25 | 3.25 | 4.00 | — |
| **aii** | se-tenant block of 4, HB (670ii–673ii) | 18.25 | 18.25 | 18.50 | — |
| **aT1** | se-tenant block of 4, untagged (error) | 400.00 | | 500.00* | |

Qty: 670/672: 7,410,000 of each; 671/673: 6,840,000 of each
* Blank corner block of 4.

So-called "missing anchor hole" (previously 672iii) is found on most copies of #672 on a sheet. Price same as with anchor hole. This issue has a number of minor varieties due to incomplete registration of the intaglio designs, colour shifts, and other problems. Prices 3x – 5x those of normal stamps.

**672**
Left: normal Right: 'short' rigging

See also 700–703, 744–747 and 776–779.

## CHRISTMAS

**674** Santa Claus — **675** Skater — **676** Child — **677** Family and Christmas

**678** Gift Box — **679** Christmas Trees

Designer: Bernard N.J. Reilander
Lithography (4 colours), panes of 50
Ashton-Potter Limited

| **1975, Oct 22** | **Tagged, GT2** | | | **Perf 13.3** | |
|---|---|---|---|---|---|
| | | **NH–VF** | **⊙F** | **PB** | **FDC** |
| **674** | **6¢ multicoloured** | .25 | .20 | | .80 |
| **T1** | untagged (error) | — | 60.00 | | |

Based on a drawing by Gillian Kelly

| | | **NH–VF** | **⊙F** | **PB** | **FDC** |
|---|---|---|---|---|---|
| **675** | **6¢ multicoloured** | .25 | .20 | | .80 |
| **T1** | untagged (error) | — | 70.00 | | |
| **a** | se-tenant pair (674, 675) | .50 | .40 | 1.00 | 1.10 |

Based on a drawing by Bill Cawsey
Qty: 73,000,000 of each
Nos 674–675 exist on non-inscripted sheets that do not have vertical perfs in the bottom selvedge. Price $15 /block of four; $20 /CB

| | | **NH–VF** | **⊙F** | **PB** | **FDC** |
|---|---|---|---|---|---|
| **676** | **8¢ multicoloured** | .25 | .20 | | .85 |
| **i** | single, black double printed* | 125.00 | — | | |
| **ii** | single, black triple printed** | | 300.00 | | |
| **T1** | untagged (error) | 60.00 | 40.00 | | |

Based on a drawing by Danielle Hébert

**Rates:**
Jan 1, 1976–Dec 31, 1976 International: 20¢ (0–1 oz), 35¢ (1–2 oz)
From Mar 1, 1976: USA (air mail): 10¢

*single usage:* USA air 10¢: 10.00 | International 20¢: $25.00

| | | NH–VF | ⊙F | PB | FDC |
|---|---|---|---|---|---|
| 677 | **8¢ multicoloured** | .25 | .20 | | .85 |
| b | single, black double printed* | 125.00 | — | | |
| T1 | untagged (error) | 60.00 | 40.00 | | |
| a | se-tenant pair (676, 677) | .60 | .40 | 1.25 | 1.25 |
| ai | pair, black double printed* (676i, 677b) | 250.00 | — | | |
| aii | missing legend on bottom margin pair† | 750.00 | — | | |
| c | pair, black triple printed** | 400.00 | — | | |

Based on a drawing by Lorraine Caldwell
Qty: 62,000,000 of each

* The strength of the doubling varies.

** Strong 2nd impression with wide separation from the 1st. Third impression just behind 2nd & weaker.

† Shifted perforations cut off the legend CHRISTMAS / NOËL leaving a wide white margin at bottom (5 pairs known).

Nos 676–677 exist on non-inscripted sheets that do not have vertical perfs in the bottom selvedge. Price $15 /block of four; $20 /CB

| | | NH–VF | ⊙F | PB | FDC |
|---|---|---|---|---|---|
| 678 | **10¢ multicoloured** | .35 | .30 | 1.75 | .90 |
| T1 | untagged (error) | 150.00 | | | |

Based on a drawing by Debbie Lovely
Qty: 20,547,000

| | | NH–VF | ⊙F | PB | FDC |
|---|---|---|---|---|---|
| 679 | **15¢ multicoloured** | .60 | .60 | 3.00 | 1.10 |
| i | missing blue "repellex" error, strip of 5 ‡ | 2,000.00 | | | |
| T1 | untagged (error) | 125.00 | 75.00 | | |

Based on a drawing by Robert Kowalski
Qty: 21,000,000

‡ Repellex error affects 5 stamps in horizontal strip with right stamp totally missing blue (see photo on page 27); a second strip is recorded missing parts of colour on all 5 stamps in strip - $800.00

**Nos. 674–679 (6) combination FDC** **2.60**

These Christmas stamps were designed by Canadian school children.

677ai 676ii 677aiii

## ROYAL CANADIAN LEGION

680
Legion Emblem and Bugle

Designer: Rudy Kovach.

Engraved (1 colour) and Photogravure (3 colours), pane of 50
British American Bank Note Company

**1975, Nov 10** **Tagged, GT2** **Perf 12.9x13.3**

| | | NH–VF | ⊙F | PB | FDC |
|---|---|---|---|---|---|
| 680 | **8¢ grey and multicoloured**, NF | .30 | .20 | 1.50 | .85 |
| i | LF | 3.00 | .50 | 15.00 | |
| ii | MF | 5.00 | 1.00 | 25.00 | |

Qty: 26,400,000

Issued to mark the 50th anniversary of the Royal Canadian Legion.

# 1976

Timeline:
**1976, Jan 7** 8¢+2¢, 10¢+5¢, 20¢+5¢ Team Sports, semi-postals (B10–B12)

## OLYMPIC CEREMONIES

681
Olympic Torch

682
Opening Ceremony

683
Medal Ceremony

Designer: Peter Swan.

Lithography (4 colours), Plates of 200 subjects in four panes of 50
Ashton-Potter Limited

**1976, Jun 18** **Tagged, GT2** **Perf 13.3**

| | | NH–VF | ⊙F | PB | FDC |
|---|---|---|---|---|---|
| 681 | **8¢ multicoloured**, LF | .25 | .20 | 1.25 | .85 |
| i | missing brown background (repellex) | *2,500.00* | | | |
| ii | NF | 5.00 | 1.00 | 25.00 | |
| T1 | untagged (error) | | 75.00 | | |

Qty: 38,500,000

| | | NH–VF | ⊙F | PB | FDC |
|---|---|---|---|---|---|
| 682 | **20¢ multicoloured**, NF | 1.00 | .85 | 5.00 | 1.20 |
| T1 | untagged (error) | — | 60.00 | | |
| i | LF | 4.00 | 1.00 | 20.00 | |

Qty: 15,400,000

| | | NH–VF | ⊙F | PB | FDC |
|---|---|---|---|---|---|
| 683 | **25¢ multicoloured** | 1.25 | 1.00 | 6.75 | 1.35 |

Qty: 12,600,000

**Nos. 681–683 (3) combination FDC** **2.60**

## OLYMPIC ARTS and CULTURE

684
Communications

685
Handicrafts

686
Performing Arts

Designer: Ray Webber.

Lithography (4 colours), Plates of 200 subjects in four panes of 50
Canadian Bank Note Company

**1976, Feb 6** **Tagged, GT2** **Perf 12.0x12.5**

| | | NH–VF | ⊙F | PB | FDC |
|---|---|---|---|---|---|
| 684 | **20¢ grey and multicoloured** | 1.75 | .85 | 8.75 | 1.20 |
| T1 | untagged (error) | 100.00 | 50.00 | | |

Qty: 11,050,000

| | | NH–VF | ⊙F | PB | FDC |
|---|---|---|---|---|---|
| 685 | **25¢ ocher and multicoloured** | 2.00 | 1.00 | 10.50 | 1.35 |

Qty: 9,450,000

| | | NH–VF | ⊙F | PB | FDC |
|---|---|---|---|---|---|
| 686 | **50¢ blue and multicoloured** | 3.25 | 1.75 | 16.25 | 2.10 |

Qty: 9,700,000

**Nos. 684–686 (3) combination FDC** **4.00**

## OLYMPIC SITES

687
Notre-Dame and Place Ville Marie

688
Olympic Stadium

Designer: Jean Mercier and Pierre Mercier.
Engraved (2 colours) and Photogravure (2 colours)
Plates of 96 subjects in twelve panes of 8
British American Bank Note Company

**1976, Mar 12** **Tagged, GT2** **Perf 13.3**

| | | NH–VF | ⊙F | PB | FDC |
|---|---|---|---|---|---|
| 687 | **$1 silver and multicoloured**, dull | 4.50 | 3.00 | 22.50 | 3.60 |
| | miniature pane of 8, dull† | 40.00 | | | |
| i | LF/F | 3.50 | 3.00 | 17.50 | |
| | pane of 8, LF/F† | 30.00 | | | |
| ii | LF | 4.50 | 3.00 | 22.50 | |
| | pane of 8, LF† | 40.00 | | | |

Qty: 4,520,000

| | | NH–VF | ⊙F | PB | FDC |
|---|---|---|---|---|---|
| 688 | **$2 gold and multicoloured**, dull | 7.00 | 6.00 | 35.00 | 6.60 |
| | minitature pane of 8, dull† | 60.00 | | | |
| T1 | untagged (error) | 125.00 | | | |
| i | F | 9.00 | 6.00 | 45.00 | |
| | pane of 8, F† | 70.00 | | | |

Qty: 4,120,000

**Nos. 687–688 (2) combination FDC** **11.20**

† Four different philatelic panes exist depending upon the position of the corner inscription.

See also 623–624, 629–632, 644–647, 656–657, 664–666, B1–B12.

689
Snowlake and Olympic Symbols

690
Flower Growing from City

## WINTER OLYMPICS

Designer: Rolf P. Harder.
Lithography (7 colours) and Embossed, Plates of 200 subjects in four panes of 50
Ashton-Potter Limited

**1976, Feb 6** **Tagged, GT2** **Perf 12.5**

| | | NH–VF | ⊙F | PB | FDC |
|---|---|---|---|---|---|
| 689 | **20¢ multicoloured** | 1.25 | .90 | 6.25 | 1.20 |
| T1 | untagged (error) | 125.00 | 100.00 | | |

Qty: 10,000,000

Issued to mark the 12th Winter Olympic Games, Innsbruck, Austria.

## UNITED NATIONS HABITAT CONFERENCE

Designer: Ian A.R. MacLeod.
Lithography (4 colours), pane of 50
Ashton-Potter Limited

**1976, May 12** **Tagged, GT2** **Perf 12.2x12.6**

| | | NH–VF | ⊙F | PB | FDC |
|---|---|---|---|---|---|
| 690 | **20¢ multicoloured** | .75 | .75 | 3.75 | 1.20 |
| T1 | untagged (error) | 100.00 | | | |

Qty: 12,100,000

Issued on the occasion of Habitat, a U.N. Conference on Human Settlements, Vancouver.

## UNITED STATES BICENTENNIAL

691
Benjamin Franklin and Map

Designer: Bernard N.J. Reilander.
Portrait engraved by Joseph S. Creamer Jr. Based on a sculpture by Jean-Jacques Caffiéri.
Based on a map by Robert Sayer and John Bennett.
Engraved (1 colour) and Photogravure (3 colours)
Plates of 300 subjects in six panes of 50 [Goebel press]
British American Bank Note Company

**1976, Jun 1** **Tagged, GT2** **Perf 13.0x13.3**

| | | NH–VF | ⊙F | PB | FDC |
|---|---|---|---|---|---|
| 691 | **10¢ multicoloured**, LF paper | .45 | .25 | 2.25 | .90 |
| i | DF paper | 3.00 | | 15.00 | |

Qty: 18,500,000

Issued to mark the U.S. Bicentennial. Benjamin Franklin was deputy postmaster general for the Colonies from 1753 to 1774. The U.S. also issued a stamp with similar design.

Joint issue with United States
**Scott # 1690**

## ROYAL MILITARY COLLEGE CENTENARY

692
Colour Parade and Memorial Arch

693
Wing parade and Mackenzie Building

Designer: Will Davies.
Lithography (6 colours), Plates of 200 subjects in four panes of 50
Canadian Bank Note Company

**1976, Jun 1** **Tagged, GT2** **Perf 12.0x12.5**

| | | NH–VF | ⊙F | PB | FDC |
|---|---|---|---|---|---|
| 692 | **8¢ multicoloured** | .25 | .20 | | .85 |
| i | red dot to left of arm (pos. 3) | 3.00 *EP* | 2.50 | | |
| ii | spots on flag (pos. 40) | 3.00 *EP* | 2.50 | | |
| T1 | untagged (error) | — | 100.00 | | |
| 693 | **8¢ multicoloured** | .25 | .20 | | .85 |
| i | "chinstrap" variety (pos. 44) | 3.00 *EP* | 2.50 | | 5.00 |
| ii | "flagstaff" variety (pos. 35) | 3.00 *EP* | 2.50 | | 5.00 |
| iii | "1'876" variety (pos. 37) | 3.00 *EP* | 2.50 | | 5.00 |
| iv | "UFO" to left of building (pos. 46) | 3.00 *EP* | 2.50 | | 5.00 |
| v | "pigeon hole" variety (pos. 13) | 3.00 *EP* | 2.50 | | 5.00 |
| vi | red thread variety (pos. 42) | 3.00 *EP* | 2.50 | | 5.00 |
| a | se-tenant pair (692, 693) | .60 | .50 | 1.25 | 1.25 |
| b | imperf. pair (and untagged) | 3,000.00 | — | 6,500.00* | — |
| c | vertical block of 10, partial imperf.† | 1,500.00 | — | 1,750.00** | — |
| d | double impression, pair | 5,000.00 | — | 12,000.00* | — |

Qty: 12,950,000 of each

* Blank corner block of 4.

** Blank corner block of 8 or 10.

† Block of 10 is imperf. through second row of stamps due to a perf shift. Scott lists 693c as a block of four.

Issued for the centenary of the Royal Military College, Kingston, Ontario. See also 1906.

692i

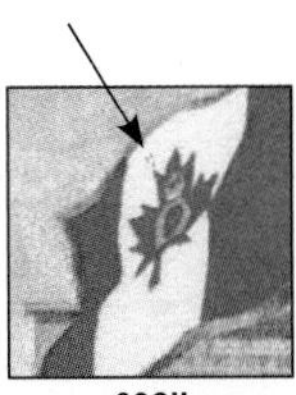
692ii

693i

693ii

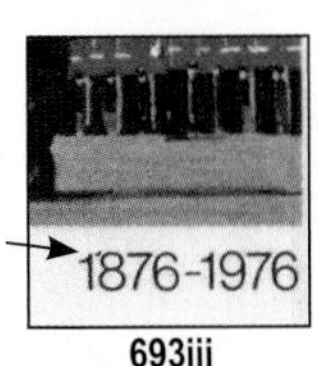

693iii

693iv

693c

693v

693vi

693d

## HANDICAPPED OLYMPICS

694
Archer in Wheelchair

Designer: Tom Bjarnason.

Lithography (5 colours), Plates of 200 subjects in four panes of 50
Canadian Bank Note Company

**1976, Aug 3** **Tagged, GT2** **Perf 12.0x12.5**

| | | NH–VF | ⊙F | PB | FDC |
|---|---|---|---|---|---|
| **694** | **20¢ green and multicoloured**, dull | .85 | .75 | 4.25 | 1.20 |
| i | HB | 5.00 | 1.50 | 25.00* | — |
| **T1** | untagged (error) | 100.00 | | | |

Qty: 12,400,000

* Blank corner block of 4; some plate blocks are known, value $50.00.

The 1976 Olympiad for the Physically Disabled (Aug 3–11 in Toronto) was the first olympiad with full competition for blind, paralyzed, and amputee athletes. More than 1,500 athletes from 38 countries took part in wheelchair (12 events), blind (8 events), and amputee (11 events) games.

## CANADIAN AUTHORS

695 The Cremation of Sam McGee
696 Le Survenant

Designer: 695: David Charles Bierk. 696: Antoine Dumas.

Lithography (4 colours), Plates of 200 subjects in four panes of 50
Ashton-Potter Limited

**1976, Aug 17** **Tagged, GT2** **Perf 13.3**

| | | NH–VF | ⊙F | PB | FDC |
|---|---|---|---|---|---|
| **695** | **8¢ multicoloured**, DF | .25 | .20 | | .85 |
| i | "glowing moon", constant tag variety (pos. 41) | 10.00 | 7.50 | | |
| ii | LF | 2.50 | .75 | | |
| **696** | **8¢ multicoloured**, DF | .25 | .20 | | .85 |
| i | "flaming dress", constant tag variety (pos. 31) | 10.00 | 7.50 | | |
| ii | LF | 2.50 | .75 | | |
| a | se-tenant pair (695, 696) | .60 | .40 | 1.50 | 1.25 |
| ai | se-tenant pair (695i, 696) | 20.00 | 15.00 | 75.00 | |
| aii | se-tenant pair (695, 696i) | 20.00 | 15.00 | 75.00 | |
| aiii | se-tenant pair (695ii, 696ii) | 5.00 | | 15.00 | |

Qty: 12,030,000 of each

Issued to honour Canadian writers Robert W. Service (1874–1958) and Germaine Guèvremont.

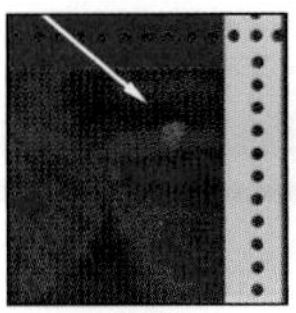
695i

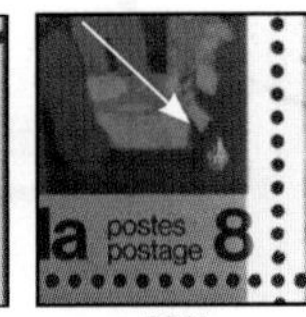
696i

**Rates:**
Sep 1, 1976 – Feb 28, 1977
Domestic: 10¢ (0–1 oz), 18¢ (1–2 oz)
3rd class (0–2 oz): 8¢
USA: 10¢ (0–1 oz), 19¢ (1–2 oz)
International: 20¢ (0–1 oz), 35¢ (1–2 oz) [from Jan 1/76]
Registration: 75¢ (up to $50)
Special delivery: 60¢

Definitive Timeline:
**1976, Sep 1** 10¢ QEII Caricature (593A)

Timeline:
**1976, Sep 17** 8¢ Iroquoian Indians (578–581)

## CHRISTMAS – NATIVITY

697
St. Michael's, Toronto

698
St. Jude, London, ON

699
Nativity by Yvonne Williams

Designer: Bernard N.J. Reilander.
Based on a stained glass windows: 8¢ by Franz Mayer of Munich, Inc.; 10¢ by G. Maile & Son Limited; 20¢ by Yvonne Williams.

Lithography (4 colours), panes of 50
Ashton-Potter Limited

| **1976, Nov 3** | **Tagged, GT2** | | | **Perf 13.3** | |
|---|---|---|---|---|---|
| | | **NH–VF** | **⊙F** | **PB** | **FDC** |
| **697** | **8¢ multicoloured** | .25 | .20 | 1.25 | .85 |
| i | missing colour (repellex error) | 900.00 | | | |
| T1 | untagged (error) | | 80.00 | | |
| Qty: 99,900,000 | | | | | |
| **698** | **10¢ multicoloured** | .25 | .20 | 1.25 | .90 |
| T1 | untagged (error) | 60.00 | 35.00 | 300.00* | |
| Qty: 84,100,000 | | | | | |
| **699** | **20¢ multicoloured** | .60 | .60 | 3.00 | 1.20 |
| Qty: 20,500,000 | | | | | |

* Blank corner block of 4.

**Nos. 697–699 (3) combination FDC** **2.00**

## INLAND VESSELS

700 Northcote — 701 Passport

702 Chicora — 703 Athabasca

Designer: Tom Bjarnason. Engraved by Yves Baril.

Engraved and Lithography, pane of 50
Canadian Bank Note Company

| **1976, Nov 19** | **Tagged, GT2** | | | **Perf 12.0x12.5** | |
|---|---|---|---|---|---|
| | | **NH–VF** | **⊙F** | **PB** | **FDC** |
| **700** | **10¢ yellow brown and black** | .50 | .45 | | .90 |
| i | stroke through 'N' of 'Northcote' (pos. 3) | 5.00 *EP* | 2.50 | | |
| ii | last bar at rear is short (pos. 23) | 5.00 *EP* | 2.50 | | |
| iii | flat bottomed second 'S' of 'POSTES' (pos. 34) | 5.00 *EP* | 2.50 | | |
| iv | short bar, second in front of flagpole (pos. 45) | 5.00 *EP* | 2.50 | 6.50 | |
| **701** | **10¢ violet and black** | .50 | .45 | | .90 |
| a | purple double printed | 375.00 | | | |
| ii | horiz. dash under flag (pos. 42) | 5.00 *EP* | 2.50 | 6.50 | |
| **702** | **10¢ light blue and black** | .50 | .45 | | .90 |
| a | blue double printed | 375.00 | | | |
| ii | break in rigging near front stack (pos. 10) | 5.00 *EP* | 2.50 | 6.50 | |
| iii | broken crossbar in A of Postage (pos. 17) | 5.00 *EP* | 2.50 | | |
| **703** | **10¢ yellow green and black** | .50 | .45 | | .90 |
| i | break in rigging below smoke (pos. 20) | 5.00 *EP* | 2.50 | | |
| a | se-tenant block (700–703) | 2.25 | 2.00 | 2.50 | 2.10 |

Qty: 700–701: 6,578,000 of each; 702–703: 6,072,000 of each
Some 28 different constant varieties have been reported; most are minor.
Normal flrsc. is DF; mint NF stamps are valued at 4x prices shown.
See also 670–673, 744–747 and 776–779.

700i 700ii 700iii 700iv

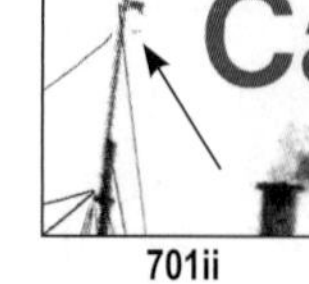

701ii

702ii

702iii

703i

## 1977

### SILVER JUBILEE

704
Queen Elizabeth II

Designer: Ken Rodmell. Based on a photograph by Peter Grugeon.

Lithography with foil stamping, sheets of 150 subjects in three panes of 50
Ashton-Potter Limited

| **1977, Feb 4** | **Tagged, GT2** | | | **Perf 12.6x12.2** | |
|---|---|---|---|---|---|
| | | **NH–VF** | **⊙F** | **PB** | **FDC** |
| **704** | **25¢ silver and multi**, LF | 1.00 | .75 | 5.00 | 1.35 |
| a | missing silver † | 1,500.00 | | | |
| ii | DF | 2.50 | 1.00 | 12.00 | |
| T1 | untagged (error) | 25.00 | 20.00 | 125.00* | |

Qty: 14,185,000
† Certificates of authenticity are important—fakes have been reported.
* Price is for inscription block of 4; blank corner $120.00

Issued to commemorate the 25th anniversary of the accession to the throne of Queen Elizabeth II.

| **Rates:** | Domestic: 12¢ (0–1 oz), 20¢ (1–2 oz) |
|---|---|
| Mar 1, 1977– | 3rd class (0–2 oz): 10¢ |
| Mar 31, 1978 | USA: 12¢ (0–1 oz), 22¢ (1–2 oz) |
| | International: 25¢ (0–1 oz), 45¢ (1–2 oz) [from Jan 1/77] |
| | Registration: $1.00 (up to $100) |
| | Special delivery: 60¢ |

*single usage:* International 25¢: $20.00

### FLORAL DEFINITIVES
### 1977–1982

705
Bottle Gentian

707
Western Columbine

708
Canada Lily

709
Hepatica

710
Shooting Star

711
Lady's Slipper

712
Jewelweed

The inks used to print the lithographic "background" of the CBN stamps (705–711) have a strong tendency to change colour when exposed to long periods of sunlight or ultraviolet light — be cautious when purchasing these so-called *printing* varieties.

Designer: Heather J. Cooper. Engraved by Yves Baril.

Engraved (1 colour) and Lithography (3 colours; 2 colours on 10¢), panes of 100
Canadian Bank Note Company

**1977, Apr 22** **Tagged, GT2** **Perf 12.0x12.5**

| | | NH–VF | ⊙F | PB | FDC |
|---|---|---|---|---|---|
| **705** | **1¢ lilac & multicoloured**, NF/NF | .25 | .20 | 1.25 | .90** |
| a | printed on gummed side (16 known, all precancelled) | 1,750.00 | | | |
| i | DF/LF | .25 | .20 | 1.25 | |
| iii | overprinted "EXUP XI/12 au 14/MAI/1978"¤ | 3.00 | — | 15.00 | |
| v | overprinted "HINTON/PEX/1977"¤ | 10.00 | | | |
| xx | No. 705, precancelled, NF/NF | .25 | .20 | 5.00† | |

Qty: 73,900,000

¤ privately produced overprint. The 'PHILABEC' overprint was applied to the BABN printing; see 781ii. These listings will likely be removed in a future edition.

** Block of 10.

No. 706 is not assigned.

| | | NH–VF | ⊙F | PB | FDC |
|---|---|---|---|---|---|
| **707** | **2¢ pale brown & multi**, NF/NF | .25 | .20 | 1.25 | .95• |
| a | printed on gum side | 1,250.00 | — | 6,000.00* | |
| i | imperf. bottom half of stamp & margin, block of 4 | 750.00 | — | 950.00* | — |
| iii | missing all purple inscriptions (four known, used); certificate of authenticity recommended | | 2,000.00 | — | |
| T1 | untagged (error) | 250.00 | 50.00 | | |

Qty: 69,300,000

• Block of 6.

| | | NH–VF | ⊙F | PB | FDC |
|---|---|---|---|---|---|
| **708** | **3¢ dull green & multi**, NF/NF | .25 | .20 | 1.25 | .95‡ |
| i | horizontal green checkmark (pos. 35) | 5.00 | 2.50 | | |
| ii | LF/MF | 2.00 | .50 | 10.00 | |
| T1 | untagged (error) | | 50.00 | | |
| xx | No. 708, precancelled, NF/NF | .25 | .20 | 5.00† | |

Qty: 69,500,000

| | | NH–VF | ⊙F | PB | FDC |
|---|---|---|---|---|---|
| **709** | **4¢ dull lavender & multi**, NF/NF | .25 | .20 | 1.25 | 1.10‡ |
| a | printed on gummed side | 400.00 | — | 2,000.00* | |

Qty: 56,800,000

* Blank corner block of 4. LL corner block has been split to make 4 singles.

| | | NH–VF | ⊙F | PB | FDC |
|---|---|---|---|---|---|
| **710** | **5¢ dull brown & multi**, NF/NF | .25 | .20 | 1.25 | .90§ |
| i | NF/DF | .25 | .20 | 1.25 | |
| T1 | untagged (error) | | 50.00 | | |
| xx | No. 710, precancelled, NF/NF | .25 | .20 | 5.00† | |

Qty: 65,300,000

**Flowers**

| Format | Sheet | | | Booklet | Precancel | |
|---|---|---|---|---|---|---|
| Method | Lithography | | Photo | Photo | Litho | Photo |
| Perf | 12x12½ | 13x13½ | 13x13½ | 12x12½ | 12x12½ | 13x13½ |
| 1¢ Gentian | 705 (Pl 1) | | 781 (Pl 2) | 781a | 705xx | |
| 2¢ Columbine | 707 (Pl 1) | | 782 (Pl 2) | 782b | | |
| 3¢ Lily | 708 (Pl 1) | | 783 (Pl 2) | | 708xx | |
| 4¢ Hepatica | 709 (Pl 1) | | 784 (Pl 2) | | | |
| 5¢ Star | 710 (Pl 1) | | 785 (Pl 2) | | 710xx | |
| 10¢ Slipper | 711 (Pl 1) | 711a (Pl 2) | 786 (Pl 3) | | 711xx | |
| 12¢ Jewelweed | | | 712 (Pl 1) | | | 712xx |
| 15¢ Violet | | | 787 (Pl 1) | | | 787xx (Pl 1) |

| | | NH–VF | ⊙F | PB | FDC |
|---|---|---|---|---|---|
| **711** | **10¢ ochre & multi**, Plate 1, NF/NF | .25 | .20 | 1.25 | .90 |
| T1 | untagged (error) | | 40.00 | | |
| a | Plate 2, perf. 13.0x13.3, NF/NF, *Oct 5, 1978* | .25 | .20 | 1.25 | |
| xx | No. 711, precancelled, NF/NF | .25 | .20 | 5.00† | |

Qty: 131,500,000 (both perfs)

‡ Block of 4.

§ Pair.

**Nos. 705–711 (6) combination FDC** **1.60**

Engraved and Photogravure, panes of 100
British American Bank Note Company

**Perf 13.0x13.3**

| | | NH–VF | ⊙F | PB | FDC |
|---|---|---|---|---|---|
| **712** | **12¢ bright green & multicoloured**, DF/DF, *Jul 6, 1978* | .40 | .25 | 5.00 | .95 |
| i | DF/MF | 1.25 | .50 | 7.50 | |
| xx | No. 712, precancelled (red lines), DF/DF | .50 | .45 | 10.00† | |
| xxi | DF/MF | 1.50 | .50 | 30.00† | |

Qty: 63,600,000

† Warning strip of 20.

705iii

705v

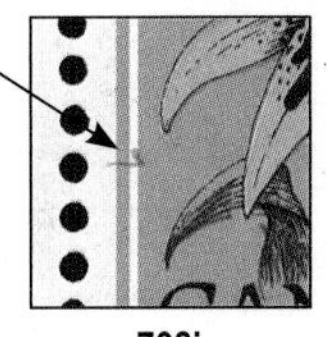
708i

## FIRST-CLASS DEFINITIVES 1977–1982

713
Queen Elizabeth II

714
Houses of Parliament

Designer: Queen: Heather Cooper; Parliament: Reinhard Derreth.

Engraved and Photogravure, pane of 100
British American Bank Note Company

**Tagged, GT2** **Perf 13.0x13.3**

| | | NH–VF | ⊙F | PB | FDC |
|---|---|---|---|---|---|
| **713** | **12¢ bright blue & black**, Plate 1 & 2, DF/DF, *Mar 1, 1977* | .35 | .20 | 1.75 | .95 |
| i | ribbed, horizontal | 5.00 | .50 | 25.00* | |
| ii | DF/LF | .50 | .25 | 3.00 | |
| iii | DF/MF | 1.50 | .35 | 7.50 | |
| iv | MF/HF | 10.00 | 1.00 | 50.00 | |
| T1 | untagged (error) | | 40.00 | | |
| a | perf 12.0x12.5, single with straight edge, from 781b, DF, *Nov 1, 1977* | .40 | .20 | | — |
| ai | as 'a', LF | .75 | .25 | | |

Qty: 633,800,000

* Blank corner block of 4.

Engraved (1 colour), pane of 100

| | | NH–VF | ⊙F | PB | FDC |
|---|---|---|---|---|---|
| **714** | **12¢ blue**, Plate 1, coated paper, LF, *May 3, 1977* | .30 | .20 | 1.50 | .95 |
| T1 | untagged (error) | | 60.00 | | |
| a | printed on gum side | 400.00 | — | | — |
| iii | double paper (repair paste-up) | 1,000.00* | — | 1,250.00 | |

Qty: BABN: 233,700,000

* Price is for block of 4 (5 blocks known).

Canadian Bank Note Company

| | | NH–VF | ⊙F | PB | FDC |
|---|---|---|---|---|---|
| iv | Plate 1 or 2, uncoated paper, LF, *Mar 1978* | .30 | .20 | 1.50 | |
| v | HB | 40.00 | 1.75 | 250.00‡ | |
| vi | DF | .50 | .20 | 2.50 | |
| ivT1 | untagged (error) | 100.00 | | 600.00 | |
| xx | No. 714iv, precancelled, DF, *May 1978* | .35 | .30 | 7.50† | |
| xxi | LF | 2.00 | .50 | 60.00† | |

Qty: CBN: 253,500,000

‡ Price shown is for plate block; blank corner block of 4 value $200.00.

† Warning strip of 20.

BABN

CBN

BABN design appears crisp and glossy; coated paper.

CBN design appears rough, faded, and dull; uncoated paper. Perforations are often rough with misaligned individual perforation holes.

715 Houses of Parliament

716 Queen Elizabeth II

Engraved (1 colour), pane of 100
Canadian Bank Note Company

**Tagged, GT2** **Perf 13.0x13.3**

| | | NH–VF | ⊙F | PB | FDC |
|---|---|---|---|---|---|
| **715** | **14¢ red**, dull paper, *Mar 7, 1978* | .30 | .20 | 1.50 | 1.00 |
| a | printed on gummed side | 50.00* | — | 250.00 | |
| b | all colour omitted (only trace of embossing) | 500.00 | — | 2,500.00** | |
| iii | "missing spire" variety (Pl. 1 & 2, pos. 34) | 5.00 *EP* | 2.50 | 50.00‡ | 7.50 |
| iv | "missing brick" variety (Pl. 1–4, pos. 1) | 5.00 | 2.50 | 10.00 | 15.00† |
| v | "light in window" variety (Pl. 1 & 2, pos. 32) | 5.00 *EP* | 2.50 | 50.00‡ | 7.50 |
| vi | imperf. bottom half of stamp & margin, block of 4 | 750.00 | | 950.00** | |
| vii | reverse offset | 200.00 | | 1,000.00** | |
| viii | "closed blind" variety (Pl. 1–4, pos. 81) | 5.00 *EP* | 2.50 | 10.00 | |
| ix | MF | .30 | .20 | 1.50 | |
| x | HF | 5.00 | 1.00 | 25.00 | |
| T1 | untagged (error) | 50.00 | 20.00 | 300.00 | |

Qty: 419,900,000

* Listed value is for VF centring, many of this variety are off-centre (F or F-VF grading) and are valued at $30–$40.

** Blank corner block of 4.

† Imprint block on FDC.

‡ Value shown is for 715iii in block of 16 or for 715v in block of 16.

Four plates were used: the tagging on plates 1 and 2 appears "more solid" or "darker"; tagging on plates 3 and 4 appears "lighter" or more "washed out".

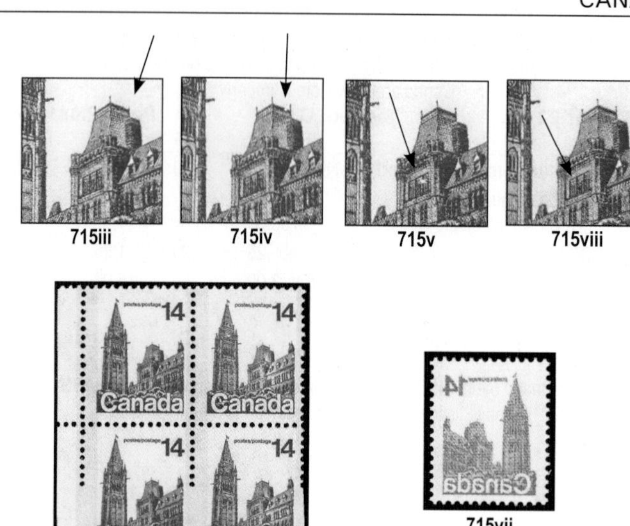
715iii 715iv 715v 715viii

715vi

715vii

Engraved and Photogravure, pane of 100
British American Bank Note Company

**Tagged, GT2** **Perf 13.0x13.3**

| | | NH–VF | ⊙F | PB | FDC |
|---|---|---|---|---|---|
| **716** | **14¢ red & black**, DF, *Mar 7, 1978* | .30 | .20 | 1.50 | 1.00 |
| ii | LF (w/HF fibres) | .30 | .20 | 1.50 | |
| c | red colour omitted, untagged† | 2,000.00 | — | 10,000.00** | |
| i | double paper (repair paste-up) | 1,000.00* | — | 1,250.00 | |
| T1 | untagged (error), DF† | 100.00 | 50.00 | | |
| T2 | untagged (error), LF | 75.00 | | | |

Qty: 392,400,000

* Price is for block of 4 (5 blocks known).

** Blank corner block of 4.

† Untagged stamps (716T1) with "pale red" shade exist from the missing colour sheets. Portion where there is still red present $200 each; transitional missing reds (716c) with part of red still present $500 to $1000.

**Booklet Issue** **Perf 12.0x12.5**

| | | | | |
|---|---|---|---|---|
| 716a | 14¢ Elizabeth II, single from 716b, perf all around | 1.00 | .75 | — |
| as | as "a", single 14¢ with straight edge, from 716b or 782a | .35 | .20 | — |
| ai | "notch in lower frame" (single 14¢ from 716b, pos. 27) | 7.50 | 5.00 | |
| aii | "scar on forehead" (from 716b, pos. 17) | 10.00 | 5.00 | |
| asi | ribbed, vertical (single 14¢ from 782ai) | 1.00 | .25 | |
| 716b | booklet pane of 25 x 14¢ (716a and 716as) + 2 labels (BK79), *Nov 13, 1978* | 7.50 | 9.00 | — |
| BK79 | pane 716b in bilingual cover $8.00 | | | |

716ai

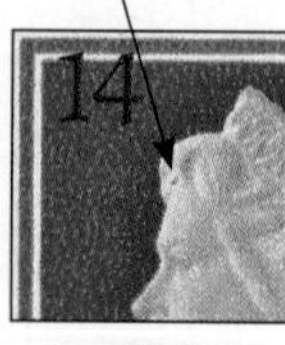
716aii

716c

716c (transition)

716b

## MEDIUM-VALUE TREE DEFINITIVES 1977–1982

717
Trembling Aspen

718
Douglas Fir

719
Sugar Maple

720
Red Oak

721
White Pine

Designer: Heather J. Cooper.
Engraved (1 colour) and Photogravure (3 colours), panes of 50
British American Bank Note Company
**Tagged, GT2** **Perf 13.3**

| | | NH–VF | ⊙F | PB | FDC |
|---|---|---|---|---|---|
| **717** | **15¢ sage green & multicoloured**, DF, *Aug 8, 1977* | .60 | .20 | 3.00 | 1.10 |
| i | LF | 3.00 | .50 | 15.00* | |

Qty: 63,400,000

| | | NH–VF | ⊙F | PB | FDC |
|---|---|---|---|---|---|
| **718** | **20¢ light blue & multicoloured**, LF, *Aug 8, 1977* | .45 | .20 | 2.25 | 1.20 |
| a | missing denomination (pos. 21) | 1,000.00 | | | |
| ii | NF | 4.00 | 1.00 | 20.00 | |

Qty: 113,300,000

| | | NH–VF | ⊙F | PB | FDC |
|---|---|---|---|---|---|
| **719** | **25¢ stone & multicoloured**, DF, *Aug 8, 1977* | .65 | .20 | 3.25 | 1.35 |
| i | LF | 3.00 | .50 | 15.00* | |

Qty: 133,800,000

| | | NH–VF | ⊙F | PB | FDC |
|---|---|---|---|---|---|
| **720** | **30¢ grey-brown & multicoloured**, *Mar 7, 1978* | .75 | .25 | 3.75 | 1.50 |

Qty: 36,500,000
The so-called "winter leaf" variety (white edges on the leaves) is due to a relatively minor colour shift. Value $10.

| | | NH–VF | ⊙F | PB | FDC |
|---|---|---|---|---|---|
| **721** | **35¢ grey-brown & multicoloured**, DF, *Mar 8, 1979* | .75 | .35 | 3.75 | 1.65 |
| i | LF | 3.00 | .50 | 15.00 | |

Qty: 117,000,000

* Blank corner block of 4.

718a

No. 722 is not assigned.

## MEDIUM-VALUE STREET DEFINITIVES 1977–1982

723
Prairie Street Scene

723C
Ontario Street Scene

724
Row Houses

725
Maritime Street Scene

Designer: Tom Bjarnason. Engraved by Arthur Ponting.
Engraved (1 colour) and Photogravure (3 colours), pane of 50
British American Bank Note Company
**Tagged, GT2** **Perf 13.3**

| | | NH–VF | ⊙F | PB | FDC |
|---|---|---|---|---|---|
| **723** | **50¢ multicoloured**, LF, *Jul 6, 1978* | 1.50 | .25 | 7.50 | 2.10 |
| i | dot above 5 (pos. 5), LF | 10.00 | 7.50 | 20.00 | |
| ii | DF | 5.00 | .50 | 25.00 | |
| iii | dot above 5 (pos. 5), DF | 25.00 | 10.00 | 60.00 | |
| T1 | untagged (error) | | 40.00 | | |

Qty: BABN: 8,650,000

Engraved (1 colour) and Lithography (3 colours), pane of 50
Canadian Bank Note Company

| | | NH–VF | ⊙F | PB |
|---|---|---|---|---|
| **723A** | **50¢ multicoloured**, plates 2 & 3, LF, *Dec 13, 1978* | 1.25 | .25 | 6.25 (LL/LR) |
| b | "ghost town" variety, brown inscriptions omitted (150 known) | 3,000.00 | — | 12,500.00* |
| c | magenta (litho.) and dark brown (engraved) missing (from foldover) | *20,000.00* | | |
| Aii | complete doubling of brown inscriptions | 1,000.00† | | |
| Aiii | "dented bumper" (pos. 6–10) | 5.00 EP | 3.50 | 15.00 (UL/UR) |
| Aiv | "black sweater" (pos. 22) | 7.50 | 5.00 | |
| Av | DF | 4.00 | .50 | 20.00 |

Qty: CBN: 85,250,000
Variety 723A shows "©1978" on the license plate of the car at the LR corner.
* Blank corner block of 4.
† Value for full doubling of inscriptions, poles and wires; both impressions of equal strength. Kiss prints showing portions of CANADA 50 shifted below the regular impression are valued at $100.00 to $300.00 depending on strength of second impression.

723i, iii

723Aiii

723Aiv

723Ab

723Ac

Engraved (1 colour) and Lithography (3 colours), pane of 50
Canadian Bank Note Company

| Tagged, GT2 | | | | Perf 13.3 | |
|---|---|---|---|---|---|
| | | NH–VF | ⊙F | PB | FDC |
| 723C | **60¢ multicoloured**, dull back, plates 1 & 2, *May 11, 1982* | 1.70 | .35 | 8.50 | 1.60 |
| Ci | flrsc. back | 2.00 | .50 | | |

Qty: 48,500,000

Engraved (1 colour) and Photogravure (3 colours), panes of 50
British American Bank Note Company

| | | NH–VF | ⊙F | PB | FDC |
|---|---|---|---|---|---|
| 724 | **75¢ multicoloured**, untagged, DF, *Jul 6,1978* | 1.75 | .40 | 8.25 | 2.85 |
| i | LF | 4.00 | .50 | 20.00 | |

Qty: 20,100,000
"Guide dots" can be found at some of the corners on many 75¢ stamps.

| | | NH–VF | ⊙F | PB | FDC |
|---|---|---|---|---|---|
| 725 | **80¢ multicoloured**, untagged, *Jul 6, 1978* | 2.00 | .45 | 10.00 | 3.00 |

Qty: 21,100,000

**Nos. 723–725 (3) combination FDC** 7.90

## HIGH-VALUE NATIONAL PARK DEFINITIVES 1979–1985

726
Fundy National Park

727
Kluane National Park

Designer: $1 Ron Bolt; $2: Based on a painting by Alan Caswell Collier.
Lettering engraved by Yves Baril.

Engraved (1 colour) and Lithography (4 colours), panes of 50
Canadian Bank Note Company

| Tagged, GT2 | | | | Perf 13.3 | |
|---|---|---|---|---|---|
| | | NH–VF | ⊙F | PB | FDC |
| 726 | **$1 multicoloured**, Plate 1, *Jan 24, 1979* | 2.00 | .75 | 10.00 | 3.60 |
| a | Plate 2, untagged, *Mar 4, 1981* | 3.50 | .95 | 15.00 | |
| b | black inscriptions omitted, untagged (approx. 200 known) | 750.00 | 750.00 | 4,000.00* | |
| ii | inscriptions doubled, kiss print | 350.00 | | 1,750.00* | |
| iii | additional inverted inscriptions, kiss print | 1,000.00† | | | |

Qty: 96,600,000
† Certificate of authenticity recommended.

| | | NH–VF | ⊙F | PB | FDC |
|---|---|---|---|---|---|
| 727 | **$2 multicoloured**, untagged, Abitibi-Price paper, LF, Plate 1, *Apr 27, 1979* | 4.00 | 1.75 | 20.00 | 6.60 |
| | plate 2, *Feb 4, 1981* | — | † | 20.00 | |
| a | silver inscriptions omitted (approx. 500–600 exist) | 400.00 | — | 2,000.00* | |
| i | NF, plate 1 or 2 | 9.00 | | 45.00 | |
| ii | silver double printed, kiss print | 250.00 | — | 1,250.00* | |
| b | silver double printed (true double) | 1,000.00 | | | |
| iii | "KLUANE" black doubled | — | *1,250.00* | | |
| iv | Plate 3, Clark paper, *Dec 14, 1984* | 7.50 | † | 35.00 | |
| v | Plate 4, Harrison paper, *Mar 15, 1985* | 10.00 | 2.25 | 45.00 | |
| vi | silver inscriptions omitted, Harrison‡ | 1,000.00 | — | *5,000.00* | |

Qty: 77,150,000
* Blank corner block of 4.
† It is not possible to separate used copies of Abitibi-Price and Clark paper stamps. Shades exist.
‡ Only 2 examples of 727vi reported to date. These have bluish tint to the gum (vs. clear white for the Abitibi, 727a error).

For additional National Park definitives, see numbers 934–937, 1084.

726b

727iii detail

727a/vi

727b

No. 728 is not assigned.

## FIRST-CLASS DEFINITIVES – COIL STAMPS 1977–1978

729

730

Rolls of 100
Canadian Bank Note Company

| Tagged, GT2 | | | Perf 10 vert | |
|---|---|---|---|---|
| | | NH–VF | ⊙F | FDC |
| 729 | **12¢ blue**, LF, (714), *May 3, 1977* | .30 | .20 | .95 |
| a | LF, imperf. pair | 200.00 | | |
| i | dull | .30 | .20 | |
| ii | dull, imperf. pair | 200.00 | | |
| iii | wide spacing strip of 4 | 15.00 | — | |
| iv | narrow spacing strip of 4 | 15.00 | — | |

Qty: 283,300,000

| | | NH–VF | ⊙F | FDC |
|---|---|---|---|---|
| 730 | **14¢ red**, dull (715), *Mar 7, 1978* | .35 | .20 | 1.00 |
| a | dull, imperf. pair | 225.00 | | |
| i | wide spacing strip of 4 | 15.00 | — | |
| iii | narrow spacing strip of 4 | 30.00 | — | |
| iv | vertical pair, imperf. between (no scoreline) | 75.00 | 75.00 | |
| ii | HB | 25.00 | 15.00 | |
| v | HB, narrow spacing strip of 4 | 200.00 | — | |
| vi | HB, wide spacing strip of 4 | 200.00 | — | |
| vii | LF/fl | 3.00 | .25 | |
| viii | LF/fl, wide spacing strip of 4 | 30.00 | — | |
| T1 | untagged (error) | — | 50.00 | |

Qty: 277,700,000

Coil pairs or larger multiples are priced in proportion.

No. 731 is not assigned.

## ENDANGERED WILDLIFE

732
Eastern Cougar

Designer: Robert McLellan Bateman.

Lithography (4 colours), pane of 50
Ashton-Potter Limited

| 1977, Mar 30 | | Tagged, GT2 | | Perf 12.5 | |
|---|---|---|---|---|---|
| | | NH–VF | ⊙F | PB | FDC |
| **732** | **12¢ multicoloured** | .30 | .20 | 1.50 | .95 |
| **T1** | untagged (error) | 90.00 | 50.00 | 450.00* | |

Qty: 25,200,000

* UL and UR imprint blocks known.

Endangered Wildlife series. See also: 752, 813, 814, 853, 854, 883, 884.

## TOM THOMSON

733 *April in Algonquin Park* (1917)
734 *Autumn Birches* (1915)

Designer: Bernard N.J. Reilander.

Lithography (5 colours), pane of 50
Ashton-Potter Limited

| 1977, May 26 | | Tagged, GT2 | | Perf 12.0 | |
|---|---|---|---|---|---|
| | | NH–VF | ⊙F | PB | FDC |
| **733** | **12¢ multicoloured** | .30 | .20 | | .95 |
| i | "extra branch" (pos. 31) | 3.50 *EP* | 1.75 | | |
| ii | black spot between trees (pos. 13) | 3.50 *EP* | 1.75 | | |
| **734** | **12¢ multicoloured** | .30 | .20 | | .95 |
| i | dot above 'r' of 'painter' (pos. 42) | 3.50 *EP* | 1.75 | 4.50 | |
| ii | stroke above 'D' of 'CANADA' (pos. 50) | 3.50 *EP* | 1.75 | 4.50 | |
| a | se-tenant pair (733, 734) | .70 | .50 | 1.50 | 1.50 |

Qty: 13,700,000 of each

Paintings by Thomas John Thomson.

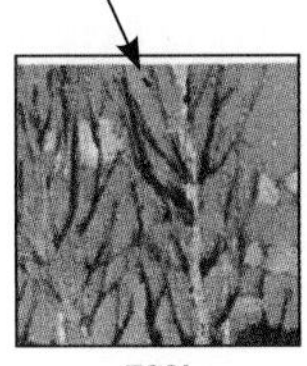
733i

733ii

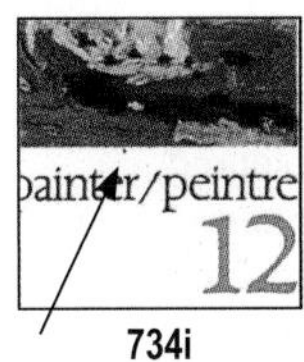

734i

734ii

## CANADIAN GOVERNORS GENERAL

735
Governor General's Standard

Designer: Anthony Hobbs.

Lithography (5 colours), pane of 50
Ashton-Potter Limited

| 1977, Jun 30 | | Tagged, GT2 | | Perf 12.5 | |
|---|---|---|---|---|---|
| | | NH–VF | ⊙F | PB | FDC |
| **735** | **12¢ multicoloured** | .30 | .20 | 1.50 | .95 |
| **T1** | untagged (error) | — | 100.00 | | |

Qty: 19,800,000

Issued to mark the 25th anniversary of the first Canadian-born Governors General: Vincent Massey (1952–1959), Georges Vanier (1959–1967), Roland Michener (1967–1974) and Jules Léger (1974–1979).

736
Order of Canada Medal

737
Peace Bridge

## ORDER OF CANADA

Designer: Anthony Hobbs. Based on a medal by Bruce Beatty.

Lithography (4 colours) and Embossed, pane of 50
Ashton-Potter Limited

| 1977, Jun 30 | | Tagged, GT2 | | Perf 12.5 | |
|---|---|---|---|---|---|
| | | NH–VF | ⊙F | PB | FDC |
| **736** | **12¢ multicoloured** | .30 | .20 | 1.50 | .95 |

Qty: 21,750,000

Issued to mark the 10th anniversary of the Order of Canada honours system.

## PEACE BRIDGE

Designer: Rolf P. Harder.

Lithography (4 colours), pane of 50
Ashton-Potter Limited

| 1977, Aug 4 | | Tagged, GT2 | | Perf 12.5 | |
|---|---|---|---|---|---|
| | | NH–VF | ⊙F | PB | FDC |
| **737** | **12¢ multicoloured**, dull/dull | .30 | .20 | 1.50 | .95 |
| i | MF/HB | 4.00 | .25 | 17.50 | |
| ii | F/F | 3.00 | .25 | 15.00 | |
| **T1** | untagged (error) | — | 100.00 | | |

Qty: 19,800,000

Issued to mark the 50th anniversary of the Peace Bridge connecting Fort Erie, Ontario and Buffalo, New York. Joint issue with the USA.

Joint issue with United States
**Scott # 1721**

## FAMOUS CANADIANS

738
Joseph E. Bernier

739
Sir Sandford Fleming

Designer: Will Davies. Engraved by Robert Couture.

Engraved (2 colours), pane of 50
British American Bank Note Company

| 1977, Sep 16 | | Tagged, GT2 | | Perf 13.0x13.3 | |
|---|---|---|---|---|---|
| | | NH–VF | ⊙F | PB | FDC |
| **738** | **12¢ blue** | .30 | .20 | | .95 |
| **T1** | untagged (error) | — | 75.00 | | |
| **739** | **12¢ brown** | .30 | .20 | | .95 |
| **T1** | untagged (error) | — | 75.00 | | |
| a | se-tenant pair (738, 739) | .70 | .60 | 1.50 | 1.50 |

Qty: 12,000,000 of each

Issued to honour Joseph E. Bernier (1852–1934), an explorer of Northern Canada, and Sir Sandford Fleming (1827–1915), who mapped the route for the Intercolonial Railway and designed Canada's first postage stamp.

## PARLIAMENTARY CONFERENCE

740
Peace Tower

Designer: Stuart Bradley Ash. Based on a photograph by Malak Karsh.
Lithography (4 colours), pane of 50
Ashton-Potter Limited

| 1977, Sep 19 | Tagged, GT2 | | | Perf 12.5 | |
|---|---|---|---|---|---|
| | | NH–VF | ⊙F | PB | FDC |
| 740 | **25¢ multicoloured**, dull | 1.00 | .90 | 5.00 | 1.35 |
| i | MF | 4.00 | 1.00 | 18.00 | |
| T1 | untagged (error) | — | 75.00 | | |

Qty: 18,430,000

Issued to mark the 23rd Commonwealth Parliamentary Conference, Ottawa.

## CHRISTMAS – FIRST CHRISTMAS CAROL

741 Hunters following star — 742 Angelic Choir — 743 Christ Child

Designer: Yon van Berkom Based on paintings by Ronald G. White.
Lithography (5 colours), panes of 50
Canadian Bank Note Company

| 1977, Oct 26 | Tagged, GT2 | | | Perf 13.3 | |
|---|---|---|---|---|---|
| | | NH–VF | ⊙F | PB | FDC |
| 741 | **10¢ multicoloured** | .25 | .20 | 1.25 | .90 |
| a | horiz. pair, imperf. between | 1,500.00 | | 3,750.00* | |
| b | printed on gum side | 1,000.00 | | 5,000.00* | |
| c | imperf. pair | 1,500.00 | | | |
| iv | black inscriptions and "© 1977" doubled, kiss print | 100.00 | | | |
| v | triple perf. (in strip of 3) | 500.00 | | | |
| T1 | untagged (error) | | 100.00 | | |

Qty: 102,500,000
* Blank corner block of 4.

| | | NH–VF | ⊙F | PB | FDC |
|---|---|---|---|---|---|
| 742 | **12¢ multicoloured** | .30 | .20 | 1.50 | .95 |
| a | left margin block of 4, left vert. pair imperf., right pair part perf. | 2,500.00† | | 2,750.00* | |
| ii | left margin horiz. pair, margin and left half of left stamp imperf. | 600.00 | | 1,250.00* | |
| iv | double black (kiss print) | 100.00 | 50.00 | | |
| b | double print of purple, blue, green; quadruple black insc. | 900.00 | | | |
| T1 | untagged (error) | 125.00 | 75.00 | | |

Qty: 80,550,000
* Blank corner blocks only.

| | | NH–VF | ⊙F | PB | FDC |
|---|---|---|---|---|---|
| 743 | **25¢ multicoloured** | .60 | .50 | 3.00 | 1.35 |
| i | kiss print, faint redoubling of JESOUS AHATONHIA | 40.00 | — | 200.00 | — |

Qty: 23,600,000

**Nos. 741–743 (3) combination FDC** 2.35

741a

from 742a

742b

## SAILING VESSELS

744 Pinky — 746 Five-Masted Schooner

745 Tern Schooner — 747 Mackinaw Boat

Designer: Tom Bjarnason. Engraved by Yves Baril.
Engraved (1 colour) and Lithography (5 colours), pane of 50
Canadian Bank Note Company

| 1977, Nov 18 | Tagged, GT2 | | | Perf 12.0x12.5 | |
|---|---|---|---|---|---|
| | | NH–VF | ⊙F | PB | FDC |
| 744 | **12¢ multicoloured** | .30 | .25 | | .95 |
| 745 | **12¢ multicoloured** | .30 | .25 | | .95 |
| 746 | **12¢ multicoloured** | .30 | .25 | | .95 |
| 747 | **12¢ multicoloured** | .30 | .25 | | .95 |
| i | "3 pulleys" (pos. 47) | 3.50 *EP* | 1.75 | 5.00(LL) | |
| a | se-tenant block of 4 (744–747) | 1.40 | 1.20 | 1.50 | 2.40 |
| b | as "a", Nos. 745, 747 imperf., Nos. 744, 746 part perf.† | *4,500.00* | | | |
| bi | vert. pair, 745 imperf., 744 part perf.† | *1,295.00* | | | |

Qty: 744–745: 8,736,000 of each; 746–747: 8,064,000 of each

† Three sheets known with bottom two rows imperf.; varieties 747b and 747bi come from these sheets. Six corner blocks known, 3 LL and 3 LR. There are three strips of 747bi recorded with bottom pair NH.

See also 670–673, 700–703 and 776–779.

747i

747bi

747b

## INUIT – HUNTING

748 Seal Hunter — 749 Fisherman's Dream

750 Disguised Archer — 751 Hunters of Old

Designer: Reinhard Derreth.

Lithography (5 colours), panes of 50
Ashton-Potter

| 1977, Nov 18 | | Tagged, GT2 | | Perf 12.2x12.7 | |
|---|---|---|---|---|---|
| | | NH–VF | ⊙F | PB | FDC |
| **748** | **12¢ multicoloured** | .30 | .20 | | .95 |
| **749** | **12¢ multicoloured** | .30 | .20 | | .95 |
| i | fluorescent ink (inscriptions) | .60 | .30 | | |
| ii | "fire in the chimney" variety (pos. 44) | 3.50 | 1.75 | 4.50 | |
| a | se-tenant pair (748, 749) | .70 | .40 | 1.50 | 1.50 |
| ai | se-tenant pair (748, 749i) | 1.20 | .75 | | |
| b | missing inscriptions on one of se-tenant pair (749a)† | 3,000.00 | | | |

Qty: 12,000,000 of each

† Grey inscriptions are missing on Fisherman's Dream (749) in se-tenant pair with normal Seal Hunter (748). There are 22 sound and 3 damaged examples known from one misprinted sheet (all are also untagged).

| | | NH–VF | ⊙F | PB | FDC |
|---|---|---|---|---|---|
| **750** | **12¢ multicoloured**, DF | .30 | .20 | | .95 |
| i | fluorescent ink (inscriptions) | .60 | .30 | | |
| ii | LF | 4.00 | .50 | | |
| **751** | **12¢ multicoloured**, DF | .30 | .20 | | .95 |
| i | fluorescent ink (inscriptions) | .60 | .30 | | |
| ii | LF | 4.00 | .50 | | |
| a | se-tenant pair, DF (750, 751) | .70 | .40 | 1.50 | 1.50 |
| ai | se-tenant pair (750i, 751i) | 1.20 | .75 | | |
| aii | se-tenant pair, LF (750ii, 751ii) | 9.00 | 3.00 | 20.00 | |

Qty: 11,900,000 of each

**Nos. 748–751 (4) combination FDC** 2.40

See also 769–772, 835–838 and 866–869.

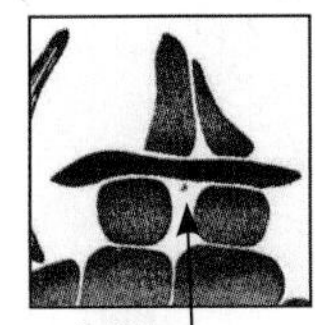

749ii

749b

## 1978

### ENDANGERED WILDLIFE

752
Peregrine Falcon

Designer: Robert McLellan Bateman.

Lithography (4 colours), pane of 50
Ashton-Potter Limited

| 1978, Jan 18 | | Tagged, GT2 | | Perf 12.5 | |
|---|---|---|---|---|---|
| | | NH–VF | ⊙F | PB | FDC |
| **752** | **12¢ multicoloured**, DF | .35 | .20 | 1.75 | .95 |
| i | pair, magenta colour missing on one stamp* | *1,000.00* | | | |
| ii | imperf. pair† | *1,000.00* | | | |
| iii | LF | 2.00 | .50 | 10.00 | |

Qty: 31,800,000

* Repellex error, one stamp in pair appears yellow instead of slate blue; second stamp in pair is normal. 10 pairs known.

† Imperforate pairs and singles (showing a portion of an adjacent stamp) exist; all are usually defective.

Endangered Wildlife series. See also: 732, 813, 814, 853, 854, 883, 884.

| **Rates:** Apr 1, 1978– Mar 31, 1979 | Domestic: 14¢ (0–1 oz), 22¢ (1–2 oz)<br>3rd class (0–2 oz): 12¢<br>USA: 14¢ (0–1 oz), 26¢ (1–2 oz)<br>International: 30¢ (0–1 oz), 54¢ (1–2 oz)<br>Registration: $1.25<br>Special delivery: 80¢ |
|---|---|

*single usage:* International 30¢: $25.00

### CAPEX '78

753
12d Queen Victoria

754
10d Jacques Cartier

755
1/2d Queen Victoria

756
6d Prince Albert

756a

Designer: Carl Brett Engraved by Robert Couture.

Engraved (1 colour) and Photogravure (2 colours), pane of 50
British American Bank Note Company

**1978** **Tagged, GT2** **Perf 13.3**

| No. | | NH–VF | ⊙F | PB | FDC |
|---|---|---|---|---|---|
| **753** | **12¢ black and multicoloured**, LF, *Jan 18, 1978* | .25 | .20 | 1.25 | .95 |
| **i** | mole on Queen's chin (left 12d stamp), (pos. 23) | 12.50 | 7.50 | | 10.00 |
| **ii** | scratch below O of Postage (left 12d stamp) (pos. 7) | 10.00 | 4.00 | 15.00 | |
| **iii** | dot between 12d stamps (pos. 1) | 5.00 | 2.50 | 10.00 | |
| **iv** | dot in T of Postage (right 12d stamp) (pos. 1) | 10.00 | 4.00 | 15.00 | |
| **v** | dot between 'Postage Postes' (pos. 12) | 10.00 | 4.00 | | |

Qty: 33,000,000

753 also exists on DF paper. Value is $3 mint/$15 PB. All varieties above valued at 3x regular price.

| No. | | NH–VF | ⊙F | PB | FDC |
|---|---|---|---|---|---|
| **754** | **14¢ blue and multi**, LF, *Jun 10* | .30 | .20 | 1.50 | 1.00 |
| **i** | DF | 4.00 | .75 | 20.00 | |

Qty: 31,600,000

| No. | | NH–VF | ⊙F | PB | FDC |
|---|---|---|---|---|---|
| **755** | **30¢ rose and multi**, *Jun 10, 1978* | .75 | .50 | 3.75 | 1.50 |

Qty: 21,600,000

| No. | | NH–VF | ⊙F | PB | FDC |
|---|---|---|---|---|---|
| **756** | **$1.25 slate-violet and multicoloured**, *Jun 10, 1978* | 2.75 | 1.50 | 13.75 | 4.35 |
| **i** | untagged (ex-souvenir sheet) | 3.00 | 3.00 | | |
| **a** | $1.69 souvenir sheet of 3, DF, *Jun 10* | 4.25 | 4.25 | — | 6.60 |
| **ai** | LF | 15.00 | | | |

Qty: $1.25: 19,000,000; souvenir sheet: 3,800,000

**Nos. 754–756 (3) combination FDC** **6.60**

Issued on the occasion of CAPEX '78, Canadian International Philatelic Exhibition, Toronto.

See Souvenir Articles section for Philatelic Exhibition Cards issued at this exhibition.

753i

753ii

753iii 753iv 753v

## 1978 COMMONWEALTH GAMES

757
Games' Emblem

758
Badminton

759
Stadium

760
Running

761 Legislature Building
762 Lawn Bowling

Designer: Stuart Bradley Ash.

Lithography (5 colours), panes of 50
Ashton-Potter Limited

**1978, Mar 31** **Tagged, GT2** **Perf 12.5**

| No. | | NH–VF | ⊙F | PB | FDC |
|---|---|---|---|---|---|
| **757** | **14¢ multicoloured** | .35 | .20 | 1.75 | 1.00 |

Qty: 43,000,000

| No. | | NH–VF | ⊙F | PB | FDC |
|---|---|---|---|---|---|
| **758** | **30¢ multicoloured** | .70 | .60 | 3.50 | 1.50 |
| **T1** | untagged (error) | | 100.00 | | |

Qty: 23,000,000

Lithography (6 colours), panes of 50

**1978, Aug 3**

| No. | | NH–VF | ⊙F | PB | FDC |
|---|---|---|---|---|---|
| **759** | **14¢ multicoloured**, DF | .30 | .20 | | 1.00 |
| **i** | LF | 3.00 | .50 | | |
| **760** | **14¢ multicoloured**, DF | .30 | .20 | | 1.00 |
| **i** | LF | 3.00 | .50 | | |
| **a** | se-tenant pair, DF (759, 760) | .70 | .40 | 1.50 | 1.70 |
| **aii** | se-tenant pair, LF (759i, 760i) | 6.00 | 1.50 | 15.00 | |
| **b** | imperf. se-tenant pair* | 1,000.00 | | | |

Qty: 21,500,000 of each

* All examples seen by the editors have wrinkles from mishandling by discoverers.

| No. | | NH–VF | ⊙F | PB | FDC |
|---|---|---|---|---|---|
| **761** | **30¢ multicoloured**, DF | .70 | .70 | | 1.50 |
| **i** | MF | 10.00 | | | |
| **762** | **30¢ multicoloured**, DF | .70 | .70 | | 1.50 |
| **i** | MF | 10.00 | | | |
| **a** | se-tenant pair, DF (761, 762) | 1.60 | 1.50 | 3.50 | 2.80 |
| **ai** | se-tenant pair, MF (761i, 762i) | 20.00 | | 30.00 | |

Qty: 11,500,000 of each

**Nos. 757–758 (2) combination FDC** **2.25**
**Nos. 759–762 (4) combination FDC** **3.80**

Issued to mark the 11th Commonwealth Games, held in Edmonton in August.

## CAPTAIN JAMES COOK

763 Captain James Cook
764 Nootka Sound

Designer: William Rueter. Paintings: 763: by Nathaniel Dance; 764: by John Webber.

Lithography (4 colours), pane of 50
Ashton-Potter Limited

**1978, Apr 26** **Tagged, GT2** **Perf 13.3**

| No. | | NH–VF | ⊙F | PB | FDC |
|---|---|---|---|---|---|
| **763** | **14¢ multicoloured** | .30 | .20 | | 1.00 |
| **764** | **14¢ multicoloured** | .30 | .20 | | 1.00 |
| **T1** | untagged (error) | — | 95.00 | | |
| **a** | se-tenant pair (763, 764) | .70 | .50 | 1.50 | 1.70 |
| **ai** | imperf. pair, untagged† | *1,000.00* | | | |

Qty: 15,675,000 of each

† All reported imperforate pairs have some degree of defect.

No. 763 has not yet been reported untagged, but must have existed.

Captain James Cook (1728–1779), explorer of Canada's East and West Coasts and bicentenary of his anchorage near Anchorage, Jun 1, 1778.

QE II — 1970's

## NATURAL RESOURCES

765
Cobalt Silver Mine

766
Athabasca Tar Sands

Designer: Will Davies.

Lithography (6 colours), pane of 50
Ashton-Potter Limited

**1978, May 19** Tagged, GT2 Perf 12.5

| | | NH–VF | ⊙F | PB | FDC |
|---|---|---|---|---|---|
| 765 | **14¢ multicoloured**, NF | .30 | .20 | | 1.00 |
| i | silver inscriptions double printed in se-tenant pair with #766 | 400.00 | | | |
| ii | "green Walkman" (pos. 35) | 7.50 | 3.50 | | |
| iii | MF | 10.00 | 3.00 | | |
| T1 | untagged (error) | | 125.00 | | |
| 766 | **14¢ multicoloured**, NF | .30 | .20 | | 1.00 |
| b | brown inscriptions double printed in se-tenant pair with #765 | 800.00 | | | |
| ii | MF | 10.00 | 3.00 | | |
| T1 | untagged (error) | | 125.00 | | |
| a | se-tenant pair, NF (765, 766) | .70 | .40 | 1.50 | 1.70 |
| ai | se-tenant pair, MF (765iii, 766ii) | 25.00 | 10.00 | 60.00 | |
| aii | se-tenant pair, doubled inscriptions on both stamps (765i, 766b) | | | | |

Qty: 16,750,000 of each

Development of natural resources.

765ii

767
Princes' Gate

768
Marguerite d'Youville

## C.N.E. CENTENNIAL

Designer: Theo Dimson.

Lithography (5 colours), pane of 50
Ashton-Potter Limited

**1978, Aug 16** Tagged, GT2 Perf 12.5

| | | NH–VF | ⊙F | PB | FDC |
|---|---|---|---|---|---|
| 767 | **14¢ multicoloured** | .30 | .20 | 1.50 | 1.00 |
| T1 | untagged (error) | — | 75.00 | | |

Qty: 31,400,000

Issued to mark the 100th anniversary of the Canadian National Exhibition.

## MARGUERITE D'YOUVILLE

Designer: Antoine Dumas.

Lithography (4 colours), pane of 50
Canadian Bank Note Company

**1978, Sep 21** Tagged, GT2 Perf 13.3

| | | NH–VF | ⊙F | PB | FDC |
|---|---|---|---|---|---|
| 768 | **14¢ multicoloured** | .30 | .20 | 1.50 | 1.00 |
| i | ghost print* | 40.00 | — | 175.00 | |

Qty: 28,400,000

* "Marguerite d'Youville" in banner at top shows distinct doubling.

Issued to honour Marguerite d'Youville (1701–1771), founder of the Grey Nuns.

## INUIT – TRAVEL

769
Woman Walking

770
Migration

771
Airplane over Village

772
Dog team and sled

Designer: Reinhard Derreth.

Lithography (5 colours), pane of 50
Ashton-Potter Limited

**1978, Sep 27** Tagged, GT2 Perf 13.3

| | | NH–VF | ⊙F | PB | FDC |
|---|---|---|---|---|---|
| 769 | **14¢ multicoloured**, LF | .30 | .20 | | 1.00 |
| i | fluorescent ink (inscriptions) | .60 | .30 | | |
| ii | DF | 2.00 | .50 | | |
| 770 | **14¢ multicoloured**, LF | .30 | .20 | | 1.00 |
| i | DF | 2.00 | .50 | | |
| a | se-tenant pair, LF (769, 770) | .70 | .50 | 1.50 | 1.70 |
| ai | se-tenant pair (769i, 770) | 1.20 | .75 | | |
| aii | se-tenant pair, DF (769ii, 770i) | 4.00 | 1.25 | 10.00 | |

Qty: 12,000,000 of each

| | | NH–VF | ⊙F | PB | FDC |
|---|---|---|---|---|---|
| 771 | **14¢ multicoloured** | .30 | .20 | | 1.00 |
| i | fluorescent ink (inscriptions) | .60 | .30 | | |
| 772 | **14¢ multicoloured** | .30 | .20 | | 1.00 |
| a | se-tenant pair (771, 772) | .70 | .50 | 1.50 | 1.70 |
| ai | se-tenant pair (771i, 772) | 1.20 | .75 | | |

Qty: 12,000,000 of each

**Nos. 769–772 (4) combination FDC** 2.65

See also 748–751, 835–838, 866–869.

## CHRISTMAS – PAINTINGS

773
*Madonna of the Flowering Pea*
(circa 1425)

774
*Virgin & Child*
by Hans Memling
(1472)

775
*Virgin & Child*
by Jacopo di Cione
(circa 1370-1380)

QE II — 1970's

Designer: Jean Morin.

Lithography (6 colours), pane of 50
Ashton-Potter Limited

| 1978, Oct 20 | | Tagged, GT2 | | Perf 12.5 | |
|---|---|---|---|---|---|
| | | NH–VF | ⊙F | PB | FDC |
| **773** | **12¢ multicoloured** | .25 | .20 | 1.25 | .95 |
| Qty: 111,000,000 | | | | | |
| **774** | **14¢ multicoloured** | .30 | .20 | 1.50 | 1.00 |
| a | black omitted | 1,500.00 | | 7,500.00* | |
| T1 | untagged (error) | 75.00 | 50.00 | | |
| Qty: 76,000,000 | | | | | |
| **775** | **30¢ multicoloured** | .70 | .60 | 3.50 | 1.50 |
| i | imperf. pair† | 1,500.00 | — | | |
| Qty: 24,000,000 | | | | | |

* Blank corner block of 4 (LR exists).
† Some of the few pairs that have come on the market are creased. They sell for half the listed price.

**Nos. 773–775 (3) combination FDC** 2.65

Nos. 773–775 occur on panes both with and without vertical perforations through the bottom margin.

Normal (774) 774a

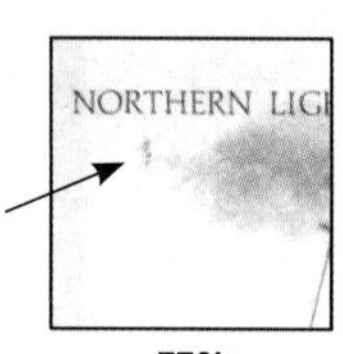

778i

779i

## ICE VESSELS

776 Chief Justice Robinson — 777 St. Roch

778 Northern Light — 779 Labrador

Designer: Tom Bjarnason. Engraved by Yves Baril

Engraved (1 colour) and Lithography (8 colours), pane of 50
Canadian Bank Note Company

| 1978, Nov 15 | | Tagged, GT2 | | Perf 13.3 | |
|---|---|---|---|---|---|
| | | NH–VF | ⊙F | PB | FDC |
| **776** | **14¢ multicoloured** | .40 | .35 | | 1.00 |
| **777** | **14¢ multicoloured** | .40 | .35 | | 1.00 |
| T1 | untagged (error) | | 75.00 | | |
| **778** | **14¢ multicoloured** | .40 | .35 | | 1.00 |
| i | "weather balloons" (pos. 6) | 4.00 | 2.50 | 6.00 | |
| **779** | **14¢ multicoloured** | .40 | .35 | | 1.00 |
| i | "weather balloons" (pos. 29) | 4.00 | 2.50 | | |
| a | se-tenant block (776–779) | 1.80 | 1.50 | 2.00 | 2.65 |
| Qty: 776/778 9,776,000 of each; 777/779: 9,024,000 of each | | | | | |

Only No. 777 has been reported untagged; the other three designs must also exist. See also 670–673, 700–703 and 744–747.

# 1979

## QUEBEC CARNIVAL

780
Winter Carnival Scene

Designer: Antoine Dumas.

Lithography (5 colours), pane of 50
Ashton-Potter Limited

| 1979, Feb 1 | | Tagged, GT2 | | Perf 13.3 | |
|---|---|---|---|---|---|
| | | NH–VF | ⊙F | PB | FDC |
| **780** | **14¢ multicoloured** | .30 | .20 | 1.50 | 1.00 |
| i | blue dot on roof of left building (pos. 32) | 3.00 *EP* | 1.50 | 6.00 | |
| ii | torn mitten on snowman (pos. 43) | 5.00 *EP* | 2.50 | | |
| iii | 'hair' under 4 of 14 (pos. 42) | 3.00 *EP* | 1.50 | | |
| Qty: 28,000,000 | | | | | |

Issued for the 25th anniversary of the Quebec Winter Carnival.

780i 780ii 780iii

| **Rates:** | Domestic: 17¢ (0–1 oz), 27¢ (1–2 oz) |
|---|---|
| Apr 1, 1979– | 3rd class (0–2 oz): 15¢ |
| Jun 30, 1979 | USA: 17¢ (0–1 oz), 31¢ (1–2 oz) |
| | International: 35¢ (0–1 oz), 63¢ (1–2 oz) |
| | Registration: $1.50 |
| | Special delivery: $1.00 |

*single usage:* International 35¢: $20.00

## FLORAL DEFINITIVES 1979–1983

781 Bottle Gentian

782 Western Columbine

783 Canada Lily

784 Hepatica — 785 Shooting Star

786 Lady's Slipper

787 Canada Violet

Nos. 781–787 were printed by British American Bank Note Company, using photogravure and steel engraving (background appears mottled). See also 705–711.

The tagging on the 1¢–15¢ BABN Flowers is very 'splotchy' with uneven edges and tag bar widths ranging from 3mm to 4½mm (and sometimes wider).

## 1972, Sep 8 — Perf 12.5x12.0

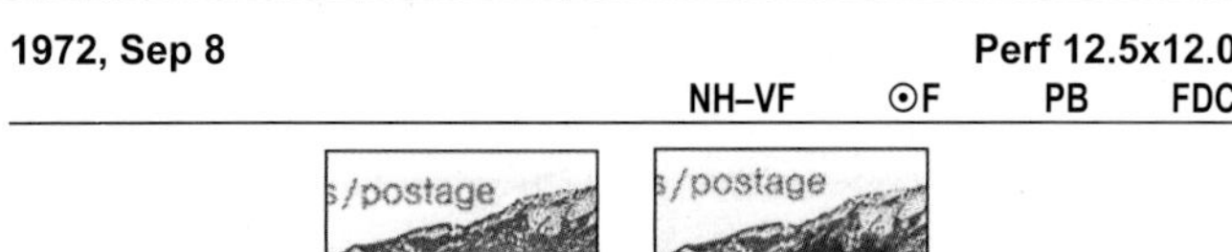

Type I Type II

Types I and II of No. 595 differ as follows: the trees (blue colour) on the hillside show clear detail on Type I, while on Type II the trees are a solid colour.

| | | NH–VF | ⊙F | PB | FDC |
|---|---|---|---|---|---|
| | **Type I** | | | | |
| 595 | **15¢ multicoloured**, (Plate 1) tagged, OP4, NF, ribbed, vert. | .75 | .20 | 4.00 | 1.10 |
| i | tagged, OP2 (3 mm), DF | 2.00 | .25 | 14.00 | |
| ii | OP2 (3 mm), DF, ribbed, vert. | .50 | .20 | 2.50 | |
| xii | "scratch in mountain" (pos. 10) | 10.00 | 5.00 | 20.00* | |
| xv | brown soil in 'a' of 'Canada' (pos. 94)§ | | | | |
| iii | tagged, W2B, NF, ribbed, vert. | 2.00 | 1.25 | 10.00* | 4.00‡ |
| xi | W2B, LF, ribbed, vert. | 10.00 | 1.50 | 60.00* | |
| xvi | brown soil in 'a' of 'Canada' (pos. 94)§ | | | | |
| | **Type II** OP2 (4mm) tagging | | | | |
| iv | NF, *Mar 1975* | 5.00 | .75 | 35.00* | |
| v | LF | 2.00 | .20 | 12.00* | |
| vi | HB (front only) | 85.00 | 15.00 | 500.00* | |
| vii | "blue tail" variety† | 5.00 | .75 | 25.00 | |
| viii | "raised rump" variety† | 5.00 | .75 | 25.00 | |
| ix | "double headed sheep" variety† | 10.00 | | 50.00 | |
| x | as 595ix, HB | 150.00 | | 900.00* | |
| xiii | "scratch in mountain" (pos. 10) | 15.00 | 10.00 | 30.00* | |
| xiv | as 595xiii, HB | | | | |
| xvii | brown soil in 'a' of 'Canada' (pos. 94)§ | | | | |

**Type II — Perf 13.3**

Plate 2, OP2 (4mm) tagging

| | | NH–VF | ⊙F | PB | FDC |
|---|---|---|---|---|---|
| 595a | LF/F, *Feb 1976* | .75 | .20 | 5.00 | |
| ai | "blue tail" variety† | 4.00 | .75 | 20.00 | |
| aii | "raised rump" variety† | 4.00 | .75 | 20.00 | |
| aiii | DF | 2.50 | .25 | 13.00 | |
| aiv | DF/LF | 2.50 | .25 | 13.00 | |
| av | DF/MF | 1.25 | .25 | 7.00 | |
| avi | brown soil in 'a' of 'Canada' (pos. 94)§ | | | | |

* Blank corner block of 4.
† Caused by colour shift, cheapest paper flrsc.
‡ With Winnipeg cancel; Ottawa *day of issue* cancel $12.50. Commercial use on cover: $10.00.
§ Exists on all printings.

(These four varieties are caused by colour shifts. As a result, the listings may be removed in the future.)

595xii/xiii

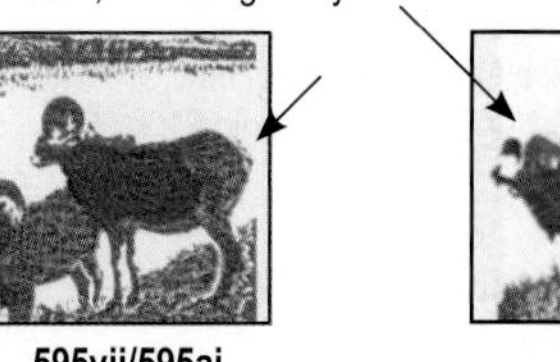
595vii/595ai 595ix

595xv/595xvi/ 595xvii/595avi

595viii/595aii

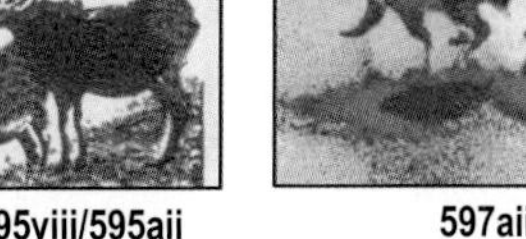

597aiii

## 1972, Sep 8 — Perf 12.5x12.0

| | | NH–VF | ⊙F | PB | FDC |
|---|---|---|---|---|---|
| 596 | **20¢ multicoloured**, (Plate 1) tagged, OP4, DF, ribbed, vert. | .75 | .20 | 4.00 | 1.20 |
| i | tagged, OP2 (3 mm) DF, ribbed, vert. | 1.00 | .20 | 5.00 | |
| ii | OP2 (3 mm) DF, horiz. ribbed | 7.00 | 1.00 | 35.00 | |
| iii | OP2 (3 mm) DF | 2.50 | .60 | 15.00 | |
| xiii | OP2 (3 mm) LF, ribbed, vert. | 10.00 | | 50.00 | |
| iv | tagged, OP2 (4 mm) DF, *Oct 1973* | 1.50 | .25 | 8.00 | |
| v | OP2 (4 mm) DF, ribbed, vert. | 8.00 | 1.25 | 50.00* | |
| vi | OP2 (4 mm) MF | 5.00 | 1.25 | 30.00 | |
| x | OP2 (4 mm) HF | 125.00 | 10.00 | 600.00* | — |
| vii | tagged, W2B, DF, ribbed, vert. | 2.50 | 1.10 | 15.00* | 4.00‡ |
| xi | W2B, DF, horiz. ribbed | 8.00 | 1.50 | 40.00* | |
| xii | W2B, LF/DF, ribbed, vert. | 5.00 | 1.00 | 35.00* | |
| viii | Repellex variety, purple partly missing in pair | 250.00 | — | | — |
| ix | double paper, repair paste-up in horiz. pair (10 known) | 500.00 | — | | — |

Plate 2 was not issued.

**Perf 13.3**

Plate 3, OP2 (4mm) tagging

| | | NH–VF | ⊙F | PB | FDC |
|---|---|---|---|---|---|
| 596a | NF, *Jan 1976* | 2.00 | .50 | 12.00 | |
| ai | DF/LF | .75 | .25 | 4.00 | |
| aii | LF/F | 1.75 | .35 | 10.00 | |
| aiii | MF | 4.00 | .75 | 20.00 | |

* Blank corner block of 4.
‡ With Winnipeg cancel; Ottawa *day of issue* cancel $12.50. Commercial use on cover: $10.00.

## 1972, Sep 8 — Perf 12.5x12.0

Type I Type II

On No. 597 the bears' shadows are evenly shaded on Type I and have a solid central area on Type II.

| | | NH–VF | ⊙F | PB | FDC |
|---|---|---|---|---|---|
| | **Type I** | | | | |
| 597 | **25¢ multicoloured**, (Plate 1) tagged, OP4, NF, ribbed, vert. | .75 | .20 | 4.00 | 1.35 |
| i | tagged, OP2 (3 mm), DF, horiz. ribbed | 3.50 | .90 | 25.00 | |
| vi | OP2 (3 mm), LF | 10.00 | 2.00 | 50.00 | |
| vii | OP2 (3 mm), LF, ribbed, vert. | 10.00 | 2.00 | 50.00 | |
| ii | OP2 (3 mm), DF, ribbed, vert. | 1.00 | .25 | 5.00 | |
| iii | tagged, W2B, ribbed, vert. | 2.50 | 1.25 | 12.50* | 5.00‡ |
| T1 | untagged (error), NF | — | 60.00 | | |
| T2 | untagged (error), LF | — | 60.00 | | |

Plate 2 was not issued.

| | | NH–VF | ⊙F | PB | FDC |
|---|---|---|---|---|---|
| | **Type II** OP2 (4mm) tagging | | | | |
| iv | NF, *Nov 1974* | 5.00 | 1.50 | 35.00* | |
| v | LF/F | 5.50 | .90 | 35.00* | |

**Type II — Perf 13.3**

Plate 3, OP2 (4mm) tagging

| | | NH–VF | ⊙F | PB | FDC |
|---|---|---|---|---|---|
| 597a | DF/LF, *May 1976* | .90 | .20 | 4.50 | |
| ai | NF/DF | 2.00 | .35 | 10.00 | |
| aii | DF/MF | 1.50 | .30 | 8.00 | |
| aiii | "Siamese twins" variety (2 bears joined) (caused by colour shift) | 10.00 | 2.00 | 50.00 | |

* Blank corner block of 4.
‡ With Winnipeg cancel; Ottawa *day of issue* cancel $15.00. Commercial use on cover: $12.00.

| 1972, Sep 8 | | | | Perf 12.5x12.0 | |
|---|---|---|---|---|---|
| | | NH–VF | ⊙F | PB | FDC |

Type I

Type II

Type II of No. 598 has darker shading and a deeper tone for the dark blue areas of the photogravure impression.

**Type I**

| No. | Description | NH–VF | ⊙F | PB | FDC |
|---|---|---|---|---|---|
| 598 | **50¢ multicoloured**, (Plate 1) tagged, OP4, NF, ribbed, vert. | 1.50 | .20 | 7.00 | 2.10 |
| i | tagged, OP2 (3 mm), DF | 10.00 | 4.00 | 60.00 | |
| ii | OP2 (3 mm), DF, ribbed, vert. | 2.00 | .30 | 10.00 | |
| v | OP2 (3 mm), LF, ribbed, vert. | 7.50 | .50 | 50.00 | |
| vi | OP2 (3 mm), F | 10.00 | | 60.00 | |
| T1 | untagged (error), LF | 100.00 | 60.00 | | |

**Type II**

Plate 1, OP2 (4mm) tagging

| No. | Description | NH–VF | ⊙F | PB | FDC |
|---|---|---|---|---|---|
| iii | LF, *Aug 1974* | 2.50 | .20 | 50.00 | |
| iv | "broken C" variety | 7.50 | 4.00 | | |

**Type II** **Perf 13.3**

Plate 2, OP2 (4mm) tagging

| No. | Description | NH–VF | ⊙F | PB | FDC |
|---|---|---|---|---|---|
| 598a | DF, *Feb 1976* | 2.50 | .20 | 13.00 | |
| ai | DF/LF (speckled paper) | 2.50 | .20 | 13.00 | |
| aii | LF/F (w/flrsc fibers) | 8.00 | .50 | 45.00* | |
| aiii | LF/MF | 10.00 | .75 | 60.00* | |
| aiv | DF/LF (non-speckled paper) | 2.50 | .20 | 13.00 | |

* Blank corner block of 4.

Six minor constant plate varieties have been reported on the 50¢ value: four are found on the Type I printings and two on the Type II printings.

**Nos. 594–598 (5) combination FDC** **4.90**

**MINT PRICING PREMIUMS**

Mint stamps from 301 to date are valued as NH-VF (Never Hinged-Very Fine). All hinged VF and NH-F copies are worth 50% of the listed values. Plate block (PB) values are for mint NH–VF plate or inscription blocks of four.

**USED, VF/XF (with in-period, circular date cancel) PRICING PREMIUM**

Single stamps with light or circular date cancels will sell for more than catalogue value (perhaps even more than a mint copy). From *1981 to 1991* single stamps from se-tenant blocks of 4 or larger will be priced at 50% or more above the fine price. From *1992* to date single stamps from se-tenant blocks of 4 or larger plus se-tenant booklet panes and souvenir sheets will be priced at 100% or more above the fine price. From *1997* to date all other stamps will be priced at 50% or more above the fine price.

## LANDSCAPE DEFINITIVES
## 1972–1977

599, 600
Vancouver
No. 599 has been redrawn from the original No. 600.

601
Quebec

600

599/599a

Designer: Reinhard Derreth.

Engraved (1 colour) and Photogravure (2 colours) , panes of 50
British American Bank Note Company

| 1973, Oct 24 | Tagged, GT2 | | | Perf 12.5x12.0 | |
|---|---|---|---|---|---|
| No. | Description | NH–VF | ⊙F | PB | FDC |
| 599 | **$1 multicoloured**, (Plate 2), DF | 3.50 | .75 | 17.50 | 15.00† |
| i | HB (front only) | 7.50 | 2.50 | 32.50* | |
| ii | NF | 5.00 | 1.00 | 25.00 | |
| iii | LF | 3.50 | .75 | 17.50 | |

† Any cover, single usage.

**Perf 13.3**

| No. | Description | NH–VF | ⊙F | PB | FDC |
|---|---|---|---|---|---|
| 599a | Revised perforation, NF, *Jul 1977* | 3.50 | .50 | 17.50 | — |
| ai | DF | 3.50 | .50 | 17.50 | |
| aii | NF/LF | 3.50 | .50 | 17.50 | |
| aiii | DF/LF | 3.50 | .50 | 17.50 | |
| aiv | MF | 5.00 | .75 | 35.00* | |

* Blank corner block of 4.

Engraved (1 colour) and Lithography (4 colours)
Sheets of 200 subjects in four panes of 50
British American Bank Note Company (engraving) and
Ashton-Potter Limited (lithography)

| 1972, Mar 17 | Untagged | | | | Perf 11 |
|---|---|---|---|---|---|
| No. | Description | NH–VF | ⊙F | PB | FDC |
| 600 | **$1 multicoloured**, (Plate 1), DF | 8.00 | 2.50 | 35.00 | 6.00‡ |
| i | DF, ribbed, horiz. | 10.00 | 3.00 | 50.00 | 7.50 |
| ii | short $ flaw (pos. 21, 23, 24) | 15.00 *EP* | 5.00 | | 25.00 |
| iii | as "ii", ribbed, horiz. | 25.00 *EP* | 7.50 | | 30.00 |
| iv | short $ flaw and dot after "Postes" (pos. 22)† | 25.00 *EP* | 10.00 | | 50.00 |
| v | as "iv", ribbed, horiz. | 50.00 *EP* | 15.00 | | 60.00 |

‡ Commercial cover, single usage $70.00.
† No. 600iv also exists without dot after "Postes" (pos. 22); price shown is for positional block of 4 from left margin $100.00.

| No. | Description | NH–VF | ⊙F | PB | FDC |
|---|---|---|---|---|---|
| 601 | **$2 multicoloured**, (Plate 1) | 6.00 | 3.50 | 30.00 | 9.00 |
| i | missing '$2' (42 recorded) | *4,500.00*‡ | | | |
| | plate 2, *Mar 28, 1978* § | — | — | 27.50 | |
| ii | "airplane in sky", (Pl 2, pos. 2) | 25.00 | 20.00 | 95.00 | |

‡ No. 601i should have a certificate of authenticity; one commercial cover known.
§ Singles from plate 2 cannot be differentiated from plate 1 singles.

**Nos. 600, 601 (2) Combination FDC** **75.00**
**Nos. 600ii, 601 (2) Combination FDC** **100.00**

Designer: Heather Cooper.

Engraved (1 colour) and Photogravure (3 colours; 2 colours on 10¢), panes of 100
British American Bank Note Company

**Tagged, GT2** **Perf 13.0x13.3**

| | | NH–VF | ⊙F | PB | FDC |
|---|---|---|---|---|---|
| **781** | **1¢ lilac & multi**, NF/NF, *Aug 16, 1979* | .25 | .20 | 1.25 | — |
| i | "hook tag flaw" | 25.00 | 20.00 | | |
| ii | overprinted "PHILABEC '80/31 MAI/ 1er JUIN"* | 10.00 | | 50.00 | |
| iii | as ii, inverted overprint | 25.00 | | | |
| iv | NF/DF | .25 | .20 | 1.25 | |

Qty: 115,200,000

* privately produced overprint. For EXUP and HINTONPEX overprints see 705. This listing will likely be removed in a future edition.

**Booklet issue** **Perf 12.0x12.5**

| | | | | | |
|---|---|---|---|---|---|
| 781a | single 1¢ with straight edge, from 781b, DF | .25 | .20 | | — |
| ai | as 'a', LF | .50 | .25 | | |
| b | booklet pane of 6, 2 x 1¢ (781a) + 4 x 12¢ (713a) (BK77), DF, *Nov 1, 1977* | 1.00 | 1.00 | | — |
| bi | as 'b', LF | 4.50 | 4.50 | | |
| BK77 | pane 781b in bilingual cover $1.25 | | | | |

**Perf 13.0x13.3**

| | | | | | |
|---|---|---|---|---|---|
| **782** | **2¢ pale brown & multi**, DF/DF, *Aug 2, 1979* | .25 | .20 | 1.25 | |
| i | "hook tag flaw" | 45.00 | 40.00 | | |
| ii | ribbed, vertical | 1.25 | .75 | 6.50 | |
| iii | DF/LF | 1.00 | .25 | 5.00 | |
| T1 | untagged (error) | | 40.00 | | |

Qty: 95,600,000

**Booklet issue** **Perf 12.0x12.5**

| | | | | | |
|---|---|---|---|---|---|
| 782a | booklet pane of 7 + label, 4 x 2¢ (782b) + 3 x 14¢ (716as) + label (BK78), DF/DF, *Apr 1, 1978* | 1.00 | 1.00 | | — |
| ai | as "a", ribbed, vertical (BK78c) | 7.00 | 7.00 | | |
| b | single 2¢ with straight edge, from 782a | .25 | .20 | | — |
| bi | ribbed, vertical (single 2¢, from 782ai) | 1.00 | .75 | | |
| BK78 | pane 782a in bilingual cover $1.25 | | | | |

781ii

781b

782a

**Perf 13.0x13.3**

| | | | | | |
|---|---|---|---|---|---|
| **783** | **3¢ dull green & multi**, DF/LF, *Apr 11, 1979* | .25 | .20 | 1.25 | |
| i | "hook tag flaw" | 35.00 | 25.00 | | |
| ii | DF/F | 1.50 | .50 | 7.50 | |

Qty: 141,800,000

| | | | | | |
|---|---|---|---|---|---|
| **784** | **4¢ dull lavender & multi**, DF/DF, *Jul 3, 1979* | .25 | .20 | 1.25 | |

Qty: 59,400,000

### Hook tag flaw:

A constant tagging flaw occurs on ***eleven*** stamps in this issue, as illustrated at right. The flaw occurs on the right-most vertical tag bar (left-most, inverted on 907). It "moves" along the pane; as such the flaw may fall entirely on a stamp or just a portion of the flaw may appear near the top or bottom of a stamp. See: 781i, 782i, 783i, 785i, 786i, 787i, 789i, 789ai, 907iv (inverted), 923i, 945ii.

Hook tag flaw

| | | NH–VF | ⊙F | PB | FDC |
|---|---|---|---|---|---|
| **785** | **5¢ dull brown & multi**, DF/DF, *Jan 24, 1979* | .25 | .20 | 1.25 | |
| i | "hook tag flaw" | 35.00 | 25.00 | | |

Qty: 114,200,000

| | | | | | |
|---|---|---|---|---|---|
| **786** | **10¢ ochre & multi**, DF/LF, Plate 3, *Oct 4, 1979* | .25 | .20 | 1.25 | |
| i | "hook tag flaw" | 35.00 | 25.00 | | |
| T1 | untagged (error) | | 40.00 | | |

Qty: 100,800,000

| | | | | | |
|---|---|---|---|---|---|
| **787** | **15¢ violet & multicoloured**, DF, *Aug 16, 1979* | .35 | .20 | 1.75 | .95 |
| i | "hook tag flaw" | 35.00 | 25.00 | | |
| ii | vertical line (10mm) down perforations between stamps 83 and 84 | 4.00 | 3.00 | | |
| iii | LF | .35 | .20 | 1.75 | |
| T1 | untagged (error) | | 75.00 | | |
| xx | No. 787 precancelled, DF | .50 | .40 | 10.00† | |
| xxi | F | 2.50 | .40 | 50.00† | |

Qty: 243,200,000

† Warning strip of 20

No. 788 is not assigned.

## FIRST-CLASS DEFINITIVES 1977–1982

789
Queen Elizabeth II

Designer: Queen: Heather Cooper; Parliament: Reinhard Derreth.

Engraved and Photogravure, pane of 100
British American Bank Note Company

**Tagged, GT2** **Perf 13.0x13.3**

| | | NH–VF | ⊙F | PB | FDC |
|---|---|---|---|---|---|
| **789** | **17¢ green & black**, DF/DF | | | | |
| | Plate 1, *Mar 8, 1979* | .35 | .20 | 1.75 | 1.00 |
| | Plate 2, *Feb 4, 1981* | — | — | 1.75 | |
| i | "hook tag flaw" | 25.00 | 20.00 | | |
| ii | NF/LF | .50 | .25 | 2.50 | |
| iii | F | 4.00 | .75 | 25.00* | |
| iv | ribbed, vert., DF/DF | 5.00 | 1.50 | 30.00* | |
| v | ribbed, vert., NF/LF | 7.00 | 2.00 | 40.00* | |
| T1 | untagged (error) | 30.00 | 10.00 | | |
| c | imperf pair | *2,750.00* | — | *3,000.00*† | — |
| d | black inscriptions omitted and printing shift (100 known) | 1,250.00 | | *5,000.00** | |

Qty: 790,200,000

* Blank corner block of 4.

† Non-inscription LL corner block of 12 (4 x 3). LL horiz. pair imperf., showing only blind perfs. between that pair and rest of block.

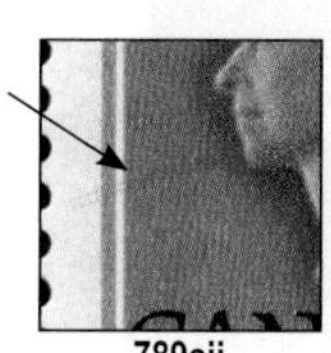
789aii

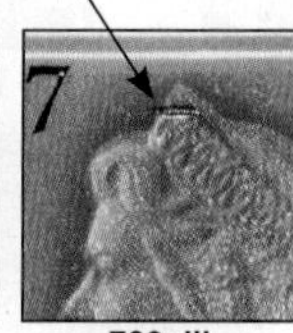
789aiii

789aiv

789d

Environment — 1979–1983

QE II — 1970's

### Booklet issue — Perf 12.0x12.5

| | | NH–VF | ⊙F | PB | FDC |
|---|---|---|---|---|---|
| 789a | single 17¢ Elizabeth II, from 789b, perf all around | 1.00 | .75 | | — |
| as | single 17¢ with straight edge, from 789b or 797a | .50 | .20 | | — |
| asi | ribbed, vertical (single 17¢) | 1.00 | .75 | | |
| ai | "hook tag flaw" | 35.00 | 30.00 | | |
| aii | horiz. grey line (797a, pos. 2) | 5.00 | 2.50 | | |
| aiii | "tarnished Tiara" (797a, pos. 3) | 5.00 | 2.50 | | |
| aiv | "scar on forehead" (789b, pos. 17) | 5.00 | 2.50 | | |
| av | "notch in lower frame" (789b, pos. 27) | 7.50 | 5.00 | | |
| aT1 | untagged (error) | 30.00 | 10.00 | | |
| 789b | booklet pane of 25 x 17¢ (789a and 789as) + 2 labels, BABN (BK81) *Jul 3, 1979* | 8.00 | 12.00 | | — |
| BK81 | pane 789b in bilingual cover $8.50 | | | | |

A single stamp with missing 'A' in Canada has been reported. A certificate of authenticity is recommended.

789b

Missing 'A'

790
Houses of Parliament

Engraved (1 colour), pane of 100
Canadian Bank Note Company

Tagged, GT2 — Perf 13.0x13.3

| | | NH–VF | ⊙F | PB | FDC |
|---|---|---|---|---|---|
| 790 | **17¢ green**, Plate 1 & 2, NF, *Mar 8, 1979* | .35 | .20 | 1.75 | 1.00 |
| a | printed on gummed side | 50.00 | | 300.00* | |
| i | ribbed, horizontal | 1.00 | .50 | | |
| ii | thin paper variety† | 450.00 | | | |
| T1 | untagged (error) | 35.00 | 20.00 | 150.00(Pl 2) | |
| iii | LF | 2.50 | .50 | 15.00 | |
| iv | DF | 1.00 | .35 | 7.50 | |

Qty: 729,600,000

* Blank corner block of 4.

† Top layer of paper peeled off before printing. 8 mint copies with full printing on thin paper are known.

**Nos. 789, 790 (2) combination FDC** 1.75

Left: normal Right: 790ii

791i

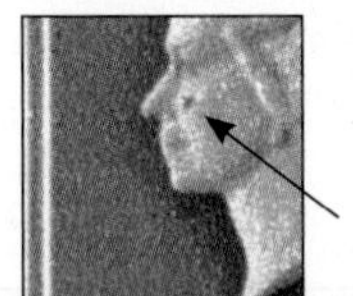

791ii

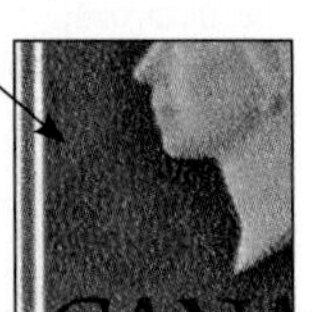

791iii

792iii

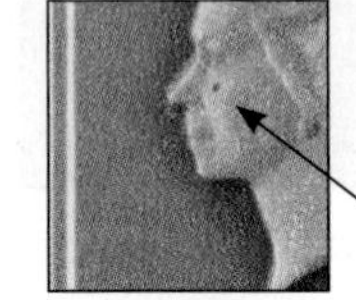

792v

791
Queen Elizabeth II

792
Queen Elizabeth II

Engraved and Photogravure, panes of 100
British American Bank Note Company

Tagged, GT2 — Perf 13.0x13.3

| | | NH–VF | ⊙F | PB | FDC |
|---|---|---|---|---|---|
| 791 | **30¢ deep magenta & black**, Plate 1 & 2, LF/fl, *May 11, 1982* | .60 | .20 | 3.00 | 1.00 |
| a | missing inscriptions (black)† | *3,000.00* | | | |
| i | "Queen's goatee" (pos. 55)‡ | 5.00 | 2.50 | | |
| ii | "crying Queen" (Pl. 2, pos. 89) | 5.00 | 2.50 | 15.00 | |
| iii | 4mm circular purple blemish, (Pl. 1, pos. 91) | 5.00 | 2.50 | 15.00 | |
| iv | DF | 3.00 | .30 | 15.00 | |
| T1 | untagged (error) | 25.00 | 5.00 | 100.00* | |

Qty: 244,600,000

† Two copies reported with inscriptions completely missing; partial missing $200 to $1,000.

‡ From plate 2, non-inscripted pane. * Blank corner block of 4.

| | | NH–VF | ⊙F | PB | FDC |
|---|---|---|---|---|---|
| 792 | **32¢ grey-blue & black**, Abitibi-Price paper, Plate 1, LF, *May 24, 1983* | .65 | .20 | 3.25 | 1.00 |
| ii | MF | 1.25 | .35 | 7.50 | |
| iii | "Queen's goatee" (pos. 55) | 5.00 | 2.50 | | |
| iv | "paleface Queen" (pos. 79) | 5.00 | 2.50 | | |
| v | "crying Queen" (pos. 89) | 5.00 | 2.50 | 15.00 | |
| i | Harrison paper, plate 2, *Aug 26, 1983* | 1.00 | .20 | 5.00 | |
| vi | as "i", "comet tag" flaw† | 25.00 | 20.00 | 45.00 (UR/LR) | |
| T1 | untagged (error) | 60.00 | 30.00 | | |

Qty: 440,400,000

† See note after No. 924.

Nos. 793–796, 798–799, 801–805, and 807–812 are not assigned.

## BOOKLET STAMPS

797
Houses of Parliament

800
Houses of Parliament

Designer: Reinhard Derreth.

Engraved
British American Bank Note Company

1979, Mar 28 — Tagged, GT2 — Perf 12.0x12.5

| | | NH–VF | ⊙F | PB | FDC |
|---|---|---|---|---|---|
| 797 | **1¢ grey blue**, single with straight edge, from 797a | 1.00 | .30 | | — |
| 797a | booklet pane of 6, 1 x 1¢ (797) + 3 x 5¢ (800) + 2 x 17¢ (789as), (BK80) | 1.00 | .60 | | 1.90 |
| ai | double paper across all 6 stamps | *2,500.00* | | | |
| BK80 | pane 797a in bilingual cover $1.25 | | | | |
| 800 | **5¢ purple**, single with straight edge, from 797a | .40 | .30 | | — |

797a

797ai

## FIRST-CLASS DEFINITIVE – COIL STAMP
## 1979

806
Houses of Parliament

Roll of 100
Canadian Bank Note Company

**1979, Mar 8** **Tagged, GT2** **Perf 10 vert**

| | | NH–VF | ⊙F | FDC |
|---|---|---|---|---|
| **806** | **17¢ green** (790), dull | .35 | .20 | 1.00 |
| i | wide spacing strip of 4 | 15.00 | | |
| ii | narrow spacing strip of 4 | 15.00 | | |
| iii | "dot at high noon/pigeon hole", (pos. 3, 15, 27) | 5.00 | 2.50 | |
| | as "iii", in strip of 4 | 20.00 | | |
| iv | F | 5.00 | 0.50 | |
| v | as "iv", jump strip of 4 | 50.00 | | |
| T1 | untagged (error) | — | 40.00 | |
| a | imperf. pair | 200.00 | | |

Qty: 793,740,000

Coil pairs or larger multiples are priced in proportion.

806iii

## ENDANGERED WILDLIFE

813
Spiny Soft-Shelled Turtle

814
Bowhead Whale

Designer: 17¢: Gary Low; 35¢: Robert McLellan Bateman.
Lithography (4 colours), panes of 50
Ashton-Potter Limited

**1979, Apr 10** **Tagged, GT2** **Perf 12.5**

| | | NH–VF | ⊙F | PB | FDC |
|---|---|---|---|---|---|
| **813** | **17¢ multicoloured**, DF | .40 | .20 | 2.00 | 1.00 |
| i | blue scratch in rocks (Type I, pos. 24) | 5.00 | 2.50 | | |
| ii | blue scratch in rocks (Type II, pos. 24) | 5.00 | 2.50 | | |
| iii | "red worm on 'n'" (pos. 46) | 5.00 | 2.50 | 7.50 | |
| iv | LF | 5.00 | | 30.00 | |

Qty: 26,500,000

| | | NH–VF | ⊙F | PB | FDC |
|---|---|---|---|---|---|
| **814** | **35¢ multicoloured** | 1.10 | .70 | 5.50 | 1.65 |

Qty: 16,000,000

Repellex error: No. 813 missing magenta colour (turtle is green instead of brown) $1,650.00 (4 known). Six copies are also known missing only part of magenta colour (turtle is part brown, part green) $375.00.

813i
Type I

813ii
Type II

813iii

Repellex error on top stamp

## POSTAL CODE

815 Female hand/red ribbon
816 Male hand/yellow ribbon

Designer: Don Haws.
Lithography (5 colours), pane of 50
Ashton-Potter Limited

**1979, Apr 27** **Tagged, GT2** **Perf 13.3**

| | | NH–VF | ⊙F | PB | FDC |
|---|---|---|---|---|---|
| **815** | **17¢ multicoloured** | .35 | .20 | | 1.00 |
| **816** | **17¢ multicoloured** | .35 | .20 | | 1.00 |
| i | "hairy knuckle" (pos. 11) | 5.00 | 2.50 | 7.50 | |
| a | se-tenant pair (815, 816) | .80 | .70 | 1.75 | 1.75 |
| b | black double printed (se-tenant pair) | 150.00 | | 400.00 | |
| c | black triple printed (se-tenant pair) | 300.00 | | | |
| d | red colour doubled (se-tenant pair) | 150.00 | | 400.00 | |

Qty: 37,500,000 of each

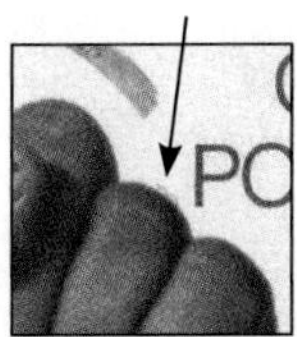

816i

## CANADIAN AUTHORS

817
*Fruits of the Earth*

818
*Le vaisseau d'or*

Designer: 817: Rosemary Elizabeth Kilbourn; 818: Monique Charbonneau.
Lithography (6 colours), pane of 50
Ashton-Potter Limited

**1979, May 3** **Tagged, GT2** **Perf 13.3**

| | | NH–VF | ⊙F | PB | FDC |
|---|---|---|---|---|---|
| **817** | **17¢ multicoloured** | .35 | .20 | | 1.85† |
| a | brown double printed | 500.00 | | | |
| T1 | untagged (error) | 100.00 | | | |
| **818** | **17¢ multicoloured** | .35 | .20 | | 1.85† |
| a | blue double printed | 500.00 | | | |
| T1 | untagged (error) | 100.00 | | | |
| b | se-tenant pair (817, 818) | .80 | .70 | 1.75 | 2.70† |
| c | left margin block of 4 with left vertical pair imperf. and right pair part perf. | 2,500.00 | | 3,000.00* | |
| ii | imperf., se-tenant horizontal pair | 1,250.00 | | | |
| bT1 | untagged (error), se-tenant pair | 200.00 | | | |

Qty: 12,500,000 of each

* Blank corner blocks only.

† FDCs were withdrawn from sale because the image used for Grove on the cachet was incorrect.

Issued to mark the 100th birth anniversaries of Frederick P. Grove (1879–1948) and Émile Nelligan (1879–1941).

## CANADIAN COLONELS

819
Colonel C.M. de Salaberry

820
Colonel John By

Designer: Theo Dimson.

Lithography (7 colours) and Embossed, pane of 50
Ashton-Potter Limited

**1979, May 11** **Tagged, GT2** **Perf 13.3**

| | | NH–VF | ⊙F | PB | FDC |
|---|---|---|---|---|---|
| **819** | **17¢ multicoloured**, DF | .35 | .20 | | 1.00 |
| i | LF | 3.00 | | | |
| ii | F | 5.00 | | | |
| **820** | **17¢ multicoloured**, DF | .35 | .20 | | 1.00 |
| i | LF | 3.00 | | | |
| ii | F | 5.00 | | | |
| **a** | se-tenant pair, DF (819, 820) | .80 | .70 | 1.75 | 1.75 |
| **ai** | se-tenant pair, LF (819i, 820i) | 6.00 | | 15.00 | |
| **aii** | se-tenant pair, F (819ii, 820ii) | 10.00 | | 25.00 | |

Qty: 13,500,000 of each

Issued to honour Charles-Michel d'Irumberry de Salaberry (1778–1829), whose forces saved Montreal from American attack at the Battle of Chateauguay; and John By (1779–1836), builder of the Rideau Canal.

## PROVINCIAL & TERRITORIAL FLAGS

821
Ontario

822
Quebec

823
Nova Scotia

824
New Brunswick

825
Manitoba

826
British Columbia

827
Prince Edward Island

828
Saskatchewan

829
Alberta

830
Newfoundland

831
Northwest Territories

832
Yukon Territory

Designer: Raymond Bellemare.

Lithography (6 colours), Plates of 144 subjects in twelve panes of 12
Ashton-Potter Limited

**1979, Jun 15** **Tagged, GT2** **Perf 13.3**

| | | NH–VF | ⊙F | PB | FDC |
|---|---|---|---|---|---|
| **821** | **17¢ Ontario** | .40 | .30 | | 1.00 |
| **822** | **17¢ Quebec** | .40 | .30 | | 1.00 |
| **823** | **17¢ Nova Scotia** | .40 | .30 | | 1.00 |
| **824** | **17¢ New Brunswick** | .40 | .30 | | 1.00 |
| **825** | **17¢ Manitoba** | .40 | .30 | | 1.00 |
| **826** | **17¢ British Columbia** | .40 | .30 | | 1.00 |
| **827** | **17¢ Prince Edward Island** | .40 | .30 | | 1.00 |
| **828** | **17¢ Saskatchewan** | .40 | .30 | | 1.00 |
| **829** | **17¢ Alberta** | .40 | .30 | | 1.00 |
| **830** | **17¢ Newfoundland** | .40 | .30 | | 1.00 |
| **831** | **17¢ Northwest Territories** | .40 | .30 | | 1.00 |
| **832** | **17¢ Yukon Territory** | .40 | .30 | | 1.00 |
| **a** | $2.04 pane of 12† (821–832) | 5.50 | 5.00 | 5.75 | 7.30 |

Qty: 5,405,000 of each

Issued for Canada Day 1979.

† Four different philatelic panes exist depending upon the position of the corner inscription, as illustrated below. Field stock includes the top and bottom inscriptions but has the side inscriptions removed.

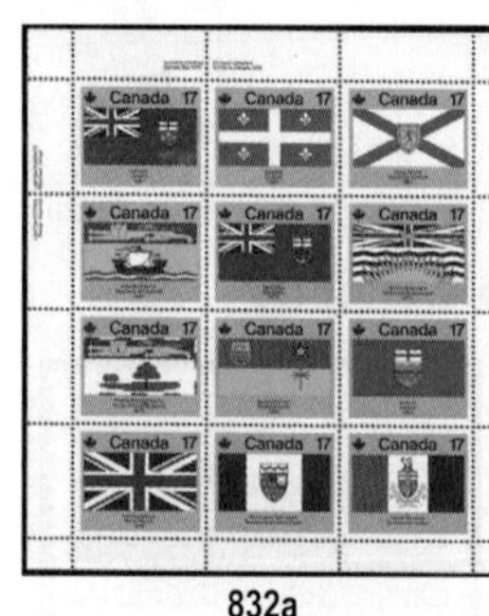

832a
upper left pane

832a
upper right pane

832a
lower left pane

832a
lower right pane

**July 1, 1979**
Canada Post goes metric: postal rates based on metric weights (grams and kilograms) instead of imperial units (ounces and pounds).

| **Rates:** | Domestic: 17¢ (0–30g), 26¢ (30–50g) |
|---|---|
| Jul 1, 1979– | 3rd class (0–50g): 15¢ |
| Dec 31, 1981 | USA: 17¢ (0–30g), 30¢ (30–50g) |
| | International: 35¢ (0–20g), 63¢ (20–50g) |
| | Registration: $1.50 |
| | Special delivery: $1.00 |

## SPORT CHAMPIONSHIPS

833
White Water Race

834
Women's Field Hockey

Designer: Jon Eby.

Lithography (4 colours), panes of 50
Ashton-Potter Limited

**1979** **Tagged, GT2** **Perf 12.5**

| | | NH–VF | ⊙F | PB | FDC |
|---|---|---|---|---|---|
| **833** | **17¢ multicoloured**, dull, *Jul 3, 1979* | .40 | .20 | 2.00 | 1.00 |
| **i** | MF | 5.00 | .50 | 25.00 | |

Qty: 25,500,000

Issued to mark the Canoe-Kayak World Championships, held at Jonquiere, Quebec.

| | | NH–VF | ⊙F | PB | FDC |
|---|---|---|---|---|---|
| **834** | **17¢ multicoloured**, dull, *Aug 16, 1979* | .40 | .20 | 2.00 | 1.00 |
| **i** | MF | 3.50 | .50 | 17.50 | |

Qty: 25,500,000

Issued to mark the Women's Field Hockey Championships, Vancouver.

## INUIT – SHELTER & COMMUNITY

835
Summer Tent

836
Building an Igloo

837
The Dance

838
Repulse Bay Soapstones

Designer: Reinhard Derreth .

Lithography (5 colours), panes of 50
Ashton-Potter Limited

**1979, Sep 13** **Tagged, GT2** **Perf 13.3**

| | | NH–VF | ⊙F | PB | FDC |
|---|---|---|---|---|---|
| **835** | **17¢ multicoloured**, DF | .35 | .20 | | 1.00 |
| **i** | nick in 'n' of 'Inuit' (pos. 17) | 5.00 *EP* | 2.50 | | |
| **ii** | LF | 5.00 | | | |
| **836** | **17¢ multicoloured**, DF | .35 | .20 | | 1.00 |
| **i** | LF | 5.00 | | | |
| **T1** | untagged (error) | 100.00 | | | |
| **a** | se-tenant pair, DF (835, 836) | .80 | .70 | 1.75 | |
| **ai** | se-tenant pair, LF (835ii, 836i) | 10.00 | | 25.00 | |

Qty: 11,000,000 of each

No. 835 has not been reported untagged, but should exist.

| | | NH–VF | ⊙F | PB | FDC |
|---|---|---|---|---|---|
| **837** | **17¢ multicoloured** | .35 | .20 | | 1.00 |
| **i** | "red stitch" (pos. 9) | 5.00 *EP* | 2.50 | 7.50 | |
| **ii** | blue scratch on feather (pos. 47) | 5.00 | 2.50 | 7.50 | |
| **838** | **17¢ multicoloured** | .35 | .20 | | 1.00 |
| **a** | se-tenant pair (837, 838) | .80 | .70 | 1.75 | |

Qty: 11,000,000 of each

**Nos. 835–838 (4) combination FDC** 2.85

See also 748–751, 769–772 and 866–869.

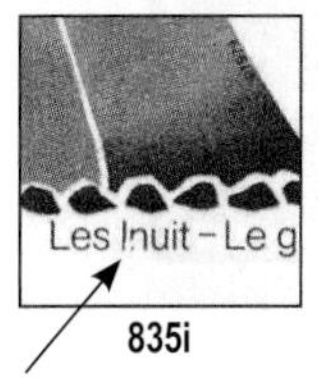

835i

837i

837ii

## CHRISTMAS – ANTIQUE TOYS

839
Wooden Train

841
Knitted Stuffed Doll

840
Wooden Horse

Designer: Arnaud Maggs.

Lithography (5 colours), panes of 50
Canadian Bank Note Company

**1979, Oct 17** **Tagged, GT2** **Perf 13.0x13.3**

| | | NH–VF | ⊙F | PB | FDC |
|---|---|---|---|---|---|
| **839** | **15¢ blue & multicoloured** | .35 | .20 | 1.75 | .95 |

Qty: 109,500,000

| | | NH–VF | ⊙F | PB | FDC |
|---|---|---|---|---|---|
| **840** | **17¢ green & multicoloured**, DF | .40 | .20 | 2.00 | 1.00 |
| **T1** | untagged (error) | 100.00 | | | |
| **i** | gutter pair (unique) due to dramatic fold-over error | *3,500.00* | | | |
| **ii** | LF | 2.50 | | 15.00 | |

Qty: 69,500,000

**Tagged, GT4** **Perf 13.3x13.0**

| | | NH–VF | ⊙F | PB | FDC |
|---|---|---|---|---|---|
| **841** | **35¢ red & multicoloured** | .80 | .60 | 4.00 | 1.65 |
| **T1** | untagged (error) | 75.00 | 50.00 | | |
| **a** | gold and tagging omitted† | 1,750.00 | 1,000.00 | 8,000.00* | |

Qty: 19,500,000

† Less than 120 copies are known. Five examples show a repellex error resulting in part of the red background missing (value $2,000 with repellex).

* Blank corner block of 4.

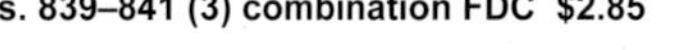

**Nos. 839–841 (3) combination FDC $2.85**

841a

## UNITED NATIONS YEAR OF THE CHILD

842
Child Watering Tree

Designer: Jean Morin. Based on a painting by Marie-Annick Viatour.

Lithography (4 colours), pane of 50
Ashton-Potter Limited

**1979, Oct 24** **Tagged, GT2** **Perf 13.3**

| | | NH–VF | ⊙F | PB | FDC |
|---|---|---|---|---|---|
| **842** | **17¢ multicoloured**, DF | .35 | .20 | 1.75 | 1.00 |
| **i** | LF | .35 | .20 | 1.75 | |

Qty: 24,000,000

## AIRCRAFT – FLYING BOATS

843 Curtiss HS-2L — 844 Canadair CL-215

845 Vickers Vedette — 846 Consolidated Canso

Designer: Jacques Charette. Based on paintings by Robert William Bradford.
Lithography (4 colours), pane of 50
Ashton-Potter Limited

**1979, Nov 15** — **Tagged, GT2** — **Perf 12.5**

| | | | NH–VF | ⊙F | PB | FDC |
|---|---|---|---|---|---|---|
| **843** | | **17¢ multicoloured** | .40 | .20 | | 1.00 |
| **844** | | **17¢ multicoloured** | .40 | .20 | | 1.00 |
| | a | se-tenant pair (843, 844) | .90 | .70 | 2.00 | |

Qty: 18,000,000 of each

| | | | NH–VF | ⊙F | PB | FDC |
|---|---|---|---|---|---|---|
| **845** | | **35¢ multicoloured** | .85 | .70 | | 1.65 |
| **846** | | **35¢ multicoloured** | .85 | .70 | | 1.65 |
| | a | se-tenant pair (845, 846) | 1.90 | 1.70 | 4.25 | |

Qty: 12,500,000 of each

**Nos. 843–846 (4) combination FDC** **4.00**

See also 873–876, 903–906 and 969–972.

## 1980

847 Map of Canada

848 Downhill Skier

## ARCTIC ISLANDS

Designer: Stuart Bradley Ash.
Lithography (4 colours), pane of 50
Ashton-Potter Limited

**1980, Jan 23** — **Tagged, GT2** — **Perf 13.3**

| | | | NH–VF | ⊙F | PB | FDC |
|---|---|---|---|---|---|---|
| **847** | | **17¢ multicoloured**, DF | .35 | .20 | 1.75 | 1.00 |
| | i | dark blue Canada (same colour as Alaska) | 1,000.00 | | | |
| | ii | "border patrol" variety (pos. 5) | 1.50 *EP* | .75 | 3.00 | |
| | iii | LF | .35 | .20 | 1.75 | |

Qty: 23,000,000

Issued to mark the 100th anniversary of Canada's acquisition of the Arctic Islands.

## WINTER OLYMPICS

Designer: Clermont Malenfant. Based on a photograph by Dinh Ngoc Mô.
Lithography (5 colours), pane of 50
Canadian Bank Note Company

**1980, Jan 23** — **Tagged, GT2** — **Perf 13.3**

| | | | NH–VF | ⊙F | PB | FDC |
|---|---|---|---|---|---|---|
| **848** | | **35¢ multicoloured**, DF | .85 | .75 | 4.25 | 1.65 |
| | i | LF | .85 | .75 | 4.25 | |

Qty: 13,000,000

Issued for the 13th Winter Olympic Games, Lake Placid, New York.

## ACADEMY OF ARTS

849 *Meeting of the School Trustees,* by Robert Harris — 850 *Inspiration,* by Louis-Phillippe Hébert

851 *Parliament Buildings,* by Thomas Fuller — 852 *Sunrise on the Saguenay,* by Lucius O'Brien

Designer: Jean Morin.
Lithography (4 colours), pane of 50
Ashton-Potter Limited

**1980, Mar 6** — **Tagged, GT2** — **Perf 13.3**

| | | | NH–VF | ⊙F | PB | FDC |
|---|---|---|---|---|---|---|
| **849** | | **17¢ multicoloured**, DF | .40 | .20 | | 1.00 |
| | i | LF | 2.00 | | | |
| | T1 | untagged (error) | | 100.00 | | |
| **850** | | **17¢ multicoloured**, DF | .40 | .20 | | 1.00 |
| | i | LF | 2.00 | | | |
| | a | se-tenant pair, DF (849, 850) | .90 | .70 | 2.00 | |
| | ai | se-tenant pair, LF (849i, 850i) | 4.00 | | | |

Qty: 12,000,000 of each

No. 850 has not been reported untagged, but it must exist.

| | | | NH–VF | ⊙F | PB | FDC |
|---|---|---|---|---|---|---|
| **851** | | **35¢ multicoloured** | .80 | .70 | | 1.65 |
| | i | vertical line over "N" of CANADA (pos. 38) | 7.50 *EP* | 5.00 | | 7.50 |
| **852** | | **35¢ multicoloured** | .80 | .70 | | 1.65 |
| | a | se-tenant pair (851, 852) | 1.60 | 1.60 | 3.25 | |

Qty: 6,500,000 of each

**Nos. 849–852 (4) combination FDC** **4.00**

Issued for the centenary of the Royal Canadian Academy of Arts, the forerunner to the National Gallery of Canada.

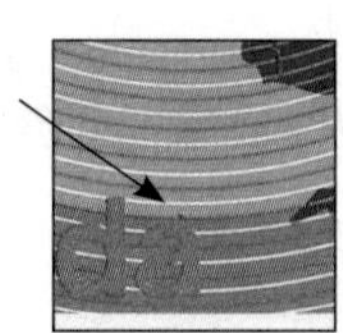

847ii

851i

## ENDANGERED WILDLIFE

853 Atlantic Whitefish

854 Greater Prairie Chicken

Designer: 853: Michael Dumas; 854: Robert McLellan Bateman.

Lithography (4 colours), panes of 50
Ashton-Potter Limited

| 1980, May 6 | Tagged, GT2 | | | Perf 12.5 |
|---|---|---|---|---|
| | NH–VF | ⊙F | PB | FDC |
| **853 17¢ multicoloured** | .45 | .20 | 2.25 | 1.00 |
| Qty: 20,500,000 | | | | |
| **854 17¢ multicoloured** | .45 | .20 | 2.25 | 1.00 |
| Qty: 20,500,000 | | | | |

## INTERNATIONAL EVENTS

855
Flower Garden

856
Helping Hands

Designer: 855: Heather J. Cooper; 856: Rolf P. Harder.

Lithography (4 colours), panes of 50
Ashton-Potter Limited

| 1980, May 29 | Tagged, GT2 | | | Perf 13.3 |
|---|---|---|---|---|
| | NH–VF | ⊙F | PB | FDC |
| **855 17¢ multicoloured** | .35 | .20 | 1.75 | 1.00 |
| Qty: 22,000,000 | | | | |
| Lithography and Embossed | | | | Perf 12.5 |
| **856 17¢ multicoloured** | .35 | .20 | 1.75 | 1.00 |
| Qty: 23,000,000 | | | | |

Issued to note Les Floralies in Montreal and the 14th World Congress of Rehabilitation International in Winnipeg.

## O CANADA CENTENARY

857
O Canada, opening bars

858
Composers

Designer: Friedrich G. Peter.

Lithography (6 colours), pane of 16
Ashton-Potter Limited

| 1980, Jun 6 | | Tagged, GT2 | | | Perf 12.5 |
|---|---|---|---|---|---|
| | | NH–VF | ⊙F | PB | FDC |
| **857** | **17¢ multicoloured** | .35 | .20 | | 1.00 |
| T1 | untagged (error) | | 100.00 | | |
| **858** | **17¢ multicoloured** | .35 | .20 | | 1.00 |
| i | dot on moustache | 3.00 | 1.00 | | 5.00 |
| T1 | untagged (error) | | 100.00 | | |
| a | se-tenant pair (857, 858) | .80 | .70 | 1.75 | 1.75 |
| | $2.72 pane of 16† (4 x 4) | 6.00 | 6.00 | 6.50 | |
| ai | se-tenant pair (857, 858i) | 4.00 | 2.00 | 8.00 | |
| | pane of 16 with 858i | 26.00 | | 27.00 | |

Qty: 30,000,000 of each

† Four different philatelic panes exist depending upon the position of the corner inscription.

There are several minor constant plate flaws on these two stamps. 858i appears on every (Composers) stamp on affected panes. The "no dot" FDC is scarcer.

Issued for the centenary of O CANADA and to mark its official proclamation as the national anthem.

858i

## JOHN DIEFENBAKER

859
John George Diefenbaker

Designer: Bernard N.J. Reilander. Portrait and lettering engraved by Yves Baril.

Engraved (1 colour), pane of 50
Canadian Bank Note Company

| 1980, Jun 20 | | Tagged, GT2 | | | Perf 13.3 |
|---|---|---|---|---|---|
| | | NH–VF | ⊙F | PB | FDC |
| **859** | **17¢ dark blue** | .35 | .20 | 1.75 | 1.00 |
| i | dot above initial "G" in legend (pos. 40) | 3.50 | 1.50 | 6.00 | 7.50 |
| T1 | untagged (error) | 100.00 | 75.00 | | |

Qty: 24,000,000

Issued in memory of John George Diefenbaker (1895–1979), Prime Minister of Canada, 1957–1963.

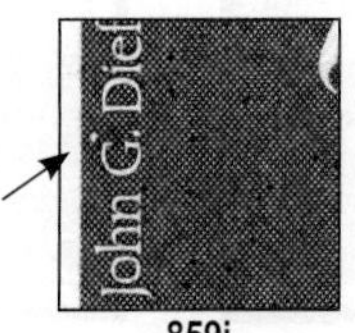

859i

## CANADIAN MUSICIANS

860
Emma Albani

861
Healey Willan

Designer: Huntley Brown.

Lithography (4 colours), pane of 50
Ashton-Potter Limited

| 1980, Jul 4 | | Tagged, GT2 | | | Perf 13.3 |
|---|---|---|---|---|---|
| | | NH–VF | ⊙F | PB | FDC |
| **860** | **17¢ multicoloured** | .35 | .20 | | 1.00 |
| **861** | **17¢ multicoloured** | .35 | .20 | | 1.00 |
| a | se-tenant pair (860, 861) | .80 | .70 | 1.75 | 1.75 |

Qty: 11,000,000 of each

Issued to honour soprano Emma Albani (1847–1930) and composer-organist Healey Willan (1880–1968).

## NED HANLAN

862

Designer: HClive Webster. Typographed by William H. Tibbles.
Lithography (4 colours), pane of 50
Ashton-Potter Limited

| 1980, Jul 4 | Tagged, GT2 | NH–VF | ⊙F | PB | FDC |
|---|---|---|---|---|---|
| 862 | 17¢ multicoloured | .35 | .20 | 1.75 | 1.00 |
| i | several blue dots below "9" of "1908" (pos. 34) | 5.00 | 2.50 | | |

Perf 13.3

Qty: 22,000,000

Issued to honour oarsman Ned Hanlan (1855–1908), first Canadian to win an international championship.
Copies of this stamp missing the blue colour are probably counterfeit.

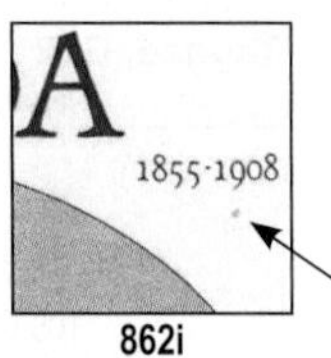


862i

## SASKATCHEWAN & ALBERTA

863
Wheat Fields, Estlin, SK

864
Strip Mining, Cowley, AB

Designer: Chris Yaneff Limited.
SK: Based on a photograph by George Hunter; AB: Based on a photograph by George Hunter.
Lithography (4 colours), panes of 50
Ashton-Potter Limited

| 1980, Aug 27 | Tagged, GT2 | NH–VF | ⊙F | PB | FDC |
|---|---|---|---|---|---|
| 863 | 17¢ multicoloured | .35 | .20 | 1.75 | 1.00 |
| 864 | 17¢ multicoloured | .35 | .20 | 1.75 | 1.00 |

Perf 13.3

Qty: 22,000,000 (863); Qty: 22,000,000 (864)

Issued to mark the 75th anniversary of the creation of the Provinces of Saskatchewan and Alberta from the Northwest Territories.

### MINT PRICING PREMIUMS

Mint stamps from 301 to date are valued as NH-VF (Never Hinged-Very Fine). All hinged VF and NH-F copies are worth 50% of the listed values. Plate block (PB) values are for mint NH–VF plate or inscription blocks of four.

### USED, VF/XF (with in-period, circular date cancel) PRICING PREMIUM

Single stamps with light or circular date cancels will sell for more than catalogue value (perhaps even more than a mint copy). From *1981 to 1991* single stamps from se-tenant blocks of 4 or larger will be priced at 50% or more above the fine price. From *1992* to date single stamps from se-tenant blocks of 4 or larger plus se-tenant booklet panes and souvenir sheets will be priced at 100% or more above the fine price. From *1997* to date all other stamps will be priced at 50% or more above the fine price.

## URANIUM

865
Uraninite Molecular Structure

Designer: Jacques Charette. Based on a photograph by Hans-Ludwig Blohm.
Lithography (4 colours), pane of 50
Canadian Bank Note Company

| 1980, Sep 3 | Tagged, GT2 | NH–VF | ⊙F | PB | FDC |
|---|---|---|---|---|---|
| 865 | 35¢ multicoloured | .80 | .70 | 4.00 | 1.65 |
| a | printed on gum side (30 known from single sheet) | 1,250.00 | | 6,000.00* | |

Perf 13.3

Qty: 11,000,000
* Blank corner block of 4 (UL and LL exist).

## INUIT – SPIRITS

866 Sedna
867 Return of the Sun

868 Bird Spirit
869 Shaman

Designer: Reinhard Derreth .
Lithography (5 colours), panes of 50
Canadian Bank Note Company

| 1980, Sep 25 | Tagged, GT2 | NH–VF | ⊙F | PB | FDC |
|---|---|---|---|---|---|
| 866 | 17¢ multicoloured | .35 | .20 | | 1.00 |
| 867 | 17¢ multicoloured | .35 | .20 | | 1.00 |
| i | vertical yellow line through 'i' of 'Inuit' (pos. 45) | 5.00 | 2.50 | 7.50 | |
| a | se-tenant pair (866, 867) | .80 | .70 | 1.75 | |
| Qty: 11,000,000 of each | | | | | |
| 868 | 35¢ multicoloured, dull | .75 | .70 | | 1.65 |
| i | F | 2.00 | 1.00 | | |
| 869 | 35¢ multicoloured, dull | .75 | .70 | | 1.65 |
| i | "Frozen Toe" variety, blue dot on toe at LR (pos. 27) | 3.00 | 1.50 | — | 7.50 |
| b | grey doubled | 900.00 | 500.00 | — | — |
| iii | F | 2.00 | 1.00 | | |
| a | se-tenant pair, dull (868, 869) | 1.70 | 1.50 | 3.75 | |
| ai | se-tenant pair, F (868i, 869iii) | 4.50 | 2.00 | 11.00 | |

Perf 13.3

Qty: 5,500,000 of each

**Nos. 866–869 (4) combination FDC** 4.00

See also 748–751, 769–772 and 835–838.

867i

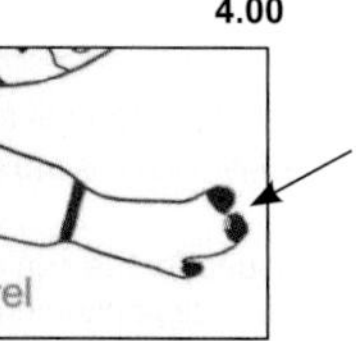

869i

## CHRISTMAS – GREETING CARDS

870
*Christmas Morning*, by Frank C. Hennessy

871
*Sleigh Ride*, by Joseph S. Hallam

872
*McGill Cab Stand*, by Kathleen Morris

Designer: Yvon Laroche.

Lithography (4 colour), panes of 50
Ashton-Potter Limited

**1980, Oct 22** **Tagged, GT2** **Perf 12.4x11.9**

| | | NH–VF | ⊙F | PB | FDC |
|---|---|---|---|---|---|
| **870** | **15¢ multicoloured**, dull | .30 | .20 | 1.50 | .95 |
| i | HB | 10.00 | .70 | 50.00 | |
| ii | "Pigeon hole in loft" (pos. 7) | 7.50 | 3.50 | 15.00 | |
| iii | two small black dots to right of 5 in 15 (pos. 39) | 3.50 | 1.50 | | |

Qty: 95,000,000

| | | NH–VF | ⊙F | PB | FDC |
|---|---|---|---|---|---|
| **871** | **17¢ multicoloured**, dull | .35 | .20 | 1.75 | 1.00 |
| i | black scratch through inscription (pos. 39) | 7.50 | 3.50 | | |
| ii | blue spot on rightmost roof (pos. 8) | 3.50 | 2.00 | | |
| iii | red dot to right of MERRY | 2.50 | 1.50 | | |
| iv | HB | 25.00 | | 125.00 | |

Qty: 65,000,000
An "imperforate piece of printer's waste" exists.

| | | NH–VF | ⊙F | PB | FDC |
|---|---|---|---|---|---|
| **872** | **35¢ multicoloured**, dull | .70 | .60 | 3.50 | 1.65 |
| i | small black dot above first S of Christmas (pos. 1) | 7.50 | 3.50 | 15.00 | |
| ii | HB | 15.00 | | 75.00 | |

Qty: 19,000,000

**Nos. 870–872 (3) combination FDC** **2.85**

There are several constant plate flaws on these Christmas stamps. The most notable are listed here.
The inscription blocks on the 15¢ and 17¢ values incorrectly reversed the names of the illustrator.

870ii

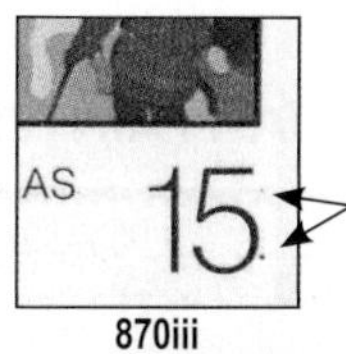

870iii

872i

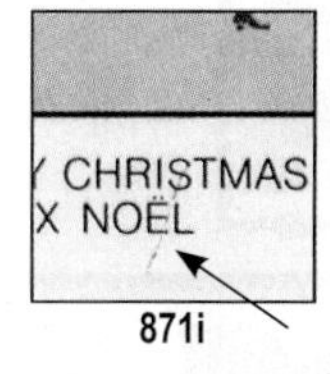

871i

871ii

871iii

**871 variety**
Imperforate printer's waste

## MILITARY AIRCRAFT

873
Avro Canada CF-100 (1950)

874
Avro Lancaster (1941)

875
Curtiss JN-4 Canuck

876
Hawker Hurricane (1935)

Designer: Jacques Charette. Based on paintings by Robert William Bradford.

Lithography (4 colours), pane of 50
Canadian Bank Note Company

**1980, Nov 10** **Tagged, GT2** **Perf 13.3**

| | | NH–VF | ⊙F | PB | FDC |
|---|---|---|---|---|---|
| **873** | **17¢ multicoloured** | .40 | .20 | | 1.00 |
| **874** | **17¢ multicoloured** | .40 | .20 | | 1.00 |
| i | "signal light" at end of wing (pos. 10) | 2.50 | 1.00 | 7.50 | |
| a | se-tenant pair (873, 874) | .90 | .70 | 2.00 | |

Qty: 14,000,000 of each

| | | NH–VF | ⊙F | PB | FDC |
|---|---|---|---|---|---|
| **875** | **35¢ multicoloured** | .85 | .75 | | 1.65 |
| **876** | **35¢ multicoloured** | .85 | .75 | | 1.65 |
| a | se-tenant pair (875, 876) | 1.90 | 1.70 | 4.25 | |

Qty: 8,500,000 of each

**Nos. 873–876 (4) combination FDC $4.00**

See also 843–846, 903–906 and 969–972.

874i

## E-P LACHAPELLE

877
Emmanuel-Persillier Lachapelle

Designer: Jean Morin. Based on a painting by Edmond Dyonnet.

Lithography (3 colours), pane of 50
Ashton-Potter Limited

**1980, Dec 5** **Tagged, GT2** **Perf 13.3**

| | | NH–VF | ⊙F | PB | FDC |
|---|---|---|---|---|---|
| **877** | **17¢ multicoloured** | .35 | .20 | 1.75 | 1.00 |

Qty: 20,000,000

Issued to mark the 100th anniversary of the founding of Notre-Dame Hospital in Montreal by physician Lachapelle (1845–1918).

## 1981

### "LOOK OF MUSIC" EXHIBITION

878
Antique Mandora

Designer: William H. Tibbles. Based on a photograph by Clive Webster.
Lithography (5 colours), pane of 50
Ashton-Potter Limited

| 1981, Jan 19 | Tagged, GT2 | | | Perf 13.3 |
|---|---|---|---|---|
| | NH–VF | ⊙F | PB | FDC |
| **878 17¢ multicoloured** | .35 | .20 | 1.75 | 1.00 |
| T1 untagged (error) | | 200.00 | | |
| i printed on gum side, missing inscriptions, untagged* | 2,000.00 | — | 9,000.00 | |

Qty: 21,500,000

* 200 examples known, approximately one half of which are sound. The remainder have minor faults and light creases and are valued at $800.00–$1,200.00.

Imperforate pairs, with brown and most of magenta missing have been seen by the editors. Value $1,500.00

A rare musical instrument exhibition held in Vancouver.

### CANADIAN FEMINISTS

879 Emily Stowe — 881 Idola Saint-Jean

880 Louise McKinney — 882 Henrietta Edwards

Designer: Dennis Goddard. Based on paintings by Muriel Wood.
Lithography (8 colours), pane of 50
Canadian Bank Note Company

| 1981, Mar 4 | Tagged, GT2 | | | Perf 13.3 |
|---|---|---|---|---|
| | NH–VF | ⊙F | PB | FDC |
| **879 17¢ multicoloured** | .45 | .30 | | 1.00 |
| i "pink brooch on collar" (pos. 1) | 7.50 *EP* | 2.50 | 10.00 | |
| **880 17¢ multicoloured** | .45 | .30 | | 1.00 |
| **881 17¢ multicoloured** | .45 | .30 | | 1.00 |
| **882 17¢ multicoloured** | .45 | .30 | | 1.00 |
| a se-tenant block of 4 (879–882) | 2.00 | 1.80 | 2.25 | 2.85 |

Qty: 879–880: 6,162,000 of each; 881–882: 5,688,000 of each

Emily Stowe (1831–1903) was the first Canadian woman physician; Louise McKinney (1868–1931) was the first woman member of a legislature in the British Commonwealth; Idola Saint-Jean (1875–1945) fought for the women's right to vote; Henrietta Edwards (1849–1931) founded the Working Girl's Association.

879i

### CANADIAN ENDANGERED WILDLIFE

883 Vancouver Island Marmot — 884 Wood Bison

Designer: 17¢: Michael Dumas. 35¢: Robert McLellan Bateman.
Lithography (4 colours), Sheets of 200 subjects in four panes of 50
Canadian Bank Note Company

| 1981, Apr 6 | Tagged, GT2 | | | Perf 13.3 |
|---|---|---|---|---|
| | NH–VF | ⊙F | PB | FDC |
| **883 17¢ multicoloured** | .40 | .20 | 2.00 | 1.00 |
| Qty: 21,500,000 | | | | |
| **884 35¢ multicoloured** | 1.00 | .90 | 5.00 | 1.65 |
| Qty: 12,500,000 | | | | |

### CANADIAN RELIGIOUS PERSONALITIES

885 Kateri Tekakwitha — 886 Marie de l'Incarnation

Designer: Laurent Marquart . Based on a sculpture by Jean-Émile Brunet.
Lithography (4 colours), Sheets of 200 subjects in four panes of 50
Ashton-Potter Limited

| 1981, Apr 24 | Tagged, GT2 | | | Perf 12.5 |
|---|---|---|---|---|
| | NH–VF | ⊙F | PB | FDC |
| **885 17¢ multicoloured** | .35 | .20 | | 1.00 |
| **886 17¢ multicoloured** | .35 | .20 | | 1.00 |
| a se-tenant pair (885, 886) | .80 | .70 | 1.75 | 1.75 |

Qty: 10,750,000 of each

Beatification of Kateri Tekakwitha (1656–1680), first North American Indian so honoured and of Marie de l'Incarnation (1599–1672), founder of Ursuline Order of Nuns.

### CANADIAN PAINTERS

887
*At Baie Saint-Paul,*
by Marc-Aurèle Fortin

888
*Self Portrait,*
by Frederick Varley

889
*Untitled No. 6,*
by Paul-Émile Borduas

Designer: Pierre Fontaine

Lithography (5 colours), Sheets of 100 subjects in four panes of 25
Ashton-Potter Limited

| 1981, May 22 | Tagged, GT4 | | | Perf 12.5 |
|---|---|---|---|---|
| | NH–VF | ⊙F | PB | FDC |
| 887 17¢ multicoloured, F | .35 | .20 | 1.75 | 1.00 |
| i dull | 3.00 | .50 | 15.00 | |
| T1 untagged (error) | — | 125.00 | | |

Qty: 18,000,000

| | NH–VF | ⊙F | PB | FDC |
|---|---|---|---|---|
| 888 17¢ multicoloured, F | .35 | .20 | 1.75 | 1.00 |
| i dull | 3.00 | .50 | 15.00 | |
| T1 untagged (error) | — | 125.00 | | |
| a imperf. pair and untagged | 2,000.00 | — | *5,000.00** | — |

Qty: 18,000,000

* Value shown is for non-inscription corner block.

No. 888a comes from a mishandled sheet. Most pairs have some creasing or gum disturbance. Value for creased pair $900. Two blocks from a second sheet have been seen by the editors.

Lithography (5 colours), pane of 25
British American Bank Note Company

| 1981, May 22 | Tagged, GT4 | | | Perf 13.0x13.4 |
|---|---|---|---|---|
| 889 35¢ multicoloured, F | .80 | .80 | 4.50 | 1.65 |
| i dull | 4.00 | 1.00 | 18.00 | |
| T1 untagged (error) | 125.00 | | | |

Qty: 11,000,000

## CANADA DAY

890
1867 Map of Canada

891
1873 Map of Canada

892
1905 Map of Canada

893
1949 Map of Canada

Designer: Raymond Bellemare.

Lithography (6 colours), pane of 16
British American Bank Note Company

| 1981, Jun 30 | Tagged, GT2 | | | Perf 13.3 |
|---|---|---|---|---|
| | NH–VF | ⊙F | PB | FDC |
| 890 17¢ 1867 Map | .40 | .30 | | 1.00 |
| T1 untagged (error) | | 100.00 | | |
| 891 17¢ 1873 Map | .40 | .30 | | 1.00 |
| T1 untagged (error) | | 100.00 | | |
| 892 17¢ 1905 Map | .40 | .30 | | 1.00 |
| T1 untagged (error) | | 100.00 | | |
| 893 17¢ 1949 Map | .40 | .30 | | 1.00 |
| T1 untagged (error) | | 100.00 | | |
| a se-tenant strip of 4 (890–893) | 1.80 | 1.75 | | 2.85 |
| se-tenant block of 8 | 3.60 | 3.50 | 4.00 | 4.30 |
| $2.72 pane of 16† (4 x 4) | 7.50 | 7.50 | 8.00 | — |

Qty: 15,000,000 of each

Four maps of Canada showing evolution from four provinces in 1867 to ten provinces and two territories in 1949, when Newfoundland joined Canada.

† Four different philatelic panes exist depending upon the position of the corner inscription.

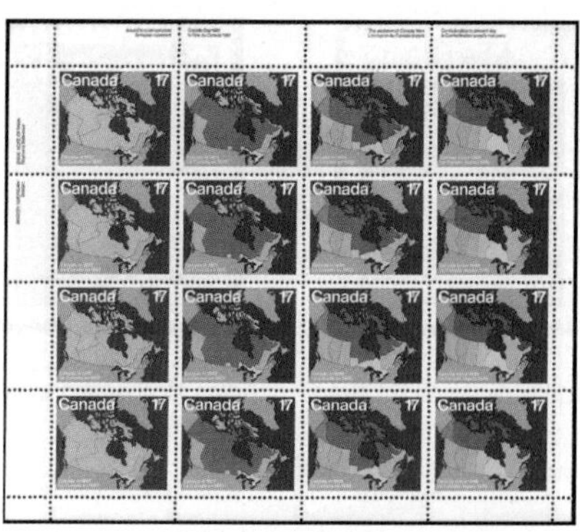

## CANADIAN BOTANISTS

894
Frère Marie-Victorin

895
John Macoun

Designer: Roger Hill.

Lithography (4 colours), Sheets of 150 subjects in three panes of 50
Ashton-Potter Limited

| 1981, Jul 22 | Tagged, GT2 | | | Perf 12.5 |
|---|---|---|---|---|
| | NH–VF | ⊙F | PB | FDC |
| 894 17¢ multicoloured | .35 | .20 | | 1.00 |
| 895 17¢ multicoloured | .35 | .20 | | 1.00 |
| a se-tenant pair (894, 895) | .80 | .70 | 1.75 | 1.75 |

Qty: 11,550,000 of each

896
Montreal Rose

897
Map of the town

## LES FLORALIES DE MONTREAL

Designer: Jean Morin, Jean-Pierre Beaudin, and Tom Yakobina.
Based on a photograph by Roméo Meloche.

Lithography (4 colours), Sheets of 200 subjects in four panes of 50
Canadian Bank Note Company

| 1981, Jul 22 | Tagged, GT2 | | | Perf 13.3 |
|---|---|---|---|---|
| | NH–VF | ⊙F | PB | FDC |
| 896 17¢ multicoloured | .35 | .20 | 1.75 | 1.00 |

Qty: 21,000,000

## NIAGARA-ON-THE-LAKE

Designer: John Mardon.

Engraved (1 colour) and Photogravure (4 colours)
Sheets of 200 subjects in four panes of 50
British American Bank Note Company

| 1981, Jul 31 | Tagged, GT2 | | | Perf 13.3 |
|---|---|---|---|---|
| | NH–VF | ⊙F | PB | FDC |
| 897 17¢ multicoloured, DF | .35 | .20 | 1.75 | 1.00 |
| i F | 4.00 | .75 | 20.00 | |

Qty: 19,500,000

Bicentenary of the first capital of Upper Canada (now Ontario).

898
L'Acadie, by Nérée De Grâce

899
Aaron Mosher and workers

## ACADIANS

Designer: Nérée DeGrâce. Typographed by William H. Tibbles.
Lithography (4 colours), Sheets of 200 subjects in four panes of 50
Ashton-Potter Limited

**1981, Aug 14** **Tagged, GT2** **Perf 13.3**

| | | NH–VF | ⊙F | PB | FDC |
|---|---|---|---|---|---|
| **898** | **17¢ multicoloured**, DF | .35 | .20 | 1.75 | 1.00 |
| i | LF | 2.50 | .50 | 15.00 | |

Qty: 20,000,000

Centenary of the first Acadian Congress.

## AARON MOSHER

Designer: Roger Hill.
Lithography (4 colours), Sheets of 200 subjects in four panes of 50
Ashton-Potter Limited

**1981, Sep 8** **Tagged, GT2** **Perf 13.3**

| | | NH–VF | ⊙F | PB | FDC |
|---|---|---|---|---|---|
| **899** | **17¢ multicoloured**, DF | .35 | .20 | 1.75 | 1.00 |
| i | LF | 2.50 | | 12.00 | |

Qty: 20,000,000

Aaron Mosher (1881–1959) was a leading founder of the Canadian Labour Congress.

## CHRISTMAS

900
Christmas Tree, 1781

901
Christmas Tree, 1881

902
Christmas Tree, 1981

Designer: Anita Kunz. Typographed by William H. Tibbles.
Lithography (4 colours), Sheets of 200 subjects in four panes of 50
Ashton-Potter Limited

**1981, Nov 16** **Tagged, GT2** **Perf 13.3**

| | | NH–VF | ⊙F | PB | FDC |
|---|---|---|---|---|---|
| **900** | **15¢ multicoloured**, DF | .30 | .20 | 1.50 | .95 |
| i | LF | 3.00 | | 15.00 | |
| **901** | **15¢ multicoloured**, DF | .30 | .20 | 1.50 | .95 |
| i | LF | 3.00 | | 15.00 | |
| **902** | **15¢ multicoloured**, DF | .30 | .20 | 1.50 | .95 |
| i | LF | 3.00 | | 15.00 | |

Qty: 33,000,000 of each

**Nos. 900–902 (3) combination FDC** **2.10**

Bicentenary of the first illuminated Christmas tree in Canada.

## CANADIAN AIRCRAFT

903
Canadair CL-41 Tutor

904
de Havilland Tiger Moth

905
Avro Canada C-102

906
de Havilland Canada Dash-7

Designer: Jacques Charette. Based on a painting by Robert William Bradford.
Lithography (4 colours), panes of 50
Ashton-Potter Limited

**1981, Nov 24** **Tagged, GT2** **Perf 12.5**

| | | NH–VF | ⊙F | PB | FDC |
|---|---|---|---|---|---|
| **903** | **17¢ multicoloured**, F | .40 | .20 | | 1.00 |
| i | DF | 2.50 | .50 | | |
| **904** | **17¢ multicoloured**, F | .40 | .20 | | 1.00 |
| i | "grounded chopper" (pos. 1) | 10.00 | 5.00 | 12.50 | |
| ii | DF | 2.50 | .50 | | |
| a | se-tenant pair, F (903, 904) | .90 | .75 | 2.00 | |
| ai | se-tenant pair, DF (903i, 904ii) | 5.00 | | 12.00 | |

Qty: 12,500,000 of each

| | | NH–VF | ⊙F | PB | FDC |
|---|---|---|---|---|---|
| **905** | **35¢ multicoloured** | .80 | .75 | | 1.65 |
| **906** | **35¢ multicoloured** | .80 | .75 | | 1.65 |
| a | se-tenant pair (905, 906) | 1.80 | 1.60 | 4.00 | |

Qty: 8,500,000 of each

**Nos. 903–906 (4) combination FDC** **4.00**

See also 843–846, 873–876 and 969–972.

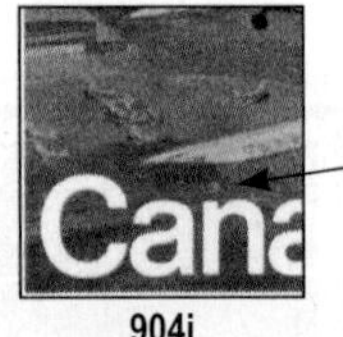
904i

## NON-DENOMINATED "A" DEFINITIVE

907

908

Designer: Raymond Bellemare. Engraved by Yves Baril.
Engraved (1 colour), pane of 100
British American Bank Note Company

**1981, Dec 29** **Tagged, GT2** **Perf 13.0x13.3**

| | | NH–VF | ⊙F | PB | FDC |
|---|---|---|---|---|---|
| **907** | **(30¢) red**, coated paper, Plate 1, LF | 2.00 | .20 | 10.00 | * |
| iv | "hook tag flaw" (inverted) ‡ | *100.00* | 50.00 | | |
| iii | MF | 1.25 | .20 | 6.00 | |
| T1 | untagged (error), LF | | 30.00 | | |
| T1a | untagged (error), MF | | 30.00 | | |

* Commercially used on domestic mail – $5.00.
‡ One mint, and one used copy reported. See note after No. 787.

Canadian Bank Note Company

| | | NH–VF | ⊙F | PB | FDC |
|---|---|---|---|---|---|
| ii | uncoated paper, plates 2, 3 | 1.00 | .20 | 5.00 | 1.00 |
| a | printed on gum side † | 1,000.00 | — | *5,000.00* | — |

† Certificate of authenticity recommended. One UR blank corner block reported.

Roll of 100
Canadian Bank Note Company

| 1981, Dec 29 | Tagged, GT2 | | Perf 10 vert | |
|---|---|---|---|---|
| | | NH–VF | ⊙F | FDC |
| **908** | **(30¢) red** (907), dull | 1.00 | .20 | * |
| | pair, dull | 2.00 | .50 | 1.60 |
| i | wide spacing, strip of 4 | 15.00 | | |
| ii | narrow spacing, strip of 4 | 15.00 | | |
| a | imperf. pair | 500.00 | 300.00 | |
| iii | LF | 2.50 | 0.20 | |
| | pair, LF | 5.00 | 0.50 | |
| iv | wide spacing, strip of 4, LF | 35.00 | | |
| v | narrow spacing, strip of 4, LF | 35.00 | | |

* Commercially used on domestic mail – $10.00.

These are Canada's first non-denominated stamps. The letter A denotes the domestic rate of 30¢.

## 1982

| **Rates:** | Domestic: 30¢ (0–30g), 45¢ (30–50g) |
|---|---|
| Jan 1, 1982– | USA: 35¢ (0–30g), 50¢ (30–50g) |
| Jan 14, 1983 | International: 60¢ (0–20g), 93¢ (20–50g) |
| | Registration: $1.85 |
| | Special delivery: $1.00 |

*single usage:* USA 35¢: $15.00 | International 60¢: $25.00

### CANADA 82

909
Three-Penny Beaver (No. 1)

910
Champlain's Departure (No. 102)

911
RCMP Constable (No. 223)

912
Mount Hurd (No. 155)

913
Bluenose (No. 158)

913a

Designer: Stuart Bradley Ash.
Lithography (4 colours; s/s: 10 colours), panes of 25
Canadian Bank Note Company

| 1982 | Tagged, GT2* | | | Perf 13.3 | |
|---|---|---|---|---|---|
| | | NH–VF | ⊙F | PB | FDC |
| **909** | **30¢ multicoloured**, *Mar 11, 1982* | .65 | .25 | 3.25 | 1.00 |
| Qty: 17,000,000 | | | | | |
| **910** | **30¢ multicoloured**, *May 20, 1982* | .65 | .25 | 3.25 | 1.00 |
| Qty: 21,600,000 | | | | | |
| **911** | **35¢ multicoloured**, DF, *Mar 11, 1982* | .75 | .75 | 3.75 | 1.10 |
| i | LF/fl | 3.00 | | 15.00 | |
| Qty: 10,000,000 | | | | | |
| **912** | **35¢ multicoloured**, *May 20, 1982* | .75 | .75 | 3.75 | 1.10 |
| Qty: 20,000,000 | | | | | |
| **913** | **60¢ multicoloured**, *May 20, 1982* | 1.50 | 1.25 | 6.50 | 1.60 |
| a | $1.90 souvenir sheet of 5 (909–913) *May 20, 1982* | 5.00 | 5.00 | | 4.20 |
| b | triple print of reddish brown | *2,000.00* | | | |
| Qty: 10,200,000; Souvenir sheet: 2,000,000 | | | | | |

* The tagging consists of vertical bars applied to the left and right white borders of the inside stamp design.

**Nos. 909, 911 (2) combination FDC** **1.70**
**Nos. 910, 912, 913 (3) combination FDC** **2.90**

Issued to commemorate "Canada 82", the International Youth Exhibition, Toronto, May 20–24.

914
Jules Léger

915
Terry Fox

### JULES LEGER

Designer: Pierre Fontaine. Based on a photograph by Michael Bedford.
Lithography (6 colours), pane of 50
Ashton-Potter Limited

| 1982, Apr 2 | Tagged, GT2 | | | Perf 13.3 | |
|---|---|---|---|---|---|
| | | NH–VF | ⊙F | PB | FDC |
| **914** | **30¢ multicoloured** | .60 | .20 | 3.00 | 1.00 |
| Qty: 21,000,000 | | | | | |

In memory of the 26th Governor-General of Canada, Jules Léger (1913–1980).

### MARATHON OF HOPE

Designer: Friedrich G. Peter.
Lithography (6 colours), pane of 50
Ashton-Potter Limited

| 1982, Apr 13 | Tagged, GT4 | | | Perf 12.5 | |
|---|---|---|---|---|---|
| | | NH–VF | ⊙F | PB | FDC |
| **915** | **30¢ multicoloured**, LF | .60 | .20 | 3.00 | 1.00 |
| i | DF | 2.50 | .75 | 13.00 | |
| T1 | untagged (error) | — | 75.00 | | |
| Qty: 44,000,000 | | | | | |

In memory of Terry Fox (1958–1981), one-legged cancer victim who raised millions by attempting a cross-country run.

Artifact — 1982–1987

## NEW CONSTITUTION

916
Constitution

Designer: Friedrich G. Peter.

Lithography (5 colours), pane of 40
Ashton-Potter Limited

1982, Apr 16 — Tagged, GT2 — Perf 12.0x12.5

| | | NH–VF | ⊙F | PB | FDC |
|---|---|---|---|---|---|
| **916** | **30¢ multicoloured**, DF | .60 | .20 | 3.00 | 1.00 |
| i | LF | 2.50 | | 12.00 | |

Qty: 35,000,000

A used example on cover, with "gold missing", has been reported. A light green cast remains where the respective book pages and 'Canada' exist, with the gold coat of arms missing. A certificate of authenticity is required.

Queen Elizabeth II visited Ottawa to officially proclaim the new Canadian Constitution.

## LOW-VALUE ARTIFACT DEFINITIVES 1982–1987

917 Decoy — 918 Fishing Spear — 919 Lantern
920 Bucket — 921 Weathercock — 922 Ice Skates

For 25¢ Butter Stamp design, see 1080.

Designer: Jean-Pierre Beaudin and Jean Morin.

Lithography (4 colours), panes of 100
Ashton-Potter Limited

Not Tagged — Perf 14.0x13.3

| | | NH–VF | ⊙F | PB |
|---|---|---|---|---|
| **917** | **1¢ light brown and multicoloured,** Abitibi-Price paper, NF/NF, *Oct 19, 1982* | .25 | .20 | 1.25 |
| i | as 917, LF/F | .25 | .20 | 1.25 |
| ii | as 917, "hair on duck's head" (pos. 89) ‡ | 5.00 | 2.50 | 10.00 |
| iii | Rolland paper, NF/LF, *Jul 4, 1986* | .25 | — | 1.25† |
| iv | as 'iii', LF/F | .25 | .20 | 1.25 |
| v | as 'iii', "hair on duck's head" (pos. 89) § | 5.00 | 2.50 | 10.00 |
| vi | as 'iii', "n apostrophe t" (pos. 97) § | 5.00 | 2.50 | |

Qty: Abitibi: 60,000,000; Rolland: 155,270,000
‡ Either paper.
† "Traffic lights" on inscriptions.
§ Variety on LF/F paper, multiply mint price by 3, used price by 2.

Canadian Bank Note Company

Perf 13.0x13.3

| | | NH–VF | ⊙F | PB |
|---|---|---|---|---|
| **917a** | Harrison paper, NF/NF, *Jan 10, 1985* | .25 | .20 | 1.25 |
| ai | as 'a', "n apostrophe t" (pos. 97) | 10.00 | 5.00 | |
| aii | Clark paper, NF/NF, *Aug 6, 1985* | 2.00 | .20 | 10.00* |
| aiii | as 'aii', "hair on duck's head" (pos. 89) | 10.00 | 5.00 | 20.00* |
| aiv | as 'aii', "n apostrophe t" (pos. 97) | 10.00 | 5.00 | |

Qty: CBN: 60,500,000
* Blank corner block of 4.

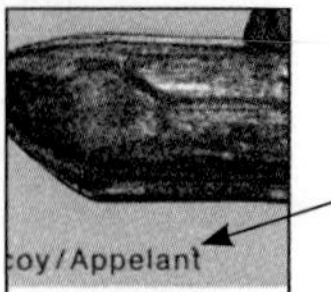

917ii/v/aiii — 917vi/ai/aiv

Ashton-Potter Limited

Not Tagged — Perf 14.0x13.3

| | | NH–VF | ⊙F | PB |
|---|---|---|---|---|
| **918** | **2¢ green and multicoloured,** Abitibi-Price paper, NF/NF, *Oct 19, 1982* | .25 | .20 | 1.25 |
| i | as 918, LF/F | .50 | .20 | 3.50 |
| ii | Rolland paper, NF/LF, *Jul 4, 1986* | .25 | — | 1.25† |
| iii | as 'ii', LF/F | .50 | .20 | 3.50 |

Qty: Abitibi: 90,000,000; Rolland: 149,170,000
† "Traffic lights" on inscriptions.

Canadian Bank Note Company

Perf 13.0x13.3

| | | NH–VF | ⊙F | PB |
|---|---|---|---|---|
| **918a** | Clark paper, NF/NF, *Feb 10, 1984* | .25 | .20 | 1.25 |
| b | imperf. bottom block margin† | 2,750.00 | — | *3,000.00** |
| c | printed on gum side | 70.00 | — | 350.00* |
| ai | Harrison paper, NF/NF, plate 2, *Jan 13, 1986* | .25 | .20 | 1.25 |
| aii | as 'ai', NF/DF | .50 | .20 | 3.50 |

Qty: CBN: 156,400,000
* Blank corner block of 4.
† The stamps in the tenth row and the bottom half of the stamps in the ninth row are imperf.

Ashton-Potter Limited

Not Tagged — Perf 14.0x13.3

| | | NH–VF | ⊙F | PB |
|---|---|---|---|---|
| **919** | **3¢ purple and multicoloured,** Abitibi-Price paper, NF/NF, *Oct 19, 1982* | .25 | .20 | 1.25 |
| i | as 919, NF/LF | .50 | .20 | 3.50 |
| ii | as 919, NF/F | .50 | .20 | 3.50 |
| iii | Rolland paper, NF/LF, *Jul 4, 1986* | .25 | — | 1.25† |
| iv | as 'iii', LF/MF | 1.50 | .50 | 7.50 |
| v | as 'iii', NF/F | .75 | .30 | 4.00 |

Qty: Abitibi: 30,000,000; Rolland: 44,405,000
† "Traffic lights" on inscriptions.

Canadian Bank Note Company

Perf 13.0x13.3

| | | NH–VF | ⊙F | PB |
|---|---|---|---|---|
| **919a** | Harrison paper, NF/NF, *Jan 10, 1985* | .25 | .20 | 1.25 |

Qty: CBN: 34,500,000

Ashton-Potter Limited

Not Tagged — Perf 14.0x13.3

| | | NH–VF | ⊙F | PB |
|---|---|---|---|---|
| **920** | **5¢ flesh and multicoloured,** Abitibi-Price paper, NF/NF, *Oct 19, 1982* | .25 | .20 | 1.25 |
| i | Rolland paper, NF/LF, *Aug 15, 1986* | .25 | — | 1.25† |
| ii | as 'i', LF/F | .50 | .20 | 3.50 |

Qty: Abitibi: 45,000,000; Rolland: 94,705,000
† "Traffic lights" on inscriptions.

Canadian Bank Note Company

Perf 13.0x13.3

| | | NH–VF | ⊙F | PB |
|---|---|---|---|---|
| **920a** | Clark paper, NF/NF, *Jul 6, 1984* | .25 | .20 | 1.25 |
| ai | Harrison paper, plate 2, NF/NF, *Mar 1, 1985* | .25 | .20 | 1.25 |

Qty: CBN: 64,000,000

Ashton-Potter Limited

Tagged, GT2 — Perf 14.0x13.3

| | | NH–VF | ⊙F | PB |
|---|---|---|---|---|
| **921** | **10¢ blue and multicoloured,** Abitibi-Price paper, NF/NF, *Oct 19, 1982* | .25 | .20 | 1.25 |
| i | Rolland paper, NF/LF, *Aug 22, 1986* | .50 | — | 2.50† |
| ii | as 'i', LF/F | .50 | .20 | 3.50 |

Qty: Abitibi: 55,000,000; Rolland: 49,100,000
† "Traffic lights" on inscriptions.

Canadian Bank Note Company

Tagged, GT4 — Perf 13.0x13.3

| | | NH–VF | ⊙F | PB |
|---|---|---|---|---|
| **921a** | Harrison paper, NF/NF, *Mar 15, 1985* | .35 | .20 | 1.75 |

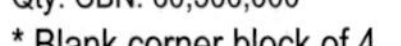

Ashton-Potter Limited

| | Tagged, GT2 | | Perf 14.0x13.3 | |
|---|---|---|---|---|
| | | NH–VF | ⊙F | PB |
| **922** | **20¢ grey-brown and multicoloured,** Abitibi-Price paper, NF/NF, *Oct 19, 1982* | .40 | .20 | 2.00 |
| v | light brown 'Canada 20' ‡ | | | |
| i | as 922, LF/LF | 2.50 | .50 | 15.00 |
| ii | Rolland Paper, NF/LF, *Jul 4, 1986* | .50 | — | 2.25† |
| iii | as 'ii', LF/F | .50 | .20 | 3.50 |
| iv | as 'ii', LF/MF | 2.50 | .50 | 15.00 |

Qty: Abitibi: 55,000,000; Rolland: 35,600,000

* Blank corner block of 4. † "Traffic lights" on inscriptions.

‡ Was 922a; Scott Publishing deleted the number in May 2016. On-going research suggests this is a major colour *shade/variety* rather than a colour *omitted* error, although the Fédération Québécoise de Philatélie gave a "missing reddish brown color ... genuine in all aspects' cert in December 1989 for a block of 30 (1 pane of 100 known)".

**Nos. 917–922 (6) combination FDC** **1.20**

922v

924c

## FIRST-CLASS DEFINITIVES 1982–1985

923
Maple Leaf

924
Maple Leaf

Designer: Raymond Bellemare

Engraved (1 colour) and Photogravure (2 colours), pane of 100
British American Bank Note Company

| 1982, May 11 | Tagged, GT2 | | | Perf 13.0x13.3 | |
|---|---|---|---|---|---|
| | | NH–VF | ⊙F | PB | FDC |
| **923** | **30¢ red on blue**, LF/fl | .75 | .20 | 3.75 | 1.00 |
| i | "hook tag flaw"† | 35.00 | 25.00 | | |
| ii | DF (no flrsc fibers) | 2.00 | .25 | 12.00 | |
| T1 | untagged (error) | — | 50.00 | | |
| T2 | light tag over entire stamp (error) | — | 50.00 | | |

Qty: 228,400,000

† See note after No. 787.

| | Booklet Issue | | Perf 12.0x12.5 | |
|---|---|---|---|---|
| 923a | booklet pane of 20 x 30¢ (923b and 923bs) + label (BK83), *Jun 30, 1982* | 15.00 | 18.00 | — |
| 923b | single 30¢ from 923a, perf all around | 2.00 | 2.00 | — |
| bs | single 30¢ with straight edge, from 923a | 1.00 | .60 | — |
| BK83 | pane 923a in bilingual cover (964,000) $16.00 | | | |

923a

924a

### Comet tag flaw:

A constant tagging flaw occurs on *three* stamps in this series, as illustrated at right. The flaw occurs on the right vertical tag bar from stamps in column 9. It "moves" along the pane; as such the flaw may fall entirely on a stamp or just a portion of the flaw may appear near the top or bottom of a stamp. See: 792vi, 924ii, 924bii.

Comet tag flaw

Engraved (1 colour) and Photogravure (2 colours), pane of 100
British American Bank Note Company

| 1983, Feb 10 | Tagged, GT2 | | | Perf 13.0x13.3 | |
|---|---|---|---|---|---|
| | | NH–VF | ⊙F | PB | FDC |
| **924** | **32¢ red on cream,** Abitibi-Price paper, Plate 1 | .65 | .20 | 3.25 | 1.00 |
| T1 | untagged (error) | 50.00 | 30.00 | 250.00* | |
| c | "Maple Leaf in Winter" error; beige (background) and tagging omitted† | 1,500.00 | — | 7,000.00* | |
| i | Harrison paper, Plate 2, *Aug 31, 1983* | .80 | .20 | 4.00 | — |
| ii | as "i", "comet tag flaw" | 30.00 | 25.00 | *75.00* (UR/LR) | |

Qty: 1,131,800,000

* Blank corner block of 4.

† 150 known; background colour partly missing (8 copies known) are valued less.

| | Booklet Issue | | Perf 12.0x12.5 | |
|---|---|---|---|---|
| 924a | booklet pane of 25 x 32¢ (924b and 924bs) + 2 labels, Abitibi-Price Paper (BK85) *Apr 8, 1983* | 16.00 | 18.00 | — |
| ai | as "a", Harrison Paper (BK85A) *Feb 15, 1984* | 16.00 | 18.00 | — |
| 924b | single 32¢ Maple Leaf, from 924a, perf all around, Abitibi-Price Paper | 1.40 | 1.00 | — |
| bs | single 32¢ with straight edge | 1.00 | .50 | — |
| bis | single 32¢ from 924ai, Harrison Paper | 1.40 | 1.00 | — |
| bisi | as "bis" with straight edge | 1.00 | .50 | — |
| bii | "comet tag flaw" | 35.00 | 35.00 | |
| BK85 | pane 924a in bilingual cover (3,009,000 including BK85b) $17.00 | | | |
| BK85b | pane 924ai in bilingual cover $17.00 | | | |

## FIRST-CLASS DEFINITIVES 1985–1987

925
Parliament Buildings

Designer: Rolf Harder.

Lithography (4 colours), pane of 100
Canadian Bank Note Company

| 1985, Jun 21 | Tagged, GT4 | | | Perf 13.3x13.0 | |
|---|---|---|---|---|---|
| | | NH–VF | ⊙F | PB | FDC |
| **925** | **34¢ multicoloured,** Harrison paper | .70 | .20 | 3.50 | 1.10 |
| T1 | untagged (error) | — | 40.00 | | |

Qty: 934,200,000

British American Bank Note Company

| | Booklet Issue | | Perf 13.3x13.0 | |
|---|---|---|---|---|
| 925a | booklet pane of 25 x 34¢ (925as) (BK89), Harrison paper, *Aug 1, 1985* | 17.00 | 20.00 | — |
| as | single from 925a | 1.00 | .20 | — |
| asi | as "as" with straight edge | 1.10 | .25 | — |
| BK89 | pane 925a in bilingual cover (1,788,000) $17.50 | | | |

Ashton-Potter Limited

| | Booklet Issue | | Perf 13.3x14.0 | |
|---|---|---|---|---|
| 925b | single 34¢ from 925c, Rolland paper | 2.00 | 1.00 | — |
| 925c | booklet pane of 25 x 34¢ (925b and 925cs) (BK89A), *Jul 4, 1986* | 17.00 | 20.00 | — |
| cs | single with straight edge, from 925c | 1.00 | .50 | — |
| BK89A | pane 925c in bilingual cover (1,999,000) $18.00 | | | |

No. 925 (CBN) has a purple sky; Nos. 925a (BABN) and 925c (AP) have a blue sky. This is the only modern Canadian definitive stamp that has had three distinct printings by all three Canadian printers: CBN, BABN, and AP.

Many minor "fly-speck" varieties have been reported on BK89 and BK89A.

925a

## FIRST-CLASS DEFINITIVES 1985–1987

926
Queen Elizabeth II

926A
Queen Elizabeth II

Designer: Raymond Bellemare

Engraved (1 colour) and Photogravure (1 colour), pane of 100
British American Bank Note Company

**1985, Jul 12** **Tagged, GT4** **Perf 13.0x13.3**

| | | NH–VF | ⊙F | PB | FDC |
|---|---|---|---|---|---|
| **926** | **34¢ dark blue** (Plate 1) | .75 | .20 | 3.50 | 1.10 |
| | Plate 2, *Sep 5, 1986* | — | — | 3.50 | |
| i | "blue paper" (improper wiping) | 200.00 | | | |
| T1 | untagged (error) | — | 25.00 | | |

Qty: 434,600,000

Engraved (1 colour) and Photogravure (1 colour), pane of 100
British American Bank Note Company

**1987, Oct 1** **Tagged, GT4** **Perf 13.0x13.3**

| | | NH–VF | ⊙F | PB | FDC |
|---|---|---|---|---|---|
| **926A** | **36¢ plum** | 4.00 | 3.00 | 20.00* | 3.00 |

Qty: 38,400,000

* Value shown is for blank corner block of 4. Plate blocks were not available for this stamp due to production difficulties.

This stamp was delayed repeatedly (from May 6, 1987) due to production difficulties and not released until near the end of the 36¢ rate period. Thus, this value was current for just 3 months, during which time the 1987 Christmas stamps would have seen most of the usage by the public. Specimens used during this period showing a clear, dated cancellation command a premium.

926i

926Bc

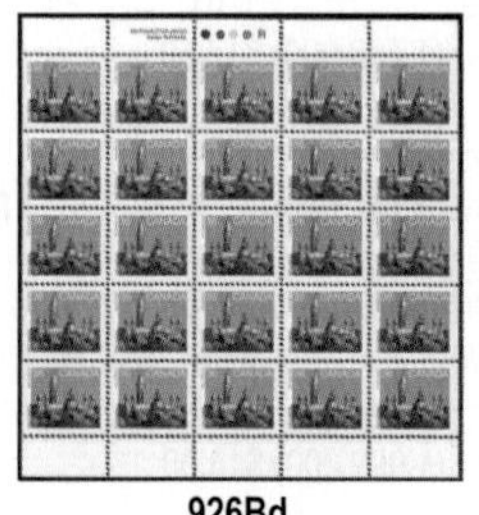
926Bd

926Bg
(gutter block)

## FIRST-CLASS DEFINITIVES 1987

926B
Parliament Buildings

Designer: Rolf Harder.

Lithography (4 colours), panes of 100
Canadian Bank Note Company

**1987, Mar 30** **Tagged, GT4** **Perf 13.3x13.0**

| | | NH–VF | ⊙F | PB | FDC |
|---|---|---|---|---|---|
| **926B** | **36¢ multicoloured**, Harrison paper | .70 | .20 | 3.75 | 1.10 |
| f | left margin block of 4, left vert. pair imperf., right pair part perf. | 2,000.00 | — | 2,500.00‡ | |
| ii | left margin block of 4, left pair part perf. | 1,000.00 | — | 1,250.00 | |
| iii | Rolland paper, LF/NF | 1.00 | .20 | 5.00 | |
| g | imperf., horiz. pair | 800.00 | | 3,500.00* | |
| h | all colour missing† | *2,000.00* | | | |
| v | as iii, Dull/Dull | 2.50 | .25 | 12.00 | |
| vi | as iii, LF/F | 2.50 | .25 | 12.00 | |

Qty: 587,700,000

‡ Value for blank corner block of 4 (20 blocks known, including 8 corner blocks).
* A gutter imprint block of 4 exists; value $3,500.00

† No. 926Bh was caused by an extraneous piece of paper overlaying the pane during printing. Two such panes are recorded, one with two colour-missing stamps and the other with 16 colour-missing stamps. All adjoining stamps have some to most colour missing, and if the panes are broken, the colour-missing variety must be left se-tenant with a partially printed stamp.

Ashton-Potter Limited

**Booklet Issue** **Perf 13.3x14.0**

| | | | | |
|---|---|---|---|---|
| 926Bc | booklet pane of 10 x 36¢ (926Bcs) (BK93), Rolland paper | 7.00 | 6.50 | — |
| Bcs | single 36¢ with straight edge, from 926Bc or 926Bd, GT4 | 1.25 | .40 | — |
| BK93 | pane 926Bc in bilingual cover $7.50 | | | |
| 926Bd | booklet pane of 25 x 36¢ (926Bcs and 926Be) (BK94), Rolland paper, *May 19, 1987* | 18.00 | 16.00 | — |
| 926Be | single 36¢ Parliament from 926Bd | 2.00 | 1.00 | — |
| BK94 | pane 926Bd in bilingual cover (1,828,000) $20.00 | | | |

## MEDIUM-VALUE ARTIFACT DEFINITIVES 1982–1987

927
Wooden Plough

928
Settle-bed

929
Cradle

930
Sleigh

932
Wood Stove

933
Spinning Wheel

For 42¢, 55¢ and 72¢ Artifact values see 1081–1083.

Designer: Jean-Pierre Beaudin and Jean Morin

Lithography (4 colours), panes of 50
Ashton-Potter Limited

**Tagged, GT2** **Perf 12.0x12.5**

| No. | Description | NH–VF | ⊙F | PB | FDC |
|---|---|---|---|---|---|
| **927** | **37¢ grey-green and multicoloured**, | | | | |
| | Abitibi-Price paper, DF, *Apr 8, 1983* | .75 | .30 | 3.75 | 1.15 |
| iii | F | 4.00 | .50 | 18.00 | |
| v | LF/fl | 5.00 | .75 | 25.00 | |
| i | Clark paper, plate 2, *May 18, 1984* | 1.25 | — | 5.00 | |
| ii | imperf. top margin single, on Clark paper | 750.00 | | 1,750.00* | |
| iv | apostrophe in "Wood'en" (pos. 40) | 30.00 | 10.00 | 30.00 | |

Qty: 94,500,000

* Blank corner block of 4.

| No. | Description | NH–VF | ⊙F | PB | FDC |
|---|---|---|---|---|---|
| **928** | **39¢ violet and multicoloured**, | | | | |
| | Harrison paper, *Aug 1, 1985* | .80 | .30 | 4.00 | 1.20 |

Qty: 63,705,000

| No. | Description | NH–VF | ⊙F | PB | FDC |
|---|---|---|---|---|---|
| **929** | **48¢ pink and multicoloured**, | | | | |
| | Abitibi-Price paper, *Apr 8, 1983* | 1.00 | .40 | 5.00 | 1.35 |
| i | brown background (colour shade)† | *50.00* | | *250.00* | |
| ii | Clark paper, Plate 2, *Dec 19, 1983* | 1.50 | — | 7.50 | |

Qty: 56,200,000

† The 48¢ Cradle stamp exists with variations in the background colour (described as 'pink' by the printers) that were previously thought to be "magenta" missing colour errors. Examination of the proof sheets in the Library and Archives Canada have conclusively determined that these are *not* missing colour errors but are some anomaly in the ink resulting in variations in the intensity of the inks used by the printer. These are shade varieties and are not a missing colour error.

| No. | Description | NH–VF | ⊙F | PB | FDC |
|---|---|---|---|---|---|
| **930** | **50¢ blue and multicoloured**, | | | | |
| | Harrison paper, *Aug 1, 1985* | 1.00 | .35 | 5.00 | 1.40 |
| i | pale blue shade | 10.00 | 1.00 | 50.00* | — |

Qty: 64,645,000

* Blank corner block of 4.

No. 931 is not assigned.

| No. | Description | NH–VF | ⊙F | PB | FDC |
|---|---|---|---|---|---|
| **932** | **64¢ grey and multicoloured**, | | | | |
| | Abitibi-Price paper, LF/fl, *Apr 8, 1983* | 1.30 | .45 | 6.50 | 1.70 |
| ii | DF | 6.00 | .50 | 30.00 | |
| i | Clark paper, plate 2, *Jun 29, 1984* | 1.75 | — | 8.75 | |

Qty: 64,650,000

**Nos. 927, 929, 932 (3) combination FDC** **3.40**

| No. | Description | NH–VF | ⊙F | PB | FDC |
|---|---|---|---|---|---|
| **933** | **68¢ tan and multicoloured**, | | | | |
| | Harrison paper, *Aug 1, 1985* | 1.50 | .50 | 7.50 | 1.75 |

Qty: 53,305,000

**Nos. 928, 930, 933 (3) combination FDC** **3.50**

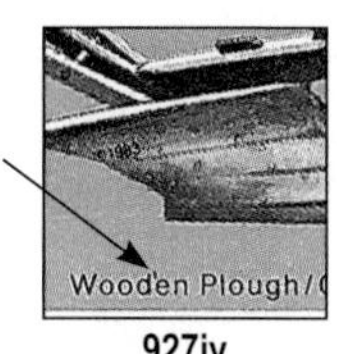


927iv

927ii

## HIGH-VALUE NATIONAL PARK DEFINITIVES 1982–1987

934
Glacier National Park

935
Waterton Lakes

936
Banff National Park

937
Point Pelee

For additional National Park definitives see 726–727 and 1084.

Designer: Brent Laycock and William Tibbles.

Engraved (1 colour) and Lithography (4 colours), panes of 25
Canadian Bank Note Company

**1984, Aug 15** **Untagged** **Perf 13.3**

| No. | Description | NH–VF | ⊙F | PB | FDC |
|---|---|---|---|---|---|
| **934** | **$1 multicoloured**, | | | | |
| | Clark paper, plate 1 | 2.00 | .70 | 10.00 | 2.40 |
| a | blue inscriptions omitted† | 1,250.00 | | 5,250.00 | |
| b | imperf. pair (12 known) | 5,000.00 | | 10,500.00* | |
| iii | Harrison paper, plate 2, *Jul 12, 1985* | 3.50 | 1.00 | 17.50 | |

Qty: CBN: 47,747,500

† All copies are off centre (F or F-VF at best).

British American Bank Note Company

| No. | Description | NH–VF | ⊙F | PB | FDC |
|---|---|---|---|---|---|
| iv | Harrison paper, plate 1, *Sep 26, 1986* | 3.50 | 1.00 | 17.50 | |
| v | double inscriptions | 300.00 | | 1,250.00* | |

Qty: BABN: 50,550,000

* Blank corner block of 4.

The inscriptions ($1 POSTES/POSTAGE and CANADA) are more pronounced on the BABN printings, compared with the CBN printings.

CBN BABN

Designer: Brent Laycock and William Tibbles.

Engraved (1 colour) and Lithography (4 colours), panes of 25
Canadian Bank Note Company

**1982, Jun 18** **Untagged** **Perf 13.3**

| No. | Description | NH–VF | ⊙F | PB | FDC |
|---|---|---|---|---|---|
| **935** | **$1.50 multicoloured**, with "beacon on mountain", NF | 4.50 | .75 | 22.50 | 3.40 |
| i | *without* "beacon in mountain", NF | 6.00 | 1.25 | | |
| ii | with 'beacon', LF | 10.00 | 2.00 | 50.00 | |
| iii | without 'beacon', LF | 15.00 | 3.00 | 50.00 | |
| a | black *completely* omitted (25 known) | *7,500.00** | | | |

Qty: 23,600,000

The "beacon in mountain" variety occurs on nearly all stamps.

* examples that are not *completely* missing the black will sell for less.

935

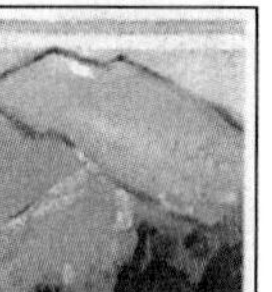

935i

Designer: George Weber and William Tibbles.

Engraved (1 colour) and Lithography (4 colours), panes of 25

Canadian Bank Note Company

**1985, Jun 21** **Untagged** **Perf 13.3**

| | | NH–VF | ⊙F | PB | FDC |
|---|---|---|---|---|---|
| **936** | **$2 multicoloured**, Harrison paper, NF | 4.50 | 1.50 | 22.50 | 4.40 |
| ii | LF | 10.00 | | 60.00* | |
| iii | HF | 25.00 | | 140.00* | |
| iv | "pink dot" in LL water, near tree (pos. 12) | 7.50 | 2.50 | | |
| v | "red spot" near top of right mountain peak (pos. 14) | 7.50 | 2.50 | | |
| vi | 2mm black scratch on right mountain peak (pos. 22) | 7.50 | 2.50 | 27.50 | |
| a | bluish green inscriptions omitted | 1,500.00 | | 6,500.00* | |

Qty: CBN: 26,650,000

* Blank corner block of 4.

British American Bank Note Company

| | | NH–VF | ⊙F | PB | FDC |
|---|---|---|---|---|---|
| i | Harrison paper, *Oct 29, 1986* | 6.00 | 1.75 | 30.00 | |
| vii | "blue spot" in LL snow bank | 7.50 | 2.50 | | |

Qty: BABN: 50,050,000

The inscriptions ($2 POSTES/POSTAGE and CANADA) are more pronounced on the BABN printings, compared with the CBN printings.

The plate varieties listed here are the most constant and prominent of many flaws found on this stamp (it is possible to plate this stamp).

CBN

BABN

936iv

936v

936vi

936vii

Designer: Wayne Terry and William Tibbles.

Engraved (1 colour) and Lithography (4 colours), panes of 25

Canadian Bank Note Company

**1983, Jan 10** **Untagged** **Perf 13.3**

| | | NH–VF | ⊙F | PB | FDC |
|---|---|---|---|---|---|
| **937** | **$5 multicoloured**, Abitibi-Price Paper, plate 1 | 12.50 | 2.75 | 62.50 | 10.40 |
| i | Clark paper, plate 2, *Dec 14, 1984* | 15.00 | — | 75.00 | |
| ii | Harrison paper, plate 3, *Aug 30, 1985* | 20.00 | 4.00 | 90.00 | |
| iii | embossing doubled | 350.00 | | | |

Qty: 19,675,000

934a

935a

936a

## BOOKLET STAMPS
## 1982–1987

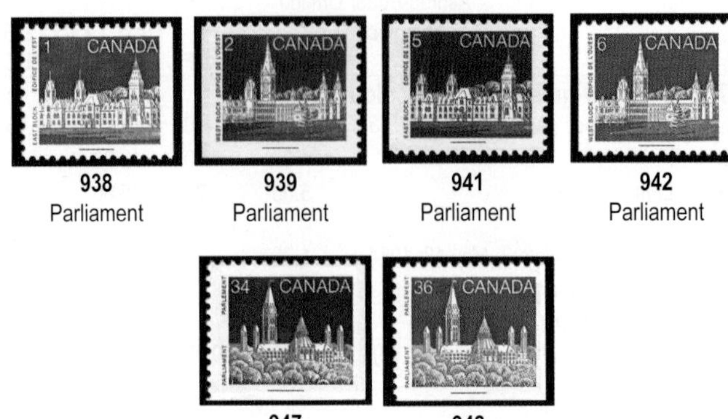


938 Parliament | 939 Parliament | 941 Parliament | 942 Parliament

947 Parliament | 948 Parliament

940 Maple Leaf | 943 Maple Leaf | 944 Maple Leaf | 945 Maple Leaf | 946 Maple Leaf

Designer: Parliament: Rolf Harder; Maple Leaf: Raymond Bellemare.

Engraved

British American Bank Note Company

**Untagged** **Perf 12.5x12.0**

| | | NH–VF | ⊙F | FDC |
|---|---|---|---|---|
| **938** | **1¢ lime green** (Parliament), Rolland paper (uncoated), with straight edge, from 948a, *Mar 30, 1987* | .30 | .20 | — |
| i | Harrison paper (coated), from 948ai, 1187a, *Oct 1, 1987* | .30 | .20 | — |
| **939** | **2¢ deep green** (Parliament), Abitibi-Price paper (uncoated), with straight edge, from 947a, *Jun 21, 1985* | .25 | .20 | — |
| i | Rolland paper (uncoated), from 947ai *Jun 21, 1985* | .25 | —† | |
| a | slate green, Harrison paper, (coated), from 1188a, *Jan 18, 1989* | .30 | .25 | — |

† Single used copies of Rolland paper cannot be differentiated from Abitibi-Price paper. No. 939/i was intended to be untagged. However, 939/i may have a narrow tag bar on either the left or right side due to its proximity to the 34¢ stamp (947/BK88), or a spot of taggant in the LL or LR corner from the 38¢ stamp (1188/BK100).

**Tagged, GT2** **Perf 12.0x12.5**

| | | NH–VF | ⊙F | FDC |
|---|---|---|---|---|
| **940** | **5¢ purple** (Maple Leaf), uncoated paper, with straight edge, from 945a, 945ax or 946b, *Mar 1, 1982* | .25 | .20 | — |
| i | coated paper, from 945ai, 945axi, *Aug 1982* | .30 | .20 | — |

**Untagged** **Perf 12.5x12.0**

| | | NH–VF | ⊙F | FDC |
|---|---|---|---|---|
| **941** | **5¢ dark brown** (Parliament), Abitibi-Price paper (uncoated), with straight edge, from 947a, *Jun 21, 1985* | .45 | .25 | — |
| i | Rolland paper (uncoated), from 947ai *Jun 21, 1985* | .45 | —† | — |

† Single used copies of Rolland paper cannot be differentiated from Abitibi-Price paper. No. 941/i was intended to be untagged. However, a narrow tag bar (or portion) may appear on the bottom due to its proximity to the 34¢ stamp (947/BK88).

| No. | Description | NH-VF | ⊙F | FDC |
|---|---|---|---|---|
| 942 | **6¢ henna brown** (Parliament), Rolland paper (uncoated), with straight edge, from 948a, *Mar 30, 1987* | .30 | .20 | — |
| i | Harrison paper (coated), from 948ai or 1187a, *Oct 1, 1987* | .50 | .20 | — |

No. 942/i was intended to be untagged.However, a narrow tag bar may appear on the bottom due to its proximity to the 36¢ stamp (948/BK92) or 37¢ stamp (1187/BK96).

**Tagged, GT2** **Perf 12.0x12.5**

| No. | Description | NH-VF | ⊙F | FDC |
|---|---|---|---|---|
| 943 | **8¢ dark blue** (Maple Leaf), uncoated paper, with straight edge, from 946b, *Feb 15, 1983* | .70 | .60 | — |
| 944 | **10¢ dark green** (Maple Leaf), uncoated paper, with straight edge, from 945a or 945ax, *Mar 1, 1982* | .60 | .45 | — |
| i | coated paper, from 945ai or 945axi, *Aug 1982* | .75 | .60 | — |
| 945 | **30¢ red** (Maple Leaf), uncoated paper, with straight edge, from 945a or 945ax *Mar 1, 1982* | 1.00 | 1.00 | — |
| ii | "hook tag flaw"† | 35.00 | 25.00 | |
| i | coated paper, from 945ai or 945axi, *Aug 1982* | 1.25 | 1.00 | — |

† See note after No. 787. Flaw can also fall on the right-hand label of the booklet pane.

| No. | Description | NH-VF | ⊙F | FDC |
|---|---|---|---|---|
| 945a | booklet pane of 4 (Maple Leaf) + 2 labels at bottom: 2 x 5¢ (940) + 1 x 10¢ (944) + 1 x 30¢ (945), uncoated paper (BK82), *Mar 1, 1982* | 1.25 | 1.75 | 1.40 |
| ai | coated paper, *Aug 1982* | 1.25 | 1.75 | |
| 945ax | as 945a, with labels in top row, uncoated paper (BK82A), *Oct 1982* | 2.00 | 3.00 | — |
| axi | coated paper, *Oct 1982* | 2.00 | 3.00 | — |
| BK82 | pane 945a in bilingual cover $1.50 | | | |

Total quantity for BK82 and BK82A (23,952,000)

| No. | Description | NH-VF | ⊙F | FDC |
|---|---|---|---|---|
| 946 | **32¢ brown** (Maple Leaf), uncoated paper, with straight edge, from 946b, *Feb 15, 1983* | .70 | .40 | — |
| 946b | booklet pane of 4 (Maple Leaf) + 2 labels: 2 x 5¢ (940) + 1 x 8¢ (943) + 1 x 32¢ (946), uncoated paper (BK84), *Feb 15, 1983* | 1.25 | 1.50 | 1.40 |
| BK84 | pane 946b in bilingual cover (19,268,000 including BK84A) $1.50 | | | |

945a 945ax 946b

**Tagged, GT4** **Perf 12.5x12.0**

| No. | Description | NH-VF | ⊙F | FDC |
|---|---|---|---|---|
| 947 | **34¢ deep slate blue** (Parliament), Abitibi-Price paper (uncoated), with straight edge, from 947a, *Jun 21, 1985* | 1.50 | 1.00 | — |
| T1 | untagged (error) | 75.00 | 50.00 | |
| i | Rolland paper (uncoated), from 947ai *Jun 21, 1985* | 1.50 | —† | — |

† Single used copies of Rolland paper cannot be differentiated from Abitibi-Price paper

| No. | Description | NH-VF | ⊙F | FDC |
|---|---|---|---|---|
| 947a | booklet pane of 6 (Parliament): 3 x 2¢ (939) + 2 x 5¢ (941) + 1 x 34¢ (947) Abitibi-Price paper (uncoated) (BK88), *Jun 21, 1985* | 2.00 | 1.75 | 1.40 |
| ai | Rolland paper (uncoated), *Jun 21, 1985* | 2.00 | 1.75 | |
| BK88 | pane 947a in bilingual cover (12,916,000) $2.50 | | | |

**Tagged, GT4** **Perf 12.5x12.0**

| No. | Description | NH-VF | ⊙F | FDC |
|---|---|---|---|---|
| 948 | **36¢ dark lilac rose** (Parliament), Rolland paper (uncoated), with straight edge, from 948a, *Mar 30, 1987* | 1.75 | 1.00 | — |
| i | Harrison paper (coated), from 948ai *Oct 1, 1987* | 2.50 | 1.00 | — |
| 948a | booklet pane of 5 (Parliament) + label: 2 x 1¢ (938) + 2 x 6¢ (942) + 1 x 36¢ (948) Rolland paper (uncoated), Plate 1 (BK92a) *Mar 30, 1987* | 2.25 | 1.75 | 1.40 |
| ai | Harrison paper (coated), Plate 2 (BK92b) *Oct 1, 1987* | 3.50 | 3.00 | |
| BK92 | pane 948a in bilingual cover (2,248,000) $2.50 | | | |

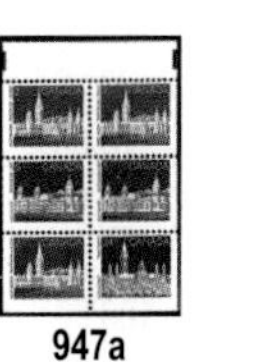
947a

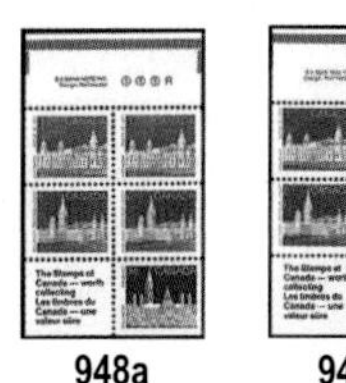
948a 948ai

No. 949 is not assigned.

## COIL STAMPS — 1982–1983

950 Maple Leaf 951 Maple Leaf

Engraved (rolls of 100)
Canadian Bank Note Company
**Tagged, GT2** **Perf 10 vert**

| No. | Description | NH-VF | ⊙F | FDC |
|---|---|---|---|---|
| 950 | **30¢ red** (945), *May 11, 1982* | 1.25 | .25 | 1.60 |
| ii | strip of 4, wide spacing | 20.00 | | |
| iii | strip of 4, narrow spacing | 20.00 | | |
| a | imperf. pair | 450.00 | | |
| 951 | **32¢ brown** (946), Abitibi-Price paper, *Feb 10, 1983* | 1.00 | .20 | 1.70 |
| i | strip of 4, wide spacing | 20.00 | | |
| ii | strip of 4, narrow spacing | 20.00 | | |
| a | imperf. pair | 225.00 | | |
| ai | imperf. strip of 4, narrow spacing | 650.00 | | 800.00† |
| T1 | untagged (error) | — | 30.00 | |
| iii | Clark paper, *Feb 15, 1984* | 1.25 | —* | — |
| iv | strip of 4, wide spacing, Clark paper | 23.00 | | |
| v | strip of 4, narrow spacing, Clark paper | 23.00 | | |

† one commercial cover known.
* used copies of Clark paper (951iii) cannot be differentiated from Abitibi-Price paper (951).

Coil pairs or larger multiples are priced in proportion.

## COIL STAMPS — 1985–1988

952
Parliament

953
Parliament

Engraved (rolls of 100)
Canadian Bank Note Company

**Tagged, GT4** — **Perf 10 horiz**

| | | NH–VF | ⊙F | FDC |
|---|---|---|---|---|
| **952** | **34¢ dull red brown**, DF, *Aug 1, 1985* | 1.00 | .20 | 1.75† |
| a | imperf. pair | 200.00 | | |
| ii | imperf. vertical block of 4, with no trace of scoreline | 75.00 | — | — |
| iii | strip of 4, narrow spacing | 20.00 | | |
| iv | strip of 4, wide spacing | 20.00 | | |
| vii | horizontal tag bar 7mm wide, in strip of 4* | 30.00 | | |
| v | F | 7.50 | 2.00 | |
| vi | strip of 4, wide spacing, F | 100.00 | | |
| viii | strip of 4, narrow spacing, F | 100.00 | | |
| T1 | untagged (error) | — | 50.00 | |

* normal tag bars are 4mm wide. Variety is only apparent in multiples.

| | | NH–VF | ⊙F | FDC |
|---|---|---|---|---|
| **953** | **36¢ dark red**, DF/F, *May 19, 1987* | 1.00 | .20 | 1.85† |
| a | imperf. pair | 375.00 | | |
| ii | strip of 4, narrow spacing, DF/F | 20.00 | | |
| iii | strip of 4, wide spacing, DF/F | 20.00 | | |
| iv | DF/DF | 2.00 | | |
| v | strip of 4, narrow spacing, DF/DF | 30.00 | | |
| vi | strip of 4, wide spacing, DF/DF | 30.00 | | |

† Available as pair on FDC only.

Several different "spacing" varieties exist on this value (953), both wide and narrow. Extremely narrow and wide spacing strips of 4 (very scarce) are worth 5x the usual wide/narrow spacing strips.

Coil pairs or larger multiples are priced in proportion.

## SALVATION ARMY CENTENARY

954
Salvation Army Volunteers

Designer: Theo Dimson.

Lithography (5 colours), pane of 50
Canadian Bank Note Company

**1982, Jun 25** — **Tagged, GT2** — **Perf 13.3**

| | | NH–VF | ⊙F | PB | FDC |
|---|---|---|---|---|---|
| **954** | **30¢ multicoloured** | .65 | .20 | 3.25 | 1.00 |
| T1 | untagged (error) | — | 90.00 | | |

Qty: 21,000,000

To honour the 100th anniversary of The Salvation Army In Canada.

## CANADA DAY

955
Yukon Territory

956
Quebec

957
Newfoundland

958
Northwest Territories

959
Prince Edward Island

960
Nova Scotia

961
Saskatchewan

962
Ontario

963
New Brunswick

964
Alberta

965
British Columbia

966
Manitoba

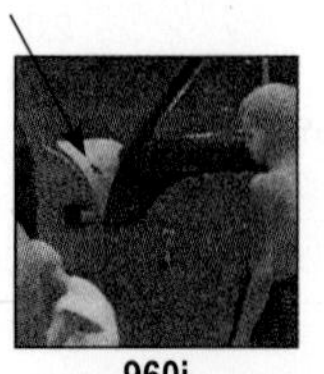
960i

966i

Designer: Jean Morin and Pierre Sasseville.
Lithography (5 colours), pane of 12
Ashton-Potter Limited

**1982, Jun 30** **Tagged, GT2** **Perf 12.5x12.0**

| | | NH–VF | ⊙F | PB | FDC |
|---|---|---|---|---|---|
| **955** | **30¢ Yukon Territory** | .90 | .90 | — | 1.00 |
| **956** | **30¢ Quebec** | .90 | .90 | — | 1.00 |
| **957** | **30¢ Newfoundland** | .90 | .90 | — | 1.00 |
| **958** | **30¢ Northwest Territories** | .90 | .90 | — | 1.00 |
| **959** | **30¢ Prince Edward Island** | .90 | .90 | — | 1.00 |
| **960** | **30¢ Nova Scotia** | .90 | .90 | — | 1.00 |
| i | "dent on car" | 5.00 | 3.50 | | |
| **961** | **30¢ Saskatchewan** | .90 | .90 | — | 1.00 |
| **962** | **30¢ Ontario** | .90 | .90 | — | 1.00 |
| **963** | **30¢ New Brunswick** | .90 | .90 | — | 1.00 |
| **964** | **30¢ Alberta** | .90 | .90 | — | 1.00 |
| **965** | **30¢ British Columbia** | .90 | .90 | — | 1.00 |
| **966** | **30¢ Manitoba** | .90 | .90 | — | 1.00 |
| i | "log in snow" | 5.00 | 3.50 | | |
| a | $3.60 pane of 12† (955–966) | 12.00 | 11.00 | 12.50 | 7.60 |
| **aT1** | untagged (error) pane of 12 | *2,000.00* | | | |

Qty: 5,771,000 of each

Twelve stamps depicting territorial and provincial scenes painted by various Canadian artists, as noted:

Yukon: Alexander Young Jackson, "The Highway near Kluane Lake", 1943
Quebec: Adrien Hébert, "Scène de rue, Montréal", circa 1933
Newfoundland: Christopher Pratt, "Breakwater", 1976
Northwest Territories: René Richard, "Le long du grand lac des Esclaves", 1960
Prince Edward Island: Molly Joan Lamb Bobak, "Tea Hill"
Nova Scotia: David Alexander Colville, "Family and Rainstorm", 1955
Saskatchewan: Dorothy Elsie Perehudoff Knowles, "Brown Shadows", 1977
Ontario: David Bruce Milne, "Red Brick House", 1931
New Brunswick: Brunislaw Jacob Bobak, "Campus Gates", 1964
Alberta: Illingworth Holey Kerr, "Prairie Town, Early Morning", 1927
British Columbia: Joseph Francis Plaskett, "Totems at Ninstints"
Manitoba: Lionel LeMoine FitzGerald, "Doc Snyder's House", 1931

† Four different philatelic panes exist depending upon the position of the corner inscription.

**966a**
upper left pane

**967**
Legislature Building

**968**
Rowing Competition

## REGINA CENTENARY

Designer: Kim Martin and Robert Russell. Based on a painting by David Allan Thauberger.
Lithography (5 colours), pane of 50
Ashton-Potter Limited

**1982, Aug 3** **Tagged, GT2** **Perf 13.6x13.0**

| | | NH–VF | ⊙F | PB | FDC |
|---|---|---|---|---|---|
| **967** | **30¢ multicoloured** | .60 | .20 | 3.00 | 1.00 |

Qty: 21,000,000

## ROYAL CANADIAN HENLEY REGATTA

Designer: Bernard N.J. Reilander. Based on a painting by Tom McNeely.
Lithography (4 colours), pane of 50
Ashton-Potter Limited

**1982, Aug 4** **Tagged, GT2** **Perf 12.5**

| | | NH–VF | ⊙F | PB | FDC |
|---|---|---|---|---|---|
| **968** | **30¢ multicoloured**, dull | .60 | .20 | 3.00 | 1.00 |
| i | stroke above last 'n' of 'Canadian' (pos. 9), dull | 5.00 | 2.50 | 7.50 | |
| ii | F | 5.00 | .50 | 25.00 | |
| iii | as i, F | 12.00 | 2.50 | 35.00 | |

Qty: 21,000,000

**968i**

## BUSH AIRCRAFT

**969** Fairchild FC-2W1 **970** de Havilland Canada Beaver

**971** Noorduyn Norseman **972** Fokker Super Universal

Designer: Jacques Charette. Based on paintings by Robert William Bradford.
Lithography (4 colours), panes of 50
Ashton-Potter Limited

**1982, Oct 5** **Tagged, GT2** **Perf 12.5**

| | | NH–VF | ⊙F | PB | FDC |
|---|---|---|---|---|---|
| **969** | **30¢ multicoloured** | 1.00 | .25 | | 1.00 |
| **970** | **30¢ multicoloured** | 1.00 | .25 | | 1.00 |
| a | se-tenant pair (969, 970) | 2.25 | 1.50 | 5.00 | |

Qty: 11,000,000 of each

| | | NH–VF | ⊙F | PB | FDC |
|---|---|---|---|---|---|
| **971** | **60¢ multicoloured**, DF | 1.50 | 1.00 | | 1.60 |
| i | LF | 2.50 | | | |
| **972** | **60¢ multicoloured**, DF | 1.50 | 1.00 | | 1.60 |
| ii | LF | 2.50 | | | |
| a | se-tenant pair, DF (971, 972) | 3.25 | 2.50 | 7.50 | |
| ai | se-tenant pair, LF (971i, 972ii) | 5.00 | | 13.00 | |
| i | vertical right margin pair (972a), missing last vertical row of perfs. and perfs. in margin | 1,000.00 | — | 1,500.00* | — |

Qty: 7,000,000 of each
* Blank corner block of 4.

**Nos. 969–972 (4) combination FDC 4.00**

See also 843–846, 873–876 and 903–906.

**972i**

## CHRISTMAS – CRECHE FIGURES

973
Holy Family

974
Shepherds

975
Three Wise Men

Designer: Jon Eby. Based on figurines by Hella Braun. Based on a photograph by Bert Bell.
Lithography (4 colours), panes of 50
Canadian Bank Note Company, Limited

**1982, Nov 3** **Tagged, GT2** **Perf 12.5x13.5**

| | | NH–VF | ⊙F | PB | FDC |
|---|---|---|---|---|---|
| **973** | **30¢ red and multicoloured** | .60 | .20 | 3.00 | 1.00 |
| a | all colours except black omitted | *20,000.00* | — | — | |
| b | printed on gum side, black omitted | *20,000.00* | — | — | |
| iii | orange background (10 known)† | 750.00 | | | |

Qty: 107,000,000

Nos. 973a and 973b are each unique and were caused by a paper fold-over.

† Repellex error, part of colour missing on part of one column of 10 stamps. Four sheets are also known with similar repellex error causing 40–80% of the background of all right margin stamps to be orange rather than bright red. Values range from $100–$350 depending on the percentage of orange background.

| | | NH–VF | ⊙F | PB | FDC |
|---|---|---|---|---|---|
| **974** | **35¢ blue and multicoloured** | .70 | .60 | 3.50 | 1.10 |

Qty: 14,000,000

| | | NH–VF | ⊙F | PB | FDC |
|---|---|---|---|---|---|
| **975** | **60¢ green and multicoloured** | 1.25 | 1.00 | 6.25 | 1.60 |
| T1 | untagged (error) | 100.00 | | | |

Qty: 14,000,000

**Nos. 973–975 (3) combination FDC** **2.90**

**973a, 973b**

## 1983

| | |
|---|---|
| **Rates:** Jan 15, 1983– Jun 23, 1985 | Domestic: 48¢ (30–50g)<br>Non-standard: 37¢ (0–30g)<br>USA: 37¢ (0–30g), 48¢ (30–50g)<br>International: 64¢ (0–20g), 99¢ (20–50g)<br>Registration: $1.96<br>Special delivery: $1.06 |

*single usage:* USA 37¢: $15.00 | International 64¢: $20.00

| | |
|---|---|
| **Rates:** Feb 15, 1983– Jun 23, 1985 | Domestic: 32¢ (0–30g) |

976
Globes

977
Map of the Earth

## UNITED NATIONS WORLD COMMUNICATIONS YEAR

Designer: Raymond Bellemare.
Lithography (6 colours), pane of 50
Ashton-Potter Limited

**1983, Mar 10** **Tagged, GT4** **Perf 12.0x12.5**

| | | NH–VF | ⊙F | PB | FDC |
|---|---|---|---|---|---|
| **976** | **32¢ multicoloured**, LF | .65 | .20 | 3.25 | 1.00 |
| i | DF | 2.50 | | 12.00 | |
| T1 | untagged (error) | — | 75.00 | | |
| a | double print* | 1,000.00 | | | |

Qty: 20,000,000

* 976a shows distinct doubling of the central 'multicoloured globe' with second impression 4 mm to the left.

## COMMONWEALTH DAY

Designer: Rolf P. Harder.
Lithography (5 colours), pane of 25
Ashton-Potter Limited

**1983, Mar 14** **Untagged** **Perf 12.5**

| | | NH–VF | ⊙F | PB | FDC |
|---|---|---|---|---|---|
| **977** | **$2 blue and multicoloured**, dull | 12.50 | 5.00 | 62.50 | 4.40 |
| i | NF paper | 20.00 | | 100.00 | |

Qty: 8,000,000

## CANADIAN WRITERS

978
Laure Conan, author
979
E.J. Pratt, poet

Designer: William H. Tibbles. 978: Based on a painting by René Milot; 979: Based on a wood engraving by Claire Pratt.
Lithography (5 colours), pane of 50
Canadian Bank Note Company, Limited

**1983, Apr 22** **Tagged, GT2** **Perf 13.5**

| | | NH–VF | ⊙F | PB | FDC |
|---|---|---|---|---|---|
| **978** | **32¢ multicoloured**, DF | .65 | .25 | | 1.00 |
| i | LF | 2.50 | | | |
| T1 | untagged (error) | — | 100.00 | | |
| **979** | **32¢ multicoloured**, DF | .65 | .25 | | 1.00 |
| i | LF | 2.50 | | | |
| T1 | untagged (error) | — | 100.00 | | |
| a | se-tenant pair, DF (978, 979) | 1.50 | 1.25 | 3.25 | 1.70 |
| ai | se-tenant pair, LF (978i, 979i) | 5.00 | | 13.00 | |
| b | missing colour on se-tenant pair† | 12,500.00 | | | |

Qty: 10,500,000 of each

† Price is for block of 24 as illustrated below.

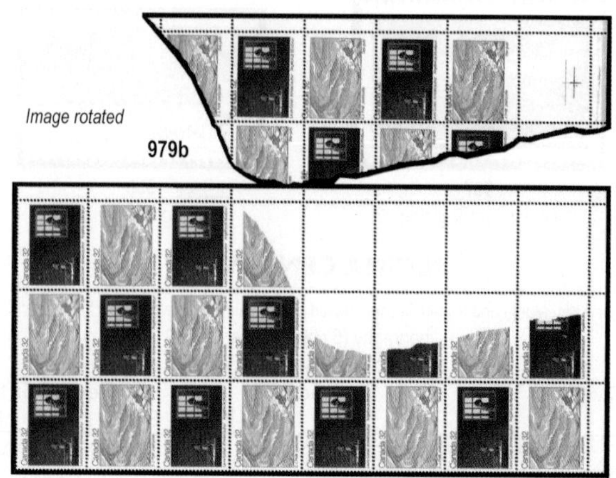
*Image rotated*
**979b**

## ST. JOHN AMBULANCE CENTENARY

980
Centenary Symbol

Designer: Louis Fishauf.

Lithography (3 colours), pane of 50
Ashton-Potter Limited

**1983, Jun 3** **Tagged, GT2** **Perf 13.5**

| | | NH–VF | ⊙F | PB | FDC |
|---|---|---|---|---|---|
| **980** | **32¢ multicoloured** | .65 | .20 | 3.25 | 1.00 |
| **T1** | untagged (error) | 100.00 | 75.00 | | |

Qty: 20,000,000

## WORLD UNIVERSITY GAMES

981 982
Universiade Edmonton Symbol

Designer: David Kilvert, Krista Huebner, and Pierre-Yves Pelletier.

Lithography (5 colours), panes of 50
Canadian Bank Note Company, Limited

**1983, Jun 28** **Tagged, GT2** **Perf 13.5**

| | | NH–VF | ⊙F | PB | FDC |
|---|---|---|---|---|---|
| **981** | **32¢ silver and multicoloured** | .65 | .20 | 3.25 | 1.00 |
| **a** | printed on gum side (50 known) | 1,250.00 | | 5,250.00* | |

Qty: 15,000,000
* Blank corner block of 4.

| | | NH–VF | ⊙F | PB | FDC |
|---|---|---|---|---|---|
| **982** | **64¢ gold and multicoloured** | 1.50 | 1.00 | 7.50 | 1.70 |

Qty: 9,000,000

**Nos. 981–982 (2) combination FDC** **2.30**

Held in Edmonton, AB from July 1 to July 11, 1983.

## CANADIAN FORTS – I

983
Fort Henry, Ontario

984
Fort William, Ontario

985
Fort Rodd Hill, British Columbia

986
Fort Wellington, Ontario

987
Fort Prince of Wales, Manitoba

988
Halifax Citadel, Nova Scotia

989
Fort Chambly, Quebec

990
Fort No. 1 Point Levis, Quebec

991
Fort Coteau-du-Lac, Quebec

992
Fort Beausejour, New Brunswick

Designer: Rolf P. Harder.

Lithography (4 colours), booklet pane of 10
Ashton-Potter Limited

**1983, Jun 30** **Tagged, GT2** **Perf 12.5x13.0**

| | | NH–VF | ⊙F | FDC |
|---|---|---|---|---|
| **983** | **32¢ Fort Henry** | 1.00 | 1.00 | |
| **984** | **32¢ Fort William** | 1.00 | 1.00 | |
| **985** | **32¢ Fort Rodd Hill** | 1.00 | 1.00 | |
| **986** | **32¢ Fort Wellington** | 1.00 | 1.00 | |
| **987** | **32¢ Fort Prince of Wales** | 1.00 | 1.00 | |
| **988** | **32¢ Halifax Citadel** | 1.00 | 1.00 | |
| **989** | **32¢ Fort Chambly** | 1.00 | 1.00 | |
| **990** | **32¢ Fort No. 1 Point Levis** | 1.00 | 1.00 | |
| **991** | **32¢ Fort Coteau-du-Lac** | 1.00 | 1.00 | |
| **992** | **32¢ Fort Beausejour** | 1.00 | 1.00 | |
| a | booklet pane of 10 different (5 x 2) (983–992) (BK86) | 11.00 | 11.00 | 6.80 |
| **BK86** | pane 992a in bilingual cover $12.00 | | | |

Qty: 2,650,000 of each

These are the first Canadian commemorative stamps to be issued in booklets only. See also 1050–1059 and 1547–1551.

992a

**MINT PRICING PREMIUMS**

Mint stamps from 301 to date are valued as NH-VF (Never Hinged-Very Fine). All hinged VF and NH-F copies are worth 50% of the listed values. Plate block (PB) values are for mint NH–VF plate or inscription blocks of four.

**USED, VF/XF (with in-period, circular date cancel) PRICING PREMIUM**

Single stamps with light or circular date cancels will sell for more than catalogue value (perhaps even more than a mint copy). From *1981 to 1991* single stamps from se-tenant blocks of 4 or larger will be priced at 50% or more above the fine price. From *1992* to date single stamps from se-tenant blocks of 4 or larger plus se-tenant booklet panes and souvenir sheets will be priced at 100% or more above the fine price. From *1997* to date all other stamps will be priced at 50% or more above the fine price.

## CANADIAN SCOUTING

993
Scout Encampment

Designer: François Dallaire. Based on a drawing by Marc Fournier .
Lithography (4 colours), pane of 50
Ashton-Potter Limited

**1983, Jul 6** **Tagged, GT2** **Perf 13.5**

| | | NH–VF | ⊙F | PB | FDC |
|---|---|---|---|---|---|
| **993** | **32¢ multicoloured**, NF | .65 | .20 | 3.25 | 1.00 |
| i | F | 3.00 | 1.50 | 30.00* | |
| ii | HB | 10.00 | 2.50 | 50.00 | |
| iii | LF/fl | 2.50 | | 13.00 | |

Qty: 20,000,000
* Non-inscription corner block – 15.00.

Commemorates the 75th anniversary of Scouting in Canada and an International Jamboree held in Alberta. Designed by 12-year old Marc Fournier, selected as winner of nation-wide poster contest.

994
Stylized Cross

995
Sir Humphrey Gilbert

## WORLD COUNCIL OF CHURCHES

Designer: Kosta (Gus) Tsetsekas.
Engraved (2 colours) and Photogravure (2 colours), pane of 50 [Goebel press]
British American Bank Note Company

**1983, Jul 22** **Tagged, GT2, Harrison Paper** **Perf 13.5**

| | | NH–VF | ⊙F | PB | FDC |
|---|---|---|---|---|---|
| **994** | **32¢ multicoloured** | .65 | .20 | 3.25 | 1.00 |
| T1 | untagged (error) | — | 75.00 | | |

Qty: 20,000,000

World Council of Churches Assembly held in Vancouver.

## NEWFOUNDLAND

Designer: Roger Hill.
Lithography (4 colours), pane of 50
Canadian Bank Note Company, Limited

**1983, Aug 3** **Tagged, GT2, Harrison Paper** **Perf 13.5**

| | | NH–VF | ⊙F | PB | FDC |
|---|---|---|---|---|---|
| **995** | **32¢ multicoloured** | .65 | .20 | 3.25 | 1.00 |
| T1 | untagged (error) | — | 125.00 | | |

Qty: 20,000,000

Marks the 400th anniversary of Sir Humphrey Gilbert claiming Newfoundland for Queen Elizabeth I of England.

## NICKEL

996
Discovery of Nickel

Designer: John Capon.
Lithography (4 colours) with foil stamping, pane of 50
Canadian Bank Note Company, Limited

**1983, Aug 12** **Tagged, GT2, Harrison Paper** **Perf 13.0x13.5**

| | | NH–VF | ⊙F | PB | FDC |
|---|---|---|---|---|---|
| **996** | **32¢ multicoloured**, DF | .75 | .20 | 3.75 | 1.00 |
| iii | F/fl | 3.00 | | 15.00 | |
| a | silver colour and tagging omitted | 900.00 | — | — | — |
| ii | silver colour shift | 500.00 | — | 2,250.00* | — |

Qty: 20,000,000
* Blank corner block of 4.

No. 996ii shows a dramatic upward shift of silver colour, with the word 'nickel' on top of 'Canada 32' at top of stamp. Less dramatic shifts are known, and are valued from $100 to $150.

996a

996ii

## CANADIAN PIONEERS

997
Josiah Henson

998
Antoine Labelle

Designer: 997: Tony Kew; 998: Jacques Hamel .
Lithography (4 colours), pane of 50
British American Bank Note Company

**1983, Sep 16** **Tagged, GT2, Clark Paper** **Perf 13.0x13.5**

| | | NH–VF | ⊙F | PB | FDC |
|---|---|---|---|---|---|
| **997** | **32¢ multicoloured** | .65 | .20 | 3.25 | 1.00 |
| T1 | untagged (error)* | 100.00 | 75.00 | | |

Qty: 20,000,000

Josiah Henson (1789–1883) was instrumental in operating the "underground railroad" which brought American black slaves to Canada.

**1983, Sep 16** **Tagged, GT2, Clark Paper** **Perf 13.0x13.5**

| | | NH–VF | ⊙F | PB | FDC |
|---|---|---|---|---|---|
| **998** | **32¢ multicoloured** | .65 | .20 | 3.25 | 1.00 |
| T1 | untagged (error)* | 100.00 | 75.00 | | |

Qty: 20,000,000

Antoine Labelle (1833–1891) colonized many of the smaller villages in Quebec.

* The tagging on #997 and #998 is known to fade under extended exposure to ultraviolet light. Genuine untagged stamps must show absolutely no trace of tagging when carefully examined under strong UV light in total darkness.

## CANADIAN LOCOMOTIVES (1836–1860) – I

999 Toronto 4-4-0 type | 1000 Dorchester 0-4-0 type

1001 Samson 0-6-0 type

1002 Adam Brown 4-4-0 type

Designer: Ernst Roch.

Lithography (6 colours), panes of 25
Ashton-Potter Limited

**1983, Oct 3 — Tagged, GT2, Harrison Paper — Perf 12.5x13.0**

| | | NH–VF | ⊙F | PB | FDC |
|---|---|---|---|---|---|
| **999** | **32¢ multicoloured** | .65 | .30 | | 1.00 |
| **1000** | **32¢ multicoloured** | .65 | .30 | | 1.00 |
| a | se-tenant pair (999, 1000) | 1.50 | 1.25 | 3.50 | |

Qty: 9,000,000 of each

| | | NH–VF | ⊙F | PB | FDC |
|---|---|---|---|---|---|
| **1001** | **37¢ multicoloured** | .90 | .75 | 4.50 | 1.15 |

Qty: 8,600,000

| | | NH–VF | ⊙F | PB | FDC |
|---|---|---|---|---|---|
| **1002** | **64¢ multicoloured**, dull | 1.50 | 1.25 | 7.50 | 1.70 |
| i | MF | 3.50 | 2.00 | 17.50 | |

Qty: 8,200,000

**Nos. 999–1002 (4) combination FDC** **3.70**

See also 1036–1039, 1071–1074 and 1118–1121.

## DALHOUSIE LAW SCHOOL CENTENARY

1003
Law School Coat-of-arms

Designer: Denise Saulnier. Based on a photograph by Don Robinson.

Lithography (5 colours), pane of 50
Canadian Bank Note Company, Limited

**1983, Oct 28 — Tagged, GT2, Harrison Paper — Perf 13.0**

| | | NH–VF | ⊙F | PB | FDC |
|---|---|---|---|---|---|
| **1003** | **32¢ multicoloured**, dull | .65 | .20 | 3.25 | 1.00 |
| i | MF | 3.50 | .50 | 17.50 | |

Qty: 18,000,000

## CHRISTMAS

1004
Urban Church

1005
Family going to Church

1006
Rural Church

Designer: Claude A. Simard.

Lithography (4 colours), panes of 50
Ashton-Potter Limited

**1983, Nov 3 — Tagged, GT2, Harrison Paper — Perf 13.3x13.4**

| | | NH–VF | ⊙F | PB | FDC |
|---|---|---|---|---|---|
| **1004** | **32¢ multicoloured** | .65 | .20 | 3.25 | 1.00 |
| i | green dot above door | 2.00 | 1.00 | | |
| ii | red and green dots in snow (pos. 47) | 2.00 | 1.00 | 5.00 | |

Qty: 106,500,000

| | | NH–VF | ⊙F | PB | FDC |
|---|---|---|---|---|---|
| **1005** | **37¢ multicoloured** | .75 | .60 | 3.75 | 1.15 |

Qty: 13,500,000

| | | NH–VF | ⊙F | PB | FDC |
|---|---|---|---|---|---|
| **1006** | **64¢ multicoloured** | 1.30 | 1.00 | 6.50 | 1.70 |

Qty: 13,000,000

**Nos. 1004–1006 (3) combination FDC** **3.10**

1004i

1004ii

## ARMY REGIMENTS

1007 Royal Canadian Regiment/ British Columbia Regiment | 1008 Royal Winnipeg Rifles/ Royal Canadian Dragoons

Designer: Ralph Tibbles. Based on paintings by William Southern.

Lithography (5 colours), pane of 50
Ashton-Potter Limited

**1983, Nov 10 — Tagged, GT4, Harrison Paper — Perf 13.3x13.0**

| | | NH–VF | ⊙F | PB | FDC |
|---|---|---|---|---|---|
| **1007** | **32¢ multicoloured**, LF/fl | .65 | .30 | | 1.00 |
| i | missing accent above "E" (pos. 49) | 2.50 | 1.50 | 6.00 (LR) | |
| ii | DF | 2.50 | | | |
| **1008** | **32¢ multicoloured**, LF/fl | .65 | .30 | | 1.00 |
| i | DF | 2.50 | | | |
| a | se-tenant pair, LF/fl (1007, 1008) | 1.50 | 1.25 | 3.25 | 1.70 |
| ai | se-tenant pair, DF (1007ii, 1008i) | 5.00 | | 13.00 | |

Qty: 11,000,000 of each

Issued to commemorate the 100th anniversary of the regiments.

1007
(normal)

1007i

QE II — 1980's

## 1984

### YELLOWKNIFE

1009
Gold mine head frame in pan

Designer: Ken Hughes.
Lithography (6 colours), pane of 50
Ashton-Potter Limited

| 1984, Mar 15 | Tagged, GT2, Clark Paper | | | Perf 13.3 |
|---|---|---|---|---|
| | NH–VF | ⊙F | PB | FDC |
| **1009 32¢ multicoloured** | .65 | .20 | 3.25 | 1.00 |

Qty: 20,000,000

Issued for the 50th anniversary of Yellowknife.

1010
Orchestra concert

1011
Cartier and ship

### MONTREAL SYMPHONY

Designer: Pierre Kohler. Based on an illustration by Jacques Delisle.
Lithography (5 colours), pane of 50
Ashton-Potter Limited

| 1984, Mar 23 | Tagged, GT2, Clark Paper | | | Perf 12.5 |
|---|---|---|---|---|
| | NH–VF | ⊙F | PB | FDC |
| **1010 32¢ multicoloured** | .65 | .20 | 3.25 | 1.00 |
| T1 untagged (error) | — | 125.00 | | |

Qty: 20,000,000

Issued for the 50th anniversary of the Montreal Symphony.

### JACQUES CARTIER

Designer: Yves Paquin. Engraved by Claude Haley.
Photogravure (4 colours) and Engraved, pane of 50
Imprimerie des Timbres-poste France

| 1984, Apr 20 | Dextrine gum, Tagged | | | Perf 13.0 |
|---|---|---|---|---|
| | NH–VF | ⊙F | PB | FDC |
| **1011 32¢ multicoloured**, F | .65 | .20 | 3.25 | 1.00 |
| i HF | 6.00 | 1.00 | 30.00 | |
| ii DF | 6.00 | 1.00 | 30.00 | |
| iii brown "anchor line" (pos. 2) | 5.00 | 2.50 | | |
| iv green "anchor line" (pos. 7) | 5.00 | 2.50 | 12.00 (w/1011iii) | |
| T1 untagged (error) | — | 100.00 | | |

Qty: 22,000,000

Commemorates the 450th anniversary of Jacques Cartier's first voyage to Canada. France issued an identical 2-franc stamp and the Canadian stamp was printed by France's national printer. A few trial colour proofs are known in private hands; value $175.00 (any colour).

First day covers with both the French 2 Fr stamp and No. 1011 on the same cover – $3.00.

Joint issue with France
**Scott # 1923**

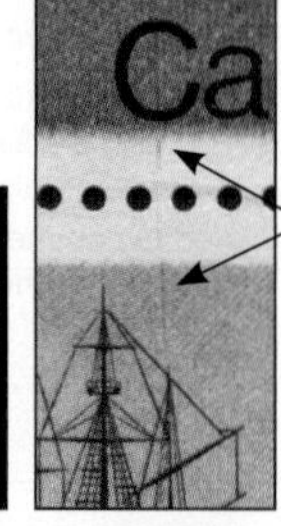

1011iii/iv

### TALL SHIPS

1012
Tall Ships regatta

Designer: Oswald Kenneth Schenk.
Lithography (4 colours), pane of 50
Ashton-Potter Limited

| 1984, May 18 | Tagged, GT4*, Harrison Paper | | | Perf 12.0x12.5 |
|---|---|---|---|---|
| | NH–VF | ⊙F | PB | FDC |
| **1012 32¢ multicoloured** | .65 | .20 | 3.25 | 1.00 |
| i "double anchor hole" (pos. 2) | 3.50 *EP* | 1.25 | 6.00 | 5.00 |

Qty: 20,000,000
* Shades exist with more brownish colour and are quite common.

As part of the Jacques Cartier celebrations, a fleet of Tall Ships visited Canada.

1012i

1013
Meritorious Service Medal

1014
'Lymphad' sailing vessels

### CANADIAN RED CROSS

Designer: William H. Tibbles. Based on a photograph by Clive Webster.
Lithography (5 colours), pane of 50
Ashton-Potter Limited

| 1984, May 28 | Tagged, GT2, Clark Paper | | | Perf 13.3 |
|---|---|---|---|---|
| | NH–VF | ⊙F | PB | FDC |
| **1013 32¢ multicoloured** | .65 | .20 | 3.25 | 1.00 |

Qty: 20,000,000

Issued to commemorate the 75th anniversary of the Canadian Red Cross.

### NEW BRUNSWICK BICENTENNIAL

Designer: Peter Dorn.
Engraved and Photogravure (4 colours), pane of 50
British American Bank Note Company

| 1984, Jun 18 | Tagged, GT2, Harrison Paper | | | Perf 13.3 |
|---|---|---|---|---|
| | NH–VF | ⊙F | PB | FDC |
| **1014 32¢ multicoloured** | .65 | .20 | 3.25 | 1.00 |

Qty: 20,000,000

## ST. LAWRENCE SEAWAY

1015
Seaway Locks

Designer: Ernst Barenscher.

Lithography (6 colours), pane of 25
Canadian Bank Note Company

| 1984, Jun 26 | Tagged, GT4, Clark Paper | | | Perf 13.3x13.0 | |
|---|---|---|---|---|---|
| | | NH–VF | ⊙F | PB | FDC |
| **1015** | **32¢ multicoloured** | .65 | .20 | 3.25 | 1.00 |
| **T1** | untagged (error) | 100.00 | 75.00 | | |

Qty: 20,000,000

**Combination FDC (No. 1015 with USA 20¢ Seaway stamp)** **1.90**

As part of the 25th anniversary celebrations, the U.S. also issued a 20¢ commemorative designed by Canadian Ernst Barenscher, but not the identical design as was employed in the joint 1959 issues.

**USA Sc# 2091**
Joint Issue

## CANADA DAY

1016
New Brunswick

1017
British Columbia

1018
Yukon Territory

1019
Quebec

1020
Manitoba

1021
Alberta

1022
Prince Edward Island

1023
Saskatchewan

1024
Nova Scotia

1025
Northwest Territories

1026
Newfoundland

1027
Ontario

Designer: Jean Morin and Tom Yakobina. Paintings by Jean Paul Lemieux.

Lithography (5 colours), pane of 12
Canadian Bank Note Company

| 1984, Jun 29 | Tagged, GT4, Clark Paper | | | Perf 13.0x13.2 | |
|---|---|---|---|---|---|
| | | NH–VF | ⊙F | PB | FDC |
| **1016** | **32¢ New Brunswick** | .75 | .50 | | 1.00 |
| **i** | "white sand on beach" | 5.00 | 2.50 | 15.00(UL pane) | |
| **1017** | **32¢ British Columbia** | .75 | .50 | | 1.00 |
| **1018** | **32¢ Yukon Territory*** | .75 | .50 | | 1.00 |
| **1019** | **32¢ Quebec** | .75 | .50 | | 1.00 |
| **1020** | **32¢ Manitoba** | .75 | .50 | | 1.00 |
| **1021** | **32¢ Alberta** | .75 | .50 | | 1.00 |
| **1022** | **32¢ Prince Edward Island** | .75 | .50 | | 1.00 |
| **1023** | **32¢ Saskatchewan** | .75 | .50 | | 1.00 |
| **1024** | **32¢ Nova Scotia** (vert §) | .75 | .50 | | 1.00 |
| **1025** | **32¢ Northwest Territories*** | .75 | .50 | | 1.00 |
| **1026** | **32¢ Newfoundland** | .75 | .50 | | 1.00 |
| **1027** | **32¢ Ontario** (vert §) | .75 | .50 | | 1.00 |
| **a** | $3.84 pane of 12† (3 x 4) (1016–1027) | 10.00 | 9.50 | 11.00 | 8.10 |

Qty: 4,568,000 of each

Provincial and territorial scenes by Jean-Paul Lemieux. Nova Scotia and Ontario stamps were issued on their sides.

* Nos. 1018 and 1025 are incorrectly inscribed: No. 1018 actually shows a church in the Northwest Territories while No. 1025 actually shows a Yukon Territory landscape.

§ 1024 and 1027, when oriented vertically, are perf. 13.2 x 13.0.

† Four different philatelic panes exist, depending upon the position of the inscription.

**1016i**

**1027a**
lower left pane

## UNITED EMPIRE LOYALISTS

1028
Loyalists and British flag

Designer: Will Davies.

Lithography (5 colours), pane of 50
British American Bank Note Company

**1984, Jul 3** **Tagged, GT2, Clark Paper** **Perf 13.1x13.3**

| | | NH–VF | ⊙F | PB | FDC |
|---|---|---|---|---|---|
| **1028** | **32¢ multicoloured** | .65 | .20 | 3.25 | 1.00 |

Qty: 20,000,000

## ROMAN CATHOLIC CHURCH

1029
Basilica of St. John's, Newfoundland

Designer: Jean Morin and Robert Ethier.

Lithography (4 colours), pane of 50
Canadian Bank Note Company

**1984, Aug 17** **Tagged, GT2, Clark Paper** **Perf 13.3**

| | | NH–VF | ⊙F | PB | FDC |
|---|---|---|---|---|---|
| **1029** | **32¢ multicoloured** | .65 | .20 | 3.25 | 1.00 |
| i | scratch above first "h" of "Church" (pos. 20) | 5.00 *EP* | 2.50 | 10.00(UR) | 7.50* |
| T1 | untagged (error) | — | 100.00 | | |

Qty: 18,000,000
* In upper right inscription block.

Commemorates the 200th anniversary of the formal establishment of the Roman Catholic Church in Newfoundland.

1029i

## PAPAL VISIT

1030
Papal coat-of-arms and map

1031
Papal coat-of-arms and map

Designer: Louis-André Rivard.

Lithography (6 colours), panes of 50
Ashton-Potter Limited

**1984, Aug 31** **Tagged, GT2, Harrison Paper** **Perf 12.5**

| | | NH–VF | ⊙F | PB | FDC |
|---|---|---|---|---|---|
| **1030** | **32¢ multicoloured** | .65 | .25 | 3.25 | 1.00 |
| **1031** | **64¢ multicoloured** | 1.50 | .90 | 7.50 | 1.70 |

Qty 1030: 20,000,000
Qty 1031: 12,000,000

**Nos. 1030–1031 (2) combination FDC** **2.30**
One combination FDC exists with the 32¢ value missing the gold, resulting in yellow-green background colour. Certificate of authenticity recommended.

Visit of Pope John Paul II to Canada.

## CANADIAN LIGHTHOUSES – I

1032 Louisbourg, NS 1734 — 1033 Fisgard, BC 1860

1034 Île Verte, PQ 1809 — 1035 Gibraltar Point, ON 1808

Designer: Ken Rodmell. Based on a painting by Dennis Noble.

Lithography (5 colours), pane of 50
Ashton-Potter Limited

**1984, Sep 21** **Tagged, GT2, Harrison Paper** **Perf 12.5**

| | | NH–VF | ⊙F | PB | FDC |
|---|---|---|---|---|---|
| **1032** | **32¢ multicoloured** | .75 | .30 | | 1.00 |
| i | "Blue, blue sea" (pos. 25) | 3.50 | 1.50 | 30.00† | |
| T1 | untagged (error) | 35.00 | 10.00 | | |
| **1033** | **32¢ multicoloured** | .75 | .30 | | 1.00 |
| T1 | untagged (error) | 35.00 | 10.00 | | |
| **1034** | **32¢ multicoloured** | .75 | .30 | | 1.00 |
| T1 | untagged (error) | 35.00 | 10.00 | | |
| **1035** | **32¢ multicoloured** | .75 | .30 | | 1.00 |
| i | scratch in sky to left of lighthouse | 3.50 | 1.50 | | 5.00 |
| T1 | untagged (error) | 35.00 | 10.00 | | |
| a | se-tenant block of 4 (1032–1035) | 3.25 | 1.60 | 3.75 | 3.00 |
| aT1 | as 1035a, untagged (error) | 140.00 | — | 150.00* | |

Qty: 1032/1034: 5,993,000 of each; 1033/1035: 5,532,000 of each
† Value shown is for blank corner block of 10. Variety appears on 1 of 4 panes.
* Blank corner block of 4.

See also 1063–1066.

1032i

1035i

## CANADIAN LOCOMOTIVES (1860–1905) – 2

1036
Scotia 0-6-0 type

1037
Countess of Dufferin 4-4-0 type

1038
GT Class E3 2-6-0 type

1039
CP Class D10a 4-6-0 type

1039i

1039ii

1039iii

1039iv

Designer: Ernst Roch.

Lithography (6 colours), panes of 25
Ashton-Potter Limited

| 1984, Oct 25 | Tagged, GT2, Harrison Paper | NH–VF | ⊙F | PB | FDC |
|---|---|---|---|---|---|
| **1036** | **32¢ green-grey and multicoloured** | .65 | .25 | | 1.00 |
| **1037** | **32¢ green-grey and multicoloured** | .65 | .25 | | 1.00 |
| a | se-tenant pair (1036, 1037) | 1.50 | 1.25 | 3.25 | |

Perf 12.5x13.1

Qty: 9,000,000 of each

| | | NH–VF | ⊙F | PB | FDC |
|---|---|---|---|---|---|
| **1038** | **37¢ green-grey and multicoloured** | 1.00 | .85 | 5.00 | 1.15 |

Qty: 8,600,000

| | | NH–VF | ⊙F | PB | FDC |
|---|---|---|---|---|---|
| **1039** | **64¢ green-grey and multicoloured** | 1.75 | 1.25 | 8.75 | 1.70 |
| a | $1.65 souvenir sheet of 4 | 4.00 | 4.00 | — | 3.70 |
| i | 32¢ Scotia, blue-grey | .65 | .65 | | |
| v | constant tag flaw on 1039i | 2.50 | 2.50 | | |
| ii | 32¢ Countess of Dufferin, blue-grey | .65 | .65 | | |
| iii | 37¢ GT Class E3, blue-grey | 1.00 | 1.00 | | |
| iv | 64¢ CP Class D10a, blue-grey | 1.75 | 1.75 | | |
| vi | as "a", with tag flaw on 1039i | 10.00 | 7.50 | | |

Qty: 1039: 8,200,000; Souvenir sheet: 700,000

**Nos. 1036–1039 (4) combination FDC** **3.70**

The backgrounds on the sheet stamps (1036–1039) are green-grey. The background on stamps from the souvenir sheet (1039ai–1039aiv) is blue-grey. The souvenir sheet was issued at Canada 84, Canada's first National Philatelic Exhibition, co-sponsored by Canada Post. Many minor varieties and shades exist.

See also 999–1002, 1071–1074 and 1118–1121.

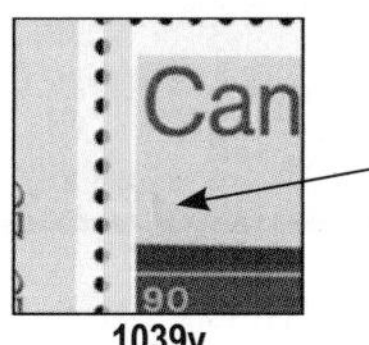
1039v

1039a

## CHRISTMAS

1040
*L'Annonciation*, by Jean Dallaire

1041
*The Three Kings*, by Simone Bouchard

1042
*Snow in Bethlehem*, by David Milne

Designer: Tom Yakobina and Jean Morin.

Lithography (4 colours), panes of 50
Ashton-Potter Limited

**1984, Nov 2** **Tagged, GT2, Harrison Paper** **Perf 13.3**

| | | NH–VF | ⊙F | PB | FDC |
|---|---|---|---|---|---|
| **1040** | **32¢ multicoloured** | .65 | .25 | 3.25 | 1.00 |

Qty: 106,500,000

| | | NH–VF | ⊙F | PB | FDC |
|---|---|---|---|---|---|
| **1041** | **37¢ multicoloured** | .75 | .75 | 3.75 | 1.15 |

Qty: 14,500,000

| | | NH–VF | ⊙F | PB | FDC |
|---|---|---|---|---|---|
| **1042** | **64¢ multicoloured** | 1.30 | 1.00 | 6.50 | 1.70 |

Qty: 14,500,000

**Nos. 1040–1042 (3) combination FDC** **3.10**

## ROYAL CANADIAN AIR FORCE

1043
Pilots in flying dress

Designer: Ralph Tibbles. Based on an illustration by William Southern.

Lithography (5 colours), pane of 50
Ashton-Potter Limited

**1984, Nov 9** **Tagged, GT4, Harrison Paper** **Perf 12.0x12.5**

| | | NH–VF | ⊙F | PB | FDC |
|---|---|---|---|---|---|
| **1043** | **32¢ multicoloured** | .65 | .25 | 3.25 | 1.00 |

Qty: 18,000,000

## TREFFLÉ BERTHIAUME

1044
Trefflé Berthiaume

Designer: Pierre-Yves Pelletier.

Lithography (3 colours), pane of 50
Ashton-Potter Limited

**1984, Nov 16** **Tagged, GT4, Harrison Paper** **Perf 13.1x13.5**

| | | NH–VF | ⊙F | PB | FDC |
|---|---|---|---|---|---|
| **1044** | **32¢ multicoloured** | .65 | .25 | 3.25 | 1.00 |

Qty: 18,000,000

## 1985

### UNITED NATIONS INTERNATIONAL YOUTH YEAR

1045
Heart and Arrow, Jeans

Designer: François Dallaire.

Lithography (4 colours), pane of 50
Ashton-Potter Limited

| 1985, Feb 8 | Tagged, GT2, Harrison Paper | | | Perf 12.5 |
|---|---|---|---|---|
| | NH–VF | ⊙F | PB | FDC |
| **1045 32¢ multicoloured** | .65 | .25 | 3.25 | 1.00 |

Qty: 19,000,000

### CANADIANS IN SPACE

1046
Astronaut and Control Panel

Designer: Les Holloway.

Lithography (6 colours), pane of 50
Ashton-Potter Limited

| 1985, Mar 15 | Tagged, GT2, Harrison Paper | | | Perf 13.4x13.3 |
|---|---|---|---|---|
| | NH–VF | ⊙F | PB | FDC |
| **1046 32¢ multicoloured** | .75 | .25 | 3.75 | 1.00 |

Qty: 18,000,000

Issued to honour Canadian achievements in space and particularly Marc Garneau, first Canadian astronaut.

### CANADIAN FEMINISTS

1047
Thérèse Casgrain

1048
Emily Murphy

Designer: Ralph Tibbles. Based on illustrations by Muriel Wood.

Lithography (6 colours), pane of 50
Ashton-Potter Limited

| 1985, Apr 17 | Tagged, GT2, Harrison Paper | | | Perf 13.3 |
|---|---|---|---|---|
| | NH–VF | ⊙F | PB | FDC |
| **1047 32¢ multicoloured** | .65 | .25 | | 1.00 |
| T1 untagged (error) | 125.00 | 75.00 | | |
| **1048 32¢ multicoloured** | .65 | .25 | | 1.00 |
| T1 untagged (error) | 125.00 | 75.00 | | |
| a se-tenant pair (1047, 1048) | 1.50 | 1.25 | 3.25 | 1.70 |
| T1 as 1048a, untagged (error)† | 300.00 | | 700.00 | |

Qty: 10,000,000 of each

† Untagged stamps come from the left-hand column of the pane; stamps from the rest of the pane are 1-bar tag. A se-tenant pair will have the left stamp untagged and the right stamp 1-bar taggged. Only UL and LL corner blocks exist.

Issued to honour Therese Casgrain (1896–1981), who fought and won the right for women to vote in Quebec; and Emily Murphy (1868–1933), the first Canadian woman judge.

### GABRIEL DUMONT

1049
Dumont and Battle of Batoche

Designer: Reinhard Derreth. Based on an illustration by Grundy.

Lithography (3 colours), pane of 50
Ashton-Potter Limited

| 1985, May 6 | Tagged, GT2, Harrison Paper | | | Perf 14.0x13.4 |
|---|---|---|---|---|
| | NH–VF | ⊙F | PB | FDC |
| **1049 32¢ multicoloured** | .65 | .25 | 3.25 | 1.00 |
| T1 untagged (error) | — | 75.00 | | |

Qty: 18,000,000

Issued to honour Métis leader Gabriel Dumont (1837–1906) on the 100th anniversary of the Northwest Rebellion.

**Rates:** Jun 24, 1985– Mar 31, 1987
Domestic: 34¢ (0–30g), 51¢ (30–50g)
Non-standard: 39¢ (0–30g)
USA: 39¢ (0–30g), 56¢ (30–50g)
International: 68¢ (0–20g), $1.05 (20–50g)
Registration: $2.46
Special delivery: $1.96

*single usage:* USA 39¢: $15.00 | International 68¢: $20.00

### CANADIAN FORTS – 2

1050
Lower Fort Garry, Manitoba

1051
Fort Anne, Nova Scotia

1052
Fort York, Ontario

1053
Castle Hill, Newfoundland

1054
Fort Whoop-Up, Alberta

1055
Fort Erie, Ontario

1056
Fort Walsh, Saskatchewan

1057
Fort Lennox, Quebec

1058
York Redoubt, Nova Scotia

1059
Fort Frederick, Ontario

Designer: Rolf P. Harder.

Lithography (4 colours), booklet pane of 10
Ashton-Potter Limited

**1985, Jun 28** **Tagged, GT2, Harrison Paper** **Perf 12.5x13.1**

| | | NH–VF | ⊙F | FDC |
|---|---|---|---|---|
| **1050** | **34¢ Lower Fort Garry** | 1.25 | .85 | — |
| **1051** | **34¢ Fort Anne** | 1.25 | .85 | — |
| **1052** | **34¢ Fort York** | 1.25 | .85 | — |
| **1053** | **34¢ Castle Hill** | 1.25 | .85 | — |
| **1054** | **34¢ Fort Whoop-Up** | 1.25 | .85 | — |
| **1055** | **34¢ Fort Erie** | 1.25 | .85 | — |
| **1056** | **34¢ Fort Walsh** | 1.25 | .85 | — |
| **1057** | **34¢ Fort Lennox** | 1.25 | .85 | — |
| **1058** | **34¢ York Redoubt** | 1.25 | .85 | — |
| **1059** | **34¢ Fort Frederick** | 1.25 | .85 | — |
| a | booklet pane of 10 different (5 x 2) (1050–1059) (BK87) | 15.00 | 18.00 | 7.20 |
| i | booklet pane of 10 (1059a) imperf. at top between stamps and tab (1 known) | *7,500.00* | | |
| **BK87** | pane 1059a in cover $16.00 | | | |

Qty: 2,801,400 of each

See also 983–992 and 1547–1551.

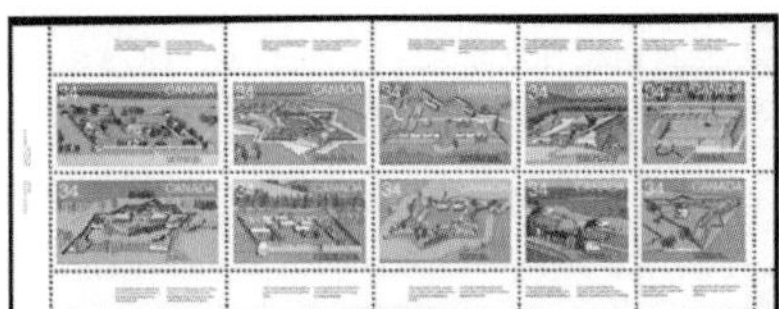

1059a

1059i

**1060**
Hébert and Apothecary objects

**1061**
Stylized map over Parliament Buildings

**1062**
Girl Guide and Brownie

## LOUIS HÉBERT

Designer: Clermont Malenfant.

Lithography (5 colours), pane of 50
Ashton-Potter Limited

**1985, Aug 30** **Tagged, GT4, Rolland Paper** **Perf 12.5**

| | | NH–VF | ⊙F | PB | FDC |
|---|---|---|---|---|---|
| **1060** | **34¢ multicoloured** | .65 | .25 | 3.25 | 1.10 |
| **i** | imperf. at top margin* | — | 750.00 | 1,500.00† | — |

Qty: 18,000,000

* Sheet reported imperf. horiz. at top margin. Two used singles and one used pair have been seen by the editors.

† Value shown is for used pair.

Louis Hébert (1575–1627) was the first French apothecary in Canada and the founder of the Canadian pharmaceutical profession.

## INTER-PARLIAMENTARY UNION CONFERENCE

Designer: Ernst Barenscher.

Lithography (4 colours), pane of 50
Ashton-Potter Limited

**1985, Sep 3** **Tagged, GT2, Rolland Paper** **Perf 13.3**

| | | NH–VF | ⊙F | PB | FDC |
|---|---|---|---|---|---|
| **1061** | **34¢ multicoloured**, LF/MF | .65 | .25 | 3.25 | 1.10 |
| i | HF/DF | 3.00 | | 15.00 | |
| ii | DF/DF | 5.00 | | 25.00 | |
| iii | LF/LF | 2.50 | | 13.00 | |

Qty: 18,000,000

Issued to commemorate the 74th Conference of the Inter-Parliamentary Union in Ottawa, Sept. 2–7.

## CANADIAN GIRL GUIDES

Designer: Barbara Griffin.

Engraved (3 colours) and Photogravure (4 colours), pane of 50
British American Bank Note Company

**1985, Sep 12** **Tagged, GT4, Harrison Paper** **Perf 13.3x12.9**

| | | NH–VF | ⊙F | PB | FDC |
|---|---|---|---|---|---|
| **1062** | **34¢ multicoloured** | .65 | .25 | 3.25 | 1.10 |

Qty: 18,000,000

Issued to honour the Canadian Girl Guide movement on the 75th anniversary of its founding.

1060i

## CANADIAN LIGHTHOUSES – 2

**1063** Sisters Islets, near Vancouver Island

**1064** Pelee Passage, Lake Erie

**1065** Haut-fond Prince, St. Lawrence River

**1066** Rose Blanche, Cains Island, NF

Designer: Louis-André Rivard.

Lithography (5 colours), pane of 50
Ashton-Potter Limited

| 1985, Oct 3 | Tagged, GT2, Rolland Paper | | | | Perf 13.3 |
|---|---|---|---|---|---|
| | | NH–VF | ⊙F | PB | FDC |
| **1063** | **34¢ multicoloured**, F/HF | 1.00 | .35 | | 1.10 |
| i | LF/DF | 1.00 | .35 | | |
| **1064** | **34¢ multicoloured**, F/HF | 1.00 | .35 | | 1.10 |
| i | LF/DF | 1.00 | .35 | | |
| **1065** | **34¢ multicoloured**, F/HF | 1.00 | .35 | | 1.10 |
| i | LF/DF | 1.00 | .35 | | |
| **1066** | **34¢ multicoloured**, F/HF | 1.00 | .35 | | 1.10 |
| i | LF/DF | 1.00 | .35 | | |
| a | se-tenant block of 4 (1063–1066) | 4.00 | 3.25 | 5.00 | 3.10 |
| ai | as 1066a, LF/DF | 4.00 | 3.25 | 4.50 | |
| b | $1.36 souvenir sheet of 4 (1063–1066) | 6.00 | 6.00 | | 3.10 |

Qty: 1063/1064: 6,848,800 of each; 1064/1066: 6,381,200 of each; Souvenir sheet: 700,000

The souvenir sheet commemorates CAPEX 87, held in Toronto, June 13–21 1987.
See also 1032–1035.

1066b

## CHRISTMAS – SANTA CLAUS PARADE

1067

1068

1069

1070

1070a

Fluorescence paper varieties described in the format of "LF/MF" indicate the fluorescence on the face of the stamp followed by the reading from the back.

Designer: Chris Yaneff. Based on paintings by Barbara Carroll.

Lithography (4 colours), panes of 50
Ashton-Potter Limited

| 1985, Oct 23 | Tagged, GT2, Harrison Paper | | | | Perf 13.3 |
|---|---|---|---|---|---|
| | | NH–VF | ⊙F | PB | FDC |
| **1067** | **34¢ multicoloured** | .65 | .25 | 3.25 | 1.10 |
| | Qty: 14,500,000 | | | | |
| **1068** | **39¢ multicoloured** | 1.00 | .75 | 5.00 | 1.20 |
| | Qty: 14,500,000 | | | | |
| **1069** | **68¢ multicoloured** | 1.75 | 1.25 | 8.75 | 1.75 |
| | Qty: 14,500,000 | | | | |
| **Nos. 1067–1069 (3) combination FDC** | | | | | **3.20** |

Booklet stamp, pane of 10

| | | NH–VF | ⊙F | PB | FDC |
|---|---|---|---|---|---|
| **1070** | **32¢ multicoloured** | 1.50 | .60 | — | — |
| a | booklet pane of 10 x 32¢ (1070) (5 x 2) (BK90) | 11.00 | 10.00 | — | — |
| **BK90** | pane 1070a in bilingual cover $12.00 | | | | |

Qty: 103,000,000

The 32¢ stamps were issued in booklet panes of 10 only and were authorized for use on greeting cards only until 31 January 1986, after which a 2¢ stamp had to be added to make up the first-class rate. No Canada Post Official FDC's exist; all privately produced FDC's bear an extra 2¢ stamp, value $20.00.

## CANADIAN LOCOMOTIVES (1906–1925) – 3

1071
GT Class K2 4-6-4T type

1072
CP Class P2a 2-8-2 type

1073
CNoR Class 010a 0-6-0 type

1074
CGR Class H4D 2-8-0 type

Designer: Ernst Roch.

Lithography (6 colours), panes of 25
Ashton-Potter Limited

| 1985, Nov 7 | Tagged, GT2, Harrison Paper | | | | Perf 12.5x13.0 |
|---|---|---|---|---|---|
| | | NH–VF | ⊙F | PB | FDC |
| **1071** | **34¢ multicoloured** | 1.00 | .35 | | 1.10 |
| **1072** | **34¢ multicoloured** | 1.00 | .35 | | 1.10 |
| a | se-tenant pair (1071, 1072) | 2.25 | 1.50 | 5.00 | |
| | Qty: 9,000,000 of each | | | | |
| **1073** | **39¢ multicoloured** | 1.00 | .90 | 5.00 | 1.20 |
| | Qty: 8,600,000 | | | | |
| **1074** | **68¢ multicoloured** | 1.75 | 1.40 | 8.75 | 1.75 |
| | Qty: 8,200,000 | | | | |
| **Nos. 1071–1074** (4) combination FDC | | | | | 3.90 |

See also 999–1002, 1036–1039 and 1118–1121

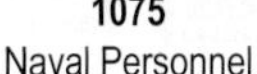

1075
Naval Personnel

1076
*The Old Holton House, Montreal, 1903–1915*
by James Wilson Morrice (1885–1924)

## ROYAL CANADIAN NAVY

Designer: Ralph Tibbles. Based on an illustration by William Southern.
Lithography (5 colours), pane of 50
Canadian Bank Note Company, Limited

**1985, Nov 8 — Tagged, GT4, Harrison Paper — Perf 13.3x13.0**

| | NH–VF | ⊙F | PB | FDC |
|---|---|---|---|---|
| **1075 34¢ multicoloured** | .65 | .25 | 3.25 | 1.10 |

Qty: 18,000,000

Issued for the 75th anniversary of the Royal Canadian Navy.

## MONTREAL MUSEUM OF FINE ARTS

Designer: .Jean Morin and Luc Parent.
Lithography (6 colours), pane of 50
Canadian Bank Note Company, Limited

**1985, Nov 15 — Tagged, GT2, Harrison Paper — Perf 13.3**

| | NH–VF | ⊙F | PB | FDC |
|---|---|---|---|---|
| **1076 34¢ multicoloured** | .65 | .25 | 3.25 | 1.10 |

Qty: 16,000,000

Issued for the 125th anniversary of the museum.

# 1986

## 1988 OLYMPIC WINTER GAMES

1077
Map

Designer: Pierre-Yves Pelletier.
Lithography (6 colours), pane of 25
Ashton-Potter Limited

**1986, Feb 13 — Tagged, GT4, Rolland Paper — Perf 12.5x13.0**

| | NH–VF | ⊙F | PB | FDC |
|---|---|---|---|---|
| **1077 34¢ multicoloured**, LF/DF | .65 | .25 | 3.25 | 1.10 |
| i F/HF | 3.00 | | 15.00 | |
| T1 untagged (error) | — | 75.00 | | |

Qty: 15,000,000

Issued to publicize the 1988 Olympic Winter Games to be held at Calgary, Alberta.
See also 1111, 1112, 1130, 1131, 1152, 1153, 1195–1198.

## EXPO 86

1078
Canada Pavilion

1079
Communications

Designer: Debbie Adams.
Photogravure (4 colours) and Engraved (1 colour), panes of 50 [Goebel press]
British American Bank Note Company

**1986, Mar 7 — Tagged, GT4, Harrison Paper — Perf 12.9x13.4**

| | NH–VF | ⊙F | PB | FDC |
|---|---|---|---|---|
| **1078 34¢ multicoloured*** | .65 | .25 | 3.25 | 1.10 |

Qty: 15,000,000
* No. 1078 has been reported with "CANADA 34" inscription omitted, value completely missing (10 reported) $1,250.00; value partly missing $200–$500 depending on how much is missing.

| | NH–VF | ⊙F | PB | FDC |
|---|---|---|---|---|
| **1079 39¢ multicoloured** | .90 | .75 | 4.50 | 1.20 |

Qty: 15,000,000

**Nos. 1078, 1079 (2) combination FDC** 1.85

Issued to publicize the International World's Fair, EXPO 86, held in Vancouver, May 2 to October 13.
See also 1092–1093.

**1078 – 'Canada 34' omitted**

## ARTIFACT DEFINITIVES 1987–1988

1080
Butter Stamp

1081
Linen Chest

1082
Iron Kettle

1083
Hand-drawn Cart

For additional Artifact definitives, see 917–922 and 927–933.

Designer: Jean-Pierre Beaudin and Jean Morin.
Lithography (4 colours), pane of 100
Ashton-Potter Limited

**1987, May 6 — Tagged, GT2, Rolland Paper — Perf 14.0x13.3**

| | NH–VF | ⊙F | PB | FDC |
|---|---|---|---|---|
| **1080 25¢ yellow and multicoloured** | .75 | .40 | 3.75 | 1.40† |

Qty: 36,100,000
† Available as pair on FDC only.

Lithography (4 colours), panes of 50

**Tagged, GT2, Rolland Paper** **Perf 12.0x12.5**

| | | NH–VF | ⊙F | PB | FDC |
|---|---|---|---|---|---|
| **1081** | **42¢ orange-brown and multicoloured**, NF | 1.40 | .25 | 7.00 | 1.25 |
| i | F | 5.00 | .50 | 25.00 | |
| iii | DF | 2.50 | | 15.00 | |
| ii | imperf at top margin (2 mint copies reported) | | | | |

Qty: 46,210,000

**Harrison Paper**

| | | NH–VF | ⊙F | PB | FDC |
|---|---|---|---|---|---|
| **1082** | **55¢ pink and multicoloured**, NF | 1.90 | .40 | 9.50 | 1.50 |
| i | MF | 5.00 | | 30.00 | |

Qty: 39,892,500

**Rolland Paper**

| | | NH–VF | ⊙F | PB | FDC |
|---|---|---|---|---|---|
| **1083** | **72¢ apple green and multicoloured**, F | 2.25 | .50 | 11.25 | 1.85 |
| a | imperforate (pair) | 1,200.00 | — | 2,500.00 | |
| ii | NF | 8.00 | 2.00 | 40.00 | |
| iii | MF | 7.50 | | 40.00 | |

Qty: 41,270,000

**Nos. 1080–1083 (4) combination FDC** **4.30**

## HIGH-VALUE NATIONAL PARK DEFINITIVE 1986

1084
La Mauricie National Park

For additional National Park definitives, see 726–727 and 934–937.

Designer: Laureat Marois and William Tibbles.

Engraved (1 colour) and Lithography (4 colours), pane of 25

Canadian Bank Note Company

**1986, Mar 14** **Untagged, Harrison Paper** **Perf 13.3**

| | | NH–VF | ⊙F | PB | FDC |
|---|---|---|---|---|---|
| **1084** | **$5 multicoloured**, plate 1 | 12.00 | 2.75 | 60.00 | 10.40 |
| a | dark blue inscriptions omitted | 3,500.00 | 2,000.00 | 15,000.00† | |

Qty: CBN: 9,000,000

British American Bank Note Company

| | | NH–VF | ⊙F | PB | FDC |
|---|---|---|---|---|---|
| ii | plate 1, *Jun 5, 1987* | 15.00 | 3.50 | 75.00 | |

Qty: BABN: 26,870,000

† Only the UR corner block remains intact.
All known mint copies of 1084a are from a single sheet of 25; 2 used copies are known from a second sheet. All are off-centre as shown in photo below.

The inscriptions ($5 POSTES/POSTAGE and CANADA) are more pronounced on the BABN printings, compared with the CBN printings.

CBN

BABN

1081ii

1084a

1090i

Nos. 1085–1089 are not assigned.

## CANADIAN PERSONALITIES

1090
Philippe Aubert de Gaspé

1091
Molly Brant

Designer: 1090: Yves Paquin. Typographed by Pierre Fontaine.
Designer: 1091: Sara Tyson.

Lithography (6 colours), panes of 50

Ashton-Potter Limited

**1986, Apr 14** **Tagged, GT4, Rolland Paper** **Perf 12.5**

| | | NH–VF | ⊙F | PB | FDC |
|---|---|---|---|---|---|
| **1090** | **34¢ multicoloured** | .65 | .25 | 3.25 | 1.10 |
| i | imperf at top margin* | — | 1,250.00 | | |

Qty: 15,000,000

* One example has been seen by the editors.

Issued to honour French-Canadian author Philippe Aubert de Gaspé (1786–1871).

**1986, Apr 14** **Tagged, GT2, Harrison Paper** **Perf 13.3**

| | | NH–VF | ⊙F | PB | FDC |
|---|---|---|---|---|---|
| **1091** | **34¢ multicoloured** | .65 | .25 | 3.25 | 1.10 |

Qty: 15,000,000

Issued to honour American Loyalist Indian, Molly Brant (1736–1796).

## EXPO 86

1092
Expo Centre

1093
Transportation

Designer: Debbie Adams.

Photogravure (4 colours) and Engraved (1 colour), panes of 50 [Goebel press]

British American Bank Note Company

**1986, Apr 28** **Tagged, GT4, Harrison Paper** **Perf 13.4x12.9**

| | | NH–VF | ⊙F | PB | FDC |
|---|---|---|---|---|---|
| **1092** | **34¢ multicoloured** | .65 | .25 | 3.25 | 1.10 |

Qty: 15,000,000

| | | NH–VF | ⊙F | PB | FDC |
|---|---|---|---|---|---|
| | | | | Perf 12.9x13.4 | |
| 1093 | **68¢ multicoloured** | 1.50 | .90 | 7.50 | 1.75 |

Qty: 15,000,000

**Nos. 1092, 1093 (2) combination FDC** 2.45

Issued to publicize the International World's Fair, EXPO 86, held in Vancouver, May 2 to October 13.
See also 1078–1079.

## CANADIAN FORCES POSTAL SERVICE

**1094**
Soldiers handling mail

Designer: Jacques DesRosiers.
Lithography (5 colours), pane of 50
Ashton-Potter Limited

**1986, May 9** **Tagged, GT2, Rolland Paper** **Perf 13.3**

| | | NH–VF | ⊙F | PB | FDC |
|---|---|---|---|---|---|
| 1094 | **34¢ multicoloured**, MF | .65 | .25 | 3.25 | 1.10 |
| i | LF | 3.00 | .50 | 15.00 | |

Qty: 15,000,000

Issued to commemorate 75 years of Canadian military postal service.

## BIRDS OF CANADA

**1095** Great Blue Heron **1096** Snow Goose

**1097** Great Horned Owl **1098** Spruce Grouse

Designer: Pierre Fontaine. Based on a painting by Jean-Luc Grondin.
Lithography (5 colours), pane of 50
Ashton-Potter Limited

**1986, May 22** **Tagged, GT2, Rolland Paper** **Perf 13.3**

| | | NH–VF | ⊙F | PB | FDC |
|---|---|---|---|---|---|
| 1095 | **34¢ multicoloured**, MF | .90 | .40 | | 1.10 |
| 1096 | **34¢ multicoloured**, MF | .90 | .40 | | 1.10 |
| 1097 | **34¢ multicoloured**, MF | .90 | .40 | | 1.10 |
| 1098 | **34¢ multicoloured**, MF | .90 | .40 | | 1.10 |
| a | se-tenant block of 4 (1095–1098) | 4.00 | 3.25 | 4.50 | 3.10 |

Qty: 1095/1097: 4,446,000 of each; 1096/1098: 4,104,000 of each
Also exists DF; same price as MF.

Issued to commemorate the XIX International Ornithological Congress, Ottawa, June 22–29, 1986.

## CANADA DAY
## SCIENCE AND TECHNOLOGY – I

**1099** Rotary Snowplow **1100** Canadarm

**1101** Anti-Gravity Flight Suit **1102** Variable Pitch Propeller

Designer: Roger Hill.
Lithography (5 colours), pane of 16
Canadian Bank Note Company, Limited

**1986, Jun 27** **Tagged, GT2, Harrison Paper** **Perf 13.3**

| | | NH–VF | ⊙F | PB | FDC |
|---|---|---|---|---|---|
| 1099 | **34¢ multicoloured** | 1.00 | .35 | | 1.25 |
| 1100 | **34¢ multicoloured** | 1.00 | .35 | | 1.25 |
| 1101 | **34¢ multicoloured** | 1.00 | .35 | | 1.25 |
| 1102 | **34¢ multicoloured** | 1.00 | .35 | | 1.25 |
| a | se-tenant block of 4 (1099–1102) | 4.50 | 3.25 | 5.00 | 3.50 |

Qty: 5,536,000 of each

Issued to honour Canadian innovations in transportation.
First commemorative issue to include colour dots and paper indicator on inscription/plate blocks.
See also 1135–1138 and 1206–1209.

H ● ● ● ● ● ● CANADIAN BANK NOTE Design: Roger Hill
Inscription with colour dots and paper indicator

## CANADIAN BROADCASTING CORPORATION

**1103**
CBC logo over 5 regions of Canada

Designer: Kosta (Gus) Tsetsekas and Raymond Mah. Computer-generated by Cliff Garbutt.
Lithography (5 colours), pane of 50
Ashton-Potter Limited

**1986, Jul 23** **Tagged, GT2, Rolland Paper** **Perf 12.5**

| | | NH–VF | ⊙F | PB | FDC |
|---|---|---|---|---|---|
| 1103 | **34¢ multicoloured**, dull | .65 | .25 | 3.25 | 1.10 |
| i | MF | 3.00 | .50 | 14.00 | |
| ii | HB | 7.00 | 1.00 | 30.00 | |
| T1 | untagged (error) | — | 125.00 | | |

Qty: 14,000,000

Issued to commemorate the 50th anniversary of the CBC.

## EXPLORATION OF CANADA – I

Discoverers

1105 The Vikings — 1104 The First Peoples

1107 Henry Hudson — 1106 John Cabot

Designer: Frederick Hagan. Typographed by J.F. Britton.
Lithography (5 colours), pane of 50
Ashton-Potter Limited

**1986, Aug 29 — Tagged, GT2, Harrison Paper — Perf 12.5x13.0**

| | | NH–VF | ⊙F | PB | FDC |
|---|---|---|---|---|---|
| **1104** | **34¢ multicoloured** | .75 | .40 | | 1.10 |
| i | crossed N (pos. 41) | 3.00 *EP* | 3.00 | 4.50 | 7.50 |
| T1 | untagged (error)* | 150.00 | 100.00 | | |
| **1105** | **34¢ multicoloured** | .75 | .40 | | 1.10 |
| T1 | untagged (error) | 150.00 | | | |
| **1106** | **34¢ multicoloured** | .75 | .40 | | 1.10 |
| T1 | untagged (error) | 150.00 | | | |
| **1107** | **34¢ multicoloured** | .75 | .40 | | 1.10 |
| i | pink print flaw (pos. 49) | 5.00 *EP* | 5.00 | 8.50 | 7.50 |
| ii | line in D of DE LA BAIE (pos. 40) | 3.00 *EP* | 3.00 | — | 5.00 |
| T1 | untagged (error) | 150.00 | | | |
| a | se-tenant block of 4 (1104–1107) | 3.40 | 3.25 | 3.75 | 3.10 |
| aT1 | untagged (error) | 600.00 | | | |
| b | $1.36 souvenir sheet of 4, *Oct 1, 1986* | 4.00 | 3.50 | | 3.10 |

Qty: 1104/1106: 5,285,000 of each; 1105/1107: 4,940,000 of each; souvenir sheet: 700,000

* Only 1104 has been reported untagged in used condition

Issued to honour discoverers of Canada. The souvenir sheet publicizes CAPEX 87 held June 13–21, 1987 in Toronto.
See also 1126–1129, 1199–1202 and 1233–1236.

1104i

1107i

1107ii

1107b

## PEACEMAKERS OF THE PRAIRIES

1108 Chief Crowfoot (1830–1890) — 1109 James F. Macleod (1836–1894)

Designer: Jean Morin and Wanda Lewicka. Based on a photograph by Alexander Ross.
Lithography (4 colours), pane of 50
Canadian Bank Note Company, Limited

**1986, Sep 5 — Tagged, GT2, Harrison Paper — Perf 13.0x13.4**

| | | NH–VF | ⊙F | PB | FDC |
|---|---|---|---|---|---|
| **1108** | **34¢ scarlet, grey and indigo** | .65 | .35 | | 1.10 |
| **1109** | **34¢ indigo, grey and scarlet** | .65 | .35 | | 1.10 |
| a | se-tenant pair (1108, 1109) | 1.50 | 1.25 | 3.25 | 1.75 |

Qty: 7,000,000 of each

Issued to commemorate the two leaders credited with preventing war between Canada and the Blackfoot during the troubled 1870's.

## UN: INTERNATIONAL YEAR OF PEACE

1110
Symbolic dove protecting the earth

Designer: Carole Jeghers.
Lithography (5 colours) and Embossed, pane of 50
Ashton-Potter Limited

**1986, Sep 16 — Tagged, GT2, Harrison Paper — Perf 13.3**

| | | NH–VF | ⊙F | PB | FDC |
|---|---|---|---|---|---|
| **1110** | **34¢ multicoloured** | .65 | .25 | 3.25 | 1.10 |

Qty: 14,000,000

Issued to commemorate the 'International Year of Peace' proclaimed by the United Nations.

## 1988 OLYMPIC WINTER GAMES

1111 Ice Hockey — 1112 Biathlon

Designer: Pierre-Yves Pelletier.
Lithography (6 colours), pane of 50
Canadian Bank Note Company, Limited

**1986, Oct 15 — Tagged, GT2, Rolland Paper — Perf 13.4x13.1**

| | | NH–VF | ⊙F | PB | FDC |
|---|---|---|---|---|---|
| **1111** | **34¢ multicoloured** | .65 | .25 | | 1.10 |
| **1112** | **34¢ multicoloured** | .65 | .25 | | 1.10 |
| a | se-tenant pair (1111, 1112) | 1.50 | 1.20 | 3.25 | 1.75 |

Qty: 7,500,000 of each

Issued to publicize the 1988 Winter Olympics, held at Calgary, Alberta.
See also 1077, 1130–1131, 1152–1153, 1195–1198.

## CHRISTMAS – ANGELS

1113

1114

1115

1116

Designer: Theo Dimson.

Lithography (5 colours), panes of 50
Ashton-Potter Limited

| 1986, Oct 29 | Tagged, GT4, Harrison Paper | | | | Perf 12.5 |
|---|---|---|---|---|---|
| | | NH–VF | ⊙F | PB | FDC |
| **1113** | **34¢ multicoloured** | .65 | .25 | 3.25 | 1.10 |
| Qty: 35,000,000 | | | | | |
| **1114** | **39¢ multicoloured** | .85 | .75 | 4.25 | 1.20 |
| Qty: 12,500,000 | | | | | |
| **1115** | **68¢ multicoloured** | 1.50 | 1.15 | 7.50 | 1.75 |
| Qty: 12,500,000 | | | | | |
| **Nos. 1113–1115 (3) combination FDC** | | | | | **3.20** |

Booklet issue

| | Tagged, GT2 | | | | Perf 13.5 horiz |
|---|---|---|---|---|---|
| **1116** | **29¢ multicoloured**, from 1116a | 2.00 | 1.50 | — | 1.00 |
| a | booklet pane of 10 x 29¢ (1116) (BK91a) | 17.00 | 16.00 | — | — |
| **BK91** | pane 1116a in cover $18.00 | | | | |
| | | | | | **Perf 12.5 horiz** |
| **1116b** | single 29¢, from 1116c | 8.00 | 3.00 | — | 15.00 |
| c | booklet pane of 10 x 29¢ (1116b) (BK91d) | 80.00 | 70.00 | — | — |

The 29¢ value (1116) was designed specifically for use on greeting card envelopes bearing a printed postal code matrix. Issued in booklet panes of 10 only, and accepted for single usage on greeting cards until January 31, 1987. Non-philatelic usage on cover during this period: $10.00.

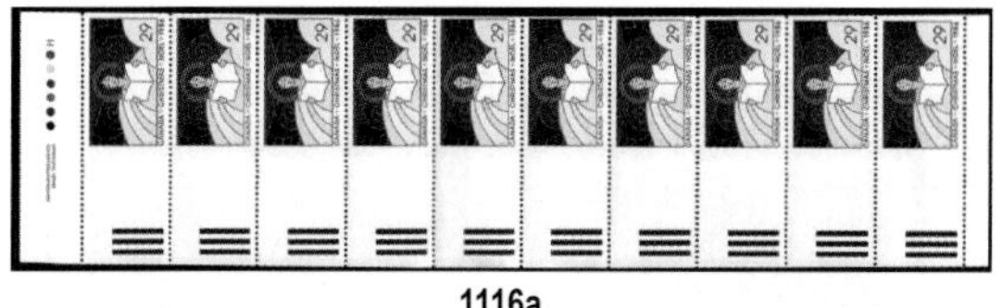
1116a

## JOHN MOLSON

1117
John Molson and his main achievements

Designer: Clermont Malenfant .

Lithography (6 colours), pane of 50
Ashton-Potter Limited

| 1986, Nov 4 | Tagged, GT2, Rolland Paper | | | | Perf 12.5 |
|---|---|---|---|---|---|
| | | NH–VF | ⊙F | PB | FDC |
| **1117** | **34¢ multicoloured**, dull | .65 | .25 | 3.25 | 1.10 |
| i | LF | 2.50 | .50 | 12.00 | |
| Qty: 14,000,000 | | | | | |

Issued on the 150th anniversary of John Molson's death (1763–1836).

## CANADIAN LOCOMOTIVES (1925–1945) – 4

1118
CN Class V-1-a 2-Do-1+1-Do-2 type

1119
CP Class T1a 2-10-4 type

1120
CN Class U-2-a 4-8-4 type

1121
CP Class H1c 4-6-4 type

Designer: Ernst Roch.

Lithography (6 colours), panes of 20
Ashton-Potter Limited

| 1986, Nov 21 | Tagged, GT2, Rolland Paper | | | Perf 12.5x13.0 | |
|---|---|---|---|---|---|
| | | NH–VF | ⊙F | PB | FDC |
| **1118** | **34¢ multicoloured**, LF/LF | 1.00 | .35 | | 1.10 |
| i | HF/LF | 3.00 | 1.00 | | |
| ii | LF/HF | 3.00 | 1.00 | | |
| **1119** | **34¢ multicoloured**, LF/LF | 1.00 | .35 | | 1.10 |
| i | HF/LF | 3.00 | 1.00 | | |
| ii | LF/HF | 3.00 | 1.00 | | |
| a | se-tenant pair, LF/LF (1118, 1119) | 2.20 | 1.50 | 5.00 | |
| ai | se-tenant pair, HF/LF (1118i, 1119i) | 7.00 | 3.50 | 15.00 | |
| aii | se-tenant pair, LF/HF (1118ii, 1119ii) | 7.00 | 3.50 | 15.00 | |
| Qty: 7,000,000 of each | | | | | |

| | | NH–VF | ⊙F | PB | FDC |
|---|---|---|---|---|---|
| **1120** | **39¢ multicoloured**, DF/MF | 1.15 | 1.00 | 5.75 | 1.20 |
| i | DF/HF | 2.50 | 1.25 | 13.00 | |
| ii | DF/LF | 3.50 | | 17.50 | |

Qty: 9,500,000

| | | NH–VF | ⊙F | PB | FDC |
|---|---|---|---|---|---|
| **1121** | **68¢ multicoloured**, MF/DF | 1.75 | 1.50 | 8.75 | 1.75 |
| i | DF/LF | 5.00 | 2.50 | 22.00 | |
| ii | DF/MF | 1.75 | 1.50 | 9.00 | |
| iii | DF/HF | 1.75 | 1.50 | 9.00 | |

Qty: 9,500,000

**Nos. 1118–1121 (4) combination FDC** 3.90

This issue comes with a variety of different fluorescent papers, both from front and back. The catalogue listings reflect the most common ones but others exist.
See also 999–1002, 1036–1039 and 1071–1074.

## 1987

### CAPEX 87

**1122**
Toronto's First Post Office

**1123**
Nelson-Miramichi Post Office

**1124**
Saint-Ours Post Office

**1125**
Battleford Post Office

Designer: John Mardon. Engraved by Gregory Prosser.
Lithography (6 colours) and Engraved (1 colour), panes of 50
British American Bank Note Company

| **1987** | **Tagged, GT4, Harrison Paper** | | | **Perf 13.0x13.3** | |
|---|---|---|---|---|---|
| | | **NH–VF** | **⊙F** | **PB** | **FDC** |
| **1122** | **34¢ multicoloured**, *Feb 16, 1987* | .65 | .25 | 3.25 | 1.10 |
| i | "twig in eavestrough" | 5.00 | 2.50 | | |

Qty: 15,000,000

| | | NH–VF | ⊙F | PB | FDC |
|---|---|---|---|---|---|
| **1123** | **36¢ multicoloured**, *Jun 12, 1987* | .75 | .30 | 3.75 | 1.10 |
| i | double tagging* | 20.00 | 5.00 | 120.00 | |

Qty: 15,000,000

| | | NH–VF | ⊙F | PB | FDC |
|---|---|---|---|---|---|
| **1124** | **42¢ multicoloured**, *Jun 12, 1987* | 1.00 | .85 | 8.00 | 1.25 |
| i | broken sidewalk (pos. 50) | 10.00 | 3.50 | 15.00 | |

Qty: 10,000,000

| | | NH–VF | ⊙F | PB | FDC |
|---|---|---|---|---|---|
| **1125** | **72¢ multicoloured**, *Jun 12, 1987* | 1.75 | 1.40 | 8.75 | 1.85 |
| T1 | untagged (error) | 100.00 | | | |

Qty: 10,000,000

**Nos. 1123–1125** (3) combination FDC 3.40

* A portion of the printing was produced with tagging on all sides (GT4), plus additional vertical tag bars (GT2).

Note: Numbers 1123, 1124 and 1125 have been reported imperforate (1 pane of each). None have come onto the market as yet so values unknown.

**1122i**

**1125Ab**
Toronto's First Post Office

**1125Ac**
Nelson-Miramichi Post Office

**1125Ad**
Saint-Ours Post Office

**1125Ae**
Battleford Post Office

| | | NH–VF | ⊙F | FDC |
|---|---|---|---|---|
| **1125A** | **$1.86 Souvenir sheet** of 4, *Jun 12, 1987* | 4.50 | 4.50 | 4.10 |
| b | 36¢ Toronto P.O. | .75 | .75 | |
| c | 36¢ Nelson-Miramichi P.O. | .75 | .75 | |
| d | 42¢ Saint-Ours P.O. | .90 | .90 | |
| e | 72¢ Battleford P.O. | 1.50 | 1.50 | |
| i | black and green inscriptions doubled | 75.00 | 40.00 | |

Qty: 1,100,000 of each

The stamps from No. 1125A differ from regular sheet stamps as all have a yellow-green inscription. No. 1125Ab issued only in souvenir sheet.

**1125A**

### EXPLORATION OF CANADA – 2
**Investigators**

**1126**
Brûlé nears Lake Superior

**1127**
Radisson and Des Groseilliers

**1128**
Father Marquette with Jolliet

**1129**
Missions in the wilderness

Designer: Frederick Hagan. Typographed by J.F. Britton.

Lithography (5 colours), pane of 50
Ashton-Potter Limited

| 1987, Mar 13 | Tagged, GT2, Rolland Paper | | | Perf 12.5x13.0 | |
|---|---|---|---|---|---|
| | | NH–VF | ⊙F | PB | FDC |
| 1126 | **34¢ multicoloured**, D/MF | .75 | .40 | | 1.10 |
| i | MF/D | 2.00 | .50 | | |
| 1127 | **34¢ multicoloured**, D/MF | .75 | .40 | | 1.10 |
| i | MF/D | 2.00 | .50 | | |
| 1128 | **34¢ multicoloured**, D/MF | .75 | .40 | | 1.10 |
| i | MF/D | 2.00 | .50 | | |
| 1129 | **34¢ multicoloured**, D/MF | .75 | .40 | | 1.10 |
| i | MF/D | 2.00 | .50 | | |
| a | se-tenant block of 4, D/MF (1126–1129) | 3.40 | 3.25 | 3.75 | 3.10 |
| ai | se-tenant block of 4, MF/D (1126i–1129i) | 10.00 | 7.00 | 12.00 | |

Qty: 1126/1128: 4,290,000 of each; 1127/1129: 3,960,000 of each

**Nos. 1126–1129 (4) combination FDC** **3.10**

Issued to commemorate explorers of New France.
See also 1104–1107, 1199–1202 and 1233–1236.

| **Rates:** Apr 1, 1987– Dec 31, 1987 | Domestic: 36¢ (0–30g), 55¢ (30–50g)<br>Non-standard: 42¢ (0–30g)<br>USA: 42¢ (0–30g), 60¢ (30–50g)<br>International: 72¢ (0–20g), $1.12 (20–50g)<br>Registration: $2.63<br>Special delivery: $1.96 |
|---|---|

*single usage:* USA 42¢: $20.00 | International 72¢: $30.00

## 1988 OLYMPIC WINTER GAMES

1130
Speed Skating

1131
Bobsleigh

Designer: Pierre-Yves Pelletier.

Lithography (5 colours), pane of 50
Canadian Bank Note Company, Limited

| 1987, Apr 3 | Tagged, GT2, Rolland Paper | | | Perf 13.4x13.1 | |
|---|---|---|---|---|---|
| | | NH–VF | ⊙F | PB | FDC |
| 1130 | **36¢ multicoloured**, dull/dull | .75 | .25 | 3.75 | 1.10 |
| i | F/F | 2.50 | 1.00 | 12.50 | |
| ii | F/dull | 2.50 | 1.00 | 12.50 | |
| iii | dull/HB | 10.00 | 5.00 | 45.00 | |

Qty: 15,000,000

| | | NH–VF | ⊙F | PB | FDC |
|---|---|---|---|---|---|
| 1131 | **42¢ multicoloured**, dull/F | 1.00 | .90 | 5.00 | 1.25 |
| i | dull/MF | 4.00 | 1.50 | 18.00 | |
| ii | dull/HB | 20.00 | 10.00 | 90.00 | |

Qty: 10,000,000

**Nos. 1130, 1131 (2) combination FDC** **2.00**

Issued to publicize the 1988 Winter Olympics to be held at Calgary, Alberta.
See also 1077, 1111–1112, 1152–1153, 1195–1198.

## VOLUNTEERS WEEK

1132
Canadian Volunteers

Designer: Will Davies.

Lithography (5 colours), pane of 25
Ashton-Potter Limited

| 1987, Apr 13 | Tagged, GT2, Rolland Paper | | | Perf 12.5x13.0 | |
|---|---|---|---|---|---|
| | | NH–VF | ⊙F | PB | FDC |
| 1132 | **36¢ multicoloured**, DF | .75 | .25 | 3.75 | 1.10 |
| i | LF | 2.50 | | 12.00 | |

Qty: 15,000,000

## CANADIAN CHARTER OF RIGHTS AND FREEDOMS

1133
Canadian Coat-of-Arms

Designer: Ralph Tibbles.

Lithography (5 colours), pane of 25
Ashton-Potter Limited

| 1987, Apr 15 | Tagged, GT4, Rolland Paper | | | Perf 14.0x13.4 | |
|---|---|---|---|---|---|
| | | NH–VF | ⊙F | PB | FDC |
| 1133 | **36¢ multicoloured**, LF | .75 | .25 | 3.75 | 1.10 |
| i | MF | 2.50 | | 12.00 | |
| a | imperf. pair | *2,000.00* | | *4,500.00** | |

Qty: 15,000,000
* Blank corner block of 4.

Issued on the 5th anniversary of the Charter of Rights and Freedoms to mark Law Day.

## ENGINEERING INSTITUTE CENTENARY

1134
Engineering Symbols

Designer: Les Holloway, Nita Wallace, and Richard Kerr.

Lithography (8 colours), pane of 25
Ashton-Potter Limited

| 1987, May 19 | Tagged, GT2, Rolland Paper | | | Perf 12.5x13.0 | |
|---|---|---|---|---|---|
| | | NH–VF | ⊙F | PB | FDC |
| 1134 | **36¢ multicoloured**, LF | .75 | .25 | 3.75 | 1.10 |
| i | DF | 2.50 | | 12.00 | |

Qty: 15,000,000

Issued on the occasion of the 100th anniversary of the Engineering Institute of Canada.

## CANADA DAY
## SCIENCE AND TECHNOLOGY – 2

1135 R.A. Fessenden, AM radio (1900) — 1136 C. Fenerty, newsprint pulp (1838)

1137 G.E. Desbarats, W. Leggo, half-tone engraving (1869) — 1138 F.N. Gisborne, undersea cable (1852)

Designer: Roger Hill.

Lithography (6 colours), pane of 16
Canadian Bank Note Company, Limited

**1987, Jun 25** — **Tagged, GT2, Rolland Paper** — **Perf 13.3**

| | | NH–VF | ⊙F | PB | FDC |
|---|---|---|---|---|---|
| **1135** | **36¢ multicoloured**, LF | .80 | .40 | | 1.10 |
| i | DF | 2.50 | .75 | | |
| ii | NF | 10.00 | 1.50 | | |
| **1136** | **36¢ multicoloured**, LF | .80 | .40 | | 1.10 |
| i | DF | 2.50 | .75 | | |
| ii | NF | 10.00 | 1.50 | | |
| **1137** | **36¢ multicoloured**, LF | .80 | .40 | | 1.10 |
| i | DF | 2.50 | .75 | | |
| ii | NF | 10.00 | 1.50 | | |
| **1138** | **36¢ multicoloured**, LF | .80 | .40 | | 1.10 |
| i | DF | 2.50 | .75 | | |
| ii | NF | 10.00 | 1.50 | | |
| a | se-tenant block of 4, LF (1135–1138) | 3.60 | 3.25 | 4.00 | 3.30 |
| ai | se-tenant block of 4, DF (1135i–1138i) | 10.00 | | 15.00 | |
| aii | se-tenant block of 4, NF (1135ii–1138ii) | 40.00 | | 50.00 | |

Qty: 5,595,000 of each

See also 1099–1102 and 1206–1209.

## CANADIAN STEAMSHIPS

1139 *Segwun*, 1887 — 1140 *Princess Marguerite*, 1948

Designer: Douglas Champion.

Lithography (5 colours), pane of 25
Canadian Bank Note Company, Limited

**1987, Jul 20** — **Tagged, GT2, Rolland Paper** — **Perf 13.0**

| | | NH–VF | ⊙F | PB | FDC |
|---|---|---|---|---|---|
| **1139** | **36¢ multicoloured** | .75 | .40 | | 1.10 |
| | | | | **Perf 13.3x13.0** | |
| **1140** | **36¢ multicoloured** | .75 | .40 | | 1.10 |
| a | se-tenant pair (1139, 1140) | 1.70 | 1.40 | 3.75 | 1.85 |

Qty: 7,575,000 of each

## SHIPWRECKS

1141 *Hamilton Scourge*, Lake Ontario 1813 — 1142 *San Juan*, Red Bay 1565

1143 *Breadalbane*, Barrow Strait 1853 — 1144 *Ericsson*, Barkley Sound 1892

Designer: Louis-André Rivard.

Lithography (5 colours), pane of 50
Ashton-Potter Limited

**1987, Aug 7** — **Tagged, GT2, Rolland Paper** — **Perf 13.5x13.1**

| | | NH–VF | ⊙F | PB | FDC |
|---|---|---|---|---|---|
| **1141** | **36¢ multicoloured** | .75 | .40 | | 1.10 |
| **1142** | **36¢ multicoloured** | .75 | .40 | | 1.10 |
| **1143** | **36¢ multicoloured** | .75 | .40 | | 1.10 |
| **1144** | **36¢ multicoloured** | .75 | .40 | | 1.10 |
| a | se-tenant block of 4 (1141–1144) | 3.40 | 3.25 | 3.75 | 3.30 |

Qty: 4,050,000 of each

1145
Jet over Globe

1146
Quebec Summit Symbol

## AIR CANADA

Designer: Debbie Adams and Derrick Carter.

Lithography (5 colours), pane of 50
Canadian Bank Note Company, Limited

**1987, Sep 1** — **Tagged, GT2, Rolland Paper** — **Perf 13.3**

| | | NH–VF | ⊙F | PB | FDC |
|---|---|---|---|---|---|
| **1145** | **36¢ multicoloured** | .75 | .25 | 3.75 | 1.10 |

Qty: 15,000,000

Issued to commemorate the 50th anniversary of Air Canada.

## QUEBEC SUMMIT

Designer: Claude Gaudreau.

Lithography (5 colours), pane of 50
Ashton-Potter Limited

**1987, Sep 2** — **Tagged, GT4, Rolland Paper** — **Perf 13.1x12.5**

| | | NH–VF | ⊙F | PB | FDC |
|---|---|---|---|---|---|
| **1146** | **36¢ multicoloured** | .75 | .25 | 3.75 | 1.10 |

Qty: 15,000,000

Issued on the occasion of the 2nd International Francophone Summit, Quebec City, Sept. 1–4.

## COMMONWEALTH MEETING

1147
Commonwealth Emblem

Designer: Kosta (Gus) Tsetsekas.

Lithography (5 colours), pane of 50
Ashton-Potter Limited

**1987, Oct 13** **Tagged, GT4, Rolland Paper** **Perf 13.1x12.5**

| | | NH–VF | ⊙F | PB | FDC |
|---|---|---|---|---|---|
| **1147** | **36¢ multicoloured**, dull/dull | .75 | .25 | 3.75 | 1.10 |
| i | F/MF | 2.00 | .75 | 10.00 | |

Qty: 15,000,000

Issued to mark the 9th Commonwealth Heads of Government Meeting, Vancouver, Oct. 13-17.

## CHRISTMAS

1148
Poinsettia

1149
Holly Wreath

1150
Mistletoe, tree

1151
Gifts under Tree

Designer: Claude A. Simard.

Lithography (5 colours), panes of 50
Ashton-Potter Limited

**1987, Nov 2** **Tagged, GT4, Slater Paper** **Perf 13.3**

| | | NH–VF | ⊙F | PB | FDC |
|---|---|---|---|---|---|
| **1148** | **36¢ multicoloured** | .75 | .25 | 3.75 | 1.10 |
| Qty: 45,000,000 | | | | | |
| **1149** | **42¢ multicoloured** | 1.00 | .90 | 5.00 | 1.25 |
| Qty: 16,000,000 | | | | | |
| **1150** | **72¢ multicoloured** | 1.65 | 1.25 | 8.25 | 1.85 |
| Qty: 12,000,000 | | | | | |

**Nos. 1148–1150 (3) combination FDC** **3.40**

Greetmore Booklet issue, pane of 10

**Tagged, GTX** **Perf 12.5x13.1**

| | | NH–VF | ⊙F | FDC |
|---|---|---|---|---|
| **1151** | **31¢ multicoloured** | 1.00 | 1.00 | 1.00 |
| a | booklet pane of 10 x 31¢ (1151) (2 x 5) (BK95) | 7.50 | 12.50 | — |
| b | horiz. pair, imperf. between, from miscut booklet pane (5 known) | *3,500.00* | | |
| BK95 | pane 1151a in bilingual cover $8.00 | | | |

Qty: 123,700,000

No. 1151 was issued in booklets only, for use on greeting card envelopes bearing a printed postal code matrix. Accepted singly until January 31, 1988 if affixed to designated envelopes.

1151a

1151b

## 1988 OLYMPIC WINTER GAMES

1152 Cross-country Skiing
1153 Ski Jumping

Designer: Pierre-Yves Pelletier.

Lithography (6 colours), pane of 50
Canadian Bank Note Company, Limited

**1987, Nov 13** **Tagged, GT4, Harrison Paper** **Perf 13.4x13.1**

| | | NH–VF | ⊙F | PB | FDC |
|---|---|---|---|---|---|
| **1152** | **36¢ multicoloured** | .75 | .35 | | 1.10 |
| **1153** | **36¢ multicoloured** | .75 | .35 | | 1.10 |
| a | se-tenant pair (1152, 1153) | 1.70 | 1.25 | 3.75 | 1.85 |

Qty: 7,500,000 of each

Issued to publicize the 1988 Winter Olympics, Calgary, Alberta.
See also 1077, 1111–1112, 1130–1131, 1195–1198.

## GREY CUP

1154
Football and Grey Cup

Designer: Les Holloway.

Lithography (5 colours), pane of 50
Ashton-Potter Limited

**1987, Nov 20** **Tagged, GT4, Slater Paper** **Perf 12.5**

| | | NH–VF | ⊙F | PB | FDC |
|---|---|---|---|---|---|
| **1154** | **36¢ multicoloured** | .75 | .25 | 3.75 | 1.10 |

Qty: 15,000,000

Issued to mark the 75th playing of the Grey Cup football game, Nov. 29 in Vancouver.

**MINT PRICING PREMIUMS**

Mint stamps from 301 to date are valued as NH-VF (Never Hinged-Very Fine). All hinged VF and NH-F copies are worth 50% of the listed values. Plate block (PB) values are for mint NH–VF plate or inscription blocks of four.

**USED, VF/XF (with in-period, circular date cancel) PRICING PREMIUM**

Single stamps with light or circular date cancels will sell for more than catalogue value (perhaps even more than a mint copy). From *1981 to 1991* single stamps from se-tenant blocks of 4 or larger will be priced at 50% or more above the fine price. From *1992* to date single stamps from se-tenant blocks of 4 or larger plus se-tenant booklet panes and souvenir sheets will be priced at 100% or more above the fine price. From *1997* to date all other stamps will be priced at 50% or more above the fine price.

## MAMMAL DEFINITIVES 1988–1992 Low Values

1155 Flying Squirrel

1156 Porcupine

1157 Muskrat

1158 Varying Hare — 1159 Red Fox — 1160 Skunk — 1161 Beaver

Designer: Gottschalk + Ash International.

Lithography (5 colours), panes of 100
Ashton-Potter Limited

**1988, Oct 3 — Untagged, Slater Paper — Perf 13.1x13.6**

| | | NH–VF | ⊙F | PB | FDC |
|---|---|---|---|---|---|
| **1155** | **1¢ multicoloured** | .25 | .20 | 1.25 | — |
| i | imperf. top pair in block of 4† | 1,500.00 | | 1,750.00 | |
| ii | Coated Papers, *Oct 25, 1991* | .25 | .20 | 1.25 | |
| b | CPP, imperf. pair | 1,000.00 | | 2,250.00 | |
| a | perf 13.1 x 12.8, SP, *Oct 1991* | 5.00 | 1.20 | 50.00* | — |

* Blank corner block of 4.

† 4 blocks and 2 vertical pairs ($750) reported from one pane.

| | | NH–VF | ⊙F | PB | FDC |
|---|---|---|---|---|---|
| **1156** | **2¢ multicoloured** | .25 | .20 | 1.25 | — |
| i | Coated Papers, *Oct 25, 1991* | .25 | .20 | 1.25 | — |
| a | CPP, imperf. pair | 1,000.00 | | 2,250.00 | |
| **1157** | **3¢ multicoloured** | .25 | .20 | 1.25 | — |
| a | imperf. pair | 1,200.00 | | 2,750.00 | |
| **1158** | **5¢ multicoloured** | .25 | .20 | 1.25 | — |
| a | imperf. pair | 2,000.00 | — | 4,500.00 | — |
| **1159** | **6¢ multicoloured** | .25 | .20 | 1.25 | — |
| a | horizontal imperf. pair | 3,000.00† | | | |

† Block of 4 with top pair imperf., from a sheet with only the top row of stamps imperforate. Vertical pair with top stamp imperf. $1,350. Three blocks and 3 sound pairs were found in Manitoba. Seven vertical pairs and three damaged pairs are known from a sheet found in British Columbia.

| | | NH–VF | ⊙F | PB | FDC |
|---|---|---|---|---|---|
| **1160** | **10¢ multicoloured**, GT4 | .25 | .20 | 1.25 | — |
| ii | Coated Papers, untagged, *Oct 25,1991* | .60 | .20 | 2.50 | — |
| b | imperf. pair | 1,000.00 | | 4,500.00 | |
| a | perf 13.1 x 12.8, SP, GT4, *Feb 1991* | 7.50 | .50 | 75.00* | — |
| iii | odourless Skunk variety (very faint shading above skunk) | 25.00 | 2.50 | 150.00* | |

* Blank corner block of 4.

| | | NH–VF | ⊙F | PB | FDC |
|---|---|---|---|---|---|
| **1161** | **25¢ multicoloured**, GT4 | .50 | .20 | 2.50 | — |
| ii | Coated Papers, untagged, *Apr 22, 1992* | 1.50 | .75 | 7.50 | — |

**Nos. 1155–1161 (7) combination FDC** — **1.45**

1155i

## DOMESTIC FIRST-CLASS RATE

1162
Queen Elizabeth II

Designer: Yousuf Karsh, Tom Yakobina, Chris Candlish.

Lithography (5 colours), pane of 100
B A Bank Note Inc.

**1987, Dec 30 — GT4, Harrison Paper — Perf 13.3x13.0**

| | | NH–VF | ⊙F | PB | FDC |
|---|---|---|---|---|---|
| **1162** | **37¢ multicoloured (blue)** | 1.00 | .20 | 5.00 | 1.15 |
| **T1** | untagged (error) | | 75.00 | | |

This was the first time that the first-class letter rate Queen Elizabeth II design did *not* appear in booklet form.

**Paper Manufacturers (water-activated gum)**

| Initials | Company | Gum colour (mint stamp) | Paper appearance (used) | First seen |
|---|---|---|---|---|
| APP | Abitibi Price | clear | | |
| HP | Harrison | blue-green tinge; paper curls | back of stamp has horizontal "lines" when viewed against a darker background | Aug 1983 |
| CLP | Clark | clear | | Dec 1983 |
| RP | Rolland | white; slight paper curl | | Aug 1985 |
| PP | Peterborough Paper Converters | greyish; very shiny | very smooth, white, crispy | Feb 1988 |
| SP | Slater | light cream colour | looks like a mixture of "pulp" and has a darker tone (beige); slightly darker than CPP | Feb 1988 |
| CPP | Coated Papers Ltd | slight blue-green tinge | textured or "indented" appearance | Dec 1990 |
| TRC | Tullis Russel Coatings | same paper as CPP; name changed | | Jan 1998 |
| SR | Spicer | | | Dec 2007 |

Definitive Series Historical Notes:

- the size of the low-value and first-class letter rate stamps were made slightly larger than previous definitive series
- first definitive series to issue booklets which did not contain any first-class letter rate stamps for domestic use only
- first time a definitive stamp's colour was printed over the entire stamp, including the perforations

1163
Houses of Parliament

Designer: Rolf Harder.

Lithography (4 colours), pane of 100
Canadian Bank Note

**1987, Dec 30** **GT4, Harrison Paper** **Perf 13.3x13.0**

| | | NH–VF | ⊙F | PB | FDC |
|---|---|---|---|---|---|
| **1163** | **37¢ multicoloured** | 1.00 | .20 | 5.00 | 1.15 |

**1988, Jan 5** **Ashton-Potter Limited** **Perf 13.3x14.0**

Harrison Paper

| | | NH–VF | ⊙F | PB | FDC |
|---|---|---|---|---|---|
| 1163a | booklet pane of 10 x 37¢ (1163cs), with perforated selvedge at bottom (BK97) | 10.00 | 10.00 | — | — |
| ai | as "a", without selvedge at bottom | 20.00 | 10.00 | — | — |
| bi | booklet pane of 25 x 37¢ (1163c and 1163cs), without selvedge at bottom (BK98c) | 35.00 | 25.00 | — | — |
| c | 37¢ single, from 1163bi, perf all around | 1.75 | .60 | | |
| cs | single with straight edge, from 1163a, 1163ai or 1163bi | 1.00 | .30 | — | — |
| BK97 | pane 1163a in cover $11.00 | | | | |
| BK98c | pane 1163bi (HP) in cover $40.00 | | | | |

Rolland Paper

| | | NH–VF | ⊙F | PB | FDC |
|---|---|---|---|---|---|
| 1163b | booklet pane of 25 x 37¢ (1163bs and 1163bsi), with perforated selvedge at bottom (BK98a/b) | 25.00 | 20.00 | — | — |
| bs | 37¢ single, from 1163b, perf all around | 2.50 | 1.25 | | |
| bsi | single with straight edge, from 1163b | 1.00 | .30 | — | — |
| BK98 | pane 1163b in cover $27.50 | | | | |

Qty: 1163 (516,500,000), BK97 (11,924,500), BK98 (3,975,600)

1164
Queen Elizabeth II

Designer: Yousuf Karsh, Tom Yakobina, Chris Candlish.

Lithography (5 colours), pane of 100
British American Bank Note

**1988, Dec 29** **GT4, Harrison Paper** **Perf 13.1x12.8**

| | | NH–VF | ⊙F | PB | FDC |
|---|---|---|---|---|---|
| **1164** | **38¢ multicoloured (red)** | 1.00 | .20 | 5.00 | 1.15 |
| c | vert. block of 10, middle pair imperf, 2nd and 4th pairs part perf | *1,500.00* | | *1,750.00** | |
| | part imperf. pair from 1164c | *500.00* | | | |
| | vertical strip of 5 from 1164c | *750.00* | | | |
| e | bottom margin horiz. pair, imperf | | | | |

**Ashton-Potter, Slater Paper** **Perf 13.1x13.6**

| | | NH–VF | ⊙F | PB | FDC |
|---|---|---|---|---|---|
| 1164a | 38¢ single, from 1164b | 2.00 | 2.00 | — | — |
| as | single with straight edge, from 1164b | 1.00 | .40 | — | — |
| aiii | horiz. pair with full perforations (no straight edge) | 150.00 | 100.00 | | |
| d | horiz. pair, imperf. between | 1,250.00 | | | |
| di | 38¢ (1164a) + label, imperf. between | 1,750.00 | | | |
| b | booklet pane of 10 x 38¢ (1164a and 1164as) + 2 labels, (BK102) | 10.00 | 9.00 | — | — |
| BK102 | pane 1164b in cover $10.00 | | | | |

* Blank corner block of 4.

Variety 1164c: 40 blocks of 10 (2 x 5) are known with middle pair imperforate and 2nd and 4th pairs part imperforate. From sheets with no horizontal perf. above rows 8 and 9, and these same rows imperf. vertically. Varieties 1164d and 1164aii are from a miscut booklet (value $5,750). Variety 1164aiii is from a pane (1164b) which was perforated on a vertical edge instead of being guillotined.

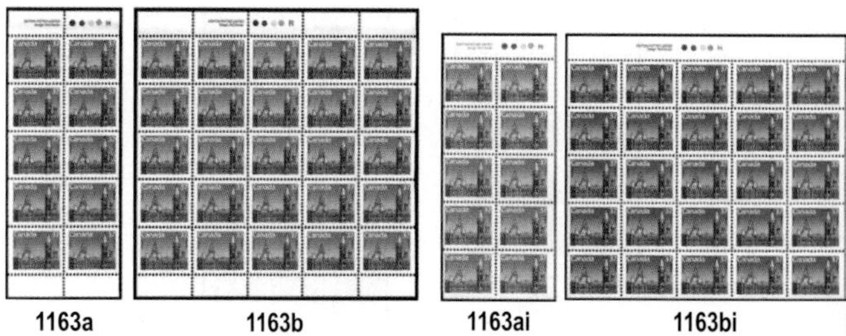

1163a 1163b 1163ai 1163bi

1164b

1164c

1164e

1164b miscut
(source of 1164aii and 1164d)

1165
Houses of Parliament

Designer: Rolf Harder.

Lithography (4 colours), pane of 100
Canadian Bank Note

**1988, Dec 29** **GT4, Slater Paper** **Perf 13.1x13.6**

| | | NH–VF | ⊙F | PB | FDC |
|---|---|---|---|---|---|
| **1165** | **38¢ multicoloured** | 1.00 | .20 | 5.00 | 1.15 |
| c | printed on gum side † | 125.00 | — | 625.00* | — |
| d | double impression of all litho colours except black, SP‡ | 300.00 | | 1,500.00 | |
| v | imperf. top margin and top portion of stamp | 1,250.00 | | 1,500.00* | |
| ii | Peterborough paper, *Nov 6, 1989* | 1.25 | .20 | 6.25 | — |
| iv | double impression of all litho colours except black, PP‡ | 300.00 | | 1,500.00 | |

**Ashton-Potter**

| | | NH–VF | ⊙F | PB | FDC |
|---|---|---|---|---|---|
| a | booklet pane of 10 x 38¢ (1165 and 1165as) + 2 labels (BK101) | 8.00 | 8.00 | | |
| as | single 38¢ with straight edge, from 1165a or 1165b | 1.25 | .50 | — | — |
| b | booklet pane of 25 x 38¢ (1165 and 1165as) + 2 labels (BK103) | 25.00 | 25.00 | — | — |
| BK101 | pane 1165a in cover $9.00 | | | | |
| BK103 | pane 1165b in cover $26.00 | | | | |

Qty: 1165 (538,000,000), BK101 (8,943,657), BK102 (4,356,160)

* Price is for blank (non-inscription) corner block of 4.
† Two variations of the "printed on gum side" error exist. The more common of the two shows poor registration with blurred printing. There also exists at least one sheet of 100 with clear, sharp printing as on properly printed stamps.
‡ Slater paper (SP) has cream-coloured gum, Peterborough paper (PP) has bluish gum.

1165a

1165v

1165b

1166
Flag over Clouds

Designer: Gottschalk + Ash International.
Lithography (5 colours), pane of 100
Canadian Bank Note

| 1989, Dec 28 | GT4, Peterborough Paper | NH–VF | ⊙F | PB | FDC |
|---|---|---|---|---|---|
| | | | | Perf 13.6x13.1 | |
| **1166** | **39¢ multicoloured**, LF | 1.00 | .20 | 5.00 | 1.30 |
| ii | DF | 10.00 | .50 | 50.00 | |
| iii | MF | 10.00 | .50 | 50.00 | |
| i | Ashton-Potter, *Feb 14, 1990* | 1.50 | .20 | 7.50 | |
| d | imperf pair | 700.00 | | 3,000.00 | |
| T1 | untagged (error) | 90.00 | 50.00 | | |
| c | AP, perf. 12.8 x 13.1, *Dec 1990* | 25.00 | 1.00 | 150.00* | — |

**Ashton-Potter, Slater Paper** **Perf 13.6x13.1**

| | | | | | |
|---|---|---|---|---|---|
| 1166a | booklet pane of 10 x 39¢ (1166as and 1166asi) + 2 labels (BK112) | 10.00 | 9.00 | — | — |
| as | single 39¢ (perforated all around), from 1166a or 1166b | 1.50 | .25 | — | — |
| asi | single 39¢ with straight edge, from 1166a or 1166b | 1.00 | .20 | — | — |
| b | booklet pane of 25 x 39¢ (1166as and 1166asi) + 2 labels (BK115) | 30.00 | 25.00 | — | — |
| BK112 | pane 1166a in cover $11.00 | | | | |
| BK115 | pane 1166b in cover $32.00 | | | | |

* Blank corner block of 4.
CBN printings have a darker blue sky; AP printings have a lighter blue sky, sometimes a violet shade.

1166a

1166b

1167
Queen Elizabeth II

Designer: Yousuf Karsh, Tom Yakobina, Chris Candlish.
Lithography (5 colours), pane of 100
British American Bank Note

| 1990, Jan 12 | GT4, Harrison Paper | NH–VF | ⊙F | PB | FDC |
|---|---|---|---|---|---|
| | | | | Perf 13.1x13.6 | |
| **1167** | **39¢ multicoloured (green)** | 1.00 | .20 | 5.00 | 1.30 |
| b | BABN, perf. 13.1 x 12.8, *Feb 1990* | 20.00 | 1.00 | 125.00* | — |

* Blank corner block of 4. Value for No. 1167b inscription block $1,000.00.

**Ashton-Potter, Slater Paper**

| | | | | | |
|---|---|---|---|---|---|
| 1167a | booklet pane of 10 x 39¢ (1167as and 1167asi) + 2 labels (BK113) | 9.00 | 8.00 | — | — |
| as | 39¢ single (perforated all around), from 1167a | 1.50 | .25 | — | — |
| asi | single with straight edge, from 1167a | 1.00 | .25 | | |
| c | imperf. pair | 700.00 | | | |
| d | horiz. pair, imperf. between | 500.00 | | | |
| di | 39¢ (1167a) + label, imperf. between | 600.00 | | | |
| BK113 | pane 1167a in cover $11.00 | | | | |

1167c

1167d

1167di

1168
Queen Elizabeth II

Designer: Yousuf Karsh, Tom Yakobina, Chris Candlish.
Lithography (5 colours), pane of 100
Ashton-Potter

| 1990, Dec 28 | GT4, Peterborough Paper | NH–VF | ⊙F | PB | FDC |
|---|---|---|---|---|---|
| | | | | Perf 13.1x13.6 | |
| **1168** | **40¢ multicoloured (brown)** | 1.00 | .20 | 5.00 | 1.30 |
| i | Harrison paper, *May 24, 1991* | 1.50 | | 7.50 | |
| a | booklet pane of 10 x 40¢, CPP (1168as and 1168asi) + 2 labels (BK126) | 10.00 | 9.00 | — | — |
| as | 40¢ single, CPP, from 1168a | 1.50 | 1.25 | — | — |
| asi | single with straight edge, from 1168a | 1.00 | .60 | — | — |
| BK126 | pane 1168a in cover $12.00 | | | | |

1167a

1168a

1169
Flag over Mountains

Designer: Gottschalk + Ash International.

Lithography (5 colours), pane of 100
Canadian Bank Note

| 1990, Dec 28 | GT4, Coated Paper | | | Perf 13.6x13.1 | |
|---|---|---|---|---|---|
| | | NH–VF | ⊙F | PB | FDC |
| **1169** | **40¢ multicoloured** | 1.00 | .20 | 5.00 | 1.30 |
| i | double print* | — | 1,350.00 | | |
| T1 | untagged (error) | 50.00 | 20.00 | | |
| | **Ashton-Potter Limited** | | | | |
| 1169a | booklet pane of 25 x 40¢ (1169 and 1169as) + 2 labels (BK125), AP | 35.00 | 25.00 | — | — |
| as | single 40¢ with straight edge, from 1169a, 1169b † | 1.25 | .25 | — | — |
| b | booklet pane of 10 x 40¢ (1169 and 1169as) + 2 labels (BK124) | 10.00 | 9.00 | — | — |
| BK124 | pane 1169b in cover $11.00 | | | | |
| BK125 | pane 1169a in cover $36.00 | | | | |

* One reported unused and creased.
† Single stamps perforated all around from 1169a or 1169b (AP) have a vertical 'texture'; those from 1169 (CBN) have a horizontal 'texture'.

1169a

1169b

## MAMMAL DEFINITIVES
## 1988–1990
## Medium Values

### USA RATE

Beginning with the medium value definitives 1172A , 1176 and 1180 issued on December 28, 1990, Canada Post offers only combination FDCs for groups of stamps considered as a single issue.

1170
Lynx

1171
Atlantic Walrus

1172
Pronghorn

1172A
Wolverine

Designer: Brian Tsang

Lithography (5 colours), panes of 50
Ashton-Potter Limited

| 1988, Jan 18 | GT4, Harrison Paper | | | Perf 12.0x12.5 | |
|---|---|---|---|---|---|
| | | NH–VF | ⊙F | PB | FDC |
| **1170** | **43¢ multicoloured** | 1.50 | .50 | 7.50 | 1.25 |

| 1989, Jan 18 | GT4, Harrison Paper | | | Perf 14.4x13.8 | |
|---|---|---|---|---|---|
| **1171** | **44¢ multicoloured** | 2.00 | .25 | 10.00 | 1.30 |
| i | Slater paper, *Jun 9, 1989* | 4.50 | — | 20.00 | — |
| c | SP, perf 13.8 x 13.1†, *Nov 1989* | 600.00 | 60.00 | 2,750.00* | —‡ |
| | **44¢ Booklet issues** | | | **Perf 12.5x13.1** | |
| 1171a | SP single, from 1171b | 3.50 | 2.00 | — | — |
| b | booklet pane of 5 x 44¢ (1171a) + label (BK104) | 16.00 | 15.00 | — | — |
| BK104 | pane 1171b in cover $17.00 | | | | |

† Only about 1000-1100 mint copies reported to date.
‡ Commercial use on cover: $70.00.

| 1990, Jan 12 | GT4, Slater Paper | | | Perf 14.4x13.8 | |
|---|---|---|---|---|---|
| **1172** | **45¢ multicoloured** | 1.25 | .35 | 6.25 | 1.40 |
| d | perf 13.1, *Jun 1990* | 27.50 | 1.50 | 150.00* | —‡ |
| h | imperf. pair | 1,200.00 | | 3,000.00* | — |
| | **45¢ Booklet issues** | | | **Perf 12.5x13.1** | |
| 1172b | booklet pane of 5 x 45¢ (1172f) + label (BK116) | 15.00 | 13.50 | — | — |
| f | single, from 1172b | 3.50 | .65 | — | — |
| BK116 | pane 1172b in cover $16.00 | | | | |

Qty: 1171b (3,273,052)
* Blank corner block of 4.
‡ Commercial use on cover: $5.00.

| 1990, Dec 28 | GT4, Peterborough Paper | | | Perf 13.1 | |
|---|---|---|---|---|---|
| **1172A** | **46¢ multicoloured** | 1.25 | .35 | 6.25 | — |
| g | perf 14.4x13.8 | 7.00 | .50 | 35.00 | — |
| | **46¢ Booklet issues** | | | **Perf 12.5x13.1** | |
| 1172c | CPP single, from 1172e | 1.75 | .65 | — | — |
| e | booklet pane of 5 x 46¢ (1172c) + label (BK128) | 8.00 | 7.00 | — | — |
| BK128 | pane 1172e in cover $9.00 | | | | |

1171b 1172b 1172Ae

### OVERWEIGHT DOMESTIC RATE

1173
Killer Whale

1174
Musk Ox

1175
Timber wolf

1176
Harbour Porpoise

Designer: Brian Tsang

Lithography (5 colours), panes of 50
Ashton-Potter Limited

| **1988, Jan 18** | **GT4, Rolland Paper** | | | **Perf 12.0x12.5** | |
|---|---|---|---|---|---|
| | | NH–VF | ⊙F | PB | FDC |
| **1173** | **57¢ multicoloured**, LF | 1.50 | .45 | 7.50 | 1.50 |
| ii | as 1173, F | 7.50 | | 35.00 | — |
| i | Harrison paper, *Sep 26, 1988* | 5.00 | .45 | 25.00 | — |

| **1989, Jan 18** | **GT4, Harrison Paper** | | | **Perf 14.4x13.8** | |
|---|---|---|---|---|---|
| **1174** | **59¢ multicoloured** | 1.75 | .45 | 7.50 | 1.60 |
| i | Slater paper, *Fall 1989* | 15.00 | 2.00 | 250.00* | — |
| a | SP, perf 13.1, *Nov 1, 1989* | 15.00 | 9.00 | 65.00 | —‡ |

* No. 1174i imprint blocks are very scarce, blank corner blocks $60.00
Imperforate pairs (3) have been reported on 1174 (printing unknown by the editors).

| **1990, Jan 12** | **GT4, Slater Paper** | | | **Perf 14.4x13.8** | |
|---|---|---|---|---|---|
| **1175** | **61¢ multicoloured** | 1.50 | .50 | 7.50 | 1.70 |
| a | perf 13.1, *Jun 1990* | 100.00 | 8.00 | 500.00* | —‡ |

* Blank corner block of 4.

| **1990, Dec 28** | **GT4, Peterborough Paper** | | | **Perf 14.4x13.8** | |
|---|---|---|---|---|---|
| **1176** | **63¢ multicoloured** | 4.00 | .50 | 20.00 | — |
| a | perf 13.1 | 9.00 | 4.00 | 40.00 | —‡ |

‡ Commercial use on cover: 1174a, 1175a: $10.00; 1176a: $8.00.

## INTERNATIONAL RATE

1177
Wapiti

Canada 76

1178
Grizzly Bear

1179
Beluga Whale

1180
Peary Caribou

Designer: Brian Tsang

Lithography (5 colours), panes of 50
Ashton-Potter Limited

| **1988, Jan 18** | **GT4, Harrison Paper** | | | **Perf 12.0x12.5** | |
|---|---|---|---|---|---|
| | | NH–VF | ⊙F | PB | FDC |
| **1177** | **74¢ multicoloured** | 2.50 | 1.00 | 12.50 | 1.90 |
| i | Rolland paper, *late 1988*† | 1,000.00 | — | 5,000.00* | |

† Only 200–300 known.
**Nos. 1170, 1173, 1177 (3) combination FDC** 3.90

| **1989, Jan 18** | **GT4, Harrison Paper** | | | **Perf 14.4x13.8** | |
|---|---|---|---|---|---|
| **1178** | **76¢ multicoloured** | 2.50 | .75 | 12.50 | 1.90 |
| i | Slater paper, *Aug 25, 1989* | 5.00 | — | 25.00 | — |
| c | SP, perf 13.1, *Nov 1989* | 50.00 | 20.00 | 275.00* | 30.00‡ |

‡ Any cover.
**Nos. 1171, 1174, 1178 (3) combination FDC** 4.00

| | **76¢ Booklet issue** | | | **Perf 12.5x13.1** | |
|---|---|---|---|---|---|
| 1178a | SP single, from 1178b | 4.00 | 3.50 | — | — |
| b | booklet pane of 5 x 76¢ (1178a) + label (BK105) | 20.00 | 20.00 | — | — |
| BK105 | pane 1178b in cover (3,378,926) $22.00 | | | | |

| **1990, Jan 12** | **GT4, Slater Paper** | | | **Perf 14.4x13.8** | |
|---|---|---|---|---|---|
| **1179** | **78¢ multicoloured** | 3.00 | 1.00 | 13.50 | 2.10 |
| d | imperf. pair | *1,200.00* | — | — | — |
| b | perf 13.1, *Apr 1990* | 45.00 | 8.00 | 250.00* | 4.00‡ |

**Nos. 1172, 1175, 1179 (3) combination FDC** 4.20

| | **78¢ Booklet issue** | | | **Perf 12.5x13.1** | |
|---|---|---|---|---|---|
| 1179a | booklet pane of 5 x 78¢ (1179c) + label (BK117) | 20.00 | 20.00 | — | — |
| c | single from 1179a | 4.00 | 2.50 | — | — |
| BK117 | pane 1179a in cover $22.00 | | | | |

‡ Commercial use on cover: $9.00.

| **1990, Dec 28** | **GT4, Peterborough Paper** | | | **Perf 13.1** | |
|---|---|---|---|---|---|
| **1180** | **80¢ multicoloured** | 2.50 | 1.00 | 12.50 | — |
| i | missing dark blue colour at top and untagged ‡ | — | *2,000.00* | | |
| ii | missing dark blue colour at top and violet background ‡ | — | *2,000.00* | | |
| d | imperf. pair | 1,500.00 | | | |
| c | perf 14.4x13.8 | 7.50 | 3.00 | 37.50 | — |
| ci | as 1180c, missing dark blue at top and violet background ‡ | — | *2,000.00* | | |

‡ Band of grey sky at top of stamp because blue colour is missing. Certificate of authenticity required on 80¢ missing colours.
**Nos. 1172A, 1176, 1180 (3) combination FDC** 4.30

**Medium-value Mammals**

| Format | Sheet | | | | | | | | Booklet | |
|---|---|---|---|---|---|---|---|---|---|---|
| Perf | 12.0x12.5 | | 14.4x13.8 | | | 13.8x13.1 | 13.1 | | 12.5x13.1 | |
| Paper | Rolland | Harrison | Harrison | Slater | Peter | Slater | Slater | Peter | Slater | Coated |
| 43¢ Lynx | | 1170 | | | | | | | | |
| 44¢ Atlantic Walrus | | | 1171 | 1171i | | 1171c | | | 1171a | |
| 45¢ Pronghorn | | | | 1172 | | | 1172d | | 1172f | |
| 46¢ Wolverine | | | | | 1172Ag | | | 1172A | | 1172Ac |
| 57¢ Killer Whale | 1173 | 1173i | | | | | | | | |
| 59¢ Musk Ox | | | 1174 | 1174i | | | 1174a | | | |
| 61¢ Timber wolf | | | | 1175 | | | 1175a | | | |
| 63¢ Harbour Porpoise | | | | | 1176 | | | 1176a | | |
| 74¢ Wapiti | 1177i | 1177 | | | | | | | | |
| 76¢ Grizzly Bear | | | 1178 | 1178i | | | 1178c | | 1178a | |
| 78¢ Beluga | | | | 1179 | | | 1179b | | 1179c | |
| 80¢ Peary Caribou | | | | | 1180c | | | 1180 | | 1180a |

1178b

1179a

1180b

**80¢ Booklet issue, Coated Paper Perf 12.5x13.1**

| | | | | | |
|---|---|---|---|---|---|
| **1180a** | single, from 1180b | 4.00 | 1.50 | — | — |
| ai | missing dark blue at top and violet background, untagged | — | *2,000.00* | | |
| b | booklet pane of 5 x 80¢ (1180a) + label (BK129) | 20.00 | 20.00 | — | — |

**BK129** pane 1180b in cover $22.00

‡ Commercial use on cover: $4.00.

* Blank corner block of 4.

## HIGH VALUES — Architecture

**1181**
Runnymede Library, Toronto, ON

Designer: Raymond Bellemare.
Lithography (6 colours) and steel engraving (1 colour), pane of 25
B A Bank Note Inc.

**1989, May 5 Untagged, Harrison Paper Perf 13.3**

| | | NH–VF | ⊙F | PB | FDC |
|---|---|---|---|---|---|
| **1181** | **$1 multicoloured (blue)**, Plate 1 | 2.00 | .70 | 10.00 | 2.40 |
| b | imperf. pair | | | | |
| i | vert. strip of 5, top pair imperf. | *2,000.00* | | | |
| | block of 10 (2x5), top 4 (2x2) imperf. | *4,000.00* | | *4,250.00** | |
| c | missing colour, inscription omitted | *2,500.00* | | | |
| ii | CBN, CPP, Plate 2, *Aug 28, 1992* | 3.50 | 1.50 | 15.00 | |
| a | engraved inscriptions inverted (1 pane of 25 known) † | *17,500.00* | | | |
| iv | CBN reprint, CPP, Plate 2, *Oct 1992* | 20.00 | 3.00 | 100.00* | |
| v | vert. strip of 5, bottom pair imperf. | *1,750.00* | | | |
| | block of 10 (2x5), bottom pair imperf. | *3,500.00* | | *4,000.00** | |

BABN/Plate 1: letters are light black; CBN/Plate 2: letters are dark blue: Aug printing: brownish roof, green header above the main door is rounded, tan bricks appear more solid; Oct printing, black roof, green header above the main door has squared ends, tan bricks are "dotted".

* Blank corner block; No. 1181iv inscription block $400.00.

† 20 copies with "$1 Canada" inverted at bottom plus 5 copies with just "$1" inverted at lower right corner of stamps (from 1st column of sheet.) These are usually offered in pair with full invert (value *$35,000.00*).

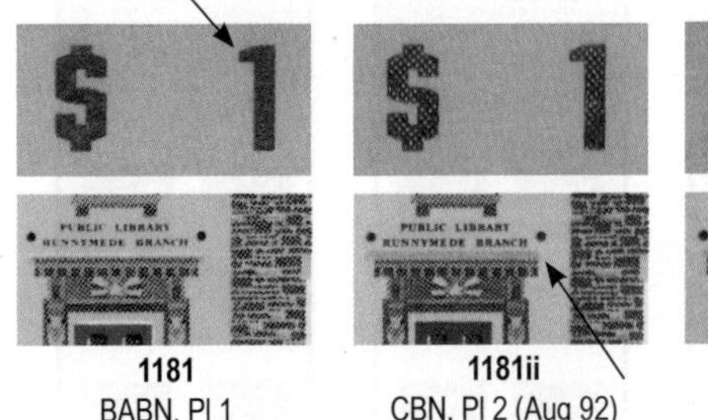


**1181** BABN, Pl 1 — **1181ii** CBN, Pl 2 (Aug 92) — **1181iv** CBN, Pl 2 (Oct 92)

**1181a**
Inverted inscriptions

**1181a**
Inverted inscriptions in left margin pair

**1182**
McAdam Railway Station, NB

Designer: Raymond Bellemare.
Lithography (6 colours) and steel engraving (1 colour), pane of 25
B A Bank Note Inc.

**1989, May 5 Untagged, Harrison Paper Perf 13.3**

| | | NH–VF | ⊙F | PB | FDC |
|---|---|---|---|---|---|
| **1182** | **$2 multicoloured (orange)**, plate 1 | 5.00 | 1.35 | 25.00 | 4.40 |
| a | imperf. pair | *1,200.00* | | *2,500.00** | |
| b | vertical strip of 5, part imperf. | *2,000.00* | | | |
| | vertical block of 10 (2 x 5), as 1182b | *4,000.00* | | *4,250.00** | |
| iii | CBN, CPP, Plate 2, *Jul 29, 1992* | 7.00 | 1.50 | 35.00 | |
| iv | CBN, CPP, Plate 2, reprint | 100.00 | 10.00 | 500.00* | |
| **Nos. 1181, 1182 (2) combination FDC** | | | | | **6.40** |

* Blank corner block.

BABN/Plate 1: roof trim is light green; CBN/Plate 2: trim is a darker green, vertical green rails at top of roof are very thick, orange dot pattern is random; Plate 2 reprint: vertical green rails at top of roof are thin, orange dot pattern is uniform.

Variety 1182a comes from imperf. pane of 25; 9 panes known. Variety 1182b is from pane of 25, imperf. above rows 3 and 4, with these same rows imperf. vertically; 5 panes recorded. One pane recorded imperf. on bottom two rows.

**1182**
BABN, Pl 1

**1182iii**
CBN, Pl 2

**1183**
Bonsecours Market, Montreal, QC

Designer: Raymond Bellemare.
Lithography (6 colours) and steel engraving (1 colour), pane of 25
B A Bank Note Inc.

**1990, May 28 Untagged, Peterborough Paper Perf 13.3**

| | | NH–VF | ⊙F | PB | FDC |
|---|---|---|---|---|---|
| **1183** | **$5 multicoloured (green)**, plate 1 | 10.00 | 3.00 | 50.00 | 10.50 |
| i | CBN, CPP, Plate 2, *Sep 11, 1992* | 20.00 | 5.00 | 100.00 | |
| a | vertical strip of 5, part imperf | *3,500.00* | | | |
| | vertical block of 10 (2x5), as 1183a | | | *7,500.00** | |

* Blank corner block.

On the CBN printing, the dome columns are darker, the two black windows at the base of the dome are "fuller", and the red X has a darker background.

1183a comes from pane of 25 with first and fourth row imperforate. Only 1 such pane has been recorded.

**1183**
BABN, Pl 1

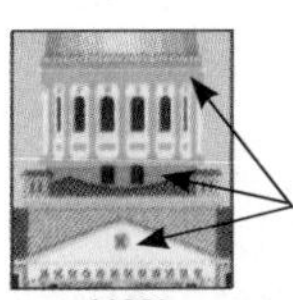

**1183i**
CBN, Pl 2

Mammal/Flag — 1987–1992

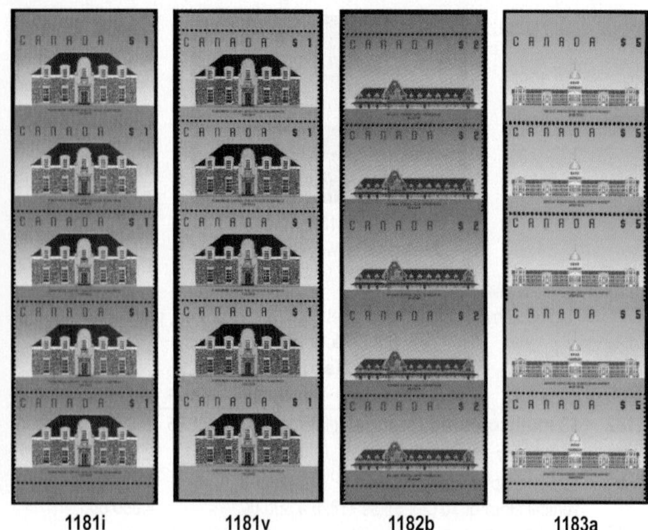
1181i 1181v 1182b 1183a

## BOOKLET ISSUES 1988–1990

1184 Canada Flag

1185 Canada Flag

1186 Parliament (East Block)

1187 Parliament

1188 Parliament

1189 Canada Flag

1190 Canada Flag

Designer: Flag: Gottschalk + Ash International.
Parliament: Rolf Harder

Lithography (5 colours)
Ashton-Potter

**1990, Jan 12** **Untagged, Slater Paper** **Perf 13.3x14.0**

| | | NH–VF | ⊙F | FDC |
|---|---|---|---|---|
| **1184** | **1¢ multicoloured (yellow)**, from 1189a | .40 | .25 | — |
| i | CPP, from 1190a, *Dec 28, 1990* | .30 | .25 | — |
| a | SP, perf 12.5 x 13.0, from 1189c, *Mar 1990* | 15.00 | 15.00 | — |
| **1185** | **5¢ multicoloured (pink)**, from 1189a | .30 | .30 | — |
| i | CPP, from 1190a, *Dec 28, 1990* | .40 | .30 | — |
| a | SP, perf 12.5 x 13.0, from 1189c, *Mar 1990* | 10.00 | 10.00 | — |

Nos. 1184 and 1185 were intended to be untagged. However, a narrow tag bar may appear on one or two sides due to the proximity to the 39¢/40¢ stamps (1189/1190).

Engraved
B A Bank Note Inc.

**Untagged, Harrison Paper** **Perf 12.5x12.0**

| | | NH–VF | ⊙F | FDC |
|---|---|---|---|---|
| **1186** | **6¢ purple**, from 1188a, *Jan 18, 1989* | .90 | .40 | — |

No. 1186 was intended to be untagged. However, a narrow tag bar may appear on the bottom due to its proximity to the 38¢ stamp (1188/BK100).

| | | NH–VF | ⊙F | FDC |
|---|---|---|---|---|
| **1187** | **37¢ blue**, GT4, from 1187a, *Feb 3, 1988* | 1.25 | 1.00 | — |
| **T1** | untagged (error) | 100.00 | | |
| a | booklet pane of 4 + 2 labels: 1 x 1¢ (938) + 2 x 6¢ (942) + 1 x 37¢ (1187) (BK96) | 1.50 | 1.50 | 1.40 |
| **BK96** | pane 1187a in cover (5,880,000) $2.00 | | | |
| **1188** | **38¢ blue**, GT4, from 1188a, *Jan 18, 1989* | 1.25 | .50 | — |
| a | booklet pane of 5 + label: 3 x 2¢ (939a) + 1 x 6¢ (1186) + 1 x 38¢ (1188) (BK100) | 1.50 | 1.50 | 1.40 |
| **BK100** | pane 1188a in cover (5,676,000) $2.00 | | | |

Lithography (5 colours)
Ashton-Potter

**1990, Jan 12** **GT4, Slater Paper** **Perf 13.3x14.0**

| | | NH–VF | ⊙F | FDC |
|---|---|---|---|---|
| **1189** | **39¢ multicoloured (blue)**, from 1189a | 1.25 | .50 | — |
| a | booklet pane of 4 (Flag): 1 x 1¢ (1184) + 2 x 5¢ (1185) +1 x 39¢ (1189) (BK111) | 2.25 | .75 | 1.50 |
| b | perf 12.5 x 13.0, from 1189c, *Mar 1990* | 15.00 | 15.00 | — |
| c | booklet pane of 4 (Flag): 1 x 1¢ (1184a) + 2 x 5¢ (1185a) + 1 x 39¢ (1189b) (BK111A) | 50.00 | 50.00 | — |
| **BK111** | pane 1189a in cover $2.50 | | | |
| **BK111A** | pane 1189c in cover $50.00 | | | |
| **1190** | **40¢ multicoloured (blue)**, CPP, from 1190a, *Dec 28, 1990* | 2.00 | .75 | |
| a | booklet pane of 4, 2 x 1¢ (1184i) + 1 x 5¢ (1185i) + 1 x 40¢ (1190) (BK123) | 3.00 | 1.50 | 1.45 |
| b | as "a", fully imperforate | *2,000.00* | | |
| **BK123** | pane 1190a in cover $3.25 | | | |

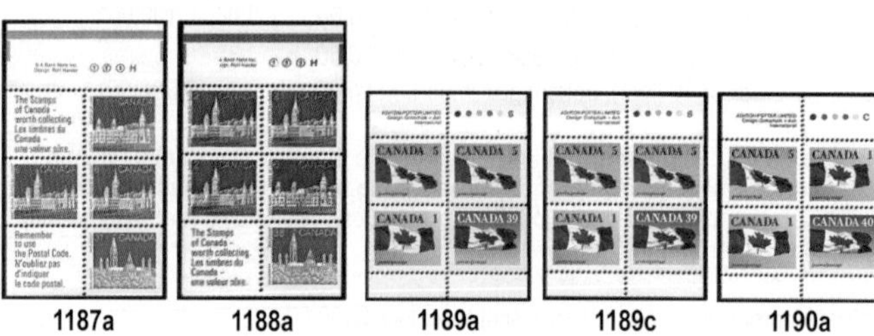
1187a 1188a 1189a 1189c 1190a

1191a

1192a

1193a

QE II — 1980's

## "QUICK STICK" BOOKLET ISSUES 1989–1991

1191
Flag over Forest

1192
Flag over Prairie

1193
Flag over Seacoast

Designer: Flag: Gottschalk + Ash International.

Lithography (5 colours)
Ashton-Potter, Self-adhesive

| 1989, Jun 30 | GT4, Slater/Fasson Paper | NH–VF | ⊙F | Die cut FDC |
|---|---|---|---|---|
| **1191** | **38¢ multicoloured**, from 1191a | 2.00 | 1.00 | 1.50 |
| b | horizontal pair, left stamp missing blue colour † | *2,500.00* | — | — |
| c | missing yellow colour (1 booklets of 12 known) | *1,250.00* | | |
| iii | partial missing colour (2 booklets of 12 known) | *1,000.00* | | |
| a | 12 x 38¢ on inside booklet cover (**BK110***) | 22.00 | | |

† Two booklets of 12 are known without blue colour on left column. One or both have been cut into 8 variety pairs (1191b) and 2 imprint blocks of 4 (2 x 1191b).
* Booklet sold for $5.00, a premium of 44¢ over face.

| | | NH–VF | ⊙F | FDC |
|---|---|---|---|---|
| **1192** | **39¢ multicoloured**, from 1192a, *Feb 8, 1990* | 1.75 | 1.00 | 1.50 |
| a | 12 x 39¢ on inside booklet cover (**BK114***) | 22.00 | | |

* Booklet sold for $5.00, a premium of 32¢ over face.
See also UO70, non-denominated special order envelope.

| | | NH–VF | ⊙F | FDC |
|---|---|---|---|---|
| **1193** | **40¢ multicoloured**, from 1193a, *Jan 11, 1991* | 1.75 | 1.00 | 1.50 |
| a | 12 x 40¢ on inside booklet cover (**BK127***) | 24.00 | | |

* Booklet sold for $5.25, a premium of 45¢ over face.

See also 1388 (42¢), 1389 (43¢).

1191b

1191c

1191iii

## ROLL STAMP ISSUES (COILS) 1988–1990

1194
Parliament

1194A
Parliament

1194B
Flag

1194C
Flag

Designer: Flag: Gottschalk + Ash International.
Parliament: Rolf Harder

Engraved (1 colour), rolls of 100
Canadian Bank Note

| 1988, Feb 22 | GT4, Peterborough Paper | NH–VF | Perf 10 horiz. ⊙F | FDC |
|---|---|---|---|---|
| **1194** | **37¢ blue**, DF* | 1.00 | .20 | 1.90† |
| iii | wide spacing strip of 4, DF | 20.00 | | |
| iv | narrow spacing strip of 4, DF | 20.00 | | |
| d | imperf. pair, creamy paper, DF | 225.00 | | |
| ii | MF* | 5.00 | .35 | |
| v | imperf. pair on MF paper | 225.00 | | |
| vii | wide spacing strip of 4, MF | 40.00 | | |
| viii | narrow spacing strip of 4, MF | 40.00 | | |
| vi | imperf. pair, NF* | 225.00 | | |
| T1 | untagged (error), NF | 100.00 | 40.00 | |
| xii | horizontally textured/ribbed paper (gum side) | 5.00 | .35 | |
| xiii | as xii, wide spacing strip of 4 | 75.00 | | |
| xiv | as xii, narrow spacing strip of 4 | 75.00 | | |
| xv | as xii, jump strip of 4 | 75.00 | | |
| i | **Rolland paper**, DF | 125.00 | — | |
| ix | as 1194i, imperf. pair | 2,000.00 | | |
| x | as 1194i, wide spacing strip of 4 | 1,250.00 | | |
| xi | as 1194i, narrow spacing strip of 4 | 1,250.00 | | |

* Due to the brilliance of the tagging, it is easier to check for paper varieties from the back of the stamps.
A double print variety exists (two strips of 6 known); see illustration below ($2,500.00)

| | | NH–VF | ⊙F | FDC |
|---|---|---|---|---|
| **1194A** | **38¢ dark green**, DF, *Feb 1, 1989* | 1.50 | .20 | 1.90† |
| Aiii | wide spacing strip of 4 | 20.00 | | |
| Aiv | narrow spacing strip of 4 | 20.00 | | |
| e | imperf. pair | 500.00 | | |
| Avii | gutter strip of 5 caused by perf shift* | *2,000.00* | | |
| Aii | MF | .70 | .25 | |
| Av | wide spacing strip of 4, MF | 15.00 | | |
| Avi | narrow spacing strip of 4, MF | 15.00 | | |

* 5 strips reported

| | | NH–VF | ⊙F | FDC |
|---|---|---|---|---|
| **1194B** | **39¢ dark violet**, DF, *Feb 8, 1990* | 1.00 | .20 | 2.10† |
| f | imperf. pair, DF | 250.00 | | |
| Biv | narrow spacing strip of 4, DF | 30.00 | | |
| Bii | HF | 2.50 | .25 | |
| Bv | narrow spacing strip of 4, HF | 40.00 | | |
| Biii | imperf. pair, HF | 250.00 | | |

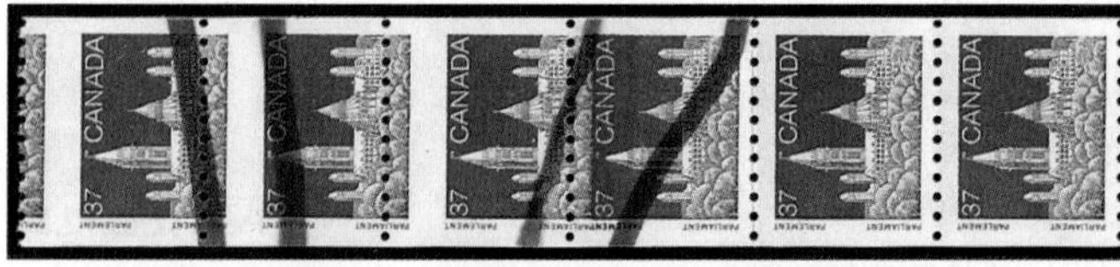

1194, double print

*Image rotated*

1194Avii

| | | NH–VF | ⊙F | FDC |
|---|---|---|---|---|
| **1194C** | **40¢ blue grey**, DF, *Dec 28, 1990* | 1.00 | .20 | 2.10† |
| **Ciii** | narrow spacing strip of 4, DF | 50.00 | | |
| **g** | imperf. pair | 375.00 | | |
| **h** | all colour omitted (tagged)‡ | *500.00* | | |
| **CT1** | untagged (error), DF | 90.00 | 60.00 | |
| **Cii** | MF | 5.00 | 1.25 | |
| **Civ** | narrow spacing strip of 4, MF | 75.00 | | |

† Value shown is for pair on FDC.
‡ No. 1194Ch must be collected in a pair with normal or misperfed stamp or (more often) in a strip of four with a pair of normal (or misperfed) stamps and a pair of the colour-omitted stamps.
Beware: Fake double perforations are known. Certificates of authenticity recommended.

Coil pairs or larger multiples are priced in proportion.

*Image rotated* **1194Ch**

## 1988

| **Rates:** | Domestic first-class (0-30g): 37¢ | |
|---|---|---|
| Jan 1/88– | Domestic first-class (30-50g): 57¢ | USA (0-30g): 43¢ |
| Dec 31/88 | Domestic oversize (30-50g): 74¢ | International (0-20g): 74¢ |

*single usage:* USA 43¢: $15.00 | International 74¢: $25.00

### 1988 OLYMPIC WINTER GAMES

**1195** Alpine Skiing **1196** Curling

**1197** Figure Skating **1198** Luge

Designer: Pierre-Yves Pelletier.
Lithography (37¢: 6 colours; others: 5 colours), pane of 50
Ashton-Potter Limited

**1988, Feb 12** **GT4, Slater Paper** **Perf 12.0x12.5**

| | | NH–VF | ⊙F | PB | FDC |
|---|---|---|---|---|---|
| **1195** | **37¢ multicoloured** | .80 | .35 | — | 1.15 |
| **i** | constant tag flaw (pos. 41) | 10.00 | 5.00 | 15.00 (LL) | |
| **1196** | **37¢ multicoloured** | .80 | .35 | — | 1.15 |
| **a** | se-tenant pair (1195, 1196) | 1.80 | 1.25 | 4.00 | |

Qty: 8,192,500 of each

**Perf 12.6x12.5**

| | | NH–VF | ⊙F | PB | FDC |
|---|---|---|---|---|---|
| **1197** | **43¢ multicoloured** | .90 | .90 | 5.00 | 1.25 |

Qty: 10,500,000

| | | NH–VF | ⊙F | PB | FDC |
|---|---|---|---|---|---|
| **1198** | **74¢ multicoloured** | 1.60 | 1.25 | 8.00 | 1.90 |

Qty: 10,912,500
**Nos. 1195–1198 (4) combination FDC** **4.20**

Issued to mark the Winter Olympic Games, Calgary, Alberta.
See also 1077, 1111–1112, 1130–1131, 1152–1153.

**1195i**

### EXPLORATION OF CANADA — 3

**Recognizers**

**1199** Anthony Henday **1200** George Vancouver

**1201** Simon Fraser **1202** John Palliser

Designer: Frederick Hagan.
Lithography (5 colours), pane of 50
Ashton-Potter Limited

**1988, Mar 17** **GT4, Slater Paper** **Perf 12.5x13.0**

| | | NH–VF | ⊙F | PB | FDC |
|---|---|---|---|---|---|
| **1199** | **37¢ multicoloured** | .75 | .45 | | 1.15 |
| **1200** | **37¢ multicoloured** | .75 | .45 | | 1.15 |
| **1201** | **37¢ multicoloured** | .75 | .45 | | 1.15 |
| **1202** | **37¢ multicoloured** | .75 | .45 | | 1.15 |
| **a** | se-tenant block of 4 (1199–1202) | 3.40 | 3.00 | 3.75 | 3.35 |

Qty: 1199, 1201: 3,963,700 each; 1200, 1202: 3,658,800 each

See also 1104–1107, 1126–1129 and 1233–1236.

### MASTERPIECES OF CANADIAN ART — I

**1203**
*The Young Reader*

Designer: Pierre-Yves Pelletier and Gregory Prosser (engraving). Based on a painting by Ozias Leduc.
Lithography (5 colours) and steel engraving (1 colour), pane of 16
British American Bank Note Company

**1988, May 20** **Untagged, Harrison Paper** **Perf 13.0x13.3**

| | | NH–VF | ⊙F | PB | FDC |
|---|---|---|---|---|---|
| **1203** | **50¢ multicoloured** (silver border), DF | 1.50 | 1.25 | 7.50 | 1.50 |
| **i** | LF | 10.00 | | 45.00 | |

Qty: 8,704,000

Issued on the occasion of the opening of Canada's National Art Gallery.
See also 1241, 1271, 1310, 1419, 1466, 1516, 1545, 1602, 1635, 1754, 1800, 1863, 1916, 1945.

## WILDLIFE CONSERVATION

1204 Duck landing — 1205 Moose feeding

Designer: Joseph Gault and Tiit Telmet.

Lithography (5 colours), pane of 50
Canadian Bank Note Company, Limited

**1988, Jun 1** **GT4, Harrison Paper** **Perf 13.1x13.4**

| | | NH–VF | ⊙F | PB | FDC |
|---|---|---|---|---|---|
| **1204** | **37¢ multicoloured** | .75 | .45 | | 1.15 |
| i | "bug on leaf" (pos. 19) | 2.50 | 1.50 | | |
| **1205** | **37¢ multicoloured** | .75 | .45 | | 1.15 |
| a | se-tenant pair (1204, 1205) | 1.70 | 1.25 | 3.75 | 1.90 |

Qty: 8,250,000 of each

Issued for the 100th birth anniversary of conservationist Archibald Belaney, known as Grey Owl, and for the 50th anniversary of Ducks Unlimited Canada.

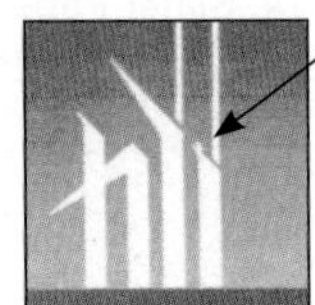

1204i

## CANADA DAY SCIENCE AND TECHNOLOGY — 3

1206 Kerosene, 1846 — 1207 Marquis Wheat, 1909

1208 Electron Microscope, 1938 — 1209 Cobalt Therapy, 1951

Designer: Roger Hill.

Lithography (5 colours), pane of 16
Ashton-Potter Limited

**1988, Jun 17** **GT4, Slater Paper** **Perf 12.5x13.0**

| | | NH–VF | ⊙F | PB | FDC |
|---|---|---|---|---|---|
| **1206** | **37¢ multicoloured** | .75 | .40 | | 1.15 |
| **1207** | **37¢ multicoloured** | .75 | .40 | | 1.15 |
| **1208** | **37¢ multicoloured** | .75 | .40 | | 1.15 |
| **1209** | **37¢ multicoloured** | .75 | .40 | | 1.15 |
| a | se-tenant block of 4 (1206–1209) | 3.60 | 3.25 | 3.75 | 3.35 |

Qty: 5,500,800 of each

See also 1099–1102 and 1135–1138.

## BUTTERFLIES

1210 Short-tailed Swallowtail — 1211 Northern Blue

1212 Macoun's Arctic — 1213 Canadian Tiger Swallowtail

Designer: Heather J. Cooper.

Lithography (5 colours), pane of 50
Ashton-Potter Limited

**1988, Jul 4** **GT4, Slater Paper** **Perf 12.0x12.5**

| | | NH–VF | ⊙F | PB | FDC |
|---|---|---|---|---|---|
| **1210** | **37¢ multicoloured** | .75 | .45 | | 1.15 |
| **1211** | **37¢ multicoloured** | .75 | .45 | | 1.15 |
| i | "caterpillar" (pos. 18) | 7.50 | 3.50 | | |
| ii | "two flies" (pos. 38) | 7.50 | 3.50 | | |
| iii | blemish on wing (pos. 42) | 7.50 | 3.50 | | |
| **1212** | **37¢ multicoloured** | .75 | .45 | | 1.15 |
| i | "black fly" (pos. 15) | 7.50 | 3.50 | | |
| **1213** | **37¢ multicoloured** | .75 | .45 | | 1.15 |
| a | se-tenant block of 4 (1210–1213) | 4.00 | 3.50 | 4.25 | 3.35 |

Qty: 1210–1211: 4,290,000 each; 1212–1213: 3,960,000 each

Issued for the 18th Entomology Congress, Vancouver, B.C.

1211iii

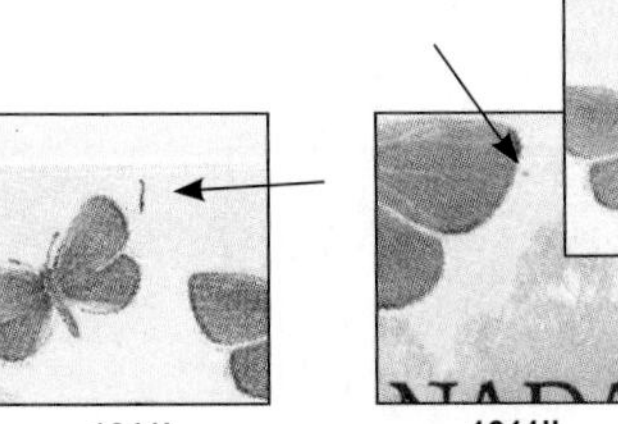

1211i

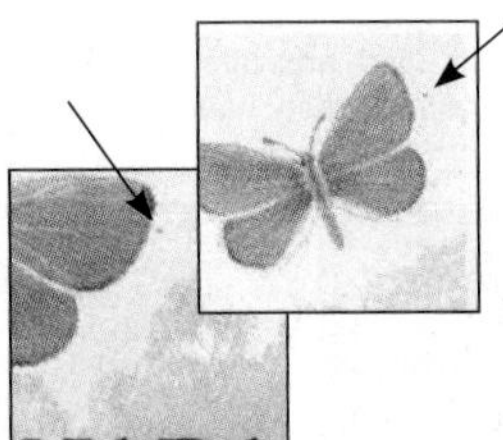

1211ii

1212i

## ST. JOHN'S CENTENNIAL

1214 St. John's Harbour

Designer: Louis-André Rivard.

Lithography (5 colours), pane of 50
Ashton-Potter Limited

**1988, Jul 22** **GT4, Slater Paper** **Perf 13.5x13.0**

| | | NH–VF | ⊙F | PB | FDC |
|---|---|---|---|---|---|
| **1214** | **37¢ multicoloured** | .75 | .25 | 3.75 | 1.15 |

Qty: 15,742,500.

Issued to commemorate the 100th anniversary of the incorporation of St. John's, capital of Newfoundland.

## 4-H CLUBS

**1215**
Rural scene and 4-H project

Designer: Debbie Adams.

Lithography (5 colours), pane of 50
Ashton-Potter Limited

**1988, Aug 5** **GT4, Slater Paper** **Perf 13.5x13.0**

| | NH–VF | ⊙F | PB | FDC |
|---|---|---|---|---|
| **1215 37¢ multicoloured** | .75 | .25 | 3.75 | 1.15 |

Qty: 16,022,500

Issued to honour 4-H Clubs in Canada on the 75th anniversary of the establishment of the first club in Roland, Manitoba.

## LES FORGES DU SAINT-MAURICE

**1216**
Ironworks blast furnace

Designer: Michèle Cayer. Engraved by Yves Baril. Based on a painting by Hélène Racicot.

Engraved and Lithography (5 colours), pane of 50
Canadian Bank Note Company, Limited

**1988, Aug 19** **GT4, Slater Paper** **Perf 13.3**

| | NH–VF | ⊙F | PB | FDC |
|---|---|---|---|---|
| **1216 37¢ multicoloured** | .75 | .25 | 3.75 | 1.15 |
| i "feather in cap" variety | 15.00 | 7.50 | 20.00 | — |
| ii "cuff link" variety (pos. 6) | 25.00 | 10.00 | | — |

Qty: 14,700,000

Issued to commemorate the 250th anniversary of Canada's first industrial complex, Les Forges du Saint-Maurice, near Trois-Rivières, Quebec.

**1216i**

**1216ii**

**MINT PRICING PREMIUMS**

Mint stamps from 301 to date are valued as NH-VF (Never Hinged-Very Fine). All hinged VF and NH-F copies are worth 50% of the listed values. Plate block (PB) values are for mint NH–VF plate or inscription blocks of four.

**USED, VF/XF (with in-period, circular date cancel) PRICING PREMIUM**

Single stamps with light or circular date cancels will sell for more than catalogue value (perhaps even more than a mint copy). From *1981 to 1991* single stamps from se-tenant blocks of 4 or larger will be priced at 50% or more above the fine price. From *1992* to date single stamps from se-tenant blocks of 4 or larger plus se-tenant booklet panes and souvenir sheets will be priced at 100% or more above the fine price. From *1997* to date all other stamps will be priced at 50% or more above the fine price.

## DOGS OF CANADA

**1217** Tahltan Bear Dog
**1218** Nova Scotia Duck Trolling Retriever

**1219** Canadian Eskimo Dog
**1220** Newfoundland

Designer: David Nethercott. Based on a painting by Mia Lane.

Lithography (5 colours), pane of 50
Ashton-Potter Limited

**1988, Aug 26** **GT4, Slater Paper** **Perf 12.5x12.0**

| | NH–VF | ⊙F | PB | FDC |
|---|---|---|---|---|
| **1217 37¢ multicoloured** | 1.25 | .50 | | 1.15 |
| **1218 37¢ multicoloured** | 1.25 | .50 | | 1.15 |
| **1219 37¢ multicoloured** | 1.25 | .50 | | 1.15 |
| **1220 37¢ multicoloured** | 1.25 | .50 | | 1.15 |
| a se-tenant block of 4 (1217–1220) | 5.40 | 4.00 | 6.25 | 3.35 |

Qty: 1217, 1220: 3,960,000 each; 1218–1219: 4,290,000 each

The stamps feature four dog breeds native to Canada, to commemorate the centennial of the Canadian Kennel Club.

## BASEBALL IN CANADA

**1221**
Ball, Glove and Diamond

Designer: Les Holloway.

Lithography (5 colours), pane of 50
Canadian Bank Note Company, Limited

**1988, Sep 14** **GT4, Slater Paper** **Perf 13.3x13.0**

| | NH–VF | ⊙F | PB | FDC |
|---|---|---|---|---|
| **1221 37¢ multicoloured** | .75 | .25 | 3.75 | 1.15 |

Qty: 15,150,000

Issued to commemorate the 150th anniversary of the first recorded baseball game in Beachville, Upper Canada.

Definitive Timeline:
**1988, Oct 3** 1–25¢ low-value Mammals (1155–1161)

## CHRISTMAS (Icons)

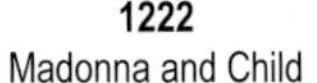

1222
Madonna and Child

1223
Madonna and Child

1224
Madonna and Child

1225
Nativity

Designer: Ernst Roch and Tom Yakobina.
Lithography (5 colours), panes of 50
Ashton-Potter Limited

**1988, Oct 27** **GT4, Slater Paper** **Perf 13.3**

| | NH–VF | ⊙F | PB | FDC |
|---|---|---|---|---|
| **1222 37¢ multicoloured**<br>Qty: 66,432,500 | .85 | .25 | 4.25 | 1.15 |
| **1223 43¢ multicoloured**<br>Qty: 18,320,000 | 1.00 | .80 | 5.00 | 1.25 |
| **1224 74¢ multicoloured**<br>Qty: 14,950,000 | 2.00 | 1.25 | 10.00 | 1.90 |
| **Nos. 1222–1224 (3) combination FDC** | | | | **3.50** |

**GTX, Greetmore Booklet** **Perf 12.5x13.0**

| | | | | |
|---|---|---|---|---|
| **1225 32¢ multicoloured**, from 1225a | 1.35 | 1.00 | | 1.00 |
| a booklet pane of 10 x 32¢ (1225) (BK99) | 12.50 | 12.00 | | |
| **BK99** pane 1225a in bilingual cover $13.00 | | | | |

Qty: 9,639, 325

Issued to commemorate the millennium of Christianity in the Ukraine.
No. 1225 was issued in booklets only, for use on greeting card envelopes bearing a printed postal code matrix. Accepted singly until January 31, 1989 if affixed to designated envelopes.

1225a

## CHARLES INGLIS

1226

Designer: Steven Slipp. Based on an illustration by Kevin Sollows.
Lithography (5 colours), pane of 50
Ashton-Potter Limited

**1988, Nov 1** **GT4, Slater Paper** **Perf 12.5x12.0**

| | NH–VF | ⊙F | PB | FDC |
|---|---|---|---|---|
| **1226 37¢ multicoloured**<br>Qty: 15,152,500 | .75 | .30 | 3.75 | 1.15 |

Issued to honour Charles Inglis (1734–1816). Canada's first Anglican Bishop, who founded an Academy at Windsor, Nova Scotia which has evolved into Kings-Edgehill School and the University of King's College at Halifax.

## CANADIAN PERSONALITIES

1227
Frances Ann Hopkins

1228
Angus Walters

### Frances Ann Hopkins

Designer: David Nethercott. Based on a photograph by William Notman. Based on a painting ("Canoe Manned by Voyageurs Passing a Waterfall (Ontario)") by Frances Anne Hopkins.
Lithography (5 colours), pane of 50
Ashton-Potter Limited

**1988, Nov 18** **GT4, Slater Paper** **Perf 13.5x13.0**

| | NH–VF | ⊙F | PB | FDC |
|---|---|---|---|---|
| **1227 37¢ multicoloured**<br>Qty: 16,500,000 | .75 | .30 | 3.75 | 1.15 |

Issued to honour Frances Ann Hopkins (1838–1918), pioneer painter of western Canada.

### Angus Walters

Designer: Roger Hill.
Lithography (5 colours), pane of 50
Ashton-Potter Limited

**1988, Nov 18** **GT4, Slater Paper** **Perf 13.3**

| | NH–VF | ⊙F | PB | FDC |
|---|---|---|---|---|
| **1228 37¢ multicoloured**<br>Qty: 16,500,000 | .80 | .30 | 4.00 | 1.15 |

Issued to honour Angus Walters (1882–1968), captain of the Bluenose which won the International Fisherman's Trophy in 1938.
See also 158, 913 and 1738.

Definitive Timeline:
**1988, Dec 29** 38¢ Queen Elizabeth II (1164)
38¢ Parliament (1165)

## 1989

**Rates:** Domestic first-class (0-30g): 38¢
Jan 1/89– Domestic first-class (30-50g): 59¢ USA (0-30g): 44¢
Dec 31/89 Domestic oversize (30-50g): 76¢ International (0-20g): 76¢

*single usage:* USA 44¢: $15.00 | International 76¢: $25.00

Definitive Timeline:
1989, Jan 18 44/59/76¢ Mammals (1171/1174/1178)
50¢ Parliament booklet (939a, 1186, 1188)

### SMALL CRAFT — I

Native Boats

1229 Chipewyan canoe — 1230 Haida canoe

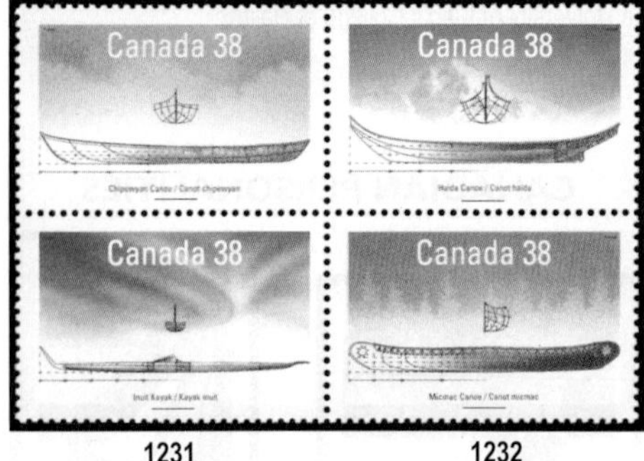


1231 Inuit kayak — 1232 Micmac canoe

Designer: Louis-André Rivard. Based on illustrations by Bernard Leduc.
Lithography (4 colours), pane of 50
Ashton-Potter Limited

| 1989, Feb 1 | GT4, Slater Paper | | | Perf 13.5x13.0 | |
|---|---|---|---|---|---|
| | | NH–VF | ⊙F | PB | FDC |
| **1229** | **38¢ multicoloured** | .80 | .45 | | 1.15 |
| **1230** | **38¢ multicoloured** | .80 | .45 | | 1.15 |
| **1231** | **38¢ multicoloured** | .80 | .45 | | 1.15 |
| **1232** | **38¢ multicoloured** | .80 | .45 | | 1.15 |
| a | se-tenant block of 4 (1229–1232) | 3.60 | 3.00 | 4.00 | 3.45 |
| ai | block of 4, imperf. at left margin (20 blocks known, from 4 panes) | 800.00 | — | 900.00* | — |

Qty: 1229, 1231: 4,290,000 each; 1230, 1232: 3,960,000 each
* Blank corner block of 4.

See also 1266–1269 and 1317–1320.

### EXPLORATION OF CANADA — 4

Realizers

1233 Matonabbee — 1234 Sir John Franklin

1235 Joseph Burr Tyrrell — 1236 Vilhjalmur Stefansson

Designer: Frederick Hagan.
Lithography (5 colours), pane of 50
Ashton-Potter Limited

| 1989, Mar 22 | GT4, Slater Paper | | | Perf 12.5x13.1 | |
|---|---|---|---|---|---|
| | | NH–VF | ⊙F | PB | FDC |
| **1233** | **38¢ multicoloured** | .80 | .45 | | 1.15 |
| **1234** | **38¢ multicoloured** | .80 | .45 | | 1.15 |
| **1235** | **38¢ multicoloured** | .80 | .45 | | 1.15 |
| **1236** | **38¢ multicoloured** | .80 | .45 | | 1.15 |
| a | se-tenant block of 4 (1233–1236) | 3.60 | 3.00 | 4.00 | 3.45 |

Qty: 1233, 1235: 4,745,250 each; 1234, 1236: 3,163,500 each

Issued to honour explorers of Canada's north.
See also 1104–1107, 1126–1129 and 1199–1202.

Canada Post's stamp announcement brochures changed from a "Commemorative Stamp Bulletin" on the Exploration's Mar 22 issue to a "Presenting" pamphlet with the Architecture definitive issues of May 5.

Definitive Timeline:
1989, May 5 $1 Architecture (1181)
$2 Architecture (1182)

### CANADIAN PHOTOGRAPHY

1237 William Notman — 1238 W. Hanson Boorne

1239 Alexander Henderson — 1240 Jules-Ernest Livernois

Designer: Jean Morin and Tom Yakobina.
Lithography (8 colours), pane of 16
Ashton-Potter Limited

| 1989, Jun 23 | GT4, Slater Paper | | | Perf 12.5x12.0 | |
|---|---|---|---|---|---|
| | | NH–VF | ⊙F | PB | FDC |
| **1237** | **38¢ multicoloured** | .80 | .45 | | 1.15 |
| **1238** | **38¢ multicoloured** | .80 | .45 | | 1.15 |
| **1239** | **38¢ multicoloured** | .80 | .45 | | 1.15 |
| **1240** | **38¢ multicoloured** | .80 | .45 | | 1.15 |
| a | se-tenant block of 4 (1237–1240) | 3.60 | 3.00 | 4.00 | 3.45 |

Qty: 3,781,200 of each

Issued to commemorate 150 years of Canadian photography, featuring trailblazing Canadian photographers: William Notman (1826-1891); Alexander Henderson (1831-1913); Jules-Ernest Livernois (1851-1933); and W. Hanson Boorne (1859-1945).

## MASTERPIECES OF CANADIAN ART — 2

1241
*Ceremonial Frontlet*

Designer: Pierre-Yves Pelletier. Based on a painting by Harry Foster.
Lithography (6 colours) and foil stamping (2 colours), pane of 16
Ashton-Potter Limited

**1989, Jun 29** **Untagged, Slater Paper** **Perf 12.5x13.3**

| | | NH–VF | ⊙F | PB | FDC |
|---|---|---|---|---|---|
| **1241** | **50¢ multicoloured** (silver border) | 1.50 | 1.20 | 7.50 | 1.40 |

Qty: 10,763,850

Inscription/plate blocks sold by Canada Post in packaged corner sets have rouletted selvedge on the top and/or sides. Blocks removed from full panes by collectors would be either torn or cut with a knife.

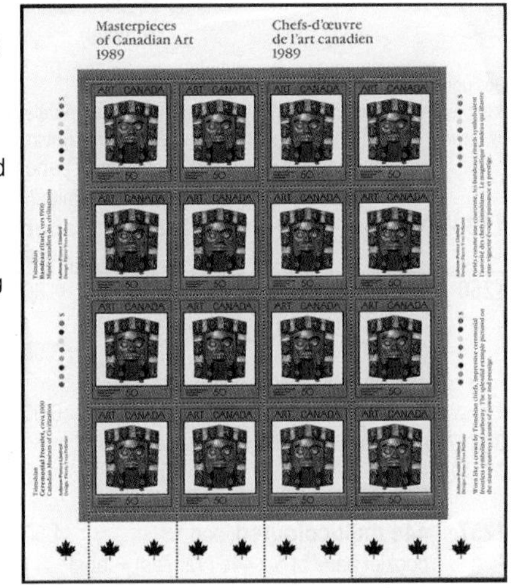


Issued to mark the opening of the Canadian Museum of Civilization.
See also 1203, 1271, 1310, 1419, 1466, 1516, 1545, 1602, 1635, 1754, 1800, 1863, 1916, 1945.

Definitive Timeline:
**1989, Jun 30** 38¢ Flag over Forest "Quick-stick" booklet (1191)
[was initially assigned Sc# 1242]

No. 1242 is not assigned.

## CANADIAN POETS

1243 Louis-H. Fréchette
1244 Archibald Lampman

Designer: René Milot.
Lithography (6 colours), pane of 50
Ashton-Potter Limited

**1989, Jul 7** **GT4, Slater Paper** **Perf 13.3**

| | | NH–VF | ⊙F | PB | FDC |
|---|---|---|---|---|---|
| **1243** | **38¢ multicoloured** | .80 | .45 | | 1.15 |
| **1244** | **38¢ multicoloured** | .80 | .45 | | 1.15 |
| a | se-tenant pair (1243, 1244) | 1.80 | 1.25 | 4.00 | 1.90 |

Qty: 7,985,000 of each

Issued for the sesquicentennial of the birth of Louis Frechette (1839-1908), and featuring one of his contemporaries, Archibald Lampman (1861-1899).

## MUSHROOMS

1245 Clavulinopsis fusiformis
1246 Boletus mirabilis

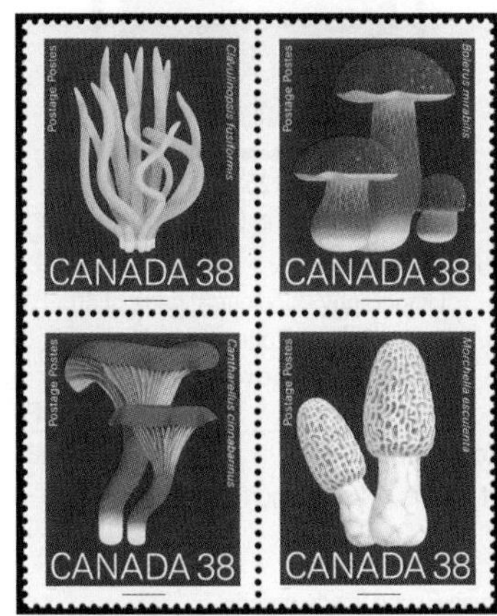

1247 Cantharellus cinnabarinus
1248 Morchella esculenta

Designer: Ernst Roch.
Lithography (9 colours), pane of 50
Ashton-Potter Limited

**1989, Aug 4** **GT4, Slater Paper** **Perf 13.3**

| | | NH–VF | ⊙F | PB | FDC |
|---|---|---|---|---|---|
| **1245** | **38¢ multicoloured** | .80 | .45 | | 1.15 |
| **1246** | **38¢ multicoloured** | .80 | .45 | | 1.15 |
| **1247** | **38¢ multicoloured** | .80 | .45 | | 1.15 |
| **1248** | **38¢ multicoloured** | .80 | .45 | | 1.15 |
| T1 | untagged, error | — | 60.00 | | |
| a | se-tenant block of 4 (1245–1248) | 3.60 | 3.00 | 4.00 | 3.45 |

Qty: 1245–1246: 3,911,050 each; 1247–1248: 3,610,200 each

1248 is known untagged in used condition (defective); the other three stamps *should* also exist untagged but have not yet been reported.

## CANADIAN INFANTRY REGIMENTS

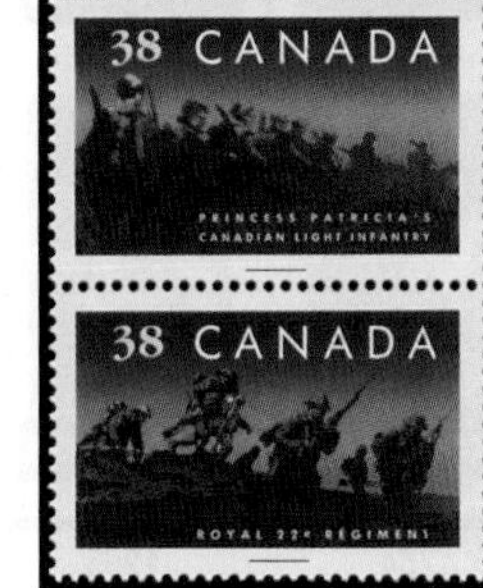

1249 Princess Patricia's Canadian Light Infantry
1250 Royal 22e Régiment

Designer: Joseph Gault, Normand Fontaine, and Tiit Telmet. Engraved by Yves Baril.
Lithography (5 colours) and steel engraving (1 colour), pane of 50
Canadian Bank Note Company, Limited

**1989, Sep 8** **GT4, Peterborough Paper** **Perf 13.0**

| | | NH–VF | ⊙F | PB | FDC |
|---|---|---|---|---|---|
| **1249** | **38¢ multicoloured** | 1.00 | .50 | | 1.15 |
| **1250** | **38¢ multicoloured** | 1.00 | .50 | | 1.15 |
| a | vertical se-tenant pair (1249, 1250) | 2.25 | 1.75 | 5.00* | 1.90* |
| ii | inscription block of 4 | | | 250.00 | 125.00 |

Qty: 3,973,350 of each

Less than 50 full panes exist with imprints. Value $1,200.00
* Value shown is for blank corner block; a significant shortage of inscription blocks resulted from technical difficulties at the printer. Most have colours out of register, most apparent in the "doubling" of the weapons. These are common and do not merit any premium.

Canada Post announcement said plates 1 *and 2* would be "on sale at the National Philatelic Centre and Philatelic Centres". Only plate 1 has been seen.

Issued to celebrate the 75th anniversaries of the two regiments.

## INTERNATIONAL TRADE

1251
World in Carton

Designer: Les Holloway and Nita Wallace.
Lithography (5 colours), pane of 50
Ashton-Potter Limited

| 1989, Oct 2 | GT4, Peterborough Paper | | Perf 13.5x13.0 | | |
|---|---|---|---|---|---|
| | | NH–VF | ⊙F | PB | FDC |
| 1251 | **38¢ multicoloured** | .80 | .30 | 4.00 | 1.15 |
| i | imperf. at left margin (2 used reported) | | | | |

Qty: 15,822,500

Issued to mark Canadian Export Trade month.

1251i

## PERFORMING ARTS

1252 Dancers — 1253 Musicians

1254 Movie director and camera — 1255 Youth and adult performers

Designer: William H. Tibbles. Based on a sculpture by Jonathan Milne.
Lithography (6 colours), pane of 50
Ashton-Potter Limited

| 1989, Oct 4 | GT4, Peterborough Paper | | Perf 13.0x13.5 | | |
|---|---|---|---|---|---|
| | | NH–VF | ⊙F | PB | FDC |
| 1252 | **38¢ multicoloured** | .80 | .45 | | 1.15 |
| 1253 | **38¢ multicoloured** | .80 | .45 | | 1.15 |
| 1254 | **38¢ multicoloured** | .80 | .45 | | 1.15 |
| 1255 | **38¢ multicoloured** | .80 | .45 | | 1.15 |
| a | se-tenant block of 4 (1252–1255) | 3.60 | 2.50 | 4.00 | 3.45* |

Qty: 1252–1253: 4,018,800 each; 1254–1255: 4,353,700 each
* Se-tenant strip of 4

Commemorating the 50th anniversaries of the National Film Board and the Royal Winnipeg Ballet; the 30th anniversary of the Vancouver Opera; and the 25th anniversary of the Confederation Centre of the Arts in Charlottetown, P.E.I.

## CHRISTMAS (Winter Landscapes)

1256
Bend in Gosselin River, Arthabaska

1257
Snow II

1258
Ste. Agnès (near La Malbaie, QC)

1259
Champ-de-Mars, Winter (Montreal)

Designer: David Nethercott and Viviane Warburton.
33¢ painting by William Brymner; 38¢ painting by Marc-Aurèle de Foy Suzor-Côté ; 44¢ painting by Lawren Stewart Harris; 76¢ painting by Albert Henry Robinson.
Lithography (5 colours), panes of 50
Ashton-Potter Limited

| 1989, Oct 26 | GT4, Slater Paper | | Perf 13.1x13.5 | | |
|---|---|---|---|---|---|
| | | NH–VF | ⊙F | PB | FDC |
| 1256 | **38¢ multicoloured** | .80 | .25 | 4.00 | 1.15 |
| a | booklet pane of 10 x 38¢ (1256b) (BK107) | 58.00 | 58.00 | — | — |
| b | single with straight edge, from 1256a, Peterborough Paper, perf 13.0x12.5 | 6.00 | 6.00 | — | — |
| BK107 | pane 1256a in bilingual cover $60.00 | | | | |

Qty: 50,975,270

| | | NH–VF | ⊙F | PB | FDC |
|---|---|---|---|---|---|
| 1257 | **44¢ multicoloured**, perf 13.3 | 1.00 | .80 | 5.00 | 1.30 |
| a | booklet pane of 5 x 44¢ (1257as) + label (BK108) | 20.00 | 20.00 | — | — |
| as | single with straight edge, from 1257a, Peterborough Paper | 5.00 | 5.00 | — | — |
| BK108 | pane 1257a in bilingual cover $22.00 | | | | |

Qty: 15,438,375

| | | NH–VF | ⊙F | PB | FDC |
|---|---|---|---|---|---|
| 1258 | **76¢ multicoloured**, perf 13.3 | 1.75 | 1.25 | 8.75 | 1.90 |
| a | booklet pane of 5 x 76¢ (1258as) + label (BK109) | 38.00 | 38.00 | — | — |
| as | single with straight edge, from 1258a, Peterborough Paper | 8.00 | 8.00 | — | — |
| BK109 | pane 1258a in bilingual cover $40.00 | | | | |

Qty: 14,968,205 BK107: 625,000; BK108: 605,175; BK109: 500,000
**Nos. 1256–1258 (3) combination FDC** 3.60

### Greetmore Booklet

| | GTX, Peterborough Paper | Perf 12.5x13.0 | | |
|---|---|---|---|---|
| | | NH–VF | ⊙F | FDC |
| 1259 | **33¢ multicoloured**, single with straight edge, from 1259a, "dead" paper | 2.00 | 2.00 | 1.10 |
| ii | HF | 15.00 | 7.00 | |
| a | booklet pane of 10 x 33¢ (1259) (2 x 5) (BK106) | 15.00 | 15.00 | |
| b | horizontal pair, imperf. between (from 'c') | *3,000.00* | | |
| c | as "a" with no vertical perf. between stamps† | *15,000.00* | | |
| BK106 | pane 1259a in bilingual cover $20.00; HF $150.00 | | | |

Qty: 1259: 71,074,210
† Resulting from a cutting error. 3 booklets recorded; 2 have been split up with 1 remaining intact.

No. 1259 was accepted singly until January 31, 1990. See note following No. 1225.

1256a 1257a 1258a 1259a

## SECOND WORLD WAR — 1939

**Reluctantly at War Again**

1260 Canada Declares War — 1261 The Army Mobiizes

1263 Air Training Plan — 1262 Convoy System Established

Designer: Pierre-Yves Pelletier. Based on an illustration by Jean-Pierre Armanville.
Lithography (5 colours), pane of 16
Canadian Bank Note Company, Limited

**1989, Nov 10** **GT4, Peterborough Paper** **Perf 13.3**

| | | NH–VF | ⊙F | PB | FDC |
|---|---|---|---|---|---|
| **1260** | **38¢ multicoloured** | 1.00 | .75 | | 1.15 |
| **1261** | **38¢ multicoloured** | 1.00 | .75 | | 1.15 |
| **1262** | **38¢ multicoloured** | 1.00 | .75 | | 1.15 |
| **1263** | **38¢ multicoloured** | 1.00 | .75 | | 1.15 |
| **a** | se-tenant block of 4 (1260–1263) | 4.50 | 4.00 | 4.50 | 3.50 |

Qty: 3,614,000 of each

Issued to mark the 50th anniversary of the outbreak of World War II.
See also 1298–1301, 1345–1348, 1448–1451, 1503–1506, 1537–1540 and 1541–1544.

Definitive Timeline:
**1989, Dec 28** 39¢ Flag over Clouds (1166)
39¢ Queen Elizabeth II (1167)

## 1990

| **Rates:** | Domestic first-class (0-30g): 39¢ | |
|---|---|---|
| Jan 1/90– | Domestic first-class (30-50g): 61¢ | USA (0-30g): 45¢ |
| Dec 31/90 | Domestic oversize (30-50g): 78¢ | International (0-20g): 78¢ |

*single usage:* USA 45¢: $15.00 | International 78¢: $25.00

Definitive Timeline:
**1990, Jan 12** 45/61/78¢ Mammals (1172/1175/1179
50¢ Flag booklet (1184, 1185, 1189)
**1990, Feb 8** 39¢ Flag over Prairie "Quick-Stick" booklet (1192)

## NORMAN BETHUNE

1264 Norman Bethune in Canada — 1265 Norman Bethune in China

Designer: Jean Morin, Wanda Lewicka. Engraved by Hu Zhenyuan and Yan Bingwu. Based on illustrations by Liu Xiangping.
Lithography (5 colours) and steel engraving (1 colour), pane of 50
Canadian Bank Note Company, Limited

**1990, Mar 2** **GT4, Peterborough Paper** **Perf 13.0x13.3**

| | | NH–VF | ⊙F | PB | FDC |
|---|---|---|---|---|---|
| **1264** | **39¢ multicoloured**, DF | 1.25 | .50 | | 1.90 |
| **i** | F | 2.00 | .75 | | |
| **1265** | **39¢ multicoloured**, DF | 1.25 | .50 | | 1.90 |
| **i** | F | 2.00 | .75 | | |
| **a** | se-tenant pair (1264, 1265), DF | 2.50 | 1.50 | 6.00 | 3.10 |
| **ai** | se-tenant pair (1264i, 1265i), F | 4.00 | 2.50 | 10.00 | |

Qty: 7,500,000 each

Issued to commemorate the centennial of the birth of Norman Bethune (1890–1939) who dedicated his life to the advancement of medicine and spent much of his adult life in China. The People's Republic of China issued a se-tenant pair of stamps with the same design.

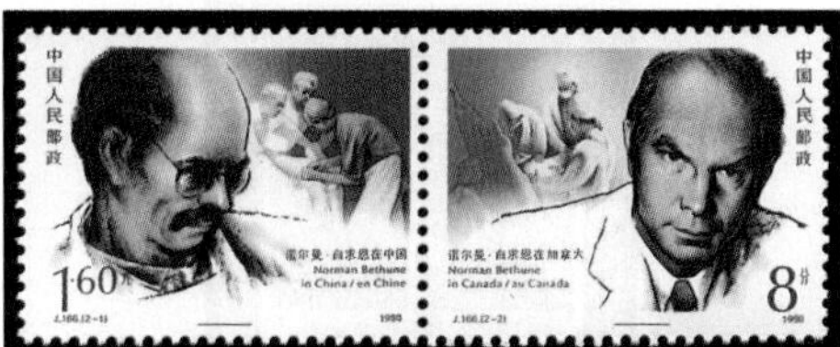

Joint issue with The People's Republic of China
**Scott # 2263–2264**

## SMALL CRAFT — 2

**Work Boats**

1266 Dory — 1267 Pointer

1268 York Boat — 1269 North Canoe

Designer: Louis-André Rivard. Based on illustrations by Bernard Leduc.
Lithography (4 colours), pane of 50
Ashton-Potter Limited

**1990, Mar 15** **GT4, Peterborough Paper** **Perf 13.5x13.0**

| | | NH–VF | ⊙F | PB | FDC |
|---|---|---|---|---|---|
| **1266** | **39¢ multicoloured** | .90 | .45 | | 1.30 |
| **1267** | **39¢ multicoloured** | .90 | .45 | | 1.30 |
| **1268** | **39¢ multicoloured** | .90 | .45 | | 1.30 |
| **1269** | **39¢ multicoloured** | .90 | .45 | | 1.30 |
| **a** | se-tenant block of 4 (1266–1269) | 4.00 | 3.50 | 4.50 | 3.65 |

Qty: 1266, 1268: 3,900,000 each; 1267, 1269: 3,600,000 each

This Small Craft issue recognizes the role played by work boats during Canada's early history.
See also 1229–1332 and 1317–1320.

## MULTICULTURALISM

**1270**
Maple leaf with multicoloured design

Designer: Friedrich G. Peter.

Lithography (4 colours) and steel engraving (1 colour), pane of 50
Canadian Bank Note Company, Limited

| **1990, Apr 5** | **GT4, Peterborough Paper** | | | **Perf 13.0** |
|---|---|---|---|---|
| | NH–VF | ⊙F | PB | FDC |
| **1270 39¢ multicoloured** | .80 | .30 | 4.00 | 1.30 |
| a black inscriptions omitted† | *1,500.00* | | | |

Qty: 15,000,000

† A certificate of authenticity is recommended.

Issued in conjunction with the opening of "A Coat of Many Colours", an exhibit tracing 200 years of Jewish life in Canada, at the Canadian Museum of Civilization in Hull, Quebec.

## MASTERPIECES OF CANADIAN ART — 3

**1271**
*The West Wind*

Designer: Pierre-Yves Pelletier. Based on a painting by Thomas John Thomson.

Lithography (6 colours) with foil stamping (2 colours), pane of 16
Ashton-Potter Limited

| **1990, May 3** | **Untagged, Slater Paper** | | | **Perf 12.5x13.3** |
|---|---|---|---|---|
| | NH–VF | ⊙F | PB | FDC |
| **1271 50¢ multicoloured** (silver border) | 1.50 | 1.25 | 6.50 | 1.50 |

Qty: 10,500,000

Four mint singles have been seen by the Editors where the bottom 11mm of silver is missing. Value $1,000.

Inscription/plate blocks sold by Canada Post in packaged corner sets have roulettted selvedge on the top and/or sides. Blocks removed from full panes by collectors would be either torn or cut with a knife.

Issued in recognition of Tom Thomson's contribution to Canada's artistic heritage.

See also 1203, 1241, 1310, 1419, 1466, 1516, 1545, 1602, 1635, 1754, 1800, 1863, 1916, 1945.

Silver missing along bottom 11mm of stamp

## CANADA POST CORPORATION

**1272** CPC van, facing left

**1273** CPC van, facing right

Designer: Alain Rochon and Jean Morin.

Lithography (5 colours), Prestige Booklet
Ashton-Potter Limited

| **1990, May 3** | **GT4, Peterborough Paper** | | **Perf 13.6** |
|---|---|---|---|
| | NH–VF | ⊙F | FDC |
| **1272 39¢ multicoloured** | 1.00 | .70 | |
| **1273 39¢ multicoloured** | 1.00 | .70 | |
| a booklet pane of 8 x 39¢ (4 x 1272, 4 x 1273) with Post Office artifacts on selvedge | 9.00 | 9.00 | |
| b booklet pane of 9 x 39¢ (5 x 1272, 4 x 1273) + 3 labels, with Post Office truck on selvedge | 14.00 | 14.00 | |
| i horiz. se-tenant pair (1272, 1273) | 3.00 | 3.00 | 2.10 |
| ii horiz. identical pair (1272, 1272) | 4.00 | 4.00 | |
| iii horiz. se-tenant strip of 3 (2 x 1272, 1273) | 10.00 | 10.00 | |
| biv booklet pane of 8 x 39¢ (4 x 1272, 4 x 1273), with illustration of postage stamp on selvedge | 9.00 | 9.00 | |
| BK118 Bilingual 16 pages Prestige booklet with 2 panes of 1273a and 1 pane of 1273b $32.00 | | | |

Qty: 1272: 6,500,000; 1273: 6,000,000 (500,000 booklets)

Canada's first Prestige Booklet with 2 panes of 8 (1273a and 1273biv), 1 pane of 9 (1273b) and 16 pages of text was issued in recognition of Canada Post Corporation's (CPC) development. Panes are stitched on the left side.

1273a

1273b 1273biv

Definitive Timeline:
1990, May 28 $5 Architecture (1183)

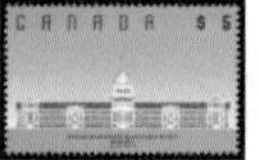

## CULTURAL TREASURES — DOLLS

1274 Native dolls (1840–1916) 1275 Settlers' dolls (1840–1900)

1276 Commercial dolls (1917–1936) 1277 Commercial dolls (1940–1960)

Designer: Nita Wallace. Based on a photograph by Michael Kohn.

Lithography (6 colours), pane of 50
Ashton-Potter Limited

| 1990, Jun 8 | GT4, Peterborough Paper | | | Perf 12.5x12.0 | |
|---|---|---|---|---|---|
| | | NH–VF | ⊙F | PB | FDC |
| **1274** | **39¢ multicoloured** | .90 | .45 | | 1.30 |
| i | "dripping barrel" (black & blue spots) (pos. 18) | 5.00 | 2.50 | | |
| **1275** | **39¢ multicoloured** | .90 | .45 | | 1.30 |
| **1276** | **39¢ multicoloured** | .90 | .45 | | 1.30 |
| **1277** | **39¢ multicoloured** | .90 | .45 | | 1.30 |
| i | line under "pé" of "Poupées" (pos. 47) | 15.00 | 7.50 | 20.00 | |
| ii | "thread" between dolls (pos. 17) | 10.00 | 5.00 | | |
| a | se-tenant block of 4 (1274–1277) | 4.00 | 3.50 | 4.50 | 3.65 |

Qty: 1274, 1276: 4,500,000 each; 1275, 1277: 3,000,000 each

All of the dolls depicted on the stamps are Canadian, and remind us about how we lived day-to-day in the past. The dolls are pictured in groups, positioned among other toys as they might be displayed in a child's room or on a toy store shelf.

This issue has many fly-speck dots, some of which are constant.

1274i

1277i

1277ii

## THE CANADIAN FLAG (1965–1990)

1278
Canadian flag with fireworks

Designer: Clermont Malenfant.

Lithography (7 colours), pane of 16
Ashton-Potter Limited

| 1990, Jun 29 | GT4, Slater Paper | | | Perf 13.3x12.5 | |
|---|---|---|---|---|---|
| | | NH–VF | ⊙F | PB | FDC |
| **1278** | **39¢ multicoloured** | .80 | .30 | 4.00 | 1.30 |
| a | silver inscriptions omitted, and untagged* | *3,000.00* | | | |
| T1 | untagged, error | 75.00 | — | | |
| T2 | tagged all over, error | — | 50.00 | | |

Qty: 15,000,000

* One pane of 16 reported.

Issued to celebrate the 25th anniversary of the Canadian flag.

## PREHISTORIC LIFE IN CANADA — I

### The Age of Primitive Life

1279 Trilobite (Cambrian Period) 1280 Sea Scorpion (Silurian Period)

1281 Fossil Algae (Precambrian Eon) 1282 Soft Invertebrate (Cambrian Period)

Designer: Rolf P. Harder. Engraved by Yves Baril.

Lithography (5 colours) and steel engraving (1 colour), pane of 20
Canadian Bank Note Company, Limited

| 1990, Jul 12 | GT4, Harrison Paper | | | Perf 13.0x13.3 | |
|---|---|---|---|---|---|
| | | NH–VF | ⊙F | PB | FDC |
| **1279** | **39¢ multicoloured** | .90 | .45 | | 1.30 |
| **1280** | **39¢ multicoloured** | .90 | .45 | | 1.30 |
| **1281** | **39¢ multicoloured** | .90 | .45 | | 1.30 |
| **1282** | **39¢ multicoloured** | .90 | .45 | | 1.30 |
| a | se-tenant block of 4 (1279–1282) | 4.00 | 3.50 | 4.50 | 3.65 |

Qty: 3,750,000 of each

The first four stamps in a four-year series, depicting organisms found fossilized in different parts of Canada from 1900 million to 10,000 years ago.
See also 1306–1309, 1495–1498 and 1529–1532.

QE II — 1990's

## MAJESTIC FORESTS OF CANADA

1283 Acadian Forest — 1284 Great Lakes-St. Lawrence Forest

1285 Coast Forest — 1286 Boreal Forest

Designer: Malcolm Waddell. Based on an illustration by Jan Waddell.
Lithography (7 colours), Sheets of 120 subjects in six panes of 20
Ashton-Potter Limited

**1990, Aug 7** **GT4, Harrison Paper** **Perf 12.5x13.1**

| | | NH–VF | ⊙F | PB | FDC |
|---|---|---|---|---|---|
| **1283** | **39¢ multicoloured** | .90 | .35 | | 1.30 |
| i | identical vert. pair | 2.00 | 1.00 | | |
| **1284** | **39¢ multicoloured** | .90 | .35 | | 1.30 |
| i | identical vert. pair | 2.00 | 1.00 | | |
| **1285** | **39¢ multicoloured** | .90 | .35 | | 1.30 |
| i | identical vert. pair | 2.00 | 1.00 | | |
| **1286** | **39¢ multicoloured** | .90 | .35 | | 1.30 |
| i | identical vert. pair | 2.00 | 1.00 | | |
| a | se-tenant block of 4 (1283–1286) | 4.00 | 3.50 | 4.50 | 3.65 |
| **1283–6** | cancelled on Petro-Canada souvenir card. | — | 15.00 | — | — |

Qty: 9,750,000 of each

Issued for the Nineteenth World Congress of the International Union of Forestry and Research Organizations, held in Montreal, Quebec.

### Souvenir Miniature panes of 4

1283a

1284a

1285a

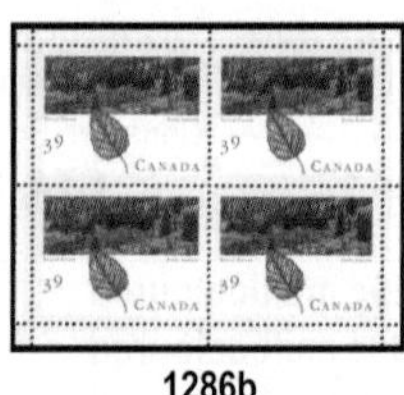

1286b

Ashton-Potter Limited, Sheets of 112 subjects in twenty-eight panes of 4

**1990, Sep 7** **GT4, Peterborough Paper** **Perf 12.5x13.1**

| | | NH–VF | ⊙F | PB | FDC |
|---|---|---|---|---|---|
| **1283a** | 39¢ multicoloured, pane of 4 | 12.50 | 10.00 | — | |
| **1284a** | 39¢ multicoloured, pane of 4 | 12.50 | 10.00 | — | |
| **1285a** | 39¢ multicoloured, pane of 4 | 12.50 | 10.00 | — | |
| **1286b** | 39¢ multicoloured, pane of 4 | 12.50 | 10.00 | — | |

The souvenir miniature panes were used for a special promotion by Petro-Canada.

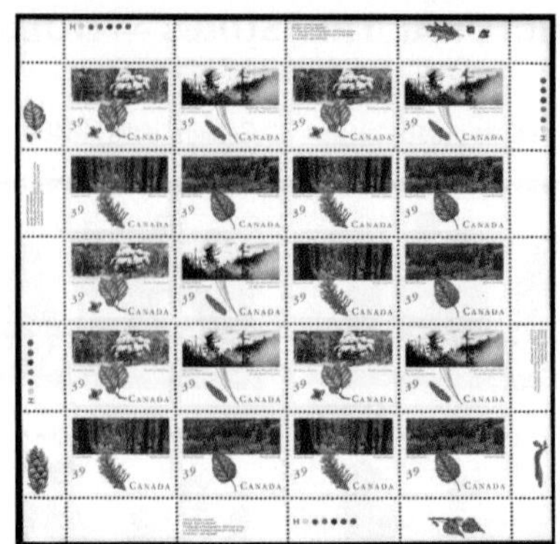

1283–1286 full pane

## WEATHER OBSERVING

1287
Rainbow in clouds

Designer: Denis L'Allier and Dominique Trudeau. Based on a photograph by David Collins.
Lithography (5 colours), pane of 50
Ashton-Potter Limited

**1990, Sep 5** **GT4, Harrison Paper** **Perf 12.5x13.3**

| | | NH–VF | ⊙F | PB | FDC |
|---|---|---|---|---|---|
| **1287** | **39¢ multicoloured**, from col. 2–4 | .80 | .30 | | 1.30 |
| i | stamp from column 1† | 1.25 | .45 | 4.00 | |
| ii | stamp from column 5† | 1.25 | .45 | 4.00 | |

Qty: 15,000,000

† Stamps in columns 1 and 5 differ slightly (in the clouds at the edges of the pane) from those in columns 2–4.

Issued to commemorate 150 years of weather observing in Canada.

**3 types of cloud formation on sides of stamp**

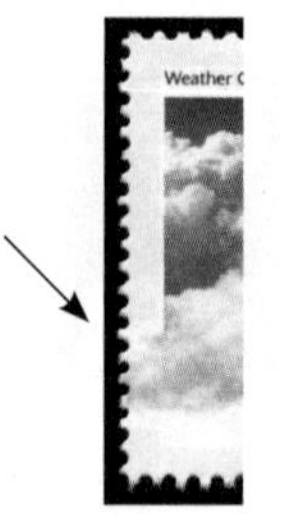

Stamps from Col 1 (left side of stamp)

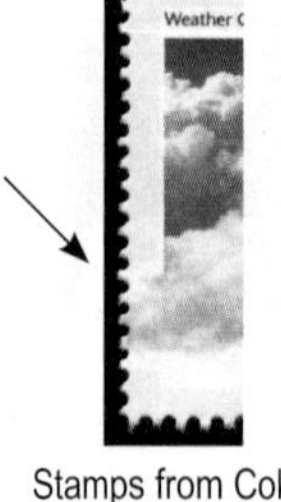

Stamps from Col 2–4 (left and right side of stamp)

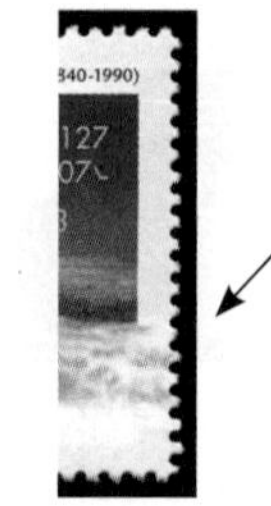

Stamps from Col 5 (right side of stamp)

## UNITED NATIONS INTERNATIONAL LITERACY YEAR

1288
Symbolic bird

Designer: Debbie Adams. Lettering engraved by Yves Baril.
Lithography (5 colours) and steel engraving (1 colour), pane of 20
Canadian Bank Note Company, Limited

| 1990, Sep 7 | GT4, Harrison Paper | | | Perf 13.3x13.1 |
|---|---|---|---|---|
| | NH–VF | ⊙F | PB | FDC |
| **1288 39¢ multicoloured** | .80 | .30 | 4.00 | 1.30 |

Qty: 15,000,000

Issued to commemorate 1990 as International Literacy Year.

## CANADIAN FOLKLORE — I

**Legendary Creatures**

1289 Sasquatch | 1290 Kraken

1291 Werewolf | 1292 Ogopogo

Designer: Ralph Tibbles. Based on illustrations by Allan Cormack and Deborah Drew-Brook.
Lithography (5 colours), pane of 50
Ashton-Potter Limited

| 1990, Oct 1 | | GT4, Peterborough Paper | | | Perf 12.5x13.3 |
|---|---|---|---|---|---|
| | | NH–VF | ⊙F | PB | FDC |
| **1289** | **39¢ multicoloured** | 1.00 | 1.00 | | |
| a | 39¢ multicoloured, perf 12.5x12.0 | 15.00 | 5.00 | | 5.00 |
| **1290** | **39¢ multicoloured** | 1.00 | 1.00 | | |
| a | 39¢ multicoloured, perf 12.5x12.0 | 15.00 | 5.00 | | 5.00 |
| **1291** | **39¢ multicoloured** | 1.00 | 1.00 | | |
| a | 39¢ multicoloured, perf 12.5x12.0 | 15.00 | 5.00 | | 5.00 |
| **1292** | **39¢ multicoloured** | 1.00 | 1.00 | | |
| a | se-tenant block of 4 (1289–1292) | 4.50 | 4.00 | 5.00 | 3.65 |
| b | as 1292a, imperf. (50 blocks exist) | 2,500.00 | | 3,000.00 | |
| ii | imperf. vert. pair (1289, 1291), from 1292b (20 pairs known) | 950.00 | | | |
| c | 39¢ multicoloured, perf 12.5x12.0 | 15.00 | 5.00 | | 5.00 |
| d | se-tenant block of 4 (1289a–1292c) | 60.00 | 40.00** | 120.00* | 25.00 |

Qty: 1289, 1291: 4,500,000 each; 1290, 1292: 3,000,000 each

* Value shown is for blank corner block only. Plate blocks of 1292d are rare. Value of plate block on FDC $50.00; mint plate block $425.

** Value shown is for regular cancel, not first day of issue cancel.

These four stamps, depicting legendary creatures, are the first in a series of stamps on Canadian folklore.

See also 1334–1337, 1432–1435 and 1491–1494.

## AGNES MACPHAIL

1293

Designer: Designed by Eskind Waddell. Based on a photograph by P. Hardy.
Lithography (7 colours), pane of 50
Ashton-Potter Limited

| 1990, Oct 9 | GT4, Slater Paper | | | Perf 13.0x13.5 |
|---|---|---|---|---|
| | NH–VF | ⊙F | PB | FDC |
| **1293 39¢ multicoloured** | .80 | .30 | 4.00 | 1.30 |

Qty: 15,000,000

Issued to celebrate the centennial of the birth of Agnes Macphail (1890–1954), Canada's first female member of parliament and Canada's first woman delegate to the League of Nations.

## CHRISTMAS (Native Nativity)

1294 Virgin Mary with Christ Child

1295 Mother and Child

1296 Children of the Raven

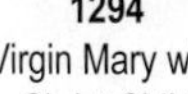

1297 Rebirth

Designer: Clermont Malenfant.
39¢: Based on a painting by Norval Morrisseau; 45¢: Based on a sculpture by Lukta Qiatsuk; 78¢: Based on a painting by William Ronald Reid; 34¢: Based on a painting by Jackson Beardy.
Lithography (5 colours; 78¢: 3 colours), panes of 50
Ashton-Potter Limited

| 1990, Oct 25 | | GT4, Slater Paper | | | Perf 13.3 |
|---|---|---|---|---|---|
| | | NH–VF | ⊙F | PB | FDC |
| **1294** | **39¢ multicoloured** | 1.00 | .25 | 5.00 | 1.30 |
| a | booklet pane of 10 x 39¢ (1294as) (BK120) | 9.00 | 12.50 | — | — |
| as | single with straight edge, from 1294a | 1.20 | .40 | — | — |
| **BK120** | pane 1294a in cover $10.00 | | | | |

Qty: 72,500,000; BK120: 17,500,000

| | | NH–VF | ⊙F | PB | FDC |
|---|---|---|---|---|---|
| **1295** | **45¢ multicoloured** | 1.25 | .90 | 6.25 | 1.40 |
| a | booklet pane of 5 x 45¢ (1295as) + label (BK121) | 6.00 | 6.50 | — | — |
| as | single with straight edge, from 1295a | 1.25 | 1.00 | — | — |
| **BK121** | pane 1295a in cover $6.50 | | | | |

Qty: 14,500,000; BK121: 3,000,000

| | | NH–VF | ⊙F | PB | FDC |
|---|---|---|---|---|---|
| **1296** | **78¢ multicoloured** | 2.00 | 1.50 | 10.00 | 2.10 |
| a | booklet pane of 5 x 78¢ (1296as) + label (BK122) | 10.00 | 8.00 | — | — |
| as | single with straight edge, from 1296a | 2.00 | 1.50 | — | — |
| **BK122** | pane 1296a in cover $11.00 | | | | |

Qty: 14,500,000; BK122: 2,000,000

**Nos. 1294–1296 (3) combination FDC** **3.75**

| | | GTX, Greetmore Booklet | | | Perf 12.5x13.1 |
|---|---|---|---|---|---|
| **1297** | **34¢ multicoloured**, from 1297a | 1.35 | .40 | — | 1.20 |
| a | booklet pane of 10 x 34¢ (1297) (2 x 5) (BK119) | 9.50 | 12.50 | — | — |
| **BK119** | pane 1297a in cover $10.00 | | | | |

Qty: 1297: 80,000,000 (8,000,000 booklets)

Number 1297 was issued in booklets only. See note following No. 1225.

The 1990 Christmas stamps feature the works of native Canadian artists: Norval Morrisseau, Ojibwa (39¢); a Cape Dorset Inuit artist, believed to be Lukta Qiatsuk (45¢); Bill Reid, Haida (78¢) and Jackson Beardy, Cree (34¢).

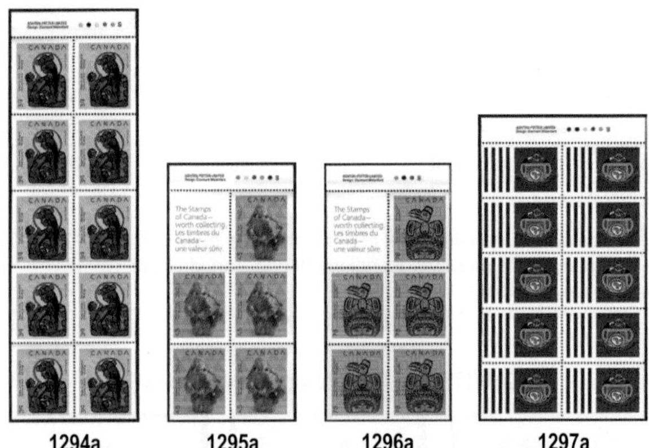

1294a 1295a 1296a 1297a

## SECOND WORLD WAR — 1940

**Canada Mobilizes its Resources**

1298 Home Front | 1299 Communal War Efforts

1300 Food Production | 1301 Science and War

Designer: Pierre-Yves Pelletier. Based on an illustration by Jean-Pierre Armanville.

Lithography (5 colours), pane of 16
Ashton-Potter, Limited

**1990, Nov 9** **GT4, Slater Paper** **Perf 12.5x12.0**

| | | NH–VF | ⊙F | PB | FDC |
|---|---|---|---|---|---|
| **1298** | **39¢ multicoloured** | 1.00 | .75 | | 1.30 |
| **1299** | **39¢ multicoloured** | 1.00 | .75 | | 1.30 |
| **1300** | **39¢ multicoloured** | 1.00 | .75 | | 1.30 |
| **1301** | **39¢ multicoloured** | 1.00 | .75 | | 1.30 |
| **a** | se-tenant block of 4 (1298–1301) | 4.50 | 4.50 | 5.00 | 4.00 |

Qty: 3,750,000 of each

The second set marking the 50th anniversary of Canada's contribution to the Allied war effort during World War II, recognizes the hardships endured by Canadians on the Home Front.

See also Nos. 1260–1263, 1345–1348, 1448–1451, 1503–1506, 1537–1540 and 1541–1544.

Canada Post's stamp announcement brochures changed from a "Presenting" pamphlet to a black and white "Canada's Stamp Details" booklet (about 5½"x7½") with the rate-change definitive issues of Dec 28. The new format included information on multiple issues, instead of just one stamp issue per pamphlet

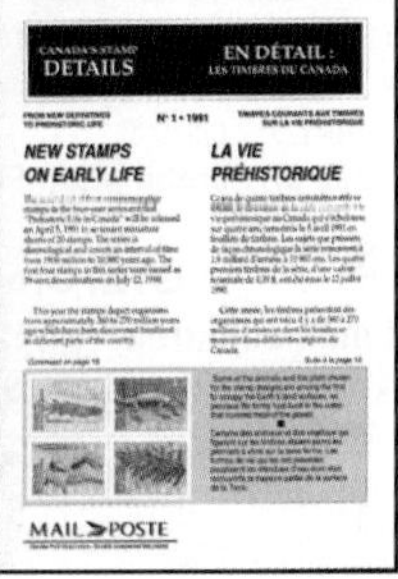


Definitive Timeline:

**1990, Dec 28** 40¢ Queen Elizabeth II (1168)
40¢ Flag over Mountains (1169)
46/63/80¢ Mammals (1172A/1176/1180
50¢ Flag Booklet (1184, 1185, 1190)

## 1991

| **Rates:** | Domestic first-class (0-30g): 40¢ | |
|---|---|---|
| Jan 1/91– | Domestic first-class (30-50g): 63¢ | USA (0-30g): 46¢ |
| Dec 31/91 | Domestic oversize (30-50g): 80¢ | International (0-20g): 80¢ |

*single usage:* USA 46¢: $15.00 | International 80¢: $25.00

Definitive Timeline:

**1991, Jan 11** 40¢ Flag over Seacoast "Quick-Stick" booklet (1193)

## CANADIAN DOCTORS

1302 Jennie K. Trout | 1303 Wilder G. Penfield

1304 Sir Frederick Banting | 1305 Harold R. Griffith

Designer: René Milot.

Lithography (5 colours), pane of 50
Ashton-Potter Limited

**1991, Mar 15** **GT4, Peterborough Paper** **Perf 13.3**

| | | NH–VF | ⊙F | PB | FDC |
|---|---|---|---|---|---|
| **1302** | **40¢ multicoloured** | .90 | .45 | | |
| **1303** | **40¢ multicoloured** | .90 | .45 | | |
| **1304** | **40¢ multicoloured** | .90 | .45 | | |
| **1305** | **40¢ multicoloured** | .90 | .45 | | |
| **a** | se-tenant block of 4 (1302–1305) | 4.00 | 3.50 | 4.50 | 3.70 |

Qty: 1302-1303: 3,900,000 each; 1304-1305: 3,600,000 each

Issued to honour the accomplishments of Canadian physicians Jennie Kidd Trout (1841-1921), Canada's first licensed woman physician; Wilder Graves Penfield (1891-1976), founder of the Montreal Neurosurgical Institute; Sir Frederick Banting (1891-1941), discoverer of insulin; and Harold Randall Griffith (1894-1985), who changed the philosophy and practice of anesthesiology.

## PREHISTORIC LIFE IN CANADA — 2

Fossils

1306 Conodonts | 1307 Archaeopteris | 1308 Eusthenopteron foordi | 1309 Hylonomus lyelli

Designer: Rolf P. Harder. Engraved by Larry Bloss.
Lithography (5 colours), pane of 20
Ashton-Potter Limited

**1991, Apr 5 — GT4, Peterborough Paper — Perf 12.5x13.5**

| | | NH–VF | ⊙F | PB | FDC |
|---|---|---|---|---|---|
| **1306** | **40¢ multicoloured** | .90 | .45 | | |
| **1307** | **40¢ multicoloured** | .90 | .45 | | |
| **1308** | **40¢ multicoloured** | .90 | .45 | | |
| **1309** | **40¢ multicoloured** | .90 | .45 | | |
| **a** | se-tenant block of 4 (1306–1309) | 4.00 | 3.50 | 4.50 | 3.70 |

Qty: 3,750,000 of each

This second set in a four part series depicts organisms from 380–270 million years ago.
See also 1279–1282, 1495–1498 and 1529–1532.

## MASTERPIECES OF CANADIAN ART — 4

1310
*Forest, British Columbia*

Designer: Pierre-Yves Pelletier based on a painting by Emily Carr.
Lithography (6 colours) with foil stamping (2 colours), pane of 16
Ashton-Potter Limited

**1991, May 7 — Untagged, Coated Papers — Perf 12.5x13.3**

| | | NH–VF | ⊙F | PB | FDC |
|---|---|---|---|---|---|
| **1310** | **50¢ multicoloured** (silver border) | 1.50 | 1.25 | 7.50 | 1.50 |

Qty: 10,500,000

Inscription/plate blocks sold by Canada Post in packaged corner sets have roulетted selvedge on the top and/or sides. Blocks removed from full panes by collectors would be either torn or cut with a knife.
See also 1203, 1241, 1271, 1419, 1466, 1516, 1545, 1602, 1635, 1754, 1800, 1863, 1916, 1945.

1315b

## PUBLIC GARDENS

1311 The Butchart Gardens, BC | 1312 International Peace Garden, MB

1313 Royal Botanical Gardens, ON | 1314 Montreal Botanical Garden, QC | 1315 Halifax Public Gardens, NS

Designer: David Wyman. Based on illustrations by Gerard Gauci.
Lithography (5 colours), booklet pane of 10
Ashton-Potter Limited

**1991, May 22 — GT4, Coated Papers — Perf 13.0x12.5**

| | | NH–VF | ⊙F | FDC |
|---|---|---|---|---|
| **1311** | **40¢ multicoloured** | 1.00 | .50 | |
| **1312** | **40¢ multicoloured** | 1.00 | .50 | |
| **1313** | **40¢ multicoloured** | 1.00 | .50 | |
| **1314** | **40¢ multicoloured** | 1.00 | .50 | |
| **1315** | **40¢ multicoloured** | 1.00 | .50 | |
| **a** | horizontal strip of 5 (1311–1315) | 5.25 | 4.50 | 4.50 |
| **ai** | never folded strip of 5 different* | 7.50 | 8.00 | |
| **b** | booklet pane of 10 (5 x 2), 2 x 1315a se-tenant (BK130) | 10.50 | 9.00 | |
| **BK130** | pane 1315b in cover $11.00 | | | |

Qty: 3,000,000 each.
* Available only in Canada Post quarterly packs and annual collections. Pane in booklet has been folded to fit cover.

## CANADA DAY

1316
Stylized Maple Leaf

Designer: Jean-Pierre Veilleux, Lisa Miller and Roger Séguin.
Based on an illustration by Laurie Lafrance.
Lithography (5 colours), Sheets of 80 subjects in four panes of 20
Canadian Bank Note Company, Limited

**1991, Jun 28 — GT4, Coated Papers — Perf 13.3x13.0**

| | | NH–VF | ⊙F | PB | FDC |
|---|---|---|---|---|---|
| **1316** | **40¢ multicoloured** | 1.00 | .50 | 5.00 | 1.30 |

Qty: 15,000,000

| | | NH–VF | ⊙F | PB | FDC |
|---|---|---|---|---|---|
| **1341** | **80¢ multicoloured** | 1.80 | 1.25 | 9.00 | |
| b | imperf. pair* | 1,000.00 | | | |
| a | booklet pane of 5 x 80¢ (1341as) + label (BK136) | 8.50 | 8.00 | — | |
| as | single with straight edge, from 1341a | 2.00 | 1.25 | — | |

BK136 pane 1341a in cover $9.00

Qty: 13,000,000; BK136: 400,000

* Most imperf. pairs seen by the editors have been mishandled and are creased due to improper handling. Creased pairs worth $250.00–$500.00

**Nos. 1339–1341 (3) combination FDC** **3.80**

**GTX, Greetmore Booklet** **Perf 12.5x13.0**

| | | NH–VF | ⊙F | PB | FDC |
|---|---|---|---|---|---|
| **1342** | **35¢ multicoloured**, from 1342a | 1.00 | .30 | — | 1.20 |
| a | booklet pane of 10 x 35¢ (1342) (BK133) | 10.00 | 6.00 | — | |

BK133 pane 1342a in cover $11.00

No. 1342 was issued in booklets only. See note following No. 1225.

Qty: 1342: 70,000,000 (7,000,000 booklets)

Four classical images of the famous "man in red", based on characters made from torn paper.

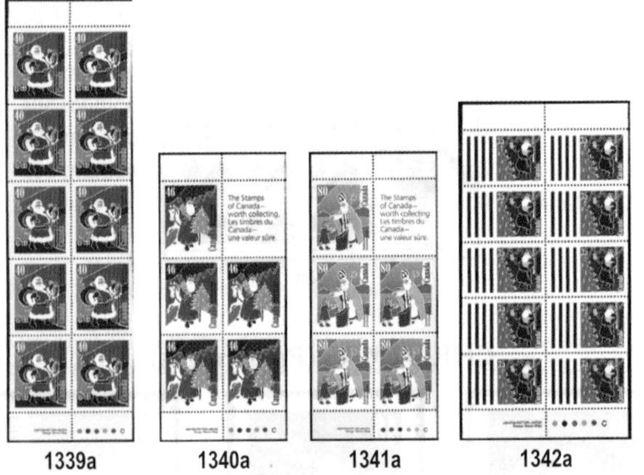

1339a 1340a 1341a 1342a

## BASKETBALL

1343

1344a

1344b

1344c

1344

Designer: Charles Reynolds, Joseph Gault and Tiit Telmet.

Lithography (7 colours; souvenir sheet: 8 colours), pane of 50

Ashton-Potter Limited

**1991, Oct 25** **GT4, Coated Papers** **Perf 13.0x13.5**

| | | NH–VF | ⊙F | PB | FDC |
|---|---|---|---|---|---|
| **1343** | **40¢ multicoloured**† | 1.00 | .30 | 5.00 | 1.30 |
| i | repellex error: blue background omitted on middle stamp in strip of 3 | *2,750.00* | *1,350.00** | — | — |

Qty: 15,000,000

* one used example reported to date (with cert.).

| | | NH–VF | ⊙F | PB | FDC |
|---|---|---|---|---|---|
| **1344** | **$1.66 souvenir sheet** of 3 | 7.00 | 7.00 | | 5.75 |
| a | 40¢ multicoloured, ex souvenir sheet† | 1.50 | 1.50 | | |
| b | 46¢ multicoloured, ex souvenir sheet | 2.00 | 2.00 | | |
| c | 80¢ multicoloured, ex souvenir sheet | 3.00 | 3.00 | | |

Qty: 500,000 souvenir sheets

Issued to commemorate the centennial of the game of basketball, invented by James A. Naismith in 1891.

† The 40¢ sheet stamp (1343) bears the name of the inventor in the legend; the three stamps from the souvenir sheet (1344) do not.

1343i

## SECOND WORLD WAR — 1941

Total War

1345 Women's Armed Forces — 1346 War industry

1347 Cadets and veterans — 1348 The defence of Hong Kong

Designer: Pierre-Yves Pelletier. Based on an illustration by Jean-Pierre Armanville.

Lithography (5 colours), pane of 16

Canadian Bank Note Company, Limited

**1991, Nov 8** **GT4, Coated Papers** **Perf 13.3**

| | | NH–VF | ⊙F | PB | FDC |
|---|---|---|---|---|---|
| **1345** | **40¢ multicoloured** | 1.00 | .70 | | |
| **1346** | **40¢ multicoloured** | 1.00 | .70 | | |
| **1347** | **40¢ multicoloured** | 1.00 | .70 | | |
| **1348** | **40¢ multicoloured** | 1.00 | .70 | | |
| a | se-tenant block of 4 (1345–1348) | 4.50 | 4.00 | 5.00 | 4.00 |

Qty: 3,750,000 of each

The third set marking the 50th anniversary of World War II.

See also Nos. 1260–1263, 1298–1301, 1448–1451, 1503–1506, 1537–1540 and 1541–1544.

## EDIBLE BERRIES DEFINITIVES 1992–1998

### Low Values — Edible Berries

1349 Blueberry

1350 Wild Strawberry

1351 Black Crowberry

1352 Rose Hip

1353 Black Raspberry

1354 Kinnikinnick

1355 Saskatoon Berry

The initial printing (1992) of the low-value Edible Berry definitives was by Ashton-Potter Limited (AP), on Coated paper.

A second printing of all values except the 1¢ (spring 1994) was printed by Canadian Bank Note (CBN) on Harrison paper.

A third printing of all values (summer 1994) was printed by Canadian Bank Note on Coated paper.

A fourth, and final, printing (summer 1995) of all values except the 6¢ was printed by Ashton-Potter Canada Ltd. (APC) (name change due to previous bankruptcy) on Coated paper.

Designer: Dennis Noble. Typographed by Tania Craan.

Lithography (5 colours), panes of 100
Ashton-Potter Limited

**1992, Aug 5** **Untagged, Coated Papers** **Perf 13.1x13.6**

| | | NH–VF | ⊙F | PB | FDC |
|---|---|---|---|---|---|
| **1349** | **1¢ multicoloured** | .25 | .20 | 1.25 | — |
| a | imperf. pair | 1,000.00 | | | |
| i | CBN, *Aug 19, 1994* | .25 | — | 1.25 | |
| ii | APC, *Apr 3, 1995* | .25 | — | 1.25 | |
| iv | "Snake in grass" (column 1, row 2–10) | 3.00 | 1.50 | 10.00 | |
| v | "blue thread" (column 5, row 2–10) | 3.00 | 1.50 | | |
| **1350** | **2¢ multicoloured** | .25 | .20 | 1.25 | — |
| a | imperf. pair | 1,000.00 | | | |
| i | CBN, Harrison paper, *Apr 22, 1994* | .30 | .20 | 1.50 | — |
| ii | CBN, Coated Papers, *Aug 19, 1994* | .25 | — | 1.25 | — |
| iii | APC, Coated Papers, *Aug 1, 1995* | .25 | — | 1.25 | — |
| v | "Rose thorn" (column 8, rows 2–10) | 3.00 | 1.50 | | |
| vi | "Snake in bush" (column 1, rows 2–10) | 3.00 | 1.50 | 10.00 | |
| vii | "blue thread" (column 5, row 2–10) | 3.00 | 1.50 | | |

| | | NH–VF | ⊙F | PB | FDC |
|---|---|---|---|---|---|
| **1351** | **3¢ multicoloured** | .25 | .20 | 1.25 | — |
| a | imperf. pair | 1,000.00 | | | |
| i | CBN, Harrison paper, *Apr 22, 1994* | .30 | .20 | 1.50 | — |
| ii | CBN, Coated Papers, *Aug 19, 1994* | .25 | — | 1.25 | — |
| iii | APC, Coated Papers, *May 2, 1997* | .25 | — | 1.25 | — |
| v | "poisoned berry" (pos 22)* | 10.00 | 5.00 | | |
| vi | "blue thread" (column 5, row 2–10) | 3.00 | 1.50 | | |
| vii | "Snake in grass" (column 1, row 2–10) | 3.00 | 1.50 | 10.00 | |

* Price for position block of 6 $30.00.

| | | NH–VF | ⊙F | PB | FDC |
|---|---|---|---|---|---|
| **1352** | **5¢ multicoloured** | .25 | .20 | 1.25 | — |
| a | imperf. pair | 1,000.00 | | | |
| i | CBN, Harrison paper, *Mar 11, 1994* | .40 | .20 | 2.00 | — |
| ii | CBN, Coated Papers, *Aug 19, 1994* | .25 | — | 1.25 | — |
| iii | APC, Coated Papers, *Sep 20, 1995* | .25 | — | 1.25 | — |
| v | "blue thread" (column 5, row 2–10) | 3.00 | 1.50 | | |
| vi | "Rose thorn" (column 8, rows 2–10) | 3.00 | 1.50 | | |
| **1353** | **6¢ multicoloured** | .25 | .20 | 1.25 | — |
| a | imperf. pair | 1,000.00 | | | |
| i | CBN, Harrison paper, *Mar 11, 1994* | .40 | .20 | 2.00 | — |
| ii | CBN, Coated Papers, *Aug 18, 1994* | .25 | — | 1.25 | — |
| iv | "blue thread" (column 5, row 2–10) | 3.00 | 1.50 | | |
| v | "leaf mold" (column 9, rows 2–10) | 3.00 | 1.50 | | |
| **1354** | **10¢ multicoloured** | .25 | .20 | 1.25 | — |
| a | horizontal pair from bottom row, imperf. except along top of stamps ‡ | 1,500.00 | — | 1,650.00 | |
| b | imperf. pair | 1,000.00 | | | |
| i | CBN, Harrison paper, *Mar 11, 1994* | .50 | .20 | 2.50 | — |
| iii | CBN, Coated Papers, *Aug 19,1994* | .25 | — | 1.25 | — |
| iv | APC, Coated Papers, *Sep 1, 1995* | .25 | — | 1.25 | — |
| vi | "blue thread" (column 5, row 2–10) | 3.00 | 1.50 | | |
| vii | "Rose thorn" (column 8, rows 2–10) | 3.00 | 1.50 | | |
| viii | "smiling berry" (column 1, rows 1–10) | 3.00 | 1.50 | 10.00 | |
| ix | stroke on 'k' (pos 91) | 10.00 | 5.00 | 15.00 | |

‡ Five panes are known.

| | | NH–VF | ⊙F | PB | FDC |
|---|---|---|---|---|---|
| **1355** | **25¢ multicoloured** | .50 | .30 | 2.50 | — |
| a | imperf. pair | 1,000.00 | | | |
| i | CBN, Harrison paper, *Apr 22, 1994* | .80 | .30 | 5.00 | — |
| ii | CBN, Coated Papers, *Aug 19, 1994* | .50 | — | 2.50 | — |
| iii | APC, Coated Papers, *May 1, 1996* | .50 | — | 2.50 | — |
| v | "Snake in grass" (column 1, row 2–10) | 3.00 | 2.00 | 10.00 | |
| vi | "blue thread" (column 5, row 2–10) | 3.00 | 2.00 | | |
| vii | "Rose thorn" (column 8, rows 2–10) | 3.00 | 2.00 | | |

**Nos. 1349–1355 (7) combination FDC** 1.50

Constant flaws on the low value berry stamps are plentiful. Many share the same printing cylinder across most values and used by different printers. These are the most prominent.

| *Flaw* | Snake in grass/bush | Blue thread | Rose thorn | Poisoned berry* | Leaf mold* | Smiling berry* | Extra stroke in K* |
|---|---|---|---|---|---|---|---|
| *Printer* | CBNs and APC | CBNs and APC | CBNs and APC | CBN (2nd) and APC | AP | AP | CBNs and APC |
| *Position* | Col 1, Row 2–10 | Col 5, Row 2–10 | Col 8, Row 2–10 | Col 2, Row 3 | Col 9, Row 2–10 | Col 1, Row 1–10 | Col 1, Row 10 |
| 1¢ | 1349iv | 1349v | | | | | |
| 2¢ | 1350vi | 1350vii | 1350v | | | | |
| 3¢ | 1351vii | 1351vi | ‡ | 1351v | | | |
| 5¢ | ‡ | 1352v | 1352vi | | | | |
| 6¢ | ‡ | 1353iv | ‡ | | 1353v | | |
| 10¢ | ‡ | 1354vi | 1354vii | | | 1354viii | 1354ix |
| 25¢ | 1355v | 1355vi | 1355vii | | | | |

* variety is unique to the value noted
‡ indicates the variety is not visible due to overlapping darker colour(s)

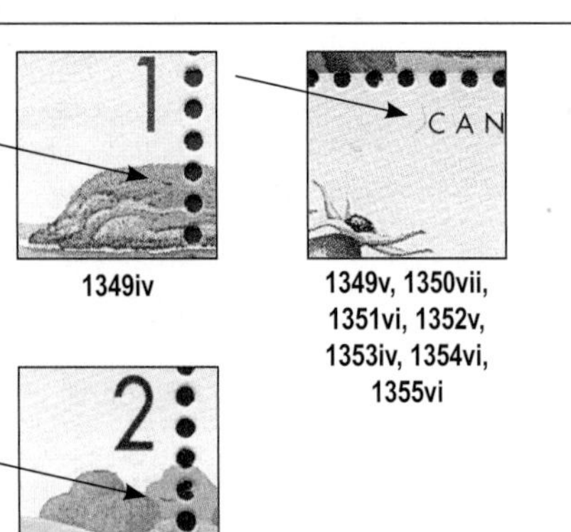

1349iv

1349v, 1350vii, 1351vi, 1352v, 1353iv, 1354vi, 1355vi

1350vi

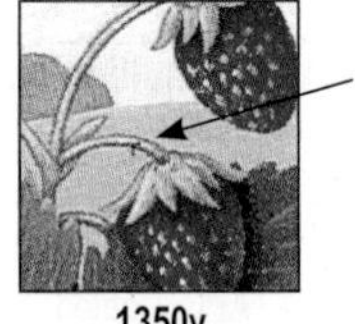

1350v

1351v

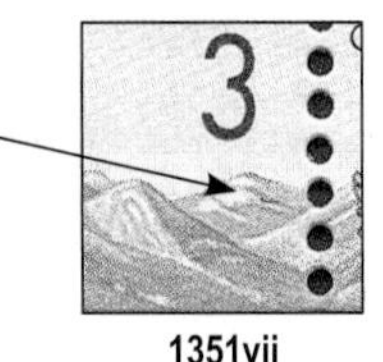

1351vii

1352vi

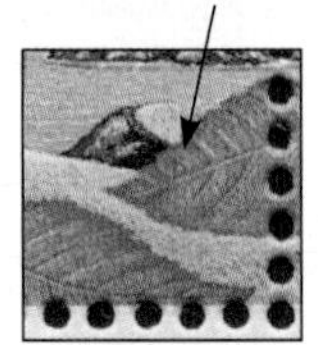

1353v

1354vii

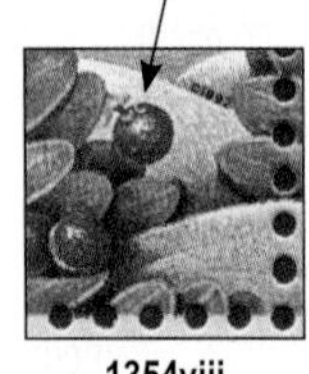

1354viii

1354ix

1355v

1355vii

1354a

## DOMESTIC FIRST-CLASS RATE

1356
Flag over Hills

1356a

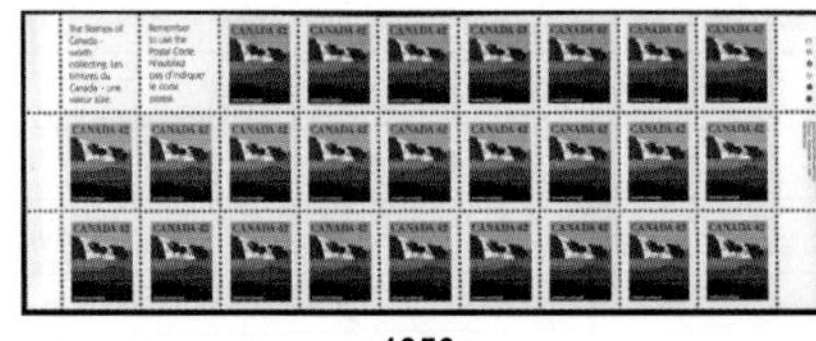

1356c

Designer: Gottschalk + Ash International.

Lithography (5 colours), pane of 100
Ashton-Potter Limited

| **1991, Dec 27** | **GT4, Coated Papers** | | | **Perf 13.6x13.1** | |
|---|---|---|---|---|---|
| | | **NH–VF** | **⊙F** | **PB** | **FDC** |
| **1356** | **42¢ multicoloured** | 1.00 | .20 | 5.00 | 1.35 |
| i | imperf. pair | 1,000.00 | | | |
| a | booklet pane of 10 x 42¢ (1356as) (BK137) | 10.00 | 8.00 | | |
| as | single with straight edge, from 1356a, 1356b or 1356c | 1.25 | .25 | | |
| b | booklet pane of 50 x 42¢ (1356 and 1356as) + 2 labels (BK139) | 120.00 | 100.00 | | |
| c | booklet pane of 25 x 42¢ (1356a and 1356as) + 2 labels (BK138) | 23.00 | 18.00 | | |
| d | vertical pair, imperf. between, from miscut pane (24 known) | 1,200.00 | | 2,750.00* | |
| i | vertical pair, imperf. between stamp and label (2 known) | *3,000.00* | | | |

* block of 8 with 2 imperf between pairs and imprints in right margin.

**BK137** pane 1356a in cover $11.00
**BK138** pane 1356c in cover $24.00
**BK139** pane 1356b in cover $125.00

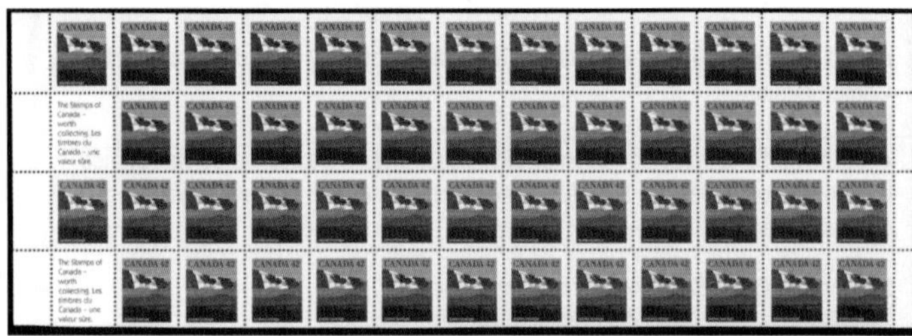

1356b

1357
Queen Elizabeth II

Designer: Yousuf Karsh, Tom Yakobina, Chris Candlish.

Lithography (5 colours), pane of 100
Ashton-Potter Limited

| **1991, Dec 27** | **GT4, Coated Papers** | | | **Perf 13.1x13.6** | |
|---|---|---|---|---|---|
| | | **NH–VF** | **⊙F** | **PB** | **FDC** |
| **1357** | **42¢ multicoloured** (purple) | 1.00 | .20 | 5.00 | 1.35 |
| **b** | imperf. pair | 1,000.00 | | | |
| a | booklet pane of 10 x 42¢ (1357as), with perforated selvedge (BK140/A) | 10.00 | 8.00 | | |
| as | single with straight edge, from 1357a or 1357ai | 1.25 | .25 | | |
| ai | booklet pane of 10 x 42¢ (1357as), with imperforate selvedge (BK140c/Ac) | 10.00 | 8.00 | | |

**BK140** pane 1357a in cover $11.00

1357a

1357ai

1358
Queen Elizabeth II

Designer: Yousuf Karsh, Tom Yakobina, Chris Candlish.

Lithography (5 colours), pane of 100
Canadian Bank Note

**1992, Dec 30** **GT4, Peterborough Paper** **Perf 13.1x13.6**

| | | NH–VF | ⊙F | PB | FDC |
|---|---|---|---|---|---|
| **1358** | **43¢ multicoloured** (grey-black), LF | 1.25 | .20 | 6.25 | 1.35 |
| ii | MF | 7.00 | .35 | 35.00 | |
| a | booklet pane of 10 x 43¢ (1358as), AP, Coated Papers (BK155) | 12.50 | 12.00 | | |
| as | single w/straight edge, from 1358a | 1.50 | .25 | | |
| b | imperf. pair, Coated Papers (from either 1358a or 1358avi) | 1,200.00 | | | |
| aiv | as 1358a, CBN, Harrison paper, (BK155A, B), *Jan 7, 1994* | 10.00 | 12.00 | | |
| aivs | single w/straight edge, from 1358aiv | 1.50 | .25 | | |
| av | as 1358a, CBN, Peterborough paper, (BK155C), *Dec 23, 1994* | 14.00 | 12.00 | | |
| avs | single w/straight edge, from 1358av | 1.75 | .25 | | |
| avi | as 1358a, APC, Coated Papers (BK155D), *Mar 27, 1995* | 11.00 | 12.00 | | |
| avis | single w/straight edge, from 1358avi | 1.25 | .25 | | |
| BK155 | pane 1358a in cover $13.00 | | | | |

1358a

1358aiv

1358av

1358avi

1359
Flag over Field

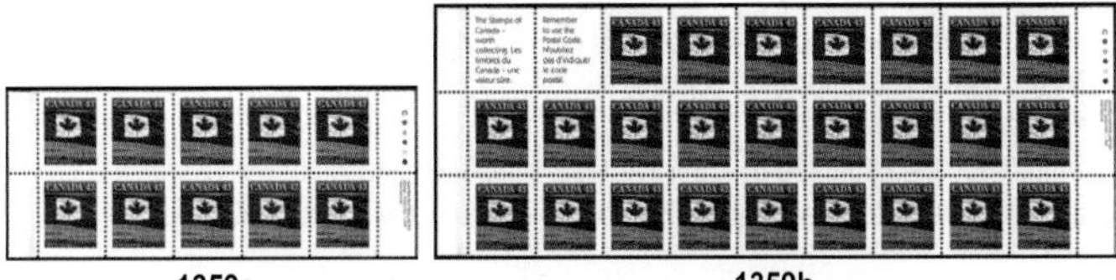
1359a
1359b

1359f x 7 and 1359fii x 2

Designer: Gottschalk + Ash International.

Lithography (5 colours), pane of 100
Ashton-Potter Limited

**1992, Dec 30** **GT4, Coated Papers** **Perf 13.6x13.1**

| | | NH–VF | ⊙F | PB | FDC |
|---|---|---|---|---|---|
| **1359** | **43¢ multicoloured** | 1.25 ‡ | .20 ‡ | 6.25 | 1.35 |
| g | imperf. pair | 1,000.00 | | | |
| ii | double print † | | | | |
| iii | imperf. at right margin | 300.00 | | 750.00* | |

* Blank corner block.
† as listed in previous editions; this may be a colour shift. Further research required.

| | | | |
|---|---|---|---|
| a | booklet pane of 10 x 43¢ (1359as) (BK153) | 10.00 | 8.00 |
| as | single with straight edge, from 1359a or 1359b | 1.50 ‡ | .25 ‡ |
| b | booklet pane of 25 x 43¢ (1359 and 1359as) + 2 labels (BK154) | 30.00 | 25.00 |
| BK153 | pane 1359a in cover $10.50 | | |
| BK154 | pane 1359b in cover $32.00 | | |

Leigh-Mardon Pty, Limited

**1994, Jan 7** **GT4, Coated Papers** **Perf 14.5x14.6**

| | | | | | |
|---|---|---|---|---|---|
| **1359c** | 43¢ multicoloured | 1.50 | .25 | 7.50 | — |
| d | booklet pane of 10 x 43¢ (1359ds) (BK153A or B) | 12.50 | 10.00 | | |
| ds | single with straight edge, from 1359d or 1359e | 1.75 | .25 | | |
| e | booklet pane of 25 x 43¢ (1359c and 1359ds) + 2 labels (BK154A or B) | 35.00 | 30.00 | | |
| f | vertical pair, imperf. between | 1,000.00 | — | | |
| fi | as 1359f, in booklet pane of 10 | 5,000.00 | | | |
| fii | vertical pair (stamp and label), imperf. between | 2,000.00 | — | | |

Blocks of 16 + 2 labels, consisting of 1359f (7 pairs) and 1359fii (2 pairs) exist.

Canadian Bank Note

**1994, Nov 14** **GT4, Coated Papers** **Perf 13.6x13.1**

| | | | | | |
|---|---|---|---|---|---|
| **1359x** | 43¢ multicoloured, *Jan 19, 1995* | 1.00 ‡ | .20 ‡ | 5.00 | — |
| xi | booklet pane of 10 x 43¢ (1359xis) (BK153C) | 14.00 | 12.50 | | |
| xis | single with straight edge, from 1359xi or 1359xii | 1.50 ‡ | .25 ‡ | | |
| xii | booklet pane of 25 x 43¢ (1359x and 1359xis) + 2 labels (BK154C) | 22.00 | 25.00 | | |

Imperforates from booklets BK153–BK155 have been seen by the editors. Quantities and values not established.

‡ Ashton-Potter (1359/1359as) and Canadian Bank Note (1359x/1359xis) examples can only be differentiated on copies with attached selvedge with imprints.

1359ii

1359iii

**1360**
Queen Elizabeth II

Designer: Yousuf Karsh, Tom Yakobina, Chris Candlish.
Lithography (5 colours), pane of 100
Canadian Bank Note

| 1995, Jul 31 | GT4, Coated Papers | | | Perf 13.1x13.6 | |
|---|---|---|---|---|---|
| | | NH–VF | ⊙F | PB | FDC |
| **1360** | **45¢ multicoloured** (turquoise) | 1.00 | .20 | 5.00 | 1.50 |
| | **Peterborough Paper** | | | | |
| 1360a | booklet pane of 10 x 45¢ (1360as) (BK179) | 10.00 | 8.00 | | |
| as | single with straight edge, from 1360a | 1.50 | .30 | | |
| BK179 | pane 1360a in cover $11.00 | | | | |

Ashton-Potter Canada Limited

| 1995, Oct 6 | Coated Papers | | | | |
|---|---|---|---|---|---|
| **1360viii** | 45¢ multicoloured | 1.00 | .20 | 5.00 | — |
| ix | booklet pane of 10 x 45¢ (1360ixs) (BK179A) | 10.00 | 8.00 | | |
| ixs | single w/straight edge, from 1360ix | 1.50 | .40 | | |

1360a

**1361**
Flag over Building

Stamp size: 22x26mm
Design size: 17x22mm
(image shown at actual size)

For smaller size stamp (20x24mm), see 1362.

Designer: Gottschalk + Ash International.
Lithography (5 colours), pane of 100
Leigh-Mardon Pty, Limited

| 1995, Jul 31 | GT4, Coated Papers | | | Perf 14.5x14.6 | |
|---|---|---|---|---|---|
| | | NH–VF | ⊙F | PB | FDC |
| **1361** | **45¢ multicoloured** | 1.00 | .20 | 5.00 | 1.50 |
| a | booklet pane of 10 x 45¢ (1361as) (BK177) | 12.50 | 10.00 | | |
| as | single with straight edge, from 1361a or 1361b | 1.50 | .40 | | |
| b | booklet pane of 25 x 45¢ (1361 and 1361as) + 2 labels (BK178) | 37.50 | 30.00 | | |
| BK177 | pane 1361a in cover $13.00 | | | | |
| BK178 | pane 1361b in cover $38.00 | | | | |

Canadian Bank Note

| 1995, Oct 6 | GT4, Coated Papers | | | Perf 13.6x13.1 | |
|---|---|---|---|---|---|
| **1361c** | **45¢ multicoloured**, NF | 1.00 | .20 | 5.00 | — |
| xxi | F paper | 1.00 | .20 | | |
| d | booklet pane of 10 x 45¢ (1361ds) (BK177A) | 10.00 | 9.00 | | |
| ds | single with straight edge, from 1361d or 1361e | 1.50 | .30 | | |
| T7 | untagged (error) (single stamp) | — | 50.00 | | |
| e | booklet pane of 25 x 45¢ (1361c and 1361ds) + 2 labels (BK178A) | 25.00 | 20.00 | | |

| 1996, Apr 5 | GT4, Peterborough Paper | | | | |
|---|---|---|---|---|---|
| **1361xiii** | 45¢ multicoloured | 1.00 | .20 | 5.00 | — |
| xiv | booklet pane of 10 x 45¢ (1361xivs) (BK177B), LF | 10.00 | 9.00 | | |
| xivs | single with straight edge, from 1361xiv or 1361xv | 1.50 | .40 | | |
| xvi | as xiv, pane of 10, dull | 20.00 | | | |
| xvii | as xiv, pane of 10, MF | 25.00 | | | |
| xv | booklet pane of 25 x 45¢ (1361xiii and 1361xivs) + 2 labels (BK178B) | 25.00 | 20.00 | | |

The so-called "snowstorm" variety: When some booklets are opened, stray spots of glue on the cover adhere to the printed face of the stamps. Ink is removed by the glue, leaving spots of "snow". These are damaged stamps.

1361a 1361b

**1362**
Flag over Building

Stamp size: 20x24mm
Design size: 16x20mm
(image shown at actual size)

For larger size stamp (22x26mm), see 1361.

Designer: Gottschalk + Ash International.
Lithography (5 colours), pane of 120 + gutter
Canadian Bank Note

| 1998, Feb 2 | GT4, Coated Papers | | | Perf 13.0x13.3 | |
|---|---|---|---|---|---|
| | | NH–VF | ⊙F | PB | FDC |
| **1362** | **45¢ multicoloured** | .90 | .20 | 4.50 | 1.50 |
| i | horizontal pair, gutter between | 5.00 | 4.00 | | |
| c | imperf. pair | 750.00 | | | |
| iii | imperf. gutter pair | 2,250.00 | | | |
| iv | offset on reverse | 125.00 | | | |
| a | booklet pane of 10 x 45¢ (1362as) (BK205) | 10.50 | 12.00 | | |
| as | single with straight edge, from 1362a | 1.00 | .35 | | |
| BK205 | pane 1362a in cover $12.00 | | | | |
| | Ashton-Potter Canada Limited | | | | |
| 1362b | booklet pane of 30 x 45¢ (1362 and 1362bs) (BK206) | 32.00 | 30.00 | | |
| bs | single with straight edge, from 1362b | 1.00 | .30 | | |
| bvi | horizontal gutter pair with straight edge, from 1362b | 5.00 | 2.00 | | |
| bvii | perforated horizontal gutter pair | 4.00 | | | |
| BK206 | pane 1362b in cover $33.00 | | | | |

Number 1362 was printed by CBN in sheets of 120 (2 sections of 5 x 12 with a perforated vertical gutter between); similar to image shown after 1682 (46¢ Flag).

For non-denominated postal card of same design, see UX120.

1362a 1362b

## FRUIT TREE DEFINITIVES 1991–1996

### USA RATE

1363
McIntosh Apple

1364
Delicious Apple

1365
Snow Apple

1366
Gravenstein Apple

Designer: Clermont Malenfant.

Lithography (5 colours), panes of 50
Ashton-Potter Limited

**1991, Dec 27** **GT4, Coated Papers** **Perf 13.1**

| | | NH–VF | ⊙F | PB | FDC |
|---|---|---|---|---|---|
| **1363** | **48¢ multicoloured** | 1.25 | .30 | 6.25 | — |
| c | imperf. pair | 1,250.00 | | | |
| ii | vertical black line in stem (pos. 1) | 5.00 | 3.50 | 15.00 | |

**GT4, Coated Papers** **Perf 14.4x13.8**

| | | | |
|---|---|---|---|
| 1363a | single with straight edge, from 1363b | 2.00 | .50 |
| b | booklet pane of 5 x 48¢ (1363a) + label (BK142) | 10.00 | 8.00 |
| BK142 | pane 1363b in cover $11.00 | | |

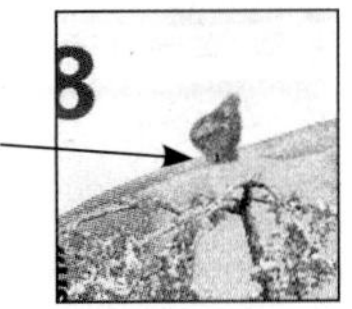

1363ii

Ashton-Potter Limited

**1992, Dec 30** **GT4, Coated Papers** **Perf 13.1**

| | | NH–VF | ⊙F | PB | FDC |
|---|---|---|---|---|---|
| **1364** | **49¢ multicoloured** | 1.25 | .30 | 6.25 | — |

**GT4, Coated Papers** **Perf 14.4x13.8**

| | | | |
|---|---|---|---|
| 1364a | single with straight edge, from 1364b | 3.50 | .45 |
| b | booklet pane of 5 x 49¢ (1364a) + label (BK156) | 17.50 | 8.00 |
| BK156 | pane 1364b in cover $20.00 | | |

Canadian Bank Note

**1994, Jan 7** **GT4, Harrison Paper** **Perf 13.1**

| | | | | | |
|---|---|---|---|---|---|
| 1364i | 49¢ multicoloured | 2.50 | .40 | 12.50 | — |
| c | booklet pane of 5 x 49¢ (1364cs) + label (BK156A) | 16.50 | 14.00 | | |
| cs | single with straight edge, from 1364c | 3.50 | 1.00 | | |

An "essay" of the Delicious Apple design with an 86¢ denomination exists in imperforate form. Value $2,000.00 (pair).

Canadian Bank Note

**1994, Feb 25** **GT4, Harrison Paper** **Perf 13.1**

| | | NH–VF | ⊙F | PB | FDC |
|---|---|---|---|---|---|
| **1365** | **50¢ multicoloured** | 1.25 | .35 | 6.25 | — |

**Peterborough Paper**

| | | | |
|---|---|---|---|
| as | single with straight edge, from 1365a | 2.00 | .45 |
| a | booklet pane of 5 x 50¢ (1365as) + label (BK167) | 9.00 | 7.00 |
| BK167 | pane 1365a in cover $10.00 | | |

Ashton-Potter Canada Limited

**1995** **GT4, Coated Papers** **Perf 13.1**

| | | | | | |
|---|---|---|---|---|---|
| 1365i | 50¢ multicoloured, *Apr 10, 1995* | 2.00 | .50 | 15.00 | — |

**Perf 14.4x13.8**

| | | | |
|---|---|---|---|
| b | single from 1365c | 3.00 | .55 |
| c | booklet pane of 5 x 50¢ (1365b) + label (BK167B), *Mar 27, 1995* | 18.00 | 16.00 |

**Fruit Trees**

| Format | Sheet | | | | | | | Booklet | | | | | | |
|---|---|---|---|---|---|---|---|---|---|---|---|---|---|---|
| Printer | AP | | CBN | | | AP | | AP | | | | CBN | | |
| Perf | 13.1 | | | | | 14.4x13.8 | | 14.4x13.8 | | 13.1 | | | | |
| Paper | Coated | | Harrison | Peterborough | | Coated | | Coated | | | | Harrison | Peterborough | |
| Tag | Block | 3-bar | Block | | 3-bar | Block | 3-bar | Block | 3-bar | Block | 3-bar | Block | | 3-bar |
| 48¢ Macintosh | 1363 | | | | | | | 1363a | | | | | | |
| 49¢ Delicious | 1364 | | 1364i | | | | | 1364a | | | | 1364cs | | |
| 50¢ Snow | 1365i | | 1365 | | | | | 1365b | | | | | 1365as | |
| 52¢ Gravenstein | 1366i | | | 1366 | | 1366b | | 1366cs | | 1366iis | | | 1366as | |
| 65¢ Walnut | 1367 | | | | | | | | | | | | | |
| 67¢ Hazelnut | 1368 | | | | | | | | | | | | | |
| 69¢ Hickory | 1369i | | 1369 | | | | | | | | | | | |
| 71¢ Chestnut | 1370i | | | 1370 | | 1370a | | | | | | | | |
| 84¢ Plum | 1371 | | | | | | | 1371a | | | | | | |
| 86¢ Pear | 1372 | | 1372i | | | | | 1372a | | | | 1372cs | | |
| 88¢ Apricot | | 1373ii | | 1373 | 1373i | | | | 1373b | | | | 1373as | 1373iiis |
| 90¢ Peach | | 1374i | | | 1374 | | 1374ii | | 1374b | | 1374iiis | | | 1374as |

Canadian Bank Note

**1995, Jul 31 — GT4, Peterborough Paper — Perf 13.1**

| | | NH–VF | ⊙F | PB | FDC |
|---|---|---|---|---|---|
| **1366** | **52¢ multicoloured** | 2.00 | .50 | 10.00 | — |
| a | booklet pane of 5 x 52¢ (1366as) + label (BK180) | 10.00 | 8.00 | | |
| as | single with straight edge, from 1366a | 2.00 | .55 | | |
| BK180 | pane 1366a in cover $11.00 | | | | |

Ashton-Potter Canada Limited

**1995, Oct 6 — GT4, Coated Papers — Perf 14.4x13.8**

| | | NH–VF | ⊙F | PB | FDC |
|---|---|---|---|---|---|
| **1366b** | 52¢ multicoloured | 3.00 | .75 | 15.00 | — |
| c | booklet pane of 5 x 52¢ (1366cs) + label (BK180A) | 13.00 | 11.00 | | |
| cs | single with straight edge, from 1366c | 2.75 | 1.00 | | |

**1996, Oct — Perf 13.1**

| | | NH–VF | ⊙F | PB | FDC |
|---|---|---|---|---|---|
| **1366i** | 52¢ multicoloured | 6.00 | .35 | 150.00* | — |
| ii | booklet pane of 5 x 52¢ (1366iii) + label (BK180B) | 16.00 | 13.00 | | |
| iis | single with straight edge, from 1366ii | 3.00 | 1.00 | | |

* Plate blocks are very scarce.

1363b 1364b 1364c

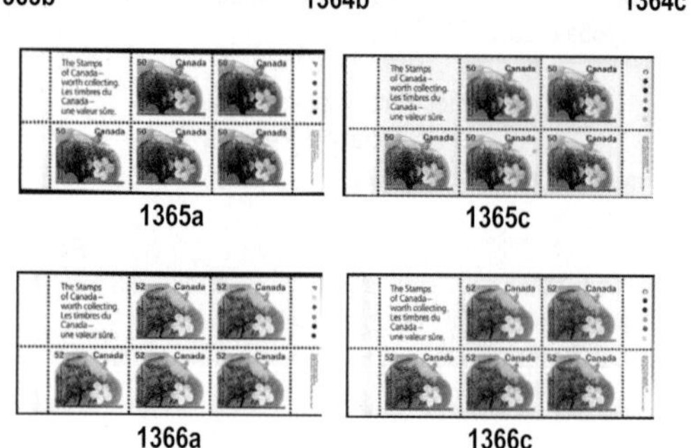

1365a 1365c

1366a 1366c

## OVERWEIGHT DOMESTIC RATE

1367
Black Walnut

1368
Beaked Hazelnut

1369
Shagbark Hickory

1370
American Chestnut

Ashton-Potter Limited

**1991, Dec 27 — GT4, Coated Papers — Perf 13.1**

| | | NH–VF | ⊙F | PB | FDC |
|---|---|---|---|---|---|
| **1367** | **65¢ multicoloured** | 1.50 | .50 | 7.50 | — |
| a | imperf. pair | 1,500.00 | | | |

Ashton-Potter Limited

**1992, Dec 30 — GT4, Coated Papers — Perf 13.1**

| | | NH–VF | ⊙F | PB | FDC |
|---|---|---|---|---|---|
| **1368** | **67¢ multicoloured** | 1.50 | .50 | 7.50 | — |
| a | imperf. pair | 2,000.00 | | | |

Canadian Bank Note

**1994, Feb 25 — GT4, Harrison Paper — Perf 13.1**

| | | NH–VF | ⊙F | PB | FDC |
|---|---|---|---|---|---|
| **1369** | **69¢ multicoloured** | 1.50 | .45 | 7.50 | — |
| i | APCL, Coated Papers, *Apr 10, 1995* | 5.00 | .75 | 25.00 | |

Canadian Bank Note

**1995, Jul 31 — GT4, Peterborough Paper — Perf 13.1**

| | | NH–VF | ⊙F | PB | FDC |
|---|---|---|---|---|---|
| **1370** | **71¢ multicoloured** | 1.50 | .45 | 7.50 | — |
| i | APCL, Coated Papers, *Oct 6, 1995* | 1.75 | .75 | 8.75 | — |
| | **Perf 14.4x13.8** | | | | |
| **1370a** | APCL, Coated Papers, *Dec 1995* | 100.00 | 10.00 | 600.00* | — |

* Blank corner block of four.

## INTERNATIONAL RATE

1371
Stanley Plum

1372
Bartlett Pear

1373
Westcot Apricot

1374
Elberta Peach

Ashton-Potter Limited

**1991, Dec 27 — GT4, Coated Papers — Perf 13.1**

| | | NH–VF | ⊙F | PB | FDC |
|---|---|---|---|---|---|
| **1371** | **84¢ multicoloured** | 2.00 | .50 | 10.00 | — |
| c | imperf. pair | 2,000.00 | | | |
| | **Perf 14.4x13.8** | | | | |
| 1371a | single with straight edge, from 1371b | 3.00 | .85 | | |
| b | booklet pane of 5 x 84¢ (1371a) + label (BK143) | 14.00 | 11.00 | | |
| BK143 | pane 1371b in cover $15.00 | | | | |

**Nos. 1363, 1367, 1371 (3) combination FDC** 4.45

49¢ denomination on 86¢ design

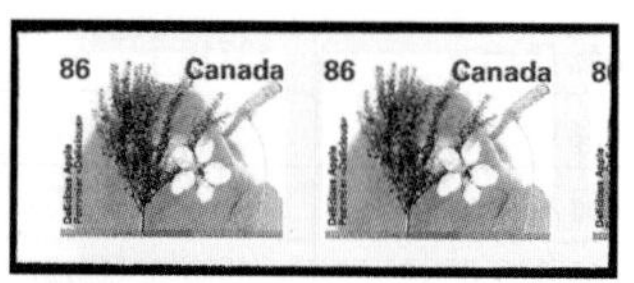


86¢ denomination on 49¢ design

Ashton-Potter Limited

**1992, Dec 30 GT4, Coated Papers Perf 13.1**

| | | NH–VF | ⊙F | PB | FDC |
|---|---|---|---|---|---|
| **1372** | **86¢ multicoloured** | 2.50 | .75 | 12.50 | |

**Perf 14.4x13.8**

| | | NH–VF | ⊙F | PB | FDC |
|---|---|---|---|---|---|
| a | single with straight edge, from 1372b | 4.00 | 2.00 | | |
| b | booklet pane of 5 x 86¢ (1372a) + label (BK157) | 18.00 | 16.00 | | |
| BK157 | pane 1372b in cover $20.00 | | | | |

Canadian Bank Note

**1994, Jan 7 GT4, Harrison Paper Perf 13.1**

| | | NH–VF | ⊙F | PB | FDC |
|---|---|---|---|---|---|
| **1372i** | **86¢ multicoloured** | 7.50 | 2.50 | 37.50 | |
| c | booklet pane of 5 x 86¢ (1372cs) + label (BK157A) | 22.00 | 20.00 | | |
| cs | single with straight edge, from 1372c | 5.50 | 2.00 | | |

An “essay” of the Bartlett Pear design with a 49¢ denomination exists in imperforate form. Value $2,000.00 (pair).

**Nos. 1364, 1368, 1372 (3) combination FDC 4.50**

Canadian Bank Note

**1994, Feb 25 GT4, Peterborough Paper Perf 13.1**

| | | NH–VF | ⊙F | PB | FDC |
|---|---|---|---|---|---|
| **1373** | **88¢ multicoloured** | 2.00 | .65 | 10.00 | |
| a | booklet pane of 5 x 88¢ (1373as) + label (BK168) | 15.00 | 11.00 | | |
| as | single with straight edge, from 1373a | 3.00 | 1.50 | | |
| BK168 | pane 1373a in cover $17.50 | | | | |

**1994, Nov 14 GT3 Perf 13.1**

| | | NH–VF | ⊙F | PB | FDC |
|---|---|---|---|---|---|
| **1373i** | 88¢ multicoloured | 2.25 | .75 | 11.25 | — |
| iii | booklet pane of 5 x 88¢ (1373iiis) + label (BK168A) | 17.50 | 14.00 | | |
| iiis | single with straight edge, from 1373iii | 3.50 | 1.50 | | |

Ashton-Potter Canada Limited

**GT3, Coated Papers Perf 13.1**

| | | NH–VF | ⊙F | PB | FDC |
|---|---|---|---|---|---|
| **1373ii** | 88¢ multicoloured, *Apr 10, 1995* | 3.00 | .75 | 15.00 | — |

**GT3, Coated Papers Perf 14.4x13.8**

| | | NH–VF | ⊙F | PB | FDC |
|---|---|---|---|---|---|
| 1373b | single with straight edge, from 1373c | 5.50 | 3.00 | | |
| c | booklet pane of 5 x 88¢ (1373b) + label (BK168B), *Mar 27, 1995* | 27.50 | 20.00 | | |

Examples of the 88¢ Westcot Apricot (CBN printing on Peterborough Paper), have been reported with four-sided tagging (1373, GT4) *along with* a central vertical tag bar (1373i, GT3) *on the same stamp.*

**Nos. 1365, 1369, 1373 (3) combination FDC 4.75**

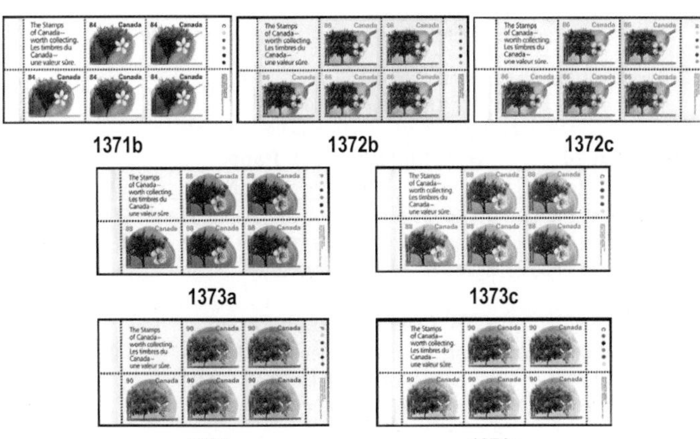

1371b 1372b 1372c

1373a 1373c

1374a 1374c

Canadian Bank Note

**1995, Jul 31 GT3, Peterborough Paper Perf 13.1**

| | | NH–VF | ⊙F | PB | FDC |
|---|---|---|---|---|---|
| **1374** | **90¢ multicoloured** | 2.50 | .65 | 12.50 | — |
| a | booklet pane of 5 x 90¢ (1374as) + label (BK181) | 15.00 | 13.00 | | |
| as | single with straight edge, from 1374a | 3.00 | .70 | | |
| BK181 | pane 1374a in cover $17.50 | | | | |

Ashton-Potter Canada Limited

**GT3, Coated Papers Perf 13.1**

| | | NH–VF | ⊙F | PB | FDC |
|---|---|---|---|---|---|
| **1374i** | 90¢ multicoloured, *Oct 6, 1995* | 2.50 | .65 | 12.50 | — |
| iii | booklet pane of 5 x 90¢ (1374iiis) + label (BK181B), *Oct 1996* | 30.00 | 25.00 | | |
| iiis | single with straight edge, from 1374iii | 6.00 | 3.00 | | |

**Perf 14.4x13.8**

| | | NH–VF | ⊙F | PB | FDC |
|---|---|---|---|---|---|
| 1374b | single from 1374c | 5.00 | 2.00 | | |
| c | booklet pane of 5 x 90¢ (1374b) + label (BK181A), *Oct 6, 1995* | 25.00 | 18.00 | | |
| **ii** | 90¢ multicoloured, *Spring 1996* | 45.00 | 4.00 | 400.00* | — |

* Plate blocks are very scarce.

**Nos. 1366, 1370, 1374 (3) combination FDC 4.85**

## ARCHITECTURE DEFINITIVES 1994–1996

**1375**
Court House, Yorkton, SK

Designer: Raymond Bellemare.

Lithography (4 colours) and Engraved (1 colour), panes of 25

Leigh-Mardon Pty, Limited

**1994, Feb 21 Untagged, Coated Papers Perf 14.6x14.0**

| | | NH–VF | ⊙F | PB | FDC |
|---|---|---|---|---|---|
| **1375** | **$1 blue and multicoloured,** central brown facade glows “orangy”† | 2.50 | .70 | 12.50 | — |
| **a** | dark blue inscriptions omitted* | 2,000.00 | — | 9,000.00 | |
| **i** | central brown facade glows “copper”† | 10.00 | 2.50 | | |

† When exposed by an ultraviolet light (in a dark room).
* One pane of 25 reported.

Canadian Bank Note

**1995, Feb 20 Perf 13.3x13.0**

| | | NH–VF | ⊙F | PB | FDC |
|---|---|---|---|---|---|
| **1375b** | $1 blue and multicoloured | 2.50 | .70 | 12.50 | — |
| **c** | dark blue inscriptions omitted* | 2,000.00 | — | 9,000.00 | |

Shades of bricks exist (notably grey and black-brown).
* One pane of 25 reported.

1375c

1376a

**1376**
Provincial Normal School, Truro, NS

Designer: Raymond Bellemare.
Lithography (5 colours) and Engraved (1 colour), panes of 25
Leigh-Mardon Pty, Limited

**1994, Feb 21 — Untagged, Coated Papers — Perf 14.6x14.0**

| | | NH–VF | ⊙F | PB | FDC |
|---|---|---|---|---|---|
| **1376** | **$2 brown and multicoloured**, building glows "orange-brown"† | 5.00 | 1.35 | 25.00 | — |
| a | inscriptions omitted (68 known) | 1,500.00 | — | 6,500.00 | |
| i | building glows "red-brown"† | 10.00 | 2.50 | | |
| ii | building glows "copper"† | 35.00 | 7.50 | | |

† When exposed by an ultraviolet light (view in a dark room).
A "philatelically created" cover of 1376a, used in period, has been seen by the Editors.

Canadian Bank Note

**1995, Feb 20 — Perf 13.3x13.0**

| | | NH–VF | ⊙F | PB | FDC |
|---|---|---|---|---|---|
| **1376c** | $2 brown and multicoloured | 5.00 | 1.35 | 25.00 | — |
| b | inscriptions inverted (70 known)* | 12,000.00 | | | |
| d | inscriptions omitted (25 known) | 2,000.00 | | 8,500.00 | |
| v | white "invert" (10 known)* | *10,000.00* | | | |
| vi | brown cutting guide "invert" (10 known)* | *10,000.00* | | | |
| vii | brown cutting guide "invert" gutter stamp (10 known)* | *10,000.00* | | | |

The 1376v–vii inverts only exist in pairs or strips of three with 1376b (see pics):
1376b & vii (10 pairs known) *22,000.00*
1376b & v & vi (7 strips remain) *32,000.00*

* Varieties 1376b, 1376v–1376vii occur on sheets discovered in Moncton, NB and Hamilton, ON. Only ten strips of three are known to exist from each discovery (as shown). Three of 1376v, three of 1376vi and 9 of 1376b were apparently destroyed when lost in shipping in 1998. After extensive investigation by two insurance companies they paid the claim.

**Nos. 1375, 1376 (2) combination FDC** **6.60**

**Top: 1376b, Bottom: 1376vii**
from Hamilton sheets

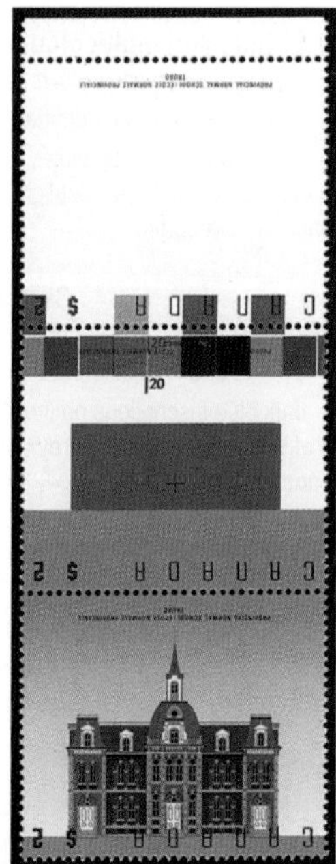

**Top: 1376v, Middle: 1376vi,**
**Bottom: 1376b**
from Moncton sheets

No. 1377 is not assigned.

**1378**
Public Library, Victoria, BC

Designer: Raymond Bellemare.
Lithography (4 colours) and Engraved (1 colour), panes of 25
Canadian Bank Note

**1996, Feb 29 — Untagged, Coated Papers — Perf 13.3x13.0**

| | | NH–VF | ⊙F | PB | FDC |
|---|---|---|---|---|---|
| **1378** | **$5 blue green and multicoloured**, Type I | 10.00 | 3.00 | 50.00 | 10.60 |
| i | reprint (Type II), *Dec 1998* | 30.00 | 5.00 | 140.00* | |

* Blank corner block of 4.

As illustrated by the yellow 'X' below, the black print in all of the windows and doors on the original printing had a 'sharper/steeper' screen angle (about 38 degrees from horizontal) whereas the black on the reprint (or second printing) had a much flatter screen angle (about 13 degrees from horizontal).

**1378 (Type I)**
Original printing: 38 degree angle

**1378i (Type II)**
Reprint: 13 degree angle

Nos. 1379–1387 are not assigned.

## "QUICK STICK" BOOKLET ISSUES 1992-1993

**1388**
Flag over Mountains

**1389**
Flag over Shoreline

Designer: Flag: Gottschalk + Ash International.
Lithography (5 colours)
Ashton-Potter, Self-adhesive booklet of 12

**1992, Jan 28 — GT4, Slater/Fasson Paper — Die cut**

| | | NH–VF | ⊙F | FDC |
|---|---|---|---|---|
| **1388** | **42¢ multicoloured**, from 1388a | 1.50 | 1.00 | 1.35 |
| a | 12 x 42¢ on inside booklet cover (**BK141***) | 24.00 | | |

* Booklet sold for $5.25, a premium of 21¢ over face.

**GT4, Coated/Fasson Paper**

| | | NH–VF | ⊙F | FDC |
|---|---|---|---|---|
| **1389** | **43¢ multicoloured**, from 1389a, *Feb 15, 1993* | 1.50 | 1.00 | 1.35 |
| a | 12 x 43¢ on inside booklet cover (**BK158***) | 24.00 | | |

* Booklet sold for $5.25, a premium of 9¢ over face.

See also 1191–1193 (38¢–40¢)

1388a

1389a

Nos. 1390–1393 are not assigned.

## ROLL STAMP ISSUES (COILS) 1991–1995

1394 Flag

1395 Flag

1396 Flag

Designer: Gottschalk + Ash International.

Engraved (1 colour), rolls of 100
Canadian Bank Note

**GT4, Peterborough Paper** **Perf 10 horiz.**

| | | NH–VF | ⊙F | FDC |
|---|---|---|---|---|
| **1394** | **42¢ red**, DF, *Dec 27, 1991* | 1.00 | .20 | 2.20† |
| a | imperf. pair, DF | 225.00 | | |
| i | narrow spacing, strip of 4, DF | 15.00 | | |
| ii | wide spacing, strip of 4, DF | 30.00 | | |
| iii | LF | 7.50 | 1.00 | |
| iv | wide spacing, strip of 4, LF | 75.00 | | |
| **1395** | **43¢ olive green**, DF, *Dec 30, 1992* | 1.00 | .20 | 2.20† |
| a | imperf. pair, DF* | 200.00 | | |
| iv | narrow spacing, strip of 4, DF | 15.00 | | |
| vii | wide spacing, strip of 4, DF | 23.00 | | |
| ii | HB | 3.00 | .25 | |
| iii | imperf. pair, HB | 250.00 | | |
| v | narrow spacing, strip of 4, HB | 40.00 | | |
| vi | wide spacing, strip of 4, HB | 60.00 | | |

* Three strips of 25 have been reported (typically this type of error is found in strips of 13).

Lithographic forgeries of the 43¢ roll stamp exist. Most of the known copies were used for postage in the Toronto area. The forgeries are not tagged and vary in shade.

| | | NH–VF | ⊙F | FDC |
|---|---|---|---|---|
| **1396** | **45¢ blue green**, HB, *Jul 31, 1995* | 1.00 | .20 | 2.40† |
| iv | narrow spacing, strip of 4, HB | 15.00 | | |
| a | imperf. pair, HB | 200.00 | | |
| ii | DF | 3.00 | .30 | |
| v | narrow spacing, strip of 4, DF | 30.00 | | |
| iii | imperf. pair, DF | 250.00 | | |
| vi | MF | 4.00 | .50 | |

† Value shown is for pair on FDC.

Coil pairs or larger multiples are priced in proportion. Narrow and wide spacing strips may exist with jumps to left or right, or no lateral misalignment.

Nos. 1397–1398 are not assigned.

## 1992

| Rates: | Domestic first-class (0-30g): 42¢ | |
|---|---|---|
| Jan 1/92– | Domestic first-class (30-50g): 65¢ | USA (0-30g): 48¢ |
| Dec 31/92 | Domestic oversize (30-50g): 84¢ | International (0-20g): 84¢ |

*single usage:* USA 48¢: $15.00 | International 84¢: $25.00

## WINTER OLYMPICS

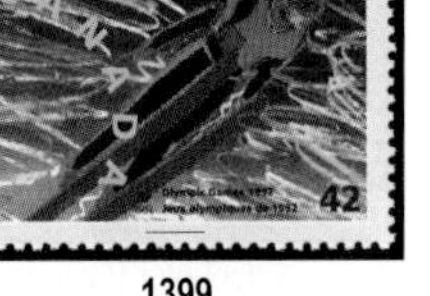
1399
Ski Jumping

1400
Figure Skating

1401
Ice Hockey

1402
Bobsleigh

1403
Alpine Skiing

Designer: Peter Adam and Katalin Kovats.

Lithography (11 colours), booklet pane of 10
Ashton-Potter Limited

**1992, Feb 7** **GT4, Harrison Paper** **Perf 12.5x13.1**

| | | NH–VF | ⊙F | FDC |
|---|---|---|---|---|
| **1399** | **42¢ multicoloured** | 1.00 | .50 | |
| **1400** | **42¢ multicoloured** | 1.00 | .50 | |
| **1401** | **42¢ multicoloured** | 1.00 | .50 | |
| **1402** | **42¢ multicoloured** | 1.00 | .50 | |
| **1403** | **42¢ multicoloured** | 1.00 | .50 | |
| a | horizontal strip of 5 (1399–1403) | 6.00 | 5.25 | 4.70 |
| ai | as 1403a without fold, from Canada Post's annual Souvenir Collection | 7.50 | 9.00 | |
| b | booklet pane of 10 x 42¢ (2 each of 1399–1403) (BK144) | 11.00 | 11.00 | |

BK144 pane 1403b in cover $12.50

Qty: 3,000,000 of each

Issued to commemorate the XVI Olympic Winter Games held in Albertville, France. The pane layout does not produce identical se-tenant pairs. See also 1414–1418.

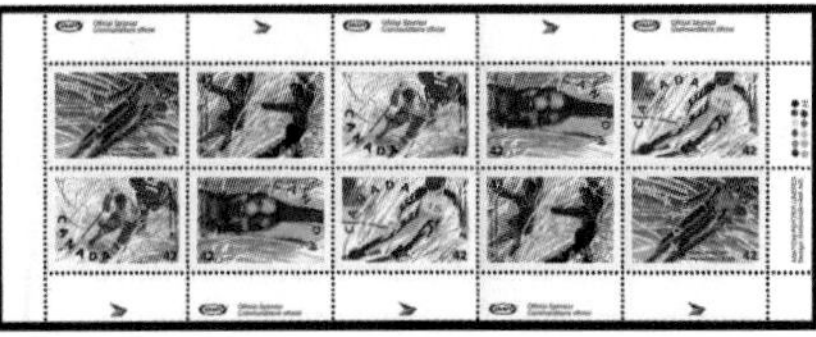
1403b

## CANADA 92

1404
Montréal

1405
Ville-Marie

1406
Exploration (Cartier)

1407
Encounter (Columbus)

Designer: Pierre-Yves Pelletier. Based on an illustration by Suzanne Duranceau.
Lithography, panes of 25
(1404–1405: 6 colours; 1406: 5 colours; 1407: 7 colours; 1407a: 11 colours)
Canadian Bank Note Company, Limited

| 1992, Mar 25 | GT4, Harrison Paper | | | | Perf 13.3 |
|---|---|---|---|---|---|
| | | NH–VF | ⊙F | PB | FDC |
| **1404** | **42¢ multicoloured** | .85 | .40 | — | — |
| **1405** | **42¢ multicoloured** | .85 | .40 | — | — |
| a | se-tenant pair (1404, 1405) | 2.00 | 1.00 | 4.25 | 2.20 |

Qty: 7,600,000 of each

| | | | | | |
|---|---|---|---|---|---|
| **1406** | **48¢ multicoloured** | 1.00 | .90 | 5.00 | 1.45 |

Qty: 15,000,000

| | | | | | |
|---|---|---|---|---|---|
| **1407** | **84¢ multicoloured** | 1.75 | 1.25 | 8.75 | 2.20 |
| a | $2.16 souvenir sheet of 4 (1404–1407), Coated Papers | 5.00 | 5.00 | — | 4.80 |
| ai | signature sheet of 4 as 1407a, with signature, Harrison Paper † | 125.00 | 150.00* | — | 350.00 |

Qty: 15,000,000; 1407a: 400,000; 1407ai: 10,000

* Postally used in period.

† Printed for the CANADA 92 catalogue, these souvenir sheets bear the marginal signature “Paul de Chomedy, De Maisonneuve”. Beware of examples being offered for sale where the blue signature has been forged. Note that this item must be on Harrison Paper.

Issued for CANADA 92, the World Philatelic Youth Exhibition held in Montreal, the stamps also celebrate the 350th anniversary of Montreal, the voyages of Jacques Cartier and the 500th anniversary of Columbus’ first voyage to the new world in 1492.

1407a

1407ai

## HERITAGE RIVERS — 2

**Waterways of Industry and Commerce**

1408
Margaree River, NS

1409
West (Eliot) River, PEI

1410
Ottawa River, ON/QC border

1411
Niagara River, ON

1412
South Saskatchewan River, AB/SK

Designer: Malcolm Waddell. Based on illustrations by Jan Waddell.
Lithography (5 colours), booklet pane of 10
Ashton-Potter Limited

| 1992, Apr 22 | GT4, Coated Papers | | Perf 12.5x12.7 | |
|---|---|---|---|---|
| | | NH–VF | ⊙F | FDC |
| **1408** | **42¢ multicoloured** | 1.00 | .50 | |
| **1409** | **42¢ multicoloured** | 1.00 | .50 | |
| **1410** | **42¢ multicoloured** | 1.00 | .50 | |
| **1411** | **42¢ multicoloured** | 1.00 | .50 | |
| **1412** | **42¢ multicoloured** | 1.00 | .50 | |
| a | horizontal strip of 5 (1408–1412) | 5.50 | 5.00 | |
| ai | as 1412a without fold, from Canada Post’s annual Souvenir Collection | 8.00 | 9.00 | |
| b | booklet pane of 10 (5 x 2), 2 x 1412a se-tenant, (BK145) | 12.00 | 12.00 | |

**BK145** pane 1412b in cover $12.50
Qty: 3,000,000 of each

**Nos. 1408–1412 (strip of 3 + pair) combination FDC** **4.70**

This is the second set in the Canadian Heritage Rivers stamps and recognizes waterways of industry and commerce. The pane layout produces vertical pairs of each of the 5 designs.
See also Nos. 1321–1325, 1485–1489 and 1511–1515.

1412b

## THE ALASKA HIGHWAY

1413
Map and Vehicle

Designer: Jacques Charette. Based on an illustration by Vivian Laliberté.
Lithography (5 colours), pane of 50
Canadian Bank Note Company, Limited

| 1992, May 15 | GT4, Harrison Paper | | | Perf 13.3 |
|---|---|---|---|---|
| | NH–VF | ⊙F | PB | FDC |
| **1413 42¢ multicoloured** | .85 | .30 | 4.25 | 1.35 |

Qty: 15,000,000

**Joint FDC with USA (USA Sc# 2635, issued May 30, 1992) 2.00**

Five sheets are known with a progressive missing colour variety due to a "repellex" error. The amount of colour missing varies with each sheet; only 2 examples are 'really good' missing all of the colour. Value $750–$3,000.

Issued to commemorate the 50th anniversary of the opening of the Alaska Highway between Canada and the USA.

Repellex on 1413

## SUMMER OLYMPICS

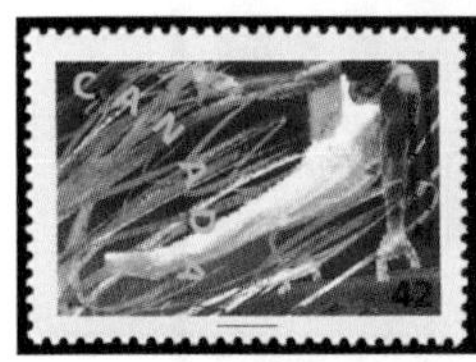

1414
Gymnastics

1415
Track and Field

1416
Diving

1417
Cycling

1418
Swimming

Designer: Peter Adam and Katalin Kovats.
Lithography (11 colours), booklet pane of 10
Ashton-Potter Limited

| 1992, Jun 15 | GT4, Harrison Paper | | Perf 12.5x13.1 | |
|---|---|---|---|---|
| | | NH–VF | ⊙F | FDC |
| **1414** | **42¢ multicoloured** | 1.00 | .50 | |
| **1415** | **42¢ multicoloured** | 1.00 | .50 | |
| **1416** | **42¢ multicoloured** | 1.00 | .50 | |
| **1417** | **42¢ multicoloured** | 1.00 | .50 | |
| **1418** | **42¢ multicoloured** | 1.00 | .50 | |
| a | horizontal strip of 5 (1414–1418) | 6.00 | 6.00 | 4.70 |
| ai | as 1418a without fold, from Canada Post's annual Souvenir Collection | 7.50 | 9.00 | |
| b | booklet pane of 10 x 42¢ (2 each of 1414–1418) (BK146) | 11.00 | 11.00 | |

**BK146** pane 1418b in cover $12.50
Qty: 3,000,000 of each

Issued to commemorate the 1992 Olympic Summer Games held in Barcelona, Spain. The pane layout does not produce identical vertical pairs. This booklet is known with inverted pane. See also 1399–1403.

1418b

## MASTERPIECES OF CANADIAN ART — 5

1419
David Milne, *Red Nasturtiums*

Designer: Pierre-Yves Pelletier. Based on a painting by David Bruce Milne.
Lithography (6 colours) with foil stamping, pane of 16
Ashton-Potter Limited

| 1992, Jun 29 | Untagged, Coated Papers | | | Perf 12.5x13.3 |
|---|---|---|---|---|
| | NH–VF | ⊙F | PB | FDC |
| **1419 50¢ multicoloured** (silver border) | 1.25 | 1.00 | 6.25 | 1.50 |

Qty: 6,700,000

Inscription/plate blocks sold by Canada Post in packaged corner sets have roulettted selvedge on the top and/or sides. Blocks removed from full panes by collectors would be either torn or cut with a knife.
See also 1203, 1241, 1271, 1310, 1466, 1516, 1545, 1602, 1635, 1754, 1800, 1863, 1916, 1945.

**MINT PRICING PREMIUMS**

Mint stamps from 301 to date are valued as NH-VF (Never Hinged-Very Fine). All hinged VF and NH-F copies are worth 50% of the listed values. Plate block (PB) values are for mint NH–VF plate or inscription blocks of four.

**USED, VF/XF (with in-period, circular date cancel) PRICING PREMIUM**

Single stamps with light or circular date cancels will sell for more than catalogue value (perhaps even more than a mint copy). From *1981 to 1991* single stamps from se-tenant blocks of 4 or larger will be priced at 50% or more above the fine price. From *1992* to date single stamps from se-tenant blocks of 4 or larger plus se-tenant booklet panes and souvenir sheets will be priced at 100% or more above the fine price. From *1997* to date all other stamps will be priced at 50% or more above the fine price.

## CANADA DAY

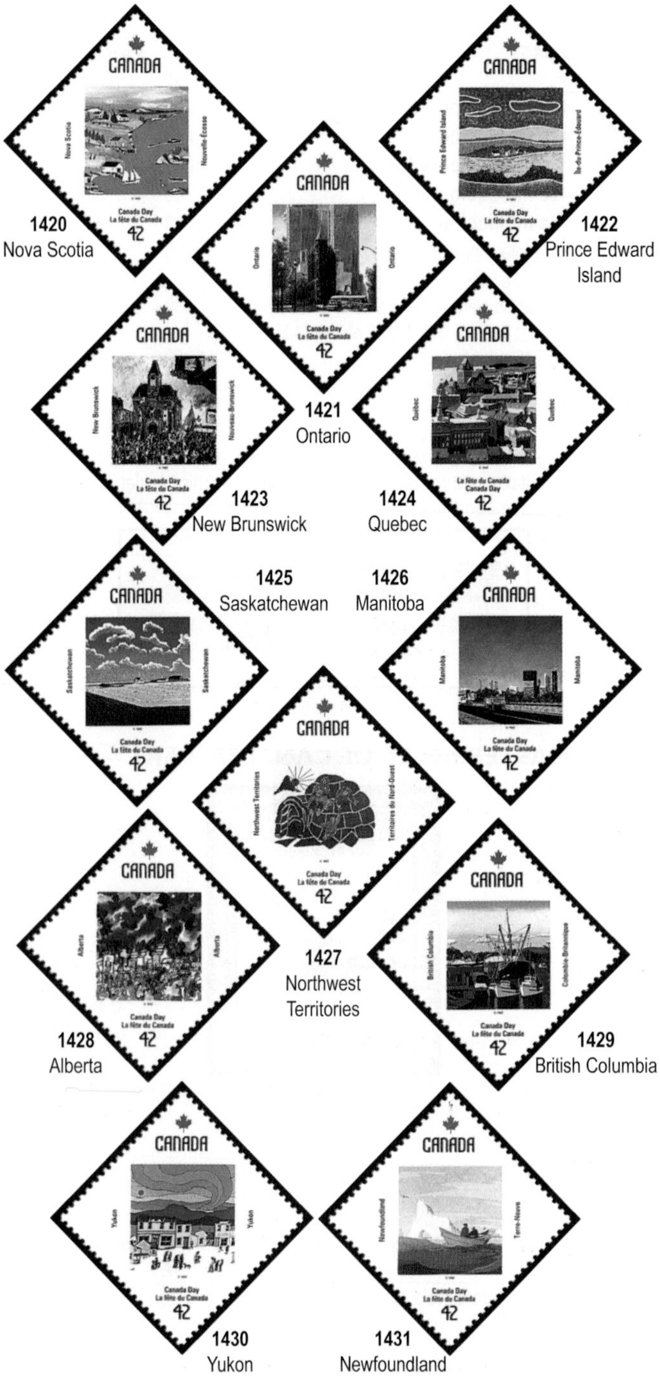

1420 Nova Scotia

1421 Ontario

1422 Prince Edward Island

1423 New Brunswick

1424 Quebec

1425 Saskatchewan

1426 Manitoba

1427 Northwest Territories

1428 Alberta

1429 British Columbia

1430 Yukon

1431 Newfoundland

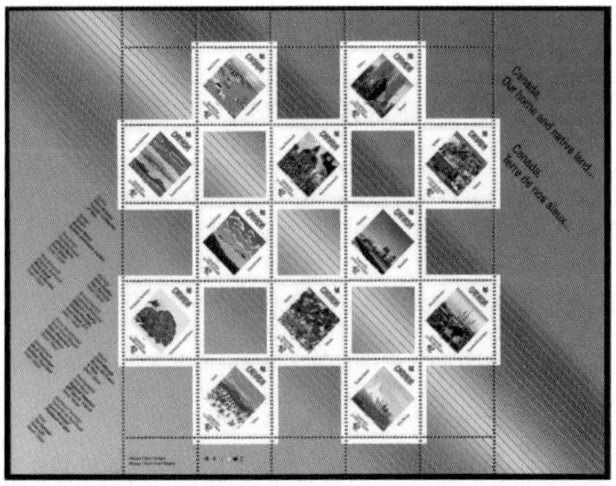

1431a

Designer: Pierre-Yves Pelletier.

Lithography (5 colours), pane of 12 plus 13 labels
Ashton-Potter Limited

**1992, Jun 29** **GT4, Coated Papers** **Perf 13.2x12.5**

| | | NH–VF | ⊙F | FDC |
|---|---|---|---|---|
| **1420** | **42¢ Nova Scotia** | 2.00 | 2.00 | |
| **1421** | **42¢ Ontario** | 2.00 | 2.00 | |
| **1422** | **42¢ Prince Edward Island** | 2.00 | 2.00 | |
| **1423** | **42¢ New Brunswick** | 2.00 | 2.00 | |
| **1424** | **42¢ Quebec** | 2.00 | 2.00 | |
| **1425** | **42¢ Saskatchewan** | 2.00 | 2.00 | |
| **1426** | **42¢ Manitoba** | 2.00 | 2.00 | |
| **1427** | **42¢ Northwest Territories** | 2.00 | 2.00 | |
| **1428** | **42¢ Alberta** | 2.00 | 2.00 | |
| **1429** | **42¢ British Columbia** | 2.00 | 2.00 | |
| **1430** | **42¢ Yukon** | 2.00 | 2.00 | |
| **1431** | **42¢ Newfoundland** | 2.00 | 2.00 | |
| **a** | $5.04 full pane of 12 (1420–1431) + 13 labels | 25.00 | 25.00 | |

Qty: 10,000,000 of each

**Nos. 1420–1431 (12 single stamps) combination FDC** **30.00**

Issued for the 125th anniversary of Confederation. Each stamp depicts a local landmark by artists from each province and territory.

Definitive Timeline:

**1992, Aug 5** 1¢–25¢ Edible Berries (1349–1355)

## CANADIAN FOLKLORE — 3

**Legendary Heroes**

1432 Jerry Potts, Plainsman

1433 William Jackman, Rescuer

1434 Laura Secord, Patriot

1435 Jos Montferrand, Lumberjack

1433i

Designer: Ralph Tibbles. Based on illustrations by Deborah Drew-Brook and Allan Cormack.

Lithography (5 colours), pane of 50

Ashton-Potter Limited

**1992, Sep 8** **GT4, Coated Papers** **Perf 12.6x12.5**

| | | NH–VF | ⊙F | PB | FDC |
|---|---|---|---|---|---|
| **1432** | **42¢ multicoloured** | 1.00 | .45 | | |
| **1433** | **42¢ multicoloured** | 1.00 | .45 | | |
| i | "Jack'man" variety | 10.00 | 3.00 | | |
| **1434** | **42¢ multicoloured** | 1.00 | .45 | | |
| **1435** | **42¢ multicoloured** | 1.00 | .45 | | |
| a | se-tenant block of 4 (1432–1435) | 4.25 | 3.50 | 5.00 | 3.85 |

Qty: 1432–1433: 6,000,000 of each; 1434–1435: 4,000,000 of each

This is the third set in a series representing Canadian folklore. See also Nos. 1289–1292, 1334–1337 and 1491–1494.

## CANADIAN MINERALS

1436
Copper

1437
Sodalite

1438
Gold

1439
Galena

1440
Grossular

Designer: Raymond Bellemare. Based on a photograph by Hans-Ludwig Blohm.

Lithography (10 colours), booklet pane of 10

Ashton-Potter Limited

**1992, Sep 21** **GT4, Coated Papers** **Perf 12.5x12.7**

| | | NH–VF | ⊙F | FDC |
|---|---|---|---|---|
| **1436** | **42¢ multicoloured** | 1.25 | .50 | |
| **1437** | **42¢ multicoloured** | 1.25 | .50 | |
| **1438** | **42¢ multicoloured** | 1.25 | .50 | |
| **1439** | **42¢ multicoloured** | 1.25 | .50 | |
| **1440** | **42¢ multicoloured** | 1.25 | .50 | |
| a | horizontal strip of 5 (1436–1440) | 6.50 | 6.00 | 4.70* |
| ai | as 1440a without fold, from Canada Post's annual Souvenir Collection | 7.50 | 9.00 | |
| b | booklet pane of 10 (5 x 2), 2 x 1440a se-tenant, (BK147) | 13.00 | 12.00 | — |

BK147 pane 1440b in cover $14.00

Qty: 3,000,000 of each

* OFDC consists of a strip of 3 and horizontal pair

Issued to commemorate the 150th anniversary of the Geological Survey of Canada. The pane layout produces vertical pairs of each stamp.

1440b

## CANADA IN SPACE

1441
ANIK E2 satellite

1442
Astronauts' achievements

Designer: Debbie Adams.

Lithography (10 colours) plus hologram, pane of 20

Canadian Bank Note Company, Limited

**1992, Oct 1** **GT4, Coated Papers** **Perf 13.1**

| | | NH–VF | ⊙F | PB | FDC |
|---|---|---|---|---|---|
| **1441** | **42¢ multicoloured** | 1.00 | 1.00 | | |
| a | silver omitted | *3,750.00* | *2,500.00* | | |
| **1442** | **42¢ multicoloured**, with holographic image | 1.50 | 1.50 | | |
| a | se-tenant pair (1441, 1442) | 2.50 | 2.50 | 5.00 | 2.20 |
| b | as "a", hologram omitted on 1442 | 2,000.00† | | 4,200.00‡ | 2,000.00 |
| iii | as "a", high orbit on 1442. Nose of shuttle above top of hologram* | 75.00 | | | |
| iv | as "a", low orbit on 1442. Map of Canada cut off at James Bay | 90.00 | | | |
| v | as "a", black hole on 1442, shows a black line beneath the earth | 200.00 | | | |
| vi | as "a", meteor shower on 1442 (streaks in sky on map) | 200.00 | | | |

Qty: 5,000,000 of each

* Nose of shuttle must be cut off at top of hologram.

† A certificate of authenticity is recommended.

‡ Imprint block of 4 with 2 missing holograms.

Variety 1442b occurs on 1, 2 or all 10 positions on the sheet; sheet with 1 or 2 missing $5,000, 10 missing $25,000.

Two panes of 60 hologram "proofs" are known in private hands. Singles have been cut from one of these panes. Value $500.

Single use on non-philatelic commercial cover: No. 1441 $5.00; No. 1442 $10.00.

Issued to honour Canadian achievements in space and space technology. No. 1442 is Canada's first hologram stamp. Soaking in water may affect the hologram.

1441a

Hologram proof

1442b

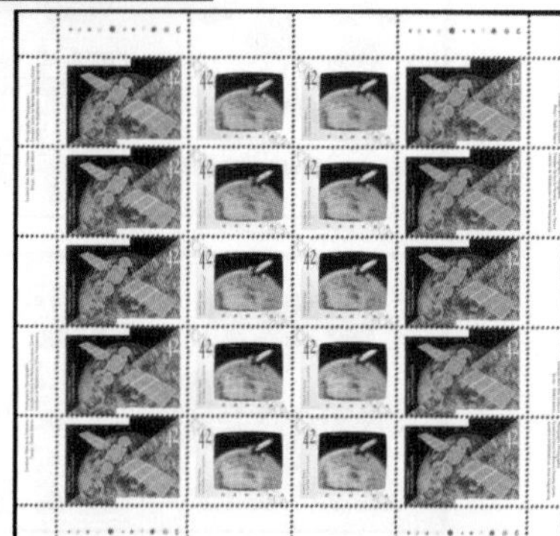

1441–1442
full pane

## NATIONAL HOCKEY LEAGUE

1443
The Early Years (1917–1942)

1444
The Six-Team Years (1942–1967)

1445
The Expansion Years (1967–1992)

Designer: Les Holloway and Designed by Richard Kerr.
Lithography (6 colours), Prestige Booklet
Ashton-Potter Limited

**1992, Oct 9** **GT4, Harrison Paper** **Perf 13.1x12.5**

| | | NH–VF | ⊙F | FDC |
|---|---|---|---|---|
| **1443** | **42¢ multicoloured** | 1.00 | .30 | — |
| a | booklet pane of 8 (1443) + 4 labels (BK148) | 8.00 | 7.00 | — |

Qty: 8,000,000

| | | NH–VF | ⊙F | FDC |
|---|---|---|---|---|
| **1444** | **42¢ multicoloured** | 1.00 | .30 | — |
| a | booklet pane of 8 (1444) + 4 labels (BK148) | 8.00 | 7.00 | — |

Qty: 8,000,000

| | | NH–VF | ⊙F | FDC |
|---|---|---|---|---|
| **1445** | **42¢ multicoloured** | 1.00 | .30 | — |
| a | booklet pane of 9 (1445) + 3 labels (BK148) | 10.00 | 8.00 | — |

Qty: 9,000,000

**BK148** 1 each of panes 1443a, 1444a, 1445a in cover $28.00

**Nos. 1443–1445 (3) Combination FDC** 3.75

This illustrated Prestige Booklet was issued to mark the 75th anniversary of the National Hockey League.

1443a

1444a

1445a

## ORDER OF CANADA / ROLAND MICHENER

1446 Order of Canada
1447 Daniel Roland Michener

Designer: Tania Craan. Based on a photograph by Michael Kohn (1446) and Artin Cavouk (1447).
Lithography (7 colours), pane of 25
Ashton-Potter Limited

**1992, Oct 21** **GT4, Coated Papers** **Perf 12.7x12.5**

| | | NH–VF | ⊙F | PB | FDC |
|---|---|---|---|---|---|
| **1446** | **42¢ multicoloured** | .85 | .30 | — | — |
| **1447** | **42¢ multicoloured** | .85 | .40 | — | — |
| a | se-tenant pair (1446, 1447) | 2.00 | 1.50 | 4.25 | 2.20 |
| i | pair of 1446 | 2.00 | 1.50 | — | — |
| ii | pair of 1447 | 2.50 | 2.00 | — | — |

Qty: 1446: 9,600,000; 1447: 5,400,000

Issued to commemorate the 25th anniversary of the Order of Canada and in memory of its first recipient, the late Governor-General Roland Michener who died in 1991.

This unique pane format of 25 stamps has 9 x 1447, surrounded by 16 x 1446.

1446–1447
full pane

## SECOND WORLD WAR — 1942

**Dark Days Indeed**

1448 War Reporting
1449 Newfoundland Air Bases

1450 The Dieppe Raid
1451 U-Boats Offshore

Designer: Pierre-Yves Pelletier. Based on an illustration by Jean-Pierre Armanville.
Lithography (5 colours), pane of 16
Canadian Bank Note Company, Limited

| 1992, Nov 10 | GT4, Peterborough Paper | NH–VF | ⊙F | PB | FDC |
|---|---|---|---|---|---|
| | Perf 13.3 | | | | |
| **1448** | **42¢ multicoloured**, MF | 1.00 | .60 | | |
| i | dull | 2.00 | 1.00 | | |
| **1449** | **42¢ multicoloured**, MF | 1.00 | .60 | | |
| i | dull | 2.00 | 1.00 | | |
| **1450** | **42¢ multicoloured**, MF | 1.00 | .60 | | |
| i | dull | 2.00 | 1.00 | | |
| **1451** | **42¢ multicoloured**, MF | 1.00 | .60 | | |
| i | dull | 2.00 | 1.00 | | |
| a | se-tenant block of 4, MF (1448–1451) | 4.50 | 4.00 | 5.00 | 3.85 |
| ai | se-tenant block of 4, dull (1448i–1451i) | 10.00 | | 12.00 | |

Qty: 3,750,000 of each

The fourth set honouring Canadian achievements and sacrifices during World War II.

See also Nos. 1260–1263, 1298–1301, 1345–1348, 1503–1506, 1537–1540 and 1541–1544.

## CHRISTMAS — PERSONAGES

1452
Jõuluvana

1453
La Befana

1454
Weihnachtsmann

1455
Santa Claus

Designer: Louis Fishauf and Stephanie Power. Based on an illustration by Anita Kunz.
Lithography (5 colours), panes of 50
Ashton-Potter Limited

| 1992, Nov 13 | GT4, Harrison Paper | NH–VF | ⊙F | PB | FDC |
|---|---|---|---|---|---|
| | Perf 12.6x12.5 | | | | |
| **1452** | **42¢ multicoloured** | .90 | .20 | 4.50 | — |
| i | imperf. pair (accent over O)* | 1,250.00 | | | |
| a | single with straight edge, from 1452b, perf 13.3* | 1.25 | .25 | — | — |
| b | booklet pane of 10 x 42¢ (1452a) (2 x 5) (BK150) | 12.50 | 7.00 | — | — |

**BK150** pane 1452b in cover $13.00
Qty: 45,000,000
On 42¢ sheets, the top "tooth" on both sides of each stamp is taller than the rest due to an improper placement of perforation pins.

| | Coated Papers | NH–VF | ⊙F | PB | FDC |
|---|---|---|---|---|---|
| | Perf 13.3 | | | | |
| **1453** | **48¢ multicoloured** | 1.50 | 1.00 | 7.50 | — |
| i | imperf. pair (correct accent over E) | 1,250.00 | | | |
| a | booklet pane of 5 x 48¢ (1453as) + label (2 x 3) (BK151) | 7.50 | 6.00 | — | — |
| as | single with straight edge, from 1453a | 1.50 | 1.25 | — | — |

**BK151** pane 1453a in cover $8.00
Qty: 8,000,000

| | Harrison Paper | NH–VF | ⊙F | PB | FDC |
|---|---|---|---|---|---|
| | Perf 13.3 | | | | |
| **1454** | **84¢ multicoloured** | 2.00 | 1.00 | 10.00 | |
| i | imperf pair (accent over O)* | 1,250.00 | | | |
| a | booklet pane of 5 x 84¢ (1454as) + label (2 x 3) (BK152) | 12.50 | 8.00 | — | — |
| as | single with straight edge, from 1454a | 2.50 | 1.50 | | |

**BK152** pane 1454a in cover $15.00
Qty: 8,000,000

* One example of 1452a is known with accent over "O" instead of "E" in NOEL. V.G. Greene Foundation certificate states: "Printer's waste, but a genuine printed stamp, likely of proof status." One bottom margin pair, imperf. between is known with same accent variety (left stamp creased). Value *$2,750.00.* One pane of 50 (25 pairs) of each of 1452i and 1454i are known.

**Nos. 1452–1454 (3) combination FDC** 4.00

| | GTX, Greetmore Booklet, Coated Papers | NH–VF | ⊙F | PB | FDC |
|---|---|---|---|---|---|
| | Perf 12.5x13.0 | | | | |
| **1455** | **37¢ multicoloured** | 1.00 | 1.00 | — | 1.25 |
| a | booklet pane of 10 x 37¢ (1455) (2 x 5) (BK149) | 11.50 | 7.50 | — | — |

**BK149** pane 1455a in cover $12.00
Qty: 58,000,000

No. 1455 was issued in booklets only, for use on greeting card envelopes bearing a printed postal code matrix. Accepted singly until January 31, 1993, if affixed to designated envelope.

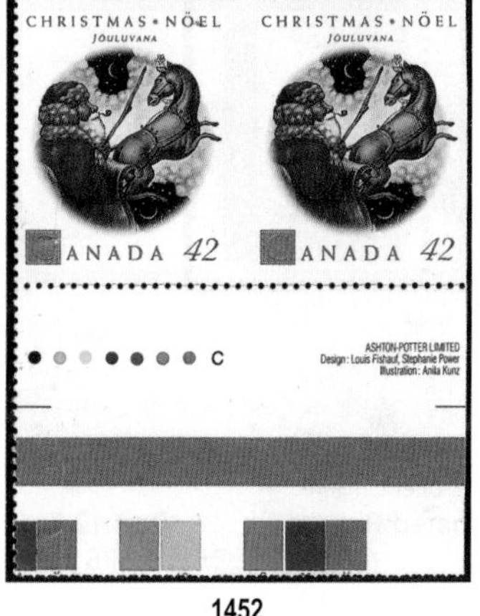

1452
(with accent over O)

1452b

1453a

1454a

1455a

Definitive Timeline:
1992, Dec 30 43¢ Queen Elizabeth II (1358)
43¢ Flag over Mountains (1359)
49/67/86¢ Fruit Trees (1364/1368/1372)

## 1993

**Rates:**
Jan 1/93–
Jul 31/95 Domestic first-class (0-30g): 43¢

**Rates:**

| | | |
|---|---|---|
| Jan 1/93– | Domestic first-class (30-50g): 67¢ | USA (0-30g): 49¢ |
| Feb 28/94 | Domestic oversize (30-50g): 86¢ | International (0-20g): 86¢ |

*single usage:* USA 49¢: $15.00 | International 86¢: $25.00

Definitive Timeline:
1993, Feb 15 43¢ Flag over Shoreline (1389)

### PROMINENT CANADIAN WOMEN

1456 Adelaide Sophia Hoodless — 1457 Marie-Joséphine Gérin-Lajoie

1458 Pitseolak Ashoona — 1459 Helen Alice Kinnear

Designer: Heather J. Cooper.
Lithography (6 colours), pane of 50
Ashton-Potter Limited

| 1993, Mar 8 | GT4, Coated Papers | | Perf 12.7x12.5 | | |
|---|---|---|---|---|---|
| | | NH–VF | ⊙F | PB | FDC |
| **1456** | **43¢ multicoloured** | .90 | .40 | | |
| **1457** | **43¢ multicoloured** | .90 | .40 | | |
| **1458** | **43¢ multicoloured** | .90 | .40 | | |
| **1459** | **43¢ multicoloured** | .90 | .40 | | |
| a | se-tenant strip or block of 4 different (1456–1459) | 4.00 | 3.50 | 4.50 | 3.95 |

Qty: 1456–1457: 3,900,000 of each; 1458–1459: 3,600,000 of each

Issued for the centennial of the National Offices of the YWCA and the NCWC, and for the 50th anniversary of the first appointment of a woman judge in Canada. Adelaide Hoodless was a founder of the Victorian Order of Nurses and helped found both the National YWCA and NCWC. Marie-Joséphine Gérin-Lajoie was the first woman to receive a BA degree from a French-Canadian institute of higher learning. Pitseolak Ashoona was one of Canada's best known Inuit graphic artists and Helen Kinnear became the first federally-appointed woman judge in Canada.

### STANLEY CUP

1460
Stanley Cup (1893–1993)

Designer: François Dallaire and Lise Giguère.
Lithography (6 colours), pane of 25
Canadian Bank Note Company, Limited

| 1993, Apr 16 | GT4, Coated Papers | | Perf 13.3x13.4 | | |
|---|---|---|---|---|---|
| | | NH–VF | ⊙F | PB | FDC |
| **1460** | **43¢ multicoloured** | 1.00 | .30 | 5.00 | 1.75 |
| **T1** | untagged (error) | 100.00 | — | | |

Qty: 15,000,000

Issued to commemorate the 100th anniversary of the Stanley Cup.

### HAND-CRAFTED TEXTILES

1461
Coverlet "Bed Rugg", New Brunswick

1462
Pieced Quilt, Ontario

1463
Doukhobor Bedcover, Saskatchewan

1464
Kwakwaka'wakw, Ceremonial Robe, BC

1465
Boutonné Coverlet, Quebec

Designer: Peter Adam. Based on a photograph by Michael Mitchell.
Lithography (6 colours), booklet pane of 10
Ashton-Potter Limited

| 1993, Apr 30 | GT4, Harrison Paper | | Perf 13.1x12.5 | |
|---|---|---|---|---|
| | | NH–VF | ⊙F | FDC |
| **1461** | **43¢ multicoloured** | 1.00 | .50 | |
| **1462** | **43¢ multicoloured** | 1.00 | .50 | |
| **1463** | **43¢ multicoloured** | 1.00 | .50 | |
| **1464** | **43¢ multicoloured** | 1.00 | .50 | |
| **1465** | **43¢ multicoloured** | 1.00 | .50 | |
| a | horizontal strip of 5 (1461–1465) | 6.50 | 5.50 | 4.80 |
| ai | as 1465a without fold, from Canada Post's annual Souvenir Collection | 7.00 | 8.00 | |
| b | booklet pane of 10 (5 x 2), (BK159) | 11.00 | 9.00 | — |

**BK159** pane 1465b in cover $12.00
Qty: 3,000,000 of each

Issued to mark the Year of the Craft in the Americas. The pane layout does not produce vertical identical pairs.

QE II — 1990's

1465b

## MASTERPIECES OF CANADIAN ART — 6

1466
Drawing for *The Owl*

Designer: Pierre-Yves Pelletier. Based on a drawing by Kenojuak Ashevak (c. 1969).
Lithography (6 colours) with foil stamping, pane of 16
Ashton-Potter Limited

**1993, May 17** **Tagged, Harrison Paper** **Perf 12.5x13.3**

| | | NH–VF | ⊙F | PB | FDC |
|---|---|---|---|---|---|
| **1466** | **86¢ multicoloured** (gold border) | 2.00 | 1.50 | 10.00 | 2.20 |

Qty: 8,700,000

General tagging around edge of white background.
Issued for the International Year of the World's Indigenous People.
See also 1203, 1241, 1271, 1310, 1419, 1516, 1545, 1602, 1635, 1754, 1800, 1863, 1916, 1945.

## HISTORIC CPR HOTELS

1467
Empress Hotel, Victoria, BC

1468
Banff Springs Hotel, Banff, AB

1469
Royal York Hotel, Toronto, ON

1470
Château Frontenac, Quebec City, QC

1471
Algonquin Hotel, St. Andrews, NB

Designer: Kosta (Gus) Tsetsekas. Based on illustrations by Heather Price.
Lithography (6 colours), booklet pane of 10
Ashton-Potter Limited

**1993, Jun 14** **GT4, Harrison Paper** **Perf 13.3**

| | | NH–VF | ⊙F | FDC |
|---|---|---|---|---|
| **1467** | **43¢ multicoloured** | 1.25 | .80 | |
| **1468** | **43¢ multicoloured** | 1.25 | .80 | |
| **1469** | **43¢ multicoloured** | 1.25 | .80 | |
| **1470** | **43¢ multicoloured** | 1.25 | .80 | |
| **1471** | **43¢ multicoloured** | 1.25 | .80 | |
| a | horizontal strip of 5 (1467–1471) | 7.00 | 4.50 | 4.80* |
| ai | as 1471a without fold, from Canada Post's annual Souvenir Collection | 8.00 | 8.00 | |
| b | booklet pane of 10 (5 x 2) 2 x 1470a se-tenant, (BK160) | 11.00 | 11.00 | — |

BK160 pane 1471a in cover $12.00
Qty: 3,000,000 of each
* OFDC consists of a strip of 3 and horizontal pair

No. 1471b consists of one vertical pair of each stamp.
Issued for the centenary of the Château Frontenac in Quebec City.

1471b



## CANADA DAY PROVINCIAL and TERRITORIAL PARKS

1472
Algonquin Park, Ontario

1473
De la Gaspésie Park, Quebec

1474
Cedar Dunes Park, PEI

1475
Cape St. Mary's Reserve, Newfoundland

1476
Mount Robson Park, British Columbia

1477
Writing-On-Stone Park, Alberta

1478
Spruce Woods Park, Manitoba

1479
Herschel Island Park, Yukon

1480
Cypress Hills Park, Saskatchewan

1481
The Rocks Park, New Brunswick

1482
Blomidon Park, Nova Scotia

1483
Katannilik Park, Northwest Territories

Designer: Malcolm Waddell. Based on illustrations by Jan Waddell.
Lithography (7 colours), pane of 12
Canadian Bank Note Company, Limited

**1993, Jun 30** **GT4, Coated Papers** **Perf 13.0**

| | | NH–VF | ⊙F | PB | FDC |
|---|---|---|---|---|---|
| **1472** | 43¢ Algonquin Park, Ontario | 1.40 | 1.40 | | |
| **1473** | 43¢ De la Gaspésie Park, Quebec | 1.40 | 1.40 | | |
| i | blue stroke to left of "Parc" | 5.00 | 2.50 | | |
| **1474** | 43¢ Cedar Dunes Park, PEI | 1.40 | 1.40 | | |
| **1475** | 43¢ Cape St. Mary's Reserve, NF | 1.40 | 1.40 | | |
| **1476** | 43¢ Mount Robson Park, BC | 1.40 | 1.40 | | |
| **1477** | 43¢ Writing-On-Stone Park, Alberta | 1.40 | 1.40 | | |
| **1478** | 43¢ Spruce Woods Park, Manitoba | 1.40 | 1.40 | | |
| **1479** | 43¢ Herschel Island Park, Yukon | 1.40 | 1.40 | | |
| **1480** | 43¢ Cypress Hills Park, SK | 1.40 | 1.40 | | |
| **1481** | 43¢ The Rocks Park, New Brunswick | 1.40 | 1.40 | | |
| **1482** | 43¢ Blomidon Park, Nova Scotia | 1.40 | 1.40 | | |
| **1483** | 43¢ Katannilik Park, NWT | 1.40 | 1.40 | | |
| a | $5.16 pane of 12 (4 x 3) (1472–1483), with full illustrated tab at top | 20.00 | 20.00 | — | 11.85† |
| ai | pane of 12 from field stock, without imprinted tabs at top and bottom | 17.50 | 17.50 | | |

Qty: 15,000,000 of each

† Three FDCs: 1) 1472, 1473, 1476, 1477 – $3.95; 2) 1474, 1475, 1478, 1479 – $3.95; 3) 1480–1483 – $3.95, in a protective folder.

1483a

1483ai

1473i

## TORONTO BICENTENNIAL

1484
Founding of Toronto

Designer: Vincent McIndoe. Typographed by Richard Heeney.
Lithography (5 colours), pane of 25
Canadian Bank Note Company, Limited

**1993, Aug 6** **GT4, Coated Papers** **Perf 13.3x13.0**

| | | NH–VF | ⊙F | PB | FDC |
|---|---|---|---|---|---|
| **1484** | **43¢ multicoloured** | .90 | .30 | 4.50 | 1.35 |

Qty: 15,000,000

## HERITAGE RIVERS — 3

**Routes of Settlement and Growth**

1485
Fraser River, BC

1486
Yukon River, Yukon Territory

1487
Red River, Manitoba

1488
St. Lawrence River, Ontario and Quebec

1489
St. John River, NB

1489b

1489c

QE II — 1990's

Designer: Malcolm Waddell. Based on illustrations by Jan Waddell.
Lithography (5 colours), booklet pane of 10
Ashton-Potter Limited

| 1993, Aug 10 | GT4, Harrison Paper | | Perf 13.1x12.5 | |
|---|---|---|---|---|
| | | NH–VF | ⊙F | FDC |
| **1485** | **43¢ multicoloured** | 1.00 | .50 | |
| **1486** | **43¢ multicoloured** | 1.00 | .50 | |
| **1487** | **43¢ multicoloured** | 1.00 | .50 | |
| **1488** | **43¢ multicoloured** | 1.00 | .50 | |
| **1489** | **43¢ multicoloured** | 1.00 | .50 | |
| a | strip of 5 (1485–1489) | 6.50 | 5.00 | 4.80 |
| ai | as 1489a without fold, from Canada Post's annual Souvenir Collection | 7.00 | 8.00 | |
| c | as "a", imperf. strip of 5* | *4,000.00* | | |
| b | booklet pane of 10 (10 x 1) (2 x 1489a), (BK161) | 11.00 | 10.00 | — |
| BK161 | pane 1489b in cover $12.00 | | | |

Qty: 3,000,000 of each
* Two booklets of 10 reported.

This is the third in a series of booklets featuring Canadian rivers.
See also 1321–1325, 1408–1412 and 1511–1515.

## HISTORIC LAND VEHICLES — I

**Personal Vehicles**

**1490a**
H.S. Taylor Steam Buggy (1867)

**1490b**
Russell Model L Touring Car (1908)

**1490c**
Ford Model T (1914)

**1490d**
Studebaker Champion Deluxe (1950)

**1490e**
McLaughlin-Buick Model 28-496 (1928)

**1490f**
Gray-Dort Model 25-SM (1923)

Designer: Joseph Gault and Tiit Telmet. Based on illustrations by Cameron Wykes.
Lithography (7 colours), Souvenir sheet of 6
Canadian Bank Note Company, Limited

| 1993, Aug 23 | GT4, Coated Papers | | Perf 12.5x13.1 | |
|---|---|---|---|---|
| | | NH–VF | ⊙F | FDC |
| **1490** | **$3.56 souvenir sheet of 6 stamps** | 10.00 | 10.00 | 8.60* |
| a | **43¢ multicoloured** | 1.00 | 1.00 | |
| b | **43¢ multicoloured** | 1.00 | 1.00 | |
| c | **49¢ multicoloured** | 1.25 | 1.25 | |
| d | **49¢ multicoloured** | 1.25 | 1.25 | |
| e | **86¢ multicoloured** | 2.00 | 1.75 | |
| f | **86¢ multicoloured** | 2.00 | 1.75 | |

Qty: 550,000

*Three FDCs: 1) a, b – $2.20; 2) c, d – $2.45; 3) e, f – $3.95, in a protective folder.
See also 1527, 1552, 1604 and 1605.

**1490**

## CANADIAN FOLKLORE — 4

**Folk Songs**

**1491** Alberta Folksong — **1492** Quebec Folksong

**1493** Newfoundland Ditty — **1494** Kanien' Kehaka Song

Designer: Ralph Tibbles. Based on illustrations by Allan Cormack and Deborah Drew-Brook.
Lithography (5 colours), pane of 50
Ashton-Potter Limited

| 1993, Sep 7 | GT4, Harrison Paper | | | Perf 12.5x12.7 | |
|---|---|---|---|---|---|
| | | NH–VF | ⊙F | PB | FDC |
| **1491** | **43¢ multicoloured** | .90 | .40 | | |
| **1492** | **43¢ multicoloured** | .90 | .40 | | |
| **1493** | **43¢ multicoloured** | .90 | .40 | | |
| **1494** | **43¢ multicoloured** | .90 | .40 | | |
| a | se-tenant block of 4 (1491–1494) | 4.00 | 3.50 | 4.50 | 3.95 |
| ai | as "a", imperforate† | 2,000.00 | | | |

Qty: 1491/1493: 4,500,000 of each; 1492/1494: 3,000,000 of each
† Ten strips reported, all have no gum.

This is the final set representing Canadian Folklore.
See also 1289–1292, 1334–1337 and 1432–1435.

## PREHISTORIC LIFE IN CANADA — 3

**Dinosaurs**

**1495** Massospondylus (Jurassic period) — **1496** Styracosaurus (Cretaceous period)

**1497** Albertosaurus (Cretaceous period) — **1498** Platecarpus (Cretaceous period)

Designer: Rolf P. Harder.

Lithography (6 colours), pane of 20
Ashton-Potter Limited

**1993, Oct 1** **GT4, Harrison Paper** **Perf 13.3**

| | | NH–VF | ⊙F | PB | FDC |
|---|---|---|---|---|---|
| **1495** | **43¢ multicoloured** | .90 | .40 | | |
| **1496** | **43¢ multicoloured** | .90 | .40 | | |
| **1497** | **43¢ multicoloured** | .90 | .40 | | |
| **1498** | **43¢ multicoloured** | .90 | .40 | | |
| a | se-tenant block of 4 (1495–1498) | 4.00 | 3.50 | 4.50 | 3.95 |
| b | as "a", imperforate | | | 4,000.00 | |

Qty: 4,250,000 of each

This is the third set in a four-part series.
See also 1279–1282, 1306–1309 and 1529–1532.

## CHRISTMAS PERSONAGES

1499
Swiety Mikolaj and Gwiazdka, Poland

1500
Russia's Ded Moroz

1501
Father Christmas from Australia

1502
North American Santa Claus

Designer: Louis Fishauf and Stephanie Power. Based on an illustration by Jeff Jackson.

Lithography (7 colours), panes of 50
Canadian Bank Note Company, Limited

**1993, Nov 4** **GT4, Coated Papers** **Perf 13.3**

| | | NH–VF | ⊙F | PB | FDC |
|---|---|---|---|---|---|
| **1499** | **43¢ multicoloured** | .90 | .20 | 4.50 | — |
| b | horizontal pair, imperf. between | 1,600.00 | — | 4,500.00* | — |
| ii | imperf. between stamp and left or right margin | 600.00 | — | — | — |
| a | booklet pane of 10 x 43¢ (1499as), (BK163) | 10.00 | 7.00 | — | — |
| as | single with straight edge, from 1499a | 1.25 | .50 | — | — |

BK163 pane 1499a in cover $11.00
Qty: 45,000,000
* Blank corner block of 6 with two pairs of 1499b and two singles of 1499ii at the margin.
1499b and 1499ii in strip of 3 (left or right margin strip of 3, imperf. between pair plus imperf. margin single), value $2,200.00

| | | NH–VF | ⊙F | PB | FDC |
|---|---|---|---|---|---|
| **1500** | **49¢ multicoloured** | 1.00 | .55 | 5.00 | — |
| a | booklet pane of 5 x 49¢ (1500as) + label (BK164) | 7.50 | 6.00 | — | — |
| as | single with straight edge, from 1500a | 1.50 | .90 | — | — |

BK164 pane 1500a in cover $8.00
Qty: 8,000,000

| | | NH–VF | ⊙F | PB | FDC |
|---|---|---|---|---|---|
| **1501** | **86¢ multicoloured** | 2.00 | .70 | 10.00 | — |
| a | booklet pane of 5 x 86¢ (1501as) + label (BK165) | 12.50 | 9.00 | — | — |
| as | single with straight edge, from 1501a | 2.50 | 1.20 | — | — |

BK165 pane 1501a in cover $13.00
Qty: 8,000,000

**Nos. 1499–1501 (3) combination FDC** **4.10**

**GTX, Greetmore Booklet** **Perf 13.0**

| | | NH–VF | ⊙F | PB | FDC |
|---|---|---|---|---|---|
| **1502** | **38¢ multicoloured** | 1.00 | .75 | — | 1.25 |
| a | booklet pane of 10 x 38¢ (1502) (BK162) | 11.00 | 10.00 | — | — |

BK162 pane 1502a in cover $12.00
Qty: 60,000,000

No. 1502 was issued for use on greeting card envelopes bearing a printed postal code matrix. Accepted singly until January 31, 1994, if affixed to designated envelope.

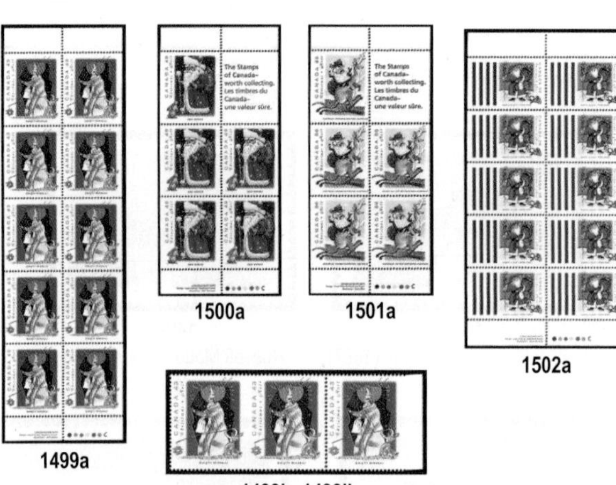

1500a 1501a 1502a 1499a 1499b, 1499ii

## SECOND WORLD WAR — 1943

**The Tide Begins to Turn**

1503
Aid to Allies

1504
Bomber Forces

1505
Battle of the Atlantic

1506
Italian Campaign

Designer: Pierre-Yves Pelletier. Based on an illustration by Jean-Pierre Armanville.
Lithography (5 colours), pane of 16
Canadian Bank Note Company, Limited

| 1993, Nov 8 | GT4, Coated Papers | | | | Perf 13.3 |
|---|---|---|---|---|---|
| | | NH–VF | ⊙F | PB | FDC |
| **1503** | **43¢ multicoloured** | 1.00 | .60 | | |
| **1504** | **43¢ multicoloured** | 1.00 | .60 | | |
| **1505** | **43¢ multicoloured** | 1.00 | .60 | | |
| **1506** | **43¢ multicoloured** | 1.00 | .60 | | |
| a | se-tenant block of 4 (1503–1506) | 4.50 | 4.00 | 5.00 | 3.95 |

Qty: 3,750,000 of each

This is the fifth set honouring Canadian achievements and sacrifices during World War II.
See also Nos. 1260–1263, 1298–1301, 1345–1348, 1448–1451, 1537–1540 and 1541–1544.

Canada Post's stamp announcement booklet ("Canada's Stamp Details") changed from a 5½"x7½" black and white format to a 6"x11" colour booklet with the first issues of 1994.

## 1994

### GREETINGS BOOKLET — I

**1507**
"Quick Stick", Canada on left

**1508**
"Quick Stick", Canada on right

Designer: Steven Spazuk, Daniel Fortin, and George Fok.
Lithography (6 colours), Self adhesive booklet of 10
Leigh-Mardon Pty Limited

| 1994, Jan 28 | Tagged, JAC Paper | | | Die cut |
|---|---|---|---|---|
| | | NH–VF | ⊙F | FDC |
| **1507** | **43¢ multicoloured** | 1.25 | .90 | — |
| i | die cut to shape from Quarterly Pack/ Annual Collection | 2.50 | — | |
| **1508** | **43¢ multicoloured** | 1.25 | .90 | — |
| i | die cut to shape from Quarterly Pack/ Annual Collection | 2.50 | — | |
| a | booklet of 10 x 43¢ (5 x 1507, 5 x 1508) + 35 greeting stickers (5 each of 7 designs) (**BK166**) | 13.00 | | — |

**Nos. 1507, 1508 (2) combination FDC** **2.30**

Booklet issued for $4.50, a premium of 20¢ over face. Names of special occasions appear in the background. The world's first customized (Quick Sticks) self-adhesive stamps.

Two booklets of 1508a are known without die cutting; one still complete and one separated as follows: strip of 4 + 10 stickers (with bends): $2,000; strip of 4 + 10 stickers (VF): $2,750; pair and 15 stickers (VF): $1,350.

The adhesive on this issue appears to be drying out, making the stamps less "sticky" over time.

See also 1568–1569, 1600–1601

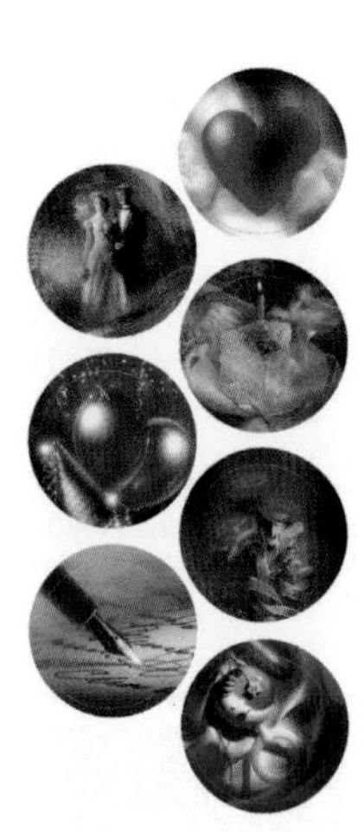

**Labels for Greetings stamps**

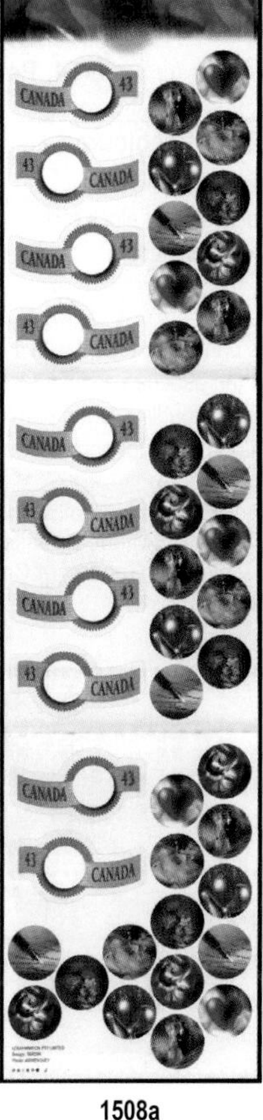

**1508a**

Definitive Timeline:
**1994, Feb 21** $1 Court House, Yorkton (1375)
$1 Provincial Normal School, Truro (1376)

**Rates:**

| Mar 1/94– Jul 31/95 | Domestic first-class (30-50g): 69¢ | USA (0-30g): 50¢ |
|---|---|---|
| | Domestic oversize (30-50g): 88¢ | International (0-20g): 88¢ |

*single usage:* USA 50¢: $15.00 | International 88¢: $20.00

## JEANNE SAUVÉ

1509
Jeanne Sauvé (1922–1993)

Designer: Jean Morin and Tom Yakobina.
Based on a photograph by André Le Coz, Greg Lorfing, Mike Pinder, and Yousuf Karsh.

Lithography (6 colours), pane of 20 plus 20 tabs
Canadian Bank Note Company, Limited

**1994, Mar 8** **GT4, Peterborough Paper** **Perf 12.5x13.1**

| | | NH–VF | ⊙F | PB | FDC |
|---|---|---|---|---|---|
| **1509** | **43¢ multicoloured**, LF | 1.00 | .40 | 5.25 | 4.00 |
| i | MF | 2.00 | 1.00 | 10.00 | |
| a | horiz. strip or block of 4 + 4 different tabs | 5.00 | 4.00 | | |

Qty: 15,000,000

No. 1509 is printed se-tenant with 4 different joining tabs in panes of 20 + 20 tabs. Stamp with tab attached commands a premium.
Kiss prints with doubling of the purple inscriptions are known. Value $500 for a block or strip of 4 and $600 for corner block.

Jeanne Sauvé was a journalist and broadcaster (1952–72), a Member of Parliament (1972–84), the Speaker of the House of Commons (1980–84) and served as Governor General of Canada (1984–90). Each tab represents one of these roles.

1509a

## T. EATON COMPANY

1510
Timothy Eaton

Designer: Louis Fishauf.

Lithography (5 colours), Prestige booklet of 10
Canadian Bank Note Company, Limited

**1994, Mar 17** **GT4, Harrison Paper** **Perf 13.3x13.0**

| | | NH–VF | ⊙F | FDC |
|---|---|---|---|---|
| **1510** | **43¢ multicoloured** | 1.00 | .40 | 1.45 |
| a | booklet pane of 10 x 43¢ (1510) + 2 labels (6 x 2) (BK169) | 10.00 | 8.00 | |

BK169 pane 1510a in cover $11.00
Qty: 7,500,000

Issued for the 125th anniversary of T. Eaton Company. The booklet contains 10 pages describing the history of the company.

1510a

## HERITAGE RIVERS — 4
Routes of the Fur Traders

1511
Saguenay River, QC

1512
French River, ON

1513
Mackenzie River, NWT

1514
Churchill River, NF

1515
Columbia River, BC

Designer: Malcolm Waddell. Based on illustrations by Jan Waddell.

Lithography (5 colours), booklet of 10
Canadian Bank Note Company, Limited

**1994, Apr 22** **GT4, Harrison Paper** **Perf 13.3**

| | | NH–VF | ⊙F | FDC |
|---|---|---|---|---|
| **1511** | **43¢ multicoloured** | 1.25 | .60 | |
| **1512** | **43¢ multicoloured** | 1.25 | .60 | |
| **1513** | **43¢ multicoloured** | 1.25 | .60 | |
| **1514** | **43¢ multicoloured** | 1.25 | .60 | |
| **1515** | **43¢ multicoloured** | 1.25 | .60 | |
| a | strip of 5 (1511–1515) | 6.50 | 5.00 | |
| ai | as 1515a without fold, from Canada Post's annual Souvenir Collection | 7.50 | 9.00 | |
| b | booklet pane of 10 (5 x 2) 2 x 1515a se-tenant (BK170) | 13.00 | 12.00 | |

BK170 pane 1515b in cover $13.50
Qty: 3,000,000 of each

**Nos. 1511–1515 (strip of 3 + pair) combination FDC** 4.90

This is the fourth and final booklet in a series depicting Canadian Heritage Rivers and features the canoe routes of the fur traders.
See also 1321–1325, 1408–1412 and 1485–1489.

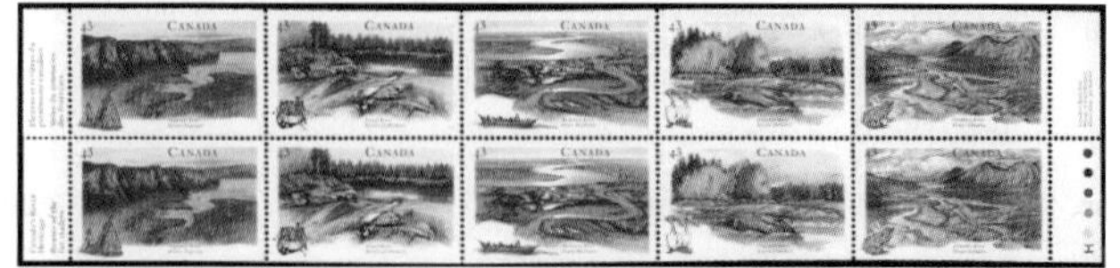

1515b

## MASTERPIECES OF CANADIAN ART — 7

**1516**
*Vera*, by Frederick H. Varley

Designer: Pierre-Yves Pelletier. Based on a painting by Frederick Horsman Varley.
Lithography (6 colours) with foil stamping, pane of 16
Leigh-Mardon Pty Limited

**1994, May 6** **Tagged, Coated Papers** **Perf 14.0x14.6**

| | | NH–VF | ⊙F | PB | FDC |
|---|---|---|---|---|---|
| **1516** | **88¢ multicoloured** (gold border) | 2.00 | 1.50 | 10.00 | 2.35 |
| i | gold bar across Vera's chest, due to a 6.5mm up colour shift (2 panes of 16 known) | *900.00* | — | *3,750.00†* | |

Qty: 8,700,000

† Corner Block (LL or LR) with gold maple leaves on bottom of lower stamps.
One "used" copy is recorded with missing yellow; has corner crease: value: $1,500.

General tagging around edge of white background.
See also 1203, 1241, 1271, 1310, 1419, 1466, 1545, 1602, 1635, 1754, 1800, 1863, 1916, 1945.

**1516i**

## XV COMMONWEALTH GAMES

**1517** Lawn bowling — **1518** Lacrosse

**1519** Wheelchair marathon — **1520** High jump

**1521** Diving — **1522** Cycling

Designer: David Coates and Roderick C.J. Roodenburg.
Lithography (5 colours) with foil stamping, panes of 25
Leigh-Mardon Pty Limited

**1994, May 20** **Tagged, Coated Papers** **Perf 14.0**

| | | NH–VF | ⊙F | PB | FDC |
|---|---|---|---|---|---|
| **1517** | **43¢ multicoloured** | 1.00 | .35 | | |
| **1518** | **43¢ multicoloured** | 1.00 | .35 | | |
| a | se-tenant pair (1517, 1518) | 2.25 | 1.50 | 5.00 | 2.30 |

Qty: 7,500,000 of each

**1994, Aug 5**

| | | NH–VF | ⊙F | PB | FDC |
|---|---|---|---|---|---|
| **1519** | **43¢ multicoloured** | 1.00 | .35 | | |
| **1520** | **43¢ multicoloured** | 1.00 | .35 | | |
| a | se-tenant pair (1519, 1520) | 2.25 | 1.50 | 5.00 | — |
| ai | se-tenant pair with silver inscriptions | *1,000.00* | | | |

Qty: 7,500,000 of each

| | | NH–VF | ⊙F | PB | FDC |
|---|---|---|---|---|---|
| **1521** | **50¢ multicoloured** | 1.25 | 1.00 | 6.25 | — |
| a | gold inscriptions omitted* | 2,000.00 | | | |

Qty: 15,000,000

* Thirty-three known. Several have disturbed gum; value $300–$1,000, depending on the degree of disturbance. A certificate of authenticity is recommended.

| | | NH–VF | ⊙F | PB | FDC |
|---|---|---|---|---|---|
| **1522** | **88¢ multicoloured** | 2.00 | 1.25 | 10.00 | |
| a | gold inscriptions omitted | 2,500.00 | — | — | — |

Qty: 15,000,000

**Nos. 1519–1522 (4) combination FDC** **5.10**

Tagging is found only on the white borders.
Issued to celebrate the Commonwealth Games held at Victoria, B.C. in August, 1994.

## UNITED NATIONS INTERNATIONAL YEAR OF THE FAMILY

**1523a** Mother and child — **1523b** Family outing

**1523c** Child with elderly woman — **1523d** Education — **1523e** Social aid

QE II — 1990's

Designer: Suzanne Duranceau.

Lithography (5 colours), Souvenir sheet of 5
Leigh-Mardon Pty Limited

| 1994, Jun 2 | FCP, Coated Papers | Perf 14.0x14.6 | | |
|---|---|---|---|---|
| | | NH–VF | ⊙F | FDC |
| 1523 | $2.15 souvenir sheet of 5 stamps | 6.00 | 6.00 | 4.90 |
| a | 43¢ multicoloured | 1.00 | 1.00 | |
| b | 43¢ multicoloured | 1.00 | 1.00 | |
| c | 43¢ multicoloured | 1.00 | 1.00 | |
| d | 43¢ multicoloured | 1.00 | 1.00 | |
| e | 43¢ multicoloured | 1.00 | 1.00 | |

Qty: 1,500,000 of each

Issued to commemorate 1994 as the United Nations International Year of the Family.

1523



## CANADA DAY — MAPLE TREES

1524a
Bigleaf Maple

1524b
Sugar Maple

1524c
Silver Maple

1524d
Striped Maple

1524e
Norway Maple

1524f
Manitoba Maple

1524g
Black Maple

1524h
Douglas Maple

1524i
Mountain Maple

1524j
Vine Maple

1524k
Hedge Maple

1524l
Red Maple

Designer: Dennis Noble. Typographed by Bernard Low.

Lithography (6 colours), pane of 12
Canadian Bank Note Company, Limited

| 1994, Jun 30 | GT4, Peterborough Paper | Perf 13.0x13.5 | | |
|---|---|---|---|---|
| | | NH–VF | ⊙F | FDC |
| 1524 | $5.16 pane of 12, LF | 15.00* | 15.00 | 12.00† |
| | MF paper | 25.00 | 25.00 | |
| a | 43¢ Bigleaf Maple | 1.00 | 1.00 | |
| b | 43¢ Sugar Maple | 1.00 | 1.00 | |
| c | 43¢ Silver Maple | 1.00 | 1.00 | |
| d | 43¢ Striped Maple | 1.00 | 1.00 | |
| e | 43¢ Norway Maple | 1.00 | 1.00 | |
| f | 43¢ Manitoba Maple | 1.00 | 1.00 | |
| g | 43¢ Black Maple | 1.00 | 1.00 | |
| h | 43¢ Douglas Maple | 1.00 | 1.00 | |
| i | 43¢ Mountain Maple | 1.00 | 1.00 | |
| j | 43¢ Vine Maple | 1.00 | 1.00 | |
| k | 43¢ Hedge Maple | 1.00 | 1.00 | |
| l | 43¢ Red Maple | 1.00 | 1.00 | |

Qty: 1,250,000 of each

* Value shown is for full philatelic pane as illustrated below. For field stock pane (without inscriptions) 12.00 12.00

† Value shown is for set of 3 FDC's: 1) a, b, e, f – $4.00; 2) c, d, g, h – $4.00; 3) i, j, k. l – $4.00, issued together in a protective folder.

1524

## GREAT CANADIANS

1525 William Avery (Billy) Bishop (1894–1956)

1526 Mary Travers – "La Bolduc" (1894–1941)

Designer: Pierre Fontaine. Based on illustrations by Bernard Leduc.
Lithography (6 colours), pane of 50
Canadian Bank Note Company, Limited

**1994, Aug 12 GT4, Peterborough Paper Perf 13.3**

| | | NH–VF | ⊙F | PB | FDC |
|---|---|---|---|---|---|
| **1525** | **43¢ multicoloured**, F (back) | .90 | .40 | | |
| i | MF (back) | 2.00 | .75 | | |
| ii | DF | 2.00 | .75 | | |
| **1526** | **43¢ multicoloured**, F (back) | .90 | .40 | | |
| i | MF (back) | 2.00 | .75 | | |
| ii | DF | 2.00 | .75 | | |
| a | se-tenant pair (1525, 1526), F (back) | 2.00 | 1.25 | 4.50 | 2.30 |
| aii | as "a", MF (back) | 5.00 | 3.00 | | |
| aiii | as "a", DF | 5.00 | 3.00 | | |

Qty: 7,500,000 of each

Issued in honour of Billy Bishop, WWI flying ace and Mary Travers, singer and song writer on the 100th anniversary of their birth.

## HISTORIC PUBLIC SERVICE VEHICLES — 2

**Public Service Vehicles**

1527a Ford Military Ambulance (1942–1943)

1527b Reo Police Wagon (1925)

1527c Sicard Snow Remover Snowblower (1927)

1527d Bickle Chieftain Fire Engine (1936)

1527e Ottawa Car Company Streetcar (1894)

1527f MCI Courier 50 Skyview Motor Coach (1950)

1527

Designer: Joseph Gault and Tiit Telmet. Based on illustrations by Cameron Wykes.
Lithography (7 colours), Souvenir sheet of 6
Canadian Bank Note Company, Limited

**1994, Aug 19 GT4, Peterborough Paper Perf 12.5x13.1**

| | | NH–VF | ⊙F | FDC |
|---|---|---|---|---|
| **1527** | **$3.62 souvenir sheet of 6 stamps**, LF | 9.00 | 9.00 | 9.00† |
| a | **43¢ multicoloured** | 1.00 | 1.00 | |
| b | **43¢ multicoloured** | 1.00 | 1.00 | |
| c | **50¢ multicoloured** | 1.20 | 1.20 | |
| d | **50¢ multicoloured** | 1.20 | 1.20 | |
| e | **88¢ multicoloured** | 2.25 | 2.00 | |
| f | **88¢ multicoloured** | 2.25 | 2.00 | |
| i | sheet of 6, MF | 20.00 | 16.00 | |

Qty: 800,000 of each

† Value shown is for set of 3 FDC's: 1) a, b – $2.30; 2) c, d – $2.60; 3) e, f – $4.10, issued together in a protective folder.

See also 1490, 1552, 1604 and 1605.

## UNITED NATIONS INTERNATIONAL CIVIL AVIATION

1528 Multi-engine Jet Aircraft

Designer: Stuart Bradley Ash, Katalin Kovats, and Silvio Napoleone.
Lithography (6 colours), pane of 25
Canadian Bank Note Company, Limited

**1994, Sep 16 GT4, Coated Papers Perf 13.1**

| | | NH–VF | ⊙F | PB | FDC |
|---|---|---|---|---|---|
| **1528** | **43¢ multicoloured** | 1.45 | .30 | 7.25 | 1.45 |

Qty: 15,000,000

Issued for the 50th anniversary of the International Civil Aviation Organization (ICAO), a UN organization with headquarters in Montreal.

## PREHISTORIC LIFE IN CANADA — 4

**Mammals**

1529 Coryphodon (Eocene Epoch)

1530 Megacerops (Oligocene Epoch)

1531 Arctodus simus (Pleistocene Epoch)

1532 Mammuthus primigenius (Pleistocene Epoch)

QE II — 1990's

Designer: Rolf P. Harder

Lithography (6 colours), pane of 20
Canadian Bank Note Company, Limited

**1994, Sep 26** **GT4, Peterborough Paper** **Perf 13.3**

| | | NH–VF | ⊙F | PB | FDC |
|---|---|---|---|---|---|
| **1529** | **43¢ multicoloured**, LF | .90 | .40 | | |
| i | HF | 2.00 | .50 | | |
| **1530** | **43¢ multicoloured**, LF | .90 | .40 | | |
| i | HF | 2.00 | .50 | | |
| **1531** | **43¢ multicoloured**, LF | .90 | .40 | | |
| i | HF | 2.00 | .50 | | |
| **1532** | **43¢ multicoloured**, LF | .90 | .40 | | |
| i | HF | 2.00 | .50 | | |
| a | se-tenant block of 4 (1529–1532), LF | 4.00 | 3.50 | 4.50 | 4.00 |
| ai | as "a", HF | 10.00 | 8.00 | 12.00 | |

Qty: 4,250,000 of each

This is the fourth and final set in the series.
See also 1279–1282, 1306–1309 and 1495–1498.

## CHRISTMAS CAROLLING

1533
Family carolling near Christmas Tree

1534
Choir

1535
Outdoor Carolling

1536
Soloist

Designer: Diti Katona and John Pylypczak. Based on an illustration by Nina Berkson.

Lithography (6 colours), pane of 50
Canadian Bank Note Company, Limited

**1994, Nov 3** **GT4, Peterborough Paper** **Perf 13.3**

| | | NH–VF | ⊙F | PB | FDC |
|---|---|---|---|---|---|
| **1533** | **43¢ multicoloured**, LF | .90 | .20 | 4.50 | |
| i | MF | 2.50 | .50 | 12.00 | |
| a | booklet pane of 10 x 43¢ (1533as), LF (BK172) | 12.00 | 9.00 | | |
| as | single with straight edge, from 1533a | 1.25 | .25 | | |
| asi | as "as", double print of red 'Canada' and green 'Christmas-Noel' | 300.00 | | | |
| ai | booklet pane of 10 x 43¢ (1533ais), MF (BK172) | 35.00 | | | |
| ais | single with straight edge, from 1533ai | 3.00 | .50 | | |
| BK172 | pane 1533a in cover $12.50 | | | | |

Qty: 44,000,000

**Peterborough Paper**

| | | NH–VF | ⊙F | PB | FDC |
|---|---|---|---|---|---|
| **1534** | **50¢ multicoloured**, LF | 1.00 | .75 | 5.00 | |
| i | MF | 3.00 | 1.25 | 15.00 | |
| ii | 52¢ denomination† | 200.00 | — | 950.00 | |

Qty: 9,000,000

**Coated Papers**

| | | NH–VF | ⊙F | PB | FDC |
|---|---|---|---|---|---|
| a | booklet pane of 5 x 50¢ (1534as) + label, LF (BK173) | 7.50 | 6.00 | | |
| as | single with straight edge, from 1534a | 1.50 | 1.50 | | |
| BK173 | pane 1534a in cover $8.00 | | | | |

| | | NH–VF | ⊙F | PB | FDC |
|---|---|---|---|---|---|
| | **Peterborough Paper** | | | | |
| **1535** | **88¢ multicoloured**, LF | 2.00 | 1.25 | 10.00 | — |
| i | MF | 5.00 | 2.00 | 25.00 | |
| ii | 90¢ denomination (1,000 known)† | 600.00 | — | — | — |

Qty: 9,000,000

**Coated Papers**

| | | NH–VF | ⊙F | PB | FDC |
|---|---|---|---|---|---|
| a | booklet pane of 5 x 88¢ (1535as) + label (BK174) | 12.50 | 9.00 | — | — |
| as | single with straight edge, from 1535a | 2.50 | 2.00 | — | — |
| BK174 | pane 1535a in cover $13.00 | | | | |

**Nos. 1533–1535 (3) combination FDC** **4.20**

† Examples of unissued 52¢ and 90¢ denominations, printed in anticipation of a rate increase which was not approved, are known in private hands. No multiples exist of the 90¢ as all of the 'find' of these were split into singles before they reached the philatelic market.

**GTX, Greetmore Booklet, Coated Papers** **Perf 13.0x13.1**

| | | NH–VF | ⊙F | FDC |
|---|---|---|---|---|
| **1536** | **(38¢) multicoloured**, single from 1536a | 1.00 | .75 | 1.35 |
| a | booklet pane of 10 x 38¢ (1536) (BK171) | 11.00 | 8.00 | — |
| BK171 | pane 1536a in cover $11.50 | | | |

Qty: 50,700,000

No. 1536 was issued in booklets only, for use on greeting card envelopes bearing a printed postal code matrix. Accepted singly until January 31, 1995, if affixed to designated envelope.

1534ii

1535ii

1533a

1534a

1535a

1536a

1533asi

## SECOND WORLD WAR — 1944

Victory in Sight

1537 D-Day Beachhead — 1538 Artillery – Normandy

1539 Tactical Air Forces — 1540 Walcheren and the Scheldt

Designer: Pierre-Yves Pelletier. Based on an illustration by Jean-Pierre Armanville.

Lithography (5 colours), pane of 16

Canadian Bank Note Company, Limited

**1994, Nov 7 — GT4, Peterborough Paper — Perf 13.3**

| | | NH–VF | ⊙F | PB | FDC |
|---|---|---|---|---|---|
| **1537** | **43¢ multicoloured**, MF | 1.25 | .50 | | |
| i | HF | 2.00 | .75 | | |
| **1538** | **43¢ multicoloured**, MF | 1.25 | .50 | | |
| i | HF | 2.00 | .75 | | |
| **1539** | **43¢ multicoloured**, MF | 1.25 | .50 | | |
| i | HF | 2.00 | .75 | | |
| **1540** | **43¢ multicoloured**, MF | 1.25 | .50 | | |
| i | HF | 2.00 | .75 | | |
| a | se-tenant block of 4 (1537–1540), MF | 5.00 | 3.00 | 6.25 | 4.00 |
| ai | as "a", HF | 8.00 | | 10.00 | |

Qty: 2,500,000 of each

This is the sixth set honouring Canadian achievements and sacrifices during World War II.

See also Nos. 1260–1263, 1298–1301, 1345–1348, 1448–1451, 1503–1506 and 1541–1544.

# 1995

## SECOND WORLD WAR — 1945

Peace

1541 Veterans Return Home — 1542 Freeing the POW

1543 Liberation of Civilians, Netherlands — 1544 Crossing the Rhine

Designer: Pierre-Yves Pelletier. Based on an illustration by Jean-Pierre Armanville.

Lithography (5 colours), pane of 16

Canadian Bank Note Company, Limited

**1995, Mar 20 — GT4, Peterborough Paper — Perf 13.3**

| | | NH–VF | ⊙F | PB | FDC |
|---|---|---|---|---|---|
| **1541** | **43¢ multicoloured**, LF | 1.25 | .50 | | |
| i | HF | 3.00 | .75 | | |
| **1542** | **43¢ multicoloured**, LF | 1.25 | .50 | | |
| i | HF | 3.00 | .75 | | |
| **1543** | **43¢ multicoloured**, LF | 1.25 | .50 | | |
| i | HF | 3.00 | .75 | | |
| **1544** | **43¢ multicoloured**, LF | 1.25 | .50 | | |
| i | HF | 3.00 | .75 | | |
| a | se-tenant block of 4, LF (1541–1544) | 5.00 | 4.00 | 6.25 | 4.00 |
| ai | se-tenant block of 4, HF (1541i–1544i) | 15.00 | 12.00 | | |

Qty: 2,500,000 of each

This is the final set honouring Canadian achievements and sacrifices during World War II.

See also Nos. 1260–1263, 1298–1301, 1345–1348, 1448–1451, 1503–1506 and 1537–1540.

## MASTERPIECES OF CANADIAN ART — 8

1545
*Floraison*, c. 1950

Designer: Pierre-Yves Pelletier. Based on a painting by Alfred Pellan (1906–1988).

Lithography (6 colours) with foil stamping, pane of 16

Canadian Bank Note Company, Limited

**1995, Apr 12 — Tagged, Coated Papers — Perf 13.0x13.3**

| | | NH–VF | ⊙F | PB | FDC |
|---|---|---|---|---|---|
| **1545** | **88¢ multicoloured** (gold border) | 2.25 | 1.50 | 11.00 | 2.35 |
| a | gold foil omitted | 2,000.00 | — | 8,000.00* | |

Qty: 8,700,000

* Blank corner block of 4.

General tagging around edge of white background.

See also 1203, 1241, 1271, 1310, 1419, 1466, 1516, 1602, 1635, 1754, 1800, 1863, 1916, 1945.

## CANADIAN FLAG

1546
Flag with scene of lake

Designer: Stuart Bradley Ash, Katalin Kovats, and Philip Unger.
Based on a photograph by Bill Brooks and J.A. Kraulis.

Lithography (6 colours), pane of 20

Canadian Bank Note Company, Limited

**1995, May 1 — GT4, Peterborough Paper — Perf 13.5x13.0**

| | | NH–VF | ⊙F | PB | FDC |
|---|---|---|---|---|---|
| **1546** | **(43¢) multicoloured**, MF | 1.20 | .30 | 5.00 | 1.45 |
| i | LF | 2.50 | .45 | 10.00 | |

Qty: 15,000,000

For non-denominated size 10 envelope of same design, see U272 (issued 2014).

Issued for the thirtieth anniversary of the Canadian flag (Maple Leaf design).

## FORTRESS OF LOUISBOURG, Nova Scotia

**1547**
Louisbourg Harbour and ships

**1548**
Town of Louisbourg

**1549**
Museum behind King's Bastion

**1550**
King's garden, convent, etc.

**1551**
Partially eroded fortifications

Designer: Rolf P. Harder.

Lithography (6 colours), booklet pane of 10
Ashton-Potter Canada Limited

**1995, May 5** **FCP, Coated Papers** **Perf 12.5x13.1**

| | | NH–VF | ⊙F | FDC |
|---|---|---|---|---|
| **1547** | **(43¢) multicoloured** | 1.00 | .50 | |
| **1548** | **(43¢) multicoloured** | 1.00 | .50 | |
| **1549** | **(43¢) multicoloured** | 1.00 | .50 | 1.45* |
| **1550** | **(43¢) multicoloured** | 1.00 | .50 | |
| **1551** | **(43¢) multicoloured** | 1.00 | .50 | |
| a | se-tenant strip of 5 (1547–1551) | 5.50 | 5.00 | |
| ai | as 1551a without fold, from Canada Post's annual Souvenir Collection | 7.00 | 8.00 | |
| b | booklet pane of 10 (5 x 2) (2 x 1551a se-tenant) (BK175) | 12.00 | 11.00 | — |
| **BK175** | pane of 1551b in cover $13.00 | | | |

Qty: 3,000,000 of each

**Nos. 1547, 1548 (2) combination FDC*** **2.30**
**Nos. 1550, 1551 (2) combination FDC*** **2.30**

* The three FDCs were issued together in a protective folder for $5.00.
No. 1551a is a continuous design. The pane layout produces identical vertical pairs of the five designs.
Issued for the 275th anniversary of the founding of the Fortress of Louisbourg.
See also 983–992 and 1050–1059.

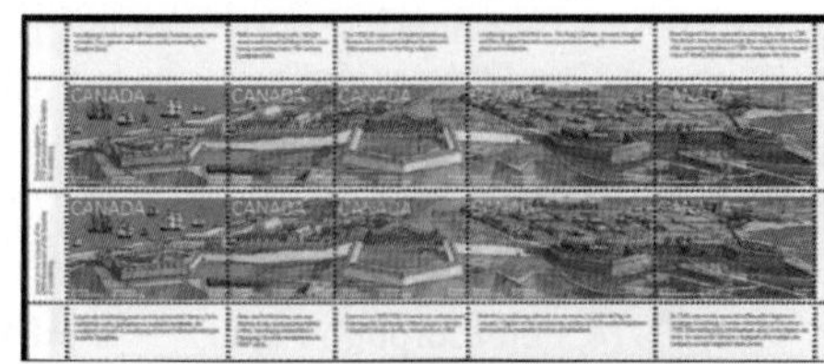

**1551b**

## HISTORIC LAND VEHICLES — 3

**Farm & Frontier Vehicles**

**1552a**
Cockshutt "30" farm tractor (1950)

**1552b**
Bombardier Ski-Doo Olympique 335 snowmobile (1970)

**1552c**
Bombardier B-12 CS multi-passenger snowmobile (1948)

**1552d**
Gotfredson Model 20 farm truck (1924)

**1552e**
Robin-Nodwell RN 110 tracked carrier (1962)

**1552f**
Massey-Harris No, 21 self-propelled combine (1942)

Designer: Joseph Gault and Tiit Telmet. Based on illustrations by Cameron Wykes.

Lithography (7 colours), Souvenir sheet of 6
Canadian Bank Note Company, Limited

**1995, May 26** **GT4, Peterborough Paper** **Perf 12.5x13.1**

| | | NH–VF | ⊙F | FDC |
|---|---|---|---|---|
| **1552** | **$3.62 souvenir sheet of 6 stamps**, LF | 9.00 | 9.00 | 9.00† |
| a | **43¢ multicoloured** | 1.00 | 1.00 | |
| b | **43¢ multicoloured** | 1.00 | 1.00 | |
| c | **50¢ multicoloured** | 1.25 | 1.25 | |
| d | **50¢ multicoloured** | 1.25 | 1.25 | |
| e | **88¢ multicoloured** | 2.25 | 2.25 | |
| f | **88¢ multicoloured** | 2.25 | 2.25 | |
| i | sheet of 6, MF | 20.00 | 12.00 | |
| ii | sheet of 6, DF | 25.00 | 22.00 | |

Qty: 800,000 of each

† Value shown is for set of 3 FDC's: 1) a, b – $2.30; 2) c, d – $2.60; 3) e, f – $4.10, issued together in a protective folder.
See also 1490, 1527, 1604 and 1605.

**1552**

## GOLF IN CANADA

**1553**
Banff Springs Golf Club, Banff, AB

**1554**
Riverside Country Club, Saint John, NB

**1555**
Glen Abbey Golf Club, Oakville, ON

**1556**
Victoria Golf Club, Victoria, BC

**1557**
Royal Montreal Golf Club, Montreal, QC

Designer: Peter Adam. Based on photographs by Michael Rafelson.
Photo imaging by Cameron Wykes.

Lithography (6 colours), booklet pane of 10
Ashton-Potter Canada Limited

**1995, Jun 6** | **GT4, Coated Papers** | **Perf 13.5x13.0**

| | | NH–VF | ⊙F | FDC |
|---|---|---|---|---|
| **1553** | **43¢ multicoloured** | 1.25 | .50 | |
| **1554** | **43¢ multicoloured** | 1.25 | .50 | |
| **1555** | **43¢ multicoloured** | 1.25 | .50 | |
| **1556** | **43¢ multicoloured** | 1.25 | .50 | |
| **1557** | **43¢ multicoloured** | 1.25 | .50 | |
| a | horizontal strip of 5 (1553–1557) | 7.00 | 5.00 | |
| ai | as 1557a without fold, from Canada Post's annual Souvenir Collection | 7.00 | 8.00 | |
| b | booklet pane of 10 (5 x 2) 2 of 1557a se-tenant (BK176) | 12.00 | 11.00 | — |

**BK176** pane 1557a in cover $13.00
Qty: 3,000,000 of each

**Nos. 1553–1557 (5) combination FDC** **4.90**

The pane layout produces no identical pairs.
Issued for the centennials of the Royal Canadian Golf Association (RCGA) and the Canadian Amateur Championship.

**1557b**

## LUNENBURG ACADEMY CENTENARY

**1558**
Lunenburg Academy

Designer: Brian MacKay-Lyons and Steven Slipp.

Lithography (6 colours), pane of 25
Canadian Bank Note Company, Limited

**1995, Jun 29** | **Tagged, Peterborough Paper** | **Perf 13.0**

| | | NH–VF | ⊙F | PB | FDC |
|---|---|---|---|---|---|
| **1558** | **43¢ multicoloured**, MF | .90 | .30 | 4.50 | 1.45 |
| **T1** | untagged (error) | 100.00 | — | 600.00 | |
| **i** | HF | 2.50 | .50 | 12.00 | |

Qty: 15,000,000

Tagging is on white edges only.
Issued for the Centennial of the Lunenburg Academy in Nova Scotia.

## CANADA DAY — GROUP OF SEVEN

**1559a**
*October Gold* (1922)
by Franklin Carmichael

**1559b**
*From the North Shore, Lake Superior* (1923)
by Lawren Harris

**1559c**
*Evening, Les Éboulements, Quebec* (1932–1933)
by A.Y. Jackson

**1560a**
*Serenity, Lake of the Woods* (1922)
by Frank H. Johnston

**1560b**
*A September Gale, Georgian Bay* (1921) by Arthur Lismer

QE II — 1990's

**1560c**
*Falls, Montreal River* (1920)
by J.E.H. MacDonald

**1560d**
*Open Window* (c. 1933)
by Frederick Horsman Varley

**1561a**
*Mill Houses* (1928) by Alfred J. Casson

**1561b**
*Pembina Valley* (1923)
by Lionel LeMoine FitzGerald

**1561c**
*The Lumberjack* (1924)
by Edwin Headley Holgate

Designer: Alain Leduc.

Lithography (7 colours), Souvenir sheets
Canadian Bank Note Company, Limited

| **1995, Jun 29** | | **FCP, Coated Papers** | | **Perf 13.0x13.3** |
|---|---|---|---|---|
| | | **NH–VF** | **⊙F** | **FDC** |
| **1559** | **$1.29 souvenir sheet** of 3 | | | |
| | Three original members | 4.00 | 4.00 | |
| a | **43¢ multicoloured** | 1.25 | 1.25 | |
| b | **43¢ multicoloured** | 1.25 | 1.25 | |
| c | **43¢ multicoloured** | 1.25 | 1.25 | |
| Qty: 870,000 of each | | | | |
| **Nos. 1559a–1559c (3) combination FDC** | | | | **3.20** |
| **1560** | **$1.72 souvenir sheet** of 4 | | | |
| | Four original members | 5.25 | 5.25 | |
| a | **43¢ multicoloured** | 1.25 | 1.25 | |
| b | **43¢ multicoloured** | 1.25 | 1.25 | |
| c | **43¢ multicoloured** | 1.25 | 1.25 | |
| d | **43¢ multicoloured** | 1.25 | 1.25 | |
| Qty: 870,000 of each | | | | |
| **Nos. 1560a–1560d (4) combination FDC** | | | | **4.00** |
| **1561** | **$1.29 souvenir sheet** of 3 | | | |
| | Three new members | 4.00 | 4.00 | |
| a | **43¢ multicoloured** | 1.25 | 1.25 | |
| b | **43¢ multicoloured** | 1.25 | 1.25 | |
| c | **43¢ multicoloured** | 1.25 | 1.25 | |
| Qty: 870,000 of each | | | | |
| **Nos. 1561a–1561c (3) combination FDC** | | | | **3.20** |

The three souvenir sheets (1559–1561) were issued together with a 12 page information booklet in a sealed cardboard envelope – $15.00.

The tagging (FCP) exists as weak (mottled) or strong and even (smooth).

Souvenir sheets (1559–1561) exist with shifted perforations. In the most severe cases '43 CANADA' would remain on the sheet if the stamps were removed. Value $100–$750 per pane, depending on the degree of perforation shift and number of stamps on the pane (3 or 4).

**1559**

**1560**

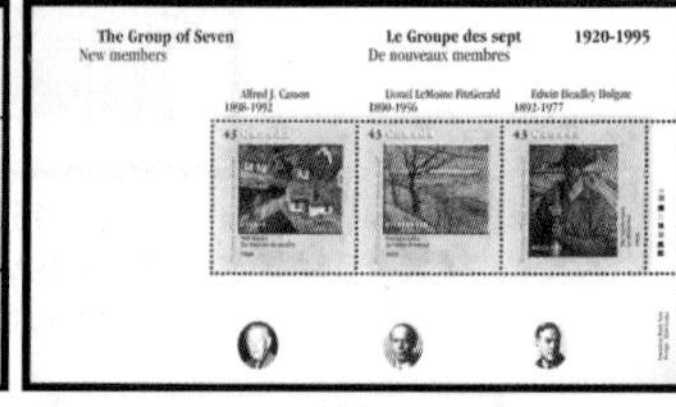

**1561**

## MANITOBA

**1562**

Designer: Steven Rosenberg and Terry Gallagher.

Lithography (5 colours), pane of 20
Ashton-Potter Canada Limited

| **1995, Jul 14** | **GT4, Coated Papers** | | **Perf 13.3x13.0** | |
|---|---|---|---|---|
| | **NH–VF** | **⊙F** | **PB** | **FDC** |
| **1562 43¢ multicoloured** | .90 | .40 | 4.50 | 1.45 |

Qty: 15,000,000

Examples on cover dated before the rate change on August 1, 1995 command a premium.

Issued to celebrate the 125th anniversary of Manitoba's entry into Confederation.

Definitive Timeline:

1995, Jul 31 — 45¢ Queen Elizabeth II (1360)
45¢ Flag over Building (1361)
52/71/90¢ Fruit Trees (1366/1370/1374)

| **Rates:** | Domestic first-class (0-30g): 45¢ | |
|---|---|---|
| Aug 1/95– | Domestic first-class (30-50g): 71¢ | USA (0-30g): 52¢ |
| Dec 31/98 | Domestic oversize (30-50g): 90¢ | International (0-20g): 90¢ |

*single usage:* USA 52¢: $10.00 | International 90¢: $15.00

## MIGRATORY WILDLIFE

1563 Monarch Butterfly — 1564, 1567 Belted Kingfisher

1565 Northern Pintail — 1566 Hoary Bat

Designer: Debbie Adams.

Lithography (7 colours), pane of 20
Canadian Bank Note Company, Limited

**1995, Aug 15** **FCP, Coated Papers** **Perf 13.1x12.5**

| | | NH–VF | ⊙F | PB | FDC |
|---|---|---|---|---|---|
| **1563** | **45¢ multicoloured** (row 1) | 1.00 | .30 | | |
| i | thicker green line (row 4) | 1.00 | .30 | | |
| **1564** | **45¢ multicoloured** ("aune")† (row 1) | 1.25 | .50 | | |
| i | pink arrow through 'a' (row 4) | 1.00 | .30 | | |
| **1565** | **45¢ multicoloured** (row 2) | 1.00 | .30 | | |
| i | thin pink line (row 3) | 1.00 | .30 | | |
| **1566** | **45¢ multicoloured** (row 2) | 1.00 | .30 | | |
| i | thick pink line (row 3) | 1.00 | .30 | | |
| a | se-tenant block or vertical strip of 4 (1563–1566) | 5.00 | 3.50 | 5.30 | 4.20 |

Qty: 4,550,000 of each

This issue exists with weak, mottled tagging. May be a "dry print" of the taggant.

**1995, Sep 26**

| | | NH–VF | ⊙F | PB | FDC |
|---|---|---|---|---|---|
| **1567** | **45¢ multicoloured** ("faune" corrected)† (row 1) | 1.25 | 1.00 | | |
| i | pink arrow through 'a' (row 4) | 1.25 | 1.00 | | |
| a | se-tenant block or vertical strip of 4 (1563, 1565, 1566 and 1567) | 5.00 | 5.50 | 6.00 | — |

Qty: 800,000

† The original printing (1564) incorrectly left off the "f" of "faune" (leaving "aune"). This was corrected with a reprint of the stamps (1567).

Subtle differences in the thickness or placement of the coloured "flight paths" results in the stamps in one row being slightly different from the same design found in another row.

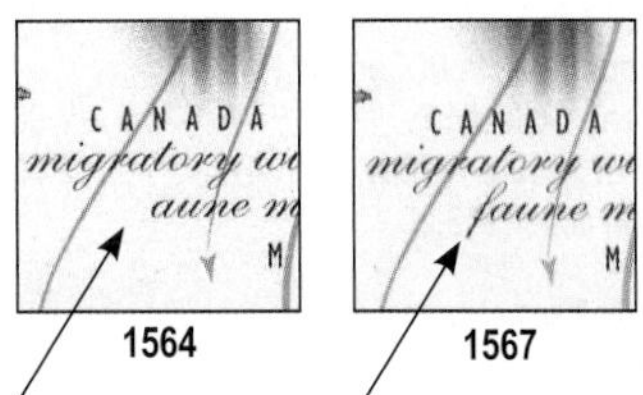


1564 — 1567

Mexico released a set of 4 'Animal Species' stamps (illustrated at left; Scott 1924a–d) on August 15 featuring similar migratory wildlife.

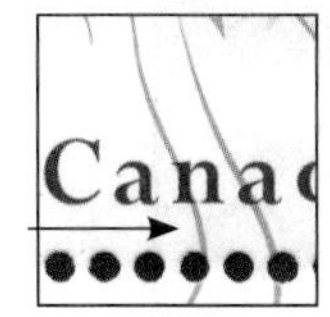
1563

1563i

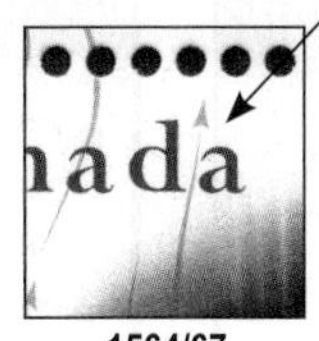
1564/67

1564i/67i

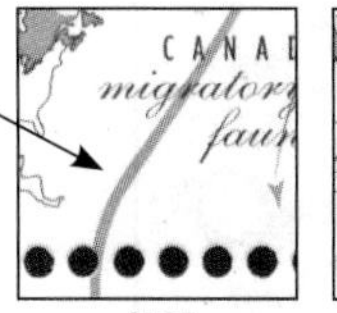
1565

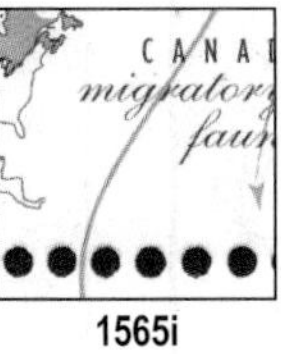
1565i

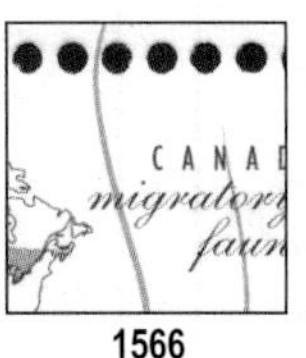
1566

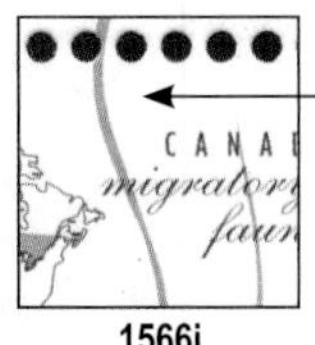
1566i

## GREETINGS BOOKLET — 2
### "Provinces" (52mmx28mm)

**1568**
"Quick Stick", Canada on left

**1569**
"Quick Stick", Canada on right

Designer: Tarzan Communication Graphique Inc. Based on illustrations by Steven Spazuk.

Lithography (6 colours), Self-adhesive booklet pane of 10
Ashton-Potter Canada Limited

**1995, Sep 1** **Tagged, JAC Paper** **Die cut**

| | | NH–VF | ⊙F | FDC |
|---|---|---|---|---|
| **1568** | **45¢ multicoloured**, HB | 1.25 | 1.00 | |
| i | Coated Papers, dull | 1.25 | 1.00 | |
| ii | die cut to shape from Quarterly Pack/ Annual Collection | 2.50 | — | |
| **1569** | **45¢ multicoloured**, HB | 1.25 | 1.00 | |
| a | booklet pane of 10 x 45¢ (5 x 1568, 5 x 1569) + 15 greeting stickers (4 each of 3 designs, 3 of 1 design) (**BK182**), HB | 16.00 | | |
| i | Coated Papers, dull | 1.25 | 1.00 | |
| iv | die cut to shape from Quarterly Pack/ Annual Collection | 2.50 | — | |
| ii | booklet pane, Coated Papers (**BK183**), dull, *Sep 15, 1995* | 16.00 | | |
| iii | booklet pane, Coated Papers (**BK200**), dull, *Aug 15, 1997* | 13.00 | | |

**Nos. 1568, 1569 (2) combination FDC** **2.40**

Booklets issued for $4.70, a premium of 20¢ over face. Tagging is on white border. See also 1507–1508 (43¢ silver border), 1600–1601 (45¢ special occasion text).

1568, 1569
Provinces

1600, 1601
Special occasions

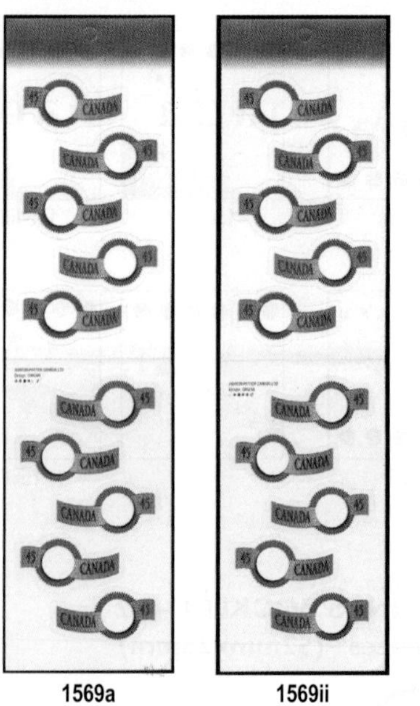

1569a 1569ii 1569iii

| Paper | JAC | Coated | |
|---|---|---|---|
| Labels | Greetings | Chiropracty | Greetings |
| | when booklet is *open*, labels are affixed at ... | | |
| 1569a (BK182) | ... bottom of top panel | | |
| 1569ii (BK183) | | ... top of bottom panel | |
| 1569iii (BK200) | | | ... top of bottom panel |

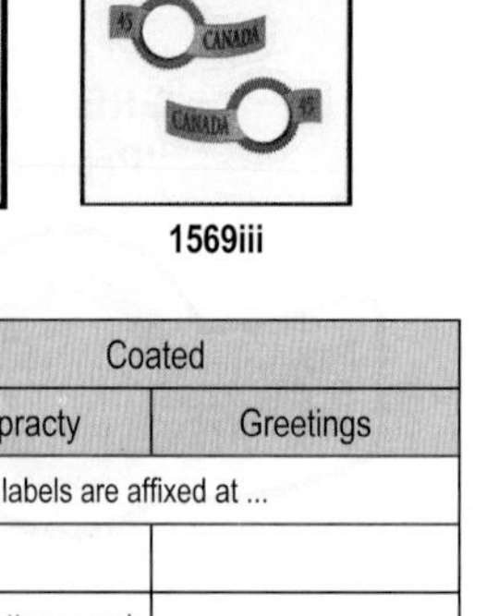

**Greetings Labels from 1569a, 1569iii**

**Chiropracty Labels from 1569ii**

**Other labels issued as promotional items**

## BRIDGES

**1570**
Quebec Bridge, Quebec, QC

**1571**
Highway 401-403-410 interchange, Mississauga,ON

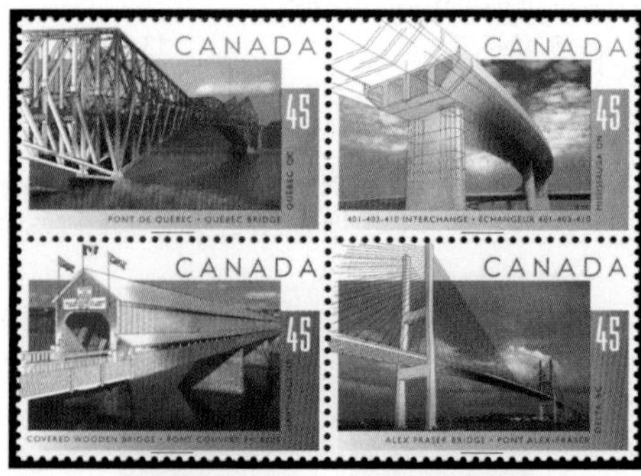

**1572**
Hartland covered wooden bridge, Hartland, NB

**1573**
Alex Fraser Bridge, Delta, BC

Designer: Tiit Telmet, Joseph Gault, and Cameron Wykes.
Based on photographs by Richard Robitaille.

Lithography (8 colours), pane of 20
Ashton-Potter Canada Limited

**1995, Sep 1 — FCP, Peterborough Paper — Perf 12.5x13.1**

| | | NH–VF | ⊙F | PB | FDC |
|---|---|---|---|---|---|
| **1570** | **45¢ multicoloured** | 1.00 | .40 | | |
| **1571** | **45¢ multicoloured** | 1.00 | .40 | | |
| **1572** | **45¢ multicoloured** | 1.00 | .40 | | |
| **1573** | **45¢ multicoloured** | 1.00 | .40 | | |
| **a** | block or strip of 4 (1570–1573) | 4.50 | 3.50 | 5.00 | 4.20 |
| **aT1** | block of 4, untagged (error) | | | 1,000.00(UL)* | |

Qty: 3,750,000 of each

* VGG cert states "trial color printing on different paper and without tagging".
This issue exists with weak, mottled tagging. May be a "dry print" of the taggant.

## THE ARCTIC

**1574**
Polar bear, caribou

**1575**
Arctic Poppy, cargo canoe

**1576**
Inuk man, igloo, sled dogs

**1577**
Dog-sled team, ski plane

**1578**
Children

Designer: Malcolm Waddell. Based on photographs by Sherman Hines.
Photo Imaging by Gary Mansbridge.

Lithography (6 colours), booklet pane of 10
Canadian Bank Note Company, Limited

**1995, Sep 15 — FCP, Coated Papers — Perf 13.1x12.5**

| | | NH–VF | ⊙F | FDC |
|---|---|---|---|---|
| **1574** | **45¢ multicoloured** | 1.00 | .40 | |
| **1575** | **45¢ multicoloured** | 1.00 | .40 | |
| **1576** | **45¢ multicoloured** | 1.00 | .40 | |
| **1577** | **45¢ multicoloured** | 1.00 | .40 | |
| **1578** | **45¢ multicoloured** | 1.00 | .40 | |
| **a** | horiz. strip of 5 x 45¢ (1574–1578) | 6.00 | 5.00 | 5.10* |
| **ai** | as 1578a without fold, from Canada Post's annual Souvenir Collection | 7.00 | 8.00 | |
| **b** | booklet pane of 10 (2 x 1578a) (BK184) | 12.00 | 12.00 | — |
| **BK184** | pane 1578b in cover $13.00 | | | |

Qty: 3,000,000 of each
* OFDC consists of a strip of 3 and horizontal pair

The pane layout produces no identical pairs.
This issue exists with weak, mottled tagging. May be a "dry print" of the taggant.

**1578b**

## COMIC BOOK SUPERHEROES

1579
Superman
(drawing by Joe Shuster)

1580
Johnny Canuck
(drawing by Leo Bachle)

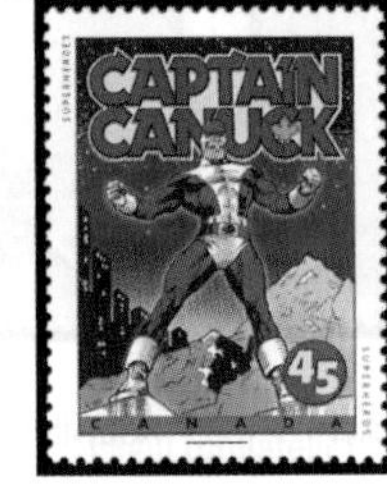

1581
Nelvana
(drawing by Adrian Dingle)

1582
Captain Canuck
(drawing by Richard Comely)

1583
Fleur de Lys
(drawing by Gabriel Morrissette)

Designer: Louis Fishauf.

Lithography (5 colours), booklet pane of 10
Ashton-Potter Canada Limited

**1995, Oct 2** **GT4, Coated Papers** **Perf 13.1x12.5**

| | | NH–VF | ⊙F | FDC |
|---|---|---|---|---|
| **1579** | **45¢ multicoloured** | 1.50 | .50 | |
| **1580** | **45¢ multicoloured** | 1.50 | .50 | |
| **1581** | **45¢ multicoloured** | 1.50 | .50 | |
| **1582** | **45¢ multicoloured** | 1.50 | .50 | |
| **1583** | **45¢ multicoloured** | 1.50 | .50 | |
| a | horizontal strip of 5 x 45¢ (1579–1583) | 7.50 | 7.00 | |
| b | booklet pane of 10 x 45¢ (2 x 1583a) (BK185) | 15.00 | 14.00 | |
| bi | as 1583b without fold (with full margins), from Quarterly Pack | 35.00 | 35.00 | |
| bii | unfolded horizontal strip of 5 (from 1583bi) | 9.00 | 8.00 | |
| BK185 | pane 1583b in cover $15.00 | | | |

Qty: 6,000,000 of each

**Nos. 1579–1583 (5) combination FDC** 5.10

The pane layout does not produce identical pairs.

1583b

## UNITED NATIONS — 50th ANNIVERSARY

1584
Prime Minister William Lyon Mackenzie King signing the UN charter in San Francisco

Designer: Les Holloway and Richard Kerr.

Lithography (6 colours) with foil stamping, pane of 10
Canadian Bank Note Company, Limited

**1995, Oct 24** **GT4, Coated Papers** **Perf 13.3**

| | | NH–VF | ⊙F | PB | FDC |
|---|---|---|---|---|---|
| **1584** | **45¢ multicoloured** | 1.60 | .30 | 8.00 | 1.50 |
| i | $4.50 full pane of 10 with header tab | 25.00 | | | |

Qty: 15,000,000

The 60 mm high header tab across the top of the 5 x 2 pane illustrates Canadian achievements at the UN from 1945 to 1955.

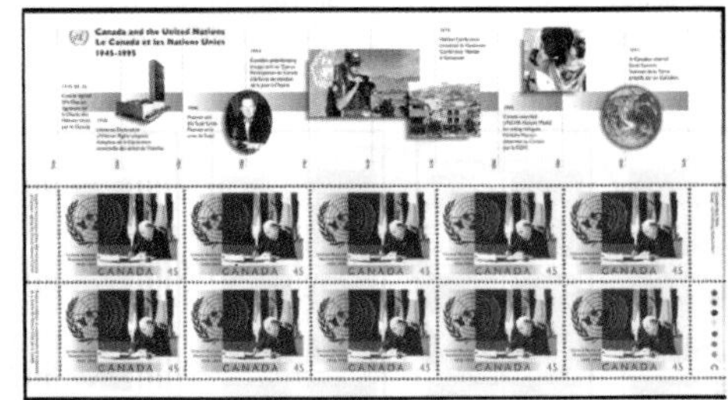

**1584 pane of 10**

## CHRISTMAS — CAPITAL SCULPTURES

1585
*The Nativity*

1586
*The Annunciation*

1587
*Flight to Egypt*

1588
Holly

Designer: Holly: François Dallaire.
Sculptured capitals: Photographs by Guy Couture, based on drawings by Jean-Émile Brunet based on sculptures by Maurice Lord at Sainte-Anne-de-Beaupré Basilica, Quebec.

Lithography (6 colours), panes of 50
Canadian Bank Note Company, Limited

**1995, Nov 2** **GT4, Coated Papers** **Perf 13.3**

| | | NH–VF | ⊙F | PB | FDC |
|---|---|---|---|---|---|
| **1585** | **45¢ multicoloured** | .90 | .25 | 4.50 | — |
| a | booklet pane of 10 x 45¢ (1585as) (BK187) | 9.50 | 8.00 | — | — |
| as | single with straight edge, from 1585a | 1.25 | .35 | — | — |
| BK187 | pane 1585a in cover $10.00 | | | | |
| Qty: 38,000,000 | | | | | |
| **1586** | **52¢ multicoloured** | 1.05 | .65 | 5.25 | — |
| a | booklet pane of 5 x 52¢ (1586as) + label (BK188) | 5.50 | 5.50 | — | — |
| as | single with straight edge, from 1586a | 1.50 | .90 | — | — |
| BK188 | pane 1586a in cover $6.00 | | | | |
| Qty: 8,850,000 | | | | | |
| **1587** | **90¢ multicoloured** | 1.80 | .75 | 9.00 | — |
| a | booklet pane of 5 x 90¢ (1587as) + label (BK189) | 10.00 | 9.00 | — | — |
| as | single with straight edge, from 1587a | 2.25 | 1.25 | — | — |
| BK189 | pane 1587a in cover $12.00 | | | | |
| Qty: 8,850,000 | | | | | |

**Nos. 1585–1587 (3) combination FDC** 4.35

Definitive Timeline:
1996, Feb 29 $5 Public Library (1378)

## MASTERPIECES OF CANADIAN ART — 9

1602
*The Spirit of Haida Gwaii*

Designer: Pierre-Yves Pelletier. Based on a photograph by Harry Foster. Based on a sculpture by William Ronald Reid.

Lithography (6 colours) with foil stamping, pane of 16
Ashton-Potter Canada Limited

| 1996, Apr 30 | FCP, Coated Papers | | Perf 12.5x13.3 | |
|---|---|---|---|---|
| | NH–VF | ⊙F | PB | FDC |
| **1602 90¢ multicoloured** (gold) | 2.00 | 1.40 | 10.00 | 2.50 |

Qty: 7,000,000

Inscription/plate blocks sold by Canada Post in packaged corner sets have roulettted selvedge on the top and/or sides. Blocks removed from full panes by collectors would be either torn or cut with a knife.
See also 1203, 1241, 1271, 1310, 1419, 1466, 1516, 1545, 1635, 1754, 1800, 1863, 1916, 1945.

## AIDS AWARENESS

1603
*One World, One Hope*

Designer: Kosta (Gus) Tsetsekas. Based on a painting by Joe Average.

Lithography (6 colours), pane of 20
Ashton-Potter Canada Limited

| 1996, May 8 | GT4, Coated Papers | | Perf 13.3 | |
|---|---|---|---|---|
| | NH–VF | ⊙F | PB | FDC |
| **1603 45¢ multicoloured** | .90 | .30 | 4.50 | 1.50 |

Qty: 15,000,000

Issued for the XI International Conference on Aids, held in Vancouver in July, 1996.

## HISTORIC LAND VEHICLES — 4

**Industrial & Commercial Vehicles**

1604a
Still Motor Co. Ltd.
Electric Van (1899)

1604b
Waterous Engine Works
Road Roller (1914)

1604c
International D-35
Delivery Truck (1938)

1604d
Champion Road Grader (1936)

1604e
White Model WA 122
Tractor-Trailer (1947)

1604f
Hayes HDX 45-115
Logging Truck (1975)

Designer: Joseph Gault and Tiit Telmet. Based on illustrations by Cameron Wykes.

Lithography (8 colours), Souvenir sheet of 6
Canadian Bank Note Company, Limited

| 1996, Jun 8 | GT4, Peterborough Paper | Perf 12.5x13.1 | | |
|---|---|---|---|---|
| | | NH–VF | ⊙F | FDC |
| 1604 | **$3.74 souvenir sheet of 6 stamps**, LF | 9.00 | 9.00 | 10.80† |
| a | **45¢ multicoloured** | 1.10 | 1.10 | |
| b | **45¢ multicoloured** | 1.10 | 1.10 | |
| c | **52¢ multicoloured** | 1.25 | 1.25 | |
| d | **52¢ multicoloured** | 1.25 | 1.25 | |
| e | **90¢ multicoloured** | 2.00 | 2.00 | |
| f | **90¢ multicoloured** | 2.00 | 2.00 | |
| i | sheet of 6, MF | 25.00 | 22.00 | |
| ii | sheet of 6, HF | 25.00 | 22.00 | |

Qty: 800,000 of each

† Set of 4 FDCs: 1) 1604a, b – $2.40; 2) 1604c, d – $2.70; 3) 1604e, f – $4.20, 4) 1605y – $1.50; issued together in a protective folder.

See also 1490, 1527, 1552 and 1605.

1604

## HISTORIC LAND VEHICLES COLLECTION — 5

1605a
H.S. Taylor Steam Buggy (1867)

1605b
Russell Model L Touring Car (1908)

1605c
Ford Military Ambulance (1942–1943)

1605d
Reo Police Wagon (1925)

## COMIC BOOK SUPERHEROES

1579
Superman
(drawing by Joe Shuster)

1580
Johnny Canuck
(drawing by Leo Bachle)

1581
Nelvana
(drawing by Adrian Dingle)

1582
Captain Canuck
(drawing by Richard Comely)

1583
Fleur de Lys
(drawing by Gabriel Morrissette)

Designer: Louis Fishauf.

Lithography (5 colours), booklet pane of 10
Ashton-Potter Canada Limited

**1995, Oct 2 GT4, Coated Papers Perf 13.1x12.5**

| | | NH–VF | ⊙F | FDC |
|---|---|---|---|---|
| **1579** | **45¢ multicoloured** | 1.50 | .50 | |
| **1580** | **45¢ multicoloured** | 1.50 | .50 | |
| **1581** | **45¢ multicoloured** | 1.50 | .50 | |
| **1582** | **45¢ multicoloured** | 1.50 | .50 | |
| **1583** | **45¢ multicoloured** | 1.50 | .50 | |
| a | horizontal strip of 5 x 45¢ (1579–1583) | 7.50 | 7.00 | |
| b | booklet pane of 10 x 45¢ (2 x 1583a) (BK185) | 15.00 | 14.00 | |
| bi | as 1583b without fold (with full margins), from Quarterly Pack | 35.00 | 35.00 | |
| bii | unfolded horizontal strip of 5 (from 1583bi) | 9.00 | 8.00 | |
| BK185 | pane 1583b in cover $15.00 | | | |

Qty: 6,000,000 of each

**Nos. 1579–1583 (5) combination FDC** 5.10

The pane layout does not produce identical pairs.

1583b

## UNITED NATIONS — 50th ANNIVERSARY

1584
Prime Minister William Lyon Mackenzie King signing the UN charter in San Francisco

Designer: Les Holloway and Richard Kerr.

Lithography (6 colours) with foil stamping, pane of 10
Canadian Bank Note Company, Limited

**1995, Oct 24 GT4, Coated Papers Perf 13.3**

| | | NH–VF | ⊙F | PB | FDC |
|---|---|---|---|---|---|
| **1584** | **45¢ multicoloured** | 1.60 | .30 | 8.00 | 1.50 |
| i | $4.50 full pane of 10 with header tab | 25.00 | | | |

Qty: 15,000,000

The 60 mm high header tab across the top of the 5 x 2 pane illustrates Canadian achievements at the UN from 1945 to 1955.

1584 pane of 10

## CHRISTMAS — CAPITAL SCULPTURES

1585
*The Nativity*

1586
*The Annunciation*

1587
*Flight to Egypt*

1588
Holly

Designer: Holly: François Dallaire.
Sculptured capitals: Photographs by Guy Couture, based on drawings by Jean-Émile Brunet based on sculptures by Maurice Lord at Sainte-Anne-de-Beaupré Basilica, Quebec.

Lithography (6 colours), panes of 50
Canadian Bank Note Company, Limited

**1995, Nov 2 GT4, Coated Papers Perf 13.3**

| | | NH–VF | ⊙F | PB | FDC |
|---|---|---|---|---|---|
| **1585** | **45¢ multicoloured** | .90 | .25 | 4.50 | — |
| a | booklet pane of 10 x 45¢ (1585as) (BK187) | 9.50 | 8.00 | — | — |
| as | single with straight edge, from 1585a | 1.25 | .35 | — | — |
| BK187 | pane 1585a in cover $10.00 | | | | |

Qty: 38,000,000

| | | NH–VF | ⊙F | PB | FDC |
|---|---|---|---|---|---|
| **1586** | **52¢ multicoloured** | 1.05 | .65 | 5.25 | — |
| a | booklet pane of 5 x 52¢ (1586as) + label (BK188) | 5.50 | 5.50 | — | — |
| as | single with straight edge, from 1586a | 1.50 | .90 | — | — |
| BK188 | pane 1586a in cover $6.00 | | | | |

Qty: 8,850,000

| | | NH–VF | ⊙F | PB | FDC |
|---|---|---|---|---|---|
| **1587** | **90¢ multicoloured** | 1.80 | .75 | 9.00 | — |
| a | booklet pane of 5 x 90¢ (1587as) + label (BK189) | 10.00 | 9.00 | — | — |
| as | single with straight edge, from 1587a | 2.25 | 1.25 | — | — |
| BK189 | pane 1587a in cover $12.00 | | | | |

Qty: 8,850,000

**Nos. 1585–1587 (3) combination FDC** 4.35

Ashton-Potter Canada Limited

**GTX, Greetmore booklet, Coated Papers** **Perf 12.5x13.1**

| | | NH–VF | ⊙F | PB | FDC |
|---|---|---|---|---|---|
| **1588** | **40¢ multicoloured**, | | | | |
| | single from 1588a | 1.00 | 1.00 | — | 1.40 |
| a | booklet pane of 10 x 40¢ (1588) (BK186) | 8.50 | 12.50 | — | — |

**BK186** pane 1588a in cover $9.00
Qty: 38,940,000

No. 1588 was issued in booklets only, for use on greeting card envelopes bearing a printed postal code matrix. Accepted singly until January 31, 1996, if affixed to designated envelope.

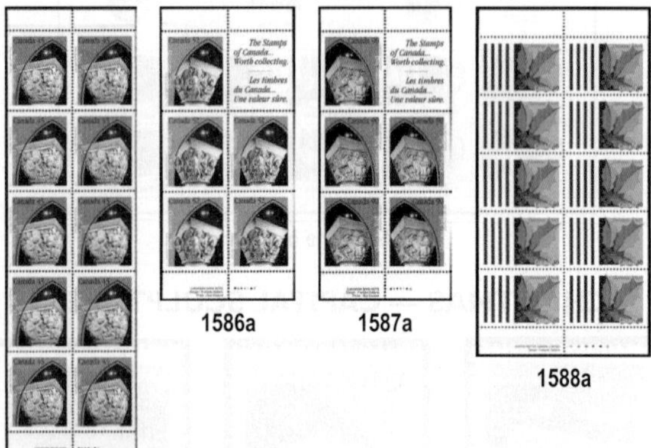

1585a 1586a 1587a 1588a

## LA FRANCOPHONIE

1589

Designer: Alain Leduc.

Lithography (4 colours), pane of 20
Ashton-Potter Canada Limited

**1995, Nov 6** **GT4, Coated Papers** **Perf 13.0x13.3**

| | | NH–VF | ⊙F | PB | FDC |
|---|---|---|---|---|---|
| **1589** | **45¢ multicoloured** | .90 | .30 | 4.50 | 1.50 |

Qty: 15,000,000

For non-denominated postal card of same design, see UX124.
25th anniversary of the Agency for Cultural and Technical Co-operation (ACCT).

## THE HOLOCAUST

1590

Designer: Glenda Rissman and Peter D.K. Scott.

Lithography (6 colours), pane of 20
Ashton-Potter Canada Limited

**1995, Nov 9** **FCP, Coated Papers** **Perf 12.5x13.1**

| | | NH–VF | ⊙F | PB | FDC |
|---|---|---|---|---|---|
| **1590** | **45¢ multicoloured** | .90 | .30 | 4.50 | 1.50 |

Qty: 15,000,000

# 1996

## BIRDS OF CANADA — I

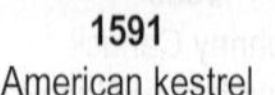

**1591**
American kestrel

**1592**
Atlantic puffin

**1593**
Pileated woodpecker

**1594**
Ruby-throated hummingbird

Designer: Raymond Bellemare. Based on paintings by Pierre Leduc.

Lithography (5 colours), pane of 12
Canadian Bank Note Company, Limited

**1996, Jan 9** **GT4, Peterborough Paper** **Perf 13.3**

| | | NH–VF | ⊙F | PB | FDC |
|---|---|---|---|---|---|
| **1591** | **45¢ multicoloured**, LF | 1.00 | .40 | — | — |
| **i** | single from philatelic pane, MF† | 1.25 | .50 | | |
| **1592** | **45¢ multicoloured**, LF | 1.00 | .40 | — | — |
| **i** | single from philatelic pane, MF† | 1.25 | .50 | | |
| **1593** | **45¢ multicoloured**, LF | 1.00 | .40 | — | — |
| **i** | single from philatelic pane, MF† | 1.25 | .50 | | |
| **1594** | **45¢ multicoloured**, LF | 1.00 | .40 | — | — |
| **i** | single from philatelic pane, MF† | 1.25 | .50 | | |
| **a** | strip of 4, LF (1591–1594) | 5.00 | 4.00 | | 4.20* |
| **ai** | strip of 4, MF (1591i–1594i) | 6.00 | 6.00 | | |
| **ii** | $5.40 field stock pane of 12 (no inscriptions), LF | 12.00 | 10.00 | | |
| **iii** | $5.40 philatelic (inscr) pane of 12, LF | 14.00 | 12.00 | | |
| **v** | as "iii", pane of 12 (insc), MF | 20.00 | 17.00 | | |
| **iv** | $27.00 uncut press sheet of 5 panes (1594iii), unsigned | 175.00 | | | |
| | as "iv", signed (issue price $69.00) | 500.00 | | | |

Qty: 3,750,000 of each; 1594ii: 9,000; 1594ii signed: 1,000

† The background dot pattern on the field and philatelic panes is printed at different angles, as illustrated below.
* The FDC consists of two pairs of stamps.

Nos. 1591–1594 were issued in rectangular panes of 12 (3 x 1594a) with no identical pairs. Philatelic panes were cut in a diamond shape with inscriptions in 1 corner. See also 1631–1634, 1710–1713, 1770–1777, 1839–1846, 1886–1893. For non-denominated stationery of same designs, see U150–U153 and UX122.

**1594ii (field stock)**

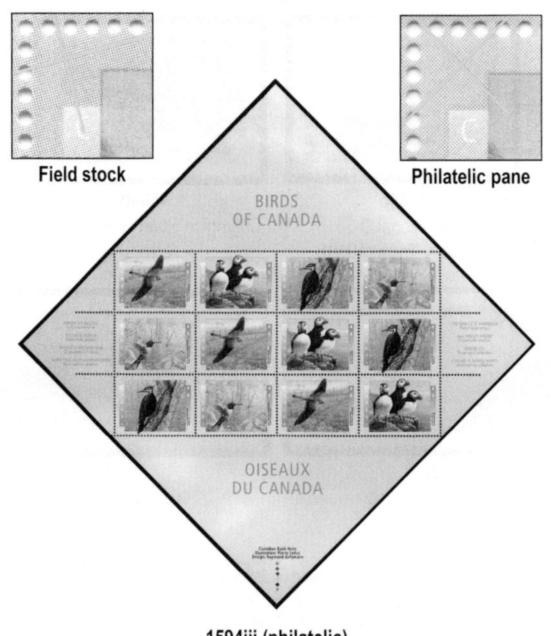


Field stock

Philatelic pane

1594iii (philatelic)

## HIGH TECHNOLOGY INDUSTRIES

1595 Ocean Technology

1596 Aerospace Technology

1597 Information Technology

1598 Biotechnology

Designer: Peter D.K. Scott, Glenda Rissman, and Darrell Corriveau.
Lithography (7 colours), booklet pane of 12
Canadian Bank Note Company, Limited

**1996, Feb 15 — FCP, Peterborough Paper — Perf 13.3**

| | | NH–VF | ⊙F | FDC |
|---|---|---|---|---|
| **1595** | **45¢ multicoloured** | 1.25 | .50 | |
| **1596** | **45¢ multicoloured** | 1.25 | .50 | |
| **1597** | **45¢ multicoloured** | 1.25 | .50 | |
| **1598** | **45¢ multicoloured** | 1.25 | .50 | |
| i | se-tenant block of 4 different (1595–1598) | 5.25 | 4.00 | |
| a | booklet pane of 12 (3 of each stamp) (BK191) | 15.00 | 10.00 | — |

**BK191** pane 1598a in cover $16.00
Qty: 3,750,000 of each

**Nos. 1595–1598 (4) combination FDC** 4.20

1598a

No. 1599 is not assigned.

## GREETINGS BOOKLET — 3
## "Special Occasions" (56mmx30mm)

**1600**
"Quick Stick",
Canada on left

**1601**
"Quick Stick",
Canada on right

Designer: Tarzan Communication Graphique Inc.
Lithography (6 colours), self-adhesive booklet of 10
Leigh-Mardon Pty Limited

**1996, Jan 15 — Tagged, Fasson Paper — Die cut**

| | | NH–VF | ⊙F | FDC |
|---|---|---|---|---|
| **1600** | **45¢ multicoloured** | 2.00 | 1.50 | — |
| **1601** | **45¢ multicoloured** | 2.00 | 1.50 | — |
| a | booklet pane of 10 (5 x 1600, 5 x 1601) + 35 greeting stickers (5 each of 7 designs) (BK190) | 20.00 | | |
| b | as "a", die cutting omitted | 5,000.00* | | |

Booklet issued for $4.70, a premium of 20¢ over face.

Nos. 1600, 1601 are the same size (56mmx30mm) as Nos. 1507, 1508 and have the same special occasions in the background, the colours and values are different (both issues were printed in Australia by Leigh-Mardon). Nos. 1568, 1569 (Sept. 1995 and August, 1997) were printed by APC; these are a smaller size (52mmx28mm) and have the names of the Provinces and Territories in the background.

* Four panes recorded; one was split into 3 sections: value for strip of 4 and 10 labels: $2,000; pair and 15 labels: $1,000.

See also 1507–1508, 1568–1569

1568, 1569
Provinces

1600, 1601
Special occasions

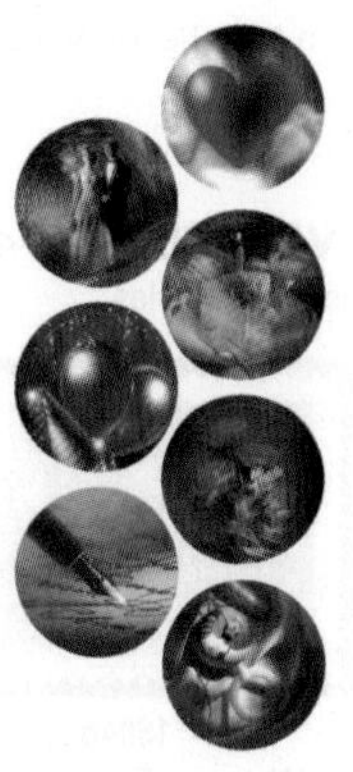

Greeting labels

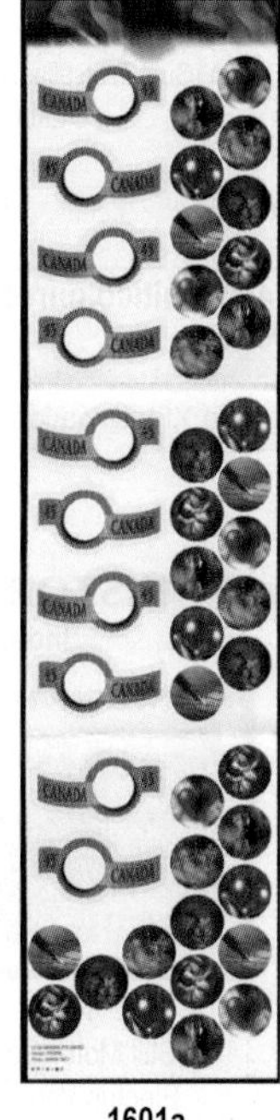

1601a

Definitive Timeline:
1996, Feb 29 $5 Public Library (1378)

## MASTERPIECES OF CANADIAN ART — 9

1602
*The Spirit of Haida Gwaii*

Designer: Pierre-Yves Pelletier. Based on a photograph by Harry Foster. Based on a sculpture by William Ronald Reid.
Lithography (6 colours) with foil stamping, pane of 16
Ashton-Potter Canada Limited

**1996, Apr 30 FCP, Coated Papers Perf 12.5x13.3**

| | | NH–VF | ⊙F | PB | FDC |
|---|---|---|---|---|---|
| **1602** | **90¢ multicoloured** (gold) | 2.00 | 1.40 | 10.00 | 2.50 |

Qty: 7,000,000

Inscription/plate blocks sold by Canada Post in packaged corner sets have rouletted selvedge on the top and/or sides. Blocks removed from full panes by collectors would be either torn or cut with a knife.
See also 1203, 1241, 1271, 1310, 1419, 1466, 1516, 1545, 1635, 1754, 1800, 1863, 1916, 1945.

## AIDS AWARENESS

1603
*One World, One Hope*

Designer: Kosta (Gus) Tsetsekas. Based on a painting by Joe Average.
Lithography (6 colours), pane of 20
Ashton-Potter Canada Limited

**1996, May 8 GT4, Coated Papers Perf 13.3**

| | | NH–VF | ⊙F | PB | FDC |
|---|---|---|---|---|---|
| **1603** | **45¢ multicoloured** | .90 | .30 | 4.50 | 1.50 |

Qty: 15,000,000

Issued for the XI International Conference on Aids, held in Vancouver in July, 1996.

## HISTORIC LAND VEHICLES — 4

**Industrial & Commercial Vehicles**

1604a
Still Motor Co. Ltd.
Electric Van (1899)

1604b
Waterous Engine Works
Road Roller (1914)

1604c
International D-35
Delivery Truck (1938)

1604d
Champion Road Grader (1936)

1604e
White Model WA 122
Tractor-Trailer (1947)

1604f
Hayes HDX 45-115
Logging Truck (1975)

Designer: Joseph Gault and Tiit Telmet. Based on illustrations by Cameron Wykes.
Lithography (8 colours), Souvenir sheet of 6
Canadian Bank Note Company, Limited

**1996, Jun 8 GT4, Peterborough Paper Perf 12.5x13.1**

| | | NH–VF | ⊙F | FDC |
|---|---|---|---|---|
| **1604** | **$3.74 souvenir sheet of 6 stamps**, LF | 9.00 | 9.00 | 10.80† |
| a | **45¢ multicoloured** | 1.10 | 1.10 | |
| b | **45¢ multicoloured** | 1.10 | 1.10 | |
| c | **52¢ multicoloured** | 1.25 | 1.25 | |
| d | **52¢ multicoloured** | 1.25 | 1.25 | |
| e | **90¢ multicoloured** | 2.00 | 2.00 | |
| f | **90¢ multicoloured** | 2.00 | 2.00 | |
| i | sheet of 6, MF | 25.00 | 22.00 | |
| ii | sheet of 6, HF | 25.00 | 22.00 | |

Qty: 800,000 of each
† Set of 4 FDCs: 1) 1604a, b – $2.40; 2) 1604c, d – $2.70; 3) 1604e, f – $4.20, 4) 1605y – $1.50; issued together in a protective folder.

See also 1490, 1527, 1552 and 1605.

1604

## HISTORIC LAND VEHICLES COLLECTION — 5

1605a
H.S. Taylor Steam Buggy (1867)

1605b
Russell Model L Touring Car (1908)

1605c
Ford Military Ambulance (1942–1943)

1605d
Reo Police Wagon (1925)

**1605e**
Bombardier Ski-Doo Olympique 335 snowmobile (1970)

**1605f**
Still Motor Co. Ltd. Electric Van (1899)

**1605g**
Waterous Engine Works Road Roller (1914)

**1605h**
Cockshutt "30" farm tractor (1950)

**1605i**
International D-35 Delivery Truck (1938)

**1605j**
Champion Road Grader (1936)

**1605k**
Ottawa Car Company Streetcar (1894)

**1605l**
MCI Courier 50 Skyview Motor Coach (1950)

**1605m**
White Model WA 122 Tractor-Trailer (1947)

**1605n**
Hayes HDX 45-115 Logging Truck (1975)

**1605o**
Ford Model T (1914)

**1605p**
Studebaker Champion Deluxe (1950)

**1605q**
Bickle Chieftain Fire Engine (1936)

**1605r**
McLaughlin-Buick Model 28-496 (1928)

**1605s**
Gray-Dort Model 25-SM (1923)

**1605t**
Sicard Snow Remover Snowblower (1927)

**1605u**
Bombardier B-12 CS multi-passenger snowmobile (1948)

**1605v**
Gotfredson Model 20 farm truck (1924)

**1605w**
Robin-Nodwell RN 110 tracked carrier (1962)

**1605x**
Massey-Harris No, 21 self-propelled combine (1942)

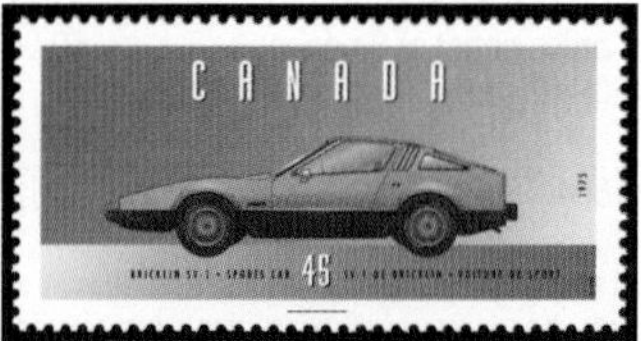

**1605y**
Bricklin SV-1 Sports Car

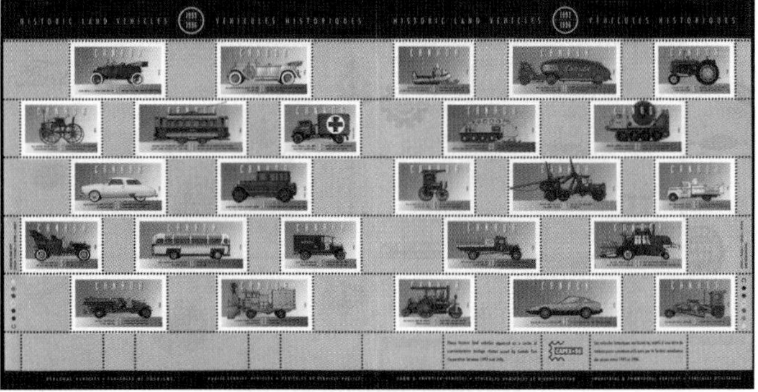

**1605**

Designer: Joseph Gault and Tiit Telmet. Based on illustrations by Cameron Wykes.
Lithography (7 colours), Souvenir sheet of 25
Canadian Bank Note Company, Limited

**1996, Jun 8 Not tagged, Peterborough Paper Perf 12.5x13.1**

| | | NH–VF | ⊙F | FDC |
|---|---|---|---|---|
| **1605** | $3.35 pane of 25 stamps + 20 labels | 10.00 | 10.00 | |
| a | **5¢ like 1490a** | .30 | .30 | |
| b | **5¢ like 1490b** | .30 | .30 | |
| c | **5¢ like 1527a** | .30 | .30 | |
| d | **5¢ like 1527b** | .30 | .30 | |
| e | **5¢ like 1552b** | .30 | .30 | |
| f | **5¢ like 1604a** | .30 | .30 | |
| g | **5¢ like 1604b** | .30 | .30 | |
| h | **5¢ like 1552a** | .30 | .30 | |
| i | **5¢ like 1604c** | .30 | .30 | |
| j | **5¢ like 1604d** | .30 | .30 | |
| k | **10¢ like 1527e** | .50 | .50 | |
| l | **10¢ like 1527f** | .50 | .50 | |
| m | **10¢ like 1604e** | .50 | .50 | |
| n | **10¢ like 1604f** | .50 | .50 | |
| o | **20¢ like 1490c** | .60 | .60 | |
| p | **20¢ like 1490d** | .60 | .60 | |
| q | **20¢ like 1527d** | .60 | .60 | |
| r | **20¢ like 1490e** | .60 | .60 | |
| s | **20¢ like 1490f** | .60 | .60 | |
| t | **20¢ like 1527c** | .60 | .60 | |
| u | **20¢ like 1552c** | .60 | .60 | |
| v | **20¢ like 1552d** | .60 | .60 | |
| w | **20¢ like 1552e** | .60 | .60 | |
| x | **20¢ like 1552f** | .60 | .60 | |
| y | **45¢ Bricklin SV-1 Sports Car, GT4** | 1.50 | 1.50 | —† |
| z | $20.00 uncut press sheet of 3 panes | 50.00 | | |

Qty: 1,000,000 of each; 1605z: 25,000

† See FDC note after 1604.

Issued for CAPEX'96.
See also 1490, 1527, 1552 and 1604.

## YUKON GOLD RUSH

**1606a**
Skookum Jim Mason staked the first claim

**1606b**
Prospectors heading for the gold fields

**1606c**
Superintendent Sam Steele, NWMP

**1606d**
Dawson City, Yukon

**1606e**
Working the gold claims

Designer: Steven Slipp.
Lithography (6 colours) with foil stamping, pane of 10
Ashton-Potter Canada Limited

**1996, Jun 13 FCP§, Coated Papers Perf 13.3**

| | | NH–VF | ⊙F | FDC |
|---|---|---|---|---|
| **1606** | 45¢ x 5 different, se-tenant horizontal strip of 5* | 8.00 | 7.00 | 6.00† |
| a | **45¢ multicoloured** | 1.50 | .75 | |
| b | **45¢ multicoloured** | 1.50 | .75 | |
| c | **45¢ multicoloured** | 1.50 | .75 | |
| d | **45¢ multicoloured** | 1.50 | .75 | |
| e | **45¢ multicoloured** | 1.50 | .75 | |
| i | pane of 10 (2 x 1606)* | 16.00 | 12.00 | |

Qty: 2,400,000 of each

§ This issue exists with weak and strong overall phosphor. Relative scarcity has not been determined.

† OFDC consists of a strip of 3 and horizontal pair

* All panes were distributed unfolded.

Issued to commemorate the centennial of the Yukon Gold Rush.
The pane contains an identical vertical pair of each design. All four selvedge areas bear inscriptions.

**1606i**

## CANADA DAY

**1607**
Maple Leaf Quilt

Designer: Raymond Bellemare. Based on a photograph by Yves Binette.
Based on quilt by Claire Brisson.
Lithography (5 colours), self adhesive pane of 12 + 5 labels
Ashton-Potter Canada Limited

**1996, Jun 28 GT4, Coated Papers Die cut**

| | | NH–VF | ⊙F | FDC |
|---|---|---|---|---|
| **1607** | **45¢ multicoloured** | 1.00 | .35 | 1.50 |
| a | pane of 12 stamps + 5 labels | 13.00 | 5.00 | |

Qty: 15,000,000

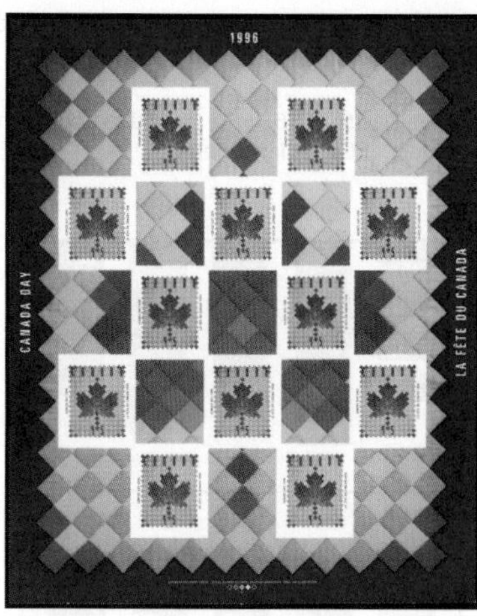

1607a

## CANADIAN OLYMPIC GOLD MEDALLISTS

1608
Ethel Catherwood,
high jump, 1928

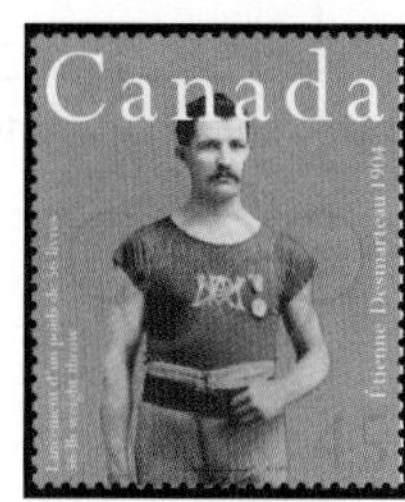

1609
Étienne Desmarteau,
56 lb. weight throw, 1904

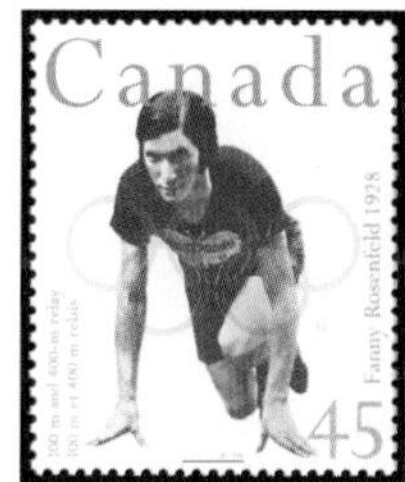

1610
Fanny Rosenfeld,
400 m relay, 1928

1611
Gerald Ouellette,
smallbore rifle, prone, 1956

1612
Percy Williams,
100 m, 200 m, 1928

Designer: Mark Koudis.
Lithography (6 colours) and Typographed with foil stamping, booklet pane of 10
Ashton-Potter Canada Limited

**1996, Jul 8** **FCP, Coated Papers** **Perf 13.2x12.5**

| | | NH–VF | ⊙F | FDC |
|---|---|---|---|---|
| **1608** | **45¢ multicoloured** | 1.40 | .75 | |
| **1609** | **45¢ multicoloured** | 1.40 | .75 | |
| **1610** | **45¢ multicoloured** | 1.40 | .75 | |
| **1611** | **45¢ multicoloured** | 1.40 | .75 | |
| **1612** | **45¢ multicoloured** | 1.40 | .75 | |
| a | se-tenant horizontal strip of 5 (1608–1612) | 7.50 | 5.00 | 6.00* |
| ai | as 1612a without fold, from Canada Post's annual Souvenir Collection | 9.00 | 8.00 | |
| b | booklet pane of 10 (2 x 1612a) (BK192) | 15.00 | 12.00 | — |
| **BK192** | pane 1612b in cover $15.00 | | | |

Qty: 2,400,000 of each
* OFDC consists of a strip of 3 and horizontal pair

1608–1612 are known with silver rings missing and untagged; 2 of each reported from one booklet. Value: $1,750.00 each.

Issued to mark the centenary of the Modern Olympics.

1612b

## BRITISH COLUMBIA

1613
Vancouver skyline

Designer: Matthew Warburton. Based on an illustration by Jeff Burgess.
Based on photographs by George M. Dawson, Roy Hamaguchi, Koos Dykstra, and Dave Watters
Lithography (6 colours), pane of 25
Ashton-Potter Canada Limited

**1996, Jul 19** **FCP, Coated Papers** **Perf 13.0x12.5**

| | | NH–VF | ⊙F | PB | FDC |
|---|---|---|---|---|---|
| **1613** | **45¢ multicoloured**, strong, clear tagging | .90 | .30 | 4.50 | 1.50 |
| i | weak, spotted tagging | 1.25 | .45 | 6.00 | |

Qty: 12,000,000

Issued in celebration of British Columbia's 125th anniversary as a province of Canada.

## CANADIAN HERALDRY

1614
Canada's heraldic tradition

Designer: Derek Sarty and Rand Gaynor.
Lithography (6 colours), pane of 25
Ashton-Potter Canada Limited

**1996, Aug 19** **FCP, Coated Papers** **Perf 12.7x12.2**

| | | NH–VF | ⊙F | PB | FDC |
|---|---|---|---|---|---|
| **1614** | **45¢ multicoloured** | .90 | .30 | 4.50 | 1.50 |

Qty: 8,000,000

Issued in honour of the 22nd International Congress of Genealogical and Heraldic Sciences, held in Ottawa in August.

## CINEMA IN CANADA

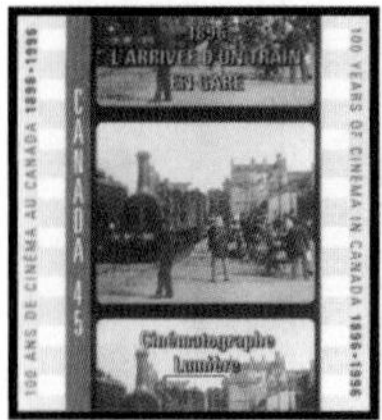
1615a
L'arrivée d'un train en gare (1896)

1615b
Back to God's Country (1919)

1615c
Hen Hop (1942)

1615d
Pour la suite du monde (1963)

1615e
Goin' Down the Road (1970)

1616a
Mon oncle Antoine (1971)

1616b
The Apprenticeship of Duddy Kravitz (1974)

1616c
Les Ordres (1974)

1616d
Les Bons Débarras (1980)

1616e
The Grey Fox (1982)

Designer: Pierre-Yves Pelletier.

Lithography (5 colours), self-adhesive souvenir sheets of 5
Canadian Bank Note Company, Limited

| 1996, Aug 22 | FCP, Coated Papers | | | Die cut |
|---|---|---|---|---|
| | | NH–VF | ⊙F | FDC |
| 1615 | $2.25 souvenir sheet of 5 different | 5.00 | 5.00 | |
| a | **45¢ multicoloured** | .90 | .90 | |
| b | **45¢ multicoloured** | .90 | .90 | |
| c | **45¢ multicoloured** | .90 | .90 | |
| d | **45¢ multicoloured** | .90 | .90 | |
| e | **45¢ multicoloured** | .90 | .90 | |
| **Nos. 1615a–1615e (5) combination FDC** | | | | 5.10 |
| 1616 | $2.25 souvenir sheet of 5 different | 5.00 | 5.00 | |
| a | **45¢ multicoloured** | .90 | .90 | |
| b | **45¢ multicoloured** | .90 | .90 | |
| c | **45¢ multicoloured** | .90 | .90 | |
| d | **45¢ multicoloured** | .90 | .90 | |
| e | **45¢ multicoloured** | .90 | .90 | |
| **Nos. 1616a–1616e (5) combination FDC** | | | | 5.10 |

The adhesive on this issue appears to dry out over time, making the stamps less adhesive and colouring the paper brownish.

The two souvenir sheets (1615, 1616) were issued to honour memorable achievements in a century of Canadian cinema.

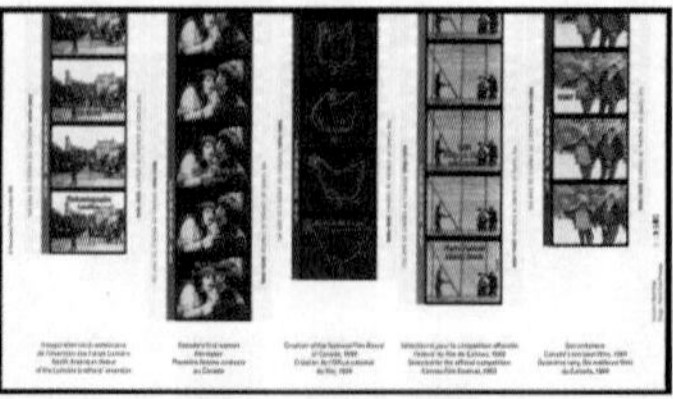
1615

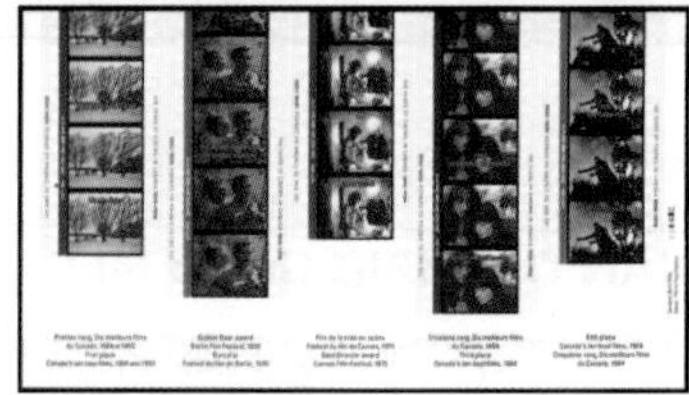
1616

Timeline:
1996, Sep 9 45¢+5¢ Literacy, semi-postal (B13)

## ÉDOUARD MONTPETIT

1617
Édouard Montpetit (1881–1954), educator

Designer: Jean R. Beauchesne. Based on a photograph by Bob Fisher and Division des archives de l'Université de Montréal

Lithography (5 colours), pane of 25
Ashton-Potter Canada Limited

| 1996, Sep 26 | GT4, Coated Papers | | | Perf 12.3x12.6 | |
|---|---|---|---|---|---|
| | | NH–VF | ⊙F | PB | FDC |
| 1617 | **45¢ multicoloured** | .90 | .30 | 4.50 | 1.50 |

Qty: 6,000,000

**MINT PRICING PREMIUMS**

Mint stamps from 301 to date are valued as NH-VF (Never Hinged-Very Fine). All hinged VF and NH-F copies are worth 50% of the listed values. Plate block (PB) values are for mint NH–VF plate or inscription blocks of four.

**USED, VF/XF (with in-period, circular date cancel) PRICING PREMIUM**

Single stamps with light or circular date cancels will sell for more than catalogue value (perhaps even more than a mint copy). From *1981 to 1991* single stamps from se-tenant blocks of 4 or larger will be priced at 50% or more above the fine price. From *1992* to date single stamps from se-tenant blocks of 4 or larger plus se-tenant booklet panes and souvenir sheets will be priced at 100% or more above the fine price. From *1997* to date all other stamps will be priced at 50% or more above the fine price.

## WINNIE THE POOH

**1618**
Winnie with Lt. Colebourn, 1914

**1619**
Winnie the Pooh with Christopher Robin, 1925

**1620**
Milne and Shepard's Winnie, 1926

**1621**
Winnie the Pooh at Walt Disney World, 1996

Designer: Wai Poon. Art direction by Anthony Van Bruggen.
Computer design by Marcelo Caetano

Lithography (5 colours), booklet pane of 16; souvenir sheet 4
Ashton-Potter Canada Limited

| **1996, Oct 1** | **GT4, Coated Papers** | | | **Perf 12.5x13.1** | |
|---|---|---|---|---|---|
| | | NH–VF | ⊙F | PB | FDC |
| **1618** | **45¢ multicoloured** | 1.00 | .50 | | |
| i | single from souvenir sheet* | 2.00 | 1.00 | | |
| **1619** | **45¢ multicoloured** | 1.00 | .50 | | |
| i | single from souvenir sheet* | 2.00 | 1.00 | | |
| **1620** | **45¢ multicoloured** | 1.00 | .50 | | |
| i | single from souvenir sheet* | 2.00 | 1.00 | | |
| **1621** | **45¢ multicoloured** | 1.00 | .50 | | |
| ii | single from souvenir sheet* | 2.00 | 1.00 | | |
| a | se-tenant block of 4 (1618–1621) | 4.25 | 3.50 | 4.50 | 4.20 |
| b | $1.80 souvenir sheet of 4 | 10.00 | 9.50 | | |
| c | booklet pane of 16 (1621a x 4) (BK194) | 16.00 | 15.00 | | |
| BK194 | pane 1621c folded and stapled as cover for Walt Disney World booklet $20.00 | | | | |

Qty: 7,500,000 of each; Souvenir sheet: 3,250,000

* Singles from the souvenir sheet have minor differences in the tagging compared to stamps from the booklet; see the illustration on the next page.

The booklet pane was used as the outer cover of a 16-page souvenir story booklet for the 25th anniversary of Walt Disney World.

1621b

1621c

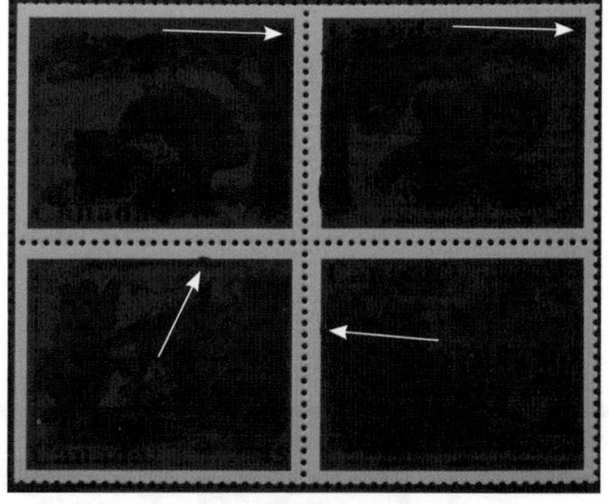

**1621b**
Tagging on souvenir sheet

The arrows indicate where indents in the tagging only occurs on stamps from the souvenir sheet.

These indents are small on a couple of stamps, but important in their appearance compared to the booklet stamps.

## CANADIAN AUTHORS

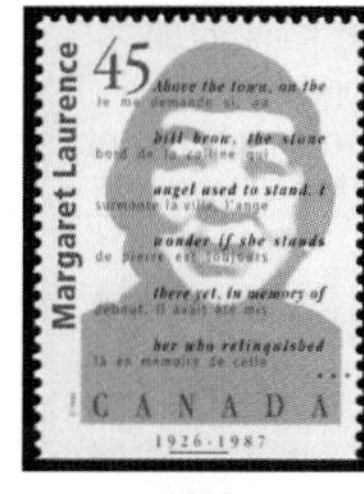

**1622**
Margaret Laurence
(1926–1987)

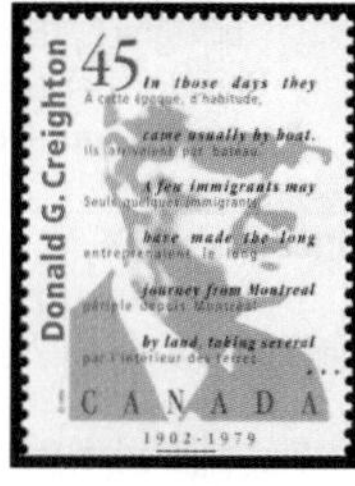

**1623**
Donald G. Creighton
(1902–1979)

**1624**
Gabrielle Roy
(1909–1983)

**1625**
Félix-Antoine Savard
(1896–1982)

**1626**
Thomas C. Haliburton
(1796–1865)

Designer: Alain Leduc.

Lithography (6 colours) and Engraved (1 colour),
Sheets of 160 subjects in sixteen booklet panes of 10
Canadian Bank Note Company, Limited

| **1996, Oct 10** | **FCP, Coated Papers** | **Perf 13.3x13.0** | | |
|---|---|---|---|---|
| | | NH–VF | ⊙F | FDC |
| **1622** | **45¢ multicoloured** | 1.50 | .50 | — |
| **1623** | **45¢ multicoloured** | 1.50 | .50 | — |
| **1624** | **45¢ multicoloured** | 1.50 | .50 | — |
| **1625** | **45¢ multicoloured** | 1.50 | .50 | — |
| **1626** | **45¢ multicoloured** | 1.50 | .50 | — |
| a | se-tenant horizontal strip of 5 (1622–1626) | 7.50 | 7.00 | 5.10 |
| ai | as 1626a without fold, from Canada Post's annual Souvenir Collection | 9.00 | 10.00 | |
| b | booklet pane of 10 (5 x 2) (2 x 1626a) (BK195) | 16.00 | 18.00 | — |
| BK195 | pane 1626b in cover $16.50 | | | |

Qty: 2,400,000 of each

The booklet pane contains a vertical pair of each design.

QE II — 1990's

1626b

## UNICEF AND CHRISTMAS

1627
Delivering gifts by sled

1628
Santa and elf skiing

1629
Children skating

Designer: Stuart Bradley Ash, Katalin Kovats, and Heather Lafleur.
Based on paintings by Edward Hardy (Ted) Harrison (45¢), Pauline Paquin (52¢), and Joan Bacquie (90¢).

Lithography (6 colours), panes of 50
Canadian Bank Note Company, Limited

**1996, Nov 1 Tagged 2-bar, Peterborough Paper Perf 13.3**

| | | NH–VF | ⊙F | PB | FDC |
|---|---|---|---|---|---|
| **1627** | **45¢ multicoloured**, DF | .90 | .25 | 4.50 | |
| i | LF | 5.00 | 1.00 | 25.00 | |
| a | booklet pane of 10 x 45¢ (1627as) (BK196) | 9.50 | 10.00 | | |
| as | single with straight edge, from 1627a | 1.25 | .25 | | |
| T1 | as "as", untagged (error) | — | 100.00 | | |
| BK196 | pane 1627a in cover $12.00 | | | | |

Qty: 40,000,000

Ashton-Potter Canada Limited
**Coated Papers**

| | | NH–VF | ⊙F | PB | FDC |
|---|---|---|---|---|---|
| | | | | **Perf 12.7x12.2** | |
| **1628** | **52¢ multicoloured** | 1.05 | .40 | 5.25 | |
| | | | | **Perf 13.3** | |
| a | booklet pane of 5 x 52¢ (1628as) + label (BK197) | 5.50 | 6.00 | | |
| as | single with straight edge, from 1628a | 1.50 | .65 | | |
| BK197 | pane 1628a in cover $6.00 | | | | |

Qty: 10,000,000

| | | NH–VF | ⊙F | PB | FDC |
|---|---|---|---|---|---|
| | | | | **Perf 12.7x12.2** | |
| **1629** | **90¢ multicoloured** | 1.80 | .65 | 9.00 | |
| | | | | **Perf 13.3** | |
| a | booklet pane of 5 x 90¢ (1629as) + label (BK198) | 10.00 | 12.00 | | |
| as | single with straight edge, from 1629a | 3.00 | .85 | | |
| BK198 | pane 1629a in cover $11.00 | | | | |

Qty: 10,000,000

**Nos. 1627–1629 (3) combination FDC** 4.35

The 1996 Christmas stamps are based on Canadian art used on UNICEF Christmas cards and celebrate the 50th anniversary of UNICEF (United Nations International Children's Emergency Fund).

1627a

1628a

1629a

## 1997

### LUNAR NEW YEAR — I
### Year of the Ox

1630
Ox and Chinese symbol

Designer: Ivy Li and Brenda Tong. Based on illustrations and calligraphy by Liu Xiangping

Lithography (6 colours), pane of 25
Ashton-Potter Canada Limited

**1997, Jan 7 GT4, Peterborough Paper Perf 13.1x12.5**

| | | NH–VF | ⊙F | PB | FDC |
|---|---|---|---|---|---|
| **1630** | **45¢ multicoloured** | 1.25 | .30 | 6.00 | 4.00 |
| a | souvenir sheet of 2 x 45¢, dull | 3.50 | 3.50 | | 6.00 |
| aii | as "a", LF | 8.00 | 8.00 | | |
| aiii | as "a", MF | 15.00 | 15.00 | | |
| aiv | $20.00 uncut press sheet of 12 souvenir sheets, *Feb 7, 1997* | 225.00 | | | |
| b | as 1630 (single from 1630c), gold inscriptions omitted | 5,000.00 | | | |
| c | as "a", gold omitted | 12,500.00 | | | |
| ai | as "a", with Hong Kong 97 logo printed at lower right of sheet | 10.00 | 10.00 | | |
| ci | as "ai", missing gold lettering in margins and leaves on UL background; diamond is orange red | 10,000.00 | | | |
| cii | single from 1630ci (missing gold) | 5,000.00 | | | |

Qty: 12,000,000; 1630a: 2,000,000; 1630ai: 150,000; 1630aiv: 15,000

Kiss prints, showing double inscriptions at bottom left, are known for Nos. 1630a ($150.00) and 1630ai ($250.00).

See also 1708, 1767–1768, 1836–1837, 1883–1884, 1933–1934, 1969–1970, 2015–2016, 2083–2084, 2140–2141, 2201–2202, 2257–2258.

1630b

1630cii

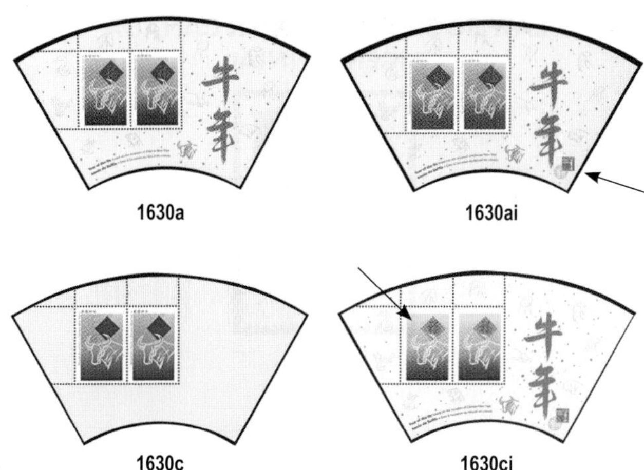

1630a 1630ai

1630c 1630ci

## BIRDS OF CANADA — 2

1631 Mountain Bluebird — 1632 Western Grebe

1633 Northern Gannet — 1634 Scarlet Tanager

Designer: Raymond Bellemare. Based on paintings by Pierre Leduc.
Lithography (5 colours), pane of 20
Ashton-Potter Canada Limited

**1997, Jan 10** — **GT4, Coated Papers** — **Perf 12.5x13.1**

| | | NH–VF | ⊙F | PB | FDC |
|---|---|---|---|---|---|
| **1631** | **45¢ multicoloured** | 1.00 | .30 | | |
| **1632** | **45¢ multicoloured** | 1.00 | .30 | | |
| **1633** | **45¢ multicoloured** | 1.00 | .30 | | |
| **1634** | **45¢ multicoloured** | 1.00 | .30 | | |
| a | se-tenant block or strip of 4 different (1631–1634) | 4.50 | 3.50 | 5.00 | 4.20 |
| i | $54.00 uncut press sheet of 6 panes, unsigned | 100.00 | | | |
| | as "i", signed (issue price $89.95) | 200.00 | | | |

Qty: 4,000,000* of each

*Quantity shown is the total issue including 10,000 uncut press sheets. 1,500 of the uncut press sheets were signed and numbered by the artist and designer.

See also 1591–1594, 1710–1713, 1770–1777, 1839–1846, 1886–1893.

For non-denominated envelopes of nos. 1631–1632, see U154–U155; for non-denominated envelope of 1634 (reversed image), see U169.

## MASTERPIECES OF CANADIAN ART — 10

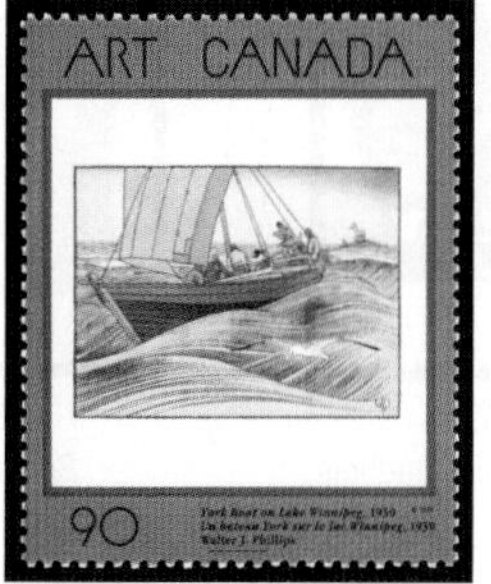


**1635**
*York Boat on Lake Winnipeg*

Designer: Pierre-Yves Pelletier. Based on a woodcut by Walter Joseph Phillips.
Lithography (6 colours) with foil stamping, pane of 16
Ashton-Potter Canada Limited

**1997, Feb 17** — **FCP, Coated Papers** — **Perf 12.5x13.3**

| | | NH–VF | ⊙F | PB | FDC |
|---|---|---|---|---|---|
| **1635** | **90¢ multicoloured** (gold) | 2.50 | 1.50 | 12.00 | 3.00 |

Qty: 6,000,000

Inscription/plate blocks sold by Canada Post in packaged corner sets have rouletted selvedge on the top and/or sides. Blocks removed from full panes by collectors would be either torn or cut with a knife.

See also 1203, 1241, 1271, 1310, 1419, 1466, 1516, 1545, 1602, 1754, 1800, 1863, 1916, 1945.

## CANADIAN TIRE — 75th ANNIVERSARY

**1636**
J.W. and A.J. Billes, founders of Canadian Tire

Designer: Richard Fisher, Mike Smalley, and John Wiltshire.
Lithography (5 colours), pane of 12
Ashton-Potter Canada Limited

**1997, Mar 3** — **GT4, Peterborough Paper** — **Perf 13.0x13.5**

| | | NH–VF | ⊙F | FDC |
|---|---|---|---|---|
| **1636** | **45¢ multicoloured**, HF | 1.00 | .30 | 1.50 |
| | full pane of 12 | 12.00 | | |
| i | thin vert. white line through 'CANADA 45', HF* | 5.00 | 1.00 | |
| ii | F | 4.00 | | |
| iii | as "i", F | 20.00 | | |

Qty: 15,000,000

* At least 3 types exist: through 'D', last 'A', or '5'.

The panes of 12 were sold in a protective cardboard envelope with a 16 page bilingual descriptive booklet. Value $15.00.

**1636i (3 types)**

**1636 full pane**

QE II — 1990's

**1637**
Charles-Émile Gadbois, musicologist

**1638**
*Blue Poppy*, by Claude A. Simard

## ABBÉ CHARLES-ÉMILE GADBOIS

Designer: Marie Lessard.

Lithography (5 colours), pane of 20
Canadian Bank Note Company, Limited

| **1997, Mar 20** | **GT4, Coated Papers** | | | **Perf 13.3x13.1** |
|---|---|---|---|---|
| | **NH–VF** | **⊙F** | **PB** | **FDC** |
| **1637 45¢ multicoloured** | 1.00 | .30 | 5.00 | 1.50 |

Qty: 7,000,000

Issued in conjunction with Semaine de la francophonie, March 16–22, this issue honours Charles-Émile Gadbois who collected and published more than 500 French language songs and is credited with composing more than 100 hymns and songs himself.

## QUÉBEC EN FLEURS 97

Designer: Claude A. Simard.

Lithography (5 colours), booklet pane of 12
Ashton-Potter Canada Limited

| **1997, Apr 4** | **GT4, Peterborough Paper** | | **Perf 13.1x12.5** |
|---|---|---|---|
| | **NH–VF** | **⊙F** | **FDC** |
| **1638 45¢ multicoloured**, HF | 1.00 | .35 | 1.50 |
| i NF | 1.25 | .30 | |
| a booklet pane of 12 (6 x 2) (BK199) | 11.00 | 12.00 | |
| **BK199** pane 1638a in cover $12.00 | | | |

Qty: 9,600,000

Issued to celebrate the international horticultural exhibition Québec en Fleurs, held at Quebec City, April 4–13, 1997.

**1638a**

## VICTORIAN ORDER OF NURSES FOR CANADA CENTENNIAL

**1639**
Nurse and Patient

Designer: Margaret Susan Issenman.

Lithography (6 colours), pane of 20
Ashton-Potter Canada Limited

| **1997, May 12** | **GT4, Peterborough Paper** | | | **Perf 12.5x13.1** |
|---|---|---|---|---|
| | **NH–VF** | **⊙F** | **PB** | **FDC** |
| **1639 45¢ multicoloured** | 1.00 | .30 | 5.00 | 1.50 |

Qty: 7,000,000

Issued for the centennial of the Victorian Order of Nurses which was created in honour of Queen Victoria's Diamond Jubilee in 1897.

## LAW SOCIETY OF UPPER CANADA BICENTENNIAL

**1640**
Osgoode Hall

Designer: Les Holloway. Based on a photograph by Robert White.

Lithography (5 colours plus varnish), Plates of 120 subjects in six panes of 20
Canadian Bank Note Company, Limited

| **1997, May 23** | **GT4, Coated Papers** | | | **Perf 13.3x13.1** |
|---|---|---|---|---|
| | **NH–VF** | **⊙F** | **PB** | **FDC** |
| **1640 45¢ multicoloured** | 1.00 | .30 | 5.00 | 1.50 |
| i nick in outer ring of wax impression (pos. 16) | 7.50 | 2.50 | 10.00 | |

Qty: 7,000,000

Issued to celebrate the Bicentennial of the Law Society of Upper Canada, the oldest and largest law society in Canada.

**1640i**

## OCEAN WATER FISH

**1641** Great White Shark — **1642** Pacific Halibut

**1643** Atlantic Sturgeon — **1644** Bluefin Tuna

Image is reduced.

Designer: Glenda Rissman, Peter D.K. Scott, and Darrell Corriveau.

Lithography (6 colours), pane of 20
Ashton-Potter Canada Limited

| **1997, May 30** | **FCP, Coated Papers** | | | **Perf 12.5x13.1** |
|---|---|---|---|---|
| | **NH–VF** | **⊙F** | **PB** | **FDC** |
| **1641 45¢ multicoloured** | .90 | .30 | | |
| **1642 45¢ multicoloured** | .90 | .30 | | |
| **1643 45¢ multicoloured** | .90 | .30 | | |
| **1644 45¢ multicoloured** | .90 | .30 | | |
| a se-tenant block or strip of 4 different (1641–1644) | 4.00 | 3.00 | 4.50 | 4.20 |

Qty: 2,500,000 of each

## CONFEDERATION BRIDGE

1645 Lighthouse and bridge

1646 Heron and bridge

Designer: Charles Burke and Jim Hudson.

Lithography (6 colours), pane of 20 + 10 tabs
Canadian Bank Note Company, Limited

**1997, May 31** **GT4, Coated Papers** **Perf 12.5x13.1**

| | | NH–VF | ⊙F | PB | FDC |
|---|---|---|---|---|---|
| **1645** | **45¢ multicoloured** | .90 | .30 | | |
| **T1** | untagged (error) | | 100.00 | | |
| **1646** | **45¢ multicoloured** | .90 | .30 | | |
| **a** | se-tenant strip of two (1645, 1646) plus tab between | 2.40 | 1.50 | 4.50 | 2.40 |
| **i** | se-tenant horizontal pair (1646 with 1645 on right) | 4.00 | 4.00 | | |

Qty: 4,000,000 of each

Issued to commemorate the opening of the Confederation Bridge between New Brunswick and Prince Edward Island.

full pane of 1645–1646

## GILLES VILLENEUVE

1647 Villeneuve and checkered flag

1648 Close-up of Villeneuve with Ferrari T-3 in background

Designer: Joseph Gault and Nigel Skinner.
Based on a photograph by Allan de la Plante.

Lithography (7 colours), panes of 16 (2 sections of 2x4)
Canadian Bank Note Company, Limited

**1997, Jun 12** **GT4, Coated Papers** **Perf 12.5x13.1**

| | | NH–VF | ⊙F | PB | FDC |
|---|---|---|---|---|---|
| **1647** | **45¢ multicoloured** | 1.00 | .30 | 4.50 | |
| **i** | vert. pair, gutter between | 3.00 | 2.50 | | |

Qty: 10,000,000

| | | NH–VF | ⊙F | PB | FDC |
|---|---|---|---|---|---|
| **1648** | **90¢ multicoloured** | 2.00 | 1.25 | 10.00 | |
| **i** | vert. pair, gutter between | 6.00 | 5.00 | | |
| **a** | se-tenant pair (1647, 1648) from 1648b | 3.00 | 3.00 | — | 3.30 |
| **b** | $5.40 souvenir sheet of 8 stamps (4 x 1648a) | 13.00 | 12.00 | — | — |

Qty: 6,000,000

The souvenir sheet was issued in a full-colour protective folder.
This issue honours Canadian race car driver Gilles Villeneuve.

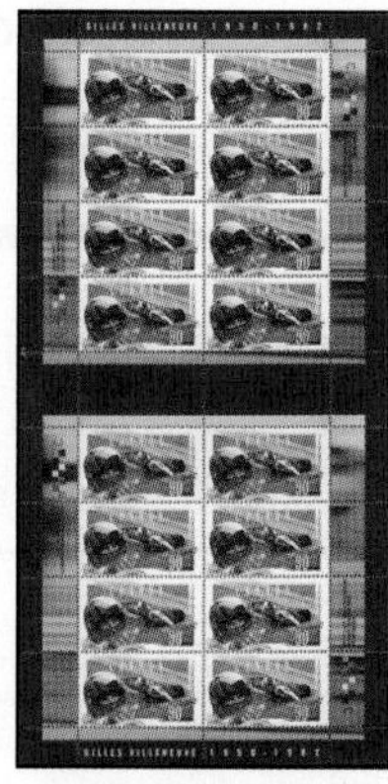

Full panes
(1647 and 1648)

1648b

## JOHN CABOT

1649
Cabot's ship, Matthew, with map and globe in background

Designer: Susan Warr. Based on a map by Juan de la Cosa.
Based on an illustration by Bonnie Ross and illustration by Ivan Murphy.
Based on photographs by Tony Stone Images and James Steeves.

Lithography (6 colours), pane of 20
Ashton-Potter Canada Limited

**1997, Jun 24** **FCP, Coated Papers** **Perf 12.5x13.1**

| | | NH–VF | ⊙F | PB | FDC |
|---|---|---|---|---|---|
| **1649** | **45¢ multicoloured** | 1.00 | .30 | 5.00 | 1.50 |
| **i** | FCP + GT4 tagging | 1.00 | .30 | 5.00 | 1.50 |

Qty: 9,000,000

Joint issue with Italy, the country of Cabot's birth.

Joint issue with Italy
**Scott # 2162**

## SCENIC HIGHWAYS — I

1650 Sea to Sky Highway, British Columbia
1651 Cabot Trail, Nova Scotia

1652 Wine Route, Ontario
1653 Big Muddy, Saskatchewan

Designer: Lou Cable. Based on photographs by Ed Gifford and Greg Griffith.
Lithography (6 colours), pane of 20
Canadian Bank Note Company, Limited

| 1997, Jun 30 | GT4, Coated Papers | | | Perf 12.5x13.1 | |
|---|---|---|---|---|---|
| | | NH–VF | ⊙F | PB | FDC |
| **1650** | **45¢ multicoloured** | .90 | .50 | | |
| **1651** | **45¢ multicoloured** | .90 | .50 | | |
| **1652** | **45¢ multicoloured** | .90 | .50 | | |
| **1653** | **45¢ multicoloured** | .90 | .50 | | |
| a | se-tenant block or strip of 4 different (1650–1653) | 4.00 | 3.50 | 4.50 | 4.20 |

Qty: 1,875,000 of each

This is the first issue in a three-year series.
See also 1739–1742 and 1780–1783. For non-denominated envelopes of nos. 1650 and 1652, see U164–U167.

## INDUSTRIAL DESIGN

1654

Designer: François Dallaire. Based on photographs by Guy Lavigueur.
Lithography (6 colours), pane of 24 + 24 tabs
Canadian Bank Note Company, Limited

| 1997, Jul 23 | GT4, Coated Papers | | | Perf 12.5x13.1 | |
|---|---|---|---|---|---|
| | | NH–VF | ⊙F | PB | FDC |
| **1654** | **45¢ multicoloured** | .90 | .40 | 4.50 | 1.50 |

Qty: 7,000,000

The pane contains 24 connecting tabs (2 each of 12 designs). Identical tab designs have different background colours. Stamp with tab attached command a premium.

Issued to commemorate the 20th International Congress of the International Council of Societies for Industrial Design, held at Toronto in August 1997.

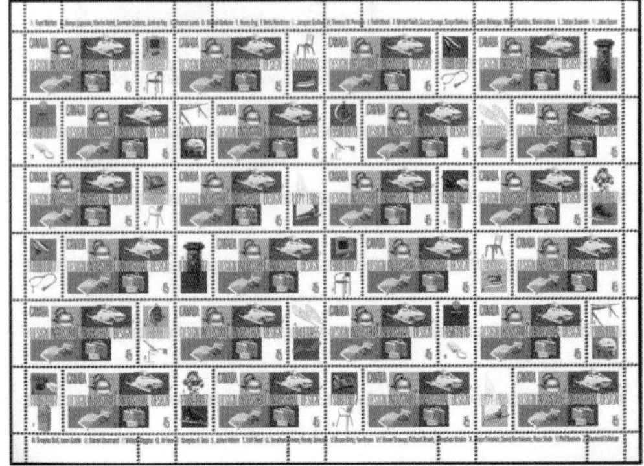

**1654 full pane**

1655 Highland Games

1656 Knights of Columbus

## HIGHLAND GAMES

Designer: Fraser Ross. Based on photographs by Andrew Balfour.
Lithography (6 colours), pane of 20
Canadian Bank Note Company, Limited

| 1997, Aug 1 | GT4, Coated Papers | | | Perf 12.5x13.1 | |
|---|---|---|---|---|---|
| | | NH–VF | ⊙F | PB | FDC |
| **1655** | **45¢ multicoloured** | .90 | .30 | 4.50 | 1.50 |

Qty: 8,000,000

Issued in honour of the fiftieth anniversary of the Glengarry Highland Games, held annually at Maxville, Ontario.

## KNIGHTS OF COLUMBUS

Designer: Alain Leduc. Based on an illustration by François Chartier.
Lithography (6 colours), pane of 25
Canadian Bank Note Company, Limited

| 1997, Aug 5 | GT4, Coated Papers | | | Perf 13.1 | |
|---|---|---|---|---|---|
| | | NH–VF | ⊙F | PB | FDC |
| **1656** | **45¢ multicoloured** | .90 | .30 | 4.50 | 1.50 |

Qty: 7,000,000

Issued to celebrate the first hundred years of the Knights of Columbus in Canada.

1657 The PTTI

1658

## WORLD CONGRESS OF THE PTTI LABOUR UNION

Designer: François Picard. Based on photographs by Jean-François Bérubé, Hiroyuki Matsumoto, and Bruce Forster.
Lithography (6 colours), pane of 20
Canadian Bank Note Company, Limited

| 1997, Aug 18 | GT4, Coated Papers | | | Perf 13.0x13.1 | |
|---|---|---|---|---|---|
| | | NH–VF | ⊙F | PB | FDC |
| **1657** | **45¢ multicoloured** | .90 | .30 | 4.50 | 1.50 |

Qty: 7,000,000

Issued to celebrate the 28th World Congress of the Postal, Telegraph and Telephone International Labour Union, held at Montreal.

## CANADA'S YEAR OF ASIA PACIFIC

Designer: Ken Fung.
Lithography (5 colours), pane of 20
Canadian Bank Note Company, Limited

| 1997, Aug 25 | GT4, Coated Papers | | | Perf 13.4x13.3 | |
|---|---|---|---|---|---|
| | | NH–VF | ⊙F | PB | FDC |
| **1658** | **45¢ multicoloured** | .90 | .30 | 4.50 | 1.50 |
| i | kiss print; black inscriptions doubled | 400.00 | | | |

Qty: 7,000,000

Issued in celebration of Canada's role as the 1997 chair of the Asia Pacific Economic Cooperation (APEC) Economic Leaders Meeting.

## THE SERIES OF THE CENTURY

1659 Paul Henderson celebrates his winning goal

1660 Team Canada celebrates the series win

Designer: Charles Vinh. Based on photographs by Denis Brodeur.
Computer graphics by Pierre Rousseau.

Lithography (5 colours), booklet pane of 10
Ashton-Potter Canada Limited

**1997, Sep 20 — GT4, Coated Papers — Perf 12.5x13.1**

| | | NH–VF | ⊙F | FDC |
|---|---|---|---|---|
| **1659** | **45¢ multicoloured** | 1.00 | .40 | |
| **1660** | **45¢ multicoloured** | 1.00 | .40 | |
| ii | se-tenant pair (1659, 1660) | 2.25 | 1.50 | 3.00 |
| a | booklet pane of 10, 5 each of 1659, 1660 (BK201) | 10.50 | 11.00 | |
| ai | overprinted unfolded pane from Collector Gift Set (issue price $39.95) | 100.00 | | |
| BK201 | pane 1660a in cover $11.00 | | | |

Qty: 9,000,000 of each

Complete Gift Set includes sweat shirt, commemorative puck and colourful print. (Complete boxed set as issued $125.00.)
Issued to celebrate the 25th anniversary of the first Canada/Soviet hockey series.

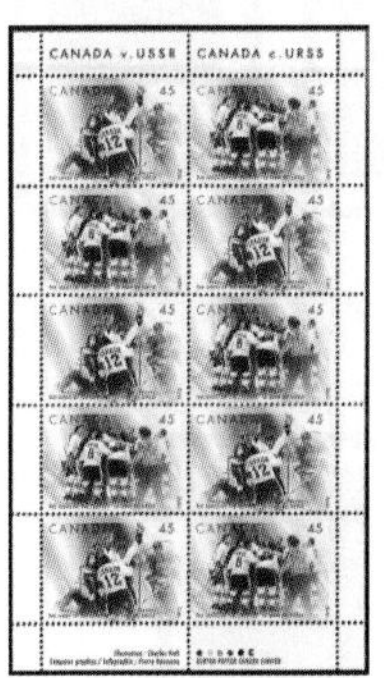

1660a

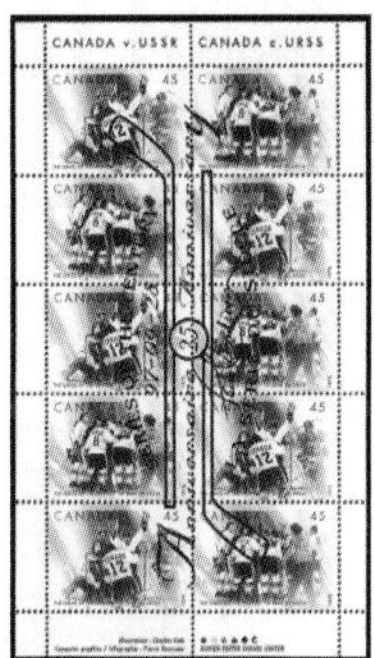

1660ai

## PROMINENT CANADIANS

1661 Martha Black (1866–1957)

1662 Lionel Chevrier (1903–1987)

1663 Judy LaMarsh (1924–1980)

1664 Réal Caouette (1917–1976)

Designer: Kosta (Gus) Tsetsekas. Based on an illustration by Steve Hepburn.

Lithography (6 colours), pane of 20
Canadian Bank Note Company, Limited

**1997, Sep 26 — GT4, Coated Papers — Perf 13.4x13.0**

| | | NH–VF | ⊙F | PB | FDC |
|---|---|---|---|---|---|
| **1661** | **45¢ multicoloured** | .90 | .50 | | |
| **1662** | **45¢ multicoloured** | .90 | .50 | | |
| **1663** | **45¢ multicoloured** | .90 | .50 | | |
| a | double print, "Canada 45" | — | 75.00* | | |
| b | quadruple print, "Canada 45" | — | 400.00* | | |
| **1664** | **45¢ multicoloured** | .90 | .50 | | |
| a | quintuple print "Canada 45" | — | 500.00* | | |
| b | se-tenant block or strip of 4 different (1661–1664) | 4.00 | 3.25 | 4.50 | 4.20 |

Qty: 1,875,000 of each
* Only used copies have been reported.

This set of stamps honours the lives and achievements of four prominent federal politicians.

1664i

## THE SUPERNATURAL

1665 Vampire

1666 Werewolf

1667 Ghost

1668 Goblin

Designer: Louis Fishauf. Based on an illustration by Blair Drawson.

Lithography (6 colours), pane of 16
Ashton-Potter Canada Limited

**1997, Oct 1 — FCP, Coated Papers — Perf 12.5x13.2**

| | | NH–VF | ⊙F | PB | FDC |
|---|---|---|---|---|---|
| **1665** | **45¢ multicoloured** | .90 | .50 | | |
| **1666** | **45¢ multicoloured** | .90 | .50 | | |
| **1667** | **45¢ multicoloured** | .90 | .50 | | |
| **1668** | **45¢ multicoloured** | .90 | .50 | | |
| a | se-tenant block of 4 different (1665–1668) | 4.00 | 3.25 | 4.50 | 4.20 |

Qty: 4,000,000 of each

Inspired by the 100th anniversary of Bram Stoker's novel Dracula, this set was issued to begin Stamp Collecting Month. A protective folder, which becomes a pop-up haunted house, was made available free to the purchaser upon request.

Definitive Timeline:
1997, Oct 15 $8 Grizzly Bear (1694)

## CHRISTMAS — MADONNA AND CHILD

1669
*Our Lady of the Rosary*, by Guido Nincheri

1670
*Nativity Scene*, by Ellen Simon

1671
*Scene from the Life of the Blessed Virgin*, by Christopher Wallis

Designer: Maggi Cash, Gary Mansbridge, Heiki Sillaste, and Malcolm Waddell. Based on stained glass windows.

Lithography (6 colours), panes of 50
Ashton-Potter Canada Limited

| 1997, Nov 3 | GT4, Coated Papers | | | Perf 12.5x13.1 | |
|---|---|---|---|---|---|
| | | NH–VF | ⊙F | PB | FDC |
| **1669** | **45¢ multicoloured** | .90 | .25 | 4.50 | |
| a | booklet pane of 10 x 45¢ (1669as) (1 x 10) (BK202) | 10.50 | 11.00 | | |
| as | single from 1669a, perf 12.5 horiz. | 1.00 | .35 | | |
| **BK202** | pane 1669a in cover $12.00 | | | | |
| Qty: 39,305,650 | | | | | |
| **1670** | **52¢ multicoloured** | 1.05 | .50 | 5.25 | |
| a | booklet pane of 5 x 52¢ (1670as) (1 x 5) (BK203) | 6.00 | 6.50 | | |
| as | single from 1670a, perf 12.5 horiz. | 1.50 | .75 | | |
| **BK203** | pane 1670a in cover $6.50 | | | | |
| Qty: 9,601,250 | | | | | |
| **1671** | **90¢ multicoloured** | 1.80 | .75 | 9.00 | |
| a | booklet pane of 5 x 90¢ (1671as) (1 x 5) (BK 204) | 10.50 | 12.00 | | |
| as | single from 1671a, perf 12.5 horiz. | 2.00 | 1.00 | | |
| **BK204** | pane 1671a in cover $11.00 | | | | |
| Qty: 10,381,900 | | | | | |

**Nos. 1669–1671 (3) combination FDC** **$4.35**

The 1997 Christmas stamps feature stained glass windows depicting the Madonna and Child by Canadian artists. No. 1669 is from the Holy Rosary Cathedral, Vancouver, B.C.; No. 1670 is from the United Church in Leith, Ontario; and No. 1671 is from St. Stephen's Ukrainian Byzantine Rite Roman Catholic Church in Calgary, Alberta.

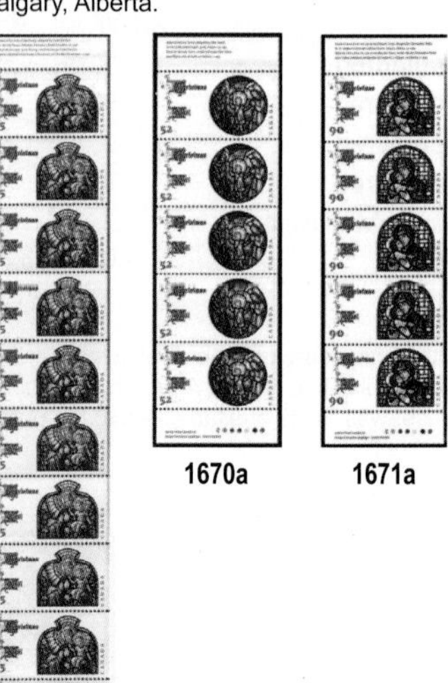

1669a 1670a 1671a

## ROYAL AGRICULTURAL WINTER FAIR

1672
Collage of events at the fair

Designer: Heather Lafleur. Based on an illustration by Shelagh Armstrong.

Lithography (7 colours), pane of 20
Canadian Bank Note Company, Limited

| 1997, Nov 6 | GT4, Coated Papers | | | Perf 12.5x13.2 | |
|---|---|---|---|---|---|
| | | NH–VF | ⊙F | PB | FDC |
| **1672** | **45¢ multicoloured** | .90 | .30 | 4.50 | 1.50 |
| Qty: 8,000,000 | | | | | |

Issued to celebrate the 75th anniversary of the Royal Agricultural Winter Fair, the world's largest indoor equestrian and agricultural competition, held annually at Toronto, Ontario.

## TRADITIONAL TRADES DEFINITIVES
## 1999–2007
### Low Values

1673
Bookbinding

1674
Decorative Ironwork

1675
Glass-blowing

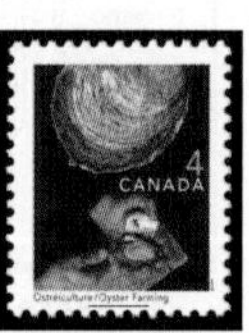

1676
Oyster Farming

1677
Weaving

1678
Quilting

1679
Artistic Woodworking

1680
Leatherworking

The initial printings of these stamps were by Ashton-Potter Canada Limited in April 1999. Reprints of some values began to appear in late 2000, printed by the Canadian Bank Note Company, Limited. Further reprints by CBN began appearing in late 2001. These printings had imperforate top and bottom selvedge with a UPC product barcode placed above (or below) the stamps in columns 5 and 6 of either the top or bottom selvedge.

It is not possible to differentiate between singles of APCL and CBN stamps.

Designer: Monique Dufour and Sophie Lafortune.
Based on photographs by Jean-Pierre Beaudin.

Lithography (5 colours), panes of 100
Ashton-Potter Canada Limited

**1999, Apr 29** **Not tagged, TRC Paper** **Perf 13.0x13.3**

| | | | NH–VF | ⊙F | PB | FDC |
|---|---|---|---|---|---|---|
| **1673** | | **1¢ multicoloured** | .20 | .20 | 1.00 | — |
| | i | CBN, *Dec 2000* | — | — | 3.50 | — |
| | ii | CBN, *Nov 15, 2001*† | — | — | 1.00 | — |
| | a | as "ii", missing grey (in numeral 1) | 400.00 | | | |
| | – | top or bottom block of 20 with UPC barcode in selvedge | — | — | 3.00 | |
| **1674** | | **2¢ multicoloured** | .20 | .20 | 1.00 | — |
| | i | CBN, *Dec 2001* | — | — | 3.50 | — |
| | ii | CBN, *Dec 13, 2002*† | — | — | 1.00 | — |
| | – | top or bottom block of 20 with UPC barcode in selvedge | — | — | 3.00 | |

A reprint of 1674ii exists with a shift in the plate inscriptions to the right, but the shift is very slight and difficult to detect.

| | | | NH–VF | ⊙F | PB | FDC |
|---|---|---|---|---|---|---|
| **1675** | | **3¢ multicoloured** | .30 | .20 | 1.50 | — |
| **1676** | | **4¢ multicoloured** | .20 | .20 | 1.00 | — |
| | i | CBN, *Oct 2005*† | — | — | 1.00 | — |
| | a | imperf. pair (CBN)† | 1,250.00 | | | |
| | – | top or bottom block of 20 with UPC barcode in selvedge | — | — | 5.00 | |
| **1677** | | **5¢ multicoloured** | .20 | .20 | 1.00 | — |
| | i | CBN, *Feb 2001* | — | — | 4.00 | — |
| | ii | CBN, *Nov 15, 2001*† | — | — | 1.00 | — |
| | – | top or bottom block of 20 with UPC barcode in selvedge | — | — | 5.00 | |
| **1678** | | **9¢ multicoloured** | .25 | .25 | 1.25 | — |
| **1679** | | **10¢ multicoloured** | .25 | .20 | 1.25 | — |
| | i | CBN, *Mar 2001* | — | — | 4.50 | — |
| | ii | CBN, *Nov 15, 2001*† | — | — | 1.25 | — |
| | – | top or bottom block of 20 with UPC barcode in selvedge | — | — | 5.00 | |
| | – | top or bottom block of 20 with UPC barcode in selvedge and plate inscriptions shifted 1.5mm to right§ | — | — | 75.00 | |
| | a | imperforate single | | | | |
| | b | block of 4, top 2 stamps imperforate (cut between) | | | | |
| | c | imperforate vertical pair | 1,000.00 | | 2,000.00 (UR, LR) | |

§ the shifted inscriptions were a new printing, available in March 2006.

| | | | NH–VF | ⊙F | PB | FDC |
|---|---|---|---|---|---|---|
| **1680** | | **25¢ multicoloured** | .50 | .20 | 2.00 | — |
| | i | CBN, *Nov 2001* | — | — | 9.00 | — |
| | ii | CBN, *Dec 15, 2001*† | — | — | 2.00 | — |
| | – | top or bottom block of 20 with inverted UPC barcode in selvedge | — | — | 15.00 | |
| | iii | white slash through '2' of '25' (pos. 95) | 10.00 | 5.00 | | |
| | – | as ii, with guide dots at edge of selvedge (block of 20) | — | — | 70.00* | |
| | – | CBN, top or bottom block of 20 with upright UPC in selvedge, *Dec 2004*† | — | — | 15.00 | |

* two different versions exist of each strip (top or bottom)

**Nos. 1673–1680 (8) Combination FDC** **1.80**

† These printings have an imperforate top and bottom selvedge with a UPC barcode in either the top or bottom selvedge.

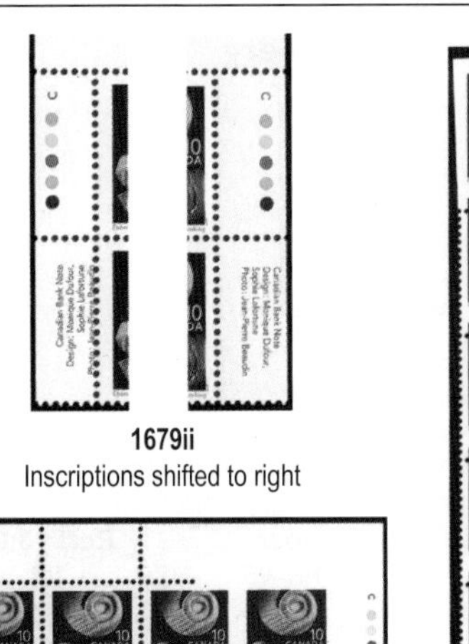

**1679ii**
Inscriptions shifted to right

**1679b**

**1679c**

**1673a**

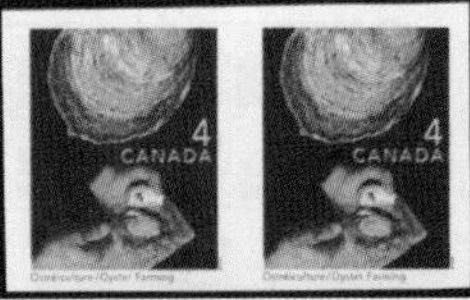


**1676ii**

**1680iii**

**1680** with inverted UPC barcode in top selvedge (Dec 2001)

**1680** with upright UPC barcode in top selvedge (Dec 2004)

## DOMESTIC FIRST-CLASS RATE
### Queen Elizabeth II

**1681**

Designer: Chris Candlish and Tom Yakobina. Based on a photograph by Yousuf Karsh.

Lithography, pane of 120
Ashton-Potter Canada Limited

**1998, Dec 28** **GT4, TRC Paper** **Perf 13.3x13.0**

| | | NH–VF | ⊙F | PB | FDC |
|---|---|---|---|---|---|
| **1681** | **46¢ multicoloured** (red) | .90 | .20 | 4.50 | 1.50 |

Pane is 12 x 10 stamps with no gutters.

## Flag over Iceberg

1682

Designer: Stuart Bradley Ash and Katalin Kovats.
Based on photographs by John Foster and J.A. Kraulis.

Lithography, pane of 120 + vertical blank gutter
Canadian Bank Note Company, Limited

| 1998, Dec 28 | GT4, TRC Paper | NH–VF | ⊙F | Perf 13.0x13.3 PB | FDC |
|---|---|---|---|---|---|
| **1682** | **46¢ multicoloured** | .90 | .20 | 4.50 | 1.50 |
| i | horizontal gutter pair | 4.00 | 3.00 | | |
| a | booklet pane of 10 x 46¢ (1682as) (BK214) | 11.50 | 14.00 | | |
| as | single with straight edge, from 1682a | 1.25 | .40 | | |
| BK214 | pane 1682a in cover $12.00 | | | | |

Pane is 10 x 12 stamps with a vertical gutter. For die cut self-adhesive see 1698.

1682a

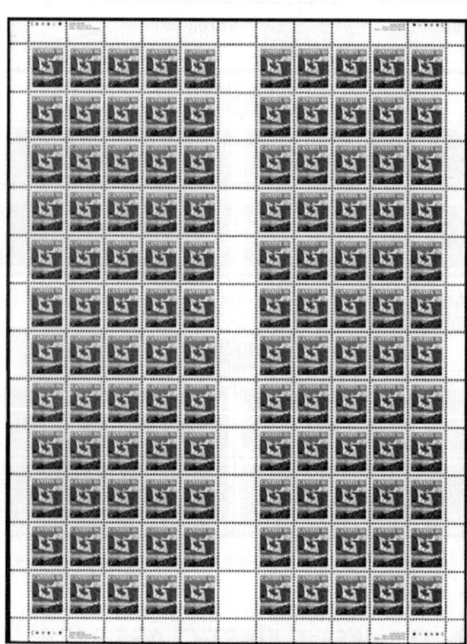

1682 full pane of 120 + gutter

## Queen Elizabeth II

1683

Lithography, pane of 100
Canadian Bank Note Company, Limited

| 2000, Dec 28 | GT4, TRC Paper | NH–VF | ⊙F | Perf 13.3x13.0 PB | FDC |
|---|---|---|---|---|---|
| **1683** | **47¢ multicoloured** (blue) | .95 | .20 | 4.75 | 1.50 |
| a | imperf. pair | 900.00 | | 2,000.00 | |
| ii | imperf. bottom pair and half of next pair in block of 4 | 1,200.00 | — | 1,500.00 | — |

## MEDIUM VALUE STYLIZED MAPLE LEAF

1684

1685

1686

Designer: Bernhard Mueller.

Lithography (3 colours), panes of 50
Ashton-Potter Canada Limited

| 1998, Dec 28 | GT4, TRC Paper | NH–VF | ⊙F | Perf 13.0x13.3 PB | FDC |
|---|---|---|---|---|---|
| **1684** | **55¢ multicoloured** (orange leaf on blue background) | 1.25 | .25 | 5.50* | — |
| a | booklet pane of 5 x 55¢ (1684as) + label (BK216) | 6.00 | 5.00 | | |
| as | single with straight edge, from 1684a | 1.75 | .45 | | |
| BK216 | pane 1684a in cover $6.50 | | | | |
| **1685** | **73¢ multicoloured** (yellow leaf on purple background) | 1.50 | .50 | 7.50* | — |
| **1686** | **95¢ multicoloured** (green leaf on peach background) | 2.25 | .60 | 9.50* | — |
| a | booklet pane of 5 x 95¢ (1686as) + label (BK217) | 11.00 | 10.00 | | |
| as | single with straight edge, from 1686a | 2.50 | 1.00 | | |
| BK217 | pane 1686a in cover $12.00 | | | | |

**Nos. 1684, 1685, 1686 (3) combination FDC** **5.50**

* All lower left inscriptions on all 3 values have a narrower line spacing than found on the other three corners.

1684a

1686a

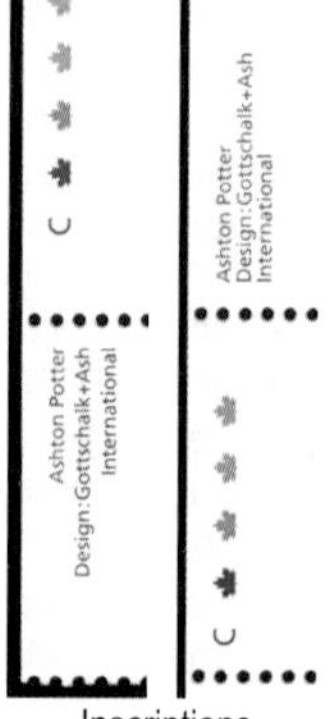


Inscriptions
Left: 'wide' line spacing
Right: narrow line spacing

## WILDLIFE DEFINITIVES
### High values

1687
Loon

For non-denominated size 10 envelopes of same high-value wildlife designs, see U251–U259.

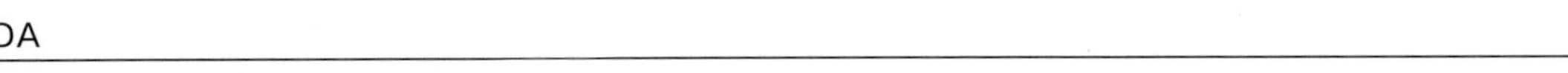

1688 White-tailed Deer    1689 Atlantic Walrus

1690
Polar Bear

1691 Peregrine Falcon    1692 Sable Island Horse

Designers: Steven Slipp and Alain Leduc. Engraved by Jorge Peral ($1) and Martin Mörck ($2). Based on illustrations by Robert-Ralph Carmichael ($1) and Brent Townsend ($2).

Lithography and Engraving (3 colours), panes of 16
Canadian Bank Note Company, Limited

**1998, Oct 27 Not tagged, Peterborough Paper Perf 13.3x13.0**

| | | NH–VF | ⊙F | PB | FDC |
|---|---|---|---|---|---|
| **1687** | **$1 multicoloured**, NF | 2.00 | .70 | 10.00 | 2.75 |
| i | LF | 10.00 | 2.00 | 45.00 | |
| ii | MF | 5.00 | 1.00 | 25.00 | |
| iii | HF | 7.00 | 1.25 | 32.00 | |
| iv | Coated (TRC) paper, *Feb 4, 2003*† | 2.00 | .50 | 10.00 | — |
| v | brown dot in water (pos. 16) | 5.00 | 2.50 | 15.00 | |

† Panes have UPC barcode in lower right inscription block.
For size 10 envelope of same design see U251.

**2005, Oct 20 GT4, TRC Paper Perf 12.5x13.1**

| | | NH–VF | ⊙F | PB | FDC |
|---|---|---|---|---|---|
| **1688** | **$1 multicoloured** | 2.00 | .70 | | |
| **1689** | **$1 multicoloured** | 2.00 | .70 | | |
| a | se-tenant pair (1688, 1689) | 4.00 | 3.00 | 10.00 | 6.00 |
| b | souvenir sheet (2 each 1688, 1689)* ‡ | 10.00 | 10.00 | | |

* Tagging is dull (not visible) under normal lighting compared to shiny (visible) tagging on the two stamps from the pane of 16.

A reprint of 1688–89 (pane of 16) was seen as early as September 2009. The reprint is on thicker paper (80lb) with a "sharper" intaglio image (CANADA appears 'bubbled' and the small scientific text is the same blue colour end to end). The plate inscriptions stayed the same as the original printing, which was on 60lb paper. [On the original, CANADA appears 'solid' and the scientific text colour progresses from blue to brown-black.]

For size 10 envelopes of same designs see U253 and U254.

1687v

**1998, Oct 27 Not tagged, Peterborough Paper Perf 13.3x13.0**

| | | NH–VF | ⊙F | PB | FDC |
|---|---|---|---|---|---|
| **1690** | **$2 multicoloured** | 4.00 | 1.35 | 20.00 | 5.00 |
| i | Coated (TRC) paper, *Feb 4, 2003*† | 4.00 | 1.25 | 20.00 | |

† Panes have UPC barcode in lower right inscription block.
For size 10 envelope of same design see U252.

**2005, Dec 19 GT4, TRC Paper Perf 12.5x13.1**

| | | NH–VF | ⊙F | PB | FDC |
|---|---|---|---|---|---|
| **1691** | **$2 multicoloured** | 4.00 | 1.35 | | |
| **1692** | **$2 multicoloured** | 4.00 | 1.35 | | |
| a | se-tenant pair (1691, 1692) | 8.00 | 6.00 | 20.00 | 10.00 |
| b | souvenir sheet (2 each 1691, 1692)* ‡ | 20.00 | 20.00 | | |

* Tagging is dull (not visible) under normal lighting compared to shiny (visible) tagging on the two stamps from the pane of 16.

‡ The souvenir sheets were originally released with UPC barcodes in the left selvedge. Sometime in 2008, Canada Post started selling off surplus stocks with this bar code trimmed off. Price shown is for panes *with* the UPC barcode; panes without barcode sell for less.

For size 10 envelopes of same designs see U255 and U256.

1689b    1692b

1693
Moose

Designer: Steven Slipp. Based on a drawing by David Preston-Smith. Engraved by Jorge Peral.

Lithography (4 colours) and Engraving (2 colours), pane of 4
Canadian Bank Note Company, Limited

**2003, Dec 19 Not tagged, TRC Paper Perf 12.5x13.1**

| | | NH–VF | ⊙F | PB | FDC |
|---|---|---|---|---|---|
| **1693** | **$5 multicoloured** | 10.00 | 2.50 | 50.00 | 12.00 |
| a | engraved colours omitted | *7,500.00* | | *35,000.00* | |
| i | vertical scratch between top pair of stamps (in pair)† | 40.00 | | | |
| ii | strong offset of the brown Moose on gum side (200 reported) | 100.00 | | | |

† Two types exist, one appears a bit lower than the other.

The moose is reproduced over a colour lithographic print of sky, woods and wetland, typical of the moose's habitat. Various security features have been imprinted on this high-denomination stamp. A Mi'kmaq petroglyph, derived from an original in Kejimkujik National Park, appears in a "latent," or hidden, image. The sky is created with an image of a moose's hoof print in a custom half-tone pattern, and two lines of microtype reproduce the Latin name of the moose. An image of a stylized moose is only visible under ultraviolet light.

The "Missing moose" error is missing the moose, grass, and trees (both engraved colours). Between 8 and 12 panes were found; most have been broken up into singles.

For size 10 envelope of same design see U257.

1693 full pane of 4

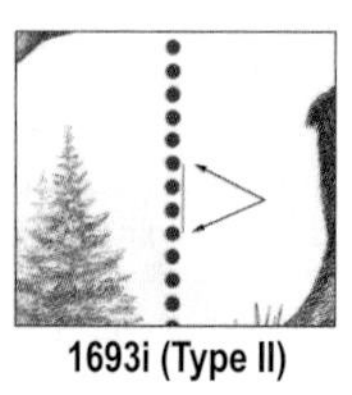

1693i (Type I)

1693i (Type II)

1693a full pane of 4

1694
Grizzly Bear

Designer: Alain Leduc. Engraved by Jorge Peral.

Lithography and Engraving (3 colours), Sheets of 36 subjects in nine panes of 4
Canadian Bank Note Company, Limited

| 1997, Oct 15 | Not tagged, TRC Paper | | | Perf 12.5x13.1 | |
|---|---|---|---|---|---|
| | | NH–VF | ⊙F | PB | FDC |
| **1694** | **$8 multicoloured** | 16.00 | 6.00 | 80.00* | 20.00 |
| i | imperforate top selvedge and top half of stamp (in full pane) | *6,000.00* | | | |
| ii | strong offset of the black Bear on gum side (exists in various stages) | 100.00 | | | |

* Price is for full pane of 4 with inscription in right selvedge. Field stock pane (no inscription) $65.00.

Canada Post issued 2,500 sets containing an imprint block of 4, with the signatures of the designer and engraver in the margin and a numbered print of the engraving of the Grizzly Bear for $95.00. Value $145.

A "We appreciate your business" presentation folder containing a single used $8 stamp cancelled "Nov./Dec. 1997" was given away by Canada Post commercial sales staff to selected customers after the 1997 postal strike. Value $25.

For size 10 envelope of same design see U258.

Philatelic pane (with inscription in right selvedge)
Field stock has the inscription trimmed from the right selvedge

For $10 Blue Whale, see Scott 2405

## ROLL STAMP (COIL)

1695
Flag

Designer: Stuart Bradley Ash and Katalin Kovats. Engraved by Yves Baril.

Engraved (1 colour), roll of 100
Canadian Bank Note Company, Limited

| 1998, Dec 28 | GT4 | | Perf 10 horiz. | |
|---|---|---|---|---|
| | | NH–VF | ⊙F | FDC |
| **1695** | **46¢ red** | 1.00 | .20 | 1.50 |
| i | wide spacing strip of 4 | 20.00 | | |
| ii | narrow spacing strip of 4 | 25.00 | | |
| a | imperf. pair | 225.00 | | |
| ai | imperf., wide spacing jump, strip of 4 | 600.00 | | |

Coil pairs or larger multiples are priced in proportion. Spacing strips may also contain an alignment "jump". Same price as the spacing strip.

## DOMESTIC FIRST-CLASS RATE STYLIZED MAPLE LEAF

1696

1697

Designer: Bernhard Mueller.

Photogravure (4 colours), self-adhesive ATM panes of 18
Avery Dennison Corporation

| 1998, Apr 14 | USA Tagging, FCP Paper | | | Die cut | |
|---|---|---|---|---|---|
| | | NH–VF | ⊙F | PB | FDC |
| **1696** | **45¢ multicoloured** | 1.75 | 2.50 | 18.00* | 1.50 |
| a | sheetlet of 18† | 35.00 | | | |

Qty: 4,500,000

* Inscribed gutter block of 6.

† The sheetlet of 18 stamps was issued through ATM machines which dispense paper currency. The purchase was automatically deducted from the user's bank account.

The printer (Avery) is also responsible for many of the self-adhesive ATM stamps issued by the USA. This Canadian stamp was tagged with the *same* taggant as used on USA stamps — it is only visible under *short wave* ultraviolet light. The tagging glows green when exposed to the UV light.

In-period usage on commercial covers is very rare; $20.00 per cover.

Flexography (3 colours) with foil stamping, self-adhesive roll of 100
Ashton-Potter Canada Limited

| 1998, Sep 30 | GT4, JAC Paper | Die cut perf 12.8x13.1 | | |
|---|---|---|---|---|
| | | NH–VF | ⊙F | FDC |
| **1697** | **45¢ multicoloured** | 1.50 | 1.00 | 1.50 |
| i | "bullet hole" (every 5th stamp on only 1 roll from larger printing sheet) | 10.00 | 5.00 | |
| | No. 1697 in full roll with dispenser box | 150.00 | — | |
| ii | backing paper rouletted horizontally, single from Canada Post's annual Souvenir Collection | 10.00 | — | |

Qty: 2,720,000

Minor constant varieties occur on green background.

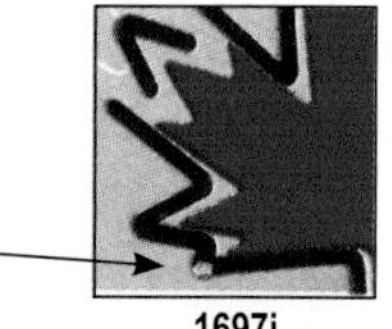

1697i

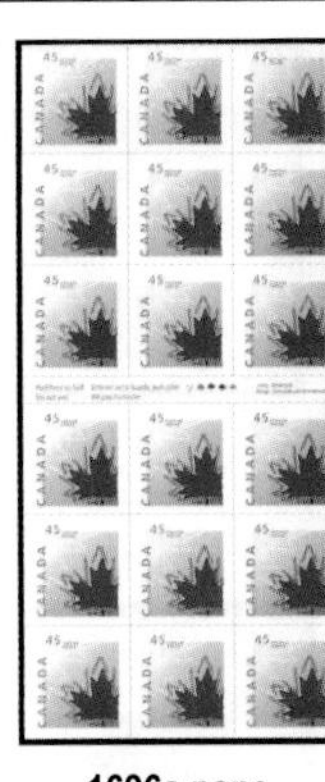
1696a pane

1699a pane

## SELF-ADHESIVE BOOKLET

1698
Flag over Iceberg

Designer: Stuart Bradley Ash and Katalin Kovats.
Based on photographs by John Foster and J.A. Kraulis.

Lithography, self-adhesive booklet pane of 30
Ashton-Potter Canada Limited

**1998, Dec 28** **GT4, JAC Paper** **Die cut**

| | | NH–VF | ⊙F | FDC |
|---|---|---|---|---|
| **1698** | **46¢ multicoloured** | 1.25 | .20 | — |
| a | booklet pane of 30 x 46¢ (1698) (**BK215**) | 30.00 | | |
| b | die cutting omitted, pair | 400.00 | | |
| ii | vertical strip of 3, imperf. between bottom pair | 150.00 | | |

Only JAC paper was used on this stamp, despite the C-paper designation shown in the booklet pane inscription.

This stamp exists with either a horizontal 'texture' or a vertical 'texture' to the paper.

For 46¢ water-activated gum, perforated stamp see 1682.

There was no Canada Post OFDC produced with the self-adhesive printing (1698). Only the PVA gum printing from panes of 120 (1682) were utilized on the OFDC.

1698a

## STYLIZED MAPLE LEAF

1699

Photogravure (4 colours), self-adhesive ATM panes of 18
Avery Dennison Corporation

**1998, Dec 28** **USA Tagging, FCP Paper** **Die cut**

| | | NH–VF | ⊙F | PB | FDC |
|---|---|---|---|---|---|
| **1699** | **46¢ multicoloured** | 3.50 | 4.00 | 35.00* | 1.50 |
| a | sheetlet of 18† | 65.00 | | | |

Qty: 2,250,000

* Inscribed gutter block of 6.

† The sheetlet of 18 stamps was issued through ATM machines which dispense paper currency. The purchase was automatically deducted from the user's bank account.

The printer (Avery) is also responsible for many of the self-adhesive ATM stamps issued by the USA. This Canadian stamp was tagged with the *same* taggant as used on USA stamps — it is only visible under *short wave* ultraviolet light. The tagging glows green when exposed to the UV light.

In-period usage on commercial covers is very rare; $20.00 per cover.

## SELF-ADHESIVE BOOKLET

1700
Flag over Inukshuk

Designer: Katalin Kovats and Doreen Colonello.
Based on photographs by Paul Eekhoff and Daryl Benson.

Lithography, self-adhesive booklet pane of 10 or 30
Canadian Bank Note Company, Limited / Ashton-Potter Canada Limited

**2000, Dec 28** **GT4, JAC Paper** **Die cut**

| | | NH–VF | ⊙F | FDC |
|---|---|---|---|---|
| **1700** | **47¢ multicoloured**, flrsc. back | 1.00 | .20 | 1.50 |
| i | back of stamp NF | – | .25 | |
| c | "blank stamp" (all colours missing), tagged | 300.00 | – | |
| a | booklet pane of 10 x 47¢ (1700) CBN (**BK236**) | 10.50 | | |
| d | booklet pane of 10 x 47¢ (1700c), 10 "blank stamps" | 3,000.00 | | |
| e | as "a", die cutting omitted (**BK236Bai**) | 2,500.00 | | |
| b | booklet pane of 30 x 47¢ (1700) APC (**BK237**) | 31.00 | | |

The back of the stamp can be either fluorescent (varying levels) (1700) or non-fluorescent (1700i); this can only be identified on used stamps.

1700a

1700b

Nos. 1701–1707 are not assigned.

## 1998

### LUNAR NEW YEAR — 2
### Year of the Tiger

**1708**
Tiger and Chinese Symbol

Designer: Raymond Mah.
Based on illustrations by Gavin Chow, Leigh Bridges, and Tammi Hall.
Calligraphed by Leung Hon Kwan.

Lithography (6 colours), pane of 25
Ashton-Potter Canada Limited

**1998, Jan 8** **GT4, TRC Paper** **Perf 13.2x12.5**

| | | NH–VF | ⊙F | PB | FDC |
|---|---|---|---|---|---|
| **1708** | **45¢ multicoloured** | 1.00 | .30 | 5.00 | 1.50 |
| a | souvenir sheet of 2 (diamond shaped) | 2.25 | 2.00 | — | 2.40 |
| ai | $24.95 uncut press sheet of 12 souvenir sheets | 85.00 | | | |
| aii | 1708a with additional imprint at bottom, *Jan 28, 1998* | 4.00 | 3.50 | | |

Qty: 13,280,000; 1708a: 2,500,000; 1708aii: 500,000; 1708ai: 30,000

Issued to celebrate Chinese New Year and usher in the lunar year of the Tiger. See also 1630, 1767–1768, 1836–1837, 1883–1884, 1933–1934, 1969–1970, 2015–2016, 2083–2084, 2140–2141, 2201–2202, 2257–2258.

**1708a**

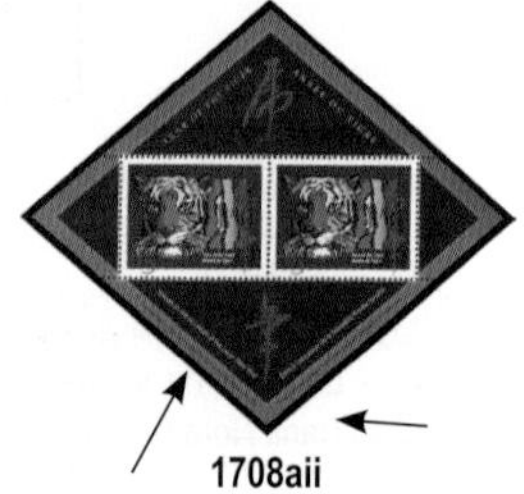

**1708aii**

The additional imprint at the bottom of 1708ii includes information about the printer and illustrators (in English and French).

Definitive Timeline:
**1998, Feb 2** 45 Flag over Building (small size) (1362)

### PROVINCIAL PREMIERS

**1709a**
John P. Robarts (1917–1982)
Ontario

**1709b**
Jean Lesage (1912–1980)
Quebec

**1709c**
John B. McNair (1889–1968)
New Brunswick

**1709d**
Tommy Douglas (1904–1986)
Saskatchewan

**1709e**
Joseph R. Smallwood (1900–1991)
Newfoundland

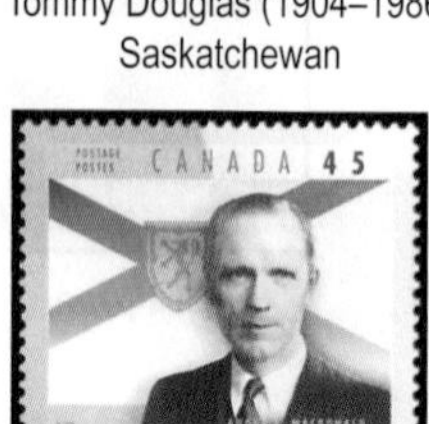

**1709f**
Angus L. MacDonald (1890–1954)
Nova Scotia

**1709g**
W.A.C. Bennett (1900–1979), BC

**1709h**
Ernest C. Manning (1908–1995), AB

**1709i**
John Bracken (1883–1969), MB

**1709j**
Walter Jones (1878–1954), PEI

Designer: Raymond Bellemare. Based on an illustration by Pierre Sasseville.
Jean-Pierre Beaudin photographed the Canadian flag that serves as background to the pane of stamps.

Lithography (5 colours), pane of 10
Canadian Bank Note Company, Limited

**1998, Feb 18** **GT4, TRC Paper** **Perf 13.4x13.3**

| | | NH–VF | ⊙F | FDC |
|---|---|---|---|---|
| **1709** | $4.50 pane of 10 | 15.00 | 12.00 | 10.20* |
| a | **45¢ Robarts (Ontario)** | 1.50 | 1.00 | |
| b | **45¢ Lesage (Quebec)** | 1.50 | 1.00 | |
| c | **45¢ McNair (New Brunswick)** | 1.50 | 1.00 | |
| d | **45¢ Douglas (Saskatchewan)** | 1.50 | 1.00 | |
| e | **45¢ Smallwood (Newfoundland)** | 1.50 | 1.00 | |
| f | **45¢ MacDonald (Nova Scotia)** | 1.50 | 1.00 | |
| g | **45¢ Bennett (British Columbia)** | 1.50 | 1.00 | |
| h | **45¢ Manning (Alberta)** | 1.50 | 1.00 | |
| i | **45¢ Bracken (Manitoba)** | 1.50 | 1.00 | |
| j | **45¢ Jones (Prince Edward Island)** | 1.50 | 1.00 | |

Qty. 1,000,000 of each
*Value shown is for two FDCs: a–e and f–j.

**1709**

## BIRDS OF CANADA — 3

1710 Hairy Woodpecker — 1711 Great Crested Flycatcher

1712 Eastern Screech-Owl — 1713 Gray-crowned Rosy-Finch

Designer: Raymond Bellemare. Based on paintings by Pierre Leduc.
Lithography (5 colours), pane of 20
Canadian Bank Note Company, Limited

**1998, Mar 13** **GT4, TRC Paper** **Perf 13.0x13.3**

| | | NH–VF | ⊙F | PB | FDC |
|---|---|---|---|---|---|
| **1710** | **45¢ multicoloured** | 1.00 | .40 | | |
| **1711** | **45¢ multicoloured** | 1.00 | .40 | | |
| **1712** | **45¢ multicoloured** | 1.00 | .40 | | |
| **1713** | **45¢ multicoloured** | 1.00 | .40 | | |
| a | se-tenant block or strip of 4 different (1710–1713) | 4.50 | 3.50 | 5.00 | 4.50 |
| i | $54.00 uncut press sheet of 6 panes, unsigned | 100.00 | | | |
| | as "i", signed (issue price $89.95) | 200.00 | | | |

Qty: 4,500,000* of each

* Quantity shown is the total issue including 10,000 uncut press sheets of six panes of 20 each; 1,500 of the uncut press sheets were signed and numbered by the artist and designer.

See also 1591–1594, 1631–1634, 1770–1777, 1839–1846, 1886–1893.
For non-denominated envelopes of these designs, see U155–U158; for non-denominated postal cards of nos. 1711–1712, see UX122.

Definitive Timeline:
**1998, Apr 14** 45¢ Stylized Maple Leaf (ATM) (1696)

1714 is not assigned.

### MINT PRICING PREMIUMS

Mint stamps from 301 to date are valued as NH-VF (Never Hinged-Very Fine). All hinged VF and NH-F copies are worth 50% of the listed values. Plate block (PB) values are for mint NH–VF plate or inscription blocks of four.

### USED, VF/XF (with in-period, circular date cancel) PRICING PREMIUM

Single stamps with light or circular date cancels will sell for more than catalogue value (perhaps even more than a mint copy). From *1981 to 1991* single stamps from se-tenant blocks of 4 or larger will be priced at 50% or more above the fine price. From *1992* to date single stamps from se-tenant blocks of 4 or larger plus se-tenant booklet panes and souvenir sheets will be priced at 100% or more above the fine price. From *1997* to date all other stamps will be priced at 50% or more above the fine price.

## FISHING FLIES

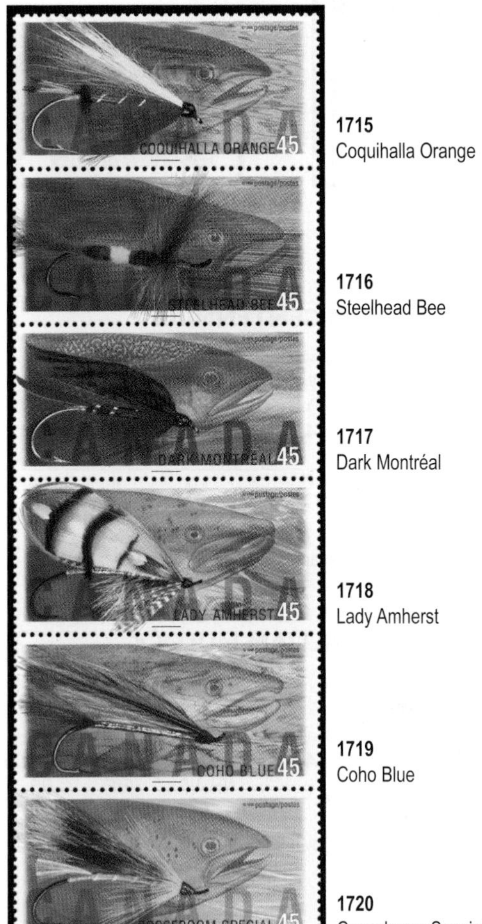

1715 Coquihalla Orange
1716 Steelhead Bee
1717 Dark Montréal
1718 Lady Amherst
1719 Coho Blue
1720 Cosseboom Special

1720a

Designer: Paul-Michael Brunelle. Based on photographs by James Steeves.
Lithography (11 colours), booklet pane of 12
Ashton-Potter Canada Limited

**1998, Apr 16** **GT4, TRC Paper** **Perf 12.5x13.1**

| | | NH–VF | ⊙F | FDC |
|---|---|---|---|---|
| **1715** | **45¢ multicoloured** | 1.25 | .60 | |
| **1716** | **45¢ multicoloured** | 1.25 | .60 | |
| **1717** | **45¢ multicoloured** | 1.25 | .60 | |
| **1718** | **45¢ multicoloured** | 1.25 | .60 | |
| **1719** | **45¢ multicoloured** | 1.25 | .60 | |
| **1720** | **45¢ multicoloured** | 1.25 | .60 | |
| a | se-tenant vertical strip of 6 different (1715–1720) | 7.50 | 6.00 | |
| aii | as "a" without fold, from Canada Post's annual Souvenir Collection, with top or bottom margin | 10.00 | 9.00 | |
| b | booklet pane of 12 (2 each of 1715–1720 in 1 x 12 format) (BK207) | 15.50 | | |
| BK207 | pane 1720b in cover $16.00 | | | |

Qty: 2,000,000 of each

**Nos. 1715–1720 (6) combination FDC (2 FDCs, 3 stamps on each)** 6.60

Issued in celebration of sport fishing in Canada.

For non-denominated envelopes of same designs, see U220–225, U230–235.

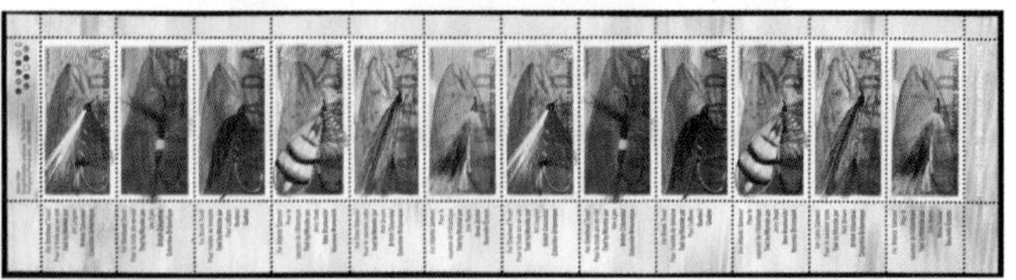

1720b

1721
Oil rig

1722
St. Edward's Crown /
2¢ Imperial Penny Postage /
Sir William Mulock

## CIM CENTENNIAL

Designer: Monique Dufour. Designed by Sophie Lafortune.
Lithography (6 colours), pane of 20
Ashton-Potter Canada Limited

**1998, May 4** **GT4, TRC Paper** **Perf 12.7x12.5**

| | | NH–VF | ⊙F | PB | FDC |
|---|---|---|---|---|---|
| **1721** | **45¢ multicoloured** | 1.00 | .30 | 5.00 | 1.50 |

Qty: 7,000,000

Issued for the centennial of the Canadian Institute of Mining, Metallurgy and Petroleum.

## SIR WILLIAM MULOCK

Designer: François Dallaire. Based on a photograph by William James Topley.
Lithography (6 colours), pane of 14 + central tab
Canadian Bank Note Company, Limited

**1998, May 29** **GT4, TRC Paper** **Perf 12.5x13.1**

| | | NH–VF | ⊙F | PB | FDC |
|---|---|---|---|---|---|
| **1722** | **45¢ multicoloured** | 1.00 | .30 | 5.00 | 1.50 |
| i | single stamp and centre crown tab, se-tenant pair | 2.00 | 1.50 | | |

Qty: 7,000,000

Horizontal or vertical 'gutter' strip of 3 with centre crown tab: $3.50.

Issued for the centennial of the 2¢ Imperial Penny Postage stamp (recognized as the world's first Christmas stamp, see No. 85 and 86) and to honour Sir William Mulock who, as Postmaster General, was instrumental in negotiating the change in the international rate from 5¢ to 2¢.

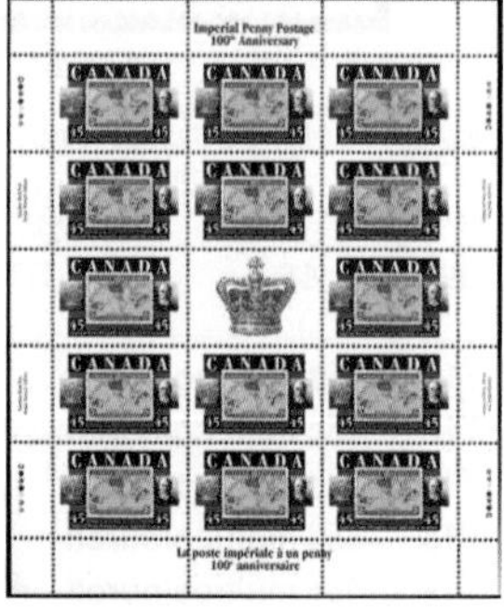

1722
pane

## SUMO CANADA BASHO

1723
Sumo wrestlers in match

1724
Sumo ceremony

Designer: Gerry Takeuchi. Based on an illustration by Stephen Dittberner.
Lithography (6 colours) and Embossed, pane of 20 + 40 tabs
Ashton-Potter Canada Limited

**1998, Jun 5** **GT4, TRC Paper** **Perf 12.5x13.1**

| | | NH–VF | ⊙F | PB | FDC |
|---|---|---|---|---|---|
| **1723** | **45¢ multicoloured** | 1.00 | .35 | | |
| **1724** | **45¢ multicoloured** | 1.00 | .35 | | |
| a | se-tenant horizontal or vertical pair (1723, 1724 *plus* 4 tabs) | 2.50 | 2.00 | 5.00 | |
| b | 90¢ souvenir sheet (1723, 1724) | 5.00 | 5.00 | | |

Qty: 4,250,000 of each; Souvenir sheet: 1,000,000

**Nos. 1723, 1724 (2) combination FDC** **2.40**

Issued in recognition of the first Japanese Sumo Basho tournament in Canada, July 6 and 7, 1998 at Vancouver. Only nine other bashos have ever been held outside Japan.

Nos. 1723 and 1724 were printed checkerwise in panes of 20 with a connecting tab imprinted 'SUMO CANADA BASHO' to the left and a tab imprinted with the Japanese equivalent to the right of each stamp (2 tabs between each pair of stamps). All perforations extend through the printed margins of the pane.

1724b

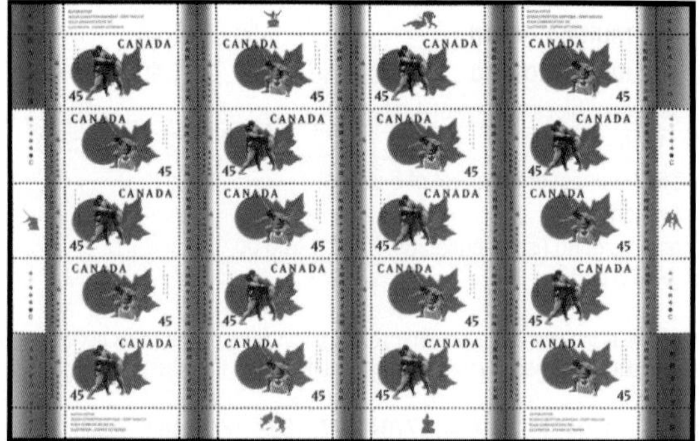

1723–24 pane

## CANALS

1725
St. Peters Canal, Nova Scotia

1726
St. Ours Canal, Quebec

1727
Port Carling Lock, Ontario

1728
Rideau Canal in summer, Ontario

1729
Trent-Severn Waterway, hydraulic lift lock, Ontario

1730
Chambly Canal, Quebec

1731
Lachine Canal, Quebec

1732
Rideau Canal in winter, Ontario

1733
Trent-Severn Waterway, marine railway, Ontario

1734
Sault Ste. Marie Canal, Ontario

Designer: Carey George and Dean Martin. Based on a painting by Vincent McIndoe.

Lithography (10 colours), booklet pane of 10
Ashton-Potter Canada Limited

**1998, Jun 17** **GT4, TRC Paper** **Perf 12.7x12.4**

| | | NH–VF | ⊙F | FDC |
|---|---|---|---|---|
| **1725** | **45¢ multicoloured** | 1.50 | 1.00 | |
| **1726** | **45¢ multicoloured** | 1.50 | 1.00 | |
| **1727** | **45¢ multicoloured** | 1.50 | 1.00 | |
| **1728** | **45¢ multicoloured** | 1.50 | 1.00 | |
| **1729** | **45¢ multicoloured** | 1.50 | 1.00 | |
| **1730** | **45¢ multicoloured** | 1.50 | 1.00 | |
| **1731** | **45¢ multicoloured** | 1.50 | 1.00 | |
| **1732** | **45¢ multicoloured** | 1.50 | 1.00 | |
| **1733** | **45¢ multicoloured** | 1.50 | 1.00 | |
| **1734** | **45¢ multicoloured** | 1.50 | 1.00 | |
| a | booklet pane of 10 x 45¢ (1725–1734) with 2 fold and complete printed borders (BK208)* | 20.00 | | |
| ai | full pane of 10 x 45¢ (1725–1734) with 1 centre fold, from Quarterly Pack/Annual Collection* | 30.00 | | |

**BK208** pane 1734a in cover $25.00
Qty: 1,030,000 of each

**Nos. 1725–1734 (10) combination FDC (2 FDCs, 5 stamps on each)** **10.20**

* The booklet pane issued at post offices has 2 folds (between stamps 4 and 5, and 8 and 9). A full pane with 1 centre fold, without the cover, was included in the Quarterly Pack and 1998 Annual Collection.

1734a

## HEALTH PROFESSIONALS

1735
Aesculapian Staff and medical cross

Designer: Pierre-Yves Pelletier

Lithography (2 colours) and Embossed with 3 foil stampings, pane of 16
Ashton-Potter Canada Limited and Gravure Choquet Inc.

**1998, Jun 25** **FCP, TRC Paper** **Perf 12.5**

| | | NH–VF | ⊙F | PB | FDC |
|---|---|---|---|---|---|
| **1735** | **45¢ multicoloured**, dull phosphor | .90 | .30 | 4.50 | 1.50 |
| i | bright phosphor | 3.00 | 1.00 | 15.00 | |

Qty: 7,000,000

Issued in honour of all Canada health professionals.

## RCMP — 125th ANNIVERSARY

1736
Historic view with mountie in old uniform

1737
Modern view with helicopter and computer operator

Designer: Robert L. Peters, Catharine Brandy, 'Segun Olude, and Susan McWatt.
Based on photographs by John McQuarrie, Brian Gould, Mike Pinder, Royal Canadian Mounted Police, and First Light.

Lithography (6 colours) and Embossed with foil stamping, pane of 20 + 25 tabs
Ashton-Potter Canada Limited

**1998, Jul 3** **GT4, TRC Paper** **Perf 12.5x13.1**

| | | NH–VF | ⊙F | PB | FDC |
|---|---|---|---|---|---|
| **1736** | **45¢ multicoloured** | .90 | .35 | | |
| **1737** | **45¢ multicoloured** | .90 | .35 | | |
| a | horizontal pair with RCMP badge or musical ride on connecting tab | 2.00 | 1.50 | 4.00 | |
| b | 90¢ souvenir sheet | 2.00 | 2.00 | | |
| c | 1737b with Lt. Col. G.A. French signature (*Jul 3, 1998*)† | 4.00 | 4.00 | | |
| d | 1737b with Portugal '98 emblem (*Sep 4, 1998*) | 6.00 | 6.00 | | |
| e | 1737b with Italia '98 emblem (*Oct 23, 1998*) | 6.00 | 6.00 | | |
| f | as "d", gold embossed emblem omitted | 1,000.00 | | | |
| i | $24.95 uncut press sheet of 10 souvenir sheets | 75.00 | | | |

Qty: 6,500,000 of each; Souvenir sheet: 3,000,000*; 1737c: 275,000; 1737d and e: 200,000 each; 1736–37i: 25,000

**Nos. 1736, 1737 (2) combination FDC** **2.40**

* Quantity includes 25,000 uncut press sheets of 10 souvenir sheets each.
† Lt. Col. G.A. French was the first commissioner of the RCMP.
Issued to celebrate the 125th anniversary of the RCMP.

1737a (2nd type)

1736–37 pane

1737b

1737c

1737d

1737e

1737f

## WILLIAM JAMES ROUÉ

1738
W.J. Roué (1879–1970) and the *Bluenose*

Designer: Louis C. Hébert.

Lithography (5 colours) and Engraved (1 colour), pane of 25
Canadian Bank Note Company, Limited

| 1998, Jul 24 | GT4, Peterborough Paper | | | Perf 13.0 |
|---|---|---|---|---|
| | NH–VF | ⊙F | PB | FDC |
| **1738 45¢ multicoloured** | 1.00 | .30 | 5.00 | 1.50 |

Qty: 9,000,000

Issued in recognition of William James Roué, the Naval Architect who designed the famous schooner *Bluenose*.

See also 158, 913, 1228.

## SCENIC HIGHWAYS — 2

1739
Dempster Highway, Yukon

1740
Dinosaur Trail, Alberta

1741
River Valley Scenic Drive, New Brunswick

1742
Blue Heron Scenic Route, PEI

Designer: Lou Cable.

Lithography (6 colours), pane of 20
Ashton-Potter Canada Limited

| 1998, Jul 28 | | GT4, TRC Paper | | Perf 12.5x13.1 | |
|---|---|---|---|---|---|
| | | NH–VF | ⊙F | PB | FDC |
| **1739** | **45¢ multicoloured** | .90 | .50 | | |
| **1740** | **45¢ multicoloured** | .90 | .50 | | |
| **1741** | **45¢ multicoloured** | .90 | .50 | | |
| **1742** | **45¢ multicoloured** | .90 | .50 | | |
| **a** | se-tenant block or strip of 4 different (1739–1742) | 4.00 | 3.25 | 4.50 | 4.20 |

Qty: 2,000,000 of each

See also 1650–1653 and 1780–1783.

## THE AUTOMATISTES

1743
*Peinture*,
by Jean-Paul Riopelle,
1947–1948

1744
*La dernière campagne de Napoléon*,
by Fernand Leduc, 1946

1745
*Jet fuligineux sur noir torturé*,
by Jean-Paul Mousseau, 1949

1746
*Le Fond du garde-robe*,
by Pierre Gauvreau, 1950

**1747**
*Joie lacustre,*
by Paul-Émile Borduas, 1948

**1748**
*Syndicat des gens de mer,*
by Marcelle Ferron, 1954

**1749**
*Le tumulte à la mâchoire crispée,*
by Marcel Barbeau, 1946

Designer: Raymond Bellemare.
Lithography (5 colours), self-adhesive booklet pane of 7
Canadian Bank Note Company, Limited

| 1998, Aug 7 | GT4, TRC Paper | | | Die cut |
|---|---|---|---|---|
| | | NH–VF | ⊙F | FDC |
| **1743** | **45¢ multicoloured** | 1.50 | 1.50 | |
| **1744** | **45¢ multicoloured** | 1.50 | 1.50 | |
| **1745** | **45¢ multicoloured** | 1.50 | 1.50 | |
| **1746** | **45¢ multicoloured** | 1.50 | 1.50 | |
| **1747** | **45¢ multicoloured** | 1.50 | 1.50 | |
| **1748** | **45¢ multicoloured** | 1.50 | 1.50 | |
| **1749** | **45¢ multicoloured** | 1.50 | 1.50 | |
| a | booklet pane of 7 (1743–1749) (**BK209**) | 11.00 | — | |

Qty: 1,000,000 of each

| | |
|---|---|
| **Nos: 1743–1746 (4) combination FDC** | **4.20** |
| **Nos: 1747-1749 (3) combination FDC** | **3.30** |

**1749a**

## LEGENDARY CANADIANS

**1750**
Napoléon-Alexandre Comeau
(1848–1923)

**1751**
Phyllis Munday
(1894–1990)

**1752**
Bill Mason
(1929–1988)

**1753**
Harry "Red" Foster
(1905–1985)

Designer: Catharine Bradbury. Based on an illustration by Dean Bartsch.
Lithography (10 colours), pane of 20
Canadian Bank Note Company, Limited

| 1998, Aug 15 | GT4, TRC Paper | | | Perf 13.4x13.3 | |
|---|---|---|---|---|---|
| | | NH–VF | ⊙F | PB | FDC |
| **1750** | **45¢ multicoloured** | .90 | .35 | | |
| **1751** | **45¢ multicoloured** | .90 | .35 | | |
| **1752** | **45¢ multicoloured** | .90 | .35 | | |
| **1753** | **45¢ multicoloured** | .90 | .35 | | |
| **a** | se-tenant block or strip of 4 different (1750–1753) | 4.00 | 3.50 | 4.50 | 4.20 |

Qty: 2,000,000 of each

## MASTERPIECES OF CANADIAN ART — 11

**1754**
*The Farmer's Family* (detail)

Designer: Pierre-Yves Pelletier. Based on a painting by Brunislaw Jacob Bobak.
Lithography (5 colours) with foil stamping, pane of 16
Ashton-Potter Canada Limited

| 1998, Sep 8 | TRC Paper | | | Perf 12.5x13.3 | |
|---|---|---|---|---|---|
| | | NH–VF | ⊙F | PB | FDC |
| **1754** | **90¢ multicoloured** (silver) | 2.00 | 1.25 | 9.00 | 2.50 |

Qty: 7,000,000

See also 1203, 1241, 1271, 1310, 1419, 1466, 1516, 1545, 1602, 1635, 1800, 1863, 1916, 1945.

QE II — 1990's

## HOUSING IN CANADA

1755a
Native Peoples

1755b
Settler

1755c
Regional

1755d
Heritage preservation

1755e
Multiple unit

1755f
Prefabricated

1755g
Veterans'

1755h
Planned community

1755i
Innovative

1755

Designer: Peter D.K. Scott, Renata Chubb, and Glenda Rissman.
Lithography (11 colours), pane of 9
Ashton-Potter Canada Limited

**1998, Sep 23** **GT4, TRC Paper** **Perf 12.5x13.1**

| | | NH–VF | ⊙F | FDC |
|---|---|---|---|---|
| **1755** | $4.05 pane of 9 different with full descriptive tabs at left and right | 15.00 | 15.00 | 9.90* |
| a | **45¢ multicoloured** | 1.50 | 1.50 | |
| b | **45¢ multicoloured** | 1.50 | 1.50 | |
| c | **45¢ multicoloured** | 1.50 | 1.50 | |
| d | **45¢ multicoloured** | 1.50 | 1.50 | |
| e | **45¢ multicoloured** | 1.50 | 1.50 | |
| f | **45¢ multicoloured** | 1.50 | 1.50 | |
| g | **45¢ multicoloured** | 1.50 | 1.50 | |
| h | **45¢ multicoloured** | 1.50 | 1.50 | |
| i | **45¢ multicoloured** | 1.50 | 1.50 | |

Qty: 1,000,000 of each

*Three FDCs: a, b, c; d, e, f and g, h, i.

## UNIVERSITY OF OTTAWA

1756
Tabaret Hall

Designer: Julia Harris and Clementina Koppman.
Based on a photograph by Michael Rafelson.
Lithography (6 colours), pane of 20
Canadian Bank Note Company, Limited

**1998, Sep 25** **GT4, TRC Paper** **Perf 13.3**

| | NH–VF | ⊙F | PB | FDC |
|---|---|---|---|---|
| **1756 45¢ multicoloured** | .90 | .30 | 4.50 | 1.50 |

Qty: 7,000,000

Issued to celebrate the sesquicentennial of the University of Ottawa.
For other University issues see 1941–1944, 1973–1977, 2033–2034, 2089, 2172, 2209–2210.

Definitive Timeline:
**1998, Sep 30** 45¢ Stylized Maple Leaf coil (1697)

## THE CIRCUS

1757 Clown / Animal acts — 1758 Clown / Equestrian acts

1759 Clown / Lion tamer — 1760 Clown / Acrobats

Designer: Sophie Lafortune and Monique Dufour.
Based on a painting by Paule Thibault. Based on a photograph by Daniel Ouellette.
Lithography (7 colours), booklet pane of 12
Ashton-Potter Canada Limited

**1998, Oct 1** — **GT4, TRC Paper** — **Perf 13.1x13.0**

| | | NH–VF | ⊙F | FDC |
|---|---|---|---|---|
| **1757** | **45¢ multicoloured** | .90 | .40 | |
| i | single from souvenir sheet (1760b)† | 1.25 | .90 | |
| **1758** | **45¢ multicoloured** | .90 | .40 | |
| i | single from souvenir sheet (1760b)† | 1.25 | .90 | |
| **1759** | **45¢ multicoloured** | .90 | .40 | |
| i | single from souvenir sheet (1760b)† | 1.25 | .90 | |
| **1760** | **45¢ multicoloured** | .90 | .40 | |
| i | single from souvenir sheet (1760b)† | 1.25 | .90 | |
| a | booklet pane of 12 x 45¢ (3 each of 1757–1760) (BK210) | 14.00 | 16.00 | |
| ai | se-tenant block or strip of 4 different (1757–1760) | 4.00 | 3.50 | |
| b | $1.80 souvenir sheet of 4 different | 6.00 | 5.00 | — |
| BK210 | pane 1760a in cover $14.50 | | | |

Qty: 2,680,000 of each; souvenir sheet: 625,000

**Nos. 1757–1760 (4) combination FDC** 4.20

The booklet pane does not produce identical pairs.
† Singles from souvenir sheet are perforated on all four sides; singles from the booklet have a straight edge on either the top or bottom.

1760b

1760a

## JOHN PETERS HUMPHREY

1761
John Humphrey (1905–1995) and page from the Universal Declaration of Human Rights

Designer: Jim Hudson. Based on a photographs by Rod Stears and McGill University Archives.
Lithography (6 colours), pane of 20
Canadian Bank Note Company, Limited

**1998, Oct 7** — **GT4, TRC Paper** — **Perf 13.0x13.3**

| | | NH–VF | ⊙F | PB | FDC |
|---|---|---|---|---|---|
| **1761** | **45¢ multicoloured** | .90 | .30 | 4.50 | 1.50 |

Qty: 7,000,000

Issued to mark the 50th anniversary of the Universal Declaration of Human Rights and to honour its Canadian author, John Peters Humphrey.

Definitive Timeline:
1998, Oct 27 $1 Loon (1687)
$2 Polar Bear (1690)

## CANADIAN NAVAL RESERVE

1762
HMCS Sackville

1763
HMCS Shawinigan

Designer: Dennis George Page. Based on an illustration by Todd Hawkins.
Lithography (6 colours), pane of 20
Canadian Bank Note Company, Limited

**1998, Nov 4** — **GT4, TRC Paper** — **Perf 12.5x13.1**

| | | NH–VF | ⊙F | PB | FDC |
|---|---|---|---|---|---|
| **1762** | **45¢ multicoloured** | 1.00 | .35 | | |
| **1763** | **45¢ multicoloured** | 1.00 | .35 | | |
| a | se-tenant pair (1762, 1763) | 2.25 | 2.00 | 4.50 | 2.50 |

Qty: 3,750,000 of each

Issued to commemorate the 75th anniversary of the Canadian Naval Reserve.

## CHRISTMAS — ANGELS

1764 Angel of the Last Judgement | 1765 Adoring Angel | 1766 Praying Angel

Designer: Anita Zeppetelli.

Lithography (5 colours), panes of 50
Ashton-Potter Canada Limited

**1998, Nov 6** **GT4, TRC Paper** **Perf 13.1**

| No. | Description | NH–VF | ⊙F | PB | FDC |
|---|---|---|---|---|---|
| **1764** | **45¢ multicoloured** (blue) | 1.00 | .25 | 5.00 | |
| a | booklet pane of 10 x 45¢ (1764as) (BK211) | 45.00 | 45.00 | — | |
| ai | as "a", with 'missing sunbeam' † | 75.00 | | | |
| as | single with straight edge, from 1764a | 5.00 | 3.00 | | |
| asi | as "as", 'missing sunbeam' † | 20.00 | 10.00 | | |
| BK211 | pane 1764a in cover $50.00 | | | | |
| | **Perf 13.1x13.6** | | | | |
| b | sheet stamp, perf change* | 500.00 | 15.00 | 2,500.00 | |
| c | booklet pane of 10 x 45¢ (1764cs) (BK211A) | 18.00 | 15.00 | — | |
| ci | as "c", with 'missing sunbeam' † | 30.00 | | | |
| cs | single with straight edge, from 1764c | 2.00 | .35 | | |
| csi | as "cs", 'missing sunbeam' † | 5.00 | 2.50 | | |
| BK211A | pane 1764ai in cover $20.00 | | | | |

Qty: 39,306,000

* Approximately 500 mint copies known; must have perforations all around (straight edged copies are 1764cs); plate blocks are very rare. One used plate block of the rare perf, on cover, is known to the editors. Value is 'at least' the value of a mint plate block.

† 'Missing sunbeam' variety is from bottom two stamps of some booklet panes. Some panes may have either the left or right stamp showing the variety, both stamps showing the variety, or neither. Price of pane is for variety occurring once; add 50% for a pane with two varieties.

| No. | Description | NH–VF | ⊙F | PB | FDC |
|---|---|---|---|---|---|
| | **Perf 13.1x13.6** | | | | |
| **1765** | **52¢ multicoloured** (reddish) | 1.05 | .60 | 5.25 | |
| a | booklet pane of 5 x 52¢ (1765as) + label (BK212A) | 30.00 | 30.00 | | |
| as | single with straight edge, from 1765a | 5.00 | 5.00 | | |
| BK212A | pane 1765a in cover $25.00 | | | | |
| | **Perf 13.1** | | | | |
| b | single with straight edge, from 1765c | 1.50 | .75 | | |
| c | booklet pane of 5 x 52¢ (1765b) + label (BK212) | 7.50 | 6.50 | | |
| BK212 | pane 1765c in cover $8.00 | | | | |

Qty: 9,601,000

| No. | Description | NH–VF | ⊙F | PB | FDC |
|---|---|---|---|---|---|
| | **Perf 13.1x13.6** | | | | |
| **1766** | **90¢ multicoloured** (green) | 2.00 | 1.00 | 10.00 | |
| ii | diagonal scratch under 'c' (pos. 41) | 7.50 | 3.50 | 15.00 (LL) | |
| a | booklet pane of 5 x 90¢ + label (1766as) (BK213A) | 50.00 | 50.00 | | |
| as | single with straight edge, from 1766a | 8.00 | 7.00 | | |
| BK213A | pane 1766a in cover $40.00 | | | | |
| | **Perf 13.1** | | | | |
| b | single with straight edge, from 1766c | 2.00 | 1.00 | | |
| c | booklet pane of 5 x 90¢ (1766b) + label (BK213) | 10.00 | 9.00 | | |
| BK213 | pane 1766c in cover $11.00 | | | | |

Qty: 9,601,000

**Nos. 1764–1766 (3) combination FDC** 4.35

1764a

1765a 1766a

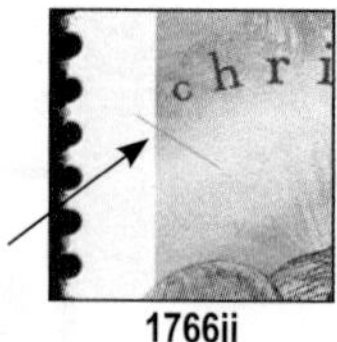

1766ii

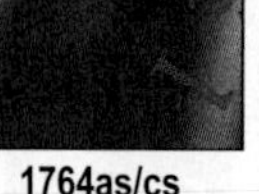

1764as/cs Normal | 1764asi/csi Missing sunbeam

Canada Post's stamp announcement booklet ("Canada's Stamp Details") changed from a 6"x11" size to the now familiar 8½"x11" size with the 46¢-era rate change definitives.

Definitive Timeline:

**1998, Dec 28**
46¢ Queen Elizabeth II (1681)
46¢ Flag over Iceberg (1682, 1698)
55/73/95¢ Stylized Maple Leaf (1684/1685/1686)
46¢ Flag coil (1695)
46¢ Stylized Maple Leaf ATM (1699)

## 1999

**Rates:** Jan 1/99– Dec 31/00
- Domestic first-class (0-30g): 46¢
- Domestic first-class (30-50g): 73¢
- Domestic oversize (30-50g): 92¢
- USA (0-30g): 55¢
- International (0-20g): 95¢

*single usage:* USA 55¢: $15.00 | International 95¢: $20.00

## LUNAR NEW YEAR — 3
### Year of the Rabbit

1767 Rabbit and Chinese Symbol

1768a Rabbit and Chinese Symbol

Designer: Ken Fung. Based on an illustration by Ken Koo. Calligraphed by Quint Li.
Lithography (7 colours), pane of 25
Ashton-Potter Canada Limited

**1999, Jan 8** **GT4, TRC Paper** **Perf 13.5x13.7**

| | | NH–VF | ⊙F | PB | FDC |
|---|---|---|---|---|---|
| **1767** | **46¢ multicoloured** | 1.00 | .30 | 4.50 | 2.00 |
| a | missing red and untagged | 1,250.00 | | | |

Qty: 13,280,000

**Perf 12.5x13.1**

| | | NH–VF | ⊙F | PB | FDC |
|---|---|---|---|---|---|
| **1768** | **95¢ souvenir sheet** | 3.00 | 2.75 | | 3.00* |
| a | single 95¢ Year of the Rabbit | 2.00 | 1.75 | — | |
| i | 1768 with China '99 logo in top of pane just above stamp† | 3.00 | 3.00 | — | |
| ii | $24.95 uncut press sheet of 12 souvenir sheets | 75.00 | | | |
| b | No. 1768 missing red and untagged | 1,250.00 | | | |
| v | No. 1768i missing red and untagged | *3,000.00* | | | |

Qty: 2,575,000; 1768i: 425,000; 1768ii: 30,000
Qty recorded: 1767i: 100; 1768b: 25; 1768v: 3 known

* Souvenir sheet on cover.
† The world philatelic exhibition taking place in August 1999, in Beijing.

See also 1630, 1708, 1836–1837, 1883–1884, 1933–1934, 1969–1970, 2015–2016, 2083–2084, 2140–2141, 2201–2202, 2257–2258.

1768 1768i 1768v

## LE THÉÂTRE DU RIDEAU VERT

1769
The masks of Tragedy and Comedy, with the profiles of the theatre's co-founders superimposed

Designer: Yves Paquin. Designed by Marie Rouleau.
Lithography (5 colours), pane of 16
Canadian Bank Note Company, Limited

**1999, Feb 17** **GT4, TRC Paper** **Perf 13.1x12.5**

| | | NH–VF | ⊙F | PB | FDC |
|---|---|---|---|---|---|
| **1769** | **46¢ multicoloured** | .90 | .30 | 4.50 | 1.50 |

Qty: 6,000,000

Issued for the 50th anniversary of Le Théâtre du Rideau Vert, Canada's first professional French theatre company, in Montreal. The company was founded by Mercedes Palomino and Yvette Brind'Amour.

## BIRDS OF CANADA — 4a

*Perforated singles from water-activated gum pane*

1770 Northern Goshawk
1771 Red-winged blackbird

1772 American goldfinch
1773 Sandhill crane

## BIRDS OF CANADA — 4b

*Die cut singles from self-adhesive booklet*

1774
Northern Goshawk

1775
Red-winged blackbird

1776
American goldfinch

1777
Sandhill crane

Designer: Raymond Bellemare. Based on paintings by Pierre Leduc.
Lithography (5 colours), water-activated gum pane of 20
Ashton-Potter Canada Limited

**1999, Feb 24** **GT4, TRC Paper** **Perf 12.5x13.1**

| | | NH–VF | ⊙F | PB | FDC |
|---|---|---|---|---|---|
| **1770** | **46¢ multicoloured** | .90 | .35 | | |
| **1771** | **46¢ multicoloured** | .90 | .35 | | |
| **1772** | **46¢ multicoloured** | .90 | .35 | | |
| **1773** | **46¢ multicoloured** | .90 | .35 | | |
| a | se-tenant block or strip of 4 different (1770–1773) | 4.00 | 2.00 | 4.50 | 4.30 |
| i | $55.20 uncut press sheet of 6 panes, unsigned | 100.00 | | | |
| | as "i", signed (issue price $89.95) | 150.00 | | | |

Qty: 3,495,000 of each; 1773i: 5,000, signed: 1,500

Lithography, self-adhesive booklet of 12
Ashton-Potter Canada Limited

**1999, Feb 24** **GT4, JAC Paper** **Die cut 11.7x11.3**

| | | NH–VF | ⊙F | FDC |
|---|---|---|---|---|
| **1774** | **46¢ multicoloured** | 1.25 | .50 | |
| **1775** | **46¢ multicoloured** | 1.25 | .50 | |
| **1776** | **46¢ multicoloured** | 1.25 | .50 | |
| **1777** | **46¢ multicoloured** | 1.25 | .50 | |

| | | NH–VF | ⊙F | FDC |
|---|---|---|---|---|
| a | booklet pane of 6 x 46¢ (1776, 1777 + 2 each of 1774, 1775) | 8.00 | — | |
| b | booklet pane of 6 x 46¢ (1774, 1775 + 2 each of 1776, 1777) | 8.00 | — | |

**BK218** one each of panes 1777a, 1777b $16.50
Qty:

See 1770–1773 for water-activated gum versions of these designs.

See also 1591–1594, 1631–1634, 1710–1713, 1770–1773, 1839–1846, 1886–1893. For non-denominated envelope of no. 1772 design, see U168.

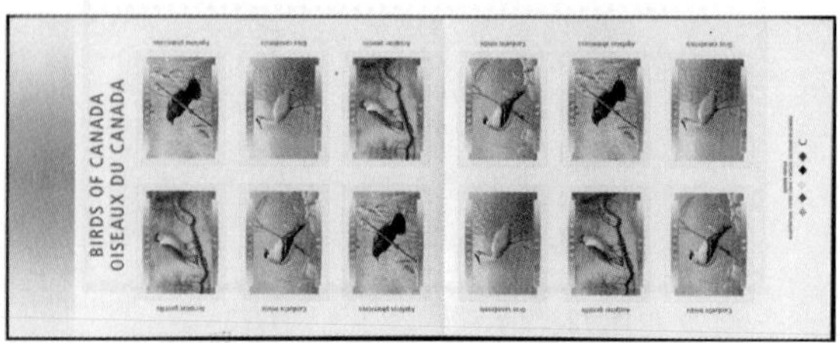


**1777a** (top half) **1777b** (bottom half)

## UBC MUSEUM OF ANTHROPOLOGY

**1778**
The Raven and the First Men and the MOA

Designer: Barbara Hodgson. Based on a sculpture by William Ronald Reid. Based on a photographs by William McLennan and Jacqueline Gijssen.
Lithography (6 colours), pane of 16
Canadian Bank Note Company, Limited

**1999, Mar 9** **GT4, TRC Paper** **Perf 13.3**

| | | NH–VF | ⊙F | PB | FDC |
|---|---|---|---|---|---|
| **1778** | **46¢ multicoloured** | .90 | .30 | 4.50 | 1.50 |

Qty: 6,000,000

## SAILING SHIP MARCO POLO

**1779**
The *Marco Polo* under full sail

Designer: A. Lee Sackett. Based on a painting by J. Franklin Wright.
Lithography (6 colours), pane of 16
Ashton-Potter Canada Limited

**1999, Mar 19** **GT4, TRC Paper** **Perf 13.1x12.5**

| | | NH–VF | ⊙F | PB | FDC |
|---|---|---|---|---|---|
| **1779** | **46¢ multicoloured** | 1.00 | .30 | 4.50 | 1.50 |
| a | $1.25 souvenir sheet † | 3.50 | 3.50 | | 3.10 |
| b | single 46¢ from souvenir sheet (1779a), perf 13.1x13.0 | 2.50 | 2.50 | | |

Qty: 16,000,000; Souvenir sheet (1779a): 500,000

† The souvenir sheet (joint issue between Canada and Australia) features the Canadian 46¢ Marco Polo issue and the Australian 85¢ Marco Polo stamp (sold for $1.25 by Canada Post). See Australia No. 1631a.

Souvenir sheet used in Canada and in Australia (proper dual usage in period) $25.00

**1779a**

## SCENIC HIGHWAYS — 3

**1780** Gaspé Peninsula, Highway 132, Quebec
**1781** Yellowhead Highway (PTH16), Manitoba

**1782** Dempster Highway 8, Northwest Territories
**1783** Discovery Trail, Route 230N, Newfoundland

Designer: Lou Cable. Based on a photograph by Peter Timmermans.
Lithography (6 colours), pane of 20
Ashton-Potter Canada Limited

**1999, Mar 31** **GT4, TRC Paper** **Perf 12.5x13.1**

| | | NH–VF | ⊙F | PB | FDC |
|---|---|---|---|---|---|
| **1780** | **46¢ multicoloured** | .90 | .50 | | |
| **1781** | **46¢ multicoloured** | .90 | .50 | | |
| **1782** | **46¢ multicoloured** | .90 | .50 | | |
| **1783** | **46¢ multicoloured** | .90 | .50 | | |
| a | se-tenant block or strip of 4 different (1780–1783) | 4.00 | 3.50 | 4.50 | 4.30 |

Qty: 2,500,000 of each

See also 1650–1653 and 1739–1742.

## CREATION OF NUNAVUT TERRITORY

**1784**
Inuit faces and landscape

Designer: Bonne Zabolotney. Based on a painting by Susan Point.
Lithography (6 colours), pane of 20
Ashton-Potter Canada Limited

| 1999, Apr 1 | GT4, TRC Paper | | Perf 12.5x13.1 | |
|---|---|---|---|---|
| | NH–VF | ⊙F | PB | FDC |
| **1784 46¢ multicoloured**<br>Qty: 7,000,000 | .90 | .30 | 4.50 | 1.50 |

Issued to celebrate the creation of Nunavut Territory, the largest aboriginal land claim agreement in Canadian history.

## INTERNATIONAL YEAR OF OLDER PERSONS

**1785**
Older couple on path of life

Designer: Paul Hodgson. Based on an illustration by Shelagh Armstrong.
Lithography (6 colours), pane of 16
Canadian Bank Note Company, Limited

| 1999, Apr 12 | GT4, TRC Paper | | Perf 13.3x13.4 | |
|---|---|---|---|---|
| | NH–VF | ⊙F | PB | FDC |
| **1785 46¢ multicoloured**<br>Qty: 8,000,000 | .90 | .30 | 5.00 | 2.00 |

## SIKH CANADIANS

**1786**
The Khanda

Designer: Stacey Zabolotney.
Lithography (5 colours), pane of 16
Canadian Bank Note Company, Limited

| 1999, Apr 19 | GT4, TRC Paper | | Perf 13.1x13.0 | |
|---|---|---|---|---|
| | NH–VF | ⊙F | PB | FDC |
| **1786 46¢ multicoloured**<br>Qty: 3,000,000 | 2.50 | .50 | 10.00 | 2.50 |

Issued to celebrate the 300th anniversary of Baisakhi, considered the Sikh New Year.

## CANADIAN ORCHIDS

**1787**
Dragon's Mouth,
*Arethusa bulbosa*

**1788**
Small round-leaved orchid,
*Amerorchis rotundifolia*

**1789**
Small purple-fringed orchid,
*Platanthera psycodes*

**1790**
Greater Yellow Lady's Slipper,
*Cypripedium pubescens*

Designer: Marlene Wou.
Lithography (7 colours), booklet pane of 12
Ashton-Potter Canada Limited

| 1999, Apr 27 | GT4, TRC Paper | | Perf 13.1x12.5 | |
|---|---|---|---|---|
| | | NH–VF | ⊙F | FDC |
| **1787** | **46¢ multicoloured**, (pos. 1, 9; s/s) | 1.25 | .40 | |
| i | stem extends through bottom perfs (pos. 11) | 3.50 | 1.00 | |
| **1788** | **46¢ multicoloured**, (pos. 2, 6; s/s) | 1.25 | .40 | |
| i | stem extends through bottom perfs (pos. 10) | 3.50 | 1.00 | |
| **1789** | **46¢ multicoloured**, left leaf extends through left perfs (pos. 4) | 1.25 | .40 | |
| i | design stops short on all four sides (pos. 8) | 1.25 | .40 | |
| ii | stem extends through bottom perfs (pos. 12) | 1.25 | .40 | |
| iii | left leaves extend through left perfs and stem extends through bottom perfs (s/s) | 2.50 | 1.00 | |
| **1790** | **46¢ multicoloured**, right leaf extends through right perfs (pos. 3, s/s) | 1.25 | .40 | |
| i | design stops short on all four sides (pos. 5) | 1.25 | .40 | |
| ii | left leaf extends through left perfs (pos. 7) | 1.25 | .40 | |
| iii | se-tenant block or strip of 4 (1787–1790) | 5.00 | 4.00 | 5.00 |
| a | booklet pane of 12 (3 each of 1787–1790) (BK219) | 15.50 | — | — |
| b | $1.84 souvenir sheet of 4 different, *Aug 21,1999* | 5.00 | 5.00 | — |
| BK219 | pane 1790a in cover $16.00 | | | |

Issued for the World Orchid Conference, held in Canada for the first time in 1999 at Vancouver, April 27–May 2. The stamp subjects are from paintings by Poon-Kuen Chow (1787, 1790) and Yukman Lai (1788, 1789).

For non-denominated envelopes of same designs, see U212–219.

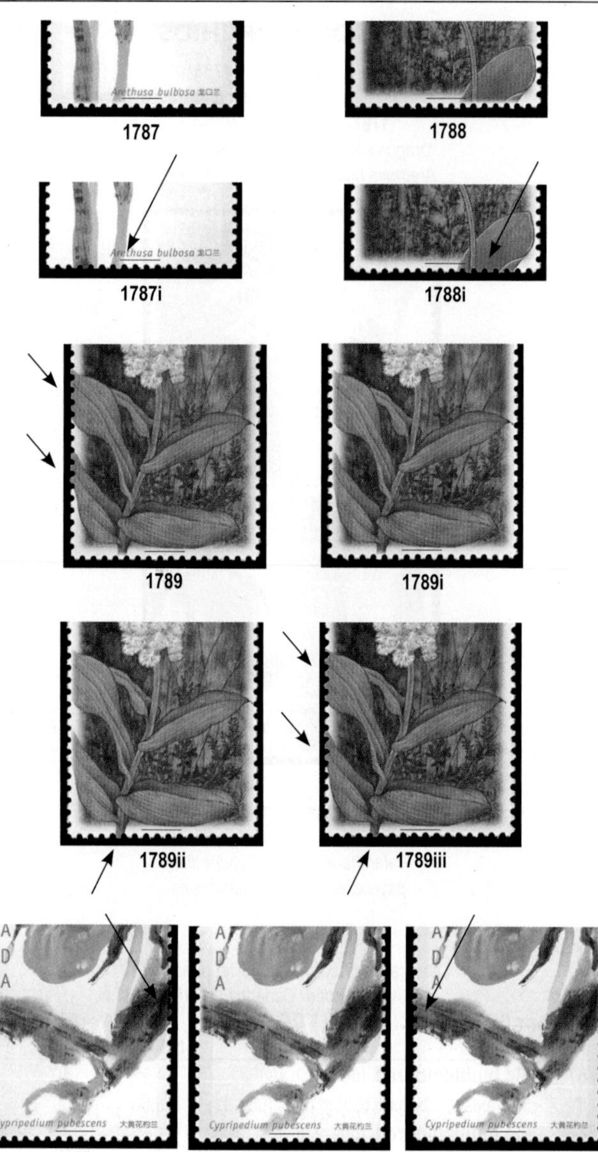

1787 1788

1787i 1788i

1789 1789i

1789ii 1789iii

1790 1790i 1790ii

1790a

1790b

Definitive Timeline:

1999, Apr 29 1–25¢ Low-value Trades definitives (1673–1680)

## CANADIAN HORSES

*Perforated singles from water-activated gum pane*

1791 Northern Dancer — 1792 Kingsway Skoal

1793 Big Ben — 1794 Armbro Flight

*Die cut singles from self-adhesive booklet*

1795 Northern Dancer

1796 Kingsway Skoal

1797 Big Ben

1798 Armbro Flight

Designer: Pierre-Yves Pelletier.

Lithography (5 colours), water-activated gum pane of 16
Ashton-Potter Canada Limited

| **1999, Jun 2** | **GT4, TRC Paper** | **Perf 13.0x13.4** | | | |
|---|---|---|---|---|---|
| | | **NH–VF** | **⊙F** | **PB** | **FDC** |
| **1791** | **46¢ multicoloured** | 1.25 | .50 | | |
| **1792** | **46¢ multicoloured** | 1.25 | .50 | | |
| **1793** | **46¢ multicoloured** | 1.25 | .50 | | |
| **1794** | **46¢ multicoloured** | 1.25 | .50 | | |
| **a** | se-tenant block or horizontal strip of 4 (1791–1794) | 5.00 | 4.00 | 6.25 | 5.00 |

Qty: 1,500,000 of each

Lithography (5 colours), Sheets of 96 subjects in 8 self-adhesive booklet panes of 12
Ashton-Potter Canada Limited

| **1999, Jun 2** | **GT4, JAC Paper** | **Serpentine die cut 11.5x11.1** | | |
|---|---|---|---|---|
| | | **NH–VF** | **⊙F** | **FDC** |
| **1795** | **46¢ multicoloured** | 1.50 | .40 | |
| **i** | pink cloud in trees | 5.00 | 2.50 | |
| **1796** | **46¢ multicoloured** | 1.50 | .40 | |
| **1797** | **46¢ multicoloured** | 1.50 | .40 | |
| **1798** | **46¢ multicoloured** | 1.50 | .40 | |
| **a** | block of 4 (1795–1798) | 6.00 | | |
| b | booklet pane of 12 (3 each of 1795–1798) (**BK220**) | 19.00 | | |

Qty: 3,000,000 of each

1795i

1798b

## QUEBEC BAR ASSOCIATION

1799
Quebec Bar Association Logo

Designer: Pierre Fontaine. Based on a sculpture by Morton Rosengarten.
Based on a photograph by Jean-Pierre Beaudin.

Lithography (5 colours), pane of 16
Canadian Bank Note Company, Limited

**1999, Jun 3** **GT4, TRC Paper** **Perf 13.3**

| | | NH–VF | ⊙F | PB | FDC |
|---|---|---|---|---|---|
| **1799** | **46¢ multicoloured** | .90 | .30 | 4.50 | 1.50 |

Qty: 6,000,000

Issued to honour the 150-year history of the Quebec Bar Association.

## MASTERPIECES OF CANADIAN ART — 12

1800
*Coq licorne*

Designer: Pierre-Yves Pelletier. Based on a painting by Jean Dallaire.

Lithography (5 colours) with foil stamping, pane of 16
Ashton-Potter Canada Limited

**1999, Jul 3** **TRC Paper** **Perf 12.5x13.3**

| | | NH–VF | ⊙F | PB | FDC |
|---|---|---|---|---|---|
| **1800** | **95¢ multicoloured** (silver) | 2.00 | 1.50 | 10.00 | 2.50 |
| **a** | silver (border) omitted* | 1,750.00 | | | |

Qty: 6,000,000
* One pane of 16 recorded.

See also 1203, 1241, 1271, 1310, 1419, 1466, 1516, 1545, 1602, 1635, 1754, 1863, 1916, 1945.

## PAN AMERICAN GAMES

1801 Track and Field — 1802 Cycling

1803 Swimming — 1804 Soccer

Designer: Robert L. Peters, Catharine Brandy, 'Segun Olude, Susan McWatt, and Carisa L. Romans. Based on illustrations by Andrew Valko.

Lithography (7 colours), pane of 16
Ashton-Potter Canada Limited

**1999, Jul 12** **GT4, TRC Paper** **Perf 13.3**

| | | NH–VF | ⊙F | PB | FDC |
|---|---|---|---|---|---|
| **1801** | **46¢ multicoloured** | .90 | .50 | | |
| **1802** | **46¢ multicoloured** | .90 | .50 | | |
| **1803** | **46¢ multicoloured** | .90 | .50 | | |
| **1804** | **46¢ multicoloured** | .90 | .50 | | |
| **a** | se-tenant block or horizontal strip of 4 (1801–1804) | 4.00 | 3.50 | 4.50 | 4.30 |

Qty: 2,500,000 of each

For non-denominated postal cards of same designs, see UX123.
Issued for the XIIIth Pan American Games, held at Winnipeg in 1999.

## WORLD ROWING CHAMPIONSHIPS

1805
Five rowers

Designer: Paul Haslip and Alan Lum. Based on photographs by Curtis Lantinga.

Lithography (9 colours), pane of 20
Ashton-Potter Canada Limited

**1999, Aug 22** **GT4, TRC Paper** **Perf 12.5x13.1**

| | | NH–VF | ⊙F | PB | FDC |
|---|---|---|---|---|---|
| **1805** | **46¢ multicoloured** | .90 | .30 | 4.50 | 1.50 |

Qty: 6,000,000

Issued for the 23rd World Rowing Championships, held at St.Catharines, ON in 1999.

## UNIVERSAL POSTAL UNION

**1806**
UPU emblem on world map

Designer: Pierre-Yves Pelletier.

Lithography (6 colours), pane of 20
Canadian Bank Note Company, Limited

**1999, Aug 26** **GT4, TRC Paper** **Perf 12.5x13.1**

| | NH–VF | ⊙F | PB | FDC |
|---|---|---|---|---|
| **1806 46¢ multicoloured** | .90 | .30 | 4.50 | 1.50 |

Qty: 6,000,000

Issued to celebrate the 125th anniversary of the Universal Postal Union.



## CANADIAN INTERNATIONAL AIR SHOW

**1807a**
Fokker DR-1 and CT-114 Tutors

**1807b**
CT-114 Tutors and H101 Salto Sailplane

**1807c**
de Havilland DH100 Vampire, MKIII

**1807d**
Stearman A-75

Designer: Tiit Telmet and Marko Barac.
Based on photographs by David Tarrant and by Roman Holowatyj.

Lithography (9 colours), souvenir sheet of 4
Canadian Bank Note Company, Limited

**1999, Sep 4** **GT4, TRC Paper** **Perf 12.5x13.1**

| | | NH–VF | ⊙F | FDC |
|---|---|---|---|---|
| **1807** | $1.84 pane of 4 | 7.50 | 7.50 | 5.00 |
| **a** | **46¢ multicoloured** | 1.50 | 1.25 | — |
| **b** | **46¢ multicoloured** | 1.50 | 1.25 | — |
| **c** | **46¢ multicoloured** | 1.50 | 1.25 | — |
| **d** | **46¢ multicoloured** | 1.50 | 1.25 | — |

Qty: 2,500,000 of each

Issued for the 50th anniversary of the Canadian International Air Show.

**1807**

## CANADIAN AIR FORCES 1924–1999

**1808a**
de Havilland Mosquito F.B.VI

**1808b**
Sopwith F1 Camel

**1808c**
de Havilland Canada DHC-3 Otter

**1808d**
de Havilland Canada CC-108 Caribou

**1808e**
Canadair CL-28 Argus MK 2

**1808f**
North American F-86 Sabre 6

**1808g**
McDonnell Douglas CF-18 Hornet

**1808h**
Sopwith 5.F.1 Dolphin

**1808i**
Armstrong Whitworth Siskin 111A

**1808j**
Canadian Vickers (Northrop) Delta II

**1808k**
Sikorsky CH-124A Sea King

**1808l**
Vickers Armstrong Wellington MK II

**1808m**
Avro Anson MK I

**1808n**
Canadair (Lockheed) CF-104G Starfighter

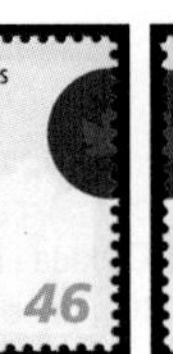

**1808o**
Burgess-Dunne seaplane

**1808p**
Avro 504K

Designer: Tiit Telmet and Marko Barac. Based on an illustration by Garry Lay.
Lithography (10 colours), pane of 16
Canadian Bank Note Company, Limited

**1999, Sep 4** — **GT4, TRC Paper** — **Perf 12.5x13.1**

| | | NH–VF | ⊙F | FDC |
|---|---|---|---|---|
| **1808** | $7.36 pane of 16 | 25.00 | 25.00 | |
| a | 46¢ de Havilland Mosquito F.B.VI | 1.25 | 1.25 | |
| b | 46¢ Sopwith F1 Camel | 1.25 | 1.25 | |
| c | 46¢ de Havilland Canada DHC-3 Otter | 1.25 | 1.25 | |
| d | 46¢ de Havilland Canada CC-108 Caribou | 1.25 | 1.25 | |
| e | 46¢ Canadair CL-28 Argus MK 2 | 1.25 | 1.25 | |
| f | 46¢ North American F-86 Sabre 6 | 1.25 | 1.25 | |
| g | 46¢ McDonnell Douglas CF-18 Hornet | 1.25 | 1.25 | |
| h | 46¢ Sopwith 5.F.1 Dolphin | 1.25 | 1.25 | |
| i | 46¢ Armstrong Whitworth Siskin 111A | 1.25 | 1.25 | |
| j | 46¢ Canadian Vickers (Northrop) Delta II | 1.25 | 1.25 | |
| k | 46¢ Sikorsky CH-124A Sea King | 1.25 | 1.25 | |
| l | 46¢ Vickers Armstrong Wellington MK II | 1.25 | 1.25 | |
| m | 46¢ Avro Anson MK I | 1.25 | 1.25 | |
| n | 46¢ Canadair (Lockheed) CF-104G Starfighter | 1.25 | 1.25 | |
| o | 46¢ Burgess-Dunne seaplane | 1.25 | 1.25 | |
| p | 46¢ Avro 504K | 1.25 | 1.25 | |

Qty: 1,250,000 of each

Plate blocks of 4: 4 different at 4.50 each.

| | |
|---|---|
| **Nos: 1808a–b, e–f (4) Combination FDC** | **5.00** |
| **Nos: 1808c–d, g–h (4) Combination FDC** | **5.00** |
| **Nos: 1808i–j, m–n (4) Combination FDC** | **5.00** |
| **Nos: 1808k–l, o–p (4) Combination FDC** | **5.00** |

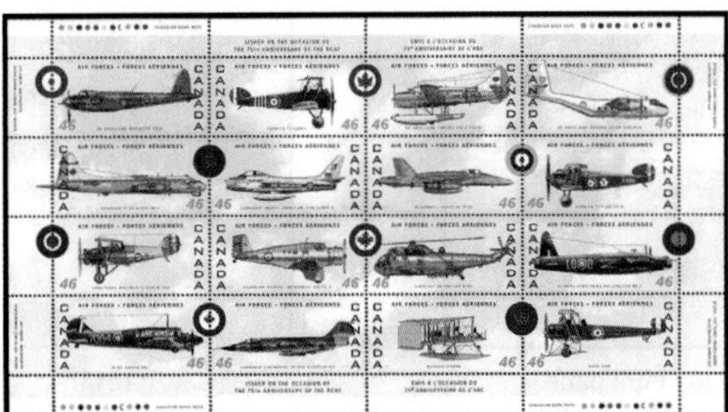

**1808**

## NATO

**1809**
NATO flags

Designer: Fraser Ross. Based on an illustration by Bonnie Ross.
Lithography (6 colours), pane of 16
Ashton-Potter Canada Limited

**1999, Sep 21** — **GT4, TRC Paper** — **Perf 12.5x13.1**

| | | NH–VF | ⊙F | PB | FDC |
|---|---|---|---|---|---|
| **1809** | **46¢ multicoloured** | 1.00 | .30 | 4.50 | 1.50 |

Qty: 7,000,000

Issued for the 50th anniversary of the North Atlantic Treaty Organization.

## FRONTIER COLLEGE

**1810**
Frontier College farmer ploughing an open book

Designer: Renata Chubb, Glenda Rissman, and Peter D.K. Scott.
Based on an illustration by Alain Massicotte.
Lithography (5 colours), pane of 16
Canadian Bank Note Company, Limited

**1999, Sep 24** — **GT4, TRC Paper** — **Perf 13.0x13.3**

| | | NH–VF | ⊙F | PB | FDC |
|---|---|---|---|---|---|
| **1810** | **46¢ multicoloured**, tag type 4 | .90 | .30 | 4.50 | 1.50 |
| i | tag type 1, pos. 1 | 1.50 | .50 | | |
| ii | tag type 2, pos. 2–4 | 1.00 | .35 | | |
| iii | tag type 3, pos. 5, 9, 13 | 1.00 | .35 | | |

Qty: 6,000,000

The four different tag types are the result of where the tagging bars have been notched. The upper left plate block contains an example of each of the four types; value $7.50.

Issued to celebrate the 100th anniversary of Frontier College.

**1810i** *tag type 1* (pos. 1)

**1810ii** *tag type 2* (pos. 2–4)

**1810iii** *tag type 3* (pos. 5, 9, 13)

**1810** *tag type 4* (pos. 6–8, 10–12, 14–16)

## KITES

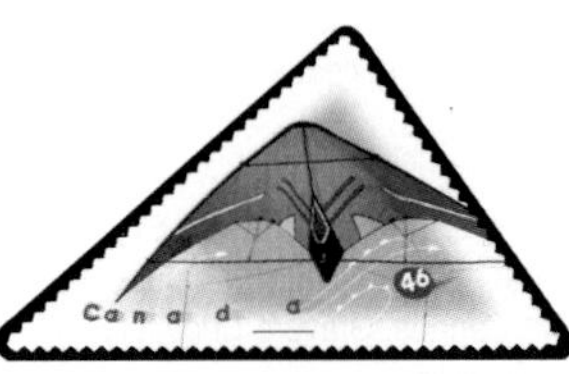

**1811a**
Master Control sport kite (triangular)

**1811b**
Indian Garden Flying Carpet (trapezoidal)

**1811c**
Gibson Girl (rectangular)

**1811d**
Dragon Centipede (oval)

Designer: Debbie Adams.

Lithography (5 colours), self-adhesive booklet pane of 8
Ashton-Potter Canada Limited

**1999, Oct 1** **GT4, JAC Paper**
**Serpentine Die cut in various patterns**

| | | NH–VF | ⊙F | FDC |
|---|---|---|---|---|
| **1811** | $3.68 booklet of 8 x 46¢ (2 each of a–d) (BK221) | 12.00 | | |
| a | **46¢ multicoloured** (triangular) | 1.25 | .50 | |
| b | **46¢ multicoloured** (trapezoidal) | 1.25 | .50 | |
| c | **46¢ multicoloured** (rectangular) | 1.25 | .50 | |
| d | **46¢ multicoloured** (oval) | 1.25 | .50 | |

Qty: 4,000,000 of each

**Nos: 1811a-d (4) Combination FDC** **4.30**

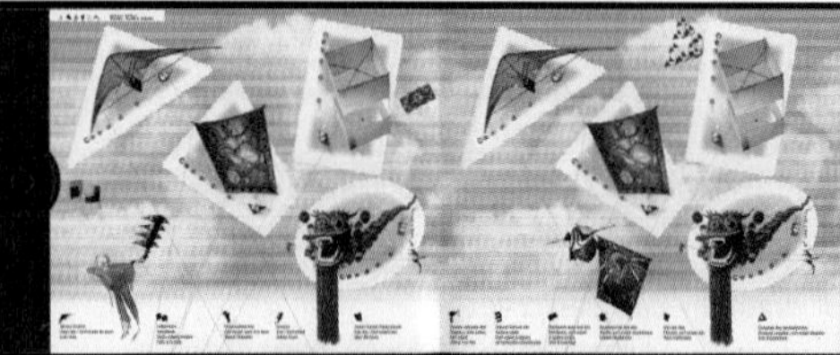
1811

## MILLENNIUM ISSUES (DOVE)

1812
Dove (hologram)

1813
Child and dove of peace

1814
Dove of peace on branch

Designer: Pierre-Yves Pelletier and Georges de Passillé.
Based on photographs by François LeClair. Holographic stereogram by George Siny.

Hologram and Lithography, pane of 4
Ashton-Potter Canada Limited, Crown Canada, Gravure Choquet Inc.

**1999, Oct 12** **GT4, JAC Paper** **Die cut**

| | | NH–VF | ⊙F | FDC |
|---|---|---|---|---|
| **1812** | **46¢ silver hologram** | 1.25 | .50 | 2.00 |
| | pane of 4 | 6.00 | 6.00 | |
| i | 46¢ souvenir sheet of 1 (1812)* | 7.50 | 7.50 | |
| ii | $79.99 uncut press sheet of 9 souvenir sheets | 130.00 | | |

Qty: 4,000,000; Souvenir sheet: 5,000,000; Uncut press sheet: 30,000

* Available in Official Millennium Keepsake and in uncut press sheets of nine souvenir sheets.

The self-adhesive backing paper on the sheets of four comes in a variety of fluorescences, from LF to HB. Individual scarcity factors have not been determined.

1812 full pane

1812i

Designer: Monique Dufour and Sophie Lafortune. Based on a photograph by François LeClair.

Lithography (5 colours), pane of 4
Ashton-Potter Canada Limited

**1999, Oct 12** **GT4, TRC Paper** **Perf 13.3**

| | | NH–VF | ⊙F | FDC |
|---|---|---|---|---|
| **1813** | **55¢ multicoloured** | 1.25 | 1.00 | 2.00 |
| | pane of 4 | 6.00 | 6.00 | |
| i | 55¢ souvenir sheet of 1 (1813)* | 7.50 | 7.50 | |

Qty: 1,000,000; Souvenir sheet: 5,000,000

* Available only in Official Millennium Keepsake.
For non-denominated postal card of same design, see UX125.

1813 full pane

1813i

Designer: Jorge Peral.

Engraved (1 colour), pane of 4
Canadian Bank Note Company, Limited

**1999, Oct 12** **GT4, Peterborough Paper** **Perf 12.9**

| | | NH–VF | ⊙F | FDC |
|---|---|---|---|---|
| **1814** | **95¢ brown** | 2.25 | 2.00 | 2.50 |
| | pane of 4 | 9.00 | 9.00 | |
| i | 95¢ souvenir sheet of 1 (1814)* | 7.50 | 7.50 | |

Qty: 1,000,000; Souvenir sheet: 5,000,000

*Available only in Official Millennium Keepsake.

1814 full pane

1814i

## OFFICIAL MILLENNIUM KEEPSAKE

The keepsake consists of a matte-finish metal box containing 1 each of the millennium souvenir sheets (1812i, 1813i, 1814i), a millennium medallion struck by the Royal Canadian Mint, a souvenir card to record millennium memories and an international pre-stamped postcard to send a millennium greeting anywhere in the world. Personal greetings from the chairman of Canada Post Corporation and an entry form for a contest called "Wonders of the World" (Canadian residents only) are also included. Issue price $8.99.

The original collection, as described above, was released Oct 12, 1999. On five additional occasions, the metal box containing 1 each of the souvenir sheets has been either sold or distributed with an appropriate wrapper:

- Canada Post (original), *Oct 12, 1999*; sold for $8.99
- launch of www.epost.ca, *Nov 26, 1999*; approximately 150 dignitaries and guests in attendance, Toronto.
- Wal-mart stores, *summer 2000*; sold for $7.97
- Hallmark stores, *fall 2000*; sold for $7.97
- *The Magazine — Not for adults, Aug 2001*; included free in the August/September issue (retail $1.95)
- Police Officers of Canada, *2002*; promotional event

Original; Canada Post

ePost

Wal-Mart

Hallmark

Police Officers

## CHRISTMAS — VICTORIAN ANGELS

1815
Angel with drum

1816
Angel with toys

1817
Angel with candle

Designer: Kosta (Gus) Tsetsekas and Bonne Zabolotney.
Based on an illustration by Tannis Hopkins.

Lithography (6 colours), panes of 50
Canadian Bank Note Company, Limited

**1999, Nov 4** **GT4, TRC Paper** **Perf 13.3x13.4**

| | | NH–VF | ⊙F | PB | FDC |
|---|---|---|---|---|---|
| **1815** | **46¢ multicoloured** | .90 | .30 | 4.50 | |
| **b** | horizontal pair, imperf. between | *2,500.00* | | | |
| a | booklet pane of 10 x 46¢ (1815as) (BK222) | 11.00 | 14.00 | | |
| as | single with straight edge, from 1815a | 1.00 | .40 | | |
| BK222 | pane 1815a in cover $12.00 | | | | |
| Qty: 25,000,000 | | | | | |
| **1816** | **55¢ multicoloured** | 1.10 | .50 | 5.50 | |
| a | booklet pane of 5 x 55¢ (1816as) (BK223) | 7.00 | 10.00 | | |
| as | single with straight edge, from 1816a | 1.25 | .75 | | |
| BK223 | pane 1816a in cover $7.50 | | | | |
| Qty: 5,000,000 | | | | | |
| **1817** | **95¢ multicoloured** | 1.90 | 1.25 | 9.50 | |
| **b** | horizontal pair, imperf. between | *1,500.00* | | | |
| a | booklet pane of 5 x 95¢ (1817as) (BK224) | 12.00 | 15.00 | | |
| as | single with straight edge, from 1817a | 2.50 | 1.50 | | |
| BK224 | pane 1817a in cover $13.00 | | | | |
| Qty: 5,000,000 | | | | | |

**Nos: 1815-1817 (3) Combination FDC** 4.50

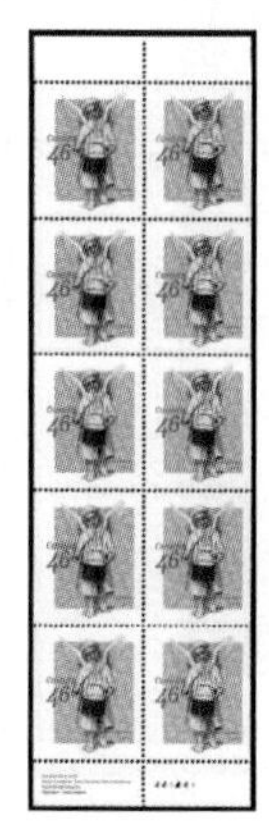

1815a

1816a

1817a

## THE MILLENNIUM COLLECTION HARDBOUND BOOK

Canada Post issued a limited edition (200,000 numbered copies) hardbound book on September 15, 1999 for $59.99 that contained 68 specially minted stamps in a unique page format created exclusively for this edition. The 94 page book included bilingual text and original black and white photography.

The stamps were printed with only two stamps per page, as illustrated at right.

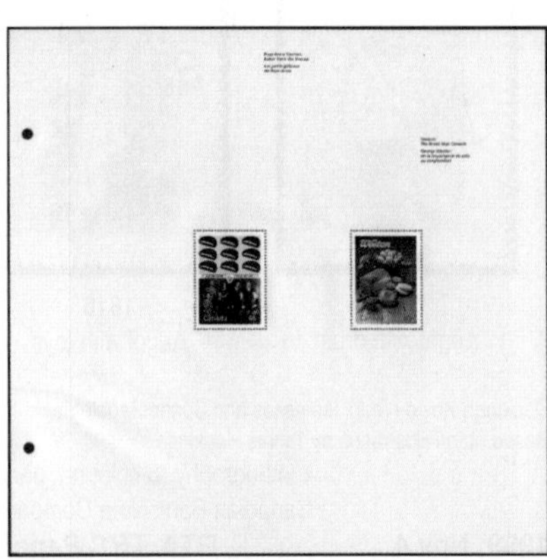

The stamp catalogues were not going to recognize the 68 stamps printed in the book because of the "limited edition" and excessive "surcharge" over face value (almost double the price of the stamps). As a result Canada Post re-issued the 68 stamps over a 3-month period in 17 different panes of 4 stamps each (Sc. 1818–1834).

There is a difference between the stamps printed in the book compared to those printed in the souvenir sheets. The 'hidden' date on the stamps from the book are slightly larger than the date on the souvenir sheet stamps.

1834d (book)

1834d (s/s)

## THE MILLENNIUM COLLECTION SOUVENIR SHEETS OF FOUR

Lithography (4 colours plus varnish), panes of 4

Images reduced (60%) Ashton-Potter Canada Limited

The panes on the official first day covers have all had their bottom selvedge removed to allow the pane to fit on the envelope.

### I — MEDIA TECHNOLOGIES

The Millennium Collection La collection du millénaire

La collection du millénaire The Millennium Collection

1818

Designer: a) Kosta (Gus) Tsetsekas and Geoff Kehrig; b) Hoover Chung; c) Darrell Corriveau, Peter D.K. Scott, and Glenda Rissman; d) Bryan Canning and Malcolm Waddell.

**1999, Dec 17** **GT4, TRC Paper** **Perf 13.3x13.4**

| | | NH–VF | ⊙F | FDC |
|---|---|---|---|---|
| **1818** | $1.84 pane of 4 x 46¢ (a–d) | 9.00 | 9.00 | 5.00 |
| a | **46¢ IMAX movies** | 2.00 | 1.50 | |
| b | **46¢ Softimage animation software** | 2.00 | 1.50 | |
| c | **46¢ Ted Rogers, Sr. and radio tube** | 2.00 | 1.50 | |
| d | **46¢ Sir Wm. Stephenson** | 2.00 | 1.50 | |

Qty: 1,000,000 of each

### 2 — CANADIAN ENTERTAINMENT

1819

Designer: a) Terry Gregoraschuk; b) Marc Serre, Daniel Fortin and George Fok; c and d) Sheri Hancock and Hélène L'Heureux.

**1999, Dec 17** **GT4, TRC Paper** **Perf 13.3x13.4**

| | | NH–VF | ⊙F | FDC |
|---|---|---|---|---|
| **1819** | $1.84 pane of 4 x 46¢ (a–d) | 9.00 | 9.00 | 5.00 |
| a | **46¢ Calgary Stampede** | 2.00 | 1.50 | |
| b | **46¢ Cirque du Soleil** | 2.00 | 1.50 | |
| c | **46¢ Hockey Night In Canada** | 2.00 | 1.50 | |
| d | **46¢ La Soirée du Hockey** | 2.00 | 1.50 | |

Qty: 1,000,000 of each

### 3 – EXTRAORDINARY ENTERTAINERS

1820

Designer: a) Fraser Ross; b) Avi Dunkelman; c) Russ Willms; d) Yvon Laroche.

**1999, Dec 17** **GT4, TRC Paper** **Perf 13.3x13.4**

| | | NH–VF | ⊙F | FDC |
|---|---|---|---|---|
| **1820** | $1.84 pane of 4 x 46¢ (a–d) | 9.00 | 9.00 | 5.00 |
| a | **46¢ Portia White, singer** | 2.00 | 1.50 | |
| b | **46¢ Glenn Gould, pianist** | 2.00 | 1.50 | |
| c | **46¢ Guy Lombardo, band leader** | 2.00 | 1.50 | |
| d | **46¢ Félix Leclerc, singer, guitarist** | 2.00 | 1.50 | |

Qty: 1,000,000 of each

## 4 – FOSTERING CANADIAN TALENT

1821

Designer: a) Jean Michaud; b) Paul Haslip; c) Geneviève Caron; d) Clermont Malenfant.

**1999, Dec 17 GT4, TRC Paper Perf 13.3x13.4**

| | | NH–VF | ⊙F | FDC |
|---|---|---|---|---|
| **1821** | $1.84 pane of 4 x 46¢ (a–d) | 9.00 | 9.00 | 5.00 |
| a | **46¢ Royal Canadian Academy of Arts** | 2.00 | 1.50 | |
| b | **46¢ Canada Council** | 2.00 | 1.50 | |
| c | **46¢ National Film Board of Canada** | 2.00 | 1.50 | |
| d | **46¢ Canadian Broadcasting Corporation** | 2.00 | 1.50 | |

Qty: 1,000,000 of each

# 2000

## 5 – MEDICAL INNOVATORS

1822

Designer: a) Louis Fishauf; b) Louise Delisle and Jean-Claude Guénette; c) Stéphane Huot; d) Tom Yakobina.

**2000, Jan 17 GT4, TRC Paper Perf 13.3x13.4**

| | | NH–VF | ⊙F | FDC |
|---|---|---|---|---|
| **1822** | $1.84 pane of 4 x 46¢ (a–d) | 9.00 | 9.00 | 5.00 |
| a | **46¢ Sir Frederic Banting, insulin** | 2.00 | 1.50 | |
| b | **46¢ Dr. Armand Frappier, microbiology** | 2.00 | 1.50 | |
| c | **46¢ Dr. Hans Selye, endocrinology** | 2.00 | 1.50 | |
| d | **46¢ Maude Abbott, pathologist** | 2.00 | 1.50 | |

Qty: 1,000,000 of each

## 6 – SOCIAL PROGRESS

1823

Designer: a) François Blais; b) Susan Lee; c) François Dallaire; d) Derek Sarty.

**2000, Jan 17 GT4, TRC Paper Perf 13.3x13.4**

| | | NH–VF | ⊙F | FDC |
|---|---|---|---|---|
| **1823** | $1.84 pane of 4 x 46¢ (a–d) | 9.00 | 9.00 | 5.00 |
| a | **46¢ From the Hospitalières de Québec to Medicare** | 2.00 | 1.50 | |
| b | **46¢ "Women are Persons . . . "** | 2.00 | 1.50 | |
| c | **46¢ Alphonse Desjardins and wife Dorimène, Credit Unions** | 2.00 | 1.50 | |
| d | **46¢ Father Moses Coady, adult education** | 2.00 | 1.50 | |

Qty: 1,000,000 of each

## 7 – HEARTS OF GOLD

1824

Designer: a) Ralph Tibbles; b) Pierre-Yves Pelletier; c) Ken Fung; d) Lou Cable.

**2000, Jan 17 GT4, TRC Paper Perf 13.3x13.4**

| | | NH–VF | ⊙F | FDC |
|---|---|---|---|---|
| **1824** | $1.84 pane of 4 x 46¢ (a–d) | 9.00 | 9.00 | 5.00 |
| a | **46¢ Canadian International Development Agency** | 2.00 | 1.50 | |
| b | **46¢ Dr. Lucille Teasdale** | 2.00 | 1.50 | |
| c | **46¢ Marathon of Hope, Terry Fox** | 2.00 | 1.50 | |
| d | **46¢ Meals On Wheels** | 2.00 | 1.50 | |

Qty: 1,000,000 of each

## 8 – HUMANITARIANS AND PEACEKEEPERS

1825

Designer: a) Raymond Bellemare; b) Margaret Susan Issenman; c) Kiky Kambylis; d) Carisa L. Romans and Robert L. Peters.

**2000, Jan 17 GT4, TRC Paper Perf 13.3x13.4**

| | | NH–VF | ⊙F | FDC |
|---|---|---|---|---|
| 1825 | $1.84 pane of 4 x 46¢ (a–d) | 9.00 | 9.00 | 5.00 |
| a | **46¢ Raoul Dandurand, Senator** | 2.00 | 1.50 | |
| b | **46¢ Pauline Vanier, Red Cross and Elizabeth Smellie, nursing** | 2.00 | 1.50 | |
| c | **46¢ Lester B. Pearson, Prime Minister and Nobel Peace Prize recipient** | 2.00 | 1.50 | |
| d | **46¢ Canada's role in banning land mines** | 2.00 | 1.50 | |

Qty: 1,000,000 of each

## 9 – CANADA'S FIRST PEOPLES

1826

Designer: a) Rolf P. Harder; b) Sunil Bhandari and Georges Khayat; c) James Skipp; d) Jerry Evans and Steven Slipp.

**2000, Feb 17 GT4, TRC Paper Perf 13.3x13.4**

| | | NH–VF | ⊙F | FDC |
|---|---|---|---|---|
| 1826 | $1.84 pane of 4 x 46¢ (a–d) | 9.00 | 9.00 | 5.00 |
| a | **46¢ Chief Pontiac** | 2.00 | 1.50 | |
| b | **46¢ Tom Longboat, runner** | 2.00 | 1.50 | |
| c | **46¢ The Power of the Inuit Shaman** | 2.00 | 1.50 | |
| d | **46¢ Healing From Within** | 2.00 | 1.50 | |

Qty: 1,000,000 of each

## 10 – CANADA'S CULTURAL FABRIC

1827

Designer: a) Susan Warr; b) Horst Deppe and Fraser Ross; c) Bruce Kierstead; d) Les Holloway.

**2000, Feb 17 GT4, TRC Paper Perf 13.3x13.4**

| | | NH–VF | ⊙F | FDC |
|---|---|---|---|---|
| 1827 | $1.84 pane of 4 x 46¢ (a–d) | 9.00 | 9.00 | 5.00 |
| a | **46¢ L'Anse aux Meadows, World Heritage Site** | 2.00 | 1.50 | |
| b | **46¢ Immigration – Pier 21, Halifax** | 2.00 | 1.50 | |
| c | **46¢ Neptune Theatre, Halifax** | 2.00 | 1.50 | |
| d | **46¢ Stratford Festival** | 2.00 | 1.50 | |

Qty: 1,000,000 of each

## 11 – LITERARY LEGENDS

1828

Designer: a) Catharine Bradbury; b) Pierre Fontaine; c) Lise Giguère; d) Gary Ludwig.

**2000, Feb 17 GT4, TRC Paper Perf 13.3x13.4**

| | | NH–VF | ⊙F | FDC |
|---|---|---|---|---|
| 1828 | $1.84 pane of 4 x 46¢ (a–d) | 9.00 | 9.00 | 5.00 |
| a | **46¢ W.O. Mitchell, novelist** | 2.00 | 1.50 | |
| b | **46¢ Gratien Gélinas, playright** | 2.00 | 1.50 | |
| c | **46¢ Le Cercle du Livre de France, book club** | 2.00 | 1.50 | |
| d | **46¢ Harlequin paperback books** | 2.00 | 1.50 | |

Qty: 1,000,000 of each

## 12 – GREAT THINKERS

1829

Designer: a) Ian Drolet; b) Brian Tsang; c) Pierre Fontaine; d) Stacey Zabolotney.

**2000, Feb 17** **GT4, TRC Paper** **Perf 13.3x13.4**

| | | NH–VF | ⊙F | FDC |
|---|---|---|---|---|
| **1829** | $1.84 pane of 4 x 46¢ (a–d) | 9.00 | 9.00 | 5.00 |
| a | **46¢ Marshall McLuhan, philosopher** | 2.00 | 1.50 | |
| b | **46¢ Northrop Frye, literary critic** | 2.00 | 1.50 | |
| c | **46¢ Roger Lemelin, novelist** | 2.00 | 1.50 | |
| d | **46¢ Hilda Marion Neatby, historian** | 2.00 | 1.50 | |

Qty: 1,000,000 of each

## 13 – A TRADITION OF GENEROSITY

1830

Designer: a) Debbie Adams; b) Dennis George Page; c) Tim Nokes; d) Rolf P. Harder.

**2000, Feb 17** **GT4, TRC Paper** **Perf 13.3x13.4**

| | | NH–VF | ⊙F | FDC |
|---|---|---|---|---|
| **1830** | $1.84 pane of 4 x 46¢ (a–d) | 9.00 | 9.00 | 5.00 |
| a | **46¢ Hart Massey, Hart House, U of T** | 2.00 | 1.50 | |
| b | **46¢ Dorothy and Isaac Killam, philanthropists and molecular model** | 2.00 | 1.50 | |
| c | **46¢ Eric Lafferty Harvie, philanthropist** | 2.00 | 1.50 | |
| d | **46¢ Macdonald Stewart Foundation** | 2.00 | 1.50 | |

Qty: 4,000,000 of each

The press sheet for the Millennium souvenir sheets consists of one pane of each sheet but *four* panes of Scott 1830. Thus, four times as many of this pane were printed compared to the other 16 panes.

## 14 – ENGINEERING AND TECHNOLOGICAL MARVELS

1831

Designer: a) Kevin van der Leek and Andrew McKinley; b) Ernst Roch; c) Tom Yakobina; d) Nigel Skinner and Joseph Gault.

**2000, Mar 17** **GT4, TRC Paper** **Perf 13.3x13.4**

| | | NH–VF | ⊙F | FDC |
|---|---|---|---|---|
| **1831** | $1.84 pane of 4 x 46¢ (a–d) | 9.00 | 9.00 | 5.00 |
| a | **46¢ Rogers Pass** | 2.00 | 1.50 | |
| b | **46¢ Manic Dams, Quebec** | 2.00 | 1.50 | |
| c | **46¢ Canada in Space** | 2.00 | 1.50 | |
| d | **46¢ CN Tower** | 2.00 | 1.50 | |

Qty: 1,000,000 of each

## 15 – FATHERS OF INVENTION

1832

Designer: a) Tiit Telmet; b) Steven Slipp; c) Julien LeBlanc; d) Michèle Cayer.

**2000, Mar 17** **GT4, TRC Paper** **Perf 13.3x13.4**

| | | NH–VF | ⊙F | FDC |
|---|---|---|---|---|
| **1832** | $1.84 pane of 4 x 46¢ (a–d) | 9.00 | 9.00 | 5.00 |
| a | **46¢ George Klein, inventor** | 2.00 | 1.50 | |
| b | **46¢ Abraham Gesner, kerosene** | 2.00 | 1.50 | |
| c | **46¢ Alexander Graham Bell, telephone** | 2.00 | 1.50 | |
| d | **46¢ Joseph-Armand Bombardier, snowmobile** | 2.00 | 1.50 | |

Qty: 1,000,000 of each

## 16 – FOOD, GLORIOUS FOOD !

1833

Designer: a) Ivan Novotny and John Taylor; b) Mark Koudis; c) Paul-Michael Brunelle; d) Jim Hudson.

| 2000, Mar 17 | GT4, TRC Paper | Perf 13.3x13.4 | | |
|---|---|---|---|---|
| | | NH–VF | ⊙F | FDC |
| 1833 | $1.84 pane of 4 x 46¢ (a–d) | 9.00 | 9.00 | 5.00 |
| a | **46¢ Sir Charles Saunders, Marquis Wheat** | 2.00 | 1.50 | |
| b | **46¢ Frederick Tisdall, Pablum** | 2.00 | 1.50 | |
| c | **46¢ Dr. Archibald G. Huntsman, pioneered packaging frozen fish** | 2.00 | 1.50 | |
| d | **46¢ McCain Food Ltd., marketer of frozen foods** | 2.00 | 1.50 | |

Qty: 1,000,000 of each

## 17 – ENTERPRISING GIANTS

1834

Designer: a) Susan Scott; b) Neville Smith; c) Monique Dufour and Sophie Lafortune; d) Doreen Colonello and Stuart Bradley Ash.

| 2000, Mar 17 | GT4, TRC Paper | Perf 13.3x13.4 | | |
|---|---|---|---|---|
| | | NH–VF | ⊙F | FDC |
| 1834 | $1.84 pane of 4 x 46¢ (a–d) | 9.00 | 9.00 | 5.00 |
| a | **46¢ Hudson's Bay Company** | 2.00 | 1.50 | |
| b | **46¢ Bell Canada Enterprises** | 2.00 | 1.50 | |
| c | **46¢ Vachon Co., snack cakes** | 2.00 | 1.50 | |
| d | **46¢ George Weston Ltd., bakers** | 2.00 | 1.50 | |

Qty: 1,000,000 of each

## CANADA MILLENNIUM PARTNERSHIP PROGRAM

1835
Canada Millennium Partnership Program Logo

Designer: Jeff Harrison and Roy White.

Lithography (4 colours), panes of 16
Canadian Bank Note Company, Limited

| 2000, Jan 1 | GT4, TRC Paper | Perf 13.1x12.5 | | | |
|---|---|---|---|---|---|
| | | NH–VF | ⊙F | PB | FDC |
| 1835 | **46¢ multicoloured** | 1.00 | .30 | 5.00 | 1.50 |

Qty: 7,000,000

## LUNAR NEW YEAR — 4
## Year of the Dragon

1836
Dragon and Chinese Symbol

1837i

Designer: Ken Fung and Ken Koo. Based on an illustration by Samuel Tseng.
Based on an embroidery by Punchline Embroidery Centre.
Based on a photograph by Clinton Hussey.

Lithography (9 colours; s/s: 10 colours) and Embossed, pane of 25
Ashton-Potter Canada Limited

| 2000, Jan 5 | GT4, TRC Paper | Perf 12.5x12.6 | | | |
|---|---|---|---|---|---|
| | | NH–VF | ⊙F | PB | FDC |
| 1836 | **46¢ multicoloured** | 1.00 | .30 | 4.50 | 2.00 |
| a | red and tagging omitted | *1,500.00* | | | |
| Qty: 16,280,000; 1836i: one pane of 25 recorded | | | | | |
| | | | | **Perf 13.7x13.3** | |
| 1837 | **95¢ souvenir sheet** | 2.25 | 2.25 | — | 2.75 |
| i | single stamp from souvenir sheet | 2.00 | 1.50 | — | |
| a | as 1837, orange and tagging omitted* | *2,000.00* | | | |
| ii | $24.95 uncut press sheet of 12 souvenir sheets | 65.00 | | | |

Qty: 1837: 4,100,000; 1837ii: 50,000
* One example reported to date with V.G. Greene certificate.

See also 1630, 1708, 1767–1768, 1883–1884, 1933–1934, 1969–1970, 2015–2016, 2083–2084, 2140–2141, 2201–2202, 2257–2258.

1836a

1837

1837a

## NHL ALL STARS — I
### 50th All-star game

1838a
Wayne Gretzky (1961– )

1838b
Gordie Howe (1928–2016)

1838c
Maurice Richard (1921–2000)

1838d
Doug Harvey (1924–1989)

1838e
Bobby Orr (1948– )

1838f
Jacques Plante (1929–1986)

Designer: Dan Fell. Based on an illustration by Vincent McIndoe.
Lithography (6 colours), pane of 6 + 6 tabs
Canadian Bank Note Company, Limited

**2000, Feb 5** **Tagged, TRC Paper** **Perf 12.9**

| | | NH–VF | ⊙F | FDC |
|---|---|---|---|---|
| **1838** | $2.76 pane of 6 x 46¢ | 6.00 | 6.00 | |
| a | **46¢ multicoloured** | 1.00 | .75 | |
| b | **46¢ multicoloured** | 1.00 | .75 | |
| c | **46¢ multicoloured** | 1.00 | .75 | |
| d | **46¢ multicoloured** | 1.00 | .75 | |
| e | **46¢ multicoloured** | 1.00 | .75 | |
| f | **46¢ multicoloured** | 1.00 | .75 | |

Qty: 6,000,000 of each

***Three combination FDCs: a+b, c+d and e+f** 7.35

No. 1838 could also be purchased with a souvenir folder for $2.99.
General tagging appears around the inner edge of the large circle on each stamp.

Used examples of 1838a, with black lettering *doubled* (value $150), and 1838e with black lettering *tripled* (value $500) are known.

Issued for the 50th National Hockey League (NHL) All-Star Game.
See also 1443–1445, 1885, 1935, 1971–1972, 2017–2018, 2085–2086. For non-denominated postal card of no. 1838a design, see UX127.

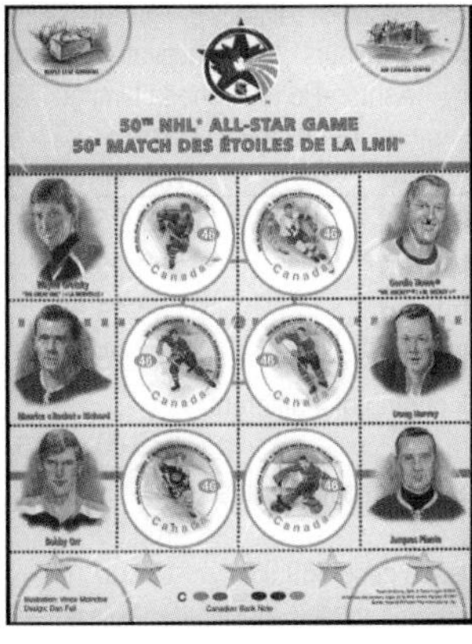

1838

## BIRDS OF CANADA — 5a

*Perforated singles from water-activated gum pane*

1839
Canadian Warbler

1840
Osprey

1841
Pacific Loon

1842
Blue Jay

## BIRDS OF CANADA — 5b

*Die cut singles from self-adhesive booklet*

1843
Canadian Warbler

1844
Osprey

1845
Pacific Loon

1846
Blue Jay

Designer: Raymond Bellemare. Based on paintings by Pierre Leduc.

Lithography (5 colours), water-activated gum pane of 20
Ashton-Potter Canada Limited

| **2000, Mar 1** | **GT4, TRC Paper** | | **Perf 12.5x13.1** | |
|---|---|---|---|---|
| | **NH–VF** | **⊙F** | **PB** | **FDC** |
| **1839 46¢ multicoloured** | 1.25 | .40 | | |
| **1840 46¢ multicoloured** | 1.25 | .40 | | |
| **1841 46¢ multicoloured** | 1.25 | .40 | | |
| **1842 46¢ multicoloured** | 1.25 | .40 | | |
| a se-tenant block or strip of 4 different (1839–1842) | 5.00 | 3.70 | 6.25 | 4.35 |
| i $55.20 uncut press sheet of 6 panes, unsigned | 100.00 | | | |
| as "i", signed (issue price $89.95) | 150.00 | | | |

Qty: 1,600,000 of each

Lithography (5 colours), self-adhesive booklet pane of 12
Ashton-Potter Canada Limited

| **2000, Mar 1** | **GT4, JAC Paper** | **Die cut perf 11.6x11.3** | |
|---|---|---|---|
| | **NH–VF** | **⊙F** | **FDC** |
| **1843 46¢ multicoloured** | 1.25 | .40 | |
| **1844 46¢ multicoloured** | 1.25 | .40 | |
| **1845 46¢ multicoloured** | 1.25 | .40 | |
| **1846 46¢ multicoloured** | 1.25 | .40 | |
| i booklet pane of 12, trimmed and unfolded* | 20.00 | | |
| a booklet pane of 6 x 46¢ (1845, 1846 + 2 each of 1843, 1844) | 7.50 | — | |
| b booklet pane of 6 x 46¢ (1843, 1844 + 2 each of 1845, 1846) | 7.50 | — | |

**BK225** one each of panes 1846a, 1846b $16.00

Qty: 4,000,000 of each

* from "Write Me" kit. Pane is unfolded but trimmed at top and bottom (there is no text at top and no inscriptions at the bottom).

See also 1591–1594, 1631–1634, 1710–1713, 1770–1773, 1774–1777, 1886–1893. For non-denominated envelopes of same nos. 1839/1843 and 1842/1846 designs, see U160–U161.

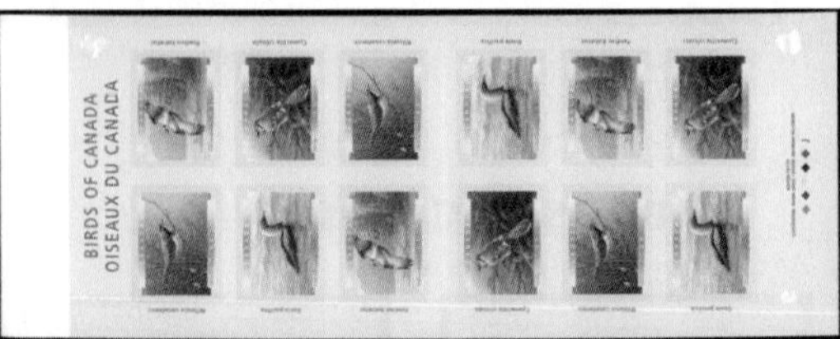


**1846a** (top half) **1846b** (bottom half)

## THE SUPREME COURT OF CANADA

**1847**
The assembled Supreme Court Justices

Designer: Claude Le Sauteur.

Lithography (4 colours), pane of 16
Canadian Bank Note Company, Limited

| **2000, Apr 10** | **GT4, TRC Paper** | | **Perf 12.5x13.1** | |
|---|---|---|---|---|
| | **NH–VF** | **⊙F** | **PB** | **FDC** |
| **1847 46¢ multicoloured** | 1.00 | .30 | 5.00 | 1.50 |

Qty: 5,000,000

Issued for the 125th anniversary of the Supreme Court of Canada.

## THE CALLING OF AN ENGINEER

**1848**
Engineering achievements

Designer: Darrell L. Freeman.
Based on photographs by Sir Alexander Galt Museum and Archives; Polysar, Bayer Rubber Division; Photolink; Photodisc.

Lithography (5 colours), pane of 16 + 4 tabs
Ashton-Potter Canada Limited

| **2000, Apr 25** | **GT4, TRC Paper** | | **Perf 12.5x13.1** | |
|---|---|---|---|---|
| | **NH–VF** | **⊙F** | **PB** | **FDC** |
| **1848 46¢ multicoloured** | 1.00 | .30 | 5.00 | |
| a vertical tête-bêche pair* | 2.00 | 1.50 | | 2.45 |
| i vertical gutter pair with tab between | 2.00 | 1.50 | | |
| b silver (Canada 46) omitted | 3,000.00 | — | — | 4,000.00† |

Qty: 7,000,000

* 1848a shows a full circle representing the iron ring worn by graduate engineers. The pane consists of 2 horizontal rows of such pairs with a row of imprinted tabs between.
† Commercial cover. One used on cover known; 17 mint copies reported including pane of 16 still intact.

Issued for the 75th anniversary of the Ritual of the Calling of an Engineer.

**1848a**

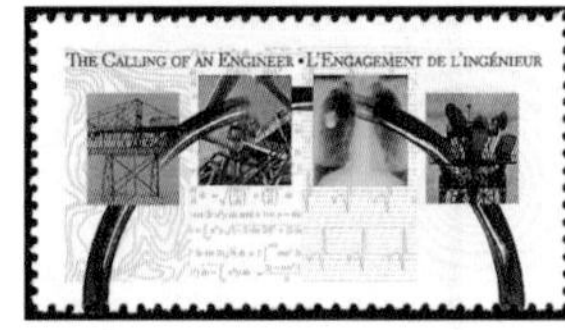


**1848b**

**1848** full pane

**MINT PRICING PREMIUMS**

Mint stamps from 301 to date are valued as NH-VF (Never Hinged-Very Fine). All hinged VF and NH-F copies are worth 50% of the listed values. Plate block (PB) values are for mint NH–VF plate or inscription blocks of four.

**USED, VF/XF (with in-period, circular date cancel) PRICING PREMIUM**

Single stamps with light or circular date cancels will sell for more than catalogue value (perhaps even more than a mint copy). From *1981 to 1991* single stamps from se-tenant blocks of 4 or larger will be priced at 50% or more above the fine price. From *1992* to date single stamps from se-tenant blocks of 4 or larger plus se-tenant booklet panes and souvenir sheets will be priced at 100% or more above the fine price. From *1997* to date all other stamps will be priced at 50% or more above the fine price.

## RURAL MAILBOXES

1849 Ship, fish, house designs — 1850 Flowered house, cow and church designs

1851 Tractor design — 1852 Goose head and house designs

Designer: Raymond Bellemare. Based on an illustration by Martin Côté.
Lithography (5 colours), booklet pane of 12
Ashton-Potter Canada Limited

**2000, Apr 28** **GT4, TRC Paper** **Perf 12.5x13.1**

| | | NH–VF | ⊙F | FDC |
|---|---|---|---|---|
| **1849** | **46¢ multicoloured** | 1.25 | .50 | |
| **1850** | **46¢ multicoloured** | 1.25 | .50 | |
| **1851** | **46¢ multicoloured** | 1.25 | .50 | |
| **1852** | **46¢ multicoloured** | 1.25 | .50 | |
| a | se-tenant block of 4 (1849–1852) | 5.00 | 4.00 | |
| b | booklet pane of 12 x 46¢ (2 x 6) 3 each of 1849–1852 | 13.00 | | |
| BK226 | pane 1852b in cover $14.00 | | | |

Qty: 3,750,000 of each

**Nos. 1849–1852 (4) combination FDC** **4.30**

1852b

## PICTURE POSTAGE™

1853
Gold leaf picture frame

Designer: Steven Spazuk.
Lithography (5 colours), self-adhesive booklet pane of 5
Ashton-Potter Canada Limited

**2000, Apr 28** **GT4, JAC Paper** **Serpentine die cut 11.7**

| | | NH–VF | ⊙F | FDC |
|---|---|---|---|---|
| **1853** | **46¢ multicoloured** | 1.25 | .75† | 1.50 |
| i | die cut to shape from Quarterly Pack/ Annual Collection | 5.00 | — | |
| a | booklet pane of 5 x 46¢ (1853) + 5 different stickers to complete the stamp image (BK227) | 6.00 | | |
| b | pane of 25 x 46¢ stamps + sheet of personalized stickers* | *100.00* | | |
| BK227 | pane 1853a in cover $6.50 | | | |

† Used price is for stamp without personalized label. With label used price is $4.00.

* No. 1853b was not sold at postal outlets or philatelic counters. The inside cover of BK227 served as an order form for a pane of 25 x 46¢ picture frames (1853), 25 return address stickers and 25 customized stickers. These stickers are reproduced from a single photograph submitted by the purchaser. The cost for 1853b was $24.95 each (1 or 2 panes) and $22.95 each for 3–10 panes. These panes were not available at post offices or through the philatelic bureau, but special orders from the printer, Ashton-Potter. Price is for full pane.

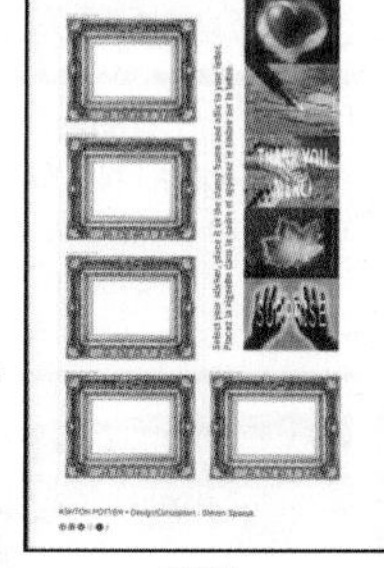

1853a

For 47¢ value of similar design see 1882b. For non-denominated value of same design see 1918b.

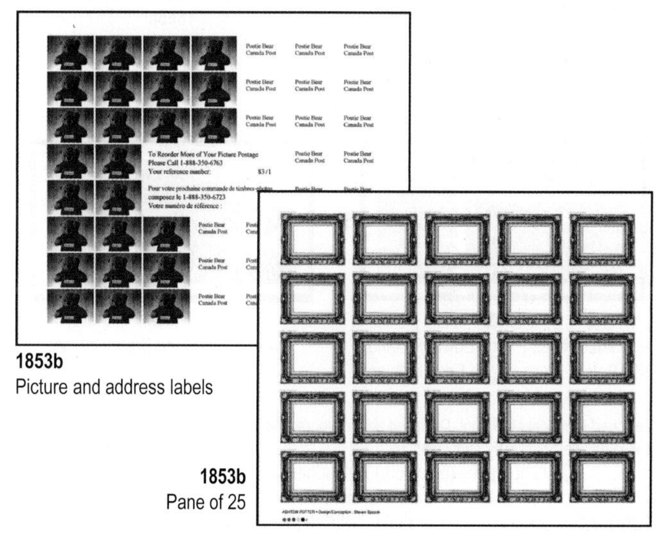

1853b
Picture and address labels

1853b
Pane of 25

## FRESH WATERS OF CANADA

1854a
Helmcken Falls, Wells Gray Park, British Columbia /
Howe Sound, between Vancouver and Squamish, British Columbia

1854b
Unnamed Lake near Baldwinton, west of Battleford, Saskatchewan /
Waterlilies, Saskatchewan

**1854c**
Cameron Lake, Waterton Lakes National Park, Alberta /
Peyto Lake, Banff National Park, Alberta

**1854d**
Red River and Lake Winnipeg, Manitoba

**1854e**
Niagara Falls, Ontario /
Hattie Cove, Pukaskwa National Park, Ontario

**1855a**
Iceberg, Newfoundland /
Western Brook Pond, Gros Morne National Park, Newfoundland

**1855b**
Grande Riviere de la Baleine, Hudson Bay, Quebec /
Broadback River, James Bay, Quebec

**1855c**
Saint John River, New Brunswick

**1855d**
DeSable River, Prince Edward Island /
St. Peters River, Prince Edward Island

**1855e**
Lake O'Law, Cape Breton Island, Nova Scotia

Designer: Clermont Malenfant. Designed and photographed by Mia Matthes.
Based on photographs by Klaus Matthes.
Lithography (5 colours), self-adhesive booklet panes of 5
Ashton-Potter

**2000, May 23** **GT4, JAC Paper**
**Serpentine die cut 2.5 horizontal**

| | | NH–VF | ⊙F | FDC |
|---|---|---|---|---|
| **1854** | $2.75 booklet of 5 x 55¢ (**BK228**) | 11.00 | — | |
| **a** | **55¢ multicoloured** | 2.00 | 1.25 | |
| **b** | **55¢ multicoloured** | 2.00 | 1.25 | |
| **c** | **55¢ multicoloured** | 2.00 | 1.25 | |
| **d** | **55¢ multicoloured** | 2.00 | 1.25 | |
| **e** | **55¢ multicoloured** | 2.00 | 1.25 | |
| **i** | as 1854, unfolded pane of 5* | 20.00 | | |

Qty: 2,500,000 of each

**Nos. 1854a-1854e (5) combination FDC** 6.25

| | | NH–VF | ⊙F | FDC |
|---|---|---|---|---|
| **1855** | $4.75 booklet of 5 x 95¢ (**BK229**) | 13.00 | — | |
| **a** | **95¢ multicoloured** | 2.50 | 2.00 | |
| **b** | **95¢ multicoloured** | 2.50 | 2.00 | |
| **c** | **95¢ multicoloured** | 2.50 | 2.00 | |
| **d** | **95¢ multicoloured** | 2.50 | 2.00 | |
| **e** | **95¢ multicoloured** | 2.50 | 2.00 | |
| **i** | as 1855, unfolded pane of 5* | 25.00 | | |

Qty: 2,500,000 of each
* The unfolded panes were distributed only in the Annual Collection.

**Nos. 1855a-1855e (5) combination FDC** 12.00

**1854**

**1855**

## A ROYAL CENTENARIAN

**1856**
Elizabeth, The Queen Mother

Designer: Ian Drolet. Based on a photograph by William Conran.
Lithography (7 colours), pane of 9
Canadian Bank Note Company, Limited

**2000, May 23** **GT4, TRC Paper** **Perf 13.1x12.5**

| | | NH–VF | ⊙F | FDC |
|---|---|---|---|---|
| **1856** | **95¢ multicoloured**, DF | 2.00 | 1.25 | 3.00 |
| **i** | F | 7.50 | | |
| **a** | imperf. pair* | 1,000.00 | | |
| | $8.55 full pane of 9 with descriptive border, DF | 20.00 | | |
| | full pane, F | 80.00 | | |

Qty: 3,870,000
* Four imperforate panes reported.

Issued to celebrate the 100th birthday of Her Majesty Queen Elizabeth the Queen Mother (the mother of Queen Elizabeth II).

**1856 pane of 9**

## BOYS AND GIRLS CLUBS OF CANADA

**1857**
Three club members

QE II — 2000's

Designer: Gary Ludwig. Based on a photograph by Silvio Calcagno.
Lithography (5 colours), pane of 16
Canadian Bank Note Company, Limited

| 2000, Jun 1 | GT4, TRC Paper | | | Perf 13.0 |
|---|---|---|---|---|
| | NH–VF | ⊙F | PB | FDC |
| **1857 46¢ multicoloured** | .90 | .30 | 4.50 | 1.50 |

Qty: 5,000,000

Issued to celebrate 100 years of service to Canadian youth by the Boys and Girls Clubs of Canada.

## SEVENTH-DAY ADVENTIST CHURCH

**1858**
Sunlight breaking through clouds

Designer: Malcolm Waddell. Based on a photograph by Carl Hiebert.
Lithography (6 colours), pane of 16
Ashton-Potter Canada Limited

| 2000, Jun 29 | GT4, TRC Paper | | | Perf 13.5x13.2 |
|---|---|---|---|---|
| | NH–VF | ⊙F | PB | FDC |
| **1858 46¢ multicoloured** | 1.25 | .30 | 5.00 | 2.00 |

Qty: 3,000,000

Issued for the 57th international meeting of the Seventh-day Adventist Church during 2000, the first to be held in Canada.

## STAMPIN' THE FUTURE

**1859**
*Astronauts*, by Anne Nardelli

**1860**
*New and High Tech*, by Sarah Lutgen

**1861**
*Building Canada*, by Christine Weera

**1862**
*Colour-blind World*, by Andrew Wright

Designer: Lise Giguère.
Lithography (6 colours), pane of 16
Canadian Bank Note Company, Limited

| 2000, Jul 1 | | GT4, TRC Paper | | | Perf 13.3 |
|---|---|---|---|---|---|
| | | NH–VF | ⊙F | PB | FDC |
| **1859** | **46¢ multicoloured** | .90 | .50 | | |
| **1860** | **46¢ multicoloured** | .90 | .50 | | |
| **1861** | **46¢ multicoloured** | .90 | .50 | | |
| **1862** | **46¢ multicoloured** | .90 | .50 | | |
| a | se-tenant block or strip of 4 different (1859–1862) | 4.00 | 3.50 | 4.50 | 4.30 |
| b | $1.84 souvenir sheet of 4 different (1859–1862) | 6.00 | 4.00 | — | — |

Qty: 1,250,000 of each; souvenir sheet: 250,000 panes

Illustrations by school children selected from more than 56,000 contest entries.

**1862b**

## MASTERPIECES OF CANADIAN ART — 13

**1863**
*The Artist at Niagara*

Designer: Pierre-Yves Pelletier. Based on a painting by Cornelius Krieghoff.
Lithography (5 colours) with foil stamping, pane of 16
Ashton-Potter Canada Limited

| 2000, Jul 7 | TRC Paper | | | Perf 12.5x13.3 |
|---|---|---|---|---|
| | NH–VF | ⊙F | PB | FDC |
| **1863 95¢ multicoloured** (silver) | 1.90 | 1.25 | 9.50 | 2.50 |

Qty: 4,000,000

See also 1203, 1241, 1271, 1310,1419, 1466, 1516, 1545, 1602, 1635, 1754, 1800, 1916, 1945.

## TALL SHIPS

**1864**
(denomination at left)

**1865**
(denomination at right)

Designer: Fraser Ross. Based on an illustration by Bonnie Ross.
Lithography (8 colours), self-adhesive booklet pane of 10
Ashton-Potter Canada Limited

2000, Jul 19 — GT4, JAC Paper — Serpentine die cut 4.8x5.0

| | | NH–VF | ⊙F | FDC |
|---|---|---|---|---|
| **1864** | **46¢ multicoloured** | 1.25 | .50 | |
| **1865** | **46¢ multicoloured** | 1.25 | .50 | |
| a | se-tenant pair (1864, 1865) | 2.50 | — | 2.45 |
| b | booklet of 10 (5 of 1865a, se-tenant) (BK230) | 13.00 | | |

Qty: 6,000,000 of each

For non-denominated postal cards of same designs, see UX126.
150 tall ships cruise into Halifax Harbour July 19 during The Race of the Century.

**1865b**

## DEPARTMENT OF LABOUR CENTENNIAL

**1866**
Images of Labour and Industry

Designer: Paul Hodgson. Based on an illustration by Sandra Dionisi.
Lithography (4 colours), pane of 16
Canadian Bank Note Company, Limited

| **2000, Sep 1** | **GT4, TRC Paper** | | **Perf 12.5x13.1** | |
|---|---|---|---|---|
| | NH–VF | ⊙F | PB | FDC |
| **1866 46¢ multicoloured** | .90 | .35 | 4.50 | 1.50 |

Qty: 3,000,000

## PETRO-CANADA

**1867**

Designer: Denis L'Allier. Based on an illustration by Raymond Gendron.
Lithography (4 colours), self-adhesive booklet pane of 12
Canadian Bank Note Company, Limited

| **2000, Sep 13** | **GT4, JAC Paper** | | **Die cut** |
|---|---|---|---|
| | NH–VF | ⊙F | FDC |
| **1867 46¢ multicoloured** | 1.25 | .50 | 1.50 |
| b inverted die cutting† | 10.00 | 10.00 | |
| a booklet pane of 12 x 46¢ (1867) (4 x 3) | 15.00 | | |
| **BK231** pane 1867a in complete booklet $16.00* | | | |

Qty: 12,000,000

† Available only in Canada Post's quarterly Collector's Pack issued October 4, 2000 and in the Canada Post annual collection.
* The booklet pane is the inside front cover of a 12-page bilingual booklet describing the history of Petro-Canada.

A single pane with missing die cutting on all stamps is known by the editors.

Issued to celebrate the 25th anniversary of Petro-Canada.

**1867b**

**1867a**

## WHALES

**1868**
Narwal (*Monodon monoceros*)

**1869**
Blue Whale (*Balaenoptera musculus*)

**1870**
Bowhead Whale (*Balaena mysticetus*)

**1871**
Beluga Whale (*Delphinapterus leucas*)

Designer: Keith Martin.
Lithography (8 colours), pane of 16
Ashton-Potter Canada Limited

| **2000, Oct 2** | **GT4, TRC Paper** | | **Perf 12.5x13.1** | |
|---|---|---|---|---|
| | NH–VF | ⊙F | PB | FDC |
| **1868 46¢ multicoloured** | 1.00 | .40 | | |
| **1869 46¢ multicoloured** | 1.00 | .40 | | |
| **1870 46¢ multicoloured** | 1.00 | .40 | | |
| **1871 46¢ multicoloured** | 1.00 | .40 | | |
| a se-tenant block of 4 different (1868–1871) | 4.50 | 3.50 | 5.00 | 4.50 |

Qty: 2,000,000 of each

## CHRISTMAS PICTURE POSTAGE™

**1872**
Christmas picture frame

Designer: Steven Spazuk.
Lithography (5 colours), self-adhesive booklet pane of 5
Ashton-Potter Canada Limited

| **2000, Oct 5** | **GT4, JAC Paper** | **Serpentine die cut 11.7** | |
|---|---|---|---|
| | NH–VF | ⊙F | FDC |
| **1872 46¢ multicoloured** | 1.25 | 1.00† | 1.50 |
| i die cut to shape from Quarterly Pack/ Annual Collection | 5.00 | — | |
| a booklet pane of 5 x 46¢ (1872) + 5 different stickers to complete the stamp image (BK232) | 6.50 | | |
| b pane of 25 x 46¢ stamps + personalized stickers* | *100.00* | | |
| **BK232** pane 1872a in cover $7.50 | | | |

† Used price is for stamp without personalized label. With label used price is $2.00.

The Christmas picture frame stamp shows "Canada 46" on 2 adjacent sides so the special order stickers can be either portrait or landscape format.

* Personalized stickers (special order) – See 1853b.

For 47¢ value of same design see 1882e.

**1872a**

## CHRISTMAS — NATIVITY

1873 *Adoration of the Shepherds*, by Susie Matthias

1874 *Christmas Creche*, by Michel Guilemette

1875 *Flight Into Egypt*, by David Allan Carter

Designer: Kelly Burke and Larry Burke.

Lithography (5 colours), panes of 50
Ashton-Potter Canada Limited

**2000, Nov 3 — GT4, Peterborough Paper — Perf 13.3**

| | | NH–VF | ⊙F | PB | FDC |
|---|---|---|---|---|---|
| **1873** | **46¢ multicoloured** | .90 | .30 | 4.50 | — |
| a | booklet pane of 10 x 46¢ (1873as) | 10.00 | 12.00 | — | — |
| as | single with straight edge, from 1873a | 1.00 | .40 | | |
| BK233 | pane 1873a in cover $11.00 | | | | |

Qty: 27,500,000

| | | NH–VF | ⊙F | PB | FDC |
|---|---|---|---|---|---|
| **1874** | **55¢ multicoloured** | 1.10 | .45 | 5.50 | — |
| a | booklet pane of 6 x 55¢ (1874as) | 8.00 | 9.00 | — | — |
| as | single with straight edge, from 1874a | 1.25 | .80 | | |
| BK234 | pane 1874a in cover $9.00 | | | | |

Qty: 6,000,000

| | | NH–VF | ⊙F | PB | FDC |
|---|---|---|---|---|---|
| **1875** | **95¢ multicoloured** | 1.80 | .85 | 9.00 | — |
| a | booklet pane of 6 x 95¢ (1875as) | 13.00 | 14.00 | — | — |
| as | single with straight edge, from 1875a | 2.00 | 1.00 | | |
| BK235 | pane 1875a in cover $14.00 | | | | |

Qty: 6,000,000

**Nos. 1873–1875 (3) combination FDC** 4.50

1873a 1874a 1875a

## CANADIAN REGIMENTS

1876 Lord Strathcona's Horse

1877 Les Voltigeurs de Québec

Designer: Pierre-Yves Pelletier. Based on an illustration by Bernard Leduc.

Lithography (5 colours), pane of 16
Canadian Bank Note Company, Limited

**2000, Nov 11 — GT4*, TRC Paper — Perf 13.3x13.0**

| | | NH–VF | ⊙F | PB | FDC |
|---|---|---|---|---|---|
| **1876** | **46¢ multicoloured** | .90 | .40 | | |
| **1877** | **46¢ multicoloured** | .90 | .40 | | |
| a | se-tenant pair (1876, 1877) | 2.00 | 1.25 | 4.50 | 2.45 |

Qty: 1,600,00 of each

* The tagging is applied to the white space framing the inside images.

## DEFINITIVES 2000–2001

Definitive Timeline:
2000, Dec 28 47¢ Queen Elizabeth II (1683)
47¢ Flag over Inukshuk (1700)

## DOMESTIC FIRST-CLASS RATE COIL

1878 Stylized Maple Leaf

Designer: Pierre-Yves Pelletier.

Lithography (6 colours), self-adhesive roll of 100
Ashton-Potter Canada Limited

**2000, Dec 28 — GT4, JAC Paper**
**Serpentine die cut 8.5 horizontal**

| | | NH–VF | ⊙F | FDC |
|---|---|---|---|---|
| **1878** | **47¢ multicoloured**, 9 peaks along top | .95 | .25 | 1.50 |
| i | gutter strip of 4 | 13.00 | | |
| | starter strip of 4 (with 10mm rouletted tab) | 13.00 | | |
| | starter strip of 4 (with 5mm wavy die-cut tab), *Nov 2001* | 15.00 | | |
| | end strip of 4 (with 5mm wavy die-cut tab), *Nov 2001* | 15.00 | | |
| a | blue inscriptions omitted | 900.00 | | *1,500.00†* |
| ai | as "a", gutter strip of 4 | *5,000.00* | | |
| iv | inverted die cutting, 10 peaks along top | * | 30.00 | |

† One used example on cover reported.
* Mint copies have not yet been reported.
For 48¢ value of similar design, see 1927.

A properly die cut stamp will have 'half a plateau' at both sides and begin with a valley (1878) or a peak (1878iv). Die cut shifts are *common* on this value.

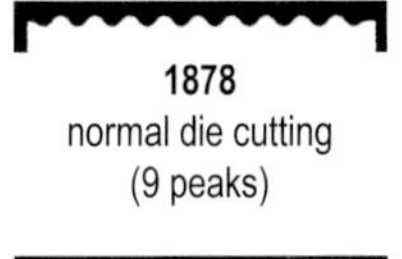

1878 normal die cutting (9 peaks)

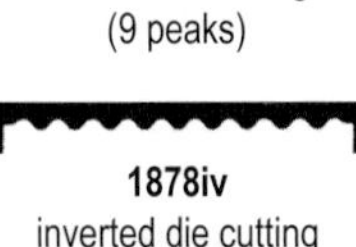

1878iv inverted die cutting (10 peaks)

Die cut shift to right

Die cut shift to left

Die cut illustrations are for informational purposes; the Unitrade catalogue does *not* list perf/die cut shifts.

1878a

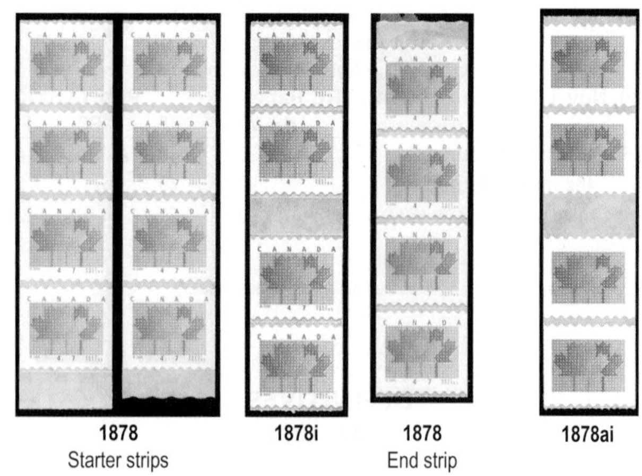
1878 Starter strips | 1878i | 1878 End strip | 1878ai

## MEDIUM-VALUE WILDLIFE DEFINITIVES

**Booklets**
(peak at upper left)

**1879iv** Red Fox | **1881ii** White-tailed Deer

**Coils**
(valley at upper left)

**1879** Red Fox | **1880** Grey Wolf | **1881** White-tailed Deer

The 60¢ and $1.05 wildlife definitives were issued in both coil and booklet formats. These can be differentiated apart by looking at the serpentine die cutting.

**Peaks and valleys**

The serpentine die cutting on these stamps have *peaks* and *valleys*: A stamp is identified as either "valley at upper left" or "peak at upper left" based on the very first die cut:

Coils (valley at upper left) have 9 peaks/10 valleys along the top; booklets (peak at upper left) have 10 peaks/9 valleys along the top.

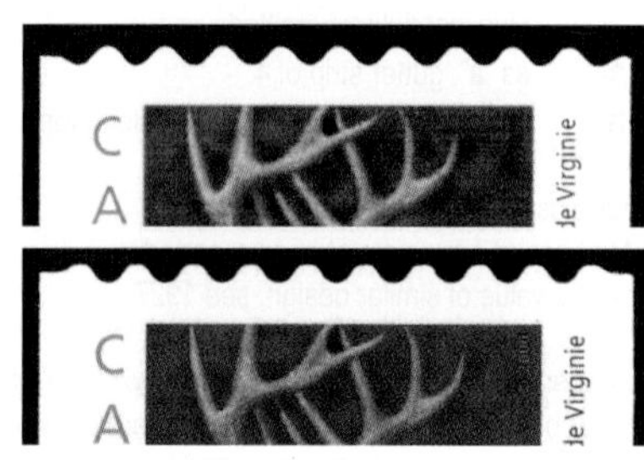
Top: coil (valley at upper left)
Bottom: booklet (peak at upper left)

Generally speaking, the three wildlife coils have a "valley at upper left" while the two booklet stamps have a "peak at upper left". With that said, the 60¢ Red Fox coil has been found with either a "valley" or a "peak" at upper left. Thankfully, there is another method available to separate our coil and booklet wildlife stamps.

**Hidden date**

The so-called "hidden date" (upper right corner of design) on the booklet stamps is lighter/brighter than that found on the coil stamps.

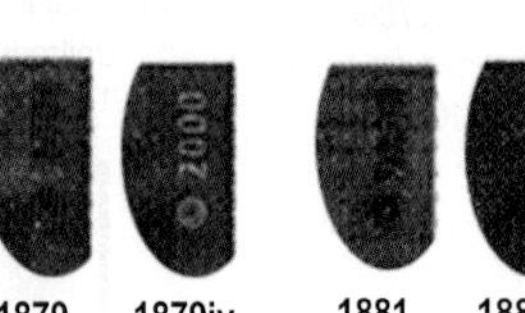
1879 | 1879iv | 1881 | 1881ii

Designer: Pierre-Yves Pelletier. Based on a painting by René Milot.
Lithography (5 colours), self-adhesive booklet pane of 6 / self-adhesive roll of 50
Ashton-Potter Canada Limited

**2000, Dec 28** **GT4, JAC Paper**
**Serpentine die cut 8.5 horizontal**

| | | NH–VF | ⊙F | FDC |
|---|---|---|---|---|
| | Coil | | | |
| **1879** | **60¢ multicoloured**, (valley at upper left) | 1.25 | .50 | — |
| i | gutter strip of 4 | 15.00 | | |
| | starter strip of 4 (with 10mm rouletted tab) | 15.00 | | |
| ii | 60¢ multicoloured (coil – peak at upper left) | 20.00 | 4.00 | |
| iii | gutter strip of 4 | 150.00 | | |
| | starter strip of 4 (with 10mm rouletted tab) | 150.00 | | |
| | Booklet | | | |
| iv | 60¢ multicoloured (peak at upper left), NF | 1.25 | .75 | |
| a | booklet pane of 6 x 60¢ (1879iv) (**BK238**) | 14.00 | | |
| v | LF (speckled) (single) | 2.50 | 1.00 | |
| ai | booklet pane of 6 x 60¢ (1879v) | 20.00 | | |
| vi | MF (single) | 2.50 | 1.00 | |
| aii | booklet pane of 6 x 60¢ (1879vi) | 20.00 | | |
| **1880** | **75¢ multicoloured** (valley at upper left) | 1.50 | .60 | — |
| i | gutter strip of 4 | 18.00 | | |
| | starter strip of 4 (with 10mm rouletted tab) | 18.00 | | |
| | Coil | | | |
| **1881** | **$1.05 multicoloured** (valley at upper left) | 2.25 | 1.00 | — |
| i | gutter strip of 4 | 21.00 | | |
| | starter strip of 4 (with 10mm rouletted tab) | 21.00 | | |
| | Booklet | | | |
| ii | $1.05 multicoloured (peak at upper left), (10 peaks), NF | 2.25 | 1.00 | |
| a | booklet pane of 6 x $1.05 (1881ii) (**BK239**) | 15.50 | | |
| iii | low fluorescence (speckled) (single) | 5.00 | 1.50 | |
| ai | booklet pane of 6 x $1.05 (1881iii) | 35.00 | | |

Counterfeit booklets of 1881 (BK239) are known to exist. These are of a very high quality.

**Nos. 1879-1881 (3) combination FDC** **5.40**
Coil display cards: 1878–1881 (set of 4) $15.00

The backing paper of the roll is rouletted between each stamp. The excess 'stamp' paper was removed between each stamp.10mm wide gutters appear every 25 stamps.

1879a | 1881a

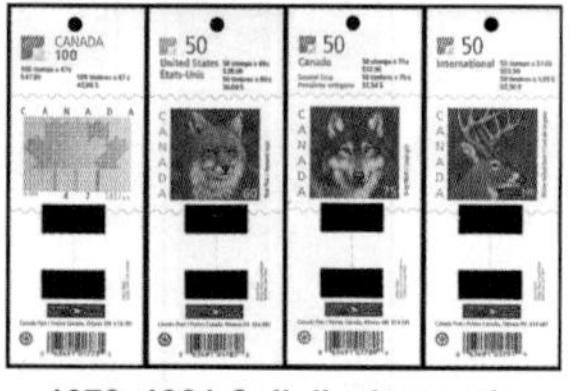
1878–1881 Coil display cards

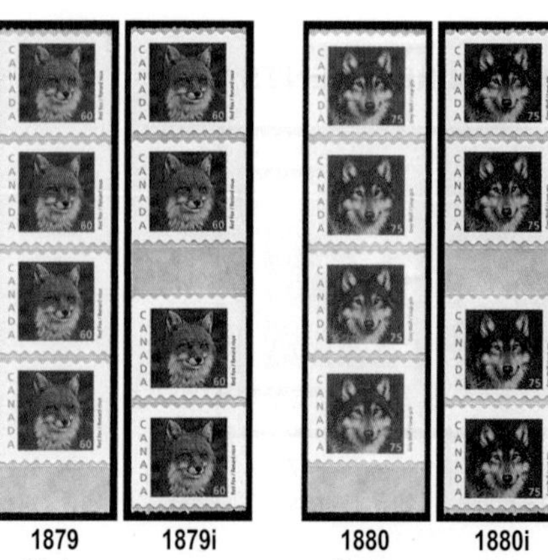
1879 Starter | 1879i | 1880 Starter | 1880i

1881 Starter | 1881i

## PICTURE POSTAGE™

**1882a**
Silver frame

**1882b**
Gold leaf frame

**1882c**
Mahogany frame

**1882d**
Love (roses) frame

**1882e**
Christmas frame

Designer: Steven Spazuk.
Lithography (10 colours), self-adhesive booklet pane of 5
Ashton-Potter Canada Limited

**2000, Dec 28** **GT4, JAC Paper** **Serpentine die cut 11.7**

| | | NH–VF | ⊙F | FDC |
|---|---|---|---|---|
| **1882** | $2.35 booklet pane of 5 x 47¢ (a–e) + 5 labels, DF | 6.50 | — | |
| a | **47¢ silver and multicoloured** | 1.25 | 1.25 | |
| b | **47¢ gold and multicoloured** | 1.25 | 1.25 | |
| c | **47¢ multicoloured** | 1.25 | 1.25 | |
| d | **47¢ red and multicoloured** | 1.25 | 1.25 | |
| e | **47¢ multicoloured** | 1.25 | 1.25 | |
| i | as 1882, pane of 5, MF | 25.00 | | |
| ii | as 1882, 'unglued' full pane of 5 † | 15.00 | | |
| f | pane of 25 x 47¢ stamps + personalized stickers* | *100.00* | | |

**BK240** pane 1882 in cover $8.00

Used prices are for a stamp without personalized label. With label used price is $2.00.

**Nos. 1882a-1882e (5) combination FDC** 5.30

† 1882 is glued to the booklet cover (BK240). The 'unglued' pane (1882ii) was distributed in the Quarterly Pack/Annual Collection and will show no signs of removal from a booklet cover.

* Personalized stickers with any frame (special order) – See 1853b.

The frames show "Canada 47" on 2 adjacent sides so the stamp can be placed in either portrait or landscape format.

For 46¢ Gold leaf frame see 1853. For 46¢ Christmas frame see 1872.

For non-denominated values of similar designs, see 1918a–e.

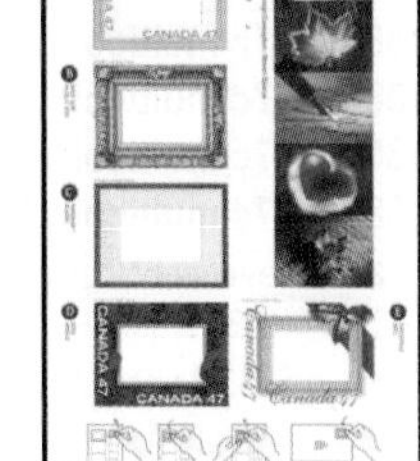

**1882**

## 2001

| | | |
|---|---|---|
| **Rates:** | Domestic first-class (0-30g): 47¢ | |
| Jan 1/01– | Domestic first-class (30-50g): 75¢ | USA (0-30g): 60¢ |
| Jan 13/02 | Domestic oversize (30-50g): 94¢ | International (0-20g): $1.05 |

*single usage:* USA 60¢: $15.00 | International $1.05: $25.00

### LUNAR NEW YEAR — 5
### Year of the Snake

**1883**
Snake and Chinese Symbol

**1884i**
Snake and Chinese Symbol

Designer: Marlene Wou. Based on a sculpture by Lyle Sopel.
Digital photography by Montizambert Photography. Calligraphed by Yukman Lai.
Lithography (9 colours; s/s: 10 colours) and Embossed, pane of 25
Ashton-Potter Canada Limited

**2001, Jan 5** **GT2, TRC Paper** **Perf 14.0x13.4**

| | | NH–VF | ⊙F | PB | FDC |
|---|---|---|---|---|---|
| **1883** | **47¢ multicoloured** | 1.00 | .30 | 4.75 | 2.00 |
| a | gold omitted* | 2,000.00 | — | 9,500.00 | |

Qty: 16,280,000
* 4 panes of 25 known.

| | | NH–VF | ⊙F | PB | FDC |
|---|---|---|---|---|---|
| **1884** | **$1.05 souvenir sheet** | 3.00 | 3.00 | — | 3.00 |
| i | $1.05 single from souvenir sheet | 2.50 | 1.50 | | |
| ii | $24.95 uncut press sheet of 12 souvenir sheets | 60.00 | | | |

Qty: 1884: 2,980,000; 1884ii: 35,000

Tagging does not extend into the top and bottom bands of colour.
See also 1630, 1708, 1767–1768, 1836–1837, 1933–1934, 1969–1970, 2015–2016, 2083–2084, 2140–2141, 2201–2202, 2257–2258.

**1883a**

**1884**

## NHL ALL STARS — 2

1885a
Jean Béliveau (1931–2014)

1885b
Terry Sawchuk (1929–1970)

1885c
Eddie Shore (1902–1985)

1885d
Denis Potvin (1953– )

1885e
Bobby Hull (1939– )

1885f
Syl Apps (1915–1998)

Designer: Stéphane Huot. Based on an illustration by Charles Vinh.
Lithography (5 colours), pane of 6 + 3 tabs
Ashton-Potter Canada Limited

**2001, Jan 18** **Tagged, TRC Paper** **Perf 12.5x13.2**

| | | NH–VF | ⊙F | FDC |
|---|---|---|---|---|
| **1885** | $2.82 pane of 6 x 47¢ | 6.00 | 6.00 | |
| a | **47¢ multicoloured** | 1.00 | .60 | |
| b | **47¢ multicoloured** | 1.00 | .60 | |
| c | **47¢ multicoloured** | 1.00 | .60 | |
| d | **47¢ multicoloured** | 1.00 | .60 | |
| e | **47¢ multicoloured** | 1.00 | .60 | |
| f | **47¢ multicoloured** | 1.00 | .60 | |
| g | strip of 3 (1885a, 1885c, 1885e), blue circle and text omitted | 8,000.00* | | |

Qty: 3,000,000 of each
* The only mint strip reported to date is damaged at bottom.

**Three combination FDCs: a+b, c+d and e+f** **7.50**

General tagging appears around the inner edge of the large circle on each stamp.
Issued for the 51st National Hockey League All-Star Game.
See also 1443–1445, 1838, 1935, 1971–1972, 2017–2018, 2085–2086.

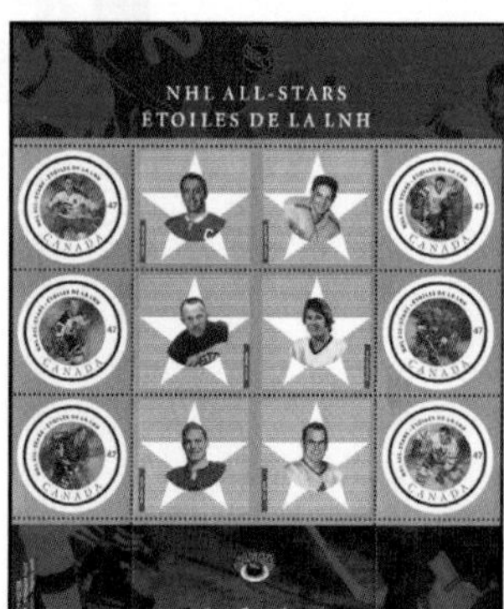


1885

## BIRDS OF CANADA — 6a

*Perforated singles from water-activated gum pane*

1886
Golden Eagle

1887
Arctic Tern

1888
Rock Ptarmigan

1889
Lapland Longspur

## BIRDS OF CANADA — 6b

*Die cut singles from self-adhesive booklet*

1890
Golden Eagle

1891
Arctic Tern

1892
Rock Ptarmigan

1893
Lapland Longspur

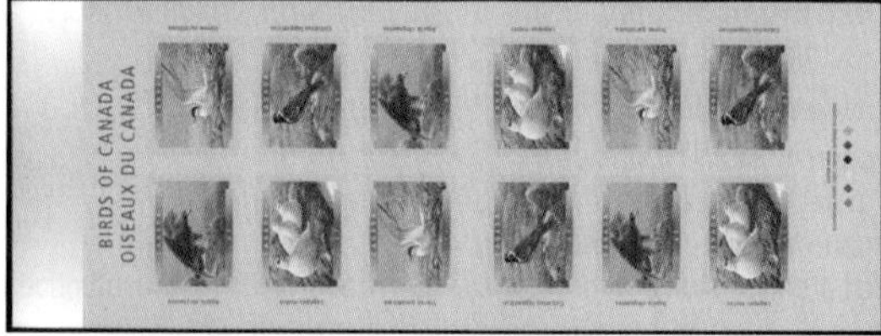


1893a
(top half)

1893b
(bottom half)

Designer: Raymond Bellemare. Based on paintings by Pierre Leduc.
Lithography (5 colours), water-activated gum pane of 20
Ashton-Potter Canada Limited

**2001, Feb 1** **GT4, TRC Paper** **Perf 12.5x13.1**

| | | NH–VF | ⊙F | PB | FDC |
|---|---|---|---|---|---|
| **1886** | **47¢ multicoloured** | 1.00 | .40 | | |
| **1887** | **47¢ multicoloured** | 1.00 | .40 | | |
| **1888** | **47¢ multicoloured** | 1.00 | .40 | | |
| **1889** | **47¢ multicoloured** | 1.00 | .40 | | |
| a | se-tenant block or strip of 4 different (1886–1889) | 4.50 | 3.50 | 5.00 | 5.00 |
| i | $56.40 uncut press sheet of 6 panes, unsigned | 200.00 | | | |
| | as "i", signed (issue price $89.95) | 300.00 | | | |

Qty: 2,099,000 of each; 1886–89i: 1,500; 1886–89i signed: 800.

On sheet stamps, two types of tagging have been reported: bright and dull (less common).

Lithography (5 colours), self-adhesive booklet pane of 12
Ashton-Potter Canada Limited

| 2001, Feb 1 | GT4, JAC Paper | Die cut perf 11.6x11.4 | | |
|---|---|---|---|---|
| | | NH–VF | ⊙F | FDC |
| **1890** | **47¢ multicoloured** | 1.25 | .50 | |
| **1891** | **47¢ multicoloured** | 1.25 | .50 | |
| **1892** | **47¢ multicoloured** | 1.25 | .50 | |
| **1893** | **47¢ multicoloured** | 1.25 | .50 | |
| i | booklet pane of 12, trimmed and unfolded* | 20.00 | | |
| a | booklet pane of 6 x 47¢ (1892, 1893 + 2 each of 1890, 1891) | 7.50 | — | |
| b | booklet pane of 6 x 47¢ (1890, 1891 + 2 each of 1892, 1893) | 7.50 | — | |

**BK241** one each of panes 1893a, 1893b $15.50
Qty: 2,100,000 of each
* from "Write Me" kit. Pane is unfolded but trimmed at top and bottom (there is no text at top and no inscriptions at the bottom).

See also 1591–1594, 1631–1634, 1710–1713, 1770–1777, 1839–1846.
For non-denominated envelopes of nos. 1886/1890 and 1889/1893 designs, see U162–U163.

## GAMES OF LA FRANCOPHONIE

**1894** High Jumper
**1895** Folk Dancer

Designer: Clermont Malenfant. Based on a photograph by M. Stirn.
Lithography (9 colours plus varnish), pane of 16
Canadian Bank Note Company, Limited

| 2001, Feb 28 | GT4, TRC Paper | | | Perf 13.3 |
|---|---|---|---|---|
| | NH–VF | ⊙F | PB | FDC |
| **1894** **47¢ multicoloured** | .95 | .35 | — | |
| **1895** **47¢ multicoloured** | .95 | .35 | — | |
| a se-tenant pair (1894, 1985) | 2.00 | 1.25 | 4.75 | 2.50 |

Qty: 2,500,000 of each

Issued for the IV games of La Francophonie, in Ottawa in 2001.

## WORLD FIGURE SKATING CHAMPIONSHIPS

**1896** Pairs
**1897** Ice Dancing

**1898** Men's Singles
**1899** Women's Singles

Designer: Barbara Hodgson. Based on photographs by Lorne Bridgman.
Lithography (9 colours), pane of 16 + horizontal gutter
Canadian Bank Note Company, Limited

| 2001, Mar 19 | GT4, TRC Paper | | | Perf 13.1x12.5 |
|---|---|---|---|---|
| | NH–VF | ⊙F | PB | FDC |
| **1896** **47¢ multicoloured** | .95 | .40 | — | — |
| **1897** **47¢ multicoloured** | .95 | .40 | — | — |
| **1898** **47¢ multicoloured** | .95 | .40 | — | — |
| **1899** **47¢ multicoloured** | .95 | .40 | — | — |
| a se-tenant block of 4 different (1896–1899) | 4.00 | 3.00 | 4.75 | 4.35 |
| i vert. pair with perforated gutter between | 3.00 | 2.00 | | |

Qty: 2,000,000 of each

The pane consists of two se-tenant blocks of 4 above and two se-tenant blocks of 4 below a horizontal perforated gutter.

Issued to celebrate the ISU World Figure Skating Championships, held in Vancouver in 2001.

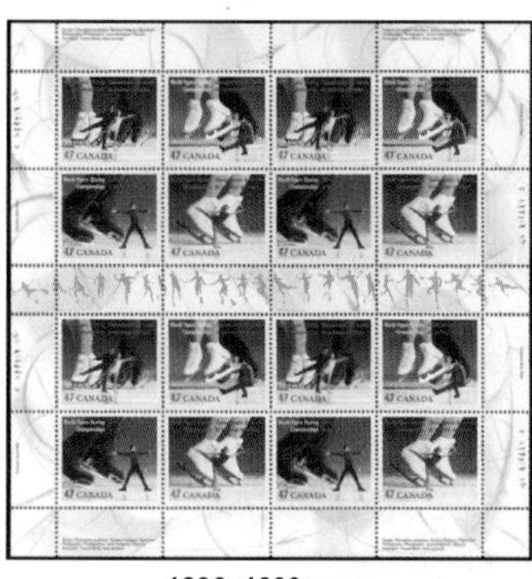

1896–1899 pane

1900 pane

## CANADA POST – 150 YEARS

**1900**
3d beaver, stamp on stamp

Designer: Tom Yakobina. Engraved by Larry O'Gorman.
Lithography (4 colours) and Engraved (1 colour), pane of 8
Canadian Bank Note Company, Limited

| 2001, Apr 6 | GT4*, TRC Paper | Perf 12.8x12.9 | | |
|---|---|---|---|---|
| | | NH–VF | ⊙F | FDC |
| **1900** | **47¢ multicoloured** | 1.00 | .35 | 1.50 |
| i | accent above R of THREE (pos. 6) | 7.50 | 2.50 | |
| | full pane of 8 | 10.00 | | |

Qty: 5,000,000

* The tagging is applied to the frame around the inside stamp image.

Pane was sold in souvenir folder containing a 12-page pamphlet. Two different UPC barcodes exist: Field stock ends with "01930 2"; philatelic stock ends with "01931 9".

Issued for the 150th anniversary of the transfer of postal authority from Britain to Canada.

1900i

QE II — 2000's

## TORONTO BLUE JAYS

**1901**
Emblem for 25th anniversary of the Toronto Blue Jays baseball team

Designer: Paul Haslip. Designed by Omar Morson.
Lithography (5 colours), self-adhesive booklet pane of 8
Ashton-Potter Canada Limited

| **2001, Apr 9** | **GT4, JAC Paper** | | | **Die cut** |
|---|---|---|---|---|
| | | NH–VF | ⊙F | FDC |
| **1901** | **47¢ multicoloured** | 1.25 | .35 | 1.50 |
| i | die cut to shape from Quarterly Pack/ Annual Collection | 3.50 | | |
| a | booklet pane of 8 x 47¢ (1901) (**BK242**) | 10.50 | — | |

Qty: 10,000,000

**1901a**

## SUMMIT OF THE AMERICAS

**1902**
The western hemisphere as if alone on the globe

Designer: Denis L'Allier. Based on a photograph by Mountain High Maps.
Lithography (5 colours), pane of 16
Ashton-Potter Canada Limited

| **2001, Apr 20** | **GT4, TRC Paper** | | | **Perf 13.3x13.0** | |
|---|---|---|---|---|---|
| | | NH–VF | ⊙F | PB | FDC |
| **1902** | **47¢ multicoloured** | 1.00 | .35 | 4.75 | 1.50 |

Qty: 3,000,000

Issued for the Third Summit of the Americas, held at Québec in 2001.

## TOURIST ATTRACTIONS

**1903a**
Butchart Gardens, BC

**1903b**
Apple Blossom Festival, NS

**1903c**
White Pass and Yukon Route

**1903d**
Sugar Bushes, QC

**1903e**
Niagara-On-The-Lake, ON

**1904a**
The Forks, MB

**1904b**
Barkerville, BC

**1904c**
Canadian Tulip Festival, ON

**1904d**
Auyuittuq National Park, NU

**1904e**
Signal Hill National Historic Site, NF

Designer: Catharine Bradbury and Jennifer Hood.
Lithography (8 colours), self-adhesive booklet panes of 5
Canadian Bank Note Company, Limited

| **2001, May 11** | **GT4, JAC Paper** | **Die cut perf 11.3x11.4** | | |
|---|---|---|---|---|
| | | NH–VF | ⊙F | FDC |
| **1903** | booklet pane of 5 x 60¢ (a–e) (**BK243**) | 7.00 | — | |
| a | **60¢ Butchart Gardens, BC** | 1.25 | 1.00 | |
| b | **60¢ Apple Blossom Festival, NS** | 1.25 | 1.00 | |
| c | **60¢ White Pass and Yukon Route** | 1.25 | 1.00 | |
| d | **60¢ Sugar Bushes, QC** | 1.25 | 1.00 | |
| e | **60¢ Niagara-On-The-Lake, ON** | 1.25 | 1.00 | |
| i | unfolded strip of 5 stamps* | 10.00 | | |

Qty: 3,750,000 of each

**Nos. 1903a–1903e (5) combination FDC** 7.50

| | | NH–VF | ⊙F | FDC |
|---|---|---|---|---|
| **1904** | booklet pane of 5 x $1.05 (a–e) (**BK244**) | 11.50 | — | |
| a | **$1.05 The Forks, MB** | 2.25 | 1.50 | |
| b | **$1.05 Barkerville, BC** | 2.25 | 1.50 | |
| c | **$1.05 Canadian Tulip Festival, ON** | 2.25 | 1.50 | |
| d | **$1.05 Auyuittuq National Park, NU** | 2.25 | 1.50 | |
| e | **$1.05 Signal Hill National Historic Site, NF** | 2.25 | 1.50 | |
| i | unfolded strip of 5 stamps* | 13.50 | | |

Qty: 3,750,000 of each

**Nos. 1904a–1904e (5) combination FDC** 12.50

* The 2001 Annual Collection included unfolded strips of 5 stamps from each pane; the top and bottom of the booklet panes were trimmed.

See also 1952–1953, 1989–1990, 2019–2023. For non-denominated postal cards of same designs, see UX127A. For non-denominated envelopes of some designs, see U184–U203.

1903

1904

## ARMENIAN CHURCH - 17 CENTURIES

**1905**
Elements of the Armenian Church

Designer: Debbie Adams. Based on photographs by Christine Guest, Brian Merrett, Hrair Hawk Khatcherian. Based on a drawing by Izit ( Psak ).

Lithography (6 colours), pane of 16 + 9 tabs
Ashton-Potter Canada Limited

**2001, May 16** **GT4, TRC Paper** **Perf 13.2x12.5**

| | | NH–VF | ⊙F | PB | FDC |
|---|---|---|---|---|---|
| **1905** | **47¢ multicoloured** | .95 | .35 | 4.75 | 1.50 |
| i | horizontal pair, gutter between | 2.00 | 1.25 | | |
| ii | vertical pair, gutter between | 2.00 | 1.50 | | |
| iii | cross gutter block of 4 | 10.00 | 6.00 | | |

Qty: 3,000,000

The pane is divided into four blocks of 4 by a vertical strip of labels and a perforated horizontal gutter through the middle of the pane.

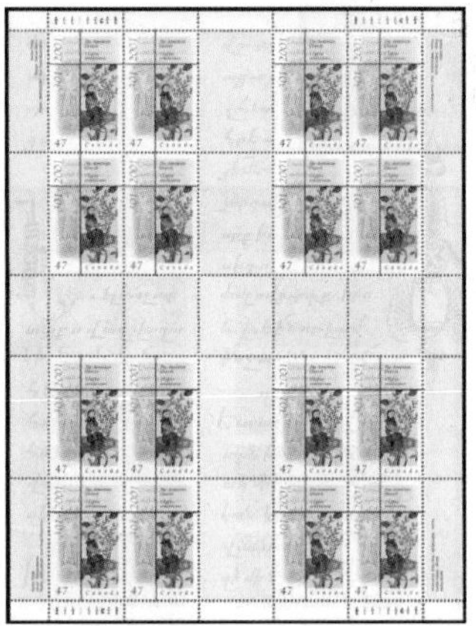
**1905** full pane

## ROYAL MILITARY COLLEGE

**1906**
Royal Military College

Designer: Jim Hudson. Based on photographs by Rod Stears; Department of National Defence; and Royal Military College Archives.

Lithography (4 colours), pane of 16
Canadian Bank Note Company, Limited

**2001, Jun 1** **GT4, TRC Paper** **Perf 12.5x13.1**

| | | NH–VF | ⊙F | PB | FDC |
|---|---|---|---|---|---|
| **1906** | **47¢ multicoloured** | .95 | .35 | 4.75 | 1.50 |

Qty: 5,000,000

Issued to celebrate the 125th anniversary of the Royal Military College of Canada. See also 692, 693.

## IAAF WORLD CHAMPIONSHIPS

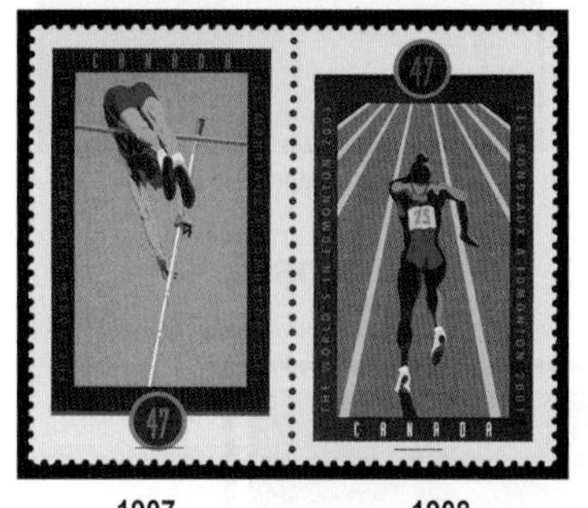

**1907** Pole vault
**1908** Runner

Designer: Tim Nokes. Produced by Neil Petrunia.

Lithography (7 colours), pane of 16
Ashton-Potter Canada Limited

**2001, Jun 25** **GT4, TRC Paper** **Perf 12.7x12.5**

| | | NH–VF | ⊙F | PB | FDC |
|---|---|---|---|---|---|
| **1907** | **47¢ multicoloured** | .95 | .35 | | |
| **1908** | **47¢ multicoloured** | .95 | .35 | | |
| **a** | se-tenant pair (1907, 1908) | 2.00 | 1.25 | 4.75 | 3.90 |

Qty: 2,000,000 of each

Issued for the International Amateur Athletic Federation's World Championships in Athletics, held at Edmonton in 2001.

## PIERRE ELLIOTT TRUDEAU

**1909**
Portrait of Trudeau

QE II — 2000's

Designer: Tom Yakobina. Based on a painting by Myfanwy Pavelic.

Lithography (7 colours), pane of 16

Ashton-Potter Canada Limited

| 2001, Jul 1 | GT4*, Peterborough Paper | | | Perf 13.1x12.5 | |
|---|---|---|---|---|---|
| | | NH–VF | ⊙F | PB | FDC |
| **1909** | **47¢ multicoloured** | .95 | .35 | 4.75 | 2.95 |
| a | $1.88 souvenir sheet of 4 (1909) | 4.50 | 4.50 | | |

Qty: 6,000,000; souvenir sheet: 500,000 panes

* The tagging is applied to the white frame surrounding the inside painting.

Pierre Elliott Trudeau (1919–2000), Prime Minister of Canada (1968–1979, 1980–1984).

1909a

## ROSES

*Perforated singles from water-activated gum souvenir sheet*

1910a
Morden Centennial

1910b
Agnes

1910c
Champlain

1910d
Canadian White Star

*Die cut singles from self-adhesive booklet*

1911
Morden Centennial

1912
Agnes

1913
Champlain

1914
Canadian White Star

Designer: Gerry Takeuchi. Based on a photograph by Alex Waterhouse-Hayward.

Lithography (9 colours), water-activated gum souvenir sheet of 4

Ashton-Potter Canada Limited

| 2001, Aug 1 | GT4, TRC Paper | | Perf 12.5x13.1 | |
|---|---|---|---|---|
| | | NH–VF | ⊙F | FDC |
| **1910** | $1.88 souvenir sheet of 4 different | 6.00 | 6.00 | |
| a | **47¢ multicoloured** | 1.50 | 1.50 | |
| b | **47¢ multicoloured** | 1.50 | 1.50 | |
| c | **47¢ multicoloured** | 1.50 | 1.50 | |
| d | **47¢ multicoloured** | 1.50 | 1.50 | |

Qty: 300,000 of each

Lithography (9 colours), self-adhesive booklet pane of 12

| 2001, Aug 1 | GT4, JAC Paper | | Die cut |
|---|---|---|---|
| **1911** | **47¢ multicoloured** | 1.00 | .40 |
| **1912** | **47¢ multicoloured** | 1.00 | .40 |
| **1913** | **47¢ multicoloured** | 1.00 | .40 |
| **1914** | **47¢ multicoloured** | 1.00 | .40 |
| a | booklet pane of 4 x 47¢ (1911–1914) | 4.00 | — |
| BK245 | booklet of 3 x 1914a $12.50 | | |

Qty: 3,000,000 of each

**Nos. 1911–1914 (4) combination FDC** 5.75

Self-adhesive single prices are for "full" examples with both left and top nib extensions. Stamps with missing nibs sell for less.

For non-denominated envelopes of same designs, see U170–U173.

1910

3 x 1914a (BK245)

## THE GREAT PEACE OF MONTRÉAL

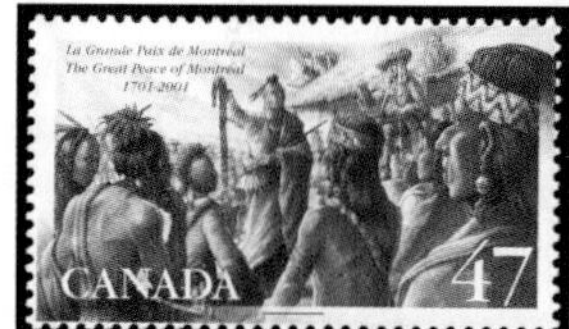

1915
Great Peace negotiations

Designer: Normand Tessier. Based on an illustration by Francis Back.
Lithography (5 colours), pane of 16 + 8 tabs
Ashton-Potter Canada Limited

| 2001, Aug 3 | GT4, TRC Paper | | | Perf 12.5x13.1 | |
|---|---|---|---|---|---|
| | | NH–VF | ⊙F | PB | FDC |
| **1915** | **47¢ multicoloured** | .95 | .35 | 4.75 | 2.95 |
| i | horizontal pair, gutter between | 2.00 | 1.50 | | |

Qty: 4,000,000

Issued to celebrate the 400th anniversary of the Great Peace of Montréal which led to peace among the French and some 30 First People's nations.

## MASTERPIECES OF CANADIAN ART — 14

1916
*The Space Between Columns #21 (Italian)*

Designer: Pierre-Yves Pelletier. Based on a painting by Jack Leonard Shadbolt.
Lithography (5 colours) with foil stamping, pane of 16
Canadian Bank Note Company, Limited

| 2001, Aug 24 | TRC Paper | | | Perf 13.0x13.3 | |
|---|---|---|---|---|---|
| | | NH–VF | ⊙F | PB | FDC |
| **1916** | **$1.05 multicoloured** (silver) | 2.25 | 1.25 | 10.50 | 5.00 |

Qty: 4,000,000

See also 1203, 1241, 1271, 1310, 1419, 1466, 1516, 1545, 1602, 1635, 1754, 1800, 1863, 1945.

## SHRINERS

1917
Clown juggling crutches and boy with braces

Designer: Monique Dufour and Sophie Lafortune. Based on a photograph by François LeClair.
Lithography (5 colours), pane of 16
Ashton-Potter Canada Limited

| 2001, Sep 19 | GT4, TRC Paper | | | Perf 13.3x13.0 | |
|---|---|---|---|---|---|
| | | NH–VF | ⊙F | PB | FDC |
| **1917** | **47¢ multicoloured** | .95 | .35 | 4.75 | 2.95 |

Qty: 5,000,000

Issued to honour the Shriners and their network of Children's Hospitals.

## PICTURE POSTAGE™

1918a
Silver frame

1918b
Gold leaf frame

1918c
Baby frame

1918d
Love (roses) frame

1918e
Christmas frame

Designer: Steven Spazuk.
Lithography (10 colours), booklet pane of 5†
Ashton-Potter Canada Limited

| 2001, Sep 21 | GT4, JAC Paper Serpentine die cut 11.7 | | | |
|---|---|---|---|---|
| | | NH–VF | ⊙F | FDC |
| **1918** | $2.35 booklet pane of 5 x (47¢) (a–e) + 5 labels | 7.50 | — | |
| a | **(47¢) silver and multicoloured** | 1.25 | 1.25 | |
| b | **(47¢) gold and multicoloured** | 1.25 | 1.25 | |
| c | **(47¢) multicoloured** | 1.25 | 1.25 | |
| d | **(47¢) red and multicoloured** | 1.25 | 1.25 | |
| e | **(47¢) multicoloured** | 1.25 | 1.25 | |
| f | pane of 25 x (47¢) stamps (any frame) + 25 personalized stickers* | *100.00* | | |
| g | pane of 10 x (47¢) stamps (1918b) + 10 personalized stickers* | *80.00* | | |
| **BK246** | pane 1918 in cover $8.00 | | | |

Used prices are for a stamp without personalized label. With label used price is $2.00.

† Booklet panes of 5 different stamps and 5 different standardized stickers.

**Nos. 1918a–1918e (5) combination FDC** **6.70**

The frames show "CANADA" on 2 adjacent sides so the stamp can be placed in either portrait or landscape format.

* Individuals or businesses could order customized stickers (reproduced from a single photograph submitted by the purchaser) with any one of the five stamp designs in panes of 25. Panes of 25 cost $24.95 each (1 or 2 panes) and $22.95 each for 3–10 panes. In addition, customized panes of 10 (gold leaf frame only) were available via a special Fuji Film promotion ($5 for a pane of 10). The stickers and stamps are printed on the same sheet. Literally thousands (or hundreds of thousands?) of different customized stickers have likely been ordered of all of the Picture Postage™ stamps (an impossible task to catalogue or collect).

For 46¢ Gold Leaf frame see 1853. For 47¢ values of similar designs, see 1882a–e.

1918

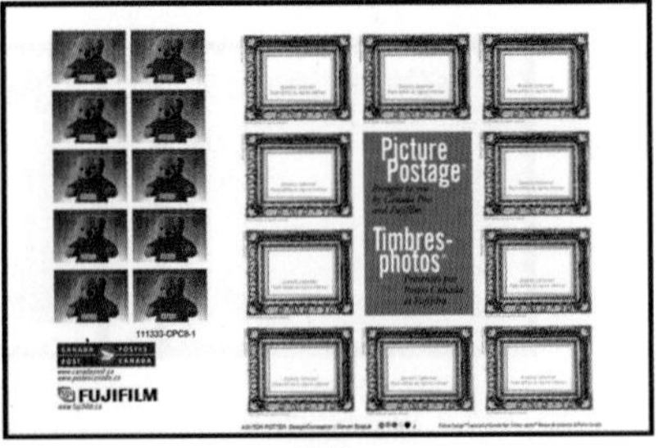
1918g

Panes of 10 (above) and 25 (below) with customized stickers; available only via special order.

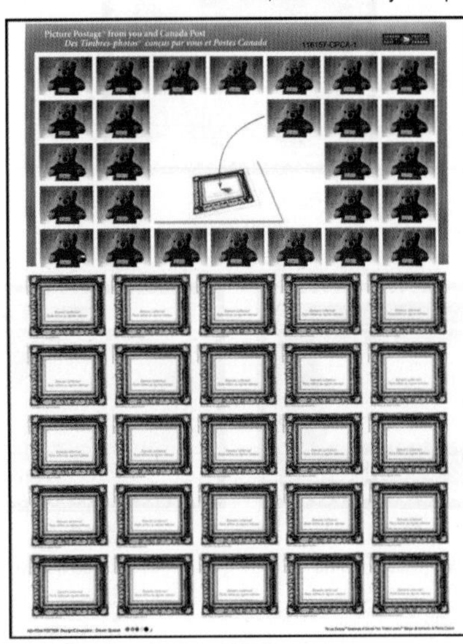
1918f

## THEATRES

1919 Théâtre du Nouveau Monde, Montréal
1920 The Grand Theatre, London

Designer: Pierre Léonard, Marc Serre, and Serge Côté.
Lithography (5 colours), pane of 16
Ashton-Potter Canada Limited

**2001, Sep 28** **GT4, TRC Paper** **Perf 12.5x12.7**

| | | NH–VF | ⊙F | PB | FDC |
|---|---|---|---|---|---|
| **1919** | **47¢ multicoloured** | 1.00 | .35 | — | |
| **1920** | **47¢ multicoloured** | 1.00 | .35 | — | |
| **a** | se-tenant horizontal pair (1919, 1920) | 2.10 | 1.25 | 4.40 | 3.90 |

Qty: 2,000,000 of each

## HOT AIR BALLOONS

1921a

1921b

1921c 1921d

Designer: Lise Giguère. Based on an illustration by Dan Fell.
Lithography (6 colours), booklet pane of 8
Canadian Bank Note Company, Limited

**2001, Oct 1** **GT4, TRC Paper** **Die cut**

| | | NH–VF | ⊙F | FDC |
|---|---|---|---|---|
| **1921** | $3.76 booklet of 8 x 47¢ (2 each of a–d) (**BK247**) | 10.50 | — | |
| **a** | **47¢ multicoloured** (green sky) | 1.25 | .50 | |
| **b** | **47¢ multicoloured** (mauve sky) | 1.25 | .50 | |
| **c** | **47¢ multicoloured** (burgundy sky) | 1.25 | .50 | |
| **d** | **47¢ multicoloured** (honey-brown sky) | 1.25 | .50 | |
| **i** | half-pane of 4 stamps, printed on gum side | 400.00 | | |

Qty: 2,000,000 of each

**Nos. 1921a–1921d (4) combination FDC** 5.75

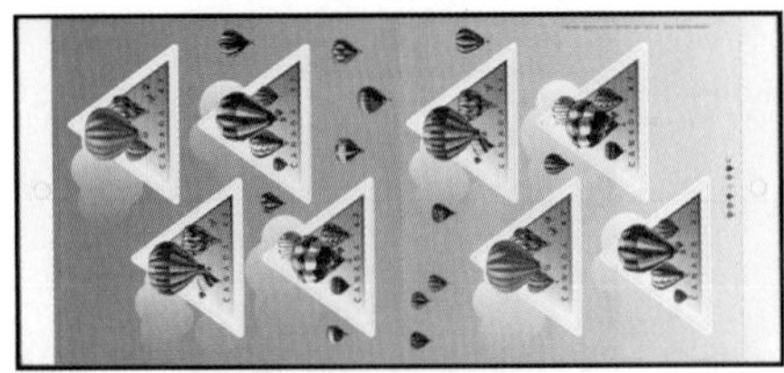
1921

## CHRISTMAS LIGHTS

1922
Sleigh Ride in an Urban Landscape

1923
Skating in the Suburbs

1924
Building a Snowman in the Country

1922a

1923a

1924a

Designer: Robert L. Peters, Carisa L. Romans, and 'Segun Olude.
Based on photographs by Malak Karsh and Mike Grandmaison.

Lithography (7 colours), panes of 25
Canadian Bank Note Company, Limited

**2001, Nov 1** **GT4, TRC Paper** **Perf 12.5x13.2**

| | | NH–VF | ⊙F | PB | FDC |
|---|---|---|---|---|---|
| **1922** | **47¢ multicoloured** | 1.00 | .30 | 4.75 | |
| a | booklet pane of 10 x 47¢ (1922) | 10.00 | | | |
| **BK248** | pane 1922a in cover $11.00 | | | | |

Qty: 64,815,000

| | | NH–VF | ⊙F | PB | FDC |
|---|---|---|---|---|---|
| **1923** | **60¢ multicoloured** | 1.20 | .50 | 6.00 | |
| a | booklet pane of 6 x 60¢ (1923) | 10.00 | | | |
| **BK249** | pane 1923a in cover $10.50 | | | | |

Qty: 10,922,000

| | | NH–VF | ⊙F | PB | FDC |
|---|---|---|---|---|---|
| **1924** | **$1.05 multicoloured** | 2.10 | .80 | 10.50 | |
| a | booklet pane of 6 x $1.05 (1924) | 13.50 | | | |
| **BK250** | pane 1924a in cover $14.00 | | | | |

Qty: 10,992,000

**Nos. 1922–1924 (3) combination FDC** **6.25**

1925
YMCA in Canada

1926
Legion badge over a portion of the National War Memorial

## YMCA

Designer: Hélène L'Heureux.

Lithography (5 colours), pane of 16
Canadian Bank Note Company, Limited

**2001, Nov 8** **GT4, TRC Paper** **Perf 13.3x13.4**

| | | NH–VF | ⊙F | PB | FDC |
|---|---|---|---|---|---|
| **1925** | **47¢ multicoloured** | 1.00 | .35 | 4.75 | 2.95 |

Qty: 4,000,000

Issued to celebrate the Young Men's Christian Association's 150 years of service in Canada.

## THE ROYAL CANADIAN LEGION, 1926–2001

Designer: Neville Smith. Based on a photograph by Veterans Affairs Canada.
Based on a sculpture designed by Vernon March.

Lithography (5 colours), pane of 16
Canadian Bank Note Company, Limited

**2001, Nov 11** **GT4, TRC Paper** **Perf 12.5x13.1**

| | | NH–VF | ⊙F | PB | FDC |
|---|---|---|---|---|---|
| **1926** | **47¢ multicoloured** | 1.00 | .35 | 4.75 | 2.95 |

Qty: 3,000,000

75th anniversary of the formation of The Canadian Legion of the British Empire Service League (became The Royal Canadian Legion in 1960).

First Canadian commemorative stamp to include a UPC barcode on pane selvedge.

**1926 full pane with UPC barcode**

# 2002

## DEFINITIVES 2002–2004

## DOMESTIC FIRST-CLASS RATE COIL

1927
Stylized Maple Leaf

Designer: Pierre-Yves Pelletier.

Lithography (5 colours), self-adhesive roll of 100
Ashton-Potter (USA) Limited

**2002, Jan 2** **GT4, TRC Paper**
**Serpentine die cut 8.5 horizontal**

| | | NH–VF | ⊙F | FDC |
|---|---|---|---|---|
| **1927** | **48¢ multicoloured**, 10 peaks along top | 1.00 | .25 | 3.00 |
| i | gutter strip of 4 | 10.00 | | |
| | starter strip of 4 (with 10mm rouletted tab) | 10.00 | | |
| | starter strip of 4 (with 5mm wavy die-cut tab), *Feb 2002* | 15.00 | | |
| | end strip of 4 (with 5mm wavy die-cut tab), *Feb 2002* | 15.00 | | |
| | starter strip of 4 (with 5mm straight die-cut tab), *Mar 2003* | 12.00 | | |
| | end strip of 4 (with 5mm straight die-cut tab), *Mar 2003* | 12.00 | | |
| iii | inverted die cutting, 9 peaks along top | * | | |

* Only 2 mint copies have been reported; no used copies have yet been reported.
For 47¢ value of similar design, see 1878.

**Coil display card: 1927, black and white logo: $0.75**
**Coil display card: 1927, colour logo: $0.75**

1927iii
Inverted die cutting
(9 peaks along top)

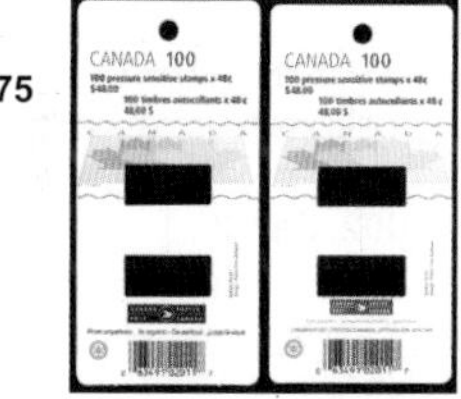
1927 Coil display cards
(left: B&W logo;
right: coloured logo)

## TRADITIONAL TRADES DEFINITIVES MEDIUM-VALUE

**Booklets**
(9 peaks/valley at upper left)

1928ii
Jewelry

1930ii
Sculpture

**Coils**
(10 peaks/peak at upper left)

1928
Jewelry

1929
Basket weaving

1930
Sculpture

The 65¢ and $1.25 Traditional Trades definitives were issued in both coil and booklet formats. These can be differentiated by looking at the serpentine die cutting.

**Peaks and valleys**

The serpentine die cutting on these stamps have *peaks* and *valleys*: A stamp is identified as either "peak at upper left" or "valley at upper left" based on the very first die cut:

The three Trades coils have a "peak at upper left" while the two booklet stamps have a "valley at upper left".

Top: coil (peak at upper left)
Bottom: booklet (valley at upper left)

Coils (peak at upper left) have 10 peaks/9 valleys along the top; booklets (valley at upper left) have 9 peaks/10 valleys along the top.

A shift in the die cutting may result in the apparent reversal of a peak/valley at the upper left. As illustrated in the bottom image above, notice that there is a plateau at the left and right side.

**Coloured "perfs"**

The two Trades booklet stamps (65¢ and $1.25) come, by design, three different ways based on the appearance of ink colour on the tips of the serpentine die cuts. This is due to the position of the stamp within the booklet pane.

The two stamps in the first row of the booklet pane will (generally) have coloured ink on the tips of both the top and bottom die cuts; stamps from the second row will have coloured ink on only the top die cuts; stamps in the third row will have coloured ink on only the bottom die cuts. If there is a shift in the die cutting, the amount of coloured ink on the die cut tips will vary. In some instances where there would generally be coloured tips, a significant shift in the die cutting will result in no ink touching the die cutting.

Designer: Monique Dufour and Sophie Lafortune.
Based on photographs by Richard Robitaille. Based on a jewel by Anne Sportun.
Lithography (5 colours), self-adhesive booklet pane of 6 / self-adhesive rolls of 50
Ashton-Potter (USA) Limited

**2002, Jan 2** **GT4, JAC Paper**
**Serpentine die cut 8.5 horizontal**

| | | NH–VF | ⊙F | FDC |
|---|---|---|---|---|
| | Coil (10 peaks along top/peak at upper left) | | | |
| **1928** | **65¢ multicoloured** | 1.30 | .40 | — |
| i | gutter strip of 4 | 13.00 | | |
| | starter strip of 4 (with 10mm rouletted tab) | 13.00 | | |
| | starter strip of 4 (with 5mm wavy die-cut tab), *Feb 2002* | 18.00 | | |
| | end strip of 4 (with 5mm wavy die-cut tab), *Feb 2002* | 18.00 | | |
| | starter strip of 4 (with 5mm straight die-cut tab), *May 2003* | 12.00 | | |
| | end strip of 4 (with 5mm straight die-cut tab), *May 2003* | 12.00 | | |
| | Booklet (9 peaks along top/valley at upper left) | | | |
| ii | 65¢ multicoloured, coloured tips at top and bottom | 1.30 | .40 | |
| iii | 65¢ multicoloured, coloured tips at top only | 1.30 | .40 | |
| iv | 65¢ multicoloured, coloured tips at bottom only | 1.30 | .40 | |
| a | booklet pane of 6 x 65¢ (2 x 1928ii, 2 x 1928iii, 2 x 1928iv) (**BK252a**) | 9.50 | | |
| | Coil (10 peaks along top/peak at upper left) | | | |
| **1929** | **77¢ multicoloured** | 1.55 | .50 | — |
| i | gutter strip of 4 | 14.00 | | |
| | starter strip of 4 (with 10mm rouletted tab) | 14.00 | | |
| | starter strip of 4 (with 5mm wavy die-cut tab), *Mar 2002* | 19.00 | | |
| | end strip of 4 (with 5mm wavy die-cut tab), *Mar 2002* | 19.00 | | |

| | | NH–VF | ⊙F | FDC |
|---|---|---|---|---|
| | Coil (10 peaks along top/peak at upper left) | | | |
| **1930** | **$1.25 multicoloured** | 2.50 | .90 | — |
| i | gutter strip of 4 | 18.00 | | |
| | starter strip of 4 (with 10mm rouletted tab) | 18.00 | | |
| | starter strip of 4 (with 5mm wavy die-cut tab), *Mar 2002* | 24.00 | | |
| | end strip of 4 (with 5mm wavy die-cut tab), *Mar 2002* | 24.00 | | |
| | Booklet (9 peaks along top/valley at upper left) | | | |
| ii | $1.25 multicoloured, coloured tips at top and bottom | 2.50 | .90 | |
| iii | $1.25 multicoloured, coloured tips at top only | 2.50 | .90 | |
| iv | $1.25 multicoloured, coloured tips at bottom only | 2.50 | .90 | |
| a | booklet pane of 6 x $1.25 (2 x 1930ii, 2 x 1930iii, 2 x 1930iv) (**BK253a**) | 16.00 | | |

**Nos. 1928–1930 (3) Combination FDC** 7.35

**Coil display cards: 1928–1930, black & white logo (set of 3) $5.00**
**Coil display cards: 1928–1930, colour logo (set of 3) $7.50**

**1928a**

**1930a**

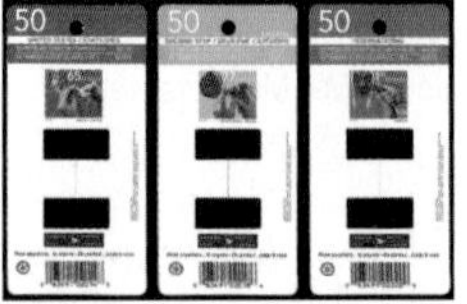

**1928–1930 Coil display cards**
(Canada Post logo is black & white)

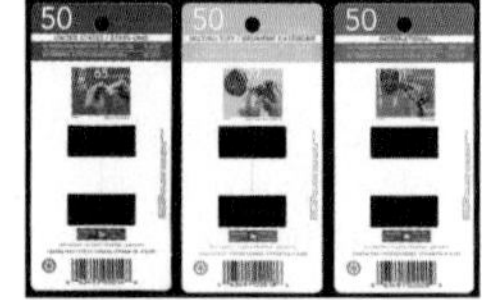

**1928–1930 Coil display cards**
(Canada Post logo is coloured)

## DOMESTIC FIRST-CLASS RATE DEFINITIVE

**1931**
Flag over Canada Post Head Office

Designer: Katalin Kovats and Stuart Bradley Ash. Based on a photograph by Paul Eekhoff.
Lithography (5 colours), self-adhesive booklet of 10/30
Ashton-Potter (USA) Limited

**2002, Jan 2** **GT4, TRC Paper** **Serpentine die cut 8.5**

| | | NH–VF | ⊙F | FDC |
|---|---|---|---|---|
| **1931** | **48¢ multicoloured**, rounded corners | 1.00 | .25 | 3.00 |
| **T1** | untagged (error) | — | 50.00 | |
| **T2** | light tag all over (error) | — | 15.00 | |
| **T3** | double tagged (error) | — | 20.00 | |
| c | missing blue colour | 500.00 | | |
| ii | square/pointed die cutting at corners, *Sep 2003* | 7.00 | 2.50 | |
| iii | single from Quarterly Pack (paper around stamp has not been removed) | 10.00 | — | |
| a | booklet of 10 x 48¢ (1931) (**BK251i, ii, iii**)* | 11.00 | — | |
| ai | booklet of 10 x 48¢ (1931ii) (from BK251C)* | 50.00 | — | |
| b | booklet of 30 x 48¢ (1931) (**BK251**) | 34.00 | — | |
| bi | booklet of 30 x 48¢ (1931ii) (**BK251C**) | 200.00 | — | |

* BK251i, ii, and iii comprise the left, centre and right thirds of BK251 respectively.

The Canadian flag is comprised of two shades of red. A minor colour shift of one will give the appearance of a doubled maple leaf — these are not 'double prints'.

For "Vancouver 2010" imprint see 1991.

The first printings of this booklet had stamps with rounded die cutting at all four corners. The "Vancouver" imprint (# 1991), released July 2003, introduced square corners to this design. The square-cornered die cutting subsequently appeared on later printings of 1931 in September 2003, shortly before the postage rates increased to 49¢.

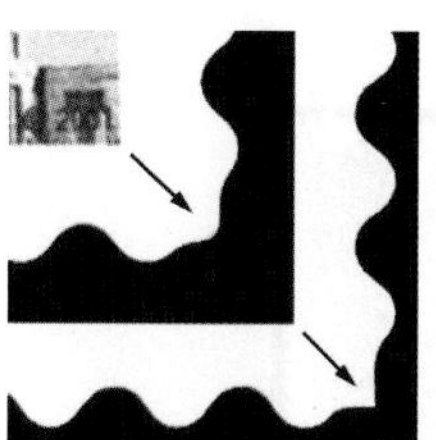

Rounded (1931) vs. square/pointed (1931ii) die cutting

1931c

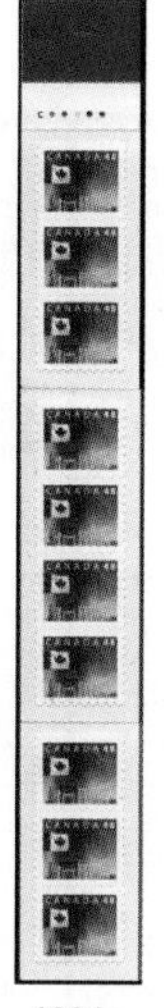

1931a

1931b

## GOLDEN JUBILEE

1932
Queen Elizabeth II

Designer: Saskia van Kampen and Stuart Bradley Ash.
Lithography (8 colours), pane of 16
Ashton-Potter Canada Limited

**2002, Jan 2** **GT4, TRC Paper** **Perf 13.2x12.5**

| | | NH–VF | ⊙F | PB | FDC |
|---|---|---|---|---|---|
| **1932** | **48¢ multicoloured** (gold) | .95 | .35 | 4.75 | 3.00 |
| **iii** | horiz. pair with right hand stamp and selvedge imperforate | 2,000.00 | | 4,000.00 | |
| **iv** | imperf. horiz. pair with perforated left selvedge | 1,500.00 | | 3,000.00 | |
| **a** | imperf. pair | 1,800.00 | — | 4,000.00 | |
| **ai** | as "a", double print of gold date | 2,000.00 | | | |
| **b** | missing gold* | — | 2,000.00 | | |

Qty: 15,000,000
* 2 used (one on piece) recorded.

Issued to celebrate 50th anniversary of ascension to the throne of Her Majesty, Queen Elizabeth II.
See 1987 for design with purple background.

1932iv

## LUNAR NEW YEAR — 6
### Year of the Horse

1933
Horse and Chinese Symbol

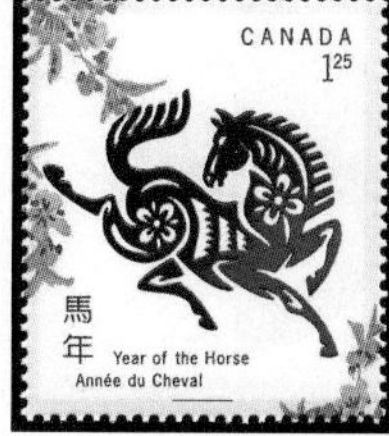

1934i
Horse and Chinese Symbol

Designer: Gilbert Li, Carey George, Ian Rapsey, Amy Chan, and Dean Martin.
Based on illustrations by Gary Alphonso and David Dao-Yan Hu.
Lithography (6 colours) and Embossed with foil stamping, pane of 25
Ashton-Potter Canada Limited

**2002, Jan 3** **GT4, TRC Paper** **Perf 13.3**

| | | NH–VF | ⊙F | PB | FDC |
|---|---|---|---|---|---|
| **1933** | **48¢ multicoloured** | 1.00 | .35 | 5.00 | 3.00 |
| **a** | foil (horse) omitted* | 1,750.00 | — | | |

Qty: 11,000,000
* 1 pane of 25 reported.

**Perf 13.4x13.3**

| | | NH–VF | ⊙F | PB | FDC |
|---|---|---|---|---|---|
| **1934** | **$1.25 souvenir sheet** | 3.00 | 3.00 | — | 4.50 |
| **i** | $1.25 single from souvenir sheet | 2.50 | 2.00 | | |
| **ii** | $26.95 uncut press sheet of 12 souvenir sheets | 75.00 | | | |

Qty: 1934: 1,700,000; 1934ii: 35,000

An essay of the souvenir sheet (1934) exists with full embossing, no tagging on the stamp and an overall quadrille grid. Value $850.00. Imperforate pairs with the horse missing (1933i) are known. Value $2,500.00.

See also 1630, 1708, 1767–1768, 1836–1837, 1883–1884, 1969–1970, 2015–2016, 2083–2084, 2140–2141, 2201–2202, 2257–2258.

1933a

1934

**MINT PRICING PREMIUMS**

Mint stamps from 301 to date are valued as NH-VF (Never Hinged-Very Fine). All hinged VF and NH-F copies are worth 50% of the listed values. Plate block (PB) values are for mint NH–VF plate or inscription blocks of four.

**USED, VF/XF (with in-period, circular date cancel) PRICING PREMIUM**

Single stamps with light or circular date cancels will sell for more than catalogue value (perhaps even more than a mint copy). From *1981 to 1991* single stamps from se-tenant blocks of 4 or larger will be priced at 50% or more above the fine price. From *1992* to date single stamps from se-tenant blocks of 4 or larger plus se-tenant booklet panes and souvenir sheets will be priced at 100% or more above the fine price. From *1997* to date all other stamps will be priced at 50% or more above the fine price.

## NHL ALL STARS — 3

**1935a**
Tim Horton (1930–1974)

**1935b**
Guy Lafleur (1951– )

**1935c**
Howie Morenz (1902–1937)

**1935d**
Glenn Hall (1931– )

**1935e**
Red Kelly (1927– )

**1935f**
Phil Esposito (1942– )

Designer: Stéphane Huot. Based on an illustration by Charles Vinh.
Lithography (8 colours), pane of 6 + 3 tabs
Canadian Bank Note Company, Limited

**2002, Jan 12** **Tagged, TRC Paper** **Perf 12.5x13.2**

| | | NH–VF | ⊙F | FDC |
|---|---|---|---|---|
| **1935** | $2.88 pane of 6 x 48¢ | 7.50 | — | |
| a | **48¢ multicoloured** | 1.00 | .75 | |
| b | **48¢ multicoloured** | 1.00 | .75 | |
| c | **48¢ multicoloured** | 1.00 | .75 | |
| d | **48¢ multicoloured** | 1.00 | .75 | |
| e | **48¢ multicoloured** | 1.00 | .75 | |
| f | **48¢ multicoloured** | 1.00 | .75 | |

Qty: 1,500,000 of each

**Three combination FDCs: a+b, c+d and e+f** **11.85**

General tagging appears around the inner edge of the large circle on each stamp. Issued for the 52nd National Hockey League All-Star Game.
See also 1443–1445, 1838, 1885, 1971–1972, 2017–2018, 2085–2086.

**1935**

| **Rates:** | Domestic first-class (0-30g): 48¢ | |
|---|---|---|
| Jan 14/02– | Domestic first-class (30-50g): 77¢ | USA (0-30g): 65¢ |
| Jan 11/04 | Domestic oversize (30-50g): 96¢ | International (0-30g): $1.25 |

*single usage:* USA 65¢: $15.00 | International $1.25: $20.00

## 2002 OLYMPIC WINTER GAMES

**1936**
Short track speed skating

**1937**
Curling

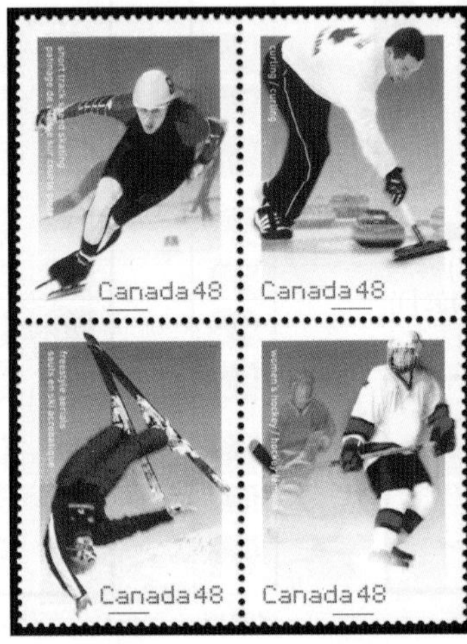


**1938**
Freestyle aerial skiing

**1939**
Women's Hockey

Designer: Sunil Bhandari and Matthew Wearn.
Lithography (8 colours), pane of 16
Ashton-Potter Canada Limited

**2002, Jan 25** **GT4, TRC Paper** **Perf 13.4x13.0**

| | | NH–VF | ⊙F | PB | FDC |
|---|---|---|---|---|---|
| **1936** | **48¢ multicoloured** | 1.00 | .40 | — | |
| **1937** | **48¢ multicoloured** | 1.00 | .40 | — | |
| **1938** | **48¢ multicoloured** | 1.00 | .40 | | |
| **1939** | **48¢ multicoloured** | 1.00 | .40 | | |
| **a** | se-tenant block or strip of 4 different (1936-1939) | 4.00 | 3.50 | 5.00 | 5.85 |

Qty: 1,250,000 of each

Issued to celebrate 2002 Olympic Winter Games held in Salt Lake City. When viewed at an angle, the Olympic symbols will be apparent in the design.

## GOVERNORS GENERAL

**1940**
Canadian Governors General

Designer: Neville Smith.
Lithography, Sheets of 96 subjects in six panes of 16
Ashton-Potter Canada Limited

**2002, Feb 1** **GT4, TRC Paper** **Perf 13.1x12.5**

| | | NH–VF | ⊙F | PB | FDC |
|---|---|---|---|---|---|
| **1940** | **48¢ multicoloured** | 1.00 | .35 | 5.00 | 3.00 |

Qty: 4,000,000

Issued to celebrate the 50th anniversary of appointment of the first Canadian Governor General.

## UNIVERSITIES

**1941**
University of Manitoba

**1942**
Laval University

**1943**
University of Trinity College

**1944**
Saint Mary's University

Designer: Steven Slipp, Semaphor Design.
Lithography (5 colours), booklet panes of 8
Ashton-Potter Canada Limited

| **2002** | **Tagged, TRC Paper** | | **Perf 13.4x13.5** | |
|---|---|---|---|---|
| | | NH–VF | ⊙F | FDC |
| **1941** | **48¢ multicoloured**, *Feb 28, 2002* | 1.00 | .35 | 3.00 |
| a | booklet pane of 8 x 48¢ (1941) (BK254) | 8.00 | — | — |
| **BK254** | pane 1941a in cover $8.50 | | | |

Qty: 3,000,000

Issued to commemorate the 125th anniversary of University of Manitoba, Winnipeg.

| | | NH–VF | ⊙F | FDC |
|---|---|---|---|---|
| **1942** | **48¢ multicoloured**, *Apr 4, 2002* | 1.00 | .35 | 3.00 |
| a | booklet pane of 8 x 48¢ (1942) (BK255) | 8.00 | — | — |
| **BK255** | pane 1942a in cover $8.50 | | | |

Qty: 3,000,000

Issued to commemorate the 150th anniversary of Laval University, Quebec City.

| | | NH–VF | ⊙F | FDC |
|---|---|---|---|---|
| **1943** | **48¢ multicoloured**, *Apr 30, 2002* | 1.00 | .35 | 3.00 |
| a | booklet pane of 8 x 48¢ (1943) (BK256) | 8.00 | — | — |
| **BK256** | pane 1943a in cover $8.50 | | | |

Qty: 3,000,000

Issued to commemorate the 150th anniversary of Trinity College, University of Toronto.

| | | NH–VF | ⊙F | FDC |
|---|---|---|---|---|
| **1944** | **48¢ multicoloured**, *May 27, 2002* | 1.00 | .35 | 3.00 |
| a | booklet pane of 8 x 48¢ (1944) (BK258) | 8.00 | — | — |
| **BK258** | pane 1944a in cover $8.50 | | | |

Qty: 3,000,000

Issued to commemorate the 200th anniversary of Saint Mary's University, Halifax.

See also 1756, 1973–1977, 2033–2034, 2089, 2172, 2209–2210.

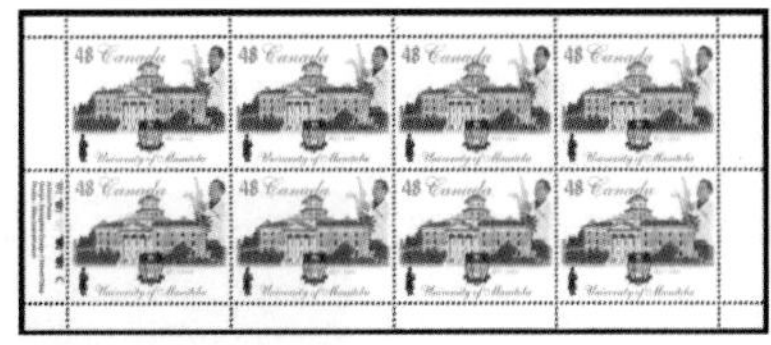

**1941a**

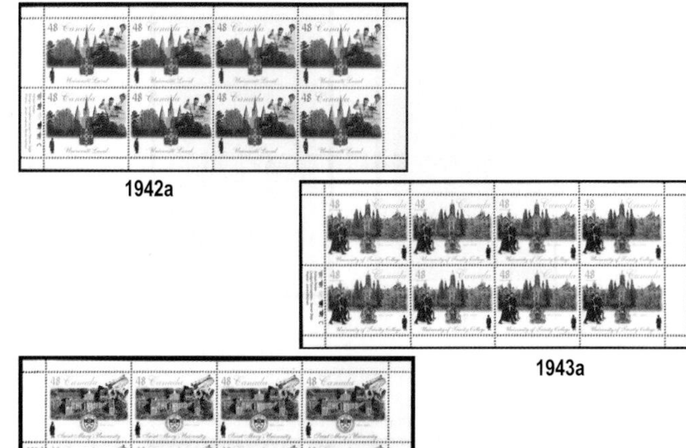

**1942a**

**1943a**

**1944a**

## MASTERPIECES OF CANADIAN ART — 15

**1945**
*Church and Horse*

Designer: Pierre-Yves Pelletier. Based on a painting by David Alexander Colville.
Lithography (5 colours) with foil stamping, pane of 16
Ashton-Potter Canada Limited

| **2002, Mar 22** | **TRC Paper** | | | **Perf 12.5x13.3** | |
|---|---|---|---|---|---|
| | | NH–VF | ⊙F | PB | FDC |
| **1945** | **$1.25 multicoloured** (silver) | 2.50 | 1.50 | 12.50 | 4.50 |
| a | foil only (all other colours and tagging omitted (16 known) | 2,000.00 | — | 8,500.00* | |
| b | imperf. pair | 1,800.00 | — | | |

Qty: 4,000,000
* Blank corner block of 4.

The last in a series that started in 1988. See also 1203, 1241, 1271, 1310, 1419, 1466, 1516, 1545, 1602, 1635, 1754, 1800, 1863, 1916.

## TULIPS

*Die cut singles from self-adhesive booklet*

**1946a**
City of Vancouver

**1946b**
Monte Carlo

QE II — 2000's

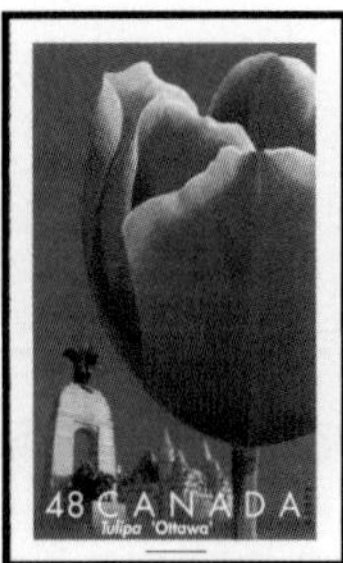

1946c
Ottawa

1946d
The Bishop

*Perforated singles from water-activated gum souvenir sheet*

1947a
City of Vancouver

1947b
Monte Carlo

1947c
Ottawa

1947d
The Bishop

Designer: Monique Dufour and Sophie Lafortune.
Based on an illustration by Ghislain Lefebvre. Based on a photograph by Peter Timmermans.

Lithography (6 colours), self-adhesive booklet pane of 8
Lowe-Martin

| **2002, May 3** | **GT4, TRC Paper** | | | **Die cut** |
|---|---|---|---|---|
| | | NH–VF | ⊙F | FDC |
| **1946** | booklet pane of 4 x 48¢ (a-d) | 4.00 | | |
| **a** | **48¢ multicoloured** (violet) | 1.00 | .40 | |
| **b** | **48¢ multicoloured** (orange-red) | 1.00 | .40 | |
| **c** | **48¢ multicoloured** (ultramarine) | 1.00 | .40 | |
| **d** | **48¢ multicoloured** (olive yellow) | 1.00 | .40 | |
| BK257 | two panes of 1946 $8.50 | | | |

Qty: 4,000,000 of each

**Nos. 1946 (a-d) (4) combination FDC** 5.85

Lithography, water-activated gum souvenir sheet of 4
Lowe-Martin

| **2002, Aug 30** | **GT4, TRC Paper** | | | **Perf 13.2x12.5** |
|---|---|---|---|---|
| | | NH–VF | ⊙F | FDC |
| **1947** | $1.92 souvenir sheet of 4 x 48¢ (a-d) | 5.00 | 5.00 | — |
| **a** | **48¢ multicoloured** (violet) | 1.00 | 1.00 | |
| **b** | **48¢ multicoloured** (orange-red) | 1.00 | 1.00 | |
| **c** | **48¢ multicoloured** (ultramarine) | 1.00 | 1.00 | |
| **d** | **48¢ multicoloured** (olive yellow) | 1.00 | 1.00 | |

Qty: 300,000 of each

First postage stamps printed by Lowe-Martin.

For non-denominated envelopes of nos. 1946c/1947c and 1946d/1947d designs, see U174–U175; for non-denominated postal cards of same designs, see UX128.

*Image rotated*

2 x 1946
(BK257)

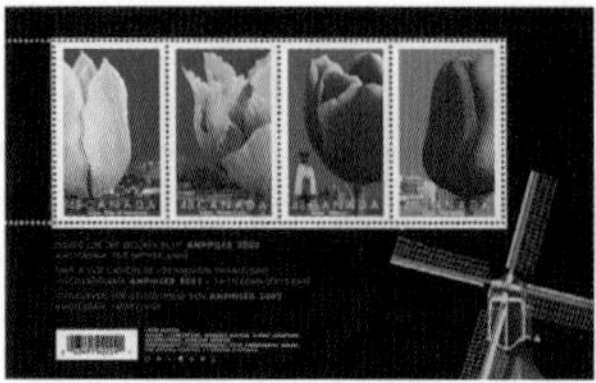

1947

## CORALS

1948
Dendronepthea Gigantea and Dendronepthea Corals

1949
Tubastrea and Echinogorgia Corals

1950
North Atlantic pink tree, Pacific orange cup and North Pacific horn corals

1951
North Atlantic Giant Orange Tree and Black Corals

Designer: 1948–1949 (Hong Kong): Bon Kwan. Based on photographs by Leslie Chan. 1950–1951 (Canada): Geoff Kehrig and Bonne Zabolotney. Based on photographs by Derek P. Jones and Bill Austin.

Lithography (6 colours) and foil stamping, pane of 16
Lowe-Martin

| **2002, May 19** | **GT4, TRC Paper** | | | | **Perf 12.5x13.1** |
|---|---|---|---|---|---|
| | | NH–VF | ⊙F | PB | FDC |
| **1948** | **48¢ multicoloured** | .95 | .40 | | |
| **i** | perf 13.3x13.1 (from souvenir sheet) | 1.00 | 1.00 | | |
| **1949** | **48¢ multicoloured** | .95 | .40 | | |
| **i** | perf 13.3x13.1 (from souvenir sheet) | 1.00 | 1.00 | | |
| **1950** | **48¢ multicoloured** | .95 | .40 | | |
| **i** | perf 13.3x13.1 (from souvenir sheet) | 1.00 | 1.00 | | |
| **1951** | **48¢ multicoloured** | .95 | .40 | | |
| **i** | perf 13.3x13.1 (from souvenir sheet) | 1.00 | 1.00 | | |
| **a** | se-tenant block of 4 different (1948-1951) | 4.00 | 3.00 | 5.00 | 5.10 |
| **b** | $1.92 souvenir sheet (Canada) | 5.00 | 5.00 | — | 5.85 |

Qty: 2,000,000 of each; souvenir sheet: 300,000

**Nos. 1950-1951 (2) and Hong Kong (2) joint combination FDC with Hong Kong** 7.20

Joint issue with Hong Kong (Scott 979–982).

1951b

## TOURIST ATTRACTIONS

1952a
Yukon Quest, YK

1952b
Icefields Parkway, AB

1952c
Agawa Canyon, ON

1952d
Old Port of Montreal, QC

1952e
Kings Landing, NB

1953a
Northern Lights, NT

1953b
Stanley Park, Vancouver, BC

1953c
Head-Smashed-In Buffalo Jump, AB

1953d
Saguenay Fjord, QC

1953e
Peggy's Cove, NS

Designer: Catharine Bradbury and Jeannine Saylor.
Lithography (8 colours), self-adhesive booklet panes of 5
Canadian Bank Note Company, Limited

**2002, Jun 1** **GT4, TRC Paper** **Die cut perf 11.3x11.4**

| | | NH–VF | ⊙F | FDC |
|---|---|---|---|---|
| **1952** | booklet pane of 5 x 65¢ (a–e) (**BK259**) | 8.50 | — | — |
| a | **65¢ Yukon Quest, YK** | 1.50 | 1.00 | |
| b | **65¢ Icefields Parkway, AB** | 1.50 | 1.00 | |
| c | **65¢ Agawa Canyon, ON** | 1.50 | 1.00 | |
| d | **65¢ Old Port of Montreal, QC** | 1.50 | 1.00 | |
| e | **65¢ Kings Landing, NB** | 1.50 | 1.00 | |
| i | unfolded strip of 5 stamps* | 10.00 | | |

Qty: 1,250,000 of each

**Nos. 1952a–1952e (5) combination FDC** **8.50**

| | | NH–VF | ⊙F | FDC |
|---|---|---|---|---|
| **1953** | booklet pane of 5 x $1.25 (a–e) (**BK260**) | 14.00 | — | — |
| a | **$1.25 Northern Lights, NT** | 2.50 | 1.50 | |
| b | **$1.25 Stanley Park, Vancouver, BC** | 2.50 | 1.50 | |
| c | **$1.25 Head-Smashed-In Buffalo Jump, AB** | 2.50 | 1.50 | |
| d | **$1.25 Saguenay Fjord, QC** | 2.50 | 1.50 | |
| e | **$1.25 Peggy's Cove, NS** | 2.50 | 1.50 | |
| i | unfolded strip of 5 stamps* | 16.00 | | |

Qty: 1,250,000 of each

**Nos. 1953a–1953e (5) combination FDC** **14.50**

* The 2002 Annual Collection included unfolded strips of 5 stamps from each pane; the top and bottom of the booklet panes were trimmed.

See also 1903–1904, 1989–1990, 2019–2023. For non-denominated postal cards of same designs, see UX129. For non-denominated envelopes of some designs, see U184–U203.

1952

1953

QE II — 2000's

## SCULPTORS

**1954**
*Embâcle*, by Charles Daudelin

**1955**
*Lumberjacks*, by Leo Mol

Designer: Suzanne Morin. Based on a photograph by François Brunelle
Based on a sculpture by Charles Daudelin (1954) and Leonid Molodoshanin (1955).
Lithography (5 colours), pane of 16
Canadian Bank Note Company, Limited

**2002, Jun 10** **GT4, TRC Paper** **Perf 13.4**

| | | NH–VF | ⊙F | PB | FDC |
|---|---|---|---|---|---|
| **1954** | **48¢ multicoloured** | 1.00 | .35 | — | |
| **1955** | **48¢ multicoloured** | 1.00 | .35 | — | |
| a | se-tenant pair (1954, 1955) | 2.25 | 1.25 | 5.00 | 3.95 |

Qty: 2,500,000 of each

## CANADIAN POSTMASTERS AND ASSISTANTS ASSOCIATION 1902–2002

**1956**
Post office in Stonewall, MB,
2¢ Victoria and 1902 date stamp

Designer: Chris Candlish. Based on a photograph by Provincial Archives of Manitoba.
Lithography (8 colours), pane of 16 + 12 labels
Canadian Bank Note Company, Limited

**2002, Jul 5** **GT4, TRC Paper** **Perf 13.1x12.5**

| | | NH–VF | ⊙F | PB | FDC |
|---|---|---|---|---|---|
| **1956** | **48¢ multicoloured** | 1.00 | .35 | 5.00 | 3.00 |
| i | vertical pair with gutter between | 2.25 | 1.25 | | |

Qty: 3,000,000

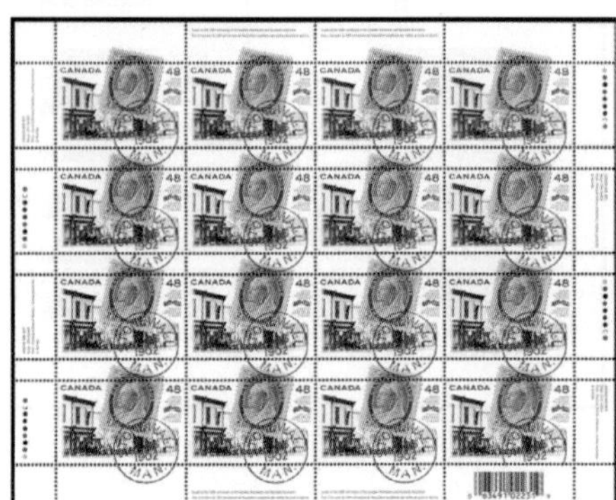

**1956 full pane of 16 and 12 labels**

## WORLD YOUTH DAY

**1957**
World Youth Day

Designer: Lise Giguère. Based on a photograph by François Brunelle.
Lithography (6 colours plus varnish), self-adhesive booklet pane of 8
Ashton-Potter Canada Limited

**2002, Jul 23** **GT4, JAC Paper** **Die cut**

| | | NH–VF | ⊙F | FDC |
|---|---|---|---|---|
| **1957** | **48¢ multicoloured** | 1.00 | .40 | 10.00 |
| i | die cut to shape from Quarterly Pack/ Annual Collection | 3.50 | | |
| a | booklet pane of 8 x 48¢ (1957a) (**BK261**) | 9.00 | — | |

Qty: 6,000,000

Issued to celebrate the 17th World Youth Day, July 28, 2002.

*Image rotated* **1957a**

**1958**
Four arms pulling a rope

**1959**
A tree depicted in 4 seasons

## PUBLIC SERVICES INTERNATIONAL CONGRESS

Designer: Denis L'Allier. Based on a photograph by Guy Lavigueur.
Lithography (6 colours), pane of 16
Lowe-Martin

**2002, Sep 4** **GT4, TRC Paper** **Perf 12.5x13.1**

| | | NH–VF | ⊙F | PB | FDC |
|---|---|---|---|---|---|
| **1958** | **48¢ multicoloured** | 1.00 | .35 | 5.00 | 3.00 |

Qty: 3,000,000

The World Congress is held every 5 years, and was held in Ottawa Sep 2–6, 2002.

## PUBLIC PENSIONS

Designer: Debbie Adams. Based on photographs by Garry Black.
Lithography (8 colours), pane of 16
Canadian Bank Note Company, Limited

**2002, Sep 10** **GT4, TRC Paper** **Perf 13.3x13.4**

| | | NH–VF | ⊙F | PB | FDC |
|---|---|---|---|---|---|
| **1959** | **48¢ multicoloured** | 1.00 | .35 | 5.00 | 3.00 |

Qty: 3,000,000

Issued to celebrate the 75th anniversary of the Old Age Pension Act.

## UNITED NATIONS INTERNATIONAL YEAR OF MOUNTAINS

**1960a**
Mount Logan, Canada

**1960b**
Mount Elbrus, Europe

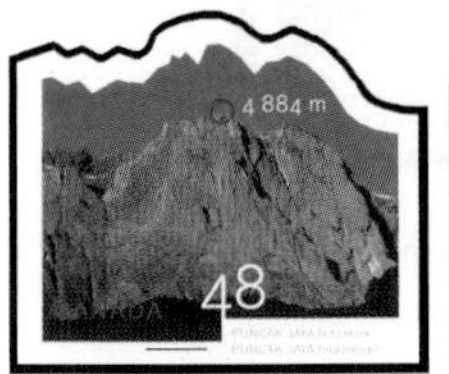

**1960c**
Puncak Jaya, Oceania

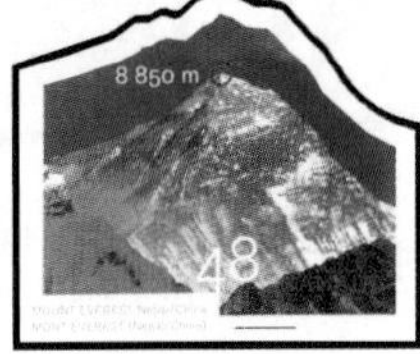

**1960d**
Mount Everest, Asia

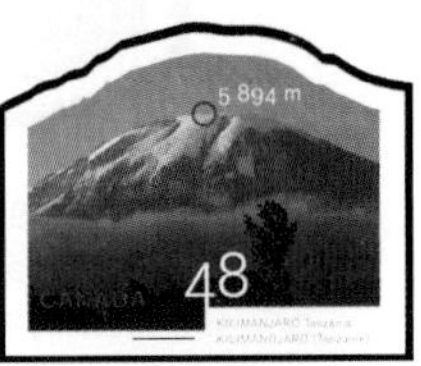

**1960e**
Kilimanjaro, Africa

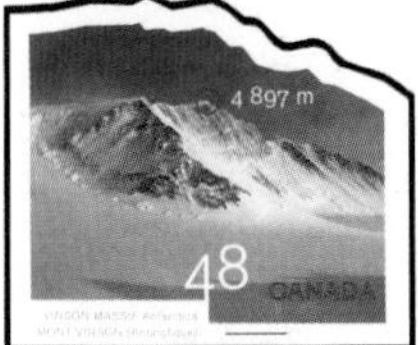

**1960f**
Vinson Massif, Antarctica

**1960g**
Aconcagua, South America

**1960h**
Mount McKinley, North America

Designer: Gildo Martino, Peter D.K. Scott, and Glenda Rissman.
Lithography (9 colours), self-adhesive souvenir sheet of 8 + 8 labels
Lowe-Martin

| 2002, Oct 1 | GT4, TRC Paper | | | Die cut |
|---|---|---|---|---|
| | | NH–VF | ⊙F | FDC |
| **1960** | $3.84 Souvenir sheet of 8 different (a-h) | 10.00 | *12.00* | — |
| a | **48¢ multicoloured** | 1.25 | *1.50* | |
| b | **48¢ multicoloured** | 1.25 | *1.50* | |
| c | **48¢ multicoloured** | 1.25 | *1.50* | |
| d | **48¢ multicoloured** | 1.25 | *1.50* | |
| e | **48¢ multicoloured** | 1.25 | *1.50* | |
| f | **48¢ multicoloured** | 1.25 | *1.50* | |
| g | **48¢ multicoloured** | 1.25 | *1.50* | |
| h | **48¢ multicoloured** | 1.25 | *1.50* | |

Qty: 1,000,000 of each

**Two combination FDCs: a+h+g+f and e+b+c+d** **11.70**

The eight stamps are spaced evenly around the circumference of the circular pane which includes geographical and ecological information for each summit.

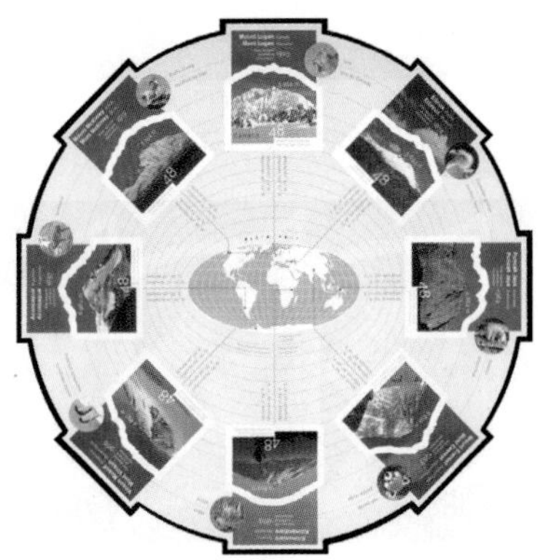

**1960**

## UNITED NATIONS TEACHER'S DAY

**1961**
Teacher writing on blackboard

Designer: Mark Koudis. Based on a photograph by Ron Baxter Smith.
Lithography (8 colours), pane of 16
Canadian Bank Note Company, Limited

| 2002, Oct 4 | GT4, TRC Paper | | | Perf 12.5x13.1 | |
|---|---|---|---|---|---|
| | | NH–VF | ⊙F | PB | FDC |
| **1961** | **48¢ multicoloured** | 1.00 | .35 | 5.00 | 3.00 |

Qty: 3,000,000

Issued to mark World Teacher's Day (Oct. 5) and as a tribute to Canadian teachers.

## TORONTO STOCK EXCHANGE

**1962**
Collage of images related to TSE

Designer: Ivan Novotny, John Taylor, and Patrick Sayers.
Based on a photograph by Tracy Clare. Based on a painting by Charles Fraser Comfort.
Lithography (5 colours), pane of 16
Canadian Bank Note Company, Limited

| 2002, Oct 24 | GT4, TRC Paper | | | Perf 12.5x13.1 | |
|---|---|---|---|---|---|
| | | NH–VF | ⊙F | PB | FDC |
| **1962** | **48¢ multicoloured** | 1.00 | .35 | 5.00 | 3.00 |

Qty: 3,000,000

Commemorating the 150th anniversary of the Toronto Stock Exchange.

## COMMUNICATIONS TECHNOLOGY

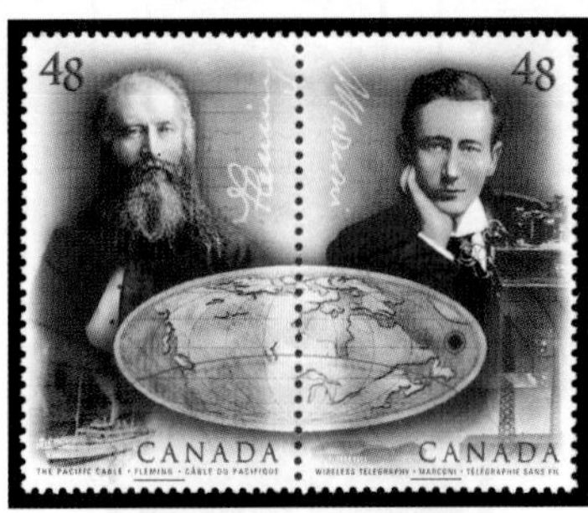


**1963** Sir Sandford Fleming
**1964** Guglielmo Marconi

Designer: Susan Warr. Based on an illustration by Bonnie Ross.
Based on a photograph by William James Topley.
Based on a photograph by Charles Bradbury.
Lithography (8 colours), pane of 16
Lowe-Martin

| 2002, Oct 31 | GT4, TRC Paper | | | Perf 13.1x12.5 | |
|---|---|---|---|---|---|
| | | NH–VF | ⊙F | PB | FDC |
| **1963** | **48¢ multicoloured** | 1.00 | .35 | | |
| **1964** | **48¢ multicoloured** | 1.00 | .35 | | |
| a | se-tenant pair (1963, 1964) | 2.00 | 1.50 | 5.00 | 3.95 |

Qty: 2,500,000 of each

On October 31, 1902, Sir Sandford Fleming's Pacific Cable was completed. On December 15, 1902, Marconi's first trans-Atlantic radio message was transmitted to England.

## CHRISTMAS — ABORIGINAL ART

**1965**
*Genesis*, by Daphne Odjig

**1966**
*Winter Travel*, by Cecil Youngfox

**1967**
*Mary and Child*, by Irene Katak Angutitaq

Designer: Keith Hamilton and Bernice Alderson.
Lithography (7 colours; $1.25: 6 colours), panes of 25
Canadian Bank Note Company, Limited

**2002, Nov 4** **GT4, TRC Paper** **Perf 12.5x13.1**

| | | NH–VF | ⊙F | PB | FDC |
|---|---|---|---|---|---|
| **1965** | **48¢ multicoloured** | 1.00 | .35 | 5.00 | |
| a | booklet pane of 10 x 48¢ (1965) | 10.00 | | | |
| **BK262** | pane 1965a in cover $11.00 | | | | |
| Qty: 53,515,000 | | | | | |
| **1966** | **65¢ multicoloured** | 1.30 | .50 | 6.50 | |
| a | booklet pane of 6 x 65¢ (1966) | 9.50 | | | |
| **BK263** | pane 1966a in cover $10.50 | | | | |
| Qty: 9,174,165 | | | | | |
| **1967** | **$1.25 multicoloured** | 2.50 | 1.00 | 12.50 | |
| a | booklet pane of 6 x $1.25 (1967) | 15.00 | | | |
| **BK264** | pane 1967a in cover $16.00 | | | | |
| Qty: 9,174,165 | | | | | |

**Nos. 1965–1967 (3) combination FDC 6.75**

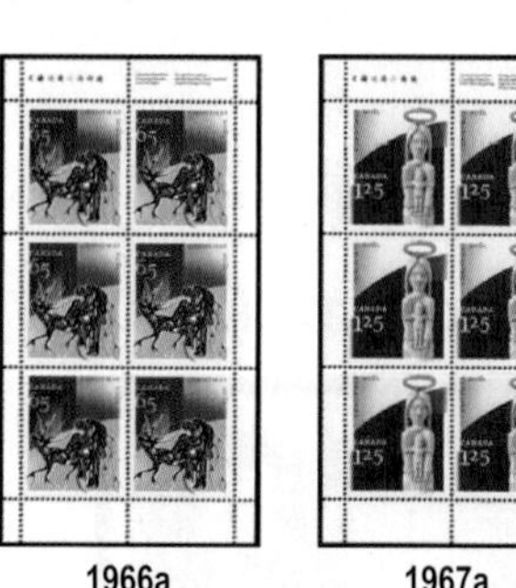

**1966a**

**1967a**

**1965a**

## QUEBEC SYMPHONY ORCHESTRA

**1968**
Conductor's hands, strings section

Designer: Monique Dufour and Sophie Lafortune.
Based on a photograph by Jules-Ernest Livernois. Based on a photograph by Digital Vision.
Lithography (6 colours plus varnish), pane of 16
Lowe-Martin

**2002, Nov 7** **GT4, TRC Paper** **Perf 12.5x13.1**

| | | NH–VF | ⊙F | PB | FDC |
|---|---|---|---|---|---|
| **1968** | **48¢ multicoloured** | 1.00 | .35 | 4.75 | 3.00 |
| Qty: 3,000,000 | | | | | |

Issued for the 100th anniversary of the orchestra.

## 2003

## LUNAR NEW YEAR — 7
### Year of the Ram

**1969**
Ram and Chinese Symbol

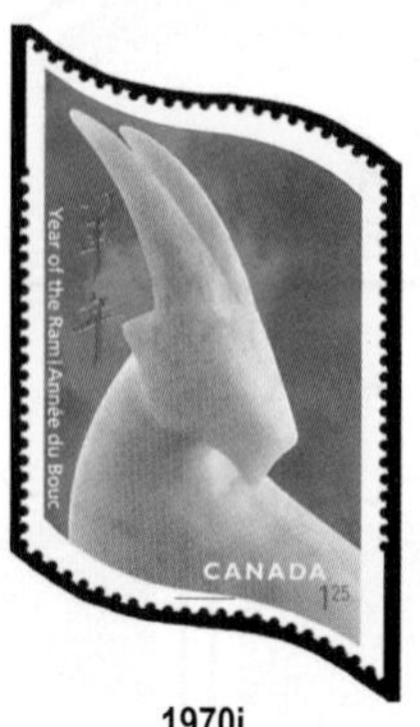

**1970i**
Ram and Chinese Symbol

Designed, illustrated and calligraphed by Rosina Li.
Based on a sculpture and an illustration by Christopher Reid.
Based on an illustration by Jason Li. Based on a photograph by Raeff Miles.
Lithography (9 colours) and Embossed with foil stamping, pane of 25
Lowe-Martin

**2003, Jan 3** **GT4, TRC Paper** **Perf 12.5x13.1**

| | | NH–VF | ⊙F | PB | FDC |
|---|---|---|---|---|---|
| **1969** | **48¢ multicoloured** | 1.00 | .35 | 5.00 | 3.00 |
| **a** | gold Chinese inscription omitted | 600.00 | | | |
| | as "a", left margin strip of 3 missing colour on 2 stamps + 1 normal | 1,200.00 | | 2,500.00* | |
| **b** | imperf. pair | *2,500.00* | | | |

Qty: 10,000,000
* UL or LL imprint block of 6
The missing gold was a "progressive" error with some sheets missing only the gold on the selvedge, a few missing only the left column (5 stamps), and some missing gold from left two columns (10 stamps).

**Perf 12.5x13.3**

| | | NH–VF | ⊙F | PB | FDC |
|---|---|---|---|---|---|
| **1970** | **$1.25 souvenir sheet** | 3.00† | 3.00† | — | 4.50* |
| i | $1.25 single from souvenir sheet | 2.50 | 2.25 | | |
| ii | $26.95 uncut press sheet of 12 souvenir sheets | 75.00 | | | |

Qty: 1970: 1,600,000; 1970ii: 35,000
† Price is for souvenir sheet with attached UPC barcode tab.
* UPC barcode tab removed on all FDCs.

See also 1630, 1708, 1767–1768, 1836–1837, 1883–1884, 1933–1934, 2015–2016, 2083–2084, 2140–2141, 2201–2202, 2257–2258.

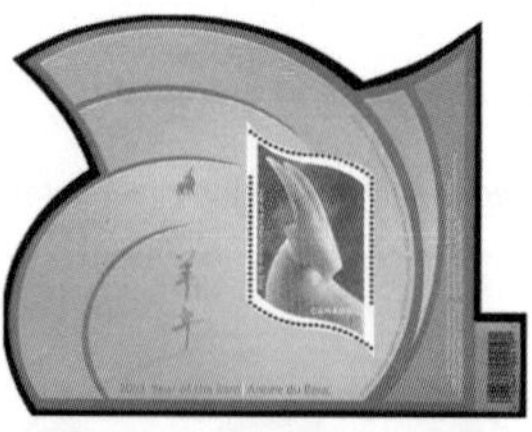

**1970**

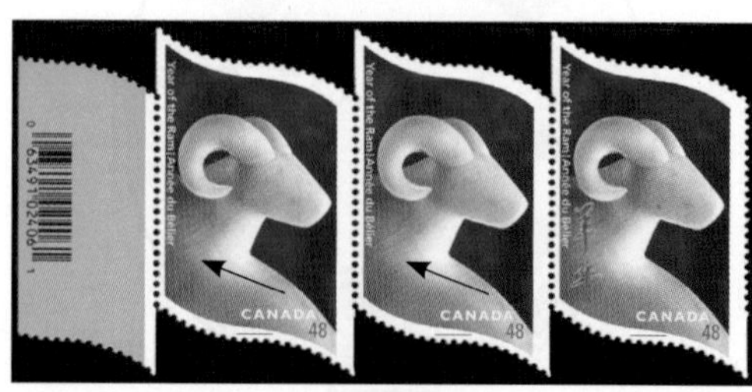

**1969a**
in left margin strip of 3

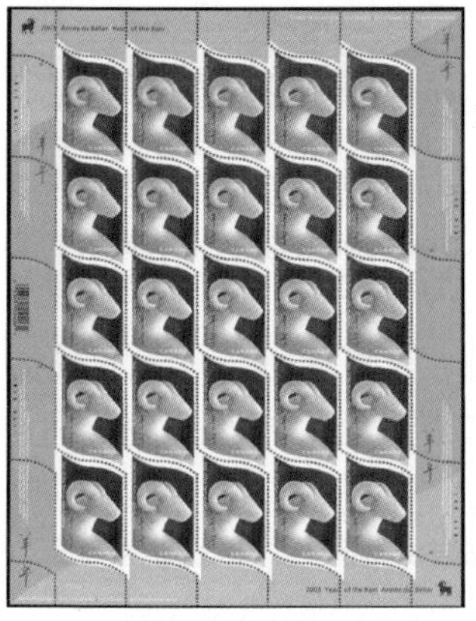
1969 full pane of 25

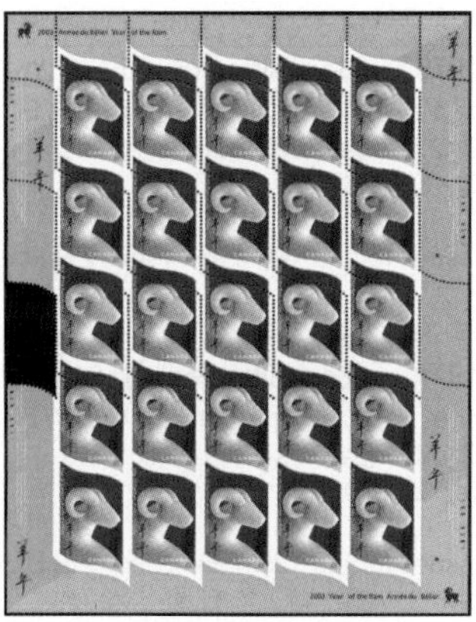
1969b full pane of 25
Bottom 2 rows imperforate due to major perforation shift

## NHL ALL STARS — 4

*Perforated singles from water-activated gum pane*

1971a
Frank Mahovlich (1938– )

1971b
Raymond Bourque (1960– )

1971c
Serge Savard (1946– )

1971d
Stan Mikita (1940–2018)

1971e
Mike Bossy (1957– )

1971f
Bill Durnan (1916–1972)

*Die cut singles from self-adhesive booklet*

1972a
Frank Mahovlich

1972b
Raymond Bourque

1972c
Serge Savard

1972d
Stan Mikita

1972e
Mike Bossy

1972f
Bill Durnan

Designer: Stéphane Huot. Based on an illustration by Charles Vinh.
Lithography (7 colours), pane of 6 + 3 tabs
Canadian Bank Note Company, Limited

| **2003, Jan 18** | **GT4, TRC Paper** | | **Perf 12.5x13.1** | |
|---|---|---|---|---|
| | | NH–VF | ⊙F | FDC |
| **1971** | $2.88 pane of 6 x 48¢ | 19.50 | — | |
| a | **48¢ multicoloured** | 3.00 | 2.00 | |
| b | **48¢ multicoloured** | 3.00 | 2.00 | |
| c | **48¢ multicoloured** | 3.00 | 2.00 | |
| d | **48¢ multicoloured** | 3.00 | 2.00 | |
| e | **48¢ multicoloured** | 3.00 | 2.00 | |
| f | **48¢ multicoloured** | 3.00 | 2.00 | |

Qty: 396,500 of each

**Three combination FDC's: a+b, c+d, e+f** 11.85

Self-adhesive booklet of 6

| **2003, Jan 18** | **GT4, JAC Paper** | | **Die cut** | |
|---|---|---|---|---|
| | | NH–VF | ⊙F | FDC |
| **1972** | $2.88 pane of 6 x 48¢ (**BK265**) | 90.00 | — | |
| a | **48¢ multicoloured** | 8.00 | 2.00 | |
| b | **48¢ multicoloured** | 8.00 | 2.00 | |
| c | **48¢ multicoloured** | 8.00 | 2.00 | |
| d | **48¢ multicoloured** | 8.00 | 2.00 | |
| e | **48¢ multicoloured** | 8.00 | 2.00 | |
| f | **48¢ multicoloured** | 8.00 | 2.00 | |

Qty: 603,500 of each

The 2003 Annual Collection did *not* include the self-adhesive booklet.
See also 1443–1445, 1838, 1885, 1935, 2017–2018, 2085–2086.

1971

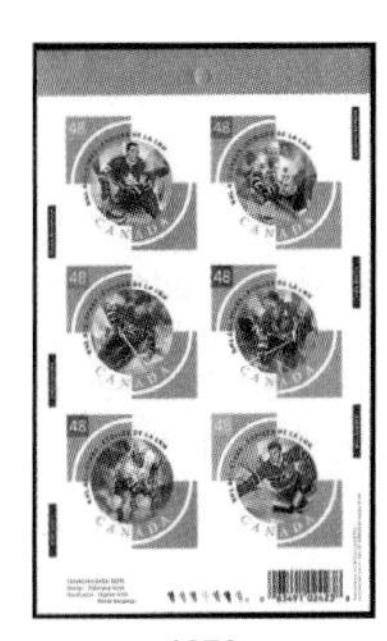
1972

## UNIVERSITIES

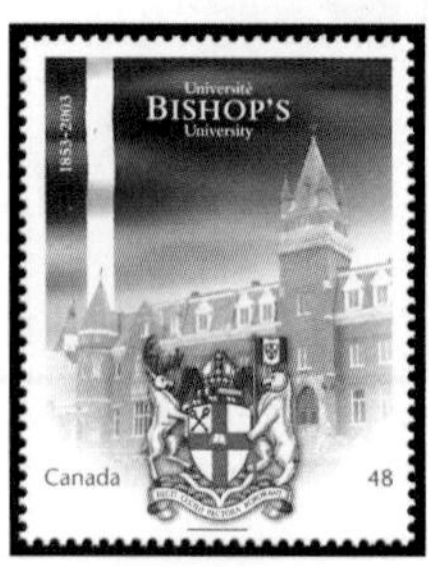
1973
Bishop's University

1974
University of Western Ontario

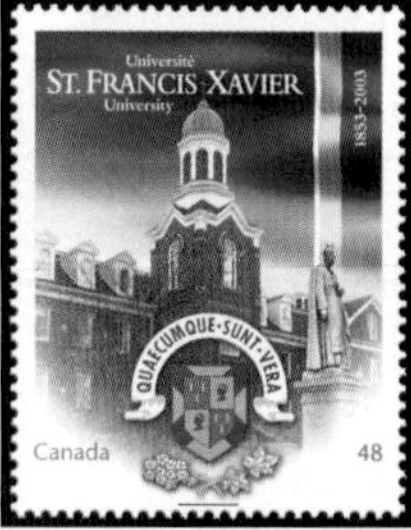
1975
St. Francis Xavier University

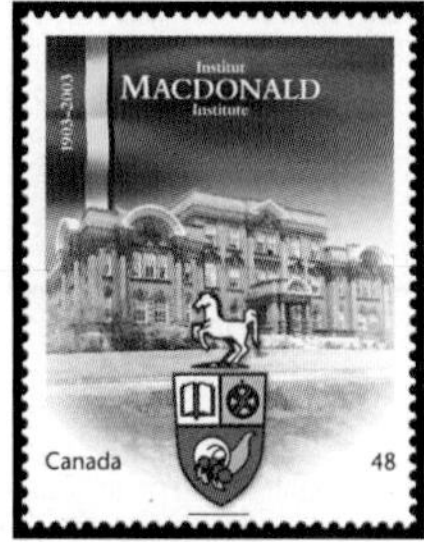
1976
Macdonald Institute

1977
Université de Montréal

Designer: Denis L'Allier.

Lithography (6 colours), booklet panes of 8
Canadian Bank Note Company, Limited

**2003** **GT4, TRC Paper** **Perf 13.4**

| | | NH–VF | ⊙F | FDC |
|---|---|---|---|---|
| **1973** | **48¢ multicoloured**, *Jan 28, 2003* | 1.00 | .35 | 3.00 |
| a | booklet pane of 8 x 48¢ (1973) (BK266) | 8.00 | — | — |
| **BK266** | pane 1973a in cover 9.00 | | | |

Qty: 3,000,000

Issued for the 150th anniversary of Bishop's University in Lennoxville, Quebec.

| | | NH–VF | ⊙F | FDC |
|---|---|---|---|---|
| **1974** | **48¢ multicoloured**, *Mar 19, 2003* | 1.00 | .35 | 3.00 |
| a | booklet pane of 8 x 48¢ (1974) (BK268) | 8.00 | — | — |
| **BK268** | pane 1974a in cover $9.00 | | | |

Qty: 3,000,000

Issued for the 125th anniversary of the University of Western Ontario at London, Ontario.

| | | NH–VF | ⊙F | FDC |
|---|---|---|---|---|
| **1975** | **48¢ multicoloured**, *Apr 4, 2003* | 1.00 | .35 | 3.00 |
| a | booklet pane of 8 x 48¢ (1975) (BK269) | 8.00 | — | — |
| **BK269** | pane 1975a in cover $9.00 | | | |

Qty: 3,000,000

Issued for the 150th anniversary of St. Francis Xavier University at Antigonish, Nova Scotia.

| | | NH–VF | ⊙F | FDC |
|---|---|---|---|---|
| **1976** | **48¢ multicoloured**, *Jun 20, 2003* | 1.00 | .35 | 3.00 |
| a | booklet pane of 8 x 48¢ (1976) (BK272) | 8.00 | — | — |
| **BK272** | pane 1976a in cover $9.00 | | | |

Qty: 3,000,000

Issued for the 100th anniversary of Macdonald Institute at Guelph, Ontario.

| | | NH–VF | ⊙F | FDC |
|---|---|---|---|---|
| **1977** | **48¢ multicoloured**, *Sep 4, 2003* | 1.00 | .35 | 3.00 |
| a | booklet pane of 8 x 48¢ (1977) (BK273) | 8.00 | — | — |
| **BK273** | pane 1977a in cover $9.00 | | | |

Qty: 3,000,000

Issued for the 125th anniversary of Université de Montréal, Montreal, Quebec.

For other University issues, see 1756, 1941–1944, 2033–2034, 2089, 2172, 2209–2210.

No. 1978 is not assigned.

1973a

1974a

1975a

1976a

1977a

## JOHN JAMES AUDUBON'S BIRDS – I

1979 Leach's storm-petrel · 1980 Brant

1981 Great cormorant · 1982 Common murre

1983
Gyrfalcon

1983a

Designer: Rolf P. Harder.

Lithography (10 colours), pane of 16
Lowe-Martin

| 2003, Feb 21 | GT4, TRC Paper | | Perf 13.3x12.5 | |
|---|---|---|---|---|
| | NH–VF | ⊙F | PB | FDC |
| **1979 48¢ multicoloured** | 1.00 | .50 | | |
| **1980 48¢ multicoloured** | 1.00 | .50 | | |
| **1981 48¢ multicoloured** | 1.00 | .50 | | |
| **1982 48¢ multicoloured** | 1.00 | .50 | | |
| a se-tenant block of 4 (1979–1982) | 4.00 | 3.00 | 5.00 | 5.85 |

Qty: 1,250,000 of each

Lithography (7 colours), Self-adhesive pane of 6
Lowe-Martin

| 2003, Feb 21 | GT4, JAC Paper | | Die cut |
|---|---|---|---|
| | NH–VF | ⊙F | FDC |
| **1983 65¢ multicoloured** | 1.50 | 1.00 | 3.30 |
| a booklet pane of 6 x 65¢ (**BK267**) | 9.50 | | |

Qty: 3,000,000

Considered one of the pioneers of wildlife art, John James Audubon was a gifted painter with a unique style and method that combined scientific accuracy with emotion.

See also: 2036–2040, 2095–2099.

## CANADIAN RANGERS

1984
Ranger with binoculars

Designer: Charles Oliver Hill and Dennis George Page.
Based on photographs by Ted Coldwell and Ed Darack.

Lithography (6 colours plus gloss spot varnish), pane of 16
Lowe-Martin

| 2003, Mar 3 | GT4, TRC Paper | | Perf 12.5x13.1 | |
|---|---|---|---|---|
| | NH–VF | ⊙F | PB | FDC |
| **1984 48¢ multicoloured** | 1.00 | .35 | 5.00 | 3.00 |

Qty: 3,000,000

Formed on March 3, 1942 in response to the threat of Japanese attack, the Pacific Coast Militia Rangers (PCMR) patrolled and watched the coasts from the Queen Charlotte Islands to the U.S. border. On May 23, 1947, the Canadian Rangers were formally established as a Corps of the Reserve Militia, expanding to include other remote and coastal parts of Canada

1985
AHEPA

1986
Firefighter carrying victim

## AMERICAN HELLENIC EDUCATIONAL PROGRESSIVE ASSOCIATION IN CANADA

Designer: Kosta (Gus) Tsetsekas and John Belisle.

Lithography (5 colours with varnish), pane of 16
Canadian Bank Note Company, Limited

| 2003, Mar 25 | GT4, TRC Paper | | Perf 12.5x13.2 | |
|---|---|---|---|---|
| | NH–VF | ⊙F | PB | FDC |
| **1985 48¢ multicoloured** | 1.00 | .35 | 5.00 | 3.00 |

Qty: 3,000,000

Issued to celebrate the 75th anniversary of AHEPA Canada.

## CANADA'S VOLUNTEER FIREFIGHTERS

Designer: François Dallaire. Based on photographs by Guy Lavigueur, Jacques Paul, and Le Courrier de Saint-Hyacinthe.

Lithography (6 colours with varnish), pane of 16
Canadian Bank Note Company, Limited

| 2003, May 30 | GT4, TRC Paper | | Perf 13.4 | |
|---|---|---|---|---|
| | NH–VF | ⊙F | PB | FDC |
| **1986 48¢ multicoloured** | 1.00 | .35 | 5.00 | 3.00 |

Qty: 4,000,000

Volunteer firefighters have long been an invaluable part of emergency response to domestic threats involving fire, medical emergencies, hazardous materials, motor vehicle accidents, and rescues across Canada.

## 50th ANNIVERSARY OF THE CORONATION OF QUEEN ELIZABETH II

1987
Queen Elizabeth II

Designer: Saskia van Kampen.

Lithography (8 colours), pane of 16
Lowe-Martin

| 2003, Jun 2 | GT4, TRC Paper | | Perf 13.2x12.5 | |
|---|---|---|---|---|
| | NH–VF | ⊙F | PB | FDC |
| **1987 48¢ multicoloured** (purple) | 1.00 | .35 | 5.00 | 3.00 |

Qty: 20,000,000

See 1932 for design with gold background.

## PEDRO DA SILVA

1988
*A General View of Quebec, from Point Levy*

Designer: Clermont Malenfant. Based on a drawing by Richard Short.
Based on a photograph by Guy Lavigueur and Archives nationales du Québec à Québec.
Calligraphed by Ginette Morin.

Lithography (6 colours), pane of 16
Canadian Bank Note Company, Limited

| 2003, Jun 6 | GT4, TRC Paper | | Perf 13.1x13.0 | |
|---|---|---|---|---|
| | NH–VF | ⊙F | PB | FDC |
| **1988 48¢ multicoloured** | 1.00 | .35 | 5.00 | 3.00 |

Qty: 3,000,000

**Combination cover (No. 1988 and Portugal stamp)** **5.00**

Issued to honour Pedro da Silva as the first courier of New France and to celebrate the 50th anniversary of Portuguese immigration to Canada.

## TOURIST ATTRACTIONS

1989a
Wilberforce Falls, NU

1989b
Inside Passage, BC

1989c
RCMP parade, SK

1989d
Casa Loma, Toronto, ON

1989e
Gatineau Park, QC

1990a
Dragon boat races, BC

1990b
Polar bear watching, Churchill, MB

1990c
Niagara Falls, ON

1990d
Magdalen Islands, QC

1990e
Charlottetown, PE

Designer: Catharine Bradbury.

Lithography (8 colours), self-adhesive booklet panes of 5
Ashton-Potter (USA) Limited

| 2003, Jun 12 | | GT4, TRC Paper | Die cut perf 11.3x11.4 | | |
|---|---|---|---|---|---|
| | | | NH–VF | ⊙F | FDC |
| 1989 | | booklet pane of 5 x 65¢ (a–e) (**BK270**) | 10.50 | — | — |
| | a | **65¢ Wilberforce Falls, NU** | 1.50 | 1.00 | |
| | b | **65¢ Inside Passage, BC** | 1.50 | 1.00 | |
| | c | **65¢ RCMP parade, SK** | 1.50 | 1.00 | |
| | d | **65¢ Casa Loma, Toronto, ON** | 1.50 | 1.00 | |
| | e | **65¢ Gatineau Park, QC** | 1.50 | 1.00 | |
| | i | unfolded strip of 5 stamps* | 12.50 | | |

Qty: 1,046,175 of each

**Nos. 1989a–1989e (5) combination FDC** **8.50**

| | | | NH–VF | ⊙F | FDC |
|---|---|---|---|---|---|
| 1990 | | booklet pane of 5 x $1.25 (a–e) (**BK271**) | 16.00 | — | — |
| | a | **$1.25 Dragon boat races, BC** | 2.50 | 1.50 | |
| | b | **$1.25 Polar bear watching, Churchill, MB** | 2.50 | 1.50 | |
| | c | **$1.25 Niagara Falls, ON** | 2.50 | 1.50 | |
| | d | **$1.25 Magdalen Islands, QC** | 2.50 | 1.50 | |
| | e | **$1.25 Charlottetown, PE** | 2.50 | 1.50 | |
| | i | unfolded strip of 5 stamps* | 17.50 | | |

Qty: 1,046,175 of each

**Nos. 1990a–1990e (5) combination FDC** **14.50**

* The 2003 Annual Collection included unfolded strips of 5 stamps from each pane; the top and bottom of the booklet panes were trimmed.
See also 1903–1904, 1952–1953, 2019–2023. For non-denominated postal cards of same designs, see UX130.

1989

1990

## VANCOUVER 2010

1991
Vancouver 2010 imprint

Designer: Katalin Kovats and Stuart Bradley Ash.
Based on a photograph by Paul Eekhoff.

Lithography, self-adhesive booklet pane of 10/30
Ashton-Potter (USA) Limited

| 2003, Jul 11 | GT4, TRC Paper | Serpentine die cut 8.5 | | |
|---|---|---|---|---|
| | | NH–VF | ⊙F | FDC |
| 1991 | **48¢ multicoloured** (1931 with 'Vancouver/ 2010' imprint in red at lower right corner) | 2.00 | 1.50 | † |
| a | booklet of 10 x 48¢ (1991) (**BK251Ai, ii, iii**)* | 20.00 | — | |
| b | booklet of 30 x 48¢ (1991) (**BK251A**) | 60.00 | — | |
| **e** | die cutting omitted, pair | *1,000.00* | | |

Qty: 3,000,000

† Canada Post did not produce Official First Day Covers for this issue. Less than 100 First Day Covers were created by private individuals.

* BK251Ai, ii, and iii comprise the left, centre and right thirds of BK251A respectively.

This stamp was *announced* on its date of issue. It commemorates the awarding of the 2010 Winter Olympics to the Vancouver/BC region. The stamp was *not* included in the 2003 Annual Collection.

The Canadian flag is comprised of two shades of red. A minor colour shift of one will give the appearance of a doubled maple leaf — these are not 'double prints'.

1991a

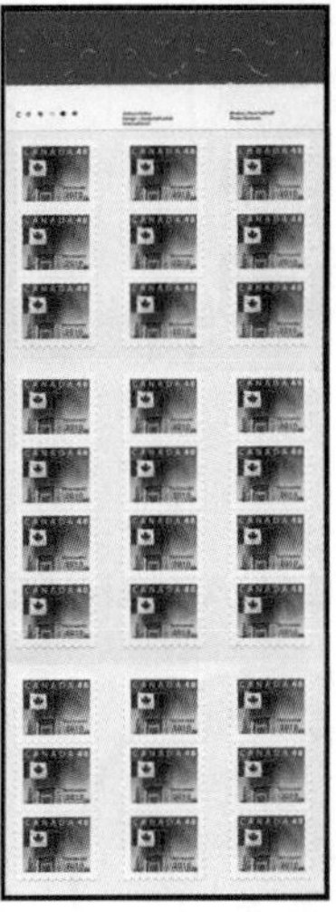
1991b

## CANADA–ALASKA CRUISE PICTURE POSTAGE™

1991C
Totem Pole

1991D
Whale's tail

Designer: Geoff Kehrig.

Lithography, self-adhesive pane of 10
Ashton-Potter (USA) Limited

| 2003, Jul 19 | GT4, TRC Paper | Die cut | | |
|---|---|---|---|---|
| | | NH–VF | ⊙F | FDC |
| 1991C | **($1.25) multicoloured** | 10.00 | 10.00 | — |
| 1991D | **($1.25) multicoloured** | 10.00 | 10.00 | — |
| **De** | horizontal pair (1991C–1991D) | 20.00 | — | † |
| | full pane of 10 | 100.00 | | |

Qty: 250,000 of each

† Canada Post did not produce Official First Day Covers for this issue.
These stamps were not announced to collectors until *after* they appeared. They were *not* included in the 2003 Annual Collection.

The pane contains 10 stamps (5 each of 2 designs) and 3 memento frames, all of which can be imprinted with the sender's photograph. Of the 50,000 panels available, only 10,000 were offered through the National Philatelic Centre. Those remaining were offered to cruise guests whose pictures were printed on the stamps. It is uncertain how many of the sheets set aside for cruises were actually sold. Only a few used singles have been seen that appear to have originated from the cruise ship, with the additional printed souvenir central design. Used price is $75.00 per single. Authentification is required. There is no denomination shown on the stamps.

1991C–1991D full pane of 10

## LUTHERAN WORLD FEDERATION TENTH ASSEMBLY

1992
Logo of 10th Assembly of the LWF

Designer: Pierre Fontaine. Based on a logo by Erik Norbraten and Richard Nostbakken.

Lithography (7 colours), pane of 16
Lowe-Martin

| 2003, Jul 21 | GT4, TRC Paper | Perf 12.5x13.2 | | | |
|---|---|---|---|---|---|
| | | NH–VF | ⊙F | PB | FDC |
| 1992 | **48¢ multicoloured** | 1.00 | .35 | 5.00 | 3.00 |

Qty: 3,000,000

Held every six years, the tenth Assembly of the Lutheran World Federation was held in Winnipeg between July 21 and July 31.

## 50th ANNIVERSARY OF THE SIGNING OF THE KOREA ARMISTICE AGREEMENT

1993
Korea Armistice

Designer: Steven Slipp.
Based on photographs by Bill Olson, Larry Milberry, and W.N. Cridland.
Lithography (9 colours), pane of 16 + gutter
Canadian Bank Note Company, Limited

| 2003, Jul 25 | GT4, TRC Paper | | | Perf 12.9 |
|---|---|---|---|---|
| | NH–VF | ⊙F | PB | FDC |
| **1993** **48¢ multicoloured** | 1.00 | .35 | 5.00 | 3.00 |
| i vertical pair with gutter between | 2.50 | 1.25 | | |

Qty: 3,000,000

## NATIONAL LIBRARY OF CANADA CANADIAN AUTHORS

1994
Anne Hébert (1916–2000)

1995
Hector de Saint-Denys Garneau (1912–1943)

1996
Morley Callaghan (1903–1990)

1997
Susanna Moodie (1803–1885) and Catharine Parr Traill (1802–1899)

Designer: Katalin Kovats.
Lithography (9 colours), booklet pane of 8
Canadian Bank Note Company, Limited

| 2003, Sep 8 | GT4, TRC Paper | Perf 13.1x12.5 | |
|---|---|---|---|
| | NH–VF | ⊙F | FDC |
| **1994** **48¢ multicoloured** | 1.00 | .50 | |
| **1995** **48¢ multicoloured** | 1.00 | .50 | |
| **1996** **48¢ multicoloured** | 1.00 | .50 | |
| i blue dot on forehead (pos. 7) | 3.50 | 2.00 | |
| **1997** **48¢ multicoloured** | 1.00 | .50 | |
| a se-tenant block of 4 (1994–1997) | 4.25 | 3.50 | 5.85 |
| b booklet pane of 2 x 1997a (BK274) | 9.00 | | |
| bi as "b", with two dashes and dot in top left pane margin above inscription, above pos. 1 | 20.00 | | |

**BK274** pane 1997b in cover $9.50
Qty: 750,000 of each

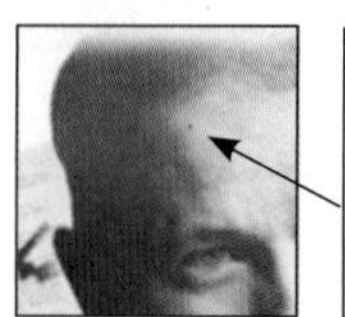
1996i

1997bi

1997b

## WORLD ROAD CYCLING CHAMPIONSHIPS

1998
Cyclists

Designer: Doreen Colonello. Based on a photograph by Peter Griffith.
Lithography (6 colours), booklet pane of 8
Canadian Bank Note Company, Limited

| 2003, Sep 10 | GT4, TRC Paper | Perf 12.5x13.1 | |
|---|---|---|---|
| | NH–VF | ⊙F | FDC |
| **1998** **48¢ multicoloured** | 1.00 | .75 | 3.00 |
| a booklet pane of 8 x 48¢ (BK275) | 9.00 | | |

**BK275** pane 1998a in cover $9.50
Qty: 4,000,000

For non-denominated postal card of same design, see UX133.
Issued for the 68th World Championships for bicycling, held in Hamilton, ON from October 6–12, 2003.

1998a

1999

## CANADIAN ASTRONAUTS

1999a
Marc Garneau

1999b
Roberta Bondar

1999c
Steve MacLean

1999d
Chris Hadfield

1999e
Robert Thirsk

1999f
Bjarni Tryggvason

1999g
Dave Williams

1999h
Julie Payette

Designer: Pierre-Yves Pelletier.
Based on photographs provided by Canadian Space Agency and the National Aeronautics and Space Administration.

Lithography (6 colours) with foil stamping and spot varnish, self-adhesive pane of 8
Lowe-Martin

**2003, Oct 1** **Tagged, TRC Paper** **Die cut**

| | | NH–VF | ⊙F | FDC |
|---|---|---|---|---|
| **1999** | $3.84 full pane of 8 x 48¢ (a–h) (**BK276**) | 12.00 | — | — |
| a | **48¢ Marc Garneau** | 1.00 | 1.00 | |
| b | **48¢ Roberta Bondar** | 1.00 | 1.00 | |
| c | **48¢ Steve MacLean** | 1.00 | 1.00 | |
| d | **48¢ Chris Hadfield** | 1.00 | 1.00 | |
| e | **48¢ Robert Thirsk** | 1.00 | 1.00 | |
| f | **48¢ Bjarni Tryggvason** | 1.00 | 1.00 | |
| g | **48¢ Dave Williams** | 1.00 | 1.00 | |
| h | **48¢ Julie Payette** | 1.00 | 1.00 | |

Qty: 750,000 of each

**Two combination FDCs a–d and e–h** **11.70**

General tagging appears on the white circular border of each stamp.
The 2003 Annual Collection included a trimmed (top and bottom) block of 8 stamps, lacking the inscription at top and image at bottom.

## NATIONAL EMBLEMS

2000
Acer Saccharum
(Canada)

2001
Cassia Fistula
(Thailand)

Designed and based on a photograph by Raymond Bellemare.

Lithography (7 colours), pane of 16
Ashton-Potter (USA) Limited

**2003, Oct 4** **FCP, TRC Paper** **Perf 12.7x12.6**

| | | NH–VF | ⊙F | PB | FDC |
|---|---|---|---|---|---|
| **2000** | **48¢ multicoloured** | 1.00 | .35 | | |
| **2001** | **48¢ multicoloured** | 1.00 | .35 | | |
| a | se-tenant pair (2000, 2001) | 2.25 | 1.50 | 4.50 | 3.95 |
| b | 96¢ souvenir sheet of 2 | 10.00 | 6.00 | — | — |
| c | as "a", imperf. pair* | 1,250.00 | — | | |
| d | as "b", imperforate | 2,000.00 | | | |

Qty: 1,650,000; Souvenir sheet: 300,000
* 40 pairs from 5 panes of 16 reported

**Joint FDC cover with Thailand** **7.20**

Joint issue with Thailand.

2001b

Joint issue with Thailand
**Scott # 2090**

## JEAN-PAUL RIOPELLE

2002a

2002b

2002c

QE II — 2000's

2002d

2002e

2002f

2003i

Designer: Steven Spazuk. Portions taken from a painting (*L'Hommage à Rosa Luxemburg*) by Jean-Paul Riopelle.

Lithography (7 colours, with varnish), pane of 6

Lowe-Martin

| 2003, Oct 7 | GT4, TRC Paper | Perf 12.5x13.3 | | |
|---|---|---|---|---|
| | | NH–VF | ⊙F | FDC |
| **2002** | $2.88 pane of 6 different (a–f) | 10.00 | 10.00 | |
| a | **48¢ multicoloured** | 1.75 | 1.75 | |
| b | **48¢ multicoloured** | 1.75 | 1.75 | |
| c | **48¢ multicoloured** | 1.75 | 1.75 | |
| d | **48¢ multicoloured** | 1.75 | 1.75 | |
| e | **48¢ multicoloured** | 1.75 | 1.75 | |
| f | **48¢ multicoloured** | 1.75 | 1.75 | |

Qty: 500,000 of each

**Three combination FDC's: a+b, c+d, e+f** 11.85

| | | Perf 12.8 | | |
|---|---|---|---|---|
| | | NH–VF | ⊙F | FDC |
| **2003** | **$1.25 souvenir sheet** | 4.00 | 4.00 | 4.50 |
| i | $1.25 single from souvenir sheet | 3.00 | 3.00 | |
| ii | as 2003, with 2 extra perf holes in wings | 4.00 | 4.00 | |
| iii | as 2003, with 1 extra perf hole (right) in wing | 7.50 | 7.50 | |

Qty: 400,000

2003 and 2003ii are believed to exist in equal quantities. Canada Post literature illustrated 2003ii.
The hidden copyright date is found in the fluorescent tagging.

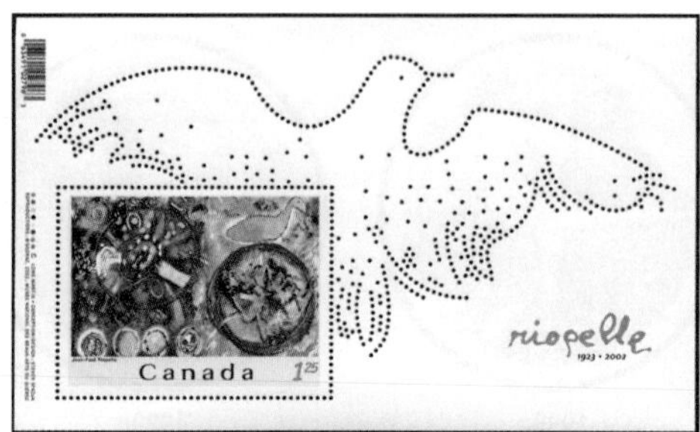

2003

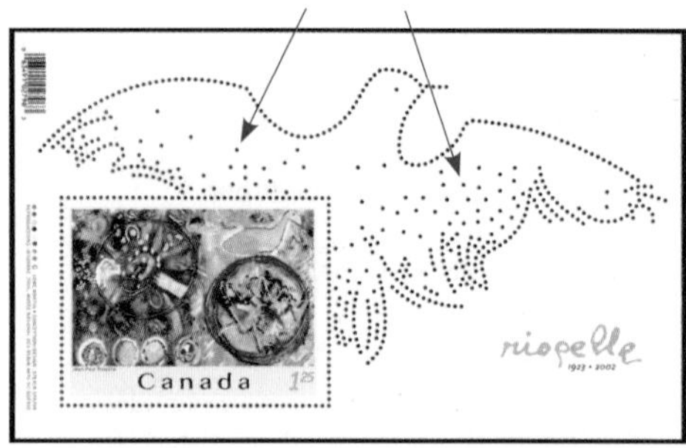

2003ii

2002

## CHRISTMAS — GIFTS

2004
Ice Skates

2005
Teddy Bear

2006
Wood Duck

Designer: Pierre David. Based on a photograph by François Brunelle.
Lithography (7 colours), self-adhesive booklet panes
Lowe-Martin

| 2003, Nov 4 | GT4, TRC Paper | NH–VF | ⊙F | Die cut FDC |
|---|---|---|---|---|
| 2004 | **48¢ multicoloured** | 1.00 | .35 | |
| i | die cut to shape from Quarterly Pack/ Annual Collection | 3.50 | | |
| a | booklet pane of 6 x 48¢ | 6.00 | | |
| b | pair, die cutting omitted | 500.00 | | |
| BK277 | two panes of 2004a $12.00 | | | |

Qty: 48,000,000

| | | NH–VF | ⊙F | FDC |
|---|---|---|---|---|
| 2005 | **65¢ multicoloured** | 1.30 | .75 | |
| i | die cut to shape from Quarterly Pack/ Annual Collection | 4.00 | | |
| c | die cutting omitted, pair | 600.00 | | |
| a | booklet pane of 6 x 65¢ (BK278) | 8.50 | | |
| b | as "a", die cutting omitted | *2,000.00* | | |

Qty: 7,500,000

| | | NH–VF | ⊙F | FDC |
|---|---|---|---|---|
| 2006 | **$1.25 multicoloured** | 2.50 | 1.25 | |
| i | die cut to shape from Quarterly Pack/ Annual Collection | 5.00 | | |
| b | die cutting omitted, pair | 600.00 | | |
| a | booklet pane of 6 x $1.25 (BK279) | 16.00 | | |

Qty: 7,500,000

**Nos. 2004–2006 (3) Combination FDC** 6.75

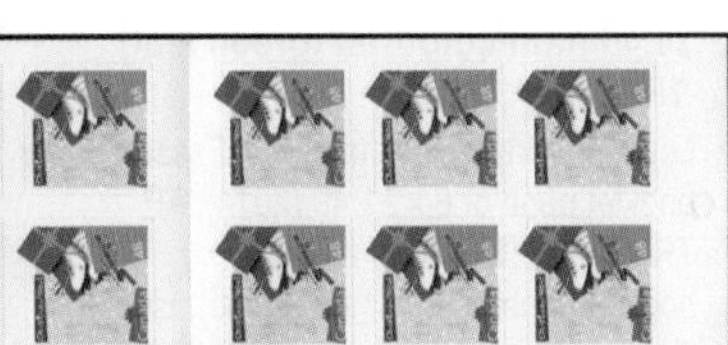

*Image rotated* 2 x 2004a (BK277)

2005a

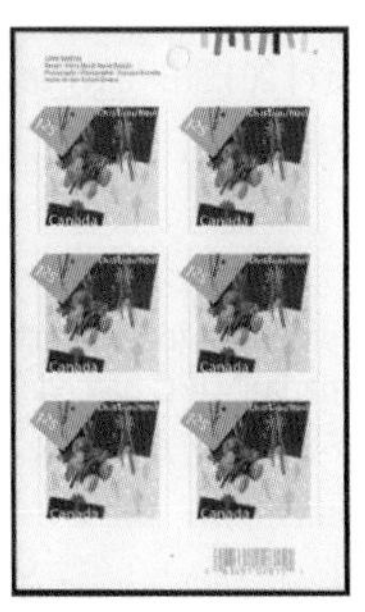

2006a

### eBay Fakes

Warning! Collectors and dealers should be aware of a large number of faked 'used' booklet and souvenir sheets being offered on auction in the past few years. These fakes originate from Montreal, and are being represented as genuinely used to appeal to the collectors of used Canadian issues. Parts of the cancellations (apparently stolen) are genuine, but fake date indicia have been added.

*Reference Manual of BNA Fakes, Forgeries and Counterfeits Series II - Release 6*, Ken Pugh, 2005

## DEFINITIVES 2003–2004

Definitive Timeline:

2003, Dec 19 $5 Moose (1693) (originally assigned 2007 and then 1699, and then 1701)

No. 2007 is not assigned.

## COILS

2008

2009

2010

Designer: Joseph Gault (49¢), Monique Dufour and Sophie Lafortune (80¢ and $1.40).
Lithography (5 colours)
Ashton Potter, Self-adhesive vertical roll of 100

**2003, Dec 19** **GT4, TRC Paper**
**Serpentine Die cut 8.1 Horiz**

| | | NH–VF | ⊙F | FDC |
|---|---|---|---|---|
| 2008 | **49¢ multicoloured** | 1.00 | .25 | 3.00 |
| i | gutter strip of 4† | 9.00 | | |
| | starter strip of 4 (wavy die cut), *Spring 2004** | 15.00 | | |
| | end strip of 4 (wavy die cut), *Spring 2004** | 15.00 | | |
| a | die cutting omitted, pair | 200.00 | | |

* The original release of this coil was separated at the start and end of the roll with just a tear of the rouletted backing paper. This can be "created" by separating at any point along the roll (thus, no premium). The Spring 2004 printing had a revised form of roll separation.

See 2053 for horizontal coil roll (die cut all around).

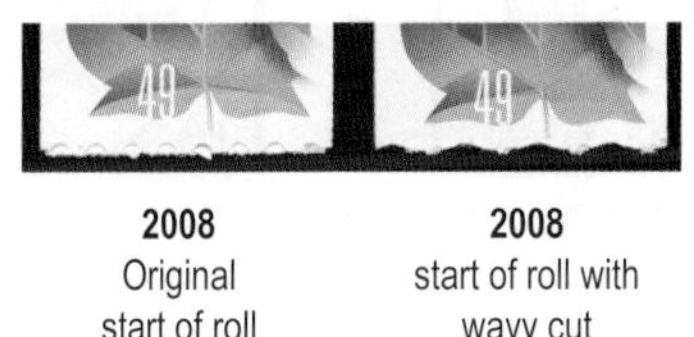

2008 Original start of roll — 2008 start of roll with wavy cut

Ashton Potter, Self-adhesive horizontal rolls of 50
**Serpentine Die cut 8.1 Vert**
**2003, Dec 19** **GT4, TRC Paper**

| | | NH–VF | ⊙F | FDC |
|---|---|---|---|---|
| 2009 | **80¢ multicoloured (red leaf)** | 1.75 | .50 | — |
| i | gutter strip of 4† | 17.00 | | |
| | starter strip of 4 (wavy die cut), *Spring 2004** | 20.00 | | |
| | end strip of 4 (wavy die cut), *Spring 2004** | 20.00 | | |
| 2010 | **$1.40 multicoloured (green leaf)** | 4.00 | .75 | — |
| i | gutter strip of 4† | 27.00 | | |
| | starter strip of 4 (wavy die cut), *Spring 2004** | 35.00 | | |
| | end strip of 4 (wavy die cut), *Spring 2004** | 35.00 | | |

**Nos. 2009–2010 (2) combination FDC** 6.40

**Coil display cards: 2008–2010 (set of 3) $5.00**

* The original release of these coils was separated at the start and end of the roll with just a tear of the rouletted backing paper. This can be "created" by separating at any point along the roll (thus, no premium). The Spring 2004 printings had a revised form of roll separation.

† Gutters appear every 23 stamps.

See 2054–2055 for vertical coil rolls (serpentine die cut at top and bottom).

For non-denominated postal card of no. 2008 design, see UX142; for non-denominated postal card of no. 2009/2013, see UX136.

2008i

2008–2010 Coil display cards

2009i

2010i

## BOOKLETS

2011
Flag over Edmonton, AB

2012
Queen Elizabeth II

2013
Red Maple Leaf on Twig

2014
Green Maple Leaf on Twig

Designer: Gottschalk+Ash Intl (Flag/Queen), Monique Dufour and Sophie Lafortune (Leaf).
Photography: Alberta Economic Development; Lee Simmons (Flag), Bryan Adams (Queen).
Lithography (Flag and QEII: 6 colours; Leaf: 5 colours)
Ashton Potter, Self-adhesive booklet of 10

**2003, Dec 19** **GT4, TRC Paper** **Die cut**

| | | NH–VF | ⊙F | FDC |
|---|---|---|---|---|
| **2011** | **49¢ multicoloured (Flag)**, TRC Paper | 1.00 | .25 | 3.00 |
| i | Fasson paper | 1.00 | .25 | |
| ii | single "no gum", printed on gum side (HB) | 10.00 | 10.00 | |
| a | booklet pane of 10 x 49¢ (2011), AP (**BK280**)[1] | 11.00 | | |
| ai | booklet pane of 10 x 49¢ (2011i), CBN, Fasson paper (philatelic) (**BK280Aa**)‡, *Jul '04* | 15.00 | | |
| aii | booklet pane of 10 x 49¢ (2011i), CBN, Fasson paper (**BK280Ab**)[3], *Sep '04* | 11.00 | | |
| c | as "aii", die cutting omitted, pane of 10, Fasson paper (**BK280Abi**) | 1,000.00 | | |
| b | die cutting omitted, pair, Fasson paper | 200.00 | | |
| aiii | booklet pane of 10 x 49¢ (2011), CBN, TRC paper, narrow roulette (**BK280Ba**)[2]*, *Sep '04* | 75.00 | | |
| aiv | booklet pane of 10 x 49¢ (2011), CBN, TRC paper, wide roulette (**BK280Bb**), *Dec '04* | 25.00 | | |
| avi | as "aiii", die cutting omitted, pane of 10, TRC paper (**BK280Bai**) | 1,200.00 | | |
| avii | as "aii", printed on gum side, pane of 10, Fasson paper (**BK280ABii**) | 125.00 | | |

* BK280Ba exists, due to a miscut, with portions of adjacent stamps tête-bêche.

Canadian Bank Note Company, Limited, Self-adhesive booklet of 10

| | | NH–VF | ⊙F | FDC |
|---|---|---|---|---|
| **2012** | **49¢ multicoloured (QE II)**, TRC paper | 1.00 | .25 | 3.00 |
| ii | pink flaw on forehead, C paper [R1/C3] | 80.00 | 10.00 | |
| i | Fasson paper | 2.00 | .40 | |
| iii | as "i", "no gum", printed on gum side (HB) | 25.00 | 25.00 | |
| a | booklet pane of 10 x 49¢ (2012), TRC paper, medium-length roulette (10 slits)[1] (**BK281**) | 11.00 | | |
| ai | as "a", with pink flaw on forehead (**BK281i**) | 100.00 | | |
| aii | booklet pane of 10 x 49¢ (2012), TRC paper, narrow roulette (23 slits)[2] (**BK281A**), *Jun '04* | 14.00 | | |
| aiii | booklet pane of 10 x 49¢ (2012i), Fasson paper, (philatelic)‡ (**BK281Ba**), *Jul '04* | 14.00 | | |
| aiv | booklet pane of 10 x 49¢ (2012i), Fasson paper, wide roulette (5 slits)[3] (**BK281Bb**) | 35.00 | | |
| av | as "aiv", printed on gum side, pane of 10, Fasson paper (**BK281Bbi**) | 250.00 | | |

Ashton Potter, Self-adhesive booklets of 6

| | | NH–VF | ⊙F | FDC |
|---|---|---|---|---|
| **2013** | **80¢ multicoloured (red leaf)**, TRC paper | 2.00 | .50 | — |
| i | Lowe-Martin ('visible' tagging), Fasson paper | 2.00 | .50 | |
| a | booklet pane of 6 x 80¢ (2013), AP, TRC paper (**BK282**) | 12.00 | | |
| ai | booklet pane of 6 x 80¢ (2013i), LM, Fasson paper (philatelic)‡ (**BK282Aa**), *Jul '04* | 16.00 | | |
| aii | booklet pane of 6 x 80¢ (2013i), LM, Fasson paper (field) (**BK282Ab**), *Sep '04* | 25.00 | | |
| **2014** | **$1.40 multicoloured (green leaf)**, TRC paper | 3.00 | 1.00 | — |
| i | Lowe-Martin ('visible' tagging), Fasson paper | 3.00 | 1.00 | |
| a | booklet pane of 6 x $1.40 (2014), AP, TRC paper (**BK283**) | 18.00 | | |
| ai | booklet pane of 6 x $1.40 (2014i), LM, Fasson paper (philatelic)‡ (**BK283Aa**), *Jul '04* | 25.00 | | |
| aii | booklet pane of 6 x $1.40 (2014i), LM, Fasson paper (field) (**BK283Ab**), *Sep '04* | 35.00 | | |

Counterfeit booklets of 2012 (BK281) and 2014 (BK283) are known to exist. These are of a very high quality.

**UPC Barcodes**

‡ Philatelic reprint [produced to 'show off' change of printer from Ashton-Potter (USA) to Lowe-Martin (Canada)]. UPC barcodes on booklet covers were "unique" for these printings, as follows:

| 0 63491 ... | Flag | Queen | 80¢ Leaf | $1.40 Leaf |
|---|---|---|---|---|
| Field | ... 02799 4 | ... 02800 7 | ... 02803 8 | ... 02805 2 |
| Philatelic | ... 03102 1 | ... 03119 9 | ... 03105 2 | ... 03106 9 |

**Rouletting**

Rouletting was applied through the middle of the 49¢ booklets (Flag and Queen) to aid in folding the pane in half, as follows:

[1] first printings: Flag: thin roulette through middle only visible from back; Queen: medium-length roulette (about 10 per booklet)

[2] narrow roulette through middle (about 23 per booklet)

[3] wide roulette through middle (about 5 per booklet); red product info bar at top is shorter to avoid die cutting

2012ii

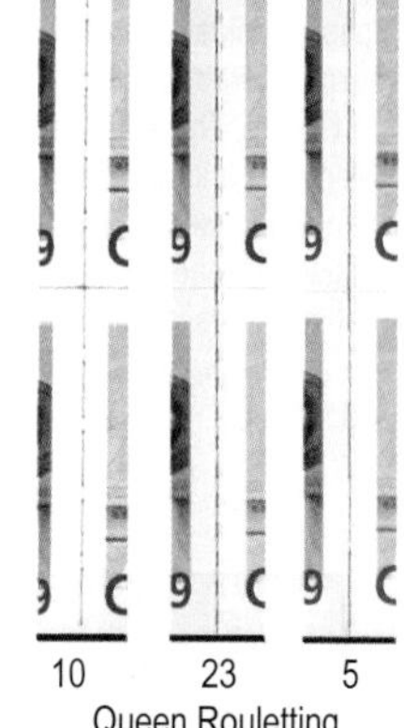
10 23 5
Queen Rouletting

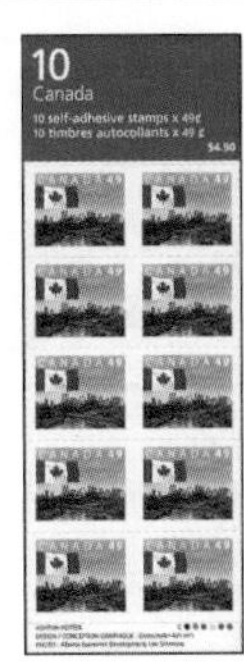
2011a

2012a

2013a

2014a

**Differentiating "C" and "F" paper**

Under 10x magnification, F paper has a smooth, flat appearance; C paper has a textured, "indented" appearance, as illustrated at right.

C paper

## 2004

| **Rates:** | Domestic first-class (0-30g): 49¢ | |
|---|---|---|
| Jan 12/04– | Domestic first-class (30-50g): 80¢ | USA (0-30g): 80¢ |
| Jan 16/05 | Domestic oversize (0-100g): 98¢ | International (0-30g): $1.40 |

*single usage:* USA 80¢: $15.00 | International $1.40: $25.00

### LUNAR NEW YEAR — 8
### Year of the Monkey

2015
Confrontation with Jade Emperor

2016i
Errand for Buddha

Designer: Louis Fishauf. Based on an illustration by Anita Kunz.
Lithography (9 colours) and clear and gold foil stamping plus embossing, pane of 25
Canadian Bank Note Company, Limited

**2004, Jan 8 — GT4, TRC Paper — Perf 13.1x12.5**

| | | NH–VF | ⊙F | PB | FDC |
|---|---|---|---|---|---|
| **2015** | **49¢ multicoloured** | 1.00 | .35 | 5.00 | 3.00 |
| **2016** | **$1.40 souvenir sheet** | 4.00† | 4.00† | — | 4.80 |
| i | $1.40 single stamp from souvenir sheet | 3.00 | 3.00 | — | |
| ii | $26.95 uncut press sheet of 12 souvenir sheets | 75.00 | | | |
| a | as 2016, with overprint | 5.00† | 5.00† | | |

Qty: 2015: 8,000,000; 2016: 1,700,000; 2016a: 200,000; 2016ii: 35,000

† Price is for souvenir sheet with attached UPC barcode tab.

*The Journey to the West* is the fabulous and funny 16th century tale of Sun Wu-k'ung, the Monkey King.

See also 1630, 1708, 1767–1768, 1836–1837, 1883–1884, 1933–1934, 1969–1970, 2083–2084, 2140–2141, 2201–2202, 2257–2258. For non-denominated postal cards of same designs, see UX134–UX135.

2016

2016a

### NHL ALL-STARS — 5

*Perforated singles from water-activated gum pane*

2017a
Larry Robinson (1951– )

2017b
Marcel Dionne (1951– )

2017c
Ted Lindsay (1925– )

2017d
Johnny Bower (1924– )

2017e
Brad Park (1948– )

2017f
Milt Schmidt (1918–2017)

*Die cut singles from self-adhesive booklet*

2018a
Larry Robinson

2018b
Marcel Dionne

2018c
Ted Lindsay

2018d
Johnny Bower

2018e
Brad Park

2018f
Milt Schmidt

Designer: Stéphane Huot. Based on an illustration by Charles Vinh and Pierre Rousseau.
Lithography (6 colours plus varnish), pane of 6 + 3 tabs
Lowe-Martin

**2004, Jan 24** **GT4, TRC Paper** **Perf 12.6x13.3**

| | | NH–VF | ⊙F | FDC |
|---|---|---|---|---|
| **2017** | $2.94 pane of 6 x 49¢ | 8.00 | — | |
| a | **49¢ multicoloured** | 1.00 | .80 | |
| b | **49¢ multicoloured** | 1.00 | .80 | |
| c | **49¢ multicoloured** | 1.00 | .80 | |
| d | **49¢ multicoloured** | 1.00 | .80 | |
| e | **49¢ multicoloured** | 1.00 | .80 | |
| f | **49¢ multicoloured** | 1.00 | .80 | |

Qty: 396,500 of each

**Three combination FDC's: a+b, c+d, e+f** **11.85**

**Self-adhesive booklet of 6**

**2004, Jan 24** **GT4, JAC Paper** **Die cut**

| | | NH–VF | ⊙F | FDC |
|---|---|---|---|---|
| **2018** | $2.94 pane of 6 x 49¢ (a–f) (**BK284**) | 10.00 | — | |
| a | **49¢ multicoloured** | 1.00 | .75 | |
| b | **49¢ multicoloured** | 1.00 | .75 | |
| c | **49¢ multicoloured** | 1.00 | .75 | |
| d | **49¢ multicoloured** | 1.00 | .75 | |
| e | **49¢ multicoloured** | 1.00 | .75 | |
| f | **49¢ multicoloured** | 1.00 | .75 | |

Qty: 603,500 of each

The 2004 Annual Collection did *not* include the self-adhesive booklet.
The fifth year of NHL All-Star stamps. See also 1443–1445, 1838, 1885, 1935, 1971–1972, 2085–2086.

**2017**

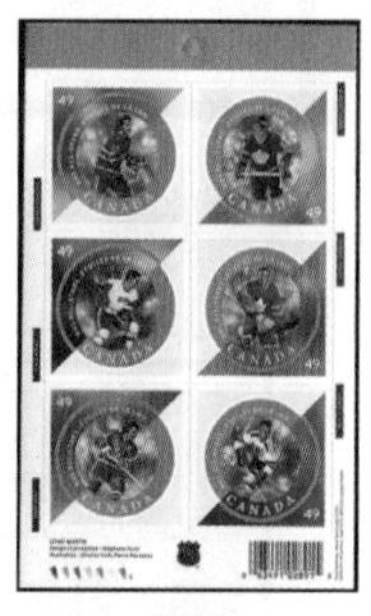
**2018**

## TOURIST ATTRACTIONS

**2019**
Quebec Winter Carnival

**2020**
St. Joseph's Oratory, Quebec

**2021**
Festival International de Jazz de Montréal

**2022**
Traversée internationale du Lac St-Jean

**2023**
Canadian National Exhibition, Toronto, ON

Designer: Bradbury Branding and Design.
Photo: Carnaval de Québec; Bernard Brault (St. Joseph's Oratory); Nadia Molinari (Jazz); Jean-François Leblanc (St-Jean); Michael Rafelson (CNE).
Lithography (8 colours plus varnish), self-adhesive booklets of 6
Lowe-Martin

**GT4, TRC Paper** **Die cut**

| | | NH–VF | ⊙F | FDC |
|---|---|---|---|---|
| **2019** | **49¢ multicoloured**, *Jan 29, 2004* | 1.00 | .50 | 3.00 |
| a | booklet pane of 6 x 49¢ (2019) (**BK285**) | 7.00 | | |
| **2020** | **49¢ multicoloured**, *Apr 2, 2004* | 1.00 | .50 | 3.00 |
| a | booklet pane of 6 x 49¢ (2020) (**BK287**) | 7.00 | | |
| **2021** | **49¢ multicoloured**, *Jun 1, 2004* | 1.00 | .50 | 3.00 |
| a | booklet pane of 6 x 49¢ (2021) (**BK293**) | 7.00 | | |
| **2022** | **49¢ multicoloured**, *Jun 18, 2004* | 1.00 | .50 | 3.00 |
| a | booklet pane of 6 x 49¢ (2022) (**BK294**) | 7.00 | | |
| **2023** | **49¢ multicoloured**, *Jul 19, 2004* | 1.00 | .50 | 3.00 |
| a | booklet pane of 6 x 49¢ (2023) (**BK295**) | 7.00 | | |

Qty: 1,500,000 (250,000 booklets) of each
Two copies of 2021 (value $1,250) and one copy of 2022 (value $1,750) have been reported with "missing metallic silver". Certification required.

See also 1903–1904, 1952–1953, 1989–1990. For non-denominated postal cards of same designs, see UX137–UX141.

**2019a**

**2020a**

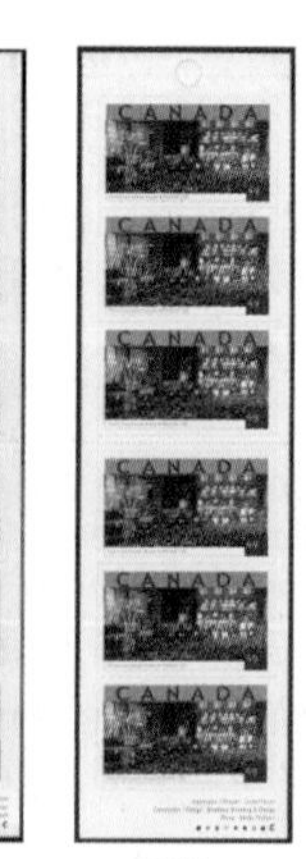
**2021a**

**2022a**

**2023a**

## GOVERNOR GENERAL RAMON HNATYSHYN

2024

Designer: Susan Mavor. Based on a photograph by Paul Chiasson.
Lithography (6 colours), pane of 16
Lowe-Martin

| 2004, Mar 16 | GT4, TRC Paper | | Perf 12.5x13.3 | |
|---|---|---|---|---|
| | NH–VF | ⊙F | PB | FDC |
| **2024 49¢ multicoloured** | 1.00 | .30 | 5.00 | 3.00 |

Qty: 2,500,000

Ramon (Ray) Hnatyshyn (1934–2002) was a lawyer and politician (serving in cabinet under two prime ministers) before becoming Governor General in 1990.

## ARMY CADETS

2025

Designer: Smith-Boake Designwerke Inc. (André Perro).
Lithography (8 colours), self-adhesive booklet of 8
Canadian Bank Note Company, Limited

| 2004, Mar 26 | GT4, TRC Paper | | Die cut |
|---|---|---|---|
| | NH–VF | ⊙F | FDC |
| **2025 49¢ multicoloured** | 1.00 | .40 | 3.00 |
| a booklet pane of 4 x 49¢ (2025) | 4.50 | | |
| BK286 two panes of 2025a $10.00 | | | |

Qty: 2,000,000

Issued to commemorate the 125th anniversary of the Royal Canadian Army Cadets (RCAC).

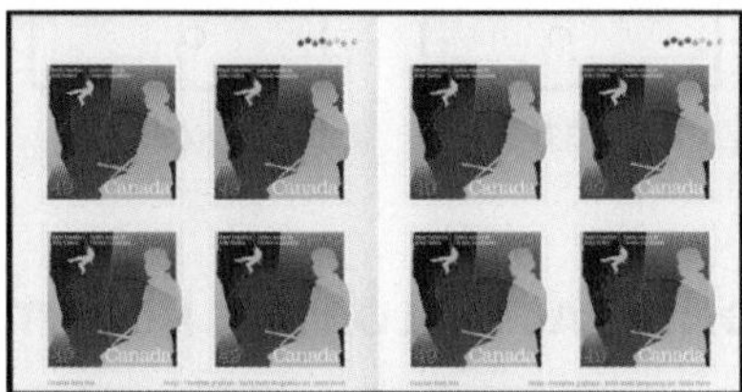

2 x 2025a (BK286)

## OTTO SVERDRUP

2026
*Fram*

2027i
*Fram*

Designed and engraved by Martin Mörk. Typographed by Morten Stürup.
Lithography (4 colours) plus engraving (1 colour), pane of 16
Post Danmark Stamps

| 2004, Mar 26 | FCP, TRC Paper | | Perf 13.2x13.1 | |
|---|---|---|---|---|
| | NH–VF | ⊙F | PB | FDC |
| **2026 49¢ multicoloured** | 1.00 | .40 | 5.00 | 3.00 |
| i flaw in 5 (higher) (pos. 11)* | 5.00 | 2.50 | 10.00 (LR) | |
| ii flaw in 5 (lower) (pos. 11)* | 5.00 | 2.50 | 10.00 (LR) | |
| **2027 $1.40 souvenir sheet** | 4.00 | 4.00 | — | 4.80 |
| i single stamp from souvenir sheet | 3.50 | 3.50 | — | |

Qty: 2026: 4,000,000; 2027: 400,000

* Three similar (but slightly different) constant flaws exist.
This issue exists with 'washed out' or 'bright' tagging.

Issued to celebrate the 150th anniversary of the birth of Norwegian explorer Otto Sverdrup (1854–1930). Joint issue with Norway and Greenland.

2027

Joint issue with Norway
**Scott # 1398–1399**

Joint issue with Greenland
**Scott # 426**

Three stamp designs are used: Sverdrup's portrait, his ship "FRAM" and a landing boat from the "FRAM" approaching an arctic island. In Canada only the "FRAM" stamp shows a denomination ($1.40).

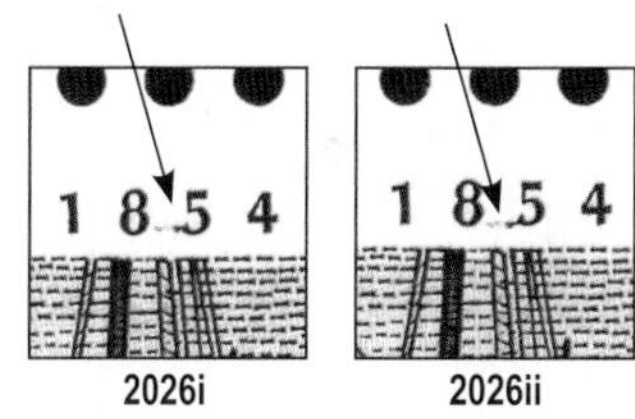


2026i 2026ii

## URBAN TRANSIT/LIGHT RAIL

2028
Toronto Transit Commission

2029
TransLink Sky-Train, Vancouver

2030
Societé de Transport de Montréal

2031
Calgary Transit Light Rail

Designer: Debbie Adams. Based on photographs by Andrew Layerle.

Lithography (11 colours plus varnish), pane of 16

Canadian Bank Note

**2004, Mar 30** **GT4, TRC Paper** **Perf 12.5x13.1**

| | | NH–VF | ⊙F | PB | FDC |
|---|---|---|---|---|---|
| **2028** | **49¢ multicoloured** | 1.00 | .50 | — | |
| **2029** | **49¢ multicoloured** | 1.00 | .50 | — | |
| **2030** | **49¢ multicoloured** | 1.00 | .50 | — | |
| **2031** | **49¢ multicoloured** | 1.00 | .50 | — | |
| a | vertical strip of four (2028–2031)* | 4.00 | 3.50 | 5.00 | 5.95 |

* Se-tenant format only available vertically.

Qty: 1,250,000 of each

Celebrating the 50th anniversary of Canada's first subway, which opened in Toronto in 1954. They depict in correct detail the trains, station names and logos of rapid transit systems in four Canadian cities: Toronto, Montreal, Calgary and Vancouver.

## HOME HARDWARE

**2032**
Map of Canada

Designer: Ron Mugford.

Lithography (6 colours), self-adhesive pane of 10 in Prestige Booklet

Lowe-Martin

**2004, Apr 19** **GT4, TRC Paper** **Die cut 11.0**

| | | NH–VF | ⊙F | FDC |
|---|---|---|---|---|
| **2032** | **49¢ multicoloured** | 1.00 | .40 | 3.00 |
| a | booklet pane of 10 x 49¢ (2032) + label | 12.00 | | |
| **BK288** | pane 2032a in Prestige Booklet $15.00 | | | |

Qty: 8,000,000

The prestige pack includes information and photos pertaining to Home Hardware and its history, including 15 special logo seals. The issue celebrates the 40th anniversary of Home Hardware.

**2032a**

**MINT PRICING PREMIUMS**

Mint stamps from 301 to date are valued as NH-VF (Never Hinged-Very Fine). All hinged VF and NH-F copies are worth 50% of the listed values. Plate block (PB) values are for mint NH–VF plate or inscription blocks of four.

**USED, VF/XF (with in-period, circular date cancel) PRICING PREMIUM**

Single stamps with light or circular date cancels will sell for more than catalogue value (perhaps even more than a mint copy). From *1981 to 1991* single stamps from se-tenant blocks of 4 or larger will be priced at 50% or more above the fine price. From *1992* to date single stamps from se-tenant blocks of 4 or larger plus se-tenant booklet panes and souvenir sheets will be priced at 100% or more above the fine price. From *1997* to date all other stamps will be priced at 50% or more above the fine price.

## UNIVERSITIES

**2033**
Université de Sherbrooke

**2034**
University of Prince Edward Island

Designer: Denis L'Allier. Based on a photograph by Guy Lavigueur.

Lithography (6 colours), booklet panes of 8

Canadian Bank Note Company, Limited

**GT4, TRC Paper** **Perf 13.3**

| | | NH–VF | ⊙F | FDC |
|---|---|---|---|---|
| **2033** | **49¢ multicoloured**, *May 4, 2004* | 1.00 | .40 | 3.00 |
| a | booklet pane of 8 x 49¢ (2033) | 8.50 | | |
| **BK289** | pane 2033a in cover $9.00 | | | |

Qty: 1,500,000

| | | NH–VF | ⊙F | FDC |
|---|---|---|---|---|
| **2034** | **49¢ multicoloured**, *May 8, 2004* | 1.00 | .40 | 3.00 |
| a | booklet pane of 8 x 49¢ (2034) | 8.50 | | |
| **BK291** | pane 2034a in cover $9.00 | | | |

Qty: 1,500,000

Issued to celebrate the 50th anniversary of Sherbrooke University, QC and the 200th anniversary of the University of Prince Edward Island.

For other Universities, see also 1756, 1941–1944, 1973–1977, 2089, 2172, 2209–2210.

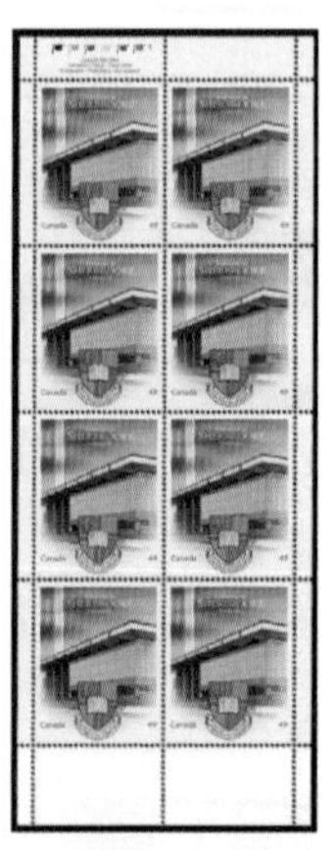

**2033a**

**2034a**

## MONTREAL CHILDREN'S HOSPITAL

**2035**
Teddy bears

Designer: Monique Dufour and Sophie Lafortune. Photography: Serge Lacroix, Digital Vision, MCH/HME.

Lithography (5 colours), self-adhesive booklet of 8
Lowe-Martin

| 2004, May 6 | GT4, TRC Paper | Die cut 9.6x10.7 | | |
|---|---|---|---|---|
| | | NH–VF | ⊙F | FDC |
| **2035** | **49¢ multicoloured** | 1.00 | .40 | 3.00 |
| a | booklet pane of 4 x 49¢ (2035) | 4.50 | | |
| BK290 | two panes of 2035a $10.00 | | | |

Qty: 2,500,000

100th anniversary of the founding of The Montreal Children's Hospital.

2 x 2035a (BK290)

## JOHN JAMES AUDUBON'S BIRDS — 2

2036 Ruby-crowned Kinglet
2037 White-winged Crossbill

2038 Bohemian Waxwing
2039 Boreal Chickadee

2040
Lincoln's Sparrow

Designer: Rolf P. Harder.

Lithography (11 colours; 80¢: 8 colours), pane of 16
Lowe-Martin

| 2004, May 14 | GT4, TRC Paper | Perf 12.4x13.3 | | | |
|---|---|---|---|---|---|
| | | NH–VF | ⊙F | PB | FDC |
| **2036** | **49¢ multicoloured** | 1.00 | .50 | | |
| **2037** | **49¢ multicoloured** | 1.00 | .50 | | |
| **2038** | **49¢ multicoloured** | 1.00 | .50 | | |
| **2039** | **49¢ multicoloured** | 1.00 | .50 | | |
| a | se-tenant block of 4 (2036–2039) | 4.00 | 3.50 | 5.00 | 5.95* |

Lowe-Martin, self-adhesive pane of 6

| 2004, May 14 | GT4, TRC Paper | Die cut | | |
|---|---|---|---|---|
| | | NH–VF | ⊙F | FDC |
| **2040** | **80¢ multicoloured** | 1.60 | 1.00 | 3.60* |
| i | 4 red dots above 8 (pos. 2) | 15.00 | 5.00 | |
| a | booklet pane of 6 x 80¢ (2040) (**BK292**) | 11.00 | | |
| ai | pane 2040a with 4 red dots at pos. 2 | 25.00 | | |

Qty: 49¢: 1,250,000 of each; 80¢: 2,100,000

* The OFDCs were incorrectly produced with a cancel of May 21. They were not reprinted to reflect the correct issue date of May 14.

See also: 1979–1983, 2095–2099.

2040a

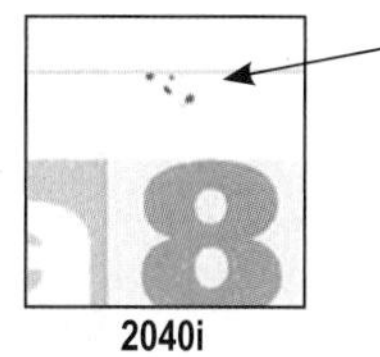

2040i

## PIONEERS OF TRANSATLANTIC MAIL SERVICE

2041 Sir Samuel Cunard
2042 Sir Hugh Allan

Designer: Dennis Page, Oliver Hill. Illustration: Bonnie Ross.

Lithography (5 colours plus varnish), self-adhesive pane of 16
Lowe-Martin

| 2004, May 28 | GT4, TRC Paper | Perf 13.4x12.6 | | | |
|---|---|---|---|---|---|
| | | VF* | ⊙F | PB* | FDC |
| **2041** | **49¢ multicoloured** | 1.00 | .40 | | |
| **2042** | **49¢ multicoloured** | 1.00 | .40 | | |
| a | se-tenant pair (2041, 2042) | 2.00 | 1.50 | 5.00 | 3.95 |
| i | se-tenant pair with 2042 on left | 3.00 | 2.50 | | |

Qty: 2,000,000 of each

* Price is for stamps with backing paper. Stamps are fully perforated – the first time self-adhesive stamps were printed this way in Canada.

Portraits of both Sir Samuel Cunard and Sir Hugh Allan, illustrated in a popular formalized period style. The two ships, Cunard's *Britannia* and Allan's *North American*, are depicted on route. The cancellation marks represent the dates of the arrival of Cunard's *Britannia* in Halifax and the departure of Allan's *North American* from Liverpool.

## D-DAY

2043
Juno Beach, Normandy

Designer: Derwyn Goodall. Painting: Canadian War Museum/O.N. Fisher.

Lithography (9 colours), pane of 16
Lowe-Martin

| 2004, Jun 6 | GT4, TRC Paper | Perf 13.3x12.6 | | | |
|---|---|---|---|---|---|
| | | NH–VF | ⊙F | PB | FDC |
| **2043** | **49¢ multicoloured** | 1.00 | .40 | 5.00* | 3.00 |

Qty: 3,000,000

60th anniversary of the landing of Canadian forces on the beaches of Normandy. The stamp depicts the initial landings and the Juno Beach sectors of the Normandy coastline.

*The artist Orville Norman Fisher's last name was spelled incorrectly on the selvedge of the stamp pane and in the credits of the OFDC.

Lowe-Martin
Design / Conception : Derwyn Goodall
Painting / Peinture : O. N. Fischer
Canadian War Museum /
Musée canadien de la guerre

QE II — 2000's

## FRENCH SETTLEMENT IN ACADIA

2044
Pierre Dugua, Sieur de Mons

Designer: Fugazi. Illustration: Suzanne Duranceau. Engraving: André Lavergne
Lithography (3 colours) plus Engraving, pane of 16
Canadian Bank Note

| 2004, Jun 26 | GT4, TRC Paper | Perf 13.1x12.5 | | | |
|---|---|---|---|---|---|
| | | NH–VF | ⊙F | PB | FDC |
| **2044** | **49¢ multicoloured** | 1.00 | .40 | 5.00 | 3.00 |

Qty: 4,000,000

**Joint FDC with France** **5.00**

Joint issue with France. Commemorating the 400th anniversary of the first French Settlement in Acadia at St. Croix Island. See also 2115, 2155, 2226, 2269.

Joint issue with France
**Scott # 3032**

## WRITE ME ... RING ME

2045
Butterfly and Flower

2046
Children on Beach

2047
Rose

2048
Pug

2045–2048
Card packages

Frame designed by Steven Spazuk. Photographs: Butterfly and Rose: Relizon Canada Inc.; Beach: Augustus Butera; Dog: Ryan McVay.
Lithography, self-adhesive panes of 2
Ashton-Potter

| 2004, Jun 1 | GT4, TRC Paper | Serpentine Die cut 11.6 | | |
|---|---|---|---|---|
| | | NH–VF | ⊙F | FDC |
| **2045** | **(49¢) multicoloured** | 30.00 | 17.50* | — |
| a | pane of 2 | 60.00 | | |
| i | complete card including phone card† | 70.00 | | |

Qty: 20,510 stamps

| | | NH–VF | ⊙F | FDC |
|---|---|---|---|---|
| **2046** | **(49¢) multicoloured** | 12.50 | 17.50* | — |
| a | pane of 2 | 25.00 | | |
| i | complete card including phone card† | 30.00 | | |

Qty: 27,370 stamps

| | | NH–VF | ⊙F | FDC |
|---|---|---|---|---|
| **2047** | **(49¢) multicoloured** | 12.50 | 17.50* | — |
| a | pane of 2 | 25.00 | | |
| i | complete card including phone card† | 30.00 | | |

Qty: 25,010 stamps

| | | NH–VF | ⊙F | FDC |
|---|---|---|---|---|
| **2048** | **(49¢) multicoloured** | 12.50 | 17.50* | — |
| a | pane of 2 | 25.00 | | |
| i | complete card including phone card† | 30.00 | | |

Qty: 27,010 stamps

* Properly used in period, with dated cancel (before Jan 17/05). Commercially used on cover during period of availability are rare ($50 each).

† Complete greeting card sold for $5.99 which includes 2 stamps and a 15 minute phone card with a matching design.

First day covers were not available for this issue. The 2004 Annual Collection did *not* include these stamps. Pane cutting varieties exist that show coloured slivers of panes from other stamps.

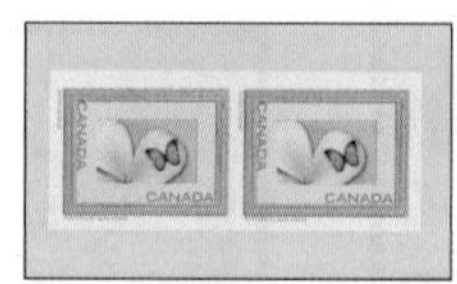

2045a

2046a

2047a

2048a

## 2004 OLYMPIC SUMMER GAMES

2049
Marathon

2050
Soccer

Designer: Pierre-Yves Pelletier. Photography: IOC/Olympic Museum Collections, Imagination (Photolux Studio).
Lithography (5 colours), pane of 16
Canadian Bank Note

| 2004, Jul 28 | GT4, TRC Paper | Perf 12.5x13.1 | | | |
|---|---|---|---|---|---|
| | | NH–VF | ⊙F | PB | FDC |
| **2049** | **49¢ multicoloured** | 1.00 | .40 | | |
| **2050** | **49¢ multicoloured** | 1.00 | .40 | | |
| a | se-tenant pair (2049, 2050) | 2.00 | 1.50 | 5.00 | 3.95 |

Qty: 2,000,000 of each

Spyros Louis was the winner of the first marathon of the modern Olympics in 1896. Women's soccer was introduced to the Olympics in 1996.

## GOLFING

2051
Golfer swinging driver on tee box

2052
Golfer putting on green

Designer: q30 design inc. Photography: Royal Canadian Golf Association
Lithography (8 colours) plus foil stamping and embossing
Lowe-Martin, self-adhesive pane of 8

**2004, Aug 12** **GT4, Fasson Paper** **Die cut**

| | | NH–VF | ⊙F | FDC |
|---|---|---|---|---|
| **2051** | **49¢ multicoloured** | 1.00 | .40 | |
| **2052** | **49¢ multicoloured** | 1.00 | .40 | |
| ii | missing silver on both stamps, horiz. pair | 3,000.00 | | |
| i | full pane of 8 (4 each of 2051 and 2052) | 10.00 | | |

Qty: 4,000,000 of each

**Nos. 2051–2052 (2) combination FDC** **3.95**

Die cut to shape singles were affixed to the "Open Championship Commemorative Frame" (a joint Royal Canadian Mint/Canada Post stamp and coin product).
2052 has been reported with partially missing silver foil stamping; value $300 – certificate of authenticity recommended.

Issued to celebrate the centenary of the Open Golf Championship in Canada in 1895. The circular stamps are the same size as a regulation golf ball. When the stamps are removed from the pane, green text is revealed reading "REPLACE DIVOT • REPLACER LA MOTTE".

2052i

2054i

2055i

## COIL REPRINTS

2053

2054

2055

2053i

Designer: Joseph Gault (49¢), Monique Dufour and Sophie Lafortune (80¢ and $1.40).
Lithography (5 colours)
Canadian Bank Note, Self-adhesive horizontal roll of 100

**2004, Sep** **GT4, TRC Paper** **Die cut**

| | | NH–VF | ⊙F | FDC |
|---|---|---|---|---|
| **2053** | **49¢ multicoloured**, 3½mm tagging | 1.00 | .25 | — |
| i | gutter strip of 4 with Maple Leafs† | 7.50 | | |
| ii | 4mm tagging with "inner frame" | 1.25 | .25 | |
| iii | as ii, gutter strip of 4 with Maple Leafs† | 7.50 | | |
| iv | reprint (lighter blue), *Nov 2004* | 3.00 | .25 | |
| v | as iv, gutter strip of 4 with Maple Leafs† | 18.00 | | |
| a | die cutting omitted, pair | 250.00 | | |
| vii | reprint, non-flourescent orange ink | 10.00 | 1.00 | |
| viii | as vii, gutter strip of 4 with Maple Leafs† | 80.00 | | |

All versions of 2053 (except 2053vii-viii) were printed with orange ink that fluoresces under UV light.

See 2008 for vertical coil roll (serpentine die cut at top and bottom).

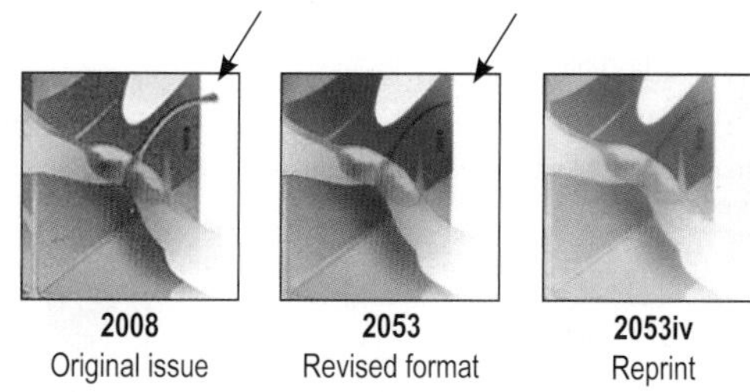

2008 Original issue — 2053 Revised format — 2053iv Reprint

Lowe-Martin, Self-adhesive vertical rolls of 50

Two different die cut patterns were used. The first pattern has a 'perf' range from 8.00 to 8.85 and does *not* have nibs. The second pattern (containing the "ski slope" anomaly; not used on the $1.40 value) has a 'perf' range of 7.75 to 8.90 *with* nibs. Every stamp on each of the 100-subject (10x10) die cutting mats is different due to variations occurring on the top and bottom of a single stamp.

**2004, Sep** **GT4, TRC Paper**
**Serpentine Die cut 7.75 to 8.90 Horiz**

| | | NH–VF | ⊙F | FDC |
|---|---|---|---|---|
| **2054** | **80¢ multicoloured (red leaf)** | 2.75 | .70 | — |
| i | gutter strip of 4 with Maple Leafs† | 16.00 | | |
| ii | with nibs | 15.00 | 2.50 | |
| iii | as 2054ii, in gutter strip of 4† | 75.00 | | |
| iv | "ski slope" die cut anomaly (between 3rd and 4th stamp above gutter, 1 in 10 rolls) | 150.00 | | |
| v | as 2054iv, in gutter strip of 6† | 255.00 | | |
| **2055** | **$1.40 multicoloured (green leaf)** | 5.00 | 1.25 | — |
| i | gutter strip of 4 with Maple Leafs† | 35.00 | | |
| a | die cutting omitted, pair | | | |

See 2009–2010 for horizontal coil rolls (serpentine die cuts at sides).

† Gutters, with coloured Maple leafs, appear every 10 stamps. Rolls of 2054 and 2055 exist wound in either direction.
No FDC's were available for 2053–2055.

2054iv
"ski slope" die cut

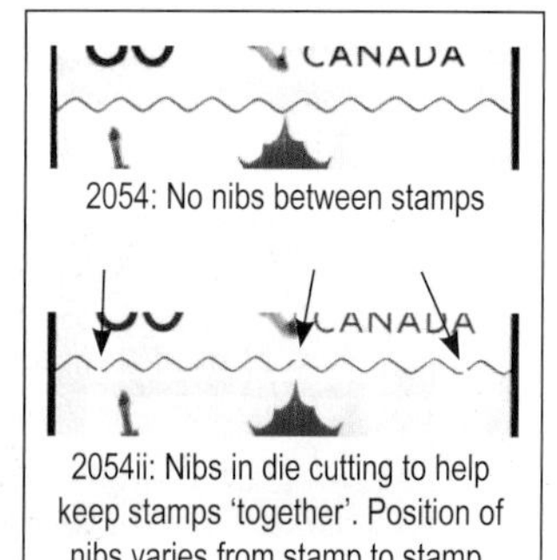

2054: No nibs between stamps

2054ii: Nibs in die cutting to help keep stamps 'together'. Position of nibs varies from stamp to stamp.

## MONTRÉAL HEART INSTITUTE

2056

Designer: Guénette + Delisle. Photography: MHI

Lithography (6 colours), self-adhesive booklet of 8

Lowe-Martin

| 2004, Sep 15 | GT4, Fasson Paper | NH–VF | ⊙F | FDC (Die cut 13.6) |
|---|---|---|---|---|
| **2056** | **49¢ multicoloured** | 1.00 | .40 | 3.00 |
| ii | die cut to shape from Quarterly Pack/ Annual Collection | 3.00 | | |
| a | booklet pane of 4 x 49¢ (2056) | 4.50 | | |
| **BK296** | two panes of 2056a $10.00 | | | |

Qty: 2,500,000

50th anniversary of the Montréal Heart Institute featuring a stylized heart graphic.

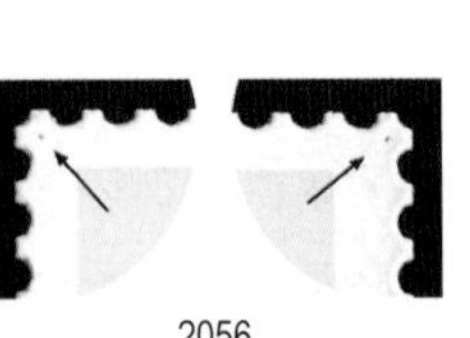
2056
"gripping indents" in corners
are found on most booklets

2 x 2056a
(BK296)

## PETS

2057 Fish — 2058 Cats

2059 Rabbit — 2060 Dog

2 x 2060a (BK297)

Image reduced.

Designer: Isabelle Toussaint. Photography: Savoie/Montplaisir. Children: Agence Joanne Sheskay Agency. Animals: CinéZoo.

Lithography (7 colours), self-adhesive booklet of 8

Lowe-Martin

| 2004, Oct 1 | GT4, Fasson Paper | NH–VF | ⊙F | FDC (Die cut) |
|---|---|---|---|---|
| **2057** | **49¢ multicoloured** | 1.00 | .50 | |
| **2058** | **49¢ multicoloured** | 1.00 | .50 | |
| **2059** | **49¢ multicoloured** | 1.00 | .50 | |
| **2060** | **49¢ multicoloured** | 1.00 | .50 | |
| a | booklet pane of 4 x 49¢ (BK297) | 4.50 | | |
| **BK297** | two panes of 2060a $10.00 | | | |

Qty: 1,250,000 of each

**Nos. 2057–2060 (4) Combination FDC** 5.95*

*Stamps on FDCs are not die cut all the way through.

October Stamp Collecting Month. The four stamps, when put together, become panes of glass, forming a window.

## NOBEL PRIZE WINNERS

2061
Dr. Gerhard Herzberg,
1971 laureate, and molecular structures

2062
Dr. Michael Smith,
1993 laureate, and DNA double helix

Designer: HM&E Communications/Paul Haslip. Photography: Ted Grant, University of British Columbia Archives

Lithography (11 colours plus varnish), pane of 16

Lowe-Martin

| 2004, Oct 4 | GT4, TRC Paper | NH–VF | ⊙F | PB | FDC (Perf 12.6x13.3) |
|---|---|---|---|---|---|
| **2061** | **49¢ multicoloured** | 1.00 | .40 | | |
| **2062** | **49¢ multicoloured** | 1.00 | .40 | | |
| a | se-tenant pair (2061, 2062) | 2.00 | 1.50 | 5.00 | 3.95 |

Qty: 1,250,000 of each

Various features fluoresce (including the hidden date) when exposed to ultraviolet light.

## PICTURE POSTAGE™

2063
Silver ribbon

2064
Picture frame

Designer: Steven Spazuk, Jean-François Renaud. Photography: Adrien Duey

Lithography ("Frame": 5 colours; "Ribbon": 6 colours, plus varnish)

Canadian Bank Note, Self-adhesive panes of 21†

| 2004, Oct 8 | GT4, TRC Paper | NH–VF | ⊙F | FDC (Die cut 12.7x13.0) |
|---|---|---|---|---|
| **2063** | **(49¢) multicoloured** | 2.00 | 1.50 | |
| | pane of 21 | 45.00 | | |
| i | die cut to shape from Quarterly Pack/ Annual Collection | 3.00 | | |
| ii | personalized pane of 21 stamps* | *50.00* | | |
| iii | personalized pane of 40 stamps* | *75.00* | | |

| | | NH–VF | ⊙F | FDC |
|---|---|---|---|---|
| **2064** | **(49¢) multicoloured** | 2.00 | 1.50 | |
| | pane of 21 | 45.00 | | |
| i | die cut to shape from Quarterly Pack/ Annual Collection | 3.00 | | |
| ii | pane of 21 stamps + personalized stickers* | *50.00* | | |
| iii | pane of 40 stamps + personalized stickers* | *75.00* | | |

Qty: 400,000 of each

† Panes contain 21 stamps but were sold by the post office as if there were only 20 stamps.

**Nos. 2063–2064 combination FDC** **3.95**

Non-denominated stamps — good for the prevailing domestic rate at time of usage. The outer frame designs could be ordered in panes of 21 or 40 with a user-supplied photograph imprinted in the central design area. Stamps ordered this way have the image printed directly onto the stamp itself; previous personalized postage was printed on small labels that were then affixed to the centre of the stamp by the mailer.

* The personalized stamps have a "© 2004" inscription printed in taggant at the upper left corner of the stamp design (inside the 4-sided tagging) visible only with an ultraviolet light.

**2063 pane of 21**

## CANADIAN VICTORIA CROSS WINNERS

**2065** Victoria Cross medal **2066** 1993 Canadian Victoria Cross illustration

Designer: Pierre-Yves Pelletier

Lithography (17 colours) plus embossing, pane of 16 + centre tab

Canadian Bank Note

**2004, Oct 21** **GT4, TRC Paper** **Perf 13.2x12.5**

| | | NH–VF | ⊙F | FDC |
|---|---|---|---|---|
| **2065** | **49¢ multicoloured** | 1.00 | .40 | |
| **2066** | **49¢ multicoloured** | 1.00 | .40 | |
| **a** | se-tenant pair (2065, 2066) | 2.00 | 1.50 | |
| | pane of 16 | 17.50 | | |

Qty: 2,000,000 of each

**Nos. 2065–2066 (2) combination FDC** **3.95**

150th anniversary of the first Canadian recipient (Lieutenant Alexander Roberts Dunn) who received the Victoria Cross. The central portion of the unique pane of 16 stamps features all 94 Canadian recipients of the Victoria Cross.

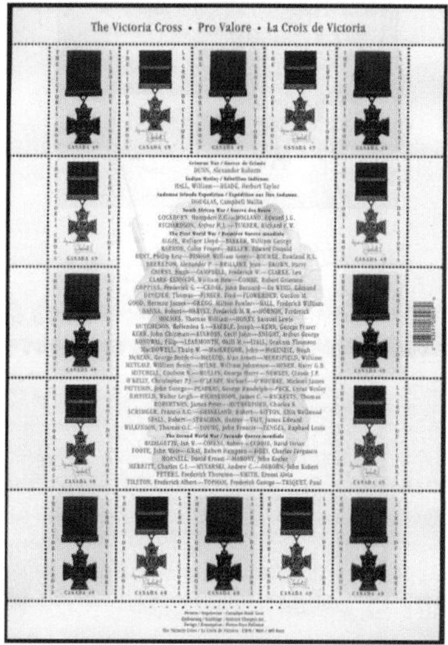


**2065–2066 pane of 16**

## *ART CANADA:* JEAN-PAUL LEMIEUX

**2067**
*Self-portrait, 1974*

**2068a**
*A June Wedding, 1972*

**2068b**
*Summer, 1959*

Designer: Gottschalk+Ash Intl.

Lithography (8 colours plus varnish), pane of 16

Lowe-Martin

**2004, Oct 22** **GT4, TRC Paper** **Perf 13.2**

| | | NH–VF | ⊙F | PB | FDC |
|---|---|---|---|---|---|
| **2067** | **49¢ multicoloured** | 1.00 | .40 | 5.00 | 3.00 |
| i | horizontal pair with gutter between | 2.50 | 1.25 | | |
| **a** | single 49¢, perf 13.2x12.9, ex. souvenir sheet | 2.00 | 2.00 | — | |
| **2068** | **$2.69 souvenir sheet** of 3 | 7.00 | 7.00 | — | 7.40 |
| **a** | single 80¢ multicoloured* | 2.00 | 2.00 | — | |
| **b** | single $1.40, perf 13.0x13.1 | 3.00 | 3.00 | — | |

Qty: 49¢: 2,000,000. Souvenir sheet: 300,000

* The 80¢ stamp has transitional perfs on the top and left sides, as illustrated below.

QE II — 2000's

2068

Transitional perfs on 80¢ (2068a)

## CHRISTMAS — TORONTO SANTA CLAUS PARADE

2069
Santa on his sled

2070
Santa in a Cadillac

2071
Santa in a train

2 x 2069a (BK298)

2070a

2071a

Designer: Gottschalk+Ash Intl.

Lithography (7 colours), self-adhesive booklets
Canadian Bank Note

**2004, Nov 2** **GT4, TRC Paper**
**Serpentine Die cut 7.1 horiz**

| | | NH–VF | ⊙F | FDC |
|---|---|---|---|---|
| **2069** | **49¢ multicoloured** | 1.00 | .25 | |
| i | single from Quarterly Pack/Annual collection* | 5.00 | | |
| b | single "no gum", printed on gum side | 15.00 | | |
| a | booklet pane of 6 x 49¢ (2069) | 6.00 | | |
| c | as BK298, printed on gum side, pane of 12 | 200.00 | | |
| BK298 | two panes of 2069a $12.00 | | | |

Qty: 60,000,000

| | | NH–VF | ⊙F | FDC |
|---|---|---|---|---|
| **2070** | **80¢ multicoloured** | 1.60 | .60 | |
| i | single from Quarterly Pack/Annual collection* | 5.00 | | |
| c | imperforate pair | *1,500.00*† | | |
| b | single "no gum", printed on gum side | | | |
| a | booklet pane of 6 x 80¢ (2070) (**BK299**) | 10.00 | | |

Qty: 7,500,000
† price is for a 'sound' pair, not creased.

| | | NH–VF | ⊙F | FDC |
|---|---|---|---|---|
| **2071** | **$1.40 multicoloured** | 2.80 | 1.00 | |
| i | single from Quarterly Pack/Annual collection* | 5.00 | | |
| b | single "no gum", printed on gum side | 60.00 | | |
| a | booklet pane of 6 x $1.40 (2071) (**BK300**) | 15.00 | | |
| c | as "a", printed on gum side, pane of 6 | *1,000.00* | | |

Qty: 7,500,000

**Nos. 2069–2071 (3) combination FDC** **7.40**

* The single stamps supplied in the Quarterly Pack / Annual collection included paper surrounding all four sides of the stamp with no trace of an adjoining stamp (a single stamp cut from a corresponding booklet would show some trace of the adjacent stamp). As well, these singles came without any printing on the backing paper (a stamp from the booklet will have some kind of cover design).

**MINT PRICING PREMIUMS**

Mint stamps from 301 to date are valued as NH-VF (Never Hinged-Very Fine). All hinged VF and NH-F copies are worth 50% of the listed values. Plate block (PB) values are for mint NH–VF plate or inscription blocks of four.

**USED, VF/XF (with in-period, circular date cancel) PRICING PREMIUM**

Single stamps with light or circular date cancels will sell for more than catalogue value (perhaps even more than a mint copy). From *1981 to 1991* single stamps from se-tenant blocks of 4 or larger will be priced at 50% or more above the fine price. From *1992* to date single stamps from se-tenant blocks of 4 or larger plus se-tenant booklet panes and souvenir sheets will be priced at 100% or more above the fine price. From *1997* to date all other stamps will be priced at 50% or more above the fine price.

## FLOWER DEFINITIVES – COILS 2004–2005

2072
Red Calla Lily

2073
Yellow Calla Lily

2074
Blue Iris

Designers: Monique Dufour, Sophie Lafortune. Photography: Serge Lacroix.
Lithography (5 colours), self-adhesive rolls of 100 (50¢) and 50 (85¢/$1.45)
Lowe-Martin

As many as four different die cut patterns were used. The first pattern (with the "ski slope" anomaly; used on all 3 values) has a 'perf' range from 7.75 to 8.90. The second pattern has a 'perf' range of 6.85 to 7.50 (used only on 50¢ and 85¢). A third pattern (rare), seen on all three values, is not yet fully plated (6.25–7.40). Every stamp on each of the 100-subject (10x10) die cutting mats is different due to variations occurring on the top and bottom of a single stamp. A fourth mat (6x6, 36-subject) was used for the Quarterly Pack/Annual Collection singles, with a range of 6.45–7.05.

**2004, Dec 20** **GT4, Fasson Paper**
**Serpentine Die cut 6.25 to 8.90 Horiz**

| | | NH–VF | ⊙F | FDC |
|---|---|---|---|---|
| **2072** | **50¢ multicoloured** | 1.00 | .25 | |
| i | gutter strip of 4 with inscription (F over R) | 6.00 | | |
| ii | "ski slope" die cut anomaly (between 3rd and 4th stamp above gutter, 1 in 10 rolls) | 4.00 | 1.00 | |
| iii | as 2072ii, in gutter strip of 6 (F over R) | 25.00 | | |
| b | die cutting omitted, pair* | 100.00 | | |
| v | as 2072b, in gutter strip of 4* | 450.00 | | |
| vi | gutter strip of 4 with inscription (F over O) | 7.50 | | |
| vii | as 2072ii, in gutter strip of 6 (F over O) | 35.00 | | |
| a | die cut 6.85–7.50 horiz, *Feb 2005* | 1.00 | .25 | |
| ai | gutter strip of 4 with inscription (F over O) | 5.00 | | |
| | starter strip of 4 (wavy die cut), *June 2005* | 7.50 | | |
| | end strip of 4 (wavy die cut), *June 2005* | 7.50 | | |
| aii | die cut to shape (6.45–7.05 horiz) from Quarterly Pack/Annual Collection | 3.00 | — | |
| aiii | as "a", turquoise green background, visible only under short wave ultraviolet light | – | 20.00 | |
| | (no mint copies of 2072aiii have yet surfaced) | | | |
| **2073** | **85¢ multicoloured** | 1.70 | .35 | |
| i | gutter strip of 4 with inscription (F over R) | 10.00 | | |
| ii | "ski slope" die cut anomaly (between 3rd and 4th stamp above gutter, 1 in 10 rolls) | 6.00 | 2.00 | |
| iii | as 2073ii, in gutter strip of 6 (F over R) | 40.00 | | |
| iv | gutter strip of 4 with inscription (F over O) | 10.00 | | |
| v | as 2073ii, in gutter strip of 6 (F over O) | 50.00 | | |
| a | die cut 6.85–7.50 horiz, *Feb 2005* | 2.00 | .35 | |
| ai | gutter strip of 4 with inscription (F over O) | 10.00 | | |
| aii | die cut to shape (6.45–7.05 horiz) from Quarterly Pack/Annual Collection | 5.00 | — | |
| **2074** | **$1.45 multicoloured** | 3.00 | .75 | |
| i | gutter strip of 4 with inscription (F over R) | 15.00 | | |
| ii | "ski slope" die cut anomaly (between 3rd and 4th stamp above gutter, 1 in 10 rolls) | 10.00 | 3.00 | |
| iii | as 2074ii, in gutter strip of 6 (F over R) | 50.00 | | |
| – | die cutting omitted, pair* | | | |
| iv | gutter strip of 4 (F over O), "0LOWE..." | 15.00 | | |
| v | gutter strip of 4 (F over O), "LOWE..." | 30.00 | | |
| vi | as 2074ii, in gutter strip of 6 (F/O), "LOWE..." | 75.00 | | |
| a | die cut 6.25–7.40 horiz †, *Feb 2005* | 7.50 | 3.00 | |
| ai | gutter strip of 4 (F over O), "0LOWE..." | 60.00 | | |
| aii | gutter strip of 4 (F over O), "LOWE..." | 120.00 | | |
| aiii | die cut to shape (6.45–7.05 horiz) from Quarterly Pack/Annual Collection | 10.00 | — | |

† must be from third die cut pattern for this set of coils.

**Nos. 2072–2074 (3) combination FDC** **6.70**

Gutters appear every 10 stamps.
* Price shown is for no trace of die cutting. Faint surface scorelines exist on all values that result in coil strips that look nearly imperforate — value 10–20x a normal single.

For non-denominated postal cards of same designs, see UX146–UX148.

**Inscriptions ("F over R" vs. "F over O")**
All three values exist with two different placements of the paper/colour dots in relation to the designer's name in the inscription:

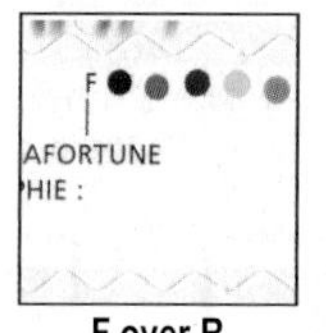


F over R

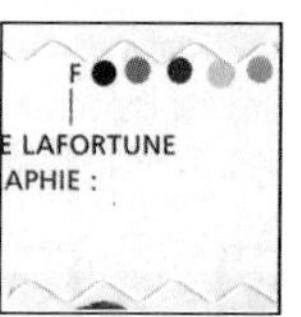


F over O

**$1.45 Printer Inscription ("LOWE" vs. "0LOWE")**
The $1.45 value exists with two types of printer name inscriptions on the "F over O" placement. A zero was inadvertently included in the front of the name on 9 out of 10 rolls; the correct inscription (without 'zero') occurs on 1 out of 10 rolls:

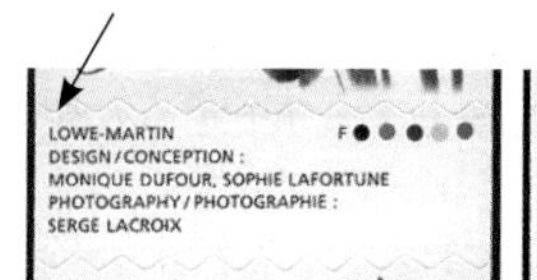


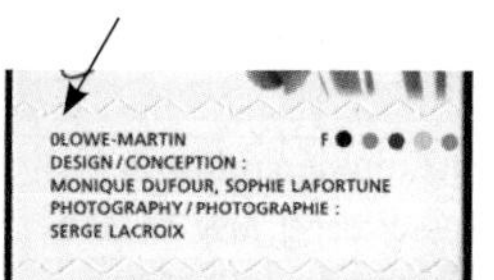


LOWE vs. 0LOWE

2072a
Wavy die cut at start of roll

2072ii
"Ski slope" die cut

| *Format:* | Coil | | | | | | Booklet | |
|---|---|---|---|---|---|---|---|---|
| | Die cut 7.75 to 8.90 horiz | | | Die cut 6.25 to 7.50 | | 6.45–7.05 | Die cut | |
| *Inscription:* | F over R | F over O | | F over O | | Qtr pack | Dots at left | Dots at right |
| 50¢ Red Calla Lily | 2072, i–v | 2072 vi–vii | | 2072 a–ai | | 2072aii | — | |
| 85¢ Yellow Calla Lily | 2073, i–iii | 2073 iv–v | | 2073 a–ai | | 2073aii | 2081 | |
| $1.45 Blue Iris | 2074, i–iii | 0LOWE 2074iv | LOWE 2074 v–vi | 0LOWE 2074 a–ai | LOWE 2074aii | 2074aiii | 2082b | 2082a |

For 51¢, 89¢, $1.05, $1.49 Flowers see 2128–2134
For P, 93¢, $1.10, $1.55 Flowers see 2187, 2194–2200
For P, 96¢, $1.15, $1.60 Flowers see 2243–2247, 2254–2256
For P, $1.00, $1.22, $1.70 Flowers see 2356–2364

## BOOKLETS

**2075**
Queen Elizabeth II

Designers: Flags: Gottschalk+Ash Int'l. Photography: B. Brooks, E. Giffor, J.A. Kraulis, M. Tomalty / Masterfile; Queen: Gottschalk+Ash Int'l. Photography: Bryan Adams.
Lithography (5 colours; QEII: 7 colours), self-adhesive booklets of 10
Canadian Bank Note

**2004, Dec 20 — GT4, TRC Paper — Die cut**

| | | NH–VF | ⊙F | FDC |
|---|---|---|---|---|
| **2075** | **50¢ multicoloured (QE II, blue)** | 1.00 | .25 | 3.00 |
| i | Fasson paper, *May 30, 2005* | 1.00 | .25 | |
| a | booklet pane of 10 x 50¢ (2075) (**BK301a**), 5 rouletted slits per pane | 12.00 | | |
| ai | as "a", with 23 rouletted slits per pane (**BK301b**), *Apr '05* | 15.00 | | |
| aii | as "a", F paper, with 29 roulettes, (**BK301Aa**) *May 30, '05* | 12.00 | | |

**2076**
Flag over Broadway Bridge, Saskatoon, SK

**2077**
Flag over Durrell, Twillingate Island, NL

**2078**
Flag over Shannon Falls, Squamish, BC

**2079**
Flag over Mont Saint-Hilaire, QC

**2080**
Flag over Toronto, ON Island Ferry

| | | NH–VF | ⊙F | FDC |
|---|---|---|---|---|
| **2076** | **50¢ multicoloured** (bridge) | 1.00 | .25 | |
| i | Fasson paper, *May 30, 2005* | 1.00 | .25 | |
| **2077** | **50¢ multicoloured** (town) | 1.00 | .25 | |
| i | Fasson paper, *May 30, 2005* | 1.00 | .25 | |
| **2078** | **50¢ multicoloured** (waterfall) | 1.00 | .25 | |
| i | Fasson paper, *May 30, 2005* | 1.00 | .25 | |
| **2079** | **50¢ multicoloured** (church) | 1.00 | .25 | |
| i | Fasson paper, *May 30, 2005* | 1.00 | .25 | |
| **2080** | **50¢ multicoloured** (boat) | 1.00 | .25 | |
| i | Fasson paper, *May 30, 2005* | 1.00 | .25 | |
| a | booklet pane of 10 x 50¢ (2 each of 2076–2080) TRC paper, (**BK302a**), 5 rouletted slits per pane | 25.00 | | |
| ai | as "a", with 29 rouletted slits per pane (**BK302b**) | 12.00 | | |
| aii | as "a", with 23 rouletted slits per pane, (**BK302c**) *Feb '05* | 250.00 | | |
| aiii | strip of 5 (2076–2080) with 12 slits, die cut to shape from Quarterly Pack | 10.00 | | |
| aiv | as "a", F paper, with 29 roulettes, (**BK302Aa**) *May 30, '05* | 12.00 | | |
| b | as "aiv", printed on gum side, pane of 10 (**BK302Ab**) | 100.00 | | |
| avi | strip of 5, TRC paper, from 2080a/BK302 | 12.50 | | |
| avii | strip of 5, F paper, from 2080aiv/BK302A | 12.50 | | |

**Nos. 2076–2080 (5) combination FDC $7.00**

For non-denominated postal cards of all five Flag over... designs, see UX155–UX159.

**Flag rouletting**

**2075a**

**2080a**

## FLOWER DEFINITIVES – BOOKLETS

**2081**
Yellow Calla Lily

**2082**
Blue Iris

Designers: Monique Dufour, Sophie Lafortune. Photography: Serge Lacroix.
Lithography (5 colours), self-adhesive booklets of 6
Lowe-Martin

**2004, Dec 20 — GT4, Fasson Paper — Die cut**

| | | NH–VF | ⊙F | FDC |
|---|---|---|---|---|
| **2081** | **85¢ multicoloured** (3mm tagging) | 2.25 | .50 | — |
| i | 4mm tagging | 1.70 | .35 | |
| ii | 4½mm tagging | 2.50 | .75 | |
| iii | 4mm tagging, TRC Paper† | 17.50 | 7.50 | |
| a | booklet pane of 6 x 85¢ (2081) (**BK303a**) | 14.00 | | |
| ai | as a, with 4mm tagging (**BK303b**) | 12.00 | | |
| aii | as a, with 4½mm tagging (**BK303c**) | 17.50 | | |
| aiii | with 4mm tagging, TRC Paper† (**BK303d**) | 150.00 | | |
| b | as 2081a, black inscriptions omitted* | *6,000.00* | | |

* Two booklets reported; two used single stamps reported (value $1,000.00). Three other booklets reported with inscriptions 'almost' missing (value $1,800.00).

| | | NH–VF | ⊙F | FDC |
|---|---|---|---|---|
| **2082** | **$1.45 multicoloured** (3mm tagging) | 2.90 | .75 | — |
| i | 4mm tagging | 2.90 | .75 | |
| ii | 4mm tagging, TRC Paper† | 10.00 | 4.00 | |
| a | booklet pane of 6 x $1.45 (2082), colour dots at right (**BK304a**) | 18.00 | | |
| ai | with 4mm tagging (**BK304b**) | 18.00 | | |
| aii | with 4mm tagging, TRC Paper† (**BK304c**) | 75.00 | | |
| aiii | booklet pane of 6 x $1.45 (2082), colour dots at left (3mm tag; Fasson) (**BK304A**) | 70.00 | | |

† The imprint indicates "F" (Fasson) paper, but the paper actually used is Tullis Russell Coatings (Coated Papers).

The 3mm tagging is "notched" around the design (i.e. flowers); the 4mm tagging passes across the design.

Unless indicated, all booklet types, tagging types, and paper types were available on the date of issue.

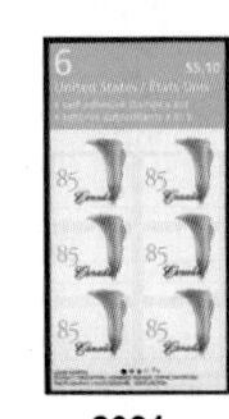

**2081a**

**2082a**

**2082aiii**

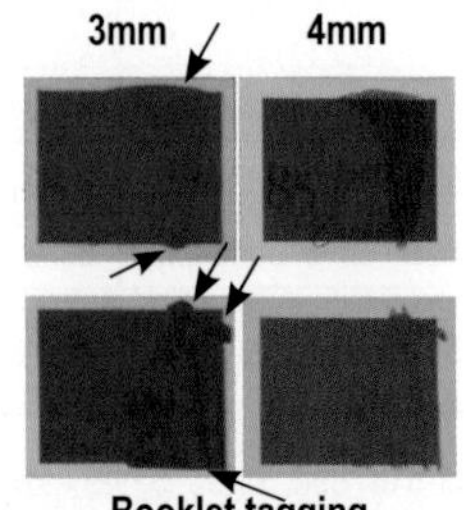

**Booklet tagging**

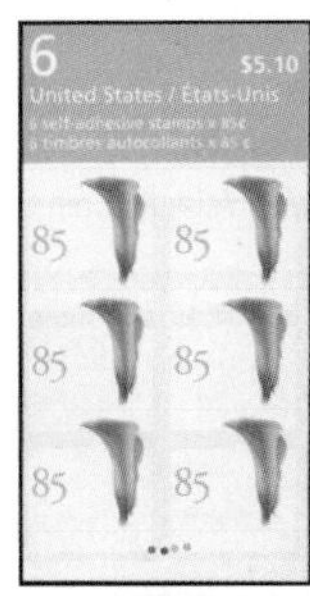

2081b
Missing inscriptions

2082a (top); 2082aiii (bottom)

## 2005

### LUNAR NEW YEAR — 9
### Year of the Rooster

2083

2084i

Designer: Gottschalk+Ash International. Illustration: Helene L'Heureux.

Lithography (6 colours) and 2 foil stampings plus embossing, pane of 25
Canadian Bank Note Company, Limited

| 2005, Jan 7 | | GT4, TRC Paper | | | Perf 13.4 |
|---|---|---|---|---|---|
| | | NH–VF | ⊙F | PB | FDC |
| **2083** | **50¢ multicoloured** | 1.00 | .40 | 5.00 | 3.00 |
| a | red colour omitted* | 2,000.00 | | | |
| i | vert. pair, with label above or below | 2.00 | 1.50 | | |

* One pane of 25 reported. No blocks exist due to staggered format of the pane.

Lithography (8 colours [press sheet: 10]) and satin gold, gloss gold and red pigment foil stamping plus embossing

| | | NH–VF | ⊙F | PB | FDC |
|---|---|---|---|---|---|
| **2084** | **$1.45 souvenir sheet** | 3.00 | 3.00 | — | 4.90 |
| i | single stamp from souvenir sheet, perf 12.5x13.1 | 2.50 | 2.00 | — | |
| ii | $26.95 uncut press sheet of 12 souvenir sheets | 75.00 | | | |
| a | as 2084, with dates, Canada and Chinese flags added to top of pane | 4.50 | 4.50 | | |

Qty: 2083: 8,000,000; 2084: 550,000; 2084a: 200,000; 2084ii: 25,000

No. 2084a exists with double and triple printing (black, most noticeable on Snake at LL and red in boxes at UL.; triple print of black on Rooster's tail feathers, double gold letters). Value $300–$900.00.

The 50¢ stamps are arranged on the pane offset to the stamps on either side making it more difficult to obtain horizontal pairs or blocks.

See also 1630, 1708, 1767–1768, 1836–1837, 1883–1884, 1933–1934, 1969–1970, 2015–2016, 2201–2202, 2257–2258.
For non-denominated postal cards of same designs, see UX143–UX144.

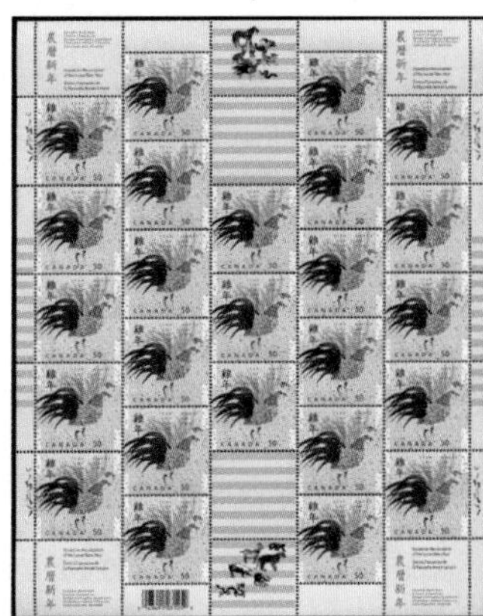

2083 full pane of 25

2084

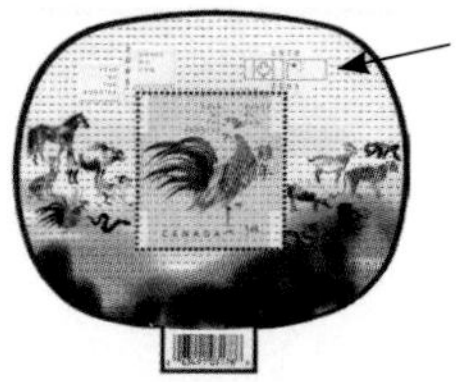

2084a

| Rates: | Domestic first-class (0-30g): 50¢ | |
|---|---|---|
| Jan 17/05– | Domestic first-class (30-50g): 85¢ | USA (0-30g): 85¢ |
| Jan 15/06 | Domestic oversize (0-100g): $1.00 | International (0-30g): $1.45 |

*single usage:* USA 85¢: $15.00 | International $1.45: $20.00

### NHL ALL-STARS — 6

*Perforated singles from water-activated gum pane*

2085a
Henri Richard (1936– )

2085b
Grant Fuhr (1962– )

2085c
Allan Stanley (1926–2013)

2085d
Pierre Pilote (1931–2017)

QE II — 2000's

2085e
Bryan Trottier (1956– )

2085f
John Bucyk (1935– )

*Die cut singles from self-adhesive booklet*

2086a
Henri Richard

2086b
Grant Fuhr

2086c
Allan Stanley

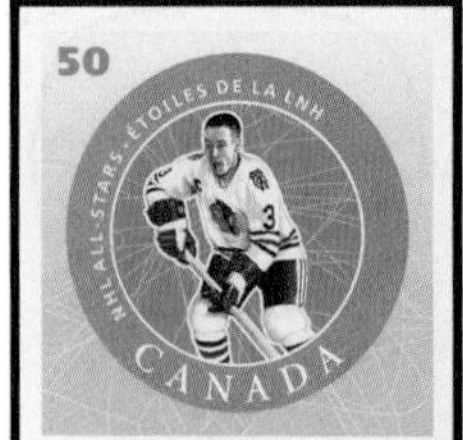

2086d
Pierre Pilote

2086e
Bryan Trottier

2086f
John Bucyk

Designer: Stéphane Huot. Based on an illustration by François Escalmel and Pierre Rousseau.
Lithography (7 colours), pane of 6 + 3 tabs
Canadian Bank Note Company

**2005, Jan 29** **GT4, TRC Paper** **Perf 12.6x13.2**

| | | NH–VF | ⊙F | FDC |
|---|---|---|---|---|
| **2085** | $3.00 pane of 6 x 50¢ | 7.00 | — | |
| a | **50¢ multicoloured** | 1.00 | .75 | |
| b | **50¢ multicoloured** | 1.00 | .75 | |
| c | **50¢ multicoloured** | 1.00 | .75 | |
| d | **50¢ multicoloured** | 1.00 | .75 | |
| e | **50¢ multicoloured** | 1.00 | .75 | |
| f | **50¢ multicoloured** | 1.00 | .75 | |

Qty: 2,215,200 of each
At least one imperforate pane is known to exist.

**Three combination FDC's: a+b, c+d, e+f** **12.00**

Self-adhesive booklet of 6

**2005, Jan 29** **GT4, TRC Paper** **Die cut**

| | | NH–VF | ⊙F | FDC |
|---|---|---|---|---|
| **2086** | $3.00 pane of 6 x 50¢ (a–f) (**BK305**) | 7.00 | — | |
| a | **50¢ multicoloured** | 1.00 | .75 | |
| b | **50¢ multicoloured** | 1.00 | .75 | |
| c | **50¢ multicoloured** | 1.00 | .75 | |
| d | **50¢ multicoloured** | 1.00 | .75 | |
| e | **50¢ multicoloured** | 1.00 | .75 | |
| f | **50¢ multicoloured** | 1.00 | .75 | |

Qty: 550,000 of each

The 2005 Annual Collection did *not* include the self-adhesive booklet.
The final year of NHL All-Star stamps. See also 1443–1445, 1838, 1885, 1935, 1971–1972, 2017–2018.

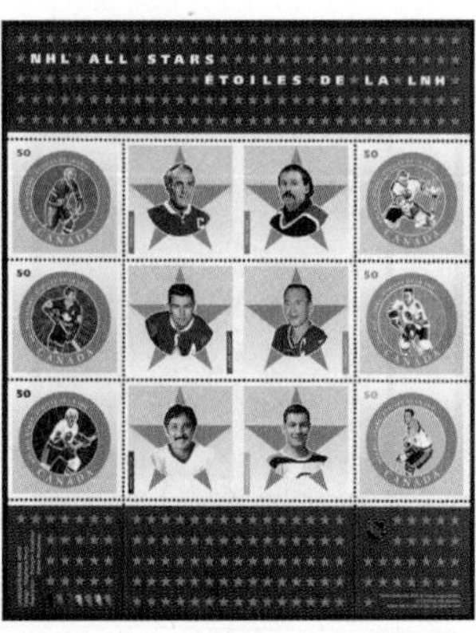

2085

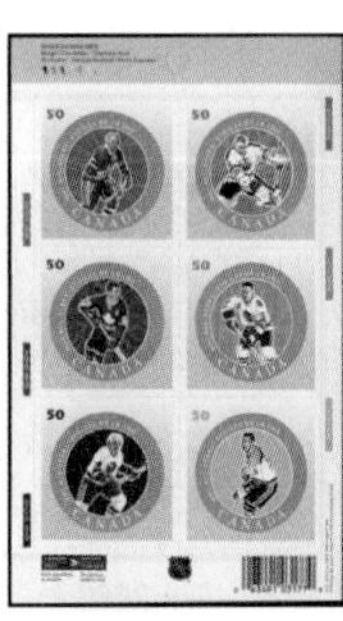
2086

## FISHING FLIES

*Perforated singles from water-activated gum souvenir sheet*

2087a
Alevin, for Rainbow Trout

2087b
Jock Scott, for Atlantic Salmon

2087c
P.E.I. Fly, for Brook Trout

2087d
Mickey Finn, for Atlantic Salmon

*Die cut singles from self-adhesive booklet*

2088a
Alevin, for Rainbow Trout

2088b
Jock Scott, for Atlantic Salmon

2088c
Mickey Finn, for Atlantic Salmon

2088d
P.E.I. Fly, for Brook Trout

Designer: Circle Design Inc. Illustration: Alain Massicotte.
Lithography (9 colours), water-activated gum souvenir sheet of 4
Canadian Bank Note Company

**2005, Feb 4** **GT4, TRC Paper** **Perf 12.5x13.1**

| | | NH–VF | ⊙F | FDC |
|---|---|---|---|---|
| **2087** | **$2.00 souvenir sheet** | 10.00 | 7.50 | 6.00* |
| a | **50¢ multicoloured** | 2.50 | 1.50 | |
| b | **50¢ multicoloured** | 2.50 | 1.50 | |
| c | **50¢ multicoloured** | 2.50 | 1.50 | |
| d | **50¢ multicoloured** | 2.50 | 1.50 | |

Qty: 225,000 of each
* Surrounding selvedge was removed.

Self-adhesive booklet of 8

**GT4, TRC Paper** **Die cut 10.1**

| | | NH–VF | ⊙F | FDC |
|---|---|---|---|---|
| **2088** | booklet pane of 4 x 50¢ (a–d) | 5.00 | — | — |
| a | **50¢ multicoloured** | 1.25 | 0.50 | |
| b | **50¢ multicoloured** | 1.25 | 0.50 | |
| c | **50¢ multicoloured** | 1.25 | 0.50 | |
| d | **50¢ multicoloured** | 1.25 | 0.50 | |
| i | strip of 4, die cut to shape from Quarterly Pack/ Annual Collection | 5.00 | — | |
| **BK306** | two panes of 2088 + biographical sketch panel $10.00 | | | |

Qty: 1,250,000 of each

The art and craft of fly-fishing in Canada. See also 1715–1720. For non-denominated postal cards of same designs, see UX149–UX152. For non-denominated envelopes of same designs, see U226–U229, U236–239.

2087

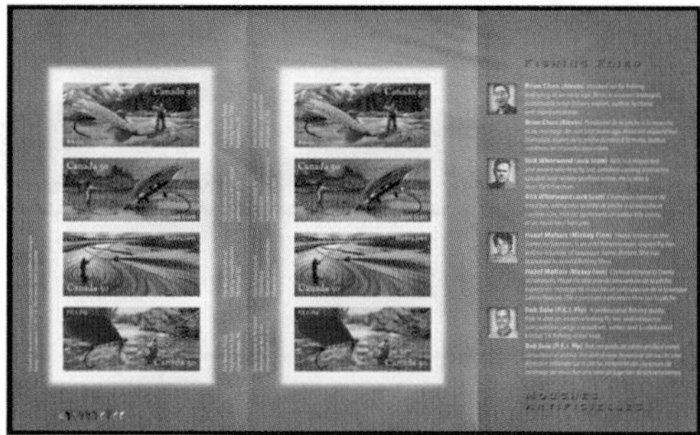

2 x 2088 (BK306)

## NOVA SCOTIA AGRICULTURAL COLLEGE

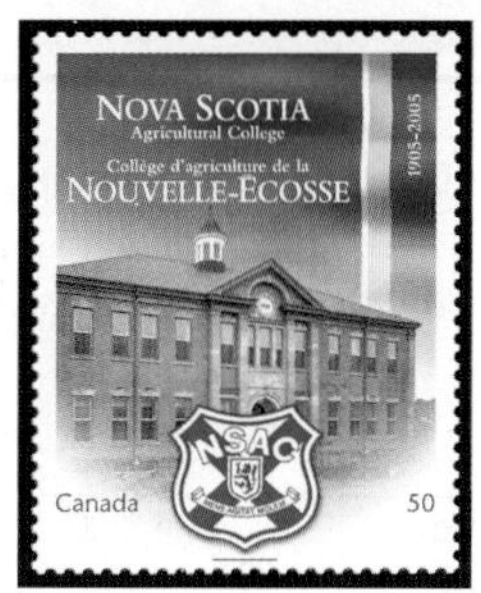

2089

Designer: Denis L'Allier. Photography: Guy Lavigueur.

Lithography (6 colours), self-adhesive booklet of 8
Lowe-Martin

| 2005, Feb 14 | GT4, Fasson Paper | Die cut 12.8x13.4 | | |
|---|---|---|---|---|
| | | NH–VF | ⊙F | FDC |
| **2089** | **50¢ multicoloured** | 1.00 | .40 | 3.00 |
| i | die cut to shape from Quarterly Pack/ Annual Collection | 1.50 | — | |
| a | booklet pane of 4 x 50¢ (2089) | 5.00 | | |
| BK307 | two panes of 2089a $10.00 | | | |

Qty: 3,000,000

100th anniversary of the Nova Scotia Agricultural College.

For other University issues, see 1756, 1941–1944, 1973–1977, 2033–2034, 2172, 2209–2210.

2 x 2089a (BK307)

## EXPO 2005

2090

Designer: HM&E Design. Photography: Curtis Lantinga

Lithography (9 colours), pane of 16
Canadian Bank Note Company

| 2005, Mar 4 | GT4, TRC Paper | Perf 13.3 | | | |
|---|---|---|---|---|---|
| | | NH–VF | ⊙F | PB | FDC |
| **2090** | **50¢ multicoloured** | 1.00 | .40 | 5.00 | 3.00 |

Qty: 3,000,000

Canada's contribution to Expo 2005, an international exhibition held in Aichi, Japan. Canada's Pavilion celebrates "Wisdom of Diversity".

## DAFFODILS

*Perforated singles from water-activated gum souvenir sheet*

2091a 2091b

*Die cut singles from self-adhesive booklet*

2092 Yellow Daffodil 2093 White Daffodil

Designer: Isabelle Toussaint.
Based on a photograph by Marc Montplaisir.

Lithography (booklet: 4 colours; s/s: 5 colours)
Lowe-Martin
Water-activated gum souvenir sheet of 2

| 2005, Mar 10 | GT4, TRC Paper | Perf 13.1x13.4 | | |
|---|---|---|---|---|
| | | NH–VF | ⊙F | FDC |
| **2091** | **$1 souvenir sheet** of 2 | 3.00 | 3.00 | — |
| a | **50¢ multicoloured** | 1.50 | 1.00 | |
| b | **50¢ multicoloured** | 1.50 | 1.00 | |
| i | se-tenant pair (2091a–b) | 3.00 | 2.50 | |

Qty: 300,000

Self-adhesive booklet of 10

| | GT4, Fasson Paper | Die cut 10.0 | | |
|---|---|---|---|---|
| | | NH–VF | ⊙F | FDC |
| **2092** | **50¢ multicoloured** | 1.00 | .40 | |
| **2093** | **50¢ multicoloured** | 1.00 | .40 | |
| a | booklet pane of 10, 5 each #2092–2093 + 10 stickers (**BK308**) | 12.00 | | |

Qty: 4,000,000 of each

**Nos. 2092–2093 (2) combination FDC** **4.00**

For non-denominated postal cards of same designs, see UX153–UX154.
For non-denominated size 10 envelopes of same designs, see U241–U242.
Daffodils are not native to Canada, but because they are winter-hardy, they thrive in most parts of the country. Symbols of hope and renewal, they have served as the ideal emblem for the Canadian Cancer Society's spring fundraising campaign for the past half-century.

2091

*Image rotated* 2093a

## TORONTO DOMINION BANK

2094
TD Bank

Designer: q30 design Inc., Photography: Bernard Bohn.
Lithography (6 colours), self-adhesive pane of 10 in Prestige Booklet
Lowe-Martin

| 2005, Mar 18 | GT4, Fasson Paper | Die cut 11.4x11.3 | | |
|---|---|---|---|---|
| | | NH–VF | ⊙F | FDC |
| **2094** | **50¢ multicoloured** | 1.00 | .40 | 3.00 |
| a | booklet pane of 10 x 50¢ (2094) | 10.00 | | |
| **BK309** | pane 2094a in Prestige Booklet $15.00 | | | |

Qty: 8,000,000

The prestige pack includes information and photos pertaining to Toronto Dominion Bank, including 15 special logo seals on the inside back cover. The issue celebrates the 150th anniversary of the TD Bank Financial Group.

2094a

2099a

## JOHN JAMES AUDUBON'S BIRDS – 3

2095 Horned Lark — 2096 Piping Plover

2097 Stilt Sandpiper — 2098 Willow Ptarmigan

2099
Double-Crested Cormorant

Designer: Rolf P. Harder.
Lithography (11 colours; 85¢: 7 colours), pane of 16
Lowe-Martin

| 2005, Mar 23 | GT4, TRC Paper | Perf 12.5x13.1 | | | |
|---|---|---|---|---|---|
| | | NH–VF | ⊙F | PB | FDC |
| **2095** | **50¢ multicoloured** | 1.00 | .50 | | |
| **2096** | **50¢ multicoloured** | 1.00 | .50 | | |
| **2097** | **50¢ multicoloured** | 1.00 | .50 | | |
| **2098** | **50¢ multicoloured** | 1.00 | .50 | | |
| a | se-tenant block of 4 (2095–2098) | 4.00 | 3.50 | 5.00 | 6.00 |

Lowe-Martin, self-adhesive booklet of 6

| 2005, Mar 23 | GT4, TRC Paper | Die cut | | |
|---|---|---|---|---|
| | | NH–VF | ⊙F | FDC |
| **2099** | **85¢ multicoloured** | 1.50 | .60 | 3.70 |
| a | booklet pane of 6 x 85¢ (2099) (**BK310**) | 10.00 | | |

Qty: 50¢: 1,250,000 of each; 85¢: 2,100,000

See also: 1979–1983, 2036–2040.

## CANADIAN BRIDGES

2100
Jacques Cartier Bridge, QC

2101
Souris Swinging Bridge, MB

2102
Angus L. Macdonald Bridge, NS

2103
Canso Causeway, NS

Designer: Smith-Boake Designwerke Inc. Photographs by Sid Tabak.
Lithography (10 colours), Self-adhesive pane of 16
Canadian Bank Note

| 2005, Apr 2 | GT4, TRC Paper | Perf 12.6x13.1 | | | |
|---|---|---|---|---|---|
| | | VF* | ⊙F | PB* | FDC |
| **2100** | **50¢ multicoloured** | 1.00 | .60 | | |
| **2101** | **50¢ multicoloured** | 1.00 | .60 | | |
| **2102** | **50¢ multicoloured** | 1.00 | .60 | | |
| **2103** | **50¢ multicoloured** | 1.00 | .60 | | |
| a | se-tenant block or strip of 4 (2100–2103) | 4.00 | 3.50 | 5.00 | 6.00† |
| b | as "a", imperforate | | | *2,000.00* | |

Qty: 1,250,000 of each

* Price is for stamps with backing paper. Stamps are fully perforated – the second time self-adhesive stamps were printed this way.

† Strip of 4 on FDC.

The backing paper includes photographs of the 4 bridges, with each picture covering four stamps.

## MACLEAN'S MAGAZINE

**2104**
Magazine covers

Designer: 52 Pick-up Inc.
Lithography (6 colours plus spot varnish), pane of 16
Lowe-Martin

| 2005, Apr 12 | GT4, TRC Paper | Perf 12.6x13.1 | | | |
|---|---|---|---|---|---|
| | | NH–VF | ⊙F | PB | FDC |
| **2104** | **50¢ multicoloured** | 1.00 | .40 | 5.00 | 3.00 |

Qty: 4,000,000

100th anniversary of Maclean's Magazine.

## BIOSPHERE RESERVES

**2105** Waterton Lakes National Park — **2106** Killarney National Park, Ireland

Designer: Xerxes Irani, nonfiction studios inc.
Lithography (9 colours), pane of 16
Lowe-Martin

| 2005, Apr 22 | GT4, TRC Paper | Perf 12.5x13.1 | | | |
|---|---|---|---|---|---|
| | | NH–VF | ⊙F | PB | FDC |
| **2105** | **50¢ multicoloured** | 1.00 | .40 | | |
| **2106** | **50¢ multicoloured** | 1.00 | .40 | | |
| a | se-tenant pair (2105, 2106) | 2.25 | 1.50 | 5.00 | 4.00 |
| b | $1 souvenir sheet of 2 | 3.00 | 3.00 | | |

Qty: 2105–2106: 2,500,000 of each; 2106b: 400,000

**Joint FDC with Ireland** **8.00**

UNESCO designated Biosphere Reserves in 1970.
Joint issue with Ireland.

**2106b**

Joint issue with Ireland
**Scott # 1611–1612**

## BATTLE OF THE ATLANTIC

**2107**
Corvette in submarine scope

Designer: Derek Sarty and Gaynor Sarty.
Based on photographs by Library and Archives Canada, Maritime Command Museum.
Lithography (8 colours plus varnish), pane of 16
Lowe-Martin

| 2005, Apr 29 | GT4, TRC Paper | Perf 12.6x13.2 | | | |
|---|---|---|---|---|---|
| | | NH–VF | ⊙F | PB | FDC |
| **2107** | **50¢ multicoloured** | 1.00 | .40 | 5.00 | 3.00 |

Qty: 2,500,000

60th anniversary of the Battle of the Atlantic, the only battle to last the entire six years of the Second World War.

## CANADIAN WAR MUSEUM

**2108**
War Museum, medal, Morse code

Designer: Tiit Telmet and Marko Barac.
Lithography (9 colours plus varnish),
Sheets of 72 subjects in nine self-adhesive booklet panes of 8
Lowe-Martin

| 2005, May 6 | GT4, TRC Paper | Die cut 8.0x8.5 | | |
|---|---|---|---|---|
| | | NH–VF | ⊙F | FDC |
| **2108** | **50¢ multicoloured** | 1.00 | .40 | 3.00 |
| i | die cut to shape from Quarterly Pack/ Annual Collection | 1.50 | — | |
| a | booklet pane of 4 x 50¢ (2108) (**BK311**) | 4.00 | — | |
| **BK311** | two panes of 2108a $10.00 | | | |

Qty: 3,000,000

Issued on the occasion of the opening of the new Canadian War Museum.

QE II — 2000's

2 x 2108a (BK311)

## *ART CANADA:* HOMER WATSON

2109
*Down in the Laurentides*

2110a
*The Flood Gate*

Designer: Hélène L'Heureux. Painting by Homer Watson, 1855–1936.

Lithography (8 colours), Sheets of 32 subjects in two panes of 16 + horizontal gutter
Lowe-Martin

| **2005, May 27** | **GT4, TRC Paper** | | **Perf 13.2x13.1** | |
|---|---|---|---|---|
| | NH–VF | ⊙F | PB | FDC |
| **2109 50¢ multicoloured** | 1.00 | .40 | 5.00 | 3.00 |
| i vertical pair, gutter between | 2.00 | 1.00 | | |
| a 50¢ single from souvenir sheet, perf 13.3x13.1 | 2.00 | 2.00 | | |
| **2110 $1.35 souvenir sheet** of 2 | 6.00 | 6.00 | | 4.70 |
| a **85¢ multicoloured**, perf 13.3x13.0 | 4.00 | 4.00 | | |

Qty: 2109: 3,000,000; 2109a/2110/2110a: 233,000

Recognizes the 150th anniversary of Watson's birth, the 125th anniversary of the National Gallery of Canada and the 125th anniversary of the Royal Canadian Academy of Art.

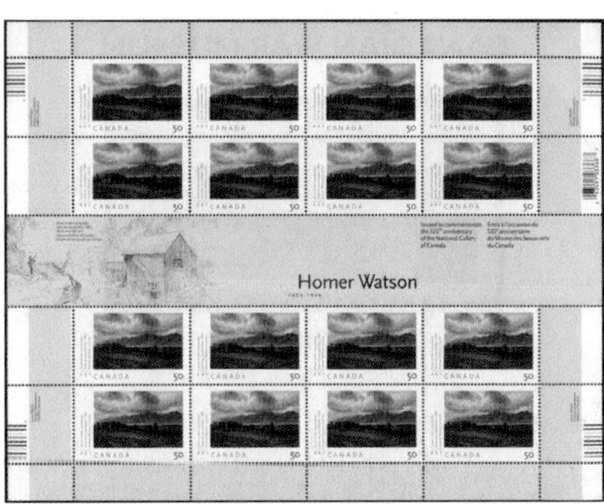


2109 full pane of 16

2110

## SEARCH and RESCUE

2111a
Ground rescue with dog

2111b
Rescue from the sea

2111c
Rescue by air

2111d
Alpine rescue

Designer: François Dallaire.

Lithography (10 colours), pane of 8
Lowe-Martin

| **2005, Jun 13** | **GT4, TRC Paper** | **Perf 13.0x13.4** | |
|---|---|---|---|
| | NH–VF | ⊙F | FDC |
| **2111** $4.00 pane of 8 (2 each #a–d) | 8.00 | | |
| i horizontal strip of 4 | 4.00 | 4.00 | 6.00 |
| a **50¢ multicoloured** (plane) | 1.00 | .75 | |
| b **50¢ multicoloured** (ship) | 1.00 | .75 | |
| bi vertical tête-bêche pair (2111b with 2111d) | 2.00 | 2.00 | |
| c **50¢ multicoloured** (helicopter) | 1.00 | .75 | |
| ci vertical tête-bêche pair (2 x 2111c) | 2.00 | 2.00 | |
| d **50¢ multicoloured** (mountain) | 1.00 | .75 | |

Qty: 1,750,000 of each

Canada's role in search-and-rescue services.

2111 full pane of 8

## ELLEN FAIRCLOUGH

2112

Designer: Katalin Kovats.

Lithography (6 colours), pane of 16
Canadian Bank Note

| 2005, Jun 21 | GT4, TRC Paper | Perf 13.1x12.5 | | |
|---|---|---|---|---|
| | NH–VF | ⊙F | PB | FDC |
| **2112 50¢ multicoloured** | 1.00 | .40 | 5.00 | 3.00 |

Qty: 2,500,000

Ellen Fairclough (1905–2004), first woman federal cabinet minister (Secretary of State, Minister of Citizenship and Immigration, Postmaster General).

## XI FINA WORLD CHAMPIONSHIPS

2113 Diver in mid-air — 2114 Butterfly stroke

Designer: Fugazi.

Lithography (2 colours including 1 special black, plus 4 metallic colours, plus varnish)
Pane of 8
Lowe-Martin

| 2005, Jul 5 | GT4, TRC Paper | | Perf 13.3 |
|---|---|---|---|
| | NH–VF | ⊙F | FDC |
| **2113 50¢ multicoloured** | 1.00 | .60 | |
| **2114 50¢ multicoloured** | 1.00 | .60 | |
| a se-tenant pair (2113, 2114) | 2.00 | 1.25 | 4.00 |
| full pane of 8 | 8.00 | | |

Qty: 1,500,000 of each

FINA World Championships held in Montreal from July 17–31 with athletes competing in swimming, diving, water polo, synchronized swimming and open water swimming.

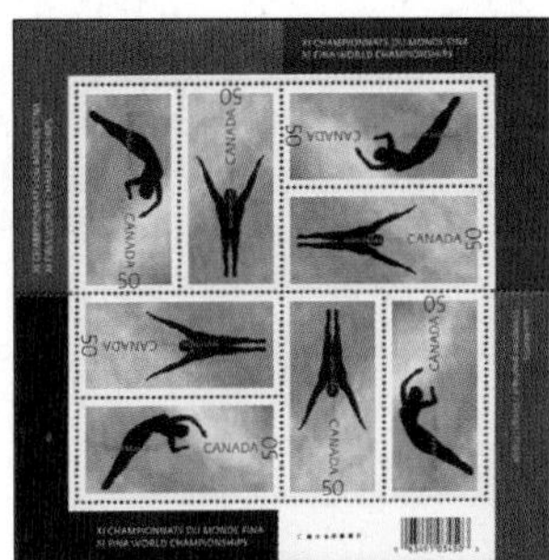

2113–2114
Pane of 8

## PORT-ROYAL 1605–2005

2115
Samuel de Champlain's drawing of settlement

Designer: Martin Côté.

Engraved (1 colour) and Lithography (3 colour process [no black] plus 3 special colours), pane of 16
Canadian Bank Note

| 2005, Jul 16 | GT4*, TRC Paper | Perf 13.1x12.5 | | |
|---|---|---|---|---|
| | NH–VF | ⊙F | PB | FDC |
| **2115 50¢ multicoloured** | 1.00 | .40 | 5.00 | 3.00 |
| i line through t of 'abitasion' (pos. 12) | 5.00 | 3.50 | 8.00(LR) | |

Qty: 3,000,000

* The tagging on this issue is somewhat lighter/paler relative to other stamp issues.
400th anniversary of the founding of Port-Royal, Nova Scotia. See also 2044, 2155, 2226, 2269.

2115i

## ALBERTA CENTENNIAL

2116
Nova Chemicals plant, Calgary's skyline, Mount Grassi

Designer: Matthias Reinicke.

Lithography (9 colours), Sheets of 96 subjects in twelve self-adhesive panes of 8
Lowe-Martin

| 2005, Jul 21 | GT4, TRC Paper | Perf 12.5x13.2† | | |
|---|---|---|---|---|
| | VF* | ⊙F | PB* | FDC |
| **2116 50¢ multicoloured** | 1.00 | .40 | 5.00 | 3.00 |
| i missing 's-shaped' die cut on backing paper | 125.00 | | | |

Qty: 3,000,000

† All stamps have transitional perfs along the top and bottom of each stamp, as illustrated below.
* Price is for stamps with backing paper. Stamps are fully perforated – the third time self-adhesive stamps were printed this way.

Issued to celebrate the 100th anniversary of Alberta's entry into Confederation.

The backing paper includes four historical images of various aspects of Alberta.

13.1 | Perf 13.3

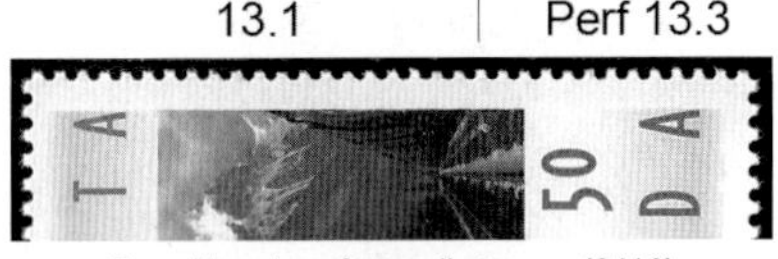

Transitional perfs on all stamps (2116)

QE II — 2000's

## SASKATCHEWAN CENTENNIAL

2117
Young woman, sunflowers, legislature building

Designer: Bradbury Branding & Design Inc..

Lithography (9 colours), Pane of 8
Canadian Bank Note

| 2005, Aug 2 | GT4, TRC Paper | Perf 13.1x12.5 | | |
|---|---|---|---|---|
| | | NH–VF | ⊙F | FDC |
| 2117 | 50¢ multicoloured | 1.00 | .40 | 3.00 |
| | full pane of 8 | 8.00 | | |

Qty: 3,000,000

Issued to celebrate the 100th anniversary of Saskatchewan's entry into Confederation.

2117 full pane

## OSCAR PETERSON

2118
Oscar Peterson (1925–2007) and keyboard

Designer: Tiit Telmet.
Based on photographs by Gilbert Duclos.

Lithography (7 colours), Pane of 16
Canadian Bank Note

| 2005, Aug 15 | GT4, TRC Paper | | | Perf 13.1x12.5 | |
|---|---|---|---|---|---|
| | | NH–VF | ⊙F | PB | FDC |
| 2118 | 50¢ multicoloured | 1.00 | .40 | 5.00 | 3.00 |
| a | $2 souvenir sheet of 4 | 4.00 | 4.00 | — | |

Qty: 4,000,000; Souvenir sheet: 500,000

Commemorates the life and achievements of internationally renowned Canadian jazz composer and musician Oscar Peterson. The date of issue marked Peterson's 80th birthday

2118a

## ACADIAN DEPORTATION

2119
Grand-Pré stamp of 1930 and Acadian flag

Designer: Pierre-Yves Pelletier.

Lithography (6 colours), Pane of 16
Canadian Bank Note

| 2005, Aug 15 | GT4*, TRC Paper | | | Perf 13.1x12.5 | |
|---|---|---|---|---|---|
| | | NH–VF | ⊙F | PB | FDC |
| 2119 | 50¢ multicoloured | 1.00 | .40 | 5.00 | 3.00 |

Qty: 2,500,000

* Tagging appears 'duller' than other issues due to underlying ink pattern.

Issued to mark the 250th anniversary of the deportation of settlers in Acadia (Nova Scotia) to the British colonies of North America.

## POLIO VACCINATION

2120
Children playing; discarded leg braces

Designer: Debbie Adams.

Lithography (10 colours), Pane of 16
Canadian Bank Note

| 2005, Sep 2 | GT4, TRC Paper | | | Perf 12.5x13.1 | |
|---|---|---|---|---|---|
| | | NH–VF | ⊙F | PB | FDC |
| 2120 | 50¢ multicoloured | 1.00 | .40 | 5.00 | 3.00 |

Qty: 2,500,000

Issued to mark the 50th anniversary of Canada's program of universal polio vaccination.

## YOUTH SPORTS

2121a
Wall climbing

2121b
Skateboarding

2121c
Mountain biking

2121d
Snowboarding

Designer: Circle Design Inc.

Lithography (7 colours), Self-adhesive booklet of 8
Lowe-Martin

**2005, Oct 1** **GT4, TRC Paper** **Die cut**

| | | NH–VF | ⊙F | FDC |
|---|---|---|---|---|
| **2121** | $4.00 pane of 8 (2 each #a–d) (**BK312**) | 8.00 | | 6.00* |
| a | **50¢ multicoloured**, climbing | 1.00 | .50 | |
| b | **50¢ multicoloured**, skateboarding | 1.00 | .50 | |
| c | **50¢ multicoloured**, biking | 1.00 | .50 | |
| d | **50¢ multicoloured**, snowboarding | 1.00 | .50 | |

Qty: 1,000,000 of each
* FDC consists of a "block" of 4 stamps which are not die cut all the way through.

October Stamp Collecting Month featuring youth-oriented, high-energy sports.

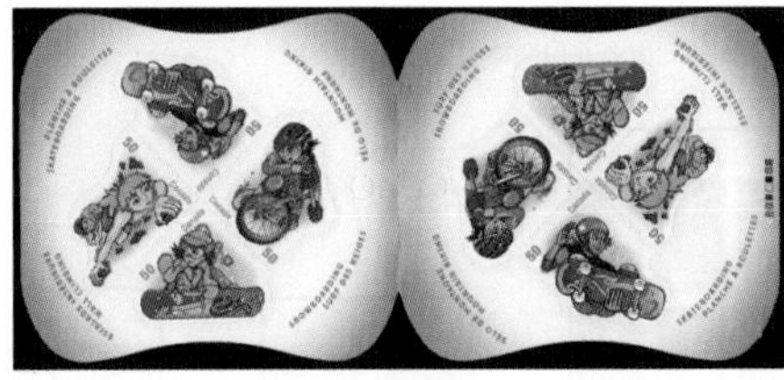

2121

**MINT PRICING PREMIUMS**

Mint stamps from 301 to date are valued as NH-VF (Never Hinged-Very Fine). All hinged VF and NH-F copies are worth 50% of the listed values. Plate block (PB) values are for mint NH–VF plate or inscription blocks of four.

**USED, VF/XF (with in-period, circular date cancel) PRICING PREMIUM**

Single stamps with light or circular date cancels will sell for more than catalogue value (perhaps even more than a mint copy). From *1981 to 1991* single stamps from se-tenant blocks of 4 or larger will be priced at 50% or more above the fine price. From *1992* to date single stamps from se-tenant blocks of 4 or larger plus se-tenant booklet panes and souvenir sheets will be priced at 100% or more above the fine price. From *1997* to date all other stamps will be priced at 50% or more above the fine price.

## BIG CATS

2122
Cougar
(*Puma concolor*)

2123
Amur leopard (from Northeast China)
(*Panthera pardus orientalis*)

Designer: Keith Martin.

Lithography (9 colours), Pane of 16
Lowe-Martin

**2005, Oct 13** **GT4, TRC Paper** **Perf 13.6x13.3**

| | | NH–VF | ⊙F | FDC |
|---|---|---|---|---|
| **2122** | **50¢ multicoloured** | 1.00 | .50 | |
| **2123** | **50¢ multicoloured** | 1.00 | .50 | |
| a | se-tenant pair (2122, 2123) | 2.00 | 1.25 | 4.00 |
| i | horizontal strip of 4, gutter between | 4.00 | 4.00 | |
| | full pane of 16 | 20.00 | | |
| b | $1 souvenir sheet of 2 | 2.50 | 2.50 | |

Qty: 2,500,000 of each; 2123b: 400,000

**Joint FDC with People's Republic of China** **6.00**

This issue represents the very first appearance of shaped perforations (Maple Leaf) on a Canadian stamp.

Joint issue with the People's Republic of China. Issued to celebrate the 35th anniversary of Canada's establishment of formal diplomatic ties with the People's Republic of China.

2123b

Joint issue with People's Republic of China
**Scott # 3458–3459**

Definitive Timeline:
**2005, Oct 20** $1 White-tailed Deer and $1 Atlantic Walrus (1688–1689)

QE II — 2000's

## CHRISTMAS

"valley" at upper left "peak" at upper left
**2124**
Snowman

Designer: Hélène L'Heureux.

Lithography (6 colours) plus 1 clear holographic stamping
Lowe-Martin, self-adhesive booklet of 12

**2005, Nov 2 GT4, TRC Paper**
**Serpentine Die cut 8.3 Horiz**

| | | NH–VF | ⊙F | FDC |
|---|---|---|---|---|
| **2124** | **50¢ multicoloured**, valley at upper left | 1.00 | .40 | 3.00 |
| i | peak at upper left | 1.00 | .40 | 3.00 |
| ii | die cut to shape from Quarterly Pack/ Annual Collection, valley at upper left | 2.00 | — | |
| iii | die cut to shape from Quarterly Pack/ Annual Collection, peak at upper left | 2.00 | — | |
| iv | with "divot" die cutting (3 types), valley at UL † | 3.00 | 1.50 | |
| v | with "divot" die cutting (3 types), peak at UL † | 3.00 | 1.50 | |
| a | booklet pane of 3 x 2124 and 3 x 2124i (**BK313**) | 6.00 | — | |
| ai | as "a", booklet pane of 6 with 'divots' at adjoining stamp corners (3 x 2124iv, 3 x 2124v) (**BK313a**) † | *25.00* | | |
| **BK313** | two panes of 2124a $12.00 | | | |

Qty: 40,000,000

The three stamps from the first row of 2124a start with a "valley" at the upper left of the serpentine die cut (2124); the three stamps from the second row of 2124a start with a "peak" (2124i).

† see images below; the "divots" produce "blunted" die cutting. Between the two types of booklets (2124a and 2124ai) there are eight different single stamp die cutting varieties available.

The 2005 holiday season marked the first time that Canada Post issued both secular- and religious-themed Christmas stamps in the same year. A non-denominated version of the Snowman design was reproduced on the 2006 Santa Claus Letter-Writing program reply envelopes (size 10 and 9x12). These had 1-bar tagging beside the indicia and were lacking the holographic-stamped snowflakes.

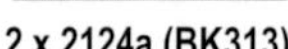

2 x 2124a (BK313)

**Die cutting at adjoining stamp corners**

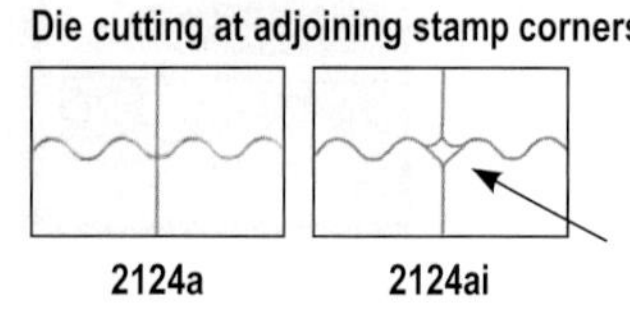

2124a 2124ai
with "divots"

Die cutting varieties
*"Normal" stamps:*

2124 2124i
"valley" at upper left "peak" at upper left

*Die cutting varieties for stamps with "blunted" corners:*

"valley" at upper left "peak" at upper left

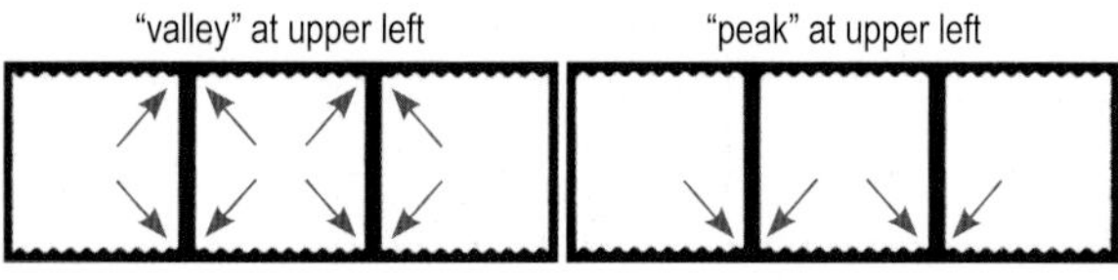

2124iv 2124v
Corners with arrows are "blunted" ('half' rounded); other corners are longer and 'pointed'

## CHRISTMAS — CRÈCHES

**2125** Nativity

**2126** Aborignal mother and child

**2127** Mary, Joseph, baby Jesus

Designer: Israël Charney.
Crèche designs: 50¢: Michel Forest; 85¢: Keena; $1.45: Sylvia Daoust.

Lithography (7 colours), self-adhesive booklet of 12 (50¢) or 6
Lowe-Martin

**2005, Nov 2 GT4, TRC Paper**
**Serpentine Die cut 6.7 Horiz**

| | | NH–VF | ⊙F | FDC |
|---|---|---|---|---|
| **2125** | **50¢ multicoloured** | 1.00 | .40 | |
| i | die cut to shape from Quarterly Pack/ Annual Collection | 2.00 | — | |
| a | booklet pane of 6 x 50¢ (2125) (**BK314**) | 6.00 | — | |
| **BK314** | two panes of 2125a $12.00 | | | |

Qty: 20,000,000

**Serpentine Die cut 6.5 Horiz**

| | | NH–VF | ⊙F | FDC |
|---|---|---|---|---|
| **2126** | **85¢ multicoloured** | 1.75 | .75 | |
| i | die cut to shape from Quarterly Pack/ Annual Collection | 4.50 | — | |
| a | booklet pane of 6 x 85¢ (2126) (**BK315**) | 11.00 | — | |

Qty: 7,500,000

**Serpentine Die cut 6.7 Horiz**

| | | NH–VF | ⊙F | FDC |
|---|---|---|---|---|
| **2127** | **$1.45 multicoloured** | 3.00 | 1.50 | |
| i | die cut to shape from Quarterly Pack/ Annual Collection | 6.00 | — | |
| a | booklet pane of 6 x $1.45 (2127) (**BK316**) | 18.00 | — | |

Qty: 7,500,000

**Nos. 2125–2127 (3) Combination FDC** **7.60**

Paper crèches selected from a collection of more than 600 crèches housed at the museum at St. Joseph's Oratory in Montréal.

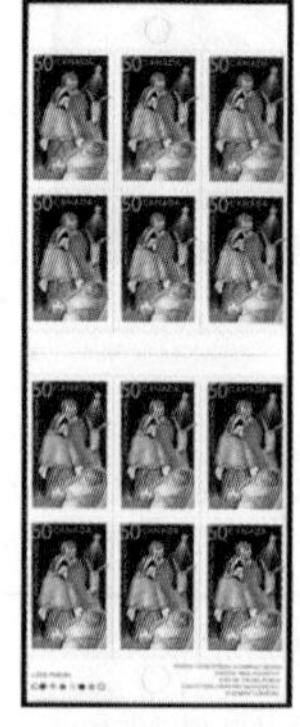

2 x 2125a (BK314)

2126a

2127a

## FLOWER DEFINITIVES – COILS 2005–2006

2128 Red Bergamot Blossom

2129 Yellow Lady's Slipper

2130 Pink Fairy Slipper

2131 Himalayan Blue Poppy

Designers: Monique Dufour, Sophie Lafortune.
Lithography (5 colours), self-adhesive rolls of 100 (51¢) and 50 (89¢–$1.49)
Lowe-Martin

Three different die cut patterns were used. The first pattern has a 'perf' range of 7.00–7.70. A second pattern appeared in July 2006 which had a 'perf' range of 7.20 to 9.30 and includes a 'compound' perf§ (not used on the $1.49; the die cutting on the 89¢ was inverted compared to the 51¢/$1.05 mat). Every stamp on each of the 100-subject (10x10) die cutting mats is different due to variations occurring on the top and bottom of a single stamp. A third mat (6x6, 36-subject) was used for the Quarterly Pack/Annual Collection singles, with a range of 6.45–7.05.

**2005, Dec 19** **GT4, TRC Paper**
**Serpentine Die cut 7.00 to 9.30 Horiz**

| | | NH–VF | ⊙F | FDC |
|---|---|---|---|---|
| **2128** | **51¢ multicoloured**, die cut 7.00–7.70 | 1.00 | .25 | |
| i | gutter strip of 4 with "high" inscription | 5.00 | | |
| ii | gutter strip of 4 with "centre" inscription, *May '06* | 5.00 | | |
| | starter strip of 4 (wavy die cut) | 7.50 | | |
| | end strip of 4 (wavy die cut) | 7.50 | | |
| iii | die cut to shape (6.45–7.05 horiz) from Quarterly Pack/Annual Collection | 3.00 | — | |
| | Fasson paper | | | |
| iv | 51¢ multicoloured, die cut 7.00–7.70, *Apr '06* | 1.00 | .25 | |
| v | gutter strip of 4 with "centre" inscription, *Apr '06* | 5.00 | | |
| | starter strip of 4 (wavy die cut), *Apr '06* | 7.50 | | |
| | end strip of 4 (wavy die cut), *Apr '06* | 7.50 | | |
| vi | die cut 7.20–9.30, TRC paper, *Jul '06* | 7.50 | 1.50 | |
| vii | gutter strip of 4, *Jul '06* | 35.00 | | |
| | starter strip of 4 (wavy die cut), *Jul '06* | 50.00 | | |
| | end strip of 4 (wavy die cut), *Jul '06* | 50.00 | | |
| viii | 'compound' die cut 7.20–7.50 one edge only§ | 9.00 | 2.50 | |
| | as viii, compound die cut in strip of 4§ | 45.00 | | |

Sc 2128/2128ii is known with an error of colour: the magenta ink is violet resulting in a brown flower. Value: $250 per stamp; gutter strip of 4 $1,500.

| | | NH–VF | ⊙F | FDC |
|---|---|---|---|---|
| | Fasson paper | | | |
| **2129** | **89¢ multicoloured**, die cut 7.00–7.70 | 1.80 | .60 | |
| i | gutter strip of 4 with "high" inscription | 9.00 | | |
| ii | gutter strip of 4 with "centre" inscription, *Feb '06* | 9.00 | | |
| | starter strip of 4 (wavy die cut), *Feb '06* | 10.50 | | |
| | end strip of 4 (wavy die cut), *Feb '06* | 10.50 | | |
| iii | die cut to shape (6.45–7.05 horiz) from Quarterly Pack/Annual Collection | 5.00 | — | |
| | TRC Paper | | | |
| iv | 89¢ multicoloured, die cut 7.00–7.70, *Jun '06* | 1.80 | .60 | |
| v | gutter strip of 4 with "high" inscription, *Jun '06* | 35.00 | | |
| vi | gutter strip of 4 with "centre" inscription, *Jun '06* | 9.00 | | |
| | starter strip of 4 (wavy die cut), *Jun '06* | 10.50 | | |
| | end strip of 4 (wavy die cut), *Jun '06* | 10.50 | | |
| vii | die cut 7.20–9.30, Fasson paper, *Sep '06* | 13.00 | 5.00 | |
| viii | gutter strip of 4, *Sep '06* | 75.00 | | |
| | starter strip of 4 (wavy die cut), *Sep '06* | 90.00 | | |
| | end strip of 4 (wavy die cut), *Sep '06* | 90.00 | | |
| ix | 'compound' die cut 7.20–7.50 one edge only§ | 17.00 | 10.00 | |
| | as ix, compound die cut in strip of 4§ | 85.00 | | |
| | TRC paper | | | |
| **2130** | **$1.05 multicoloured**, die cut 7.00–7.70 | 2.10 | .75 | |
| i | gutter strip of 4 with "high" inscription | 10.50 | | |
| ii | gutter strip of 4 with "centre" inscription, *Feb '06* | 10.50 | | |
| | starter strip of 4 (wavy die cut), *Feb '06* | 12.50 | | |
| | end strip of 4 (wavy die cut), *Feb '06* | 12.50 | | |
| iii | die cut to shape (6.45–7.05 horiz) from Quarterly Pack/Annual Collection | 6.00 | — | |
| iv | die cut 7.20–9.30, TRC paper, *Dec '06* | 20.00 | 10.00 | |
| v | gutter strip of 4, *Dec '06* | 120.00 | | |
| | starter strip of 4 (wavy die cut), *Dec '06* | 140.00 | | |
| | end strip of 4 (wavy die cut), *Dec '06* | 140.00 | | |
| vi | 'compound' die cut 7.20–7.50 one edge only§ | 24.00 | 15.00 | |
| | as vi, compound die cut in strip of 4§ | 120.00 | | |
| | TRC paper | | | |
| **2131** | **$1.49 multicoloured**, die cut 7.00–7.70 | 3.00 | 1.25 | |
| i | gutter strip of 4 with "high" inscription | 15.00 | | |
| ii | gutter strip of 4 with "centre" inscription, *Jul '06* | 25.00 | | |
| iii | die cut to shape (6.45–7.05 horiz) from Quarterly Pack/Annual Collection | 9.00 | — | |

**Nos. 2128–2131 (4) combination FDC** **9.90**

Gutters appear every 10 stamps. "High" inscriptions are 2.5mm below the stamp design from above, 5.0mm above the stamp design below. "Centre" inscriptions are 3.8mm below/above the respective designs.

§ One of the eleven rows of die cutting from this printing had a measurement of 7.20–7.50. The adjacent rows measure 8.40 to 9.30. This is a full 1½ 'perf' difference on the same stamp. See illustration after 2187.

| *Format:* | Coil | | | | | | | Booklet | |
|---|---|---|---|---|---|---|---|---|---|
| | Die cut 7.00–7.70 horiz | | | | 6.45–7.05 | Die cut 7.20–9.30§ | | Die cut | |
| *Paper:* | TRC | | Fasson | | Qtr pack | TRC | Fasson | | |
| *Inscription:* | High | Centre | High | Centre | | | | C over S | C over O |
| 51¢ Red Bergamot Blossom | 2128, i | 2128ii | | 2128 iv–v | 2128iii | 2128 vi–viii | | | |
| 89¢ Yellow Lady's Slipper | 2129 iv–v | 2129vi | 2129, i | 2129ii | 2129iii | | 2129 vii–ix | 2132 | |
| $1.05 Pink Fairy Slipper | 2130, i | 2130ii | | | 2130iii | 2130 iv–vi | | 2133 | |
| $1.49 Himalayan Blue Poppy | 2131, i | 2131ii | | | 2131iii | | | 2134a | 2134ai |

For non-denominated envelopes of same flower designs, see U176–U183.

For 50¢, 85¢, $1.45 Flowers see 2072–2074, 2081–2082
For P, 93¢, $1.10, $1.55 Flowers see 2187, 2194–2200
For P, 96¢, $1.15, $1.60 Flowers see 2243–2247, 2254–2256
For P, $1.00, $1.22, $1.70 Flowers see 2356–2364

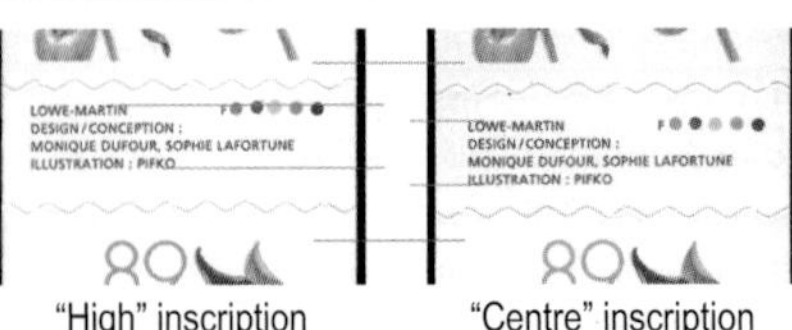

"High" inscription "Centre" inscription

Straight cut (can be 'created' with scissors from any gutter)

Wavy die cut at start of roll

## FLOWER DEFINITIVES – BOOKLETS

**2132**
Yellow Lady's Slipper

**2133**
Pink Fairy Slipper

**2134**
Himalayan Blue Poppy

Designers: Monique Dufour, Sophie Lafortune. Photography: Serge Lacroix.

Lithography (5 colours), self-adhesive booklets of 6
Lowe-Martin

| **2005, Dec 19** | **GT4, TRC Paper** | | | **Die cut** |
|---|---|---|---|---|
| | | NH–VF | ⊙F | FDC |
| **2132** | **89¢ multicoloured** | 2.00 | .60 | — |
| a | booklet pane of 6 x 89¢ (2132) (**BK318**) | 14.00 | | |
| **2133** | **$1.05 multicoloured** | 2.50 | .80 | — |
| a | booklet pane of 6 x $1.05 (2133) (**BK319**) | 18.00 | | |
| **2134** | **$1.49 multicoloured** | 3.00 | 1.25 | — |
| a | booklet pane of 6 x $1.49 (2134), "C over S" (**BK320**) | 21.00 | | |
| ai | booklet pane of 6 x $1.49 (2134), "C over O" (**BK320A**), *Feb '06* | 21.00 | | |
| T1 | untagged (error) [single stamp] | 150.00 | | |

**2132a**

**2133a**

**2134a**

**C over S** **C over O**

## FLAG BOOKLET

**2135**
Flag over (near) New Glasgow, PEI

**2136**
Flag over The Bridge, Bouctouche, NB

**2137**
Flag over turbines, Pincher Creek, AB

**2138**
Flag over Lower Fort Garry, MB

**2139**
Flag over dogsled, YK

Designer: Gottschalk+Ash International.
Photos: John Sylvester, Tourism Moncton, Janet Foster, Peter Langer, Pat Morrow.

Lithography (5 colours), self-adhesive booklet of 10
Canadian Bank Note

| **2005, Dec 19** | **GT4, Fasson Paper** | | | **Die cut** |
|---|---|---|---|---|
| | | NH–VF | ⊙F | FDC |
| **2135** | **51¢ multicoloured** (houses) | 1.00 | .25 | |
| i | TRC paper (Lowe-Martin), *Jul 31, 2006* | 1.00 | .25 | |
| **2136** | **51¢ multicoloured** (bridge) | 1.00 | .25 | |
| i | TRC paper (Lowe-Martin), *Jul 31, 2006* | 1.00 | .25 | |
| **2137** | **51¢ multicoloured** (windmills) | 1.00 | .25 | |
| i | TRC paper (Lowe-Martin), *Jul 31, 2006* | 1.00 | .25 | |
| **2138** | **51¢ multicoloured** (fort) | 1.00 | .25 | |
| i | TRC paper (Lowe-Martin), *Jul 31, 2006* | 1.00 | .25 | |
| **2139** | **51¢ multicoloured** (dogsled) | 1.00 | .25 | |
| i | TRC paper (Lowe-Martin) | 1.00 | .25 | |
| a | booklet pane of 10 x 51¢ (2 each of 2135–2139) (**BK317a**), with roulettes, CBN, Fasson paper | 12.00 | | |
| ai | as a, no vert. roulettes, (**BK317b**) | 200.00 | | |
| aii | booklet pane of 10 x 51¢ (2 each of 2135i–2139i) (**BK317Aa**), Lowe-Martin, TRC paper, 29 rouletted slits per pane, *Jul 31, 2006* | 15.00 | | |
| aiii | as "aii", 32 rouletted slits per pane, (**BK317Ab**), *Dec '06* | 50.00 | | |
| aiv | printed on gum side, pane of 10, (**BK317i**) | 200.00 | | |
| **av** | strip of 5, Fasson paper, from 2139a/BK317a | 6.00 | | |
| **avi** | strip of 5, TRC paper, from 2139aii/BK317A | 7.50 | | |
| b | as "a", die cutting omitted, (**BK317ii**) | 2,000.00 | | |

Beware of fake imperforate booklets (2139b) that have been hand cut from printer's waste that began appearing on the market in early 2012.

**Nos. 2135–2139 (5) combination FDC** **7.10**

**2139a**

Definitive Timeline:
**2005, Dec 19** $2 Peregrine Falcon and $2 Sable Island Horse (1691–1692)

## 2006

### LUNAR NEW YEAR — 10
### Year of the Dog

2140

2141i

Designer: Joseph Gault.
Lithography (8 colours) and 1 pearlescent colour and 2 foil stampings plus embossing, pane of 25
Lowe-Martin

**2006, Jan 6** **GT4, TRC Paper** **Perf 13.3**

| | | NH–VF | ⊙F | PB | FDC |
|---|---|---|---|---|---|
| **2140** | **51¢ multicoloured** | 1.00 | .40 | 5.00 | 3.00 |

Qty: 8,000,000

| | | | | | |
|---|---|---|---|---|---|
| **2141** | **$1.49 souvenir sheet** | 3.00 | 3.00 | — | 5.00* |
| i | $1.49 single stamp from souvenir sheet | 2.50 | 2.00 | — | |
| ii | $26.95 uncut press sheet of 12 souvenir sheets | 75.00 | | | |

Qty: 2141: 950,000; 2141ii: 20,000
* UPC barcode removed from all souvenir sheets on FDC. Two types exists: price shown is for 'straight cut' where tab was mechanically-removed; a second type has rouletting where the tab was hand-removed – value $25.00.

See also 1630, 1708, 1767–1768, 1836–1837, 1883–1884, 1933–1934, 1969–1970, 2015–2016, 2201–2202, 2257–2258. For non-denominated postal cards of same designs, see UX160–UX161.

2141

### QUEEN ELIZABETH II, 80th BIRTHDAY

2142

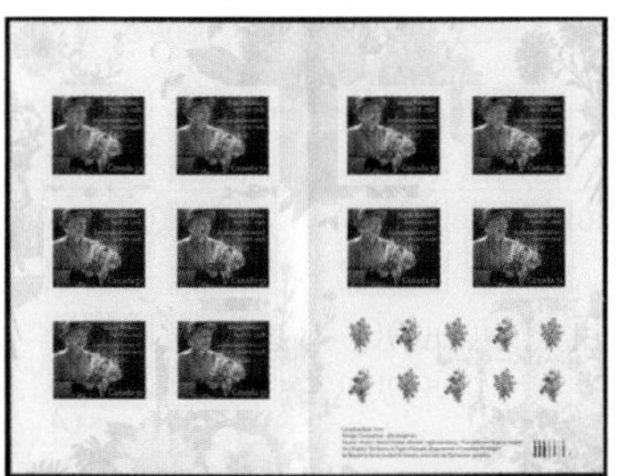
2142a

Designer: q30 design Inc. Photograph of Queen by Victor Pilon.
Lithography (7 colours), self-adhesive booklet of 10
Canadian Bank Note

**2006, Jan 12** **GT4, Fasson Paper**
**Serpentine Die cut 10.0**

| | | NH–VF | ⊙F | FDC |
|---|---|---|---|---|
| **2142** | **51¢ multicoloured** | 1.00 | .40 | 3.00 |
| i | die cut to shape from Quarterly Pack/ Annual Collection | 2.00 | — | |
| **b** | die cutting omitted, pair | 350.00 | | |
| **T1** | untagged (error) | — | 100.00 | |
| a | booklet pane of 10 x 51¢ (2142) + 10 stickers (**BK321**) | 10.00 | | |

Qty: continuous printing.

Beware of fake imperforate booklets that have been hand cut from printer's waste that began appearing on the market in early 2012.

For $1.49 value of similar design, see 2150a.

| **Rates:** | Domestic first-class (0-30g): 51¢ | |
|---|---|---|
| Jan 16/06– | Domestic first-class (30-50g): 89¢ | USA (0-30g): 89¢ |
| Jan 15/07 | Domestic oversize (0-100g): $1.05 | International (0-30g): $1.49 |

*single usage:* USA 89¢: $15.00 | International $1.49: $20.00

### XX OLYMPIC WINTER GAMES

2143 Team pursuit speed skating
2144 Skeleton

Designer: Metaform Communication Design.
Lithography (7 colours), pane of 16
Lowe-Martin

**2006, Feb 3** **GT4, TRC Paper** **Perf 12.5x13.1**

| | | NH–VF | ⊙F | PB | FDC |
|---|---|---|---|---|---|
| **2143** | **51¢ multicoloured** | 1.00 | .40 | | |
| i | blue smudge on lower back of left-most skater (pos. 11) | 5.00 | 2.00 | | |
| **2144** | **51¢ multicoloured** | 1.00 | .40 | | |
| **a** | se-tenant pair (2143, 2144) | 2.00 | 1.25 | 5.00 | 4.00 |
| **ai** | se-tenant pair (2143i, 2144) | 7.50 | 5.00 | 20.00 | 25.00 |

Qty: 2,000,000 of each

2143i

### GARDENS

2145a
Shade garden,
Black-throated blue warbler

2145b
Flower garden,
American painted lady butterfly

**2145c**
Water garden,
Green darner dragonfly

**2145d**
Rock garden,
Blue-spotted salamander

Designer: Debbie Adams.

Lithography (8 colours), Sheets of 64 subjects in eight self-adhesive booklets of 8
Lowe-Martin

**2006, Mar 8** **GT4, TRC Paper** **Serpentine Die cut 10.1**

| | | NH–VF | ⊙F | FDC |
|---|---|---|---|---|
| **2145** | $4.08 pane of 8 (2 each #a–d) (**BK322**) | 8.00 | | |
| a | **51¢ multicoloured**, shade | 1.00 | .60 | |
| b | **51¢ multicoloured**, flower | 1.00 | .60 | |
| c | **51¢ multicoloured**, water | 1.00 | .60 | |
| d | **51¢ multicoloured**, rock | 1.00 | .60 | |
| i | strip of 4, die cut to shape from Quarterly Pack/Annual Collection | 8.00 | — | |

Qty: 1,250,000 of each

**Nos. 2145a–d (4) combination FDC** **6.10**

Gardening is the number one hobby in Canada. Issued in conjunction with the Canada Blooms Garden Show in Toronto, ON.

For non-denominated envelopes of same designs, see U204–211.

2145

2146a

## BIRTHDAY

**2146**
Balloons

Designer: Designwerke Inc.

Lithography (8 colours), self-adhesive booklet of 6
Lowe-Martin

**2006, Apr 3** **GT4, TRC Paper**
**Serpentine Die cut 6.7 horiz**

| | | NH–VF | ⊙F | FDC |
|---|---|---|---|---|
| **2146** | **51¢ multicoloured** | 1.00 | .40 | 3.00 |
| i | die cut to shape from Quarterly Pack/ Annual Collection | 2.00 | — | |
| a | booklet pane of 6 x 51¢ (2146) (**BK323**) | 6.00 | | |

Qty: 10,000,000

## *ART CANADA:* DOROTHY KNOWLES

**2147**
*The Field of Rapeseed*

**2148a**
*North Saskatchewan River*

Designer: Hélène L'Heureux. Painting by Dorothy Knowles, 1927–

Lithography (9 colours), pane of 16 + gutter
Lowe-Martin

**2006, Apr 7** **GT4, TRC Paper** **Perf 13.2x12.5**

| | | NH–VF | ⊙F | PB | FDC |
|---|---|---|---|---|---|
| **2147** | **51¢ multicoloured** | 1.00 | .40 | 5.00 | 3.00 |
| i | vertical pair, gutter between | 2.00 | 1.25 | | |
| a | 51¢ single from souvenir sheet, perf 12.8x12.5 | 2.00 | 2.00 | | |
| **2148** | **$1.40 souvenir sheet** of 2 | 5.00 | 5.00 | | 4.80 |
| a | **89¢ multicoloured**, perf 13.1 x * | 3.00 | 3.00 | | |

Qty: 2147: 3,000,000; 2147a/2148/2148a: 300,000

* The 89¢ stamp has transitional perfs on the sides, as illustrated below.

2148

Transitional perfs on 89¢ (2148a)

## CANADIAN LABOUR CONGRESS

**2149**
Hands holding globe

Designer: Steven Spazuk.

Lithography (7 colours), pane of 16
Canadian Bank Note

**2006, Apr 20** **GT4, TRC Paper** **Perf 13.3**

| | | NH–VF | ⊙F | PB | FDC |
|---|---|---|---|---|---|
| **2149** | **51¢ multicoloured** | 1.00 | .40 | 5.00 | 3.00 |

Qty: 3,000,000

50th anniversary of the Canadian Labour Congress.

## QUEEN ELIZABETH II, 80th BIRTHDAY

2150a

Designer: q30 design Inc. Photograph of Queen by Victor Pilon.

Lithography (7 colours), souvenir sheet of 2
Canadian Bank Note

| 2006, Apr 21 | GT4, TRC Paper | | Perf 12.5x13.1 | |
|---|---|---|---|---|
| | | NH–VF | ⊙F | FDC |
| 2150 | **$2.98 souvenir sheet** of 2 | 6.00 | 6.00 | 8.00 |
| a | $1.49 single from souvenir sheet | 3.00 | 3.00 | |

Qty: 400,000 souvenir sheets

For 51¢ value of similar design, see 2142.

2150

## McCLELLAND & STEWART CENTENARY

2151
Horse and charioteer

Designer: James Roberts, Overdrive (Design Limited).

Lithography (2 colours), self-adhesive booklet of 8
Lowe-Martin

| 2006, Apr 26 | GT4, TRC Paper | | Die cut 11.3x11.1 | |
|---|---|---|---|---|
| | | NH–VF | ⊙F | FDC |
| 2151 | **51¢ multicoloured** | 1.00 | .40 | 3.00 |
| i | die cut to shape from Quarterly Pack/ Annual Collection | 2.00 | — | |
| a | booklet pane of 4 x 51¢ (2151) + 4 stickers | 4.00 | | |
| BK324 | two panes of 2151a $8.00 | | | |

Qty: 3,000,000

Publishers McClelland & Stewart on their 100th anniversary.

2 x 2151a (BK324)

## CANADIAN MUSEUM OF CIVILIZATION

2152
Northwest Coast Transformation Mask

Designer: Neville Smith.

Lithography (6 colours), self-adhesive booklet of 8
Lowe-Martin

| 2006, May 11 | GT4, TRC Paper | | | Die cut |
|---|---|---|---|---|
| | | NH–VF | ⊙F | FDC |
| 2152 | **89¢ multicoloured** | 1.80 | 1.00 | 3.80 |
| i | die cut to shape from Quarterly Pack/ Annual Collection | 4.00 | — | |
| ii | die cutting omitted, pair | *1,000.00* | | |
| a | booklet pane of 4 x 89¢ (2152) | 6.00 | | |
| b | as "a", die cutting omitted | *2,000.00* | | |
| BK325 | two panes of 2152a $15.00 | | | |

Qty: 3,000,000

Celebrating the 150th anniversary of the Canadian Museum of Civilization in Gatineau, Quebec.

2 x 2152a (BK325)

## CANADIANS IN HOLLYWOOD

*Perforated singles from water-activated gum souvenir sheet*

2153a
John Candy / *SCTV*
(1950–1994)

2153b
Fay Wray / *King Kong*
(1907–2004)

2153c
Lorne Greene / *Bonanza*
(1915–1987)

2153d
Mary Pickford / *Vaudeville*
(1892–1979)

*Die cut singles from self-adhesive booklet*

2154a
John Candy / *SCTV*

2154b
Mary Pickford / *Vaudeville*

2154c
Fay Wray / *King Kong*

2154d
Lorne Greene / *Bonanza*

Designer: John Belisle, Kosta Tsetsekas.

Lithography (5 colours) and 2 varnishes, water-activated gum souvenir sheet of 4
Lowe-Martin

**2006, May 26 GT4, TRC Paper Perf 13.1x12.5**

| | | NH–VF | ⊙F | FDC |
|---|---|---|---|---|
| 2153 | **$2.04 souvenir sheet** of 4 | 6.00 | 6.00 | 6.10 |
| a | **51¢ multicoloured** | 1.50 | 1.25 | |
| b | **51¢ multicoloured** | 1.50 | 1.25 | |
| c | **51¢ multicoloured** | 1.50 | 1.25 | |
| d | **51¢ multicoloured** | 1.50 | 1.25 | |

Qty: 600,000

Lithography (5 colours) and 2 varnishes, self-adhesive booklet of 8
Lowe-Martin

**2006, May 26 GT4, TRC Paper**
**Serpentine Die cut 9.9x10.0**

| | | NH–VF | ⊙F | FDC |
|---|---|---|---|---|
| 2154 | booklet pane of 4 x 51¢ (a–d) + 4 stickers (BK326), pane with John Candy at upper left | 4.00 | — | — |
| a | **51¢ multicoloured** | 1.00 | .60 | |
| b | **51¢ multicoloured** | 1.00 | .60 | |
| c | **51¢ multicoloured** | 1.00 | .60 | |
| d | **51¢ multicoloured** | 1.00 | .60 | |
| i | booklet pane of 4 x 51¢ (a–d) + 4 stickers (BK327), pane with Fay Wray at upper left | 4.00 | — | — |
| ii | booklet pane of 4 x 51¢ (a–d) + 4 stickers (BK328), pane with Lorne Greene at upper left | 4.00 | — | — |
| iii | booklet pane of 4 x 51¢ (a–d) + 4 stickers (BK329), pane with Mary Pickford at upper left | 4.00 | — | — |
| BK326 | two panes of 2154 (John Candy cover) $8.00 | | | |
| BK327 | two panes of 2154i (Fay Wray cover) $8.00 | | | |
| BK328 | two panes of 2154ii (Lorne Greene cover) $8.00 | | | |
| BK329 | two panes of 2154iii (Mary Pickford cover) $8.00 | | | |

Qty: 1,500,000 of each stamp.

Honouring the accomplishments of film and television Canadian actors who became stars in Hollywood.

For non-denominated postal cards of same designs, see UX162–UX165.

2153

2 x 2154 (BK326)

2 x 2154i (BK327)

2 x 2154ii (BK328)

2 x 2154iii (BK329)

## CHAMPLAIN SURVEYS THE EAST COAST

2155
Two-masted sailing ship

Designer: Fugazi.

Lithography (6 colours) plus Engraving, pane of 16
Canadian Bank Note

**2006, May 28 GT4, TRC Paper Perf 13.1x12.5**

| | | NH–VF | ⊙F | PB | FDC |
|---|---|---|---|---|---|
| 2155 | **51¢ multicoloured** | 1.00 | .40 | 5.00 | 3.00 |

Qty: 4,000,000

Imperforate pairs (and blocks) with black engraving omitted, from two panes, appeared on the market in 2013.

Ashton-Potter (USA) Ltd.

| | | NH–VF | ⊙F | PB | FDC |
|---|---|---|---|---|---|
| 2156 | **$2 souvenir sheet** of 4 | 10.00 | 10.00* | | — |
| a | 51¢ single from souvenir sheet, perf 11.0 | 2.00 | 2.00 | | |

Qty: 500,000†

† Quantity of souvenir sheets produced and distributed by each country: Canada Post and the United States Postal Service.

* Postally used in *both* countries $25.00

The Canadian souvenir sheet has a UPC barcode in the lower left corner; the USA souvenir sheet does not. Otherwise, the stamps themselves are identical.

**Joint FDC with USA** **6.00**

Joint issue with USA. Commemorating the 400th anniversary of the mapping of the East Coast by Samuel de Champlain. See also 2044, 2115, 2226, 2269.

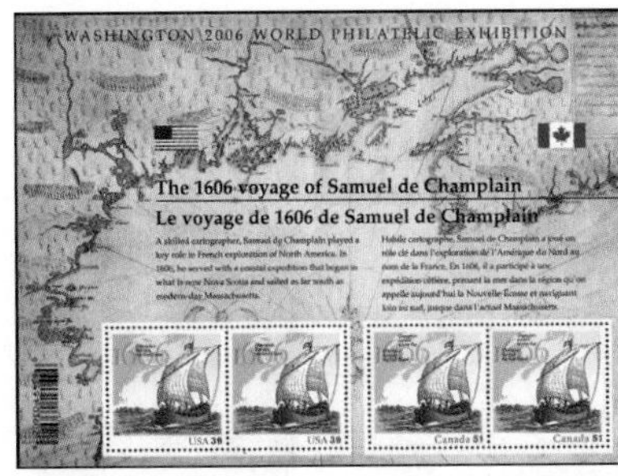


**2156**
Canadian version (with UPC barcode at lower left)

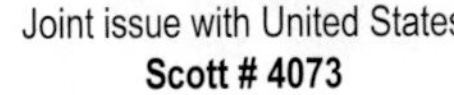

Joint issue with United States
**Scott # 4073**

Joint issue with United States
**Scott # 4074a**

## VANCOUVER AQUARIUM

**2157**
Child viewing beluga whale

Designer: Kevin van der Leek.

Lithography (7 colours plus varnish), self-adhesive booklet of 10
Lowe-Martin

**2006, Jun 15** **GT4, TRC Paper**
**Serpentine Die cut 9.6**

| | | NH–VF | ⊙F | FDC |
|---|---|---|---|---|
| **2157** | **51¢ multicoloured** | 1.00 | .40 | 3.00 |
| i | die cut to shape from Quarterly Pack/ Annual Collection | 2.00 | — | |
| a | booklet pane of 5 x 51¢ (2157) | 5.00 | | |
| BK330 | two panes of 2157a $10.00 | | | |

Qty: 5,000,000

50th anniversary of the Vancouver Aquarium.

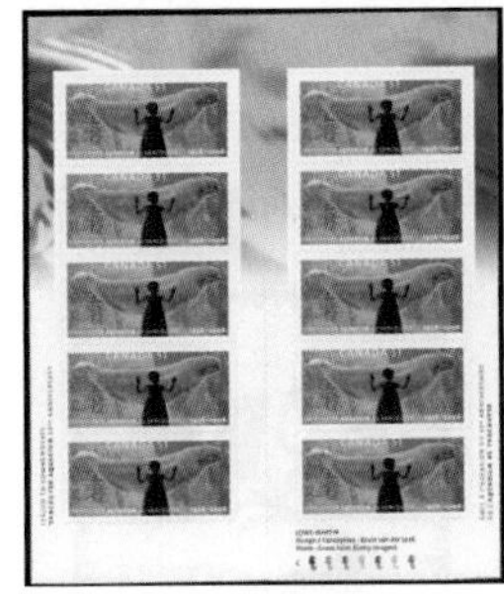

**2 x 2157a (BK330)**

## CANADIAN FORCES SNOWBIRDS

**2158**
Pilot and two planes

**2159**
3 planes in front of 9-plane formation

Designer: Wade Stewart and Tilt Telmet.

Lithography (9 colours), pane of 16
Canadian Bank Note

**2006, Jun 28** **GT4, TRC Paper** **Perf 12.5x13.1**

| | | NH–VF | ⊙F | PB | FDC |
|---|---|---|---|---|---|
| **2158** | **51¢ multicoloured** | 1.00 | .40 | | |
| **2159** | **51¢ multicoloured** | 1.00 | .40 | | |
| a | se-tenant pair (2158, 2159) | 2.25 | 1.50 | 5.00 | 4.00 |
| b | $1.02 souvenir sheet of 2 | 3.00 | 3.00 | | 4.00 |
| i | $38.75 uncut press sheet of 4 panes of 2158–59 and 6 panes of 2159b | 250.00 | — | | |

Qty: 2158–2159: 2,500,000 of each; 2159b: 400,000, 2159i: 1,000.

25th anniversary of formation of the "Snowbirds". For non-denominated postal cards of same designs, see UX166–UX167.
An overprinted souvenir sheet was available in the *Snowbirds Stamp and Coin Set* (Thematic collection 147).

**2159b**

**2159b (overprinted)**

## ATLAS OF CANADA CENTENARY

**2160**
Dividers and map of Canada

Designer: Karen Smith.

Lithography (9 colours), Sheets of 96 subjects in six panes of 16 + gutter + 4 tabs
Lowe-Martin

**2006, Jun 30** **GT4, TRC Paper** **Perf 13.1x12.5**

| | | NH–VF | ⊙F | FDC |
|---|---|---|---|---|
| **2160** | **51¢ multicoloured** | 1.00 | .40 | 3.00 |
| i | vertical pair, gutter between | 2.00 | 1.00 | |
| | full pane of 16 | 16.00 | | |

Qty: 2,500,000

100th anniversary of the creation of the first atlas of Canada by James White, Canada's Chief Geographer.

**2160 full pane**

## 2006 WORLD LACROSSE CHAMPIONSHIPS

2161
Lacrosse player

Designer: Tom Yakobina.

Lithography (6 colours), self-adhesive booklet of 8
Lowe-Martin

**2006, Jul 6** **GT4, TRC Paper**
**Serpentine Die cut 11.7 horiz**

| | | NH–VF | ⊙F | FDC |
|---|---|---|---|---|
| **2161** | **51¢ multicoloured** | 1.00 | .40 | 3.05 |
| i | die cut to shape from Quarterly Pack/ Annual Collection | 1.50 | — | |
| a | booklet pane of 8 x 51¢ (2161) (**BK331**) | 8.00 | | |

Qty: 3,000,000

The 2006 World Lacrosse Championships held in London, ON from July 13–22.

2161a

2162a

## MOUNTAINEERING CENTENARY

2162
Climbers

Designer: Xerxes Irani.

Lithography (7 colours and spot gloss varnish), self-adhesive booklet of 8
Lowe-Martin

**2006, Jul 19** **GT4, TRC Paper** **Die cut 12.5x13.1**

| | | NH–VF | ⊙F | FDC |
|---|---|---|---|---|
| **2162** | **51¢ multicoloured** | 1.00 | .40 | 3.00 |
| i | die cut to shape from Quarterly Pack/ Annual Collection | 1.50 | — | |
| a | booklet pane of 8 x 51¢ (2162) + 8 stickers (**BK332**) | 8.00 | | |

Qty: 4,000,000

100 year anniversary of the founding of The Alpine Club of Canada in Winnipeg, MB. The stamps were placed at a slant in the booklet and on all FDCs to symbolize the slope of a mountain side.

## DUCK DECOYS

2163 Barrow's golden eye — 2164 Mallard

2165 Black duck — 2166 Red-breasted merganser

Designer: Oliver Hill and Dennis Page.

Lithography (4 colours), pane of 16
Canadian Bank Note

**2006, Aug 3** **GT4, TRC Paper** **Perf 13.1x12.5**

| | | NH–VF | ⊙F | PB | FDC |
|---|---|---|---|---|---|
| **2163** | **51¢ multicoloured** | 1.00 | .60 | | |
| **2164** | **51¢ multicoloured** | 1.00 | .60 | | |
| **2165** | **51¢ multicoloured** | 1.00 | .60 | | |
| **2166** | **51¢ multicoloured** | 1.00 | .60 | | |
| a | se-tenant block of 4 (2163–2166) | 4.00 | 3.00 | 5.00 | 6.10 |
| b | $2.04 souvenir sheet of 4 | 5.00 | 5.00 | | |

Qty: 1,125,000 of each; 400,000 of souvenir sheet.

For non-denominated postal cards of same designs, see UX168–UX171.

2166b

## SOCIETY OF GRAPHIC DESIGNERS

2167
Beaver

Designer: David Coates, FDGC, Rod Roodenburg, MGDC.
Lithography (5 colours), pane of 16
Lowe-Martin

| 2006, Aug 16 | GT4, TRC Paper | | Perf 12.5x13.2 | |
|---|---|---|---|---|
| | NH–VF | ⊙F | PB | FDC |
| **2167 51¢ multicoloured** | 1.00 | .40 | 5.00 | 3.00 |

Qty: 2,500,000

50th anniversary of the founding of The Society of Graphic Designers of Canada.

## CANADIAN WINE and CHEESE

2168
Three wines

2169
Red wine and barrels

2170
Four types of cheese

2171
Serving cheese

Designer: Derwyn Goodall. Photography: Robert Wigington.
Lithography (8 colours), self-adhesive booklet of 8
Lowe-Martin

| 2006, Aug 23 | GT4, TRC Paper | | Die cut |
|---|---|---|---|
| | NH–VF | ⊙F | FDC |
| **2168 51¢ multicoloured** | 1.00 | .60 | |
| **2169 51¢ multicoloured** | 1.00 | .60 | |
| **2170 51¢ multicoloured** | 1.00 | .60 | |
| **2171 51¢ multicoloured** | 1.00 | .60 | |
| a booklet pane of 8 x 51¢ (2 each, 2168–2171) (BK333) | 8.00 | — | — |

Qty: 1,125,000 of each stamp.

**Nos. 2168–2171 (4) combination FDC 6.10**

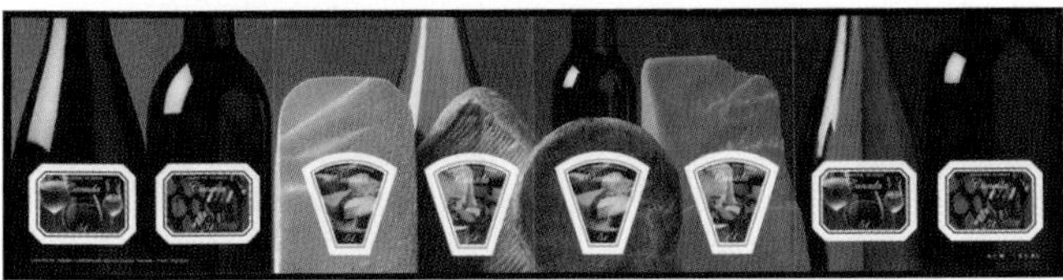

2171a

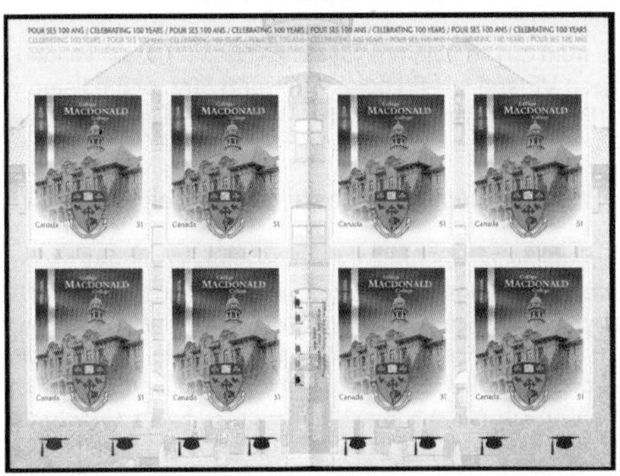

2 x 2172a (BK334)

## MACDONALD COLLEGE

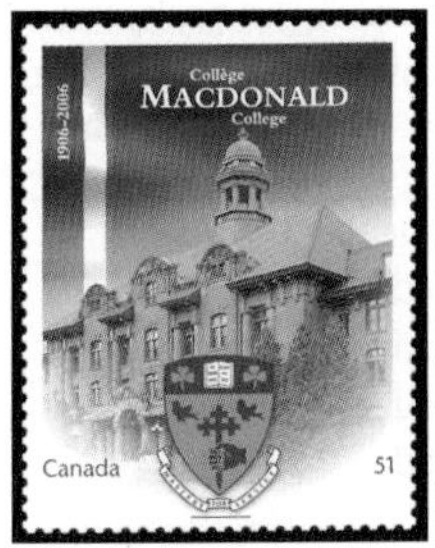

2172

Designer: Denis L'Allier. Photography: Guy Lavigueur.
Lithography (6 colours), self-adhesive booklet of 8
Lowe-Martin

| 2006, Sep 26 | GT4, TRC Paper | Die cut 12.8x13.4 | |
|---|---|---|---|
| | NH–VF | ⊙F | FDC |
| **2172 51¢ multicoloured** | 1.00 | .40 | 3.00 |
| i die cut to shape from Quarterly Pack/ Annual Collection | 1.50 | — | |
| a booklet pane of 4 x 51¢ (2172) | 5.00 | | |
| BK334 two panes of 2172a $10.00 | | | |

Qty: 3,000,000

100th anniversary of Macdonald College, Sainte-Anne-de-Bellevue, Quebec.

For other University issues, see 1756, 1941–1944, 1973–1977, 2033–2034, 2089, 2209–2210.

## ENDANGERED SPECIES — I

*Perforated singles from water-activated gum souvenir sheet*

2173a
Newfoundland marten

2173b
Blotched tiger salamander

2173c
Blue racer snake

2173d
Swift fox

*Die cut singles from self-adhesive booklet*

2174
Newfoundland marten

2175
Blotched tiger salamander

2176
Blue racer snake

2177
Swift fox

Designer: Sputnik Design Partners.

Lithography (8 colours)
Lowe-Martin
Water-activated gum souvenir sheet of 4 + 4 tabs

**2006, Sep 29** **GT4, TRC Paper** **Perf 13.4**

| | | NH–VF | ⊙F | FDC |
|---|---|---|---|---|
| 2173 | **$2.04 souvenir sheet** of 4 | 7.50 | 6.50 | — |
| a | **51¢ multicoloured** | 1.50 | 1.25 | |
| b | **51¢ multicoloured** | 1.50 | 1.25 | |
| c | **51¢ multicoloured** | 1.50 | 1.25 | |
| d | **51¢ multicoloured** | 1.50 | 1.25 | |

Qty: 400,000

Self-adhesive booklet of 8
**GT4, TRC Paper** **Die cut**

| | | NH–VF | ⊙F | FDC |
|---|---|---|---|---|
| 2174 | **51¢ multicoloured** | 1.00 | .60 | |
| 2175 | **51¢ multicoloured** | 1.00 | .60 | |
| 2176 | **51¢ multicoloured** | 1.00 | .60 | |
| 2177 | **51¢ multicoloured** | 1.00 | .60 | |
| a | block of four (2174–2177) | 5.00 | | 6.10* |
| b | booklet pane, 2 # 2177a (**BK335**) | 10.00 | | |

Qty: 1,000,000 of each

* Stamps on FDCs are not die cut all the way through.

The 2006 series features four endangered Canadian animals that live on land. A second set in 2007 features water creatures (see 2229–2233); a third set in 2008 features animals that live in the air (see 2285–2289).

2173

2177b

## OPERA

**2178**
Maureen Forrester (1930–2010)
[Place des Art, Montréal]

**2179**
Raoul Jobin (1906–1974)
[Palais Garnier opera house, Paris]

**2180**
Léopold Simoneau (1916–2006) and
Pierrette Alarie (1921–2011)
[Opéra-Comique, Paris]

**2181**
Jon Vickers (1926–2015)
[La Scala opera house, Milan, Italy]

**2182**
Edward Johnson (1878–1959)
[Metropolitan Opera House, New York]

Designer: Paul Haslip and Judith Lacerte.

Lithography (11 colours), pane of 10
Canadian Bank Note

**2006, Oct 17** **GT4, TRC Paper** **Perf 12.6x13.1**

| | | NH–VF | ⊙F | FDC |
|---|---|---|---|---|
| 2178 | **51¢ multicoloured** | 1.00 | .60 | |
| 2179 | **51¢ multicoloured** | 1.00 | .60 | |
| 2180 | **51¢ multicoloured** | 1.00 | .60 | |
| 2181 | **51¢ multicoloured** | 1.00 | .60 | |
| 2182 | **51¢ multicoloured** | 1.00 | .60 | |
| a | vertical se-tenant strip of 5 (2178–2182) | 5.00 | 5.00 | 7.10* |

Qty:600,000 of each

* The First Day Cover consists of a strip of three and a pair, adjacent to each other.

## CHRISTMAS

**2183**
Madonna and Child,
by Antoine-Sébastien Falardeau (1822–1889)

Designer: Pierre Fontaine.

Lithography (6 colours) plus 1 varnish
Lowe-Martin, self-adhesive booklet of 12

**2006, Nov 1** **GT4, TRC Paper** **Die cut**

| | | NH–VF | ⊙F | FDC |
|---|---|---|---|---|
| 2183 | **51¢ multicoloured** | 1.00 | .30 | 3.00 |
| a | booklet pane of 12 x 2183 (**BK336**) | 12.00 | — | |

Qty: 35,000,000

**MINT PRICING PREMIUMS**

Mint stamps from 301 to date are valued as NH-VF (Never Hinged-Very Fine). All hinged VF and NH-F copies are worth 50% of the listed values. Plate block (PB) values are for mint NH–VF plate or inscription blocks of four.

**USED, VF/XF (with in-period, circular date cancel) PRICING PREMIUM**

Single stamps with light or circular date cancels will sell for more than catalogue value (perhaps even more than a mint copy). From *1981 to 1991* single stamps from se-tenant blocks of 4 or larger will be priced at 50% or more above the fine price. From *1992* to date single stamps from se-tenant blocks of 4 or larger plus se-tenant booklet panes and souvenir sheets will be priced at 100% or more above the fine price. From *1997* to date all other stamps will be priced at 50% or more above the fine price.

## CHRISTMAS CARDS

**2184**
*Snowman*,
by Yvonne McKague Housser

**2185**
*Winter Joys*,
by J.E. Sampson

**2186**
*Contemplation*,
by Edwin Holgate

Designer: Peter Steiner.
Lithography (51¢ and $1.49 in 7 colours, 89¢ in 6 colours)
Self-adhesive booklet of 12 (51¢) or 6
Canadian Bank Note

**2006, Nov 1** **GT4, TRC Paper**
**Serpentine Die cut 13.3 Horiz**

| | | | NH–VF | ⊙F | FDC |
|---|---|---|---|---|---|
| **2184** | | **51¢ multicoloured** | 1.00 | .30 | |
| | i | die cut to shape from Quarterly Pack/ Annual Collection | 2.00 | — | |
| | a | booklet pane of 12 x 51¢ (2184) (**BK337**) | 12.00 | — | |
| Qty: 30,000,000 | | | | | |
| **2185** | | **89¢ multicoloured** | 1.80 | .75 | |
| | i | die cut to shape from Quarterly Pack/ Annual Collection | 4.50 | — | |
| | a | booklet pane of 6 x 89¢ (2185) (**BK338**) | 11.00 | — | |
| Qty: 6,900,000 | | | | | |
| **2186** | | **$1.49 multicoloured** | 3.00 | 1.25 | |
| | i | die cut to shape from Quarterly Pack/ Annual Collection | 6.00 | — | |
| | a | booklet pane of 6 x $1.49 (2186) (**BK339**) | 18.00 | — | |
| Qty: 6,800,000 | | | | | |
| **Nos. 2184–2186 (3) combination FDC** | | | | | **7.80** |

A tribute to the art and tradition of Christmas cards.

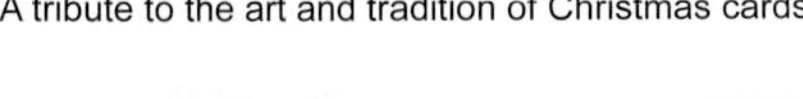

2183a

2184a

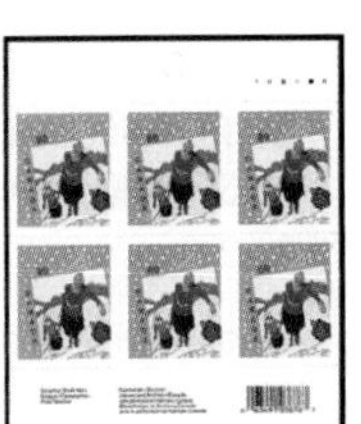

2185a

2186a

## PERMANENT™ COIL

**2187**
Spotted Coralroot

Designers: Monique Dufour, Sophie Lafortune.
Lithography (5 colours), self-adhesive rolls of 100
Lowe-Martin

Five different die cut patterns were used. The first pattern has a 'perf' range of 7.20–9.30 and includes a 'compound' perf§. A second pattern had a range of 7.80 to 8.75. A third pattern appeared in February 2007 which had a 'perf' range of 7.85 to 9.40. A fourth pattern appeared in July 2007 with a range of 8.35 to 9.10. Every stamp on each of the 100-subject (10x10) die cutting mats is different due to variations occurring on the top and bottom of a single stamp. A fifth mat (6x6, 36-subject) was used for the Quarterly Pack singles, with a range of 6.45–7.05.

**2006, Nov 16** **GT4*, TRC Paper**
**Serpentine Die cut 7.20 to 9.40 Horiz**

| | | | NH–VF | ⊙F | FDC |
|---|---|---|---|---|---|
| **2187** | | **multicoloured** †, die cut 7.20–9.30 | 1.70 | .25 | 3.00 |
| | i | gutter strip of 4 with inscription | 8.50 | | |
| | | starter strip of 4 (wavy die cut) | 11.00 | | |
| | | end strip of 4 (wavy die cut) | 11.00 | | |
| | ii | 'compound' die cut 7.20–7.50 one edge only§ | 5.00 | 1.50 | 15.00 |
| | | as ii, compound die cut in strip of 4§ | 25.00 | | |
| | iii | die cut 7.80–8.75 | 1.70 | .25 | |
| | iv | gutter strip of 4 with inscription | 8.50 | | |
| | | starter strip of 4 (wavy die cut) | 11.00 | | |
| | | end strip of 4 (wavy die cut) | 11.00 | | |
| | v | die cut to shape (6.45–7.05) from Quarterly Pack, *Apr '07* | 5.00 | — | |

* original printings of 2187 had weak, washed out tagging. 2187iii (normally with bright tagging) also exists with weak, washed out tagging; value is 5x normal price.

§ One of the eleven rows of die cutting from this printing had a measurement of 7.20–7.50. The adjacent rows measure 8.40 to 9.30. This is a full 1½ 'perf' difference on the same stamp.

One "double roll" (error) of 100 exists, producing *horizontal* uncut pairs. Value: $125.00 per pair; $750.00 for gutter block of 8.

For water-activated gum from souvenir sheet see 2194a.

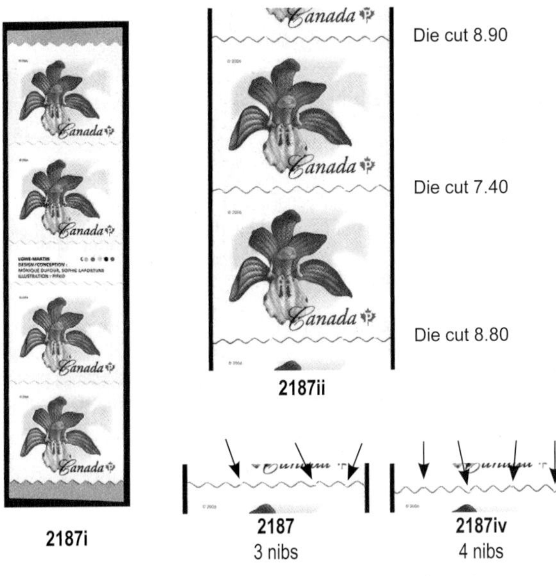


2187i

2187ii

2187
3 nibs

2187iv
4 nibs

The exact position of the nibs varies from stamp to stamp.

## PERMANENT™ BOOKLETS

**2188**
Queen Elizabeth II

Designers: Flags: Gottschalk+Ash Int'l.; Queen: q30 Design Inc.
Lithography (5 colours), self-adhesive booklets of 10 and 30
Canadian Bank Note

**2006, Nov 16** — **GT4, Fasson Paper** — **Die cut**

| | | NH–VF | ⊙F | FDC |
|---|---|---|---|---|
| **2188** | **P multicoloured (QE II)** † | 1.70 | .25 | 3.00 |
| i | TRC paper, *Apr 5, 2007* | 1.70 | .25 | |
| a | booklet pane of 10 x P (2188), Fasson paper (**BK340**) | 17.00 | | |
| aii | as "a", die cutting omitted, pane of 10, Fasson paper (**BK340i**) | 1,200.00 | | |
| ai | booklet pane of 10 x P (2188i), TRC paper (**BK340A**), *Apr 5, 2007* | 17.00 | | |

A single, used counterfeit of the P Queen has been reported.

**2189**
Flag over Sirmilik National Park, Nunavut

**2190**
Flag over Cliff near Chemainus, BC

**2191**
Flag over Polar Bears near Churchill, MB

**2192**
Flag over Bras d'Or Lake, NS

**2193**
Flag over Tuktut Nogait National Park, NWT

**GT4, TRC Paper** — **Die cut**

| | | NH–VF | ⊙F | FDC |
|---|---|---|---|---|
| **2189** | **P multicoloured**, ice fields † | 1.70 | .25 | |
| **2190** | **P multicoloured**, coastline † | 1.70 | .25 | |
| **2191** | **P multicoloured**, polar bears † | 1.70 | .25 | |
| **2192** | **P multicoloured**, lighthouse † | 1.70 | .25 | |
| **2193** | **P multicoloured**, river † | 1.70 | .25 | |
| a | booklet pane of 10 x P (2 each of 2189–2193) (**BK341**) | 17.00 | | |
| b | booklet pane of 30 x P (6 each of 2189–2193 in 3 panels) (**BK342**) | 50.00 | | |
| **ai** | strip of 5, from 2193a/BK341 or 2193b/BK342 | 8.50 | | |

**Nos. 2189–2193 (5) combination FDC** 7.10

Beware of die cutting omitted booklets (2188a, 2193a, 2193b) that have been hand cut from Canadian Bank Note printer's waste that began appearing on the market in early 2012. They are faked booklets due to the hand cutting (i.e. stamps printed by CBN modified by hand cutting to make them appear to be legitimately released die cutting omitted booklets).

**2188a**

**2193a**

**2193b**

## FLOWER DEFINITIVES – SOUVENIR SHEET

**2194a**
Spotted Coralroot

**2194b**
Flat-leaved Bladderwort

**2194c**
The Marsh Skullcap

**2194d**
The Little Larkspur

Designers: Monique Dufour, Sophie Lafortune.
Lithography (5 colours)
Lowe-Martin
Water-activated gum souvenir sheet of 4

**2006, Dec 19** — **GT4, TRC Paper** — **Perf 13.4x13.1**

| | | NH–VF | ⊙F | FDC |
|---|---|---|---|---|
| **2194** | **$4.09 souvenir sheet** of 4 † | 9.25 | 8.50 | 10.20 |
| a | **P multicoloured** | 1.70 | 1.25 | |
| b | **93¢ multicoloured** | 2.00 | 1.50 | |
| c | **$1.10 multicoloured** | 2.25 | 1.75 | |
| d | **$1.55 multicoloured** | 3.00 | 2.50 | |

Qty: unknown

† Face value of $4.09 at time of issue; the face value of the P stamp changed from 51¢ to 52¢ on January 16, 2007 (making the face value of the souvenir sheet $4.10 as of that date).

**2194**

**† PERMANENT™ non-denominated stamps**

The stamps identified with the symbol of a letter "P" within a red maple leaf are valid indefinitely for use within Canada. Regardless of rate increases, these definitives will be worth the Canadian domestic basic letter rate in effect, and can be used to mail a letter that weighs up to 30 grams to any address in Canada. At time of issue, the P stamp was valued at 51¢; this changed to 52¢ on January 16, 2007.

## FLOWER DEFINITIVES – COILS

| 2195 | 2196 | 2197 |
|---|---|---|
| Flat-leaved Bladderwort | The Marsh Skullcap | The Little Larkspur |

Designers: Monique Dufour, Sophie Lafortune.
Lithography (5 colours), self-adhesive rolls of 50
Lowe-Martin

As many as four different die cut patterns were used. The first pattern has a 'perf' range of 7.80 to 8.75. A second pattern appeared in February 2007 which had a 'perf' range of 7.85 to 9.40 (used on 93¢ and $1.10). A third pattern appeared in July 2007 which had a 'perf' range of 8.35 to 9.10 (used on $1.10 and $1.55) Every stamp on each of the 100-subject (10x10) die cutting mats is different due to variations occurring on the top and bottom of a single stamp. A fourth mat (6x6, 36-subject) was used for the Quarterly Pack singles, with a range of 6.45–7.05.

**2006, Dec 19** **GT4, TRC Paper**
**Serpentine Die cut 7.80 to 9.40 Horiz**

| | | NH–VF | ⊙F | FDC |
|---|---|---|---|---|
| **2195** | **93¢ multicoloured** | 1.85 | .50 | — |
| i | gutter strip of 4 with inscription | 9.00 | | |
| | starter strip of 4 (wavy die cut) | 10.50 | | |
| | end strip of 4 (wavy die cut) | 10.50 | | |
| ii | die cut to shape (6.45–7.05) from Quarterly Pack, *Apr '07* | 5.00 | — | |
| **2196** | **$1.10 multicoloured** | 2.25 | .75 | — |
| i | gutter strip of 4 with inscription | 10.50 | | |
| | starter strip of 4 (wavy die cut) | 12.50 | | |
| | end strip of 4 (wavy die cut) | 12.50 | | |
| ii | die cut to shape (6.45–7.05) from Quarterly Pack, *Apr '07* | 6.00 | — | |
| **2197** | **$1.55 multicoloured** | 3.10 | .75 | — |
| i | gutter strip of 4 with inscription | 15.00 | | |
| | starter strip of 4 (wavy die cut) | 17.50 | | |
| | end strip of 4 (wavy die cut) | 17.50 | | |
| ii | die cut to shape (6.45–7.05) from Quarterly Pack, *Apr '07* | 9.00 | — | |

Coil (2187, 2195–2197) tagging: under an ultraviolet light, tagging on the initial printings has a "washed out" appearance (generally dull with ghost bars and smearing). Subsequent printings have tagging that is "bright" (sharp edges). The two types are very distinctive. The bright tagging on the $1.55 coil (seen in late September) is valued at $15 for a single, $110 for a gutter strip of 4, and $150 for start/end strip of 4. Only a few rolls of this tagging variety have been found. The other denominations (P/93¢/$1.10) with bright tagging do not command a premium.

2197
Left: "washed out" tagging
Right: "bright" tagging

## FLOWER DEFINITIVES – BOOKLETS

| 2198 | 2199 | 2200 |
|---|---|---|
| Flat-leaved Bladderwort | The Marsh Skullcap | The Little Larkspur |

Designers: Monique Dufour, Sophie Lafortune.
Lithography (5 colours), self-adhesive booklets of 6
Lowe-Martin

**2006, Dec 19** **GT4, TRC Paper** **Die cut**

| | | NH–VF | ⊙F | FDC |
|---|---|---|---|---|
| **2198** | **93¢ multicoloured** | 2.00 | .75 | — |
| a | booklet pane of 6 x 93¢ (2198) (**BK343**) | 12.00 | | |
| ai | as "a", with F-paper designation (**BK343a**) | 15.00 | | |
| **2199** | **$1.10 multicoloured** | 2.50 | 1.00 | — |
| a | booklet pane of 6 x $1.10 (2199) (**BK344**) | 15.00 | | |
| **2200** | **$1.55 multicoloured** | 3.25 | 1.50 | — |
| a | booklet pane of 6 x $1.55 (2200) (**BK345**) | 19.50 | | |

2198 appeared with both C- and F-paper designations. The F-paper booklets are actually printed on C-paper (TRC). Both versions were distributed from the initial release.

The tagging on the initial printings was dull with ghost bars and smearing. Subsequent printings have tagging that includes a smooth, lacquer-type (shiny) and another type that appears dull with crisp edges.

All three booklets (about every second booklet of the first printing) exist with a small portion of the bottom of the UPC barcode thickened.

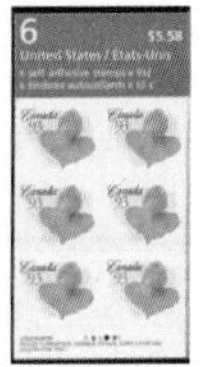
2198a

2199a

2200a

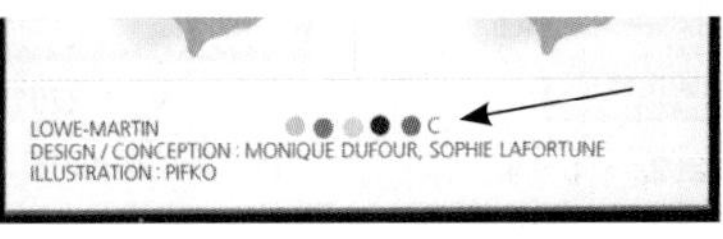

2198: C- and F-paper designations

Doubling of black at bottom of back panel

| Format: | Coil | | | Souvenir sheet | Booklet |
|---|---|---|---|---|---|
| *Die cut/perf:* | 7.20–9.30 horiz | 7.80–8.75 horiz | 6.45–7.05 horiz Qtr pack | Perf 13.4x13.1 | Die cut |
| Spotted Coralroot | 2187, i–ii | 2187 iii–iv | 2187v | 2194a | |
| 93¢ Flat-leaved Bladderwort | | 2195, i | 2195ii | 2194b | 2198 |
| $1.10 The Marsh Skullcap | | 2196, i | 2196ii | 2194c | 2199 |
| $1.55 The Little Larkspur | | 2197, i | 2197ii | 2194d | 2200 |

For 50¢, 85¢, $1.45 Flowers see 2072–2074, 2081–2082
For 51¢, 89¢, $1.05, $1.49 Flowers see 2128–2134
For P, 96¢, $1.15, $1.60 Flowers see 2243–2247, 2254–2256
For P, $1.00, $1.22, $1.70 Flowers see 2356–2364

## 2007

### LUNAR NEW YEAR — II
### Year of the Pig

2201

2202i

Designers: John Belisle, Kosta Tsetsekas (Signals).
Lithography (8 colours, souvenir sheet: 9 colours) and 2 foil stampings plus embossing, pane of 25
Lowe-Martin

**2007, Jan 5** **GT4, TRC Paper** **Perf 13.3x13.1**

| | | NH–VF | ⊙F | PB | FDC |
|---|---|---|---|---|---|
| **2201** | **52¢ multicoloured** | 1.00 | .40 | 5.00 | 3.00 |
| a | missing foil stampings (gold and rainbow)* | *100.00* | | *500.00* | |

Qty: 8,000,000
* Beware of fakes.

| | | NH–VF | ⊙F | PB | FDC |
|---|---|---|---|---|---|
| **2202** | **$1.55 souvenir sheet** of 1 | 3.00 | 3.00 | — | 5.10 |
| i | $1.55 single stamp from souvenir sheet | 2.50 | 2.00 | — | |
| ii | $26.95 uncut press sheet of 12 souvenir sheets | 125.00 | | | |
| iii | $1.55 souvenir sheet from uncut press sheet (2202ii), without UPC barcode | *20.00* | | | |

Qty: 2202: 700,000; 2202ii: 15,000

One example of 2202 exists with "missing rainbow" on both designs, with a red rejection mark on front of pane. Value: *$5,000.*

See also 1630, 1708, 1767–1768, 1836–1837, 1883–1884, 1933–1934, 1969–1970, 2015–2016, 2140–2141, 2257–2258. For non-denominated postal cards of same designs, see UX172–UX173. Souvenir sheets from the uncut press sheet differ in design from those released singly as they do not contain the bar code symbol.

2202

2201a

### CELEBRATIONS

2203
Ribbons and confetti

Designer: Karen Smith, Trivium Design Inc.
Lithography (9 colours), Sheets of 192 subjects in 32 self-adhesive booklets of 6
Lowe-Martin

**2007, Jan 15** **GT4, TRC Paper**
**Serpentine Die cut 6.7 horiz**

| | | NH–VF | ⊙F | FDC |
|---|---|---|---|---|
| **2203** | **52¢ multicoloured** | 1.00 | .40 | 3.00 |
| i | die cut to shape from Quarterly Pack/ Annual Collection | 2.00 | — | |
| a | booklet pane of 6 x 52¢ (2203) (**BK346**) | 6.00 | | |

Qty: continuous printing

*Image rotated* **2203a**

| **Rates:** | Domestic first-class (0-30g): 52¢ | |
|---|---|---|
| Jan 16/07– | Domestic first-class (30-50g): 93¢ | USA (0-30g): 93¢ |
| Jan 13/08 | Domestic oversize (0-100g): $1.10 | International (0-30g): $1.55 |

*single usage:* USA 93¢: $15.00 | International $1.55: $20.00

### INTERNATIONAL POLAR YEAR

**2204** Male King Eider
**2205** Deep-sea jellyfish *Crossota norvegica*

Designer: q30 design inc.
Lithography (9 colours), pane of 16 + gutter
Lowe-Martin

**2007, Feb 12** **GT 3 sides, TRC Paper** **Perf 13.5x13.4**

| | | NH–VF | ⊙F | FDC |
|---|---|---|---|---|
| **2204** | **52¢ multicoloured** | 1.00 | .40 | |
| **2205** | **52¢ multicoloured** | 1.00 | .40 | |
| a | se-tenant pair (2204, 2205) | 2.25 | 1.25 | 4.10 |
| i | horizontal pair, gutter between (2205 at left) | 3.00 | 2.50 | |
| | full pane of 16 | 16.00 | | |
| b | souvenir sheet of 2 | 3.00 | 3.00 | |

Qty: 2204–2205: 2,000,000 of each; 2205b: 350,000.

Canada Post sold "gutter strips of 8". These can be created by cutting a pane of 16. Price: $12.00. The general tagging is *not* applied to the side with the Maple Leaf-shaped perforation.

Eight countries issued identical-sized souvenir sheets to inform people about the sensitivity of the northern environment and to mark the advent of the 2007 International Polar Year.

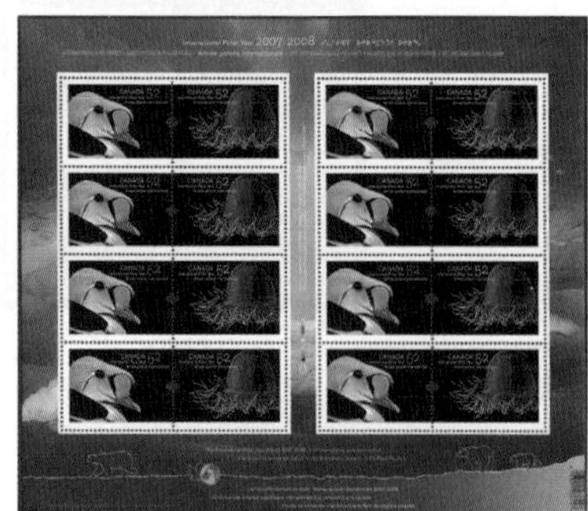
2204–2205 full pane

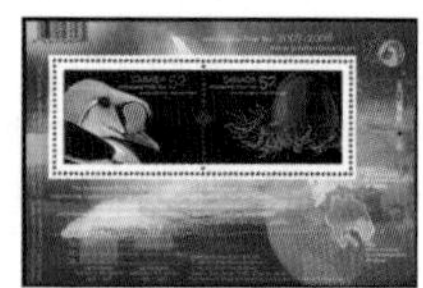
2205b

## LILACS

*Perforated singles from water-activated gum souvenir sheet*

2206a 2206b

*Die cut singles from self-adhesive booklet*

2207 White lilac 'Princess Alexandra'

2208 Pale purple lilac 'Isabella'

Designer: Isabelle Toussaint.

Lithography (4 colours)
Canadian Bank Note Company
Water-activated gum souvenir sheet of 2

| 2007, Mar 1 | GT4, TRC Paper | | Perf 13.0x12.7 | |
|---|---|---|---|---|
| | | NH–VF | ⊙F | FDC |
| **2206** | **$1.04 souvenir sheet** of 2 | 3.00 | 3.00 | — |
| a | **52¢ multicoloured** | 1.50 | 1.00 | |
| b | **52¢ multicoloured** | 1.50 | 1.00 | |
| i | se-tenant pair (2206a–b) | 3.00 | 2.50 | |
| c | as 2206, imperforate | *3,000.00* | | |

Qty: 300,000

Sheets of 130 subjects in thirteen self-adhesive booklets of 10

| | GT4, TRC Paper | | Die cut | |
|---|---|---|---|---|
| | | NH–VF | ⊙F | FDC |
| **2207** | **52¢ multicoloured** | 1.00 | .40 | |
| **2208** | **52¢ multicoloured** | 1.00 | .40 | |
| i | se-tenant pair (2207–08), die cut to shape from Quarterly Pack | 4.50 | — | |
| a | booklet pane of 10, 5 each #2207–2208 + 10 stickers (**BK347**) | 12.00 | | |

Qty: 5,000,000 of each

**Nos. 2207–2208 (2) combination FDC** **4.10**

For non-denominated postal cards of same designs, see UX174–UX175.
For non-denominated size 10 envelopes of same designs, see U243–U244.
The 'Princess Alexandra' (*Syringa vulgaris*) was one of the first lilacs to be planted in Canada (1874); The 'Isabella' (*Syringa x prestoniae*) originated in 1927.

2206

*Image rotated* 2208a

**Rates:** USA (30-50g): $1.10
Apr 16/07– Jan 13/08 International (30-50g): $2.20

## HIGHER LEARNING

2209
HEC Montréal

2210
University of Saskatchewan

Designer: Denis L'Allier. Photography: Guy Lavigueur.

Lithography (6 colours), self-adhesive booklets of 8
Lowe-Martin

| | GT4, TRC Paper | | Die cut 12.8x13.4 | |
|---|---|---|---|---|
| | | NH–VF | ⊙F | FDC |
| **2209** | **52¢ multicoloured**, *Mar 12, 2007* | 1.00 | .40 | 3.00 |
| i | die cut to shape from Quarterly Pack/ Annual Collection | 1.50 | — | |
| a | booklet pane of 4 x 52¢ (2209) | 5.00 | | |
| **BK348** | two panes of 2209a $10.00 | | | |

Qty: 2,500,000

| | | NH–VF | ⊙F | FDC |
|---|---|---|---|---|
| **2210** | **52¢ multicoloured**, *Apr 3, 2007* | 1.00 | .40 | 3.00 |
| i | die cut to shape from Quarterly Pack/ Annual Collection | 1.50 | — | |
| a | booklet pane of 4 x 52¢ (2210) | 5.00 | | |
| **BK349** | two panes of 2210a $10.00 | | | |

Qty: 2,500,000

Issued to celebrate the 100th anniversaries of École des hautes études commerciales of Montréal (HEC Montréal) and the University of Saskatchewan, Saskatoon, SK.

For other University issues, see 1756, 1941–1944, 1973–1977, 2033–2034, 2089, 2172.

2 x 2209a (BK348)

2 x 2210a (BK349)

## *ART CANADA:* MARY PRATT

2211
*Jelly Shelf*

2212a
*Iceberg in the North Atlantic*

Designer: Hélène L'Heureux. Paintings by Mary Pratt, 1935–2018
Lithography (9 colours), Sheets of 64 subjects in four panes of 16 + gutter
Canadian Bank Note Company

**2007, Mar 15** **GT4, TRC Paper** **Perf 13.1x12.5**

| | | NH–VF | ⊙F | PB | FDC |
|---|---|---|---|---|---|
| **2211** | **52¢ multicoloured** | 1.00 | .40 | 5.00 | 3.00 |
| i | vertical pair, gutter between | 2.00 | 1.00 | | |

Lithography (10 colours), Sheets of 24 subjects in twelve panes of 2

| | | NH–VF | ⊙F | PB | FDC |
|---|---|---|---|---|---|
| **2212** | **$2.07 souvenir sheet** of 2 | 5.00 | 5.00 | | 6.15 |
| a | **$1.55 multicoloured** | 3.00 | 3.00 | | |

Qty: 2211: 2,500,000; 2212/2212a: 300,000

2212

## OTTAWA, CAPITAL SESQUICENTENNIAL

*Perforated singles from water-activated gum souvenir sheet*

2213b

2213a

*Die cut single from self-adhesive booklet*

2214

2213

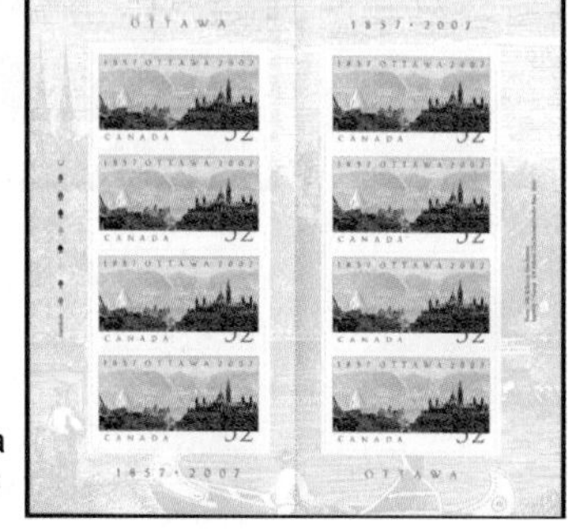

2 x 2214a
(BK350)

Designer: John McQuarrie.
Lithography (8 colours plus embossing and foil stamping on $1.55)
Water-activated souvenir sheet of 2
Lowe-Martin

**2007, May 3** **Perf 13.1**

| | | NH–VF | ⊙F | FDC |
|---|---|---|---|---|
| **2213** | **$2.07 souvenir sheet** of 2 | 5.00 | 5.00 | 6.15 |
| a | **52¢ multicoloured** | 1.50 | 1.50 | |
| b | **$1.55 multicoloured** | 3.00 | 3.00 | |

Qty: 300,000

Lithography (8 colours), Sheets of 72 subjects in nine self-adhesive booklets of 8
**GT4, TRC Paper**
**Serpentine Die cut 7.3 horiz**

| | | NH–VF | ⊙F | FDC |
|---|---|---|---|---|
| **2214** | **52¢ multicoloured** | 1.00 | .40 | 3.00 |
| i | die cut to shape from Quarterly Pack | 1.50 | — | |
| a | booklet pane of 4 x 52¢ (2214) | 4.00 | | |
| BK350 | two panes of 2214a $8.00 | | | |

Qty: 3,000,000

Celebrating the 150th anniversary of the selection of Ottawa as Canada's national capital.

## ROYAL ARCHITECTURAL INSTITUTE

2215
University of Lethbridge (Lethbridge, AB) by Arthur Erickson

2216
St. Mary's Church (Red Deer, AB) by Douglas Cardinal

2217
Ontario Science Centre (Toronto, ON) by Raymond Moriyama

2218
National Gallery of Canada (Ottawa, ON) by Moshe Safdie

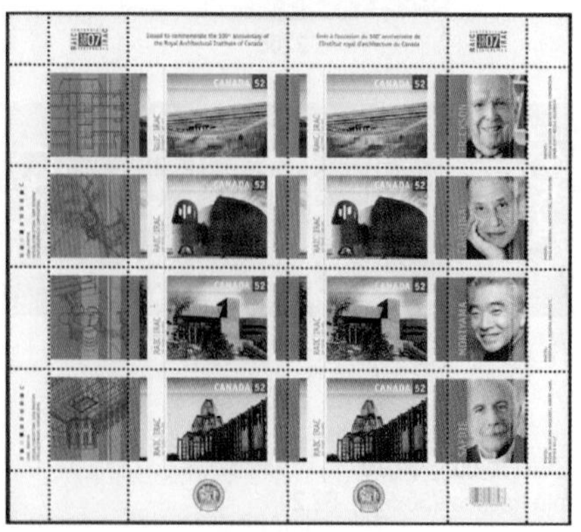

2215–2218 full pane

Designer: Ivan Novotny, Taylor|Sprules Corporation.
Lithography (9 colours), Sheets of 72 subjects in nine panes of 8 + 8 tabs
Lowe-Martin

| 2007, May 9 | GT, TRC Paper | | | Perf 13.1 |
|---|---|---|---|---|
| | | NH–VF | ⊙F | FDC |
| **2215** | **52¢ multicoloured + label** | 1.00 | .60 | |
| **2216** | **52¢ multicoloured + label** | 1.00 | .60 | |
| **2217** | **52¢ multicoloured + label** | 1.00 | .60 | |
| **2218** | **52¢ multicoloured + label** | 1.00 | .60 | |
| a | vertical se-tenant strip of 4 + 4 labels (2215–2218) | 4.00 | 3.00 | 6.15* |
| | full pane of 8 | 8.00 | | |
| i | $37.44 uncut press sheet of 9 panes, signed | 100.00 | | |

Qty: 750,000 of each; 2215–18i: 2,000

* The first day cover consists of two pairs of two stamps, without attached labels.

Printed in panes containing two of each stamp. Labels flank the stamps, with labels on the left showing drawings of the buildings and the labels on the right showing the architect.

Centennial of the Royal Architectural Institute of Canada (RAIC). The tagging is not applied to the four sides.

## CAPTAIN GEORGE VANCOUVER

2219
Captain Vancouver and signature

Designer: Niko Potton, Fleming Design.
Lithography (7 colours plus embossing)
Sheets of 27 subjects in three panes of 8 and three souvenir sheets of 1
Lowe-Martin

| 2007, Jun 22 | GT4, TRC Paper | | | Perf 13.1x12.5 |
|---|---|---|---|---|
| | | NH–VF | ⊙F | FDC |
| **2219** | **$1.55 multicoloured** | 3.00 | 1.25 | 5.10 |
| | full pane of 8 | 24.00 | | |
| | | | **Perf 13.1** | |
| a | $1.55 souvenir sheet of 1 | 3.00 | 3.00 | |
| ai | $1.55 single from souvenir sheet | 2.50 | 2.50 | |

Qty: 4,000,000; souvenir sheet: 400,000

250th anniversary of Captain Vancouver's birth. This is the first time that Canada Post has not shown the face of a person commemorated on a stamp.

2219a

## FIFA U-20 WORLD YOUTH CHAMPIONSHIPS

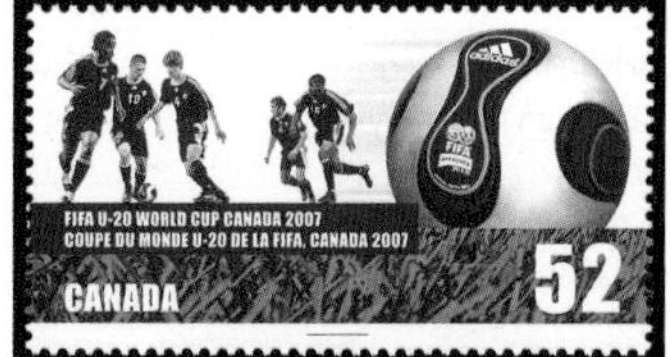


2220
Soccer players and ball

Designer: Debbie Adams; photography: Dale MacMillan
Lithography (8 colours), pane of 16
Canadian Bank Note Company

| 2007, Jun 26 | GT4, TRC Paper | | | Perf 12.5x13.1 | |
|---|---|---|---|---|---|
| | | NH–VF | ⊙F | PB | FDC |
| **2220** | **52¢ multicoloured** | 1.00 | .40 | 5.00 | 3.00 |
| a | imperf. pair | 1,300.00 | | | |

Qty: 3,000,000

## CANADIAN RECORDING ARTISTS

*Perforated singles from water-activated gum souvenir sheet*

2221a
Gordon Lightfoot (1938– )

2221b
Joni Mitchell (1943– )

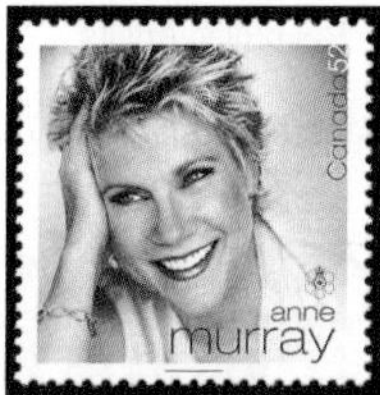


2221c
Anne Murray (1945– )

2221d
Paul Anka (1941– )

*Die cut singles from self-adhesive booklet*

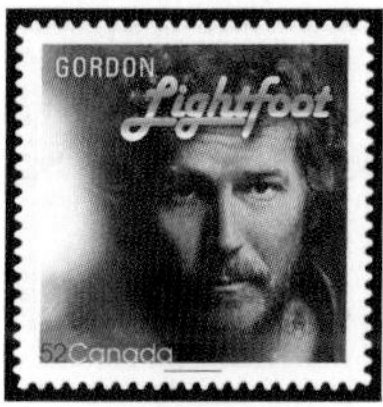


2222a

2222b

2222c

2222d

Designer: Circle Design Inc.
Lithography (9 colours), water-activated gum souvenir sheet of 4
Lowe-Martin

| 2007, Jun 29 | GT4, TRC Paper | | | Perf 12.5x13.1 |
|---|---|---|---|---|
| | | NH–VF | ⊙F | FDC |
| **2221** | **$2.08 souvenir sheet** of 4 | 4.00 | 4.00 | 6.15 |
| a | **52¢ multicoloured** | 1.00 | 1.00 | |
| b | **52¢ multicoloured** | 1.00 | 1.00 | |
| c | **52¢ multicoloured** | 1.00 | 1.00 | |
| d | **52¢ multicoloured** | 1.00 | 1.00 | |

Qty: 300,000

2221

QE II — 2000's

Lithography (9 colours), self-adhesive booklet of 8
Lowe-Martin

**2007, Jun 29** **GT4, TRC Paper**
**Serpentine Die cut 13.5**

| | | NH–VF | ⊙F | FDC |
|---|---|---|---|---|
| **2222** | booklet pane of 4 x 52¢ + 4 stickers, pane with Gordon Lightfoot at upper left | 4.00 | | |
| a | **52¢ multicoloured** | 1.00 | .50 | |
| b | **52¢ multicoloured** | 1.00 | .50 | |
| c | **52¢ multicoloured** | 1.00 | .50 | |
| d | **52¢ multicoloured** | 1.00 | .50 | |
| i | booklet pane of 4 x 52¢ + 4 stickers, pane with Joni Mitchell at upper left | 4.00 | | |
| ii | booklet pane of 4 x 52¢ + 4 stickers, pane with Anne Murray at upper left | 4.00 | | |
| iii | booklet pane of 4 x 52¢ + 4 stickers, pane with Paul Anka at upper left | 4.00 | | |

BK351 two panes of 2222 (Gordon Lightfoot cover) $8.00
BK352 two panes of 2222i (Joni Mitchell cover) $8.00
BK353 two panes of 2222ii (Anne Murray cover) $8.00
BK354 two panes of 2222iii (Paul Anka cover) $8.00
Qty: 1,502,000 of each stamp.

Honouring the accomplishments of Canadian Recording Artists.

For non-denominated postal cards of same designs, see UX176–UX179.

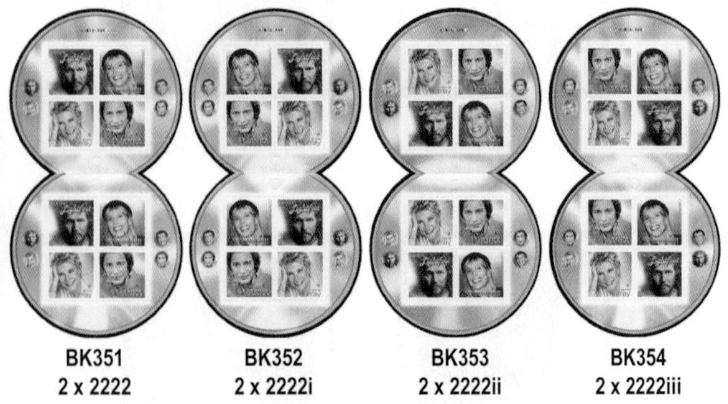

BK351 2 x 2222 · BK352 2 x 2222i · BK353 2 x 2222ii · BK354 2 x 2222iii

## NATIONAL PARKS

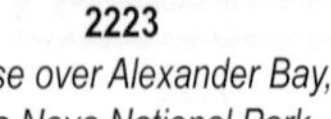

**2223**
*Sunrise over Alexander Bay, Terra Nova National Park*

**2224**
Jasper National Park

Designer: Saskia van Kampen.

Lithography (6 colours), self-adhesive booklets of 10
Lowe-Martin

**2007** **GT4, TRC Paper**
**Serpentine Die cut 13.4**

| | | NH–VF | ⊙F | FDC |
|---|---|---|---|---|
| **2223** | **52¢ multicoloured**, *Jul 6* | 1.00 | .40 | 3.00 |
| i | die cut to shape from Quarterly Pack/ Annual Collection | 2.00 | — | |
| a | booklet pane of 5 x 52¢ (2223) | 5.00 | | |

BK355 two panes of 2223a $10.00
Qty: 3,000,000

50th anniversary of Terra Nova National Park, Newfoundland. The illustration at the top of the stamp depicts the park's horizon. The top band of tagging also includes the park's horizon line with a mirror image appearing in the bottom band of tagging.

| | | NH–VF | ⊙F | FDC |
|---|---|---|---|---|
| **2224** | **52¢ multicoloured**, *Jul 20* | 1.00 | .40 | 3.00 |
| i | die cut to shape from Quarterly Pack/ Annual Collection | 2.00 | — | |
| a | booklet pane of 5 x 52¢ (2224) | 5.00 | | |
| b | gutter pane, 2223a and 2224a | 15.00 | | |

BK356 two panes of 2224a $10.00
Qty: 3,000,000; 2224b gutter pane: 25,000

100th anniversary of Jasper National Park, Alberta. The illustration at the top of the stamp depicts the park's horizon. The top band of tagging also includes the park's horizon line with a mirror image appearing in the bottom band of tagging.

2 x 2223a (BK355)

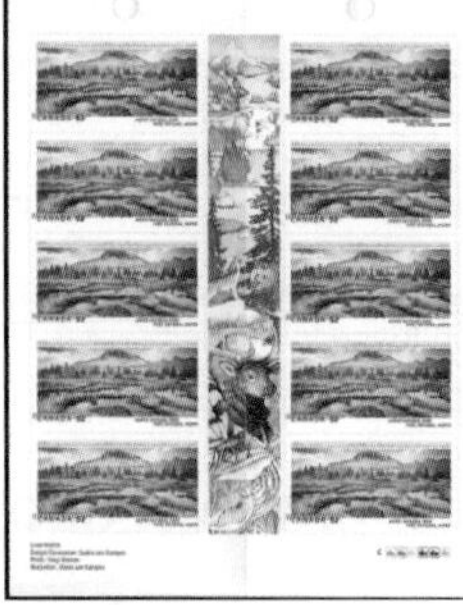

2 x 2224a (BK356)

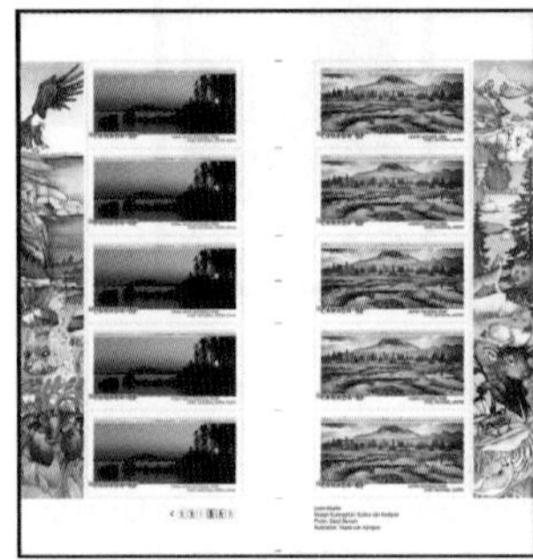

**2224b**
Gutter pane: 2223a and 2224a

## 100 YEARS OF SCOUTING

**2225**
Organization logo and activities

Designer: Matthias Reinicke, Lime Design Inc.

Lithography (7 colours plus spot gloss varnish), self-adhesive booklet of 8
Lowe-Martin

**Serpentine Die cut 13.4**
**2007, Jul 25** **GT4, TRC Paper**

| | | NH–VF | ⊙F | FDC |
|---|---|---|---|---|
| **2225** | **52¢ multicoloured** | 1.00 | .40 | 3.00 |
| i | die cut to shape from Quarterly Pack/ Annual Collection | 2.00 | — | |
| a | booklet pane of 4 x 52¢ (2225) + 4 stickers | 4.00 | | |

BK357 two panes of 2225a $8.00
Qty: 4,000,000

100th anniversary of Scouting, founded by Robert Baden-Powell. The five youth programs are featured (from bottom to top): Beavers, Cubs, Scouts, Venturers, Rovers.

2 x 2225a (BK357)

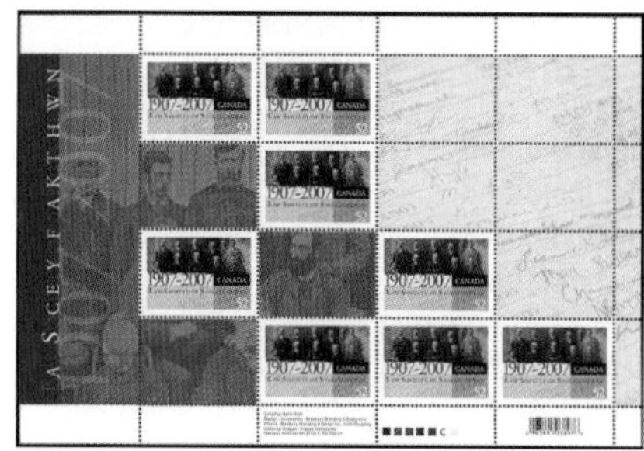

2227 full pane

## CHIEF MEMBERTOU

**2226**
Chief Henri Membertou, Grand Chief of the Mi'kmaq

Designer: Fugazi. Engraver: Jorge Peral.

Engraved (3 colours), pane of 16
Canadian Bank Note

**2007, Jul 26** **GT4, TRC Paper** **Perf 13.1x12.5**

| | | NH–VF | ⊙F | PB | FDC |
|---|---|---|---|---|---|
| **2226** | **52¢ deep grey-blue, sepia, bistre** | 1.00 | .40 | 5.00 | 3.00 |

Qty: 3,000,000

In 1607, the French returned to France, leaving the habitation of Port-Royal (see Scott 2115) in the care of Membertou. See also 2044, 2115, 2155, 2269.

## LAW SOCIETIES CENTENNIALS

**2227**
Law Society of Saskatchewan Benchers (founding members of the law society)

**2228**
Law Society of Alberta Books, gavel, photo of James Muir

Designer: Bradbury Branding & Design Inc.

Lithography (6 colours), Sheets of 48 subjects in six panes of 8 + 8 tabs
Canadian Bank Note

**2007, Sep 13** **GT4, TRC Paper** **Perf 12.9**

| | | NH–VF | ⊙F | FDC |
|---|---|---|---|---|
| **2227** | **52¢ multicoloured** | 2.00 | 1.00 | 3.00 |
| | full pane of 8 | 16.00 | | |

Qty: 2,000,000

Designer: Xerxes Irani, nonfiction studios inc.

Lithography (8 colours) plus spot varnish, pane of 16
Lowe-Martin

**2007, Sep 13** **GT4, TRC Paper** **Perf 12.5x13.1**

| | | NH–VF | ⊙F | PB | FDC |
|---|---|---|---|---|---|
| **2228** | **52¢ multicoloured** | 1.00 | .40 | 5.00 | 3.00 |

Qty: 2,000,000

## ENDANGERED SPECIES — 2

*Perforated singles from water-activated gum souvenir sheet*

**2229a**
North Atlantic Right Whale

**2229b**
Northern Cricket Frog

**2229c**
White Sturgeon

**2229d**
Leatherback Turtle

*Die cut singles from self-adhesive booklet*

**2230**
North Atlantic Right Whale

**2231**
Northern Cricket Frog

**2232**
White Sturgeon

**2233**
Leatherback Turtle

Designer: Sputnik Design Partners.

Lithography (9 colours)
Lowe-Martin
Water-activated gum souvenir sheet of 4 + 4 tabs

**2007, Oct 1** **GT4, TRC Paper** **Perf 13.4**

| | | NH–VF | ⊙F | FDC |
|---|---|---|---|---|
| **2229** | **$2.08 souvenir sheet** of 4 | 4.00 | 4.00 | |
| a | **52¢ multicoloured** | 1.00 | 1.00 | |
| b | **52¢ multicoloured** | 1.00 | 1.00 | |
| c | **52¢ multicoloured** | 1.00 | 1.00 | |
| d | **52¢ multicoloured** | 1.00 | 1.00 | |

Qty: 400,000

Self-adhesive booklet of 8

**GT4, TRC Paper** **Die cut**

| | | NH–VF | ⊙F | FDC |
|---|---|---|---|---|
| **2230** | **52¢ multicoloured** | 1.00 | .40 | |
| **2231** | **52¢ multicoloured** | 1.00 | .40 | |
| **2232** | **52¢ multicoloured** | 1.00 | .40 | |
| **2233** | **52¢ multicoloured** | 1.00 | .40 | |
| a | block of four (2230–2233) | 5.00 | | 6.15* |
| b | booklet pane, 2 # 2233a (**BK358**) | 10.00 | | |

Qty: 1,000,000 of each

* Stamps on FDCs are not die cut all the way through.

The 2007 series features four endangered water creatures. See also 2173–2177, 2285–2289.

2229

2233b

## BENEFICIAL INSECTS
## 2007– ...
## Low Value Definitives

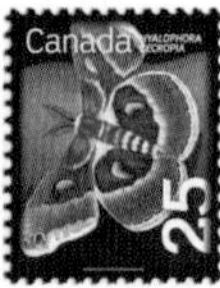

| 2234 | 2235 | 2236 | 2237 | 2238 |
|---|---|---|---|---|
| Convergent Lady Beetle | Golden-eyed Lacewing | Northern Bumblebee | Canada Darner (dragonfly) | Cecropia Moth |

For 2¢ value see Sc. 2328. For 4¢, 6¢–9¢ values, see Sc. 2406–10. For 22¢ value see Sc. 2708.

2235 space after 'Canada' — 2235a *no* space after 'Canada'

*Hidden features*

2235b

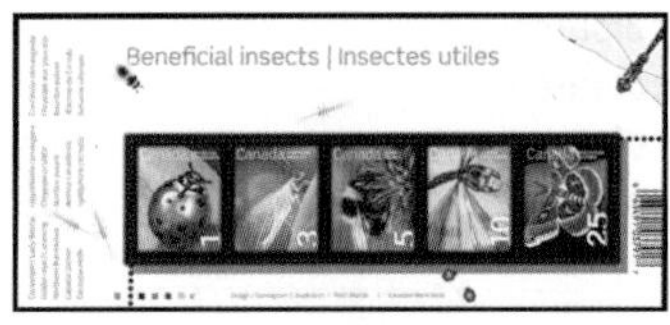


2238a

Designer: Keith Martin.

Lithography (5 colours), panes of 50

Canadian Bank Note

**Not tagged**

**2007, Oct 12** **TRC Paper (blue-green gum)** **Perf 13.0x13.4**

| | | NH–VF | ⊙F | PB | FDC |
|---|---|---|---|---|---|
| **2234** | **1¢ multicoloured** | .25 | .25 | .25 | |
| **2235** | **3¢ multicoloured** | .25 | .25 | .30 | |
| i | as 2235, transparent gum (colourless/ white), *2014* § | .25 | — | .30 | |
| a | 'Canada' shifted to right, touching 'OCULATA' (pos. 11–14) † | .50 | .25 | 1.50(UL) | |
| b | dated '2012', with added microprinting and small design features (from 2409b), *Oct 16, 2012* § | .25 | .25 | | |
| **2236** | **5¢ multicoloured** | .25 | .25 | .50 | |
| i | transparent gum (colourless/white), *May 2015* § | .25 | — | .50 | |
| **2237** | **10¢ multicoloured** | .25 | .25 | 1.00 | |
| i | transparent gum (colourless/white), *Jun 2014* § | .25 | — | 1.00 | |
| | as 'i', Lowe-Martin printing°, *Dec 2016* | — | — | 1.00 | |
| **2238** | **25¢ multicoloured** | .50 | .25 | 2.50 | |
| i | $28.00 uncut press sheet of 8 panes* | 60.00 | | | |
| ii | transparent gum (colourless/white), *Dec 2012* § | .50 | — | 2.50 | |
| a | souvenir sheet of 5 | 1.00 | 1.00 | | 2.90 |

Qty: 2238a: 350,000

* The uncut press sheet consists of 3 panes of 2234, 1 pane of 2235, 1 pane of 2236, 2 panes of 2237, and 1 pane of 2238. Qty: 2,500 (all signed by the designer).

† 2235a occurs on 4 of the 50 stamps on all panes from the initial printing. A reprint in December 2009 corrected the mistake; panes of 50 from this second printing no longer show the mistake.

§ transparent gum (colourless); back of paper appears white instead of blue-green.

° Lowe-Martin printing: there is no discernable difference between singles stamps of the CBN and LM printings. Only the 4 stamps with selvedge attached, containing the name of the printer, positively identify the different printings.

**Reprints** by CBN of the 3¢ (Dec 2009), 5¢ and 10¢ (2010) appear to have narrower black borders around the individual stamps, most noticeable at the base of the denomination. Prices: 3¢ (same as original printing); 5¢ and 10¢: $1.25 for mint singles and $7.50 for plate blocks.

These stamps were purposely designed to be oriented either horizontally or vertically. The souvenir sheet, uncut press sheet and Canada Post illustrations place the stamps vertically, with the denomination on the right side reading up.

## CHRISTMAS

2239 Reindeer

Designer: Hélène L'Heureux.

Lithography (5 colours) plus 1 clear holographic stamping

Lowe-Martin, self-adhesive booklet of 12

**Serpentine Die cut 8.4 horiz**

**2007, Nov 1** **GT4, TRC Paper**

| | | NH–VF | ⊙F | FDC |
|---|---|---|---|---|
| **2239** | **P multicoloured** | 1.70 | .25 | 3.00 |
| i | die cut to shape from Quarterly Pack/ Annual Collection | 2.50 | — | |
| a | booklet pane of 6 x P (2239) | 10.00 | — | |
| b | die cutting omitted, pair | 675.00 | | |
| BK359 | two panes of 2239a $15.00 | | | |

Qty: 44,000,000

At time of issue, the P stamp was valued at 52¢.
This design was also used on the 2008 and 2009 *Santa Claus* envelopes.

## HOPE, JOY and PEACE

**2240**
Hope
(nativity scene)

**2241**
Joy
(trumpeting angel)

**2242**
Peace
(dove)

Designer: Tandem Design Associates Ltd.
Lithography (P and 93¢ in 5 colours, $1.55 in 4 colours)
Self-adhesive booklet of 12 (P) or 6
Lowe-Martin

**2007, Nov 1** **GT4, TRC Paper**
**Serpentine Die cut 13.4**

| | | NH–VF | ⊙F | FDC |
|---|---|---|---|---|
| **2240** | **multicoloured** | 1.25 | .25 | |
| i | die cut to shape from Quarterly Pack/ Annual Collection | 2.50 | — | |
| a | booklet pane of 6 x P (2240) | 7.50 | — | |
| BK360 | two panes of 2240a $15.00 | | | |

Qty: 27,000,000

At time of issue, the P stamp was valued at 52¢.

| | | NH–VF | ⊙F | FDC |
|---|---|---|---|---|
| **2241** | **93¢ multicoloured** | 1.80 | .50 | |
| i | die cut to shape from Quarterly Pack/ Annual Collection | 4.50 | — | |
| a | booklet pane of 6 x 93¢ (2241) (**BK361**) | 11.00 | — | |

Qty: 6,900,000
One imperforate pane of 2241a (BK361) has been reported.

| | | NH–VF | ⊙F | FDC |
|---|---|---|---|---|
| **2242** | **$1.55 multicoloured** | 3.00 | .75 | |
| i | die cut to shape from Quarterly Pack/ Annual Collection | 6.00 | — | |
| b | die cutting omitted, pair | 750.00 | | |
| a | booklet pane of 6 x $1.55 (2242) (**BK362**) | 18.00 | — | |

Qty: 6,000,000

**Nos. 2240–2242 (3) combination FDC** **8.00**

The Hope, Joy, and Peace stamps each have two star-shaped cutouts in the tagging around the edge of the stamp (top and bottom margin). In addition, the Permanent™ stamp has tagging within the star found in the design of the stamp.

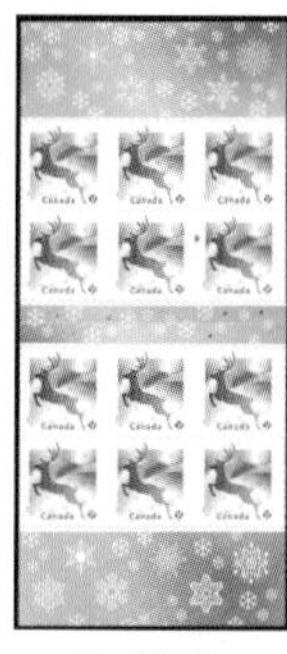

**2 x 2239a**
**(BK359)**

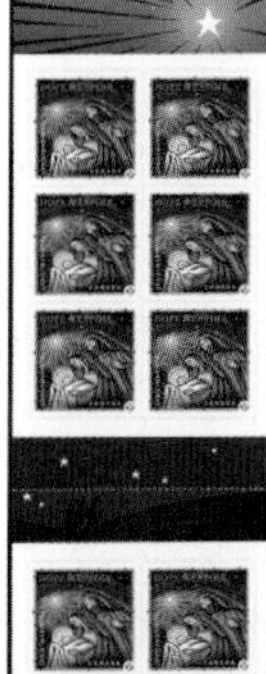

**2 x 2240a**
**(BK360)**

**2241a**

**2242a**

## FLOWER DEFINITIVES – SOUVENIR SHEET

**2243a**
Island Red flowers

**2243b**
Janet Elizabeth 'Fire Dancer'

**2243c**
Memoria Evelyn Light

**2243d**
Kaleidoscope 'Conni'

Designers: Monique Dufour, Sophie Lafortune.
Lithography (5 colours)
Lowe-Martin
Water-activated gum souvenir sheet of 4

**2007, Dec 27** **GT4, TRC Paper** **Perf 13.4x13.1**

| | | NH–VF | ⊙F | FDC |
|---|---|---|---|---|
| **2243** | **$4.23 souvenir sheet** of 4 † | 9.25 | 9.25 | 10.45 |
| a | **multicoloured** | 1.75 | 1.50 | |
| b | **96¢ multicoloured** | 2.00 | 1.75 | |
| c | **$1.15 multicoloured** | 2.25 | 2.00 | |
| d | **$1.60 multicoloured** | 3.00 | 2.75 | |

Qty: 320,000

† Face value of $4.23 at time of issue; the face value of the P stamp was 52¢.

The stamps have extra tagging elements throughout the white portions of the design.

**2243**

Tagging (as viewed under an ultraviolet light) on Flower definitives. The tagging is the same on stamps from coils, booklets, and the souvenir sheet.

## FLOWER DEFINITIVES – COILS

2244 2244A
Island Red flowers

2245 Janet Elizabeth 'Fire Dancer'
2246 Memoria Evelyn Light
2247 Kaleidoscope 'Conni'

Designers: Monique Dufour, Sophie Lafortune.
Lithography (5 colours), self-adhesive rolls of 100 (P) and 50 (96¢, $1.15, $1.60)
Lowe-Martin

As many as four different die cut patterns were used. The first pattern has a 'perf' range of 8.35 to 9.10. A second pattern appeared in April 2008 which had a 'perf' range of 7.90 to 8.80 (used on P and 96¢). A third pattern appeared in July 2008 with a range of 8.10 to 9.60 (used on P, $1.15 and $1.60). Every stamp on each of the 100-subject (10x10) die cutting mats is different due to variations occurring on the top and bottom of a single stamp. A fourth mat (6x6, 36-subject) was used for the Quarterly Pack singles, with a range of 6.45–7.05 (inverted compared to previous Flower Quarterly Pack stamps).



**2007, Dec 27 GT4, TRC Paper**
**Serpentine Die cut 7.90 to 9.60 Horiz**

| | | NH–VF | ⊙F | FDC |
|---|---|---|---|---|
| **2244** | **P multicoloured** † | 1.70 | .25 | — |
| i | gutter strip of 4 with inscription | 8.50 | | |
| | starter strip of 4 (wavy die cut) | 11.00 | | |
| | end strip of 4 (wavy die cut) | 11.00 | | |
| ii | die cut to shape (6.45–7.05) from Quarterly Pack, *Apr '08* | 4.00 | — | |

2244 exists with faint surface scorelines that result in coil strips that look nearly imperforate — value 10–20x a normal single.

| | | | |
|---|---|---|---|
| **2244A** | die cut 9.2 horiz., *Feb 1/08* ‡ | 2.00 | 2.00 |

‡ from horizontal rolls of 3,000 or 5,000. Individual stamps do not touch along the horizontal roll. Sold in strips of 4 or 10 by the National Philatelic Centre; single stamps included in the Quarterly Pack/Annual Collection. Die cutting on 2244A is consistent across the entire stamp (with rounded tips), compared to the irregular die cutting on 2244 (with sawtooth tips).

| | | NH–VF | ⊙F | FDC |
|---|---|---|---|---|
| **2245** | **96¢ multicoloured** | 1.85 | .45 | — |
| i | gutter strip of 4 with inscription | 9.00 | | |
| | starter strip of 4 (wavy die cut) | 10.50 | | |
| | end strip of 4 (wavy die cut) | 10.50 | | |
| ii | die cut to shape (6.45–7.05) from Quarterly Pack, *Apr '08* | 5.50 | — | |
| **2246** | **$1.15 multicoloured** | 2.25 | .75 | — |
| i | gutter strip of 4 with inscription | 10.50 | | |
| | starter strip of 4 (wavy die cut) | 12.50 | | |
| | end strip of 4 (wavy die cut) | 12.50 | | |
| ii | die cut to shape (6.45–7.05) from Quarterly Pack, *Apr '08* | 6.00 | — | |
| **2247** | **$1.60 multicoloured** | 3.10 | 1.00 | — |
| i | gutter strip of 4 with inscription | 15.00 | | |
| | starter strip of 4 (wavy die cut) | 17.50 | | |
| | end strip of 4 (wavy die cut) | 17.50 | | |
| ii | die cut to shape (6.45–7.05) from Quarterly Pack, *Apr '08* | 8.00 | — | |

## QUEEN ELIZABETH II

2248
Queen Elizabeth II

Designers: Gottschalk+Ash Int'l.
Lithography (5 colours), self-adhesive booklets of 10
Canadian Bank Note

**2007, Dec 27 GT4, Spicer Paper**
**Serpentine Die cut 13.4**

| | | NH–VF | ⊙F | FDC |
|---|---|---|---|---|
| **2248** | **P multicoloured (QE II)** † | 1.70 | .25 | 3.00 |
| i | die cut to shape from Quarterly Pack/ Annual Collection | 3.50 | — | |
| a | booklet pane of 10 x P (2248) (**BK363**) | 17.00 | | |

The tagging on the left and bottom of each stamp (2248) is comprised of small crowns.

**2248a**

| Format: | Coil | | | Souvenir sheet | Booklet |
|---|---|---|---|---|---|
| *Die cut/perf:* | 7.90–9.60 horiz | 9.2 horiz | 6.45–7.05 horiz Qtr pack | Perf 13.4x13.1 | Die cut |
| P Island Red flowers | 2244, i | 2244A | 2244ii | 2243a | |
| 96¢ Janet Elizabeth 'Fire Dancer' | 2245, i | | 2245ii | 2243b | 2254 |
| $1.15 Memoria Evelyn Light | 2246, i | | 2246ii | 2243c | 2255 |
| $1.60 Kaleidoscope 'Conni' | 2247, i | | 2247ii | 2243d | 2256 |

For 50¢, 85¢, $1.45 Flowers see 2072–2074, 2081–2082
For 51¢, 89¢, $1.05, $1.49 Flowers see 2128–2134
For P, 93¢, $1.10, $1.55 Flowers see 2187, 2194–2197
For P, $1.00, $1.22, $1.70 Flowers see 2356–2364

**† PERMANENT™ non-denominated stamps**

The stamps identified with the symbol of a letter "P" within a red maple leaf are valid indefinitely for use within Canada. Regardless of rate increases, these definitives will be worth the Canadian domestic basic letter rate in effect, and can be used to mail a letter that weighs up to 30 grams to any address in Canada. At time of issue, the P stamps on these two pages were valued at 52¢.

## PERMANENT™ LIGHTHOUSES BOOKLETS

2249
Flag over Sambro Island Lighthouse, NS

2250
Flag over Point Clark Lighthouse, ON

2251
Flag over Cap-des-Rosiers Lighthouse, QC

2252
Flag over Warren Landing Lighthouse, MB

2253
Flag over Pachena Point Lighthouse, BC (flipped image)

2253B
Flag over Pachena Point Lighthouse, BC (corrected image)

Designer: Gottschalk+Ash Int'l.
Lithography (5 colours), self-adhesive booklets of 10 and 30
Canadian Bank Note

**2007, Dec 27 — GT4, TRC Paper**
**Serpentine Die cut 13.4**

| | | NH–VF | ⊙F | FDC |
|---|---|---|---|---|
| **2249** | P **multicoloured** (striped lighthouse) † | 1.70 | .25 | |
| **2250** | P **multicoloured** (trees to left) † | 1.70 | .25 | |
| **2251** | P **multicoloured** (water to left) † | 1.70 | .25 | |
| **2252** | P **multicoloured** (field to left) † | 1.70 | .25 | |
| **2253** | P **multicoloured** (house to left), flipped image † | 1.70 | .25 | |
| **i** | se-tenant strip of 5 (2249–2253), die cut to shape from Quarterly Pack/Annual Collection | 12.50 | — | |
| a | booklet pane of 10 x P (2 each of 2249–2253) (**BK364**) | 17.00 | | |
| **ai** | strip of 5, from 2253a/BK364 | 8.50 | | |
| **2253B** | P **multicoloured** (house at right), correct image of 2253, *May 1, 2008* † | 1.70 | .25 | * |
| **Bi** | die cut to shape from Quarterly Pack/ Annual Collection | 2.50 | — | |
| c | booklet pane of 10 x P (2 each of 2249–2252, 2253B), *Jul 2, 2008* (**BK385**) | 17.00 | | |
| d | booklet pane of 30 x P (6 each of 2249–2252, 2253B), *May 1, 2008* (**BK375**) | 50.00 | | |
| **ci** | strip of 5, from 2253c/BK385 or 2253d/BK375 | 8.50 | | |

* OFDC was not produced by Canada Post; less than 20 privately produced FDCs have been reported.

2253 and 2253B: the image supplied to Canada Post for the Pachena Point Lighthouse (2253) was incorrectly "flipped". A corrected image (2253B) was subsequently provided and issued.

Hidden within each of the Lighthouse designs, in very fine black micro-printing, is the geographical location of the illustrated lighthouse. The tagging on the left and bottom of each stamp (2249–2253B) is comprised of small waves of water.

Counterfeit booklets of 2253c (BK385) are known to exist. These are untagged.

**Nos. 2249–2253 (5) combination FDC** 7.20

2253a

2253c

2253d

## FLOWER DEFINITIVES – BOOKLETS

2254
Janet Elizabeth 'Fire Dancer'

2255
Memoria Evelyn Light

2256
Kaleidoscope 'Conni'

Designers: Monique Dufour, Sophie Lafortune.
Lithography (5 colours), self-adhesive booklets of 6
Lowe-Martin

**2007, Dec 27 — GT4, TRC Paper — Die cut**

| | | NH–VF | ⊙F | FDC |
|---|---|---|---|---|
| **2254** | **96¢ multicoloured** | 2.00 | .45 | |
| a | booklet pane of 6 x 96¢ (2254) (**BK365**) | 12.00 | | |
| **2255** | **$1.15 multicoloured** | 2.50 | .75 | |
| a | booklet pane of 6 x $1.15 (2255) (**BK366**) | 15.00 | | |
| **2256** | **$1.60 multicoloured** | 3.25 | 1.00 | |
| a | booklet pane of 6 x $1.60 (2256) (**BK367**) | 19.50 | | |

2254a

2255a

2256a

## 2008

### LUNAR NEW YEAR — 12
### Year of the Rat

2257
Bride holding parasol

2258i
Groom holding fan

Designers: Harvey Chan (i2iArt).
Lithography (9 colours) plus 1 pearlescent foil and
1 gold foil stampings plus embossing, Sheets of 50 subjects in two panes of 25
Lowe-Martin

| **2008, Jan 8** | **GT4, TRC Paper** | | **Perf 13.3x13.5** | | |
|---|---|---|---|---|---|
| | | NH–VF | ⊙F | PB | FDC |
| **2257** | **52¢ multicoloured** | 1.00 | .40 | 5.00 | 3.00 |
| Qty: 8,000,000 | | | | | |
| **2258** | **$1.60 souvenir sheet** of 1 | 4.00 | 4.00 | — | 5.20 |
| i | $1.60 single stamp from souvenir sheet | 3.50 | 3.50 | — | |
| ii | $26.95 uncut press sheet of 12 souvenir sheets | 125.00 | | | |

Qty: 2258: 750,000; 2258ii: 15,000

See also 1630, 1708, 1767–1768, 1836–1837, 1883–1884, 1933–1934, 1969–1970, 2015–2016, 2140–2141, 2201–2202. For non-denominated postal cards of same designs, see UX180–UX181.

2258

2259a

| **Rates:** | Domestic first-class (0-30g): 52¢ | |
|---|---|---|
| Jan 14/08– | Domestic first-class (30-50g): 96¢ | USA (0-30g): 96¢ |
| Jan 11/09 | Domestic oversize (0-100g): $1.15 | International (0-30g): $1.60 |

*single usage:* USA 96¢: $15.00 | International $1.60: $20.00

### CELEBRATIONS

2259
Fireworks

Designer: Michael Zavacky, McMillan.
Lithography (7 colours), self-adhesive booklet of 6
Lowe-Martin

| **2008, Jan 15** | **GT4, TRC Paper** | | | |
|---|---|---|---|---|
| | **Serpentine Die cut 13.4 horiz** | NH–VF | ⊙F | FDC |
| **2259** | **P multicoloured** | 1.70 | .40 | 3.00 |
| i | die cut to shape from Quarterly Pack/ Annual Collection | 2.50 | — | |
| a | booklet pane of 6 x P (2259) (**BK368**) | 10.00 | | |

Qty: continuous printing

At time of issue, the P stamp was valued at 52¢.

### PEONIES

*Perforated singles from water-activated gum souvenir sheet*

2260a 2260b

*Die cut singles from self-adhesive booklet*

2261
Elgin

2262
Coral 'n Gold

Designer: Isabelle Toussaint.
Lithography (6 colours)
Lowe-Martin
Water-activated gum souvenir sheet of 2

| **2008, Mar 3** | **GT4, TRC Paper** | **Perf 13.2x13.4** | | |
|---|---|---|---|---|
| | | NH–VF | ⊙F | FDC |
| **2260** | **$1.04 souvenir sheet** of 2 | 3.00 | 3.00 | — |
| a | **52¢ multicoloured** | 1.50 | 1.25 | |
| b | **52¢ multicoloured** | 1.50 | 1.25 | |
| i | se-tenant pair (2260a–b) | 3.00 | 2.50 | |

Qty: 275,000

Self-adhesive booklet of 10
**GT4, TRC Paper**
**Serpentine Die cut 13.4**

| | | NH–VF | ⊙F | FDC |
|---|---|---|---|---|
| **2261** | **52¢ multicoloured** | 1.00 | .45 | |
| **2262** | **52¢ multicoloured** | 1.00 | .45 | |
| a | se-tenant pair (2261, 2262) | 2.00 | | 4.10 |
| ai | se-tenant pair (2261, 2262), die cut to shape from Quarterly Pack | 2.00 | — | |
| c | die cutting omitted, se-tenant pair | *500.00* | | |
| b | booklet pane of 10, 5 each #2261–2262 + 10 stickers (**BK369**) | 10.00 | | |

Qty: 6,000,000 of each

For non-denominated postal cards of same designs, see UX182–UX183.
For non-denominated size 10 envelopes of same designs, see U245–U246.
The blooms of the 'Elgin' (1952) last for two to three weeks. The 'Coral 'n Gold' features a cup of bright petals surrounding golden stamens.

2260 *Image rotated* 2262b

### UNIVERSITIES

2263
University of Alberta

2264
University of British Columbia

Designer: Metaform Communication Design.

Lithography (6 colours), self-adhesive booklets of 8
Lowe-Martin

**2008, Mar 7** **GT4, TRC Paper** **Die cut 13.4**

| | | NH–VF | ⊙F | FDC |
|---|---|---|---|---|
| **2263** | **52¢ multicoloured** | 1.00 | .40 | 3.00 |
| i | die cut to shape from Quarterly Pack/ Annual Collection | 1.50 | — | |
| b | die cutting omitted, pair | *500.00* | | |
| a | booklet pane of 8 x 52¢ (2263) (**BK370**) | 8.00 | | |

Qty: 1,500,000

| | | NH–VF | ⊙F | FDC |
|---|---|---|---|---|
| **2264** | **52¢ multicoloured** | 1.00 | .40 | 3.00 |
| i | die cut to shape from Quarterly Pack/ Annual Collection | 1.50 | — | |
| a | booklet pane of 8 x 52¢ (2264) (**BK371**) | 8.00 | | |
| b | gutter pane of 4 each #2263–2264 | 15.00 | | |

Qty: 1,500,000

Issued to celebrate the 100th anniversaries of the University of Alberta and The University of British Columbia. Tagged images of the respective university logos appear in the top selvedge above each column of stamps.

For other University issues, see 1756, 1941–1944, 1973–1977, 2033–2034, 2089, 2172.

2263a

2264a

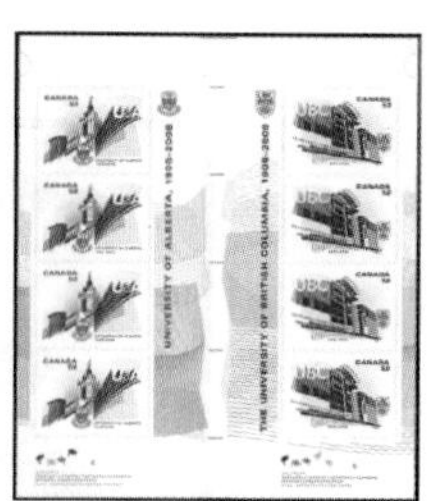
2264b

## 2008 IIHF WORLD CHAMPIONSHIP

2265
Hockey Players

Designer: Lionel Gadoury, Dave Hurds (Context Creative).

Lithography (7 colours), self-adhesive booklet of 10
Lowe-Martin

**2008, Apr 3** **GT4, TRC Paper** **Die cut 13.4x13.3**

| | | NH–VF | ⊙F | FDC |
|---|---|---|---|---|
| **2265** | **52¢ multicoloured** | 1.00 | .40 | 3.00* |
| i | die cut to shape from Quarterly Pack/ Annual Collection | 1.50 | — | |
| b | die cutting omitted, pair | *400.00* | | |
| a | booklet pane of 10 x 52¢ (2265), with Halifax images (**BK372**) | 10.00 | | |
| ai | booklet pane of 10 x 52¢ (2265), with Québec City images (**BK373**) | 10.00 | | |

Qty: 2,500,000
* Two different cachets/city cancellations produced.

International Ice Hockey Federation (IIHF) Men's World Championship held in Halifax and Québec City.

Two different booklet covers (and inside pane illustrations) were issued.

2265a

2265ai

## GUIDE DOGS

2266

Designer: Designwerke Inc.

Lithography (4 colours plus varnish) and Embossed, self-adhesive booklet of 10
Lowe-Martin

**2008, Apr 21** **GT4, TRC Paper** **Die cut 13.5x13.0**

| | | NH–VF | ⊙F | FDC |
|---|---|---|---|---|
| **2266** | **52¢ multicoloured** | 1.00 | .40 | 3.00 |
| i | die cut to shape from Quarterly Pack/ Annual Collection | 1.50 | — | |
| a | booklet pane of 10 x 52¢ (2266) (**BK374**) | 10.00 | | |

Qty: 3,500,000

Issued to coincide with the Montreal Association for the Blind's 100th anniversary. The braille within the design reads '52'.

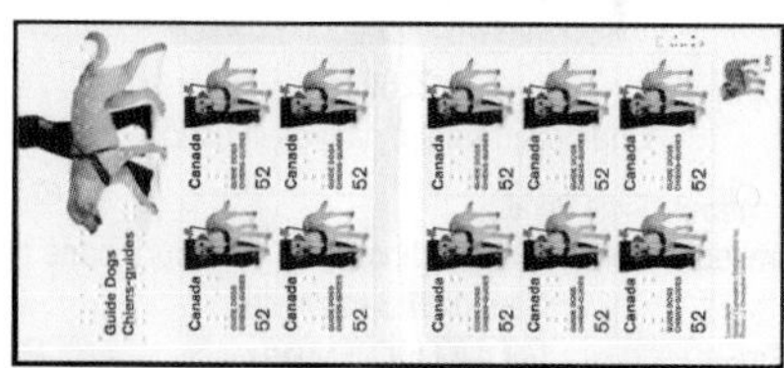
*Image rotated* 2266a

Definitive Timeline:
2008, May 1 P (52¢) Flag over Pachena Point Lighthouse (corrected image) (2253B)

## INDUSTRIES: OIL AND GAS

2267
Welder welding TransCanada Pipeline

2268
James M. Williams & Charles Tripp, Oil Springs, Ontario oil field



QE II — 2000's

Designer: Tim Nokes.

Lithography (6 colours), self-adhesive booklet of 10
Lowe-Martin

| 2008, May 2 | GT4, TRC Paper | Die cut 13.4 | | |
|---|---|---|---|---|
| | | NH–VF | ⊙F | FDC |
| **2267** | **52¢ multicoloured** | 1.00 | .40 | |
| i | die cut to shape from Quarterly Pack/ Annual Collection | 1.50 | — | |
| a | die cutting omitted, pair | 1,000.00 | | |
| **2268** | **52¢ multicoloured** | 1.00 | .40 | |
| i | die cut to shape from Quarterly Pack/ Annual Collection | 1.50 | — | |
| a | die cutting omitted, pair | 1,000.00 | | |
| b | booklet pane of 10, 5 x 52¢ (2267) and 5 x 52¢ (2268) (**BK376**) | 10.00 | | |

Qty: 1,125,000 of each

**Nos. 2267–2268 (2) combination FDC** 4.10

Commemorating the country's first commercial oil well (1858) and first transcontinental pipeline (1958).

2268b

## FOUNDING OF QUEBEC CITY

**2269**
Champlain's ship, natives in canoe

Designer: Fugazi. Engraver: Jorge Peral.

Engraved (3 colours) and Lithography (1 colour), pane of 16
Canadian Bank Note

| 2008, May 16 | GT4, TRC Paper | Perf 13.1x12.5 | | | |
|---|---|---|---|---|---|
| | | NH–VF | ⊙F | PB | FDC |
| **2269** | **52¢ deep grey-blue, sepia, brown** | 1.00 | .45 | 5.00 | 3.00 |
| i | 52¢ design printed by France, *Jun 14, 2008* † | 12.00 | 15.00* | | |
| ii | s/s, 2269i and France 3437 | 20.00 | 35.00** | | |

Qty: 2,500,000; 2269i/ii: ?

† Canadian denominated stamp printed by France on souvenir sheet with France stamp; s/s sold via Canada Post at $4.99. Stamp differences (2269i) include: tagging is pink on all four sides, the hidden Château Frontenac image is not included, paper is HB, gum is white.

* postally used in period.

** Value is for Canadian only usage; cancelled in both countries during rate period $45.00.

**Joint FDC with France** 7.00

400th anniversary of the founding of Québec City. Under an ultraviolet light, a "pink" Château Frontenac appears on the cliff in the upper right corner. Joint issue with France. See also 2044, 2115, 2155, 2226.

Joint issue with France
**Scott # 3437**

France joint issue souvenir sheet

## *ART CANADA:* YOUSUF KARSH

*Perforated singles from water-activated gum souvenir sheet*

**2270**
Yousuf Karsh (self-portrait)

**2271a**
Audrey Hepburn

**2271b**
Sir Winston Churchill

*Die cut singles from self-adhesive booklet*

**2272**
Audrey Hepburn

**2273**
Sir Winston Churchill

Designer: Hélène L'Heureux. Portraits by Yousuf Karsh, 1908–2002.

Lithography (6 colours plus varnish), pane of 16 + gutters
Lowe-Martin

| 2008, May 21 | GT4, TRC Paper | Perf 13.1x12.5 | | | |
|---|---|---|---|---|---|
| | | NH–VF | ⊙F | PB | FDC |
| **2270** | **52¢ multicoloured** | 1.00 | .45 | 5.00 | 3.00 |
| i | horizontal pair, gutter between | 2.00 | 1.00 | | |
| ii | vertical pair, gutter between | 2.00 | 1.00 | | |

Qty: 1,750,000

| | | NH–VF | ⊙F | PB | FDC |
|---|---|---|---|---|---|
| **2271** | **$3.08 souvenir sheet** of 3 | 6.00 | 6.00 | | 8.15 |
| a | **96¢ multicoloured** | 2.00 | 1.75 | | |
| b | **$1.60 multicoloured** | 3.20 | 3.00 | | |
| i | $35.12 uncut press sheet of 6 souvenir sheets and 2 panes of 2270 | 75.00 | | | |

Qty: 325,000; uncut press sheet: 3,000

Self-adhesive booklets of 8

| | GT4, TRC Paper | Die cut | | |
|---|---|---|---|---|
| | | NH–VF | ⊙F | FDC |
| **2272** | **96¢ multicoloured** | 2.00 | .90 | |
| a | booklet pane of 4 x 96¢ (2272) | 8.00 | | |
| **BK377** | two panes of 2272a $16.00 | | | |

Qty: 1,600,000

| | | NH–VF | ⊙F | FDC |
|---|---|---|---|---|
| **2273** | **$1.60 multicoloured** | 3.20 | 1.50 | |
| a | booklet pane of 4 x 1.60 (2273) | 13.00 | | |
| b | gutter pane (2272a and 2273a) | 21.00 | | |
| **BK378** | two panes of 2273a $26.00 | | | |

Qty: 1,600,000; gutter pane: 10,000

For non-denominated postal cards of same designs, see UX184–UX187.

2 x 2272a (BK377)

2 x 2273a (BK378)

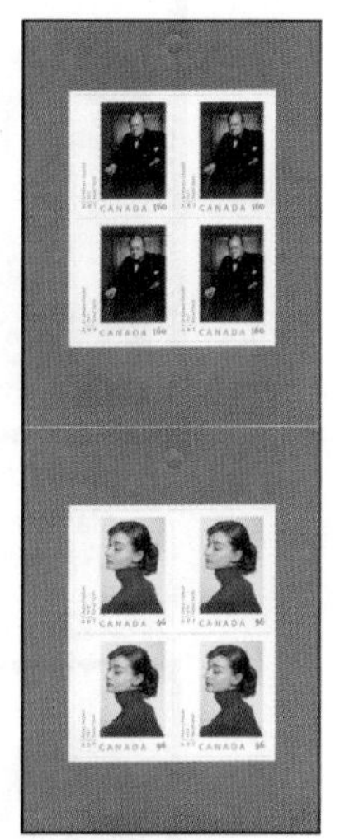

2273b

2271

2274i

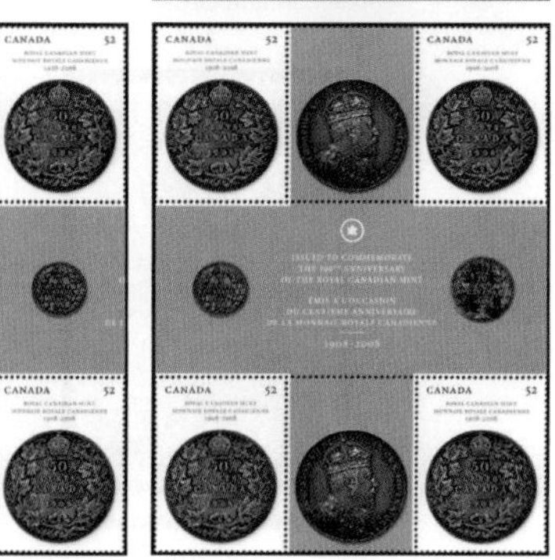

2274ii 2274iii

## ROYAL CANADIAN MINT

2274
50¢ Coin from 1908

Designer: Stéphane Huot

Lithography (6 colours) and Embossed, pane of 16 + gutters

Lowe-Martin

| 2008, Jun 4 | | GT4, TRC Paper | | Perf 12.9x13.3 | |
|---|---|---|---|---|---|
| | | NH–VF | ⊙F | PB | FDC |
| **2274** | **52¢ multicoloured** | 1.00 | .45 | 5.00 | 3.00 |
| i | horizontal pair, gutter between | 3.00 | 1.50 | | |
| ii | vertical pair, gutter between | 3.00 | 1.50 | | |
| iii | cross gutter block of 4 | 6.00 | 6.00 | | |

Qty: 2,000,000

100th anniversary of the Royal Canadian Mint in Ottawa.

## CANADIAN NURSES ASSOCIATION

2275
Working nurse in her greens

Designer: Gottschalk+Ash International

Lithography (8 colours), self-adhesive booklet of 10

Canadian Bank Note

| 2008, Jun 16 | | GT4, TRC Paper | Die cut 13.3 | |
|---|---|---|---|---|
| | | NH–VF | ⊙F | FDC |
| **2275** | **52¢ multicoloured** | 1.00 | .40 | 3.00 |
| i | die cut to shape from Quarterly Pack/ Annual Collection | 1.50 | — | |
| a | booklet pane of 10 x 52¢ (2275) (**BK379**) | 10.00 | | |

Qty: 2,500,000

100th anniversary of the Canadian Nurses Association.

2275a

## ANNE OF GREEN GABLES

*Perforated singles from water-activated gum souvenir sheet*

2276a 2276b

*Die cut singles from self-adhesive booklet*

2277
Anne of Green Gables

2278
Green Gables

2276

Designer: Dennis Page, Oliver Hill (Trampoline)

Lithography (7 colours)
Lowe-Martin
Water-activated gum souvenir sheet of 2

**2008, Jun 20** **GT 3 sides, TRC Paper** **Perf 13.5x13.3**

| | | NH–VF | ⊙F | FDC |
|---|---|---|---|---|
| **2276** | **$1.04 souvenir sheet** of 2 | 3.00 | 3.00 | 4.10 |
| a | **52¢ multicoloured** | 1.50 | 1.25 | |
| b | **52¢ multicoloured** | 1.50 | 1.25 | |
| i | se-tenant pair (2276a–b) | 3.00 | 2.50 | |

Qty: 350,000

Self-adhesive booklet of 10
**GT 3 sides, TRC Paper**
**Serpentine Die cut 13.3x13.0**

| | | NH–VF | ⊙F | FDC |
|---|---|---|---|---|
| **2277** | **52¢ multicoloured** | 1.00 | .45 | |
| **2278** | **52¢ multicoloured** | 1.00 | .45 | |
| i | se-tenant pair (2277, 2278), die cut to shape from Quarterly Pack | 3.00 | — | |
| b | die cutting omitted, pair (2277, 2278) | *500.00* | | |
| a | booklet pane of 10, 5 each #2277–2278 + 10 stickers (**BK380**) | 10.00 | | |

Qty: 6,000,000 of each

**Nos. 2277–2278 (2) combination FDC** 4.10*
* Two different cachets produced.

For non-denominated postal cards of same designs, see UX188–UX189.
100th anniversary of publication of *Anne of Green Gables* in Boston by Lucy Maud Montgomery.
Joint issue with Japan.

2278a

Joint issue with Japan
**Scott # 3028**

## CANADIANS IN HOLLYWOOD: THE SEQUEL

*Perforated singles from water-activated gum souvenir sheet*

**2279a**
Norma Shearer
(1900–1983)

**2279b**
Chief Dan George
(1899–1981)

**2279**

**2279c**
Marie Dressler
(1868–1934)

**2279d**
Raymond Burr
(1917–1993)

*Die cut singles from self-adhesive booklet*

**2280a**
Marie Dressler

**2280b**
Chief Dan George

**2280c**
Norma Shearer

**2280d**
Raymond Burr

**2 x 2280 (BK381)**

**2 x 2280i (BK382)**

**2 x 2280ii (BK383)**

**2 x 2280iii (BK384)**

Designer: John Belisle, Kosta Tsetsekas, Geoff Kehrig (Signals).

Lithography (5 colours) and varnish, water-activated gum souvenir sheet of 4
Canadian Bank Note

| 2008, Jun 30 | GT4, Spicer Paper | Perf 13.1x12.5 | | |
|---|---|---|---|---|
| | | NH–VF | ⊙F | FDC |
| 2279 | **$2.08 souvenir sheet** of 4 | 6.00 | 6.00 | 6.15 |
| a | **52¢ multicoloured** | 1.50 | 1.25 | |
| b | **52¢ multicoloured** | 1.50 | 1.25 | |
| c | **52¢ multicoloured** | 1.50 | 1.25 | |
| d | **52¢ multicoloured** | 1.50 | 1.25 | |

Qty: 300,000

Lithography (5 colours plus varnish),
Sheets of 96 subjects in 12 self-adhesive booklets of 8
Canadian Bank Note

| 2008, Jun 30 | GT4, Spicer Paper<br>Serpentine Die cut 13.3 | | | |
|---|---|---|---|---|
| | | NH–VF | ⊙F | FDC |
| 2280 | booklet pane of 4 x 52¢ (a–d) + 4 stickers, pane with Marie Dressler at upper left | 4.00 | — | |
| a | **52¢ multicoloured** | 1.00 | .40 | |
| b | **52¢ multicoloured** | 1.00 | .40 | |
| c | **52¢ multicoloured** | 1.00 | .40 | |
| d | **52¢ multicoloured** | 1.00 | .40 | |
| i | booklet pane of 4 x 52¢ (a–d) + 4 stickers, pane with Chief Dan George at upper left | 4.00 | — | |
| ii | booklet pane of 4 x 52¢ (a–d) + 4 stickers, pane with Norma Shearer at upper left | 4.00 | — | |
| iii | booklet pane of 4 x 52¢ (a–d) + 4 stickers, pane with Raymond Burr at upper left | 4.00 | — | |
| BK381 | two panes of 2280 (Marie Dressler cover) $8.00 | | | |
| BK382 | two panes of 2280i (Chief Dan George cover) $8.00 | | | |
| BK383 | two panes of 2280ii (Norma Shearer cover) $8.00 | | | |
| BK384 | two panes of 2280iii (Raymond Burr cover) $8.00 | | | |

Qty: 1,125,000 of each stamp.

Honouring the accomplishments of film and television Canadian actors who became stars in Hollywood.

For non-denominated postal cards of same designs, see UX190–UX193.

## 2008 BEIJING SUMMER OLYMPICS

2281
Athlete and Flag

Designer: q30design inc.

Lithography (6 colours), self-adhesive booklet of 10
Lowe-Martin

| 2008, Jul 18 | GT4, TRC Paper | Die cut 13.4 | | |
|---|---|---|---|---|
| | | NH–VF | ⊙F | FDC |
| 2281 | **52¢ multicoloured** | 1.00 | .40 | 3.00 |
| i | die cut to shape from Quarterly Pack/ Annual Collection | 1.50 | — | |
| b | die cutting omitted, strip of 3 | *1,250.00* | | |
| a | booklet pane of 10 x 52¢ (2281) (BK386) | 10.00 | | |

Qty: 2,500,000

2281a

*Image rotated*

## LIFESAVING SOCIETY CENTENNIAL

2282
"valley" at upper left

2282i
"peak" at upper left

Designer: Derwin Goodall.

Lithography (7 colours plus varnish), self-adhesive booklet of 10
Lowe-Martin

| 2008, Jul 25 | GT4, TRC Paper | Die cut 13.3x12.7 | | |
|---|---|---|---|---|
| | | NH–VF | ⊙F | FDC |
| 2282 | **52¢ multicoloured**, valley at upper left | 1.00 | .40 | 3.00 |
| i | peak at upper left | 1.00 | .40 | 3.00 |
| ii | as 2282, die cut to shape from Quarterly Pack/ Annual Collection | 1.50 | — | |
| iii | as 2282i, die cut to shape from Quarterly Pack/ Annual Collection | 1.50 | — | |
| a | booklet pane of 10 x 52¢ (5 x 2282 and 5 x 2282i) (BK387) | 10.00 | | |

Qty: 2,250,000

The five stamps from the left panel of the booklet start with a "valley" at the upper left of the die cut (2282); the five stamps from the right panel start with a "peak" at the upper left (2282i).

2282a

## BRITISH COLUMBIA SESQUICENTENNIAL

2283
Map of BC, panning for gold

Designer: Subplot Design Inc.

Lithography (6 colours plus varnish), self-adhesive pane of 16
Lowe-Martin

| 2008, Aug 1 | GT4, TRC Paper | Perf 12.5x13.1 | | | |
|---|---|---|---|---|---|
| | | VF* | ⊙F | PB* | FDC |
| 2283 | **52¢ multicoloured** | 1.00 | .45 | 5.00(LL) | 3.00 |

Qty: 2,000,000

* Price is for stamps with backing paper. Stamps are fully perforated — the fourth time self-adhesive stamps were printed this way in Canada. Only the lower left imprint block includes the colour dots and paper designation. The backing paper includes nine images, some covering several stamps.

150th anniversary of the founding of the Province of British Columbia.

## ROBERT SAMUEL McLAUGHLIN

**2284**
McLaughlin-Buick, McLaughlin (1871–1972)

Designer: Tiit Telmet, Marko Barac.

Lithography (7 colours), Sheets of 64 subjects in four panes of 16
Lowe-Martin

| 2008, Sep 8 | GT4, TRC Paper | Perf 12.5x13.1 | | |
|---|---|---|---|---|
| | VF | ⊙F | PB | FDC |
| **2284 52¢ multicoloured** | 1.00 | .45 | 5.00 | 3.00 |

Qty: 2,000,000

## ENDANGERED SPECIES — 3

*Perforated singles from water-activated gum souvenir sheet*

**2285a**
Prothonotary Warbler

**2285b**
Taylor's Checkerspot Butterfly

**2285c**
Roseate Tern

**2285d**
Burrowing Owl

*Die cut singles from self-adhesive booklet*

**2286**
Prothonotary Warbler

**2287**
Taylor's Checkerspot Butterfly

**2288**
Roseate Tern

**2289**
Burrowing Owl

Designer: Sputnik Design Partners Inc.

Lithography (9 colours)
Lowe-Martin
Water-activated gum souvenir sheet of 4 + 4 tabs

| 2008, Oct 1 | GT4, TRC Paper | Perf 13.4 | | |
|---|---|---|---|---|
| | | NH–VF | ⊙F | FDC |
| 2285 | **$2.08 souvenir sheet** of 4 | 4.00 | 4.00 | — |
| a | **52¢ multicoloured** | 1.00 | 1.00 | |
| b | **52¢ multicoloured** | 1.00 | 1.00 | |
| c | **52¢ multicoloured** | 1.00 | 1.00 | |
| d | **52¢ multicoloured** | 1.00 | 1.00 | |

Qty: 200,000

Self-adhesive booklet of 8

| | GT4, TRC Paper | | | Die cut |
|---|---|---|---|---|
| | | NH–VF | ⊙F | FDC |
| **2286** | **52¢ multicoloured** | 1.00 | .45 | |
| **2287** | **52¢ multicoloured** | 1.00 | .45 | |
| **2288** | **52¢ multicoloured** | 1.00 | .45 | |
| **2289** | **52¢ multicoloured** | 1.00 | .45 | |
| a | block of four (2286–2289) | 5.00 | | 6.15* |
| b | booklet pane, 2 # 2289a (**BK388**) | 10.00 | | |

Qty: 750,000 of each

* Stamps on FDCs are not die cut all the way through.

The 2008 series features four endangered creatures of the sky. See also 2173–2177, 2229–2233.

**2285**

**2289b**

Timeline:
2008, Oct 6 (52¢)+10¢ Mental Health, semi-postal (B14)

## XII SUMMIT OF LA FRANCOPHONIE

**2290**
Skyline of Québec City

Designer: Marc-André Grenier.

Lithography (7 colours plus varnish), pane of 16
Canadian Bank Note

| 2008, Oct 15 | GT4, TRC Paper | Perf 12.5x13.2 | | |
|---|---|---|---|---|
| | VF | ⊙F | PB | FDC |
| **2290 52¢ multicoloured** | 1.00 | .45 | 5.00 | 3.00 |

Qty: 1,500,000

Issued to mark the XII Summit of la Francophonie that took place in Québec City from October 17–19, 2008. The names of the participating countries are listed across the top half of the stamp.

## CHRISTMAS

*Perforated singles from water-activated gum souvenir sheet*

**2291a**

**2291b**

**2291c**

*Die cut singles from self-adhesive booklet*

2293
Snow Angel

2294
Skiing

2295
Tobogganing

2292
The Nativity

Designer: Susan Scott.

Lithography (8 colours)
Lowe-Martin
Water-activated gum souvenir sheet of 3

**2008, Nov 3** **GT4, TRC Paper** **Perf 13.4**

| | | NH–VF | ⊙F | FDC |
|---|---|---|---|---|
| **2291** | **$3.08 souvenir sheet** of 3 | 7.00 | 7.00 | 8.15 |
| a | **P multicoloured** | 1.75 | 1.50 | |
| b | **96¢ multicoloured** | 2.00 | 2.00 | |
| c | **$1.60 multicoloured** | 3.20 | 3.20 | |

Qty: 250,000

Designer: Joseph Gault. Sculptor: Antonio Caruso.

Lithography (6 colours), self-adhesive booklet of 12
Lowe-Martin

**2008, Nov 3** **GT4, TRC Paper** **Serpentine Die cut 13.4**

| | | NH–VF | ⊙F | FDC |
|---|---|---|---|---|
| **2292** | **P multicoloured** * | 1.70 | .25 | 3.00 |
| i | die cut to shape from Quarterly Pack/ Annual Collection | 2.50 | — | |
| b | die cutting omitted, pair | *800.00* | | |
| a | booklet pane of 6 x P (2292) | 10.00 | — | |
| BK390 | two panes of 2292a $20.00 | | | |

Qty: 24,000,000
* See 2343a for water-activated gum single from souvenir sheet, perf 13.0x12.5 variety of 2292.

Designer: Susan Scott.

Lithography (8 colours), self-adhesive booklet of 12 (P) or 6
Lowe-Martin

**2008, Nov 3** **GT4, TRC Paper**
**Serpentine Die cut 13.7**

| | | NH–VF | ⊙F | FDC |
|---|---|---|---|---|
| **2293** | **P multicoloured** | 1.70 | .25 | — |
| i | die cut to shape from Quarterly Pack | 2.50 | — | |
| a | booklet pane of 6 x P (2293) | 10.00 | — | |
| BK391 | two panes of 2293a $20.00 | | | |

Qty: 30,000,000

| | | NH–VF | ⊙F | FDC |
|---|---|---|---|---|
| **2294** | **96¢ multicoloured** | 2.00 | .75 | — |
| i | die cut to shape from Quarterly Pack | 3.00 | — | |
| a | booklet pane of 6 x 96¢ (2294) (BK392) | 12.00 | — | |

Qty: 6,600,000

| | | NH–VF | ⊙F | FDC |
|---|---|---|---|---|
| **2295** | **$1.60 multicoloured** | 3.20 | 1.25 | — |
| i | die cut to shape from Quarterly Pack | 5.00 | — | |
| a | booklet pane of 6 x $1.60 (2295) (BK393) | 19.50 | — | |
| b | gutter pane, 2294a and 2295a | 35.00 | | |

Qty: 6,000,000; gutter pane: 8,000

At time of issue, the P Christmas stamps were valued at 52¢.

2291

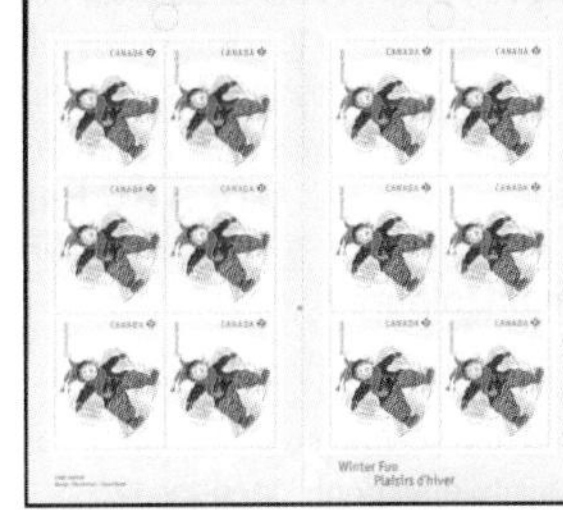
2 x 2293a (BK391)

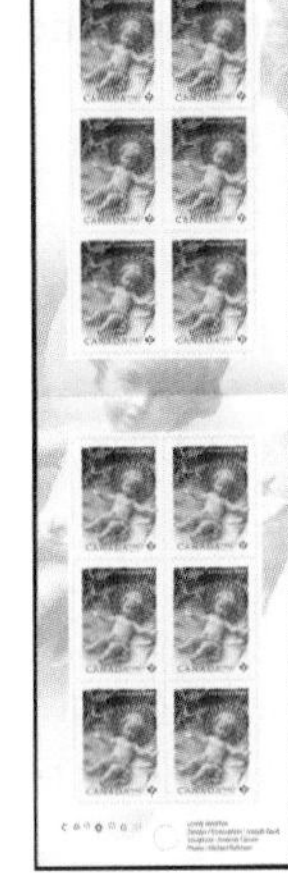
2 x 2292a (BK390)

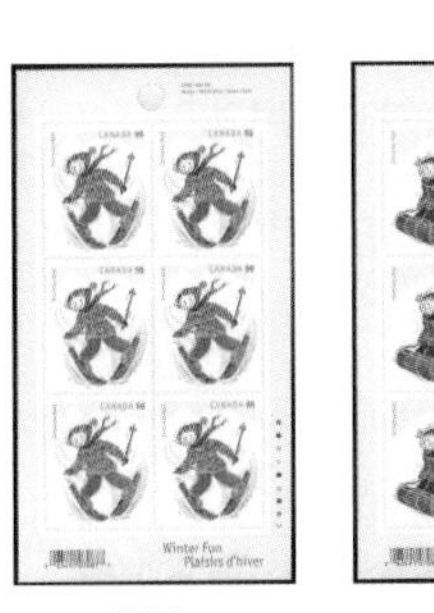
2294a 2295a

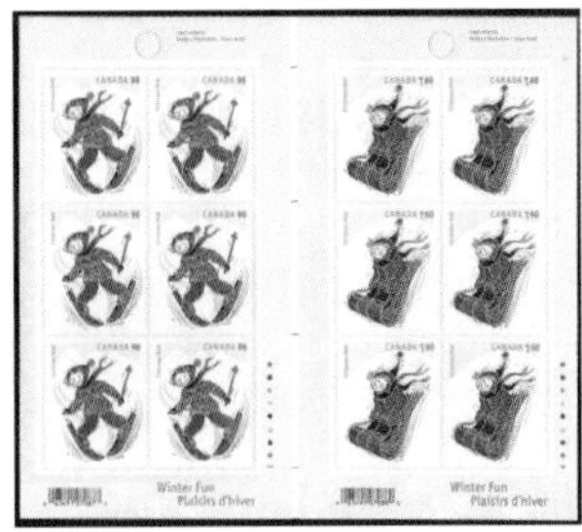
2295b

## 2009

### LUNAR NEW YEAR (Series 2) — I
### Year of the Ox

2296
Ox

2297i
Pottery

2297

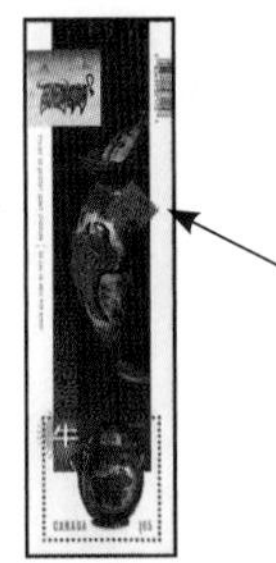
2297a

QE II — 2000's

Designer: Ivan Novotny (Taylor|Sprules Corporation). Pottery: Shu-Hwei Kao.
Lithography (6 colours) plus 2 foil stampings and embossing plus varnish, pane of 25
Lowe-Martin, Gravure Choquet

**2009, Jan 8** **GT4, TRC Paper** **Perf 12.5**

| | | NH–VF | ⊙F | PB | FDC |
|---|---|---|---|---|---|
| **2296** | **multicoloured** | 1.70 | .40 | 8.50 | 3.10 |

Qty: 7,500,000

At time of issue, the P stamp was valued at 54¢ even though the 54¢ domestic rate did not go into effect until January 12.

**Single stamp General Tagged on left, right and bottom**

| | | | | | |
|---|---|---|---|---|---|
| 2297 | **$1.65 souvenir sheet** of 1 | 3.30 | 3.30 | — | 5.30 |
| a | overprinted souvenir sheet of 1 | 4.50 | 4.50 | — | |
| i | $1.65 single stamp from souvenir sheet | 3.00 | 3.00 | — | |
| ii | $28.95 uncut press sheet of 12 souvenir sheets | 75.00 | | | |

Qty: 2297: 750,000; 2297a:200,000; 2297ii: 25,000

For non-denominated postal cards of same designs, see UX194–UX195.

| **Rates:** | Domestic first-class (0-30g): 54¢ | USA (0-30g): 98¢ |
|---|---|---|
| Jan 12/09– | Domestic first-class (30-50g): 96¢ | USA (30-50g): $1.18 |
| Jan 10/10 | Domestic oversize (0-100g): $1.15 | International (0-30g): $1.65 |

*single usage:* USA 98¢: $15.00 | International $1.65: $20.00

## QUEEN ELIZABETH II

**2298**
Queen Elizabeth II

Designers: Gottschalk+Ash International.
Lithography (5 colours), self-adhesive booklet of 10
Canadian Bank Note

**2009, Jan 12** **GT4, TRC Paper**
**Serpentine Die cut 13.4**

| | | NH–VF | ⊙F | FDC |
|---|---|---|---|---|
| **2298** | **multicoloured (QE II)** † | 1.70 | .25 | 3.00 |
| i | die cut to shape from Quarterly Pack/ Annual Collection | 2.50 | — | |
| a | booklet pane of 10 x P (2298) (BK394) | 17.00 | | |

Some of the tagging along the top right portion of each stamp (2298) is comprised of small crowns.

Counterfeit booklets of 2298a (BK394) are known to exist. These are untagged.

**2298a**

## OLYMPIC SPORTING EVENTS – DEFINITIVES SOUVENIR SHEET

*Perforated singles from water-activated gum souvenir sheet*

**2299a**
Curling

**2299b**
Bobsledding

**2299c**
Snowboarding

**2299d**
Freestyle skiing

**2299e**
Ice-sled hockey

Designers: John Belisle, Kosta Tsetsekas (Signals Vancouver).
Lithography (5 colours)
Canadian Bank Note
Water-activated gum souvenir sheet of 5

**2009, Jan 12** **GT4, TRC Paper** **Perf 13.4x13.0**

| | | NH–VF | ⊙F | FDC |
|---|---|---|---|---|
| **2299** | **$2.70 souvenir sheet** of 5 † | 8.50 | 8.50 | 7.50 |
| a | **multicoloured**, curling | 1.70 | 1.50 | |
| b | **multicoloured**, bobsledding | 1.70 | 1.50 | |
| c | **multicoloured**, snowboarding | 1.70 | 1.50 | |
| d | **multicoloured**, freestyle skiing | 1.70 | 1.50 | |
| e | **multicoloured**, ice-sled hockey | 1.70 | 1.50 | |
| f | souvenir sheet with silver 'VANCOUVER/2010' overprint in selvedge*, *Jun 15/09* | 25.00 | | |

Qty: 2299f: 50,000

* available in coin/stamp set ($49.95); released at face value ($2.70) Feb 12/10. One sheet with the overprint in *gold* has been reported.

The stamps have extra tagging elements (tiny maple leafs) throughout the white portions of the design. Hidden within each of the Olympic sporting designs, in very fine micro-printing, is the name of the sport.

For non-denominated postal cards of same designs, see UX196–UX200.

**2299**

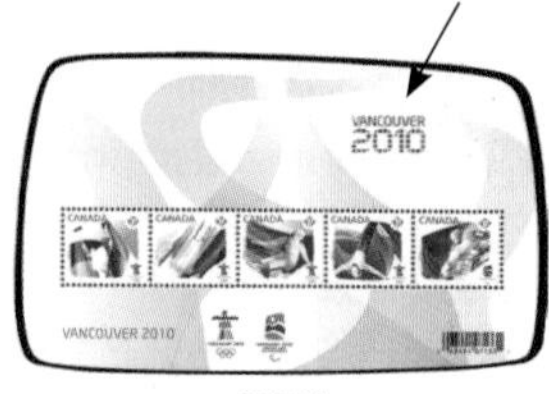

**2299f**

Tagging (as viewed under an ultraviolet light) on Olympic Sporting Event definitives. The tagging is the same on stamps from booklets and the souvenir sheet.

## OLYMPIC DEFINITIVES – BOOKLETS

*Die cut singles from self-adhesive booklet*

**2300**
Freestyle skiing

**2301**
Ice-sled hockey

**2302**
Bobsledding

**2303**
Curling

**2304**
Snowboarding

Designer: John Belisle, Kosta Tsetsekas (Signals Vancouver).
Lithography (5 colours), self-adhesive booklets of 10 and 30
Canadian Bank Note

**2009, Jan 12** **GT4, TRC Paper**
**Serpentine Die cut 13.4**

| | | NH–VF | ⊙F | FDC |
|---|---|---|---|---|
| **2300** | **multicoloured**, freestyle skiing † | 1.70 | .25 | — |
| **2301** | **multicoloured**, ice-sled hockey † | 1.70 | .25 | — |
| **2302** | **multicoloured**, bobsledding † | 1.70 | .25 | — |
| **2303** | **multicoloured**, curling † | 1.70 | .25 | — |
| **2304** | **multicoloured**, snowboarding † | 1.70 | .25 | — |
| i | se-tenant strip of 5 (2300–2304), die cut to shape from Quarterly Pack/Annual Collection | 12.50 | — | |
| a | booklet pane of 10 x P (2 each of 2300–2304) (**BK395**) | 17.00 | | |
| b | booklet pane of 30 x P (6 each of 2300–2304) (**BK396**) | 50.00 | | |
| **ai** | strip of 5, from 2304a/BK395 or 2304b/BK396 | 8.50 | | |

The stamps have extra tagging elements (tiny maple leafs) throughout the white portions of the design. Hidden within each of the Olympic sporting designs, in very fine micro-printing, is the name of the sport.

Counterfeit booklets of 2304a (BK395) are known to exist. These are untagged.

**2304a**

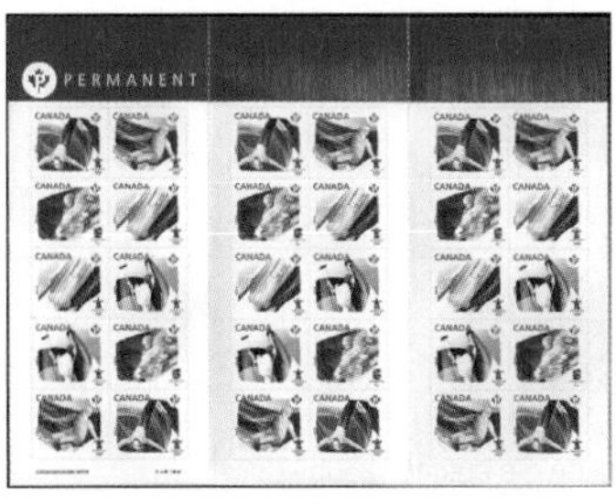

**2304b**

† **PERMANENT™ non-denominated stamps**

The stamps identified with the symbol of a letter "P" within a red maple leaf are valid indefinitely for use within Canada. Regardless of rate increases, these definitives will be worth the Canadian domestic basic letter rate in effect, and can be used to mail a letter that weighs up to 30 grams to any address in Canada. At time of issue, the P stamps issued in January and February 2009 were valued at 54¢.

## OLYMPIC EMBLEMS and MASCOTS – DEFINITIVES SOUVENIR SHEET

**2305a**
Vancouver 2010 emblem

**2305b**
Paralympic emblem

**2305c**
Miga

**2305d**
Sumi

**2305e**
Quatchi

Designers: VANOC/COVAN; Tandem Design Associates Ltd.
Lithography (5 colours)
Lowe-Martin
Water-activated gum souvenir sheet of 5

**2009, Feb 12** **GT4, TRC Paper** **Perf 13.4x13.0**

| | | NH–VF | ⊙F | FDC |
|---|---|---|---|---|
| **2305** | **$4.89 souvenir sheet** of 5 † | 11.25 | 11.25 | 11.75 |
| a | **multicoloured**, Vancouver 2010 | 1.75 | 1.50 | |
| b | **multicoloured**, Paralympics | 1.75 | 1.50 | |
| c | **98¢ multicoloured** | 2.00 | 2.00 | |
| d | **$1.18 multicoloured** | 2.40 | 2.40 | |
| e | **$1.65 multicoloured** | 3.30 | 3.30 | |
| f | souvenir sheet with bronze 'VANCOUVER/2010' overprint in selvedge*, *Jun 15/09* | 25.00 | | |

Qty: 2305f: 50,000
* available in coin/stamp set ($49.95); released at face value ($4.89) Feb 12/10.

A single souvenir sheet (Scott 2305) has been reported imperforate.

The stamps have extra tagging elements throughout the white portions of the design.

For non-denominated postal cards of same designs, see UX201–UX203.

**2305**

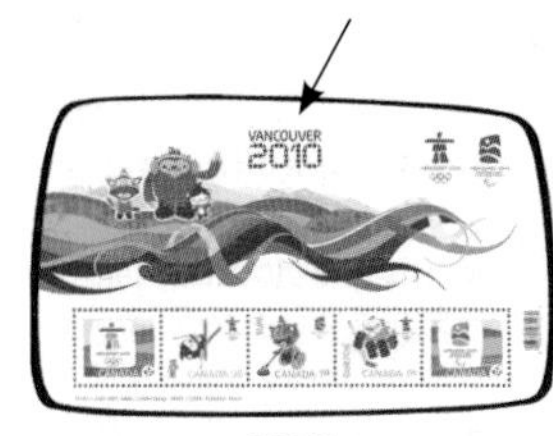

**2305f**

Tagging (as viewed under an ultraviolet light) on Olympic Emblem and Mascot definitives. The tagging is the same on stamps from coils, booklets, and the souvenir sheet.

## OLYMPIC EMBLEMS and MASCOTS – DEFINITIVES COILS

**2306**
Vancouver 2010 emblem

**2307**
Paralympic emblem

**2307A**
Vancouver 2010 emblem

**2307B**
Paralympic emblem

**2308**
Miga

**2309**
Sumi

**2310**
Quatchi

Designers: VANOC/COVAN; Tandem Design Associates Ltd.
Lithography (5 colours), self-adhesive rolls of 100 (P) and 5,000 (P) and 50 (98¢, $1.18, $1.65)
Lowe-Martin

**2009, Jan 12 GT4, TRC Paper**
**Serpentine Die cut 9.2 horiz (Rounded tips)**

| | | NH–VF | ⊙F | FDC |
|---|---|---|---|---|
| **2306** | **multicoloured**, Vancouver 2010 † | 2.00 | 2.00 | — |
| **2307** | **multicoloured**, Paralympics † | 2.00 | 2.00 | — |

2306 and 2307 issued in separate horizontal rolls of 5,000 each. Individual stamps do not touch along the horizontal roll; rounded 'perf tips' start with a valley. Sold in strips of 4 or 10 by the National Philatelic Centre; single stamps included in the Quarterly Pack/Annual Collection.

Three different die cut patterns were used. The first pattern had a 'perf' range of 8.10–9.60 (with 4 nibs). A second pattern has a range of 7.85 to 8.85 (with 3 nibs; used only on P and 98¢ stamps). A third pattern (used on the P, 98¢ and $1.18 stamps) is a combination of the first two patterns — the ninth row of die cutting is from the first pattern (measuring 9.35–9.60 with 4 nibs) while the other rows are from the second pattern (with 3 nibs, 7.85–8.85). This produces a full 1½ 'perf' difference on the same stamp. Every stamp on each of the 100-subject (10x10) die cutting mats is different due to variations occurring on the top and bottom of a single stamp.

**2009, Jan 12 GT4, TRC Paper**
**Serpentine Die cut 7.85 to 9.60 Horiz (Sawtooth tips)**

| | | NH–VF | ⊙F | FDC |
|---|---|---|---|---|
| **2307A** | **multicoloured**, Vancouver 2010 † | 1.70 | .25 | — |
| i | die cut to shape (9.2 horiz) from Quarterly Pack, *Apr '09* ‡ | 4.00 | — | |
| ii | 'compound' die cut 9.30–9.60 one edge only§ | 4.00 | 1.50 | |
| **2307B** | **multicoloured**, Paralympics † | 1.70 | .25 | — |
| c | se-tenant pair (vert.), 2307A–2307B | 3.40 | | |
| i | gutter strip of 4 (2 each 2307A, 2307B), with inscription | 8.50 | | |
| | starter strip of 4 (2 each 2307A, 2307B), (wavy die cut) | 12.50 | | |
| | end strip of 4 (2 each 2307A, 2307B), (wavy die cut) | 12.50 | | |

| | | NH–VF | ⊙F | FDC |
|---|---|---|---|---|
| ii | die cut to shape (9.2 horiz) from Quarterly Pack, *Apr '09* ‡ | 4.00 | — | |
| iii | 'compound' die cut 9.30–9.60 one edge only§ | 4.00 | 1.50 | |
| | as iii, compound die cut in gutter strip of 6§ | 20.00 | | |
| **2308** | **98¢ multicoloured** | 2.00 | .45 | — |
| i | gutter strip of 4 with inscription | 14.00 | | |
| | starter strip of 4 (wavy die cut) | 16.00 | | |
| | end strip of 4 (wavy die cut) | 16.00 | | |
| ii | die cut to shape (9.2 horiz) from Quarterly Pack, *Apr '09* ‡ | 5.50 | — | |
| iii | 'compound' die cut 9.30–9.60 one edge only§ | 15.00 | 4.00 | |
| | as iii, compound die cut in gutter strip of 6§ | 45.00 | | |
| **2309** | **$1.18 multicoloured**, *Feb 12, 2009* | 2.50 | .75 | 4.35 |
| i | gutter strip of 4 with inscription | 15.50 | | |
| | starter strip of 4 (wavy die cut) | 18.00 | | |
| | end strip of 4 (wavy die cut) | 18.00 | | |
| ii | die cut to shape (9.2 horiz) from Quarterly Pack, *Apr '09* ‡ | 6.50 | — | |
| iii | 'compound' die cut 9.30–9.60 one edge only§ | 20.00 | 5.00 | |
| | as iii, compound die cut in gutter strip of 6§ | 55.00 | | |
| **2310** | **$1.65 multicoloured** | 3.30 | 1.00 | — |
| i | gutter strip of 4 with inscription | 19.00 | | |
| | starter strip of 4 (wavy die cut) | 22.00 | | |
| | end strip of 4 (wavy die cut) | 22.00 | | |
| ii | die cut to shape (9.2 horiz) from Quarterly Pack, *Apr '09* ‡ | 8.00 | — | |

‡ Single coil stamps supplied in the Quarterly Pack have rounded tips, starting with a peak at upper left; stamps from the full rolls have sawtooth tips.

§ One of the eleven rows of die cutting from this printing had a measurement of 9.30–9.60. The adjacent rows measure 7.85 to 8.20. This is a full 1½ 'perf' difference on the same stamp.

| | |
|---|---|
| **Nos. 2307A–2307B (2) combination FDC** | **4.15** |
| **Nos. 2308, 2310 (2) combination FDC** | **7.25** |

Serpentine die cutting (2306–2313):

| "Saw tooth" | "Rounded"; valley start | "Rounded"; peak start |
|---|---|---|
| Rolls of 50/100 (2307A–2310) (peak/valley purely random) | Booklet of 6 and booklet singles from Qtr pack Roll of 5,000 (2306–2307, 2311–2313, 2311i, 2312i, 2313i) | Single coil from Qtr pack (2307Ai, 2307Bii, 2308ii, 2309ii, 2310ii) |

| *Format:* | Coil | | | Souvenir sheet | Booklet | |
|---|---|---|---|---|---|---|
| *Die cut/perf:* | 7.85–9.60 horiz | 9.2 horiz | 9.2 horiz Qtr pack | Perf 13.4x13.1 | 9.2 horiz | 9.2 horiz Qtr pack |
| Vancouver 2010 emblem | 2307A | 2306 | 2307Ai | 2305a | | |
| Paralympic emblem | 2307B | 2307 | 2307Bii | 2305b | | |
| 98¢ Miga | 2308 | | 2308ii | 2305c | 2311 | 2311i |
| $1.18 Sumi | 2309 | | 2309ii | 2305d | 2312 | 2312i |
| $1.65 Quatchi | 2310 | | 2310ii | 2305e | 2313 | 2313i |

## OLYMPIC EMBLEMS and MASCOTS – DEFINITIVES BOOKLETS

2311
Miga

2312
Sumi

2313
Quatchi

Designers: VANOC/COVAN; Tandem Design Associates Ltd.
Lithography (5 colours), self-adhesive booklets of 6
Lowe-Martin

**2009, Jan 12 GT4, TRC Paper**
**Serpentine Die cut 9.2 horiz (Rounded tips)**

| | | NH–VF | ⊙F | FDC |
|---|---|---|---|---|
| **2311** | **98¢ multicoloured** | 2.00 | .45 | — |
| i | die cut to shape from Quarterly Pack ‡ | 5.50 | — | |
| a | booklet pane of 6 x 98¢ (2311) (**BK397**) | 12.00 | | |
| **2312** | **$1.18 multicoloured**, *Feb 12, 2009* | 2.50 | .75 | — |
| i | die cut to shape from Quarterly Pack ‡ | 6.50 | — | |
| a | booklet pane of 6 x $1.18 (2312) (**BK398**) | 15.00 | | |
| **2313** | **$1.65 multicoloured** | 3.30 | 1.00 | — |
| i | die cut to shape from Quarterly Pack ‡ | 8.00 | — | |
| a | booklet pane of 6 x $1.65 (2313) (**BK399**) | 19.50 | | |

A single used counterfeit of the $1.65 has been reported.

‡ Single stamps from booklets of 6 *and* single stamps supplied in the Quarterly packs all start with a valley at the upper left.

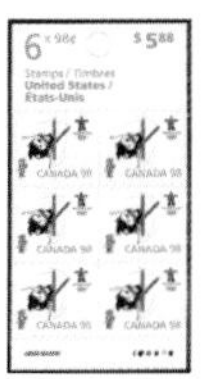
2311a

2312a

2313a

## CELEBRATION

2314
'Celebration in the Mail'

Designer: Debbie Adams.
Lithography (7 colours), self-adhesive booklet of 6
Lowe-Martin

**2009, Feb 2 GT4, TRC Paper**
**Serpentine Die cut 13.4 horiz**

| | | NH–VF | ⊙F | FDC |
|---|---|---|---|---|
| **2314** | **P multicoloured** | 1.70 | .40 | 3.00 |
| i | die cut to shape from Quarterly Pack/ Annual Collection | 2.50 | — | |
| a | booklet pane of 6 x P (2314) (**BK400**) | 10.00 | | |

Qty: continuous printing

At time of issue, the P stamp was valued at 54¢.

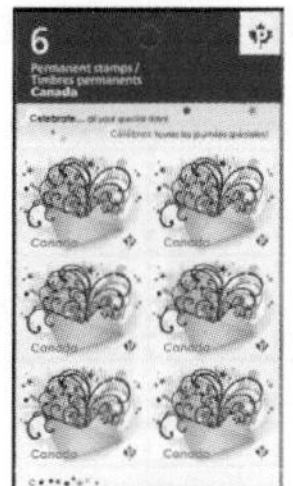
2314a

## BLACK HISTORY MONTH

2315
Rosemary Brown
(1930–2003)

2316
Abraham Doras Shadd
(1801–1882)

Designer: Lime Design Inc.
Lithography (5 colours plus varnish), pane of 16 + horizontal gutter
Canadian Bank Note

**2009, Feb 2 GT4, TRC Paper Perf 13.1x12.5**

| | | NH–VF | ⊙F | PB | FDC |
|---|---|---|---|---|---|
| **2315** | **54¢ multicoloured** | 1.00 | .40 | | |
| **2316** | **54¢ multicoloured** | 1.00 | .40 | | |
| **a** | se-tenant pair (2315, 2316) | 2.00 | 1.50 | 5.00(LR) | 4.15 |
| **i** | vertical pair (2315, 2316), gutter between | 2.00 | 1.50 | | |

Qty: 1,000,000 of each

These stamps were initially announced as Permanent™-valued but released denominated at 54¢. Brown was the first Black woman elected to public office in Canada; Shadd played a major role in the Undergound Railroad and was the first Black person to serve in Canadian public office.

## FIRST FLIGHT IN CANADA

2317
*Silver Dart*'s maiden flight

Designer: Crystal Oicle, Dennis Page (trampoline).
Lithography (5 colours), Self-adhesive pane of 16
Lowe-Martin

**2009, Feb 23 GT4, TRC Paper Perf 12.5x13.1**

| | | VF* | ⊙F | PB | FDC |
|---|---|---|---|---|---|
| **2317** | **P multicoloured** | 1.70 | .45 | 8.50 | 3.00 |

Qty: 3,000,000

* Price is for stamps on original backing paper. Stamps are fully perforated — the fifth time self-adhesive stamps were printed this way in Canada. The backing paper includes design elements on the reverse. At time of issue, the P stamp was valued at 54¢.

| **Rates:** | Domestic first-class (30-50g): 98¢ |
|---|---|
| Feb 23/09– Jan 10/10 | Domestic oversize (0-100g): $1.18 |

## RHODODENDRONS

*Perforated singles from water-activated gum souvenir sheet*

2318a 2318b

*Die cut singles from self-adhesive booklet*

2319 R. yakushimanum 'Mist Maiden' 2320 R. Minas Maid

Designer: Isabelle Toussaint, Design graphique.

Lithography (6 colours)
Lowe-Martin
Water-activated gum souvenir sheet of 2

**2009, Mar 13** **GT4, TRC Paper** **Perf 13.2x13.4**

| | | NH–VF | ⊙F | FDC |
|---|---|---|---|---|
| **2318** | **$1.08 souvenir sheet** of 2 | 3.00 | 3.00 | — |
| a | **54¢ multicoloured** | 1.50 | 1.25 | |
| b | **54¢ multicoloured** | 1.50 | 1.25 | |
| i | se-tenant pair (2318a–b) | 3.00 | 2.50 | |

Qty: 275,000

Self-adhesive booklet of 10
**GT4, TRC Paper**
**Serpentine Die cut 13.4x12.8**

| | | NH–VF | ⊙F | FDC |
|---|---|---|---|---|
| **2319** | **54¢ multicoloured**, white and pink flowers | 1.00 | .45 | |
| **2320** | **54¢ multicoloured**, pink flowers | 1.00 | .45 | |
| i | se-tenant pair (2319, 2320), die cut to shape from Quarterly Pack | 4.00 | — | |
| b | die cutting omitted, se-tenant pair | 750.00 | | |
| a | booklet pane of 10, 5 each #2319–2320 + 10 stickers (**BK401**) | 10.00 | | |

Qty: 6,500,000 of each

**Nos. 2319–2320 (2) combination FDC** **4.15***
* Stamps on FDCs are not die cut all the way through.

For non-denominated postal cards of same designs, see UX204–UX205.
For non-denominated size 10 envelopes of same designs, see U247–U248.
Rhododendron is Greek for "red tree" but blooms can also be found in magenta, purple, pink and white shades, often blotted with speckles and splashes of colour.

2318

*Image rotated* 2320a

## *ART CANADA:* JACK BUSH

2321 *Striped Column* 2322a *Chopsticks*

Designer: Hélène L'Heureux. Paintings by Jack Bush, 1909–1977.

Lithography (7 colours), pane of 16
Lowe-Martin

**2009, Mar 20** **GT4, TRC Paper** **Perf 13.0x13.4**

| | | NH–VF | ⊙F | PB | FDC |
|---|---|---|---|---|---|
| **2321** | **54¢ multicoloured** | 1.00 | .45 | 5.00 | 3.00 |
| a | 54¢ single from souvenir sheet, perf 12.5x13.4 | 1.50 | 1.50 | | |
| **2322** | **$2.19 souvenir sheet** of 2 | 5.00 | 5.00 | | 6.15 |
| a | **$1.65 multicoloured**, perf 12.5x13.4 | 3.00 | 3.00 | | |

Qty: 2321: 1,750,000; 2321a/2322/2322a: 250,000

2322

## INTERNATIONAL YEAR OF ASTRONOMY

*Perforated singles from water-activated gum souvenir sheet*

2323a 2323b

*Die cut singles from self-adhesive booklet*

2324 Horsehead Nebula Dominion Astrophysical Observatory (Saanich, BC)

2325 Eagle Nebula Canada-France-Hawaii Telescope (Mauna Kea summit, Hawaii)

Designer: Keith Martin.

Lithography (10 colours)
Lowe-Martin
Water-activated gum souvenir sheet of 2

| **2009, Apr 2** | **GT4, TRC Paper** | | **Perf 13.1x13.0** | |
|---|---|---|---|---|
| | | NH–VF | ⊙F | FDC |
| **2323** | **$1.08 souvenir sheet** of 2 | 3.00 | 3.00 | 4.15 |
| a | **54¢ multicoloured**, telescope at left | 1.50 | 1.25 | |
| b | **54¢ multicoloured**, telescope at right | 1.50 | 1.25 | |
| i | se-tenant pair (2323a, 2323b) | 3.00 | 2.50 | |
| c | overprinted souvenir sheet | 5.00 | 5.00 | |
| ci | $19.95 uncut press sheet of 14 souvenir sheets (2323c) | 100.00 | | |

Qty: 250,000; 2323c: 80,000; 2323ci: 7,500

The UPC barcode on 2323 is '... 07203 1' on a white background. On 2323c the barcode is '... 07202 4' on a buff background. The overprint on 2323c is visible under a UV light.

Self-adhesive booklet of 10
**GT4, TRC Paper**
**Serpentine Die cut 13.4**

| | | NH–VF | ⊙F | FDC |
|---|---|---|---|---|
| **2324** | **54¢ multicoloured**, telescope at left | 1.00 | .45 | — |
| **2325** | **54¢ multicoloured**, telescope at right | 1.00 | .45 | — |
| i | se-tenant pair (2324, 2325), die cut to shape from Quarterly Pack | 4.00 | — | |
| a | booklet pane of 10, 5 each #2324–2325 + 10 stickers (**BK402**) | 10.00 | | |

Qty: 3,000,000 of each

2323

2323c
Upper left portion of s/s showing overprint under UV light

2325a

## PRESERVING THE POLES

2326
Polar bear

2327
Arctic tern

Designer: Tiit Telmet, Wade Stewart.

Lithography (6 colours), pane of 16
Lowe-Martin

| **2009, Apr 9** | **GT4, TRC Paper** | | | **Perf 12.9** | |
|---|---|---|---|---|---|
| | | NH–VF | ⊙F | PB | FDC |
| **2326** | **54¢ multicoloured** | 1.00 | .45 | | |
| **2327** | **54¢ multicoloured** | 1.00 | .45 | | |
| a | se-tenant pair (2326, 2327) | 2.00 | 1.25 | 5.00 | 4.15 |
| b | $1.08 souvenir sheet of 2 | 2.50 | 2.50 | | |

Qty: 2326–2327: 1,000,000 of each; 2327b: 225,000

Issued in partnership with approximately 30 countries from around the world under the theme "Preserve the Polar Regions and Glaciers" to raise awareness of the dangers of climate change as well as the many creatures impacted by its effects.

2327b

## BENEFICIAL INSECT – DEFINITIVE

2328
Monarch Caterpillar

Designer: Keith Martin.

Lithography (5 colours), pane of 50
Canadian Bank Note

| **2009, Apr 22** | **Not tagged, TRC Paper** | | | **Perf 13.0x13.4** | |
|---|---|---|---|---|---|
| | | NH–VF | ⊙F | PB | FDC |
| **2328** | **2¢ multicoloured** | .25 | .25 | .25 | 2.05* |

For 1¢, 3¢–25¢ values see Sc. 2234–2238. For 4¢, 6¢–9¢ values see Sc. 2406–10.
For 22¢ value see Sc. 2708.
* The FDC contains only a single 2¢ stamp.

## CANADIAN HORSES

2329 The Canadian Horse
2330 Newfoundland Pony

Designer: Wilco Design (Bonnie Yam).

Lithography (5 colours), self-adhesive booklet of 10
Lowe-Martin

| **2009, May 15** | **GT 3 sides, TRC Paper** | | **Die cut 13.4** | |
|---|---|---|---|---|
| | | NH–VF | ⊙F | FDC |
| **2329** | **54¢ multicoloured** | 1.00 | .40 | |
| **2330** | **54¢ multicoloured** | 1.00 | .40 | |
| i | se-tenant pair (2329, 2330) die cut to shape from Quarterly Pack/Annual Collection | 3.00 | — | |
| a | booklet pane of 10 x 54¢ (2329–30) (**BK403**) | 15.00 | | |

Qty: 2,000,000 of each

**Nos. 2329–2330 (2) combination FDC** **4.15***
* Stamps on FDCs are not die cut all the way through.
The general tagging is *not* applied to the side with the illustration passing through the die cutting.

2330a

## CANADIAN DIPLOMACY

2331
Canadian flag intersecting globe

Designer: Parable Communications.
Lithography (7 colours plus varnish), pane of 16 + horizontal gutter
Lowe-Martin

| 2009, Jun 1 | GT4, TRC Paper | | Perf 13.4x13.1 | |
|---|---|---|---|---|
| | NH–VF | ⊙F | PB | FDC |
| **2331 54¢ multicoloured** | 1.00 | .45 | 4.00 | 3.10 |
| i vertical pair, gutter between | 4.00 | 1.00 | | |

Qty: 1,750,000

Issued on the 100th anniversary of the Department of Foreign Affairs and International Trade.

## BOUNDARY WATERS TREATY

2332
Niagara Falls USA side, and at night

Designer: Paul Haslip.
Lithography (8 colours), Sheets of 64 subjects in four panes of 16 + vertical gutter
Lowe-Martin

| 2009, Jun 12 | GT4, TRC Paper | | Perf 13.4 | |
|---|---|---|---|---|
| | NH–VF | ⊙F | PB | FDC |
| **2332 54¢ multicoloured** | 1.00 | .45 | 4.00 | 3.10 |
| i horizontal pair, gutter between | 4.00 | 1.00 | | |

Qty: 2,500,000

Issued on the 100th anniversary of the Boundary Waters Treaty between Canada and the United States which established the International Joint Commission.

### MINT PRICING PREMIUMS

Mint stamps from 301 to date are valued as NH-VF (Never Hinged-Very Fine). All hinged VF and NH-F copies are worth 50% of the listed values. Plate block (PB) values are for mint NH–VF plate or inscription blocks of four.

### USED, VF/XF (with in-period, circular date cancel) PRICING PREMIUM

Single stamps with light or circular date cancels will sell for more than catalogue value (perhaps even more than a mint copy). From *1981 to 1991* single stamps from se-tenant blocks of 4 or larger will be priced at 50% or more above the fine price. From *1992* to date single stamps from se-tenant blocks of 4 or larger plus se-tenant booklet panes and souvenir sheets will be priced at 100% or more above the fine price. From *1997* to date all other stamps will be priced at 50% or more above the fine price.

## CANADIAN RECORDING ARTISTS

*Perforated singles from water-activated gum souvenir sheet*

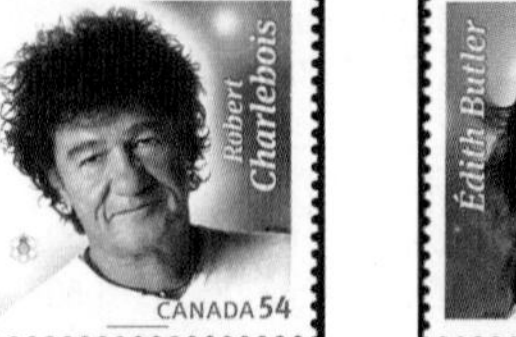


2333a
Robert Charlebois (1944– )

2333b
Édith Butler (1942– )

2333c
Stompin' Tom Connors (1936–2013)

2333d
Bryan Adams (1959– )

*Die cut singles from self-adhesive booklet*

2334a
Bryan Adams

2334b
Stompin' Tom Connors

2334c
Édith Butler



2334d
Robert Charlebois

Designer: Circle Design Inc.
Lithography (9 colours plus varnish), water-activated gum souvenir sheet of 4
Lowe-Martin

| 2009, Jul 2 | GT4, TRC Paper | Perf 12.5x13.1 | |
|---|---|---|---|
| | NH–VF | ⊙F | FDC |
| **2333 $2.16 souvenir sheet** of 4 | 4.00 | 4.00 | 6.30 |
| a **54¢ multicoloured** | 1.00 | 1.00 | |
| b **54¢ multicoloured** | 1.00 | 1.00 | |
| c **54¢ multicoloured** | 1.00 | 1.00 | |
| d **54¢ multicoloured** | 1.00 | 1.00 | |

Qty: 275,000

2333

Lithography (9 colours), self-adhesive booklet of 8
Lowe-Martin

**2009, Jul 2** **GT4, TRC Paper**
**Serpentine Die cut 13.5**

| | | NH–VF | ⊙F | FDC |
|---|---|---|---|---|
| **2334** | booklet pane of 4 x 54¢ + 4 stickers, pane with Bryan Adams at upper left | 4.00 | | — |
| a | **54¢ multicoloured** | 1.00 | .60 | |
| b | **54¢ multicoloured** | 1.00 | .60 | |
| c | **54¢ multicoloured** | 1.00 | .60 | |
| d | **54¢ multicoloured** | 1.00 | .60 | |
| i | booklet pane of 4 x 54¢ + 4 stickers, pane with Stompin' Tom Connors at upper left | 4.00 | | |
| ii | booklet pane of 4 x 54¢ + 4 stickers, pane with Édith Butler at upper left | 4.00 | | |
| iii | booklet pane of 4 x 54¢ + 4 stickers, pane with Robert Charlebois at upper left | 4.00 | | |
| BK404 | two panes of 2334 (Adams cover) $8.00 | | | |
| BK405 | two panes of 2334i (Connors cover) $8.00 | | | |
| BK406 | two panes of 2334ii (Butler cover) $8.00 | | | |
| BK407 | two panes of 2334iii (Charlebois cover) $8.00 | | | |

Qty: 1,000,000 of each stamp

Honouring the accomplishments of Canadian Recording Artists.

For non-denominated postal cards of same designs, see UX206–UX209. Beware of so-called "double impression errors" on the booklet stamps — these are the result of a minor shift of one of the two black colours.

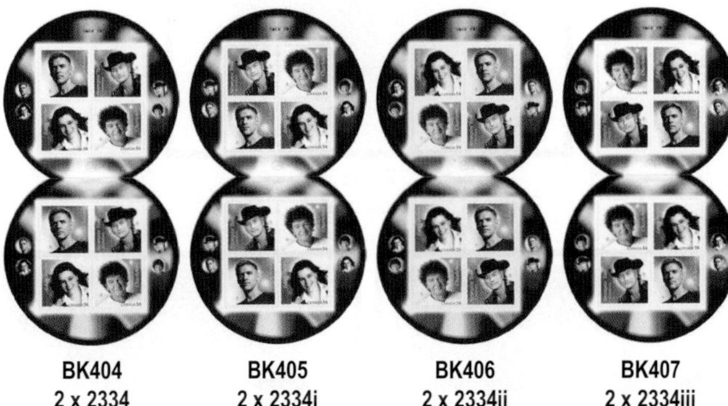

**BK404** 2 x 2334 **BK405** 2 x 2334i **BK406** 2 x 2334ii **BK407** 2 x 2334iii

## ROADSIDE ATTRACTIONS — I

*Perforated singles from water-activated gum souvenir sheet*

**2335a** *Mr. PG*, Prince George, BC

**2335b** *Watson Lake Signpost Forest*, Watson Lake, YK

**2335c** *Inukshuk*, Hay River, NWT

**2335d** *Pysanka*, Vegreville, AB

*Die cut singles from self-adhesive booklet*

**2336a** *Mr. PG*, Prince George, BC

**2336b** *Watson Lake Signpost Forest*, Watson Lake, YK

**2336c** *Inukshuk*, Hay River, NWT

**2336d** *Pysanka*, Vegreville, AB

Designer: Fraser Ross (Semaphor Design Company).
Lithography (7 colours plus varnish), water-activated gum souvenir sheet of 4
Lowe-Martin

**2009, Jul 6** **GT4, TRC Paper** **Perf 12.8x12.9**

| | | NH–VF | ⊙F | FDC |
|---|---|---|---|---|
| **2335** | **$2.16 souvenir sheet** of 4 | 4.00 | 4.00 | — |
| a | **54¢ multicoloured** | 1.00 | 1.00 | |
| b | **54¢ multicoloured** | 1.00 | 1.00 | |
| c | **54¢ multicoloured** | 1.00 | 1.00 | |
| d | **54¢ multicoloured** | 1.00 | 1.00 | |

Qty: 250,000

Lithography (9 colours), self-adhesive booklet of 8
**Serpentine Die cut 13.4 on 3 sides**

| | | NH–VF | ⊙F | FDC |
|---|---|---|---|---|
| **2336** | booklet pane of 4 x 54¢ + 4 stickers (BK408) | 4.00 | | 6.30 |
| a | **54¢ multicoloured** | 1.00 | .60 | |
| b | **54¢ multicoloured** | 1.00 | .60 | |
| c | **54¢ multicoloured** | 1.00 | .60 | |
| d | **54¢ multicoloured** | 1.00 | .60 | |
| BK408 | two panes of 2336 $8.00 | | | |

Qty: 1,000,000 of each stamp

For non-denominated postal cards of same designs, see UX210–UX213. First of a three-year series. See also 2397–2401, 2484–2485.

**2335**

**2 x 2336 (BK408)**

## CAPTAIN ROBERT A. BARTLETT

**2337**
Bartlett (1875–1946) and *Roosevelt*

Designer: Karen Smith Design.
Lithography (7 colours plus varnish), pane of 16 + vertical gutter
Lowe-Martin

**2009, Jul 10** **GT4, TRC Paper** **Perf 13.0x13.1**

| | | NH–VF | ⊙F | PB | FDC |
|---|---|---|---|---|---|
| **2337** | **54¢ multicoloured** | 1.00 | .45 | 4.00 | 3.10 |
| i | horizontal pair, gutter between | 2.00 | 1.00 | | |

Qty: 1,750,000

100th anniversary of Bartlett's attempt to reach the North Pole.

## CANADIAN INVENTIONS: SPORTS

**2338a**
Five-pin bowling

**2338b**
Ringette

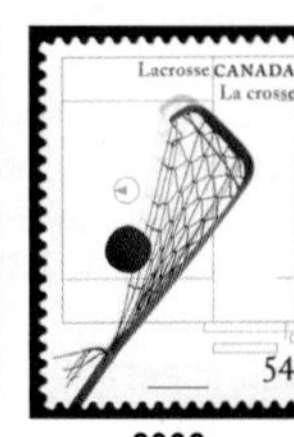


**2338c**
Lacrosse

**2338d**
Basketball

Designer: q30design inc.
Lithography (4 colours), self-adhesive booklet of 8
Lowe-Martin

**2009, Aug 10** **GT4, TRC Paper**
**Serpentine Die cut 13.4**

| | | NH–VF | ⊙F | FDC |
|---|---|---|---|---|
| **2338** | booklet pane of 4 x 54¢ + 4 stickers | 4.00 | | 6.30 |
| a | **54¢ multicoloured** | 1.00 | .60 | |
| b | **54¢ multicoloured** | 1.00 | .60 | |
| c | **54¢ multicoloured** | 1.00 | .60 | |
| d | **54¢ multicoloured** | 1.00 | .60 | |
| **BK409** | two panes of 2338 $8.00 | | | |

Qty: 625,000 of each stamp

**2 x 2338**
**(BK409)**

Timeline:
**2009, Sep 14** (54¢)+10¢ Mental Health, semi-postal (B15)

## MONTREAL CANADIENS 100TH ANNIVERSARY

**2339**
Montreal Canadiens Hockey Jersey

Designer: Stéphane Huot.
Lithography (6 colours), self-adhesive booklet of 10
Lowe-Martin

**2009, Oct 17** **GT4, TRC Paper** **Serpentine Die cut 13.4**

| | | NH–VF | ⊙F | FDC |
|---|---|---|---|---|
| **2339** | **multicoloured** | 1.70 | .40 | 3.10 |
| i | die cut to shape from Quarterly Pack/ Annual Collection | 2.50 | — | |
| a | booklet pane of 10 x P (2339) (**BK411**) | 17.00 | | |

Qty: 6,000,000

At time of issue, the P stamp was valued at 54¢. Features game-worn #9 hockey sweater of Maurice "Rocket" Richard currently housed in the Montreal Canadiens Hall of Fame.

**2340a**
Replay of 500th goal of Maurice Richard

**2340b**
Replay of 500th goal of Jean Béliveau

**2340c**
Replay of 500th goal of Guy Lafleur

Designer: Stéphane Huot.
Lithography (6 colours) plus Lenticular, self-adhesive souvenir sheet of 3
Lowe-Martin and Outer Aspect

**2009, Oct 17** **Not tagged, TRC Paper**
**Serpentine Die cut 13.1 x 13.3**

| | | NH–VF | ⊙F | FDC |
|---|---|---|---|---|
| **2340** | **$9 souvenir sheet of 3** | 20.00 | 20.00 | 20.00 |
| a | **$3 Maurice Richard** (1957.10.19) | 6.00 | 6.00 | |
| b | **$3 Jean Béliveau** (1971.02.11) | 6.00 | 6.00 | |
| c | **$3 Guy Lafleur** (1983.12.20) | 6.00 | 6.00 | |
| d | as 2340, die cutting omitted, pane of 3 | *2,500.00* | | |

Qty: 375,000

Be careful when soaking any used copies of these three stamps; they may separate into 'layers' and leave gum residue on the back of the stamp. Any cancellation may also 'disappear'.

Using an action-oriented printing process called Motionstamp™ technology, these stamps feature replays of the historic 500th goals of each player.

*Image rotated* **2339a**

**2340**

QE II — 2000's

## LEST WE FORGET

*Perforated single from water-activated gum souvenir sheet*

2341

2342

*Die cut single from self-adhesive booklet*

Detail of National War Memorial in Ottawa, ON

Designer: Lionel Gadoury, Michael Wandelmaier (Context Creative).

Lithography (7 colours), Water-activated souvenir sheet of 2

Lowe-Martin

**2009, Oct 19** **GT4, TRC Paper** **Perf 12.5**

| | | NH–VF | ⊙F | FDC |
|---|---|---|---|---|
| **2341** | **P multicoloured** | 1.70 | 1.25 | — |
| a | souvenir sheet of 2 | 3.50 | 3.50 | |

Qty: 225,000 souvenir sheets

Lithography (7 colours), self-adhesive booklet of 10

**Serpentine Die cut 13.4**

| | | NH–VF | ⊙F | FDC |
|---|---|---|---|---|
| **2342** | **P multicoloured** | 1.70 | .40 | 3.10 |
| i | die cut to shape from Quarterly Pack/ Annual Collection | 2.50 | — | |
| a | booklet pane of 10 x P (2342) (**BK412**) | 17.00 | | |

Qty: 6,000,000

At time of issue, the P stamp was valued at 54¢.

2341a

2342a

## CHRISTMAS: THE NATIVITY SCENE

*Perforated singles from water-activated gum souvenir sheet*

2343a

2343b

2343c

2343d

*Die cut singles from self-adhesive booklet*

2345

2346

2347

2344
Christmas Tree

Designer: Joseph Gault. Sculptor: Antonio Caruso.

Lithography (9 colours)

Lowe-Martin

Water-activated gum souvenir sheet of 4

**2009, Nov 2** **GT4, TRC Paper** **Perf 13.0x12.5**

| | | NH–VF | ⊙F | FDC |
|---|---|---|---|---|
| **2343** | **$3.71 souvenir sheet** of 4 | 7.75 | 7.75 | 9.40 |
| a | **P multicoloured*** | 1.75 | 1.50 | |
| b | **P multicoloured** | 1.75 | 1.50 | |
| c | **98¢ multicoloured** | 2.00 | 2.00 | |
| d | **$1.65 multicoloured** | 3.20 | 3.20 | |

Qty: 240,000

* See 2292 for self-adhesive, serpentine die cut variety of 2343a.

Designer: Hélène L'Heureux.

Lithography (5 colours) plus holographic foil

Lowe-Martin, self-adhesive booklet of 12

**2009, Nov 2** **GT4, TRC Paper**

**Serpentine Die cut 8.3 horiz**

| | | NH–VF | ⊙F | FDC |
|---|---|---|---|---|
| **2344** | **P multicoloured** | 1.70 | .25 | 3.10 |
| i | die cut to shape from Quarterly Pack/ Annual Collection | 2.50 | — | |
| a | booklet pane of 6 x P (2344) | 10.00 | — | |
| **BK413** | two panes of 2344a $20.00 | | | |

Qty: 12,000,000

This design was also used on the 2010 *Santa Claus* envelopes.

Designer: Joseph Gault. Sculptor: Antonio Caruso.

Lithography (8 colours), self-adhesive booklet of 12 (P) or 6

Lowe-Martin

**2009, Nov 2** **GT4, TRC Paper**

**Serpentine Die cut 13.4**

| | | NH–VF | ⊙F | FDC |
|---|---|---|---|---|
| **2345** | **P multicoloured** | 1.70 | .25 | — |
| i | die cut to shape from Quarterly Pack | 2.50 | — | |
| a | booklet pane of 6 x P (2345) | 10.00 | — | |
| **BK414** | two panes of 2345a $20.00 | | | |

Qty: 12,000,000

| | | NH–VF | ⊙F | FDC |
|---|---|---|---|---|
| **2346** | **98¢ multicoloured** | 2.00 | .75 | — |
| i | die cut to shape from Quarterly Pack | 3.00 | — | |
| a | booklet pane of 6 x 98¢ (2346) (**BK415**) | 12.00 | — | |

Qty: 5,400,000

| | | NH–VF | ⊙F | FDC |
|---|---|---|---|---|
| **2347** | **$1.65 multicoloured** | 3.20 | 1.25 | — |
| i | die cut to shape from Quarterly Pack | 5.00 | — | |
| a | booklet pane of 6 x $1.65 (2347) (**BK416**) | 19.50 | — | |
| b | gutter pane, 2346a and 2347a | 35.00 | | |

Qty: 5,400,000; gutter pane: 5,000

At time of issue, the P Christmas stamps were valued at 54¢.

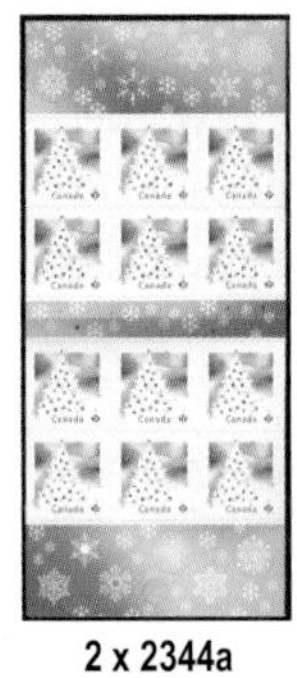
2 x 2344a
(BK413)

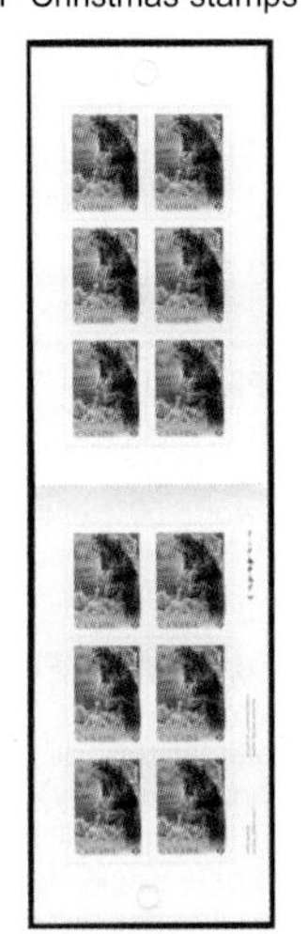
2 x 2345a
(BK414)

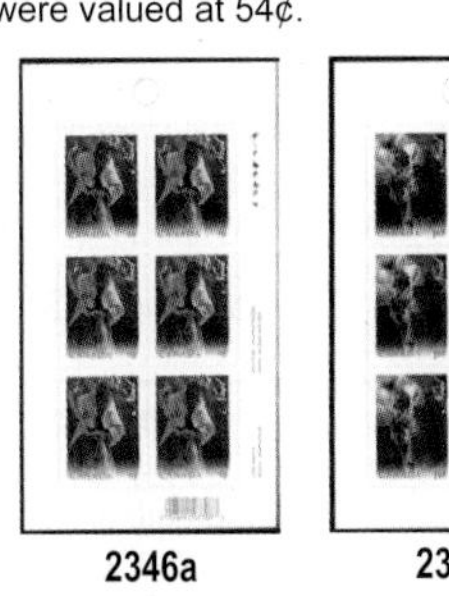
2346a

2347a

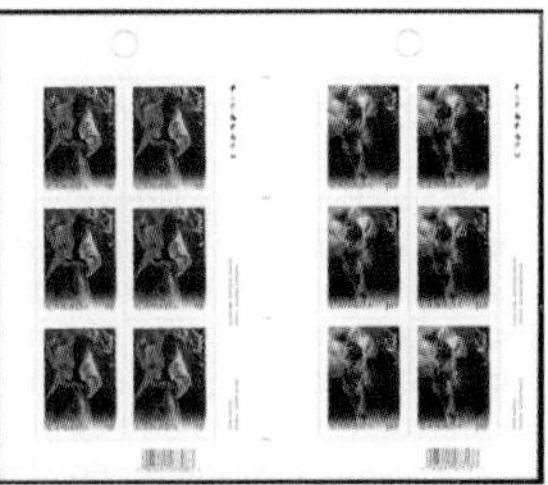
2347b

2343

## 2010

### LUNAR NEW YEAR (Series 2) — 2
### Year of the Tiger

2348 Seal impression of tiger in circle

2349i Sculpted tiger seal

Designer: Wilson Chi Ian Lam (Wilco Design). Sculpture: Bill Lao.

Lithography (5 colours) plus 2 foil stampings and embossing/debossing plus varnish, Sheets of 50 subjects in two panes of 25
Lowe-Martin, Gravure Choquet

**2010, Jan 8** **GT4, TRC Paper** **Perf 12.5**

| | | NH-VF | ⊙F | PB | FDC |
|---|---|---|---|---|---|
| **2348** | P **multicoloured** | 1.70 | .60 | 8.50 | 3.15 |

Qty: 6,500,000

At time of issue, the P stamp was valued at 57¢ even though the 57¢ domestic rate did not go into effect until January 11.

**Single stamp General Tagged on left, right and bottom**

| | | NH-VF | ⊙F | PB | FDC |
|---|---|---|---|---|---|
| **2349** | **$1.70 souvenir sheet** of 1 | 3.30 | 3.30 | — | 5.40 |
| i | $1.70 single stamp from souvenir sheet | 3.00 | 3.00 | — | |
| ii | $28.95 uncut press sheet of 12 souvenir sheets | 60.00 | | | |

Qty: 2349: 750,000; 2349ii: 25,000

For non-denominated postal cards of same designs, see UX214–UX215.

*Image rotated* 2349

**Rates:**

| | | |
|---|---|---|
| Jan 11/10– | Domestic first-class (0-30g): 57¢ | USA (0-30g): $1.00 |
| Jan 16/11 | Domestic first-class (30-50g): $1.00 | USA (30-50g): $1.22 |
| | Domestic oversize (0-100g): $1.22 | International (0-30g): $1.70 |

*single usage:* USA $1.00: $15.00 | International $1.70: $20.00

**MINT PRICING PREMIUMS**

Mint stamps from 301 to date are valued as NH-VF (Never Hinged-Very Fine). All hinged VF and NH-F copies are worth 50% of the listed values. Plate block (PB) values are for mint NH–VF plate or inscription blocks of four.

**USED, VF/XF (with in-period, circular date cancel) PRICING PREMIUM**

Single stamps with light or circular date cancels will sell for more than catalogue value (perhaps even more than a mint copy). From *1981 to 1991* single stamps from se-tenant blocks of 4 or larger will be priced at 50% or more above the fine price. From *1992* to date single stamps from se-tenant blocks of 4 or larger plus se-tenant booklet panes and souvenir sheets will be priced at 100% or more above the fine price. From *1997* to date all other stamps will be priced at 50% or more above the fine price.

### PERMANENT™ FLAG OVER MILLS

*Perforated singles from water-activated gum souvenir sheet*

2350a Flag over Watson's Mill, Manotick, ON

2350b Flag over Keremeos Grist Mill, Keremeos, BC

2350c Flag over Old Stone Mill Natl. Historic Site, Delta, ON

2350d Flag over Riordon Grist Mill, Caraquet, NB

2350e Flag over Cornell Mill, Stanbridge East, QC

*Die cut singles from self-adhesive booklet*

2351 2352 2353 2354 2355

Designers: Gottschalk+Ash International.

Lithography (5 colours)
Canadian Bank Note
Water-activated gum souvenir sheet of 5

**2010, Jan 11** **GT4, TRC Paper** **Perf 13.0x13.3**

| | | NH-VF | ⊙F | FDC |
|---|---|---|---|---|
| **2350** | **$2.85 souvenir sheet** of 5 † | 8.50 | 8.50 | 7.70 |
| a | P **multicoloured**, Watson's Mill | 1.70 | 1.50 | |
| b | P **multicoloured**, Keremeos Grist Mill | 1.70 | 1.50 | |
| c | P **multicoloured**, Stone Mill | 1.70 | 1.50 | |
| d | P **multicoloured**, Riordon Grist Mill | 1.70 | 1.50 | |
| e | P **multicoloured**, Cornell Mill | 1.70 | 1.50 | |

Qty: 220,000

Self-adhesive booklets of 10 and 30

**2010, Jan 11** **GT4, TRC Paper**
**Serpentine Die cut 13.4**

| | | NH-VF | ⊙F | FDC |
|---|---|---|---|---|
| **2351** | P **multicoloured**, Watson's Mill | 1.70 | .25 | — |
| **2352** | P **multicoloured**, Keremeos Grist Mill | 1.70 | .25 | — |
| **2353** | P **multicoloured**, Stone Mill | 1.70 | .25 | — |
| **2354** | P **multicoloured**, Riordon Grist Mill | 1.70 | .25 | — |
| **2355** | P **multicoloured**, Cornell Mill | 1.70 | .25 | — |
| i | se-tenant strip of 5 (2351–2355), die cut to shape from Quarterly Pack | 12.50 | — | |
| a | booklet pane of 10 x P (2 each of 2351–2355) (**BK417**) | 17.00 | | |
| b | booklet pane of 30 x P (6 each of 2351–2355) (**BK418**) | 50.00 | | |
| ai | strip of 5, from 2355a/BK417 or 2355b/BK418 | 8.50 | | |

Hidden within each of the designs, in very fine micro-printing, is the location of the mill.

For non-denominated postal cards of same designs, see UX216–UX220.

2350

2355a

2355b

## FLOWER DEFINITIVES — SOUVENIR SHEET

2356a
Striped Coralroot

2356b
Giant Helleborine

2356c
Rose Pogonia

2356d
Grass Pink

Designers: Monique Dufour, Sophie Lafortune.
Lithography (8 colours)
Lowe-Martin
Water-activated gum souvenir sheet of 4

**2010, Jan 11 — GT4, TRC Paper — Perf 13.4x13.1**

| | | NH–VF | ⊙F | FDC |
|---|---|---|---|---|
| 2356 | **$4.49 souvenir sheet** of 4 † | 9.00 | 9.00 | 11.00 |
| a | **multicoloured** | 1.75 | 1.50 | |
| b | **$1.00 multicoloured** | 2.00 | 1.75 | |
| c | **$1.22 multicoloured** | 2.25 | 2.00 | |
| d | **$1.70 multicoloured** | 3.00 | 2.75 | |

Qty: 220,000

† Face value of $4.49 at time of issue; the face value of the P stamp was 57¢.

2356

## FLOWER DEFINITIVES – COILS

2357

2361

Striped Coralroot

2358
Giant Helleborine

2359
Rose Pogonia

2360
Grass Pink

Designers: Monique Dufour, Sophie Lafortune.
Lithography (5 colours), self-adhesive rolls of 100 (P) and 50 ($1.00, $1.22, $1.70)
Lowe-Martin

Three different die cut patterns were used. On the first pattern, one of the eleven rows of die cutting from this first printing had a measurement of 9.35–9.60. The adjacent rows measure 7.85–8.20. This is a full 1½ 'perf' difference on the same stamp. The second and third patterns was used on the P, $1.00 and $1.22 rolls. Pattern 2 ranges from 7.90–9.25; Pattern 3 ranges from 7.80–8.70. Every stamp on each of the 100-subject (10x10) die cutting mats is different due to variations occurring on the top and bottom of a single stamp.

**2010, Jan 11 — GT4, TRC Paper**
**Serpentine Die cut 7.85 to 9.60 Horiz**
**(Sawtooth tips)**

| | | NH–VF | ⊙F | FDC |
|---|---|---|---|---|
| 2357 | **multicoloured** † | 1.70 | .25 | — |
| i | gutter strip of 4 with inscription | 8.50 | | |
| | starter strip of 4 (wavy die cut) | 11.00 | | |
| | end strip of 4 (wavy die cut) | 11.00 | | |
| ii | die cut to shape (9.2 horiz) from Quarterly Pack, *Apr '10* ‡ | 2.50 | — | |
| iii | $57 uncut press panel of 100, *Sep '10* | 170.00 | | |
| iv | horiz. pair, imperf. between, from 2357iii | 4.00 | 4.00 | |
| v | block of 4, imperf. vert. with insc., from 2357iii | 10.00 | 10.00 | |
| vi | 'compound' die cut 9.30–9.60 one edge only§ | 4.00 | 1.50 | |
| | as vi, compound die cut in gutter strip of 6§ | 15.00 | | |
| 2358 | **$1.00 multicoloured** | 1.85 | .45 | — |
| i | gutter strip of 4 with inscription | 11.00 | | |
| | starter strip of 4 (wavy die cut) | 13.00 | | |
| | end strip of 4 (wavy die cut) | 13.00 | | |
| ii | die cut to shape (9.2 horiz) from Quarterly Pack, *Apr '10* ‡ | 2.75 | — | |
| iii | 'compound' die cut 9.30–9.60 one edge only§ | 10.00 | 4.00 | |
| | as iii, compound die cut in gutter strip of 6§ | 24.00 | | |
| 2359 | **$1.22 multicoloured** | 2.50 | .75 | — |
| i | gutter strip of 4 with inscription | 14.00 | | |
| | starter strip of 4 (wavy die cut) | 15.00 | | |
| | end strip of 4 (wavy die cut) | 15.00 | | |
| ii | die cut to shape (9.2 horiz) from Quarterly Pack, *Apr '10* ‡ | 3.75 | — | |
| iii | 'compound' die cut 9.30–9.60 one edge only§ | 11.00 | 5.00 | |
| | as iii, compound die cut in gutter strip of 6§ | 28.00 | | |
| 2360 | **$1.70 multicoloured** | 3.40 | 1.00 | — |
| i | gutter strip of 4 with inscription | 18.00 | | |
| | starter strip of 4 (wavy die cut) | 22.00 | | |
| | end strip of 4 (wavy die cut) | 22.00 | | |
| ii | die cut to shape (9.2 horiz) from Quarterly Pack, *Apr '10* ‡ | 5.00 | — | |
| iii | 'compound' die cut 9.30–9.60 one edge only§ | 10.00 | 5.00 | |
| | as iii, compound die cut in gutter strip of 6§ | 32.00 | | |

‡ Single stamps supplied in the Quarterly Pack have rounded tips (backing paper is 'plain'), starting with a peak at upper left; stamps from the full rolls have sawtooth tips.
§ One of the eleven rows of die cutting from this printing had a measurement of 9.30–9.60. The adjacent rows measure 7.85 to 8.20. This is a full 1½ 'perf' difference on the same stamp.

**2010, Jan 11 — GT4, TRC Paper**
**Serpentine Die cut 9.2 Horiz**
**(Rounded tips)**

| | | NH–VF | ⊙F | FDC |
|---|---|---|---|---|
| 2361 | **multicoloured** † | 2.00 | 2.00 | — |

2357 issued in horizontal rolls of 5,000. Individual stamps do not touch along the horizontal roll; rounded 'perf tips' start with a peak. Sold in strips of 4 or 10 by the National Philatelic Centre; single stamps included in the Quarterly Pack/Annual Collection.

| *Format:* | Coil | | | Souvenir sheet | Booklet | |
|---|---|---|---|---|---|---|
| *Die cut/perf:* | 7.85–9.60 horiz | 9.2 horiz | 9.2 horiz Qtr pack | Perf 13.4x13.1 | 9.2 horiz | 9.2 horiz Qtr pack |
| Striped Coralroot | 2357, i | 2361 | 2357ii | 2356a | | |
| $1.00 Giant Helleborine | 2358, i | | 2358ii | 2356b | 2362 | 2362i |
| $1.22 Rose Pogonia | 2359, i | | 2359ii | 2356c | 2363 | 2363i |
| $1.70 Grass Pink | 2360, i | | 2360ii | 2356d | 2364 | 2364i |

**† PERMANENT™ non-denominated stamps**

The stamps identified with the symbol of a letter "P" within a red maple leaf are valid indefinitely for use within Canada. Regardless of rate increases, these definitives will be worth the Canadian domestic basic letter rate in effect, and can be used to mail a letter that weighs up to 30 grams to any address in Canada. At time of issue, the P stamps on these pages (Jan 11/10 issue date) were valued at 57¢.

For 50¢, 85¢, $1.45 Flowers see 2072–2074, 2081–2082
For 51¢, 89¢, $1.05, $1.49 Flowers see 2128–2134
For P, 93¢, $1.10, $1.55 Flowers see 2187, 2194–2197
For P, 96¢, $1.15, $1.60 Flowers see 2243–2247, 2254–2256

Flower/Flag — 2010

## FLOWER DEFINITIVES – BOOKLETS

2362 Giant Helleborine · 2363 Rose Pogonia · 2364 Grass Pink

Designers: Monique Dufour, Sophie Lafortune.

Lithography (5 colours), self-adhesive booklets of 6
Lowe-Martin

**2010, Jan 11** **GT4, TRC Paper**
**Serpentine Die cut 9.2 horiz (Rounded tips)**

| | | NH–VF | ⊙F | FDC |
|---|---|---|---|---|
| **2362** | **$1.00 multicoloured** | 2.00 | .45 | — |
| i | die cut to shape from Quarterly Pack ‡ | 3.00 | — | |
| a | booklet pane of 6 x $1.00 (2362) (**BK419**) | 12.00 | | |
| **2363** | **$1.22 multicoloured** | 2.50 | .75 | — |
| i | die cut to shape from Quarterly Pack ‡ | 3.75 | — | |
| a | booklet pane of 6 x $1.22 (2363) (**BK420**) | 15.00 | | |
| **2364** | **$1.70 multicoloured** | 3.40 | 1.00 | — |
| i | die cut to shape from Quarterly Pack ‡ | 5.00 | — | |
| a | booklet pane of 6 x $1.70 (2364) (**BK421**) | 19.50 | | |

‡ Single stamps supplied in the Quarterly packs start with a peak at the upper left (backing paper contains some form of printing from backside of booklet); single stamps from booklets of 6 start with a valley at the upper left.

Serpentine die cutting (2357–2364):

| "Saw tooth" Rolls of 50/100 (2357–2360) (peak/valley purely random) | "Rounded"; valley start Booklet of 6 (2362–2364) | "Rounded"; peak start Single coil and booklet from Qtr pack Roll of 5,000 (2357ii, 2358ii, 2359ii, 2360ii, 2361, 2362i, 2363i, 2364i) |
|---|---|---|

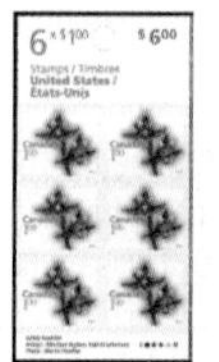
2362a

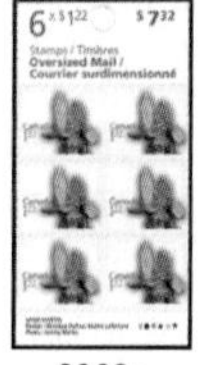
2363a

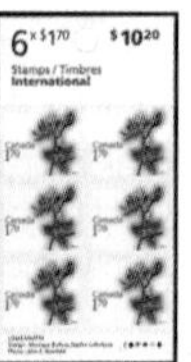
2364a

2357iv

The inscription on the $1.70 flower stamps incorrectly spells "Neufeld" as "Newfeld".

2357v

QE II — 2010's

## QUEEN ELIZABETH II

2365

Designers: Gottschalk+Ash International.

Lithography (5 colours), self-adhesive booklet of 10
Canadian Bank Note

**2010, Jan 11** **GT4, TRC Paper**
**Serpentine Die cut 13.4**

| | | NH–VF | ⊙F | FDC |
|---|---|---|---|---|
| **2365** | **multicoloured (QE II)** † | 1.70 | .25 | 3.15 |
| i | die cut to shape from Quarterly Pack/ Annual Collection | 2.50 | — | |
| a | booklet pane of 10 x P (2365) (**BK422**) | 17.00 | | |

2365a

## VANCOUVER 2010 OLYMPIC WINTER GAMES

*Perforated singles from water-activated gum souvenir sheet*

2366a Whistler, BC

2366b Vancouver, BC

*Die cut singles from self-adhesive booklet*

2367

2368

Designer: Tandem Design Associates Ltd.

Lithography (6 colours plus varnish)
Lowe-Martin
Water-activated gum souvenir sheet of 2

**2010, Jan 12** **GT4, TRC Paper** **Perf 13.4**

| | | NH–VF | ⊙F | FDC |
|---|---|---|---|---|
| **2366** | **$1.14 souvenir sheet** of 2 | 3.00 | 3.00 | 4.30 |
| a | **57¢ multicoloured**, Whistler | 1.50 | 1.25 | |
| b | **57¢ multicoloured**, Vancouver | 1.50 | 1.25 | |
| i | se-tenant pair (2366a, 2366b) | 3.00 | 2.50 | |
| c | souvenir sheet with gold 'VANCOUVER/2010' overprint in selvedge* | 15.00 | | |

* available in coin/stamp set ($49.95); released at face value ($1.14) Feb 12/10.
Qty: 300,000; 2366c: 50,000

Self-adhesive booklet of 10 + 10 labels
**GT4, TRC Paper**
**Serpentine Die cut 13.4**

| | | NH–VF | ⊙F | FDC |
|---|---|---|---|---|
| **2367** | **57¢ multicoloured**, Whistler | 1.00 | .45 | 3.15 |
| i | die cut to shape from Quarterly Pack | 1.50 | — | |
| **2368** | **57¢ multicoloured**, Vancouver | 1.00 | .45 | 3.15 |
| i | die cut to shape from Quarterly Pack | 1.50 | — | |
| a | booklet pane of 10, 5 each #2367–2368 + 10 stickers (**BK423**) | 10.00 | | |

Qty: 2,275,000 of each

For non-denominated postal cards of same designs, see UX221–UX222.

2366

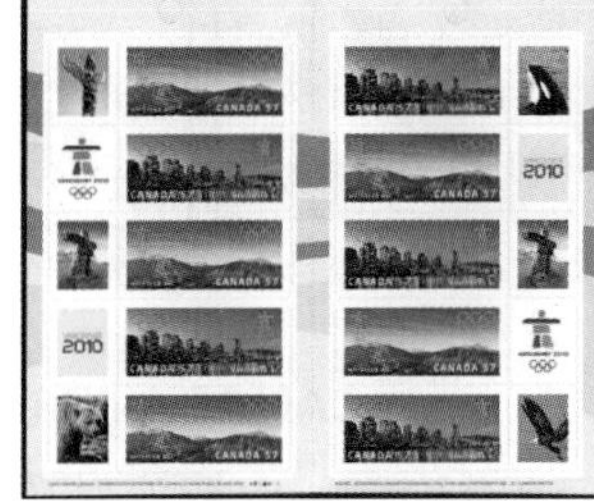
2368a

2366c

## BLACK HISTORY MONTH

2369
William Hall V.C.
(circa 1825–1904)

Designer: Lara Minja (Lime Design Inc.).

Lithography (7 colours plus varnish)
Sheets of 64 subjects in four panes of 16 + horizontal gutter
Lowe-Martin

| 2010, Feb 1 | GT4, TRC Paper | | | Perf 12.5* | |
|---|---|---|---|---|---|
| | | NH–VF | ⊙F | PB | FDC |
| **2369** | **57¢ multicoloured** | 1.00 | .40 | 5.00 | 3.15 |
| i | vertical pair, gutter between | 2.00 | 1.50 | | |

Qty: 1,600,000

* All stamps have transitional perfs along the top and bottom of each stamp, as illustrated below.

Hall was the first black person, first Nova Scotian, and third Canadian to receive the Victoria Cross.

Transitional perfs on all stamps (2369)

## THE RIGHT HONOURABLE ROMÉO LEBLANC

2370
LeBlanc's official portrait
(1927–2009)

Designer: Christan Nicholson.

Lithography (8 colours), pane of 16
Lowe-Martin

| 2010, Feb 8 | GT4, TRC Paper | | | Perf 12.5 | |
|---|---|---|---|---|---|
| | | NH–VF | ⊙F | PB | FDC |
| **2370** | **57¢ multicoloured** | 1.00 | .40 | 5.00 | 3.15 |

Qty: 1,500,000

First Acadian Governor General of Canada (Feb 8/95–Oct 8/99). The three flags in the lower corner of the design are Canada, New Brunswick and Acadia.

## CANADA STRIKES GOLD!

*Perforated single from water-activated gum souvenir sheet*

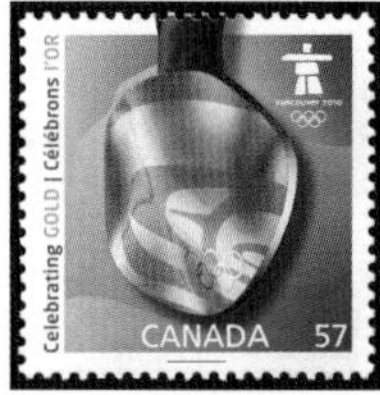
2371a

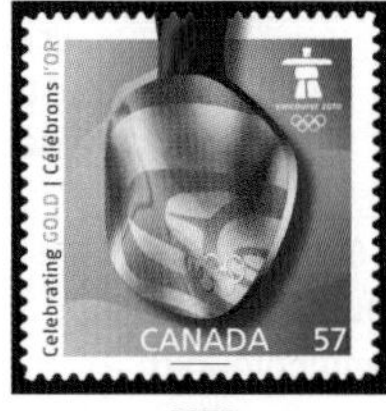
2372

*Die cut single from self-adhesive booklet*

Vancouver 2010 Winter Olympic Games Gold Medal

This stamp was *announced* by Canada Post on the evening of Sunday, February 14, 2010, approximately one hour *after* a Canadian Olympian won a gold medal at the Vancouver 2010 Winter Olympic Games.

Designer: Tandem Design Associates Ltd.

Lithography (6 colours plus varnish)
Lowe-Martin
Water-activated gum souvenir sheet of 2

| 2010, Feb 14 | GT4, TRC Paper | | Perf 12.5 | |
|---|---|---|---|---|
| | | NH–VF | ⊙F | FDC |
| **2371** | **$1.14 souvenir sheet** of 2 | 3.00 | 3.00 | * |
| a | **57¢ multicoloured**, single from souvenir sheet | 1.50 | 1.25 | |

Qty: 300,000

A few "FDCs" of the souvenir sheets were prepared and cancelled on Feb 15/10, the "first day of availability".

Self-adhesive booklet of 10
**GT4, TRC Paper**
**Serpentine Die cut 13.5**

| | | NH–VF | ⊙F | FDC |
|---|---|---|---|---|
| **2372** | **57¢ multicoloured** | 1.00 | .45 | 3.15 |
| i | die cut to shape from Quarterly Pack | 1.50 | — | |
| a | booklet pane of 10 x 57¢ (2372) (**BK424**) | 10.00 | | |

Qty: 5,000,000

Issued on the occasion of Canada's first Olympic gold medal won on home soil (Alexandre Bilodeau). The stamps were made available for ordering on Canada Post's website on the evening of February 14. The stamps were placed on sale at post offices in Vancouver, BC on February 15 and nationwide thereafter.

2371

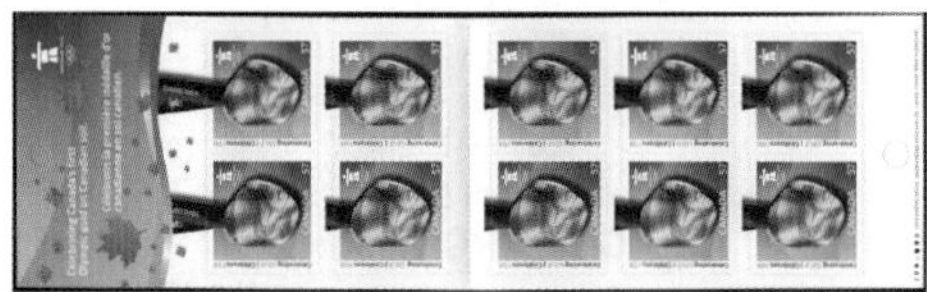
*Image rotated* 2372a

## CELEBRATING THE OLYMPIC SPIRIT

*Perforated singles from water-activated gum souvenir sheet*

2373a 2373b

*Die cut singles from self-adhesive booklet*

2374
Women's cross-country sprint, Canadian cross-country skier Chandra Crawford receiving gold medal at Torino 2006 Olympic Winter Games in Italy

2375
Men's four-man bobsleigh, men's short track relay speed skating

QE II — 2010's

Designer: Signals Design Group.

Lithography (5 colours)
Lowe-Martin
Water-activated gum souvenir sheet of 2

**2010, Feb 22** **GT 3-sided, TRC Paper** **Perf 13.1x13.0**

| | | NH–VF | ⊙F | FDC |
|---|---|---|---|---|
| **2373** | **$1.14 souvenir sheet** of 2 | 3.00 | 3.00 | 4.30 |
| a | **57¢ multicoloured** | 1.50 | 1.25 | |
| b | **57¢ multicoloured** | 1.50 | 1.25 | |
| i | se-tenant pair (2373a, 2373b) | 3.00 | 2.50 | |

Qty: 220,000

Self-adhesive booklet of 10
**GT 3-sided, TRC Paper**
**Serpentine Die cut 13.4x13.6**

| | | NH–VF | ⊙F | FDC |
|---|---|---|---|---|
| **2374** | **57¢ multicoloured** | 1.00 | .45 | — |
| **2375** | **57¢ multicoloured** | 1.00 | .45 | — |
| i | vertical pair (2374–2375), die cut to shape from Quarterly Pack | 4.00 | — | |
| a | booklet pane of 10, 5 each #2374–2375(**BK425**) 10.00 | | | |

Qty: 1,500,000 of each

The general tagging was *not* applied to the side with the illustration passing through the perfs/die cutting.

2373

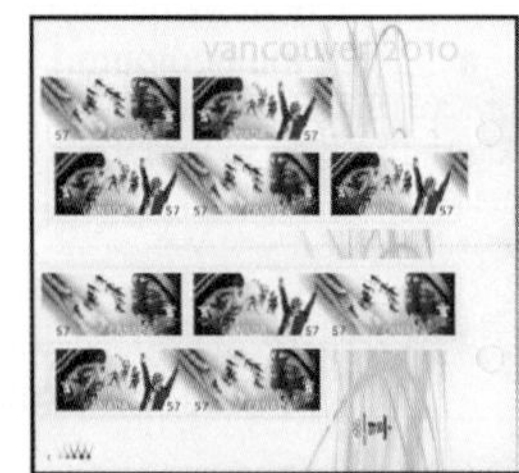
2375a

## AFRICAN VIOLETS

*Perforated singles from souvenir sheet* *Die cut singles from self-adhesive booklet*

2376a 2376b 2377 Decelles' Avalanche 2378 Picasso

Designer: Isabelle Toussaint, Design graphique.

Lithography (5 colours)
Lowe-Martin
Water-activated gum souvenir sheet of 2

**2010, Mar 3** **GT4, TRC Paper** **Perf 13.1x13.2**

| | | NH–VF | ⊙F | FDC |
|---|---|---|---|---|
| **2376** | **$1.14 souvenir sheet** of 2 | 3.40 | 3.40 | — |
| a | **multicoloured**, red flowers | 1.70 | 1.50 | |
| b | **multicoloured**, purple flowers | 1.70 | 1.50 | |
| i | se-tenant pair (2376a–b) | 3.40 | 3.00 | |

Qty: 225,000

Sheets of 120 subjects in twelve self-adhesive booklets of 10
**GT4, TRC Paper**
**Serpentine Die cut 13.4x13.5**

| | | NH–VF | ⊙F | FDC |
|---|---|---|---|---|
| **2377** | **multicoloured**, red flowers | 1.70 | .45 | |
| **2378** | **multicoloured**, purple flowers | 1.70 | .45 | |
| i | se-tenant pair (2377, 2378), die cut to shape from Quarterly Pack | 5.00 | — | |
| a | booklet pane of 10, 5 each #2377–2378 + 10 stickers (**BK426**) | 17.00 | | |

Qty: 6,500,000 of each

**Nos. 2377–2378 (2) combination FDC** **4.30***
* Stamps on FDCs are not die cut all the way through.

At time of issue, the P stamps were valued at 57¢.
For non-denominated postal cards of same designs, see UX223–UX224.
For non-denominated size 10 envelopes of same designs, see U249–U250.

2376

*Image rotated* 2378a

## CANADA–ISRAEL FRIENDSHIP

2379
National emblems

Designer: Yarek Waszul.

Lithography (4 colours), self-adhesive booklet of 6
Lowe-Martin

**2010, Apr 14** **GT4, TRC Paper** **Serpentine Die cut 13.3**

| | | NH–VF | ⊙F | FDC |
|---|---|---|---|---|
| **2379** | **$1.70 multicoloured** | 3.50 | 1.50 | 5.40 |
| i | die cut to shape from Quarterly Pack/ Annual Collection | 5.00 | — | |
| a | booklet pane of 3 x $1.70 (2379) | 10.50 | | |
| **BK427** | two panes of 2379a $21.00 | | | |

Qty: 660,000

**Joint FDC with Israel** **8.00**
Celebrating 60 years of friendship between the two countries. Joint issue with Israel.

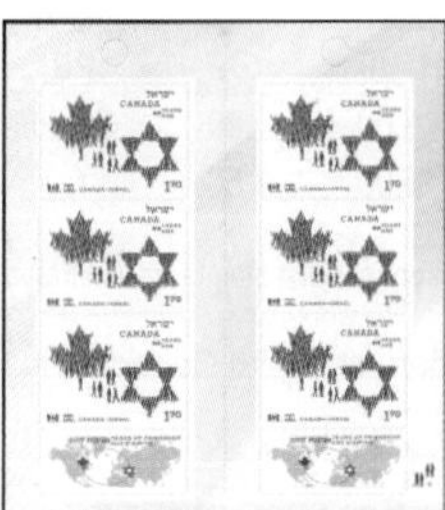
2379a

Joint issue with Israel
**Scott # 1812**

## FOUR INDIAN KINGS

2380 Tee Yee Neen Ho Ga Row
2381 Sa Ga Yeath Qua Pieth Tow

2382 Ho Nee Yeath Taw No Row
2383 Etow Oh Koam

Designer: Sputnik Design Partners Inc.

Lithography (9 colours), pane of 16 and souvenir sheet of 4
Lowe-Martin

| 2010, Apr 19 | GT4, TRC Paper | | | Perf 12.5 | |
|---|---|---|---|---|---|
| | | NH–VF | ⊙F | PB | FDC |
| 2380 | **57¢ multicoloured** | 1.00 | .60 | | |
| 2381 | **57¢ multicoloured** | 1.00 | .60 | | |
| 2382 | **57¢ multicoloured** | 1.00 | .60 | | |
| 2383 | **57¢ multicoloured** | 1.00 | .60 | | |
| a | se-tenant block, or strip of 4 (2380–83) | 4.00 | 3.00 | 5.00 | 6.55* |
| b | $2.28 souvenir sheet of 4 | 5.00 | 5.00 | | |
| c | $2.28 overprinted souvenir sheet of 4 | 7.50 | 7.50 | | |

Qty: 375,000 of each; 150,000 of souvenir sheet; 80,000 of overprinted souvenir sheet.
* Strip of 4 on first day cover.

Issued on the 300th anniversary of the painting of four portraits of First Nations "Kings" while on a visit with the British Queen in London on April 19, 1710.

2383b

2383c

## CANADIAN NAVY CENTENNIAL

*Perforated singles from water-activated gum souvenir sheet*

2384a 2384b

*Die cut singles from self-adhesive booklet*

2385
*HMCS Niobe*

2386
*HMCS Halifax*

Designer: Designwerke Inc.

Lithography (6 colours plus varnish)
Lowe-Martin
Water-activated gum souvenir sheet of 2

| 2010, May 4 | GT 3-sided, TRC Paper | | Perf 12.5 | |
|---|---|---|---|---|
| | | NH–VF | ⊙F | FDC |
| 2384 | **$1.14 souvenir sheet** of 2 | 3.00 | 3.00 | 4.30 |
| a | **57¢ multicoloured** | 1.50 | 1.25 | |
| b | **57¢ multicoloured** | 1.50 | 1.25 | |
| i | se-tenant pair (2384a, 2384b) | 3.00 | 2.50 | |

Qty: 225,000

Self-adhesive booklet of 10
**GT 3-sided, TRC Paper**
**Serpentine Die cut 13.3x13.5**

| | | NH–VF | ⊙F | FDC |
|---|---|---|---|---|
| 2385 | **57¢ multicoloured** | 1.00 | .45 | — |
| 2386 | **57¢ multicoloured** | 1.00 | .45 | — |
| i | se-tenant pair, die cut to shape from Quarterly Pack | 3.00 | — | |
| a | booklet pane of 10, 5 each #2385–2386 (**BK428**) | 10.00 | | |

Qty: 1,500,000 of each

The general tagging was *not* applied to the side with the illustration passing through the perfs/die cutting.

2384

2386a

## MARINE LIFE

2387a 2387b

2387c 2387d
Harbour Porpoise Sea Otter

Designer: Martin Mörck. Engraving: Lars Sjööblom.

Lithography (3 colours) and intaglio (2 colours)
Sweden Post Stamps
Water-activated gum souvenir sheet of 2 and booklet of 8

| 2010, May 13 | GT4 | | Perf 12.9x12.8 | |
|---|---|---|---|---|
| | | NH–VF | ⊙F | FDC |
| 2387 | **$1.14 souvenir sheet** of 2* | 3.00 | 3.00 | — |
| a | **57¢ multicoloured,** porpoise | 1.50 | 1.25 | |
| b | **57¢ multicoloured,** otter | 1.50 | 1.25 | |
| i | se-tenant pair from souvenir sheet (2387a, 2387b) | 3.00 | 2.50 | |
| c | **57¢ multicoloured,** porpoise † | 1.00 | .45 | — |
| ci | 'longer' dash to left of small porpoise (pos. 3) | 3.00 | 1.00 | |
| cii | 'shorter' dash to left of small porpoise (pos. 7) | 3.00 | 1.00 | |
| d | **57¢ multicoloured,** otter † | 1.00 | .45 | — |
| di | two extra brown dots in white wave (pos. 2 on panes with blue '1') | 3.00 | 1.00 | |
| e | booklet pane of 8, 4 each #2387c–2387d (**BK429**) | 8.00 | | |

Qty: 2387: 225,000, 2387c–d: 1,100,000 of each
* Middle column of souvenir sheet, with Maple Leaf-shaped perforation, is perf 12.0. Elliptical perfs on opposite side to Maple-Leaf shaped perf. That is, elliptical perf to left of porpoises and right of otters.
† From booklet pane; elliptical perfs between pair of stamps (2387c–d); a first in Canada. That is, elliptical perf to right of porpoises and left of otters.
Booklet panes exist with markings on the right selvedge: blue 1 or 2; black 6-digit serial number. 2387ci/ii varieties occur on some panes with blue '2'.

| | |
|---|---|
| **Nos. 2387c–2387d (2) combination FDC** | **4.30** |
| **Joint FDC with Sweden** | **12.00** |

Joint issue with Sweden. Sweden's issue had four designs.

2387

2387e

QE II — 2010's

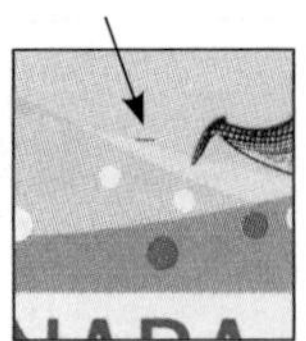
2387ci

2387cii

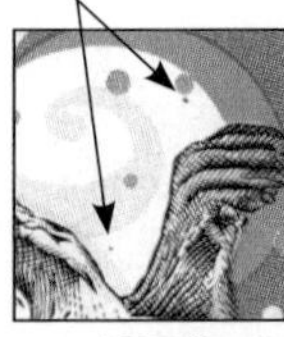
2387di

Joint issue with Sweden (4 designs, **Scott # 2638**)

## WILDLIFE PHOTOGRAPHY

*Perforated singles from water-activated gum souvenir sheet*

2388a

2388b

2388c

2388d

2388e

*Die cut singles from self-adhesive booklet*

2389
Hummingbird

2390
Tree Swallows

2391
Katydid

2392
Red Fox

2393
Great Blue Heron

2388

*Image rotated* 2393a

Designer: Susan Scott.
Contest winners: Martin Cooper (Birds), Ben Boulter (Mammals), Julie Bazinet (Insects), Mark Bradley (Urban wildlife), Wing Yan Tam (Junior, 15 and under).

Lithography (5 colours)
Canadian Bank Note
Water-activated gum souvenir sheet of 5

**2010, May 22** **GT4, TRC Paper** **Perf 12.5x13.1**

| | | NH–VF | ⊙F | FDC |
|---|---|---|---|---|
| **2388** | **$2.85 souvenir sheet** of 5 | 6.00 | 6.00 | 7.70 |
| a | **57¢ multicoloured**, heron | 1.50 | 1.25 | |
| b | **57¢ multicoloured**, fox | 1.50 | 1.25 | |
| c | **57¢ multicoloured**, katydid | 1.50 | 1.25 | |
| d | **57¢ multicoloured**, swallows | 1.50 | 1.25 | |
| e | **57¢ multicoloured**, hummingbird | 1.50 | 1.25 | |

Qty: 225,000

The lower right corner of the souvenir sheet shows contest runners-up photographs.

Self-adhesive booklet of 10
**GT4, TRC Paper**
**Serpentine Die cut 13.4**

| | | NH–VF | ⊙F | FDC |
|---|---|---|---|---|
| **2389** | **57¢ multicoloured**, hummingbird | 1.00 | .45 | — |
| i | die cut to shape from Quarterly Pack | 1.50 | — | |
| **2390** | **57¢ multicoloured**, swallows | 1.00 | .45 | — |
| i | die cut to shape from Quarterly Pack | 1.50 | — | |
| **2391** | **57¢ multicoloured**, katydid | 1.00 | .45 | — |
| i | die cut to shape from Quarterly Pack | 1.50 | — | |
| **2392** | **57¢ multicoloured**, fox | 1.00 | .45 | — |
| i | die cut to shape from Quarterly Pack | 1.50 | — | |
| **2393** | **57¢ multicoloured**, heron | 1.00 | .45 | — |
| i | die cut to shape from Quarterly Pack | 1.50 | — | |
| a | booklet pane of 10, 2 each #2389–2393 (**BK430**) | 10.00 | | |

Qty: 400,000 of each

Images selected from winners of 2009 Wildlife Photography contest with *Canadian Geographic* magazine (celebrating 80th anniversary in 2010), in partnership with the Canadian Museum of Nature.

## ROTARY INTERNATIONAL CENTENNIAL

2394
Traditional Rotary Vest

Designer: Xerxes Irani.

Lithography (6 colours plus varnish), self-adhesive booklet of 8
Lowe-Martin

**2010, Jun 18** **GT4, TRC Paper**
**Serpentine Die cut 13.4x13.0**

| | | NH–VF | ⊙F | FDC |
|---|---|---|---|---|
| **2394** | **57¢ multicoloured** | 1.00 | .40 | 3.10 |
| i | die cut to shape from Quarterly Pack/ Annual Collection | 1.50 | — | |
| a | booklet pane of 8 x 57¢ (2394) (**BK431**) | 8.00 | | |

Qty: 2,000,000

100th anniversary of Rotary International in Canada.
For non-denominated postal card of same design, see UX225.

2394a

## *ART CANADA:* PRUDENCE HEWARD

2395
*Rollande*

2396a
*At the Theatre*

Designer: Hélène L'Heureux. Paintings by Prudence Heward, 1896–1947.
Lithography (7 colours), pane of 16
Lowe-Martin

**2010, Jul 2** **GT4, TRC Paper** **Perf 13.3x13.0**

| | | NH–VF | ⊙F | PB | FDC |
|---|---|---|---|---|---|
| **2395** | **57¢ multicoloured** | 1.00 | .45 | 5.00 | 3.10 |
| Qty: 1,500,000 | | | | | |
| **2396** | **$2.27 souvenir sheet** of 2 | 5.00 | 5.00 | | 6.15 |
| a | **$1.70 multicoloured** | 3.00 | 3.00 | | |
| Qty: 220,000 | | | | | |

Transparent gum (i.e. colourless) on water-activated TRC paper was introduced with this issue.

2396

## ROADSIDE ATTRACTIONS — 2

*Perforated singles from water-activated gum souvenir sheet*

2397a
*Coffee Pot*, Davidson, SK

2397b
*Happy Rock*, Gladstone, MB

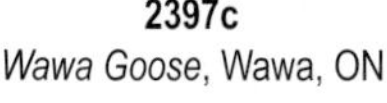

2397c
*Wawa Goose*, Wawa, ON

2397d
*Puffin*, Longue-Pointe-de-Mingan, QC

*Die cut singles from self-adhesive booklet*

2398
*Coffee Pot*, Davidson, SK

2399
*Happy Rock*, Gladstone, MB

2400
*Wawa Goose*, Wawa, ON

2401
*Puffin*, Longue-Pointe-de-Mingan, QC

Designer: Fraser Ross (Semaphor Design Company).
Lithography (8 colours plus varnish), water-activated gum souvenir sheet of 4
Lowe-Martin

**2010, Jul 5** **GT4, TRC Paper** **Perf 12.8x12.9**

| | | NH–VF | ⊙F | FDC |
|---|---|---|---|---|
| **2397** | **$2.28 souvenir sheet** of 4 | 7.00 | 7.00 | — |
| a | **P multicoloured** | 1.70 | 1.50 | |
| b | **P multicoloured** | 1.70 | 1.50 | |
| c | **P multicoloured** | 1.70 | 1.50 | |
| d | **P multicoloured** | 1.70 | 1.50 | |
| Qty: 210,000 | | | | |

Lithography (8 colours), self-adhesive booklet of 8
**Serpentine Die cut 13.4 on 3 sides**

| | | NH–VF | ⊙F | FDC |
|---|---|---|---|---|
| **2398** | **P multicoloured** | 1.70 | .60 | |
| **2399** | **P multicoloured** | 1.70 | .60 | |
| **2400** | **P multicoloured** | 1.70 | .60 | |
| **2401** | **P multicoloured** | 1.70 | .60 | |
| a | booklet pane of 4 x P (2398–2401) + 4 stickers | 6.80 | | 6.30 |
| **BK432** | two panes of 2401a $13.50 | | | |
| Qty: 970,000 of each stamp | | | | |

At time of issue, the P stamps were valued at 57¢.
For non-denominated postal cards of same designs, see UX226–UX229. Second of a three-year series. See also 2335–2336, 2484–2485.

2397

2 x 2401a (BK432)

## GIRL GUIDES OF CANADA

**2402**
Girl Guides and Badges

Designer: Derwyn Goodall.
Lithography (6 colours plus varnish), self-adhesive booklet of 10
Lowe-Martin

**2010, Jul 8** **GT4, TRC Paper**
**Serpentine Die cut 13.7**

| | | NH–VF | ⊙F | FDC |
|---|---|---|---|---|
| **2402** | **P multicoloured** | 1.70 | .40 | 3.10 |
| i | die cut to shape from Quarterly Pack/ Annual Collection | 2.50 | — | |
| a | booklet pane of 10 x P (2402) + 10 stickers (**BK433**) | 17.00 | | |

Qty: 3,000,000

At time of issue, the P stamp was valued at 57¢.
100th anniversary of Girl Guides of Canada.

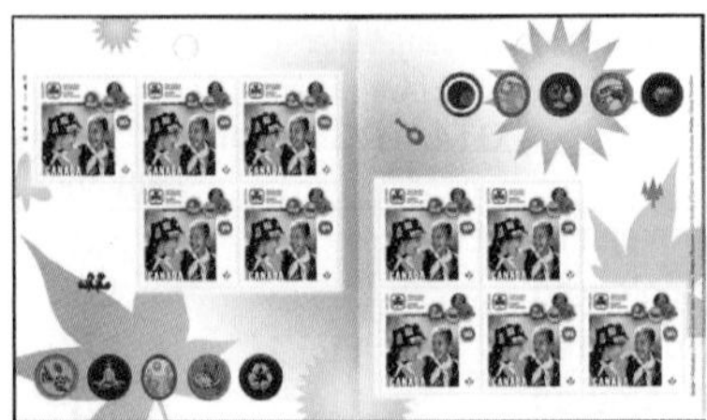

**2402a**

## CUPIDS

**2403**
Map, artifacts (coins, beads)

Designer: Steven Slipp (Semaphor Design).
Lithography (9 colours), pane of 16
Lowe-Martin

**2010, Aug 17** **GT4, TRC Paper** **Perf 12.5***

| | | NH–VF | ⊙F | PB | FDC |
|---|---|---|---|---|---|
| **2403** | **57¢ multicoloured** | 1.00 | .45 | 4.00 | 3.10 |

Qty: 1,750,000
* All stamps have transitional perfs along the top and bottom of each stamp, as illustrated below.

400th anniversary of the settlement of Cupids (then Cuppers Cove), Newfoundland.

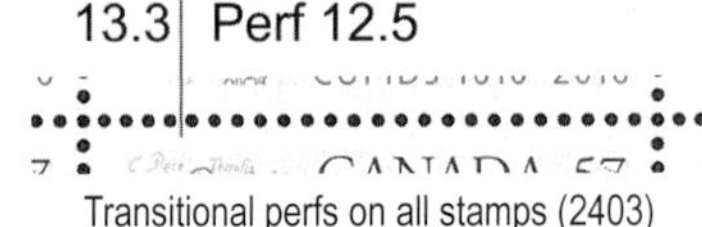

Transitional perfs on all stamps (2403)

## HOME CHILDREN

**2404**
Photograph, Farming, *SS Sardinian*

Designer: Debbie Adams.
Lithography (6 colours plus varnish), pane of 16
Lowe-Martin

**2010, Sep 1** **GT4, TRC Paper** **Perf 12.5**

| | | NH–VF | ⊙F | PB | FDC |
|---|---|---|---|---|---|
| **2404** | **57¢ multicoloured** | 1.00 | .45 | 4.00* | 3.10 |

Qty: 1,750,000
* Only the lower right block of the pane included a full inscription and paper/colour designations.

The Government of Canada proclaimed 2010 the Year of the British Home Child. Starting in 1869, and continuing into the years following the Second World War, more than 100,000 orphaned, abandoned and pauper children were sent to Canada by British churches and philanthropic organizations.

Timeline:
**2010, Sep 7** P (57¢)+10¢ Mental Health, semi-postal (B16)

## WILDLIFE DEFINITIVE

*Scaled to 70%*
**2405**
Blue Whale

Designer: Fugazi. Engraved by Jorge Peral.
Lithography (4 colours), Silkscreen and Engraving
Sheets of 18 subjects in nine panes of 2
Canadian Bank Note

**2010, Oct 4** **Not tagged, TRC Paper** **Perf 12.5x13.1**

| | | NH–VF | ⊙F | PB | FDC |
|---|---|---|---|---|---|
| **2405** | **$10 multicoloured** | 20.00 | 7.50 | 45.00* | 22.00 |
| i | $180 uncut press sheet of 9 panes | 425.00 | | | |

Qty: 2405: 1,500,000; 2405i: 1,000.

VF used examples with an in-period cancellation may sell for more than the face value.
* Price is for full pane of 2 with inscription in left selvedge.
For size 10 envelope of same design see U259.

For other $1–$8 high-value Wildlife definitives, see Scott 1687–1694.

## BENEFICIAL INSECTS
### Low Value Definitives

**2406**
Paper wasp

**2407**
Assassin bug

**2408**
Large milkweed bug

**2409**
Margined leatherwing

**2410**
Dogbane beetle

Designer: Keith Martin.

Lithography (5 colours), panes of 50
Canadian Bank Note

| 2010, Oct 19 | Not tagged, TRC Paper | | | Perf 13.0x13.4 | |
|---|---|---|---|---|---|
| | | NH–VF | ⊙F | PB | FDC |
| **2406** | **4¢ multicoloured** | .25 | .25 | .30 | |
| a | dated '2012', with added microprinting and small design features (from 2409b), *Oct 16, 2012* | .25 | .25 | | |
| **2407** | **6¢ multicoloured** | .25 | .25 | .50* | |
| **2408** | **7¢ multicoloured** | .25 | .25 | .55 | |
| **2409** | **8¢ multicoloured** | .25 | .25 | .65 | |
| a | dated '2012', with added microprinting and small design features (from 2409b), *Oct 16, 2012* | .25 | .25 | | |
| b | 15¢ souvenir sheet of 3 (2235b, 2406a, 2409a), *Oct 16, 2012* | 2.00 | .30 | | 2.30 |
| **2410** | **9¢ multicoloured** | .25 | .25 | .70 | |
| i | $30 uncut press sheet of 8 panes † | 60.00 | | | |
| a | 34¢ souvenir sheet of 5 ‡ | 3.00 | .50 | | 2.70 |

Qty: 2409b: 700,000; 2410i: 5,000; 2410a: 400,000

* The printer inscription in all four corners on the 6¢ value incorrectly reads "Lowe Martin" instead of "Canadian Bank Note".
† The uncut press sheet consists of 3 panes of 2410, 2 panes of 2409, and 1 pane each of 2406, 2407, 2408.
‡ The gum on the souvenir sheet (2410a) has a green-coloured tinge; the gum on the stamps from panes of 50 is transparent (i.e. colourless).

For 1¢, 3¢–25¢ values see Sc. 2234–2238. For 2¢ value see Sc. 2328. For 22¢ value see Sc. 2708.

*Hidden features*

2406a

2409a

2409b

2410a

2407 – inscription error

## CHRISTMAS: ORNAMENTS

*Perforated singles from water-activated gum souvenir sheet*

2411a

2411b

2411c

2412

*Die cut singles from self-adhesive booklet*

2413

2414

2415

Designer: Michael Zavacky, McMillan.

Lithography (8 colours plus varnish)
Lowe-Martin
Water-activated gum souvenir sheet of 3

| 2010, Nov 1 | GT4, TRC Paper | | Perf 12.5 | |
|---|---|---|---|---|
| | | NH–VF | ⊙F | FDC |
| **2411** | **$3.27 souvenir sheet** of 3 | 7.25 | 7.25 | 8.55 |
| a | **P multicoloured** | 1.75 | 1.50 | |
| b | **$1.00 multicoloured** | 2.00 | 2.00 | |
| c | **$1.70 multicoloured** | 3.40 | 3.40 | |

Qty: 200,000

Designer: Joseph Gault. Sculptor: Antonio Caruso.

Lithography (7 colours plus varnish), self-adhesive booklet of 12
Lowe-Martin

| 2010, Nov 1 | GT4, TRC Paper | Serpentine Die cut 13.4 | | |
|---|---|---|---|---|
| | | NH–VF | ⊙F | FDC |
| **2412** | **P multicoloured** | 1.70 | .25 | 3.15 |
| i | die cut to shape from Quarterly Pack/ Annual Collection | 2.50 | — | |
| a | booklet pane of 6 x P (2412) | 10.00 | — | |
| BK435 | two panes of 2412a $20.00 | | | |

Qty: 8,500,000

Designer: Michael Zavacky, McMillan.

Lithography (5 colours plus varnish), self-adhesive booklet of 12 (P) or 6
Lowe-Martin

| 2010, Nov 1 | GT4, TRC Paper | Serpentine Die cut 13.5 | | |
|---|---|---|---|---|
| | | NH–VF | ⊙F | FDC |
| **2413** | **P multicoloured** | 1.70 | .25 | — |
| i | die cut to shape from Quarterly Pack | 2.50 | — | |
| a | booklet pane of 6 x P (2413) | 10.00 | — | |
| BK436 | two panes of 2413a $20.00 | | | |
| Qty: 23,000,000 | | | | |
| **2414** | **$1.00 multicoloured** | 2.00 | .75 | — |
| i | die cut to shape from Quarterly Pack | 3.00 | — | |
| a | booklet pane of 6 x $1.00 (2414) (**BK437**) | 12.00 | — | |
| Qty: 3,720,000 | | | | |
| **2415** | **$1.70 multicoloured** | 3.40 | 1.25 | — |
| i | die cut to shape from Quarterly Pack | 5.00 | — | |
| a | booklet pane of 6 x $1.70 (2415) (**BK438**) | 20.50 | — | |
| b | gutter pane, 2414a and 2415a | 35.00 | | |

Qty: 3,720,000; gutter pane: 4,500

At time of issue, the P Christmas stamps were valued at 57¢.

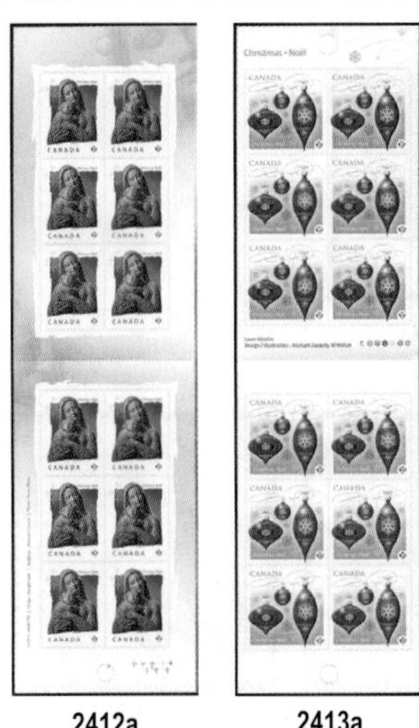

2412a 2413a

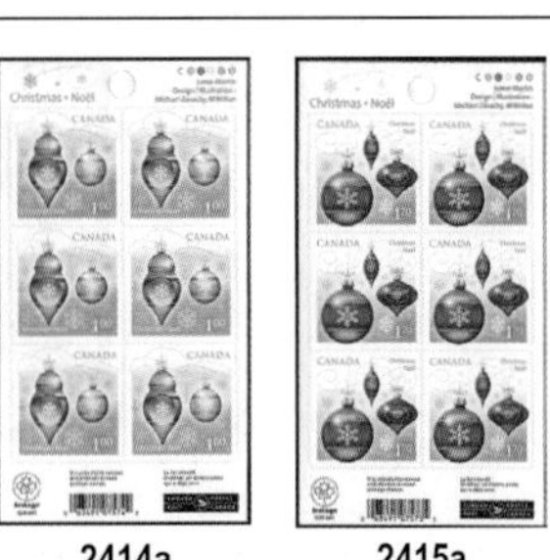

2414a 2415a

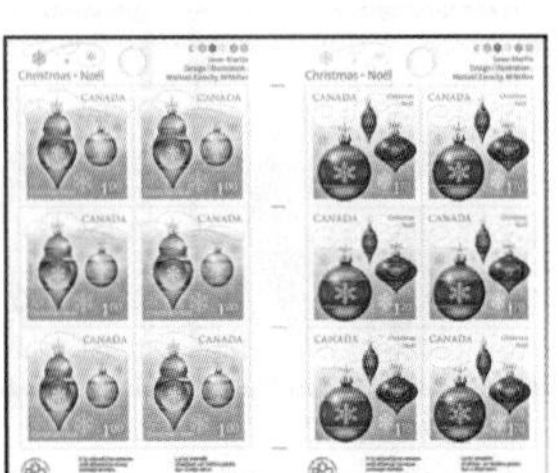

2415b

2411

## 2011

### LUNAR NEW YEAR (Series 2) — 3
### Year of the Rabbit

2416
Hopping rabbit

2417i
Rabbits chasing each other

Designer: Paul Haslip, Lauren Rand (HM&E Design).

Lithography (6 colours) plus 1 foil stamping and embossing plus varnish, pane of 25
Lowe-Martin, Gravure Choquet

**2011, Jan 7** **GT4, TRC Paper** **Perf 12.5**

| | | NH–VF | ⊙F | PB | FDC |
|---|---|---|---|---|---|
| **2416** | **multicoloured** | 1.70 | .60 | 8.50 | 3.20 |

Qty: 5,500,000

At time of issue, the P stamp was valued at 59¢ even though the 59¢ domestic rate did not go into effect until January 17.

**Single stamp General Tagged on left, right and bottom**

| | | | | | |
|---|---|---|---|---|---|
| **2417** | **$1.75 souvenir sheet** of 1 | 3.50 | 3.50 | — | 5.50 |
| i | $1.75 single stamp from souvenir sheet | 3.00 | 3.00 | — | |
| ii | $29.95 uncut press sheet of 12 souvenir sheets | 60.00 | | | |

Qty: 2417: 550,000; 2417ii: 20,000

Scott 2496a (Year of the Dragon 'transitional' souvenir sheet) also produces a 2417i single.

For non-denominated postal cards of same designs, see UX230–UX231.

*Image rotated* 2417

| Rates: | Domestic first-class (0-30g): 59¢ | USA (0-30g): $1.03 |
|---|---|---|
| Jan 17/11– | Domestic first-class (30-50g): $1.03 | USA (30-50g): $1.25 |
| Jan 15/12 | Domestic oversize (0-100g): $1.25 | International (0-30g): $1.75 |

*single usage:* USA $1.03: $15.00 | International $1.75: $20.00

### PERMANENT™ CANADIAN PRIDE (O CANADA)

*Perforated singles from water-activated gum souvenir sheet*

| **2418a** | **2418b** | **2418c** | **2418d** | **2418e** |
|---|---|---|---|---|
| Flag on Soldier's Uniform | Flag on Hot-air Balloon | Flag on Search and Rescue Team's Uniform | Flag on Canadarm | Flag on Backpack |

*Die cut singles from self-adhesive booklet*

**2419** **2420** **2421** **2422** **2423**

Designers: Lionel Gadoury, Terry Popik (Context Creative).

Lithography (4 colours)
Canadian Bank Note
Water-activated gum souvenir sheet of 5; Sheets of 75 subjects in fifteen panes of 5

**2011, Jan 17** **GT4, TRC Paper** **Perf 13.0x13.3**

| | | NH–VF | ⊙F | FDC |
|---|---|---|---|---|
| **2418** | **$2.95 souvenir sheet** of 5 † | 8.50 | 8.50 | 7.80 |
| a | **multicoloured**, Soldier's uniform | 1.70 | 1.50 | |
| b | **multicoloured**, Hot-air balloon | 1.70 | 1.50 | |
| c | **multicoloured**, Search and rescue | 1.70 | 1.50 | |
| d | **multicoloured**, Canadarm | 1.70 | 1.50 | |
| e | **multicoloured**, Backpack | 1.70 | 1.50 | |

Qty: 205,000

Self-adhesive booklets of 10 and 30

**2011, Jan 17** **GT4, TRC Paper**
**Serpentine Die cut 13.4**

| | | NH–VF | ⊙F | FDC |
|---|---|---|---|---|
| **2419** | **multicoloured**, Soldier's uniform | 1.70 | .25 | — |
| i | non-fluorescent yellow ink | 2.00 | .25 | |
| **2420** | **multicoloured**, Hot-air balloon | 1.70 | .25 | — |
| i | non-fluorescent yellow ink | 2.00 | .25 | |
| **2421** | **multicoloured**, Search and rescue | 1.70 | .25 | — |
| i | non-fluorescent yellow ink | 2.00 | .25 | |
| **2422** | **multicoloured**, Canadarm | 1.70 | .25 | — |
| **2423** | **multicoloured**, Backpack | 1.70 | .25 | — |
| ii | non-fluorescent yellow ink | 2.00 | .25 | |
| i | se-tenant strip of 5 (2419–2423), die cut to shape from Quarterly Pack | 12.50 | — | |
| a | booklet pane of 10 x P (2 each of 2419–2423) (**BK439**) | 17.00 | | |
| ai | as "a", non-fluorescent yellow ink (**BK439i**) | 25.00 | | |
| b | booklet pane of 30 x P (6 each of 2419–2423) (**BK440**) | 50.00 | | |
| bi | as "b", non-fluorescent yellow ink (**BK440i**) | 70.00 | | |
| aii | strip of 5, from 2423a/BK439 or 2423b/BK440 | 8.50 | | |
| aiii | strip of 5, from 2423ai/BK439i or 2423bi/BK440i | 12.50 | | |

The original printings of 2419–23, 2423a (BK439) and 2423b (BK440) have fluorescent yellow ink; reprints (2423ai/2423bi) with non-fluorescent ink appeared mid-2011. An ultraviolet light is required to spot these. 2422 does not show this variety.

2423ai/BK439i exists with "weak pink tagging" (the maple leaves); value same as normal.

Counterfeits of 2419–2423 exist. These are untagged.

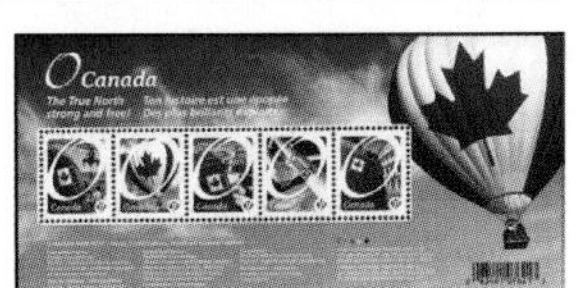
2418

2423a

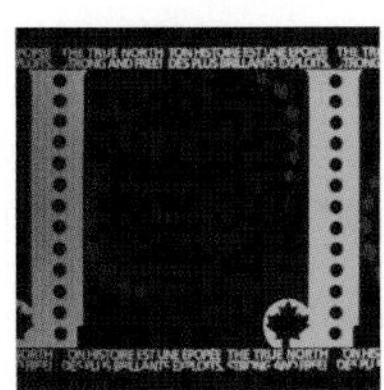
Tagging on 'Canadian Pride' definitives

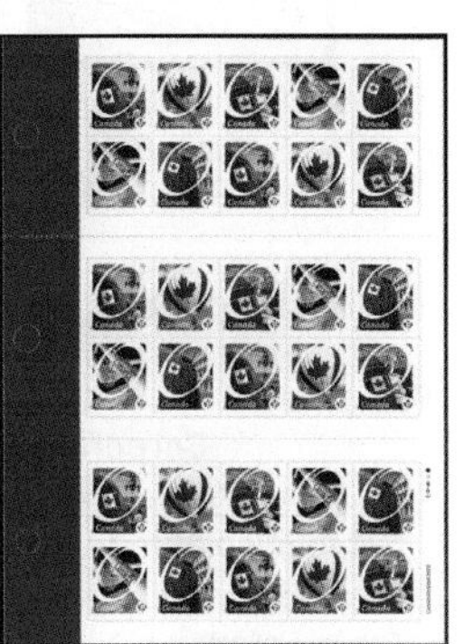
2423b

## BABY WILDLIFE DEFINITIVES — SOUVENIR SHEET

| 2424a | 2424b | 2424c | 2424d |
|---|---|---|---|
| Arctic Hare | Red Fox | Canada Geese | Polar Bear |

Designers: Monique Dufour, Sophie Lafortune.
Lithography (8 colours)
Lowe-Martin
Water-activated gum souvenir sheet of 4

**2011, Jan 17** **GT4, TRC Paper** **Perf 13.4x13.1**

| | | NH–VF | ⊙F | FDC |
|---|---|---|---|---|
| **2424** | **$4.62 souvenir sheet** of 4 * | 9.75 | 9.75 | 11.25 |
| a | **multicoloured** † | 1.75 | 1.50 | |
| b | **$1.03 multicoloured** | 2.00 | 1.75 | |
| c | **$1.25 multicoloured** | 2.50 | 2.25 | |
| d | **$1.75 multicoloured** | 3.50 | 3.25 | |

Qty: 205,000

* Face value of $4.62 at time of issue; the face value of the P stamp was 59¢.

2424

Tagging and 'hidden' footprints on Baby Wildlife definitives.

## BABY WILDLIFE DEFINITIVES – COILS

2425 2426
Arctic Hare

| 2427 | 2428 | 2429 |
|---|---|---|
| Red Fox | Canada Geese | Polar Bear |

Designers: Monique Dufour, Sophie Lafortune.
Lithography (5 colours), self-adhesive rolls of 100 (P) and 50 ($1.03, $1.25, $1.75)
Lowe-Martin

**2011, Jan 17** **GT4, TRC Paper**
**Serpentine Die cut 9.2 Horiz**
**(Rounded tips)**

| | | NH–VF | ⊙F | FDC |
|---|---|---|---|---|
| **2425** | **multicoloured**, (starts w/peak) † | 2.00 | 2.00 | — |
| i | inverted die cutting, (starts w/valley) | * | 2.00 | |

* mint copies have not yet been reported

2425 issued in horizontal rolls of 5,000. Individual stamps do not touch along the horizontal roll; rounded 'perf tips' start with a peak (or a valley). Sold in strips of 4 or 10 by the National Philatelic Centre; single stamps included in the Quarterly Pack/ Annual Collection.

| 2425 | 2425i | 2426 |
|---|---|---|
| starts with peak | starts with valley | variable |

Arctic Hare – die cutting (actual size)

**Serpentine Die cut 8.15 to 8.50 Horiz**
**(Rounded tips with 4 or 5 'nibs' between stamps)**

To date, one die cut pattern has been used on these stamps and has been used both upright and inverted.

**2011, Jan 17** **GT4, TRC Paper**

| | | NH–VF | ⊙F | FDC |
|---|---|---|---|---|
| **2426** | **multicoloured** † | 1.70 | .25 | — |
| i | gutter strip of 4 with inscription | 8.50 | | |
| | starter strip of 4 (wavy die cut) | 11.00 | | |
| | end strip of 4 (wavy die cut) | 11.00 | | |
| ii | die cut to shape (9.2 horiz) from Quarterly Pack, *Apr '11* ‡ | 2.50 | — | |
| iii | $59 uncut press panel of 100 | 170.00 | | |
| iv | horiz. pair, imperf. between, from 2426iii | 4.00 | 4.00 | |
| v | block of 4, imperf. vert. with insc., from 2426iii | 10.00 | 10.00 | |

Qty: 2426iii: 1,100

| Format: | Coil | | | Souvenir sheet | Booklet | |
|---|---|---|---|---|---|---|
| Die cut/perf: | 8.15–8.50 horiz | 9.2 horiz | 9.2 horiz Qtr pack | Perf 13.4x13.1 | 9.2 horiz | 9.2 horiz Qtr pack |
| Arctic Hare | 2426, i | 2425 | 2426ii | 2424a | | |
| $1.03 Red Fox | 2427, i | | 2427ii | 2424b | 2430 | 2430i |
| $1.25 Canada Geese | 2428, i | | 2428ii | 2424c | 2431 | 2431i |
| $1.75 Polar Bear | 2429, i | | 2429ii | 2424d | 2432 | 2432i |

For P, $1.05, $1.29, $1.80 Baby Wildlife see 2504–2512
For P, $1.10, $1.34, $1.85 Baby Wildlife see 2....

**† PERMANENT™ non-denominated stamps**

The stamps identified with the symbol of a letter "P" within a red maple leaf are valid indefinitely for use within Canada. Regardless of rate increases, these definitives will be worth the Canadian domestic basic letter rate in effect, and can be used to mail a letter that weighs up to 30 grams to any address in Canada. At time of issue, the P stamps on these pages (Jan 17/11 issue date) were valued at 59¢.

| | | NH–VF | ⊙F | FDC |
|---|---|---|---|---|
| **2427** | **$1.03 multicoloured** | 1.85 | .45 | — |
| i | gutter strip of 4 with inscription | 9.00 | | |
| | starter strip of 4 (wavy die cut) | 10.50 | | |
| | end strip of 4 (wavy die cut) | 10.50 | | |
| ii | die cut to shape (9.2 horiz) from Quarterly Pack, *Apr '11* ‡ | 2.75 | — | |
| **2428** | **$1.25 multicoloured** | 2.50 | .75 | — |
| i | gutter strip of 4 with inscription | 10.00 | | |
| | starter strip of 4 (wavy die cut) | 11.00 | | |
| | end strip of 4 (wavy die cut) | 11.00 | | |
| ii | die cut to shape (9.2 horiz) from Quarterly Pack, *Apr '11* ‡ | 3.75 | — | |
| **2429** | **$1.75 multicoloured** | 3.50 | 1.00 | — |
| i | gutter strip of 4 with inscription | 17.00 | | |
| | starter strip of 4 (wavy die cut) | 19.00 | | |
| | end strip of 4 (wavy die cut) | 19.00 | | |
| ii | die cut to shape (9.2 horiz) from Quarterly Pack, *Apr '11* ‡ | 5.25 | — | |

‡ Single stamps supplied in the Quarterly Pack have rounded tips (backing paper is 'plain'), starting with a peak at upper left; stamps from the full rolls are perf 8.15 to 8.50.

For non-denominated postal cards of same designs, see UX232–UX235.
For size 10 envelopes of same designs see U260–U263.

## BABY WILDLIFE DEFINITIVES – BOOKLETS

2430
Red Fox

2431
Canada Geese

2432
Polar Bear

Designers: Monique Dufour, Sophie Lafortune.
Lithography (5 colours), self-adhesive booklets of 6
Lowe-Martin

**2011, Jan 17** **GT4, TRC Paper**
**Serpentine Die cut 9.2 horiz (Rounded tips)**

| | | NH–VF | ⊙F | FDC |
|---|---|---|---|---|
| **2430** | **$1.03 multicoloured** | 2.00 | .45 | — |
| i | die cut to shape from Quarterly Pack ‡ | 3.00 | — | |
| a | booklet pane of 6 x $1.03 (2430) (**BK441**) | 12.00 | | |
| **2431** | **$1.25 multicoloured** | 2.50 | .75 | — |
| i | die cut to shape from Quarterly Pack ‡ | 3.75 | — | |
| a | booklet pane of 6 x $1.25 (2431) (**BK442**) | 15.00 | | |
| **2432** | **$1.75 multicoloured** | 3.50 | 1.00 | — |
| i | die cut to shape from Quarterly Pack ‡ | 5.25 | — | |
| a | booklet pane of 6 x $1.75 (2432) (**BK443**) | 19.50 | | |

2432a exists imperforate (BK443i).

‡ Single stamps supplied in the Quarterly packs start with a peak at the upper left (backing paper contains some form of printing from backside of booklet); single stamps from booklets of 6 start with a valley at the upper left.

2430a 2431a 2432a



## BLACK HISTORY MONTH

2433
Carrie Best
(1903–2001)

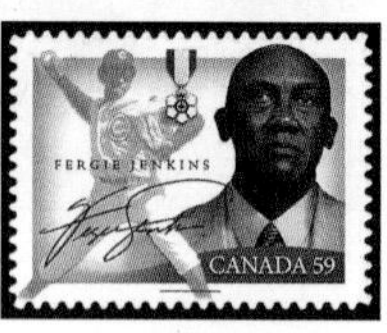


2434
Ferguson Jenkins
(1942– )

Designer: Lara Minja (Lime Design Inc.).
Lithography (7 colours plus varnish), self-adhesive booklets of 10
Lowe-Martin

**2011, Feb 1** **GT4, TRC Paper**
**Serpentine Die cut 13.5x13.9**

| | | NH–VF | ⊙F | FDC |
|---|---|---|---|---|
| **2433** | **59¢ multicoloured** | 1.20 | .45 | 3.20 |
| i | die cut to shape from Quarterly Pack/ Annual Collection | 1.80 | — | |
| a | booklet pane of 10 x 59¢ (2433) (**BK444**) | 12.00 | | |

Qty: 1,700,000

Publisher of *The Clarion*, one of Nova Scotia's first newspapers for Black Canadians.

| | | NH–VF | ⊙F | FDC |
|---|---|---|---|---|
| **2434** | **59¢ multicoloured** | 1.20 | .45 | 3.20 |
| i | die cut to shape from Quarterly Pack/ Annual Collection | 1.80 | — | |
| a | booklet pane of 10 x 59¢ (2434) (**BK445**) | 12.00 | | |

Qty: 4,000,000

Pitcher and only Canadian honoured in the National Baseball Hall of Fame in Cooperstown, NY (inducted July 21, 1991).

For non-denominated postal cards of same designs, see UX236–UX237.

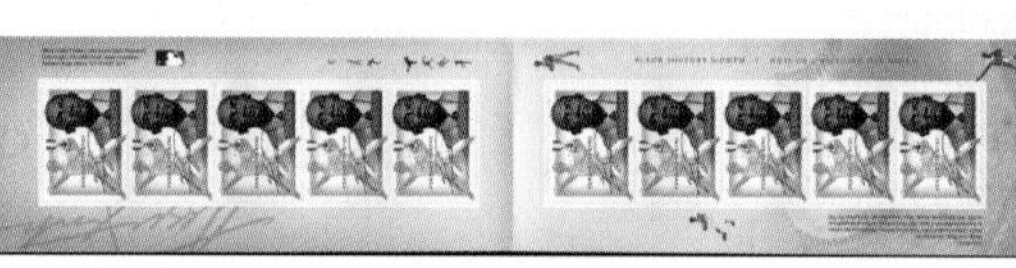

*Image rotated* 2434a

2433a

## CELEBRATION

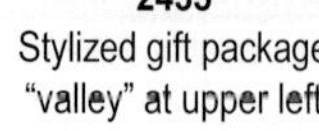

2435
Stylized gift package
"valley" at upper left

2435i
Stylized gift package
"peak" at upper left

2435a

Designer: Debbie Adams.

Lithography (5 colours), self-adhesive booklet of 6
Canadian Bank Note

**2011, Feb 7** **GT4, TRC Paper**
**Serpentine Die cut 13.4 horiz**

| | | NH–VF | ⊙F | FDC |
|---|---|---|---|---|
| **2435** | **multicoloured**, valley at upper left | 1.70 | .40 | 3.20 |
| i | peak at upper left | 1.70 | .40 | 3.20 |
| ii | as 2435, die cut to shape from Quarterly Pack/ Annual Collection | 2.50 | — | |
| iii | as 2435i, die cut to shape from Quarterly Pack/ Annual Collection | 2.50 | — | |
| a | booklet pane of 6 x P (3 x 2435 and 3 x 2435i) (**BK446**) | 10.00 | | |

Qty: 6,000,000

The three stamps from the left column of the booklet start with a "valley" at the upper left of the die cut (2435); the three stamps from the right column of the booklet start with a "peak" at the upper left (2435i).

At time of issue, the P stamp was valued at 59¢.

## *ART CANADA*: DAPHNE ODJIG

**2436**
*Pow-wow Dancer*

*Perforated singles from water-activated gum souvenir sheet*

**2437a**
*Pow-wow*

**2437b**
*Spiritual Renewal*

*Die cut singles from self-adhesive booklet*

**2438**
*Pow-wow*

**2439**
*Spiritual Renewal*

**2437**

Designer: Hélène L'Heureux. Paintings by Daphne Odjig, 1919–.

Lithography (7 colours), pane of 16
Lowe-Martin

**2011, Feb 21** · **GT4, TRC Paper** **Perf 12.5**

| | | NH–VF | ⊙F | PB | FDC |
|---|---|---|---|---|---|
| **2436** | **59¢ multicoloured** | 1.00 | .40 | 5.00 | 3.20 |
| i | $32.36 uncut press sheet of 2 panes of 2436 and 4 panes of 2437 | 75.00 | | | |

Qty: 1,552,000; 2436i: 1,500

| | | NH–VF | ⊙F | FDC |
|---|---|---|---|---|
| **2437** | **$3.37 souvenir sheet** of 3 | 6.75 | 6.75 | 8.75 |
| a | **$1.03 multicoloured** | 2.00 | 2.00 | |
| b | **$1.75 multicoloured** | 3.50 | 3.50 | |

Qty: 200,000

Lithography (6 colours), self-adhesive booklet of 6
Lowe-Martin
**GT4, TRC Paper**
**Serpentine Die cut 13.5x13.3 horiz**

| | | NH–VF | ⊙F | FDC |
|---|---|---|---|---|
| **2438** | **$1.03 multicoloured** | 2.00 | .90 | — |
| i | die cut to shape from Quarterly Pack/ Annual Collection | 3.00 | — | |
| a | booklet pane of 6 x $1.03 (2438) (**BK447**) | 12.00 | | |

Qty: 600,000

Lithography (7 colours), self-adhesive booklet of 6

| | | NH–VF | ⊙F | FDC |
|---|---|---|---|---|
| **2439** | **$1.75 multicoloured** | 3.50 | 1.50 | — |
| i | die cut to shape from Quarterly Pack/ Annual Collection | 5.25 | — | |
| a | booklet pane of 6 x $1.75 (2439) (**BK448**) | 21.00 | | |

Qty: 600,000

**2438a**

**2439a**

## SUNFLOWERS

*Perforated singles from water-activated gum souvenir sheet*

**2440a** **2440b**

**2441**
Prado Red

*Die cut singles from self-adhesive booklet*


**2443** Prado Red
**2444** Sunbright


**2442**
Sunbright

Designer: Isabelle Toussaint, Design graphique.

Lithography (6 colours)
Lowe-Martin
Water-activated gum souvenir sheet of 2

**2011, Mar 3** **GT4, TRC Paper** **Perf 13.1x13.2**

| | | NH–VF | ⊙F | FDC |
|---|---|---|---|---|
| **2440** | **$1.18 souvenir sheet** of 2 | 3.50 | 3.50 | — |
| a | **P multicoloured**, red flower | 1.75 | 1.50 | |
| b | **P multicoloured**, yellow flower | 1.75 | 1.50 | |
| i | se-tenant pair (2440a–b) | 3.25 | 3.00 | |

Qty: 200,000

Self-adhesive roll of 50
**GT4, TRC Paper**
**Serpentine Die cut 8.15 to 8.50 Horiz**
**(Rounded tips with 4 or 5 'nibs' between stamps)**

One die cut pattern exists on these stamps and has been used both upright and inverted.

| | | NH–VF | ⊙F | FDC |
|---|---|---|---|---|
| **2441** | **P multicoloured**, red flower | 1.70 | .60 | — |
| **2442** | **P multicoloured**, yellow flower | 1.70 | .60 | — |
| a | se-tenant pair (vert.), 2441–42 | 3.40 | | |
| i | gutter strip of 4 with inscription | 8.50 | | |
| | starter strip of 4 (wavy die cut) | 11.00 | | |
| | end strip of 4 (wavy die cut) | 11.00 | | |
| ii | se-tenant pair (2441–42), die cut to shape (9.2 horiz) from Quarterly Pack | 5.00 | — | |

Qty: 2,000,000 of each

These stamps were printed se-tenant along the roll. Two different rolls were produced; one starting with the red flower, the other starting with the yellow flower. As such, two types of each of the gutter, starter and end strips of 4 exist.

**Nos. 2441–2442 (2) combination FDC** **4.35**

Self-adhesive booklet of 10
**GT4, TRC Paper**
**Serpentine Die cut 13.4x13.5**

| | | NH–VF | ⊙F | FDC |
|---|---|---|---|---|
| **2443** | **P multicoloured**, red flower | 1.70 | .45 | |
| **2444** | **P multicoloured**, yellow flower | 1.70 | .45 | |
| i | se-tenant pair (2443, 2444), die cut to shape from Quarterly Pack | 5.00 | — | |
| a | booklet pane of 10, 5 each #2443–2444 + 10 stickers (**BK449**) | 17.00 | | |

Qty: 6,000,000 of each

**Nos. 2443–2444 (2) combination FDC** **4.35***

* Stamps on FDCs are not die cut all the way through.

At time of issue, the P stamps were valued at 59¢.
For non-denominated postal cards of same designs, see UX238–UX239.

**2440**

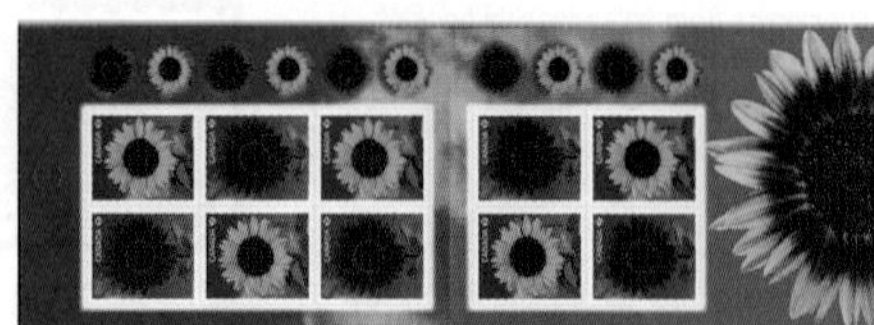
*Image rotated* **2444a**

## SIGNS OF THE ZODIAC

*Perforated singles from water-activated gum souvenir sheet*

**2445a** Aries: The Ram
**2445b** Taurus: The Bull

**2445c** Gemini: The Twins
**2445d** Cancer: The Crab

**2446a** Leo: The Lion
**2446b** Virgo: The Maiden

**2446c** Libra: The Scales
**2446d** Scorpio: The Scorpion

**2447a** Sagittarius: The Archer
**2447b** Capricorn: The Sea-Goat

**2447c** Aquarius: The Water-Bearer
**2447d** Pisces: The Fishes

**2445**

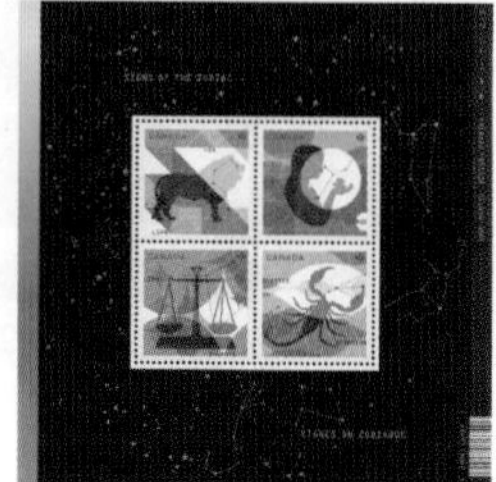
**2446**

2447

Designer: Paprika.

Lithography (7 colours), water-activated gum souvenir sheet of 4
Sheets of 48 subjects in twelve panes of 4
Lowe-Martin

**2011, Jun 22** **GT4, TRC Paper** **Perf 12.5**

| | | NH–VF | ⊙F | FDC |
|---|---|---|---|---|
| **2445** | **$2.36 souvenir sheet of 4** | 6.80 | 6.80 | |
| a | **Aries** | 1.70 | 1.50 | |
| b | **Taurus** | 1.70 | 1.50 | |
| c | **Gemini** | 1.70 | 1.50 | |
| d | **Cancer** | 1.70 | 1.50 | |

Qty: 205,000

At time of issue, the 2011-year P stamps were valued at 59¢.
For non-denominated postal cards of same designs, see UX240–UX243.

**2012, Jul 23** **GT4, TRC Paper** **Perf 12.5**

| | | NH–VF | ⊙F | FDC |
|---|---|---|---|---|
| **2446** | **$2.44 souvenir sheet of 4** | 6.80 | 6.80 | |
| a | **Leo** | 1.70 | 1.50 | |
| b | **Virgo** | 1.70 | 1.50 | |
| c | **Libra** | 1.70 | 1.50 | |
| d | **Scorpio** | 1.70 | 1.50 | |

Qty: 175,000

At time of issue, the 2012-year P stamps were valued at 61¢.
For non-denominated postal cards of same designs, see UX295–UX298.

**2013, Feb 20** **GT4, TRC Paper** **Perf 12.5**

| | | NH–VF | ⊙F | FDC |
|---|---|---|---|---|
| **2447** | **$2.52 souvenir sheet of 4** | 6.80 | 6.80 | |
| a | **Sagittarius** | 1.70 | 1.50 | |
| b | **Capricorn** | 1.70 | 1.50 | |
| c | **Aquarius** | 1.70 | 1.50 | |
| d | **Pisces** | 1.70 | 1.50 | |

Qty: 155,000

At time of issue, the 2013-year P stamps were valued at 63¢.
For non-denominated postal cards of same designs, see UX318–UX322.

Lithography (8 colours), water-activated gum pane of 12

**2013, Feb 20** **GT4, TRC Paper** **Perf 12.5x13.2**

| | | NH–VF | ⊙F | FDC |
|---|---|---|---|---|
| **2448** | **$7.56 pane of 12** | 25.00 | 25.00 | |
| a | **Aries** | 2.00 | 2.00 | |
| b | **Taurus** | 2.00 | 2.00 | |
| c | **Gemini** | 2.00 | 2.00 | |
| d | **Cancer** | 2.00 | 2.00 | |
| e | **Leo** | 2.00 | 2.00 | |
| f | **Virgo** | 2.00 | 2.00 | |
| g | **Libra** | 2.00 | 2.00 | |
| h | **Scorpio** | 2.00 | 2.00 | |
| i | **Sagittarius** | 2.00 | 2.00 | |
| j | **Capricorn** | 2.00 | 2.00 | |
| k | **Aquarius** | 2.00 | 2.00 | |
| l | **Pisces** | 2.00 | 2.00 | |

Qty: 50,000 panes

At time of issue, the 2013-year P stamps were valued at 63¢.

*Die cut singles from self-adhesive booklet*

2449
Aries: The Ram

2450
Taurus: The Bull

2451
Gemini: The Twins

2452
Cancer: The Crab

2453
Leo: The Lion

2454
Virgo: The Maiden

2455
Libra: The Scales

2456
Scorpio: The Scorpion

2457
Sagittarius: The Archer

2458
Capricorn: The Sea-Goat

2459
Aquarius: The Water-Bearer

2460
Pisces: The Fish

Designer: Paprika.

Lithography (7 colours), self-adhesive booklet of 10
Lowe-Martin

**2011** **GT4, TRC Paper** **Serpentine Die cut 13.3**

| | | NH–VF | ⊙F | FDC |
|---|---|---|---|---|
| **2449** | **Aries**, *Mar 21/11* | 1.70 | .45 | 3.20 |
| i | die cut to shape from Quarterly Pack | 2.50 | — | |
| a | booklet pane of 10 x P (2449) (**BK450**) | 17.00 | | |

Qty: 4,000,000

| | | NH–VF | ⊙F | FDC |
|---|---|---|---|---|
| **2450** | **Taurus**, *Apr 21/11* | 1.70 | .45 | 3.20 |
| i | die cut to shape from Quarterly Pack | 2.50 | — | |
| a | booklet pane of 10 x P (2450) (**BK451**) | 17.00 | | |
| b | gutter pane of 12, 6 x P (2449) and 6 x P (2450) | 20.00 | | |

Qty: 4,000,000; 2450b: 4,500

| | | NH–VF | ⊙F | FDC |
|---|---|---|---|---|
| **2451** | **Gemini**, *May 20/11* | 1.70 | .45 | 3.20 |
| i | die cut to shape from Quarterly Pack | 2.50 | — | |
| a | booklet pane of 10 x P (2451) (**BK456**) | 17.00 | | |

Qty: 4,000,000

| | | NH–VF | ⊙F | FDC |
|---|---|---|---|---|
| **2452** | **Cancer**, *Jun 22/11* | 1.70 | .45 | 3.20 |
| i | die cut to shape from Quarterly Pack | 2.50 | — | |
| a | booklet pane of 10 x P (2452) (**BK458**) | 17.00 | | |
| b | gutter pane of 12, 6 x P (2451) and 6 x P (2452) | 20.00 | | |

Qty: 4,000,000; 2452b: 4,500

At time of issue, the 2011-year P stamps were valued at 59¢.
For non-denominated postal cards of same designs, see UX240–UX243.

## 2012, Jul 23 — GT4, TRC Paper — Serpentine Die cut 13.3

| | | NH–VF | ⊙F | FDC |
|---|---|---|---|---|
| **2453** | Leo | 1.70 | .45 | 3.20 |
| i | die cut to shape from Quarterly Pack | 2.50 | — | |
| a | booklet pane of 10 x P (2453) (**BK495**) | 17.00 | | |
| Qty: 3,000,000 | | | | |
| **2454** | Virgo | 1.70 | .45 | 3.20 |
| i | die cut to shape from Quarterly Pack | 2.50 | — | |
| a | booklet pane of 10 x P (2454) (**BK496**) | 17.00 | | |
| Qty: 3,000,000 | | | | |
| **2455** | Libra | 1.70 | .45 | 3.20 |
| i | die cut to shape from Quarterly Pack | 2.50 | — | |
| a | booklet pane of 10 x P (2455) (**BK497**) | 17.00 | | |
| Qty: 3,000,000 | | | | |
| **2456** | Scorpio | 1.70 | .45 | 3.20 |
| i | die cut to shape from Quarterly Pack | 2.50 | — | |
| a | booklet pane of 10 x P (2456) (**BK498**) | 17.00 | | |
| b | gutter pane of 24, 6 x P (2453) and 6 x P (2454) and 6 x P (2455) and 6 x P (2456) | 40.00 | | |
| Qty: 3,000,000; 2456b: 4,000 | | | | |

At time of issue, the 2012-year P stamps were valued at 61¢.
For non-denominated postal cards of same designs, see UX295–UX298.

## 2013, Feb 20 — GT4, TRC Paper — Serpentine Die cut 13.3

| | | NH–VF | ⊙F | FDC |
|---|---|---|---|---|
| **2457** | Sagittarius | 1.70 | .45 | 3.25 |
| i | die cut to shape from Quarterly Pack | 2.50 | — | |
| a | booklet pane of 10 x P (2457) (**BK527**) | 17.00 | | |
| Qty: 2,250,000 | | | | |
| **2458** | Capricorn | 1.70 | .45 | 3.25 |
| i | die cut to shape from Quarterly Pack | 2.50 | — | |
| a | booklet pane of 10 x P (2458) (**BK528**) | 17.00 | | |
| Qty: 2,250,000 | | | | |
| **2459** | Aquarius | 1.70 | .45 | 3.25 |
| i | die cut to shape from Quarterly Pack | 2.50 | — | |
| a | booklet pane of 10 x P (2459) (**BK529**) | 17.00 | | |
| Qty: 2,250,000 | | | | |
| **2460** | Pisces | 1.70 | .45 | 3.25 |
| i | die cut to shape from Quarterly Pack | 2.50 | — | |
| a | booklet pane of 10 x P (2460) (**BK530**) | 17.00 | | |
| b | gutter pane of 24, 6 x P (2457) and 6 x P (2458) and 6 x P (2459) and 6 x P (2460) | 40.00 | | |
| Qty: 2,250,000; 2460b: 3,500 | | | | |

At time of issue, the 2013-year P stamps were valued at 63¢.
For non-denominated postal cards of same designs, see UX319–UX322.

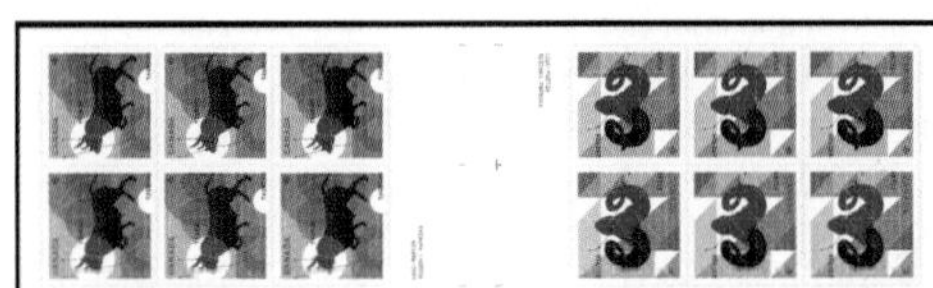

*Image rotated* 2450b

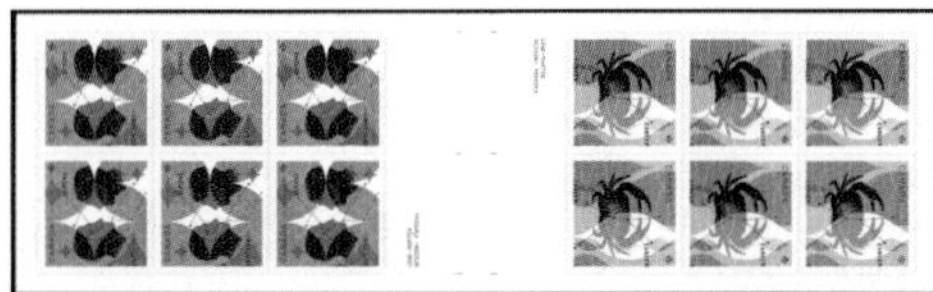

*Image rotated* 2452b

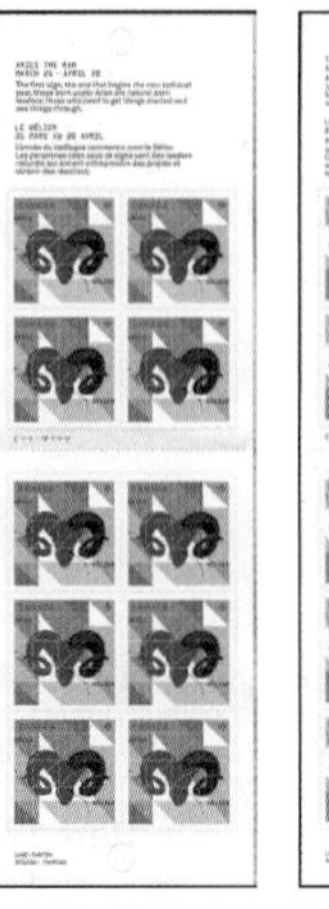

2449a

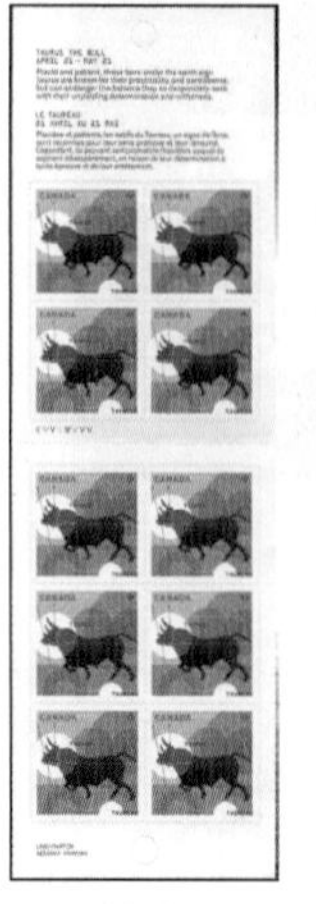

2450a

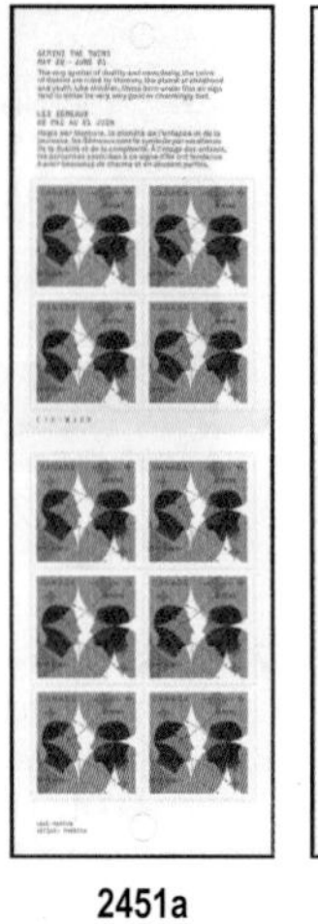

2451a

2452a

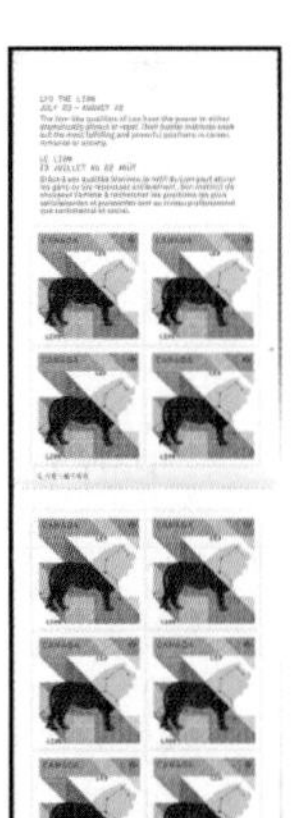

2453a

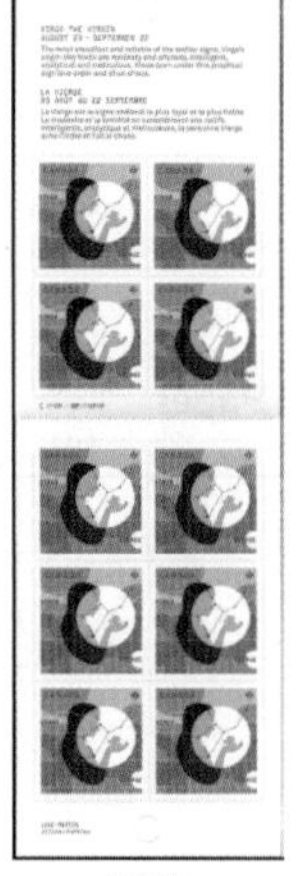

2454a

2455a

2456a

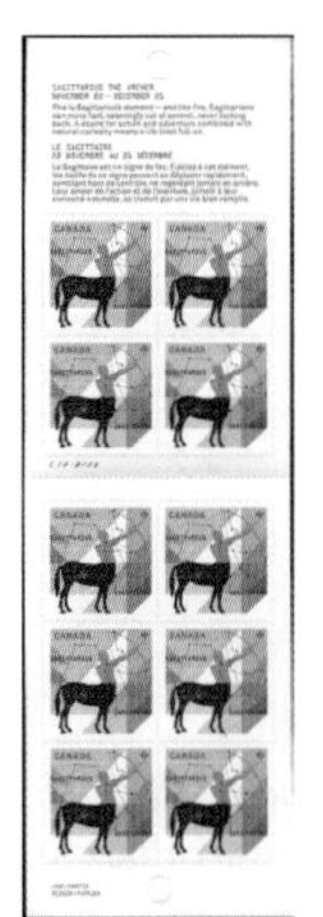

2457a

2458a

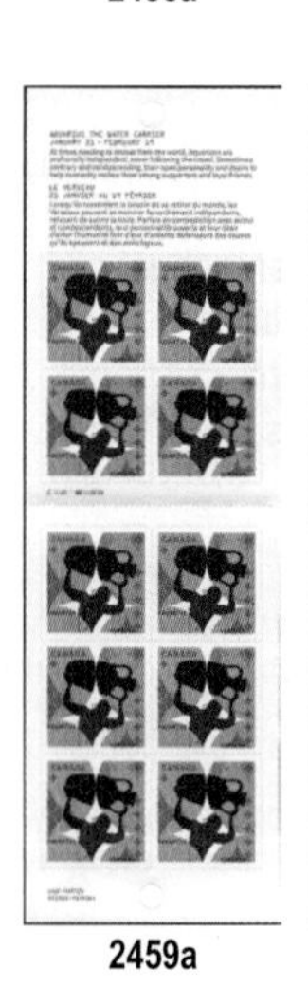

2459a

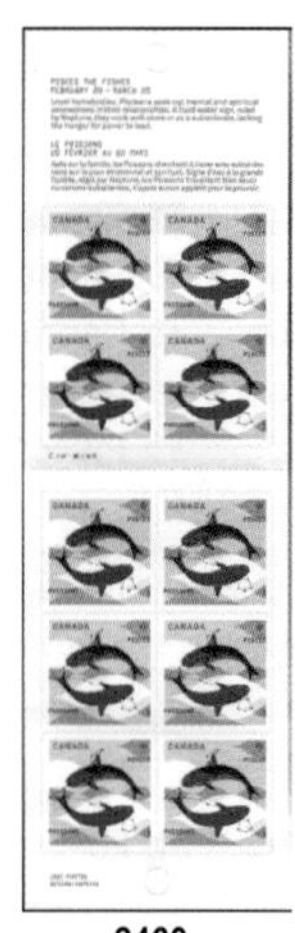

2460a

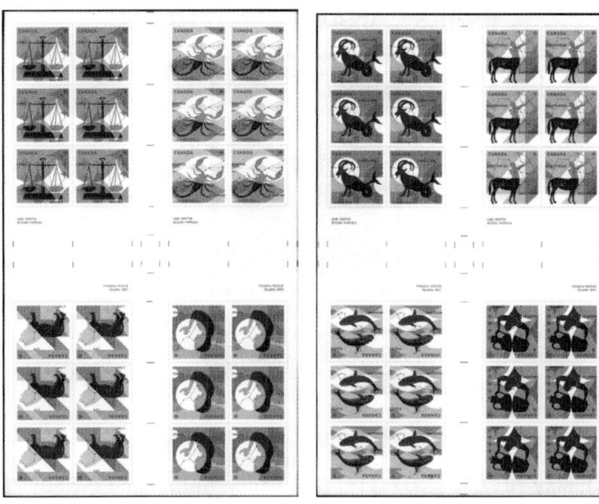

2456b 2460b

## INTERNATIONAL YEAR OF FORESTS

2461a Tree

2462 Tree

*Perforated singles from water-activated gum souvenir sheet*

*Die cut singles from self-adhesive booklet*

2461b Forest floor, mushrooms

2463 Forest floor, mushrooms

Designer: Subplot Design Inc.

Lithography (8 colours)
Lowe-Martin
Water-activated gum souvenir sheet of 2

**2011, Apr 21** **GT 3-sided, TRC Paper** **Perf 13.4x13.1**

| | | NH–VF | ⊙F | FDC |
|---|---|---|---|---|
| **2461** | **$1.18 souvenir sheet** of 2 | 3.50 | 3.50 | — |
| a | P **multicoloured**, tree | 1.70 | 1.50 | |
| b | P **multicoloured**, mushrooms | 1.70 | 1.50 | |
| i | se-tenant pair (2461a–b) | 3.40 | 3.00 | |

Qty: 200,000

Self-adhesive booklet of 8
**GT 3-sided, TRC Paper**
**Serpentine Die cut 13.1x13.3**

| | | NH–VF | ⊙F | FDC |
|---|---|---|---|---|
| **2462** | P **multicoloured**, tree | 1.70 | .45 | |
| **2463** | P **multicoloured**, mushrooms | 1.70 | .45 | |
| i | die cut to shape pair from Quarterly Pack/ Annual Collection | 5.00 | — | |
| a | booklet pane of 8 x P (2462–2463) (**BK452**) | 13.50 | | |

Qty: 1,350,000 of each

**Nos. 2462–2463 (2) combination FDC** **4.35**

The general tagging was *not* applied to the side with the illustration passing through the perfs/ die cutting.

At time of issue, the P stamps were valued at 59¢.
The United Nations declared 2011 as International Year of Forests. Under an ultraviolet light, "hidden" animals become visible on the right side of the souvenir sheet.

2461

2463a

## ROYAL WEDDING

2464 Catherine Middleton and Prince William

2465 Prince William and Catherine Middleton

2466 Catherine Middleton and Prince William

2467 Prince William and Catherine Middleton

Designer: Isabelle Toussaint, Design graphique.

Lithography (7 colours; s/s in 8 colours), pane of 16 and souvenir sheet of 2
Lowe-Martin

**2011, Apr 29** **GT4, TRC Paper** **Perf 12.8x13.4**

| | | NH–VF | ⊙F | PB | FDC |
|---|---|---|---|---|---|
| **2464** | P **multicoloured** | 1.70 | .40 | | |
| **2465** | **$1.75 multicoloured** | 3.50 | 1.50 | | |
| a | se-tenant pair (2464–65)* | 5.25 | 4.00 | 9.50 | |
| b | $2.34 souvenir sheet of 2 | 5.25 | 5.25 | | 6.75 |
| c | $2.34 overprinted souvenir sheet of 2 | 6.00 | 6.00 | | |

Qty: 760,000 of each; 800,000 of souvenir sheet; 100,000 of overprinted souvenir sheet.
* the *reversed* se-tenant pair (2465, 2464) from the middle two columns of the pane of 16 commands a premium; value $7.50.

Self-adhesive booklets of 10
**GT4, TRC Paper**
**Serpentine Die cut 13.2x13.4**

| | | NH–VF | ⊙F | FDC |
|---|---|---|---|---|
| **2466** | P **multicoloured** | 1.70 | .45 | |
| i | die cut to shape from Quarterly Pack/ Annual Collection | 2.50 | — | |
| a | booklet pane of 10 x P (2466) (**BK453**) | 17.00 | | |

Qty: 11,000,000; gutter pane: 4,000

| | | NH–VF | ⊙F | FDC |
|---|---|---|---|---|
| **2467** | **$1.75 multicoloured** | 3.50 | 1.50 | |
| i | die cut to shape from Quarterly Pack/ Annual Collection | 5.25 | — | |
| a | booklet pane of 10 x $1.75 (2467) (**BK454**) | 35.00 | | |
| b | gutter pane, 6 x 2466 and 4 x 2467 | 75.00 | | |

Qty: 2,000,000

**Nos. 2466–2467 (2) combination FDC** **6.75**

Issued for the Royal Wedding of His Royal Highness Prince William of Wales and Miss Catherine Middleton at Westminster Abbey on April 29, 2011.

At time of issue, the P stamps were valued at 59¢. For non-denominated size 10 envelope of P design see U240; for non-denominated postal card of P design, see UX244.

2465b

2465c

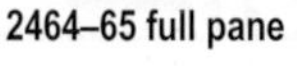
2464–65 full pane

2466a 2467a 2467b

## METHODS OF MAIL DELIVERY

2468 Winter Magdalen mail
2469 Mail delivery by dog team

Designer: Karen Smith Design.

Lithography (7 colours plus varnish), pane of 16
Lowe-Martin

**2011, May 13** **GT 3-sided, TRC Paper** **Perf 12.5***

| | | NH–VF | ⊙F | PB | FDC |
|---|---|---|---|---|---|
| **2468** | **59¢ multicoloured** | 1.20 | .45 | | |
| **2469** | **59¢ multicoloured** | 1.20 | .45 | | |
| a | se-tenant pair (2468–69) | 2.40 | 1.50 | 6.00† | 4.35 |

Qty: 750,000 of each

* All stamps have transitional perfs along the top and bottom of each stamp, starting with perf 13.3 for the first few perfs, then 12.5 for the majority of the distance. See illustration after 2403.

† Only the lower right block of the pane included a full inscription and paper/colour designations.

The general tagging was *not* applied to the side with the illustration passing through the perfs.

In the winter of 1910, a *ponchon* (large barrel used for transporting molasses) was rigged with a rudder and sail to deliver mail between the people of the Magdalen Islands north of Cape Breton and the mainland. The only reliable method of mail delivery in northern Canada prior to air mail advances of World War I was by dog team.

## PARKS CANADA CENTENNIAL

2470
Montage of images representing national parks

Designer: Tim Nokes.

Lithography (5 colours), self-adhesive booklet of 10
Canadian Bank Note

**2011, May 19** **GT4, TRC Paper** **Serpentine Die cut 13.3**

| | | NH–VF | ⊙F | FDC |
|---|---|---|---|---|
| **2470** | **59¢ multicoloured** | 1.20 | .45 | 3.20 |
| i | die cut to shape from Quarterly Pack/ Annual Collection | 1.80 | — | |
| a | booklet pane of 10 x 59¢ (2470) (**BK455**) | 12.00 | | |

Qty: 4,000,000

Celebrating the 100th anniversay of national parks in Canada, the first being in Banff, Alberta.

For non-denominated postal card of same design, see UX245.

*Image rotated* 2470a

## ARCHITECTURE: ART DECO

*Perforated singles from water-activated gum souvenir sheet*

2471a Burrard Bridge, Vancouver, BC
2471b Cormier House, Montreal, QC
2471c Harris Plant, Toronto, ON
2471d Supreme Court of Canada, Ottawa, ON
2471e Dominion Bldg, Regina, SK

*Die cut singles from self-adhesive booklet*

2472 Burrard Bridge, Vancouver, BC
2473 Cormier House, Montreal, QC
2474 Harris Plant, Toronto, ON
2475 Supreme Court of Canada, Ottawa, ON
2476 Dominion Bldg, Regina, SK

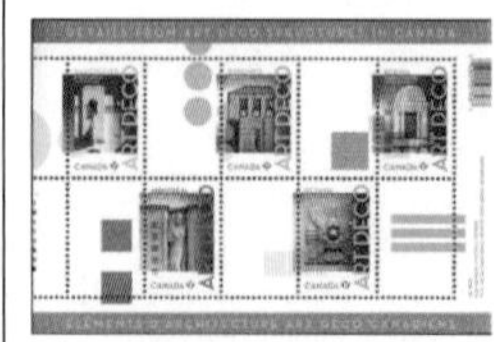
2471

*Image rotated* 2476a

Designer: Ivan Novotny (Taylor | Sprules).
Lithography (8 colours), water-activated gum souvenir sheet of 5
Lowe-Martin

**2011, Jun 9** **GT 3-sided, TRC Paper** **Perf 13.1x12.5**

| | | NH–VF | ⊙F | FDC |
|---|---|---|---|---|
| **2471** | **$2.95 souvenir sheet** of 5 + 5 labels | 8.75 | 8.75 | 7.90 |
| a | P **Vancouver** | 1.75 | 1.50 | |
| b | P **Montreal** | 1.75 | 1.50 | |
| c | P **Toronto** | 1.75 | 1.50 | |
| d | P **Ottawa** | 1.75 | 1.50 | |
| e | P **Regina** | 1.75 | 1.50 | |
| i | $53.10 uncut press sheet of 18 souvenir sheets | 160.00 | | |

Qty: 205,000; 2471i: 1,500.

Self-adhesive booklet of 10
**GT 3-sided, TRC Paper**
**Serpentine Die cut 13.5**

| | | NH–VF | ⊙F | FDC |
|---|---|---|---|---|
| **2472** | P **Vancouver** | 1.70 | .45 | |
| i | die cut to shape from Quarterly Pack | 2.50 | — | |
| **2473** | P **Montreal** | 1.70 | .45 | |
| i | die cut to shape from Quarterly Pack | 2.50 | — | |
| **2474** | P **Toronto** | 1.70 | .45 | |
| i | die cut to shape from Quarterly Pack | 2.50 | — | |
| **2475** | P **Ottawa** | 1.70 | .45 | |
| i | die cut to shape from Quarterly Pack | 2.50 | — | |
| **2476** | P **Regina** | 1.70 | .45 | |
| i | die cut to shape from Quarterly Pack | 2.50 | — | |
| a | booklet pane of 10 x P (2472–2476) (**BK457**) | 17.00 | | |

Qty: 440,000 of each design.

The general tagging was *not* applied to the left side of each stamp.
At time of issue, the P stamps were valued at 59¢. For non-denominated postal cards of same designs, see UX246–UX250.

## WEDDING DAY

*Perforated single from water-activated gum souvenir sheet*

**2477a**
Duke and Duchess of Cambridge

**2478**
Duke and Duchess of Cambridge

*Die cut single from self-adhesive booklet*

**2477**

**2477b**

*Image rotated* **2478a**

Designer: Isabelle Toussaint, Design graphique.
Lithography (7 colours plus foil stamping on 2477b), souvenir sheet of 2
Lowe-Martin

**2011, Jun 22** **GT4, TRC Paper** **Perf 12.8x13.4**

| | | NH–VF | ⊙F | FDC |
|---|---|---|---|---|
| **2477** | **$1.18 souvenir sheet** of 2, with Westminster Abbey at left | 5.00 | 3.50 | 4.35 |
| a | P multicoloured, single from souvenir sheet (either 2477 or 2477b) | 2.00 | 1.25 | |
| b | $1.18 souvenir sheet of 2, with Canada's Parliament Building at left and Royal Tour emblem overprint | 5.00 | 3.50 | 4.35 |

Qty: 250,000 of souvenir sheet; 250,000 of overprinted souvenir sheet.

Lithography (7 colours), self-adhesive booklet of 10
**GT4, TRC Paper**
**Serpentine Die cut 13.2x13.4**

| | | NH–VF | ⊙F | FDC |
|---|---|---|---|---|
| **2478** | P **multicoloured** | 1.70 | .45 | |
| i | die cut to shape from Quarterly Pack/ Annual Collection | 2.50 | — | |
| a | booklet pane of 10 x P (2478) (**BK459**) | 17.00 | | |

Qty: 10,000,000

At time of issue, the P stamp was valued at 59¢. For non-denominated postal card of P design, see UX251.

## CANADIAN RECORDING ARTISTS

*Perforated singles from water-activated gum panes and s/s*

**2479/a**
Ginette Reno (1946– )

**2480/a**
Bruce Cockburn (1945– )

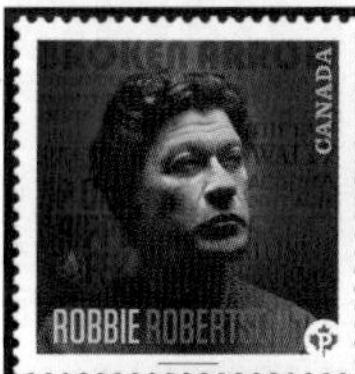

**2481/a**
Robbie Robertson (1943– )

**2482/a**
Kate (1946–2010) and Anna (1944– ) McGarrigle

*Die cut singles from self-adhesive booklet*

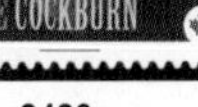

**2483a**

**2483b**

**2483c**

**2483d**

Designer: Circle Design Inc.

Lithography (8 colours plus varnish), water-activated gum panes of 16
Lowe-Martin

**2011, Jul 30** **GT4, TRC Paper** **Perf 12.5**

| | | NH–VF | ⊙F | FDC |
|---|---|---|---|---|
| **2479** | **multicoloured**, Reno | 2.50 | 2.50 | |
| **2480** | **multicoloured**, Cockburn | 2.50 | 2.50 | |
| **2481** | **multicoloured**, Robertson | 2.50 | 2.50 | |
| **2482** | **multicoloured**, McGarrigles | 2.50 | 2.50 | |

Qty: 160,000 of each
Value for full panes of 16 (each), $40.00

Water-activated gum souvenir sheet of 4
Lowe-Martin

**2011, Jun 30** **GT4, TRC Paper** **Perf 12.5x13.1**

| | | NH–VF | ⊙F | FDC |
|---|---|---|---|---|
| **2479a** | **multicoloured**, Reno | 1.75 | 1.50 | |
| **2480a** | **multicoloured**, Cockburn | 1.75 | 1.50 | |
| **2481a** | **multicoloured**, Robertson | 1.75 | 1.50 | |
| **2482a** | **multicoloured**, McGarrigles | 1.75 | 1.50 | |
| b | $2.36 souvenir sheet of 4 (2479a, 2480a, 2481a, 2482a) | 7.00 | 7.00 | 6.70 |

Qty: 205,000

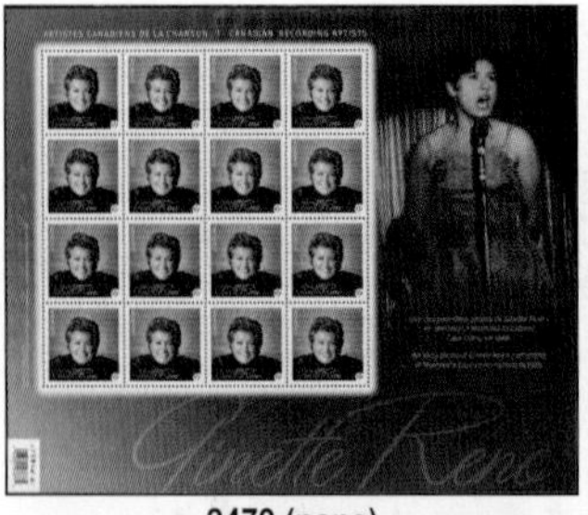

2479 (pane)

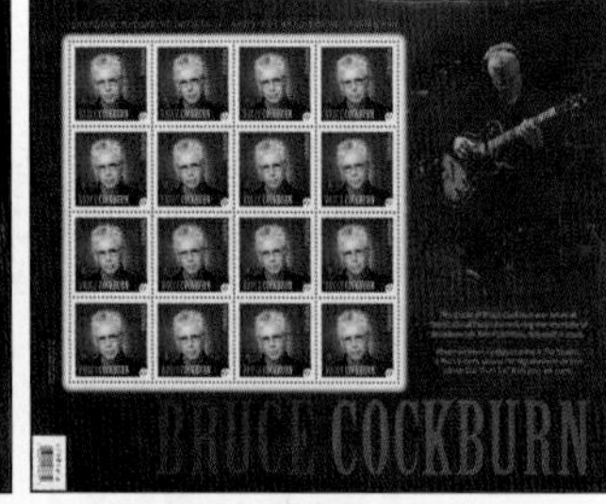

2480 (pane)

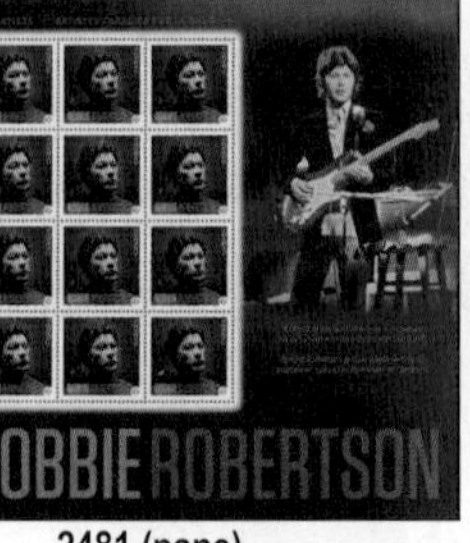

2481 (pane)

2482 (pane)

Lithography (8 colours plus varnish), self-adhesive booklet of 8
Lowe-Martin

**2011, Jun 30** **GT4, TRC Paper**
**Serpentine Die cut 13.5**

| | | NH–VF | ⊙F | FDC |
|---|---|---|---|---|
| **2483** | booklet pane of 4 x P + 4 stickers, pane with Bruce Cockburn at upper left | 6.80 | | — |
| a | **multicoloured**, Cockburn | 1.70 | .60 | |
| b | **multicoloured**, McGarrigles | 1.70 | .60 | |
| c | **multicoloured**, Reno | 1.70 | .60 | |
| d | **multicoloured**, Robertson | 1.70 | .60 | |
| i | booklet pane of 4 x P + 4 stickers, pane with Kate & Anna McGarrigle at upper left | 6.80 | | |
| ii | booklet pane of 4 x P + 4 stickers, pane with Ginette Reno at upper left | 6.80 | | |
| iii | booklet pane of 4 x P + 4 stickers, pane with Robbie Robertson at upper left | 6.80 | | |

BK460 two panes of 2483 (Cockburn cover) $13.50
BK461 two panes of 2483i (McGarrigle cover) $13.50
BK462 two panes of 2483ii (Reno cover) $13.50
BK463 two panes of 2483iii (Robertson cover) $13.50
Qty: 900,000 of each stamp

Honouring the accomplishments of Canadian Recording Artists.

At time of issue, the P stamps were valued at 59¢.
For non-denominated postal cards of same designs, see UX252–UX255.

2482b

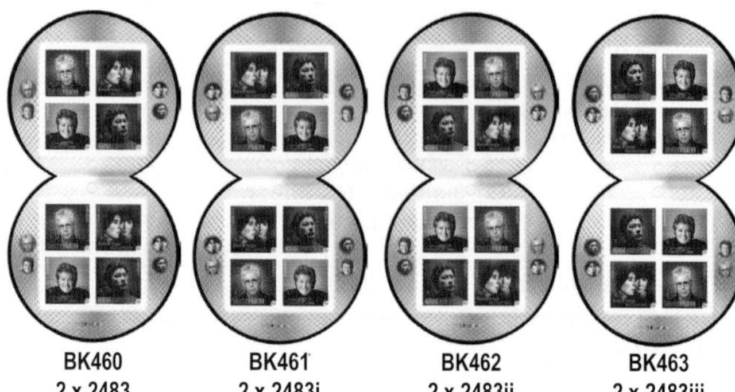
BK460 2 x 2483 | BK461 2 x 2483i | BK462 2 x 2483ii | BK463 2 x 2483iii

## ROADSIDE ATTRACTIONS — 3

*Perforated singles from water-activated gum souvenir sheet*

**2484a**
*World's Largest Lobster*, Shediac, NB

**2484b**
*Wild Blueberry*, Oxford, NS

**2484c**
*Big Potato*, O'Leary, PEI

**2484d**
*Giant Squid*, Glover's Harbour, NL

*Die cut singles from self-adhesive booklet*

**2485a**
*World's Largest Lobster*, Shediac, NB

**2485b**
*Wild Blueberry*, Oxford, NS

**2485c**
*Big Potato*, O'Leary, PEI

**2485d**
*Giant Squid*,
Glover's Harbour, NL

Designer: Fraser Ross (Semaphor Design Company).
Lithography (8 colours plus varnish), water-activated gum souvenir sheet of 4
Lowe-Martin

**2011, Jul 7** **GT4, TRC Paper** **Perf 12.5x13.1**

| | | NH–VF | ⊙F | FDC |
|---|---|---|---|---|
| **2484** | **$2.36 souvenir sheet** of 4 | 7.00 | 7.00 | — |
| a | **P multicoloured** | 1.75 | 1.50 | |
| b | **P multicoloured** | 1.75 | 1.50 | |
| c | **P multicoloured** | 1.75 | 1.50 | |
| d | **P multicoloured** | 1.75 | 1.50 | |

Qty: 185,000

Self-adhesive booklet of 8
**Serpentine Die cut 13.5 on 3 sides**

| | | NH–VF | ⊙F | FDC |
|---|---|---|---|---|
| **2485** | booklet pane of 4 x P + 4 stickers (BK464) | 6.80 | | 6.70 |
| a | **P multicoloured** | 1.70 | .60 | |
| b | **P multicoloured** | 1.70 | .60 | |
| c | **P multicoloured** | 1.70 | .60 | |
| d | **P multicoloured** | 1.70 | .60 | |

**BK464** two panes of 2485 $13.50
Qty: 860,000 of each stamp

At time of issue, the P stamps were valued at 59¢.
For non-denominated postal cards of same designs, see UX256–UX259. Last of a three-year series. See also 2335–2336, 2397–2401.

**2484**

**2 x 2485 (BK464)**

## MISS SUPERTEST

*Perforated singles from water-activated gum souvenir sheet*

**2486a**
*Miss Supertest III*, front view

**2486b**
*Miss Supertest III*, side view

*Die cut single from self-adhesive booklet*

**2487**
*Miss Supertest III*, front view

Designer: Ivan Novotny (Taylor|Sprules Corporation)
Lithography (7 colours plus spot varnish)
Lowe-Martin
Water-activated gum souvenir sheet of 2

**2011, Aug 8** **GT4, TRC Paper** **Perf 13.4x13.1**

| | | NH–VF | ⊙F | FDC |
|---|---|---|---|---|
| **2486** | **$2.34 souvenir sheet** of 2 | 5.25 | 5.00 | 6.70 |
| a | **P multicoloured** | 1.75 | 1.50 | |
| b | **$1.75 multicoloured** | 3.50 | 3.25 | |
| i | se-tenant pair (2486a–b) | 5.00 | 4.75 | |

Qty: 190,000

Lithography (6 colours plus spot varnish), self-adhesive booklet of 10
**GT4, TRC Paper**
**Serpentine Die cut 13.2 horiz**

| | | NH–VF | ⊙F | FDC |
|---|---|---|---|---|
| **2487** | **P multicoloured** | 1.70 | .45 | — |
| i | die cut to shape from Quarterly Pack | 2.50 | — | |
| a | booklet pane of 10 x P (2487) + 10 stickers (**BK465**) | 17.00 | | |

Qty: 2,800,000

At time of issue, the P stamp was valued at 59¢.

**2486**

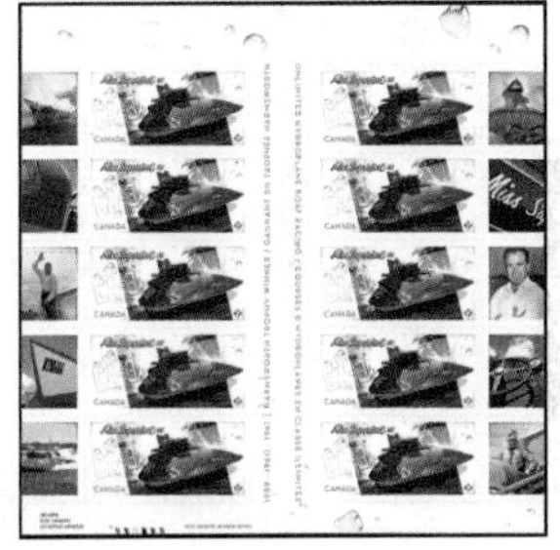

**2487a**

## CANADIAN INNOVATIONS

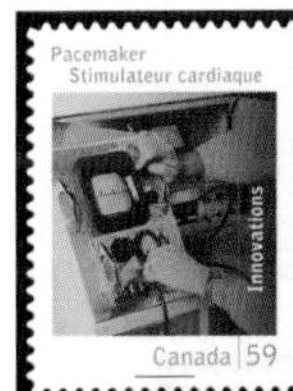

**2488a**
Pacemaker
(Dr. John Hopps)

**2488b**
BlackBerry
(Research in Motion)

**2488c**
Electric oven
(Thomas Ahearn)

**2488d**
Electric wheelchair
(George J. Klein)

Designer: q30 deisgn inc.
Lithography (9 colours), Self-adhesive booklet of 8
Lowe-Martin

**2011, Aug 17** **GT4, TRC Paper** **Serpentine Die cut 13.4**

| | | NH–VF | ⊙F | FDC |
|---|---|---|---|---|
| **2488** | booklet pane of 4 x 59¢ (BK466) | 4.75 | | 6.70 |
| a | **59¢ multicoloured** | 1.20 | .60 | |
| b | **59¢ multicoloured** | 1.20 | .60 | |
| c | **59¢ multicoloured** | 1.20 | .60 | |
| d | **59¢ multicoloured** | 1.20 | .60 | |

**BK466** two panes of 2488 $9.50
Qty: 281,250 of each stamp

Canadian inventions.

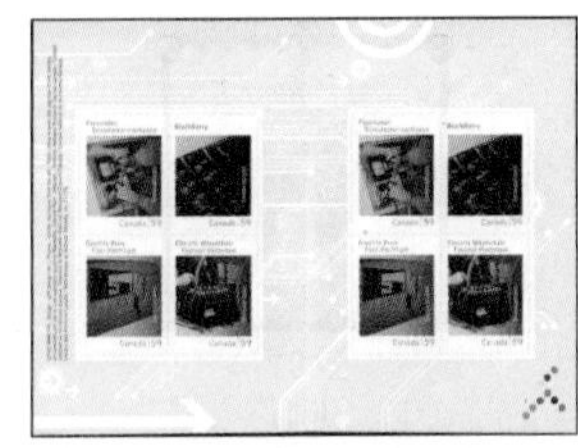

**2 x 2488 (BK466)**

QE II — 2010's

Timeline:
**2011, Sep 6** P (59¢)+10¢ Mental Health, semi-postal (B17, B18)

## INTERNATIONAL YEAR OF CHEMISTRY

**2489**
Dr. John Charles Polanyi

Designer: q30 design inc.

Lithography (6 colours), self-adhesive booklet of 10
Lowe-Martin

**2011, Oct 3** **GT4, TRC Paper**
**Serpentine Die cut 13.5x13.8**

| | | NH–VF | ⊙F | FDC |
|---|---|---|---|---|
| **2489** | **P multicoloured** | 1.70 | .45 | 3.20 |
| i | die cut to shape from Quarterly Pack/ Annual Collection | 2.50 | — | |
| a | booklet pane of 10 x P (2489) (**BK468**) | 17.00 | | |

Qty: 2,250,000

At time of issue, the P stamp was valued at 59¢.
Polanyi was awarded the Nobel Prize for Chemistry in 1986 for his "groundbreaking research in reaction dynamics".

**2489a**

## CHRISTMAS: STAINED GLASS

*Perforated singles from water-activated gum souvenir sheet*

**2490a** **2490b** **2490c**

*Die cut singles from self-adhesive booklets*

**2492** **2493** **2494**

**2491**
Holly

Designer: Andrew Perro.

Lithography (7 colours plus spot varnish)
Lowe-Martin
Water-activated gum souvenir sheet of 3

**2011, Nov 1** **GT4, TRC Paper** **Perf 13.0x12.4**

| | | NH–VF | ⊙F | FDC |
|---|---|---|---|---|
| **2490** | **$3.37 souvenir sheet** of 3 | 7.25 | 7.25 | 8.75 |
| a | **P multicoloured** | 1.75 | 1.50 | |
| b | **$1.03 multicoloured** | 2.00 | 2.00 | |
| c | **$1.75 multicoloured** | 3.50 | 3.25 | |

Qty: 190,000

Designer: Hélène L'Heureux.

Lithography (5 colours) plus holographic foil
Lowe-Martin, self-adhesive booklet of 12

**2011, Nov 1** **GT4, TRC Paper** **Serpentine Die cut 8.4**

| | | NH–VF | ⊙F | FDC |
|---|---|---|---|---|
| **2491** | **P multicoloured** | 1.70 | .25 | 3.20 |
| i | die cut to shape from Quarterly Pack/ Annual Collection | 2.50 | — | |
| a | booklet pane of 6 x P (2491) | 10.00 | — | |
| **BK469** | two panes of 2491a $20.00 | | | |

Qty: 27,000,000

This design was also used on the 2011 *Santa Claus* envelopes.
For special order envelope of P Holly design, see UO77.

Designer: Andrew Perro.

Lithography (7 colours plus spot varnish), self-adhesive booklet of 12 (P) or 6
Lowe-Martin

**2011, Nov 1** **GT4, TRC Paper** **Serpentine Die cut 13.4**

| | | NH–VF | ⊙F | FDC |
|---|---|---|---|---|
| **2492** | **P multicoloured** | 1.70 | .25 | — |
| i | die cut to shape from Quarterly Pack | 2.50 | — | |
| a | booklet pane of 6 x P (2492) | 10.00 | — | |
| **BK470** | two panes of 2492a $20.00 | | | |

Qty: 13,000,000

| | | NH–VF | ⊙F | FDC |
|---|---|---|---|---|
| **2493** | **$1.03 multicoloured** | 2.00 | .75 | — |
| i | die cut to shape from Quarterly Pack | 3.00 | — | |
| a | booklet pane of 6 x $1.03 (2493) (**BK471**) | 12.00 | — | |

Qty: 4,260,000

| | | NH–VF | ⊙F | FDC |
|---|---|---|---|---|
| **2494** | **$1.75 multicoloured** | 3.50 | 1.25 | — |
| i | die cut to shape from Quarterly Pack | 5.25 | — | |
| a | booklet pane of 6 x $1.75 (2494) (**BK472**) | 22.00 | — | |
| b | gutter pane, 2493a and 2494a | 35.00 | | |

Qty: 4,080,000; gutter pane: 3,500

At time of issue, the P Christmas stamps were valued at 59¢.

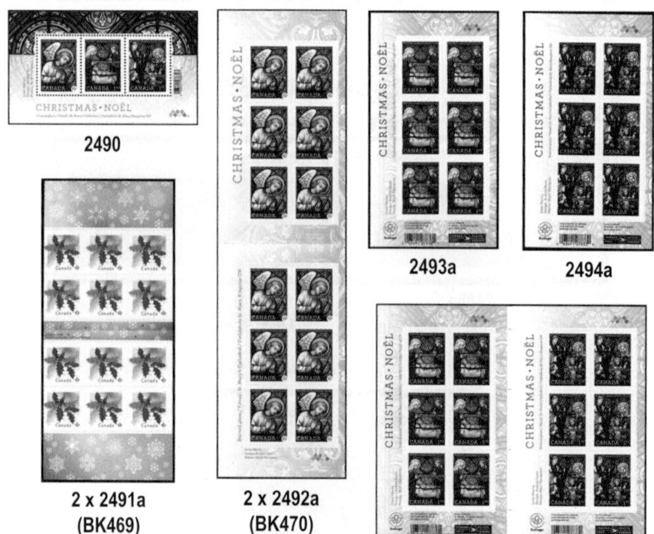

**2490** **2 x 2491a (BK469)** **2 x 2492a (BK470)** **2493a** **2494a** **2494b**

Timeline:
**2011, Sep–Nov** Canada Post produced Picture Postage™ (PP1–PP9)

## 2012

### LUNAR NEW YEAR (Series 2) — 4
### Year of the Dragon

*Perforated single from souvenir sheet* | *Die cut single from self-adhesive booklet*

2495
Dragon

2496i
Head of dragon

2497
Head of dragon

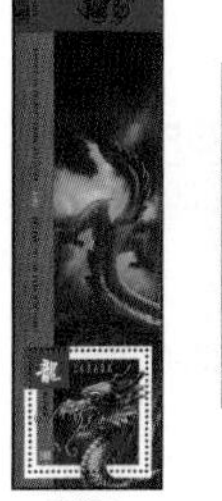
2496

2496a

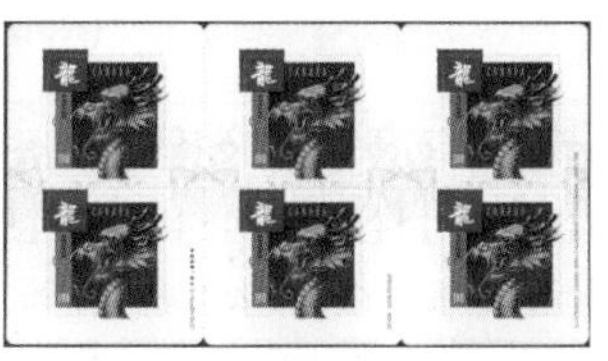
2497a

Designer: Louis Fishauf/Charles Vinh.

Lithography (6 colours) plus 1 foil stamping and embossing plus varnish, pane of 25
Lowe-Martin, Gravure Choquet

**2012, Jan 10** **GT4, TRC Paper** **Perf 12.5**

| | | NH–VF | ⊙F | PB | FDC |
|---|---|---|---|---|---|
| **2495** | **multicoloured** | 1.70 | .60 | 8.50 | 3.20 |

Qty: 5,250,000

At time of issue, the P stamp was valued at 61¢ even though the 61¢ domestic rate did not go into effect until January 16.

**GT4 (except where design passes through edge of stamp)**

| | | | | | |
|---|---|---|---|---|---|
| **2496** | **$1.80 souvenir sheet** of 1 | 3.50 | 3.50 | — | 5.60 |
| i | $1.80 single stamp from souvenir sheet | 3.00 | 3.00 | — | |
| ii | $29.95 uncut press sheet of 12 souvenir sheets | 80.00 | | | |
| a | $3.55 'transitional' souvenir sheet of 2, #2417, 2496 | 7.00 | 7.00 | — | |

Qty: 2496: 500,000; 2496ii: 15,000; 2496a: 200,000

Scott 2600a (Year of the Snake 'transitional' souvenir sheet) also produces a 2496i single.

Lithography (6 colours) plus varnish
Lowe-Martin, self-adhesive booklet of 6

**GT4 (except where design passes through edge of stamp)**
**TRC Paper** **Serpentine Die cut 13.5**

| | | NH–VF | ⊙F | FDC |
|---|---|---|---|---|
| **2497** | **$1.80 multicoloured** | 3.50 | 1.50 | |
| i | die cut to shape from Quarterly Pack | 5.25 | — | |
| a | booklet pane of 6 x $1.80 (2497) (**BK473**) | 21.50 | — | |

Qty: 1,800,000

For non-denominated postal cards of same designs, see UX263–UX264.



| Rates: | Domestic first-class (0-30g): 61¢ | USA (0-30g): $1.05 |
|---|---|---|
| Jan 16/12– | Domestic first-class (30-50g): $1.05 | USA (30-50g): $1.29 |
| Jan 13/13 | Domestic oversize (0-100g): $1.29 | International (0-30g): $1.80 |

*single usage:* USA $1.05: $15.00 | International $1.80: $20.00

### PERMANENT™ CANADIAN PRIDE

*Perforated singles from water-activated gum souvenir sheet*

2498a Flag on CCGS *Louis S. St-Laurent* | 2498b Flag in Van Window | 2498c Olympic Athlete Carrying Flag | 2498d Flag on Bobsled | 2498e Inuit Child Waving Flag

*Die cut singles from self-adhesive booklets*

2499 | 2500 | 2501 | 2502 | 2503

Designers: Gottschalk+Ash International

Lithography (4 colours)
Canadian Bank Note

Water-activated gum souvenir sheet of 5; Sheets of 100 subjects in twenty panes of 5

**2012, Jan 16** **GT4, TRC Paper** **Perf 13.0x13.4**

| | | NH–VF | ⊙F | FDC |
|---|---|---|---|---|
| **2498** | **$3.05 souvenir sheet** of 5 † | 8.75 | 8.75 | 8.10 |
| a | **multicoloured**, Coast Guard ship | 1.75 | 1.50 | |
| b | **multicoloured**, Van | 1.75 | 1.50 | |
| c | **multicoloured**, Olympic athlete | 1.75 | 1.50 | |
| d | **multicoloured**, Bobsled | 1.75 | 1.50 | |
| e | **multicoloured**, Inuit child | 1.75 | 1.50 | |

Qty: 197,000

Self-adhesive booklets of 10 and 30

**2012, Jan 16** **GT4, TRC Paper**
**Serpentine Die cut 13.4**

| | | NH–VF | ⊙F | FDC |
|---|---|---|---|---|
| **2499** | **multicoloured**, Coast Guard ship | 1.70 | .25 | — |
| a | repeating 'Canada' underprint, *Nov 2012* | 3.00 | .50 | |
| **2500** | **multicoloured**, Van | 1.70 | .25 | — |
| a | repeating 'Canada' underprint, *Nov 2012* | 3.00 | .50 | |
| **2501** | **multicoloured**, Olympic athlete | 1.70 | .25 | — |
| a | repeating 'Canada' underprint, *Nov 2012* | 3.00 | .50 | |
| **2502** | **multicoloured**, Bobsled | 1.70 | .25 | — |
| a | microprinting with corrected spelling of "Lueders", *Sep 28, 2012* | 2.00 | .25 | |
| b | repeating 'Canada' underprint, *Nov 2012* | 3.00 | .50 | |
| **2503** | **multicoloured**, Inuit child | 1.70 | .25 | — |
| i | se-tenant strip of 5 (2499–2503), die cut to shape from Quarterly Pack | 12.50 | — | |
| a | booklet pane of 10 x P (2 each of 2499–2503) (**BK474**) | 17.00 | | |
| b | booklet pane of 30 x P (6 each of 2499–2503) (**BK475**) | 50.00 | | |
| ai | strip of 5, from 2503a/BK474 or 2503b/BK475 | 8.50 | | |
| c | booklet pane of 10 x P (2 each of 2499–2501, 2502a, 2503) (**BK474A**), *Sep 28, 2012* | 25.00 | | |
| ci | strip of 5, from 2503c/BK474A | 12.50 | | |
| d | repeating 'Canada' underprint, *Nov 2012* | 3.00 | .50 | |
| e | booklet pane of 10 x P (2 each of 2499a–2501a, 2502b, 2503d) (**BK474B**), *Nov 2012* | 35.00 | | |
| ei | strip of 5, from 2503e/BK474B | 17.50 | | |

The Coast Guard ship is the CCGS *Louis S. St-Laurent*; the issue marks the 50th anniversary of the Canadian Coast Guard in 2012. The Olympic athlete is Nicolas Gill shown during the 2004 Summer Olympic Games in Athens, Greece. The bobsled design features Pierre Lueders, but is incorrectly noted (on the original printing) as

"Leuders" in the micro-printing, tagging, booklet cover, souvenir sheet text and pre-paid postal cards.
The tagging includes an incorrect spelling of "Permanent" (as "Permanant").
For non-denominated postal cards of same designs, see UX271–UX275.

Tagging on 'Canadian Pride' definitives (including incorrect spelling of "Permanent")

**2499a, 2500a, 2501a, 2502b, 2503d**
Repeating 'Canada' underprint

Incorrect spelling "Leuders" should be "Lueders"

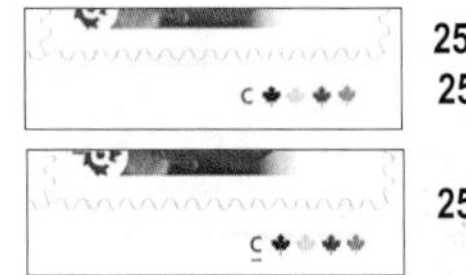

**2503a, 2503c**

**2503e**

Imprint on booklet of 10 (underlined C is for pane with repeating 'Canada' underprint)

**2498**

**2503a, 2503c**

**2503e**

**2503b**

## BABY WILDLIFE DEFINITIVES — SOUVENIR SHEET

| **2504a** | **2504b** | **2504c** | **2504d** |
|---|---|---|---|
| Racoons | Caribou | Loons | Moose |

Designers: Monique Dufour, Sophie Lafortune.
Lithography (8 colours)
Lowe-Martin
Water-activated gum souvenir sheet of 4; Sheets of 80 subjects in twenty panes of 4

**2012, Jan 16 GT4, TRC Paper Perf 13.4x13.0**

| | | NH–VF | ⊙F | FDC |
|---|---|---|---|---|
| **2504** | **$4.75 souvenir sheet** of 4 * | 10.00 | 10.00 | 11.50 |
| a | P **multicoloured** † | 1.75 | 1.50 | |
| b | **$1.05 multicoloured** | 2.00 | 1.75 | |
| c | **$1.29 multicoloured** | 2.50 | 2.25 | |
| d | **$1.80 multicoloured** | 3.50 | 3.25 | |

Qty: 197,000

* Face value of $4.75 at time of issue; the face value of the P stamp was 61¢.

**2504**

## BABY WILDLIFE DEFINITIVES – COILS

**2505**

**2506**

Racoons

**2507**
Caribou

**2508**
Loons

**2509**
Moose

Designers: Monique Dufour, Sophie Lafortune.
Lithography (5 colours), self-adhesive rolls of 100 (P) and 50 ($1.05, $1.29, $1.80)
Lowe-Martin

**2012, Jan 16 GT4, TRC Paper**
**Serpentine Die cut 9.2 Horiz**
**(Rounded tips)**

| | | NH–VF | ⊙F | FDC |
|---|---|---|---|---|
| **2505** | P **multicoloured** † | 2.00 | 2.00 | — |
| i | jump strip of 4 | 25.00 | | |

2505 issued in horizontal rolls of 5,000. Individual stamps do not touch along the horizontal roll; rounded 'perf tips' start with a peak. Sold in strips of 4 or 10 by the National Philatelic Centre; single stamps included in the Quarterly Pack/Annual Collection.

**Serpentine Die cut 8.15 to 8.50 Horiz**
**(Rounded tips with 4 or 5 'nibs' between stamps)**

To date, one die cut pattern has been used on these stamps and has been used both upright and inverted.

**2012, Jan 16 GT4, TRC Paper**

| | | NH–VF | ⊙F | FDC |
|---|---|---|---|---|
| **2506** | P **multicoloured** † | 1.70 | .25 | — |
| i | gutter strip of 4 with inscription | 8.50 | | |
| | starter strip of 4 (wavy die cut) | 11.00 | | |
| | end strip of 4 (wavy die cut) | 11.00 | | |
| ii | die cut to shape (9.2 horiz) from Quarterly Pack, *Apr '12* ‡ | 2.50 | — | |
| **2507** | **$1.05 multicoloured** | 2.10 | .45 | — |
| i | gutter strip of 4 with inscription | 10.00 | | |
| | starter strip of 4 (wavy die cut) | 12.00 | | |
| | end strip of 4 (wavy die cut) | 12.00 | | |
| ii | die cut to shape (9.2 horiz) from Quarterly Pack, *Apr '12* ‡ | 3.15 | — | |
| **2508** | **$1.29 multicoloured** | 2.50 | 1.00 | — |
| i | gutter strip of 4 with inscription | 12.00 | | |
| | starter strip of 4 (wavy die cut) | 15.00 | | |
| | end strip of 4 (wavy die cut) | 15.00 | | |
| ii | die cut to shape (9.2 horiz) from Quarterly Pack, *Apr '12* ‡ | 3.75 | — | |

| | | NH–VF | ⊙F | FDC |
|---|---|---|---|---|
| **2509** | **$1.80 multicoloured** | 3.60 | 1.25 | — |
| i | gutter strip of 4 with inscription | 17.00 | | |
| | starter strip of 4 (wavy die cut) | 19.00 | | |
| | end strip of 4 (wavy die cut) | 19.00 | | |
| ii | die cut to shape (9.2 horiz) from Quarterly Pack, *Apr '12* ‡ | 5.40 | — | |

‡ Single stamps supplied in the Quarterly Pack have rounded tips (backing paper is 'plain'), starting with a peak at upper left; stamps from the full rolls are perf 8.15 to 8.50.

Gutter strips are collected in strips of 4 with the gutter in the middle.

## BABY WILDLIFE DEFINITIVES – BOOKLETS

2510 Caribou | 2511 Loons | 2512 Moose

Designers: Monique Dufour, Sophie Lafortune.

Lithography (5 colours), self-adhesive booklets of 6
Lowe-Martin

**2012, Jan 16 GT4, TRC Paper**
**Serpentine Die cut 9.2 horiz (Rounded tips)**

| | | NH–VF | ⊙F | FDC |
|---|---|---|---|---|
| **2510** | **$1.05 multicoloured** | 2.10 | .45 | — |
| i | die cut to shape from Quarterly Pack | 3.15 | — | |
| a | booklet pane of 6 x $1.05 (2510) (**BK476**) | 12.50 | | |

A single used $1.05 counterfeit has been reported.

| | | NH–VF | ⊙F | FDC |
|---|---|---|---|---|
| **2511** | **$1.29 multicoloured** | 2.50 | .75 | — |
| i | die cut to shape from Quarterly Pack | 3.75 | — | |
| a | booklet pane of 6 x $1.29 (2511) (**BK477**) | 15.50 | | |
| **2512** | **$1.80 multicoloured** | 3.60 | 1.25 | — |
| i | die cut to shape from Quarterly Pack | 5.40 | — | |
| a | booklet pane of 6 x $1.80 (2512) (**BK478**) | 21.50 | | |

Single stamps from booklets of 6 *and* the single stamps supplied in the Quarterly Packs *all* start with a valley at the upper left.

For non-denominated postal cards of same designs, see UX276–UX279.
For size 10 envelopes of same designs see U264–U267.

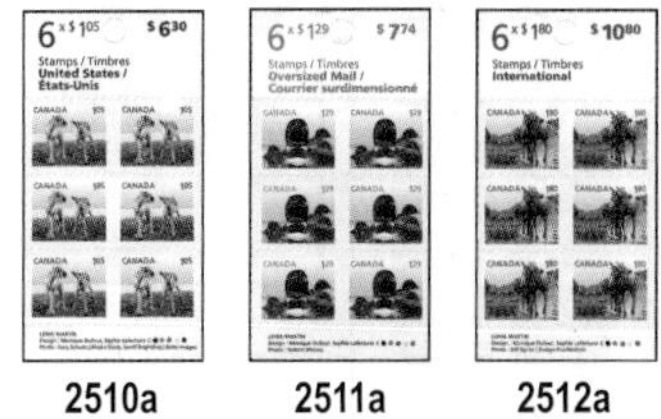

2510a 2511a 2512a

**† PERMANENT™ non-denominated stamps**

The stamps identified with the symbol of a letter "P" within a red maple leaf are valid indefinitely for use within Canada. Regardless of rate increases, these definitives will be worth the Canadian domestic basic letter rate in effect, and can be used to mail a letter that weighs up to 30 grams to any address in Canada. At time of issue, the P stamps on these pages (Jan 16/12 issue date) were valued at 61¢.

## QUEEN ELIZABETH II DIAMOND JUBILEE

2513
Crown, Sc. 330

2514
Map, Sc. 471

2515
Document pen, Sc. 704

2516
Flowers, Sc. 1168

2517
Crown, Sc. 1932

*Perforated single from mini sheet*

2518
Queen Elizabeth II

2513i 2514i 2515i

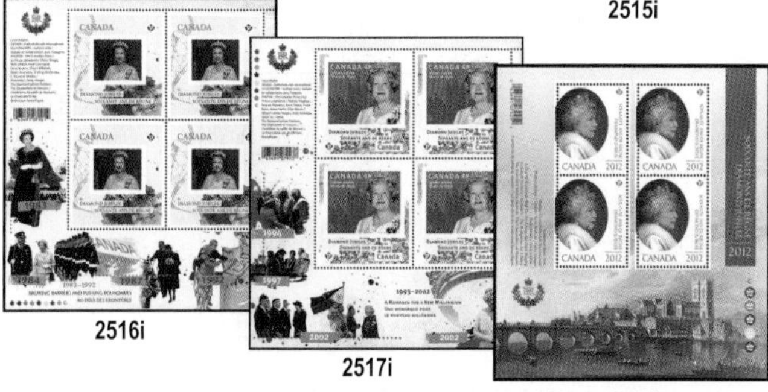

2516i 2517i 2518i

Wildlife/Canada Pride — 2012

QE II — 2010's

Designer: Gottschalk+Ash International

Lithography (5 colours), Sheets of 48 subjects in twelve mini panes of 4

Lowe-Martin

| 2012 | GT4, TRC Paper | | Perf 13.4 | |
|---|---|---|---|---|
| | | NH–VF | ⊙F | FDC |
| **2513** | **P multicoloured**, *Jan 16* | 1.70 | *1.50* | 3.20 |
| i | mini pane of 4 | 7.00 | *7.00* | |
| **2514** | **P multicoloured**, *Feb 6* | 1.70 | *1.50* | 3.20 |
| i | mini pane of 4 | 7.00 | *7.00* | |
| **2515** | **P multicoloured**, *Mar 6* | 1.70 | *1.50* | 3.20 |
| i | mini pane of 4 | 7.00 | *7.00* | |
| **2516** | **P multicoloured**, *Apr 10* | 1.70 | *1.50* | 3.20 |
| i | mini pane of 4 | 7.00 | *7.00* | |
| **2517** | **P multicoloured**, *May 7* | 1.70 | *1.50* | 3.20 |
| i | mini pane of 4 | 7.00 | *7.00* | |

**GT4 (except where design passes through edge of stamp)**

**Perf 13.1x12.5**

| | | NH–VF | ⊙F | FDC |
|---|---|---|---|---|
| **2518** | **P multicoloured**, *Jun 1* | 1.70 | *1.50* | — |
| i | mini pane of 4 | 7.00 | *7.00* | |

Qty: 800,000 of each

Postal outlets only sold these stamps in individual "Keepsake folders" which included a pane of 4, pre-paid postal card (see UX265–UX270) and a fact-filled booklet. Each sold for $5.95 ($7.95 for Keepsake 5). Mini panes were available on-line via the Canada Post website or through the National Philatelic Centre.

At time of issue, the P stamps were valued at 61¢.
Each stamp represents a 10-year reign of Queen Elizabeth II.

*Die cut single from self-adhesive booklet*

**2519**
Queen Elizabeth II

Designer: Gottschalk+Ash International

Lithography (5 colours), self-adhesive booklet of 10

Canadian Bank Note

**GT4 (except where design passes through edge of stamp)**

| 2012, Jan 16 | TRC Paper | Serpentine Die cut 13.4 | | |
|---|---|---|---|---|
| | | NH–VF | ⊙F | FDC |
| **2519** | **P multicoloured** | 1.70 | .45 | 3.20 |
| i | die cut to shape from Quarterly Pack/ Annual Collection | 2.50 | — | |
| a | booklet pane of 10 x P (2519) (**BK479**) | 17.00 | | |

Qty: 6,000,000

At time of issue, the P stamp was valued at 61¢.

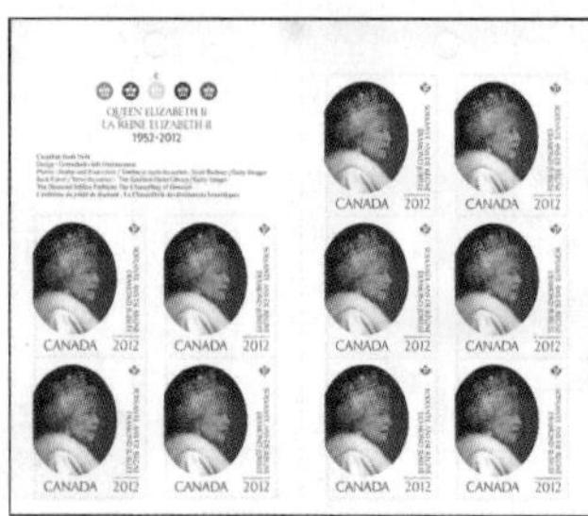

**2519a**

## BLACK HISTORY MONTH

**2520**
John Ware
(c. 1845–1905)

**2521**
Viola Desmond
(1914–1965)

Designer: Lara Minja (Lime Design Inc.).

Lithography (8 colours plus varnish), self-adhesive booklets of 10

Lowe-Martin

**2012, Feb 1 GT4, TRC Paper**

**Serpentine Die cut 13.5x13.3**

| | | NH–VF | ⊙F | FDC |
|---|---|---|---|---|
| **2520** | **P multicoloured** | 1.70 | .45 | 3.20 |
| i | die cut to shape from Quarterly Pack/ Annual Collection | 2.50 | — | |
| a | booklet pane of 10 x P (2520) (**BK480**) | 17.00 | | |

Qty: 4,000,000

Ware brought the first cattle to Southern Alberta in 1882, helping to create that province's important ranching industry.

| | | NH–VF | ⊙F | FDC |
|---|---|---|---|---|
| **2521** | **P multicoloured** | 1.70 | .45 | 3.20 |
| i | die cut to shape from Quarterly Pack/ Annual Collection | 2.50 | — | |
| a | booklet pane of 10 x P (2521) (**BK481**) | 17.00 | | |
| b | gutter pane, 6 each 2520 and 2521 | 20.00 | | |

Qty: 2,650,000; gutter pane: 4,000

Desmond was arrested in 1946 for sitting in the "whites-only" section of New Glasgow's Roseland theatre (Nova Scotia).

At time of issue, the P stamps were valued at 61¢.

**2520a** **2521a**

**2521b**

## *ART CANADA:* JOE FAFARD

**2522**
*Smoothly She Shifted*

*Perforated singles from water-activated gum souvenir sheet*

**2523a**
*Dear Vincent*

**2523b**
*Capillery*

*Die cut singles from self-adhesive booklets*

**2524**

**2525**

**2523**

**2524a**

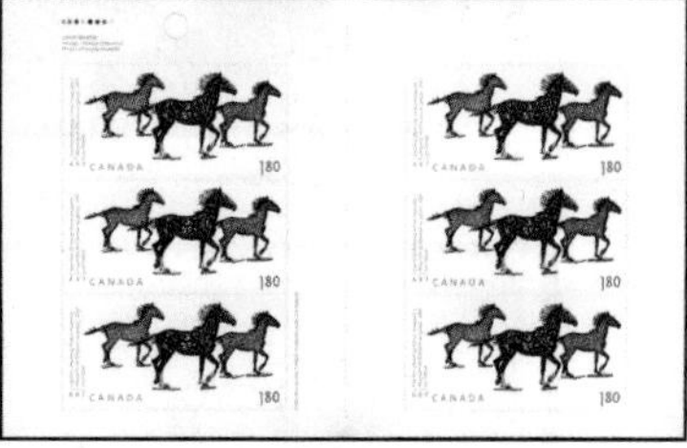
**2525a**

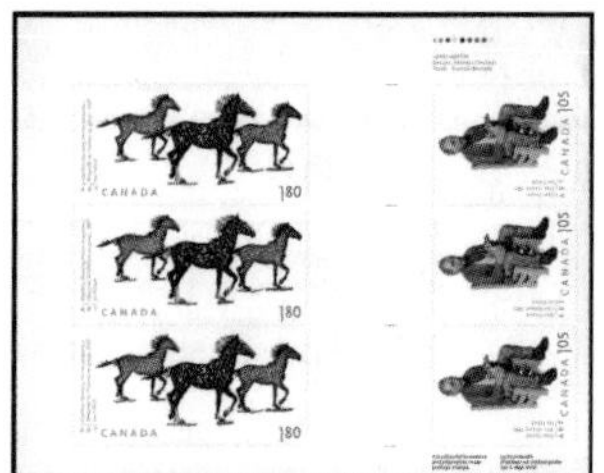
**2525b**

Designer: Hélène L'Heureux. Paintings by Joe Fafard, 1919–.

Lithography (6 colours plus varnish), pane of 16
Lowe-Martin

**2012, Feb 23 — GT4, TRC Paper — Perf 12.5**

| | | NH–VF | ⊙F | PB | FDC |
|---|---|---|---|---|---|
| **2522** | **P multicoloured** | 1.70 | .45 | 8.50 | 3.20 |
| i | $33.36 uncut press sheet of 2 panes of 2522 and 4 panes of 2523 | 75.00 | | | |

Qty: 1,600,000; 2522i: 1,500

At time of issue, the P stamp was valued at 61¢.

Lithography (7 colours plus varnish)

| | | NH–VF | ⊙F | FDC |
|---|---|---|---|---|
| **2523** | **$3.46 souvenir sheet** of 3 | 6.75 | 6.75 | 8.90 |
| a | **$1.05 multicoloured** | 2.00 | 2.00 | |
| b | **$1.80 multicoloured** | 3.50 | 3.50 | |

Qty: 200,000

Lithography (7 colours plus varnish), self-adhesive booklet of 6
Lowe-Martin
**GT4, TRC Paper**
**Serpentine Die cut 13.5 horiz**

| | | NH–VF | ⊙F | FDC |
|---|---|---|---|---|
| **2524** | **$1.05 multicoloured** | 2.00 | .90 | — |
| i | die cut to shape from Quarterly Pack | 3.00 | — | |
| a | booklet pane of 6 x $1.05 (2524) (**BK482**) | 12.50 | | |

Qty: 1,200,000

**Serpentine Die cut 13.4x13.5 horiz**

| | | NH–VF | ⊙F | FDC |
|---|---|---|---|---|
| **2525** | **$1.80 multicoloured** | 3.50 | 1.50 | — |
| i | die cut to shape from Quarterly Pack | 5.25 | — | |
| a | booklet pane of 6 x $1.80 (2525) (**BK483**) | 21.50 | | |
| b | gutter pane, 3 each 2524 and 2525 | 20.00 | | |

Qty: 1,200,000; gutter pane: 3,500

## DAYLILIES

*Perforated singles from water-activated gum souvenir sheet*

**2526a** **2526b**

**2527**
Orange

*Die cut singles from self-adhesive booklet*

**2529** Orange **2530** Purple

**2528**
Purple

**2526**

*Image rotated* **2530a**

QE II — 2010's

Designer: Isabelle Toussaint, Design graphique.

Lithography (6 colours)
Lowe-Martin
Water-activated gum souvenir sheet of 2

**2012, Mar 1** **GT4, TRC Paper** **Perf 13.2x13.4**

| | | NH–VF | ⊙F | FDC |
|---|---|---|---|---|
| **2526** | **$1.22 souvenir sheet** of 2 | 3.50 | 3.50 | — |
| a | P **multicoloured**, orange flower | 1.75 | 1.50 | |
| b | P **multicoloured**, purple flower | 1.75 | 1.50 | |
| i | se-tenant pair (2526a–b) | 3.50 | 3.00 | |

Qty: 210,000

Self-adhesive roll of 50

**GT4, TRC Paper**

**Serpentine Die cut 8.15 to 8.50 Horiz**

**(Rounded tips with 4 or 5 'nibs' between stamps)**

One die cut pattern exists on these stamps.

| | | NH–VF | ⊙F | FDC |
|---|---|---|---|---|
| **2527** | P **multicoloured**, orange flower | 1.70 | .60 | — |
| **2528** | P **multicoloured**, purple flower | 1.70 | .60 | — |
| a | se-tenant pair (vert.), 2527–28 | 3.40 | | |
| i | gutter strip of 4 with inscription | 8.50 | | |
| | starter strip of 4 (wavy die cut) | 11.00 | | |
| | end strip of 4 (wavy die cut) | 11.00 | | |
| ii | se-tenant pair (2527–28), die cut to shape (9.2 horiz) from Quarterly Pack | 5.00 | — | |

Qty: 3,000,000 of each

These stamps were printed se-tenant along the roll. Two different rolls were produced; one starting with the orange flower, the other starting with the purple flower. As such, two types of each of the gutter, starter and end strips of 4 exist.

Self-adhesive booklet of 10

**GT4, TRC Paper**

**Serpentine Die cut 13.5**

| | | NH–VF | ⊙F | FDC |
|---|---|---|---|---|
| **2529** | P **multicoloured**, orange flower | 1.70 | .45 | |
| **2530** | P **multicoloured**, purple flower | 1.70 | .45 | |
| i | se-tenant pair (2529, 2530), die cut to shape from Quarterly Pack | 7.00 | — | |
| a | booklet pane of 10, 5 each #2529–2530 + 10 stickers (**BK484**) | 17.00 | | |

Qty: 7,000,000 of each

**Nos. 2529–2530 (2) combination FDC** **4.45***

* Stamps on FDCs are not die cut all the way through.

At time of issue, the P stamps were valued at 61¢.

For non-denominated postal cards of same designs, see UX283–UX284.

**MINT PRICING PREMIUMS**

Mint stamps from 301 to date are valued as NH-VF (Never Hinged-Very Fine). All hinged VF and NH-F copies are worth 50% of the listed values. Plate block (PB) values are for mint NH–VF plate or inscription blocks of four.

**USED, VF/XF (with in-period, circular date cancel) PRICING PREMIUM**

Single stamps with light or circular date cancels will sell for more than catalogue value (perhaps even more than a mint copy). From *1981 to 1991* single stamps from se-tenant blocks of 4 or larger will be priced at 50% or more above the fine price. From *1992* to date single stamps from se-tenant blocks of 4 or larger plus se-tenant booklet panes and souvenir sheets will be priced at 100% or more above the fine price. From *1997* to date all other stamps will be priced at 50% or more above the fine price.

## TITANIC

**2531** Bow of Titanic, map of Halifax, Nova Scotia

**2532** Bow of Titanic, map showing Southampton, England

**2533** Propellers of Titanic, three men

**2534** Propellers of Titanic, six men

*Perforated single from water-activated gum souvenir sheet*

**2535i**

Titanic, map of North Atlantic, flag of the White Star Line

*Die cut singles from self-adhesive booklets*

**2536** **2537**

**2538**

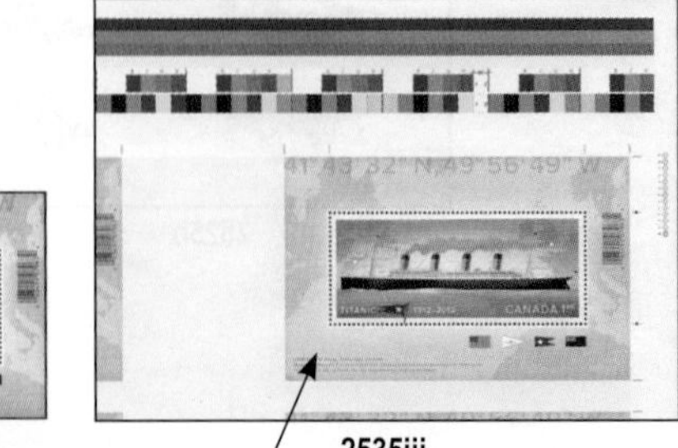

**2535** **2535iii**

QE II — 2010's

Designers: Dennis Page, Oliver Hill.

Lithography (8 colours), pane of 16 + vertical gutter
Lowe-Martin

**2012, Apr 5** **GT 3 sides, TRC Paper** **Perf 12.5**

| | | NH–VF | ⊙F | PB | FDC |
|---|---|---|---|---|---|
| **2531** | **P multicoloured** | 1.75 | .60 | | |
| **2532** | **P multicoloured** | 1.75 | .60 | | |
| **2533** | **P multicoloured** | 1.75 | .60 | | |
| **2534** | **P multicoloured** | 1.75 | .60 | | |
| a | se-tenant block of 4 (2531–34) | 7.00 | 3.00 | 8.75 | 6.90 |
| i | horizontal pair (2532, 2531), gutter between | 5.00 | 3.50 | | |
| ii | horizontal pair (2534, 2533), gutter between | 5.00 | 3.50 | | |

Qty: 800,000 of each

Lithography (7 colours), Water-activated gum souvenir sheet of 1
**GT4, TRC Paper** **Perf 12.9x12.8**

| | | NH–VF | ⊙F | FDC |
|---|---|---|---|---|
| **2535** | **$1.80 souvenir sheet** of 1 | 3.50 | 3.50 | 5.60 |
| i | $1.80 single from souvenir sheet | 3.40 | 3.40 | |
| ii | $26.95 uncut press sheet of 12 souvenir sheets | 90.00 | | |
| iii | single souvenir sheet from uncut press sheet (2535ii) with colour dots/'stars' missing* | *20.00* | | |

Qty: 300,000; 2535ii: 5,000; 2535iii: 15,000

* The three panes on the top right hand side of the uncut press sheet.

Lithography (8 colours), self-adhesive booklet of 10
Lowe-Martin
**GT 3 sides, TRC Paper**
**Serpentine Die cut 13.4**

| | | NH–VF | ⊙F | FDC |
|---|---|---|---|---|
| **2536** | **P multicoloured** | 1.70 | .45 | — |
| **2537** | **P multicoloured** | 1.70 | .45 | — |
| i | se-tenant pair, die cut to shape from Quarterly Pack | 5.00 | — | |
| a | booklet pane of 10, 5 each #2536–2537 (**BK485**) | 17.00 | | |

Qty: 2,000,000 of each

The general tagging on the Permanent™ stamps was *not* applied to the side with the illustration passing through the perfs/die cutting.

Lithography (7 colours), self-adhesive booklet of 6
**GT4, TRC Paper**
**Serpentine Die cut 13.5x13.7**

| | | NH–VF | ⊙F | FDC |
|---|---|---|---|---|
| **2538** | **$1.80 multicoloured** | 3.50 | 2.00 | — |
| i | die cut to shape from Quarterly Pack | 5.25 | — | |
| a | booklet pane of 6 x $1.80 (2538) (**BK486**) | 21.50 | | |

Qty: 1,200,000

Issued on the 100th anniversary of the sinking of the Titanic.

At time of issue, the P stamps were valued at 61¢.
For non-denominated postal cards of same designs, see UX285–UX287.

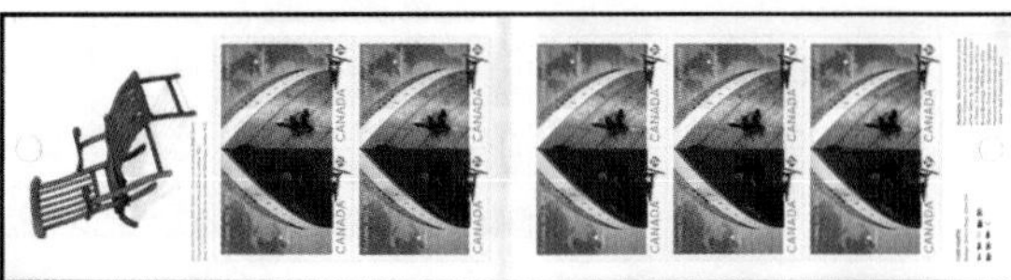
*Image rotated* **2537a**

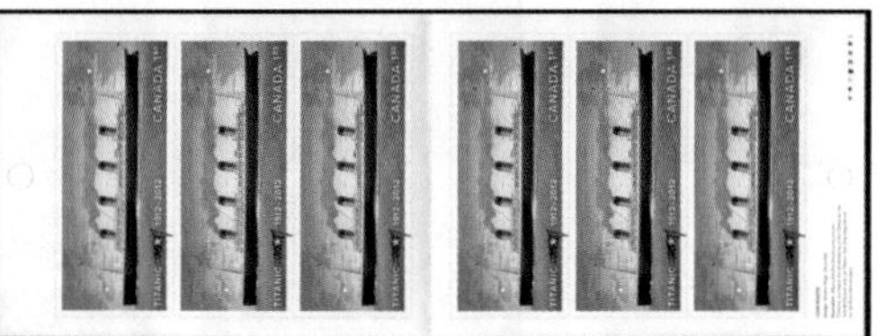
*Image rotated* **2538a**

## RED RIVER SETTLEMENT

**2539**
Métis, local trappers, native Chief and settlers; Lord Selkirk

Designer: Mark Heine.

Lithography (5 colours), pane of 16
Canadian Bank Note

**2012, May 3** **GT4, TRC Paper** **Perf 12.5**

| | | NH–VF | ⊙F | PB | FDC |
|---|---|---|---|---|---|
| **2539** | **P multicoloured** | 1.70 | .45 | 8.50* | 3.20 |

Qty: 1,200,000

* The upper right block has the inscription; the lower right block of the pane included the paper/colour designations.

Bicentennial of the Red River Settlement in the Assiniboia territory.

At time of issue, the P stamp was valued at 61¢.

## QUEEN ELIZABETH II DIAMOND JUBILEE

**2540**
Queen Elizabeth II

Designer: Mark Heine.

Intaglio (1 colour) and silkscreen, pane of 8
Intaglio (1 colour), silkscreen and silver foil, souvenir sheet of 1
Canadian Bank Note

**2012, May 7** **Not tagged, TRC Paper** **Perf 11.6**

| | | NH–VF | ⊙F | FDC |
|---|---|---|---|---|
| **2540** | **$2.00 purple** | 4.00 | 2.00 | 6.00 |
| | full pane of 8 | 32.00 | | |
| i | imperf. bottom margin | 1,000.00 | | |
| a | souvenir sheet of 1 | 5.00 | 5.00 | |
| ai | $80 signed uncut press sheet of 8 souvenir sheets and 4 panes of 8 | 200.00 | | |

Qty: 1,400,000; s/s: 350,000; 2540ai: 2,500

60th anniversary of the reign of Queen Elizabeth II featuring a design that mirrors the 1897 Queen Victoria Diamond Jubilee issue.
These stamps were sold by Canada Post early (May 5) at the ORAPEX 2012 stamp show in Ottawa, ON.

**2540, pane of 8**

**2540i**

**2540a**

QE II — 2010's

## FRANKLIN THE TURTLE

*Perforated singles from water-activated gum souvenir sheet*

2541a Franklin & Beaver | 2541b Franklin & Harriet | 2541c Franklin & Snail | 2541d Franklin & Bear

*Die cut singles from self-adhesive booklet*

2542 | 2543 | 2544 | 2545

Designer: q30 design inc.; Illustrations by Brenda Clark.

Lithography (7 colours), water-activated gum souvenir sheet of 4

Lowe-Martin

**2012, May 11** **GT4, TRC Paper** **Perf 13.0x12.5**

| | | NH–VF | ⊙F | FDC |
|---|---|---|---|---|
| **2541** | **$2.44 souvenir sheet** of 4 | 7.00 | 7.00 | 6.90 |
| a | **P multicoloured** | 1.75 | 1.50 | |
| b | **P multicoloured** | 1.75 | 1.50 | |
| c | **P multicoloured** | 1.75 | 1.50 | |
| d | **P multicoloured** | 1.75 | 1.50 | |

Qty: 300,000

Self-adhesive booklet of 12

**Serpentine Die cut 13.4**

| | | NH–VF | ⊙F | FDC |
|---|---|---|---|---|
| **2542** | **P multicoloured** | 1.70 | .60 | |
| **2543** | **P multicoloured** | 1.70 | .60 | |
| **2544** | **P multicoloured** | 1.70 | .60 | |
| **2545** | **P multicoloured** | 1.70 | .60 | |
| a | booklet pane of 12 x P + 12 stickers (**BK487**) | 20.00 | | — |

Qty: 1,800,000 of each stamp

At time of issue, the P stamps were valued at 61¢.

For non-denominated postal cards of same designs, see UX288–UX291.

2541

2545a

## CALGARY STAMPEDE

*Perforated singles from water-activated gum souvenir sheet*

**2546b**

**2546a**

*Die cut singles from self-adhesive booklets*

**2547**
Saddled rodeo horse

**2548**
Silver and gold belt buckle

Designer: Xerxes Irani.

Lithography (8 colours plus spot varnish), water-activated gum souvenir sheet of 2

Lowe-Martin

**2012, May 17** **GT4, TRC Paper** **Perf 13.0x13.3**

| | | NH–VF | ⊙F | PB | FDC |
|---|---|---|---|---|---|
| **2546** | **$1.66 souvenir sheet** of 2 | 4.50 | 4.50 | | 5.30 |
| a | **P multicoloured** | 1.75 | 1.50 | | |
| b | **$1.05 multicoloured** | 2.50 | 2.25 | | |

Qty: 325,000

Lithography (7 colours plus spot varnish), self-adhesive booklets of 10

Lowe-Martin

**GT4, TRC Paper**

**Serpentine Die cut 13.3x13.0**

| | | NH–VF | ⊙F | FDC |
|---|---|---|---|---|
| **2547** | **P multicoloured** | 1.70 | .45 | — |
| i | die cut to shape from Quarterly Pack | 2.50 | — | |
| a | booklet pane of 10 x P (2547) (**BK488**) | 17.00 | | |

Qty: 4,000,000

| | | NH–VF | ⊙F | FDC |
|---|---|---|---|---|
| **2548** | **$1.05 multicoloured** | 2.10 | .90 | — |
| i | die cut to shape from Quarterly Pack | 3.15 | — | |
| a | booklet pane of 10 x $1.05 (2548) (**BK489**) | 21.00 | | |
| b | gutter pane, 6 of 2547 and 4 of 2548 | 20.00 | | |

Qty: 2,250,000; gutter pane: 3,500

Centennial of the Calgary Stampede.

At time of issue, the P stamps were valued at 61¢.

For non-denominated postal cards of same designs, see UX292–UX293.

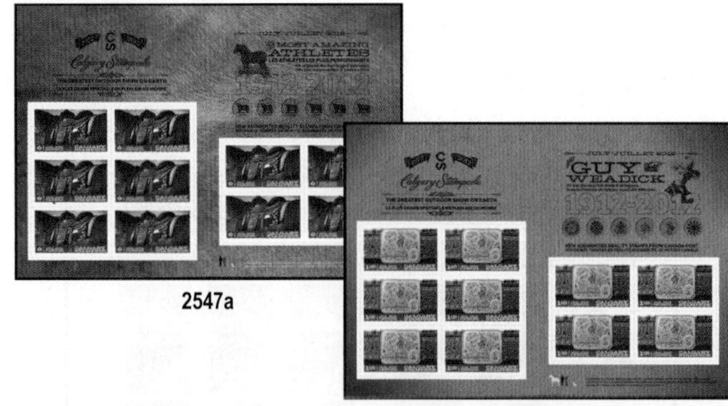

2547a

2548a

2546

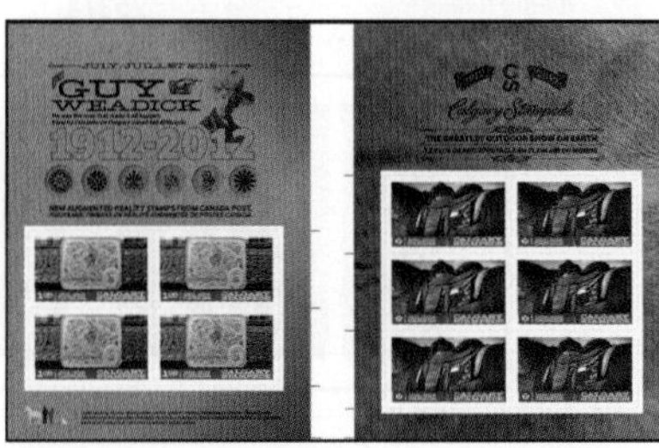

2548b

## DIFFERENCE MAKERS

*Perforated singles from water-activated gum souvenir sheet*

**2549a**
Louise Arbour
(1947– )

**2549b**
Rick Hansen
(1957– )

**2549c**
Sheila Watt-Cloutier
(1953– )

**2549d**
Michael J. Fox
(1961– )

*Die cut singles from self-adhesive booklets*

**2550**

**2551**

**2552**

**2553**

Designer: Paprika.

Lithography (5 colours plus varnish), water-activated gum souvenir sheet of 4
Lowe-Martin

**2012, May 22** **GT4, TRC Paper** **Perf 13.0x12.5**

| | | NH–VF | ⊙F | FDC |
|---|---|---|---|---|
| **2549** | **$2.44 souvenir sheet** of 4 | 7.00 | 7.00 | 6.90 |
| a | **purple, grey, red**, Arbour | 1.75 | 1.50 | |
| b | **blue, grey, red**, Hansen | 1.75 | 1.50 | |
| c | **sea green, grey, red**, Watt-Cloutier | 1.75 | 1.50 | |
| d | **bright green, grey, red**, Fox | 1.75 | 1.50 | |

Qty: 225,000

Lithography (3 colours), Self-adhesive booklets of 10
**Serpentine Die cut 13.4**

| | | NH–VF | ⊙F | FDC |
|---|---|---|---|---|
| **2550** | **purple, grey, red**, Arbour | 1.70 | .45 | |
| i | die cut to shape from Quarterly Pack | 2.50 | — | |
| a | booklet pane of 10 x P (2550) (**BK490**) | 17.00 | | |

Qty: 2,000,000

| | | NH–VF | ⊙F | FDC |
|---|---|---|---|---|
| **2551** | **blue, grey, red**, Hansen | 1.70 | .45 | |
| i | die cut to shape from Quarterly Pack | 2.50 | — | |
| a | booklet pane of 10 x P (2551) (**BK491**) | 17.00 | | |

Qty: 4,000,000

| | | NH–VF | ⊙F | FDC |
|---|---|---|---|---|
| **2552** | **sea green, grey, red**, Watt-Cloutier | 1.70 | .45 | |
| i | die cut to shape from Quarterly Pack | 2.50 | — | |
| a | booklet pane of 10 x P (2552) (**BK492**) | 17.00 | | |

Qty: 2,000,000

| | | NH–VF | ⊙F | FDC |
|---|---|---|---|---|
| **2553** | **bright green, grey, red**, Fox | 1.70 | .45 | |
| i | die cut to shape from Quarterly Pack | 2.50 | — | |
| a | booklet pane of 10 x P (2553) (**BK493**) | 17.00 | | |

Qty: 3,000,000

At time of issue, the P stamps were valued at 61¢.

**2549**

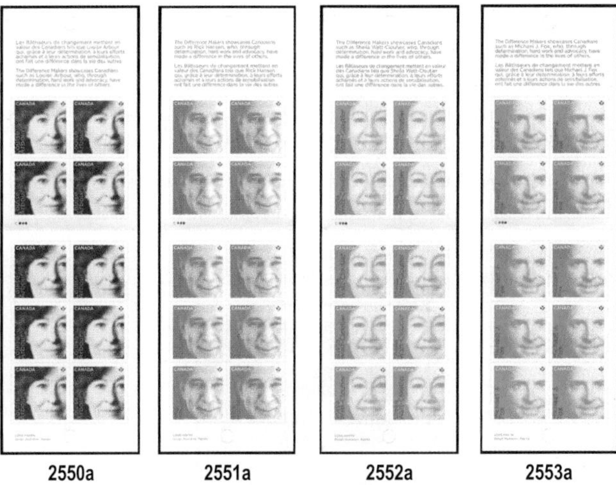

**2550a** **2551a** **2552a** **2553a**

## THE WAR OF 1812

**2554**
Sir Isaac Brock
(1769–1812)

**2555**
War Chief Tecumseh
(1768–1813)

Designer: Susan Scott.

Lithography (6 colours), pane of 16
Lowe-Martin

**2012, Jun 15** **GT 3-sided, TRC Paper** **Perf 13.1x12.5**

| | | NH–VF | ⊙F | PB | FDC |
|---|---|---|---|---|---|
| **2554** | **multicoloured** | 1.70 | .45 | | |
| **2555** | **multicoloured** | 1.70 | .45 | | |
| a | se-tenant pair (2554, 2555) | 3.40 | 1.50 | 8.50* | 4.45 |

Qty: 750,000 of each

* Only the lower right block has the inscription and paper/colour designations.

The general tagging was *not* applied to the side with the illustration passing through the perfs.

**Joint FDC with Guernsey** **11.00**

Joint issue with Guernsey (where Brock was born). The first in a multi-year series commemorating the War of 1812. At time of issue, the P stamps were valued at 61¢.

Joint issue with Guernsey
**Scott # 1172**

## LONDON 2012 SUMMER OLYMPICS

**2556**
Rowing

Designer: Kosta Tsetsekas, Mike Savage | Signals.
Lithography (7 colours plus varnish), self-adhesive booklet of 10
Lowe-Martin

**2012, Jun 27** **GT4, TRC Paper**
**Serpentine Die cut 8.1x8.2**

| | | NH–VF | ⊙F | FDC |
|---|---|---|---|---|
| **2556** | ⚘ **multicoloured** | 1.70 | .45 | 3.20 |
| i | die cut to shape from Quarterly Pack/ Annual Collection | 2.50 | — | |
| a | booklet pane of 10 x P (2556) (**BK494**) | 17.00 | | |

Qty: 4,000,000

London 2012 Summer Olympics (XXX Olympiad) scheduled for July 27 to August 12.

At time of issue, the P stamp was valued at 61¢.
For non-denominated postal card of same design, see UX294.

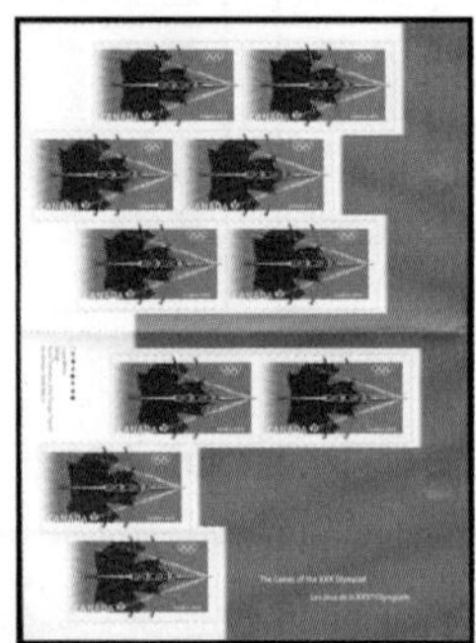

**2556a**

## TOMMY DOUGLAS

**2557**
Tommy Douglas
(1905–1986)

Designer: Derwyn Goodall.
Lithography (7 colours plus varnish), pane of 16
Lowe-Martin

**2012, Jun 29** **GT4, TRC Paper** **Perf 12.5**

| | | NH–VF | ⊙F | PB | FDC |
|---|---|---|---|---|---|
| **2557** | ⚘ **multicoloured** | 1.70 | .45 | 8.50 | 3.20 |

Qty: 1,600,000

50th anniversary of the birth of Medicare with the passing of Saskatchewan's 1962 Medical Care Insurance Act.

At time of issue, the P stamp was valued at 61¢.

## CFL TEAMS

*Perforated singles from water-activated gum souvenir sheet*

**2558a**
BC Lions

**2558b**
Edmonton Eskimos

**2558c**
Calgary Stampeders

**2558d**
Saskatchewan Roughriders

**2558e**
Winnipeg Blue Bombers

**2558f**
Hamilton Tiger-Cats

**2558g**
Toronto Argonauts

**2558h**
Montréal Alouettes

*Self-adhesive coils*

**2559**
BC Lions

**2560**
Edmonton Eskimos

**2561**
Calgary Stampeders

**2562**
Saskatchewan Roughriders

**2563**
Winnipeg Blue Bombers

**2564**
Hamilton Tiger-Cats

**2565**
Toronto Argonauts

**2566**
Montréal Alouettes

Designer: Filip Mroz, David Rosenberg | Bensimon Byrne.
Lithography (9 colours)
Lowe-Martin
Water-activated gum souvenir sheet of 8; Sheets of 160 subjects in 20 panes of 8

**2012, Jun 29** **GT4, TRC Paper** **Perf 13.3x13.0**

| | | NH–VF | ⊙F | FDC |
|---|---|---|---|---|
| **2558** | **$4.88 souvenir sheet** of 8 | 14.00 | 14.00 | 11.75 |
| a | ⚘ **multicoloured**, BC Lions | 1.75 | 1.50 | |
| b | ⚘ **multicoloured**, Edmonton Eskimos | 1.75 | 1.50 | |
| c | ⚘ **multicoloured**, Calgary Stampeders | 1.75 | 1.50 | |
| d | ⚘ **multicoloured**, Saskatchewan Roughriders | 1.75 | 1.50 | |
| e | ⚘ **multicoloured**, Winnipeg Blue Bombers | 1.75 | 1.50 | |
| f | ⚘ **multicoloured**, Hamilton Tiger-Cats | 1.75 | 1.50 | |
| g | ⚘ **multicoloured**, Toronto Argonauts | 1.75 | 1.50 | |
| h | ⚘ **multicoloured**, Montréal Alouettes | 1.75 | 1.50 | |

Qty: 200,000

Self-adhesive rolls of 50
**GT4, TRC Paper**
**Serpentine Die cut 8.25 to 8.35 Horiz**
**(Rounded tips with 3 'nibs' between stamps)**
One die cut pattern was used on the BC, Sask., Winnipeg and Hamilton stamps, a different die cut pattern was used on Edmonton, Calgary, Toronto and Montréal.

| | | NH–VF | ⊙F | FDC |
|---|---|---|---|---|
| **2559** | ⚘ **multicoloured**, BC Lions | 1.70 | .60 | — |
| i | gutter strip of 4 with inscription | 8.50 | | |
| | starter strip of 4 (wavy die cut) | 11.00 | | |
| | end strip of 4 (wavy die cut) | 11.00 | | |
| ii | die cut to shape (9.2 horiz) from Qtr Pack ‡ | 2.50 | — | |
| **2560** | ⚘ **multicoloured**, Edmonton Eskimos | 1.70 | .60 | — |
| i | gutter strip of 4 with inscription | 8.50 | | |
| | starter strip of 4 (wavy die cut) | 11.00 | | |
| | end strip of 4 (wavy die cut) | 11.00 | | |
| ii | die cut to shape (9.2 horiz) from Qtr Pack ‡ | 2.50 | — | |

| | | NH–VF | ⊙F | FDC |
|---|---|---|---|---|
| 2561 | P **multicoloured**, Calgary Stampeders | 1.70 | .60 | — |
| i | gutter strip of 4 with inscription | 8.50 | | |
| | starter strip of 4 (wavy die cut) | 11.00 | | |
| | end strip of 4 (wavy die cut) | 11.00 | | |
| ii | die cut to shape (9.2 horiz) from Qtr Pack ‡ | 2.50 | — | |
| 2562 | P **multicoloured**, Saskatchewan Roughriders | 1.70 | .60 | — |
| i | gutter strip of 4 with inscription | 8.50 | | |
| | starter strip of 4 (wavy die cut) | 11.00 | | |
| | end strip of 4 (wavy die cut) | 11.00 | | |
| ii | die cut to shape (9.2 horiz) from Qtr Pack ‡ | 2.50 | — | |
| 2563 | P **multicoloured**, Winnipeg Blue Bombers | 1.70 | .60 | — |
| i | gutter strip of 4 with inscription | 8.50 | | |
| | starter strip of 4 (wavy die cut) | 11.00 | | |
| | end strip of 4 (wavy die cut) | 11.00 | | |
| ii | die cut to shape (9.2 horiz) from Qtr Pack ‡ | 2.50 | — | |
| 2564 | P **multicoloured**, Hamilton Tiger-Cats | 1.70 | .60 | — |
| i | gutter strip of 4 with inscription | 8.50 | | |
| | starter strip of 4 (wavy die cut) | 11.00 | | |
| | end strip of 4 (wavy die cut) | 11.00 | | |
| ii | die cut to shape (9.2 horiz) from Qtr Pack ‡ | 2.50 | — | |
| 2565 | P **multicoloured**, Toronto Argonauts | 1.70 | .60 | — |
| i | gutter strip of 4 with inscription | 8.50 | | |
| | starter strip of 4 (wavy die cut) | 11.00 | | |
| | end strip of 4 (wavy die cut) | 11.00 | | |
| ii | die cut to shape (9.2 horiz) from Qtr Pack ‡ | 2.50 | — | |
| 2566 | P **multicoloured**, Montréal Alouettes | 1.70 | .60 | — |
| i | gutter strip of 4 with inscription | 8.50 | | |
| | starter strip of 4 (wavy die cut) | 11.00 | | |
| | end strip of 4 (wavy die cut) | 11.00 | | |
| ii | die cut to shape (9.2 horiz) from Qtr Pack ‡ | 2.50 | — | |

Qty: 2,000,000 of each

‡ Single stamps supplied in the Quarterly Pack have rounded tips (die cut 9.2 horiz), starting with a peak at upper left; stamps from the full rolls are die cut 8.25 to 8.35.

For Ottawa Redblacks coil design see 2754. At time of issue, the P stamps were valued at 61¢.

2558

Timeline:
2012, Jul 23 P (61¢) Signs of the Zodiac (2446, 2453–2456)

## 100th GREY CUP GAME

*Perforated singles from water-activated gum souvenir sheet*

**2567a**
Grey Cup

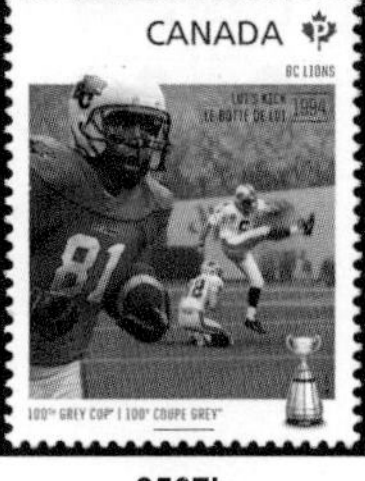

**2567b**
BC Lions
Geroy Simon (1975- ),
'Lui's Kick'

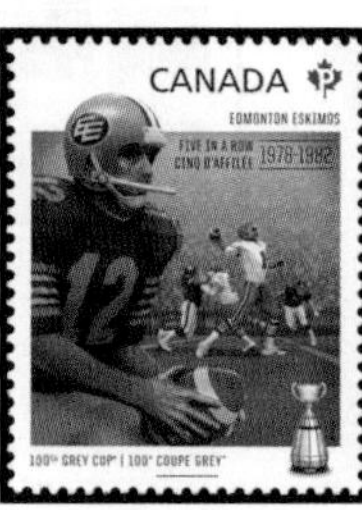

**2567c**
Edmonton Eskimos
Tom Wilkinson (1943- ),
'Five in a Row'

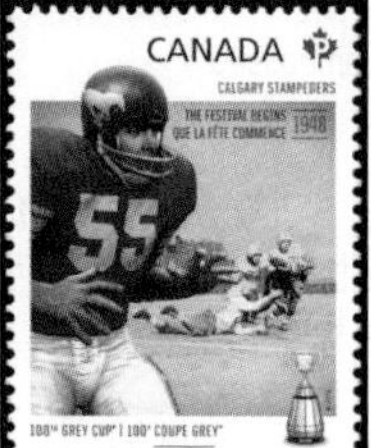

**2567d**
Calgary Stampeders
Wayne Harris (1938-2015),
'The Festival Begins'

**2567e**
Saskatchewan Roughriders
George Reed (1939- ),
'A True Classic'

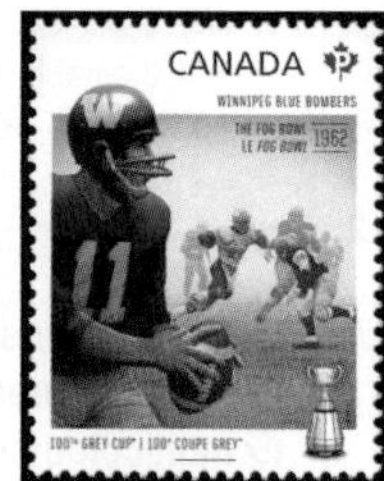

**2567f**
Winnipeg Blue Bombers
Ken Ploen (1935- ),
'The Fog Bowl'

**2567g**
Hamilton Tiger-Cats
Danny McManus (1965- ),
'Hometown Heroes'

**2567h**
Toronto Argonauts
Michael Clemons (1965- ),
'The Mud Bowl'

**2567i**
Montréal Alouettes
Anthony Calvillo (1972- ),
'The Ice Bowl'

*Die cut singles from self-adhesive booklets*

**2568**
Grey Cup

**2569**
BC Lions
Geroy Simon (1975- ),
'Lui's Kick'

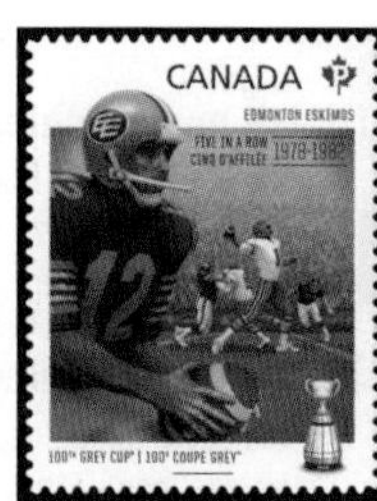

**2570**
Edmonton Eskimos
Tom Wilkinson (1943- ),
'Five in a Row'

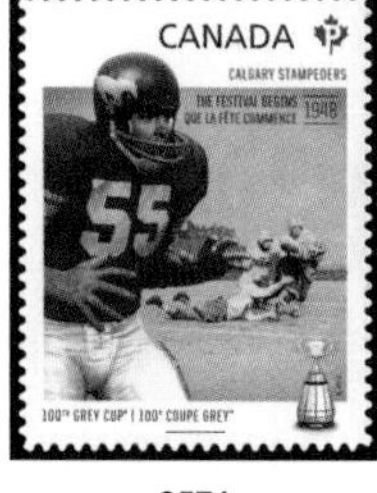

**2571**
Calgary Stampeders
Wayne Harris (1938-2015),
'The Festival Begins'

**2572**
Saskatchewan Roughriders
George Reed (1939- ),
'A True Classic'

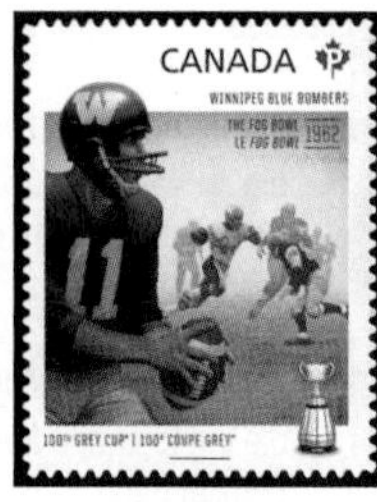

**2573**
Winnipeg Blue Bombers
Ken Ploen (1935- ),
'The Fog Bowl'

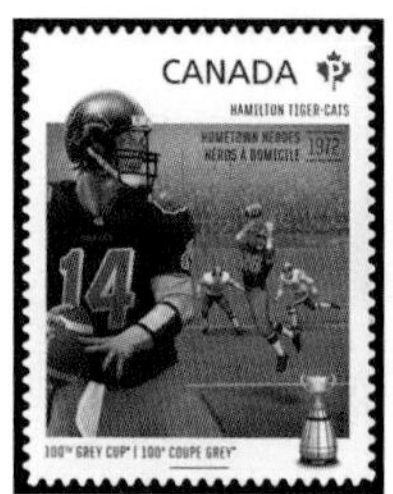

**2574**
Hamilton Tiger-Cats
Danny McManus (1965- ),
'Hometown Heroes'

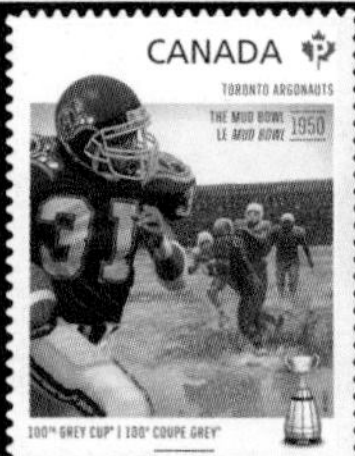

**2575**
Toronto Argonauts
Michael Clemons (1965- ),
'The Mud Bowl'

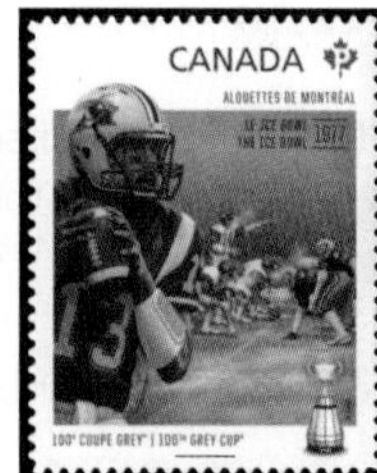

**2576**
Montréal Alouettes
Anthony Calvillo (1972- ),
'The Ice Bowl'

Designer: Filip Mroz, David Rosenberg | Bensimon Byrne.

Lithography (5 colours plus varnish) and embossed, water-activated gum pane of 9

Lowe-Martin

**2012, Aug 16** **GT4, TRC Paper** **Perf 12.5**

| | | NH–VF | ⊙F | FDC |
|---|---|---|---|---|
| **2567** | **$5.49 souvenir sheet** of 9 | 15.75 | 15.75 | |
| a | **P multicoloured**, Grey Cup | 1.75 | 1.50 | |
| b | **P multicoloured**, Lions | 1.75 | 1.50 | |
| c | **P multicoloured**, Eskimos | 1.75 | 1.50 | |
| d | **P multicoloured**, Stampeders | 1.75 | 1.50 | |
| e | **P multicoloured**, Roughriders | 1.75 | 1.50 | |
| f | **P multicoloured**, Blue Bombers | 1.75 | 1.50 | |
| g | **P multicoloured**, Tiger-Cats | 1.75 | 1.50 | |
| h | **P multicoloured**, Argonauts | 1.75 | 1.50 | |
| i | **P multicoloured**, Alouettes | 1.75 | 1.50 | |

Qty: 3,600,000

Lithography (5 colours plus varnish), Self-adhesive booklets of 10

**Serpentine Die cut 13.5x13.4**

| | | NH–VF | ⊙F | FDC |
|---|---|---|---|---|
| **2568** | **P multicoloured**, Grey Cup | 1.70 | .45 | 3.20 |
| i | die cut to shape from Quarterly Pack | 2.50 | — | |
| a | booklet pane of 10 x P (2568) (**BK499**) | 17.00 | | |

Qty: 4,000,000

For overprinted stamp (with Toronto Argonauts logo), see 2598.

| | | NH–VF | ⊙F | FDC |
|---|---|---|---|---|
| **2569** | **P multicoloured**, Lions | 1.70 | .45 | 3.20 |
| i | die cut to shape from Quarterly Pack | 2.50 | — | |
| a | booklet pane of 10 x P (2569) (**BK500**) | 17.00 | | |

Qty: 3,500,000

| | | NH–VF | ⊙F | FDC |
|---|---|---|---|---|
| **2570** | **P multicoloured**, Eskimos | 1.70 | .45 | 3.20 |
| i | die cut to shape from Quarterly Pack | 2.50 | — | |
| a | booklet pane of 10 x P (2570) (**BK501**) | 17.00 | | |

Qty: 3,000,000

| | | NH–VF | ⊙F | FDC |
|---|---|---|---|---|
| **2571** | **P multicoloured**, Stampeders | 1.70 | .45 | 3.20 |
| i | die cut to shape from Quarterly Pack | 2.50 | — | |
| a | booklet pane of 10 x P (2571) (**BK502**) | 17.00 | | |

Qty: 3,000,000

| | | NH–VF | ⊙F | FDC |
|---|---|---|---|---|
| **2572** | **P multicoloured**, Roughriders | 1.70 | .45 | 3.20 |
| i | die cut to shape from Quarterly Pack | 2.50 | — | |
| a | booklet pane of 10 x P (2572) (**BK503**) | 17.00 | | |

Qty: 4,000,000

| | | NH–VF | ⊙F | FDC |
|---|---|---|---|---|
| **2573** | **P multicoloured**, Blue Bombers | 1.70 | .45 | 3.20 |
| i | die cut to shape from Quarterly Pack | 2.50 | — | |
| a | booklet pane of 10 x P (2573) (**BK504**) | 17.00 | | |

Qty: 3,500,000

| | | NH–VF | ⊙F | FDC |
|---|---|---|---|---|
| **2574** | **P multicoloured**, Tiger-Cats | 1.70 | .45 | 3.20 |
| i | die cut to shape from Quarterly Pack | 2.50 | — | |
| a | booklet pane of 10 x P (2574) (**BK505**) | 17.00 | | |

Qty: 3,000,000

| | | NH–VF | ⊙F | FDC |
|---|---|---|---|---|
| **2575** | **P multicoloured**, Argonauts | 1.70 | .45 | 3.20 |
| i | die cut to shape from Quarterly Pack | 2.50 | — | |
| a | booklet pane of 10 x P (2575) (**BK506**) | 17.00 | | |

Qty: 3,500,000

| | | NH–VF | ⊙F | FDC |
|---|---|---|---|---|
| **2576** | **P multicoloured**, Alouettes | 1.70 | .45 | 3.20 |
| i | die cut to shape from Quarterly Pack | 2.50 | — | |
| a | booklet pane of 10 x P (2576) (**BK507**) | 17.00 | | |

Qty: 4,000,000

For non-denominated postal cards of same designs, see UX299–UX307.

For Ottawa Redblacks team player design see 2755. At time of issue, the P stamps were valued at 61¢.

2567

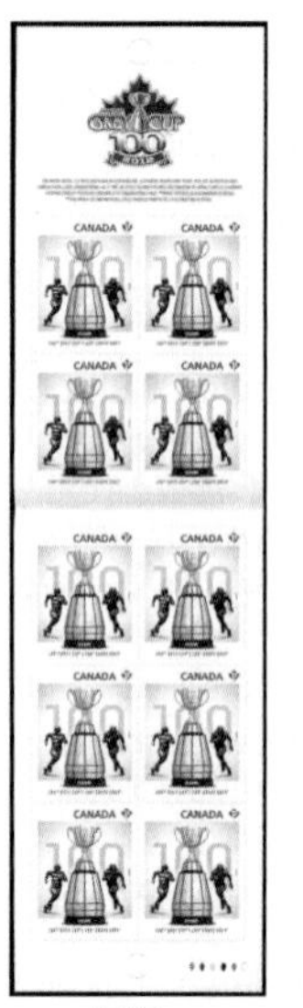
2568a

2569a

2570a

2571a

2572a

2573a

2574a

2575a

2576a

Timeline:
**2012, Sep 17** P (61¢)+10¢ Canada Post Community Foundation, semi-postal (B19)

## THE REGIMENTS

*Perforated singles from water-activated gum souvenir sheet*

| 2577a | 2577b | 2577c |
|---|---|---|
| The Black Watch | The Royal Hamilton Light Infantry | The Royal Regiment of Canada |

*Die cut singles from self-adhesive booklet*

2578
The Black Watch

2579
The Royal Hamilton Light Infantry

2580
The Royal Regiment of Canada

Designer: Sputnik Design Partners Inc.
Lithography (7 colours), water-activated gum souvenir sheet of 3
Sheets of 36 subjects in twelve panes of 3
Lowe-Martin

**2012, Oct 11** **GT4, TRC Paper** **Perf 13.0x13.4**

| | | NH–VF | ⊙F | FDC |
|---|---|---|---|---|
| **2577** | **$1.83 souvenir sheet** of 3 | 5.25 | 5.25 | |
| **a** | **P multicoloured** | 1.75 | 1.50 | |
| **b** | **P multicoloured** | 1.75 | 1.50 | |
| **c** | **P multicoloured** | 1.75 | 1.50 | |

Qty: 250,000

Self-adhesive booklets of 10
**Serpentine Die cut 13.4x13.0**

| | | NH–VF | ⊙F | FDC |
|---|---|---|---|---|
| **2578** | **P multicoloured** | 1.70 | .60 | 3.20 |
| **i** | die cut to shape from Quarterly Pack | 2.50 | — | |
| a | booklet pane of 10 x P (2578) (**BK509**) | 17.00 | | |
| **2579** | **P multicoloured** | 1.70 | .60 | 3.20 |
| **i** | die cut to shape from Quarterly Pack | 2.50 | — | |
| a | booklet pane of 10 x P (2579) (**BK510**) | 17.00 | | |
| **2580** | **P multicoloured** | 1.70 | .60 | 3.20 |
| **i** | die cut to shape from Quarterly Pack | 2.50 | — | |
| a | booklet pane of 10 x P (2580) (**BK511**) | 17.00 | | |

Qty: 2,500,000 of each stamp

At time of issue, the P stamps were valued at 61¢.

2577

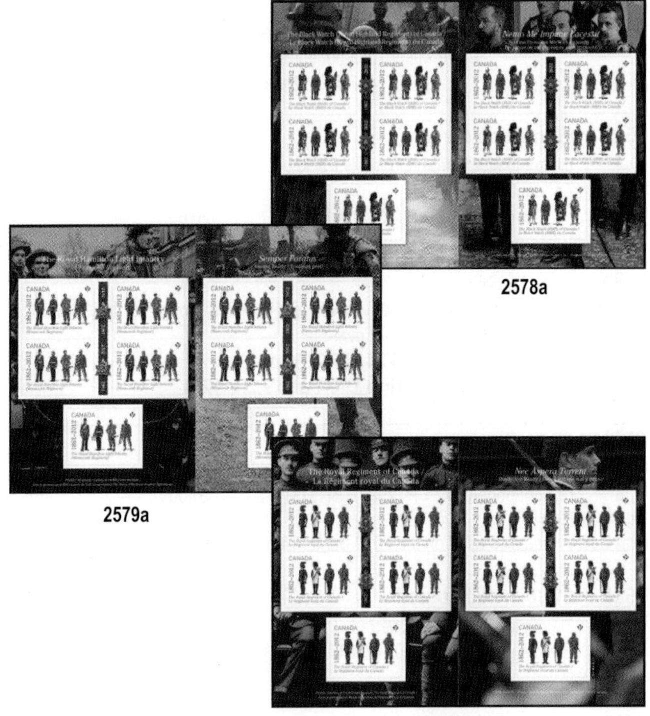

2578a

2579a

2580a

## CHRISTMAS COOKIES

*Perforated singles from water-activated gum souvenir sheet*

| 2581a | 2581b | 2581c |
|---|---|---|

*Die cut singles from self-adhesive booklets*

| 2583 | 2584 | 2585 |
|---|---|---|
| Man and Woman | Five-pointed stars | Snowflake |

## CHRISTMAS: STAINED GLASS

2582

Designer: Hélène L'Heureux.
Lithography (7 colours plus spot varnish)
Lowe-Martin
Water-activated gum souvenir sheet of 3; Sheets of 75 subjects in 25 panes of 3

**2012, Oct 15** **GT4, TRC Paper** **Perf 13.7x13.4**

| | | NH–VF | ⊙F | FDC |
|---|---|---|---|---|
| **2581** | **$3.46 souvenir sheet** of 3 | 7.50 | 7.50 | 8.90 |
| **a** | **P multicoloured** | 1.75 | 1.50 | |
| **b** | **$1.05 multicoloured** | 2.10 | 2.10 | |
| **c** | **$1.80 multicoloured** | 3.60 | 3.60 | |

Qty: 195,000

Designer: Andrew Perro.

Lithography (6 colours plus spot varnish)
Lowe-Martin, self-adhesive booklet of 12
**GT4, TRC Paper Serpentine Die cut 13.4**

| | | NH–VF | ⊙F | FDC |
|---|---|---|---|---|
| **2582** | **P multicoloured** | 1.70 | .25 | 3.20 |
| i | die cut to shape from Quarterly Pack/ Annual Collection | 2.50 | — | |
| a | booklet pane of 12 x P (2582) (**BK512**) | 20.00 | — | |

Qty: 18,000,000

Designer: Hélène L'Heureux.

Lithography (5 colours plus spot varnish), self-adhesive booklet of 12 (P) or 6
Lowe-Martin
**GT4, TRC Paper**
**Serpentine Die cut 13.2 x 12.9**

| | | NH–VF | ⊙F | FDC |
|---|---|---|---|---|
| **2583** | **P multicoloured** | 1.70 | .25 | — |
| i | die cut to shape from Quarterly Pack | 2.50 | — | |
| a | booklet pane of 12 x P (2583) (**BK513**) | 20.00 | — | |

Qty: 21,000,000

This design was also used on the 2012 *Santa Claus* envelopes and postcard.

| | | NH–VF | ⊙F | FDC |
|---|---|---|---|---|
| **2584** | **$1.05 multicoloured** | 2.10 | .75 | — |
| i | die cut to shape from Quarterly Pack | 3.15 | — | |
| a | booklet pane of 6 x $1.05 (2584) (**BK514**) | 12.50 | — | |

Qty: 4,200,000

| | | NH–VF | ⊙F | FDC |
|---|---|---|---|---|
| **2585** | **$1.80 multicoloured** | 3.60 | 1.25 | — |
| i | die cut to shape from Quarterly Pack | 5.40 | — | |
| a | booklet pane of 6 x $1.80 (2585) (**BK515**) | 21.50 | — | |

Qty: 4,200,000

At time of issue, the P Christmas stamps were valued at 61¢.

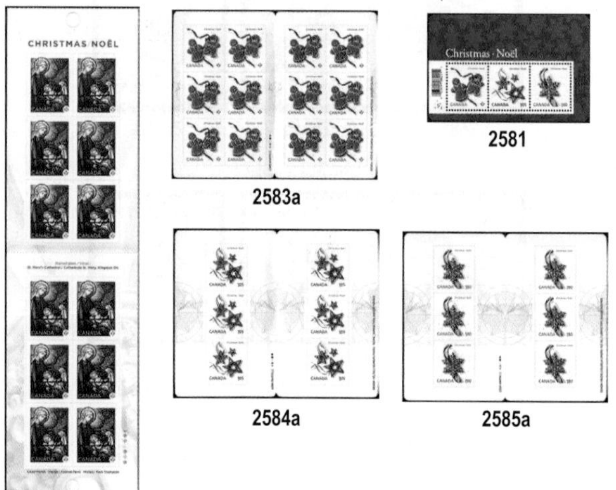

2582a 2583a 2581 2584a 2585a

## PICTURE POSTAGE™

2586 Dots | 2587 Shadow (frame) | 2588 Love Hearts | 2589 Little Creatures

2590 Butterflies | 2591 Maple Leaves | 2592 Flowers | 2593 Snowflakes

2594 Wedding Bells | 2595 Wedding Doves | 2596 Celebration (balloons) | 2597 Christmas (holly)

Designer: Stéphane Huot.

Self-adhesive, 4 colour process
Lowe-Martin
**2012, Nov 5 GT4, TRC Paper Serpentine Die cut 13.4**

| | | NH–VF | ⊙F | FDC |
|---|---|---|---|---|
| **2586** | **P grey**, dots | 3.00 | 3.00 | |
| a | personalized version* | | | |
| **2587** | **P grey**, shadow (frame) | 3.00 | 3.00 | |
| a | personalized version* | | | |
| **2588** | **P multicoloured**, love hearts | 3.00 | 3.00 | |
| a | personalized version* | | | |
| **2589** | **P multicoloured**, little creatures | 3.00 | 3.00 | |
| a | personalized version* | | | |
| **2590** | **P multicoloured**, butterflies | 3.00 | 3.00 | |
| a | personalized version* | | | |
| **2591** | **P multicoloured**, maple leaves | 3.00 | 3.00 | |
| a | personalized version* | | | |
| **2592** | **P multicoloured**, flowers | 3.00 | 3.00 | |
| a | personalized version* | | | |
| **2593** | **P multicoloured**, snowflakes | 3.00 | 3.00 | |
| a | personalized version* | | | |
| **2594** | **P multicoloured**, wedding bells | 3.00 | 3.00 | |
| a | personalized version* | | | |
| **2595** | **P grey**, wedding doves | 3.00 | 3.00 | |
| a | personalized version* | | | |
| **2596** | **P multicoloured**, celebration (balloons) | 3.00 | 3.00 | |
| a | personalized version* | | | |
| **2597** | **P multicoloured**, Christmas (holly) | 3.00 | 3.00 | |
| a | personalized version* | | | |

Qty: 10,000 of each die cut single

**Combination FDC (set of 2 covers) † 18.65**

† cover 1 has horizontally-oriented stamps: 2590a, 2596a, 2597a, 2586a, 2595a and 2589a; cover 2 has stamps: 2588a, 2591a, 2593a, 2587a, 2594a, and 2592a. Each are blocks of 6 with the stamps not die cut all the way through.

Nos. 2586–2597 were sold as die cut to shape single stamps, together in a *Picture Postage™ Collector's Pack* of 12 stamps. This package sold at the face value of $7.32. Each mint single (available only in a vertical orientation) had a light grey image area.

* Nos. 2586a–2597a have personalized photographs in the image area. They are available either horizontally or vertically, with four different denominations (Permanent™, domestic oversize, USA, International), and in three different formats (booklets of 12, panes of 25+1, panes of 50). These are only available via on-line

ordering. The selling prices of the personalized sheets and booklets are substantially higher than the face value of the stamps within them.

From Nov. 16–24 personalized stamps were offered for sale on iPad and iPhone apps at the P rate (with a franking value of 61¢), $1.05, $1.29 and $1.80. It is not known if any personalized stamps of the $1.05, $1.29 and $1.80 denominations were created for customers during this brief period. On Nov. 24 stamps at the P rate (with a franking value of 61¢), $1.10, $1.34 and $1.85 were offered to customers through the Picture Postage™ page of the Canada Post website, as well as through the apps. Additional stamps with different denominations may be offered for sale later as rates change.

A $1.29 stamp featuring the image of a Turtle was made available on Nov. 1. It was only available affixed to packages containing a box of Nestlé's Turtles chocolate. A box of candy and affixed stamp sold at post offices for $4.99 (later discounted to $2.95), and the package could only be sent to Canadian addresses. The Turtles Picture Postage™ stamp, and the box of chocolates, were a private order item by Nestlé, outside the scope of this catalogue (we recognize that this item had a strong collector interest). It was sold at Canada Post outlets but is not a Canada Post product.

Vertically oriented stamps have the denomination in the lower right corner of the stamp, with the "C" of "Canada" at the upper left of the stamp, as shown. Horizontally oriented stamps have the denomination in the lower right corner of the stamps, with the "C" of "Canada" at the lower left corner. The dots, frame, hearts, little creatures and butterflies images on horizontally-oriented stamps different from those shown on the vertically-oriented stamps.

At time of issue, the P stamps were valued at 61¢.

## 100th GREY CUP GAME WINNER: TORONTO ARGONAUTS

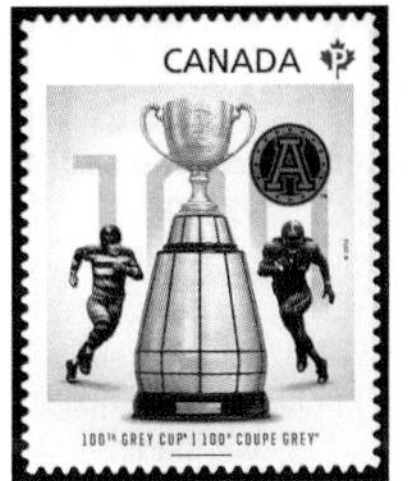


**2598**
Grey Cup with Toronto
Argonauts logo overprint

Lithography (5 colours plus varnish), Self-adhesive booklet of 10
Lowe-Martin

**2012, Nov 28** — **GT4, TRC Paper**
**Serpentine Die cut 13.5x13.4**

| | | NH–VF | ⊙F | FDC |
|---|---|---|---|---|
| **2598** | **multicoloured**, Grey Cup with Toronto Argonauts overprinted logo | 1.70 | .75 | |
| i | die cut to shape from Quarterly Pack | 2.50 | — | |
| a | booklet pane of 10 x P (2598) (**BK516**) | 17.00 | | |
| ai | as "a", unfolded booklet pane of 10 x P (2598) (**BK516a**) | *40.00* | | |

Qty: 300,000

The die cut to shape single (2598i) was available only in the Jan–Mar 2013 Quarterly Pack.

Saluting the champion of the historic 100th Grey Cup Game played at Toronto's Roger's Centre on November 25, 2012 between the Calgary Stampeders (west champions) and Toronto Argonauts (east champions). Toronto won 35-22.

At time of issue, the P stamp was valued at 61¢.

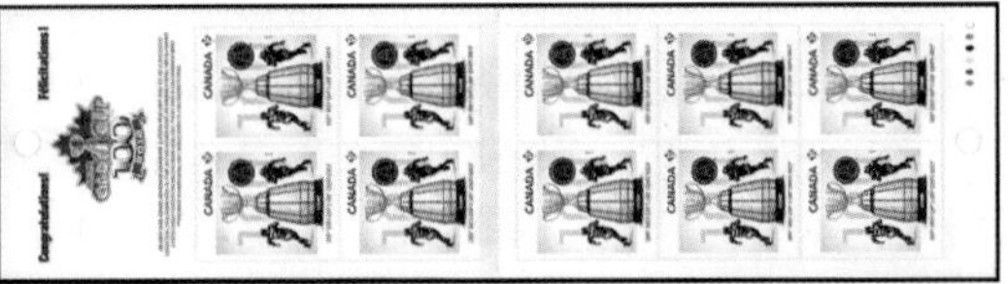

*Image rotated* **2598a**

## 2013

### LUNAR NEW YEAR (Series 2) — 5
### Year of the Snake

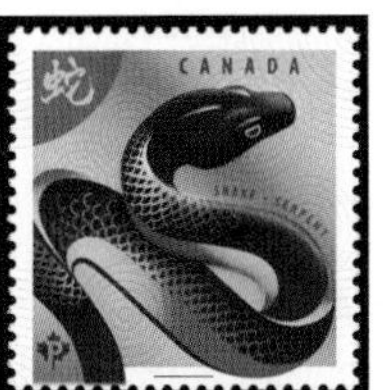


**2599**
Snake

*Perforated single from souvenir sheet*

**2600i**
Head of snake

*Die cut single from self-adhesive booklet*

**2601**
Head of snake

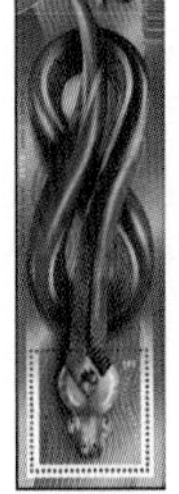

**2600**

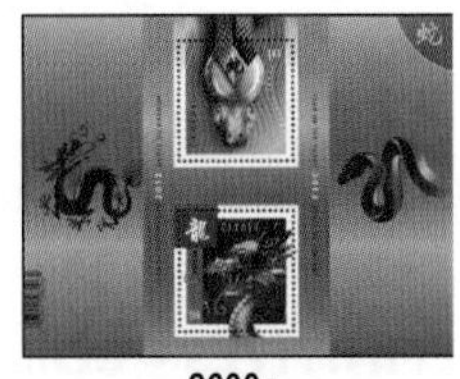

**2600a**

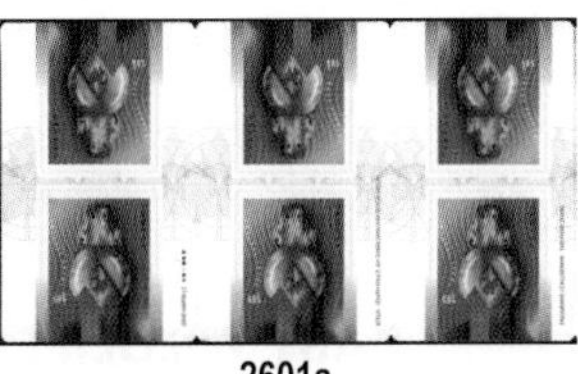

**2601a**

Designer: Joseph Gault, Avi Dunkelman (Mix Design Group).
Lithography (6 colours) plus 1 foil stamping and embossing plus varnish, pane of 25
Lowe-Martin, Gravure Choquet

**2013, Jan 8** — **GT4, TRC Paper** — **Perf 12.5**

| | | NH–VF | ⊙F | PB | FDC |
|---|---|---|---|---|---|
| **2599** | **multicoloured** | 1.70 | .60 | 8.50 | 3.25 |

Qty: 5,000,000

At time of issue, the P stamp was valued at 63¢ even though the 63¢ domestic rate did not go into effect until January 14.

**GT4 (except where design passes through edge of stamp)**

| | | NH–VF | ⊙F | PB | FDC |
|---|---|---|---|---|---|
| **2600** | **$1.85 souvenir sheet** of 1 | 3.75 | 3.75 | — | 5.70 |
| i | $1.85 single stamp from souvenir sheet | 3.25 | 3.25 | — | |
| ii | $29.95 uncut press sheet of 12 souvenir sheets | 60.00 | | | |
| a | $3.65 'transitional' souvenir sheet of 2, #2496, 2600 | 7.25 | 7.25 | — | |

Qty: 2600: 455,000; 2600ii: 15,000; 2600a: 190,000

Lithography (6 colours) plus varnish
Lowe-Martin, self-adhesive booklet of 6
**GT4 (except where design passes through edge of stamp)**
**TRC Paper** — **Serpentine Die cut 13.5**

| | | NH–VF | ⊙F | FDC |
|---|---|---|---|---|
| **2601** | **$1.85 multicoloured** | 3.75 | 1.50 | — |
| i | die cut to shape from Quarterly Pack | 5.60 | — | |
| a | booklet pane of 6 x $1.85 (2601) (**BK517**) | 22.25 | — | |

Qty: 2,250,000

For non-denominated postal cards of same designs, see UX308–UX309.

| **Rates:** | Domestic first-class (0-30g): 63¢ | USA (0-30g): $1.10 |
|---|---|---|
| Jan 14/13– | Domestic first-class (30-50g): $1.10 | USA (30-50g): $1.34 |
| Mar 30/14 | Domestic oversize (0-100g): $1.34 | International (0-30g): $1.85 |

*single usage:* USA $1.10: $15.00 | International $1.85: $20.00

QE II — 2010's

Wildlife/Canada Pride — 2013

## BABY WILDLIFE DEFINITIVES — SOUVENIR SHEET

2602a Woodchucks | 2602b Porcupine | 2602c Fawn | 2602d Black bear

Designers: Monique Dufour, Sophie Lafortune.

Lithography (8 colours)
Lowe-Martin
Water-activated gum souvenir sheet of 4

**2013, Jan 14** **GT4, TRC Paper** **Perf 13.4x13.0**

| | | NH–VF | ⊙F | FDC |
|---|---|---|---|---|
| **2602** | **$4.92 souvenir sheet** of 4 * | 10.00 | 10.00 | 11.85 |
| a | **P multicoloured** † | 1.75 | 1.50 | |
| b | **$1.10 multicoloured** | 2.00 | 1.75 | |
| c | **$1.34 multicoloured** | 2.50 | 2.25 | |
| d | **$1.85 multicoloured** | 3.50 | 3.25 | |

Qty: 170,000

* Face value of $4.92 at time of issue; the face value of the P stamp was 63¢.

## BABY WILDLIFE DEFINITIVES – COILS

2603 2604
Woodchucks

2605 Porcupine | 2606 Fawn | 2607 Black bear

Designers: Monique Dufour, Sophie Lafortune.
Lithography (5 colours), self-adhesive rolls of 100 (P) and 50 ($1.10, $1.34, $1.85)
Lowe-Martin

**2013, Jan 14** **GT4, TRC Paper**
with repeating 'Canada' underprint
**Serpentine Die cut 9.2 Horiz**
**(Rounded tips)**

| | | NH–VF | ⊙F | FDC |
|---|---|---|---|---|
| **2603** | **P multicoloured** | 2.00 | 2.00 | — |

2603 issued in horizontal rolls of 5,000. Individual stamps do not touch along the horizontal roll; rounded 'perf tips' start with a peak. Sold in strips of 4 or 10 by the National Philatelic Centre; single stamps included in the Quarterly Pack/Annual Collection.

**Serpentine Die cut 8.15 to 8.50 Horiz**
**(Rounded tips with 3 'nibs' between stamps)**

To date, one die cut pattern has been used on these stamps and has been used both upright and inverted.

**2013, Jan 14** **GT4, TRC Paper**
with repeating 'Canada' underprint

| | | NH–VF | ⊙F | FDC |
|---|---|---|---|---|
| **2604** | **P multicoloured** | 1.70 | .25 | — |
| i | gutter strip of 4 with inscription | 8.50 | | |
| | starter strip of 4 (wavy die cut) | 11.00 | | |
| | end strip of 4 (wavy die cut) | 11.00 | | |
| ii | die cut to shape (9.2 horiz) from Quarterly Pack, *Apr '13* ‡ | 3.50 | — | |
| **2605** | **$1.10 multicoloured** | 2.20 | .50 | — |
| i | gutter strip of 4 with inscription | 10.00 | | |
| | starter strip of 4 (wavy die cut) | 12.00 | | |
| | end strip of 4 (wavy die cut) | 12.00 | | |
| ii | die cut to shape (9.2 horiz) from Quarterly Pack, *Apr '13* ‡ | 3.30 | — | |
| **2606** | **$1.34 multicoloured** | 2.70 | .75 | — |
| i | gutter strip of 4 with inscription | 10.00 | | |
| | starter strip of 4 (wavy die cut) | 11.00 | | |
| | end strip of 4 (wavy die cut) | 11.00 | | |
| ii | die cut to shape (9.2 horiz) from Quarterly Pack, *Apr '13* ‡ | 3.75 | — | |
| **2607** | **$1.85 multicoloured** | 3.75 | 1.25 | — |
| i | gutter strip of 4 with inscription | 17.00 | | |
| | starter strip of 4 (wavy die cut) | 19.00 | | |
| | end strip of 4 (wavy die cut) | 19.00 | | |
| ii | die cut to shape (9.2 horiz) from Quarterly Pack, *Apr '13* ‡ | 5.60 | — | |

‡ Single stamps supplied in the Quarterly Pack have rounded tips (backing paper is 'plain' with the repeating 'Canada' underprint visible), starting with a valley at upper left; stamps from the full rolls are die cut 8.15 to 8.50.

For 63¢ denominated version of Woodchucks coil, see Scott 2692–2692A.

## BABY WILDLIFE DEFINITIVES – BOOKLETS

2608 Porcupine | 2609 Fawn | 2610 Black bear

Designers: Monique Dufour, Sophie Lafortune.
Lithography (5 colours), self-adhesive booklets of 6
Lowe-Martin

**2013, Jan 14** **GT4, TRC Paper**
with repeating 'Canada' underprint
**Serpentine Die cut 9.2 horiz (Rounded tips)**

| | | NH–VF | ⊙F | FDC |
|---|---|---|---|---|
| **2608** | **$1.10 multicoloured** | 2.20 | .50 | — |
| i | die cut to shape from Quarterly Pack ‡ | 3.30 | — | |
| a | booklet pane of 6 x $1.10 (2608) (**BK518**) | 13.25 | | |
| **2609** | **$1.34 multicoloured** | 2.70 | .75 | — |
| i | die cut to shape from Quarterly Pack ‡ | 4.00 | — | |
| a | booklet pane of 6 x $1.34 (2609) (**BK519**) | 16.25 | | |
| **2610** | **$1.85 multicoloured** | 3.75 | 1.25 | — |
| i | die cut to shape from Quarterly Pack ‡ | 5.64 | — | |
| a | booklet pane of 6 x $1.85 (2610) (**BK520**) | 22.25 | | |

‡ Single stamps supplied in the Quarterly packs start with a peak at the upper left (backing paper contains some form of printing from backside of booklet); single stamps from booklets of 6 start with a valley at the upper left.

For non-denominated postal cards of same designs, see UX310–UX313.

2602

2608a

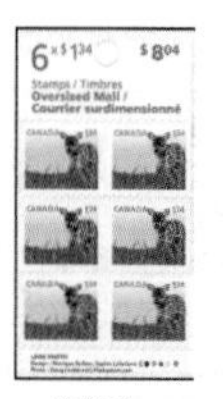

2609a

2610a

QE II — 2010's

## PERMANENT™ CANADIAN PRIDE

*Perforated singles from water-activated gum souvenir sheet*

| 2611a | 2611b | 2611c | 2611d | 2611e |
|---|---|---|---|---|
| Chairs on dock | Hay bale | Sailboat | 'Living Flag' | Fishing hut |

*Die cut singles from self-adhesive booklets*

2612 2613 2614 2615 2616

Designer: Gottschalk+Ash International.

Lithography (4 colours, with red fluorescent ink)
Canadian Bank Note
Water-activated gum souvenir sheet of 5

**2013, Jan 14 GT4, TRC Paper Perf 13.0x13.4**

| | | NH–VF | ⊙F | FDC |
|---|---|---|---|---|
| **2611** | **$3.15 souvenir sheet** of 5 | 8.75 | 8.75 | 8.30 |
| a | **P multicoloured**, chairs on dock | 1.75 | 1.50 | |
| b | **P multicoloured**, hay bale | 1.75 | 1.50 | |
| c | **P multicoloured**, sailboat | 1.75 | 1.50 | |
| d | **P multicoloured**, 'living flag' | 1.75 | 1.50 | |
| e | **P multicoloured**, fishing hut | 1.75 | 1.50 | |

Qty: 170,000

Self-adhesive booklets of 10 and 30

**2013, Jan 14 GT4, TRC Paper**
**Serpentine Die cut 13.4**

| | | NH–VF | ⊙F | FDC |
|---|---|---|---|---|
| **2612** | **P multicoloured**, chairs on dock | 1.70 | .25 | — |
| a | repeating 'Canada' underprint, *Jan 31, 2013* | 1.70 | .25 | |
| **2613** | **P multicoloured**, hay bale | 1.70 | .25 | — |
| a | repeating 'Canada' underprint, *Jan 31, 2013* | 1.70 | .25 | |
| **2614** | **P multicoloured**, sailboat | 1.70 | .25 | — |
| a | repeating 'Canada' underprint, *Jan 31, 2013* | 1.70 | .25 | |
| **2615** | **P multicoloured**, 'living flag' | 1.70 | .25 | — |
| a | repeating 'Canada' underprint, *Jan 31, 2013* | 1.70 | .25 | |
| **2616** | **P multicoloured**, fishing hut | 1.70 | .25 | — |
| a | repeating 'Canada' underprint, *Jan 31, 2013* | 1.70 | .25 | |
| i | se-tenant strip of 5 (2612–2616), die cut to shape from Quarterly Pack | 12.50 | — | |
| b | booklet pane of 10 x P (2 each of 2612–2616) (**BK521**) | 17.00 | | |
| c | booklet pane of 10 x P (2 each of 2612a–2616a) (**BK521A**), *Jan 31, 2013* | 17.00 | | |
| d | booklet pane of 30 x P (6 each of 2612–2616) (**BK522**) | 50.00 | | |
| e | booklet pane of 30 x P (6 each of 2612a–2616a) (**BK522A**), *Jan 31, 2013* | 50.00 | | |
| bi | strip of 5, from 2616b/BK521 or 2616d/BK522 | 8.50 | | |
| ci | strip of 5, from 2616c/BK521A or 2616e/BK522A | 8.50 | | |

For 63¢ denominated version of this Canadian Pride booklet, see Scott 2693–2697.
For non-denominated postal cards of same designs, see UX314–UX318.

Tagging and red fluorescent ink on Canadian Pride definitives.

2611

2616b

2616c

2616d

2616e

2616b, 2616d

2616c, 2616e

Imprint on Flag booklets of 10/30 (underlined C is for pane with repeating 'Canada' underprint)

2617a

2617c

Imprint on QEII booklet of 10 (underlined C is for pane with repeating 'Canada' underprint)

## QUEEN ELIZABETH II

2617

Designer: Entro | G+A.

Lithography (5 colours), self-adhesive booklet of 10
Canadian Bank Note

**2013, Jan 14 GT4, TRC Paper**
**Serpentine Die cut 13.4**

| | | NH–VF | ⊙F | FDC |
|---|---|---|---|---|
| **2617** | **P multicoloured (QE II)** | 1.70 | .25 | 3.25 |
| b | as above, with repeating 'Canada' underprint, *Jun 1, 2013* | 1.70 | .25 | |
| i | die cut to shape from Quarterly Pack/ Annual Collection | 2.50 | — | |
| a | booklet pane of 10 x P (2617) (**BK523**) | 17.00 | | |
| c | booklet pane of 10 x P with repeating 'Canada' underprint (**BK523A**), *Jun 1, 2013* | 17.00 | | |

The tagging includes an incorrect spelling of "Anniversary" (as "Anniversery").

For 63¢ denominated version of Queen Elizabeth II booklet, see Scott 2698.

**2612a–2616a, 2617b**
Repeating 'Canada' underprint

Tagging on QEII definitive (2617) (including incorrect spelling of "Anniversary")

**2617a**

At time of issue, the P stamps on these pages (Jan 14/13 issue date) were valued at 63¢.

## RAOUL WALLENBERG

**2618**
Wallenberg with Schutz-Pass

Designer: q30 design inc.
Lithography (5 colours plus varnish), self-adhesive booklet of 6
Lowe-Martin

**2013, Jan 17** **GT4, TRC Paper**
**Serpentine Die cut 13.3x13.5**

| | | NH–VF | ⊙F | FDC |
|---|---|---|---|---|
| **2618** | **$1.85 multicoloured** | 3.75 | 2.00 | 5.70 |
| i | die cut to shape from Quarterly Pack/ Annual Collection | 5.60 | — | |
| a | booklet pane of 6 x $1.85 (2618) (**BK524**) | 22.25 | | |

Qty: 900,000

Swedish-born Raoul Wallenberg (1912–1945?) became Canada's first honorary citizen in 1985 for saving as many as 100,000 Jewish people in Budapest, Hungary during the Second World War.

**2618a**

## BLACK HISTORY MONTH

**2619**
Oliver Jones
(1934– )

**2620**
Joe Fortes
(1863–1922)

Designer: Lara Minja (Lime Design Inc.).
Lithography (4 colours), self-adhesive booklet of 10
Lowe-Martin

**2013, Feb 1** **GT4, TRC Paper**
**Serpentine Die cut 13.5x13.3**

| | | NH–VF | ⊙F | FDC |
|---|---|---|---|---|
| **2619** | P **multicoloured** (Jones) | 1.70 | .50 | 3.25 |
| i | die cut to shape from Quarterly Pack/ Annual Collection | 2.50 | — | |
| a | booklet pane of 10 x P (2619) (**BK525**) | 17.00 | | |

Qty: 2,200,000

Jazz musician who has won five Junos. At time of issue, the P stamp was valued at 63¢.

*Image rotated* **2619a**

Lithography (5 colours), self-adhesive booklet of 10
**Serpentine Die cut 13.3x13.0**

| | | NH–VF | ⊙F | FDC |
|---|---|---|---|---|
| **2620** | P **multicoloured** (Fortes) | 1.70 | .50 | 3.25 |
| i | die cut to shape from Quarterly Pack/ Annual Collection | 2.50 | — | |
| a | booklet pane of 10 x P (2620) (**BK526**) | 17.00 | | |

Qty: 2,200,000

Swimming instructor and lifeguard in Vancouver, BC. At time of issue, the P stamp was valued at 63¢.

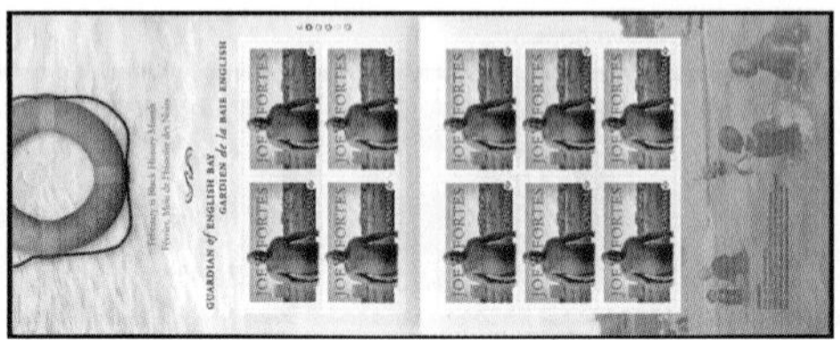

*Image rotated* **2620a**

Timeline:
**2013, Feb 20** P (63¢) Signs of the Zodiac (2447, 2448, 2457–2460)

## MAGNOLIAS

*Perforated singles from water-activated gum souvenir sheet*

**2621a**

**2621b**

*Die cut singles from self-adhesive booklet*

**2624**
Yellow Bird

**2625**
Eskimo

**2622**
Yellow Bird

**2623**
Eskimo

**2621**

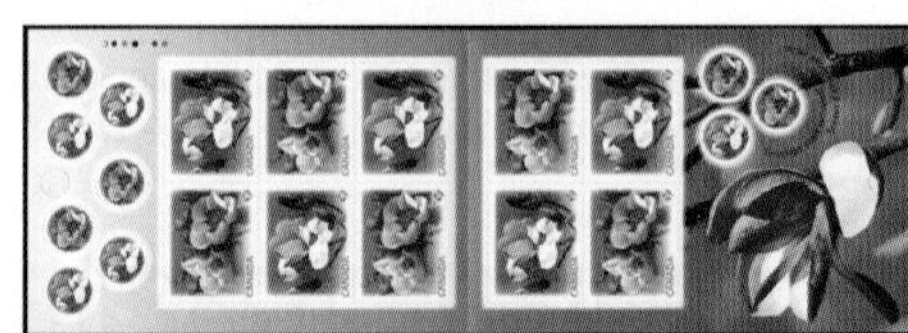

*Image rotated* **2625a**

Designer: Isabelle Toussaint, Design graphique.

Lithography (6 colours)
Lowe-Martin
Water-activated gum souvenir sheet of 2

**2013, Mar 4** **GT4, TRC Paper** **Perf 13.2x13.4**

| | | NH–VF | ⊙F | FDC |
|---|---|---|---|---|
| **2621** | **$1.26 souvenir sheet** of 2 | 3.60 | 3.60 | — |
| a | P **multicoloured**, yellow flower | 1.75 | 1.50 | |
| b | P **multicoloured**, lilac and white flower | 1.75 | 1.50 | |
| i | se-tenant pair (2621a–b) | 3.50 | 3.00 | |

Qty: 170,000

Self-adhesive roll of 50
**GT4, TRC Paper**
**Serpentine Die cut 8.15 to 8.50 Horiz**
**(Rounded tips with 3 'nibs' between stamps)**

One die cut pattern exists on these stamps.

| | | NH–VF | ⊙F | FDC |
|---|---|---|---|---|
| **2622** | P **multicoloured**, yellow flower | 1.70 | .60 | — |
| **2623** | P **multicoloured**, lilac and white flower | 1.70 | .60 | — |
| a | se-tenant pair (vert.), 2622–23 | 3.40 | | |
| i | gutter strip of 4 with inscription | 8.50 | | |
| | starter strip of 4 (wavy die cut) | 11.00 | | |
| | end strip of 4 (wavy die cut) | 11.00 | | |
| ii | se-tenant pair (2622–23), die cut to shape (9.2 horiz) from Quarterly Pack | 5.00 | — | |

Qty: 7,500,000 of each

These stamps were printed se-tenant along the roll. Two different rolls were produced; one starting with the yellow flower, the other starting with the lilac and white flower. As such, two types of each of the gutter, starter and end strips of 4 exist.

Self-adhesive booklet of 10
**GT4, TRC Paper**
**Serpentine Die cut 13.5**

| | | NH–VF | ⊙F | FDC |
|---|---|---|---|---|
| **2624** | P **multicoloured**, yellow flower | 1.70 | .50 | |
| **2625** | P **multicoloured**, lilac and white flower | 1.70 | .50 | |
| i | se-tenant pair (2624, 2625), die cut to shape from Quarterly Pack | 5.00 | — | |
| a | booklet pane of 10, 5 each #2624–2625 + 10 stickers (**BK531**) | 17.00 | | |

Qty: 7,000,000 of each

**Nos. 2624–2625 (2) combination FDC** **4.50***
* Stamps on FDCs are not die cut all the way through.

At time of issue, the P stamps were valued at 63¢.
For non-denominated postal cards of same designs, see UX323–UX324.

## CANADIAN PHOTOGRAPHY — I

*Perforated singles from water-activated gum souvenir sheet*

2626a
*Louis-Joseph Papineau*

2626b
*The Kitchen Sink*

2626c
*Koo-tuck-tuck*

2627a
*Hot Properties #1*

2627b
*Andor Pasztor*

2627c
*Basement Camera Shop*

2627d
*Yousuf Karsh*

*Die cut singles from self-adhesive booklets*

2628

2629

2630

2631

2632

2633

2634

Designer: Stephane Huot

Lithography (8 colours)
Lowe-Martin
Water-activated gum souvenir sheets of 3 and 4

**2013, Mar 22** **GT4, TRC Paper** **Perf 13.4**

| | | NH–VF | ⊙F | FDC |
|---|---|---|---|---|
| **2626** | **$1.89 souvenir sheet** of 3 | 5.25 | 5.25 | 5.75 |
| a | P **multicoloured**, Louis-Joseph Papineau | 1.75 | 1.50 | |
| b | P **multicoloured**, The Kitchen Sink | 1.75 | 1.50 | |
| c | P **multicoloured**, Koo-tuck-tuck | 1.75 | 1.50 | |

Qty: 140,000

| | | NH–VF | ⊙F | FDC |
|---|---|---|---|---|
| **2627** | **$4.21 souvenir sheet** of 4 | 9.50 | 9.50 | 10.40 |
| a | P **multicoloured**, Hot Properties #1 | 1.75 | 1.50 | |
| b | P **multicoloured**, Andor Pasztor | 1.75 | 1.50 | |
| c | **$1.10 multicoloured**, Camera Shop | 2.20 | 2.00 | |
| d | **$1.85 multicoloured**, Karsh | 3.70 | 3.50 | |

Qty: 140,000

Incorrectly perforated essays of #2627, from printer's waste produced by "Colour Innovations Inc.", appeared on the market in May 2014.

2626

2627

Self-adhesive booklet of 10
**GT4, TRC Paper**
**Serpentine Die cut 13.7**

| | | NH–VF | ⊙F | FDC |
|---|---|---|---|---|
| **2628** | **multicoloured**, Hot Properties #1 | 1.70 | .50 | — |
| i | die cut to shape from Quarterly Pack | 2.50 | — | |
| **2629** | **multicoloured**, Louis-Joseph Papineau | 1.70 | .50 | — |
| i | die cut to shape from Quarterly Pack | 2.50 | — | |
| **2630** | **multicoloured**, The Kitchen Sink | 1.70 | .50 | — |
| i | die cut to shape from Quarterly Pack | 2.50 | — | |
| **2631** | **multicoloured**, Andor Pasztor | 1.70 | .50 | — |
| i | die cut to shape from Quarterly Pack | 2.50 | — | |
| **2632** | **multicoloured**, Koo-tuck-tuck | 1.70 | .50 | — |
| i | die cut to shape from Quarterly Pack | 2.50 | — | |
| a | booklet pane of 10, 2 each #2628–2632 (**BK532**) | 17.00 | | |

Qty: 400,000 of each

Self-adhesive booklets of 6

| | | NH–VF | ⊙F | FDC |
|---|---|---|---|---|
| **2633** | **$1.10 multicoloured**, Camera Shop | 2.20 | 1.15 | — |
| i | die cut to shape from Quarterly Pack | 3.30 | — | |
| a | booklet pane of 6 (**BK533**) | 13.25 | | |

Qty: 840,000

| | | NH–VF | ⊙F | FDC |
|---|---|---|---|---|
| **2634** | **$1.85 multicoloured**, Karsh | 3.75 | 2.00 | — |
| i | die cut to shape from Quarterly Pack | 5.60 | — | |
| a | booklet pane of 6 (**BK534**) | 22.25 | | |

Qty: 840,000

At time of issue, the P stamps were valued at 63¢.
For non-denominated postal cards of same designs, see UX325–UX331. See also 2756–2764, 2814–2822, and 2814–2822

2632a

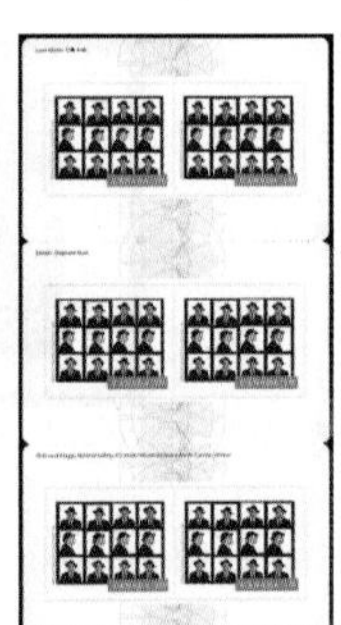
2634a

2633a

## REGIMENT

2635
The Princess of Wales' Own Regiment

Designer: Sputnik Design Partners Inc.
Lithography (7 colours), self-adhesive booklet of 10
Lowe-Martin
**2013, Apr 9** **GT4, TRC Paper**
**Serpentine Die cut 13.4x13.0**

| | | NH–VF | ⊙F | FDC |
|---|---|---|---|---|
| **2635** | **multicoloured** | 1.70 | .50 | 3.25 |
| i | die cut to shape from Quarterly Pack | 3.50 | — | |
| a | booklet pane of 10 x P (2635) (**BK535**) | 17.00 | | |

Qty: 2,000,000

At time of issue, the P stamp was valued at 63¢.

2635a

## ADOPT A PET

*Perforated singles from water-activated gum souvenir sheet*

2636a
Cat with bird on branch

2636b
Parrot

2636c
Dog with squirrel, butterfly, flower

2636d
Dog with fireplace, bed

2636e
Cat with toys

*Die cut singles from self-adhesive booklet*

2637

2638

2639

2640

2641

2636

Designer: Monika Melnychuk.

Lithography (6 colours plus varnish)
Lowe-Martin
Water-activated gum souvenir sheet of 5

**2013, Apr 22** **GT 3 sides, TRC Paper**

| | | NH–VF | ⊙F | FDC |
|---|---|---|---|---|
| **2636** | **$3.15 souvenir sheet** of 5 | 8.75 | 8.75 | 8.30 |
| a | **P multicoloured**, cat (perf 12.5) | 1.75 | 1.50 | |
| b | **P multicoloured**, parrot (perf 13.3) | 1.75 | 1.50 | |
| c | **P multicoloured**, dog (perf 12.5x13.3) | 1.75 | 1.50 | |
| d | **P multicoloured**, dog (perf 12.5x13.3) | 1.75 | 1.50 | |
| e | **P multicoloured**, cat (perf 12.5) | 1.75 | 1.50 | |

Qty: 180,000

Self-adhesive booklet of 10
**GT 3 sides, TRC Paper**

| | | NH–VF | ⊙F | FDC |
|---|---|---|---|---|
| | **Serpentine Die cut 13.0x13.5** | | | |
| **2637** | **P multicoloured**, cat | 1.70 | .60 | — |
| | **Serpentine Die cut 12.9x13.0** | | | |
| **2638** | **P multicoloured**, parrot | 1.70 | .60 | — |
| | **Serpentine Die cut 13.8x13.5** | | | |
| **2639** | **P multicoloured**, dog | 1.70 | .60 | — |
| | **Serpentine Die cut 13.4x13.5** | | | |
| **2640** | **P multicoloured**, dog | 1.70 | .60 | — |
| | **Serpentine Die cut 13.0x13.5** | | | |
| **2641** | **P multicoloured**, cat | 1.70 | .60 | — |
| a | booklet pane of 10, 2 each #2637–2641 (**BK536**) | 17.00 | | |

Qty: 1,000,000 of each

At time of issue, the P stamps were valued at 63¢.

The general tagging was *not* applied to the bottom of each stamp; the tagging on the sides stops short of the bottom by about 3mm on 2636a–b/2637–38 and 6mm on 2636c–e/2639–41.

2641a

## CHINATOWN GATES

*Perforated singles from water-activated gum souvenir sheet*

**2642a**
Toronto, ON

**2642b**
Montréal, QC

**2642c**
Winnipeg, MB

**2642d**
Edmonton, AB

**2642e**
Vancouver, BC

**2642f**
Ottawa, ON

**2642g**
Mississauga, ON

**2642h**
Victoria, BC

*Die cut singles from self-adhesive booklet*

**2643a**
Toronto, ON

**2643b**
Montréal, QC

**2643c**
Winnipeg, MB

**2643d**
Vancouver, BC

**2643e**
Edmonton, AB

**2643f**
Ottawa, ON

**2643g**
Mississauga, ON

**2643h**
Victoria, BC

Designer: Hélène L'Heureux.

Lithography (6 colours, one foil stamping)
Lowe-Martin
Water-activated gum souvenir sheet of 8

**2013, May 1** **GT4, TRC Paper** **Perf 12.5**

| | | NH–VF | ⊙F | FDC |
|---|---|---|---|---|
| **2642** | **$5.04 souvenir sheet** of 8 | 14.00 | 14.00 | 12.10 |
| a | **P multicoloured**, Toronto | 1.75 | 1.50 | |
| b | **P multicoloured**, Montréal | 1.75 | 1.50 | |
| c | **P multicoloured**, Winnipeg | 1.75 | 1.50 | |
| d | **P multicoloured**, Edmonton | 1.75 | 1.50 | |
| e | **P multicoloured**, Vancouver | 1.75 | 1.50 | |
| f | **P multicoloured**, Ottawa | 1.75 | 1.50 | |
| g | **P multicoloured**, Mississauga | 1.75 | 1.50 | |
| h | **P multicoloured**, Victoria | 1.75 | 1.50 | |
| i | $25.20 uncut press sheet of 5 souvenir sheets | 70.00 | | |
| ii | imperf. pane of 8* | *180.00* | | |

Qty: 250,000; i: 2,500; ii: 8,888 * only available in *Chinatown Gates Collection*

Self-adhesive booklet of 8
**GT4, TRC Paper Serpentine Die cut 13.5**

| | | NH–VF | ⊙F | FDC |
|---|---|---|---|---|
| **2643** | booklet pane of 8 (**BK537**) | 13.50 | | |
| a | **P multicoloured**, Toronto | 1.70 | .60 | — |
| b | **P multicoloured**, Montréal | 1.70 | .60 | — |
| c | **P multicoloured**, Winnipeg | 1.70 | .60 | — |
| d | **P multicoloured**, Vancouver | 1.70 | .60 | — |
| e | **P multicoloured**, Edmonton | 1.70 | .60 | — |
| f | **P multicoloured**, Ottawa | 1.70 | .60 | — |
| g | **P multicoloured**, Mississauga | 1.70 | .60 | — |
| h | **P multicoloured**, Victoria | 1.70 | .60 | — |

Qty: 480,000 of each

At time of issue, the P stamps were valued at 63¢.
For non-denominated postal cards of same designs, see UX332–UX339.

2642

2643

## QUEEN ELIZABETH II: 60th ANNIVERSARY OF HER MAJESTY'S CORONATION

2644
Portrait of Queen Elizabeth II

Designer: Entro, Doreen Colonello.
Lithography (5 colours), self-adhesive booklet of 10
Lowe-Martin
**2013, May 8** **GT4, TRC Paper**
**Serpentine Die cut 13.4**

| | | | NH–VF | ⊙F | FDC |
|---|---|---|---|---|---|
| **2644** | | **multicoloured** | 1.70 | .50 | 3.25 |
| | i | die cut to shape from Quarterly Pack/ Annual Collection | 2.50 | — | |
| | a | booklet pane of 10 x P (2644) (**BK538**) | 17.00 | | |

Qty: 3,500,000

Princess Elizabeth became Queen on February 6, 1952. The Coronation occurred June 2, 1953. This portrait was painted by Canadian artist Philip James Richards on the occasion of Her Majesty's Diamond Jubilee.

At time of issue, the P stamp was valued at 63¢.

2644a

## BIG BROTHERS BIG SISTERS OF CANADA

2645
Boy and Girl

Designer: Dennis Page, Oliver Hill.
Lithography (5 colours), self-adhesive booklet of 10
Lowe-Martin
**2013, May 14** **GT4, TRC Paper**
**Serpentine Die cut 13.0x13.5**

| | | | NH–VF | ⊙F | FDC |
|---|---|---|---|---|---|
| **2645** | | **multicoloured** | 1.70 | .50 | 3.25 |
| | i | die cut to shape from Quarterly Pack/ Annual Collection | 3.50 | — | |
| | a | booklet pane of 10 x P (2645) (**BK539**) | 17.00 | | |

Qty: 1,800,000

Centennial of Big Brothers agency in Canada.

At time of issue, the P stamp was valued at 63¢.

*Image rotated* 2645

## MOTORCYCLES

*Perforated singles from water-activated gum souvenir sheet*

2646a 1908 CCM
2646b 1914 Indian

*Die cut singles from self-adhesive booklet*

2647 1908 CCM
2648 1914 Indian

Designer: Matthew Warburton (Emdoubleyu Design).
Lithography (5 colours)
Lowe-Martin
Water-activated gum souvenir sheet of 2
**2013, Jun 5** **GT4, TRC Paper** **Perf 12.5x13.1**

| | | | NH–VF | ⊙F | FDC |
|---|---|---|---|---|---|
| **2646** | | **$1.26 souvenir sheet** of 2 | 3.50 | 3.50 | 4.50* |
| | a | **multicoloured**, CCM | 1.75 | 1.50 | |
| | b | **multicoloured**, Indian | 1.75 | 1.50 | |
| | i | $17.99 uncut press sheet of 12 souvenir sheets | 42.00 | | |

Qty: 170,000; i: 5,000
* horizontal pair removed from souvenir sheet

Self-adhesive booklet of 10
**GT4, TRC Paper Serpentine Die cut 13.8**

| | | | NH–VF | ⊙F | FDC |
|---|---|---|---|---|---|
| **2647** | | **multicoloured**, CCM | 1.70 | .50 | — |
| **2648** | | **multicoloured**, Indian | 1.70 | .50 | — |
| | i | se-tenant pair, die cut to shape from Quarterly Pack | 5.00 | — | |
| | a | booklet pane of 10 (5 each 2647–48) (**BK540**) | 17.00 | | |

Qty: 1,750,000 of each

At time of issue, the P stamps were valued at 63¢.
For non-denominated postal cards of same designs, see UX340–UX341.

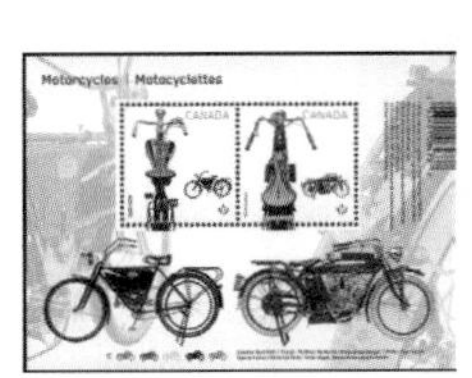
2646

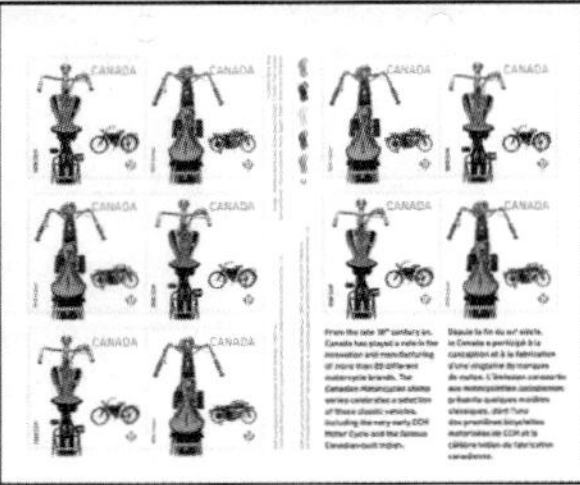
2648a

## 250 YEARS OF POSTAL HISTORY

2649
Benjamin Franklin and Quebec City

Designer: Andrew Perro.

Lithography (7 colours), self-adhesive booklet of 10
Lowe-Martin

**2013, Jun 10** **GT4, TRC Paper**
**Serpentine Die cut 13.4x13.8**

| | | NH–VF | ⊙F | FDC |
|---|---|---|---|---|
| **2649** | **P multicoloured** | 1.70 | .50 | 3.25 |
| i | die cut to shape from Quarterly Pack/ Annual Collection | 2.50 | — | |
| a | booklet pane of 10 x P (2649) (**BK541**) | 17.00 | | |

Qty: 1,350,000

Benjamin Franklin was the joint deputy postmaster general for the British colonies in 1753 and opened the first Canadian post office in Halifax.

At time of issue, the P stamp was valued at 63¢.

*Image rotated* 2649a

## THE WAR OF 1812

2650 Charles de Salaberry (1778–1829)
2651 Laura Secord (1775–1868)

Designer: Susan Scott.

Lithography (5 colours), pane of 16
Canadian Bank Note

**2013, Jun 20** **GT 3-sided, TRC Paper** **Perf 13.1x12.5**

| | | NH–VF | ⊙F | PB | FDC |
|---|---|---|---|---|---|
| **2650** | **P multicoloured** | 1.70 | .50 | | |
| **2651** | **P multicoloured** | 1.70 | .50 | | |
| **a** | horiz. se-tenant pair (2650, 2651) | 3.40 | 1.50 | 8.50* | 4.50 |

Qty: 800,000 of each

* Only the lower right block has the inscription and paper/colour designations.

The general tagging was not applied to the side with the illustration passing through the perfs.

The second in a multi-year series commemorating the War of 1812. See 2554–2555.
At time of issue, the P stamps were valued at 63¢.

## STELLA

*Perforated singles from water-activated gum souvenir sheet*

2652a Hanging from tree
2652b Reading book

*Die cut singles from self-adhesive booklet*

2653 Hanging from tree
2654 Reading book

Designer: Q30 design Inc.

Lithography (7 colours)
Lowe-Martin
Water-activated gum souvenir sheet of 2

**2013, Jul 5** **GT4, TRC Paper** **Perf 12.5**

| | | NH–VF | ⊙F | FDC |
|---|---|---|---|---|
| **2652** | **$1.26 souvenir sheet** of 2 | 3.50 | 3.50 | 4.50 |
| **a** | **P multicoloured**, tree | 1.75 | 1.50 | |
| **b** | **P multicoloured**, reading book | 1.75 | 1.50 | |

Qty: 200,000

Self-adhesive booklet of 10
**GT4, TRC Paper** **Serpentine Die cut 13.5**

| | | NH–VF | ⊙F | FDC |
|---|---|---|---|---|
| **2653** | **P multicoloured**, tree | 1.70 | .50 | — |
| **2654** | **P multicoloured**, reading book | 1.70 | .50 | — |
| i | se-tenant pair (2653, 2654), die cut to shape from Quarterly Pack | 5.00 | — | |
| a | booklet pane of 10, 5 each #2653–54 + 8 stickers (**BK542**) | 17.00 | | |

Qty: 2,000,000 of each

At time of issue, the P stamps were valued at 63¢.
For non-denominated postal cards of same designs, see UX342–UX343.

2652

2654a

## CANADIAN RECORDING ARTISTS: The Bands

*Perforated singles from water-activated gum souvenir sheet*

2655a The Tragically Hip (Gordon Downie, Paul Langlois, Rob Baker, Gord Sinclair, Johnny Fay)

2655b Rush

QE II — 2010's

**2655c**
Beau Dommage
(Pierre Bertrand, Pierre Huet, Robert Léger, Michel Rivard, Marie-Michèle Desrosiers, Réal Desrosiers, Michel Hinton)

**2655d**
The Guess Who

*Die cut singles from self-adhesive booklets*

**2656**

**2657**

**2658**

**2659**

Designer: Paprika.

Lithography (5 colours), water-activated gum souvenir sheet of 4
Lowe-Martin

| **2013, Jul 19** | **GT4, TRC Paper** | | | **Perf 12.5** |
|---|---|---|---|---|
| | | NH–VF | ⊙F | FDC |
| **2655** | **$2.52 souvenir sheet** of 4 | 7.00 | 7.00 | |
| a | P **multicoloured**, The Tragically Hip | 1.75 | 1.50 | |
| b | P **multicoloured**, Rush | 1.75 | 1.50 | |
| c | P **multicoloured**, Beau Dommage | 1.75 | 1.50 | |
| d | P **multicoloured**, The Guess Who | 1.75 | 1.50 | |

Qty: 200,000

Lithography (5 colours; 6 colours for 2656), self-adhesive booklets of 10
**Serpentine Die cut 13.3x13.5** (2656/58), **13.5** (2657/59)

| | | NH–VF | ⊙F | FDC |
|---|---|---|---|---|
| **2656** | P **multicoloured**, The Tragically Hip | 1.70 | .50 | 3.25 |
| i | die cut to shape from Quarterly Pack | 2.50 | — | |
| a | booklet pane of 10 x P (2656) (**BK543**) | 17.00 | | |

Qty: 2,500,000

| | | NH–VF | ⊙F | FDC |
|---|---|---|---|---|
| **2657** | P **multicoloured**, Rush | 1.70 | .50 | 5.00 |
| i | die cut to shape from Quarterly Pack | 2.50 | — | |
| a | booklet pane of 10 x P (2657) (**BK544**) | 17.00 | | |

Qty: 2,500,000

| | | NH–VF | ⊙F | FDC |
|---|---|---|---|---|
| **2658** | P **multicoloured**, Beau Dommage | 1.70 | .50 | 3.25 |
| i | die cut to shape from Quarterly Pack | 2.50 | — | |
| a | booklet pane of 10 x P (2658) (**BK545**) | 17.00 | | |

Qty: 1,000,000

| | | NH–VF | ⊙F | FDC |
|---|---|---|---|---|
| **2659** | P **multicoloured**, The Guess Who | 1.70 | .50 | 3.25 |
| i | die cut to shape from Quarterly Pack | 2.50 | — | |
| a | booklet pane of 10 x P (2659) (**BK546**) | 17.00 | | |

Qty: 2,500,000

At time of issue, the P stamps were valued at 63¢.
For non-denominated postal cards of same designs, see UX344–UX347.

**2655**

**2656a** **2657a** **2658a** **2659a**

## ROBERTSON DAVIES

**2660**
Robertson Davies (1913–1995)

Designer: Steven Slipp; photo by Yousuf Karsh.

Lithography (6 colours), self-adhesive booklet of 10
Lowe-Martin

| **2013, Aug 28** | **GT4, TRC Paper**<br>**Serpentine Die cut 13.3** | | | |
|---|---|---|---|---|
| | | NH–VF | ⊙F | FDC |
| **2660** | **63¢ multicoloured** | 1.25 | .50 | 3.25 |
| i | die cut to shape from Quarterly Pack/ Annual Collection | 2.50 | — | |
| a | booklet pane of 10 x 63¢ (2660) (**BK547**) | 12.50 | | |

Qty: 2,000,000

Canadian novelist, playwright, critic, journalist, and professor; became the founding master of Massey College, which opened in 1963.

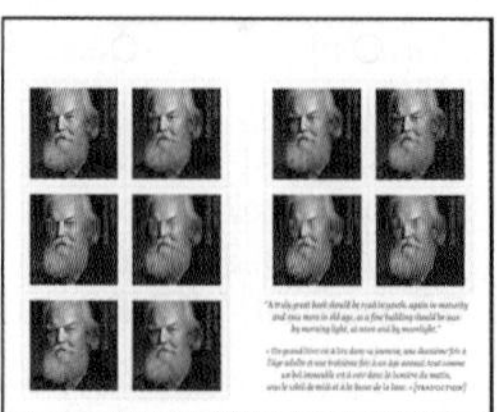

**2660a**



QE II — 2010's

## CANADIAN NHL® TEAM LOGOS

*Perforated singles from water-activated gum souvenir sheet*

**2661a** Vancouver Canucks · **2661b** Edmonton Oilers · **2661c** Toronto Maple Leafs

**2661d** Montreal Canadiens · **2661e** Calgary Flames · **2661f** Winnipeg Jets · **2661g** Ottawa Senators

*Self-adhesive coils*

**2662** Vancouver Canucks · **2663** Edmonton Oilers · **2664** Toronto Maple Leafs

**2665** Montreal Canadiens · **2666** Calgary Flames · **2667** Winnipeg Jets · **2668** Ottawa Senators

Designer: Avi Dunkelman, Joseph Gault | MIX Design Group.

Lithography (5 colours)
Lowe-Martin
Water-activated gum souvenir sheet of 7

**2013, Sep 3** **GT4, TRC Paper** **Perf 13.3x13.0**

| | | NH–VF | ⊙F | FDC |
|---|---|---|---|---|
| 2661 | **$4.41 souvenir sheet** of 7 | 9.00 | 9.00 | 10.80 |
| a | **63¢ multicoloured**, Vancouver Canucks | 1.25 | 1.00 | |
| b | **63¢ multicoloured**, Edmonton Oilers | 1.25 | 1.00 | |
| c | **63¢ multicoloured**, Toronto Maple Leafs | 1.25 | 1.00 | |
| d | **63¢ multicoloured**, Montreal Canadiens | 1.25 | 1.00 | |
| e | **63¢ multicoloured**, Calgary Flames | 1.25 | 1.00 | |
| f | **63¢ multicoloured**, Winnipeg Jets | 1.25 | 1.00 | |
| g | **63¢ multicoloured**, Ottawa Senators | 1.25 | 1.00 | |

Qty: 230,000

Self-adhesive rolls of 50
Lithography (5 colours: 2662–64 ; others are 4 colours)
**GT4, TRC Paper**
with repeating 'Canada' underprint
**Serpentine Die cut 8.2 Horiz**
**(Rounded tips with 3 'nibs' between stamps)**

| | | NH–VF | ⊙F | FDC |
|---|---|---|---|---|
| 2662 | **63¢ multicoloured**, Vancouver Canucks | 1.25 | .60 | — |
| i | gutter strip of 4 with inscription | 6.00 | | |
| | starter strip of 4 (wavy die cut) | 8.00 | | |
| | end strip of 4 (wavy die cut) | 8.00 | | |
| ii | die cut to shape (9.2 horiz) from Qtr Pack ‡ | 1.90 | — | |

Qty: 1,050,000

| | | NH–VF | ⊙F | FDC |
|---|---|---|---|---|
| 2663 | **63¢ multicoloured**, Edmonton Oilers | 1.25 | .60 | — |
| i | gutter strip of 4 with inscription | 6.00 | | |
| | starter strip of 4 (wavy die cut) | 8.00 | | |
| | end strip of 4 (wavy die cut) | 8.00 | | |
| ii | die cut to shape (9.2 horiz) from Qtr Pack ‡ | 1.90 | — | |

Qty: 1,050,000

| | | NH–VF | ⊙F | FDC |
|---|---|---|---|---|
| 2664 | **63¢ multicoloured**, Toronto Maple Leafs | 1.25 | .60 | — |
| i | gutter strip of 4 with inscription | 6.00 | | |
| | starter strip of 4 (wavy die cut) | 8.00 | | |
| | end strip of 4 (wavy die cut) | 8.00 | | |
| ii | die cut to shape (9.2 horiz) from Qtr Pack ‡ | 1.90 | — | |

Qty: 1,750,000

| | | NH–VF | ⊙F | FDC |
|---|---|---|---|---|
| 2665 | **63¢ multicoloured**, Montreal Canadiens | 1.25 | .60 | — |
| i | gutter strip of 4 with inscription | 6.00 | | |
| | starter strip of 4 (wavy die cut) | 8.00 | | |
| | end strip of 4 (wavy die cut) | 8.00 | | |
| ii | die cut to shape (9.2 horiz) from Qtr Pack ‡ | 1.90 | — | |

Qty: 1,750,000

| | | NH–VF | ⊙F | FDC |
|---|---|---|---|---|
| 2666 | **63¢ multicoloured**, Calgary Flames | 1.25 | .60 | — |
| i | gutter strip of 4 with inscription | 6.00 | | |
| | starter strip of 4 (wavy die cut) | 8.00 | | |
| | end strip of 4 (wavy die cut) | 8.00 | | |
| ii | die cut to shape (9.2 horiz) from Qtr Pack ‡ | 1.90 | — | |

Qty: 1,050,000

| | | NH–VF | ⊙F | FDC |
|---|---|---|---|---|
| 2667 | **63¢ multicoloured**, Winnipeg Jets | 1.25 | .60 | — |
| i | gutter strip of 4 with inscription | 6.00 | | |
| | starter strip of 4 (wavy die cut) | 8.00 | | |
| | end strip of 4 (wavy die cut) | 8.00 | | |
| ii | die cut to shape (9.2 horiz) from Qtr Pack ‡ | 1.90 | — | |

Qty: 700,000

| | | NH–VF | ⊙F | FDC |
|---|---|---|---|---|
| 2668 | **63¢ multicoloured**, Ottawa Senators | 1.25 | .60 | — |
| i | gutter strip of 4 with inscription | 6.00 | | |
| | starter strip of 4 (wavy die cut) | 8.00 | | |
| | end strip of 4 (wavy die cut) | 8.00 | | |
| ii | die cut to shape (9.2 horiz) from Qtr Pack ‡ | 1.90 | — | |

Qty: 1,050,000

‡ Single stamps supplied in the Quarterly Pack have rounded tips (die cut 9.2 horiz), starting with a peak at upper left; stamps from the full rolls are die cut 8.2.

**2661**

## CANADIAN NHL® TEAM JERSEYS

*Perforated singles from water-activated gum souvenir sheet*

**2669a** Vancouver Canucks · **2669b** Montreal Canadiens

**2669c**
Edmonton Oilers

2669d
Ottawa Senators

2669e
Calgary Flames

2669f
Winnipeg Jets

2669g
Toronto Maple Leafs

*Die cut singles from self-adhesive booklets*

2670
Vancouver Canucks

2671
Montreal Canadiens

2672
Edmonton Oilers

2673
Ottawa Senators

2674
Calgary Flames

2675
Winnipeg Jets

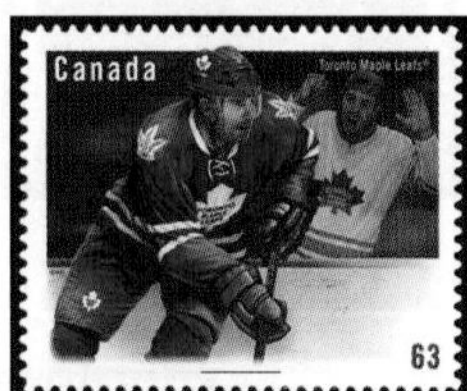

2676
Toronto Maple Leafs

Designer: Avi Dunkelman, Joseph Gault | MIX Design Group.
Lithography (7 colours) and embossed,
Water-activated gum pane of 7
Lowe-Martin

**2013, Sep 30*** **GT4, TRC Paper** **Perf 12.5x12.6**

| | | NH–VF | ⊙F | FDC |
|---|---|---|---|---|
| **2669** | **$4.41 souvenir sheet** of 7 | 9.00 | 9.00 | |
| a | **63¢ multicoloured**, Vancouver Canucks | 1.25 | 1.00 | |
| b | **63¢ multicoloured**, Montreal Canadiens | 1.25 | 1.00 | |
| c | **63¢ multicoloured**, Edmonton Oilers | 1.25 | 1.00 | |
| d | **63¢ multicoloured**, Ottawa Senators | 1.25 | 1.00 | |
| e | **63¢ multicoloured**, Calgary Flames | 1.25 | 1.00 | |
| f | **63¢ multicoloured**, Winnipeg Jets | 1.25 | 1.00 | |
| g | **63¢ multicoloured**, Toronto Maple Leafs | 1.25 | 1.00 | |

Qty: 250,000
* delayed from announced date of Sep 3 due to printing difficulties.

Lithography (5 colours: 2674; 7 colours: 2671–72, 2676; others are 6 colours)
Self-adhesive booklets of 10

**2013, Sep 3** **Serpentine Die cut 13.3x13.5**

| | | NH–VF | ⊙F | FDC |
|---|---|---|---|---|
| **2670** | **63¢ multicoloured**, Vancouver Canucks | 1.25 | .50 | 3.25 |
| i | die cut to shape from Quarterly Pack | 1.90 | — | |
| a | booklet pane of 10 x 63¢ (2670) (**BK548**) | 12.50 | | |
| Qty: 2,100,000 | | | | |
| **2671** | **63¢ multicoloured**, Montreal Canadiens | 1.25 | .50 | 3.25 |
| i | die cut to shape from Quarterly Pack | 1.90 | — | |
| a | booklet pane of 10 x 63¢ (2671) (**BK549**) | 12.50 | | |
| Qty: 2,800,000 | | | | |
| **2672** | **63¢ multicoloured**, Edmonton Oilers | 1.25 | .50 | 3.25 |
| i | die cut to shape from Quarterly Pack | 1.90 | — | |
| a | booklet pane of 10 x 63¢ (2672) (**BK550**) | 12.50 | | |
| Qty: 2,100,000 | | | | |
| **2673** | **63¢ multicoloured**, Ottawa Senators | 1.25 | .50 | 3.25 |
| i | die cut to shape from Quarterly Pack | 1.90 | — | |
| a | booklet pane of 10 x 63¢ (2673) (**BK551**) | 12.50 | | |
| Qty: 2,100,000 | | | | |
| **2674** | **63¢ multicoloured**, Calgary Flames | 1.25 | .50 | 3.25 |
| i | die cut to shape from Quarterly Pack | 1.90 | — | |
| a | booklet pane of 10 x 63¢ (2674) (**BK552**) | 12.50 | | |
| Qty: 2,100,000 | | | | |
| **2675** | **63¢ multicoloured**, Winnipeg Jets | 1.25 | .50 | 3.25 |
| i | die cut to shape from Quarterly Pack | 1.90 | — | |
| a | booklet pane of 10 x 63¢ (2675) (**BK553**) | 12.50 | | |
| Qty: 1,400,000 | | | | |
| **2676** | **63¢ multicoloured**, Toronto Maple Leafs | 1.25 | .50 | 3.25 |
| i | die cut to shape from Quarterly Pack | 1.90 | — | |
| a | booklet pane of 10 x 63¢ (2676) (**BK554**) | 12.50 | | |
| Qty: 2,800,000 | | | | |

For non-denominated postal cards of same designs, see UX348–UX354.

2669

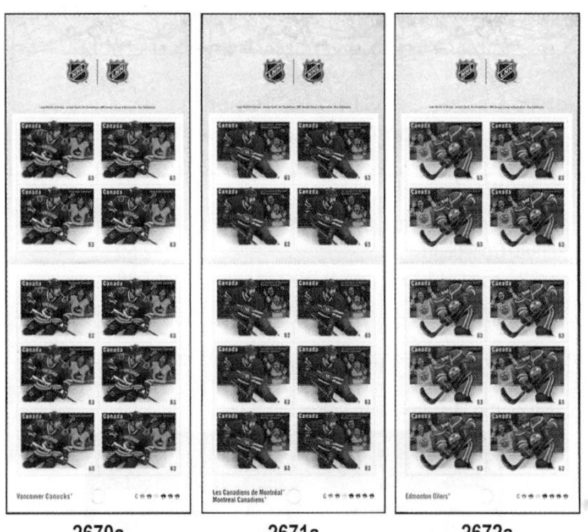

2670a 2671a 2672a

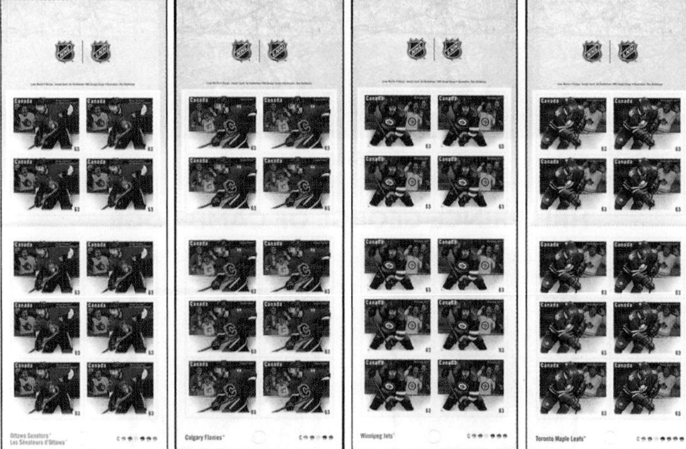

2673a 2674a 2675a 2676a

## SUPERMAN

*Perforated singles from water-activated gum souvenir sheet*

2677a
Superman #1 (1939)
Joe Shuster

2677b
Superman #32 (1945)
Wayne Boring

2677c
Superman #233 (1971)
Neal Adams

2677d
Superman #204 (2004)
Jim Lee

2677e
Superman Annual #1 (2012)
Kenneth Rocafort

*Die cut singles from self-adhesive booklet*

2679

2680

2681

2682

2683

2678
Man of Steel #1 (1986)
John Byrne

Designer: Kosta Tsetsekas, Jasper Murphy | Signals.

Lithography (6 colours), water-activated gum souvenir sheet of 5
Lowe-Martin

| 2013, Sep 10 | GT4, TRC Paper | Perf 12.6x12.5 | | |
|---|---|---|---|---|
| | | NH–VF | ⊙F | FDC |
| 2677 | **$3.15 souvenir sheet** of 5 | 8.75 | 8.75 | 8.30 |
| a | **P multicoloured**, (1939) | 1.75 | 1.50 | |
| b | **P multicoloured**, (1945) | 1.75 | 1.50 | |
| c | **P multicoloured**, (1971) | 1.75 | 1.50 | |
| d | **P multicoloured**, (2004) | 1.75 | 1.50 | |
| e | **P multicoloured**, (2012) | 1.75 | 1.50 | |
| i | $24.95 uncut press sheet of 6 souvenir sheets | 55.00 | | |

Qty: 250,000; 2677i: 7,500

The souvenir sheets from the uncut press sheet (2677i) do not contain a UPC barcode.

Lithography (6 colours), self-adhesive roll of 75
Lowe-Martin

| | GT4, TRC Paper | Die cut 13.5 | | |
|---|---|---|---|---|
| | | NH–VF | ⊙F | FDC |
| 2678 | **P multicoloured**, (1939) | 1.70 | .70 | 3.25 |
| i | single from Quarterly Pack/Annual Collection w/*rouletted* backing paper and *no* backprint | 2.50 | — | |

Qty: 3,750,000

At time of issue, the P stamps were valued at 63¢.

The reverse of the coil stamp backing material has a secret message written in Superman's mother tongue (Kryptonian). The full bilingual message covers just about 32 stamps:

> "The S shield is more than Supermans family crest its Kryptonian symbol that means hope" (in English)

> "Le cusson S est bien plus que blason de la famille de Superman ce symbole signifie espoir en Kryptonien" (in French)

Lithography (6 colours), self-adhesive booklet of 10
**Serpentine Die cut 13.4x13.3**

| | | NH–VF | ⊙F | FDC |
|---|---|---|---|---|
| 2679 | **multicoloured**, (1939) | 1.70 | .60 | |
| 2680 | **multicoloured**, (1945) | 1.70 | .60 | |
| 2781 | **multicoloured**, (1971) | 1.70 | .60 | |
| 2682 | **multicoloured**, (2004) | 1.70 | .60 | |
| 2683 | **multicoloured**, (2012) | 1.70 | .60 | |
| i | vertical strip of 5 (2679–83), die cut to shape from Quarterly Pack (with imperforate gutter) | 12.50 | — | |
| a | booklet pane of 10 x P (2679–83) (**BK555***) | 17.00 | | |

Qty: 1,200,000 of each design

* Five different booklet covers were released. Each different booklet consists of the same pane layout of 10 stamps but with different groupings of circular stickers:

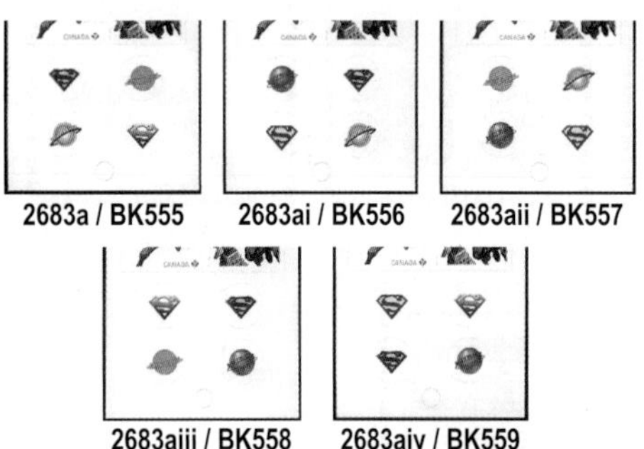

2683a / BK555 2683ai / BK556 2683aii / BK557

2683aiii / BK558 2683aiv / BK559

2683a

The die cut to shape strip of 5 from the Quarterly Pack is not rouletted in the gutter between the third and fourth stamp.

For non-denominated postal cards of same stamp designs, see UX355–UX359. For non-denominated postal cards of same booklet cover designs, see UX360–UX364.

Portion of "Kryptonian" text on reverse of 2678

2677

2683i (imperforate gutter)

Timeline:
2013, Sep 30 63¢+10¢ Canada Post Community Foundation, semi-postal (B20)

## THE HASTINGS AND PRINCE EDWARD REGIMENT

2684
Poppies over painting, *Assault on Assoro* by Ted Zuber

Designer: Sputnik Design Partners Inc.
Lithography (6 colours), self-adhesive booklet of 10
Lowe-Martin
**2013, Oct 18 GT4, TRC Paper**
**Serpentine Die cut 13.4x13.0**

| | | NH–VF | ⊙F | FDC |
|---|---|---|---|---|
| 2684 | **multicoloured** | 1.70 | .50 | 3.25 |
| i | die cut to shape from Quarterly Pack/ Annual Collection | 2.50 | — | |
| a | booklet pane of 10 x P (2684) (**BK561**) | 17.00 | | |

Qty: 1,500,000

150th anniversary of The Hastings and Prince Edward Regiment.

At time of issue, the P stamp was valued at 63¢.

2684a

## HRH PRINCE GEORGE OF CAMBRIDGE

*Perforated single from water-activated gum souvenir sheet*

2685a

*Die cut single from self-adhesive booklet*

2686

Prince George of Cambridge with Prince William, Duke of Cambridge, and Catherine, Duchess of Cambridge

Designer: Isabelle Toussaint Design Graphique.
Lithography (7 colours)
Lowe-Martin
Water-activated gum souvenir sheet of 2
**2013, Oct 22 GT4, TRC Paper Perf 12.5**

| | | NH–VF | ⊙F | FDC |
|---|---|---|---|---|
| 2685 | **$1.26 souvenir sheet** of 2 | 3.50 | 3.50 | 6.75 |
| a | **multicoloured** | 1.75 | 1.50 | |

Qty: 250,000

Self-adhesive booklet of 10
**GT4, TRC Paper Serpentine Die cut 13.5**

| | | NH–VF | ⊙F | FDC |
|---|---|---|---|---|
| 2686 | **multicoloured** | 1.70 | .50 | — |
| i | die cut to shape from Quarterly Pack | 2.50 | — | |
| a | booklet pane of 10 x P (2686) (**BK562**) | 17.00 | | |

Qty: 3,000,000

Birth of His Royal Highness Prince George Alexander Louls of Cambridge on July 22, 2013.

At time of issue, the P stamps were valued at 63¢.

2685

*Image rotated* 2686a

## CHRISTMAS CRAFT

*Perforated singles from water-activated gum souvenir sheet*

2687a

2687b

2687c

*Die cut singles from self-adhesive booklets*

2689 Cross-stitched horn

2690 Cross-stitched reindeer

2691 Cross-stitched Christmas tree

## CHRISTMAS: SAINT ANNE WITH THE CHRIST CHILD

2688
Painting by Georges de La Tour

Designer: Hélène L'Heureux.

Lithography (7 colours)
Lowe-Martin
Water-activated gum souvenir sheet of 3

**2013, Oct 22** **GT4, TRC Paper** **Perf 13.7x13.3**

| | | NH–VF | ⊙F | FDC |
|---|---|---|---|---|
| **2687** | **$3.58 souvenir sheet** of 3 | 7.60 | 7.60 | 9.15 |
| a | **63¢ multicoloured** | 1.25 | 1.25 | |
| b | **$1.10 multicoloured** | 2.20 | 2.10 | |
| c | **$1.85 multicoloured** | 3.70 | 3.60 | |

Qty: 160,000

Designer: Louise Méthé.

Lithography (6 colours)
Self-adhesive booklet of 12
**GT4, TRC Paper Serpentine Die cut 13.5**

| | | NH–VF | ⊙F | FDC |
|---|---|---|---|---|
| **2688** | **63¢ multicoloured** | 1.25 | .25 | 3.25 |
| i | die cut to shape from Quarterly Pack/ Annual Collection | 1.90 | — | |
| a | booklet pane of 12 x 63¢ (2688) (**BK563**) | 15.00 | — | |

Qty: 9,600,000

Designer: Hélène L'Heureux.

Lithography (7 colours), self-adhesive booklet of 12 (63¢) or 6
Lowe-Martin
**GT4, TRC Paper**
**Serpentine Die cut 13.3 x 13.0**

| | | NH–VF | ⊙F | FDC |
|---|---|---|---|---|
| **2689** | **63¢ multicoloured** | 1.25 | .25 | — |
| i | die cut to shape from Quarterly Pack | 1.90 | — | |
| a | booklet pane of 12 x 63¢ (2689) (**BK564**) | 15.00 | — | |

Qty: 20,400,000

| | | NH–VF | ⊙F | FDC |
|---|---|---|---|---|
| **2690** | **$1.10 multicoloured** | 2.20 | .75 | — |
| i | die cut to shape from Quarterly Pack | 3.30 | — | |
| a | booklet pane of 6 x $1.10 (2690) (**BK565**) | 13.00 | — | |

Qty: 3,780,000

| | | NH–VF | ⊙F | FDC |
|---|---|---|---|---|
| **2691** | **$1.85 multicoloured** | 3.75 | 1.25 | — |
| i | die cut to shape from Quarterly Pack | 5.60 | — | |
| a | booklet pane of 6 x $1.85 (2691) (**BK566**) | 22.00 | — | |

Qty: 3,660,000

2687

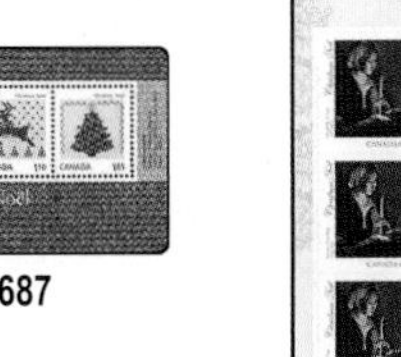
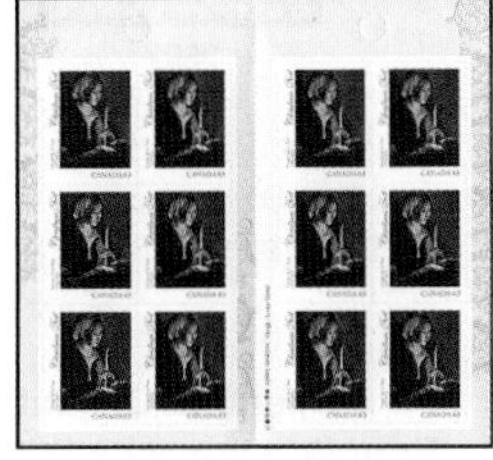
2688a

2689a

2690a

2691a

**PERMANENT™ non-denominated stamps**

On December 11, 2013 Canada Post announced a new set of postal rates to take effect on March 31, 2014 which included the increase of domestic lettermail from 63¢ to 85¢. This large increase dictated that all on-hand Permanent™ stamps would be temporarily withdrawn from sale until the rate increase went into affect. Usage of any Permanent™ stamps was still allowed, but sales of these stamps were on hold for some 3½ months.

New 63¢ denominated definitives (Scott 2692–2698) became available at post offices within a couple of days (typically by December 13).

Canada Post's stamp announcement magazine ("Details") changed from an 8½"x11" size to a 6"x8¼" size with the start of the 2014 calendar year.

Three versions are available: English only, French only, and bilingual.

**Addressed Admail**

Canada Post has introduced Customized Postal Indicia that includes artwork and a perforated edge look. The Perforated Edge Design Postal Indicia is only available for Addressed Admail™ (including Dimensional Addressed Admail), Lettermail™, Incentive Lettermail™ and Publications Mail™.

Postal indicia are pre-printed markings on mail showing that postage has been prepaid by the sender. This material, like Picture Postage™, is outside the scope of the *Unitrade Specialized Catalogue of Canadian Stamps.*

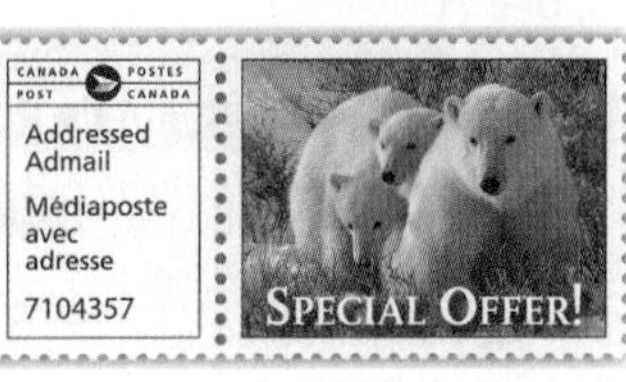

## BABY WILDLIFE DEFINITIVES – COILS

2692 2692A

Woodchucks

Designers: Monique Dufour, Sophie Lafortune.

Lithography (5 colours), self-adhesive roll of 100

Lowe-Martin

**Serpentine Die cut 8.15 to 8.50 Horiz**
**(Rounded tips with 3 'nibs' between stamps)**

One die cut pattern was used on this stamp.

**2013, Dec 11** **GT4, TRC Paper**

with repeating 'Canada' underprint

| | | NH–VF | ⊙F | FDC |
|---|---|---|---|---|
| **2692** | **63¢ multicoloured** | 1.25 | .25 | — |
| i | gutter strip of 4 with inscription | 6.00 | | |
| | starter strip of 4 (wavy die cut) | 8.00 | | |
| | end strip of 4 (wavy die cut) | 8.00 | | |
| ii | die cut to shape (9.2 horiz) from Quarterly Pack, *Apr '14* ‡ | 1.90 | — | |
| b | ***without*** repeating 'Canada' underprint | *100.00* | *10.00* | — |
| bi | as "b", gutter strip of 4 with inscription | *600.00* | | |
| | as "b", starter strip of 4 (wavy die cut) | *800.00* | | |
| | as "b", end strip of 4 (wavy die cut) | *800.00* | | |

‡ Single stamps supplied in the Quarterly Pack have rounded tips (backing paper is 'plain' with the repeating 'Canada' underprint visible), starting with a valley at upper left; stamps from the full rolls are die cut 8.15 to 8.50.

Lithography (5 colours), self-adhesive roll of 5,000

**2013, Dec 11** **GT4, TRC Paper**

with repeating 'Canada' underprint

**Serpentine Die cut 9.2 Horiz**
**(Rounded tips)**

| | | NH–VF | ⊙F | FDC |
|---|---|---|---|---|
| **2692A** | **63¢ multicoloured** | 1.50 | 1.50 | — |

2692A issued in horizontal rolls of 5,000. Individual stamps do not touch along the horizontal roll; rounded 'perf tips' start with a valley. Sold in strips of 4 or 10 by the National Philatelic Centre; single stamps included in the Quarterly Pack/Annual Collection.



## PERMANENT™ CANADIAN PRIDE

*Die cut singles from self-adhesive booklet*

2693 2694 2695 2696 2697

Designer: Gottschalk+Ash International.

Lithography (4 colours)

Canadian Bank Note

Self-adhesive booklet of 10

**2013, Dec 11** **GT4, TRC Paper**

with repeating 'Canada' underprint

**Serpentine Die cut 13.4**

| | | NH–VF | ⊙F | FDC |
|---|---|---|---|---|
| **2693** | **63¢ multicoloured**, chairs on dock | 1.25 | .25 | — |
| **2694** | **63¢ multicoloured**, hay bale | 1.25 | .25 | — |
| **2695** | **63¢ multicoloured**, sailboat | 1.25 | .25 | — |
| **2696** | **63¢ multicoloured**, 'living flag' | 1.25 | .25 | — |
| **2697** | **63¢ multicoloured**, fishing hut | 1.25 | .25 | — |
| i | se-tenant strip of 5 (2693–2697), die cut to shape from Quarterly Pack | 9.35 | — | |
| a | booklet pane of 10 x 63¢ (2 each of 2693–2697) (**BK567**) | 12.50 | | |
| ai | strip of 5, from 2697a/BK567 | 6.25 | | |

For Permanent™ versions of these definitives, see Scott 2603–2604/2612–16/2617.

## QUEEN ELIZABETH II

2698

Designer: Entro | G+A.

Lithography (5 colours), self-adhesive booklet of 10

Canadian Bank Note

**2013, Dec 11** **GT4, TRC Paper**

with repeating 'Canada' underprint

**Serpentine Die cut 13.4**

| | | NH–VF | ⊙F | FDC |
|---|---|---|---|---|
| **2698** | **63¢ multicoloured (QE II)** | 1.25 | .25 | — |
| i | die cut to shape from Quarterly Pack/ Annual Collection | 1.90 | — | |
| a | booklet pane of 10 x 63¢ (2698) (**BK568**) | 12.50 | | |

The tagging includes an incorrect spelling of "Anniversary" (as "Anniversery").

2697a 2698a

# 2014

## LUNAR NEW YEAR (Series 2) — 6
## Year of the Horse

2699
Bucking Horse

*Perforated single from souvenir sheet*

2700i
Horse

*Die cut single from self-adhesive booklet*

2701
Horse

Designer: Paprika.

Lithography (4 colours) plus embossing plus varnish, pane of 25

Lowe-Martin, Gravure Choquet

**2014, Jan 13** **GT4, TRC Paper** **Perf 12.5**

| | | NH–VF | ⊙F | PB | FDC |
|---|---|---|---|---|---|
| **2699** | **63¢ multicoloured** | 1.25 | .40 | 5.00 | 3.25 |

Qty: 2,500,000

Lithography (4 colours) plus 1 foil stamping, embossing plus varnish

**GT4 (except where design passes through edge of stamp)**

| | | | | | |
|---|---|---|---|---|---|
| **2700** | **$1.85 souvenir sheet** of 1 | 3.75 | 3.75 | — | 5.70 |
| i | $1.85 single stamp from souvenir sheet | 3.25 | 3.25 | — | |
| ii | $29.95 uncut press sheet of 12 souvenir sheets | 60.00 | | | |
| a | $3.70 'transitional' souvenir sheet of 2, #2600, 2700 | 7.25 | 7.25 | — | |

Qty: 2700: 400,000; 2700ii: 13,000; 2700a: 175,000

Lithography (1 colour) plus 1 foil stamping
Lowe-Martin, self-adhesive booklet of 6
**GT4 (except where design passes through edge of stamp)**
**TRC Paper Serpentine Die cut 13.5**

| | | NH–VF | ⊙F | FDC |
|---|---|---|---|---|
| **2701** | **$1.85 multicoloured** | 3.75 | 2.25 | — |
| i | die cut to shape from Quarterly Pack | 5.60 | — | |
| ii | gold horse omitted (one pane reported) | *9,000.00* | | |
| a | booklet pane of 6 x $1.85 (2701) (**BK569**) | 22.25 | — | |

Qty: 900,000

One complete booklet with missing gold horse on all stamps is known to the editors.

For non-denominated postal cards of same designs, see UX365–UX366.

2700

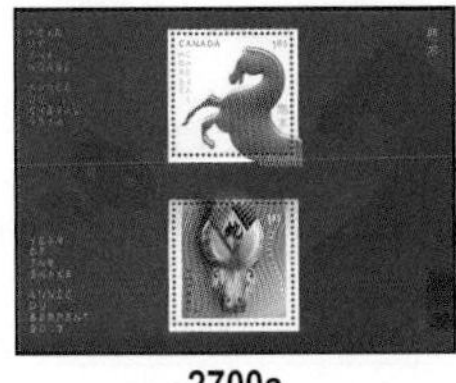
2700a

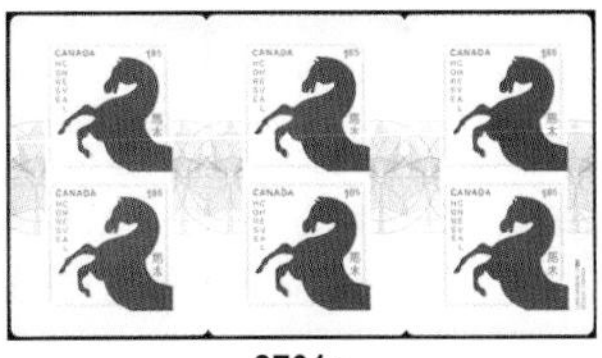
2701a

## BLACK HISTORY MONTH

2702
Africville
Halifax, NS

2703
Hogan's Alley
Vancouver, BC

Designer: Karen Smith Design.

Lithography (5 colours), self-adhesive booklets of 10
Lowe-Martin
**2014, Jan 30 GT4, TRC Paper**
**Serpentine Die cut 13.5**

| | | NH–VF | ⊙F | FDC |
|---|---|---|---|---|
| **2702** | **63¢ multicoloured**, Africville | 1.25 | .50 | 3.25 |
| i | die cut to shape from Quarterly Pack/ Annual Collection | 1.90 | — | |
| a | booklet pane of 10 x 63¢ (2702) (**BK570**) | 12.50 | | |

Qty: 2,000,000

| | | NH–VF | ⊙F | FDC |
|---|---|---|---|---|
| **2703** | **63¢ multicoloured**, Hogan's Alley | 1.25 | .50 | 3.25 |
| i | die cut to shape from Quarterly Pack/ Annual Collection | 1.90 | — | |
| a | booklet pane of 10 x 63¢ (2703) (**BK571**) | 12.50 | | |

Qty: 2,000,000

African-Canadian neighbourhoods.

*Image rotated* 2702a

*Image rotated* 2703a

## PIONEERS OF WINTER SPORTS

*Perforated singles from water-activated gum souvenir sheet*

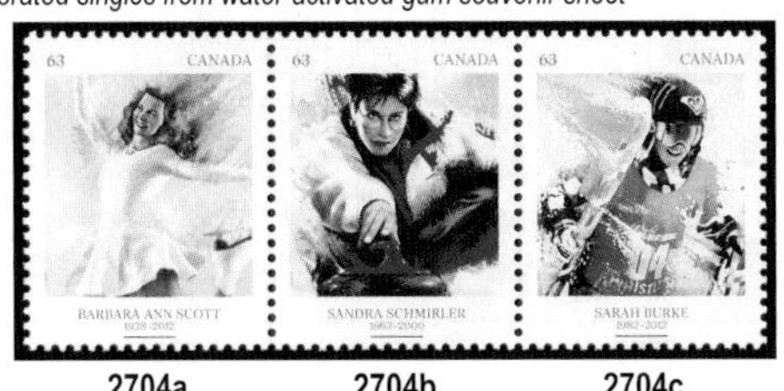
2704a 2704b 2704c

*Die cut singles from self-adhesive booklets*

2705
Barbara Ann Scott
(1928–2012)

2706
Sandra Schmirler
(1963–2000)

2707
Sarah Burke
(1982–2012)

Designer: Paprika.

Lithography (8 colours)
Lowe-Martin
Water-activated gum souvenir sheet of 3
**2014, Feb 3 GT4, TRC Paper Perf 13.1x13.2**

| | | NH–VF | ⊙F | FDC |
|---|---|---|---|---|
| **2704** | **$1.89 souvenir sheet** of 3 | 3.75 | 3.75 | — |
| a | **63¢ multicoloured**, Scott | 1.25 | 1.25 | |
| b | **63¢ multicoloured**, Schmirler | 1.25 | 1.25 | |
| c | **63¢ multicoloured**, Burke | 1.25 | 1.25 | |

Qty: 200,000

Lithography (6 colours), self-adhesive booklets of 10
**GT4, TRC Paper**
**Serpentine Die cut 13.5**

| | | NH–VF | ⊙F | FDC |
|---|---|---|---|---|
| **2705** | **63¢ multicoloured**, Scott | 1.25 | .50 | 3.25 |
| i | die cut to shape from Quarterly Pack/ Annual Collection | 1.90 | — | |
| a | booklet pane of 10 x 63¢ (2705) (**BK572**) | 12.50 | | |

Qty: 2,000,000

Lithography (7 colours)

| | | NH–VF | ⊙F | FDC |
|---|---|---|---|---|
| **2706** | **63¢ multicoloured**, Schmirler | 1.25 | .50 | 3.25 |
| i | die cut to shape from Quarterly Pack/ Annual Collection | 1.90 | — | |
| a | booklet pane of 10 x 63¢ (2706) (**BK573**) | 12.50 | | |

Qty: 2,000,000

| | | NH–VF | ⊙F | FDC |
|---|---|---|---|---|
| **2707** | **63¢ multicoloured**, Burke | 1.25 | .50 | 3.25 |
| i | die cut to shape from Quarterly Pack/ Annual Collection | 1.90 | — | |
| a | booklet pane of 10 x 63¢ (2707) (**BK574**) | 12.50 | | |

Qty: 2,000,000

Female athletes who were history-makers and record-breakers in their respective sport: Scott in figure skating; Schmirler in curling; Burke in freestyle skiing.

2704

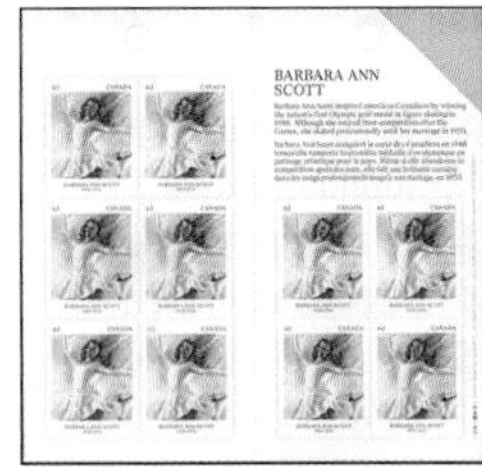
2705a

2706a

2707a

| Rates: | Domestic first-class (0-30g): 85¢ * | USA (0-30g): $1.20 |
|---|---|---|
| Mar 31/14– | Domestic first-class (30-50g): $1.20 | USA (30-50g): $1.80 |
| | Domestic oversize (0-100g): $1.80 | International (0-30g): $2.50 |

*single usage:* USA $1.20: $10.00 | International $2.50: $15.00

* Single purchase stamp(s): $1.00; metered mail: 75¢

## INSECT – DEFINITIVE

2708
Monarch Butterfly

Designer: Keith Martin.

Lithography (5 colours), pane of 50
Canadian Bank Note

**2014, Mar 31** **Not tagged, TRC Paper** **Perf 13.0x13.4**

| | | NH–VF | ⊙F | PB | FDC |
|---|---|---|---|---|---|
| **2708** | **22¢ multicoloured** | .40 | .25 | 1.80 | 2.45* |

* The FDC contains only a single 22¢ stamp.

For 1¢, 3¢–25¢ values see Sc. 2234–2238. For 2¢ value see Sc. 2328. For 4¢, 6¢–9¢ values see Sc. 2406–10.

Canada Post did not refer to this issue as a "beneficial" insect, as they have with previous stamps in this series.



## BABY WILDLIFE DEFINITIVES — SOUVENIR SHEET

2709a
Beavers

2709b
Burrowing Owl

2709c
Mountain Goat

2709d
Atlantic Puffin

2709e
Wapiti

Designers: Monique Dufour, Sophie Lafortune.

Lithography (9 colours)
Lowe-Martin
Water-activated gum souvenir sheet of 5

**2014, Mar 31** **GT4, TRC Paper** **Perf 13.4x13.0**

| | | NH–VF | ⊙F | FDC |
|---|---|---|---|---|
| **2709** | **$7.35 souvenir sheet** of 5 * | 15.00 | 15.00 | 16.70 |
| a | **P multicoloured** | 1.70 | 1.50 | |
| b | **$1.00 multicoloured** | 2.00 | 2.00 | |
| c | **$1.20 multicoloured** | 2.40 | 2.25 | |
| d | **$1.80 multicoloured** | 3.60 | 3.50 | |
| e | **$2.50 multicoloured** | 5.00 | 5.00 | |

Qty: 155,000

* Face value of $7.35 at time of issue; the face value of the P stamp was 85¢.

## BABY WILDLIFE DEFINITIVES – COILS

2710
Burrowing Owl

2710A
(roll of 5,000)

2711
Beavers

2712
Mountain Goat

2713
Atlantic Puffin

2714
Wapiti

Designers: Monique Dufour, Sophie Lafortune.

Lithography (5 colours), self-adhesive roll of 50
Lowe-Martin

**2014, Mar 31** **GT4, TRC Paper** **Die cut 13.5**
with repeating 'Canada' underprint

| | | NH–VF | ⊙F | FDC |
|---|---|---|---|---|
| **2710** | **$1.00 multicoloured** | 2.00 | .25 | — |
| *with counting number on back of coil backing paper (Jan 2016): †* | | | | |
| i | single stamp, with back #, *Jan 2016* | 2.50 | — | |
| b | missing yellow inscriptions ('CANADA 100') | 600.00 | | |

The backing paper is rouletted between each stamp. The reverse of the coil stamp backing material (original March 2014 printing) had a dot-matrix printed text inscription every 10 stamps. The January 2016 reprint had counting numbers every 5 stamps.

Lithography (5 colours), self-adhesive roll of 5,000
**GT4, TRC Paper**
with repeating 'Canada' underprint
**Serpentine Die cut 9.2 Horiz**
**(Rounded tips)**

| | | NH–VF | ⊙F | FDC |
|---|---|---|---|---|
| **2710A** | **P multicoloured** | 2.00 | 2.00 | — |

2710A issued in horizontal rolls of 5,000. Individual stamps do not touch along the horizontal roll; rounded 'perf tips' start with a valley. Sold in strips of 4 or 10 by the National Philatelic Centre; single stamps included in the Quarterly Pack/Annual Collection.

Lithography (5 colours), self-adhesive rolls of 100 (P) and 50 ($1.20, $1.80, $2.50)
**GT4, TRC Paper**
with repeating 'Canada' underprint
**Serpentine Die cut 8.15 to 8.50 Horiz**
**(Rounded tips with 3 'nibs' between stamps)**
To date, one die cut pattern has been used on these stamps.

| | | NH–VF | ⊙F | FDC |
|---|---|---|---|---|
| **2711** | **P multicoloured** | 1.70 | .25 | — |
| i | gutter strip of 4 with inscription | 8.50 | | |
| | starter strip of 4 (wavy die cut) | 11.00 | | |
| | end strip of 4 (wavy die cut) | 11.00 | | |
| ii | die cut to shape (9.2 horiz) from Quarterly Pack, *Jul '14* ‡ | 2.50 | — | |
| *with counting number on back of coil backing paper (Jan 2016): †* | | | | |
| iii | single stamp, with back #, *Jan 2016* | 2.50 | — | |
| iv | as "iii", gutter strip of 4 with inscription | 8.50 | | |
| | as "iii", starter strip of 4 (wavy die cut) | 11.00 | | |

This stamp was released in rolls of 300 and 500 on May 1, 2014. There is no difference between stamps from the rolls of 100, 300 or 500.

| | | NH–VF | ⊙F | FDC |
|---|---|---|---|---|
| **2712** | **$1.20 multicoloured** | 2.40 | .50 | — |
| i | gutter strip of 4 with inscription | 11.00 | | |
| | starter strip of 4 (wavy die cut) | 13.00 | | |
| | end strip of 4 (wavy die cut) | 13.00 | | |
| ii | die cut to shape (9.2 horiz) from Quarterly Pack, *Jul '14* ‡ | 3.60 | — | |
| *with counting number on back of coil backing paper (Feb 2016): †* | | | | |
| iii | single stamp, with back #, *Feb 2016* | 2.75 | — | |
| iv | as "iii", gutter strip of 4 with inscription | 11.00 | | |
| | as "iii", starter strip of 4 (wavy die cut) | 13.00 | | |
| **2713** | **$1.80 multicoloured** | 3.60 | .80 | — |
| i | gutter strip of 4 with inscription | 17.00 | | |
| | starter strip of 4 (wavy die cut) | 18.00 | | |
| | end strip of 4 (wavy die cut) | 18.00 | | |
| ii | die cut to shape (9.2 horiz) from Quarterly Pack, *Jul '14* ‡ | 5.40 | — | |
| *with counting number on back of coil backing paper (Jan 2016): †* | | | | |
| iii | single stamp, with back #, *Jan 2016* | 5.00 | — | |
| iv | as "iii", gutter strip of 4 with inscription | 17.00 | | |
| | as "iii", starter strip of 4 (wavy die cut) | 18.00 | | |
| **2714** | **$2.50 multicoloured** | 5.00 | 1.50 | — |
| i | gutter strip of 4 with inscription | 24.00 | | |
| | starter strip of 4 (wavy die cut) | 25.00 | | |
| | end strip of 4 (wavy die cut) | 25.00 | | |
| ii | die cut to shape (9.2 horiz) from Quarterly Pack, *Jul '14* ‡ | 7.50 | — | |
| *with counting number on back of coil backing paper (Jan 2016): †* | | | | |
| iii | single stamp, with back #, *Jan 2016* | 6.00 | — | |
| iv | as "iii", gutter strip of 4 with inscription | 24.00 | | |
| | as "iii", starter strip of 4 (wavy die cut) | 25.00 | | |

‡ Single stamps supplied in the Quarterly Pack have rounded tips (backing paper is 'plain' with the repeating 'Canada' underprint visible), starting with a peak at upper left; stamps from the full rolls are die cut 8.15 to 8.50.

† A dot-matrix printed 'counting number', found every 5 stamps on the backing paper of the coil (illustrated below). Rolls of 100 start with '100' on the first stamp of the roll (found on the starter strip) and count down to 5, by 5. Rolls of 50 start with '50' on the first stamp of the roll. These 'counting numbers' began to appear on rolls from coil boxes dated in January and February 2016.

Inscription on backing paper of 2710 (about every 10 stamps)

100 95

Counting number on backing paper of 2711 (every 5 stamps); 2710 and 2712–14 start at 50

2709

2710b

2715a

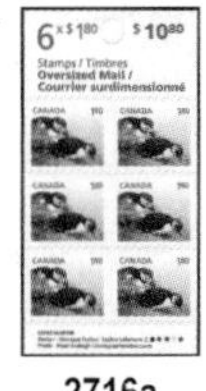

2716a

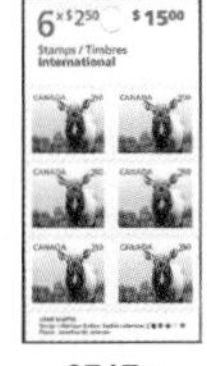

2717a

## BABY WILDLIFE DEFINITIVES – BOOKLETS

**2715** Mountain Goat

**2716** Atlantic Puffin

**2717** Wapiti

Designers: Monique Dufour, Sophie Lafortune.

Lithography (5 colours), self-adhesive booklets of 6
Lowe-Martin

**2014, Mar 31** **GT4, TRC Paper**
with repeating 'Canada' underprint
**Serpentine Die cut 9.2 horiz (Rounded tips)**

| | | NH–VF | ⊙F | FDC |
|---|---|---|---|---|
| **2715** | **$1.20 multicoloured** | 2.40 | .50 | — |
| i | die cut to shape from Quarterly Pack ‡ | 3.60 | — | |
| a | booklet pane of 6 x $1.20 (2715) (**BK575**) | 14.50 | | |
| **2716** | **$1.80 multicoloured** | 3.60 | .80 | — |
| i | die cut to shape from Quarterly Pack ‡ | 5.40 | — | |
| a | booklet pane of 6 x $1.80 (2716) (**BK576**) | 21.60 | | |
| **2717** | **$2.50 multicoloured** | 5.00 | 1.50 | — |
| i | die cut to shape from Quarterly Pack ‡ | 7.50 | — | |
| a | booklet pane of 6 x $2.50 (2717) (**BK577**) | 30.00 | | |

‡ Single stamps supplied in the Quarterly packs start with a peak at the upper left (backing paper contains some form of printing from backside of booklet); single stamps from booklets of 6 start with a valley at the upper left.

For non-denominated postal cards of same designs, see UX367–UX371.

## UNESCO WORLD HERITAGE SITES IN CANADA

*Perforated singles from water-activated gum souvenir sheet*

**2718a** Gros Morne National Park, NL

**2718b** Joggins Fossil Cliffs, NS

**2718c** Canadian Rocky Mountain Parks, AB and BC

**2718d** Nahanni National Park, NT

**2718e** Miguasha National Park, QC

*Die cut singles from self-adhesive booklets*

**2719**

**2720**

**2721** **2722**

**2723**

Designer: Lime Design.

Lithography (5 colours)
Canadian Bank Note
Water-activated gum souvenir sheet of 5

**2014, Mar 31** **GT4, TRC Paper** **Perf 13.3x13.0**

| | | NH–VF | ⊙F | FDC |
|---|---|---|---|---|
| 2718 | **$4.25 souvenir sheet** of 5 | 8.50 | 8.50 | 10.50 |
| a | **multicoloured**, Gros Morne | 1.70 | 1.50 | |
| b | **multicoloured**, Joggins | 1.70 | 1.50 | |
| c | **multicoloured**, Rocky Mountain | 1.70 | 1.50 | |
| d | **multicoloured**, Nahanni | 1.70 | 1.50 | |
| e | **multicoloured**, Miguasha | 1.70 | 1.50 | |

Qty: 160,000

Self-adhesive booklets of 10 and 30

**2014, Mar 31** **GT4, TRC Paper**
with repeating 'Canada' underprint
**Serpentine Die cut 13.4**

| | | NH–VF | ⊙F | FDC |
|---|---|---|---|---|
| 2719 | **multicoloured**, Gros Morne | 1.70 | .25 | — |
| 2720 | **multicoloured**, Nahanni | 1.70 | .25 | — |
| 2721 | **multicoloured**, Joggins | 1.70 | .25 | — |
| 2722 | **multicoloured**, Miguasha | 1.70 | .25 | — |
| 2723 | **multicoloured**, Rocky Mountain | 1.70 | .25 | — |
| i | se-tenant strip of 5 (2719–2723), die cut to shape from Quarterly Pack | 12.50 | — | |
| a | booklet pane of 10 x P (2 each of 2719–2723) (**BK578**) | 17.00 | | |
| b | booklet pane of 30 x P (6 each of 2719–2723) (**BK579**) | 50.00 | | |
| ai | strip of 5, from 2723a/BK578 or 2723b/BK579 | 8.50 | | |

At time of issue, all of the P stamps issued March 31, 2014 were valued at 85¢.
For non-denominated postal cards of same designs, see UX372–UX376.

The United Nations Educational, Scientific and Cultural Organization (UNESCO) is a specialized agency of the United Nations.

2718

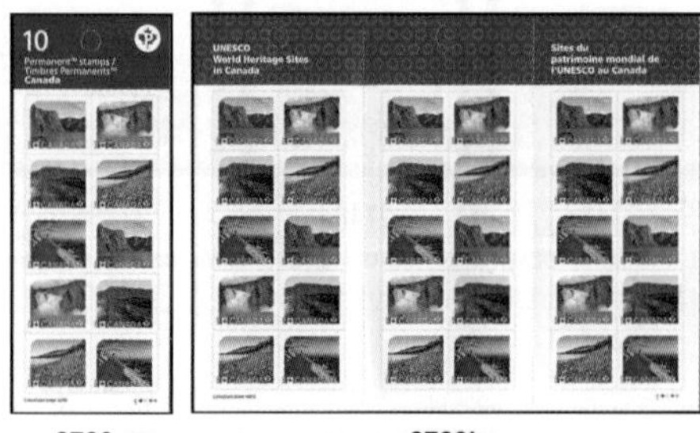

2723a 2723b

## ROYAL ONTARIO MUSEUM

*Perforated singles from water-activated gum souvenir sheet*

**2724a**
Shiva Nataraja Sculpture, Mummified Cat, Bison

**2724b**
Hadrasaur skeleton and Luohan Chinese Sculpture

*Die cut singles from self-adhesive booklet*

**2725** **2726**

Designer: Gerald Querubin of Entro Communications/Gottschalk+Ash.

Lithography (5 colours)
Lowe-Martin
Water-activated gum souvenir sheet of 2

**2014, Apr 14** **GT 3-sided, TRC Paper** **Perf 12.5**

| | | NH–VF | ⊙F | FDC |
|---|---|---|---|---|
| 2724 | **$1.70 souvenir sheet** of 2 | 3.50 | 3.50 | 5.40 |
| a | **multicoloured**, cat | 1.70 | 1.50 | |
| b | **multicoloured**, statue | 1.70 | 1.50 | |
| i | se-tenant pair (2724a–b) | 3.40 | 3.00 | |

Qty: 150,000

Self-adhesive booklet of 10
**GT 3 sides, TRC Paper**
**Serpentine Die cut 13.5x13.3**

| | | NH–VF | ⊙F | FDC |
|---|---|---|---|---|
| 2725 | **multicoloured**, cat | 1.70 | .50 | — |
| 2726 | **multicoloured**, statue | 1.70 | .50 | — |
| i | se-tenant pair, die cut to shape from Quarterly Pack | 5.00 | — | |
| a | booklet pane of 10 (5 each 2725–26) (**BK580**) | 17.00 | | |

Qty: 1,500,000 of each

The general tagging was not applied to the side with the illustration passing through the perfs.

At time of issue, the P stamps were valued at 85¢.
For non-denominated postal cards of same designs, see UX377–UX379.

2724

2726a

## ROSES

*Perforated singles from water-activated gum souvenir sheet*

*Die cut singles from self-adhesive booklet*

2727a 2727b 2730 Konrad Henkel 2731 Maid of Honour

2728 Maid of Honour 2729 Konrad Henkel

2727

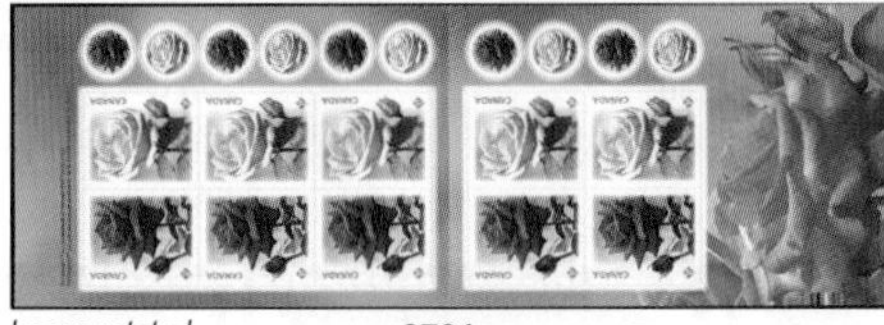

*Image rotated* 2731a

Designer: Isabelle Toussaint, Design graphique.

Lithography (6 colours)
Lowe-Martin
Water-activated gum souvenir sheet of 2

**2014, Apr 23** **GT4, TRC Paper** **Perf 13.1**

| | | NH–VF | ⊙F | FDC |
|---|---|---|---|---|
| **2727** | **$1.70 souvenir sheet** of 2 | 3.50 | 3.50 | — |
| a | **multicoloured**, red rose | 1.70 | 1.50 | |
| b | **multicoloured**, yellow rose | 1.70 | 1.50 | |
| i | se-tenant pair (2727a–b) | 3.40 | 3.00 | |

Qty: 155,000

Self-adhesive roll of 50
**GT4, TRC Paper**
with repeating 'Canada' underprint
**Serpentine Die cut 8.15 to 8.50 Horiz**
**(Rounded tips with 3 'nibs' between stamps)**

One die cut pattern exists on these stamps.

| | | NH–VF | ⊙F | FDC |
|---|---|---|---|---|
| **2728** | **multicoloured**, yellow rose | 1.70 | .60 | — |
| **2729** | **multicoloured**, red rose | 1.70 | .60 | — |
| a | se-tenant pair (vert.), 2728–29 | 5.00 | | |
| i | gutter strip of 4 with inscription | 8.50 | | |
| | starter strip of 4 (wavy die cut) | 10.00 | | |
| | end strip of 4 (wavy die cut) | 10.00 | | |
| ii | se-tenant pair (2728–29), die cut to shape (9.2 horiz) from Quarterly Pack | 6.50 | — | |

Qty: 6,250,000 of each

These stamps were printed se-tenant along the roll. Two different rolls were produced; one starting with the red rose, the other starting with the yellow rose. As such, two types of each of the gutter, starter and end strips of 4 exist.

Self-adhesive booklet of 10
**GT4, TRC Paper Serpentine Die cut 13.5**

| | | NH–VF | ⊙F | FDC |
|---|---|---|---|---|
| **2730** | **multicoloured**, red rose | 1.70 | .50 | |
| **2731** | **multicoloured**, yellow rose | 1.70 | .50 | |
| i | se-tenant pair (2730, 2731), die cut to shape from Quarterly Pack | 5.00 | — | |
| a | booklet pane of 10, 5 each #2730–2731 + 10 stickers (**BK581**) | 17.00 | | |

Qty: 7,000,000 of each

**Nos. 2730–2731 (2) combination FDC** 5.40*

* Stamps on FDCs are not die cut all the way through.

At time of issue, the P stamps were valued at 85¢.
For non-denominated postal cards of same designs, see UX380–UX381.

## KOMAGATA MARU

2732
Sikhs, *Komagata Maru*

Designer: Paprika.

Lithography (5 colours), self-adhesive booklet of 6
Canadian Bank Note

**2014, May 1** **GT4, TRC Paper**
**Serpentine Die cut 13.0x12.8**

| | | NH–VF | ⊙F | FDC |
|---|---|---|---|---|
| **2732** | **$2.50 multicoloured** | 5.00 | 2.50 | 7.00* |
| i | die cut to shape from Quarterly Pack/ Annual Collection | 7.50 | — | |
| a | booklet pane of 6 x $2.50 (2732) (**BK582**) | 30.00 | | |

Qty: 1,500,000
* Two different cachets produced.

Commemorates the centennial of the struggle of the *Komagata Maru* passengers; issued on the first day of Asian Heritage Month.

2732a

## NATIONAL FILM BOARD OF CANADA

*Perforated singles from water-activated gum souvenir sheet*

2733a

2733b

2733c 2733d

2733e

*Die cut singles from self-adhesive booklet*

**2734**
*Flamenco at 5:15* (1983)

**2735**
*The Railrodder* (1965)

**2736**
*Mon oncle Antoine* (1971)

**2737**
*Log Driver's Waltz* (1979)

**2738**
*Neighbours* (1952)

Designer: Paprika.

Lithography (6 colours)
Canadian Bank Note
Water-activated gum souvenir sheet of 5

**2014, May 2** **GT4, TRC Paper** **Perf 13.1x12.5**

| | | NH–VF | ⊙F | FDC |
|---|---|---|---|---|
| 2733 | **$4.25 souvenir sheet** of 5 | 8.50 | 8.50 | 10.50 |
| a | P **multicoloured**, *Flamenco at 5:15* | 1.70 | 1.50 | |
| b | P **multicoloured**, *The Railrodder* | 1.70 | 1.50 | |
| c | P **multicoloured**, *Mon oncle Antoine* | 1.70 | 1.50 | |
| d | P **multicoloured**, *Log Driver's Waltz* | 1.70 | 1.50 | |
| e | P **multicoloured**, *Neighbours* | 1.70 | 1.50 | |

Qty: 130,000

Self-adhesive booklet of 10
**GT4, TRC Paper** **Serpentine Die cut 13.4**

| | | NH–VF | ⊙F | FDC |
|---|---|---|---|---|
| 2734 | P **multicoloured**, *Flamenco at 5:15* | 1.70 | .50 | — |
| 2735 | P **multicoloured**, *The Railrodder* | 1.70 | .50 | — |
| 2736 | P **multicoloured**, *Mon oncle Antoine* | 1.70 | .50 | — |
| 2737 | P **multicoloured**, *Log Driver's Waltz* | 1.70 | .50 | — |
| 2738 | P **multicoloured**, *Neighbours* | 1.70 | .50 | — |
| i | vertical strip of 5 (2734–38), die cut to shape from Quarterly Pack ‡ | 12.50 | — | |
| a | booklet pane of 10, 2 each #2734–2738 (**BK583**) | 17.00 | | |

Qty: 500,000 of each

‡ The die cut to shape strip of 5 from the Quarterly Pack is not rouletted in the gutter between the second and third stamps.

At time of issue, the P stamps were valued at 85¢.
75th anniversary of the founding of the National Film Board of Canada.

**2733**

*Image rotated* **2738a**

**2738i (imperforate gutter)**

## UNESCO WORLD HERITAGE SITES IN CANADA

*Perforated singles from water-activated gum souvenir sheet*

**2739a**

**2739b**

**2739c**

**2739d**

**2739e**

*Die cut singles from self-adhesive booklets*

**2740**
Old Town Lunenburg, NS

**2741**
Head-Smashed-In Buffalo Jump, AB

**2742**
The Landscape of Grand Pré, NS

**2743**
SGang Gwaay, BC

**2744**
The Rideau Canal, ON

Designer: Lime Design.

Lithography (5 colours)
Lowe-Martin
Water-activated gum souvenir sheet of 5

**2014, May 16** **GT4, TRC Paper** **Perf 12.5**

| | | NH–VF | ⊙F | FDC |
|---|---|---|---|---|
| 2739 | **$8.60 souvenir sheet** of 5 | 17.20 | 17.20 | 19.20 |
| a | **$1.20 multicoloured**, Buffalo Jump | 2.40 | 2.00 | |
| b | **$1.20 multicoloured**, Lunenburg | 2.40 | 2.00 | |
| c | **$1.20 multicoloured**, Grand Pré | 2.40 | 2.00 | |
| d | **$2.50 multicoloured**, SGang Gwaay | 5.00 | 4.75 | |
| e | **$2.50 multicoloured**, Rideau Canal | 5.00 | 4.75 | |

Qty: 160,000

Self-adhesive booklets of 6
**GT4, TRC Paper**
**Serpentine Die cut 13.3x13.5**

| | | NH–VF | ⊙F | FDC |
|---|---|---|---|---|
| 2740 | **$1.20 multicoloured**, Lunenburg | 2.40 | 1.50 | — |
| 2741 | **$1.20 multicoloured**, Buffalo Jump | 2.40 | 1.50 | — |
| 2742 | **$1.20 multicoloured**, Grand Pré | 2.40 | 1.50 | — |
| i | horizontal strip of 3 (2740–42), die cut to shape from Quarterly Pack (with imperforate gutters) ‡ | 11.00 | — | |
| a | booklet pane of 6, 2 each #2740–2742 (**BK584**) | 14.50 | | |

Qty: 320,000 of each

| | | | | |
|---|---|---|---|---|
| **2743** | **$2.50 multicoloured**, SGang Gwaay | 5.00 | 3.00 | — |
| **2744** | **$2.50 multicoloured**, Rideau Canal | 5.00 | 3.00 | — |
| a | booklet pane of 6, 3 each #2743–2744 (**BK585**) | 30.00 | | |

Qty: 480,000 of each

‡ The die cut to shape strip of 3 from the Quarterly Pack is not rouletted in the two gutters between the stamps.

For non-denominated postal cards of same designs, see UX382–UX386.

The United Nations Educational, Scientific and Cultural Organization (UNESCO) is a specialized agency of the United Nations.

See also 2844–2849.

2739

2742a

2742i (imperforate gutter)

2744a

## RMS *EMPRESS OF IRELAND*

*Perforated single from water-activated gum pane of 16*

*Die cut singles from self-adhesive booklet*

2745

2747

RMS *Empress of Ireland*

2746i

RMS *Empress of Ireland* and SS *Storstad*

Designers: Isabelle Toussaint; Susan Scott.

Lithography (7 colours), pane of 16 + horizontal and vertical gutters

Lowe-Martin

**2014, May 29** **GT4, TRC Paper** **Perf 12.5**

| | | NH–VF | ⊙F | PB | FDC |
|---|---|---|---|---|---|
| **2745** | **P multicoloured** | 1.70 | .80 | 8.50* | 3.70 |
| i | horizontal pair, gutter between | 3.50 | 3.00 | | |
| ii | vertical pair, gutter between | 3.50 | 3.00 | | |

Qty: 1,200,000

* Only the lower right block has the inscription and paper/colour designations.

Sold only in a shrink-wrapped package containing one pane of 16 stamps.

Lithography (6 colours), water-activated gum souvenir sheet of 1

**GT4, TRC Paper** **Perf 12.9**

| | | NH–VF | ⊙F | FDC |
|---|---|---|---|---|
| **2746** | **$2.50 souvenir sheet** of 1 | 5.00 | 4.50 | 7.00 |
| i | $2.50 single from souvenir sheet | 4.75 | 4.00 | |
| ii | $30.00 uncut press sheet of 12 souvenir sheets | 60.00 | | |

Qty: 200,000; 2746ii: 5,000

Lithography (7 colours), self-adhesive booklet of 10

**GT4, TRC Paper**

**Serpentine Die cut 13.5**

| | | NH–VF | ⊙F | FDC |
|---|---|---|---|---|
| **2747** | **P multicoloured** | 1.70 | .50 | — |
| i | die cut to shape from Quarterly Pack/ Annual Collection | 2.50 | — | |
| a | booklet pane of 10 x P (2747) (**BK586**) | 17.00 | | |

Qty: 2,000,000 of each

Issued on the 100th anniversary of the sinking of the RMS *Empress of Ireland*.

At time of issue, the P stamps were valued at 85¢.

For non-denominated postal cards of same designs, see UX387–UX388.

2746

2747a

## HAUNTED CANADA

*Perforated singles from water-activated gum souvenir sheet*

2748a

2748b

2748c

2748d

2748e

*Die cut singles from self-adhesive booklet*

**2749**
The Ghost Bride of the Fairmont Banff Springs Hotel, AB

**2750**
The Fiery Ships of the Northumberland Strait, NS/PE

**2751**
The St. Louis Light Phantom Train, SK

**2752**
The Fairmont Le Château Frontenac's Ghostly Governor Louis de Buade, Count of Frontenac, QC

**2753**
Niagara-on-the-Lake's haunted Fort George, ON

Designer: Lionel Gadoury, Terry Popik, Context Creative.
Lithography (5 colours) plus holographic foil
Lowe-Martin
Water-activated gum souvenir sheet of 5

**2014, Jun 13** **GT4, TRC Paper** **Perf 12.5**

| | | NH–VF | ⊙F | FDC |
|---|---|---|---|---|
| **2748** | **$4.25 souvenir sheet** of 5 | 8.50 | 8.50 | 10.50 |
| a | **P multicoloured**, Ghost Bride | 1.70 | 1.50 | |
| b | **P multicoloured**, Phantom Train | 1.70 | 1.50 | |
| c | **P multicoloured**, Fort George | 1.70 | 1.50 | |
| d | **P multicoloured**, Count of Frontenac | 1.70 | 1.50 | |
| e | **P multicoloured**, Fiery Ships | 1.70 | 1.50 | |
| i | $34.00 uncut press sheet of 8 souvenir sheets | 68.00 | | |

Qty: 200,000; i: 5,000

Self-adhesive booklet of 10
**GT4, TRC Paper Serpentine Die cut 13.4**

| | | NH–VF | ⊙F | FDC |
|---|---|---|---|---|
| **2749** | **P multicoloured**, Ghost Bride | 1.70 | .60 | — |
| **2750** | **P multicoloured**, Fiery Ships | 1.70 | .60 | — |
| **2751** | **P multicoloured**, Phantom Train | 1.70 | .60 | — |
| **2752** | **P multicoloured**, Count of Frontenac | 1.70 | .60 | — |
| **2753** | **P multicoloured**, Fort George | 1.70 | .60 | — |
| i | vertical strip of 5, die cut to shape from Quarterly Pack (with imperforate gutter) ‡ | 12.50 | — | |
| a | booklet pane of 10, 2 each #2749–53 (**BK587**) | 17.00 | | |

Qty: 800,000 of each

‡ The die cut to shape strip of 5 from the Quarterly Pack is not rouletted in the gutter between the second and third stamps.
At time of issue, the P stamps were valued at 85¢.
For non-denominated postal cards of same designs, see UX389–UX393.
See also 2860–2865, 2935–2940.

2748

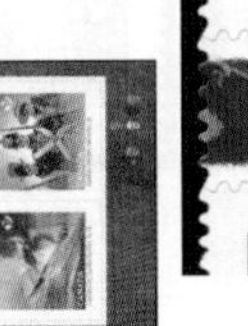

*Image rotated* 2753a

(imperforate gutter)

## OTTAWA REDBLACKS

**2754**
Ottawa Redblacks

**2755**
Ottawa Redblacks; Russ Jackson (1936- )

Designer: Filip Mroz, David Rosenberg | Bensimon Byrne.
Lithography (2 colours), Self-adhesive roll of 50
Lowe-Martin

**2014, Jun 19** **GT4, TRC Paper**
with repeating 'Canada' underprint
**Serpentine Die cut 8.25 to 8.35 Horiz**
**(Rounded tips with 3 'nibs' between stamps)**

| | | NH–VF | ⊙F | FDC |
|---|---|---|---|---|
| **2754** | **P multicoloured**, Ottawa Redblacks | 1.70 | .60 | — |
| i | gutter strip of 4 with inscription | 8.50 | | |
| | starter strip of 4 (wavy die cut) | 11.00 | | |
| | end strip of 4 (wavy die cut) | 11.00 | | |
| ii | die cut to shape (9.2 horiz) from Qtr Pack | 2.50 | — | |

Qty: 1,000,000
For eight other CFL team logo designs see 2558–2566.

Lithography (6 colours), Self-adhesive booklet of 10
Canadian Bank Note
**GT4, TRC Paper Serpentine Die cut 13.4**

| | | NH–VF | ⊙F | FDC |
|---|---|---|---|---|
| **2755** | **P multicoloured**, Russ Jackson | 1.70 | .50 | |
| i | die cut to shape from Quarterly Pack/ Annual Collection | 2.50 | — | |
| a | booklet pane of 10 x P (2755) (**BK588**) | 17.00 | | |

Qty: 1,500,000

**Nos. 2754–2755 (2) combination FDC** **5.40**

Saluting the return of professional football to Ottawa, Ontario; the Ottawa Redblacks of the Canadian Football League.
For eight other CFL team players see 2567–2576.

*Image rotated* **2755a**

## CANADIAN PHOTOGRAPHY — 2

*Perforated singles from water-activated gum souvenir sheets*

**2756a**
*Unidentified Chinese Man*

**2756b**
*St. Joseph's Convent School*

**2756c**
*Sitting Bull and Buffalo Bill*

**2757a**
*Untitled*

**2757b**
*La ville de Québec en hiver*

2757c
*Bogner's Grocery*

2757d
*Railcuts: #1*

*Die cut singles from self-adhesive booklets*

2758

2759

2760

2761
2762

2763
2764

2756

2757

2762a

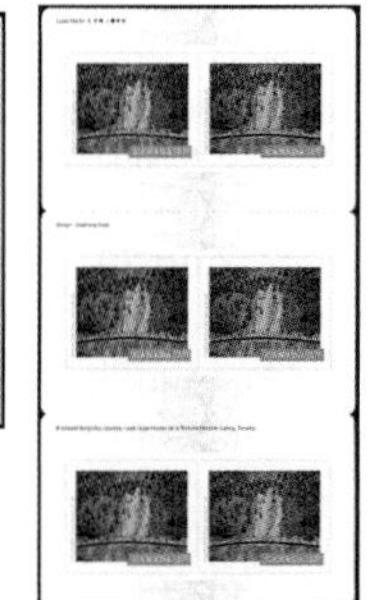
2764a

2763a

Designer: Stéphane Huot

Lithography (3 colours)
Lowe-Martin
Water-activated gum souvenir sheets of 3 and 4

**2014, Jul 7** **GT4, TRC Paper** **Perf 13.4**

| | | NH–VF | ⊙F | FDC |
|---|---|---|---|---|
| **2756** | **$2.90 souvenir sheet** of 3 | 6.00 | 6.00 | 7.80 |
| **a** | **multicoloured**, Unidentified Chinese Man | 1.75 | 1.50 | |
| **b** | **multicoloured**, St. Joseph's Convent | 1.75 | 1.50 | |
| **c** | **$1.20 multicoloured**, Sitting Bull | 2.40 | 2.25 | |

Qty: 130,000

Lithography (4 colours)

| | | NH–VF | ⊙F | FDC |
|---|---|---|---|---|
| **2757** | **$5.05 souvenir sheet** of 4 | 10.10 | 10.10 | 12.10 |
| **a** | **multicoloured**, Untitled | 1.75 | 1.50 | |
| **b** | **multicoloured**, La ville de Québec | 1.75 | 1.50 | |
| **c** | **multicoloured**, Bogner's Grocery | 1.75 | 1.50 | |
| **d** | **$2.50 multicoloured**, Railcuts | 5.00 | 5.00 | |

Qty: 130,000

Lithography (6 colours), self-adhesive booklet of 10
**GT4, TRC Paper**
**Serpentine Die cut 13.7**

| | | NH–VF | ⊙F | FDC |
|---|---|---|---|---|
| **2758** | **multicoloured**, Bogner's Grocery | 1.70 | .60 | — |
| i | die cut to shape from Quarterly Pack | 2.50 | — | |
| **2759** | **multicoloured**, St. Joseph's Convent | 1.70 | .60 | — |
| i | die cut to shape from Quarterly Pack | 2.50 | — | |
| **2760** | **multicoloured**, La ville de Québec | 1.70 | .60 | — |
| i | die cut to shape from Quarterly Pack | 2.50 | — | |
| **2761** | **multicoloured**, Untitled | 1.70 | .60 | — |
| i | die cut to shape from Quarterly Pack | 2.50 | — | |
| **2762** | **multicoloured**, Unidentified Chinese Man | 1.70 | .60 | — |
| i | die cut to shape from Quarterly Pack | 2.50 | — | |
| a | booklet pane of 10, 2 each #2758–2762 (**BK589**) | 17.00 | | |

Qty: 460,000 of each

Lithography (3 colours), self-adhesive booklet of 6

| | | NH–VF | ⊙F | FDC |
|---|---|---|---|---|
| **2763** | **$1.20 multicoloured**, Sitting Bull | 2.40 | 1.25 | — |
| i | die cut to shape from Quarterly Pack | 3.60 | — | |
| a | booklet pane of 6 x $1.20 (2763) (**BK590**) | 14.50 | | |

Qty: 840,000

Lithography (6 colours), self-adhesive booklet of 6

| | | NH–VF | ⊙F | FDC |
|---|---|---|---|---|
| **2764** | **$2.50 multicoloured**, Railcuts | 5.00 | 2.75 | — |
| i | die cut to shape from Quarterly Pack | 7.50 | — | |
| a | booklet pane of 6 x $2.50 (2764) (**BK591**) | 30.00 | | |

Qty: 840,000

At time of issue, the P stamps were valued at 85¢.
For non-denominated postal cards of same designs, see UX394–UX400. See also 2626–2634, 2814–2822, and 2814–2822

## CANADIAN COUNTRY ARTISTS

*Perforated singles from water-activated gum souvenir sheet*

2765a

2765b

2765c

2765d

2765e

QE II — 2010's

*Die cut singles from self-adhesive booklets*

**2766**
Hank Snow (1914-1999)

**2767**
Renée Martel (1947- )

**2768**
Shania Twain (1965- )

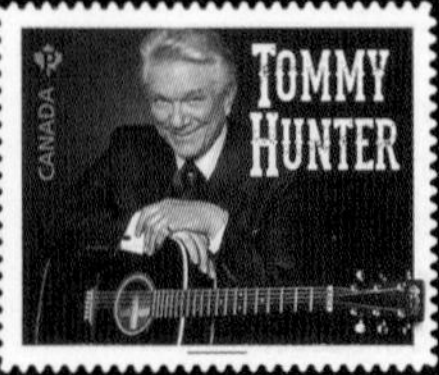

**2769**
Tommy Hunter (1937- )

**2770**
k.d. lang (1961- )

**2765**

**2766a**

**2767a**

**2768a**

**2769a**

**2770a**

Designer: Sabrina McAllister, Xerxes Irani, Roy White, Subplot Design Inc.
Lithography (8 colours)
Lowe-Martin
Water-activated gum souvenir sheet of 5

**2014, Jul 31** **GT4, TRC Paper** **Perf 12.5**

| | | NH–VF | ⊙F | FDC |
|---|---|---|---|---|
| **2765** | **$4.25 souvenir sheet** of 5 | 8.50 | 8.50 | — |
| a | **multicoloured**, Snow | 1.75 | 1.50 | |
| b | **multicoloured**, Martel | 1.75 | 1.50 | |
| c | **multicoloured**, Twain | 1.75 | 1.50 | |
| d | **multicoloured**, Hunter | 1.75 | 1.50 | |
| e | **multicoloured**, lang | 1.75 | 1.50 | |

Qty: 250,000

Lithography (5 colours), self-adhesive booklets of 10
**GT4, TRC Paper**
**Serpentine Die cut 13.3x13.5**

| | | NH–VF | ⊙F | FDC |
|---|---|---|---|---|
| **2766** | **multicoloured**, Snow | 1.70 | .50 | 3.70 |
| i | die cut to shape from Quarterly Pack | 2.50 | — | |
| a | booklet pane of 10 x P (2766) (**BK592**) | 17.00 | | |

Qty: 2,500,000 of each

| | | NH–VF | ⊙F | FDC |
|---|---|---|---|---|
| **2767** | **multicoloured**, Martel | 1.70 | .50 | 3.70 |
| i | die cut to shape from Quarterly Pack | 2.50 | — | |
| a | booklet pane of 10 x P (2767) (**BK593**) | 17.00 | | |

Qty: 2,000,000 of each

| | | NH–VF | ⊙F | FDC |
|---|---|---|---|---|
| **2768** | **multicoloured**, Twain | 1.70 | .50 | 3.70 |
| i | die cut to shape from Quarterly Pack | 2.50 | — | |
| a | booklet pane of 10 x P (2768) (**BK594**) | 17.00 | | |

Qty: 4,000,000 of each

Lithography (4 colours), self-adhesive booklets of 10

| | | NH–VF | ⊙F | FDC |
|---|---|---|---|---|
| **2769** | **multicoloured**, Hunter | 1.70 | .50 | 3.70 |
| i | die cut to shape from Quarterly Pack | 2.50 | — | |
| a | booklet pane of 10 x P (2769) (**BK595**) | 17.00 | | |

Qty: 2,500,000 of each

| | | NH–VF | ⊙F | FDC |
|---|---|---|---|---|
| **2770** | **multicoloured**, lang | 1.70 | .50 | 3.70 |
| i | die cut to shape from Quarterly Pack | 2.50 | — | |
| a | booklet pane of 10 x P (2770) (**BK596**) | 17.00 | | |

Qty: 3,000,000 of each

At time of issue, the P stamps were valued at 85¢.
For non-denominated postal cards of same designs, see UX401–UX405.

## CANADIAN MUSEUM FOR HUMAN RIGHTS

**2771**
Museum, Winnipeg, MB

Designer: Adrian Shum, Circle.
Lithography (6 colours plus spot varnish), Self-adhesive booklet of 10
Lowe-Martin

**2014, Aug 20** **GT4, TRC Paper** **Serpentine Die cut 13.3**

| | | NH–VF | ⊙F | FDC |
|---|---|---|---|---|
| **2771** | **multicoloured** | 1.70 | .50 | 3.70 |
| i | die cut to shape from Quarterly Pack/ Annual Collection | 2.50 | — | |
| a | booklet pane of 10 x P (2771) (**BK597**) | 17.00 | | |

Qty: 2,000,000

Opening of Canadian Museum for Human Rights in Winnipeg, MB.

At time of issue, the P stamp was valued at 85¢.

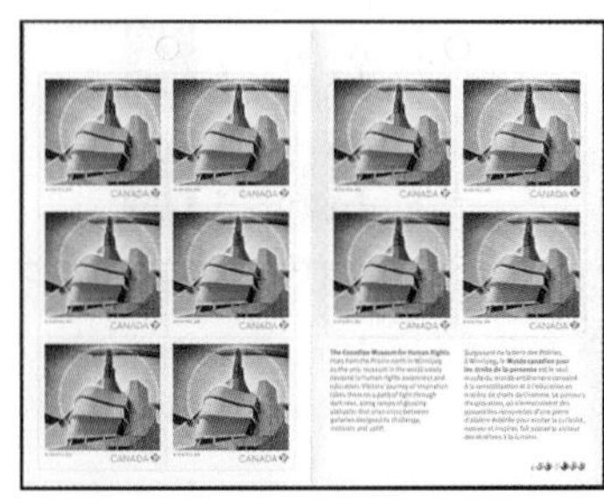

**2771a**

## GREAT CANADIAN COMEDIANS

*Perforated singles from water-activated gum souvenir sheet*

2772a

2772b

2772c

2772d

2772e

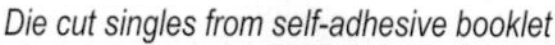

*Die cut singles from self-adhesive booklet*

2773
Mike Myers (1963- )

2774
Martin Short (1950- )

2775
Catherine O'Hara (1954- )

2776
Olivier Guimond (1914-1971)

2777
Jim Carrey (1962- )

Designer: Kosta Tsetsekas, Mike Savage, John Belisle (Signals).

Lithography (8 colours)
Lowe-Martin
Water-activated gum souvenir sheet of 5

**2014, Aug 29** **GT2, TRC Paper** **Perf 12.5x13.1**

| | | NH–VF | ⊙F | FDC |
|---|---|---|---|---|
| **2772** | **$4.25 souvenir sheet** of 5 | 8.50 | 8.50 | — |
| a | **multicoloured**, Myers | 1.75 | 1.50 | |
| b | **multicoloured**, Short | 1.75 | 1.50 | |
| c | **multicoloured**, O'Hara | 1.75 | 1.50 | |
| d | **multicoloured**, Guimond | 1.75 | 1.50 | |
| e | **multicoloured**, Carrey | 1.75 | 1.50 | |
| i | $19.95 uncut press sheet of 4 souvenir sheets | 40.00 | | |

Qty: 250,000; 2772i: 7,500

Lithography (5 colours), self-adhesive booklets of 10

**GT2, TRC Paper Serpentine Die cut 13.4**

| | | NH–VF | ⊙F | FDC |
|---|---|---|---|---|
| **2773** | **multicoloured**, Myers | 1.70 | .50 | 3.70 |
| i | die cut to shape from Quarterly Pack | 2.50 | — | |
| a | booklet pane of 10 x P (6 x 2773, 1 each 2774–77) (**BK598**) | 17.00 | | |

Qty: 600,000 of each

| | | NH–VF | ⊙F | FDC |
|---|---|---|---|---|
| **2774** | **multicoloured**, Short | 1.70 | .50 | 3.70 |
| i | die cut to shape from Quarterly Pack | 2.50 | — | |
| a | booklet pane of 10 x P (6 x 2774, 1 each 2773, 2775–77) (**BK599**) | 17.00 | | |

Qty: 600,000 of each

| | | NH–VF | ⊙F | FDC |
|---|---|---|---|---|
| **2775** | **multicoloured**, O'Hara | 1.70 | .50 | 20.00† |
| | revised (corrected) OFDC, *Sep* | | | 3.70 |
| i | die cut to shape from Quarterly Pack | 2.50 | — | |
| a | booklet pane of 10 x P (6 x 2775, 1 each 2773–74, 2776–77) (**BK600**) | 17.00 | | |

Qty: 600,000 of each

| | | NH–VF | ⊙F | FDC |
|---|---|---|---|---|
| **2776** | **multicoloured**, Guimond | 1.70 | .50 | 3.70 |
| i | die cut to shape from Quarterly Pack | 2.50 | — | |
| a | booklet pane of 10 x P (6 x 2776, 1 each 2773–75, 2777) (**BK601**) | 17.00 | | |

Qty: 600,000 of each

| | | NH–VF | ⊙F | FDC |
|---|---|---|---|---|
| **2777** | **multicoloured**, Carrey | 1.70 | .50 | 3.70 |
| i | die cut to shape from Quarterly Pack | 2.50 | — | |
| a | booklet pane of 10 x P (6 x 2777, 1 each 2773–76) (**BK602**) | 17.00 | | |

Qty: 600,000 of each

At time of issue, the P stamps were valued at 85¢.

† The Catherine O'Hara OFDC was recalled in early September due to text on the back crediting her for an award she did not receive. A corrected, replacement OFDC, was released in mid-September.

2772

2773a

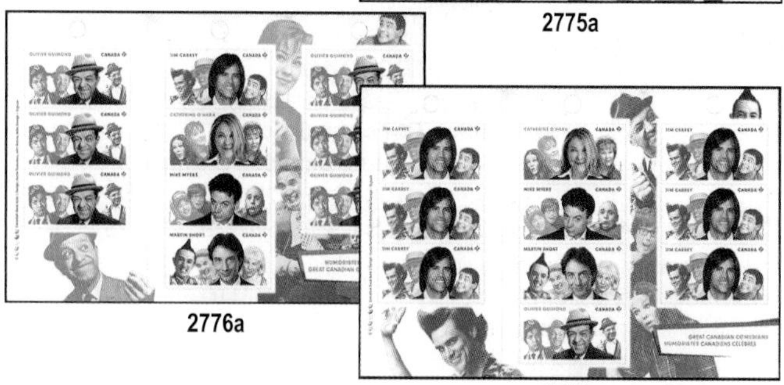
2774a  2775a 2776a 2777a

QE II — 2010's

Timeline:
2014, Sep 29 P +10¢ Canada Post Community Foundation, semi-postal (B21)

## NHL® ZAMBONI ICE RESURFACING MACHINES

*Perforated singles from water-activated gum souvenir sheet*

2778a
Winnipeg Jets

2778b
Ottawa Senators

2778c
Toronto Maple Leafs

2778d
Montreal Canadiens

2778e
Vancouver Canucks

2778f
Calgary Flames

2778g
Edmonton Oilers

*Self-adhesive coils*

2779
Winnipeg Jets

2780
Ottawa Senators

2781
Toronto Maple Leafs

2782
Montreal Canadiens

2783
Vancouver Canucks

2784
Calgary Flames

2785
Edmonton Oilers

Designer: Avi Dunkelman, Joseph Gault (MIX Design Group).
Lithography (6 colours)
Lowe-Martin
Water-activated gum souvenir sheet of 7

**2014, Oct 3** **GT4, TRC Paper** **Perf 13.3x13.1**

| | | NH–VF | ⊙F | FDC |
|---|---|---|---|---|
| 2778 | **$5.95 souvenir sheet** of 7 | 12.00 | 12.00 | 13.90 |
| a | P **multicoloured**, Winnipeg Jets | 1.70 | 1.50 | |
| b | P **multicoloured**, Ottawa Senators | 1.70 | 1.50 | |
| c | P **multicoloured**, Toronto Maple Leafs | 1.70 | 1.50 | |
| d | P **multicoloured**, Montreal Canadiens | 1.70 | 1.50 | |
| e | P **multicoloured**, Vancouver Canucks | 1.70 | 1.50 | |
| f | P **multicoloured**, Calgary Flames | 1.70 | 1.50 | |
| g | P **multicoloured**, Edmonton Oilers | 1.70 | 1.50 | |

Qty: 200,000

Self-adhesive rolls of 50
Lithography (6 colours)
**GT4, TRC Paper**
with repeating 'Canada' underprint
**Serpentine Die cut 8.3 Horiz**
**(Rounded tips with 3 'nibs' between stamps)**

| | | NH–VF | ⊙F | FDC |
|---|---|---|---|---|
| 2779 | P **multicoloured**, Winnipeg Jets | 1.70 | .75 | — |
| i | gutter strip of 4 with inscription | 8.50 | | |
| | starter strip of 4 (wavy die cut) | 11.00 | | |
| | end strip of 4 (wavy die cut) | 11.00 | | |
| ii | die cut to shape (9.2 horiz) from Qtr Pack ‡ | 2.50 | — | |

Qty: 1,000,000

| | | NH–VF | ⊙F | FDC |
|---|---|---|---|---|
| 2780 | P **multicoloured**, Ottawa Senators | 1.70 | .75 | — |
| i | gutter strip of 4 with inscription | 8.50 | | |
| | starter strip of 4 (wavy die cut) | 11.00 | | |
| | end strip of 4 (wavy die cut) | 11.00 | | |
| ii | die cut to shape (9.2 horiz) from Qtr Pack ‡ | 2.50 | — | |

Qty: 1,000,000

| | | NH–VF | ⊙F | FDC |
|---|---|---|---|---|
| 2781 | P **multicoloured**, Toronto Maple Leafs | 1.70 | .75 | — |
| i | gutter strip of 4 with inscription | 8.50 | | |
| | starter strip of 4 (wavy die cut) | 11.00 | | |
| | end strip of 4 (wavy die cut) | 11.00 | | |
| ii | die cut to shape (9.2 horiz) from Qtr Pack ‡ | 2.50 | — | |

Qty: 2,000,000

| | | NH–VF | ⊙F | FDC |
|---|---|---|---|---|
| 2782 | P **multicoloured**, Montreal Canadiens | 1.70 | .75 | — |
| i | gutter strip of 4 with inscription | 8.50 | | |
| | starter strip of 4 (wavy die cut) | 11.00 | | |
| | end strip of 4 (wavy die cut) | 11.00 | | |
| ii | die cut to shape (9.2 horiz) from Qtr Pack ‡ | 2.50 | — | |

Qty: 2,000,000

| | | NH–VF | ⊙F | FDC |
|---|---|---|---|---|
| 2783 | P **multicoloured**, Vancouver Canucks | 1.70 | .75 | — |
| i | gutter strip of 4 with inscription | 8.50 | | |
| | starter strip of 4 (wavy die cut) | 11.00 | | |
| | end strip of 4 (wavy die cut) | 11.00 | | |
| ii | die cut to shape (9.2 horiz) from Qtr Pack ‡ | 2.50 | — | |

Qty: 1,500,000

| | | NH–VF | ⊙F | FDC |
|---|---|---|---|---|
| 2784 | P **multicoloured**, Calgary Flames | 1.70 | .75 | — |
| i | gutter strip of 4 with inscription | 8.50 | | |
| | starter strip of 4 (wavy die cut) | 11.00 | | |
| | end strip of 4 (wavy die cut) | 11.00 | | |
| ii | die cut to shape (9.2 horiz) from Qtr Pack ‡ | 2.50 | — | |

Qty: 1,000,000

| | | NH–VF | ⊙F | FDC |
|---|---|---|---|---|
| 2785 | P **multicoloured**, Edmonton Oilers | 1.70 | .75 | — |
| i | gutter strip of 4 with inscription | 8.50 | | |
| | starter strip of 4 (wavy die cut) | 11.00 | | |
| | end strip of 4 (wavy die cut) | 11.00 | | |
| ii | die cut to shape (9.2 horiz) from Qtr Pack ‡ | 2.50 | — | |

Qty: 1,000,000

‡ Single stamps supplied in the Quarterly Pack have rounded tips (die cut 9.2 horiz), starting with a peak at upper left; stamps from the full rolls are die cut 8.3.

At time of issue, the P stamps were valued at 85¢.
For non-denominated postal cards of same designs, see UX406–UX412.

2778

## ORIGINAL SIX™

*Perforated singles from water-activated gum souvenir sheet*

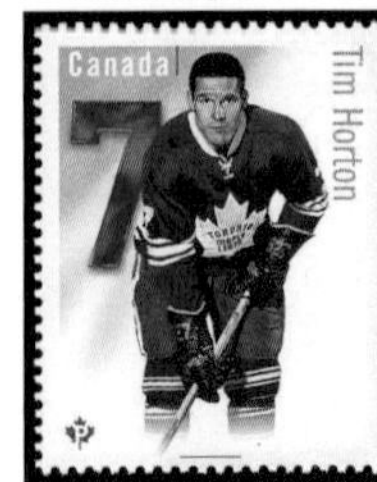

2786a
Tim Horton
(1930-1974)

2786b
Doug Harvey
(1924-1989)

2786c
Bobby Orr
(1948- )

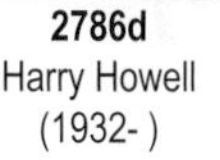

| 2786d | 2786e | 2786f |
|---|---|---|
| Harry Howell (1932- ) | Pierre Pilote (1931-2017) | Red Kelly (1927- ) |

*Die cut singles from self-adhesive booklet*

**2787a** Tim Horton — **2787b** Doug Harvey — **2787c** Bobby Orr

**2787d** Harry Howell — **2787e** Pierre Pilote — **2787f** Red Kelly

Designer: Avi Dunkelman, Joseph Gault (MIX Design Group).

Lithography (7 colours, one foil stamping plus embossing*)
Lowe-Martin
Water-activated gum pane of 6

**2014, Oct 3** **GT4, TRC Paper** **Perf 12.5x13.2**

| | | NH–VF | ⊙F | FDC |
|---|---|---|---|---|
| **2786** | **$5.10 souvenir sheet** of 6 | 10.50 | 10.50 | |
| a | P **multicoloured**, Tim Horton | 1.70 | 1.50 | |
| b | P **multicoloured**, Doug Harvey | 1.70 | 1.50 | |
| c | P **multicoloured**, Bobby Orr | 1.70 | 1.50 | |
| d | P **multicoloured**, Harry Howell | 1.70 | 1.50 | |
| e | P **multicoloured**, Pierre Pilote | 1.70 | 1.50 | |
| f | P **multicoloured**, Red Kelly | 1.70 | 1.50 | |

Qty: 180,000

* The pane had embossing in the selvedge; the stamps themselves do not have any embossing.

Lithography (7 colours)
Self-adhesive booklet of 6
**Serpentine Die cut 13.5**

| | | NH–VF | ⊙F | FDC |
|---|---|---|---|---|
| **2787** | **$5.10 booklet pane** of 6 (**BK604**) | 10.20 | – | |
| a | P **multicoloured**, Tim Horton | 1.70 | 0.50 | 3.70 |
| ai | die cut to shape from Quarterly Pack | 2.50 | — | |
| b | P **multicoloured**, Doug Harvey | 1.70 | 0.50 | 3.70 |
| bi | die cut to shape from Quarterly Pack | 2.50 | — | |
| c | P **multicoloured**, Bobby Orr | 1.70 | 0.50 | 3.70 |
| ci | die cut to shape from Quarterly Pack | 2.50 | — | |
| d | P **multicoloured**, Harry Howell | 1.70 | 0.50 | 3.70 |
| di | die cut to shape from Quarterly Pack | 2.50 | — | |
| e | P **multicoloured**, Pierre Pilote | 1.70 | 0.50 | 3.70 |
| ei | die cut to shape from Quarterly Pack | 2.50 | — | |
| f | P **multicoloured**, Red Kelly | 1.70 | 0.50 | 3.70 |
| fi | die cut to shape from Quarterly Pack | 2.50 | — | |

Qty: 750,000 of each stamp

At time of issue, the P stamps were valued at 85¢.

**2788**
Tim Horton

**2789**
Doug Harvey

**2790**
Bobby Orr

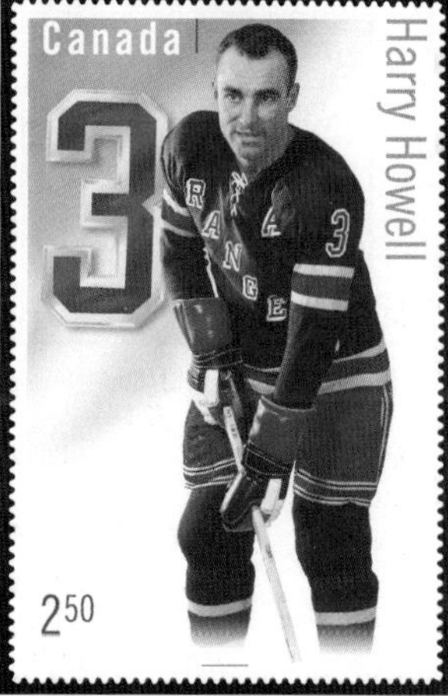


**2791**
Harry Howell

**2792**
Pierre Pilote

**2793**
Red Kelly

Designer: Avi Dunkelman, Joseph Gault (MIX Design Group).

Lithography (7 colours)
Lowe-Martin
Self-adhesive souvenir sheets of 1

**2014, Oct 3** **GT4, TRC Paper**
**Serpentine Die cut 13.5x13.3**

| | | NH–VF | ⊙F | FDC |
|---|---|---|---|---|
| **2788** | **$2.50 multicoloured**, Tim Horton | 5.00 | 4.00 | |
| **2789** | **$2.50 multicoloured**, Doug Harvey | 5.00 | 4.00 | |
| **2790** | **$2.50 multicoloured**, Bobby Orr | 5.00 | 4.00 | |
| i | autographed card | *350.00* | | |
| **2791** | **$2.50 multicoloured**, Harry Howell | 5.00 | 4.00 | |
| i | autographed card | *185.00* | | |
| **2792** | **$2.50 multicoloured**, Pierre Pilote | 5.00 | 4.00 | |
| i | autographed card | *185.00* | | |
| **2793** | **$2.50 multicoloured**, Red Kelly | 5.00 | 4.00 | |
| i | autographed card | *185.00* | | |

Qty: 125,000 of each; 2790i: 1,000; 2791i/2792i/2793i: 500 of each

The autographed souvenir sheets have a holographic Canada Post circular sticker of authenticity placed near the lower left of the stamp.
These souvenir sheets were only sold in packages of all six. They were not included in the Quarterly Pack or Annual collection.

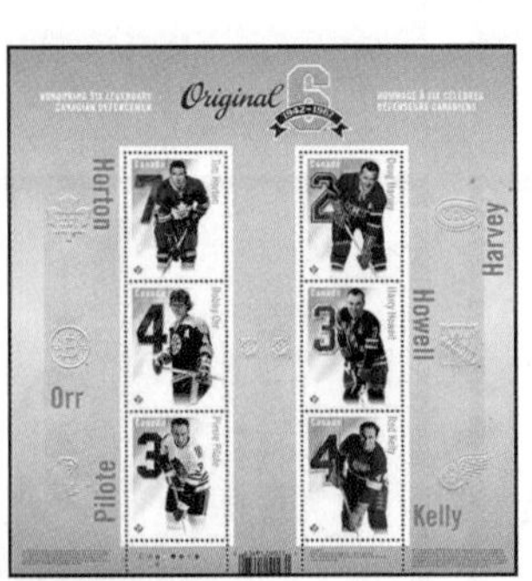
2786

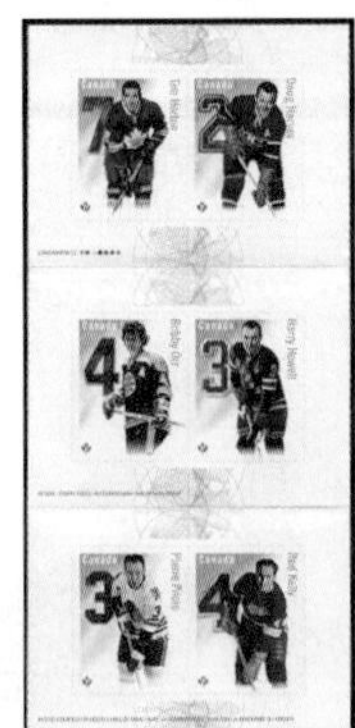
2787

*Full souvenir sheets*

*Autographed souvenir sheets*

2790i

2791i

2792i

2793i

## *WAIT FOR ME, DADDY*

*Perforated single from water-activated gum pane of 5*

2794

2795

*Die cut single from self-adhesive booklet*

Warren "Whitey" Bernard (1935– ) running to his father

Designer: Susan Mavor (Metaform). Original photograph by Claude P. Dettloff, staff photographer, The Vancouver Daily Province.

Lithography (6 colours), water-activated gum pane of 5
Lowe-Martin

**2014, Oct 4** **GT4, TRC Paper** **Perf 13.3**

| | | NH–VF | ⊙F | FDC |
|---|---|---|---|---|
| **2794** | **multicoloured** | 1.70 | 1.00 | |
| | full pane of 5 | 8.50 | | |
| i | white spot below 'R' of 'FOR' (pos. 3) | 5.00 | 2.50 | |

Qty: 375,000

Sold only in a shrink-wrapped package containing one pane of 5 stamps.

Lithography (6 colours), self-adhesive booklet of 10
Lowe-Martin
**GT4, TRC Paper**
**Serpentine Die cut 13.4**

| | | NH–VF | ⊙F | FDC |
|---|---|---|---|---|
| **2795** | **multicoloured** | 1.70 | .50 | 3.70 |
| i | die cut to shape from Quarterly Pack/ Annual Collection | 2.50 | — | |
| a | booklet pane of 10 x P (2795) + 6 stickers (**BK605**) | 17.00 | | |

Qty: 4,000,000

At time of issue, the P stamp was valued at 85¢.
For non-denominated postal cards of same designs, see UX413– UX414.

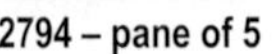
2794 – pane of 5

2795a

2794i

## SANTA

*Perforated singles from water-activated gum souvenir sheet*

2796a

2796b

2796c

*Die cut singles from self-adhesive booklets*

2798
Letter writing

2799
Santa with his magical bag

2800
Elegant coat and decorative trimmings

## CHRISTMAS: MADONNA AND CHILD

2797
Painting by Abraham Janssens van Nuyssen

Designer: Hélène L'Heureux.

Lithography (8 colours)
Lowe-Martin
Water-activated gum souvenir sheet of 3

**2014, Oct 23** **GT4, TRC Paper** **Perf 13.6x13.4**

| | | NH–VF | ⊙F | FDC |
|---|---|---|---|---|
| **2796** | **$4.55 souvenir sheet** of 3 | 9.25 | 9.75 | 11.10 |
| a | **P multicoloured** | 1.70 | 1.50 | |
| b | **$1.20 multicoloured** | 2.40 | 2.10 | |
| c | **$2.50 multicoloured** | 5.00 | 4.75 | |

Qty: 140,000

Designer: Louise Méthé.

Lithography (7 colours)
Self-adhesive booklet of 12
**GT4, TRC Paper Serpentine Die cut 13.5**

| | | NH–VF | ⊙F | FDC |
|---|---|---|---|---|
| **2797** | **P multicoloured** | 1.70 | .25 | 3.70 |
| i | die cut to shape from Quarterly Pack/ Annual Collection | 2.50 | — | |
| a | booklet pane of 12 x P (2797) (**BK606**) | 20.40 | — | |

Qty: 4,200,000

Designer: Hélène L'Heureux.

Lithography (6 colours), self-adhesive booklet of 12 (P) or 6
Lowe-Martin
**GT4, TRC Paper**
**Serpentine Die cut 13.3 x 13.0**

| | | NH–VF | ⊙F | FDC |
|---|---|---|---|---|
| **2798** | **P multicoloured** | 1.70 | .25 | — |
| i | die cut to shape from Quarterly Pack | 2.50 | — | |
| a | booklet pane of 12 x P (2798) (**BK607**) | 20.40 | — | |

Qty: 24,000,000

| | | NH–VF | ⊙F | FDC |
|---|---|---|---|---|
| **2799** | **$1.20 multicoloured** | 2.40 | 1.00 | — |
| i | die cut to shape from Quarterly Pack | 3.60 | — | |
| a | booklet pane of 6 x $1.20 (2799) (**BK608**) | 14.40 | — | |

Qty: 3,420,000

| | | NH–VF | ⊙F | FDC |
|---|---|---|---|---|
| **2800** | **$2.50 multicoloured** | 5.00 | 1.75 | — |
| i | die cut to shape from Quarterly Pack | 7.50 | — | |
| a | booklet pane of 6 x $2.50 (2800) (**BK609**) | 30.00 | — | |

Qty: 3,540,000

At time of issue, the P stamps were valued at 85¢.

2796

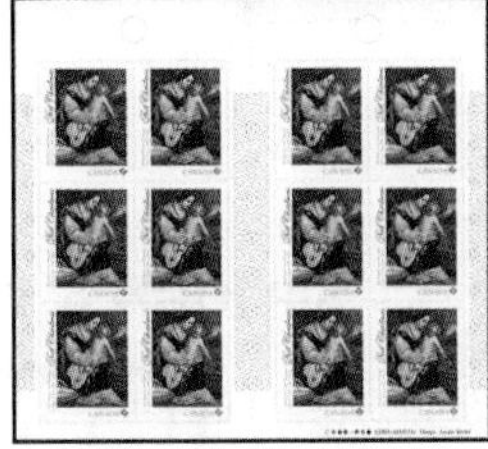
2797a

2798a

2799a

2800a

## 2015

### LUNAR NEW YEAR (Series 2) — 7
### Year of the Ram

2801
Three Rams

*Perforated single from souvenir sheet*

2802i
Ram

*Die cut single from self-adhesive booklet*

2803
Ram

Designer: Hélène L'Heureux.

Lithography (7 colours) plus embossing plus foil stamping, pane of 25
Lowe-Martin

**2015, Jan 8** **GT4, TRC Paper** **Perf 12.5**

| | | NH–VF | ⊙F | PB | FDC |
|---|---|---|---|---|---|
| **2801** | **P multicoloured** | 1.70 | .65 | 8.50 | 3.70 |

Qty: 3,125,000

Lithography (7 colours) plus embossing

| | | NH–VF | ⊙F | PB | FDC |
|---|---|---|---|---|---|
| **2802** | **$2.50 souvenir sheet** of 1 | 5.00 | 5.00 | — | 7.00 |
| i | $2.50 single stamp from souvenir sheet | 4.00 | 3.75 | — | |
| ii | $30.00 uncut press sheet of 12 souvenir sheets | 60.00 | | | |
| a | $4.35 'transitional' souvenir sheet of 2, #2700, 2802 | 8.75 | 8.75 | — | |
| b | single from 2885a, perf 13.1, *Feb 1/16* | 5.00 | 4.75 | — | |

Qty: 2802: 300,000; 2802ii: 11,000; 2802a: 150,000; 2802b: 115,000

Lithography (5 colours) plus 1 foil stamping, self-adhesive booklet of 6
**Serpentine Die cut 13.5**

| | | NH–VF | ⊙F | FDC |
|---|---|---|---|---|
| **2803** | **$2.50 multicoloured** | 5.00 | 2.75 | — |
| i | die cut to shape from Quarterly Pack | 7.50 | — | |
| a | booklet pane of 6 x $2.50 (2803) (**BK610**) | 30.00 | — | |

Qty: 1,080,000

For non-denominated postal cards of same designs, see UX415–UX416.
At time of issue, the P stamp was valued at 85¢.

2802

2802a

2803a

## SIR JOHN A. MACDONALD

2804
Sir John A. Macdonald

Designer: Paprika.

Lithography (5 colours), self-adhesive booklet of 10
Lowe-Martin

**2015, Jan 11** **GT4, TRC Paper** **Serpentine Die cut 13.4**

| | | NH–VF | ⊙F | FDC |
|---|---|---|---|---|
| **2804** | **multicoloured** | 1.70 | .50 | 3.70 |
| i | die cut to shape from Quarterly Pack/ Annual Collection | 2.50 | — | |
| a | booklet pane of 10 x P (2804) (**BK611**) | 17.00 | | |

Qty: 1,500,000

200th anniversary of the birth of Canada's first prime minister.

At time of issue, the P stamp was valued at 85¢.

*Image rotated* 2804a

## BLACK HISTORY

2805i

2806

Nelson Mandela (1918–2013)

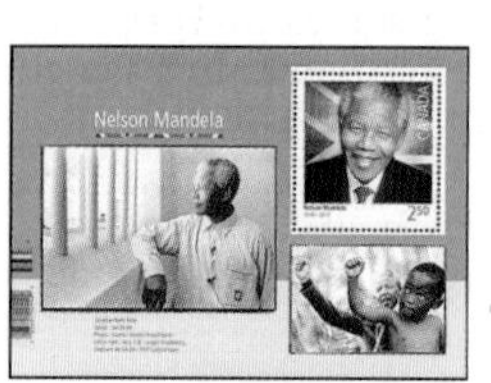
2805

2806a

Designers: Ian Drolet.

Lithography (6 colours), water-activated gum souvenir sheet of 1
Canadian Bank Note

**2015, Jan 30** **GT4, TRC Paper** **Perf 12.5x13.2**

| | | NH–VF | ⊙F | FDC |
|---|---|---|---|---|
| **2805** | **$2.50 souvenir sheet** of 1 | 5.00 | 4.50 | — |
| i | $2.50 single from souvenir sheet | 4.75 | 4.00 | |

Qty: 150,000

Lithography (6 colours), self-adhesive booklet of 10
**GT4, TRC Paper**
**Serpentine Die cut 13.4**

| | | NH–VF | ⊙F | FDC |
|---|---|---|---|---|
| **2806** | **multicoloured** | 1.70 | .50 | 3.70 |
| i | die cut to shape from Quarterly Pack | 2.50 | — | |
| a | booklet pane of 10 (2806) (**BK612**) | 17.00 | | |

Qty: 5,000,000

Issued for Black History Month.
At time of issue, the P stamp was valued at 85¢.

## CANADA'S FLAG

2807
Flag of Canada

2808i
Flag of Canada

Designer: Kosta Tsetsekas, Defne Corbacioglu (Signals).

Lithography (5 colours), self-adhesive booklet of 10
Lowe-Martin

**2015, Feb 15** **GT4, TRC Paper**
**Serpentine Die cut 13.3x13.5**

| | | NH–VF | ⊙F | FDC |
|---|---|---|---|---|
| **2807** | **multicoloured** | 1.70 | .50 | 3.70 |
| i | die cut to shape from Quarterly Pack/ Annual Collection | 2.50 | — | |
| a | booklet pane of 10 x P (2807) (**BK613**) | 17.00 | | |

Qty: 5,000,000

For non-denominated postal card of same design, see UX417.
At time of issue, the P stamp was valued at 85¢.

Lithography (6 colours), acqueous plus invisible red tagging on self-adhesive fabric
Canadian Bank Note
**Not tagged, Wausau Coated Products**
**Serpentine Die cut 9.2**

| | | | | |
|---|---|---|---|---|
| **2808** | **$5.00 souvenir sheet** of 1 | 10.00 | 10.00 | |
| i | $5.00 single stamp from souvenir sheet | 9.50 | 9.00 | |
| ii | $5.00 'rotated' single stamp from uncut press sheet ‡ | *50.00* | *50.00* | 12.00 |
| iii | $115.00 uncut press sheet of 20 souvenir (2808) sheets and 3 stamps (2808ii) ‡ | 275.00 | | |

Qty: 2808: 300,000; 2808iii: 1,000

‡ The printing on fabric results in a distinct pattern/grain. The 3 stamps (2808ii) at the

## SANTA

*Perforated singles from water-activated gum souvenir sheet*

2796a

2796b

2796c

*Die cut singles from self-adhesive booklets*

2798
Letter writing

2799
Santa with his magical bag

2800
Elegant coat and decorative trimmings

## CHRISTMAS: MADONNA AND CHILD

2797
Painting by Abraham Janssens van Nuyssen

Designer: Hélène L'Heureux.

Lithography (8 colours)
Lowe-Martin
Water-activated gum souvenir sheet of 3

**2014, Oct 23** **GT4, TRC Paper** **Perf 13.6x13.4**

| | | NH–VF | ⊙F | FDC |
|---|---|---|---|---|
| **2796** | **$4.55 souvenir sheet** of 3 | 9.25 | 9.75 | 11.10 |
| a | **P multicoloured** | 1.70 | 1.50 | |
| b | **$1.20 multicoloured** | 2.40 | 2.10 | |
| c | **$2.50 multicoloured** | 5.00 | 4.75 | |

Qty: 140,000

Designer: Louise Méthé.

Lithography (7 colours)
Self-adhesive booklet of 12
**GT4, TRC Paper Serpentine Die cut 13.5**

| | | NH–VF | ⊙F | FDC |
|---|---|---|---|---|
| **2797** | **P multicoloured** | 1.70 | .25 | 3.70 |
| i | die cut to shape from Quarterly Pack/ Annual Collection | 2.50 | — | |
| a | booklet pane of 12 x P (2797) (**BK606**) | 20.40 | — | |

Qty: 4,200,000

Designer: Hélène L'Heureux.

Lithography (6 colours), self-adhesive booklet of 12 (P) or 6
Lowe-Martin
**GT4, TRC Paper**
**Serpentine Die cut 13.3 x 13.0**

| | | NH–VF | ⊙F | FDC |
|---|---|---|---|---|
| **2798** | **P multicoloured** | 1.70 | .25 | — |
| i | die cut to shape from Quarterly Pack | 2.50 | — | |
| a | booklet pane of 12 x P (2798) (**BK607**) | 20.40 | — | |

Qty: 24,000,000

| | | NH–VF | ⊙F | FDC |
|---|---|---|---|---|
| **2799** | **$1.20 multicoloured** | 2.40 | 1.00 | — |
| i | die cut to shape from Quarterly Pack | 3.60 | — | |
| a | booklet pane of 6 x $1.20 (2799) (**BK608**) | 14.40 | — | |

Qty: 3,420,000

| | | NH–VF | ⊙F | FDC |
|---|---|---|---|---|
| **2800** | **$2.50 multicoloured** | 5.00 | 1.75 | — |
| i | die cut to shape from Quarterly Pack | 7.50 | — | |
| a | booklet pane of 6 x $2.50 (2800) (**BK609**) | 30.00 | — | |

Qty: 3,540,000

At time of issue, the P stamps were valued at 85¢.

2796

2797a

2798a

2799a

2800a

## 2015

### LUNAR NEW YEAR (Series 2) — 7
### Year of the Ram

2801
Three Rams

*Perforated single from souvenir sheet*
2802i
Ram

*Die cut single from self-adhesive booklet*
2803
Ram

Designer: Hélène L'Heureux.

Lithography (7 colours) plus embossing plus foil stamping, pane of 25
Lowe-Martin

**2015, Jan 8** **GT4, TRC Paper** **Perf 12.5**

| | | NH–VF | ⊙F | PB | FDC |
|---|---|---|---|---|---|
| **2801** | **P multicoloured** | 1.70 | .65 | 8.50 | 3.70 |

Qty: 3,125,000

Lithography (7 colours) plus embossing

| | | NH–VF | ⊙F | PB | FDC |
|---|---|---|---|---|---|
| **2802** | **$2.50 souvenir sheet** of 1 | 5.00 | 5.00 | — | 7.00 |
| i | $2.50 single stamp from souvenir sheet | 4.00 | 3.75 | — | |
| ii | $30.00 uncut press sheet of 12 souvenir sheets | 60.00 | | | |
| a | $4.35 'transitional' souvenir sheet of 2, #2700, 2802 | 8.75 | 8.75 | — | |
| b | single from 2885a, perf 13.1, *Feb 1/16* | 5.00 | 4.75 | — | |

Qty: 2802: 300,000; 2802ii: 11,000; 2802a: 150,000; 2802b: 115,000

Lithography (5 colours) plus 1 foil stamping, self-adhesive booklet of 6
**Serpentine Die cut 13.5**

| | | NH–VF | ⊙F | FDC |
|---|---|---|---|---|
| **2803** | **$2.50 multicoloured** | 5.00 | 2.75 | — |
| i | die cut to shape from Quarterly Pack | 7.50 | — | |
| a | booklet pane of 6 x $2.50 (2803) (**BK610**) | 30.00 | — | |

Qty: 1,080,000

For non-denominated postal cards of same designs, see UX415–UX416.
At time of issue, the P stamp was valued at 85¢.

2802

2802a

2803a

## SIR JOHN A. MACDONALD

2804
Sir John A. Macdonald

Designer: Paprika.

Lithography (5 colours), self-adhesive booklet of 10
Lowe-Martin

**2015, Jan 11** **GT4, TRC Paper** **Serpentine Die cut 13.4**

| | | NH–VF | ⊙F | FDC |
|---|---|---|---|---|
| **2804** | **multicoloured** | 1.70 | .50 | 3.70 |
| i | die cut to shape from Quarterly Pack/ Annual Collection | 2.50 | — | |
| a | booklet pane of 10 x P (2804) (**BK611**) | 17.00 | | |

Qty: 1,500,000

200th anniversary of the birth of Canada's first prime minister.

At time of issue, the P stamp was valued at 85¢.

*Image rotated* 2804a

## BLACK HISTORY

2805i

2806

Nelson Mandela (1918–2013)

2805

2806a

Designers: Ian Drolet.

Lithography (6 colours), water-activated gum souvenir sheet of 1
Canadian Bank Note

**2015, Jan 30** **GT4, TRC Paper** **Perf 12.5x13.2**

| | | NH–VF | ⊙F | FDC |
|---|---|---|---|---|
| **2805** | **$2.50 souvenir sheet** of 1 | 5.00 | 4.50 | — |
| i | $2.50 single from souvenir sheet | 4.75 | 4.00 | |

Qty: 150,000

Lithography (6 colours), self-adhesive booklet of 10
**GT4, TRC Paper**
**Serpentine Die cut 13.4**

| | | NH–VF | ⊙F | FDC |
|---|---|---|---|---|
| **2806** | **multicoloured** | 1.70 | .50 | 3.70 |
| i | die cut to shape from Quarterly Pack | 2.50 | — | |
| a | booklet pane of 10 (2806) (**BK612**) | 17.00 | | |

Qty: 5,000,000

Issued for Black History Month.
At time of issue, the P stamp was valued at 85¢.

## CANADA'S FLAG

2807
Flag of Canada

2808i
Flag of Canada

Designer: Kosta Tsetsekas, Defne Corbacioglu (Signals).

Lithography (5 colours), self-adhesive booklet of 10
Lowe-Martin

**2015, Feb 15** **GT4, TRC Paper**
**Serpentine Die cut 13.3x13.5**

| | | NH–VF | ⊙F | FDC |
|---|---|---|---|---|
| **2807** | **multicoloured** | 1.70 | .50 | 3.70 |
| i | die cut to shape from Quarterly Pack/ Annual Collection | 2.50 | — | |
| a | booklet pane of 10 x P (2807) (**BK613**) | 17.00 | | |

Qty: 5,000,000

For non-denominated postal card of same design, see UX417.
At time of issue, the P stamp was valued at 85¢.

Lithography (6 colours), acqueous plus invisible red tagging on self-adhesive fabric
Canadian Bank Note
**Not tagged, Wausau Coated Products**
**Serpentine Die cut 9.2**

| | | NH–VF | ⊙F | FDC |
|---|---|---|---|---|
| **2808** | **$5.00 souvenir sheet** of 1 | 10.00 | 10.00 | |
| i | $5.00 single stamp from souvenir sheet | 9.50 | 9.00 | |
| ii | $5.00 'rotated' single stamp from uncut press sheet ‡ | *50.00* | *50.00* | 12.00 |
| iii | $115.00 uncut press sheet of 20 souvenir (2808) sheets and 3 stamps (2808ii) ‡ | 275.00 | | |

Qty: 2808: 300,000; 2808iii: 1,000

‡ The printing on fabric results in a distinct pattern/grain. The 3 stamps (2808ii) at the

right side of the uncut press sheet (2808iii) are oriented vertically in relation to the other 20 souvenir sheets which results in these 3 stamps having a different pattern/grain than the souvenir sheets.

50th anniversary of the Canada's flag featuring the red Maple Leaf.
At time of issue, the P stamp was valued at 85¢.

2807a

2808

2808iii

## PANSIES

*Perforated singles from water-activated gum souvenir sheet*

2809a 2809b

*Die cut singles from self-adhesive booklet*

2812 Delta Premium Pure Light Blue
2813 Midnight Glow

2810 Delta Premium Pure Light Blue

2811 Midnight Glow

2809

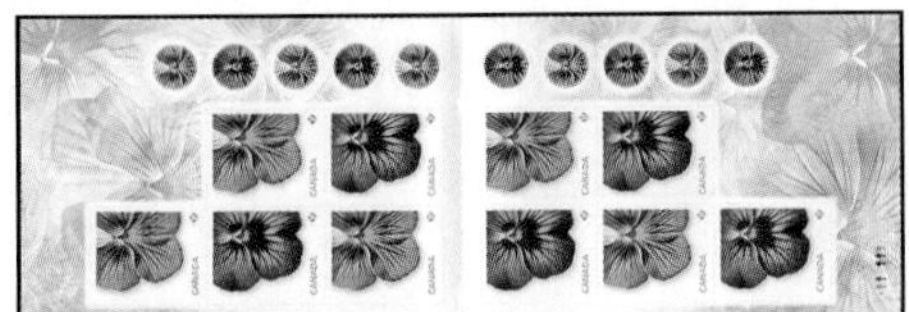
*Image rotated* 2813a

Designer: Marcio Morgado, Paul Haslip (HM & E).
Lithography (6 colours)
Lowe-Martin
Water-activated gum souvenir sheet of 2

**2015, Mar 2 GT4, TRC Paper Perf 13.1**

| | | NH–VF | ⊙F | FDC |
|---|---|---|---|---|
| **2809** | **$1.70 souvenir sheet** of 2 | 3.50 | 3.50 | — |
| a | **multicoloured**, blue pansy | 1.70 | 1.50 | |
| b | **multicoloured**, purple pansy | 1.70 | 1.50 | |
| i | se-tenant pair (2809a–b) | 3.40 | 3.00 | |

Qty: 135,000

Self-adhesive roll of 50
**GT4, TRC Paper**
with repeating 'Canada' underprint
**Serpentine Die cut 8.15 to 8.50 Horiz**
**(Rounded tips with 3 'nibs' between stamps)**

One die cut pattern exists on these stamps.

| | | NH–VF | ⊙F | FDC |
|---|---|---|---|---|
| **2810** | **multicoloured**, blue pansy | 1.70 | .60 | — |
| **2811** | **multicoloured**, purple pansy | 1.70 | .60 | — |
| a | se-tenant pair (vert.), 2810–11 | 7.00 | | |
| i | gutter strip of 4 with inscription | 8.50 | | |
| | starter strip of 4 (wavy die cut) | 10.00 | | |
| | end strip of 4 (wavy die cut) | 10.00 | | |
| ii | se-tenant pair (2810–11), die cut to shape (9.2 horiz) from Quarterly Pack | 5.00 | — | |

Qty: 3,000,000 of each

These stamps were printed se-tenant along the roll. Two different rolls were produced; one starting with the blue pansy, the other starting with the purple pansy. As such, two types of each of the gutter, starter and end strips of 4 exist.

Self-adhesive booklet of 10
**GT4, TRC Paper Serpentine Die cut 13.5**

| | | NH–VF | ⊙F | FDC |
|---|---|---|---|---|
| **2812** | **multicoloured**, blue pansy | 1.70 | .50 | |
| **2813** | **multicoloured**, purple pansy | 1.70 | .50 | |
| i | se-tenant pair (2812, 2813), die cut to shape from Quarterly Pack | 5.00 | — | |
| a | booklet pane of 10, 5 each #2812–2813 + 10 stickers (**BK614**) | 17.00 | | |

Qty: 3,000,000 of each

**Nos. 2812–2813 (2) combination FDC** 5.40*
* Stamps on FDCs are not die cut all the way through.

At time of issue, the P stamps were valued at 85¢.
For non-denominated postal cards of same designs, see UX418–UX419.

## CANADIAN PHOTOGRAPHY — 3

*Perforated singles from water-activated gum souvenir sheets*

2814a *Shoeshine Stand*

2814b *Southam Sisters*

2814c *La Voie Lactée*

**2815a**
*Angels, Saint-Jean-Baptiste Day, Montreal, Quebec*

**2815b**
*Isaac's First Swim*

**2815c**
*Friends and Family and Trips. In Front of Simpsons*

**2815d**
*Alex Colville on the Tantramar Marshes*

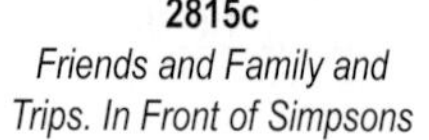

*Die cut singles from self-adhesive booklets*

**2816** **2817** **2818**

**2819**

**2820**

**2821**

**2822**

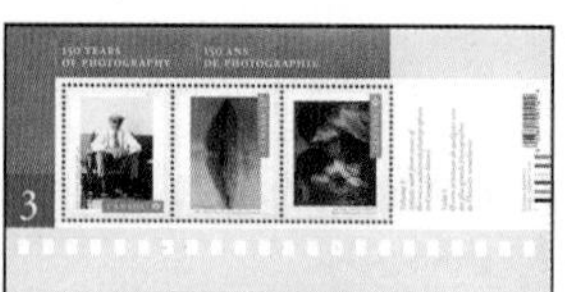

**2814**

**2815**

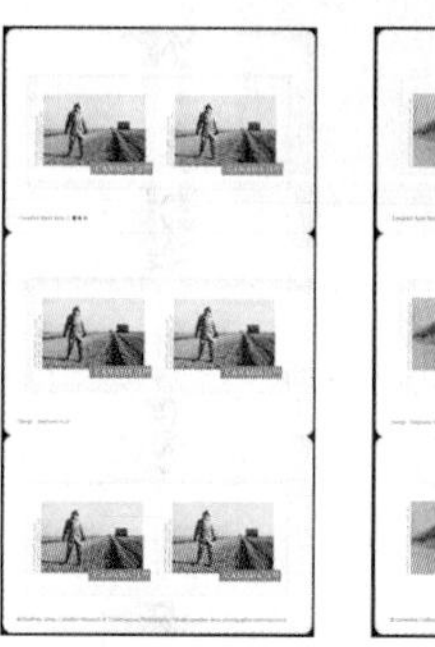

**2821a**

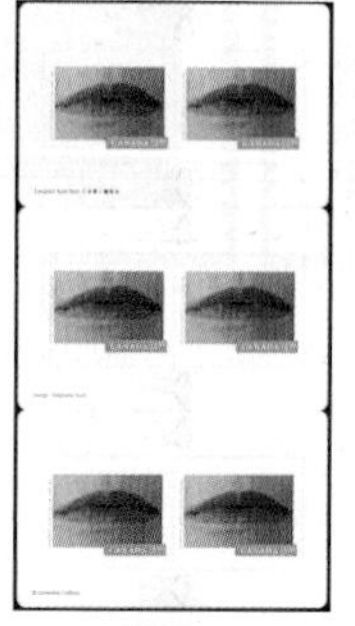

**2822a**

**2820a**

Designer: Stéphane Huot.

Lithography (7 colours)
Canadian Bank Note
Water-activated gum souvenir sheets of 3 and 4

**2015, Apr 8** **GT4, TRC Paper**

| | | NH–VF | ⊙F | FDC |
|---|---|---|---|---|
| **2814** | **$4.20 souvenir sheet** of 3 | 8.60 | 8.60 | 10.40 |
| a | P **multicoloured**, Shoeshine Stand | 1.75 | 1.50 | |
| b | P **multicoloured**, Southam Sisters | 1.75 | 1.50 | |
| c | **$2.50 multicoloured**, La Voie Lactée | 5.00 | 5.00 | |

Qty: 130,000

Lithography (5 colours)

| | | NH–VF | ⊙F | FDC |
|---|---|---|---|---|
| **2815** | **$3.75 souvenir sheet** of 4 | 7.50 | 7.50 | 9.50 |
| a | P **multicoloured**, Angels | 1.75 | 1.50 | |
| b | P **multicoloured**, Isaac's First Swim | 1.75 | 1.50 | |
| c | P **multicoloured**, Friends and Family | 1.75 | 1.50 | |
| d | **$1.20 multicoloured**, Alex Colville | 2.40 | 2.00 | |

Qty: 130,000

2814a is perf. 12.7x12.8; all other single perforated stamps are perf 12.8x12.7.

Lithography (8 colours), self-adhesive booklet of 10
**GT4, TRC Paper**
**Serpentine Die cut 13.4**

| | | NH–VF | ⊙F | FDC |
|---|---|---|---|---|
| **2816** | P **multicoloured**, Angels | 1.70 | .75 | — |
| i | die cut to shape from Quarterly Pack | 2.50 | — | |
| **2817** | P **multicoloured**, Southam Sisters | 1.70 | .75 | — |
| i | die cut to shape from Quarterly Pack | 2.50 | — | |
| **2818** | P **multicoloured**, Friends and Family | 1.70 | .75 | — |
| i | die cut to shape from Quarterly Pack | 2.50 | — | |
| **2819** | P **multicoloured**, Isaac's First Swim | 1.70 | .75 | — |
| i | die cut to shape from Quarterly Pack | 2.50 | — | |
| **2820** | P **multicoloured**, Shoeshine Stand | 1.70 | .75 | — |
| i | die cut to shape from Quarterly Pack | 2.50 | — | |
| a | booklet pane of 10, 2 each #2816–2820 (**BK615**) | 17.00 | | |

Qty: 440,000 of each

Lithography (5 colours), self-adhesive booklet of 6

| | | NH–VF | ⊙F | FDC |
|---|---|---|---|---|
| **2821** | **$1.20 multicoloured**, Alex Colville | 2.40 | 1.50 | — |
| i | die cut to shape from Quarterly Pack | 3.60 | — | |
| a | booklet pane of 6 x $1.20 (2821) (**BK616**) | 14.50 | | |

Qty: 840,000

Lithography (7 colours), self-adhesive booklet of 6

| | | NH–VF | ⊙F | FDC |
|---|---|---|---|---|
| **2822** | **$2.50 multicoloured**, La Voie Lactée | 5.00 | 3.00 | — |
| i | die cut to shape from Quarterly Pack | 7.50 | — | |
| a | booklet pane of 6 x $2.50 (2822) (**BK617**) | 30.00 | | |

Qty: 840,000

At time of issue, the P stamps were valued at 85¢.
For non-denominated postal cards of same designs, see UX420–UX426. See also 2626–2634, 2756–2764, and 2814–2822

**2823**

**2828a**

## DINOS OF CANADA

**2823a/2827**
Euoplocephalus tutus

**2823b/2826**
Chasmosaurus belli

**2823c/2824**
Tyrannosaurus rex

**2823d/2828**
Ornithomimus edmontonicus

**2823e/2825**
Tylosaurus pembinensis

Designer: Andrew Perro.

Lithography (4 colours) plus foil stamping plus embossing
Lowe-Martin
Self-adhesive souvenir sheet of 5

**2015, Apr 13** **GT4, TRC Paper**
**Serpentine Die cut 13.3**

| | | NH–VF | ⊙F | FDC |
|---|---|---|---|---|
| **2823** | **$4.25 souvenir sheet** of 5 | 8.75 | 8.75 | 10.50 |
| a | **multicoloured**, Euoplocephalus | 1.75 | 1.50 | |
| b | **multicoloured**, Chasmosaurus | 1.75 | 1.50 | |
| c | **multicoloured**, Tyrannosaurus | 1.75 | 1.50 | |
| d | **multicoloured**, Ornithomimus | 1.75 | 1.50 | |
| e | **multicoloured**, Tylosaurus | 1.75 | 1.50 | |
| i | $34.00 uncut press sheet of 8 souvenir sheets | 68.00 | | |

Qty: 2823: 200,000; 2823i: 5,000

Lithography (4 colours) plus foil stamping, self-adhesive booklet of 10

| | | NH–VF | ⊙F | FDC |
|---|---|---|---|---|
| **2824** | **multicoloured**, Tyrannosaurus | 1.70 | .75 | — |
| i | partially notched tagging at left | 1.70 | .75 | |
| ii | as 2824, die cut to shape from Quarterly Pack | 2.50 | — | |
| iii | as 2824i, die cut to shape from Quarterly Pack | 2.50 | — | |
| **2825** | **multicoloured**, Tylosaurus | 1.70 | .75 | — |
| i | fully notched tagging at left | 1.70 | .75 | |
| ii | as 2825, die cut to shape from Quarterly Pack | 2.50 | — | |
| iii | as 2825i, die cut to shape from Quarterly Pack | 2.50 | — | |
| **2826** | **multicoloured**, Chasmosaurus | 1.70 | .75 | — |
| i | partially notched tagging at bottom | 1.70 | .75 | |
| ii | as 2826, die cut to shape from Quarterly Pack | 2.50 | — | |
| iii | as 2826i, die cut to shape from Quarterly Pack | 2.50 | — | |
| **2827** | **multicoloured**, Euoplocephalus | 1.70 | .75 | — |
| i | partially notched tagging at bottom | 1.70 | .75 | |
| ii | as 2827, die cut to shape from Quarterly Pack | 2.50 | — | |
| iii | as 2827i, die cut to shape from Quarterly Pack | 2.50 | — | |
| **2828** | **multicoloured**, Ornithomimus | 1.70 | .75 | — |
| i | die cut to shape from Quarterly Pack | 2.50 | — | |
| a | booklet pane of 10, 2 each #2824–2828 (**BK618**) | 17.00 | | |

Qty: 1,000,000 of each

Single stamps from the souvenir sheet are embossed; those from the booklet pane are not.

Four of the booklet single stamps have two tagging varieties each: *fully* notched tagging (i.e. there is no tagging where the design extends near the edge of the stamp) and *partially* notched. 2824i/2825i/2826i/2827i are from the right panel of the booklet pane. 2827 (from the left panel of the booklet pane) includes the 'paper tear' design element at upper left which is the extension from 2826; 2827i (from the right panel) does not have this 'tear extension'.

At time of issue, the P stamps were valued at 85¢.

**2824**
Fully notched tagging at left

**2824i**
Partially notched tagging at left

**2825**
Partially notched tagging at left

**2825i**
Fully notched tagging at left

**2826**
Fully notched tagging at left

**2826i**
Partially notched tagging at left

**2827**
Fully notched tagging at bottom

**2827i**
Partially notched tagging at bottom

## LOVE YOUR PET

*Perforated singles from water-activated gum souvenir sheet*

**2829a** **2829b**

**2829c**

**2829d**

**2829e**

**2829**

**2834a**

QE II — 2010's

*Die cut singles from self-adhesive booklet*

**2830**
Spay/neuter: cat in head cone

**2831**
Exercise: dog chasing snowball

**2832**
Vet care: examining cat

**2833**
Identification: cat on leash

**2834**
Keep pets cool: dog drinking

Designer: Lara Minja (Lime Design).

Lithography (6 colours) plus varnish
Lowe-Martin
Water-activated gum souvenir sheet of 5

| **2015, May 2** | **GT4, TRC Paper** | | | **Perf 13.0** |
|---|---|---|---|---|
| | | **NH–VF** | **⊙F** | **FDC** |
| **2829** | **$4.25 souvenir sheet** of 5 | 8.50 | 8.50 | 10.50 |
| a | **P multicoloured**, spay/neuter | 1.75 | 1.50 | |
| b | **P multicoloured**, exercise | 1.75 | 1.50 | |
| c | **P multicoloured**, vet care | 1.75 | 1.50 | |
| d | **P multicoloured**, keep pets cool | 1.75 | 1.50 | |
| e | **P multicoloured**, identification | 1.75 | 1.50 | |

Qty: 150,000

Self-adhesive booklet of 10
**Serpentine Die cut 13.3**

| | | **NH–VF** | **⊙F** | **FDC** |
|---|---|---|---|---|
| **2830** | **P multicoloured**, spay/neuter | 1.70 | .75 | — |
| i | die cut to shape from Quarterly Pack | 2.50 | — | |
| **2831** | **P multicoloured**, exercise | 1.70 | .75 | — |
| i | die cut to shape from Quarterly Pack | 2.50 | — | |
| **2832** | **P multicoloured**, vet care | 1.70 | .75 | — |
| i | die cut to shape from Quarterly Pack | 2.50 | — | |
| **2833** | **P multicoloured**, identification | 1.70 | .75 | — |
| i | die cut to shape from Quarterly Pack | 2.50 | — | |
| **2834** | **P multicoloured**, keep pets cool | 1.70 | .75 | — |
| i | die cut to shape from Quarterly Pack | 2.50 | — | |
| a | booklet pane of 10, 2 each #2830–2834 (**BK619**) | 17.00 | | |

Qty: 800,000 of each

At time of issue, the P stamps were valued at 85¢.

## *IN FLANDERS FIELDS*

*Perforated single from water-activated gum pane of 5*

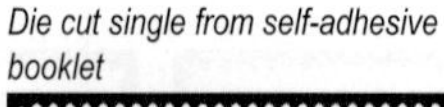

*Die cut single from self-adhesive booklet*

**2835** **2836**
Poppy, field of crosses, larks

Designer: q30 Design.

Lithography (5 colours), water-activated gum pane of 5
Lowe-Martin

| **2015, May 3** | **GT4, TRC Paper** | | | **Perf 12.5** |
|---|---|---|---|---|
| | | **NH–VF** | **⊙F** | **FDC** |
| **2835** | **P multicoloured** | 1.70 | 1.00 | — |
| | full pane of 5 | 8.50 | | |

Qty: 350,000

Sold only in a shrink-wrapped package containing one pane of 5 stamps.

Lithography (5 colours), self-adhesive booklet of 10
Lowe-Martin
**GT4, TRC Paper**
**Serpentine Die cut 13.3x13.5**

| | | **NH–VF** | **⊙F** | **FDC** |
|---|---|---|---|---|
| **2836** | **P multicoloured** | 1.70 | .50 | 3.70 |
| i | die cut to shape from Quarterly Pack/ Annual Collection | 2.50 | — | |
| a | booklet pane of 10 x P (2836) (**BK620**) | 17.00 | | |

Qty: 4,000,000

One hundredth anniversary of the writing of the poem *In Flanders Fields* by Major (later Lieutenant Colonel) John McCrae during the Second Battle of Ypres.

At time of issue, the P stamp was valued at 85¢.

**2835 – pane of 5**

**2836a**

## FIFA WOMEN'S WORLD CUP CANADA 2015™

**2837**
Christine Sinclair (#12), Kadeisha Buchanan (#14), Ayumi Kaihori (#21, Japan)

Designer: Debbie Adams.

Lithography (8 colours), self-adhesive booklet of 10
Lowe-Martin

**2015, May 6** **GT4, TRC Paper**
**Serpentine Die cut 13.3x13.5**

| | | NH–VF | ⊙F | FDC |
|---|---|---|---|---|
| **2837** | **P multicoloured** | 1.70 | .50 | 3.70 |
| i | die cut to shape from Quarterly Pack/ Annual Collection | 2.50 | — | |
| a | booklet pane of 10 x P (2837) + 10 stickers (**BK621**) | 17.00 | | |

Qty: 2,000,000

FIFA Women's World Cup held in several Canadian cities from June 6 through July 5. At time of issue, the P stamp was valued at 85¢.

*Image rotated* **2837a**

## WEATHER WONDERS

*Perforated singles from water-activated gum souvenir sheet*

**2838a**

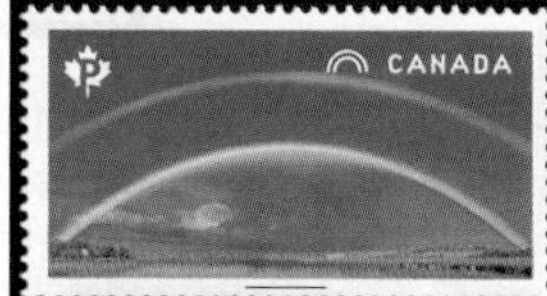


**2838b**

**2838c**

**2838d**

**2838e**

*Die cut singles from self-adhesive booklet*

**2839**

**2840**

**2841**

**2842**

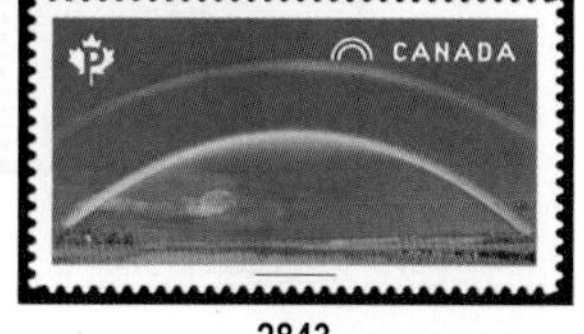


**2843**

Designer: Kosta Tsetsekas, Defne Corbacioglu (Signals).

Lithography (6 colours) plus varnish
Canadian Bank Note
Water-activated gum souvenir sheet of 5

**2015, Jun 18** **GT4, TRC Paper** **Perf 12.5x13.1**

| | | NH–VF | ⊙F | FDC |
|---|---|---|---|---|
| **2838** | **$4.25 souvenir sheet** of 5 | 8.50 | 8.50 | 10.50 |
| a | **P multicoloured**, lightning | 1.75 | 1.50 | |
| b | **P multicoloured**, double rainbow | 1.75 | 1.50 | |
| c | **P multicoloured**, sun dogs | 1.75 | 1.50 | |
| d | **P multicoloured**, fog | 1.75 | 1.50 | |
| e | **P multicoloured**, hoar frost | 1.75 | 1.50 | |
| i | $25.50 uncut press sheet of 6 souvenir sheets | 51.00 | | |

Qty: 140,000

Self-adhesive booklet of 10
**Serpentine Die cut 13.4**

| | | NH–VF | ⊙F | FDC |
|---|---|---|---|---|
| **2839** | **P multicoloured**, lightning | 1.70 | .75 | — |
| i | die cut to shape from Quarterly Pack | 2.50 | — | |
| **2840** | **P multicoloured**, hoar frost | 1.70 | .75 | — |
| i | die cut to shape from Quarterly Pack | 2.50 | — | |
| **2841** | **P multicoloured**, fog | 1.70 | .75 | — |
| i | die cut to shape from Quarterly Pack | 2.50 | — | |
| **2842** | **P multicoloured**, sun dogs | 1.70 | .75 | — |
| i | die cut to shape from Quarterly Pack | 2.50 | — | |
| **2843** | **P multicoloured**, double rainbow | 1.70 | .75 | — |
| i | die cut to shape from Quarterly Pack | 2.50 | — | |
| a | booklet pane of 10, 2 each #2839–43 (**BK622**) | 17.00 | | |

Qty: 700,000 of each

Photographs of weather phenomena from across Canada: lightning near Winnipeg, Manitoba; double rainbow in Saint-Gédéon, Quebec; sun dogs in Iqaluit, Nunavut; early-morning fog at Cape Spear Lighthouse National Historic Site in Newfoundland; hoar frost near Beaumont, Alberta.
At time of issue, the P stamp was valued at 85¢.

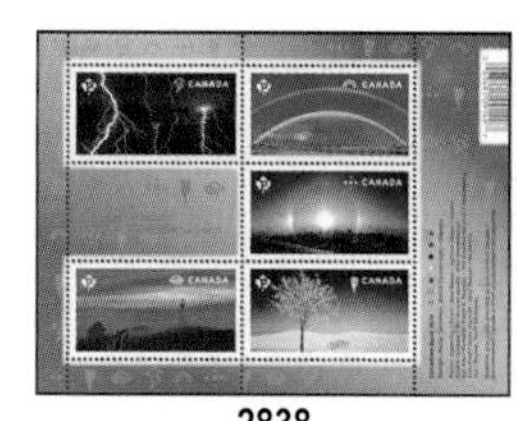

**2838**

**2843a**

## UNESCO WORLD HERITAGE SITES IN CANADA

*Perforated singles from water-activated gum souvenir sheet*

**2844a**

**2844b**

**2844c**

**2844d**

**2844e**

*Die cut singles from self-adhesive booklets*

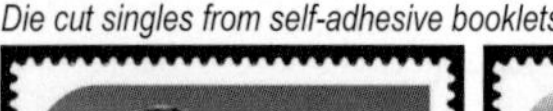

**2845**
Dinosaur Provincial Park, AB (incorrect image showing Hoodoos)

**2846**
Red Bay Basque Whaling Station, NL

**2847**
Wood Buffalo National Park, AB/NT

**2848**
Waterton-Glacier International Peace Park, AB/MT

**2849**
Kluane/Wrangell-St. Elias/ Glacier Bay, BC/YK

Designer: Lara Minja (Lime Design).

Lithography (5 colours)
Lowe-Martin
Water-activated gum souvenir sheet of 5

**2015, Jul 3** **GT4, TRC Paper** **Perf 12.5**

| | | NH–VF | ⊙F | FDC |
|---|---|---|---|---|
| **2844** | **$8.60 souvenir sheet** of 5 | *100.00* | *100.00* | *500.00†* |
| **a** | **$1.20 multicoloured**, Dinosaur * | *85.00* | | |
| **b** | **$1.20 multicoloured**, Wood Buffalo | 2.40 | | |
| **c** | **$1.20 multicoloured**, Red Bay | 2.40 | | |
| **d** | **$2.50 multicoloured**, Waterton-Glacier | 5.00 | | |
| **e** | **$2.50 multicoloured**, Kluane | 5.00 | | |

Qty: 140,000; quantity sold before recall is unknown.

Self-adhesive booklets of 6
**GT4, TRC Paper**
**Serpentine Die cut 13.3x13.5**

| | | NH–VF | ⊙F | FDC |
|---|---|---|---|---|
| **2845** | **$1.20 multicoloured**, Dinosaur * | *30.00* | *25.00* | — |
| **2846** | **$1.20 multicoloured**, Red Bay | 2.40 | 2.00 | |
| **i** | die cut to shape from Quarterly Pack | 3.60 | — | |
| **2847** | **$1.20 multicoloured**, Wood Buffalo | 2.40 | 2.00 | |
| **i** | die cut to shape from Quarterly Pack | 3.60 | — | |
| **a** | booklet pane of 6, 2 each #2845–47 (**BK623**) | *75.00* | | |

Qty: 320,000 of each; quantity sold before recall is unknown.

| | | NH–VF | ⊙F | FDC |
|---|---|---|---|---|
| **2848** | **$2.50 multicoloured**, Waterton-Glacier | 5.00 | 3.00 | — |
| **i** | die cut to shape from Quarterly Pack | 7.50 | — | |
| **2849** | **$2.50 multicoloured**, Kluane | 5.00 | 3.00 | — |
| **i** | die cut to shape from Quarterly Pack | 7.50 | — | |
| **a** | booklet pane of 6, 3 each #2848–49 (**BK624**) | 30.00 | | |

Qty: 480,000 of each

The United Nations Educational, Scientific and Cultural Organization (UNESCO) is a specialized agency of the United Nations.

† The price shown for the FDC is for Canada Post's Official First Day Cover (OFDC). Beware of any privately produced FDCs as these can be easily backdated, even weeks or months after the issue date.
* An incorrect image, showing 'Hoodoos', was used for the Dinosaur Provincial Park stamp. All related products bearing this image were recalled on July 7, 2015. These include the booklet (BK623), souvenir sheet (2844), OFDC and postal card (UX427). A corrected image was issued August 21 (2857–2858).

See also 2739–2744, 2857–2858.
For non-denominated postal cards of same designs, see UX427–UX431.

**2844**

**2847a**

**2849a**

## ALICE MUNRO

**2850**
(1931– )

Designer: Paul Haslip, Marcio Morgado (HM&E design).

Lithography (7 colours), self-adhesive booklet of 10
Colour Innovations Inc.

**2015, Jul 10** **GT4, TRC Paper**
**Serpentine Die cut 13.9x13.8**

| | | NH–VF | ⊙F | FDC |
|---|---|---|---|---|
| **2850** | **P multicoloured** | 1.70 | .50 | 3.70 |
| **i** | die cut to shape from Quarterly Pack/ Annual Collection | 2.50 | — | |
| a | booklet pane of 10 x P (2850) (**BK625**) | 17.00 | | |

Qty: 1,500,000

First Canada stamp issue for Colour Innovations Inc.

First Canadian woman to win the Nobel prize in Literature (in 2013).

At time of issue, the P stamp was valued at 85¢.

**2850a**

## THE FRANKLIN EXPEDITION

*Perforated singles from water-activated gum pane of 16*

**2851**
HMS *Erebus*

**2852**
Map, text in Inuktut

Die cut singles from self-adhesive booklet

2854 2855

Perforated single from water-activated gum souvenir sheet

2853i

Die cut single from self-adhesive booklet

2856

Sonar image and 19th-century style diagram deck plan of HMS *Erebus*

Designers: Subplot.

Lithography (6 colours) and embossed, pane of 16 + vertical gutter
Lowe-Martin

**2015, Aug 6** **GT4, TRC Paper** **Perf 12.5**

| | | NH–VF | ⊙F | PB | FDC |
|---|---|---|---|---|---|
| **2851** | **P multicoloured** | 1.75 | .80 | | |
| **2852** | **P multicoloured** | 1.75 | .80 | | |
| a | se-tenant horiz. pair (2851–52) | 3.50 | 1.50 | 4.00 | 5.40 |

Qty: 480,000 of each

Lithography (6 colours), Water-activated gum souvenir sheet of 1
**GT4, TRC Paper** **Perf 13.4**

| | | NH–VF | ⊙F | FDC |
|---|---|---|---|---|
| **2853** | **$2.50 souvenir sheet** of 1 | 5.00 | 5.00 | 7.00 |
| i | $2.50 single from souvenir sheet | 4.50 | 4.25 | |
| ii | $30.00 uncut press sheet of 12 souvenir sheets | 60.00 | | |

Qty: 150,000; 2853ii: 5,000

Lithography (6 colours) and embossed, self-adhesive booklet of 10
**GT4, TRC Paper**
**Serpentine Die cut 13.5x13.3**

| | | NH–VF | ⊙F | FDC |
|---|---|---|---|---|
| **2854** | **P multicoloured** | 1.70 | .50 | — |
| **2855** | **P multicoloured** | 1.70 | .50 | — |
| i | se-tenant pair (2854–55), die cut to shape from Quarterly Pack | 5.00 | — | |
| a | booklet pane of 10, 5 each #2854–2855 (**BK626**) | 17.00 | | |

Qty: 1,250,000 of each

Lithography (7 colours), self-adhesive booklet of 6
**GT4, TRC Paper**
**Serpentine Die cut 13.2x13.8**

| | | NH–VF | ⊙F | FDC |
|---|---|---|---|---|
| **2856** | **$2.50 multicoloured** | 5.00 | 2.75 | — |
| i | die cut to shape from Quarterly Pack | 7.50 | — | |
| a | booklet pane of 6 x $2.50 (2856) (**BK627**) | 30.00 | | |

Qty: 780,000

Issued on the 170th anniversary of Sir John Franklin and his expedition entering Arctic waters. The remains of the HMS *Erebus* were discovered in September 2014 near King William Island, Nunavut.

At time of issue, the P stamps were valued at 85¢.

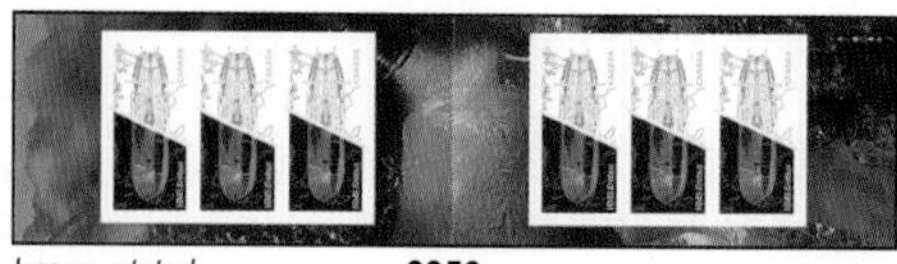

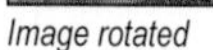

*Image rotated* 2856a

2853

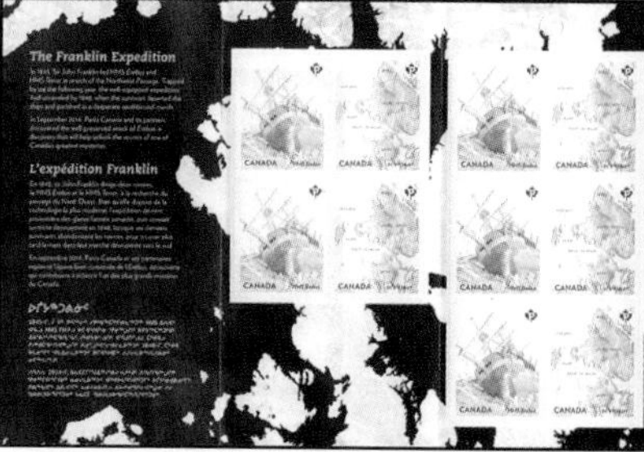

2855a

## UNESCO WORLD HERITAGE SITES IN CANADA

Perforated single from water-activated gum souvenir sheet

2857a

Die cut single from self-adhesive booklet

2858

Dinosaur Provincial Park, AB (corrected image)

Designer: Lara Minja (Lime Design).

Lithography (5 colours)
Lowe-Martin
Water-activated gum souvenir sheet of 5

**2015, Aug 21** **GT4, TRC Paper** **Perf 12.5**

| | | NH–VF | ⊙F | FDC |
|---|---|---|---|---|
| **2857** | **$8.60 souvenir sheet** of 5 * | 17.00 | 17.00 | 19.20 |
| a | **$1.20 multicoloured**, Dinosaur | 2.40 | 2.25 | |

Qty: 130,000

* Souvenir sheet consists of 2844b-2844e and 2857a.

Self-adhesive booklet of 6
**GT4, TRC Paper**
**Serpentine Die cut 13.3x13.5**

| | | NH–VF | ⊙F | FDC |
|---|---|---|---|---|
| **2858** | **$1.20 multicoloured**, Dinosaur | 2.40 | 1.50 | |
| i | die cut to shape from Quarterly Pack | 3.60 | — | |
| a | booklet pane of 6, 2 each #2846–47, 2858 (**BK628**) | 14.50 | | |

Qty: 260,000

This design was a replacement stamp for the incorrect image of Dinosaur Provincial Park first released July 3 (Scott 2844a, 2845).
See also 2739–2744, 2844–2849.
For non-denominated postal cards of same designs, see UX428–UX432.

2857

2858a

## A HISTORIC REIGN: QUEEN ELIZABETH II

**2859**
Queen Elizabeth II

Designer: Entro Communications.
Lithography (6 colours), self-adhesive booklet of 10
Lowe-Martin

**2015, Sep 9** **GT4, TRC Paper**
**Serpentine Die cut 13.3x13.5**

| | | NH–VF | ⊙F | FDC |
|---|---|---|---|---|
| **2859** | **multicoloured** | 1.70 | .50 | 3.70 |
| i | die cut to shape from Quarterly Pack/ Annual Collection | 2.50 | — | |
| a | booklet pane of 10 x P (2859) (**BK629**) | 17.00 | | |

Qty: 4,000,000

On September 9, 2015, Her Majesty Queen Elizabeth II reigned over the United Kingdom, Canada and all other realms of the Commonwealth for 63 years, seven months, three days, surpassing the reign of her great-great-grandmother, Queen Victoria.

At time of issue, the P stamp was valued at 85¢.

**2859a**

## HAUNTED CANADA – 2

*Perforated singles from water-activated gum souvenir sheet*

**2860a**

**2860b**

**2860c**

**2860d**

**2860e**

*Die cut singles from self-adhesive booklet*

**2861**
Brakeman Ghost, Vancouver, BC

**2862**
Ghost of Marie-Josephte Corriveau, Lévis, QC

**2863**
Gray Lady of the Citadel, Halifax, NS

**2864**
Red River Trail Oxcart, Winnipeg, MB

**2865**
Ghost of Caribou Hotel, Carcross, YT

Designer: Lionel Gadoury, Kammy Ahuja – Context Creative.
Lithography (5 colours) plus holographic foil
Canadian Bank Note
Water-activated gum souvenir sheet of 5

**2015, Sep 14** **GT4, TRC Paper** **Perf 12.5x13.2**

| | | NH–VF | ⊙F | FDC |
|---|---|---|---|---|
| **2860** | **$4.25 souvenir sheet** of 5 | 8.50 | 8.50 | 10.50 |
| a | **multicoloured**, Brakeman Ghost | 1.70 | 1.50 | |
| b | **multicoloured**, Red River | 1.70 | 1.50 | |
| c | **multicoloured**, Halifax Citadel | 1.70 | 1.50 | |
| d | **multicoloured**, Marie-Josephte Corriveau | 1.70 | 1.50 | |
| e | **multicoloured**, Caribou Hotel | 1.70 | 1.50 | |
| i | $34.00 uncut press sheet of 8 souvenir sheets | 68.00 | | |

Qty: 125,000; i: 2,000

Self-adhesive booklet of 10
**GT4, TRC Paper** **Serpentine Die cut 13.4**

| | | NH–VF | ⊙F | FDC |
|---|---|---|---|---|
| **2861** | **multicoloured**, Brakeman Ghost | 1.70 | .75 | — |
| i | die cut to shape from Quarterly Pack | 2.50 | — | |
| **2862** | **multicoloured**, Marie-Josephte Corriveau | 1.70 | .75 | — |
| i | die cut to shape from Quarterly Pack | 2.50 | — | |
| **2863** | **multicoloured**, Halifax Citadel | 1.70 | .75 | — |
| i | die cut to shape from Quarterly Pack | 2.50 | — | |
| **2864** | **multicoloured**, Red River | 1.70 | .75 | — |
| i | die cut to shape from Quarterly Pack | 2.50 | — | |
| **2865** | **multicoloured**, Caribou Hotel | 1.70 | .75 | — |
| i | die cut to shape from Quarterly Pack | 2.50 | — | |
| a | booklet pane of 10, 2 each #2861–65 (**BK630**) | 17.00 | | |

Qty: 680,000 of each

At time of issue, the P stamps were valued at 85¢.
For non-denominated postal cards of same designs, see UX433–UX437.
Second in a three-year series. See also 2748–2753, 2935–2940.

**2860**

*Image rotated* **2865a**

Timeline:
**2015, Sep 28** (85¢)+10¢ Canada Post Community Foundation, semi-postal (B22)

QE II — 2010's

## GREAT CANADIAN GOALIES

*Perforated singles from water-activated gum souvenir sheet*

**2866a**
Ken Dryden
(1947- )

**2866b**
Tony Esposito
(1943- )

**2866c**
Johnny Bower
(1924- )

**2866d**
Gump Worsley
(1929-2007)

**2866e**
Bernie Parent
(1945- )

**2866f**
Martin Brodeur
(1972- )

*Die cut singles from self-adhesive booklet*

**2867**
Ken Dryden

**2868**
Tony Esposito

**2869**
Johnny Bower

**2870**
Gump Worsley

**2871**
Bernie Parent

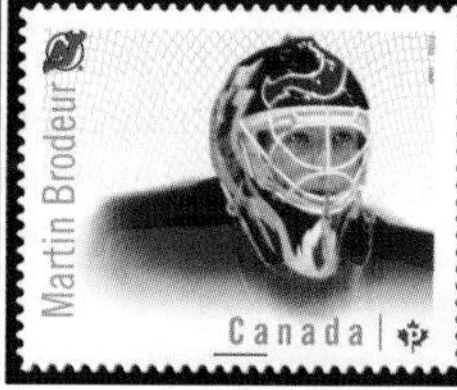


**2872**
Martin Brodeur

Designer: Avi Dunkelman, Joseph Gault (MIX Design Group).
Lithography (8 colours, one foil stamping plus embossing*)
Lowe-Martin
Water-activated gum pane of 6

**2015, Oct 2** **GT4, TRC Paper** **Perf 12.5**

| | | NH–VF | ⊙F | FDC |
|---|---|---|---|---|
| 2866 | **$5.10 souvenir sheet** of 6 | 10.50 | 10.50 | |
| a | **multicoloured**, Ken Dryden | 1.70 | 1.50 | |
| b | **multicoloured**, Tony Esposito | 1.70 | 1.50 | |
| c | **multicoloured**, Johnny Bower | 1.70 | 1.50 | |
| d | **multicoloured**, Gump Worsley | 1.70 | 1.50 | |
| e | **multicoloured**, Bernie Parent | 1.70 | 1.50 | |
| f | **multicoloured**, Martin Brodeur | 1.70 | 1.50 | |

Qty: 152,000
* The pane has embossing in the selvedge; the stamps themselves do not have any embossing.

Lithography (8 colours)
Self-adhesive booklet of 6
**Serpentine Die cut 13.3x13.5**

| | | NH–VF | ⊙F | FDC |
|---|---|---|---|---|
| 2867 | **multicoloured**, Ken Dryden | 1.70 | 0.75 | 3.70 |
| i | die cut to shape from Quarterly Pack | 2.50 | — | |
| 2868 | **multicoloured**, Tony Esposito | 1.70 | 0.75 | 3.70 |
| i | die cut to shape from Quarterly Pack | 2.50 | — | |
| 2869 | **multicoloured**, Johnny Bower | 1.70 | 0.75 | 3.70 |
| i | die cut to shape from Quarterly Pack | 2.50 | — | |
| 2870 | **multicoloured**, Gump Worsley | 1.70 | 0.75 | 3.70 |
| i | die cut to shape from Quarterly Pack | 2.50 | — | |
| 2871 | **multicoloured**, Bernie Parent | 1.70 | 0.75 | 3.70 |
| i | die cut to shape from Quarterly Pack | 2.50 | — | |
| 2872 | **multicoloured**, Martin Brodeur | 1.70 | 0.75 | 3.70 |
| i | die cut to shape from Quarterly Pack | 2.50 | — | |
| a | booklet pane of 6, 1 each #2867–72 (**BK632**) | 10.20 | | |

Qty: 600,000 of each stamp

At time of issue, the P stamps were valued at 85¢.

**2866**

**2872a**

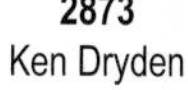

**2873**
Ken Dryden

**2874**
Tony Esposito

**2875**
Johnny Bower

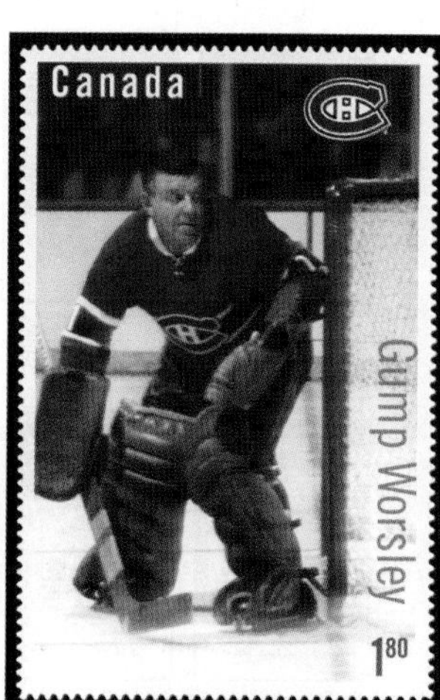


**2876**
Gump Worsley

QE II — 2010's

2877
Bernie Parent

2878
Martin Brodeur

Designer: Avi Dunkelman, Joseph Gault (MIX Design Group).

Lithography (8 colours)
Lowe-Martin
Self-adhesive souvenir sheets of 1

**2015, Oct 2** **GT4, TRC Paper**
**Serpentine Die cut 13.5x13.3**

| | | NH–VF | ⊙F | FDC |
|---|---|---|---|---|
| 2873 | **$1.80 multicoloured**, Ken Dryden | 3.60 | 3.25 | |
| 2874 | **$1.80 multicoloured**, Tony Esposito | 3.60 | 3.25 | |
| i | autographed card | *175.00* | | |
| 2875 | **$1.80 multicoloured**, Johnny Bower | 3.60 | 3.25 | |
| i | autographed card | *125.00* | | |
| 2876 | **$1.80 multicoloured**, Gump Worsley | 3.60 | 3.25 | |
| 2877 | **$1.80 multicoloured**, Bernie Parent | 3.60 | 3.25 | |
| i | autographed card | *125.00* | | |
| 2878 | **$1.80 multicoloured**, Martin Brodeur | 3.60 | 3.25 | |
| i | autographed card | *850.00* | | |

Qty: 100,000 of each; 2874i: 400; 2875i/2877i: 1,000 of each; 2878i: 100

The autographed souvenir sheets have a holographic Canada Post circular sticker of authenticity.
These souvenir sheets were only sold in packages of all six. They *were* included in the Quarterly Pack.

*Full souvenir sheets*

*Autographed souvenir sheets*

2874i

2875i

2877i

2878i

## CHRISTMAS ANIMALS

*Perforated singles from water-activated gum souvenir sheet*

2879a

2879b

2879c

*Die cut singles from self-adhesive booklets*

2881
Moose

2882
Beaver

2883
Polar Bear

## CHRISTMAS: MADONNA AND CHILD

2880
Painting by Adriaen Isenbrandt

Designer: Paprika.

Lithography (7 colours)
Lowe-Martin
Water-activated gum souvenir sheet of 3

**2015, Nov 2** **GT4, TRC Paper** **Perf 13.6x13.4**

| | | NH–VF | ⊙F | FDC |
|---|---|---|---|---|
| 2879 | **$4.55 souvenir sheet** of 3 | 9.25 | 9.25 | 11.10 |
| a | **(P) multicoloured** | 1.70 | 1.50 | |
| b | **$1.20 multicoloured** | 2.40 | 2.10 | |
| c | **$2.50 multicoloured** | 5.00 | 4.75 | |

Qty: 110,000

Designer: Louise Méthé.

Lithography (6 colours)
Canadian Bank Note
Self-adhesive booklet of 12
**GT4, TRC Paper**
**Serpentine Die cut 13.3x13.4**

| | | NH–VF | ⊙F | FDC |
|---|---|---|---|---|
| 2880 | **(P) multicoloured** | 1.70 | .25 | 3.70 |
| i | die cut to shape from Quarterly Pack/ Annual Collection | 2.50 | — | |
| a | booklet pane of 12 x P (2880) (**BK633**) | 20.40 | — | |

Qty: 8,400,000

Designer: Paprika.

Lithography (5 colours), self-adhesive booklet of 12 (P) or 6
Lowe-Martin
**GT4, TRC Paper**
**Serpentine Die cut 13.2 x 13.0**

| | | NH–VF | ⊙F | FDC |
|---|---|---|---|---|
| 2881 | **(P) multicoloured** | 1.70 | .25 | — |
| i | die cut to shape from Quarterly Pack | 2.50 | — | |
| a | booklet pane of 12 x P (2881) (**BK634**) | 20.40 | — | |

Qty: 14,400,000

| | | NH–VF | ⊙F | FDC |
|---|---|---|---|---|
| 2882 | **$1.20 multicoloured** | 2.40 | 1.25 | — |
| i | die cut to shape from Quarterly Pack | 3.60 | — | |
| a | booklet pane of 6 x $1.20 (2882) (**BK635**) | 14.40 | — | |

Qty: 2,400,000

| | | NH–VF | ⊙F | FDC |
|---|---|---|---|---|
| **2883** | **$2.50 multicoloured** | 5.00 | 2.00 | — |
| i | die cut to shape from Quarterly Pack | 7.50 | — | |
| a | booklet pane of 6 x $2.50 (2883) (**BK636**) | 30.00 | — | |

Qty: 2,400,000

At time of issue, the P stamps were valued at 85¢.

2879

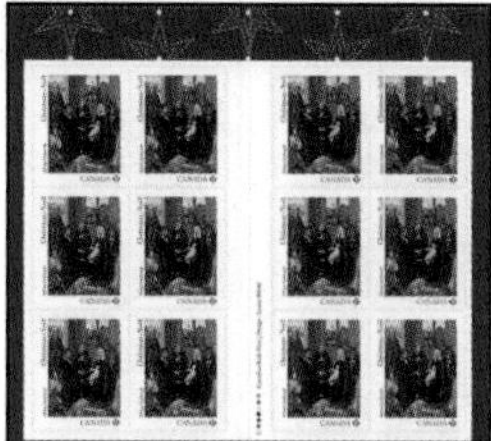
2880a

2881a

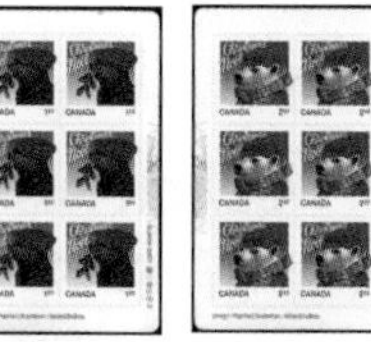
2882a 2883a

## 2016

### LUNAR NEW YEAR (Series 2) — 8
### Year of the Monkey

*Perforated single from wag pane of 25*

2884
Monkey King

*Perforated single from souvenir sheet*

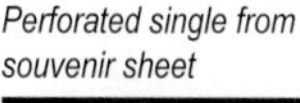

2885i
Monkey's head

*Die cut single from self-adhesive booklets*

2886

2887

2885

2885a

Designer: Albert Ng and Linna Xu.

Lithography (7 colours) plus embossing plus foil stamping, pane of 25
Colour Innovations

**2016, Jan 11** **GT4, TRC Paper** **Perf 13.1**

| | | NH–VF | ⊙F | PB | FDC |
|---|---|---|---|---|---|
| **2884** | **P multicoloured** | 1.70 | .75 | 8.50 | 3.70 |

Qty: 2,500,000

**2016, Feb 1**

| | | NH–VF | ⊙F | FDC |
|---|---|---|---|---|
| **2885** | **$2.50 souvenir sheet** of 1 | 5.00 | 5.00 | 7.00 |
| i | $2.50 single stamp from souvenir sheet | 4.00 | 3.75 | |
| ii | $30.00 uncut press sheet of 12 souvenir sheets | 60.00 | | |
| a | $5.00 'transitional' souvenir sheet of 2, #2802b, 2885 | 10.00 | 10.00 | |
| b | single from 2960a, perf 12.5, *Jan 9/17* | 5.00 | 4.75 | — |

Qty: 2885: 130,000; 2885ii: 8,000; 2885a: 115,000

The two souvenir sheets (2885 and 2885a) were not distributed to post offices/collectors until approximately the beginning of March.

Lithography (7 colours), self-adhesive booklet of 10

**2016, Jan 11** **Serpentine Die cut 13.4**

| | | | | |
|---|---|---|---|---|
| **2886** | **P multicoloured** | 1.70 | .60 | — |
| i | die cut to shape from Quarterly Pack | 2.50 | — | |
| a | booklet pane of 10 x P (2886) (**BK640**) | 17.00 | — | |

Qty: 2,500,000

Lithography (7 colours), self-adhesive booklet of 6

**2016, Feb 1**

| | | | | |
|---|---|---|---|---|
| **2887** | **$2.50 multicoloured** | 5.00 | 3.00 | — |
| i | die cut to shape from Quarterly Pack | 7.50 | — | |
| a | booklet pane of 6 x $2.50 (2887) (**BK641**) | 30.00 | — | |

Qty: 840,000

At time of issue, the P stamp was valued at 85¢.
For non-denominated postal cards of same designs, see UX438–UX439.

2886a

2887a

### QUEEN ELIZABETH II

2888

Designer: Steven Slipp.

Lithography (4 colours), self-adhesive booklet of 10
Lowe-Martin

**2016, Jan 11** **GT4, TRC Paper**
with repeating 'Canada' underprint
**Serpentine Die cut 13.4x13.7**

| | | NH–VF | ⊙F | FDC |
|---|---|---|---|---|
| **2888** | **P multicoloured (QE II)** | 1.70 | .25 | 3.70 |
| i | die cut to shape from Quarterly Pack/ Annual Collection | 2.50 | — | |
| a | booklet pane of 10 x P (2888) (**BK637**) | 17.00 | | |

## UNESCO WORLD HERITAGE SITES IN CANADA

*Perforated singles from water-activated gum souvenir sheet*

**2889a** Landscape of Grand Pré, NS
**2889b** Rideau Canal, ON

**2889c** SGang Gwaay, BC
**2889d** Head-Smashed-In Buffalo Jump, AB
**2889e** Old Town Lunenburg, NS

*Die cut singles from self-adhesive booklets*

**2890** **2891**

**2892** **2893** **2894**

Designer: Lime Design.

Lithography (5 colours)
Lowe-Martin
Water-activated gum souvenir sheet of 5

**2016, Jan 11** **GT4, TRC Paper** **Perf 13.3x13.0**

| | | NH–VF | ⊙F | FDC |
|---|---|---|---|---|
| **2889** | **$4.25 souvenir sheet** of 5 | 8.50 | 8.50 | 10.50 |
| a | **multicoloured**, Grand Pré | 1.70 | 1.50 | |
| b | **multicoloured**, Rideau Canal | 1.70 | 1.50 | |
| c | **multicoloured**, SGang Gwaay | 1.70 | 1.50 | |
| d | **multicoloured**, Buffalo Jump | 1.70 | 1.50 | |
| e | **multicoloured**, Lunenburg | 1.70 | 1.50 | |

Qty: 160,000

Self-adhesive booklets of 10 and 30
**GT4, TRC Paper**
with repeating 'Canada' underprint
**Serpentine Die cut 13.8x13.6**

| | | NH–VF | ⊙F | FDC |
|---|---|---|---|---|
| **2890** | **multicoloured**, Grand Pré | 1.70 | .25 | — |
| **2891** | **multicoloured**, SGang Gwaay | 1.70 | .25 | — |
| **2892** | **multicoloured**, Lunenburg | 1.70 | .25 | — |
| **2893** | **multicoloured**, Rideau Canal | 1.70 | .25 | — |
| **2894** | **multicoloured**, Buffalo Jump | 1.70 | .25 | — |
| i | se-tenant strip of 5 (2890–2894), die cut to shape from Quarterly Pack | 12.50 | — | |
| a | booklet pane of 10 x P (2 each of 2890–2894) (**BK638**) | 17.00 | | |
| b | booklet pane of 30 x P (6 each of 2890–2894) (**BK639**) | 50.00 | | |
| ai | strip of 5, from 2894a/BK638 or 2894b/BK639 | 8.50 | | |

At time of issue, all of the P stamps issued January 11, 2016 were valued at 85¢.

The United Nations Educational, Scientific and Cultural Organization (UNESCO) is a specialized agency of the United Nations.

**2888a**

**2889**

**2894a** **2894b**

## BLACK HISTORY MONTH

**2895**
No. 2 Construction Battalion

Designer: Lime Design.

Lithography (6 colours), self-adhesive booklet of 10
Lowe-Martin

**2016, Feb 1** **GT4, TRC Paper**
**Serpentine Die cut 13.5**

| | | NH–VF | ⊙F | FDC |
|---|---|---|---|---|
| **2895** | **multicoloured** | 1.70 | .65 | 3.70 |
| i | die cut to shape from Quarterly Pack/ Annual Collection | 2.50 | — | |
| a | booklet pane of 10 x P (2895) (**BK642**) | 17.00 | | |

Qty: 1,400,000

The No. 2 Construction Battalion was formed of black Canadians who served their country as part of the Forestry Corps in France.
At time of issue, the P stamp was valued at 85¢.

*Image rotated* **2895a**

## HYDRANGEAS

*Perforated singles from water-activated gum souvenir sheet*

**2896a** **2896b**

**2897** *Hydrangea macrophylla*

**2898** *Hydrangea arborescens*

*Die cut singles from self-adhesive booklet*

2899 2900 — "valley" at upper left

2899i 2900i — "peak" at upper left

Designer: Sputnik Design Partners Inc.

Lithography (6 colours)
Canadian Bank Note
Water-activated gum souvenir sheet of 2

**2016, Mar 1** **GT4, TRC Paper** **Perf 13.1**

| | | NH–VF | ⊙F | FDC |
|---|---|---|---|---|
| **2896** | **$1.70 souvenir sheet** of 2 | 3.50 | 3.50 | — |
| a | **multicoloured**, pink | 1.70 | 1.50 | |
| b | **multicoloured**, white | 1.70 | 1.50 | |
| i | se-tenant pair (2896a–b) | 3.40 | 3.00 | |

Qty: 120,000

Lowe-Martin, Self-adhesive roll of 50
**GT4, TRC Paper**
with repeating 'Canada' underprint
**Serpentine Die cut 8.15 to 8.50 Vertical**
**(Rounded tips with 3 'nibs' between stamps)**

One die cut pattern exists on these stamps.

| | | NH–VF | ⊙F | FDC |
|---|---|---|---|---|
| **2897** | **multicoloured**, pink | 1.70 | .65 | — |
| **2898** | **multicoloured**, white | 1.70 | .65 | — |
| a | se-tenant pair (horiz.), 2897–98 | 3.40 | | |
| i | gutter strip of 4 with inscription | 8.50 | | |
| | starter strip of 4 (wavy die cut) | 10.00 | | |
| | end strip of 4 (wavy die cut) | 10.00 | | |
| ii | se-tenant pair (2897–98), die cut to shape (9.2 vert.) from Quarterly Pack | 5.00 | — | |

Qty: 3,250,000 of each

These stamps were printed se-tenant along the same roll. A dot-matrix printed 'counting number' is printed on the backing paper of the coil, found every 5 stamps. The roll of 50 starts with '50' on the first stamp of the roll and counts down to '5'.

Canadian Bank Note
Self-adhesive booklet of 10
**GT4, TRC Paper Serpentine Die cut 13.3**

| | | NH–VF | ⊙F | FDC |
|---|---|---|---|---|
| **2899** | **multicoloured**, pink; valley at upper left | 1.70 | .65 | |
| i | peak at upper left | 1.70 | .65 | |
| **2900** | **multicoloured**, white; valley at upper left | 1.70 | .65 | |
| i | peak at upper left | 1.70 | .65 | |
| ii | se-tenant pair (2899, 2900), die cut to shape from Quarterly Pack; valley at UL | 5.00 | — | |
| iii | se-tenant pair (2899i, 2900i), die cut to shape from Quarterly Pack; peak at UL | 5.00 | — | |
| a | booklet pane of 10, 5 each #2899/i–2900/i + 10 stickers (**BK643**) | 17.00 | | |

Qty: 5,000,000 of each

The stamps from the left panel of the booklet start with a "valley" at the upper left of the die cut (2899, 2900); the stamps from the right panel of the booklet start with a "peak" at the upper left (2899i, 2900i).

**Nos. 2899–2900 (2) combination FDC** 5.40*

* Stamps on FDCs are not die cut all the way through.

At time of issue, the P stamps were valued at 85¢.

For non-denominated postal cards of same designs, see UX440-UX441.

2896

2900a

## WOMEN'S SUFFRAGE

2901
"Vote"

Designer: Tétro Design.

Lithography (3 colours), self-adhesive booklet of 10
Lowe-Martin

**2016, Mar 8** **GT4, TRC Paper**
**Serpentine Die cut 13.5x13.8**

| | | NH–VF | ⊙F | FDC |
|---|---|---|---|---|
| **2901** | **multicoloured** | 1.70 | .65 | 3.70 |
| i | die cut to shape from Quarterly Pack/ Annual Collection | 2.50 | — | |
| a | booklet pane of 10 x P (2901) (**BK644**) | 17.00 | | |

Qty: 1,400,000

100th anniversary of the first Canadian women getting the right to vote.

At time of issue, the P stamp was valued at 85¢.

*Image rotated* 2901a

## CANADIAN PHOTOGRAPHY — 4

*Perforated singles from water-activated gum souvenir sheets*

2902a
*Toronto*

2902b
*Window*

2902c
*Victoria Bridge, Grand Trunk Railway*

2902d
*Freighter's Boat on the Banks of the Red River, MB*

**2903a**
*Sans titre 0310/ La Chambre noire*

**2903b**
*Climbing Mt. Habel*

**2903c**
*Grey Owl*

*Die cut singles from self-adhesive booklets*

**2904**

**2905**

**2906**

**2907**

**2908**

**2909**

**2910**

**2902**

**2903**

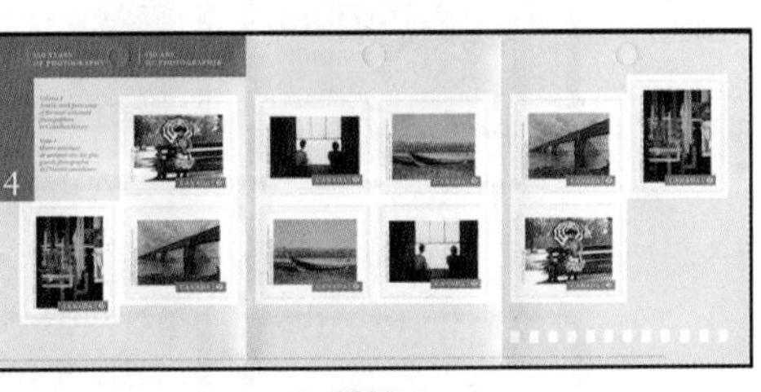

**2908a**

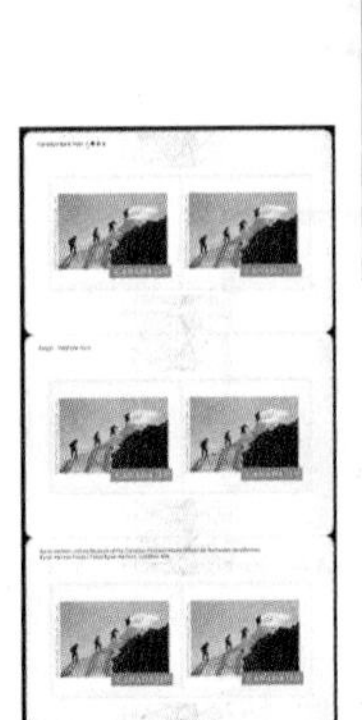

**2909a**

**2910a**

Designer: Stéphane Huot.

Lithography (6 colours)
Canadian Bank Note
Water-activated gum souvenir sheets of 3 and 4

**2016, Apr 13** **GT4, TRC Paper**

| | | NH–VF | ⊙F | FDC |
|---|---|---|---|---|
| **2902** | **$3.40 souvenir sheet** of 4 | 6.80 | 6.80 | 8.80 |
| a | P **multicoloured**, Toronto | 1.75 | 1.50 | |
| b | P **multicoloured**, Window | 1.75 | 1.50 | |
| c | P **multicoloured**, Victoria Bridge | 1.75 | 1.50 | |
| d | P **multicoloured**, Freighter's Boat | 1.75 | 1.50 | |

Qty: 100,000

| | | | | |
|---|---|---|---|---|
| **2903** | **$4.55 souvenir sheet** of 3 | 9.10 | 9.10 | 11.10 |
| a | P **multicoloured**, Sans titre | 1.75 | 1.50 | |
| b | **$1.20 multicoloured**, Mt. Habel | 2.40 | 2.00 | |
| c | **$2.50 multicoloured**, Grey Owl | 5.00 | 4.75 | |

Qty: 100,000

2903a and 2903c are perf. 12.7x12.8; all other single perforated stamps are perf 12.8x12.7.

Lithography (6 colours), self-adhesive booklet of 10
**GT4, TRC Paper**
**Serpentine Die cut 13.4**

| | | NH–VF | ⊙F | FDC |
|---|---|---|---|---|
| **2904** | P **multicoloured**, Toronto | 1.70 | .75 | — |
| i | die cut to shape from Quarterly Pack | 2.50 | — | |
| **2905** | P **multicoloured**, Window | 1.70 | .75 | — |
| i | die cut to shape from Quarterly Pack | 2.50 | — | |
| **2906** | P **multicoloured**, Freighter's Boat | 1.70 | .75 | — |
| i | die cut to shape from Quarterly Pack | 2.50 | — | |
| **2907** | P **multicoloured**, Victoria Bridge | 1.70 | .75 | — |
| i | die cut to shape from Quarterly Pack | 2.50 | — | |
| **2908** | P **multicoloured**, Sans titre | 1.70 | .75 | — |
| i | die cut to shape from Quarterly Pack | 2.50 | — | |
| a | booklet pane of 10, 2 each #2904–2908 (**BK645**) | 17.00 | | |

Qty: 260,000 of each

Lithography (6 colours), self-adhesive booklet of 6

| | | | | |
|---|---|---|---|---|
| **2909** | **$1.20 multicoloured**, Mt. Habel | 2.40 | 1.50 | — |
| i | die cut to shape from Quarterly Pack | 3.60 | — | |
| a | booklet pane of 6 x $1.20 (2909) (**BK646**) | 14.50 | | |

Qty: 780,000

Lithography (7 colours), self-adhesive booklet of 6

| | | | | |
|---|---|---|---|---|
| **2910** | **$2.50 multicoloured**, Grey Owl | 5.00 | 3.00 | — |
| i | die cut to shape from Quarterly Pack | 7.50 | — | |
| a | booklet pane of 6 x $2.50 (2910) (**BK647**) | 30.00 | | |

Qty: 780,000

At time of issue, the P stamps were valued at 85¢.
For non-denominated postal cards of same designs, see UX442–UX448. See also 2626–2634, 2756–2764, and 2814–2822.

**MINT PRICING PREMIUMS**

Mint stamps from 301 to date are valued as NH-VF (Never Hinged-Very Fine). All hinged VF and NH-F copies are worth 50% of the listed values. Plate block (PB) values are for mint NH–VF plate or inscription blocks of four.

**USED, VF/XF (with in-period, circular date cancel) PRICING PREMIUM**

Single stamps with light or circular date cancels will sell for more than catalogue value (perhaps even more than a mint copy). From *1981 to 1991* single stamps from se-tenant blocks of 4 or larger will be priced at 50% or more above the fine price. From *1992* to date single stamps from se-tenant blocks of 4 or larger plus se-tenant booklet panes and souvenir sheets will be priced at 100% or more above the fine price. From *1997* to date all other stamps will be priced at 50% or more above the fine price.

## STAR TREK

*Perforated singles from water-activated gum souvenir sheets*

**2912a**
Captain James T. Kirk
(William Shatner, 1931– )

**2912b**
Commander Kor
(John Colicos, 1928–2000)

**2912c**
Dr. Leonard "Bones" McCoy
(DeForest Kelley, 1920–1999)

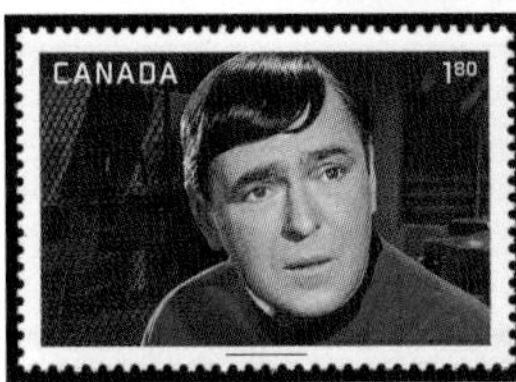
**2912d**
Lt. Commander Montgomery "Scotty" Scott
(James Doohan, 1920–2005)

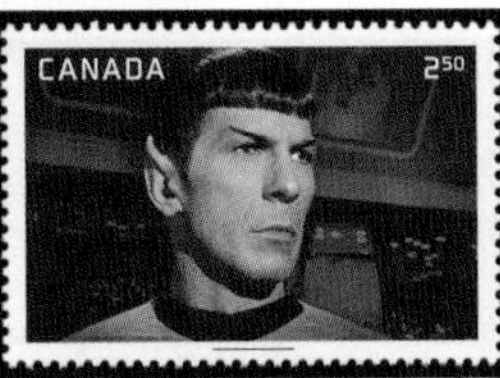
**2912e**
Commander Spock
(Leonard Nimoy, 1931–2015)

*Die cut singles from self-adhesive booklet*

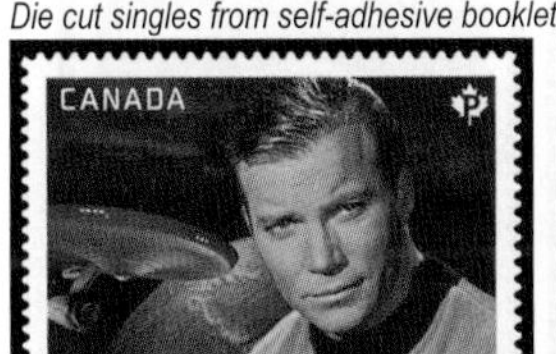
**2917**

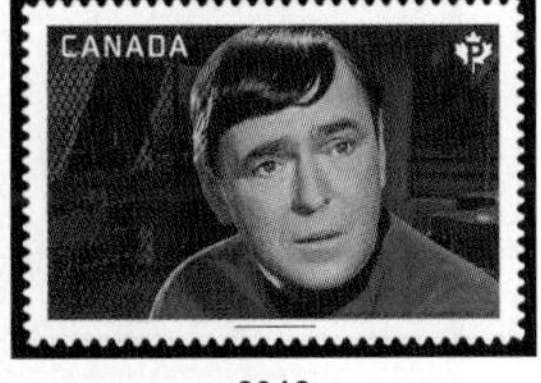
**2918**

**2919**

**2920**

**2921**

**2911**

**2922**

*Perforated singles from water-activated gum souvenir sheet*

**2911a** **2911b**

*Die cut singles from self-adhesive booklet pane*

**2915** **2916**

**2913**
*U.S.S. Enterprise NCC-1701*

**2914**
Klingon battle cruiser

**2922a–b**

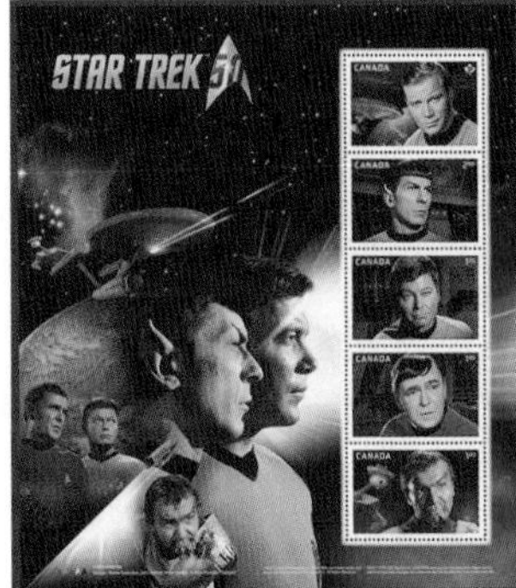
**2912**

**2921a**

**2912f**

**2912g**

**2912h**

**2912i**

**2916a**

Designer: Kosta Tsetsekas, John Belisle, Mike Savage, Adrian Horvath (Signals).

Lithography (5 colours)
Lowe-Martin
Water-activated gum souvenir sheet of 2

**2016, May 5** **GT4, TRC Paper** **Perf 13.3x13.0**

| | | NH–VF | ⊙F | FDC |
|---|---|---|---|---|
| **2911** | **$1.70 souvenir sheet** of 2 | 3.50 | 3.50 | — |
| a | **P multicoloured**, *Enterprise* | 1.75 | 1.50 | |
| b | **P multicoloured**, Klingon | 1.75 | 1.50 | |

Qty: 160,000

Lithography (5 colours)
Water-activated gum pane of 5
**GT4, TRC Paper** **Perf 13.3**

| | | NH–VF | ⊙F | FDC |
|---|---|---|---|---|
| **2912** | **$7.35 pane** of 5 | 15.00 | 15.00 | — |
| a | **P multicoloured**, Kirk | 1.75 | 1.50 | |
| b | **$1.00 multicoloured**, Kor | 2.00 | 1.75 | |
| c | **$1.20 multicoloured**, McCoy | 2.40 | 2.00 | |
| d | **$1.80 multicoloured**, Scott | 3.60 | 3.25 | |
| e | **$2.50 multicoloured**, Spock | 5.00 | 4.75 | |
| f | booklet pane of 4 x P, #2912a | 6.80 | *6.00* | |
| g | booklet pane of 3, #2912c–e | 11.00 | *10.00* | |
| h | booklet pane of 1, #2912b | 2.00 | *1.75* | |
| i | booklet pane of 5, #2912a–e | 15.00 | *12.50* | |
| ii | $44.10 uncut press sheet of 6 souvenir sheets (2912i) | 90.00 | | |

Qty: 2912: 75,000; 2912f–i: 200,000 panes of each; 2912ii: 10,000

Self-adhesive roll of 50
with repeating 'Canada' underprint
**Serpentine Die cut 8.15 to 8.50 Horiz**

| | | NH–VF | ⊙F | FDC |
|---|---|---|---|---|
| **2913** | **P multicoloured**, *Enterprise* | 1.70 | .75 | 3.70 |
| i | die cut to shape (9.2 horiz) from Quarterly Pack | 2.50 | — | |
| **2914** | **P multicoloured**, Klingon | 1.70 | .75 | 3.70 |
| a | se-tenant pair (vert.), 2813–14 | 7.00 | | |
| i | gutter strip of 4 with inscription | 8.50 | | |
| | starter strip of 4 (wavy die cut) | 10.00 | | |
| | end strip of 4 (wavy die cut) | 10.00 | | |
| ii | die cut to shape (9.2 horiz) from Quarterly Pack | 2.50 | — | |

Qty: 1,250,000 of each
These stamps were printed se-tenant along the same roll.

Lithography (5 colours), self-adhesive booklet pane of 2
**GT4, TRC Paper**
**Serpentine Die cut 13.8x13.5**

| | | NH–VF | ⊙F | FDC |
|---|---|---|---|---|
| **2915** | **P multicoloured**, *Enterprise* | *4.00* | *4.00* | |
| **2916** | **P multicoloured**, Klingon | *4.00* | *4.00* | |
| a | booklet pane of 2, #2915–16 | *8.00* | *8.00* | |
| | $19.95 Prestige booklet* (**BK649**) | 40.00 | | |

Qty: 200,000
* The Prestige booklet is comprised of 5 stamp panes: 2912f, 2912g, 2912h, 2912i, 2916a along with 17 pages of memorable moments from the original television series.

Lithography (4 colours), self-adhesive booklet of 10
**GT4, TRC Paper**
**Serpentine Die cut 13.1x13.7**

| | | NH–VF | ⊙F | FDC |
|---|---|---|---|---|
| **2917** | **P multicoloured**, Kirk | 1.70 | .75 | 3.70 |
| i | die cut to shape from Quarterly Pack | 2.50 | — | |
| **2918** | **P multicoloured**, Scott | 1.70 | .75 | 3.70 |
| i | die cut to shape from Quarterly Pack | 2.50 | — | |
| **2919** | **P multicoloured**, Kor | 1.70 | .75 | 3.70 |
| i | die cut to shape from Quarterly Pack | 2.50 | — | |
| **2920** | **P multicoloured**, Spock | 1.70 | .75 | 3.70 |
| i | die cut to shape from Quarterly Pack | 2.50 | — | |
| **2921** | **P multicoloured**, McCoy | 1.70 | .75 | 3.70 |
| i | die cut to shape from Quarterly Pack | 2.50 | — | |
| a | booklet pane of 10, 2 each #2917–2921 (**BK648**) | 17.00 | | |

Qty: 640,000 of each

Lithography plus lenticular †, self-adhesive souvenir sheet of 2
Outer Aspect
**Not tagged** **Perf 15.8x14.7**

| | | NH–VF | ⊙F | FDC |
|---|---|---|---|---|
| **2922** | **$10.00 souvenir sheet** of 2 | 20.00 | 20.00 | 22.00 |
| a | **$5 multicoloured**, transporter | 10.00 | 9.00 | |
| b | **$5 multicoloured**, "The City on the Edge of Forever" | 10.00 | 9.00 | |
| i | $120.00 uncut press sheet of 12 souvenir sheets | 240.00 | | |

Qty: 350,000; 2292i: 2,000

† 2922: A complex "lenticular" printing process that makes images appear to move when viewed from different angles. The stamps show crew members magically appearing and disappearing: on the transporter platform of the *U.S.S. Enterprise* (2922a) and through a time portal known as the Guardian of Forever (2922b).

A lenticular souvenir sheet 'enlargement' (560mmx360mm; qty: 3,500) was sold for $140. The 'stamps' appear to be valid for postage.

Issued on the 50th anniversary of the *Star Trek* television series.

At time of issue, the P stamps were valued at 85¢.
For non-denominated postal cards of same designs, see UX449–UX453.

Space, the Final Frontier... - Kirk | I'm a doctor, not a
Espace, frontière de l'infini... - Kirk | Je suis un docteu

Inscription on backing paper of 2913–14 (eleven different quotes from the TV series are printed along the entire length of the roll)

## DINOS OF CANADA

*Perforated singles from water-activated gum souvenir sheet*

**2923a**
Troodon inequalis
(from AB)

**2923b**
Dimetrodon borealis
(from PEI)

**2923c**
Comox Valley elasmosaur
(from BC)

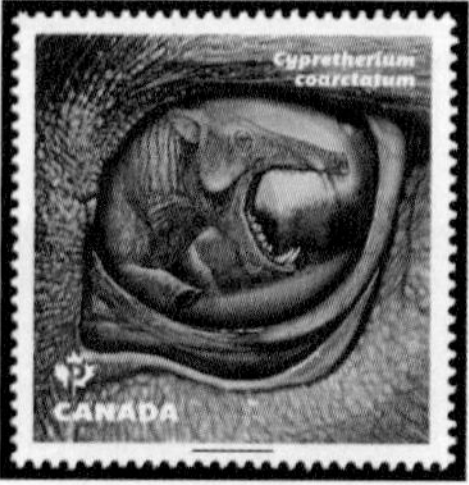


**2923d**
Cypretherium coarctatum
(from SK)

**2923e**
Acrotholus audeti
(from AB)

*Die cut singles from self-adhesive booklet*

2924

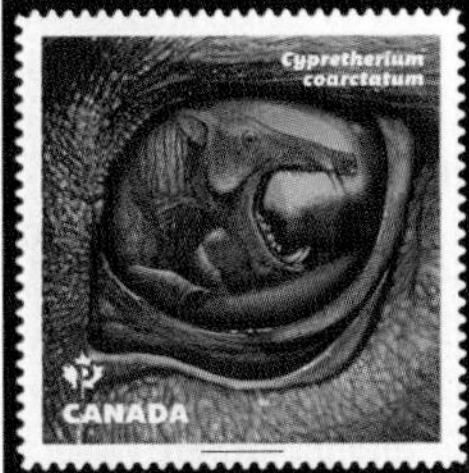
2925

2926

2927

2928

Designer: Subplot Design Inc.

Lithography (4 colours) plus varnish
Lowe-Martin
Water-activated gum souvenir sheet of 5

**2016, May 26** **GT4, TRC Paper** **Perf 13.0**

| | | NH–VF | ⊙F | FDC |
|---|---|---|---|---|
| **2923** | **$4.25 souvenir sheet** of 5 | 8.75 | 8.75 | 10.50 |
| a | **multicoloured**, Troodon | 1.75 | 1.50 | |
| b | **multicoloured**, Dimetrodon | 1.75 | 1.50 | |
| c | **multicoloured**, Comox Valley | 1.75 | 1.50 | |
| d | **multicoloured**, Cypretherium | 1.75 | 1.50 | |
| e | **multicoloured**, Acrotholus | 1.75 | 1.50 | |
| i | $30.60 uncut press sheet of 7 souvenir sheets + 1 single stamp | 62.00 | | |

Qty: 2923: 140,000; 2923i: 2,500

Self-adhesive booklet of 10
**Serpentine Die cut 13.3**

| | | NH–VF | ⊙F | FDC |
|---|---|---|---|---|
| **2924** | **multicoloured**, Troodon | 1.70 | .75 | — |
| i | die cut to shape from Quarterly Pack | 2.50 | — | |
| **2925** | **multicoloured**, Cypretherium | 1.70 | .75 | — |
| i | die cut to shape from Quarterly Pack | 2.50 | — | |
| **2926** | **multicoloured**, Dimetrodon | 1.70 | .75 | — |
| i | die cut to shape from Quarterly Pack | 2.50 | — | |
| **2927** | **multicoloured**, Acrotholus | 1.70 | .75 | — |
| i | die cut to shape from Quarterly Pack | 2.50 | — | |
| **2928** | **multicoloured**, Comox Valley | 1.70 | .75 | — |
| i | die cut to shape from Quarterly Pack | 2.50 | — | |
| a | booklet pane of 10, 2 each #2924–2928 (**BK650**) | 17.00 | | |

Qty: 520,000 of each

At time of issue, the P stamps were valued at 85¢.
See also 2823–2828.

2923

2928a

## BIRDS OF CANADA — I

*Perforated singles from water-activated gum souvenir sheet*

2929a Rock ptarmigan (from NU)

2929b Great horned owl (from AB)

2929c Common raven (from YT)

2929d Altantic puffin (from NL)

2929e Sharp-tailed grouse (from SK)

*Die cut singles from self-adhesive booklet*

2930

2931

2932

2933

2934

Designer: Kosta Tsetsekas, John Belisle (Signals).

Lithography (7 colours)
Colour Innovations
Water-activated gum souvenir sheet of 5

**2016, Jul 12** **GT4, TRC Paper** **Perf 13.0x13.4**

| | | NH–VF | ⊙F | FDC |
|---|---|---|---|---|
| **2929** | **$4.25 souvenir sheet** of 5 | 8.75 | 8.75 | 10.50 |
| a | **multicoloured**, Rock ptarmigan | 1.75 | 1.50 | |
| b | **multicoloured**, Owl | 1.75 | 1.50 | |
| c | **multicoloured**, Raven | 1.75 | 1.50 | |
| d | **multicoloured**, Atlantic puffin | 1.75 | 1.50 | |
| e | **multicoloured**, Grouse | 1.75 | 1.50 | |

Qty: 130,000

Self-adhesive booklet of 10
**Serpentine Die cut 13.4x13.8**

| | | NH–VF | ⊙F | FDC |
|---|---|---|---|---|
| **2930** | **multicoloured**, Grouse | 1.70 | .75 | — |
| i | die cut to shape from Quarterly Pack | 2.50 | — | |
| **2931** | **multicoloured**, Owl | 1.70 | .75 | — |
| i | die cut to shape from Quarterly Pack | 2.50 | — | |
| **2932** | **multicoloured**, Atlantic puffin | 1.70 | .75 | — |
| i | die cut to shape from Quarterly Pack | 2.50 | — | |
| **2933** | **multicoloured**, Raven | 1.70 | .75 | — |
| i | die cut to shape from Quarterly Pack | 2.50 | — | |
| **2934** | **multicoloured**, Rock ptarmigan | 1.70 | .75 | — |
| i | die cut to shape from Quarterly Pack | 2.50 | — | |
| a | booklet pane of 10, 2 each #2930–2934 (**BK651**) | 17.00 | | |

Qty: 800,000 of each

At time of issue, the P stamps were valued at 85¢.
For non-denominated postal cards of same designs, see UX454–UX458. See also 3017–3022.

2929

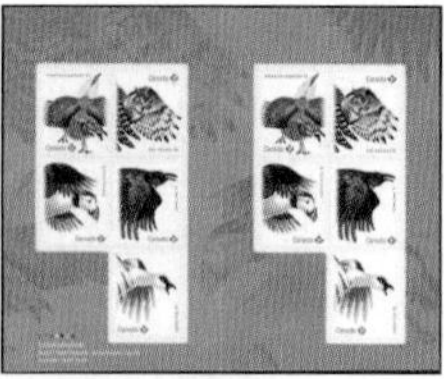
2934a

## HAUNTED CANADA – 3

*Perforated singles from water-activated gum souvenir sheet*

2935a

2935b

2935c

2935d

2935e

*Die cut singles from self-adhesive booklet*

2936
Bell Island Hag, NL

2937
Dungarvon Whooper, NB

2938
Lady in White, QC

2939
Winter Garden Theatre, ON

2940
Phantom Bell Ringers, PE

2935

*Image rotated* 2940a

Designer: Lionel Gadoury, Kammy Ahuja – Context Creative.

Lithography (5 colours) plus holographic foil
Colour Innovations
Water-activated gum souvenir sheet of 5

**2016, Sep 8** **GT4, TRC Paper** **Perf 13.2**

| | | NH–VF | ⊙F | FDC |
|---|---|---|---|---|
| **2935** | **$4.25 souvenir sheet** of 5 | 8.50 | 8.50 | 10.50 |
| a | **P multicoloured**, Bell Island Hag | 1.70 | 1.50 | |
| b | **P multicoloured**, Dungarvon Whooper | 1.70 | 1.50 | |
| c | **P multicoloured**, Winter Garden Theatre | 1.70 | 1.50 | |
| d | **P multicoloured**, Lady in White | 1.70 | 1.50 | |
| e | **P multicoloured**, Phantom Bell Ringers | 1.70 | 1.50 | |
| i | $34.00 uncut press sheet of 8 souvenir sheets | 68.00 | | |

Qty: 125,000; i: 2,000

Self-adhesive booklet of 10

**GT4, TRC Paper** **Serpentine Die cut 13.5**

| | | NH–VF | ⊙F | FDC |
|---|---|---|---|---|
| **2936** | **P multicoloured**, Bell Island Hag | 1.70 | .75 | — |
| i | die cut to shape from Quarterly Pack | 2.50 | — | |
| **2937** | **P multicoloured**, Dungarvon Whooper | 1.70 | .75 | — |
| i | die cut to shape from Quarterly Pack | 2.50 | — | |
| **2938** | **P multicoloured**, Lady in White | 1.70 | .75 | — |
| i | die cut to shape from Quarterly Pack | 2.50 | — | |
| **2939** | **P multicoloured**, Winter Garden Theatre | 1.70 | .75 | — |
| i | die cut to shape from Quarterly Pack | 2.50 | — | |
| **2940** | **P multicoloured**, Phantom Bell Ringers | 1.70 | .75 | — |
| i | die cut to shape from Quarterly Pack | 2.50 | — | |
| a | booklet pane of 10, 2 each #2936–40 (**BK652**) | 17.00 | | |

Qty: 400,000 of each

At time of issue, the P stamps were valued at 85¢.
For non-denominated postal cards of same designs, see UX459–UX463.
Last of a three-year series. See also 2748–2753, 2860–2865.

## GREAT CANADIAN FORWARDS

*Perforated singles from water-activated gum souvenir sheet*

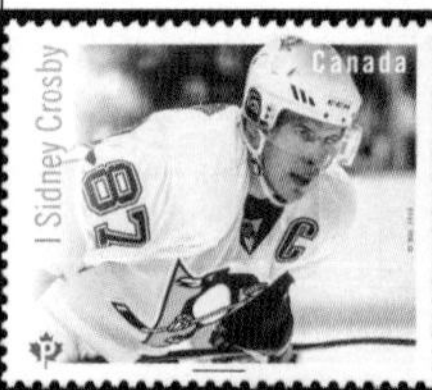
2941a
Sidney Crosby
(1987- )

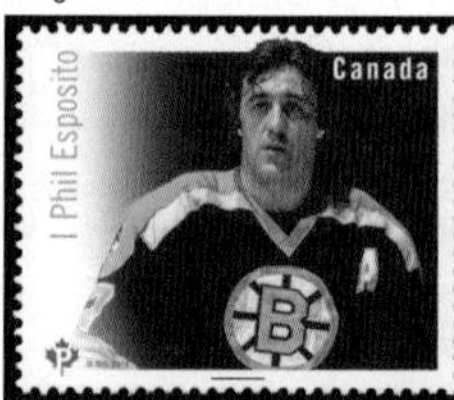
2941b
Phil Esposito
(1942- )

2941c
Guy Lafleur
(1951- )

2941d
Steve Yzerman
(1965- )

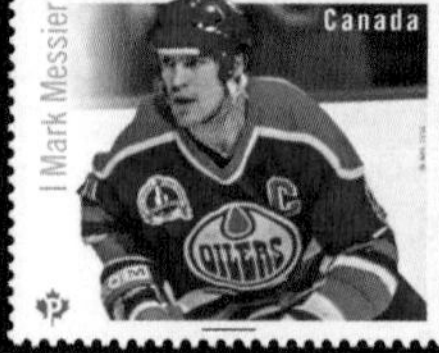
2941e
Mark Messier
(1961- )

2941f
Darryl Sittler
(1950- )

*Die cut singles from self-adhesive booklet*

2942
Sidney Crosby

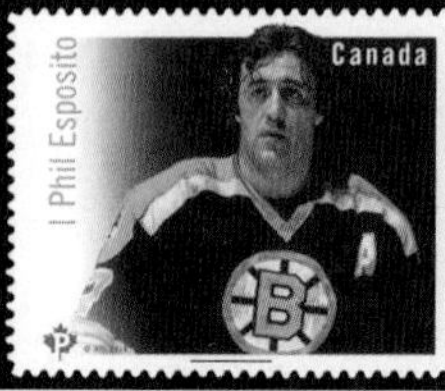
2943
Phil Esposito

2944
Guy Lafleur

**2945**
Steve Yzerman

**2946**
Mark Messier

**2947**
Darryl Sittler

Designer: Avi Dunkelman, Joseph Gault (MIX Design Group).

Lithography (7 colours, one foil stamping plus embossing*)
Lowe-Martin
Water-activated gum pane of 6

| **2016, Sep 23** | **GT4, TRC Paper** | **Perf 12.5x13.2** | | |
|---|---|---|---|---|
| | | NH–VF | ⊙F | FDC |
| **2941** | **$5.10 souvenir sheet** of 6 | 10.50 | 10.50 | |
| a | P **multicoloured**, Sidney Crosby | 1.70 | 1.50 | |
| b | P **multicoloured**, Phil Esposito | 1.70 | 1.50 | |
| c | P **multicoloured**, Guy Lafleur | 1.70 | 1.50 | |
| d | P **multicoloured**, Steve Yzerman | 1.70 | 1.50 | |
| e | P **multicoloured**, Mark Messier | 1.70 | 1.50 | |
| f | P **multicoloured**, Darryl Sittler | 1.70 | 1.50 | |

Qty: 90,000

* The pane has embossing in the selvedge; the stamps themselves do not have any embossing.

Lithography (7 colours)
Self-adhesive booklet of 6
**Serpentine Die cut 13.3x13.5**

| | | NH–VF | ⊙F | FDC |
|---|---|---|---|---|
| **2942** | P **multicoloured**, Sidney Crosby | 1.70 | 0.75 | 3.70 |
| i | die cut to shape from Quarterly Pack | 2.50 | — | |
| **2943** | P **multicoloured**, Phil Esposito | 1.70 | 0.75 | 3.70 |
| i | die cut to shape from Quarterly Pack | 2.50 | — | |
| **2944** | P **multicoloured**, Guy Lafleur | 1.70 | 0.75 | 3.70 |
| i | die cut to shape from Quarterly Pack | 2.50 | — | |
| **2945** | P **multicoloured**, Steve Yzerman | 1.70 | 0.75 | 3.70 |
| i | die cut to shape from Quarterly Pack | 2.50 | — | |
| **2946** | P **multicoloured**, Mark Messier | 1.70 | 0.75 | 3.70 |
| i | die cut to shape from Quarterly Pack | 2.50 | — | |
| **2947** | P **multicoloured**, Darryl Sittler | 1.70 | 0.75 | 3.70 |
| i | die cut to shape from Quarterly Pack | 2.50 | — | |
| a | booklet pane of 6, 1 each #2942–47 (**BK653**) | 10.20 | | |

Qty: 580,000 of each stamp

At time of issue, the P stamps were valued at 85¢.

**2941**

**2947a**

**2948**
Sidney Crosby

**2949**
Phil Esposito

**2950**
Guy Lafleur

**2951**
Steve Yzerman

**2952**
Mark Messier

**2953**
Darryl Sittler

QE II — 2010's

Designer: Avi Dunkelman, Joseph Gault (MIX Design Group).

Lithography (7 colours)
Lowe-Martin
Self-adhesive souvenir sheets of 1

**2016, Sep 23** **GT4, TRC Paper**
**Serpentine Die cut 13.5x13.3**

| | | NH–VF | ⊙F | FDC |
|---|---|---|---|---|
| **2948** | **$1.80 multicoloured**, Sidney Crosby | 3.60 | 3.25 | |
| i | autographed card | *1,200.00* | | |
| **2949** | **$1.80 multicoloured**, Phil Esposito | 3.60 | 3.25 | |
| i | autographed card | *150.00* | | |
| **2950** | **$1.80 multicoloured**, Guy Lafleur | 3.60 | 3.25 | |
| i | autographed card | *125.00* | | |
| **2951** | **$1.80 multicoloured**, Steve Yzerman | 3.60 | 3.25 | |
| i | autographed card | *125.00* | | |
| **2952** | **$1.80 multicoloured**, Mark Messier | 3.60 | 3.25 | |
| i | autographed card | *125.00* | | |
| **2953** | **$1.80 multicoloured**, Darryl Sittler | 3.60 | 3.25 | |
| i | autographed card | *125.00* | | |

Qty: 100,000 of each; 2948i: 100; 2949i: 400; 2950i/2951i/2952i/2953i: 500 of each

The autographed souvenir sheets have a holographic Canada Post circular sticker of authenticity.
These souvenir sheets were only sold in packages of all six. They *were* included in the Quarterly Pack.

*Full souvenir sheets*

*Autographed souvenir sheets*

2948i

2949i

2950i

2951i

2952i

2953i

Timeline:
**2016, Sep 26** (85¢)+10¢ Canada Post Community Foundation, semi-postal (B23–B24)

## CHRISTMAS: Christmas Tree

*Perforated singles from water-activated gum souvenir sheet*

2954a

2954b

2954c

*Die cut singles from self-adhesive booklets*

2956
Santa Claus

2957
Hat on tree

2958
Dove

## CHRISTMAS: MADONNA AND CHILD

2955
*Virgin and Child*

Designer: Hélène L'Heureux.

Lithography (5 colours)
Canadian Bank Note
Water-activated gum souvenir sheet of 3

**2016, Nov 1** **GT4, TRC Paper** **Perf 12.7x12.5**

| | | NH–VF | ⊙F | FDC |
|---|---|---|---|---|
| **2954** | **$4.55 souvenir sheet** of 3 | 9.25 | 9.25 | 11.10 |
| a | **(P) multicoloured** | 1.70 | 1.50 | |
| b | **$1.20 multicoloured** | 2.40 | 2.10 | |
| c | **$2.50 multicoloured** | 5.00 | 4.75 | |

Qty: 110,000

Designer: Louise Méthé.

Lithography (6 colours)
Self-adhesive booklet of 12
**GT4, TRC Paper**
**Serpentine Die cut 13.3x13.4**

| | | NH–VF | ⊙F | FDC |
|---|---|---|---|---|
| **2955** | **(P) multicoloured** | 1.70 | .25 | 3.70 |
| i | die cut to shape from Quarterly Pack/ Annual Collection | 2.50 | — | |
| a | booklet pane of 12 x P (2955) (**BK655**) | 20.40 | — | |

Qty: 7,800,000

Designer: Hélène L'Heureux.

Lithography (5 colours), self-adhesive booklet of 12 (P) or 6
**GT4, TRC Paper**
**Serpentine Die cut 13.0**

| | | NH–VF | ⊙F | FDC |
|---|---|---|---|---|
| **2956** | **(P) multicoloured** | 1.70 | .25 | — |
| i | die cut to shape from Quarterly Pack | 2.50 | — | |
| a | booklet pane of 12 x P (2956) (**BK656**) | 20.40 | — | |

Qty: 9,600,000

| | | NH–VF | ⊙F | FDC |
|---|---|---|---|---|
| **2957** | **$1.20 multicoloured** | 2.40 | 1.20 | — |
| i | die cut to shape from Quarterly Pack | 3.60 | — | |
| a | booklet pane of 6 x $1.20 (2957) (**BK657**) | 14.40 | — | |

Qty: 2,100,000

| | | NH–VF | ⊙F | FDC |
|---|---|---|---|---|
| **2958** | **$2.50 multicoloured** | 5.00 | 2.50 | — |
| i | die cut to shape from Quarterly Pack | 7.50 | — | |
| a | booklet pane of 6 x $2.50 (2958) (**BK658**) | 30.00 | — | |

Qty: 2,100,000

At time of issue, the P stamps were valued at 85¢.

2954

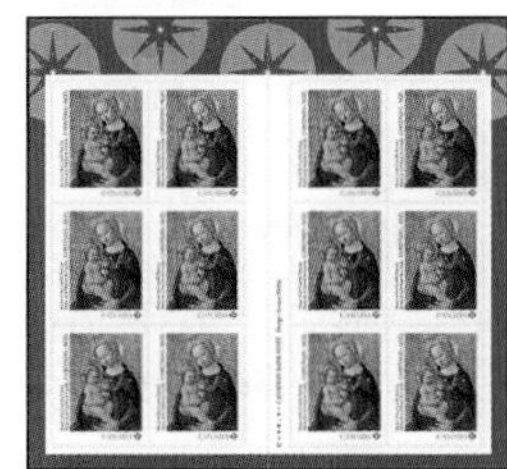

2955a

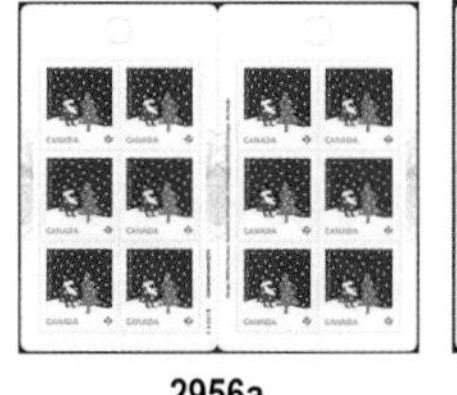

2956a

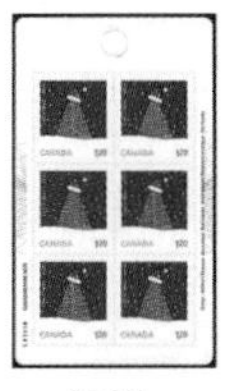

2957a 2958a

## 2017

All of the 2017 stamp issues recognize Canada's 150th anniversary of confederation with some kind of 'hidden' design element: some have either text or the Canada 150 logo visible in the design while others have the text/logo included in the tagging element that requires an ultraviolet light to view.

### LUNAR NEW YEAR (Series 2) — 9
### Year of the Rooster

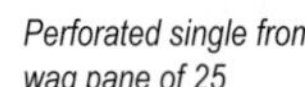

*Perforated single from wag pane of 25*

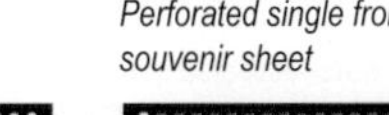

*Perforated single from souvenir sheet*

2959

2960i

*Die cut single from self-adhesive booklets*

2961

2962

2960 2960a

Designer: Paprika.

Lithography (4 colours) plus embossing plus foil stamping, pane of 25 Lowe-Martin

**2017, Jan 9 GT4, TRC Paper Perf 12.5x13.2**

| | | NH–VF | ⊙F | PB | FDC |
|---|---|---|---|---|---|
| **2959** | **(P) multicoloured** | 1.70 | .75 | | 3.70 |
| a | perf 13.2 x 12.5 | 1.70 | .75 | | 3.70 |
| b | se-tenant pair, 2959, 2959a* | 3.50 | 2.50 | 8.50 | |

Qty: 2,000,000

* The stamps are rotated 90 degrees to each other. A se-tenant pair will have one stamp upright and one stamp rotated. Blocks of four contain stamps with four different orientations.

**GT 3 sides Perf 12.5**

| | | NH–VF | ⊙F | FDC |
|---|---|---|---|---|
| **2960** | **$2.50 souvenir sheet** of 1 | 5.00 | 5.00 | 7.00 |
| i | $2.50 single stamp from souvenir sheet | 4.00 | 3.75 | |
| ii | $30.00 uncut press sheet of 12 souvenir sheets | 60.00 | | |
| a | $5.00 'transitional' souvenir sheet of 2, #2885b, 2960 | 10.00 | 10.00 | |

Qty: 2960: 200,000; 2960ii: 8,000; 2960a: 100,000

Lithography (4 colours) plus foil stamping, self-adhesive booklet of 10

**GT4 Serpentine Die cut 13.5**

| | | | | |
|---|---|---|---|---|
| **2961** | **(P) multicoloured** | 1.70 | .75 | — |
| i | die cut to shape from Quarterly Pack | 2.50 | — | |
| a | booklet pane of 10 x P (2961) (**BK659**) | 17.00 | — | |

Qty: 2,700,000

Lithography (4 colours) plus foil stamping, self-adhesive booklet of 6

**GT 3 sides**

| | | | | |
|---|---|---|---|---|
| **2962** | **$2.50 multicoloured** | 5.00 | 3.00 | — |
| i | die cut to shape from Quarterly Pack | 7.50 | — | |
| a | booklet pane of 6 x $2.50 (2962) (**BK660**) | 30.00 | — | |

Qty: 600,000

'CANADA 150' is visible within the tagging when viewed with an ultraviolet/black light.

For non-denominated postal cards of same designs, see UX464–UX465.

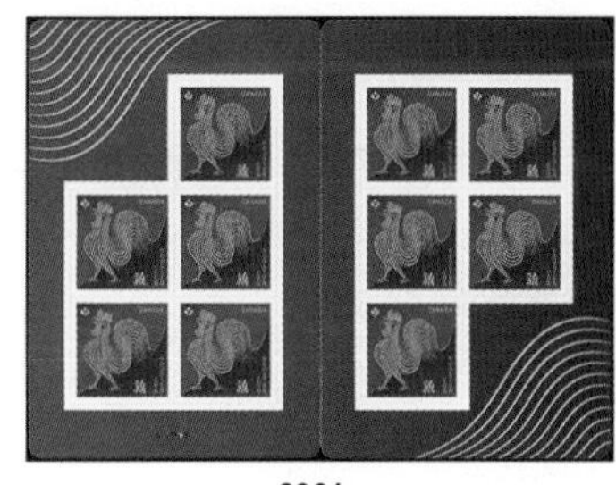

2961a

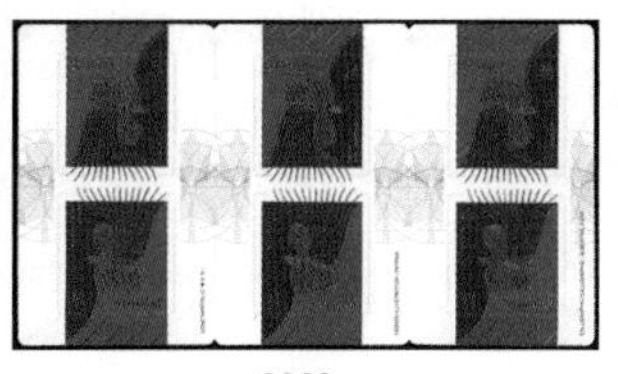

2962a

### UNESCO WORLD HERITAGE SITES IN CANADA

*Perforated singles from water-activated gum souvenir sheet*

2963a Dinosaur Provincial Park, AB

2963b Mistaken Point, NL

2963c Historic District of Old Québec, QC

2963d L'Anse aux Meadows National Historic Site, NL

2963e Red Bay Basque Whaling Station, NL

*Die cut singles from self-adhesive booklets*

2964 2965

2966 2967 2968

Designer: Lara Minja, Lime Design Inc.

Lithography (4 colours)
Canadian Bank Note
Water-activated gum souvenir sheet of 5

**2017, Jan 16** **GT4, TRC Paper** **Perf 13.4x13.0**

| | | NH–VF | ⊙F | FDC |
|---|---|---|---|---|
| **2963** | **$4.25 souvenir sheet** of 5 | 8.50 | 8.50 | 10.50 |
| a | P **multicoloured**, Dinosaur Provincial Park | 1.70 | 1.50 | |
| b | P **multicoloured**, Mistaken Point | 1.70 | 1.50 | |
| c | P **multicoloured**, Old Québec | 1.70 | 1.50 | |
| d | P **multicoloured**, L'Anse aux Meadows | 1.70 | 1.50 | |
| e | P **multicoloured**, Red Bay Basque | 1.70 | 1.50 | |

Qty: 100,000

Self-adhesive booklets of 10 and 30
**GT4, TRC Paper**
with repeating 'Canada' underprint
**Serpentine Die cut 13.0**

| | | NH–VF | ⊙F | FDC |
|---|---|---|---|---|
| **2964** | P **multicoloured**, Dinosaur Provincial Park | 1.70 | .25 | — |
| **2965** | P **multicoloured**, Old Québec | 1.70 | .25 | — |
| **2966** | P **multicoloured**, Red Bay Basque | 1.70 | .25 | — |
| **2967** | P **multicoloured**, Mistaken Point | 1.70 | .25 | — |
| **2968** | P **multicoloured**, L'Anse aux Meadows | 1.70 | .25 | — |
| i | se-tenant strip of 5 (2964–2968), die cut to shape from Quarterly Pack | 12.50 | — | |
| a | booklet pane of 10 x P (2 each of 2964–2968) (**BK661**) | 17.00 | | |
| b | booklet pane of 30 x P (6 each of 2964–2968) (**BK662**) | 50.00 | | |
| ai | strip of 5, from 2968a/BK661 or 2968b/BK662 | 8.50 | | |

The Canada 150 logo is visible within the tagging when viewed with an ultraviolet/black light.

At time of issue, all of the P stamps issued January 16, 2017 were valued at 85¢.
For non-denominated postal cards of same designs, see UX428, UX432, UX466–UX468.

The United Nations Educational, Scientific and Cultural Organization (UNESCO) is a specialized agency of the United Nations.

2963

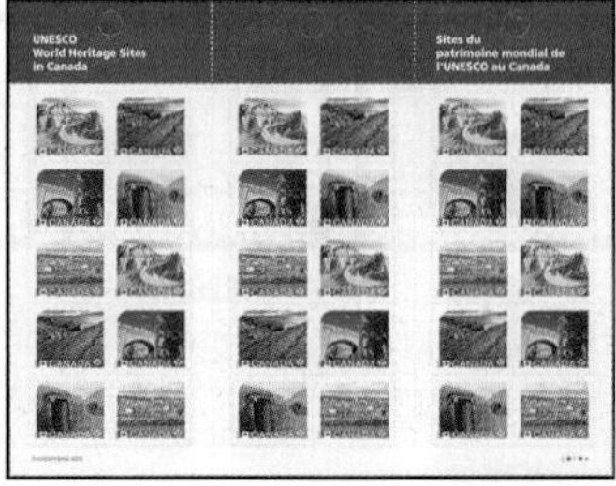

2968a 2968b

## BLACK HISTORY MONTH

2969
Mathieu Da Costa

Designer: Andrew Perro.

Lithography (5 colours), self-adhesive booklet of 10
Canadian Bank Note

**2017, Feb 1** **GT4, TRC Paper**
**Serpentine Die cut 13.4**

| | | NH–VF | ⊙F | FDC |
|---|---|---|---|---|
| **2969** | P **multicoloured** | 1.70 | .65 | 3.70 |
| i | die cut to shape from Quarterly Pack/ Annual Collection | 2.50 | — | |
| a | booklet pane of 10 x P (2969) (**BK663**) | 17.00 | | |

Qty: 1,400,000

Mathieu Da Costa is believed to be the first person of African descent to reach Canada whose name survived history.

The Canada 150 logo in red tagging is visible when viewed with an ultraviolet/black light.

At time of issue, the P stamp was valued at 85¢.

*Image rotated* 2969a

## CANADIAN OPERA

*Perforated singles from water-activated gum souvenir sheet*

2970a *Filumena*; 2970b Gerald Finley (1960– ); 2970c Adrianne Pieczonka (1963– )

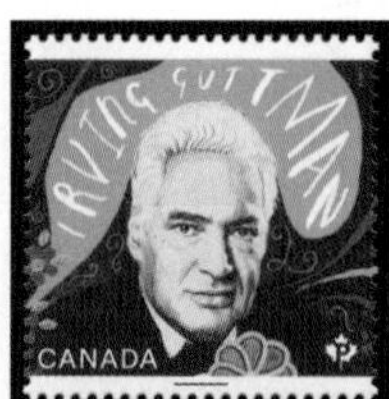

2970d Irving Guttman (1928–2014); 2970e *Louis Riel*

*Die cut singles from self-adhesive booklets*

2971 2972 2973

2974

2975

Designer: Parcel.

Lithography (6 colours)
Colour Innovations
Water-activated gum souvenir sheet of 5

**2017, Feb 4** **GT*, TRC Paper** **Perf 13.1**

| | | NH–VF | ⊙F | FDC |
|---|---|---|---|---|
| **2970** | **$4.25 souvenir sheet** of 5 | 8.50 | 8.50 | 10.50 |
| a | **multicoloured**, Filumena | 1.70 | 1.50 | |
| b | **multicoloured**, Finley | 1.70 | 1.50 | |
| c | **multicoloured**, Pieczonka | 1.70 | 1.50 | |
| d | **multicoloured**, Guttman | 1.70 | 1.50 | |
| e | **multicoloured**, Louis Riel | 1.70 | 1.50 | |

Qty: 100,000

Lithography (6 colours)
Self-adhesive booklet of 10
**Serpentine Die cut 13.4x13.5**

| | | NH–VF | ⊙F | FDC |
|---|---|---|---|---|
| **2971** | **multicoloured**, Filumena | 1.70 | 0.75 | |
| i | die cut to shape from Quarterly Pack | 2.50 | — | |
| **2972** | **multicoloured**, Finley | 1.70 | 0.75 | |
| i | die cut to shape from Quarterly Pack | 2.50 | — | |
| **2973** | **multicoloured**, Pieczonka | 1.70 | 0.75 | |
| i | die cut to shape from Quarterly Pack | 2.50 | — | |
| **2974** | **multicoloured**, Guttman | 1.70 | 0.75 | |
| i | die cut to shape from Quarterly Pack | 2.50 | — | |
| **2975** | **multicoloured**, Louis Riel | 1.70 | 0.75 | |
| i | die cut to shape from Quarterly Pack | 2.50 | — | |
| a | booklet pane of 10, 2 each #2971–75 (**BK664**) | 17.00 | | |

Qty: 260,000 of each stamp

* The tagging is applied to white border of the stamp (three-sided on the Filumena/ Louis Riel stamps, and two-sided on the other stamps).

'CANADA 150' is visible within the tagging when viewed with an ultraviolet/black light.

At time of issue, the P stamps were valued at 85¢.

2970

2975a

## DAISIES

*Perforated singles from water-activated gum souvenir sheet*

2976a 2976b

2977
Fleabane Daisy
*Erigeron speciosus*

2978
Lakeshore Daisy
*Tetraneuris herbacea*

*Die cut singles from self-adhesive booklets*

2979 2980

Designer: Debbie Adams.

Lithography (4 colours)
Lowe-Martin
Water-activated gum souvenir sheet of 2

**2017, Mar 1** **GT2, TRC Paper** **Perf 13.1**

| | | NH–VF | ⊙F | FDC |
|---|---|---|---|---|
| **2976** | **$1.70 souvenir sheet** of 2 | 3.50 | 3.50 | — |
| a | **multicoloured**, purple | 1.70 | 1.50 | |
| b | **multicoloured**, yellow | 1.70 | 1.50 | |
| i | se-tenant pair (2976a–b) | 3.40 | 3.00 | |

Qty: 100,000

Self-adhesive roll of 50
**GT4, TRC Paper**
with repeating 'Canada' underprint
**Serpentine Die cut 8.15 to 8.50 Vertical**
**(Rounded tips with 3 'nibs' between stamps)**

One die cut pattern exists on these stamps.

| | | NH–VF | ⊙F | FDC |
|---|---|---|---|---|
| **2977** | **multicoloured**, purple | 1.70 | .75 | — |
| **2978** | **multicoloured**, yellow | 1.70 | .75 | — |
| a | se-tenant pair (horiz.), 2977–78 | 3.40 | | |
| i | gutter strip of 4 with inscription | 8.50 | | |
| | starter strip of 4 (wavy die cut) | 10.00 | | |
| | end strip of 4 (wavy die cut) | 10.00 | | |
| ii | se-tenant pair (2977–78), die cut to shape (9.2 vert.) from Quarterly Pack | 5.00 | — | |

Qty: 3,250,000 of each

These stamps were printed se-tenant along the same roll.

Self-adhesive booklet of 10
**GT2, TRC Paper**
**Serpentine Die cut 13.6x13.5**

| | | NH–VF | ⊙F | FDC |
|---|---|---|---|---|
| **2979** | **multicoloured**, purple | 1.70 | .65 | |
| **2980** | **multicoloured**, yellow | 1.70 | .65 | |
| i | se-tenant pair (2979, 2980), die cut to shape from Quarterly Pack | 5.00 | — | |
| a | booklet pane of 10, 5 each #2979–2980 + 10 stickers (**BK665**) | 17.00 | | |

Qty: 5,000,000 of each

**Nos. 2979–2980 (2) combination FDC** **5.40***

* Stamps on FDCs are not die cut all the way through.

Microprinted 'CANADA 150' is 'hidden' within the design of each stamp.
At time of issue, the P stamps were valued at 85¢.
For non-denominated postal cards of same designs, see UX469-UX470.

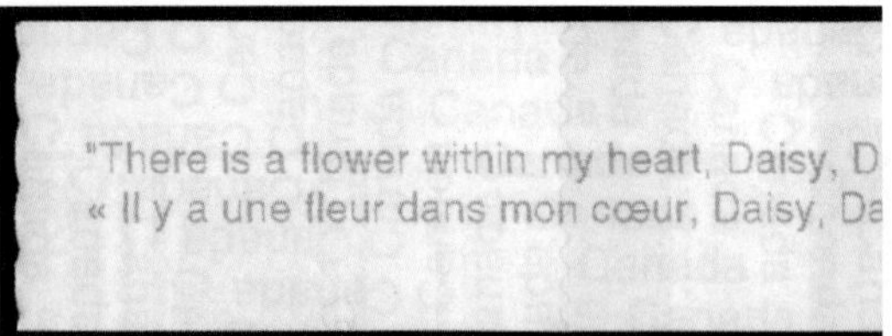


The refrain of the classic song 'Daisy, Daisy' is printed on the backing paper along the entire length of the roll.

2976

*Image rotated* **2980a**

## BATTLE OF VIMY RIDGE

**2981a**
Pillars and statue

**2981b**
Statue of weeping woman

**2982**
Canadian National Vimy Memorial
*die cut type 1*

**2982i**
*die cut type 2*

**2982ii**
*die cut type 3*

**2982iii**
*die cut type 4*

**2982iv**
*die cut type 5*

**2982v**
*die cut type 6*

**2982vi**
*die cut type 7*

Designer: Susan Scott (Canada), Sarah Bougault (France).

Lithography (5 colours plus 1 engraving)
Colour Innovations
Water-activated gum souvenir sheet of 2

**2017, Apr 8** **GT4 (inset), TRC Paper** **Perf 13.3**

| | | NH–VF | ⊙F | FDC |
|---|---|---|---|---|
| **2981** | **$5.00 souvenir sheet** of 2 | 10.00 | 10.00 | — |
| **a** | **$2.50 multicoloured** | 5.00 | 4.75 | |
| **b** | **$2.50 multicoloured** | 5.00 | 4.75 | |

Qty: 130,000

The souvenir sheet did not ship to post offices and collectors until nearly three weeks after the issue date.

Lithography (6 colours), self-adhesive booklet of 10
**GT4, TRC Paper**
**Serpentine Die cut 13.4**

| | | NH–VF | ⊙F | FDC |
|---|---|---|---|---|
| **2982** | P **multicoloured**, Type 1 die cutting (pos. 1) | 1.70 | .65 | 3.70 |
| **i** | Type 2 die cutting (pos. 2) | 1.70 | .65 | |
| **ii** | Type 3 die cutting (pos. 3) | 1.70 | .65 | |
| **iii** | Type 4 die cutting (pos. 4, 8) | 1.70 | .65 | |
| **iv** | Type 5 die cutting (pos. 5, 9) | 1.70 | .65 | |
| **v** | Type 6 die cutting (pos. 6, 10) | 1.70 | .65 | |
| **vi** | Type 7 die cutting (pos. 7) | 1.70 | .65 | |
| | *Die cut to shape singles, from Quarterly Pack/Annual Collection:* | | | |
| **vii** | as 2982, Type 1 die cutting | 2.50 | — | |
| **viii** | as 2982i, Type 2 die cutting | 2.50 | — | |
| **ix** | as 2982ii, Type 3 die cutting | 2.50 | — | |
| **x** | as 2982iii, Type 4 die cutting | 2.50 | — | |
| **xi** | as 2982iv, Type 5 die cutting | 2.50 | — | |
| **xii** | as 2982v, Type 6 die cutting | 2.50 | — | |
| **xiii** | as 2982vi, Type 7 die cutting | 2.50 | — | |
| a | booklet pane of 10 x P (2982–vi) (**BK666**) | 17.00 | | |

Qty: 2,000,000

The seven different die cutting varieties are noticeable at the four corners of the stamps. Complete sets of the die cut to shape singles are extremely difficult to obtain as one must purchase *many* Quarterly Packs (at $44.65 per pack).

Joint issue with France. France souvenir sheet sold by Canada Post for C$3.50.

Microprinted 'Canada 150' is 'hidden' within the design of each stamp. The souvenir sheet also has the Canada 150 logo.

Centennial of the Battle of Vimy Ridge (four-day battle which began at 5:30am on April 9, 1917) is considered by many to be a defining moment in Canadian history.

At time of issue, the P stamp was valued at 85¢.

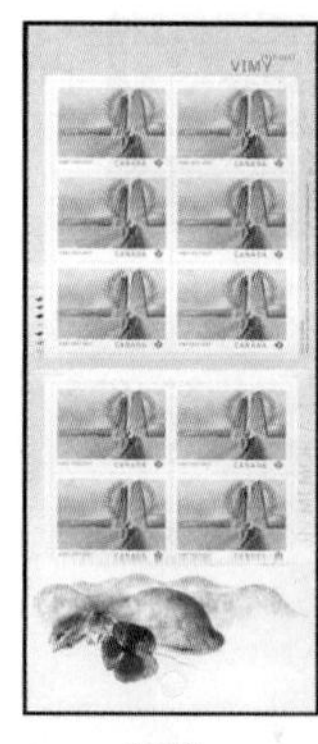

**2982a**

**2981**

Joint issue with France
**Scott # 5216**

## *STAR TREK* (Year 2): Captains

*Perforated singles from water-activated gum souvenir sheets*

**2983a**
Admiral Kirk vs. Khan Noonien Singh
(William Shatner, 1931– )
(Ricardo Montalbán, 1920–2009)

**2983b**
Captain Archer vs. Commander Dolim
[*Star Trek: Enterprise*]
(Scott Bakula, 1954– )
(Scott MacDonald, 1959– )

**2983c**
Captain Janeway vs. the Borg Queen
[*Star Trek: Voyager*]
(Kate Mulgrew, 1955– )
(Alice Krige, 1954– )

**2983d**
Captain Sisko vs. Dukat
[*Star Trek: Deep Space Nine*]
(Avery Brooks, 1948– )
(Marc Alaimo, 1942– )

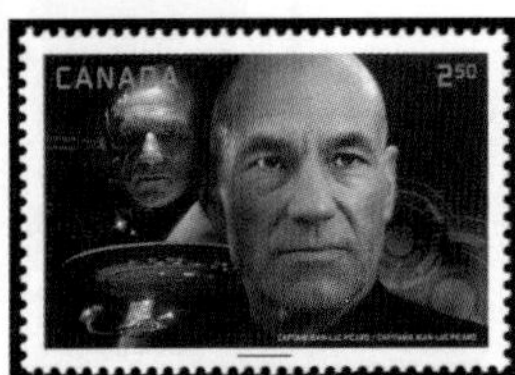

**2983e**
Captain Picard vs. Locutus of Borg
(Patrick Stewart, 1940– )

*Die cut singles from self-adhesive booklet*

**2986**

**2987**

**2988**

**2989**

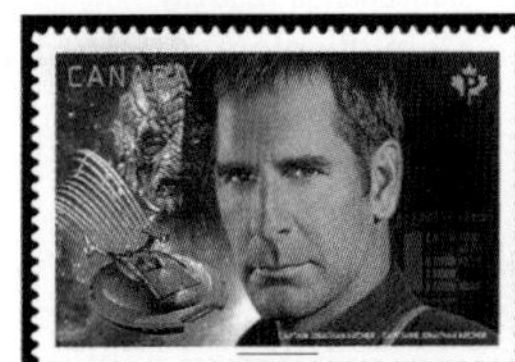

**2990**

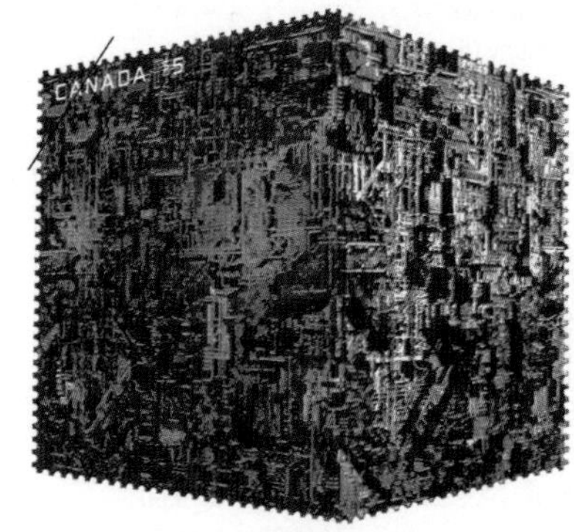

**2984**
The Borg cube

*Die cut single from self-adhesive booklet pane*

**2991**
*Galileo* (NCC-1701/7)

**2985**
*Galileo* (NCC-1701/7)

**2983**

**2990a**

**2983f**

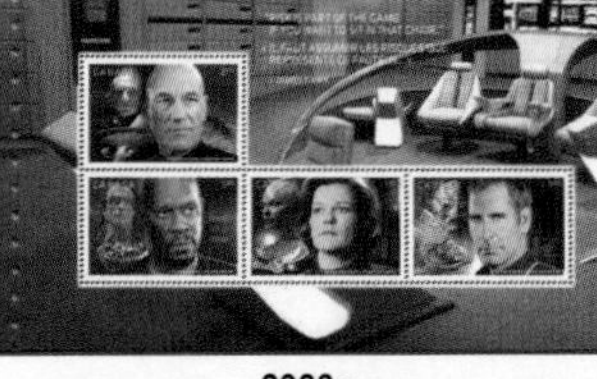

**2983g**

**2983h**

**2984a**

**2991a**

"Set a course ... for home." – Kathryn Janeway "Let us mak
« Changez de cap. On rentre à la maison. » – Kathryn Janew

Inscription on backing paper of 2985 (11 different quotes from the movie and TV series are printed along the entire length of the roll)

QE II — 2010's

Designer: Kosta Tsetsekas, Adrian Horvath (Signals).

Lithography (5 colours)
Lowe-Martin
Water-activated gum pane of 5

**2017, Apr 27** **GT4, TRC Paper** **Perf 13.3**

| | | NH–VF | ⊙F | FDC |
|---|---|---|---|---|
| **2983** | **$7.35 pane** of 5 | 15.00 | 15.00 | — |
| a | **P multicoloured**, Kirk | 1.75 | 1.50 | |
| b | **$1.00 multicoloured**, Archer | 2.00 | 1.75 | |
| c | **$1.20 multicoloured**, Janeway | 2.40 | 2.00 | |
| d | **$1.80 multicoloured**, Sisko | 3.60 | 3.25 | |
| e | **$2.50 multicoloured**, Picard | 5.00 | 4.75 | |
| f | booklet pane of 3 x P, #2983a | 6.80 | *6.00* | |
| g | booklet pane of 4, #2983b–e | 11.00 | *10.00* | |
| h | booklet pane of 5, #2983a–e | 15.00 | *12.50* | |
| i | $44.10 uncut press sheet of 6 souvenir sheets (2983h) | 90.00 | | |

Qty: 2983: 85,000; 2983f–h: 75,000 panes of each; 2983i: 5,000

Lithography (5 colours), booklet pane of 1

**Not tagged, TRC Paper** **Perf 13.2**

| | | NH–VF | ⊙F | FDC |
|---|---|---|---|---|
| **2984** | **$5 multicoloured**, Borg cube | 10.00 | *10.00* | 12.00 |
| a | booklet pane of 1, #2984 | 10.00 | *10.00* | |

Qty: 75,000

Self-adhesive roll of 50
with repeating 'Canada' underprint

**Serpentine Die cut 8.15 to 8.50 Horiz**

| | | NH–VF | ⊙F | FDC |
|---|---|---|---|---|
| **2985** | **P multicoloured**, *Galileo* | 1.70 | .75 | 3.70 |
| i | die cut to shape (9.2 horiz) from Quarterly Pack | 2.50 | — | |
| ii | gutter strip of 4 with inscription | 8.50 | | |
| | starter strip of 4 (wavy die cut) | 10.00 | | |
| | end strip of 4 (wavy die cut) | 10.00 | | |

Qty: 3,000,000

Lithography (4 colours), self-adhesive booklet of 10

**GT4, TRC Paper**

**Serpentine Die cut 13.1x13.7**

| | | NH–VF | ⊙F | FDC |
|---|---|---|---|---|
| **2986** | **P multicoloured**, Kirk | 1.70 | .75 | 3.70 |
| i | die cut to shape from Quarterly Pack | 2.50 | — | |
| **2987** | **P multicoloured**, Picard | 1.70 | .75 | 3.70 |
| i | die cut to shape from Quarterly Pack | 2.50 | — | |
| **2988** | **P multicoloured**, Sisko | 1.70 | .75 | 3.70 |
| i | die cut to shape from Quarterly Pack | 2.50 | — | |
| **2989** | **P multicoloured**, Janeway | 1.70 | .75 | 3.70 |
| i | die cut to shape from Quarterly Pack | 2.50 | — | |
| **2990** | **P multicoloured**, Archer | 1.70 | .75 | 3.70 |
| i | die cut to shape from Quarterly Pack | 2.50 | — | |
| a | booklet pane of 10, 2 each #2986–2990 (**BK667**) | 17.00 | | |

Qty: 700,000 of each

Lithography (4 colours), self-adhesive booklet pane of 1

**GT4, TRC Paper**

**Serpentine Die cut 13.8x13.5**

| | | NH–VF | ⊙F | FDC |
|---|---|---|---|---|
| **2991** | **P multicoloured**, *Galileo* | *5.00* | *5.00* | |
| a | booklet pane of 1, #2991 | 5.00 | *5.00* | |
| | $21.95 Prestige booklet* (**BK668**) | 45.00 | | |

Qty: 75,000

* The Prestige booklet is comprised of 5 stamp panes: 2983f, 2983g, 2983h, 2984a, 2991a along with 17 pages of memorable moments from the various movie and television series.

The 'Captains' stamps have 'CANADA 150' and two Canada 150 logos visible within the tagging when viewed with an ultraviolet/black light. The *Galileo* and Borg cube stamps have microprinted 'CANADA 150' 'hidden' within the design of each stamp.

At time of issue, the P stamps were valued at 85¢.
For non-denominated postal cards of same designs, see UX471–UX475.

## FORMULA I IN CANADA

*Perforated singles from water-activated gum souvenir sheets*

**2992a**
Sir Jackie Stewart
(1939– )

**2992b**
Gilles Villeneuve
(1950–1982)

**2992c**
Ayrton Senna
(1960–1994)

**2992d**
Michael
Schumacher
(1969– )

**2992e**
Lewis Hamilton
(1985– )

*Die cut singles from self-adhesive booklet*

**2993**

**2994**

**2995**

**2996**

**2997**

Designer: Paprika.

Lithography (5 colours + MFX)
Colour Innovations
Water-activated gum pane of 5

**2017, May 16** **GT4, TRC Paper** **Perf 13.1**

| | | NH–VF | ⊙F | FDC |
|---|---|---|---|---|
| **2992** | **$4.25 pane** of 5 | 8.50 | 8.50 | — |
| a | **P multicoloured**, Stewart | 1.75 | 1.50 | |
| ai | identical pair (2992a)* | 5.00 | *6.00* | |
| b | **P multicoloured**, Villeneuve | 1.75 | 1.50 | |
| bi | identical pair (2992b)* | 5.00 | *6.00* | |
| c | **P multicoloured**, Senna | 1.75 | 1.50 | |
| ci | identical pair (2992c)* | 5.00 | *6.00* | |
| d | **P multicoloured**, Schumacher | 1.75 | 1.50 | |
| di | identical pair (2992d)* | 5.00 | *6.00* | |
| e | **P multicoloured**, Hamilton | 1.75 | 1.50 | |
| ei | identical pair (2992e)* | 5.00 | *6.00* | |
| i | $21.25 uncut press sheet of 5 strips of 5 stamps | 45.00 | | |

Qty: 2992: 80,000; 2992i: 2,000

* the uncut press sheet (2992i) produces identical pairs, strips of 3, 4 and 5.

Lithography (5 colours + MFX), self-adhesive booklet of 10
**GT4, TRC Paper**
**Serpentine Die cut 16.6**

| | | NH–VF | ⊙F | FDC |
|---|---|---|---|---|
| **2993** | P **multicoloured**, Stewart | 1.70 | .75 | 3.70 |
| i | die cut to shape from Quarterly Pack | 2.50 | — | |
| **2994** | P **multicoloured**, Villeneuve | 1.70 | .75 | 75.00 |
| | revised (corrected) OFDC†, *Jun* | | | 3.70 |
| i | die cut to shape from Quarterly Pack | 2.50 | — | |
| **2995** | P **multicoloured**, Senna | 1.70 | .75 | 3.70 |
| i | die cut to shape from Quarterly Pack | 2.50 | — | |
| **2996** | P **multicoloured**, Schumacher | 1.70 | .75 | 3.70 |
| i | die cut to shape from Quarterly Pack | 2.50 | — | |
| **2997** | P **multicoloured**, Hamilton | 1.70 | .75 | 3.70 |
| i | die cut to shape from Quarterly Pack | 2.50 | — | |
| a | booklet pane of 10, 2 each #2993–2997 (**BK669**) | 17.00 | | |

Qty: 600,000 of each

† The Gilles Villeneuve OFDC was recalled three days after its release due to text on the back showing an incorrect birthplace in the French translation. A corrected, replacement OFDC, was released in June.

A pink fluorescent '150' is visible within the tagging (following 'CANADA') when viewed with an ultraviolet/black light.

At time of issue, the P stamps were valued at 85¢.

2997a

2992

## EID

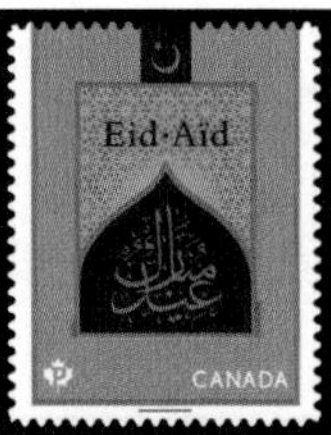

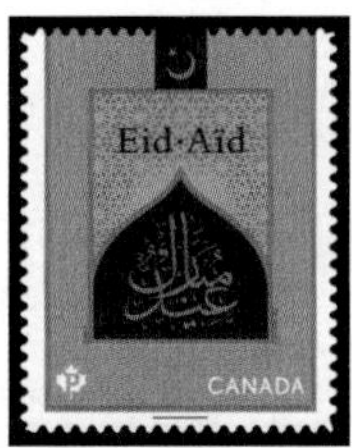

Arabic phrase "Eid Mubarak" in a pointed arch

| 2998 | 2998i | 2998ii |
|---|---|---|
| *die cut type 1* | *die cut type 2* | *die cut type 3* |

Designer: Doreen Colonello and Erin Enns of Entro Communications.
Lithography (6 colours + varnish), self-adhesive booklet of 10
Colour Innovations
**2017, May 24** **GT4, TRC Paper**
**Serpentine Die cut 13.5x13.3**

| | | NH–VF | ⊙F | FDC |
|---|---|---|---|---|
| **2998** | P **multicoloured** , Type 1 die cutting (col. 1) | 1.70 | .65 | 3.70 |
| i | Type 2 die cutting (col. 2 & 4) | 1.70 | .65 | |
| ii | Type 3 die cutting (col. 3 & 5) | 1.70 | .65 | |
| | *Die cut to shape singles, from Quarterly Pack/Annual Collection:* | | | |
| iii | as 2998, Type 1 die cutting | 2.50 | — | |
| iv | as 2998i, Type 2 die cutting | 2.50 | — | |
| v | as 2998ii, Type 3 die cutting | 2.50 | — | |
| a | booklet pane of 10 x P (2998–ii) (**BK670**) | 17.00 | | |

Qty: 2,000,000
The three different die cutting varieties are noticeable at the four corners of the stamps.
Microprinted 'Canada 150' is 'hidden' within the design of each stamp.

Celebrating Eid-al-Fitr – the Festival of Breaking the Fast (around June 26, 2017), and Eid al-Adha – the Festival of Sacrifice (around September 2, 2017). At time of issue, the P stamp was valued at 85¢.

2998

## CANADA 150

2999a
1967: Expo 67

2999b
1971: Trans-Canada Highway

2999c
1972: Summit Series

2999d
1980: Marathon of Hope

2999e
1981: Canadarm

2999f
1982: The Constitution

2999g
1999: Nunavut

2999h
2005: Marriage Equality

**2999i**
1976 1988 2010: Olympic Games

**2999j**
1976 2010: Paralympic Glory

**3000**

**3001**

**3002**

**3003**

**3004**

**3005**

**3006**

**3007**

**3008**

**3009**

Designer: Subplot Design Inc.

Lithography (6 colours), water-activated gum pane of 10
Lowe-Martin

**2017, Jun 1** **GT*, TRC Paper** **Perf 13.6**

| | | NH–VF | ⊙F | FDC |
|---|---|---|---|---|
| **2999** | **$8.50 pane** of 10 | 17.00 | 17.00 | — |
| a | **multicoloured**, Expo 67 | 1.75 | 1.50 | |
| b | **multicoloured**, Trans-Canada Highway | 1.75 | 1.50 | |
| c | **multicoloured**, Summit Series | 1.75 | 1.50 | |
| d | **multicoloured**, Marathon of Hope | 1.75 | 1.50 | |
| e | **multicoloured**, Canadarm | 1.75 | 1.50 | |
| f | **multicoloured**, The Constitution | 1.75 | 1.50 | |
| g | **multicoloured**, Nunavut | 1.75 | 1.50 | |
| h | **multicoloured**, Marriage Equality | 1.75 | 1.50 | |
| i | **multicoloured**, Olympic Games | 1.75 | 1.50 | |
| j | **multicoloured**, Paralympic Glory | 1.75 | 1.50 | |

Qty: 80,000
Used price is for copies with full perfs (they are easily damaged during separation).

Self-adhesive booklet of 10

**Die cut**

| | | NH–VF | ⊙F | FDC |
|---|---|---|---|---|
| **3000** | **multicoloured**, Expo 67 | 1.70 | .75 | 3.70 |
| i | die cut to shape from Quarterly Pack | 2.50 | — | |
| **3001** | **multicoloured**, Trans-Canada Highway | 1.70 | .75 | 3.70 |
| i | die cut to shape from Quarterly Pack | 2.50 | — | |
| **3002** | **multicoloured**, Summit Series | 1.70 | .75 | 3.70 |
| i | die cut to shape from Quarterly Pack | 2.50 | — | |
| **3003** | **multicoloured**, Marathon of Hope | 1.70 | .75 | 3.70 |
| i | die cut to shape from Quarterly Pack | 2.50 | — | |
| **3004** | **multicoloured**, Canadarm | 1.70 | .75 | 3.70 |
| i | die cut to shape from Quarterly Pack | 2.50 | — | |
| **3005** | **multicoloured**, The Constitution | 1.70 | .75 | 3.70 |
| i | die cut to shape from Quarterly Pack | 2.50 | — | |
| **3006** | **multicoloured**, Nunavut | 1.70 | .65 | 3.70 |
| i | die cut to shape from Quarterly Pack | 2.50 | — | |
| a | booklet pane of 8 x P (3006) (**BK672**) | 13.60 | | |
| **3007** | **multicoloured**, Marriage Equality | 1.70 | .65 | 3.70 |
| i | die cut to shape from Quarterly Pack | 2.50 | — | |
| a | booklet pane of 8 x P (3007) (**BK673**) | 13.60 | | |
| **3008** | **multicoloured**, Olympic Games | 1.70 | .75 | 3.70 |
| i | die cut to shape from Quarterly Pack | 2.50 | — | |
| **3009** | **multicoloured**, Paralympic Glory | 1.70 | .75 | 3.70 |
| i | die cut to shape from Quarterly Pack | 2.50 | — | |
| a | booklet pane of 10 x P #3000–3009 (**BK671**) | 17.00 | | |

Qty: 500,000 of each; Nunavut (3006): 1,300,000; Equality (3007): 2,100,000

* the tagging is a 1mm band around the outside of the maple leaf.

**3006a**

**2999**

**3007a**

**3009a**

QE II — 2010's

## CANADIAN PHOTOGRAPHY — 5

*Perforated singles from water-activated gum souvenir sheets*

**3010a** *Enlacées, Montréal* — **3010b** *Sir John A. Macdonald*

**3011a** *Ontario, Canada* — **3011b** *Construction of the Parliament Buildings, Centre Block* — **3011c** *Ti-Noir Lajeunesse, The Blind Violinist, Disraeli, Quebec*

*Die cut singles from self-adhesive booklet*

**3012** — **3013** — **3014**

**3015** — **3016**

Designer: Stéphane Huot.

Lithography (4 colours)
Canadian Bank Note
Water-activated gum souvenir sheets of 2 and 3

**2017, Jul 4** **GT4, TRC Paper** **Perf 12.7x12.8**

| | | NH–VF | ⊙F | FDC |
|---|---|---|---|---|
| **3010** | **$1.70 souvenir sheet** of 2 | 3.50 | 3.50 | 5.40 |
| a | P **multicoloured**, Enlacées | 1.75 | 1.50 | |
| b | P **multicoloured**, Macdonald | 1.75 | 1.50 | |

Qty: 100,000

Lithography (5 colours)
**Perf 12.8x12.7**

| | | NH–VF | ⊙F | FDC |
|---|---|---|---|---|
| **3011** | **$2.55 souvenir sheet** of 3 | 5.25 | 5.25 | 7.10 |
| a | P **multicoloured**, Ontario | 1.75 | 1.50 | |
| b | P **multicoloured**, Centre Block | 1.75 | 1.50 | |
| c | P **multicoloured**, Blind Violinist | 1.75 | 1.50 | |

Qty: 100,000

Lithography (6 colours), self-adhesive booklet of 10
**GT4, TRC Paper**
**Serpentine Die cut 13.4**

| | | NH–VF | ⊙F | FDC |
|---|---|---|---|---|
| **3012** | P **multicoloured**, Blind Violinist | 1.70 | .75 | — |
| i | die cut to shape from Quarterly Pack | 2.50 | — | |
| **3013** | P **multicoloured**, Enlacées | 1.70 | .75 | — |
| i | die cut to shape from Quarterly Pack | 2.50 | — | |
| **3014** | P **multicoloured**, Ontario | 1.70 | .75 | — |
| i | die cut to shape from Quarterly Pack | 2.50 | — | |
| **3015** | P **multicoloured**, Centre Block | 1.70 | .75 | — |
| i | die cut to shape from Quarterly Pack | 2.50 | — | |
| **3016** | P **multicoloured**, Macdonald | 1.70 | .75 | — |
| i | die cut to shape from Quarterly Pack | 2.50 | — | |
| a | booklet pane of 10, 2 each #3012–3016 (**BK674**) | 17.00 | | |

Qty: 280,000 of each

The Canada 150 logo is visible within the vertical tagging bars when viewed with an ultraviolet/black light.
At time of issue, the P stamps were valued at 85¢.
For non-denominated postal cards of same designs, see UX476–UX480. See also 2626–2634, 2756–2764, 2814–2822, and 2902–2910.

**3010** — **3011**

**3016a**

## BIRDS OF CANADA — 2

*Perforated singles from water-activated gum souvenir sheet*

**3017a** Blue jay (from PE) — **3017b** Gyrfalcon (from NT) — **3017c** Great gray owl (from MB) — **3017d** Osprey (from NS) — **3017e** Common loon (from ON)

*Die cut singles from self-adhesive booklet*

**3018** — **3019** — **3020** — **3021** — **3022**

Designer: Kosta Tsetsekas, Adrian Horvath, Mike Savage (Signals).

Lithography (6 colours)
Canadian Bank Note
Water-activated gum souvenir sheet of 5

**2017, Aug 1** **GT4, TRC Paper** **Perf 13.0x13.3**

| | | NH–VF | ⊙F | FDC |
|---|---|---|---|---|
| **3017** | **$4.25 souvenir sheet** of 5 | 8.75 | 8.75 | 10.50 |
| a | P **multicoloured**, Blue jay | 1.75 | 1.50 | |
| b | P **multicoloured**, Gyrfalcon | 1.75 | 1.50 | |
| c | P **multicoloured**, Great gray owl | 1.75 | 1.50 | |
| d | P **multicoloured**, Osprey | 1.75 | 1.50 | |
| e | P **multicoloured**, Common loon | 1.75 | 1.50 | |

Qty: 110,000

Self-adhesive booklet of 10
**Serpentine Die cut 13.0x12.9**

| | | NH–VF | ⊙F | FDC |
|---|---|---|---|---|
| 3018 | P **multicoloured**, Osprey | 1.70 | .75 | — |
| i | die cut to shape from Quarterly Pack | 2.50 | — | |
| 3019 | P **multicoloured**, Gyrfalcon | 1.70 | .75 | — |
| i | die cut to shape from Quarterly Pack | 2.50 | — | |
| 3020 | P **multicoloured**, Blue jay | 1.70 | .75 | — |
| i | die cut to shape from Quarterly Pack | 2.50 | — | |
| 3021 | P **multicoloured**, Great gray owl | 1.70 | .75 | — |
| i | die cut to shape from Quarterly Pack | 2.50 | — | |
| 3022 | P **multicoloured**, Common loon | 1.70 | .75 | — |
| i | die cut to shape from Quarterly Pack | 2.50 | — | |
| a | booklet pane of 10, 2 each #3018–3022 (**BK675**) | 17.00 | | |

Qty: 800,000 of each

The Canada 150 logo appears in a spot varnish on each stamp.
At time of issue, the P stamps were valued at 85¢.
For non-denominated postal cards of same designs, see UX481–UX485. See also 2929–2934.

3017

3022a

## DIWALI

*Perforated single from water-activated gum souvenir sheet*

3023a

*Die cut singles from self-adhesive booklet*

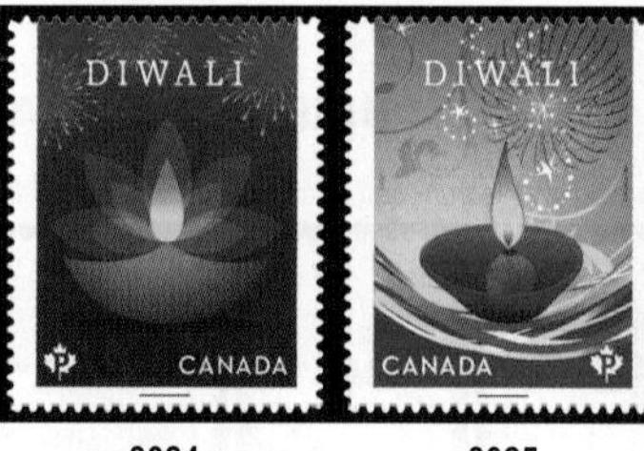
3024 3025
Clay lamps

Designer: Entro Communications.
Lithography (5 colours) plus varnish
Lowe-Martin
Water-activated gum souvenir sheet of 2

**2017, Sep 21** **GT4, TRC Paper** **Perf 13.3**

| | | NH–VF | ⊙F | FDC |
|---|---|---|---|---|
| 3023 | **$3.00 souvenir sheet** of 1 x $2.50 + 1 x $25.00 rupees | 6.00 | 6.00 | 5.50 |
| a | $2.50 single stamp from souvenir sheet | 5.00 | 4.75 | |

Qty: 75,000

Lithography (5 colours), self-adhesive booklet of 10
**Serpentine Die cut 13.7**

| | | NH–VF | ⊙F | FDC |
|---|---|---|---|---|
| 3024 | P **multicoloured** | 1.70 | .75 | — |
| 3025 | P **multicoloured** | 1.70 | .75 | — |
| i | se-tenant pair (3024, 3025), die cut to shape from Quarterly Pack | 5.00 | — | |
| a | booklet pane of 10, 2 each #3024–3025 (**BK676**) | 17.00 | — | |

Qty: 1,500,000 of each

Microprinted 'CANADA 150' is at right side of each stamp. Joint issue with India Post.
At time of issue, the P stamps were valued at 85¢.

3023

3025a

Joint issue with India Post
**Scott # 2962b**

Timeline:
2017, Sep 25 P (85¢)+10¢ Canada Post Community Foundation, semi-postal (B25–B26)

## NHL: The ULTIMATE SIX

*Perforated singles from water-activated gum souvenir sheet*

**3026a**
Maurice Richard
(1921-2000)

**3026b**
Jean Béliveau
(1931-2014)

**3026c**
Gordie Howe
(1928-2016)

**3026d**
Bobby Orr
(1948- )

**3026e**
Mario Lemieux
(1965- )

**3026f**
Wayne Gretzky
(1961- )

*Die cut singles from self-adhesive booklet*

3027

3028

3029

3030

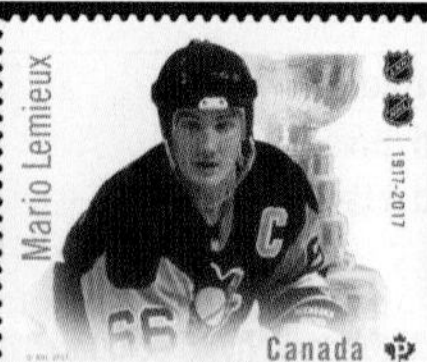
3031

3032

3026

3032a

Designer: Avi Dunkelman, Joseph Gault (MIX Design Group).

Lithography (7 colours, one foil stamping plus embossing*)
Lowe-Martin
Water-activated gum pane of 6

**2017, Sep 28** **GT4, TRC Paper** **Perf 12.5x13.2**

| | | NH–VF | ⊙F | FDC |
|---|---|---|---|---|
| 3026 | **$5.10 souvenir sheet** of 6 | 10.50 | 10.50 | |
| a | P **multicoloured**, Maurice Richard | 1.70 | 1.50 | |
| b | P **multicoloured**, Jean Béliveau | 1.70 | 1.50 | |
| c | P **multicoloured**, Gordie Howe | 1.70 | 1.50 | |
| d | P **multicoloured**, Bobby Orr | 1.70 | 1.50 | |
| e | P **multicoloured**, Mario Lemieux | 1.70 | 1.50 | |
| f | P **multicoloured**, Wayne Gretzky | 1.70 | 1.50 | |

Qty: 90,000

* The pane has embossing in the selvedge; the stamps themselves do not have any embossing.

Lithography (7 colours)
Self-adhesive booklet of 6
**Serpentine Die cut 13.3x13.5**

| | | NH–VF | ⊙F | FDC |
|---|---|---|---|---|
| 3027 | P **multicoloured**, Maurice Richard | 1.70 | 0.75 | 3.70 |
| i | die cut to shape from Quarterly Pack | 2.50 | — | |
| 3028 | P **multicoloured**, Jean Béliveau | 1.70 | 0.75 | 3.70 |
| i | die cut to shape from Quarterly Pack | 2.50 | — | |
| 3029 | P **multicoloured**, Gordie Howe | 1.70 | 0.75 | 3.70 |
| i | die cut to shape from Quarterly Pack | 2.50 | — | |
| 3030 | P **multicoloured**, Bobby Orr | 1.70 | 0.75 | 3.70 |
| i | die cut to shape from Quarterly Pack | 2.50 | — | |
| 3031 | P **multicoloured**, Mario Lemieux | 1.70 | 0.75 | 3.70 |
| i | die cut to shape from Quarterly Pack | 2.50 | — | |
| 3032 | P **multicoloured**, Wayne Gretzky | 1.70 | 0.75 | 3.70 |
| i | die cut to shape from Quarterly Pack | 2.50 | — | |
| a | booklet pane of 6, 1 each #3027–32 (BK678) | 10.20 | | |

Qty: 580,000 of each stamp

The Canada 150 logo in red tagging is visible when viewed with an ultraviolet/black light.

At time of issue, the P stamps were valued at 85¢.

3033
Maurice Richard

3034
Jean Béliveau

3035
Gordie Howe

3036
Bobby Orr

3037
Mario Lemieux

3038
Wayne Gretzky

Designer: Avi Dunkelman, Joseph Gault (MIX Design Group).

Lithography (7 colours)
Lowe-Martin
Self-adhesive souvenir sheets of 1

**2017, Sep 28** **GT4, TRC Paper**
**Serpentine Die cut 13.5x13.3**

| | | NH–VF | ⊙F | FDC |
|---|---|---|---|---|
| 3033 | **$1.80 multicoloured**, Maurice Richard | 3.60 | 3.25 | |
| 3034 | **$1.80 multicoloured**, Jean Béliveau | 3.60 | 3.25 | |
| 3035 | **$1.80 multicoloured**, Gordie Howe | 3.60 | 3.25 | |
| 3036 | **$1.80 multicoloured**, Bobby Orr | 3.60 | 3.25 | |
| i | autographed card | *150.00* | | |
| 3037 | **$1.80 multicoloured**, Mario Lemieux | 3.60 | 3.25 | |
| i | autographed card | *250.00* | | |
| 3038 | **$1.80 multicoloured**, Wayne Gretzky | 3.60 | 3.25 | |

Qty: 100,000 of each; 3036i: 2,000; 3037i: 500

'CANADA 150' is visible within the top bar of tagging when viewed with an ultraviolet/black light.

The autographed souvenir sheets have a holographic Canada Post circular sticker of authenticity.

These souvenir sheets were only sold in packages of all six. They *were* included in the Quarterly Pack.

*Full souvenir sheets*

*Autographed souvenir sheets*

3036i

3037i

## HISTORY OF HOCKEY

*Perforated singles from water-activated gum souvenir sheet*

3039a

3039b

*Die cut singles from self-adhesive booklets*

3040

3041

Designer: Subplot Design Inc.

Lithography (6 colours)
Lowe-Martin
Water-activated gum souvenir sheet of 2

**2017, Oct 20** **GT 3 sides, TRC Paper** **Perf 13.0**

| | | NH–VF | ⊙F | FDC |
|---|---|---|---|---|
| **3039** | **$1.70 souvenir sheet** of 2 | 3.50 | 3.50 | 5.50 |
| a | **P multicoloured** | 1.70 | 1.50 | |
| b | **P multicoloured** | 1.70 | 1.50 | |
| i | se-tenant pair (3039a–b) | 3.40 | 3.00 | |

Qty: 100,000

Self-adhesive booklet of 10
**GT 3 sides, TRC Paper**
**Serpentine Die cut 13.5x13.3**

| | | NH–VF | ⊙F | FDC |
|---|---|---|---|---|
| **3040** | **P multicoloured** | 1.70 | .65 | |
| **3041** | **P multicoloured** | 1.70 | .65 | |
| i | se-tenant pair (3040, 3041), die cut to shape from Quarterly Pack | 5.00 | — | |
| a | booklet pane of 10, 5 each #3040–3041 + 10 stickers (**BK679**) | 17.00 | | |

Qty: 1,000,000 of each

**Joint FDC with USA** **8.00**

Microprinted 'CANADA 150' is 'hidden' on the hockey sticks of each stamp. Joint with the USA.

At time of issue, the P stamps were valued at 85¢.

3039

Joint issue with United States
**Scott # 5253c**

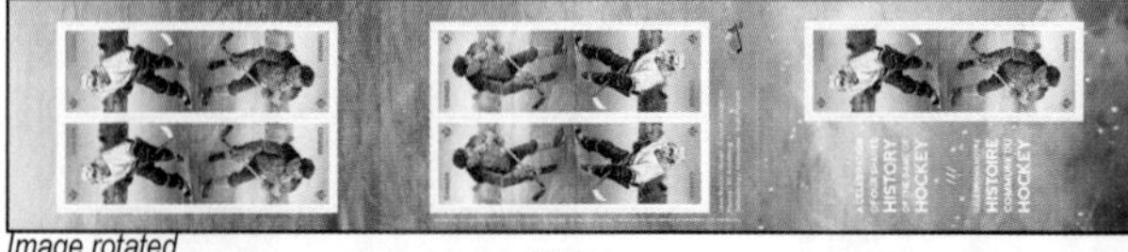
*Image rotated*
3041a

## TORONTO MAPLE LEAFS®

3042i

3043

3044

Designer: Context Creative.

Lithography (4 colours), varnish, special cloth patch logo
Lowe-Martin
Water-activated gum souvenir sheet of 1

**2017, Oct 24** **Not tagged, TRC Paper** **Perf 13.0x13.4**

| | | NH–VF | ⊙F | FDC |
|---|---|---|---|---|
| **3042** | **$5 multicoloured** | 10.00 | *10.00* | 12.00 |
| i | $5.00 single stamp from souvenir sheet | 9.50 | 9.00 | |

Qty: 200,000

Lithography (2 colours)
Self-adhesive coil of 50, sold with hockey puck-shaped dispenser with repeating 'Canada' underprint
**GT4, TRC Paper** **Die cut**

| | | NH–VF | ⊙F | FDC |
|---|---|---|---|---|
| **3043** | **P blue and black** | 1.70 | .85 | 3.70 |

Qty: 3,750,000

Microprinted 'CANADA 150' is 'hidden' in the design of the stamp.

Lithography (2 colours), 1 special ink, varnish
Self-adhesive booklet of 10
**GT4, TRC Paper**
**Serpentine Die cut 13.5**

| | | NH–VF | ⊙F | FDC |
|---|---|---|---|---|
| **3044** | **P multicoloured** | 1.70 | .65 | 3.70 |
| i | die cut to shape from Quarterly Pack | 2.50 | — | |
| a | booklet pane of 10 x P (3044) (**BK680**) | 17.00 | | |

Qty: 3,000,000

'CANADA 150' is visible within the tagging when viewed with an ultraviolet/black light.

100th anniversary of the Toronto Maple Leafs® hockey team.

Microprinted 'CANADA 150' is 'hidden' in the collar of the sweater.

At time of issue, the P stamps were valued at 85¢.

*Image rotated*
3044a

3042

## CHRISTMAS: Animals

*Perforated singles from water-activated gum souvenir sheet*

3045a 3045b 3045c

*Die cut singles from self-adhesive booklets*

3047 Polar bear · 3048 Cardinal · 3049 Caribou

## CHRISTMAS: MADONNA AND CHILD

3046

*The Adoration of the Shepherds*

Designer: Hélène L'Heureux.

Lithography (6 colours)
Colour Innovations
Water-activated gum souvenir sheet of 3

**2017, Nov 3** **GT4, TRC Paper** **Perf 13.7x13.3**

| | | NH–VF | ⊙F | FDC |
|---|---|---|---|---|
| **3045** | **$4.55 souvenir sheet** of 3 | 9.25 | 9.25 | 11.10 |
| a | **P multicoloured** | 1.70 | 1.50 | |
| b | **$1.20 multicoloured** | 2.40 | 2.10 | |
| c | **$2.50 multicoloured** | 5.00 | 4.75 | |
| **T1** | untagged souvenir sheet (error) | | | |

Qty: 100,000

'CANADA 150' is visible within the upper left tagging bar on each of the three stamps from the souvenir sheet when viewed with an ultraviolet/black light.

Designer: Louise Méthé.

Lithography (6 colours)
Lowe-Martin
Self-adhesive booklet of 12

**GT4, TRC Paper** **Serpentine Die cut 13.5**

| | | NH–VF | ⊙F | FDC |
|---|---|---|---|---|
| **3046** | **P multicoloured** | 1.70 | .25 | 3.70 |
| i | die cut to shape from Quarterly Pack/ Annual Collection | 2.50 | — | |
| a | booklet pane of 12 x P (3046) (**BK681**) | 20.40 | — | |

Qty: 8,400,000

The Canada 150 logo is printed in the lower left corner of the stamp.

Designer: Hélène L'Heureux.

Lithography (6 colours), self-adhesive booklet of 12 (P) or 6
Colour Innovations
**GT4, TRC Paper**
**Serpentine Die cut 13.2x13.0**

| | | NH–VF | ⊙F | FDC |
|---|---|---|---|---|
| **3047** | **P multicoloured** | 1.70 | .25 | — |
| i | die cut to shape from Quarterly Pack | 2.50 | — | |
| a | booklet pane of 12 x P (3047) (**BK682**) | 20.40 | — | |

Qty: 12,000,000

| | | NH–VF | ⊙F | FDC |
|---|---|---|---|---|
| **3048** | **$1.20 multicoloured** | 2.40 | 1.25 | — |
| i | die cut to shape from Quarterly Pack | 3.60 | — | |
| a | booklet pane of 6 x $1.20 (3048) (**BK683**) | 14.40 | — | |

Qty: 1,620,000

| | | NH–VF | ⊙F | FDC |
|---|---|---|---|---|
| **3049** | **$2.50 multicoloured** | 5.00 | 2.75 | — |
| i | die cut to shape from Quarterly Pack | 7.50 | — | |
| a | booklet pane of 6 x $2.50 (3049) (**BK684**) | 30.00 | — | |

Qty: 1,920,000

The self-adhesive animal Christmas stamps have a repeating 'Canada 150' printed on the gum side of the paper.

At time of issue, the P stamps were valued at 85¢.

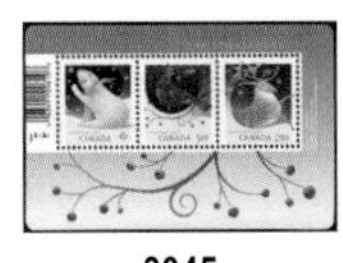

3045

3046a

3047a

3048a

3049a

## HALIFAX EXPLOSION

3050

*Halifax Herald*

Designer: Burke & Burke.

Lithography (4 colours), self-adhesive booklet of 10
Colour Innovations

**2017, Nov 6** **GT4, TRC Paper**
**Serpentine Die cut 13.5**

| | | NH–VF | ⊙F | FDC |
|---|---|---|---|---|
| **3050** | **P multicoloured** | 1.70 | .65 | 3.70 |
| i | die cut to shape from Quarterly Pack/ Annual Collection | 2.50 | — | |
| a | booklet pane of 10 x P (3050) (**BK685**) | 17.00 | | |

Qty: 1,400,000

100th anniversary of the Halifax Explosion, when the cargo ship *Imo* collided with *Mont-Blanc* on December 6, 1917.

Repeating 'Canada 150' is printed on the gum side of the paper.

At time of issue, the P stamp was valued at 85¢.

'Canada 150' underprint

3050a

## HANUKKAH

3051
Menorah

Designer: Entro Communcations.

Lithography (6 colours), self-adhesive booklet of 10
Lowe-Martin

**2017, Nov 14** **GT 3 sides, TRC Paper**
**Serpentine Die cut 13.3x13.5**

| | | NH–VF | ⊙F | FDC |
|---|---|---|---|---|
| **3051** | **P multicoloured** | 1.70 | .65 | 3.70† |
| i | die cut to shape from Quarterly Pack/ Annual Collection ‡ | 2.50 | — | |
| a | booklet pane of 10 x P (3051) (**BK686**) | 50.00 | | |
| ai | booklet pane of 10 x P (3051) (**BK686A**), ≈ *Nov 22/17* | 17.00 | | |

Qty: 3,000,000
† without Star of David on back side

Recalled Canada Post OFDC (with single Star of David on back side) *400.00*

Booklets, and the official first day cover, were recalled on the day of issue. Reprinted booklets (3051ai/BK686A) appeared in post offices around November 22. Canada Post said the following about the cover design of the booklet: "We replaced the image of the lit shamash with another part of the stylized menorah that reflects the celebration of Hanukkah." There is no change in the individual stamps. The recalled booklet pane has 'Star of David' colour dots in the right selvedge; the reprinted booklet pane has round circles.

‡ All die cut to shape singles are from the recalled booklet.

UPC barcode on back of booklet cover: recalled booklet – 0 63491 09611 2; reprinted booklet – 0 63491 09715 7.

UPC barcode on back of OFDC: recalled OFDC – 0 63491 09612 9; reprinted OFDC – 0 63491 09714 0. All OFDCs, including reprints, are dated Nov 14.

Honouring the Jewish Festival of Lights which takes place in Canada from December 12 to 20.

Microprinted 'CANADA 150' is at right side of each stamp.

At time of issue, the P stamp was valued at 85¢.

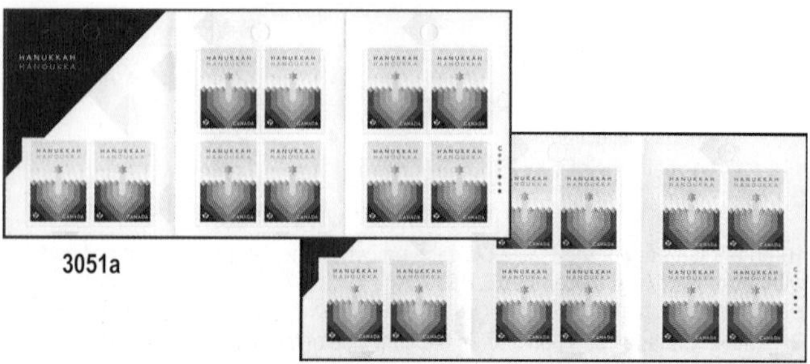

3051a

3051ai

## 2018

### LUNAR NEW YEAR (Series 2) — 10
### Year of the Dog

*Perforated single from wag pane of 25*

*Perforated single from souvenir sheet*

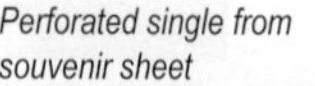

3052

3053i

*Die cut single from self-adhesive booklets*

3054

3055

3053 3053a

Designer: Subplot Design Inc.

Lithography (4 colours) plus embossing plus foil stamping, pane of 25
Lowe-Martin

**2018, Jan 15** **GT4, TRC Paper** **Perf 12.5**

| | | NH–VF | ⊙F | PB | FDC |
|---|---|---|---|---|---|
| **3052** | **P multicoloured** | 1.70 | .75 | | 3.70 |

Qty: 1,550,000

**GT 3 sides** **Perf 12.5**

| | | NH–VF | ⊙F | FDC |
|---|---|---|---|---|
| **3053** | **$2.50 souvenir sheet** of 1 | 5.00 | 5.00 | 7.00 |
| i | $2.50 single stamp from souvenir sheet | 4.00 | 3.75 | |
| ii | $30.00 uncut press sheet of 12 souvenir sheets | 60.00 | | |
| a | $5.00 'transitional' souvenir sheet of 2, #2960, 3054 | 10.00 | 10.00 | |

Qty: 3053: 170,000; 3053ii: 8,000; 3053a: 90,000

Lithography (4 colours) plus foil stamping, self-adhesive booklet of 10
**GT4** **Serpentine Die cut 13.5**

| | | | | |
|---|---|---|---|---|
| **3054** | **P multicoloured** | 1.70 | .75 | — |
| i | die cut to shape from Quarterly Pack | 2.50 | — | |
| a | booklet pane of 10 x P (3054) (**BK687**) | 17.00 | — | |

Qty: 2,750,000

Lithography (4 colours) plus foil stamping, self-adhesive booklet of 6
**GT 3 sides**

| | | | | |
|---|---|---|---|---|
| **3055** | **$2.50 multicoloured** | 5.00 | 3.00 | — |
| i | die cut to shape from Quarterly Pack | 7.50 | — | |
| a | booklet pane of 6 x $2.50 (3055) (**BK688**) | 30.00 | — | |

Qty: 540,000

For non-denominated postal cards of same designs, see UX486–UX487.

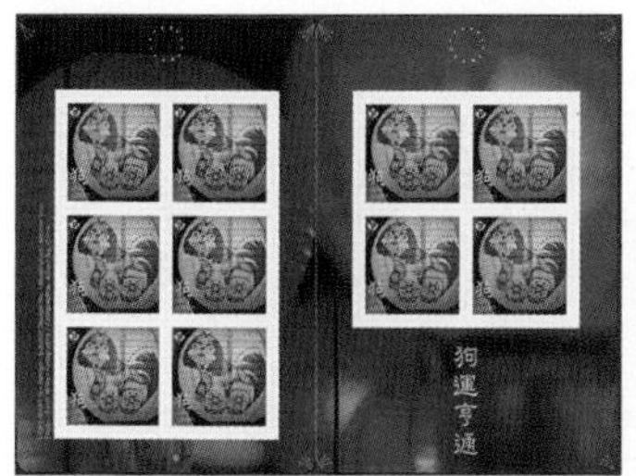

3054a

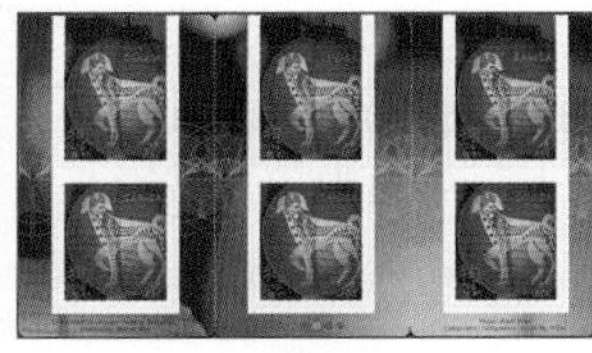

3055a

## FROM FAR AND WIDE — SOUVENIR SHEET

**3056a**
St. John's (NL)

**3056b**
Hopewell Rocks (NB)

**3056c**
MacMillan Provincial Park (BC)

**3056d**
Prince Edward Island National Park (PE)

**3056e**
Parc national de l'Île-Bonaventure-et-du-Rocher-Percé (QC)

**3056f**
Pisew Falls Provincial Park (MB)

**3056g**
Point Pelee National Park (ON)

**3056h**
Nááts'įhch'oh National Park Reserve (NT)

**3056i**
Arctic Bay (NU)

Designers: Stéphane Huot.

Lithography (6 colours)
Lowe-Martin
Water-activated gum souvenir sheet of 9

**2018, Jan 15** **GT4, TRC Paper** **Perf 13.4x13.0**

| | | NH–VF | ⊙F | FDC |
|---|---|---|---|---|
| **3056** | **$10.75 souvenir sheet** of 9 * | 10.00 | 10.00 | 23.50 |
| a | **P multicoloured**, NL | 1.75 | 1.50 | |
| b | **P multicoloured**, NB | 1.75 | 1.50 | |
| c | **P multicoloured**, BC | 1.75 | 1.50 | |
| d | **P multicoloured**, PE | 1.75 | 1.50 | |
| e | **P multicoloured**, QC | 1.75 | 1.50 | |
| f | **$1.00 multicoloured** | 2.00 | 1.75 | |
| g | **$1.20 multicoloured** | 2.00 | 1.75 | |
| h | **$1.80 multicoloured** | 2.50 | 2.25 | |
| i | **$2.50 multicoloured** | 3.50 | 3.25 | |

Qty: 80,000

* Face value of $10.75 at time of issue; the face value of the P stamp was 85¢.

3056

## FROM FAR AND WIDE — COILS

*From horizontal roll of 5,000*

**3057**
St. John's (NL)

**3058**
Hopewell Rocks (NB)

**3059**
MacMillan Provincial Park (BC)

**3060**
Parc national de l'Île-Bonaventure-et-du-Rocher-Percé (QC)

**3061**
Prince Edward Island National Park (PE)

*From vertical roll of 100*

**3062**
St. John's (NL)

**3063**
Hopewell Rocks (NB)

**3064**
MacMillan Provincial Park (BC)

**3065**
Parc national de l'Île-Bonaventure-et-du-Rocher-Percé (QC)

**3066**
Prince Edward Island National Park (PE)

*From vertical rolls of 50*

**3067**
Point Pelee National Park (ON)

**3068**
Nááts'įhch'oh National Park Reserve (NT)

**3069**
Arctic Bay (NU)

*From horizontal roll of 50*

**3070**
Pisew Falls Provincial Park (MB)

Tagging on From Far and Wide souvenir sheet and booklet definitives. The coils do not have these features.

Designers: Stéphane Huot.

Lithography (5 colours), self-adhesive roll of 5,000

**GT4, TRC Paper**

with repeating 'Canada' underprint

**Serpentine Die cut 9.2 Horiz**

**(Rounded tips)**

| | | NH–VF | ⊙F | FDC |
|---|---|---|---|---|
| **3057** | **multicoloured**, NL | 2.00 | 2.00 | — |
| **3058** | **multicoloured**, NB | 2.00 | 2.00 | — |
| **3059** | **multicoloured**, BC | 2.00 | 2.00 | — |
| **3060** | **multicoloured**, QC | 2.00 | 2.00 | — |
| **3061** | **multicoloured**, PE | 2.00 | 2.00 | — |
| a | horizontal strip of 5 (3057–3061) | 11.00 | | |

3057–3061 were issued in horizontal rolls of 5,000. Individual stamps do not touch along the horizontal roll; rounded 'perf tips' start with a peak. Sold in strips of 5 or 10 by the National Philatelic Centre; single stamps included in the Quarterly Pack/ Annual Collection.

Lithography (5 colours), self-adhesive rolls of 100 (P) and 50 ($1.20, $1.80, $2.50)

**GT4, TRC Paper**

with repeating 'Canada' underprint

*and counting number on back of coil backing paper every 5 stamps*

**Serpentine Die cut 8.15 to 8.50 Horiz**

**(Rounded tips with 3 'nibs' between stamps)**

To date, one die cut pattern has been used on these stamps.

| | | NH–VF | ⊙F | FDC |
|---|---|---|---|---|
| **3062** | **multicoloured**, NL | 1.70 | .25 | — |
| **3063** | **multicoloured**, NB | 1.70 | .25 | — |
| **3064** | **multicoloured**, BC | 1.70 | .25 | — |
| **3065** | **multicoloured**, QC | 1.70 | .25 | — |
| **3066** | **multicoloured**, PE | 1.70 | .25 | — |
| a | se-tenant vertical strip of 5 (3062–3066) | 8.50 | | |
| i | single stamp, with back # | 2.50 | — | |
| ii | gutter strip of 5 with inscription | 10.00 | | |
| | starter strip of 5 (wavy die cut) | 12.50 | | |
| | end strip of 5 (wavy die cut) | 12.50 | | |
| **3067** | **$1.20 multicoloured** | 2.40 | .50 | — |
| i | single stamp, with back # | 2.75 | — | |
| ii | gutter strip of 4 with inscription | 11.00 | | |
| | starter strip of 4 (wavy die cut) | 13.00 | | |
| | end strip of 4 (wavy die cut) | 13.00 | | |
| iii | die cut to shape (9.2 horiz) from Quarterly Pack, *Apr '18* ‡ | 3.60 | — | |
| **3068** | **$1.80 multicoloured** | 3.60 | .90 | — |
| i | single stamp, with back # | 5.00 | — | |
| ii | gutter strip of 4 with inscription | 17.00 | | |
| | starter strip of 4 (wavy die cut) | 18.00 | | |
| | end strip of 4 (wavy die cut) | 18.00 | | |
| iii | die cut to shape (9.2 horiz) from Quarterly Pack, *Apr '18* ‡ | 5.40 | — | |
| **3069** | **$2.50 multicoloured** | 5.00 | 1.25 | — |
| i | single stamp, with back # | 6.00 | — | |
| ii | gutter strip of 4 with inscription | 24.00 | | |
| | starter strip of 4 (wavy die cut) | 25.00 | | |
| | end strip of 4 (wavy die cut) | 25.00 | | |
| iii | die cut to shape (9.2 horiz) from Quarterly Pack, *Apr '18* ‡ | 7.50 | — | |

‡ Single stamps supplied in the Quarterly Pack have rounded tips (backing paper is 'plain' with the repeating 'Canada' underprint visible), starting with a peak at upper left; stamps from the full rolls are die cut 8.15 to 8.50.

None of the 'From Far and Wide' definitives were available on the day of issue. Some stamps were not available at post offices until two weeks after the day of issue. Many post offices were still selling the high-value Baby Wildlife coils (Sc. 2712–2714) into May and refusing to sell the new 'From Far and Wide' coils until stocks of the Baby Wildlife coils were depleted.

Lithography (5 colours), self-adhesive roll of 50

Lowe-Martin

**GT4, TRC Paper** **Die cut 13.5**

with repeating 'Canada' underprint

| | | NH–VF | ⊙F | FDC |
|---|---|---|---|---|
| **3070** | **$1.00 multicoloured** | 2.00 | .25 | — |
| i | single stamp, with back # | 2.50 | — | |

The backing paper is roulletted between each stamp. The reverse of the coil stamp backing material had a dot-matrix printed text inscription every 10 stamps.

## FROM FAR AND WIDE — BOOKLETS

*Die cut single from self-adhesive booklets*

**3071**
St. John's (NL)

**3072**
MacMillan Provincial Park (BC)

**3073**
Prince Edward Island National Park (PE)

**3074**
Hopewell Rocks (NB)

**3075**
Parc national de l'Île-Bonaventure-et-du-Rocher-Percé (QC)

**3076**
Point Pelee National Park (ON)

**3077**
Náátsʼįhchʼoh National Park Reserve (NT)

**3078**
Arctic Bay (NU)

Designer: Stéphane Huot.

Lithography (6 colours), Self-adhesive booklets of 10 and 30

**2018, Jan 15** **GT4, TRC Paper**

with repeating 'Canada' underprint

**Serpentine Die cut 13.8x13.6**

| | | NH–VF | ⊙F | FDC |
|---|---|---|---|---|
| **3071** | **multicoloured**, NL | 1.70 | .25 | — |
| **3072** | **multicoloured**, BC | 1.70 | .25 | — |
| **3073** | **multicoloured**, PE | 1.70 | .25 | — |
| **3074** | **multicoloured**, NB | 1.70 | .25 | — |
| **3075** | **multicoloured**, QC | 1.70 | .25 | — |
| i | se-tenant strip of 5 (3071–3075), die cut to shape from Quarterly Pack | 12.50 | — | |
| a | booklet pane of 10 x P (2 each of 3071–3075) (**BK689**) | 17.00 | | |
| b | booklet pane of 30 x P (6 each of 3071–3075) (**BK690**) | 50.00 | | |
| **ai** | strip of 5, from 3075a/BK689 or 3075b/BK690 | 8.50 | | |

Lithography (5 colours), self-adhesive booklets of 6

Lowe-Martin

**2018, Jan 15** **GT4, TRC Paper**

with repeating 'Canada' underprint

**Serpentine Die cut 9.2 horiz (Rounded tips)**

| | | NH–VF | ⊙F | FDC |
|---|---|---|---|---|
| **3076** | **$1.20 multicoloured** | 2.40 | .50 | — |
| i | die cut to shape from Quarterly Pack ‡ | 3.60 | — | |
| a | booklet pane of 6 x $1.20 (3076) (**BK691**) | 14.50 | | |

| | | | | |
|---|---|---|---|---|
| **3077** | **$1.80 multicoloured** | 3.60 | .90 | — |
| i | die cut to shape from Quarterly Pack ‡ | 5.40 | — | |
| a | booklet pane of 6 x $1.80 (3077) (**BK692**) | 21.60 | | |
| **3078** | **$2.50 multicoloured** | 5.00 | 1.25 | — |
| i | die cut to shape from Quarterly Pack ‡ | 7.50 | — | |
| a | booklet pane of 6 x $2.50 (3078) (**BK693**) | 30.00 | | |

At time of issue, all of the P stamps issued January 15, 2018 were valued at 85¢.
For non-denominated postal cards of same designs, see UX488–UX496.

"From Far and Wide" are lyrics from Canada's national anthem (music by Calixa Lavallée, English lyrics by Robert Stanley Weir, based on the French lyrics by Sir Adolphe-Basile Routhier).

3075a

3075b

3076a

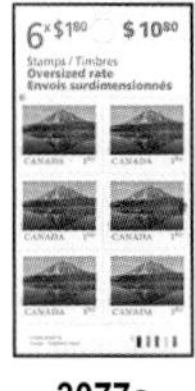
3077a

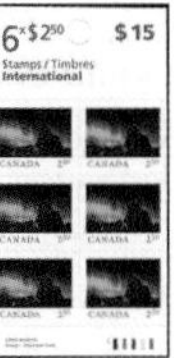
3078a

‡ Identifying 'look-alike' die cut varieties:

Stamps from coils of 50 or 100 will have 3 'nibs' in the top and bottom die cutting. These nibs keep the stamps joined while affixed to the roll.

Single from coils of 5,000:

- die cut 9.2
- no 'nibs'
- starts with peak

Single from coils of 50 or 100:

- die cut 8.15 to 8.50
- 3 'nibs' along top and bottom

Single die cut to shape from coils of 50 or 100:

- die cut 9.2
- no 'nibs' along top and bottom
- two nibs at left and right
- starts with peak

Single from booklets of 6:

- die cut 9.2
- no 'nibs'
- starts with valley

Single die cut to shape from booklets of 6:

- die cut 9.2
- 2 'nibs' along top and bottom (always in same place)
- starts with valley

## WOMEN IN WINTER SPORTS

*Perforated singles from water-activated gum souvenir sheet*

**3079a**
Nancy Greene
(1943– )
*alpine skier*

**3079b**
Shirley (1953–2013) and
Sharon Firth (1953– )
*cross-country skiers*

**3079c**
Danielle Goyette
(1966– )
*hockey*

**3079d**
Clara Hughes
(1972– )
*speed skater*

**3079e**
Sonja Gaudet
(1966– )
*wheelchair curler*

*Die cut singles from self-adhesive booklet*

**3080**

**3081**

**3082**

**3083**

**3084**

Designer: Subplot Design Inc.

Lithography (7 colours)
Colour Innovations
Water-activated gum pane of 5

**2018, Jan 24** **GT4, TRC Paper** **Perf 13.0x13.3**

| | | NH–VF | ⊙F | FDC |
|---|---|---|---|---|
| **3079** | **$4.25 souvenir sheet** of 5 | 8.75 | 8.75 | |
| a | **P multicoloured**, Greene | 1.75 | 1.50 | |
| b | **P multicoloured**, Firths | 1.75 | 1.50 | |
| c | **P multicoloured**, Goyette | 1.75 | 1.50 | |
| d | **P multicoloured**, Hughes | 1.75 | 1.50 | |
| e | **P multicoloured**, Gaudet | 1.75 | 1.50 | |

Qty: 50,000

Self-adhesive booklet of 10
**Serpentine Die cut 13.0x12.9**

| | | NH–VF | ⊙F | FDC |
|---|---|---|---|---|
| **3080** | **P multicoloured**, Greene | 1.70 | .75 | 3.70 |
| i | die cut to shape from Quarterly Pack | 2.50 | — | |
| **3081** | **P multicoloured**, Firths | 1.70 | .75 | 3.70 |
| i | die cut to shape from Quarterly Pack | 2.50 | — | |
| **3082** | **P multicoloured**, Goyette | 1.70 | .75 | 3.70 |
| i | die cut to shape from Quarterly Pack | 2.50 | — | |
| **3083** | **P multicoloured**, Hughes | 1.70 | .75 | 3.70 |
| i | die cut to shape from Quarterly Pack | 2.50 | — | |
| **3084** | **P multicoloured**, Gaudet | 1.70 | .75 | 3.70 |
| i | die cut to shape from Quarterly Pack | 2.50 | — | |
| a | booklet pane of 10, 2 each #3080–3084 (**BK694**) | 17.00 | | |

Qty: 400,000 of each

At time of issue, the P stamps were valued at 85¢.

Celebrating the achievements of six Canadian superstars who topped the podium in a variety of winter sports.

QE II — 2010's

3079

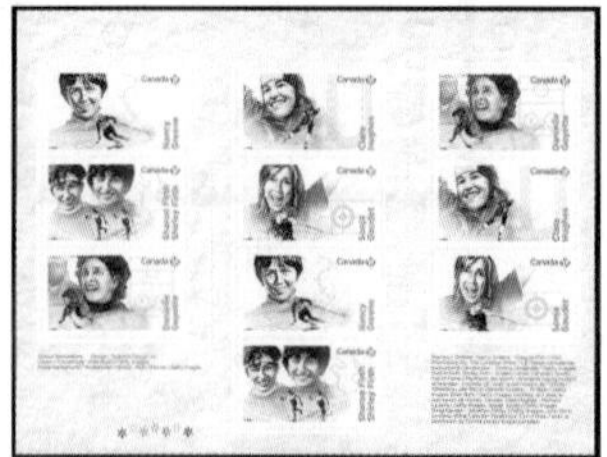
3084a

## BLACK HISTORY MONTH

3085
Kay Livingstone
(1918–1975)

3086
Lincoln M. Alexander
(1922–2012)

Designer: Tétro.

Lithography (6 colours), self-adhesive booklets of 10
Lowe-Martin

**2018, Feb 1** **GT4, TRC Paper**
**Serpentine Die cut 13.5x13.3**

| | | NH–VF | ⊙F | FDC |
|---|---|---|---|---|
| **3085** | **P multicoloured**, Livingstone | 1.70 | .65 | 3.70 |
| i | die cut to shape from Quarterly Pack/ Annual Collection | 2.50 | — | |
| a | booklet pane of 10 x P (3085) (**BK695**) | 17.00 | | |

Qty: 1,300,000

| | | NH–VF | ⊙F | FDC |
|---|---|---|---|---|
| **3086** | **P multicoloured**, Alexander | 1.70 | .65 | 3.70 |
| i | die cut to shape from Quarterly Pack/ Annual Collection | 2.50 | — | |
| a | booklet pane of 10 x P (3086) (**BK696**) | 17.00 | | |

Qty: 1,300,000

Prominent, ground-breaking Canadians.
At time of issue, the P stamps were valued at 85¢.

*Image rotated* 3085a

*Image rotated* 3086a

## LOTUS

*Perforated singles from water-activated gum souvenir sheet*

3087a 3087b

3088
*Nelumbo nucifera*

3089
*Nelumbo lutea*

*Die cut singles from self-adhesive booklets*

3090 3091

Designer: Parcel.

Lithography (5 colours) plus varnish
Lowe-Martin
Water-activated gum souvenir sheet of 2

**2018, Mar 1** **GT 3 sides, TRC Paper** **Perf 13.1x13.2**

| | | NH–VF | ⊙F | FDC |
|---|---|---|---|---|
| **3087** | **$1.70 souvenir sheet** of 2 | 3.50 | 3.50 | — |
| a | **P multicoloured**, pink petals | 1.70 | 1.50 | |
| b | **P multicoloured**, yellow petals | 1.70 | 1.50 | |
| i | se-tenant pair (3087a–b) | 3.40 | 3.00 | |

Qty: 85,000

Self-adhesive roll of 50
**GT4, TRC Paper**
with repeating 'Canada' underprint
*and counting number on back of coil backing paper every 5 stamps*
**Serpentine Die cut 8.15 to 8.50 Vertical**
**(Rounded tips with 3 'nibs' between stamps)**

One die cut pattern exists on these stamps.

| | | NH–VF | ⊙F | FDC |
|---|---|---|---|---|
| **3088** | **P multicoloured**, pink petals | 1.70 | .75 | — |
| i | single stamp, with back # | 2.50 | — | |
| **3089** | **P multicoloured**, yellow petals | 1.70 | .75 | — |
| a | se-tenant pair (horiz.), 3088–89 | 3.40 | | |
| ai | se-tenant pair (horiz.), 3088–89, with back # on one stamp | 4.50 | — | |
| i | single stamp, with back # | 2.50 | — | |
| ii | gutter strip of 4 with inscription | 8.50 | | |
| | starter strip of 4 (wavy die cut) | 10.00 | | |
| | end strip of 4 (wavy die cut) | 10.00 | | |
| iii | se-tenant pair (3088–89), die cut to shape (9.2 vert.) from Quarterly Pack | 5.00 | — | |

Qty: 3,250,000 of each

3088–89 were printed se-tenant along the same roll.

Self-adhesive booklet of 10
**GT 3 sides, TRC Paper**
**Serpentine Die cut 13.5**

| | | NH–VF | ⊙F | FDC |
|---|---|---|---|---|
| **3090** | **P multicoloured**, pink petals | 1.70 | .65 | |
| **3091** | **P multicoloured**, yellow petals | 1.70 | .65 | |
| i | se-tenant pair (3090, 3091), die cut to shape from Quarterly Pack | 5.00 | — | |
| a | booklet pane of 10, 5 each #3090–3091 + 10 stickers (**BK697**) | 17.00 | | |

Qty: 5,000,000 of each

**Nos. 3090–3091 (2) combination FDC** 5.40*

* Stamps on FDCs are not die cut all the way through.

At time of issue, the P stamps were valued at 85¢.

3087

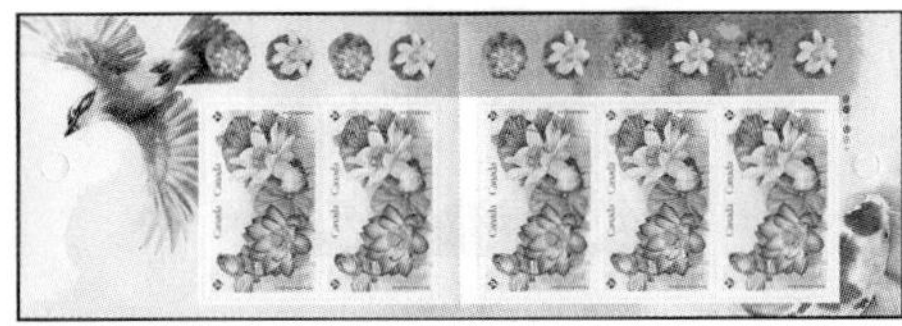

*Image rotated* 3091a

## GREAT CANADIAN ILLUSTRATORS

*Perforated singles from water-activated gum souvenir sheets*

3092a
*Best Friends*
Anita Kunz, O.C.
(1956– )

3092b
*Untitled*
Will Davies
(1924–2016)

3092c
*Stage Fright*
Blair Drawson

3092d
*It's Not a Streem of Consciousness*
Gérard Dubois
(1968– )

3092e
*Untitled*
James Hill
(1930–2004)

*Die cut singles from self-adhesive booklet*

3093

3094

3095

3096

3097

Designer: Lime Design.

Lithography (5 colours)
Lowe-Martin
Water-activated gum souvenir sheet of 5

**2018, Apr 5 GT2 (side and bottom), TRC Paper Perf 12.5**

| | | NH–VF | ⊙F | FDC |
|---|---|---|---|---|
| **3092** | **$4.25 pane** of 5 | 8.50 | 8.50 | 8.50 |
| a | **P multicoloured**, Kunz | 1.75 | 1.50 | |
| b | **P multicoloured**, Davies | 1.75 | 1.50 | |
| c | **P multicoloured**, Drawson | 1.75 | 1.50 | |
| d | **P multicoloured**, Dubois | 1.75 | 1.50 | |
| e | **P multicoloured**, Hill | 1.75 | 1.50 | |

Qty: 80,000

Self-adhesive booklet of 10
**GT2 (side and bottom), TRC Paper**
**Serpentine Die cut 13.5x13.3**

| | | NH–VF | ⊙F | FDC |
|---|---|---|---|---|
| **3093** | **P multicoloured**, Kunz | 1.70 | .75 | — |
| i | die cut to shape from Quarterly Pack | 2.50 | — | |
| **3094** | **P multicoloured**, Drawson | 1.70 | .75 | — |
| i | die cut to shape from Quarterly Pack | 2.50 | — | |
| | **Serpentine Die cut 13.5** | | | |
| **3095** | **P multicoloured**, Hill | 1.70 | .75 | |
| i | die cut to shape from Quarterly Pack | 2.50 | — | |
| | **Serpentine Die cut 13.5x13.3** | | | |
| **3096** | **P multicoloured**, Davies | 1.70 | .75 | — |
| i | die cut to shape from Quarterly Pack | 2.50 | — | |
| | **Serpentine Die cut 13.5** | | | |
| **3097** | **P multicoloured**, Dubois | 1.70 | .75 | — |
| i | die cut to shape from Quarterly Pack | 2.50 | — | |
| a | booklet pane of 10, 2 each #3093–3097 (**BK698**) | 17.00 | | |

Qty: 3,000,000 of each

At time of issue, the P stamps were valued at 85¢.

3092

3097a

## QUEEN ELIZABETH II

3098
Her Royal Highness Princess Elizabeth,
July 1951 portrait by Yousuf Karsh

Designer: Paprika.

Lithography (3 colours), self-adhesive booklet of 10
Lowe-Martin

**2018, Apr 20 GT 3 sides, TRC Paper**
**Serpentine Die cut 13.5x13.2**

| | | NH–VF | ⊙F | FDC |
|---|---|---|---|---|
| **3098** | **P multicoloured** | 1.70 | .65 | 3.70 |
| i | die cut to shape from Quarterly Pack/ Annual Collection | 2.50 | — | |
| ii | $102.00 uncut press sheet of 12 booklet panes | 205.00 | | |
| a | booklet pane of 10 x P (3098) (**BK699**) | 17.00 | | |

Qty: 3098: 3,000,000; 3098i: 1,000

The panes from the uncut press sheet are not rouletted and do not have the die cut 'peg' hole. Any pane removed from the uncut press sheet will lie flat (i.e. unfolded in the centre).

65th anniversary of Her Majesty Queen Elizabeth II Coronation.
At time of issue, the P stamp was valued at 85¢.

3098a

## NATIVE BEES

3099 Rusty-patched bumble bee *Bombus affinis*

3100 Metallic green bee *Agapostemon virescens*

Designer: Andrew Perro.

Lithography (4 colours)
Canadian Bank Note
Self-adhesive booklet of 10

**2018, May 1** **GT4, TRC Paper** **Serpentine Die cut 13.0**

| | | NH–VF | ⊙F | FDC |
|---|---|---|---|---|
| **3099** | **multicoloured**, bumble bee | 1.70 | .65 | — |
| **3100** | **multicoloured**, green bee | 1.70 | .65 | — |
| i | se-tenant pair (3099, 3100), die cut to shape from Quarterly Pack | 5.00 | — | |
| a | booklet pane of 10, 5 each #3099–3100 (**BK700**) | 17.00 | | |

Qty: 2,800,000 of each

**Nos. 3099–3100 (2) combination FDC** 5.40*

* Stamps on FDCs are not die cut all the way through.

At time of issue, the P stamps were valued at 85¢.

*Image rotated* 3100a

## MEMORIAL CUP

3101
Vintage and current uniforms of Regina Pats

Designer: Paprika.

Lithography (5 colours), self-adhesive booklet of 10
Lowe-Martin

**2018, May 18** **GT4, TRC Paper**
**Serpentine Die cut 13.2x13.8**

| | | NH–VF | ⊙F | FDC |
|---|---|---|---|---|
| **3101** | **multicoloured** | 1.70 | .65 | 3.70 |
| i | die cut to shape from Quarterly Pack/ Annual Collection | 2.50 | — | |
| a | booklet pane of 10 x P (3101) (**BK701**) | 17.00 | | |

Qty: 1,400,000

Presentation of the Memorial Cup trophy for the 100th time.
At time of issue, the P stamp was valued at 85¢.

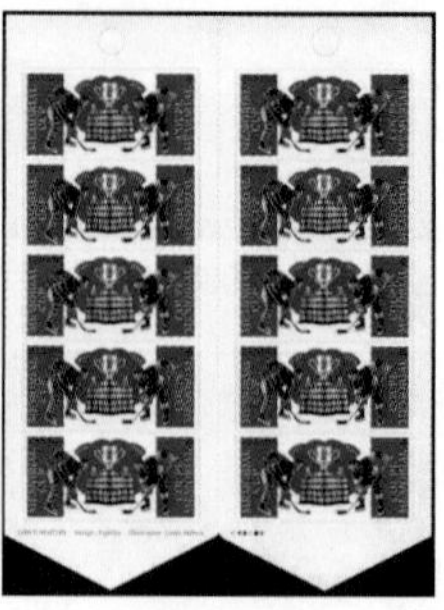

3101a

**The following stamps of 2018 had not yet been assigned a catalogue number by Scott Publishing at the time this publication went to press. Please check the *Scott Stamp Monthly* for all of the latest numbers. Booklet numbers could change.**

## ASTRONOMY

*Perforated singles from water-activated gum souvenir sheet*

Milky Way Northern Lights

*Die cut singles from self-adhesive booklets*

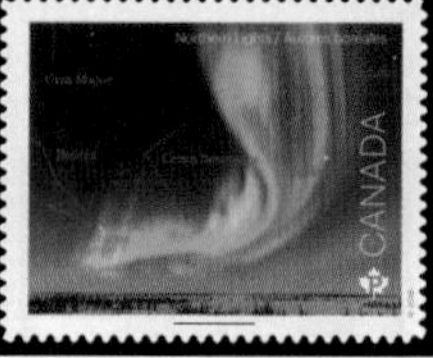

Designer: Parcel Design.

Lithography (7 colours)
Colour Innovations
Water-activated gum souvenir sheet of 2

**2018, Jun 29** **GT4 sides, TRC Paper** **Perf 13.2x13.3**

| | | NH–VF | ⊙F | FDC |
|---|---|---|---|---|
| | **$1.70 souvenir sheet** of 2 | 3.50 | 3.50 | 5.40 |
| a | **multicoloured**, Milky Way | 1.70 | 1.50 | |
| b | **multicoloured**, Northern Lights | 1.70 | 1.50 | |
| i | se-tenant pair (31*nna*–b) | 3.40 | 3.00 | |

Qty: 85,000

Self-adhesive booklet of 10
**GT4, TRC Paper**
**Serpentine Die cut 14.0x14.4**

| | | NH–VF | ⊙F | FDC |
|---|---|---|---|---|
| | **multicoloured**, Milky Way | 1.70 | .65 | — |
| | **multicoloured**, Northern Lights | 1.70 | .65 | — |
| i | se-tenant vertical pair (31*nn*, 31*nn*), die cut to shape from Quarterly Pack | 5.00 | — | |
| a | booklet pane of 10, 5 each #31*nn*–31*nn* (**BK702**) | 17.00 | | |

Qty: 900,000 of each

150th anniversary of the Royal Astronomical Society of Canada.
At time of issue, the P stamps were valued at 85¢.

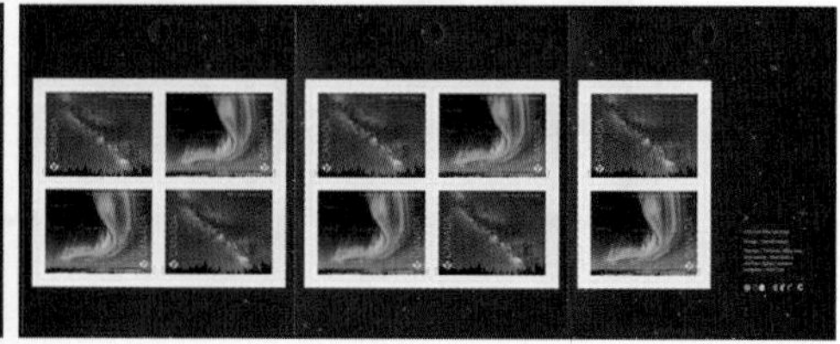

# UNI-SAFE "G" STAMP MOUNTS

## (SPLIT-BACK)

A complete line of quality mounts made solely for Unitrade. Easy-to-Use UNI-SAFE mounts are available for all sizes of stamps. Protect your stamps with UNI-SAFE "G" mounts.

| Size | | No. Pcs. | Ref. # Black | Ref. # Clear | Price |
|---|---|---|---|---|---|
| 20 | MINI STAMPS | 20 | G1020 | G2020 | 8.50 |
| 22 | CND., U.S., G.B. DEF. | 20 | G1022 | G2022 | 8.50 |
| 24 | CDN., U.S., G.B. HORIZ. COMM. | 20 | G1024 | G2024 | 8.50 |
| 25 | CAN., U.S. REG., COMM. ISSUES | 20 | G1025 | G2025 | 8.50 |
| 27 | U.S. FAM. AMER, U.N. | 20 | G1027 | G2027 | 8.50 |
| 28 | U.S., FOREIGN ISSUES | 20 | G1028 | G2028 | 8.50 |
| 29 | CAN, US ISSUES | 20 | G1029 | G2029 | 8.50 |
| 30 | CAN. INDIANS, CHRISTMAS | 20 | G1030 | G2030 | 8.50 |
| 31 | CAN., U.S. JUMBO | 20 | G1031 | G2031 | 8.50 |
| 33 | CAN. KREIGHOFF, U.N. | 20 | G1033 | G2033 | 8.50 |
| 36 | CAN. JUMBO COMM. | 20 | G1036 | G2036 | 10.95 |
| 39 | CAN. VERT. COMM. | 20 | G1039 | G2039 | 10.95 |
| 40 | U.S. SEMI-JUMBO | 20 | G1040 | G2040 | 10.95 |
| 41 | CAN., U.S., ISRAEL VERT. COMM. | 20 | G1041 | G2041 | 10.95 |
| 44 | CAN. REG. BL. OF 4 | 20 | G1044 | G2044 | 10.95 |
| 48 | CAN. BLOCK, GUTTER PAIR | 20 | G1048 | G2048 | 10.95 |
| 50 | CAN. BLOCK & JUMBO | 20 | G1050 | G2050 | 10.95 |
| 51 | CAN. BLOCK | 20 | G1051 | G2051 | 10.95 |
| 52 | CAN. U.S. HORIZ. COMM. BLOCK | 20 | G1052 | G2052 | 10.95 |
| 55 | U.S. LARGE | 20 | G1055 | G2055 | 10.95 |
| 57 | CAN., U.S. REG. PL. BLOCKS | 10 | G1057 | G2057 | 9.95 |
| 59 | VARIOUS BLOCKS | 10 | G1059 | G2059 | 9.95 |
| 61 | CN. HORIZ. COMM. PL. BL. | 10 | G1061 | G2061 | 9.95 |
| 63 | U.S. JUMBO COMM. | 10 | G1063 | G2063 | 9.95 |
| 66 | CAN. JUMBO PL. BL. | 10 | G1066 | G2066 | 9.95 |
| 68 | CAN. XMAS PL. BL. | 10 | G1068 | G2068 | 9.95 |
| 70 | JUMBO COMM. PL. BL. | 10 | G1070 | G2070 | 9.95 |
| 74 | CAN. PL. BL. | 10 | G1074 | G2074 | 9.95 |
| 79 | VARIOUS BLOCKS | 10 | G1079 | G2079 | 9.95 |
| 80 | U.S. VERT. PL. BL. | 10 | G1080 | G2080 | 9.95 |

| Size | | No. Pcs. | Ref. # Black | Ref. # Clear | Price |
|---|---|---|---|---|---|
| 100 | U.N. MARGIN BL. | 7 | G1100 | G2100 | 9.95 |
| 105 | U.S. STRIPS | 7 | G1105 | G2105 | 9.95 |
| 107 | U.S. STRIPS WIDE | 7 | G1107 | G2107 | 9.95 |
| 111 | U.S. PL. # STRIPS | 7 | G1111 | G2111 | 9.95 |
| 120 | VARIOUS BLOCKS | 10 | G1120 | G2120 | 9.95 |
| 127 | U.S. JUMBO COMM. | 7 | G1127 | G2127 | 9.95 |
| 137 | GR. BR. CORON. | 7 | G1137 | G2137 | 9.95 |
| 150 | SOUV. SHEETS | 5 | G1150 | G2150 | 9.95 |
| 158 | SOUV. SHEETS | 5 | G1158 | G2158 | 9.95 |
| 165/95 | F.D.C. | 10 | G1165 | G2165 | 9.95 |
| 187/144 | SOUV. SHEETS | 5 | G1187 | G2187 | 9.95 |
| ASST'D | ASSORTIMENT | 12 | G1000 | G2000 | 9.95 |
| 204/153 | SOUV. SHEETS | 5 | G1204 | G2204 | 10.95 |
| 264/171 | SOUV. SHEETS | 3 | G1264 | G2264 | 10.95 |
| 265/231 | SOUV. SHEETS | 5 | G1265 | G2265 | 19.95 |
| 50/31 | CANADA HIGH VALUE REGULAR ISSUES | 45 | G1301 | G2301 | 2.95 |
| 31/50 | SAME VERTICAL | 40 | G1302 | G2302 | 2.95 |
| 41/31 | U.S. HORIZONTAL SEMI-JUMBO | 45 | G1303 | G2303 | 2.95 |
| 31/41 | SAME VERTICAL | 45 | G1304 | G2304 | 2.95 |
| 25/22 | CANADA HORIZONTAL REGULAR ISSUES | 45 | G1305 | G2305 | 2.95 |
| 22/25 | SAME VERTICAL | 45 | G1306 | G2306 | 2.95 |
| 40/25 | CANADA HORIZONTAL COMMEMS. | 45 | G1307 | G2307 | 2.95 |
| 25/40 | CANADA VERTICAL COMMEMS. | 45 | G1308 | G2308 | 2.95 |
| 25/27 | U.S. FAMOUS AMERICANS | 40 | G1309 | G2309 | 2.95 |
| 33/27 | UNITED NATIONS | 40 | G1310 | G2310 | 2.95 |
| 40/27 | UNITED NATIONS | 45 | G1311 | G2311 | 2.95 |
| 57/55 | CANADIAN REG. ISSUE PLATE BLOCKS | 30 | G1312 | G2312 | 9.95 |
| 106/55 | CANADIAN HORIZ. COMMEMS. PLATE BLOCK | 25 | G1313 | G2313 | 9.95 |
| 105/57 | CANADIAN VERT. | | | | |

## COMPLETE BOOKLETS

**Prices shown are for complete, clean unmarked booklets; booklets with opening "bends" or notes on the covers sell for 20–50% less.**
**Multi pane booklets are priced according to the usual condition of panes found in a mint booklet.**
**All complete booklets are priced in F condition to BK44, for VF add 50%.**
**Booklets after BK44 are priced in VF condition.**

### QUEEN VICTORIA
### Numeral Issue (1900–1903)

| | | English | French |
|---|---|---|---|
| BK1 | 2¢ carmine (77bs), 2 panes of 6 (77b), *Jun 11, 1900* | 4,500.00 | — |

### KING EDWARD VII (1903–1911)

| | | English | French |
|---|---|---|---|
| BK2 | 2¢ carmine (90bs), 2 panes of 6 (90b), *Jul 1, 1903* | 4,750.00 | — |

### KING GEORGE V
### Admiral Issue (1912–1930)

| | | English | French |
|---|---|---|---|
| BK3 | 1¢ green, shades (104as), 4 panes of 6 (104a), *Mar 1913* | | |
| a | deep blue green, 18 mm x 21 mm, squat printing | 1,250.00 | 1,500.00 |
| b | blue green, 18 mm x 21 mm, squat printing | 1,000.00 | 3,000.00 |
| c | yellow green (104fs), 17.75 mm x 21.5 mm, vertical wove paper, serif capitals on rate sheet | 250.00 | 500.00 |
| d | as "c", sans serif capitals rate sheet | 350.00 | 1,200.00 |
| e | as "c", rate change overprinted on cover, serif capitals on rate sheet | 250.00 | 1,600.00 |
| f | as "c", sans serif capitals, plus war tax rates, cover not overprinted | 900.00 | 1,800.00 |
| BK4 | 1¢ yellow (105as), 4 panes of 6 (105b), *Dec 1922* | | |
| a | sans serif capitals with war tax rate | 700.00 | 800.00 |
| b | slogans inside, large capitals | 600.00 | 700.00 |
| c | slogans inside, small capitals | 500.00 | 700.00 |

| | | English | French |
|---|---|---|---|
| BK5 | 2¢ carmine (106as), 2 panes of 6 (106a), *Jan 1912* | | |
| a | stamps: 17.7 mm x 21.5 mm, horizontal wove paper | 750.00 | N/A |
| b | stamps: 18 mm x 21 mm, squat printing, horiz. wove | 1,000.00 | 2,500.00 |
| c | stamps: 17.7 mm x 21.5 mm, vertical wove paper, small type I text ["For Canada and the United States..."] | 200.00 | N/A |
| d | as "c", small type II text ["For Canada see Parcel Post in Postal Guide..."] | 150.00 | 350.00 |
| e | as "c", rate change overprint on cover | 250.00 | 375.00 |
| f | as "d", rate change overprint on cover | 150.00 | 225.00 |
| BK6 | 2¢ yellow green (107bs), 2 panes of 6 (107c), *Dec 1922* | | |
| a | sans serif capitals with war tax information | 1,100.00 | 1,300.00 |
| b | as "a", no binding tape | 1,100.00 | 1,300.00 |
| c | slogans inside, small capitals | 1,250.00 | 1,400.00 |
| d | slogans inside, large capitals | 1,500.00 | — |
| BK7 | 3¢ brown (108as), 2 panes of 4 + 2 labels (108a), *Mar 1922* | | |
| a | sans serif capitals, dark brown arms | 750.00 | 2,000.00 |
| b | as "a", black arms | 750.00 | 1,500.00 |

| | | English | French |
|---|---|---|---|
| BK8 | 3¢ carmine (109as), 2 panes of 4 + 2 labels (109a), *Dec 1923* | | |
| a | sans serif capitals with war tax information | 650.00 | — |
| b | red cover, slogans inside, large capitals | 450.00 | 900.00 |
| c | red cover, slogans inside, small capitals | 550.00 | 1,000.00 |
| BK9 | 1 pane each of 4 + 2 labels: 1¢ yellow (105a), 2¢ yellow green (107b), 3¢ brown (108a), *Jul 1922* | | |
| a | sans serif capitals with war tax information | 750.00 | 1,300.00 |
| b | as "a", bright blue covers, dark blue tape | 650.00 | |
| c | as "b", no tape | 750.00 | |
| BK10 | 1 pane each of 4 + 2 labels: 1¢ yellow (105a), 2¢ green (107b), 3¢ carmine (109a), *Dec 1923* | | |
| a | sans serif capitals with war tax information | 700.00 | |
| b | slogans inside, large capitals | 500.00 | 1,250.00 |
| c | slogans inside, small capitals | 600.00 | 1,250.00 |

### KING GEORGE V
### Scroll Issue (1928–1929)

BK11

BK12

BK13a

| | | English | French |
|---|---|---|---|
| BK11 | 1¢ orange (149as), 4 panes of 6 (149a), typographed covers, no binding, *Oct 25, 1928* | 200.00 | 750.00 |
| BK12 | 2¢ green (150as), 2 panes of 6 (150a), typographed covers, no tape, *Oct 16, 1928* | 125.00 | 500.00 |
| BK13 | 1¢ orange (149as), 3 panes of 6 (149a); 2¢ green (150as), 2 panes of 6 (150a); 5¢ violet (153as), 1 pane of 6 (153a), *Jan 6, 1929* | | |
| a | plain manila cover, no printing | 800.00 | — |
| b | as "a", handstamp on cover | 5,000.00 | — |
| c | as "b", 1928 in centre of handstamp | 3,850.00 | — |

### Arch or Leaf Issue (1930–1931)

BK15

BK16

BK17

| | | English | French |
|---|---|---|---|
| BK14 | 1¢ deep green (163cs), 4 panes of 6 (163c), *Jul 21, 1931* | | |
| a | typographed covers, no tape | 250.00 | 450.00 |
| b | as "a", with "PLATE" or "NO. 4" on tab | 400.00 | 600.00 |
| BK15 | 2¢ dull green (164as), 2 panes of 6 (164a), *Jun 17, 1930* | | |
| a | typographed covers, no tape | 250.00 | 500.00 |
| b | as "a", with "PLATE", "NO. 4" or "NO. 5" on tab | 500.00 | 600.00 |
| c | as "a," rotary press printing | 600.00 | 800.00 |
| d | as "a", panes perforated at right side only | 600.00 | — |
| e | as "d", panes perforated both left & right side | 700.00 | — |
| f | as "c", partial 3 on tab | 1,000.00 | — |
| BK16 | 2¢ deep red (165bs), 2 panes of 6 (165b), *Nov 17, 1930* | | |
| a | typographed covers, no tape | 125.00 | 375.00 |
| b | as "a", with PLATE, NO. 4 or NO. 5 on tab | 350.00 | 500.00 |
| BK17 | 2¢ dark brown, Die I (166cs), 2 panes of 6 (166c), *Jul 23, 1931* | | |
| a | typographed covers, no tape | 300.00 | 1,000.00 |
| b | as "a", with "PLATE" or "NO. 4" on tab | 1,000.00 | 1,500.00 |

| | | English | French |
|---|---|---|---|
| **BK18** | 3¢ deep red (167as), 2 panes of 4 + 2 labels (167a), *Jul 13, 1931* | | |
| a | typographed covers, no tape | 150.00 | 250.00 |
| b | as "a", with PLATE, NO. 1 or NO. 2 on tab | 600.00 | 1,200.00 |
| **BK19** | 1¢ deep green (163as), 2¢ dark brown (166as), 3¢ deep red (167as), 1 pane each of 4 + 2 labels (163a, 166a and 167a), *Nov 13, 1931* | | |
| a | typographed covers, no tape | 600.00 | 1,200.00 |
| b | as "a", with PLATE, NO. 1 or NO. 2 on tab, the latter on 2¢ and 3¢ only | 875.00 | 1,700.00 |

## Medallion Issue (1933–1934)

Type I "Post Office" or "Les Mandats"
Type II "Register" or "Recommendez"

BK21b

BK23b

| | | English | French |
|---|---|---|---|
| **BK20** | 1¢ dark green (195as), 4 panes of 6 (195b), *Dec 28, 1933* | | |
| a | Type I | 325.00 | 520.00 |
| b | Type II | 360.00 | 600.00 |
| c | as "a", with PLATE or NO. 2 on tab | 500.00 | 900.00 |
| d | as "b", with PLATE or NO. 2 on tab | 650.00 | 1,000.00 |
| **BK21** | 2¢ black brown (196as), 2 panes of 6 (196b), *Sep 7, 1933* | | |
| a | Type I | 500.00 | 1,000.00 |
| b | Type II | 600.00 | 1,200.00 |
| c | as "a", with PLATE, NO. 1 or NO. 2 on tab | 600.00 | 1,200.00 |
| d | as "b", with PLATE, NO. 1 or NO. 2 on tab | 700.00 | 1,400.00 |
| **BK22** | 3¢ deep red (197ds), 2 panes of 4 + 2 labels (197d), *Sep 19, 1933* | | |
| a | Type I | 170.00 | 300.00 |
| b | Type II | 200.00 | 350.00 |
| c | as "a", with PLATE, NO. 1 or NO. 2 on tab | 450.00 | — |
| d | as "b", with PLATE, NO. 1 or NO. 2 on tab | 500.00 | 600.00 |
| **BK23** | 1¢ dark green (195as), 2¢ black brown (196as), 3¢ deep red (197ds), 1 pane each of 4 + 2 labels (195a, 196a and 197d), *Sep 19, 1933* | | |
| a | Type I | 350.00 | 500.00 |
| b | Type II | 400.00 | 600.00 |
| c | as "a", with PLATE, NO. 1 or NO. 2 on tab | 600.00 | 800.00 |
| d | as "b", with PLATE, NO. 1 or NO. 2 on tab | 650.00 | 850.00 |

## 1935 Issue

| | | English | French |
|---|---|---|---|
| **BK24** | 1¢ green (217as), 4 panes of 6 (217b), *Aug 19, 1935* | 175.00 | 350.00 |
| **BK25** | 2¢ brown (218as), 2 panes of 6 (218b), *Nov 16, 1935* | 175.00 | 350.00 |
| **BK26** | 3¢ dark carmine (219as), 2 panes of 4 + 2 labels (219a), *Jun 1, 1935* | 140.00 | 300.00 |
| **BK27** | 1¢ green (217as), 2¢ brown (218as), 3¢ dark carmine (219as), 1 pane each of 4 + 2 labels (217a, 218a and 219a), *Jul 22, 1935* | 300.00 | 400.00 |

## KING GEORGE VI

## Mufti Issue (1937–1942)

Front Cover Types: Type I Arms and "Canada Postage"
Type II Arms and Contents – text 57 mm wide
Type III Arms and Contents – text 63 mm wide

BK28b (English)

BK28b (French)

| | | English | French |
|---|---|---|---|
| **BK28** | 1¢ green (231as), 4 panes of 6 (231b), *May 18, 1937* | | |
| a | Type I | 55.00 | 100.00 |
| b | Type II, no rate page | 45.00 | 75.00 |
| c | as "b", with 6¢ airmail rate | 50.00 | 90.00 |
| d | as "c", with "X" on rate page | 50.00 | 100.00 |
| e | Type III, no rate page | 150.00 | 250.00 |
| f | as "c", 12 mm staple | 75.00 | — |
| g | as "f", with "X" on rate page | 75.00 | — |

BK29c

BK30a (English)

BK30a (French)

| | | English | French |
|---|---|---|---|
| **BK29** | 2¢ brown (232as), 2 panes of 6 (232b), *May 14, 1937* | | |
| a | Type I | 60.00 | 100.00 |
| b | Type II, no rate page | 45.00 | 110.00 |
| c | as "b", with 6¢ airmail rate | 70.00 | 140.00 |
| d | as "c", with "X" on rate page | 70.00 | 150.00 |
| e | Type III, no rate page | 100.00 | 200.00 |
| **BK30** | 3¢ carmine (233as), 2 panes of 4 + 2 labels (233a), *Apr 14, 1937* | | |
| a | Type I | 25.00 | 40.00 |
| b | Type II, no rate page | 25.00 | 40.00 |
| c | as "b", with 6¢ airmail rate | 17.50 | 37.50 |
| d | as "c", with "X" on rate page | 17.50 | 37.50 |
| e | Type III, no rate page | 60.00 | 200.00 |

BK31a

BK31d (English)

BK31d (French)

| | | English | French |
|---|---|---|---|
| **BK31** | 1¢ green (231as), 2¢ brown (232as), 3¢ carmine (233as), 1 pane each of 4 + 2 labels (231a, 232a and 233a), *Apr 14, 1937* | | |
| a | Type I, blue cover | 90.00 | 180.00 |
| b | as "a", no rate page | 90.00 | 180.00 |
| c | Type II, blue cover, no rate page | 65.00 | 140.00 |
| d | as "c", with turquoise cover | 65.00 | 140.00 |
| e | Type II, with 6¢ airmail rate, blue cover | 65.00 | 140.00 |
| f | as "e", with turquoise cover | 70.00 | 160.00 |
| g | as "e", with purple cover | 75.00 | 160.00 |
| h | as "e", red "X" on rate page | 65.00 | 140.00 |
| j | Type III, blue cover, no rate page | 120.00 | 250.00 |

## War Issue (1942–1947)

Back Cover Slogans: Type I "Post Office" or "Les Mandats"
Type II "Postal Note" or "Bons Postaux"
Type IIa "Post Master" (two words)

Rates refer to last line on rate page.

BK32a (English)

BK32a (French)

BK33a

| | | English | French | Bilingual |
|---|---|---|---|---|
| **BK32** | 1¢ green (249as), 4 panes of 6 (249b), *Nov 24, 1942* | | | |
| a | Type I, 6¢ rate | 35.00 | 55.00 | N/A |
| b | as "a", with "X" on rate page | 35.00 | 55.00 | N/A |
| c | as "a", surcharged rate page | 28.00 | 45.00 | N/A |
| d | Type II, 7¢ & 6¢ rates | 28.00 | 45.00 | 48.00 |
| e | Type II, 7¢ & 5¢ rates | 47.00 | 55.00 | 52.00 |
| f | Type IIa, 7¢ & 6¢ rates | 50.00 | N/A | 60.00 |
| g | Type IIa, 7¢ & 5¢ rates | 50.00 | | |
| **BK33** | 2¢ brown (250as), 2 panes of 6 (250b), *Oct 6, 1942* | | | |
| a | Type 1, 6¢ rate | 45.00 | 90.00 | N/A |
| b | as "a", with "X" on rate page | 45.00 | 90.00 | N/A |
| c | as "a", no rate page | 45.00 | 90.00 | N/A |
| d | Type I, 7¢ & 6¢ rate page | 45.00 | 90.00 | N/A |
| e | as "d", surcharged rate page | 45.00 | 90.00 | N/A |
| **BK34** | 3¢ dark carmine (251as), 2 panes of 4 + 2 labels (251a), *Aug 20, 1942* | | | |
| a | Type I, 6¢ rate | 14.00 | 18.00 | N/A |
| b | as "a", with "X" on rate page | 14.00 | 18.00 | N/A |
| c | as "a", no rate page | 14.00 | 18.00 | N/A |
| d | as "a", surcharged rate page | 35.00 | 75.00 | N/A |

BK35 (English)

BK35 (French)

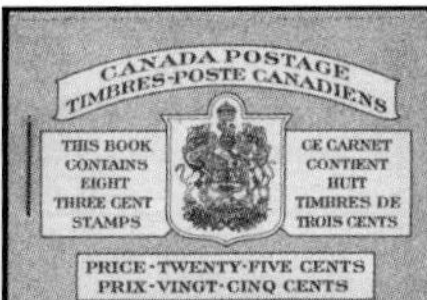

BK35 (Bilingual)

| | | English | French | Bilingual |
|---|---|---|---|---|
| **BK35** | 3¢ rose violet (252as), 2 panes of 4 + 2 labels (252a), *Aug 28, 1943* | | | |
| a | Type IIa, 7¢ & 6¢ surcharged rates | 11.00 | | |
| b | Type II, 7¢ & 6¢ rates | 7.50 | 24.00 | 20.00 |
| c | Type IIa, 7¢ & 6¢ rates | 7.50 | N/A | 20.00 |
| d | Type II, 7¢ & 5¢ rates | 11.00 | 30.00 | 35.00 |
| **BK36** | 4¢ dark carmine (254as), 1 pane of 6 (254a), *May 3, 1943* | | | |
| a | Type I, 6¢ rate | 8.75 | 20.00 | N/A |
| b | Type I, no rate page | 8.75 | 20.00 | N/A |
| c | Type I, surcharged 7¢ & 6¢ rates | 8.75 | 12.00 | N/A |
| d | Type II, 7¢ & 6¢ rates | 8.75 | 12.00 | 15.00 |
| e | Type II, 7¢ & 5¢ rates | 26.00 | N/A | 34.00 |
| f | Type IIa, surcharged 7¢ & 6¢ rates | 8.75 | 8.75 | N/A |
| g | Type IIa, 7¢ & 6¢ rates | 8.75 | N/A | 15.00 |
| h | Type IIa, 7¢ & 5¢ rates | 26.00 | N/A | 34.00 |
| **BK37** | 1¢ green (249as), 2¢ brown (250as), 3¢ dark carmine (251as), 1 pane each of 4 + 2 labels (249a, 250a and 251a), *Sep 14, 1942* | | | |
| a | Type I, 6¢ rate | 30.00 | 60.00 | N/A |
| b | Type I, no rate page | 30.00 | 60.00 | N/A |
| c | Type I, 7¢ & 6¢ rate page | 30.00 | 60.00 | N/A |
| d | as "a", "X" on rate page | 30.00 | 60.00 | N/A |
| e | Type I, surcharged rate page | 30.00 | 60.00 | N/A |

BK38 (English)

BK38 (French)

BK38 (Bilingual)

| | | English | French | Bilingual |
|---|---|---|---|---|
| **BK38** | 1¢ green (249cs), 3¢ rose violet (252bs), 4¢ dark carmine (254bs), 1 pane of 3 each (249c, 252b and 254b), *Sep 1, 1943* | | | |
| a | Type II, 7¢ & 6¢ rates | 15.00 | 25.00 | 32.00 |
| b | Type II, 7¢ & 5¢ rates | 22.50 | 30.00 | 32.00 |
| c | as "b", with rate sheet in back of booklet | 45.00 | N/A | 60.00 |
| d | Type IIa, 7¢ & 6¢ rates | 45.00 | | * |

* an example has been reported to the editors

BK39 (English)

BK39 (French)

| | | English | French | Bilingual |
|---|---|---|---|---|
| **BK39** | 3¢ rose violet (252as), 1 pane of 6 (252c); 4¢ dark carmine (254as), 1 pane of 6 (254ai); 7¢ blue (C9as), 2 panes of 4 (C9a); blue airmail labels, 2 panes of 4, *Dec 1, 1947* | | | |
| a | pane C9a is normal | 44.00 | 48.00 | N/A |
| b | pane C9a is reversed | 70.00 | N/A | N/A |

## 1949–1951 Issue

Back Cover Slogans: Type I — "Postal Note" or "Bons Postaux"
Type II — "Avoid Loss" or "Evitez Les Pertes"

| | | English | Bilingual |
|---|---|---|---|
| **BK40** | 3¢ rose violet (286bs), 2 panes of 4 + 2 labels (286b), *Apr 12, 1950* | | |
| a | Type I, 7¢ & 5¢ rates | 11.00 | 15.00 |
| b | Type II, no rate page | 9.00 | 13.00 |

BK41a (English)

BK41a (Bilingual)

BK41b (Stitched)

| | | English | Bilingual |
|---|---|---|---|
| **BK41** | 4¢ dark carmine (287bs), 1 pane of 6 (287b), *May 5, 1950* | | |
| a | Type I, 7¢ & 5¢ rates | 30.00 | 50.00 |
| b | Type II, no rate page | 30.00 | 50.00 |
| c | as "b", stitched (287bi) | 100.00 | N/A |
| **BK42** | 4¢ orange (306bs), 1 pane of 6 (306b), *Jan 2, 1951* | | |
| a | Type II, no rate page | 9.00 | 13.00 |
| b | as "a", stitched (306bi) | 18.00 | N/A |

BK43 (English)

BK43 (Bilingual)

| | | English | Bilingual |
|---|---|---|---|
| **BK43** | 1¢ green (284as), 3¢ rose violet (286as), 4¢ dark carmine (287as), 1 pane of 3 each (284a, 286a and 287a), *May 18, 1950* | | |
| a | Type I, 7¢ & 5¢ rates | 28.00 | 40.00 |
| b | Type II, no rate page | 28.00 | 40.00 |
| **BK44** | 1¢ green (284as), 3¢ rose violet (286as), 4¢ orange (306as), 1 pane of 3 each, Type II, no rate page (284a, 286a and 306a), *Oct 25, 1951* | 17.50 | 30.00 |

## QUEEN ELIZABETH II

### Karsh Issue (1953)

BK45 (Bilingual)

BK46 (English)

BK47 (English)

| | | English | Bilingual |
|---|---|---|---|
| **BK45** | 4¢ violet (328bs), 1 pane of 6 (328b), Type II, no rate page, *Jul 6, 1953* | 2.50 | 2.50 |
| **BK46** | 3¢ carmine rose (327bs), 2 panes of 4 + 2 labels (327b), Type II, no rate page, *Jul 17, 1953* | 4.00 | 6.00 |
| **BK47** | 1¢ violet brown (325as), 3¢ carmine rose (327as), 4¢ violet (328as), 1 pane each of 3 (325a, 327a and 328a), Type II, no rate page, *Aug 12, 1953* | 12.00 | 20.00 |

## Wildlife Issue (1954)

**BK48** 5¢ blue (336as), 1 pane of 5 + label (336a), *Apr 1, 1954*

a stapled 3.00

b stitched (336ai) 4.75

## Wilding Issue (1954–1962)

Back Cover Slogans: Type I "Use Air Parcel Post"
Type II "Use Your Post Office"
Type III "Postal Zoning"

BK49a

BK50

BK51a

**BK49** 5¢ blue (341as), 1 pane of 5 + label (341a), *Jul 14, 1954*

a Type I 2.75

b Type I, stitched (341aiii) 7.00

c Type II 3.00

d Type III 5.00

**BK50** 4¢ violet (340as), 1 pane of 6 (340b), Type I, *Jul 7, 1955* 4.50

a LF pane 30.00

**BK51** 1¢ violet brown (337as), 4¢ violet (340as),
1 pane each of 5 + label (337a, 340a), *Jan 1, 1956*

a Type II 4.00

b Type III 4.00

Cutting guide lines may appear on any selvedge of 337a, 340a or 341a, in the upper or lower left corner. Value is 8 x normal.

BK51b exists with cutting lines on front and/or back cover. Value: 4x listed price.

## Cameo Issue (1962–1967)

Inside Front Cover: Type I Rubber-stamped "Local Letters"
Type II "Local 4¢ 1st ounce" (no rubber stamp)
Type III as Type II with GIVE STAMPS TO SHUT-INS – DONNEZ DES TIMBRES AUX MALADES added, front cover design 62 mm wide
Type IV as "III", design 65 mm wide


BK52a

BK53c

**BK52** 5¢ blue (405as), 1 pane of 5 + label (405a), *Oct 3, 1962*

a Type I 10.00

ai missing rubber stamped "Local Letters" 100.00

b Type II 10.00

c Type III 5.00

d Type IV 30.00

e "Centennial" Cover 30.00

BK52e exists with cutting lines on front cover. Value: 5x listed price.

**BK53** 1¢ brown (401as), 4¢ carmine (404as),
1 pane each of 5 + label (401a, 404a), *Feb 4, 1963*

a Type I 9.00

b Type II 9.00

c Type III 10.00

Panes may be low fluorescent.

## Centennial Issue (1967–1973)

BK54

BK55

**BK54** 1¢ brown (454as), 4¢ carmine rose (457as)
1 pane each of 5 + label (454a [NF], 457a [NF]), DEX, *Feb 1967* 2.50

a 454aii (DF) and 457a (NF) 3.50

b 454aii (DF) and 457ai (DF) 3.50

c 454aii (DF) and 457aiii (MF) 9.00

d 454aiii (DF/fl) and 457aii (DF/fl) 15.00

e 454ai (LF) and 457ai (DF) 8.00

f 454ai (LF) and 457aiii (MF) 25.00

BK54 exists with cutting lines on front and/or back cover. Lowest price: $30 (one cover) $50 (both covers).

**BK55** 5¢ blue (458as), 1 pane of 5 + label, NF, DEX (458a), *Mar 1967* 8.00

a LF/fl (458ai) 20.00

BK55 exists with cutting lines on front and/or back cover. Value: 4x listed price.

**Beginning with BK56 (through BK100), all booklets printed by BABN have a 'counting mark' on every 50th booklet. Price is 2.5 times normal.**

Counting mark

**BK56** 1¢ brown (454d) x 5 + 4¢ carmine rose (457ds) x 5,
pane of 10 se-tenant, DF, DEX (454c), *Sep 1968* 5.00

a NF/fl (454ci) 10.00

BK56 was the first "integral" booklet where the cover is folded in half and the pane is affixed to the inside of the cover. Some larger panes from this point on are also folded within the covers. This was also Canada's first booklet to contain se-tenant designs and Canada's first two-colour booklet pane.

BK57

BK58

**BK57** 4¢ carmine rose (457d and 457cs), pane of 25 + 2 labels, NF, DEX (457c), *Jan 1968* 12.50

a NF/fl (457ci) 17.50

**BK58a** 5¢ blue (458d), pane of 20 (458c), DF, DEX, *Aug 1968* 10.50

b "Extended Line from Lobster Trap" 12.00

BK59

**BK59** 1¢ brown (454d) x 1 + 6¢ orange (459viiis) x 4,
se-tenant pane of 5 (454b), DEX, *Oct 1968*

a DF (454b) 5.00

b LF (454bi) 14.00

c HB (454bii) 30.00

d as "a", fluorescent orange ink on 6¢ orange 60.00

e as "b", fluorescent orange ink on 6¢ orange 65.00

BK60

BK61

**BK60** 6¢ orange (459 and 459as), pane of 25 + 2 labels, NF (459a), DEX, *Dec 1968*
- a top row of pane: Label-Label-Stamp 10.50
- b "cutting error", top row of pane: Label–Stamp–Label *5,000.00*
- c as "a", LF/fl (459ai) 17.50

**BK61** 6¢ black, Die I (460g), pane of 25 + 2 labels, perf. 10, (460a), DEX, *Jan 1970*
- a NF (460a) 15.00
- b LF (460ai) 17.50
- c MF (460aii) 30.00
- d HB* (460aiii) *4,500.00*

*This paper is very bright, similar to "OPAL" BK63.

BK62

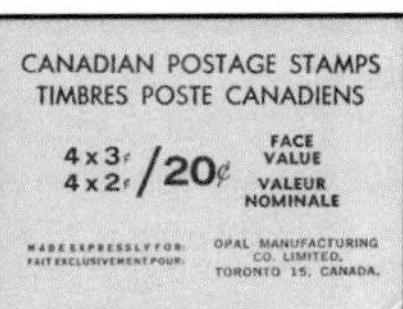

BK63

BK65

**BK62** 6¢ black, Die II (460h), 1 pane of 4 (460e) (25¢ booklet), DF, DEX, *May 1970* 15.00

**BK63** 2¢ green (455x) x 4 + 3¢ dull purple (456x) x 4, pane of 8 + 2 labels (OPAL) (455a), *Oct 26, 1970*
- a pane with vertical perforated gutter 2.50
- b pane with vertical & horizontal perforated gutter (455ai) 300.00

**BK64** 6¢ black, Die I (460 and 460bs), pane of 25 + 2 labels (460b) (perf. 12½ x 12) (top row: Label–Label–Stamp), DEX, *Dec 1970* 22.50
- a "cutting error", top row of pane: Stamp–Label–Label *3,000.00*

**BK65** 6¢ black, Die II (460ds), 1 pane of 4 (460d) (perf. 12½ x 12) (25¢ booklet), *Nov 1970*
- a DEX gum 6.00
- b DF, PVA gum (460di), wax coating on inside of cover 5.00
- c DF, PVA gum (460di), *no* wax coating on inside of cover 7.00

| | |
|---|---|
| Type I | Back Cover Slogan "Free Dispenser" |
| Type II | Back Cover Slogan "Prestamped" |
| Type III | 10 Cover Designs in Brown |

BK66d

**BK66** 1¢ brown (454ei) x 1 + 3¢ dull purple (456ai) x 1 + 7¢ slate green (543x) x 3; pane of 5 se-tenant + label (543a), PVA *Jun 30, 1971*
- a Type I, black sealing strip, LF 6.00
- ai as "a", DF 10.00
- aii as "a", MF 8.00
- b Type II, black sealing strip, LF 6.00
- bi as "b", DF 10.00
- bii as "b", MF 8.00
- c Type I, clear sealing strip, LF 8.00
- ci as "c", DF 10.00
- d Type II, clear sealing strip, LF 8.00
- di as "d", DF 10.00

BK67 BK68b

**BK67** 1¢ brown (454e) x 4 + 3¢ dull purple (456a) x 4 + 7¢ slate green (543bs) x 12 (543b), se-tenant pane of 20, DF, DEX *Jun 30, 1971* 12.50

**BK68** 1¢ brown (454ei) x 1 + 3¢ dull purple (456ai) x 1 + 7¢ slate green (543x) x 3; 2 panes of 5 + label each (543a), PVA, *Aug 1971*
- a Type I, large sticker (33 mm x 19 mm), MF/LF panes 20.00
- ai as 'a', LF/LF panes 35.00
- b Type II, large sticker (33 mm x 19 mm), MF/LF panes 20.00
- bi as 'b', LF/LF panes 35.00
- c Type I, small sticker (28 mm x 14 mm), MF/LF panes 25.00
- d Type II, small sticker (28 mm x 14 mm), MF/LF panes 25.00

These were experimental booklets to test public reaction to 50¢ vending machine booklets.

BK69d

BK71

**BK69** 1¢ brown (454eiv) x 3 + 6¢ black, Die II (460cx) x 1 + 8¢ slate (544x) x 2; se-tenant pane of 6 (544a), PVA, *Dec 30, 1971*
- a Type I or II, HF (544aiii), black sealing strip 4.00
- ai as "a", DF (544a) 10.00
- aii as "a", MF (544aii) 6.00
- b Type I or II, HF, Ottawa (OP4) tagging (544qii), black sealing strip 6.00
- bi as "b", MF (544qi) 6.00
- bii as "b", LF (544q) 10.00
- c Type I or II, HB, black sealing strip (544aiv) 4.00
- d Type III, HF, black sealing strip (544aiii) 4.00
- di as "d", LF (544ai) 6.00
- dii as "d", MF (544aii) 5.00
- e Type III, HF, Ottawa (OP4) tagging, black sealing strip (544qii) 3.00
- ei as "e", LF (544q) 4.00
- eii as "e", MF (544qi) 4.00
- f Type III, HF, Ottawa (OP2) tagging, clear sealing strip (544qv) 2.50
- fi as "f", DF (544qvi) 3.50
- fii as "f", MF (544qiv) 3.00
- g Type III, HB, black sealing strip 3.50
- gi as 'g', MF 4.00
- gii as 'g', HF 5.00
- h Type III, HB, clear sealing strip 4.50
- hi as 'h', LF 6.00
- hii as 'h', MF 6.00
- hiii as 'h', HF 5.00
- j Type III, NF, black sealing strip 2.50
- ji as 'j', LF 2.50
- k Type III, NF, Ottawa (OP2) tagging, clear sealing strip (544qiii) 22.00

**BK70** 1¢ brown (454eiv) x 6 + 6¢ black, Die II (460cx) x 1 + 8¢ slate (544x) x 11; se-tenant pane of 18, PVA, *Dec 30, 1971*
- a DF (544b) 7.50
- b as "a", Ottawa tagging (OP4) (544r) 5.00
- c part of design missing from right margin 8¢ stamp in 4th row (about 100 known) 250.00

**BK71** 1¢ brown (454ev) x 4 + 6¢ black, Die II (460cxi) x 1 + 8¢ slate (544xi) x 5; se-tenant pane of 10, PVA, ribbed, vert. *Aug 1972*
- a black sealing strip, LF (544c) 4.00
- b black sealing strip, MF (544ci) 3.00
- c clear sealing strip, MF (544ci) 4.00

| | | |
|---|---|---|
| d | black sealing strip, MF, Ottawa (OP4) tagging (544s) | 4.00 |
| e | clear sealing strip, MF, Ottawa (OP4) tagging (544s) | 4.00 |
| f | clear sealing strip, LF (544c) | 5.00 |

These booklets were issued with 10 pictorial cover designs similar to Type III, but printed in blue.

**Christmas Issue (1968)**

| | | |
|---|---|---|
| **BK72** | 5¢ blue & black (488as), 2 panes of 10 | |
| a | untagged, tab left (488a), *Nov 1, 1968* | 9.00 |
| b | as "a", tab right (488ai) | 9.00 |
| c | Winnipeg tagged, tab left (488q), *Nov 15, 1968* | 10.00 |
| d | as "c", tab right (488qi) | 10.00 |

**Christmas Issue (1969)**

| | | |
|---|---|---|
| **BK73** | 5¢ multicoloured (502as), 2 panes of 10, *Oct 8, 1969* | |
| a | untagged, tab left (502a) | 9.00 |
| b | as "a", tab right (502ai) | 9.00 |
| c | Winnipeg tagged, tab left (502q) | 12.00 |
| d | as "c", tab right (502qi) | 12.00 |

## Caricature Issue (1972–1976)

BK74

BK76

| | | |
|---|---|---|
| **BK74** | 1¢ orange (586as) x 3 + 6¢ dark red (591vii) x 1 + 8¢ ultramarine (593xxi) x 2; 1 pane of 6 se-tenant (586a), *Apr 10, 1974* | |
| a | DF paper | 2.00 |
| b | HF paper (586ai) | 2.00 |
| c | broken tiara on 8¢ (No. 593), DF paper | 2.00 |
| d | broken "1" on 1¢ (No. 586), DF paper | 2.50 |
| e | missing "1" on 1¢ (No. 586), DF paper | 100.00 |
| f | missing "1" on two 1¢ stamps (No. 586) | 150.00 |
| g | as "a", on horizontal ribbed paper (586av) | 10.00 |
| i | bottom half of "Canada 8" missing from both 8¢ stamps (593) | 350.00 |
| j | stuttering "C" | 75.00 |
| k | re-entry in "age" of "Postage" on 6¢ stamp (591viii) | 30.00 |
| l | LF paper (586aiv) | 2.50 |
| T1 | untagged (error), ribbed, horiz. | 175.00 |
| T2 | one tagging bar missing, LF paper, ribbed, horiz. | 30.00 |
| T3 | two tagging bars missing, ribbed, horiz. | 75.00 |

BK74 booklets were issued with 10 pictorial cover designs, in red, depicting aircraft. The cover stock and stamp paper exist with all grades of fluorescence. Booklets T2 and T3 sometimes have ghost tagging bar(s) running vertically across stamps to the right of the issuing bar. No difference in price.

| | | |
|---|---|---|
| **BK75** | 1¢ orange (586as) x 6 + 6¢ dark red (591vii) x 1 + 8¢ ultramarine (593xxi) x 11; 1 pane of 18, se-tenant (586b), *Jan 17, 1975* | |
| a | MF paper | 2.50 |
| b | orange on Queen's hair | 3.00 |
| c | right tag bar missing | 30.00 |
| T1 | untagged (error) | 750.00 |
| **BK76** | 1¢ orange (586as) x 2 + 2¢ green (587viii) x 4 + 10 dark carmine (593Ac) x 4; 1 pane of 10 se-tenant (586c), *Sep 1, 1976* | |
| a | LF paper | 2.00 |
| b | doubling under "10s", LF | 10.00 |
| c | repeating "10s", LF | 30.00 |
| d | green or orange on reverse | 2.50 |
| h | orange line 1 mm wide at right side of 1¢ stamp, LF | 30.00 |

BK76 with "wavy lines" on inside of cover:

| | | |
|---|---|---|
| e | LF paper | 2.25 |
| f | repeating "10s", LF | 27.50 |
| fi | repeating "10s", HB paper | 90.00 |
| g | partial numbers on tab, MF | 30.00 |

BK76 booklets were issued with the 10 aircraft covers (as BK74) in mauve.

## Floral Issue (1977–1979)

BK77

BK78

BK79

| | | |
|---|---|---|
| **BK77** | 1¢ Gentian (781a) x 2 + 12¢ Queen (713a) x 4; 1 se-tenant pane of 6 (781b), *Nov 1, 1977* | |
| a | DF | 1.25 |
| b | cameo "doubled" (colour shift) | 1.50 |
| c | LF | 5.00 |

BK77 booklets were issued with 10 pictorial cover designs in brown (with wavy lines on outside covers) depicting flora. Misregistration of colours on the 1¢ is common.

| | | |
|---|---|---|
| **BK78** | 2¢ Columbine (782b) x 4 + 14¢ Queen (716as) x 3; 1 se-tenant pane of 7 + label (782a), *Apr 1, 1978* | |
| a | pane width is 92 mm (most common), smooth paper | 1.25 |
| b | pane width is 100 mm with extra left tag bar (vert. ribbed paper) | 7.00 |
| c | as "a", on vertical ribbed paper (from 782ai) | 7.00 |
| d | as "b", on smooth paper | 10.00 |

These booklets were issued with the 10 flora pictorial covers in green. The pane widths vary from 89.2 mm to 100 mm. Misregistration of colours is common.

| | | |
|---|---|---|
| **BK79** | 14¢ Queen (716a and 716as); pane of 25 + 2 labels (716b), *Nov 13, 1978* | |
| a | dull paper | 8.00 |
| b | "notch in lower frame" on 3/9 | 15.00 |
| c | vertical guide line through 7th column | 9.00 |
| d | vertical black or red 'wedges' on tab (2 diff. black) | 30.00 |

BK79 booklets were issued with 5 pictorial cover designs in black depicting cartoons of the Postal Code.

## Parliament Issue (1979)

BK80

BK81

| | | |
|---|---|---|
| **BK80** | 1¢ Parliament (797) x 1 + 5¢ Parliament (800) x 3 + 17¢ Queen (789as) x 2; pane of 6 se-tenant (797a), *Mar 28, 1979* | |
| a | dull paper | 1.25 |
| b | as "a", broken "1" | 5.00 |
| bi | as "a", partially missing "1" | 10.00 |
| bii | as "a", missing "1" | 75.00 |
| c | as "a", cameo "doubled" (colour shift) | 1.50 |
| d | as "a", line through tiara | 2.50 |
| e | lower left corner of 2/1 broken | 2.00 |
| f | vertical green line on tab of pane width 77 mm | 10.00 |
| fi | vertical green line on tab of pane width 70 mm | 10.00 |
| g | double paper on pane 797a, affecting all 6 stamps* | *2,500.00* |

BK80 booklets were issued with 10 floral pictorial covers in blue. Pane widths vary from 70 mm to 77 mm. Many non-constant flaws exist. Tagging bar widths vary from 3½mm (normal) to 4½mm (3x price shown).

* Only one copy of BK80g has been reported.

BK80g

| | | |
|---|---|---|
| **BK81** | 17¢ Queen (789a and 789as); pane of 25 + 2 labels, (789b), *Jul 3, 1979* | |
| a | dull paper | 12.00 |
| b | as "a", on vertical ribbed paper | 8.50 |
| c | as "a", "notch in lower frame" on 3/9 | 10.00 |
| d | as "a", vertical guide line through 7th column | 10.00 |
| e | wavy lines on cover | 10.00 |
| f | vertical black or green 'wedges' on tab (2 diff. black) | 50.00 |
| T1 | as "a" (plain cover), untagged pane of 25 + 2 labels | 750.00 |
| T1i | as "T1", on vertical ribbed paper | 750.00 |
| T2 | as "e" (wavy lines on cover), untagged pane of 25 + 2 labels | 750.00 |

BK81 booklets were issued with 5 Postal Code cover designs in violet.

## Maple Leaf Issue (1982–1985)

BK82

BK83

| | | |
|---|---|---|
| **BK82** | 5¢ deep claret (940) x 2 + 10¢ dark green (944) x 1 + 30¢ red (945) x 1; pane of 4 + 2 labels (945a), *Mar 1, 1982* | |
| a | uncoated paper | 1.50 |
| ai | as 'a', with vertical green line on tab of pane | 30.00 |
| c | coated paper (945ai), *Aug 1982* | 1.50 |
| d | with "hook tag flaw" (see note after No. 787) | 50.00 |
| **BK82A** | labels in top row rather than bottom. *Oct 1982* | |
| a | uncoated paper (945x) | 2.50 |
| b | coated paper (945xi) | 2.50 |

BK82/A booklets were issued with 10 pictorial cover designs depicting Legislative Buildings, black on cream.

| | | |
|---|---|---|
| **BK83** | 30¢ light blue, blue & red (923b and 923bs); pane of 20 + label (923a), *Jun 30, 1982* | 16.00 |

BK84

BK84c

BK85b

| | | |
|---|---|---|
| **BK84** | 5¢ deep claret (940) x 2 + 8¢ dark blue (943) x 1 + 32¢ brown (946) x 1; pane of 4 se-tenant + 2 labels (946b), *Feb 15, 1983* | |
| a | Abitibi paper stock | 1.50 |
| c | cover in orange stock | 2.50 |
| T1 | untagged pane | 125.00 |

BK84 booklets were issued with 10 pictorial Legislative cover designs in red.

| | | |
|---|---|---|
| **BK85** | 32¢ beige, red & brown (924b and 924bs), pane of 25 + 2 labels | |
| a | Abitibi paper stock (924a), *Apr 1, 1983* | 17.00 |
| b | Harrison paper stock, cover dated "1984" (924ai), *Feb 15, 1984* | 17.00 |

BK85 booklets were issued on cream-coloured stock depicting the Centre Block of the Parliament Buildings in red ink.

### Canadian Forts (1983, 1985)

| | | |
|---|---|---|
| **BK86** | 32¢ Forts of Canada (992a), se-tenant pane of 10 different designs (cover in blue), *Jun 30, 1983* | 12.00 |
| **BK87** | 34¢ Forts of Canada (1059a), se-tenant pane of 10 different designs (cover in brown), *Jun 28, 1985* | 16.00 |
| a | imperforate top margin between stamps and labels (1 known) (1059ai) | *7,500.00* |

## Parliament Buildings (1985)

BK88

BK89

| | | |
|---|---|---|
| **BK88** | 2¢ dark green (939) x 3 + 5¢ dark brown (941) x 2 + 34¢ deep slate blue (947) x 1; pane of 6 se-tenant (947a) | |
| a | uncoated Abitibi paper, *Jun 21, 1985* | 2.50 |
| b | Rolland paper (small "R" on back cover) (947ai), *Jun 21, 1985* | 2.50 |
| T1 | untagged 34¢ (error) | 175.00 |

BK88 booklets were issued with 10 pictorial cover designs (brown ink on light brown) depicting stone work details from the Parliament Buildings.

| | | |
|---|---|---|
| **BK89** | 34¢ Parliament Buildings; pane of 25 (925a), Harrison Paper perf. 13.3 x 13.0 (925as and 925asi), *Aug 1, 1985* | |
| a | tag passes through both top and bottom selvedge | 17.50 |
| b | tag passes through top selvege only | 18.00 |
| c | tag passes through bottom selvege only | 18.00 |
| **BK89A** | 34¢ Parliament Buildings; pane of 25 (925c), Rolland Paper, perf. 13.3 x 14.0 (925cs and 925b), *Jul 4, 1986* | 20.00 |

A single cover design depicts a view of the Parliament Buildings from the Ottawa River, white on black-brown.

| | | |
|---|---|---|
| **BK90** | 32¢ Christmas (1070), pane of 10 (1070a), *Oct 23, 1985* | 12.00 |
| **BK91** | 29¢ Christmas Greet More (1116); pane of 10, perf. 13½ horiz. (1116a), *Oct 29, 1986* | |
| a | left and right tagging | 18.00 |
| b | left tag only | 75.00 |
| c | right tag only | 75.00 |
| d | 29¢ multicoloured (1116b), pane of 10, left and right tagging, perf. 12½ horiz. (1116c) | 100.00 |

## Parliament Buildings Issue (1987)

BK92

BK94

| | | |
|---|---|---|
| **BK92** | 1¢ sage green (938) x 2 + 6¢ henna brown (942) x 2 + 36¢ dark lilac rose (948) x 1 + label se-tenant (948a) | |
| a | uncoated Rolland paper, Plate 1 (948a), *Mar 30, 1987* | 2.50 |
| b | coated Harrison paper, Plate 2 (948ai), *Oct 1, 1987* | 4.00 |
| c | double paper on BK92b, affecting right column | *1,500.00* |

Cover designs as BK88 in black-green ink on light brown. Imprinted booklet pane tabs include printer, designer, colour indicators and paper manufacturer.

| | | |
|---|---|---|
| **BK93** | 36¢ multicoloured (926Bcs); pane of 10 (926Bc), *Mar 30, 1987* | 7.50 |

Cover design as BK89, gold on brown. Pane includes imprinted tab as BK92.

| | | |
|---|---|---|
| **BK94** | 36¢ multicoloured (926Be); pane of 25 (926Bd), *May 19, 1987* | 20.00 |

Cover design BK89, gold on brown. Pane has imprinted tab as BK92.

| | | |
|---|---|---|
| **BK95** | 31¢ Christmas Greet More (1151); pane of 10 (1151a), *Nov 2/87* | 8.00 |

BK95 exists with covers showing at least 3 different fluorescences (DF, LF and MF).

Booklets

## Parliament Buildings Issue (1988)

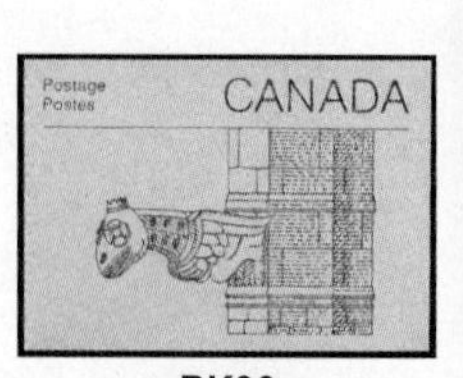


BK96

BK97a

BK97b

**BK96** 1¢ sage green (938) x 1 + 6¢ henna brown (942) x 2 + 37¢ blue (1187) x 1, se-tenant + 2 labels (1187a), *Feb 3, 1988*
- a blue tab markings 2.00
- b green tab markings 2.00
- T1 as "a", untagged 37¢ (error) 150.00
- T2 as "b", untagged 37¢ (error) 175.00

Cover design as BK88, blue ink on light brown.

**BK97** 37¢ Parliament (1163cs); pane of 10 (1163a), *Jan 5, 1988*
- a Stamp Pack text 11.00
- b Lunch Saver text 11.00
- c as "a", missing black inscription on the green cover 200.00
- d HP (1163ai) (s/e at bottom) 20.00

**BK98** 37¢ Parliament (1163bs); pane of 25 (1163b)
- a Stamp Pack text, RP, *Jan 5, 1988* 27.50
- b Lunch Saver text, RP, *Jan 5, 1988* 27.50
- c as "a", HP (1163bi) (s/e at bottom), *May 2, 1988* 40.00

**Christmas (1988)**

**BK99** 32¢ Christmas Greet More (1225), pane of 10 (1225a), *Oct 27/88* 13.00

BK99 exists in two versions: with extra tagging at top of binding margin and without.

## Parliament Buildings Issue (1989)

BK101c

BK104b

**BK100** 2¢ slate green (939a) x 3 + 6¢ dark purple (1186) x 1 + 38¢ dark blue (1188) x 1; se-tenant + blue label (1188a), plate 1, coated Harrison paper, *Jan 18, 1989*
- a Abitibi cover 2.00
- b Rolland cover 2.00
- T1 untagged 38¢ (error) 150.00

Cover design as BK88, red ink on light brown. Tab imprints as BK96, in green.

**BK101** 38¢ Parliament (1165 and 1165as); pane of 10 + 2 labels (1165a), *Dec 29 ,1988*
- a Stamps by Mail 9.00
- b Lunch Saver 9.00
- c Priority Post and New Logo 12.00

**BK102** 38¢ Queen Elizabeth II (1164a and 1164as); pane of 10 + 2 labels (1164b), *Dec 29, 1988*
- a Stamps by Mail 10.00
- b Lunch Saver 9.00
- c Priority Post and New Logo 12.00
- ci as "c", with pane perforated on right side† 500.00
- cii as "c", with pane perforated on both sides† 750.00

† Only a few booklets reported; pane normally has straight edges on both sides.

**BK103** 38¢ Parliament (1165 and 1165as); pane of 25 + 2 labels (1165b), *Dec 29, 1988*
- a Stamps by Mail 26.00
- b Lunch Saver 26.00
- c Priority Post and New Logo 30.00

**BK104** 44¢ Walrus (1171a), pane of 5 + label (1171b), *Jan 18, 1989*
- a Stamps by Mail 17.00
- b Lunch Saver 17.00
- c Priority Post and New Logo 20.00

**BK105** 76¢ Grizzly Bear (1178a), pane of 5 + label (1178b), *Jan 18, 1989*
- a Stamps by Mail 22.00
- b Lunch Saver 22.00
- c Priority Post and New Logo 26.00

**BK106** 33¢ Greet More, NF (1259), pane of 10 (1259a), *Oct 26/89* 20.00
- a HF 150.00

**BK107** 38¢ Christmas (1256b), pane of 10 (1256a), *Oct 26, 1989* 60.00

**BK108** 44¢ Christmas (1257as), pane of 5 + label (1257a), *Oct 26/89* 22.00

**BK109** 76¢ Christmas (1258as), pane of 5 + label (1258a), *Oct 26/89* 40.00

## Definitive Issues (1989)

BK110a

BK115

**BK110** 38¢ "Quick Sticks" Flag (1191); booklet of 12, *Jun 30, 1989*
- a hilltop to right on cover (no tag at right edge) 22.00
- b hilltop to left on cover (tag covers both sides) 22.00
- c hilltop to right on cover (no tag at left edge) 22.00

**BK111** 50¢ Flag, perf 13½ x 14, 1¢ yellow (1184) x 1 + 5¢ pink (1185) x 2 + 39¢ blue (1189) x 1; pane of 4 se-tenant, SP (1189a), *Jan 12, 1990* 2.50

**BK111A** 50¢ Flag, perf. 12½ x 13, 1¢ yellow (1184a) x 1 + 5¢ pink (1185a) x 2 + 39¢ blue (1189b) x 1; pane of 4 se-tenant, (1189c), *Mar 1, 1990* 50.00

**BK112** 39¢ Flag (1166as and 1166asi), pane of 10 + 2 labels, perf. 13½ x 13 (1166a), *Dec 28, 1989* 11.00

**BK113** 39¢ Queen Elizabeth II (1167as and 1167asi), pane of 10 + 2 labels (1167a), *Jan 12, 1990* 11.00

**BK114** 39¢ "Quick Sticks" Flag (1192), booklet of 12, *Feb 8, 1990*
- a building at right on cover (tag covers both sides) 22.00
- b building at left on cover (no tag at right edge) 22.00
- c building at left on cover (no tag at left edge) 22.00

**BK115** 39¢ Flag (1166as and 1166asi), pane of 25 + 2 labels, (1166b), *Dec 28, 1989* 32.00

**BK116** 45¢ Pronghorn Deer (1172f), pane of 5 + label (1172b), *Jan 12/90* 16.00

**BK117** 78¢ Beluga Whale (1179c); pane of 5 + label, (1179a), *Jan 12/90* 22.00

## 1990

**BK118** 39¢ Canada Post mail vans, (12 x 1272, 13 x 1273); 2 panes of 8 (1273a, 1273biv) + 1 pane of 9 + 3 labels (1273b), with 16 pages of text, *May 3, 1990* 32.00

This booklet exists with one pane inverted – $500.

**BK119** 34¢ Christmas Greet More (1297), pane of 10 (1297a), *Oct 25/90* 10.00

**BK120** 39¢ Christmas, (1294as), pane of 10 (1294a), *Oct 25/90* 10.00

**BK121** 45¢ Christmas (1295as), pane of 5 + label (1295a), *Oct 25/90* 6.50

**BK122** 78¢ Christmas (1296as), pane of 5 + label (1296a), *Oct 25/90* 11.00

### Definitive Issues (1990–1991)

BK123 BK126 BK127b

**BK123** 50¢ Flag, 1¢ yellow (1184) x 2 + 5¢ pink (1185) x 1 + 40¢ blue (1190) x 1; pane of 4 se-tenant, perf. 13 x 14, CPP (1190a), 50¢ booklet (tax included), *Dec 28, 1990* 3.25

**BK124** 40¢ Flag and mountains (1169 and 1169as); pane of 10 + 2 labels (1169b), *Dec 28, 1990* 11.00

**BK125** 40¢ Flag and mountains (1169 and 1169as); pane of 25 + 2 labels (1169a), *Dec 28, 1990* 36.00

**BK126** 40¢ Queen Elizabeth II (1168as and 1168asi); pane of 10 + 2 labels (1168a), *Dec 28, 1990* 12.00

**BK127** 40¢ "Quick Sticks" Flag (1193), booklet of 12 (1193a), *Jan 11/91*
- a distant cliffs at right on cover, no label (no tag at right edge) 24.00
- b distant cliffs at left on cover, no label (tag covers both sides) 24.00
- e distant cliffs at right on cover, no label (no tag at left edge) 24.00
- c as "a", with label on back 70.00
- d as "b", with label on back 70.00
- i inverted "label" on back 300.00

**BK128** 46¢ Wolverine (1172c), pane of 5 + label (1172e), *Dec 28/90* 9.00

**BK129** 80¢ Peary Caribou (1180a), pane of 5 + label (1180b), *Dec 28/90* 22.00

## 1991

**BK130** 40¢ Public Gardens, 5 different in horizontal strip of 5 (1315a), pane of 10 (5 x 2) (1315b), *May 22, 1991*
- a glued flap, with TI 11.00
- b open cover, with TI 11.00

**BK131** 40¢ Heritage Rivers, 5 different in horizontal strip of 5 (1325a), pane of 10 (5 x 2) (1325b), *Aug 20, 1991*
- a glued flap, with TI 11.00
- b open cover, with TI 11.00

**BK132** 40¢ Queen's University (1338); pane of 10 + 2 labels (1338a), with 10 pages of illustrated text, *Oct 16, 1991*
- a sealed in cellophane, no TI 11.00
- b open, no TI 11.00

One booklet of BK132b has been reported with the back cover inverted, and another with two front covers, values not established.

**BK133** 35¢ Christmas Greet More (1342), pane of 10 (1342a), *Oct 23/91*
- a glued flap, with TI 11.00
- b open cover, with TI 11.00

**BK134** 40¢ Santa Claus (1339as), pane of 10 (1339a), *Oct 23, 1991*
- a glued flap, with TI 11.00
- b open cover, with TI 11.00

**BK135** 46¢ Bonhomme Noël (1340as), pane of 5 + label (1340a), *Oct 23/91*
- a glued flap, with TI 5.50
- b open cover, with TI 5.50

**BK136** 80¢ Sinterklaas (1341as), pane of 5 + label (1341a), *Oct 23/91*
- a glued flap, with TI 9.00
- b open cover, with TI 9.00

**Beginning with BK137, until BK291, most non self-adhesive booklets are available in two versions:**
from field stock, with glued flaps, and bearing no tab inscriptions (no TI);
or from philatelic stock, with open flaps, and having inscriptions on the tabs (with TI).

### Definitive Issues (1991–1992)

BK138 BK140 BK142

**BK137** 42¢ Flag and hills (1356as), pane of 10 (1356a), *Dec 27, 1991*
- a glued flap, no TI, "Canada 92" ad inside 14.00
- b open cover, with TI, "Canada 92" ad inside 11.00
- c glued flap, with TI, "Canada 92" ad inside 14.00
- d glued flap, no TI, "1991 Souvenir Collection" ad inside 25.00

**BK138** 42¢ Flag (1356 and 1356as), pane of 25 + 2 labels (1356c), Canada 92 on back cover, *Dec 27, 1991*
- a glued flap, no TI 27.00
- b open cover, with TI 24.00
- c glued flap, with TI 27.00

**BK138A** 42¢ Flag (1356 and 1356as), pane of 25 + 2 labels (1356c), 1991 Souvenir Collection on back cover
- a glued flap, no TI 28.00

**BK139** 42¢ Flag (1356 and 1356as), pane of 50 + 2 labels (1356b), *Dec 27, 1991*
- a glued flap, with TI 125.00
- b glued flap, no TI 125.00
- c open cover, with TI 125.00

Covers of BK139 are rouletted to allow for separation into two booklets of 25.

**BK140** 42¢ Queen Elizabeth II (1357as), pane of 10 (1357a), 1991 Souvenir Collection inside, *Dec 27, 1991*
- a glued flap, no TI, perforated selvedge 14.00
- b open cover, with TI, perforated selvedge 11.00
- c open cover, with TI, imperforate selvedge 11.00

**BK140A** 42¢ Queen Elizabeth II (1357as), pane of 10 (1357a), Canada 92 inside
- a glued flap, no TI 14.00
- b open cover, with TI, perforated selvedge 11.00
- c open cover, with TI, imperforate selvedge 11.00

**BK141** 42¢ "Quick Sticks" Flag (1388), booklet of 12, *Jan 28, 1992*
- a mountain top leans to right on cover (tag covers both sides) 24.00
- b mountain top leans to left on cover (no tag at right edge) 24.00
- c mountain top leans to left on cover (no tag at left edge) 24.00

| | | |
|---|---|---|
| **BK142** | 48¢ McIntosh Apple (1363a), pane of 5 + label (1363b), *Dec 27/91* | |
| a | glued flap, no TI | 14.00 |
| b | open cover, with TI | 11.00 |
| c | glued flap, with TI | 14.00 |
| **BK143** | 84¢ Stanley Plum (1371a), pane of 5 + label CPP (1371b), *Dec 27, 1991* | |
| a | glued flap, no TI | 18.00 |
| b | open cover, with TI | 15.00 |
| c | glued flap, with TI | 18.00 |

## 1992

| | | |
|---|---|---|
| **BK144** | 42¢ Olympic Winter Games (1399–1403), 5 different (1403a), pane of 10 (1403b), *Feb 7, 1992* | |
| a | flame at right on cover, glued flap, no TI | 12.50 |
| b | flame at right on cover, open cover, with TI | 12.50 |
| c | flame at left on cover, glued flap, no TI | 12.50 |
| d | flame at left on cover, open cover, with TI | 12.50 |
| **BK145** | 42¢ Heritage Rivers (1408–12), 5 different (1412a), pane of 10 (1412b), *Apr 22, 1992* | |
| a | glued flap, no TI | 12.50 |
| b | open cover, with TI | 12.50 |
| **BK146** | 42¢ Olympic Summer Games (1414–18), 5 different (1418a), pane of 10 (1418b), *Jun 15, 1992* | |
| a | white area to right on cover, glued flap, no TI | 12.50 |
| b | white area to right on cover, open cover, with TI | 12.50 |
| c | white area to left on cover, glued flap, no TI | 12.50 |
| d | white area to left on cover, open cover, with TI | 12.50 |
| **BK147** | 42¢ Canadian Minerals (1436–40), 5 different (1440a), pane of 10 (1440b), *Sep 21, 1992* | |
| a | glued flap, no TI | 14.00 |
| b | open cover, with TI | 14.00 |
| **BK148** | 42¢ NHL (1443–45), 3 different; 1 pane of 8 (1443) + 4 labels and printed tab (1443a); 1 pane of 8 (1444) + 4 labels and printed tab (1444a); 1 pane of 9 (1445) + 3 labels and printed tab (1445a). Unsealed, with descriptive copy on 6 leaves, *Oct 9, 1992* 1 fold out leaf and covers, no TI | 28.00 |
| a | sealed in cellophane, no TI | 28.00 |

BK148 is known with an "extra pane", and another with two "extra panes", values not established.

| | | |
|---|---|---|
| **BK149** | 37¢ Christmas Greet More (1455); pane of 10 (1455a), *Nov 13/92* | |
| a | glued flap, no TI | 12.00 |
| b | open cover, with TI | 12.00 |
| **BK150** | 42¢ Jõuluvana (1452a), pane of 10 (1452b), *Nov 13, 1992* | |
| a | glued flap, no TI | 13.00 |
| b | open cover, with TI | 13.00 |
| **BK151** | 48¢ La Befana (1453as), pane of 5 + label (1453a), *Nov 13/92* | |
| a | glued flap, no TI | 8.00 |
| b | open cover, with TI | 8.00 |
| **BK152** | 84¢ Weihnachtsmann (1454as), pane of 5 + label (1454a), *Nov 13/92* | |
| a | glued flap, no TI | 15.00 |
| b | open cover, with TI | 15.00 |

BK153

BK153A

BK155A

BK157A

## Definitive Issues (1992–1994)

| | | |
|---|---|---|
| **BK153** | 43¢ Flag over Prairie perf. 13½ x 13, AP, CPP (1359as); pane of 10 (1359a), 2 overlapped stamps, *Dec 30, 1992* | |
| a | glued flap, no TI | 10.50 |
| b | open cover, with TI | 10.50 |
| **BK153A** | 43¢ Flag over Prairie perf. 14½, LM, CPP (1359ds); pane of 10 (1359d), 4 overlapped stamps, XpressPost ad on back, Canada Post address on back cover in lowercase, *Jan 7, 1994* | |
| a | glued flap, no TI | 16.00 |
| b | open cover, with TI | 13.00 |
| c | glued flap, no TI, address on back in full uppercase | 15.00 |
| **BK153B** | as BK153A, new U.S. and International postal rates inside (50¢ and 88¢), 4 overlapped stamps, *Summer 1994* | |
| a | glued flap, no TI | 15.00 |

Miscut booklets occur on BK153A and BK153B; values vary from $200 to $350 depending on the degree of error.

**Miscut BK153A**

| | | |
|---|---|---|
| **BK153C** | As BK153, CBN, 4 overlapped stamps, 30% recycle symbol on back cover, *Nov 14, 1994* | |
| a | glued flap, no TI | 25.00 |
| b | open cover, with TI | 18.00 |
| | *Does BK153Cb exist? Confirmation is requested.* | |
| c | glued flap, no TI, 50% recycle symbol | 15.00 |
| d | open cover, with TI, 50% recycle symbol | 13.00 |
| **BK154** | 43¢ Flag over Prairie, perf. 13½ x 13, AP, CPP (1359 and 1359as); pane of 25 + 2 labels (1359b), 3 overlapped stamps, 49¢ US and 86¢ International rates on inside cover, *Dec 30, 1992* | |
| a | glued flap, no TI | 32.00 |
| b | open cover, with TI | 32.00 |
| **BK154A** | 43¢ Flag over Prairie, perf. 14½, LM, CPP (1359 and 1359ds); pane of 25 + 2 labels (1359e), large Bluenose on back cover; 49¢ US and 86¢ International rates on inside cover 5 overlapped stamps, Canada Post address in lowercase text, *Jan 7, 1994* | |
| a | glued flap, no TI | 40.00 |
| b | open cover, with TI | 36.00 |
| c | glued flap, no TI, tag bar at top of label | 40.00 |
| d | open cover, with TI, tag bar at top of label | *375.00* |
| e | glued flap, no TI, address on back in full uppercase | 40.00 |
| f | open flap, with TI, address on back in full uppercase | 36.00 |
| **BK154B** | as BK154A, new U.S. and International postal rates inside (50¢ and 88¢), LM, small Bluenose on back cover, 5 overlapped stamps, *Summer 1994* | |
| a | glued flap, no TI | 40.00 |
| b | open cover, with TI | 36.00 |
| **BK154C** | as BK154, CBN, CPP, new U.S. and International postal rates inside (50¢ and 88¢), No Bluenose on back cover, 50% recycle symbol, *Nov 14, 1994* | |
| a | glued flap, no TI | 35.00 |
| b | open cover, with TI | 32.00 |

| | | |
|---|---|---|
| **BK155** | 43¢ Queen Elizabeth II, perf. 13 x 13½, AP, CPP, (1358as), pane of 10 (1358a), 2 overlapped stamps, *Dec 30/92* | |
| a | glued flap, no TI | 15.00 |
| b | open cover, with TI | 13.00 |
| **BK155A** | as BK155, CBN, HP, 3 overlapped stamps, *Jan 7, 1994* | |
| a | glued flap, no TI | 15.00 |
| b | open cover, with TI | 12.00 |
| **BK155B** | as BK155A, new U.S. and International postal rates inside (50¢ and 88¢), 3 overlapped stamps, *1994* | |
| a | glued flap, no TI | 14.00 |
| **BK155C** | as BK155, CBN, PP, 3 overlapped stamps, *Dec 23, 1994* | |
| a | glued flap, no TI | 15.00 |
| b | open cover, with TI | 12.00 |
| **BK155D** | as BK155, APC, 3 overlapped stamps, *Mar 27, 1995* | |
| a | glued flap, no TI | 15.00 |
| b | open cover, with TI | 12.00 |
| **BK156** | 49¢ Delicious Apple, perf. 14½ x 14, AP, CPP (1364a); pane of 5 + label (1364b), 2 overlapped stamps, *Dec 30, 1992* | |
| a | glued flap, no TI | 23.00 |
| b | open cover, with TI | 20.00 |
| c | glued flap, no TI, tag bar on label | 23.00 |
| d | open cover, with TI, tag bar on label | 20.00 |
| **BK156A** | 49¢ Delicious Apple, perf. 13, CBN, HP (1364cs); pane of 5 + label (1364c), 4 overlapped stamps, *Jan 7, 1994* | |
| a | glued flap, no TI | 20.00 |
| b | open cover, with TI | 17.50 |
| c | glued flap, no TI, tag bar on label | 20.00 |
| d | open cover, with TI, tag bar on label | 17.50 |

Two booklets of BK156A containing 86¢ stamps have been reported; value $250.00.

| | | |
|---|---|---|
| **BK157** | 86¢ Bartlett Pear, perf. 14½ x 14, AP, CPP (1372a); pane of 5 + label (1372b), 2 overlapped stamps, *Dec 30, 1992* | |
| a | glued flap, no TI | 23.00 |
| b | open cover, with TI | 20.00 |
| c | glued flap, no TI, tag bar on label | 23.00 |
| d | open cover, with TI, tag bar on label | 20.00 |
| **BK157A** | 86¢ Bartlett Pear, perf. 13, CBN, HP (1372cs); pane of 5 + label (1372c), 4 overlapped stamps, *Jan 7, 1994* | |
| a | glued flap, no TI | 25.00 |
| b | open cover, with TI | 22.00 |
| c | glued flap, no TI, tag bar on label | 25.00 |
| d | open cover, with TI, tag bar on label | 22.00 |
| **BK158** | 43¢ "Quick Sticks" Flag over lake (1389), pane of 12, AP, *Feb 15/93* | |
| a | shoreline at right on cover (tag covers both sides) | 24.00 |
| b | shoreline at left on cover (no tag at right edge) | 24.00 |
| c | shoreline at left on cover (no tag at left edge) | 24.00 |

## 1993

| | | |
|---|---|---|
| **BK159** | 43¢ Hand-Crafted Textiles (1461–65), 5 different (1465a), pane of 10 (1465b), *Apr 30, 1993* | |
| a | glued flap, no TI | 12.00 |
| b | open cover, with TI | 12.00 |
| **BK160** | 43¢ Historic CPR Hotels (1467–71), 5 different (1471a), pane of 10 (1471b), *Jun 14, 1993* | |
| a | glued flap, no TI | 12.00 |
| b | open cover, with TI | 12.00 |
| **BK161** | 43¢ Heritage Rivers (1485–89), 5 different (1489a), pane of 10 (10 x 1) (1489b), *Aug 10, 1993* | |
| a | glued flap, no TI | 12.00 |
| b | open cover, with TI | 12.00 |
| **BK162** | 38¢ Christmas Greet More (1502), pane of 10 (1502a), *Nov 4/93* | |
| a | glued flap, no TI | 12.00 |
| b | open cover, with TI | 12.00 |
| **BK163** | 43¢ Poland Santa (1499as), pane of 10 (1499a), *Nov 4, 1993* | |
| a | glued flap, no TI | 11.00 |
| b | open cover, with TI | 11.00 |
| **BK164** | 49¢ Russia Santa (1500as), pane of 5 + label (1500a), *Nov 4/93* | |
| a | glued flap, no TI | 8.00 |
| b | open cover, with TI | 8.00 |
| **BK165** | 86¢ Australia Santa (1501as), pane of 5 + label (1501a), *Nov 4/93* | |
| a | glued flap, no TI | 13.00 |
| b | open cover, with TI | 13.00 |

**Definitive Issues (1994)**

BK167 BK168

| | | |
|---|---|---|
| **BK166** | 43¢ Greetings, pane of 10 (5 x 1507, 5 x 1508), plus 5 each of 7 different self-stick circular labels, *Jan 28/94* | |
| a | glued flap, with TI | 13.00 |
| b | open cover, with TI | 13.00 |
| **BK167** | 50¢ Snow Apple, perf. 13, CBN, PP (1365as); pane of 5 + labe (1365a), Xpresspost ad on back cover, *Feb 25/94* | |
| a | glued flap, no TI | 12.50 |
| b | open cover, with TI | 10.00 |
| c | glued flap, no TI, tag bar on label | 12.50 |
| d | open cover, with TI, tag bar on label | 10.00 |
| **BK167A** | as BK167, CP Customer Service ad and 800 phone number on back cover | |
| a | glued flap, no TI | 13.00 |
| b | open cover, with TI | 10.00 |
| **BK167B** | 50¢ Snow Apple, perf. 14½ x 14, APC, CPP (1365b); pane of 5 + label (1365c), inside back cover is blank, *Mar 27/95* | |
| a | glued flap, no TI | 24.00 |
| b | open cover, with TI | 20.00 |
| **BK168** | 88¢ Westcot Apricot, perf. 13, CBN, PP (1373as); pane of 5 + label (1373a), Xpresspost ad on back cover, *Feb 25/94* | |
| a | glued flap, no TI | 20.00 |
| b | open cover, with TI | 17.50 |
| c | glued flap, no TI, tag bar on label | 20.00 |
| d | open cover, with TI, tag bar on label | 17.50 |
| **BK168A** | As BK168, CP, GT3; pane of 5 + label (1373iiis) Customer Service ad on back cover, *Nov 14, 1994* | |
| a | glued flap, no TI | 20.00 |
| b | open cover, with TI | 17.50 |
| c | glued flap, no TI, tag bar on label | 20.00 |
| d | open cover, with TI, tag bar on label | 17.50 |
| **BK168B** | 88¢ Westcot Apricot, perf. 14½ x 14, APC, CPP, (1373b); pane of 5 + label (1373c) CP Customer Service ad on back cover, inside cover is blank, *Mar 27, 1995* | |
| a | glued flap, no TI | 34.00 |
| b | open cover, with TI | 30.00 |

"Tag bar on label" varieties from BK156/A, BK157/A, BK167, BK168/A and BK178/A/B (and perhaps others?) consist of a *horizontal* tag bar along the *top* of the label due to the placement next to adjacent booklet panes.

## 1994

**BK169** 43¢ Timothy Eaton (1510); pane of 10 + 2 labels (1510a), 10 pages describing the history of the T. Eaton Company stores, *Mar 17, 1994*

| | | |
|---|---|---|
| a | open booklet, no TI | 11.00 |
| b | sealed booklet in cello pack with red printing, no TI | 11.00 |
| c | sealed booklet in cello pack with blue printing and inserted card (delivery truck illustration); sold only at Eaton stores, no TI | 15.00 |

**BK170** 43¢ Heritage Rivers (1511–15), 5 different (1515a); pane of 10 (1515b), *Apr 22, 1994*

| | | |
|---|---|---|
| a | glued flap, no TI | 13.50 |
| b | open cover, with TI | 13.50 |

**BK171** 38¢ Christmas Greet More (1536); pane of 10 (1536a), *Nov 3, 1994*

| | | |
|---|---|---|
| a | glued flap, no TI | 11.50 |
| b | open cover, with TI | 11.50 |

**BK172** 43¢ Indoor carolling (1533as), pane of 10 (1533a), *Nov 3, 1994*

| | | |
|---|---|---|
| a | glued flap, no TI | 12.50 |
| b | open cover, with TI | 12.50 |

**BK173** 50¢ Choir (1534as), pane of 5 + label (1534a), *Nov 3, 1994*

| | | |
|---|---|---|
| a | glued flap, no TI | 8.00 |
| b | open cover, with TI | 8.00 |

**BK174** 88¢ Outdoor carolling (1535as), pane of 5 + label (1535a), *Nov 3/94*

| | | |
|---|---|---|
| a | glued flap, no TI | 13.00 |
| b | open cover, with TI | 13.00 |

## 1995

**BK175** (43¢) Fortress of Louisbourg (1547–51), 5 different (1551a), pane of 10 (1551b), *May 5, 1995*

| | | |
|---|---|---|
| a | glued flap, no TI | 13.00 |
| b | open cover, with TI | 13.00 |

**BK176** 43¢ Golf in Canada (1553–57), 5 different (1557a), pane of 10 (1557b), *Jun 6, 1995*

| | | |
|---|---|---|
| a | glued flap, no TI | 13.00 |
| b | open cover, with TI | 13.00 |

### Definitive Issues (1995)

BK178

BK179

BK180

**BK177** 45¢ Flag and office bldg., perf. 14½, LM, CPP (1361); pane of 10 (1361a) 30% recycle symbol on back cover, *Jul 31, 1995*

| | | |
|---|---|---|
| a | 8 line text on back cover; glued flap, no TI | 15.00 |
| b | 8 line text on back cover; open cover, with TI * | 13.00 |
| c | glued flap, no TI, 50% recycle symbol on back cover | *15.00* |
| d | open cover, with TI, 50% recycle symbol on back cover | *15.00* |
| e | glued flap, no TI, 5 line text on back cover, 30% recycle | 75.00 |

* BK177b (philatelic stock) has more descriptive text on back cover, including "... Postal Service Customer Council ...", which is not seen on any of the other 45¢ booklets of 10.

**BK177A** 45¢ Flag and office bldg., perf. 13½ x 13, CBN, CPP (1361c); pane of 10 (1361d) 50% recycle symbol on back cover, *Oct 6, 1995*

| | | |
|---|---|---|
| a | glued flap, no TI | 13.00 |
| b | open cover, with TI | 11.00 |

**BK177B** 45¢ Flag and office bldg., perf. 13½ x 13, CBN, PP (1361xivs); pane of 10 (1361xiv) 50% recycle symbol on back cover, *Apr 5, 1996*

| | | |
|---|---|---|
| a | glued flap, no TI | 13.00 |
| b | open cover, with TI | 11.00 |

**BK178** 45¢ Flag and office bldg., perf. 14½ , LM, CPP (1361); pane of 25 + 2 labels (1361b) 30% recycle symbol on back cover, *Jul 31, 1995*

| | | |
|---|---|---|
| a | glued flap, no TI | 44.00 |
| b | open cover, with TI | 38.00 |
| c | glued flap, no TI, tag bar across tab | 44.00 |
| d | open cover, with TI, tag bar across tab | 38.00 |

**BK178A** 45¢ Flag and office bldg., perf. 13½ x 13, CBN, CPP, (1361c); pane of 25 + 2 labels (1361e) 50% recycle symbol on back cover, *Oct 6, 1995*

| | | |
|---|---|---|
| a | glued flap, no TI | 44.00 |
| b | open cover, with TI | 38.00 |
| c | glued flap, no TI, tag bar across tab | 44.00 |
| d | open cover, with TI, tag bar across tab | 38.00 |

**BK178B** 45¢ Flag and office bldg., perf. 13½ x 13, CBN, PP (1361xiii and 1361xivs); pane of 25 + 2 labels (1361xv), 50% recycle symbol on back cover, *Apr 5, 1996*

| | | |
|---|---|---|
| a | glued flap, no TI | 44.00 |
| b | open cover, with TI | 38.00 |
| c | glued flap, no TI, tag bar across tab | 44.00 |
| d | open cover, with TI, tag bar across tab | 38.00 |

**BK179** 45¢ Queen Elizabeth II, perf. 13 x 13½, CBN, PP (1360as); pane of 10 (1360a), *Jul 31, 1995*

| | | |
|---|---|---|
| a | glued flap, no TI | 13.00 |
| b | open cover, with TI | 11.00 |

**BK179A** 45¢ Queen Elizabeth II, perf. 13 x 13½, APC, CPP (1360ixs); pane of 10 (1360ix), *Oct 6, 1995*

| | | |
|---|---|---|
| a | glued flap, no TI | 13.00 |
| b | open cover, with TI | 11.00 |

**BK180** 52¢ Gravenstein Apple, perf. 13, CBN, PP (1366as); pane of 5 + label (1366a), 30% recycle symbol on back cover, *Jul 31, 1995*

| | | |
|---|---|---|
| a | glued flap, no TI | 12.00 |
| b | open cover, with TI | 10.00 |

**BK180A** 52¢ Gravenstein Apple, perf. 14½ x 14, APC, CPP (1366cs); pane of 5 + label (1366c), 50% recycle symbol on back cover, *Oct 6, 1995*

| | | |
|---|---|---|
| a | glued flap, no TI | 17.00 |
| b | open cover, with TI | 14.00 |

**BK180B** 52¢ Gravenstein Apple, perf. 13, CBN, CPP (1366iis); pane of 5 + label (1366ii), *Oct 1996*

| | | |
|---|---|---|
| a | glued flap, no TI | 20.00 |

**BK181** 90¢ Elberta Peach, perf. 13, CBN, PP (1374as); pane of 5 + label (1374a), 30% recycle symbol on back cover, *Jul 31, 1995*

| | | |
|---|---|---|
| a | glued flap, no TI | 17.50 |
| b | open cover, with TI | 17.50 |

**BK181A** 90¢ Elberta Peach, perf. 14½ x 14, APC, CPP (1374b); pane of 5 + label (1374c), 50% recycle symbol on back cover, *Oct 6, 1995*

| | | |
|---|---|---|
| a | glued flap, no TI | 30.00 |
| b | open cover, with TI | 27.50 |

**BK181B** 90¢ Elberta Peach, perf. 13, APC, CPP (1374iv); pane of 5 + label (1374iii), *Oct 1996*

| | | |
|---|---|---|
| a | glued flap, no TI | 35.00 |

## 1995

**BK182** 45¢ "Quick Sticks" Greetings, booklet of 10 (5 x 1568, 5 x 1569), plus 4 each of 3 different self-stick circular labels and 3 of one label, APC, JP, *Sep 1, 1995*

- **a** glued flap, with TI — 16.00
- **b** open cover, with TI — 16.00

**BK183** 45¢ "Quick Sticks" Chiropractic Greetings, booklet of 10 (5 x 1568i, 5 x 1569i), plus 4 each of 3 different chiropractic label designs and 3 of one chiropractic label design, APC, CPP, *Sep 15, 1995*

- **a** glued flap, with TI — 16.00
- **b** open cover, with TI — 16.00

**BK184** 45¢ Arctic Institute (1574–78), 5 different (1578a); pane of 10 (1578b), *Sep 15, 1995*

- **a** glued flap, no TI — 13.00
- **b** open cover, with TI — 13.00

**BK185** 45¢ Comic Book Superheroes (1579–83), 5 different (1583a); pane of 10 (1583b), *Oct 2, 1995*

- **a** glued flap, no TI — 15.00
- **b** open cover, with TI — 15.00

**BK186** 40¢ Christmas Greet More (1588), pane of 10 (1588a), *Nov 2/95*

- **a** glued flap, no TI — 9.00
- **b** open cover, with TI — 9.00

**BK187** 45¢ The Nativity (1585as), pane of 10 (1585a), *Nov 2, 1995*

- **a** glued flap, no TI — 10.00
- **b** open cover, with TI — 10.00

**BK188** 52¢ The Annunciation (1586as), pane of 5 + label (1586a), *Nov 2/95*

- **a** glued flap, no TI — 6.00
- **b** open cover, with TI — 6.00

**BK189** 90¢ Flight to Egypt (1587as), pane of 5 + label (1587a), *Nov 2/95*

- **a** glued flap, no TI — 12.00
- **b** open cover, with TI — 12.00

## 1996

**BK190** 45¢ "Quick Sticks" Greetings, booklet of 10 (5 x 1600, 5 x 1601), plus 5 each of 7 different self-stick circular stickers, LM, F paper, *Jan 15, 1996*

- **a** glued flap, with TI — 23.00
- **b** open cover, with TI — 20.00

**BK191** 45¢ Hi Tech, 4 different (1595–1598), pane of 12 (1598a), *Feb 15/96*

- **a** glued flap, no TI — 16.00
- **b** open cover, with TI — 16.00

**BK192** 45¢ Olympic Gold Medallists (1608–12), 5 different (1612a) pane of 10 (1612b), *Jul 8, 1996*

- **a** glued flap, no TI — 15.00
- **b** open cover, with TI — 15.00

**BK193** 45¢ Literacy + 5¢ surcharge (B13); pane of 10 (B13a), *Sep 9/96*

- **a** sealed booklet, no TI — 15.00
- **b** open cover, with TI — 15.00

**BK194** 45¢ Winnie the Pooh (1618–21), 4 different (1621a); pane of 16 (1621c). The halves of the pane are arranged tête-bêche with a 4 cm gutter between. The pane was used as an outer cover for a 16 page descriptive booklet, *Oct 1, 1996;* open cover, with TI — 20.00

**BK195** 45¢ Authors, 5 different (1626a); pane of 10 (1626b), *Oct 10, 1996*

- **a** glued flap, no TI — 16.50
- **b** open cover, with TI — 16.50

**BK196** 45¢ Gifts by Sled (1627as), pane of 10 (1627a), *Nov 1, 1996*

- **a** glued flap, no TI — 12.00
- **b** open cover, with TI — 12.00

**BK197** 52¢ Santa skiing (1628as), pane of 5 + label (1628a), *Nov 1/96*

- **a** glued flap, no TI — 6.00
- **b** open cover, with TI — 6.00

**BK198** 90¢ Skaters (1629as), pane of 5 + label (1629a), *Nov 1, 1996*

- **a** glued flap, no TI — 11.00
- **b** open cover, with TI — 11.00

## 1997

**BK199** 45¢ Blue Poppy (1638), pane of 12 (1638a), *Apr 4, 1997*

- **a** glued flap, no TI — 12.00
- **b** open cover, with TI — 12.00

**BK200** 45¢ x 2 Quick Stick Greetings (1568i, 1569i), pane of 10 (1569aiii) plus 4 each of 3 different self-stick circular stickers and 3 maple leaf stickers, APC, CPP, *Aug 15, 1997*

- **a** glued flap, with TI — 13.00
- **b** open cover, with TI — 13.00

**BK201** 45¢ Hockey Series of the Century (1659–60), 2 different, pane of 10 (1660a), *Sep 20, 1997*

- **a** glued flap, no TI — 11.00
- **b** open cover, with TI — 11.00

**BK202** 45¢ Madonna and Child (1669as); pane of 10 (1669a), *Nov 3/97*

- **a** glued flap, no TI — 12.00
- **b** open cover, with TI — 12.00

**BK203** 52¢ Jesus and Mary (1670as), pane of 5 + label (1670a), *Nov 3/97*

- **a** glued flap, no TI — 6.50
- **b** open cover, with TI — 6.50

**BK204** 90¢ Madonna and Child (1671as), pane of 5 + label (1671a), *Nov 3/97*

- **a** glued flap, no TI — 11.00
- **b** open cover, with TI — 11.00

## Definitive Issues (1998)

BK205

BK205A

BK206

**BK205** 45¢ Flag and office building, new smaller size, perf. 13 x 13½, CBN, CPP (1362as), pane of 10 (1362a), 5 overlapped stamps, "In Business to Serve", *Feb 2, 1998*

- **a** glued flap, no TI — 12.00
- **b** open cover, with TI — 12.00

When BK205 opens to right, pane is upright.

**BK205A** 45¢ Flag and office building, new smaller size, perf. 13 x 13½, CBN, CPP (1362as); pane of 10 (1362a), 3 flags over building on front cover, "The Right Way to Address...", *Fall 1998*

- **a** glued flap, no TI — 25.00
- **b** as above, pane not glued to cover — 30.00
- **c** as above, pane upright* — 250.00

BK205A was only available without inscriptions; not available from Antigonish. When BK205A opens to right, pane is inverted.

* Less than 100 booklets have been reported to date.

**BK206** 45¢ Flag and office building, new smaller size, perf. 13 x 13½, APC, CPP (1362 and 1362bs); pane of 30 + 3 blank labels in centre (1362b), 7 overlapped stamps, "In Business to Serve", *Feb 2, 1998*

- **a** glued flap, no TI — 33.00
- **b** open cover, with TI — 33.00

**BK206A** 45¢ Flag and office building, new smaller size, perf. 13 x 13½, APC, CPP (1362 and 1362bs); pane of 30 + 3 blank labels in centre (1362b), 3 flags over building on front cover, "The Right Way to Address", *Fall 1998*

- **a** glued flap, with TI — 60.00

BK206A was only available in field stock (glued flap) but all have inscriptions; not available from Antigonish.

## 1998

**BK207** 45¢ Fishing Flies (1715–20), 6 different (1720a), vertical pane of 12 (1720b), *Apr 16, 1998*
a glued flap, with TI 16.00
b open cover, with TI 16.00

**BK208** 45¢ Canals (1725–34), 10 different, horizontal pane of 10 (1734a), *Jun 17, 1998*
a glued flap, with TI 25.00
b open cover, with TI 25.00

**BK209** 45¢ Automatistes (1743–49), 7 different, pane of 7 (1749a), *Aug 7, 1998*
a open cover, with TI 11.00

**BK210** 45¢ Circus (1757–60), 4 different, pane of 12 (1760a), *Oct 1/98*
a glued flap, with TI 14.50
b open cover, with TI 14.50

**BK211** 45¢ Angel, perf. 13 x 13 (1764as), pane of 10 (1764a), *Nov 6/98*
a glued flap, with TI 50.00
b open cover, with TI 50.00

**BK211A** 45¢ Angel, perf. 13 x 13½, (1764cs), pane of 10 (1764c), *Nov 6/98*
a glued flap, with TI 20.00
b open cover, with TI 20.00

**BK212** 52¢ Adoring Angel, perf. 13 x 13 (1765b), pane of 5 + label (1765c), *Nov 6, 1998*
a glued flap, with TI 8.00
b open cover, with TI 8.00

**BK212A** 52¢ Adoring Angel, perf. 13 x 13½ (1765as), pane of 5 + label (1765a), *Nov 6, 1998*
a glued flap, with TI 40.00

**BK213** 90¢ Praying Angel, perf. 13 x 13 (1766b), pane of 5 + label (1766c), *Nov 6, 1998*
a glued flap, with TI 11.00
b open cover, with TI 11.00

**BK213A** 90¢ Praying Angel, perf. 13 x 13½ (1766as), pane of 5 + label (1766a), *Nov 6, 1998*
a glued flap, with TI 60.00

## Definitive Issues (1998–1999)

BK215

BK215A

BK215C

**BK214** 46¢ Flag and Iceberg, perf. 13 x 13½, CBN, TRC, (1682as); pane of 10 (1682a), *Dec 28, 1998*
a glued flap, no TI 12.00
b open cover, with TI 12.00

**BK215** 46¢ Flag and Iceberg, APC, C-paper designation†, (1698); pane of 30 (1698a), (UPC barcode ... 01518 2), *Dec 28, 1998*
a glued flap, with TI 30.00
b open cover, with TI 30.00

**BK215A** 46¢ Flag and Iceberg, APC, J-paper designation, (1698); pane of 30 (1698a), Pressure Sensitive logo on front cover
a glued flap, with TI, (UPC barcode ... 01518 2), dull, *Jul 1999* 35.00
c die cutting omitted *3,000.00*

**BK215B** 46¢ Flag and Iceberg, APC, C-paper designation†, (1698); pane of 30 (1698a), Pressure Sensitive logo on front cover
a open cover, with TI, (UPC barcode ... 01718 6), *Spring 2000* 35.00
b glued flap, with TI, (UPC barcode ... 01518 2), *Jul 2000* 60.00

† Although the panes of BK215 and BK215B show "C"-type paper, it is actually JAC.

**BK215C** 46¢ Flag and Iceberg, APC, J-paper designation, (1698); pane of 30 (1698a), "Scratch & WIN"
a glued flap, with TI, (UPC barcode ... 01587 8), *Sep 1, 2000* 30.00
b open cover, with TI, (UPC barcode ... 01588 5), *Sep 1, 2000* 35.00

BK216

BK217

**BK216** 55¢ Maple Leaf (1684as), pane of 5 + label (1684a), *Dec 28, 1998*
a glued flap, with TI 6.50
b open cover, with TI 6.50

**BK217** 95¢ Maple Leaf (1686as), pane of 5 + label (1686a), *Dec 28, 1998*
a glued flap, with TI 12.00
b open cover, with TI 12.00

## 1999

**BK218** 46¢ Birds of Canada (1774–77), 4 different; 2 panes of 6 (1777a, 1777b) 1777a (1776, 1777+2 ea. of 1774, 1775) and 1777b (1774, 1775+2 ea. of 1776, 1777), *Feb 24, 1999*
a glued flap, with TI 16.50
b open cover, with TI 16.50

**BK219** 46¢ Orchids (1787–90), 4 different, pane of 12 (1790a), *Apr 27/99*
a glued flap, with TI 16.00
b open cover, with TI 16.00

**BK220** 46¢ Horses (1795–98), 4 different, pane of 12 (1798b), *Jun 2/99*
a glued flap, with TI 19.00
b open cover, with TI 19.00

Booklet with 'pink cloud' variety (1795i): $25.00

**BK221** 46¢ Kites (1811a–d), 4 different, pane of 8 (1811), *Oct 1, 1999*
a glued flap, with TI 12.00
b open cover, with TI 12.00
c "no gum", cover printed on gum side* (pane of 4) 300.00

* About 10 half-panes and 2 full booklets (value $750.00) reported.

**BK222** 46¢ Angel with drum (1815as); pane of 10 (1815a), *Nov 4, 1999*
a glued flap, with TI 12.00
b open cover, with TI 12.00

**BK223** 55¢ Angel with toys (1816as); pane of 5 + label (1816a), *Nov 4/99*
a glued flap, with TI 7.50
b open cover, with TI 7.50

**BK224** 95¢ Angel with candle (1817as); pane of 5 + label (1817a), *Nov 4/99*
a glued flap, with TI 13.00
b open cover, with TI 13.00

## 2000

**BK225** 46¢ Birds of Canada (1843–46), 4 different; 2 panes of 6 (1846a, 1846b)* *1886a (1845, 1846+2 ea. of 1843, 1844) and 1846b (1843, 1844+2 ea. of 1845, 1846), *Mar 1, 2000*
a glued flap, with TI (UPC barcode ...01581 6) 16.00
b open cover, with TI (UPC barcode ...01582 3) 16.00

First booklet to have different UPC barcodes for field and philatelic stock.

**BK226** 46¢ Rural Mailboxes (1849–52), 4 different, pane of 12 (1852a), *Apr 28, 2000*
a glued flap, with TI (UPC barcode ...01635 6) 14.00
b open cover, with TI (UPC barcode ...01636 3) 14.00

**BK227** 46¢ Picture Postage Greetings (1853), pane of 5 plus 5 different stickers (1853a), *Apr 28, 2000*
a glued flap, with TI (UPC barcode ...01736 0) 6.50
b open cover, with TI (UPC barcode ...01740 7) 6.50

**BK228** 55¢ Fresh waters of Canada (1854a–e), 5 different, pane of 5 (1854), *May 23, 2000*

| | | |
|---|---|---|
| a | glued flap, with TI (UPC barcode ...01646 2) | 11.00 |
| b | open cover, with TI (UPC barcode ...01644 8) | 11.00 |

BK229a

BK229b

All Canada Post UPC barcodes begin with 0 63491. From BK225 to BK291, most booklets were issued with two different barcodes, one to signify "field" stock, the other to signify "philatelic" stock.

**BK229** 95¢ Fresh waters of Canada (1855a–e), 5 different, pane of 5 (1855), *May 23, 2000*

| | | |
|---|---|---|
| a | glued flap, with TI (UPC barcode ...01647 9) | 13.00 |
| b | open cover, with TI (UPC barcode ...01645 5) | 13.00 |

**BK230** 46¢ Tall ships (1864–65), 2 different pane of 10 (1865b), *Jul 19, 2000*

| | | |
|---|---|---|
| a | glued flap, with TI (UPC barcode ...01670 7) | 13.00 |
| b | open cover, with TI (UPC barcode ...01671 4) | 13.00 |

**BK231** 46¢ Petro Canada (1867), pane of 12 (1867a), *Sep 13, 2000*

| | | |
|---|---|---|
| a | field stock, with TI (UPC barcode ...01742 1) | 16.00 |
| b | philatelic stock, with TI (UPC barcode ...01743 8) | 16.00 |

**BK232** 46¢ Christmas Picture Postage (1872), pane of 5 plus 5 different stickers (1872a), *Oct 5, 2000*

| | | |
|---|---|---|
| a | glued flap, with TI (UPC barcode ...01826 8) | 7.50 |
| b | open cover, with TI (UPC barcode ...01755 1) | 7.50 |

**BK233** 46¢ Shepherds (1873as), pane of 10 (1873a), *Nov 3, 2000*

| | | |
|---|---|---|
| a | glued flap, with TI (UPC barcode ...01684 4) | 11.00 |
| b | open cover, with TI (UPC barcode ...01685 1) | 11.00 |

**BK234** 55¢ Christmas Creche (1874as), pane of 6 (1874a), *Nov 3, 2000*

| | | |
|---|---|---|
| a | glued flap, with TI (UPC barcode ...01691 2) | 9.00 |
| b | open cover, with TI (UPC barcode ...01692 9) | 9.00 |

**BK235** 95¢ Flight Into Egypt (1875as), pane of 6 (1875a), *Nov 3, 2000*

| | | |
|---|---|---|
| a | glued flap, with TI (UPC barcode ...01698 1) | 14.00 |
| b | open cover, with TI (UPC barcode ...01699 8) | 14.00 |

## Definitive Issues (2000–2001)

BK236b

BK236Aa

BK236Ba

BK239b

**BK236** 47¢ Flag and Inukshuk, CBN, JAC (1700); pane of 10 (1700a), "Collection 2000", NF/NF *Dec 28, 2000*

| | | |
|---|---|---|
| a | field stock, with TI (UPC barcode ...01776 6) | 10.50 |
| b | philatelic stock, with TI (UPC barcode ...01777 3) | 10.50 |
| c | "no gum", cover printed on gum side | 350.00 |

Stamp pane of BK236 exists also on NF/LF and DF/MF paper. Price 3x and 5x normal pane/booklet respectively.

**BK236A** 47¢ Flag and Inukshuk, CBN, JAC (1700); pane of 10 (1700a), "Moving?", *Mar 2001*

| | | |
|---|---|---|
| a | field stock, with TI (UPC barcode ...01776 6) | 15.00 |

**BK236B** 47¢ Flag and Inukshuk, CBN, JAC (1700); pane of 10 (1700a), "Prepaid Card", *Jul 2001*

| | | |
|---|---|---|
| a | field stock, with TI (UPC barcode ...01776 6) | 15.00 |
| ai | die cutting omitted (1700e) | 2,500.00 |

**BK237** 47¢ Flag and Inukshuk, APC, JAC (1700); pane of 30 (1700b), "Collection 2000", *Dec 28, 2000*

| | | |
|---|---|---|
| a | glued flap, with TI (UPC barcode ...01779 7) | 31.00 |
| b | open cover, with TI (UPC barcode ...01780 3) | 31.00 |

**BK237A** 47¢ Flag and Inukshuk, APC, JAC (1700); pane of 30 (1700b), "Moving?"

| | | |
|---|---|---|
| a | glued flap, with TI (UPC barcode ...01779 7), *Mar 2001* | 34.00 |
| b | open cover, with TI (UPC barcode ...01780 3), *Sep 2001* | 50.00 |

**BK237B** 47¢ Flag and Inukshuk, APC, JAC (1700); pane of 30 (1700b), "Prepaid Card"

| | | |
|---|---|---|
| a | glued flap, with TI (UPC barcode ...01779 7), *Jul 2001* | 45.00 |

**BK237C** 47¢ Flag and Inukshuk, APC, JAC (1700); pane of 30 (1700b), "XpressPost"

| | | |
|---|---|---|
| a | glued flap, with TI (UPC barcode ...01779 7), *Nov 2001* | 50.00 |

**BK238** 60¢ Red fox (1879iv), pane of 6 (1879a), *Dec 28, 2000*

| | | |
|---|---|---|
| a | field stock (UPC barcode ...01787 2) | 16.00 |
| b | philatelic stock (UPC barcode ...01788 9) | 14.00 |

**BK239** $1.05 White-tailed deer (1881ii), pane of 6 (1881a), *Dec 28, 2000*

| | | |
|---|---|---|
| a | field stock (UPC barcode ...01793 3) | 18.00 |
| b | philatelic stock (UPC barcode ...01794 0) | 15.50 |

Counterfeit booklets of BK239 are known to exist. These are of a very high quality.

**BK240** 47¢ Picture Postage Greetings (1882a–e), 5 different, pane of 5 plus 5 different stickers (1882), *Dec 28, 2000*

| | | |
|---|---|---|
| a | glued flap (UPC barcode ...01796 4) | 8.00 |
| b | open cover (UPC barcode ...01797 1), DF | 8.00 |
| bi | as "b", MF | 25.00 |

## 2001

**BK241** 47¢ Birds of Canada, 4 different (1890–93); pane of 12 (1893a+1893b), *Feb 1, 2001*

| | | |
|---|---|---|
| a | glued flap, no TI (UPC barcode ...01817 6) | 15.50 |
| b | open cover, with TI (UPC barcode ...01816 9) | 15.50 |

**BK242** 47¢ Toronto Blue Jays (1901), pane of 8 (1901a), *Apr 9, 2001*

| | | |
|---|---|---|
| a | glued flap, with TI (UPC barcode ...01903 6) | 10.50 |
| b | open cover, with TI (UPC barcode ...01904 3) | 10.50 |

**BK243** 60¢ Tourist attractions (1903a–e), 5 different, pane of 5 (1903), *May 11, 2001*

| | | |
|---|---|---|
| a | glued flap, with TI (UPC barcode ...01923 4) | 7.00 |
| b | open cover, with TI (UPC barcode ...01924 1) | 7.00 |

**BK244** $1.05 Tourist attractions (1904a–e), 5 different, pane of 5 (1904), *May 11, 2001*

| | | |
|---|---|---|
| a | glued flap, with TI (UPC barcode ...01925 8) | 11.50 |
| b | open cover, with TI (UPC barcode ...01926 5) | 11.50 |

**BK245** 47¢ Roses (1911–1914), 4 different, pane of 12 (1914a), *Aug 1, 2001*

| | | |
|---|---|---|
| a | glued flap, with TI (UPC barcode ...01927 2) | 12.50 |
| b | open cover, with TI (UPC barcode ...01928 9) | 12.50 |

**BK246** (47¢) Picture Postage™ Greetings (1918a–e), 5 different, pane of 5 plus 5 different stickers (1918), *Sep 21, 2001*

| | | |
|---|---|---|
| a | glued flap (UPC barcode ...02040 7) | 8.00 |
| b | open cover (UPC barcode ...02041 4) | 8.00 |

**BK247** 47¢ Hot air balloons (1921a–d), 4 different, 2 of each in pane of 8 (1921), *Oct 1, 2001*

| | | |
|---|---|---|
| a | glued flap (UPC barcode ...02037 7) | 10.50 |
| b | open cover (UPC barcode ...02038 4) | 10.50 |
| i | "no gum" (BK247), cover printed on gum side | 800.00 |

**BK248** 47¢ Horse-drawn sleigh (1922), pane of 10 (1922a), *Nov 1, 2001*

| | | |
|---|---|---|
| a | glued flap (UPC barcode ...01999 9) | 11.00 |
| b | open cover (UPC barcode ...02000 1) | 11.00 |

**BK249** 60¢ Skaters (1923), pane of 6 (1923a), *Nov 1, 2001*

| | | |
|---|---|---|
| a | field stock (UPC barcode ...02001 8) | 10.50 |
| b | philatelic stock (UPC barcode ...02002 5) | 10.50 |

**BK250** $1.05 Snowman (1924), pane of 6 (1924a), *Nov 1, 2001*

a field stock (UPC barcode ...02003 2) 14.00

b philatelic stock (UPC barcode ...02004 9) 14.00

## Definitive Issues (2002)

BK251

BK252b

BK253a

**BK251** 48¢ Flag and Canada Post head office, AP, TRC, (rounded corners), (1931); pane of 30 (1931b), *Jan 2, 2002*

a field stock (UPC barcode ...02025 4) 34.00

b philatelic stock (UPC barcode ...02026 1) 34.00

i as previous; pane of 10 (1931a) consisting of the left 1/3 of BK251 when 1931b is separated into 3 parts along rouletted margins 11.00

ii as previous; pane of 10 (1931a) consisting of the middle 1/3 of BK251 when 1931b is separated into 3 parts along rouletted margins 11.00

iii as previous; pane of 10 (1931a) consisting of the right 1/3 of BK251 when 1931b is separated into 3 parts along rouletted margins 11.00

**BK251A** 48¢ Flag and Canada Post head office with "Vancouver/2010" imprint in red at lower right corner, AP, TRC, self-adhesive, die-cut, (1991); booklet of 30 (1991b)

a field stock (UPC barcode ...02025 4), *Jul 11, 2003* 60.00

**BK251B** 48¢ Flag and Canada Post head office, AP, TRC (rounded corners), (1931); booklet of 30 (1931b), with Canada Post website information

a field stock (UPC barcode ...02025 4), *Mar 2002* 45.00

b philatelic stock (UPC barcode ...02026 1), *Jan 2003* 65.00

**BK251C** 48¢ Flag and Canada Post head office, AP, TRC, (1931ii); booklet of 30 (1931bi), with Canada Post website information; 90 degree die cutting at corners of stamps (pointed)

a field stock (UPC barcode ...02025 4), *Sep 2003* 200.00

BK251A, BK251B, and BK251C are listed as "booklets of 30". As with BK251, the booklet of 30 can be separated into 3 parts along rouletted margins. These are all numbered as i, ii, and iii, respectively; price: 1/3 of full booklet of 30.

**BK252** 65¢ Jewelry (1928ii/iii/iv), pane of 6 (1928a)

a black and white Canada Post logo (UPC barcode ...02016 2), *Jan 2, 2002* 9.50

b Canada Post logo is in colour (UPC barcode ...02016 2), *Mar 2002* 15.00

**BK253** $1.25 Sculpture (1930ii/iii/iv), pane of 6 (1930a)

a black and white Canada Post logo (UPC barcode ...02022 3) *Jan 2, 2002* 16.00

b Canada Post logo is in colour (UPC barcode ...02022 3), *Mar 2002* 23.00

## 2002

**BK254** 48¢ University of Manitoba (1941), pane of 8 (1941a), *Feb 28/02*

a glued flap (UPC barcode ...02094 0) 8.50

b open cover (UPC barcode ...02095 7) 8.50

**BK255** 48¢ Laval University (1942), pane of 8 (1942a), *Apr 4, 2002*

a glued flap (UPC barcode ...02147 3) 8.50

b open cover (UPC barcode ...02148 0) 8.50

**BK256** 48¢ University of Trinity College (1943), pane of 8 (1943a), *Apr 30/02*

a glued flap (UPC barcode ...02166 4) 8.50

b open cover (UPC barcode ...02167 1) 8.50

**BK257** 48¢ Tulips (1946a–d), 4 different, 2 of each in pane of 8 (1946), *May 3, 2002*

a glued flap (UPC barcode ...02221 0) 8.50

b open cover (UPC barcode ...02222 7) 8.50

**BK258** 48¢ Saint Mary's University (1944), pane of 8 (1944a), *May 27/02*

a glued flap (UPC barcode ...02169 5) 8.50

b open cover (UPC barcode ...02170 1) 8.50

**BK259** 65¢ Tourist attractions (1952a–e), 5 different, pane of 5 (1952), *Jun 1, 2002*

a glued flap (UPC barcode ...02213 5) 8.50

b open cover (UPC barcode ...02214 2) 8.50

**BK260** $1.25 Tourist attractions (1953a–e), 5 different, pane of 5 (1953), *Jun 1, 2002*

a glued flap (UPC barcode ...02216 6) 14.00

b open cover (UPC barcode ...02217 3) 14.00

**BK261** 48¢ World Youth Day (1957), pane of 8 (1957a), *Jul 23, 2002*

a glued flap (UPC barcode ...02308 8) 9.00

b open cover (UPC barcode ...02309 5) 9.00

**BK262** 48¢ Genesis (1965), pane of 10 (1965a), *Nov 4, 2002*

a glued flap (UPC barcode ...02385 9) 11.00

b open cover (UPC barcode ...02386 6) 11.00

**BK263** 65¢ Winter Travel (1966), pane of 6 (1966a), *Nov 4, 2002*

a glued flap (UPC barcode ...02387 3) 10.50

b open cover (UPC barcode ...02388 0) 10.50

**BK264** $1.25 Mary and Child (1967), pane of 6 (1967a), *Nov 4, 2002*

a glued flap (UPC barcode ...02389 7) 16.00

b open cover (UPC barcode ...02390 3) 16.00

## 2003

**BK265** 48¢ NHL All-Stars (1972a-b), 6 different, pane of 6 (1972), *Jan 18, 2003* 90.00

**BK266** 48¢ Bishop's University (1973); pane of 8 (1973a), *Jan 28, 2003*

a glued flap (UPC barcode 02550 1) 9.00

b open cover (UPC barcode 02551 8) 9.00

**BK267** 65¢ Gyrfalcon (1983), pane of 6 (1983a), *Feb 21, 2003* 9.50

**BK268** 48¢ University of Western Ontario (1974) pane of 8 (1974a), *Mar 19, 2003*

a glued flap (UPC barcode 02536 5) 9.00

b open cover (UPC barcode 02537 2) 9.00

**BK269** 48¢ St. Francis Xavier University (1975), pane of 8 (1975a), *Apr 4/03*

a glued flap (UPC barcode 02533 4) 9.00

b open cover (UPC barcode 02534 1) 9.00

**BK270** 65¢ Tourist Attractions (1989a–e), 5 different, *Jun 12, 2003*

a glued flap (UPC barcode 02628 7) 10.50

b open cover (UPC barcode 02629 4) 10.50

**BK271** $1.25 Tourist Attractions (1990a–e), 5 different, *Jun 12, 2003*

a glued flap (UPC barcode 02630 0) 16.00

b open cover (UPC barcode 02631 7) 16.00

**BK272** 48¢ Macdonald Institute (1976); pane of 8 (1976a), *Jun 20, 2003*

a glued flap (UPC barcode 02603 4) 9.00

b open cover (UPC barcode 02604 1) 9.00

**BK273** 48¢ Université de Montréal (1977); pane of 8 (1977a), *Sep 4, 2003*

a glued flap (UPC barcode 02606 5) 9.00

b open cover (UPC barcode 02607 2) 9.00

**BK274** 48¢ Canadian Authors (1994–97), 4 different, 2 panes of 4 (1997b), *Sep 8, 2003*

a glued flap (UPC barcode 02776 5) 9.50

b open cover (UPC barcode 02777 2) 9.50

**BK275** 48¢ Road Cycling (1998), pane of 8 (1998a), *Sep 10, 2003*

a glued flap (UPC barcode 02770 3), glossy cover 9.50

ai "flat" appearance cover (cover printed on wrong side) 60.00

b open cover (UPC barcode 02771 0) 9.50

**BK276** 48¢ Canadian Astronauts (1999a-h), pane of 8 (1999), *Oct 1/03* 12.00

**BK277** 48¢ Ice Skates (2004), 2 panes of 6 (2004a), *Nov 4, 2003* 12.00

i die cutting omitted

**BK278** 65¢ Teddy Bear (2005), pane of 6 (2005a), *Nov 4, 2003* 8.50

i die cutting omitted (2005b) *2,000.00*

**BK279** $1.25 Wood Duck (2006) pane of 6 (2006a), *Nov 4, 2003* 16.00

## Definitive Issues (2003–2004)

BK280 BK280Ab BK281 BK281A

**BK280** 49¢ Flag (City of Edmonton), AP, TRC (2011), pane of 10 (2011a), "Complete Year", (UPC barcode ... 02799 4), thin roulette on back only *Dec 19, 2003* 11.00

**BK280A** 49¢ Flag (City of Edmonton), CBN, Fasson (2011), pane of 10 (2011a), "Share Canada", wide roulette

- **a** philatelic reprint (UPC barcode ... 03102 1), *Jul 2004* 15.00
- **b** field stock (UPC barcode ... 02799 4), *Sep 2004* 11.00
- **bi** die cutting omitted (2011c) 1,000.00
- **bii** "no gum", cover printed on gum side 125.00

**BK280B** 49¢ Flag (City of Edmonton), CBN, TRC (2011), pane of 10 (2011a), "Share Canada"

- **a** narrow roulette, (UPC barcode ... 02799 4), *Sep 2004* 75.00
- **ai** die cutting omitted 1,200.00
- **b** wide roulette, (UPC barcode ... 02799 4), *Dec 2004* 25.00

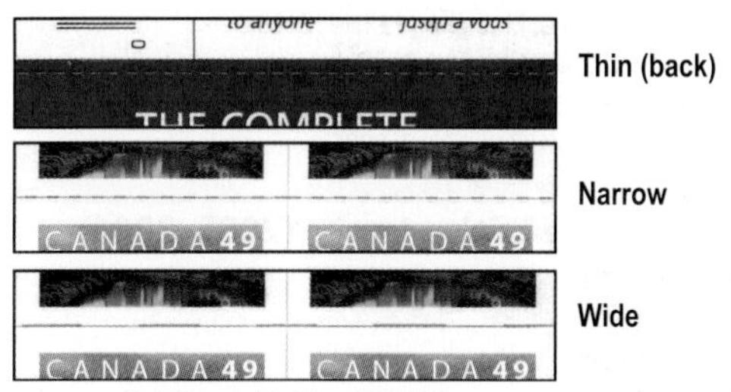

49¢ Flag rouletting (BK280)

**BK281** 49¢ Queen Elizabeth II, CBN, TRC (2012), pane of 10 (2012a), "Complete Year", (UPC barcode ... 02800 7), medium-length roulette, *Dec 19, 2003* 11.00

- **i** as BK281, with pink flaw on forehead (2012ai) 100.00

Counterfeit booklets of BK281 are known to exist. These are of a very high quality.

**BK281A** 49¢ Queen Elizabeth II, CBN, TRC (2012), pane of 10 (2012a), "Share Canada", (UPC barcode ... 02800 7), narrow roulette, *Jun 2004* 14.00

**BK281B** 49¢ Queen Elizabeth II, CBN, Fasson (2012i), pane of 10 (2012a), "Share Canada", wide roulette

- **a** philatelic reprint (UPC barcode ... 03119 9), *Jul 2004* 14.00
- **b** field stock (UPC barcode ... 02800 7), *Dec 2004* 35.00
- **bi** "no gum", cover printed on gum side 250.00

BK282 BK283Aa

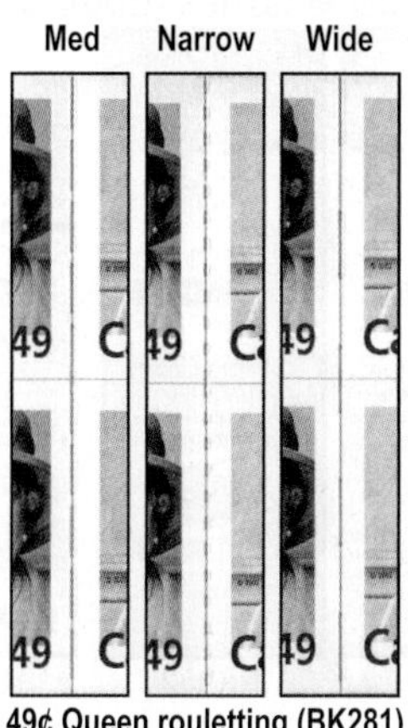

49¢ Queen rouletting (BK281)

**BK282** 80¢ Red Maple Leaf and twig, AP, TRC (2013), pane of 6 (2013a) (UPC barcode ... 02803 8), *Dec 19, 2003* 12.00

**BK282A** 80¢ Red Maple Leaf and twig, LMG, Fasson (2013i) pane of 6 (2013ai)

- **a** philatelic reprint (UPC barcode ... 03105 2), *Jul 2004* 16.00
- **b** field stock (UPC barcode ... 02803 8), *Sep 2004* 25.00

**BK283** $1.40 Green Maple Leaf and twig, AP, TRC (2014), pane of 6 (2014a) (UPC barcode ... 02805 2), *Dec 19, 2003* 18.00

**BK283A** $1.40 Green Maple Leaf and twig, LMG, Fasson (2014i), pane of 6 (2014ai)

- **a** philatelic reprint (UPC barcode ... 03106 9), *Jul 2004* 25.00
- **b** field stock (UPC barcode ... 02805 2), *Sep 2004* 35.00

Counterfeit booklets of BK283 are known to exist. These are of a very high quality.

## 2004

**BK284** 49¢ NHL All-Stars (2018a-f), pane of 6 different, *Jan 24, 2004* 8.00

**BK285** 49¢ Quebec Winter Carnival (2019), pane of 6 (2019a), *Jan 29/04* 7.00

**BK286** 49¢ Army Cadets (2025), pane of 8 (2025a), *Mar 26, 2004* 10.00

**BK287** 49¢ St. Joseph's Oratory (2020), pane of 6 (2020a), *Apr 2, 2004* 7.00

**BK288** 49¢ Home Hardware (2032) pane of 10 (2032a) in Prestige Booklet, *Apr 19, 2004* 15.00

**BK289** 49¢ Sherbrooke University (2033), pane of 8 (2033a), *May 4, 2004*

- **a** glued flap (UPC barcode 02929 5) 9.00
- **b** open cover (UPC barcode 02930 1) 11.00

**BK290** 49¢ Montreal Children's Hospital (2035), pane of 8 (2035a), *May 6, 2004* 10.00

**BK291** 49¢ University of PEI (2034), pane of 8 (2034a), *May 8, 2004*

- **a** glued flap (UPC barcode 02979 0) 9.00
- **b** open cover (UPC barcode 02980 6) 11.00

**BK292** 80¢ Lincoln's sparrow (2040) pane of 6 (2040a), *May 14, 2004* 11.00

**BK293** 49¢ Festival International de Jazz de Montréal (2021), pane of 6 (2021a), *Jun 1, 2004* 7.00

**BK294** 49¢ Traversée Internationale de Lac St-Jean (2022), pane of 6 (2022a), *Jun 18, 2004* 7.00

**BK295** 49¢ Canadian National Exhibition (2023), pane of 6 (2023a), *Jul 19, 2004* 7.00

**BK296** 49¢ Montreal Heart Institute (2056), 2 panes of 4 (2056a), *Sep 15, 2004* 10.00

**BK297** 49¢ Pets (2057–2060), 2 panes of 4 (2060a), *Oct 1, 2004* 10.00

**BK298** 49¢ Santa on his sled (2069), 2 panes of 6 (2069a), *Nov 2/04* 12.00

- **a** "no gum" (2069b), cover printed on gum side 200.00

**BK299** 80¢ Santa in a Cadillac (2070), pane of 6 (2070a), *Nov 2/04* 10.00

**BK300** $1.40 Santa in a Train (2071), pane of 6 (2071a), *Nov 2/04* 15.00

- **a** "no gum" (2071b), cover printed on gum side (1 reported) *1,000.00*

## Definitive Issues (2004–2005)

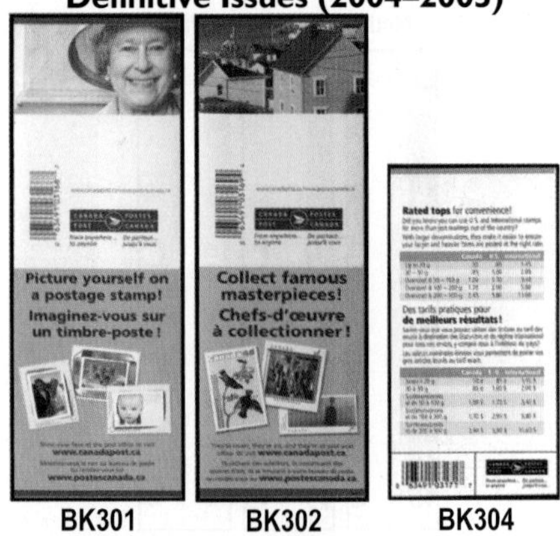

BK301 BK302 BK304

**BK301** 50¢ Queen Elizabeth II, CBN, TRC (2075), pane of 10 (2075a)
- **a** wide roulette (5 slits per pane), *Dec 20, 2004* 12.00
- **b** narrow roulette (23 slits per pane), *Apr 2005* 15.00

**BK301A** 50¢ Queen Elizabeth II, CBN, Fasson (2075i), pane of 10 (2075aii)
- **a** narrow roulette (29 slits per pane), *May 30, 2005* 12.00

BK301a/b and BK301Aa each come with five cover designs of each (different ads, noted by a letter A–E in the lower right corner on the cover side). A bundle of 50 booklets, as distributed to post offices, contains only one cover design. Only BK301Aa was offered in a set of 5 covers directly from the Philatelic Centre.

5 23 29

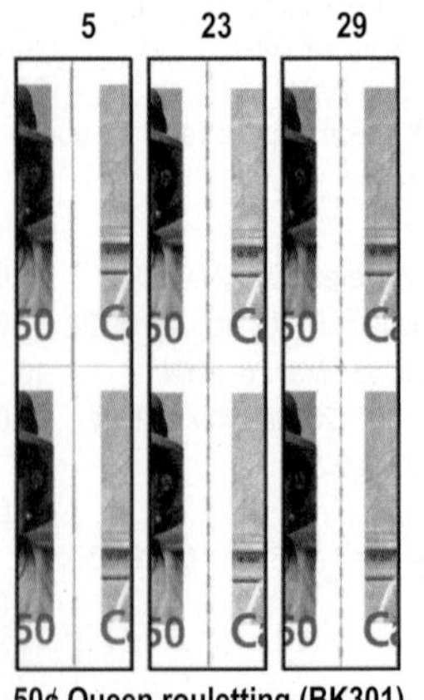

50¢ Queen rouletting (BK301)

5 29 23

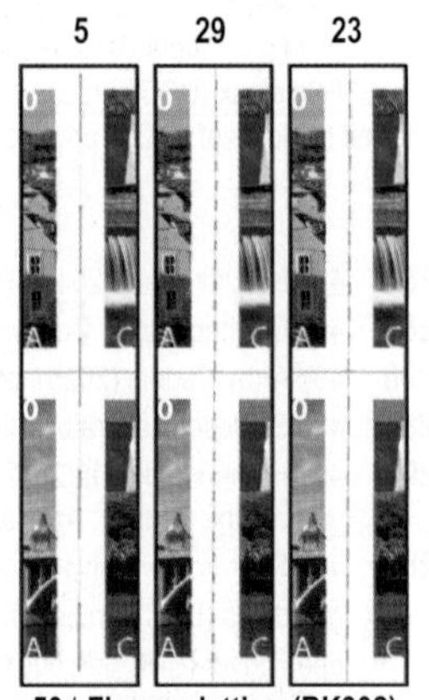

50¢ Flag rouletting (BK302)

**BK302** 50¢ Flag Over..., CBN, TRC (2076–2080), pane of 10 (2080a)
- **a** wide roulette (5 slits per pane), *Dec 20, 2004* 25.00
- **b** narrow roulette (29 slits per pane), *Dec 20, 2004* 12.00
- **c** narrow roulette (23 slits per pane), *Feb 2005* 250.00

**BK302A** 50¢ Flag Over..., CBN, Fasson (2076i–2080i), pane of 10 (2080aiv)
- **a** narrow roulette (29 slits per pane), *May 30, 2005* 12.00
- **b** "no gum" (BK302Aa), cover printed on gum side (2080b) 100.00

BK302a/b/c and BK302Aa each come with twenty-five cover designs of each (five different ads, noted by a letter A–E, combined with five different scenes at the top of the cover, noted by letter, in the lower right corner on the cover side). A bundle of 50 booklets, as distributed to post offices, contains only one cover design. Only BK302Aa was offered in a set of 25 covers directly from the Philatelic Centre.

**BK303** 85¢ Yellow Calla Lily (2081), pane of 6 (2081a), *Dec 20, 2004*
- **a** 3mm tagging 14.00
- **b** 4mm tagging 12.00
- **c** 4.5mm tagging 17.50
- **d** 4mm tagging, TRC paper* 150.00
- **i** missing black inscriptions (no trace of any black) *6,000.00*
- **ii** missing yellow on the flower on UR stamp *1,500.00*
- **iii** missing yellow on right side of flower on UR stamp *500.00*

**BK304** $1.45 Blue Iris (2082), pane of 6 (2082a), shiny tagging, *Dec 20/04*
- **a** colour dots at right, 3mm tagging 18.00
- **b** colour dots at right, 4mm tagging 18.00
- **c** colour dots at right, 4mm tagging, TRC paper* 75.00
- **d** colour dots at right, 4mm tagging, dull tagging** 25.00

**BK304A** $1.45 Blue Iris (2082), pane of 6 (2082aiii), colour dots at left, *Dec 20, 2004* 70.00

* paper surface is coarser than "F" paper, but booklet still has the "F" designation
** all of these booklets show multiple phantom tagging bars both horizontally and vertically in top margin.

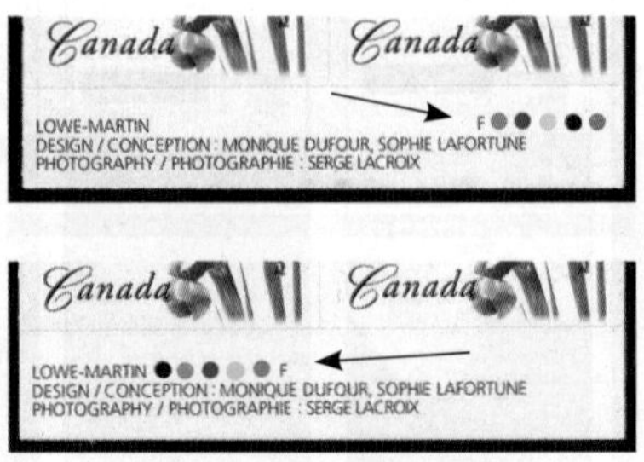


BK304 (top); BK304A (bottom)

## 2005

**BK305** 50¢ NHL All-Stars (2086a-f), pane of 6 different, *Jan 29, 2005* 7.00

**BK306** 50¢ Fishing Flies (2088a–d), 2 panes of 4 (2088), *Feb 4, 2005* 10.00

**BK307** 50¢ Nova Scotia Agricultural College (2089), 2 panes of 4 (2089a), *Feb 14, 2005* 10.00

**BK308** 50¢ Daffodils (2092–2093), pane of 10 (2093a), *Mar 10, 2005* 12.00

**BK309** 50¢ Toronto Dominion Bank (2094), pane of 10 (2094a) in Prestige Booklet, *Mar 18, 2005* 15.00

**BK310** 85¢ Double-Crested Cormorant (2099), pane of 6 (2099a), *Mar 23, 2005* 10.00

**BK311** 50¢ Canadian War Museum (2108), 2 panes of 4 (2108a), *May 6, 2005* 10.00

**BK312** 50¢ Youth Sports (2121a-d), pane of 8 (2121), *Oct 1, 2005* 8.00

**BK313** 50¢ Snowman (2124/i), 2 panes of 6 (2124a), *Nov 2, 2005* 12.00
- **a** 'divots' at adjoining stamp corners (2124iv/v), 2 panes of 6 (2124ai) *50.00*

**BK314** 50¢ Nativity (2125), 2 panes of 6 (2125a), *Nov 2, 2005* 12.00

**BK315** 85¢ Aboriginal Mother and Child (2126), pane of 6 (2126a), *Nov 2, 2005* 11.00

**BK316** $1.45 Mary, Joseph, baby Jesus (2127), pane of 6 (2127a), *Nov 2, 2005* 18.00

## Definitive Issues (2005–2006)

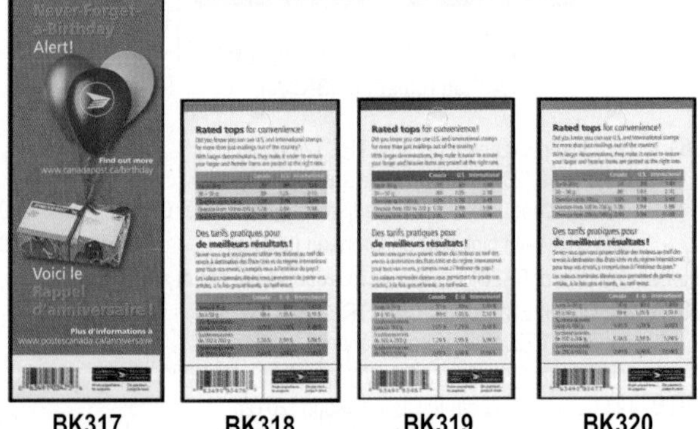


BK317 BK318 BK319 BK320

**BK317** 51¢ Flag Over..., CBN, Fasson (2135-2139), pane of 10 (2139a), *Dec 19, 2005*
- **a** with 29 vertical roulettes 12.00
- **b** without vertical roulettes; shallow vertical die cuts, *Dec 19, 2005* 200.00
- **i** "no gum" (BK317), cover printed on gum side 200.00
- **ii** as BK317 (2139b), die cutting omitted 2,000.00

**BK317A** 51¢ Flag Over..., LMG, TRC (2135i-2139i), pane of 10 (2139aii), roulette on back cover
- **a** 29-slit roulette, *Jul 31, 2006* 15.00
- **b** 32-slit roulette, *Dec 2006* 50.00

A "Sun ray" flaw occurs on Sc. 2139 of BK317Ab (6 diff. known), as illustrated. Value $75.00 for pane of 10. This variety is not "truly" constant and may be removed in a future edition.

BK317a BK317b BK317Aa BK317Ab

**51¢ Flag rouletting (BK317)**

**BK317Ab — Sun ray flaw on Sc. 2139 (6 types)**

**BK318** 89¢ Yellow Lady's Slipper (2132), pane of 6 (2132a), 4mm tagging, *Dec 19/05* 14.00
- i 5.5mm weak tagging* 20.00

* Improperly cleaned tagging mats result in "messy", wider appearing bars (5.5mm vs 4mm), and a tag "wash" over the entire pane on some booklets of BK318.

**BK319** $1.05 Pink Fairy Slipper (2133), pane of 6 (2133a), *Dec 19/05* 18.00

**BK320** $1.49 Himalayan Blue Poppy (2134), pane of 6 (2134a), "C over S", *Dec 19, 2005* 21.00
- T1 missing tagging on left column (error) 450.00

**BK320A** $1.49 Himalayan Blue Poppy (2134), pane of 6 (2134ai), "C over O", *Feb 2006* 21.00
- i die cutting omitted *2,000.00*

C over S (BK320) C over O (BK320A)

## 2006

**BK321** 51¢ Queen Elizabeth II 80th Birthday (2142), pane of 10 (2142a), *Jan 12, 2006* 10.00

Die cutting omitted booklets (see note below) have been reported.

**BK322** 51¢ Gardens (2145a–d), pane of 8 (2145), *Mar 8, 2006* 8.00

**BK323** 51¢ Birthdays (2146), pane of 6 (2146a), *Apr 3, 2006* 6.00

**BK324** 51¢ McClelland & Stewart (2151), 2 panes of 4 (2151a), *Apr 26/06* 8.00

**BK325** 89¢ Museum of Civilization (2152), 2 panes of 4 (2152a), *May 11, 2006* 15.00
- i die cutting omitted *4,000.00*

**BK326** 51¢ John Candy (2154a), 2 panes of 4 (2154), *May 26, 2006* 8.00

**BK327** 51¢ Fay Wray (2154c), 2 panes of 4 (2154i), *May 26, 2006* 8.00

**BK328** 51¢ Lorne Greene (2154d), 2 panes of 4 (2154ii), *May 26, 2006* 8.00

**BK329** 51¢ Mary Pickford (2154b), 2 panes of 4 (2154iii), *May 26, 2006* 8.00

**BK330** 51¢ Vancouver Aquarium (2157), 2 panes of 5 (2157a), *Jun 15/06* 10.00

**BK331** 51¢ Lacrosse (2161), pane of 8 (2161a), *Jul 6, 2006* 8.00

**BK332** 51¢ Mountaineering (2162), pane of 8 (2162a), *Jul 19, 2006* 8.00

**BK333** 51¢ Wine and Cheese (2168–2171), pane of 8 (2171a), *Aug 23/06* 8.00

**BK334** 51¢ Macdonald College (2172), 2 panes of 4 (2172a), *Sep 26/06* 10.00

**BK335** 51¢ Endangered Species (2174-77), pane of 8 (2177b), *Sep 29/06* 10.00

**BK336** 51¢ Madonna and Child (2183), pane of 12 (2183a), *Nov 1, 2006* 12.00

**BK337** 51¢ Snowman (2184), pane of 12 (2184a), *Nov 1, 2006* 12.00

**BK338** 89¢ Winter Joys (2185), pane of 6 (2185a), *Nov 1, 2006* 11.00

**BK339** $1.49 Contemplation (2186), pane of 6 (2186a), *Nov 1, 2006* 18.00

## Definitive Issues (2006–2007)

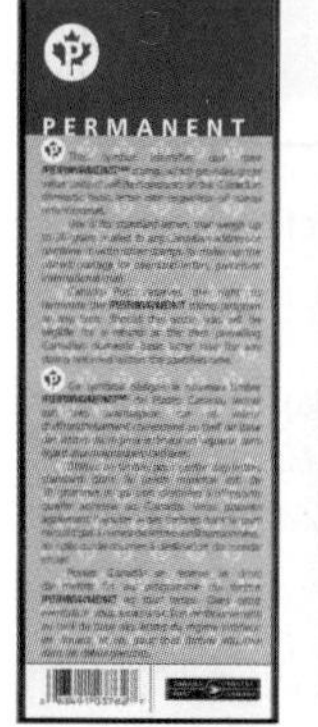

BK340 BK342 BK342A

**BK340** (P) Queen Elizabeth II, CBN, Fasson (2188), pane of 10 (2188a), *Nov 16, 2006* 17.00
- i die cutting omitted 1,200.00

A used counterfeit single of 2188 is known. No mint booklets yet reported.

**BK340A** (P) Queen Elizabeth II, CBN, TRC (2188), pane of 10 (2188ai), *Apr 5, 2007* 17.00

**BK341** (P) Flag Over..., CBN, TRC (2189-2193), pane of 10 (2193a), *Nov 16, 2006* 17.00

**BK342** (P) Flag Over..., CBN, TRC (2189-2193), pane of 30 (2193b), UPC barcode at lower left of back cover, *Nov 16, 2006* 50.00

**BK342A** (P) Flag Over..., CBN, TRC (2189-2193), pane of 30 (2193b), UPC barcode on top of panel, to left of stamps, *Apr 5, 2007* 70.00

BK345 BK345A

**BK343** 93¢ Flat-leaved Bladderwort (2198), pane of 6 (2198a), "Collection 2006", C-paper (dull, washed out tagging), *Dec 19/06* 12.00
- i shiny 'lacquer' tagging, *Spring 2007* 22.00
- ii tagging 'invisible' to naked eye, *Spring 2007* 22.00
- a 93¢ Flat-leaved Bladderwort (2198), pane of 6 (2198ai), F-paper designation, *Dec 19, 2006* 15.00

**BK343A** 93¢ Flat-leaved Bladderwort (2198), pane of 6 (2198a), Postal rates, C-paper, *Mar 2007* 12.00

**BK344** $1.10 The Marsh Skullcap (2199), pane of 6 (2199a), "Collection 2006" (dull, washed out tagging), *Dec 19, 2006* 15.00
- i shiny 'lacquer' tagging, *Spring 2007* 26.00
- ii tagging 'invisible' to naked eye, *Spring 2007* 26.00

**BK344A** $1.10 The Marsh Skullcap (2199), pane of 6 (2199a), Postal rates, *May 2007* 15.00

**BK345** $1.55 The Little Larkspur, LMG, TRC (2200), pane of 6 (2200a), "Collection 2006" (dull, washed out tagging), *Dec 19, 2006* 19.50
- i shiny 'lacquer' tagging, *Spring 2007* 34.00
- ii tagging 'invisible' to naked eye, *Spring 2007* 34.00

**BK345A** $1.55 The Little Larkspur (2200), pane of 6 (2200a), Postal rates, *May 2007* 19.50

The three types of tagging on BK343–BK345 are easily distinguishable.

BK343 exists with misaligned back cover printing relative to the booklet front. Several different versions known. Value $75.

About every second booklet of the first printing of all three Flower booklets (BK343–BK345) exist with a small portion of the bottom of the UPC barcode thickened.

**Beware of die cutting omitted booklets that have been hand cut from Canadian Bank Note printer's waste that began appearing on the market in early 2012. They are *faked booklets* due to the *hand cutting* (i.e. stamps printed by CBN modified by hand cutting to make them appear to be legitimately released die cutting omitted booklets). Examples of BK317ii, BK321, BK340, BK341 and BK342 are known.**

Doubling of black at bottom of back panel

## 2007

**BK346** 52¢ Celebrations (2203), pane of 6 (2203a), *Jan 15, 2007* 6.00
**BK347** 52¢ Lilacs 2207–08, pane of 10 (2208a), *Mar 1, 2007* 12.00
**BK348** 52¢ HEC Montreal (2209), 2 panes of 4 (2209a), *Mar 12, 2007* 10.00
**BK349** 52¢ University of Saskatchewan (2210), 2 panes of 4 (2210a), *Apr 3, 2007* 10.00
**BK350** 52¢ Ottawa (2214), 2 panes of 4 (2214a), *May 3, 2007* 8.00
**BK351** 52¢ Gordon Lightfoot (2222a–d), 2 panes of 4 (2222), *Jun 29, 2007* 8.00
**BK352** 52¢ Joni Mitchell (2222a–d), 2 panes of 4 (2222i), *Jun 29, 2007* 8.00
**BK353** 52¢ Anne Murray (2222a–d), 2 panes of 4 (2222ii), *Jun 29, 2007* 8.00
**BK354** 52¢ Paul Anka (2222a–d), 2 panes of 4 (2222iii), *Jun 29, 2007* 8.00
**BK355** 52¢ Terra Nova National Park (2223), 2 panes of 4 (2223a), *Jul 6, 2007* 10.00
**BK356** 52¢ Jasper National Park (2224), 2 panes of 4 (2224a), *Jul 20/07* 10.00
**BK357** 52¢ Scouting (2225), 2 panes of 4 (2225a), *Jul 25, 2007* 8.00
**BK358** 52¢ Endangered Species (2230–33), pane of 8 (2233b), *Oct 1/07* 10.00
**BK359** Reindeer (2239), 2 panes of 6 (2239a), *Nov 1, 2007* 20.00
i die cutting omitted *4,000.00*
**BK360** Hope (2240), 2 panes of 6 (2240a), *Nov 1/07* 20.00
**BK361** 93¢ Joy (2241), pane of 6 (2241a), *Nov 1, 2007* 14.00
**BK362** $1.55 Peace (2242), pane of 6 (2242a), *Nov 1, 2007* 18.00
i die cutting omitted *2,250.00*

## Definitive Issues (2007–2008)

BK363 BK365 BK366 BK367

**BK363** Queen Elizabeth II, CBN, Spicer (2248), pane of 10 (2248a), *Dec 27, 2007* 17.00
**BK364** Flag Over Lighthouses, CBN, TRC (2249–53), pane of 10 (2253a), *Dec 27, 2007* 17.00
**BK365** 96¢ Janet Elizabeth 'Fire Dancer' (2254), pane of 6 (2254a), *Dec 27, 2007* 12.00
i red ink on back cover is non-fluorescent, *Summer 2008* 26.00
**BK366** $1.15 Memoria Evelyn Light (2255), pane of 6 (2255a), *Dec 27/07* 15.00
i red ink on back cover is non-fluorescent, *Summer 2008* 32.00
**BK367** $1.60 Kaleidoscope 'Conni' (2256), pane of 6 (2256a), *Dec 27/07* 19.50
i red ink on back cover is non-fluorescent, *Summer 2008* 40.00

The initial printing of BK365–BK367 had fluorescent red ink on the cover side.

## 2008

**BK368** Celebrations (2259), pane of 6 (2259a), *Jan 15, 2008* 13.50
**BK369** 52¢ Peonies (5 each 2261–62), pane of 10 (2262b), *Mar 3, 2008* 10.00
i die cutting omitted *2,500.00*
**BK370** 52¢ University of Alberta (2263), pane of 8 (2263a), *Mar 7, 2008* 8.00
i die cutting omitted *2,000.00*
**BK371** 52¢ University of British Columbia (2264), pane of 8 (2264a), *Mar 7/08* 8.00
**BK372** 52¢ IIHF Championship (2265), pane of 10 (2265a) with Halifax cover, *Apr 3, 2008* 10.00
i die cutting omitted *2,000.00*
**BK373** 52¢ IIHF Championship (2265), pane of 10 (2265ai) with Québec City cover, *Apr 3, 2008* 10.00
i die cutting omitted *2,000.00*
**BK374** 52¢ Guide Dogs (2266), pane of 10, (2266a), *Apr 21, 2008* 10.00
**BK375** Flag Over Lighthouses, CBN, TRC (2249–52, 2253B), pane of 30 (2253d), *May 1, 2008* 50.00
**BK376** 52¢ Oil and Gas (2267–68), pane of 10, (2268a), *May 2, 2008* 10.00
i die cutting omitted
**BK377** 96¢ Audrey Hepburn (2272), 2 panes of 4 (2272a), *May 21/08* 16.00
**BK378** $1.60 Sir Winston Churchill (2273), 2 panes of 4 (2273a), *May 21, 2008* 26.00
**BK379** 52¢ Nurses (2275), pane of 10 (2275a), *Jun 16, 2008* 10.00
**BK380** 52¢ Anne of Green Gables (2277–78), pane of 10 (2278a), *Jun 20, 2008* 10.00
i die cutting omitted *2,500.00*
**BK381** 52¢ Marie Dressler (2280a–d), 2 panes of 4 (2280), *Jun 30, 2008* 8.00
**BK382** 52¢ Chief Dan George (2280a–d), 2 panes of 4 (2280i), *Jun 30/08* 8.00
**BK383** 52¢ Norma Shearer (2280a–d), 2 panes of 4 (2280ii), *Jun 30/08* 8.00
**BK384** 52¢ Raymond Burr (2280a–d), 2 panes of 4 (2280iii), *Jun 30/08* 8.00
**BK385** Flag Over Lighthouses, CBN, TRC (2249–52, 2253B), pane of 10 (2253c), *Jul 2, 2008* 17.00

Counterfeit booklets of BK385 are known to exist. These are untagged.

**BK386** 52¢ Beijing Olympics (2281), pane of 10, (2281a), *Jul 18, 2008* 10.00
i die cutting omitted *4,000.00*
**BK387** 52¢ Life Saving (2282, 2282i), pane of 10 (2282a), *Jul 25/08* 10.00
**BK388** 52¢ Endangered Species (sky) (2286–89), pane of 8 (2289b), *Oct 1, 2008* 10.00
**BK389** + 10¢ Mental Health (B14), pane of 10 (B14a), *Oct 6, 2008* 19.00
**BK390** The Nativity (2292), 2 panes of 6 (2292a), *Nov 3, 2008* 20.00
**BK391** Snow Angel (2293), 2 panes of 6 (2293a), *Nov 3, 2008* 20.00
**BK392** 96¢ Skiing (2294), pane of 6 (2294a), *Nov 3, 2008* 12.00
**BK393** $1.60 Toboganning (2295), pane of 6 (2295a), *Nov 3, 2008* 19.50

## Definitive Issues (2009)

BK394 BK395 BK396 BK399

**BK394** Queen Elizabeth II, CBN, TRC (2298), pane of 10 (2298a), *Jan 12, 2009* 17.00
**BK395** Olympic Sports, CBN, TRC (2300–04), pane of 10 (2304a), *Jan 12, 2009* 17.00

BK395 was issued with 24 different cover designs (numbered *n*/24) featuring Olympic moments. A complete set of 24 booklets was available from the Philatelic Centre. Counterfeit booklets of BK394 and BK395 are known to exist. These are untagged.

**BK396** Olympic Sports, CBN, TRC (2300–04), pane of 30 (2304b), *Jan 12, 2009* 50.00
**BK397** 98¢ Miga Olympic Mascot (2311), pane of 6 (2311a), *Jan 12/09* 12.00
**BK398** $1.18 Sumi Olympic Mascot (2312), pane of 6 (2312a), *Feb 12/09* 15.00
**BK399** $1.65 Quatchi Olympic Mascot (2313), pane of 6 (2313a), *Jan 12, 2009* 19.50

## 2009

| | | |
|---|---|---|
| **BK400** | P Celebration (2314), pane of 6 (2314a), *Feb 2/09* | 10.00 |
| **BK401** | 54¢ Rhododendrons (2319–20), pane of 10 (2320a), *Mar 13, 2009* | 10.00 |
| i | die cutting omitted | *3,750.00* |
| **BK402** | 54¢ Astronomy (2324–25), pane of 10 (2325a), *Apr 2/09* | 10.00 |
| **BK403** | 54¢ Horse and Pony (2329–30), pane of 10 (2330a), *May 15/09* | 15.00 |
| **BK404** | 54¢ Bryan Adams (2334a–d), 2 panes of 4 (2334), *Jul 2/09* | 8.00 |
| **BK405** | 54¢ Tom Connors (2334a–d), 2 panes of 4 (2334i), *Jul 2/09* | 8.00 |

One booklet of BK405 has been reported with “missing gold inscriptions”.

| | | |
|---|---|---|
| **BK406** | 54¢ Édith Butler (2334a–d), 2 panes of 4 (2334ii), *Jul 2/09* | 8.00 |
| **BK407** | 54¢ Robert Charlebois (2334a–d), 2 panes of 4 (2334iii), *Jul 2/09* | 8.00 |
| **BK408** | 54¢ Roadside Attractions (2336a–d), 2 panes of 4 (2336), *Jul 6/09* | 8.00 |
| **BK409** | 54¢ Sport Inventions (2338a–d), 2 panes of 4 (2338), *Aug 10/09* | 8.00 |
| **BK410** | P + 10¢ Mental Health (B15), pane of 10 (B15a), *Sep 14/09* | 19.00 |
| **BK411** | P Montreal Canadiens (2339), pane of 10 (2339a), *Oct 17/09* | 17.00 |
| **BK412** | P Lest We Forget (2342), pane of 10 (2342a), *Oct 19/09* | 17.00 |
| **BK413** | P Christmas Tree (2344), 2 panes of 6 (2344a), *Nov 2/09* | 20.00 |
| **BK414** | P Nativity (2345), 2 panes of 6 (2345a), *Nov 2/09* | 20.00 |
| **BK415** | 98¢ Nativity (2346), pane of 6 (2346a), *Nov 2/09* | 12.00 |
| **BK416** | $1.65 Nativity (2347), pane of 6 (2347a), *Nov 2/09* | 19.50 |

## Definitive Issues (2010)

BK417 BK418 BK419 BK420

| | | |
|---|---|---|
| **BK417** | P Flag over Mills (2351–55), pane of 10 (2355a), *Jan 11/10* | 17.00 |
| **BK418** | P Flag over Mills (2351–55), pane of 30 (2355b), *Jan 11/10* | 50.00 |
| **BK419** | $1.00 Giant Helleborine (2362), pane of 6 (2362a), *Jan 11/10* | 12.00 |
| **BK420** | $1.22 Rose Pogonia (2363), pane of 6 (2363a), *Jan 11/10* | 15.00 |
| **BK421** | $1.70 Grass Pink (2364), pane of 6 (2364a), *Jan 11/10* | 19.50 |
| **BK422** | P Queen Elizabeth II (2365), pane of 10 (2365a), *Jan 11/10* | 17.00 |
| **BK423** | 57¢ Olympic Venues (2367–68), pane of 10 (2368a), *Jan 12/10* | 10.00 |
| **BK424** | 57¢ Gold Medal (2372), pane of 10 (2372a), *Feb 14/10* | 10.00 |
| **BK425** | 57¢ Olympic Spirit (2374–75), pane of 10 (2375a), *Feb 22/10* | 10.00 |
| **BK426** | P Violets (2377–78), pane of 10 (2378a), *Mar 3/10* | 17.00 |
| i | die cutting omitted | |
| **BK427** | $1.70 Israel (2379), 2 panes of 3 (2379a), *Apr 14/10* | 21.00 |
| **BK428** | 57¢ Navy (2385–86), pane of 10 (2386a), *May 4/10* | 10.00 |
| **BK429** | 57¢ Marine Life (2387c–87d), pane of 8 (2387e), pane has blank right selvedge, *May 13/10* | 8.00 |
| a | as BK429, pane has blue cylinder number (“1” *or* “2”) on right selvedge | 10.00 |
| b | as BK429, pane has black, 6-digit dot matrix, control number on right selvedge (opposite bottom stamp) | 12.00 |
| bi | as “b”, 6-digit control number opposite top stamp | *125.00* |
| c | as BK429, pane w/blue 1 *or* 2, *and* black 6-digit control number | 30.00 |

BK429 also exists with a 2x10mm black counting “tab”, found at the lower right of the front cover (and around to back) on every 50th booklet; its position and intensity varies. Price is 5 times normal.

| | | |
|---|---|---|
| **BK430** | 57¢ Photography (2389–93), pane of 10 (2393a), *May 22/10* | 10.00 |
| **BK431** | 57¢ Rotary (2394), pane of 8 (2394a), *Jun 18/10* | 8.00 |
| **BK432** | P Roadside Attractions (2398–2401), 2 panes of 4 (2401a), *Jul 5/10* | 13.50 |
| **BK433** | P Girl Guides (2402), pane of 10 (2402a), *Jul 8/10* | 17.00 |
| **BK434** | P + 10¢ Mental Health (B16), pane of 10 (B16a), *Sep 7/10* | 19.00 |
| **BK435** | P Nativity (2412), 2 panes of 6 (2412a), *Nov 1/10* | 20.00 |
| **BK436** | P Ornaments (2413), 2 panes of 6 (2413a), *Nov 1/10* | 20.00 |
| **BK437** | $1.00 Ornaments (2414), pane of 6 (2414a), *Nov 1/10* | 12.00 |
| **BK438** | $1.70 Ornaments (2415), pane of 6 (2415a), *Nov 1/10* | 20.50 |

## Definitive Issues (2011)

BK439 BK440 BK441 BK443

| | | |
|---|---|---|
| **BK439** | P Flag/Canada Pride (2419–23), pane of 10 (2423a), *Jan 17/11* | 17.00 |
| i | non-fluorescent yellow ink (2423ai) | 25.00 |
| **BK440** | P Flag/Canada Pride (2419–23), pane of 30 (2423b), *Jan 17/11* | 50.00 |
| i | non-fluorescent yellow ink (2423bi) | 70.00 |

The original printings of BK439 and BK440 have fluorescent yellow ink; reprints (i) appeared mid-2011. Weak pink ‘tagging’ on BK439 exists; value $25.00.

| | | |
|---|---|---|
| **BK441** | $1.03 Red fox (2430), pane of 6 (2430a), *Jan 17/11* | 12.00 |
| **BK442** | $1.25 Canada geese (2431), pane of 6 (2431a), *Jan 17/11* | 15.00 |
| **BK443** | $1.75 Polar bear (2432), pane of 6 (2432a), *Jan 17/11* | 19.50 |
| i | die cutting omitted | |

## 2011

| | | |
|---|---|---|
| **BK444** | 59¢ Carrie Best (2433), pane of 10 (2433a), *Feb 7/11* | 12.00 |
| **BK445** | 59¢ Ferguson Jenkins (2434), pane of 10 (2434a), *Feb 7/11* | 12.00 |
| **BK446** | P Celebrations (2435, 2435i), pane of 6 (2435a), *Feb 7, 2011* | 10.00 |
| **BK447** | $1.03 Daphne Odjig (2438), pane of 6 (2438a), *Feb 21/11* | 12.00 |
| **BK448** | $1.75 Daphne Odjig (2439), pane of 6 (2439a), *Feb 21/11* | 21.00 |
| **BK449** | P Sunflowers (2443–44), pane of 10 (2444a), *Mar 3, 2011* | 17.00 |
| **BK450** | P Zodiac: Aries (2449), pane of 10 (2449a), *Mar 21, 2011* | 17.00 |
| **BK451** | P Zodiac: Taurus (2450), pane of 10 (2450a), *Apr 21, 2011* | 17.00 |
| **BK452** | P Int'l Year of Forests (2462–63), pane of 8 (2463a), *Apr 21, 2011* | 13.50 |
| **BK453** | P Royal Wedding (2466), pane of 10 (2466a), *May 2, 2011* | 17.00 |
| **BK454** | $1.75 Royal Wedding (2467), pane of 10 (2467a), *May 2, 2011* | 35.00 |
| **BK455** | 59¢ Parks Canada (2470), pane of 10 (2470a), *May 19, 2011* | 12.00 |
| **BK456** | P Zodiac: Gemini (2451), pane of 10 (2451a), *May 20, 2011* | 17.00 |
| **BK457** | P Art Deco (2472–76), pane of 10 (2476a), *Jun 9, 2011* | 17.00 |
| **BK458** | P Zodiac: Cancer (2452), pane of 10 (2452a), *Jun 22, 2011* | 17.00 |
| **BK459** | P Wedding Day (2478), pane of 10 (2478a), *Jun 22, 2011* | 17.00 |
| **BK460** | P Bruce Cockburn (2483a–d), 2 panes of 4 (2483), *Jun 30/11* | 13.50 |
| **BK461** | P McGarrigle sisters (2483a–d), 2 panes of 4 (2483i), *Jun 30/11* | 13.50 |
| **BK462** | P Ginette Reno (2483a–d), 2 panes of 4 (2483ii), *Jun 30/11* | 13.50 |
| **BK463** | P Robbie Robertson (2483a–d), 2 panes of 4 (2483iii), *Jun 30/11* | 13.50 |
| **BK464** | P Roadside Attractions (2485a–d), 2 panes of 4 (2485), *Jul 7/11* | 13.50 |
| **BK465** | P Miss Supertest (2487), pane of 10 (2487a), *Aug 8, 2011* | 17.00 |
| **BK466** | 59¢ Canadian Innovations (2488a–d), 2 panes of 4 (2488), *Aug 17/11* | 9.50 |
| **BK467** | P + 10¢ Mental Health (B18), pane of 10 (B18a), *Sep 6/11* | 19.00 |
| **BK468** | P Year of Chemistry (2489), pane of 10 (2489a), *Oct 3/11* | 17.00 |
| **BK469** | P Holly (2491), 2 panes of 6 (2491a), *Nov 1/11* | 20.00 |
| **BK470** | P Stained glass (2492), 2 panes of 6 (2492a), *Nov 1/11* | 20.00 |
| **BK471** | $1.03 Stained glass (2493), pane of 6 (2493a), *Nov 1/11* | 12.00 |
| **BK472** | $1.75 Stained glass (2494), pane of 6 (2494a), *Nov 1/11* | 21.00 |

## 2012

**BK473** $1.80 Year of the Dragon (2497), pane of 6 (2497a), *Jan 10/12* 21.50

### Definitive Issues (2012)

BK474

BK475

BK477

BK478

**BK474** Flag/Canada Pride (2499–03), pane of 10 (2503a), *Jan 16/12* 17.00

**BK474A** Flag/Canada Pride (2499–01, 2502a, 2503), with corrected spelling of "Lueders" in microprinting on 2502a, pane of 10 (2503c), *Sep 28/12* 25.00

**BK474B** Flag/Canada Pride (2499a–2501a, 2502b, 2503d), with repeating 'Canada' underprint, pane of 10 (2503e), *Nov 2012* 35.00

**BK475** Flag/Canada Pride (2499–03), pane of 30 (2503b), *Jan 16/12* 50.00

**BK476** $1.05 Caribou (2510), pane of 6 (2510a), *Jan 16/12* 12.50

**BK477** $1.29 Loons (2511), pane of 6 (2511a), *Jan 16/12* 15.50

**BK478** $1.80 Moose (2512), pane of 6 (2512a), *Jan 16/12* 21.50

## 2012

**BK479** QEII Diamond Jubilee (2519), pane of 10 (2519a), *Jan 16/12* 17.00

**BK480** John Ware (2520), pane of 10 (2520a), *Feb 1/12* 17.00

**BK481** Viola Desmond (2521), pane of 10 (2521a), *Feb 1/12* 17.00

**BK482** $1.05 Art: Fafard (2524), pane of 6 (2524a), *Feb 23/12* 12.50

**BK483** $1.80 Art: Fafard (2525), pane of 6 (2525a), *Feb 23/12* 21.50

**BK484** Daylilies (2529–30), pane of 10 (2530a), *Mar 1/12* 17.00

**BK485** Titanic (2536–37), pane of 10 (2537a), *Apr 5/12* 17.00

**BK486** $1.80 Titanic (2538), pane of 6 (2538a), *Apr 5/12* 21.50

**BK487** Franklin the Turtle (2542–45), pane of 12 (2545a), *May 11/12* 20.00

**BK488** Calgary Stampede (2547), pane of 10 (2547a), *May 17/12* 17.00

**BK489** $1.05 Calgary Stampede (2548), pane of 10 (2548a), *May 17/12* 21.00

**BK490** Arbour (2550), pane of 10 (2550a), *May 22/12* 17.00

**BK491** Hansen (2551), pane of 10 (2551a), *May 22/12* 17.00

**BK492** Watt-Cloutier (2552), pane of 10 (2552a), *May 22/12* 17.00

**BK493** Fox (2553), pane of 10 (2553a), *May 22/12* 17.00

**BK494** London Olympics (2556), pane of 10 (2556a), *Jun 27/12* 17.00

**BK495** Zodiac: Leo (2453), pane of 10 (2453a), *Jul 23/12* 17.00

**BK496** Zodiac: Virgo (2454), pane of 10 (2454a), *Jul 23/12* 17.00

**BK497** Zodiac: Libra (2455), pane of 10 (2455a), *Jul 23/12* 17.00

**BK498** Zodiac: Scorpio (2456), pane of 10 (2456a), *Jul 23/12* 17.00

**BK499** CFL: Grey Cup (2568), pane of 10 (2568a), *Aug 16/12* 17.00

**BK500** CFL: Lions (2569), pane of 10 (2569a), *Aug 16/12* 17.00

**BK501** CFL: Eskimos (2570), pane of 10 (2570a), *Aug 16/12* 17.00

**BK502** CFL: Stampeders (2571), pane of 10 (2571a), *Aug 16/12* 17.00

**BK503** CFL: Roughriders (2572), pane of 10 (2572a), *Aug 16/12* 17.00

**BK504** CFL: Blue Bombers (2573), pane of 10 (2573a), *Aug 16/12* 17.00

**BK505** CFL: Tiger-Cats (2574), pane of 10 (2574a), *Aug 16/12* 17.00

**BK506** CFL: Argonauts (2575), pane of 10 (2575a), *Aug 16/12* 17.00

**BK507** CFL: Alouettes (2576), pane of 10 (2576a), *Aug 16/12* 17.00

**BK508** + 10¢ Canada Post Community Foundation (B19), pane of 10 (B19a), *Sep 17/12* 19.00

**BK509** Black Watch (2578), pane of 10 (2578a), *Oct 11/12* 17.00

**BK510** Royal Hamilton (2579), pane of 10 (2579a), *Oct 11/12* 17.00

**BK511** Royal Regiment (2580), pane of 10 (2580a), *Oct 11/12* 17.00

**BK512** Stained glass (2582), pane of 12 (2582a), *Oct 15/12* 20.00

**BK513** Cookies (2583), pane of 12 (2583a), *Oct 15/12* 20.00

**BK514** $1.05 Cookies (2584), pane of 6 (2584a), *Oct 15/12* 12.50

**BK515** $1.80 Cookies (2585), pane of 6 (2585a), *Oct 15/12* 21.50

**BK516** Grey Cup Winner (2598), pane of 10 (2598a), *Nov 28/12* 17.00

**a** as BK516, unfolded *40.00*

## 2013

**BK517** $1.85 Year of the Snake (2601), pane of 6 (2601a), *Jan 8/13* 22.25

### Definitive Issues (2013)

BK518

BK521

BK522

BK523

**BK518** $1.10 Porcupine (2608), pane of 6 (2608a), *Jan 14/13* 13.25

**BK519** $1.34 Fawn (2609), pane of 6 (2609a), *Jan 14/13* 16.25

**BK520** $1.85 Black Bear (2610), pane of 6 (2610a), *Jan 14/13* 22.25

**BK521** Flag/Canada Pride (2612–16), pane of 10 (2616b), *Jan 14/13* 17.00

**BK521A** Flag/Canada Pride (2612a–16a), with repeating 'Canada' underprint, pane of 10 (2616c), *Jan 31/13* 17.00

**BK522** Flag/Canada Pride (2612–16), pane of 30 (2616d), *Jan 14/13* 50.00

**BK522A** Flag/Canada Pride (2612a–16a), with repeating 'Canada' underprint, pane of 30 (2616e), *Jan 31/13* 50.00

**BK523** Queen Elizabeth II (2617), pane of 10 (2617a), *Jan 14/13* 17.00

**BK523A** Queen Elizabeth II (2617b), with repeating 'Canada' underprint, pane of 10 (2617c), *Jun 1/13* 17.00

## 2013

**BK524** $1.85 Wallenberg (2618), pane of 6 (2618a), *Jan 17/13* 22.25

**BK525** Oliver Jones (2619), pane of 10 (2619a), *Feb 1/13* 17.00

**BK526** Joe Fortes (2620), pane of 10 (2620a), *Feb 1/13* 17.00

**BK527** Zodiac: Sagitarius (2457), pane of 10 (2457a), *Feb 20/13* 17.00

**BK528** Zodiac: Capricorn (2458), pane of 10 (2458a), *Feb 20/13* 17.00

**BK529** Zodiac: Aquarius (2459), pane of 10 (2459a), *Feb 20/13* 17.00

**BK530** Zodiac: Pisces (2460), pane of 10 (2460a), *Feb 20/13* 17.00

**BK531** Magnolias (2624–25), pane of 10 (2625a), *Mar 4/13* 17.00

**BK532** Photography [1] (2628–32), pane of 10 (2632a), *Mar 22/13* 17.00

**BK533** $1.10 Photography (2633), pane of 6 (2633a), *Mar 22/13* 13.25

**BK534** $1.85 Photography (2634), pane of 6 (2634a), *Mar 22/13* 22.25

**BK535** Wales' Own Regiment (2635), pane of 10 (2635a), *Apr 9/13* 17.00

**BK536** Adopt a Pet (2637–41), pane of 10 (2641a), *Apr 22/13* 17.00

**BK537** Chinatown Gates (2643a–h), pane of 8 (2643), *May 1/13* 10.00

**BK538** QEII Coronation (2644), pane of 10 (2644a), *May 8/13* 17.00

**BK539** Big Brothers Big Sisters (2645), pane of 10 (2645a), *May 14/13* 17.00

**BK540** Motorcycles (2647–48), pane of 10 (2648a), *Jun 5/13* 17.00

**BK541** 250 Years Postal History (2649), pane of 10 (2649a), *Jun 10/13* 17.00

**BK542** Stella (2653-54), pane of 10 (2654a), *Jul 5/13* 17.00

**BK543** The Tragically Hip (2656), pane of 10 (2656a), *Jul 19/13* 17.00

**BK544** Rush (2657), pane of 10 (2657a), *Jul 19/13* 17.00

**BK545** Beau Dommage (2658), pane of 10 (2658a), *Jul 19/13* 17.00

**BK546** The Guess Who (2659), pane of 10 (2659a), *Jul 19/13* 17.00

**BK547** 63¢ Robertson Davies (2660), pane of 10 (2660a), *Aug 28/13* 12.50

**BK548** 63¢ NHL: Canucks (2670), pane of 10 (2670a), *Sep 3/13* 12.50

**BK549** 63¢ NHL: Canadiens (2671), pane of 10 (2671a), *Sep 3/13* 12.50

**BK550** 63¢ NHL: Oilers (2672), pane of 10 (2672a), *Sep 3/13* 12.50

**BK551** 63¢ NHL: Senators (2673), pane of 10 (2673a), *Sep 3/13* 12.50

| | | |
|---|---|---|
| **BK552** | 63¢ NHL: Flames (2674), pane of 10 (2674a), *Sep 3/13* | 12.50 |
| **BK553** | 63¢ NHL: Jets (2675), pane of 10 (2675a), *Sep 3/13* | 12.50 |
| **BK554** | 63¢ NHL: Maple Leafs (2676), pane of 10 (2676a), *Sep 3/13* | 12.50 |
| **BK555** | Superman [1939] (2679–83), pane of 10 (2683a), *Sep 10/13* | 17.00 |
| **BK556** | Superman [1939/train] (2679–83), pane of 10 (2683ai), *Sep 10/13* | 17.00 |
| **BK557** | Superman [1986] (2679–83), pane of 10 (2683aii), *Sep 10/13* | 17.00 |
| i | die cutting omitted | *3,000.00* |
| **BK558** | Superman [2004] (2679–83), pane of 10 (2683aiii), *Sep 10/13* | 17.00 |
| **BK559** | Superman [2012] (2679–83), pane of 10 (2683aiv), *Sep 10/13* | 17.00 |
| **BK560** | 63¢ + 10¢ Canada Post Community Foundation (B20), pane of 10 (B20a), *Sep 30/13* | 15.00 |
| **BK561** | Hastings and Prince Edward Regiment (2684), pane of 10 (2684a), *Oct 18/13* | 17.00 |
| **BK562** | HRH Prince George of Cambridge (2686), pane of 10 (2686a), *Oct 22/13* | 17.00 |
| **BK563** | 63¢ Saint Anne (2688), pane of 12 (2688a), *Oct 22/13* | 15.00 |
| **BK564** | 63¢ Craft: Horn (2689), pane of 12 (2689a), *Oct 22/13* | 15.00 |
| **BK565** | $1.10 Craft: Reindeer (2690), pane of 6 (2690a), *Oct 22/13* | 13.00 |
| **BK566** | $1.85 Craft: Christmas Tree (2691), pane of 6 (2691a), *Oct 22/13* | 22.00 |
| **BK567** | 63¢ Flag/Canada Pride (2693–97), with repeating 'Canada' underprint, pane of 10 (2697a), *Dec 11/13* | 12.50 |
| **BK568** | 63¢ Queen Elizabeth II (2698), with repeating 'Canada' underprint, pane of 10 (2698a), *Dec 11/13* | 12.50 |

## 2014

| | | |
|---|---|---|
| **BK569** | $1.85 Year of the Horse (2701), pane of 6 (2701a), *Jan 13/14* | 22.25 |
| **BK570** | 63¢ Africville (2702), pane of 10 (2702a), *Jan 30/14* | 12.50 |
| **BK571** | 63¢ Hogan's Alley (2703), pane of 10 (2703a), *Jan 30/14* | 12.50 |
| **BK572** | 63¢ Barbara Ann Scott (2705), pane of 10 (2705a), *Feb 3/14* | 12.50 |
| **BK573** | 63¢ Sandra Schmirler (2706), pane of 10 (2706a), *Feb 3/14* | 12.50 |
| **BK574** | 63¢ Sarah Burke (2707), pane of 10 (2707a), *Feb 3/14* | 12.50 |

### Definitive Issues (2014)

BK575

BK577

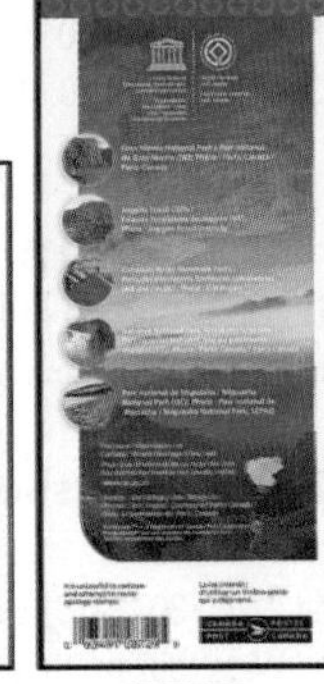
BK578

BK579

| | | |
|---|---|---|
| **BK575** | $1.20 Mountain Goat (2715), pane of 6 (2715a), *Mar 31/14* | 14.50 |
| **BK576** | $1.80 Puffin (2716), pane of 6 (2716a), *Mar 31/14* | 21.60 |
| **BK577** | $2.50 Wapiti (2717), pane of 6 (2717a), *Mar 31/14* | 30.00 |
| **BK578** | UNESCO (2719–23), pane of 10 (2723a), *Mar 31/14* | 17.00 |
| **BK579** | UNESCO (2719–23), pane of 30 (2723b), *Mar 31/14* | 50.00 |
| **BK580** | Royal Ontario Museum (2725–26), pane of 10 (2726a), *Apr 14/14* | 17.00 |
| **BK581** | Roses (2730–31), pane of 10 (2731a), *Apr 23/14* | 17.00 |
| **BK582** | $2.50 Komagata Maru (2732), pane of 6 (2732a), *May 1/14* | 30.00 |
| **BK583** | NFB (2734–38), pane of 10 (2738a), *May 2/14* | 17.00 |
| **BK584** | $1.20 UNESCO (2740–42), pane of 6 (2742a), *May 16/14* | 14.50 |
| **BK585** | $2.50 UNESCO (2743–44), pane of 6 (2744a), *May 16/14* | 30.00 |
| **BK586** | *Empress of Ireland* (2747), pane of 10 (2747a), *May 29/14* | 17.00 |
| **BK587** | Haunted Canada [1] (2749–53), pane of 10 (2753a), *Jun 13/14* | 17.00 |
| **BK588** | CFL: Ottawa (2755), pane of 10 (2755a), *Jun 19/14* | 17.00 |
| **BK589** | Photography [2] (2758–62), pane of 10 (2762a), *Jul 7/14* | 17.00 |
| **BK590** | $1.20 Photography (2763), pane of 6 (2763a), *Jul 7/14* | 14.50 |
| **BK591** | $2.50 Photography (2764), pane of 6 (2764a), *Jul 7/14* | 30.00 |
| **BK592** | Hank Snow (2766), pane of 10 (2766a), *Jul 31/14* | 17.00 |
| **BK593** | Rene Martel (2767), pane of 10 (2767a), *Jul 31/14* | 17.00 |
| **BK594** | Shania Twain (2768), pane of 10 (2768a), *Jul 31/14* | 17.00 |
| **BK595** | Tommy Hunter (2769), pane of 10 (2769a), *Jul 31/14* | 17.00 |
| **BK596** | k.d. lang (2770), pane of 10 (2770a), *Jul 31/14* | 17.00 |
| **BK597** | Museum Human Rights (2771), pane of 10 (2771a), *Aug 20/14* | 17.00 |
| **BK598** | Mike Myers (2773), pane of 10 (2773a), *Aug 29/14* | 17.00 |
| **BK599** | Martin Short (2774), pane of 10 (2774a), *Aug 29/14* | 17.00 |
| **BK600** | Catherine O'Hara (2775), pane of 10 (2775a), *Aug 29/14* | 17.00 |
| **BK601** | Olivier Guimond (2776), pane of 10 (2776a), *Aug 29/14* | 17.00 |
| **BK602** | Jim Carrey (2777), pane of 10 (2777a), *Aug 29/14* | 17.00 |
| **BK603** | + 10¢ Canada Post Community Foundation (B21), pane of 10 (B21a), *Sep 29/14* | 19.00 |
| **BK604** | Original Six™ (2787a–f), pane of 6 (2787), *Oct 3/14* | 10.20 |
| **BK605** | Wait for Me Daddy (2795), pane of 10 (2795a), *Oct 4/14* | 17.00 |
| **BK606** | Madonna and Child (2797), pane of 12 (2797a), *Oct 23/14* | 20.40 |
| **BK607** | Santa (2798), pane of 12 (2798a), *Oct 23/14* | 20.40 |
| **BK608** | $1.20 Santa (2799), pane of 6 (2799a), *Oct 23/14* | 14.40 |
| **BK609** | $2.50 Santa (2800), pane of 6 (2800a), *Oct 23/14* | 30.00 |

## 2015

| | | |
|---|---|---|
| **BK610** | $2.50 Year of the Ram (2803), pane of 6 (2803a), *Jan 8/15* | 30.00 |
| **BK611** | Macdonald (2804), pane of 10 (2804a), *Jan 11/15* | 17.00 |
| **BK612** | Mandela (2806), pane of 10 (2806a), *Jan 30/15* | 17.00 |
| **BK613** | Canada Flag (2807), pane of 10 (2807a), *Feb 15/15* | 17.00 |
| **BK614** | Pansies (2812–13), pane of 10 (2813a), *Mar 2/15* | 17.00 |
| **BK615** | Photography [3] (2816–20), pane of 10 (2820a), *Apr 8/15* | 17.00 |
| **BK616** | $1.20 Photography (2821), pane of 6 (2821a), *Apr 8/15* | 14.50 |
| **BK617** | $2.50 Photography (2822), pane of 6 (2822a), *Apr 8/15* | 30.00 |
| **BK618** | Dinos of Canada [1] (2824–28), pane of 10 (2828a), *Apr 13/15* | 17.00 |
| **BK619** | Love your pet (2830–34), pane of 10 (2834a), *May 2/15* | 17.00 |
| **BK620** | *In Flanders Fields* (2836), pane of 10 (2836a), *May 3/15* | 17.00 |
| **BK621** | FIFA (2837), pane of 10 (2837a), *May 6/15* | 17.00 |
| **BK622** | Weather Wonders (2839–43), pane of 10 (2843a), *Jun 18/15* | 17.00 |
| **BK623** | $1.20 UNESCO (2845–47), pane of 6 (2847a), *Jul 3/15* | *75.00* |

BK623 was recalled on July 7, 2015 due to an incorrect image being used on the Dinosaur Provincial Park stamp.

| | | |
|---|---|---|
| **BK624** | $2.50 UNESCO (2848–49), pane of 6 (2849a), *Jul 3/15* | 30.00 |
| **BK625** | Alice Munro (2850), pane of 10 (2850a), *Jul 10/15* | 17.00 |
| **BK626** | Franklin Expedition (2854–55), pane of 10 (2855a), *Aug 6/15* | 17.00 |
| **BK627** | $2.50 Franklin Expedition (2856), pane of 6 (2856a), *Aug 6/15* | 30.00 |
| **BK628** | $1.20 UNESCO (2846–47, 2858), pane of 6 (2858a), *Aug 21/15* | 14.50 |
| **BK629** | QE II Historic Reign (2859), pane of 10 (2859a), *Sep 9/15* | 17.00 |
| **BK630** | Haunted Canada [2] (2861–65), pane of 10 (2865a), *Sep 14/15* | 17.00 |
| **BK631** | + 10 Canada Post Community Foundation (B22), pane of 10 (B22a), *Sep 28/15* | 19.00 |
| **BK632** | Canadian Goalies (2867–72), pane of 6 (2872a), *Oct 2/15* | 10.20 |
| **BK633** | Madonna and Child (2880), pane of 12 (2880a), *Nov 2/15* | 20.40 |
| **BK634** | Moose (2881), pane of 12 (2881a), *Nov 2/15* | 20.40 |
| **BK635** | $1.20 Beaver (2882), pane of 6 (2882a), *Nov 2/15* | 14.40 |
| **BK636** | $2.50 Polar Bear (2883), pane of 6 (2883a), *Nov 2/15* | 30.00 |

## Definitive Issues (2016)

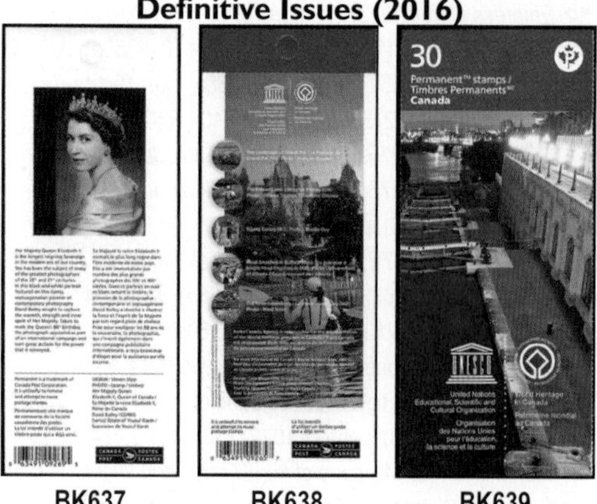


BK637 BK638 BK639

| | | |
|---|---|---|
| BK637 | Queen Elizabeth II (2888), pane of 10 (2888a), *Jan 11/16* | 17.00 |
| BK638 | UNESCO (2890–94), pane of 10 (2894a), *Jan 11/16* | 17.00 |
| BK639 | UNESCO (2890–94), pane of 30 (2894b), *Jan 11/16* | 50.00 |

## 2016

| | | |
|---|---|---|
| BK640 | Year of the Monkey (2886), pane of 10 (2886a), *Jan 11/16* | 17.00 |
| BK641 | $2.50 Year of the Monkey (2887), pane of 6 (2887a), *Feb 1/16* | 30.00 |
| BK642 | No. 2 Construction Battalion (2895), pane of 10 (2895a), *Feb 1/16* | 17.00 |
| BK643 | Hydrangeas (2899–2900), pane of 10 (2900a), *Mar 1/16* | 17.00 |
| BK644 | Women's Suffrage (2901), pane of 10 (2901a), *Mar 8/16* | 17.00 |
| BK645 | Photography [4] (2904–08), pane of 10 (2908a), *Apr 13/16* | 17.00 |
| BK646 | $1.20 Photography (2909), pane of 6 (2909a), *Apr 13/16* | 14.50 |
| BK647 | $2.50 Photography (2910), pane of 6 (2910a), *Apr 13/16* | 30.00 |
| BK648 | Star Trek (2917–2921), pane of 10 (2921a), *May 5/16* | 17.00 |
| BK649 | Star Trek Prestige booklet ($19.95), five panes (2912f, 2912g, 2912h, 2912i, 2916a), *May 5/16* | 40.00 |
| BK650 | Dinos of Canada [2] (2924–28), pane of 10 (2928a), *May 26/16* | 17.00 |
| BK651 | Birds of Canada [1] (2930–34), pane of 10 (2934a), *Jul 12/16* | 17.00 |
| BK652 | Haunted Canada [3] (2936–2940), pane of 10 (2940a), *Sep 8/16* | 17.00 |
| BK653 | Canadian Forwards (2942–2947), pane of 6 (2947a), *Sep 23/16* | 10.20 |
| BK654 | + 10 Canada Post Community Foundation (B23–B24), pane of 10 (B24a), *Sep 26/16* | 19.00 |
| BK655 | Madonna and Child (2955), pane of 12 (2955a), *Nov 1/16* | 20.40 |
| BK656 | Santa (2956), pane of 12 (2956a), *Nov 1/16* | 20.40 |
| BK657 | $1.20 Christmas Tree (2957), pane of 6 (2957a), *Nov 1/16* | 14.40 |
| BK658 | $2.50 Dove (2958), pane of 6 (2958a), *Nov 1/16* | 30.00 |

## 2017

| | | |
|---|---|---|
| BK659 | Year of the Rooster (2961), pane of 10 (2961a), *Jan 9/17* | 17.00 |
| BK660 | $2.50 Year of the Rooster (2962), pane of 6 (2962a), *Jan 9/17* | 30.00 |

## Definitive Issues (2017)

BK661 BK662

| | | |
|---|---|---|
| BK661 | UNESCO (2964–68), pane of 10 (2968a), *Jan 16/17* | 17.00 |
| BK662 | UNESCO (2964–68), pane of 30 (2968b), *Jan 16/17* | 50.00 |

## 2017

| | | |
|---|---|---|
| BK663 | Mathieu Da Costa (2969), pane of 10 (2969a), *Feb 1/17* | 17.00 |
| BK664 | Canadian Opera (2971–75), pane of 10 (2975a), *Feb 4/17* | 17.00 |
| BK665 | Daisies (2979–80), pane of 10 (2980a), *Mar 1/17* | 17.00 |
| BK666 | Vimy Ridge (2982), pane of 10 (2982a), *Apr 8/17* | 17.00 |
| BK667 | Star Trek [Captains] (2986–90), pane of 10 (2990a), *Apr 27/17* | 17.00 |
| BK668 | Star Trek [Captains] Prestige booklet ($21.95), five panes (2983f, 2983g, 2983h, 2984a, 2991a), *Apr 27/17* | 45.00 |
| BK669 | Formula 1 (2993–97), pane of 10 (2997a), *May 16/17* | 17.00 |
| BK670 | Eid (2998), pane of 10 (2998a), *May 24/17* | 17.00 |
| BK671 | Canada 150 (3000–09), pane of 10 (3009a), *Jun 1/17* | 17.00 |
| BK672 | Nunavut (3006), pane of 8 (3006a), *Jun 1/17* | 13.60 |
| BK673 | Equality (3007), pane of 8 (3007a), *Jun 1/17* | 13.60 |
| BK674 | Photography [5] (3012–16), pane of 10 (3016a), *Jul 4/17* | 17.00 |
| BK675 | Birds of Canada [2] (3018–22), pane of 10 (3022a), *Aug 1/17* | 17.00 |
| BK676 | Diwali (3024–25), pane of 10 (3025a), *Sep 21/17* | 17.00 |
| BK677 | + 10 Canada Post Community Foundation (B25–B26), pane of 10 (B26a), *Sep 25/17* | 19.00 |
| BK678 | NHL: Ultimate Six (3027–3032), pane of 6 (3032a), *Sep 28/17* | 10.20 |
| BK679 | History of Hockey (3040–41), pane of 10 (3041a), *Oct 20/17* | 17.00 |
| BK680 | Toronto Maple Leafs (3044), pane of 10 (3044a), *Oct 24/17* | 17.00 |
| BK681 | Madonna and Child (3046), pane of 12 (3046a), *Nov 3/17* | 20.40 |
| BK682 | Polar Bear (3047), pane of 12 (3047a), *Nov 3/17* | 20.40 |
| BK683 | $1.20 Cardinal (3048), pane of 6 (3048a), *Nov 3/17* | 14.40 |
| BK684 | $2.50 Caribou (3049), pane of 6 (3049a), *Nov 3/17* | 30.00 |
| BK685 | Halifax Explosion (3050), pane of 10 (3050a), *Nov 6/17* | 17.00 |

BK686 BK686A

| | | |
|---|---|---|
| BK686 | Hanukkah (3051), pane of 10 (3051a), *Nov 14/17* | 50.00 |
| BK686A | Hanukkah (3051), pane of 10 (3051ai), ≈ *Nov 22/17* | 17.00 |

## 2018

| | | |
|---|---|---|
| BK687 | Year of the Dog (3054), pane of 10 (3054a), *Jan 15/18* | 17.00 |
| BK688 | $2.50 Year of the Dog (3055), pane of 6 (3055a), *Jan 15/18* | 30.00 |

## Definitive Issues (2018)

| | | |
|---|---|---|
| BK689 | From Far and Wide (3071–75), pane of 10 (3075a), *Jan 15/18* | 17.00 |
| BK690 | From Far and Wide (3071–75), pane of 30 (3075b), *Jan 15/18* | 50.00 |
| BK691 | $1.20 From Far and Wide (3076), pane of 6 (3076a), *Jan 15/18* | 14.50 |
| BK692 | $1.80 From Far and Wide (3077), pane of 6 (3077a), *Jan 15/18* | 21.60 |
| BK693 | $2.50 From Far and Wide (3078), pane of 6 (3078a), *Jan 15/18* | 30.00 |

## 2018

| | | |
|---|---|---|
| BK694 | Women in Sports (3080-84), pane of 10 (3084a), *Jan 24/18* | 17.00 |
| BK695 | Kay Livingstone (3085), pane of 10 (3085a), *Feb 1/18* | 17.00 |
| BK696 | Lincoln Alexander (3086), pane of 10 (3086a), *Feb 1/18* | 17.00 |
| BK697 | Lotuses (3090–91), pane of 10 (3091a), *Mar 1/18* | 17.00 |
| BK698 | Canadian Illustrators (3093–97), pane of 10 (3097a), *Apr 5/18* | 17.00 |
| BK699 | QEII Coronation (3098), pane of 10 (3098a), *Apr 20/18* | 17.00 |
| i | "no gum", cover printed on gum side | 50.00 |
| BK700 | Native bees (3099–3100), pane of 10 (3100a), *May 1/18* | 17.00 |
| BK701 | Memorial Cup (3101), pane of 10 (3101a), *May 18/18* | 17.00 |

**The following stamps of 2018 had not yet been assigned a catalogue number by Scott Publishing at the time this publication went to press. Please check the *Scott Stamp Monthly* for all of the latest numbers. Booklet numbers could change.**

| | | |
|---|---|---|
| BK702 | Astronomy (31*nn–nn*), pane of 10 (31*nna*), *Jun 29/18* | 17.00 |

# UNI-SAFE BLOCK STOCKBOOKS

With 3 or 4 strips per page, these are specifically made for holding plate block or blocks of 4 stamp sheets. Padded leatherette covers, size 9″ x 12″, with black or white pages available.

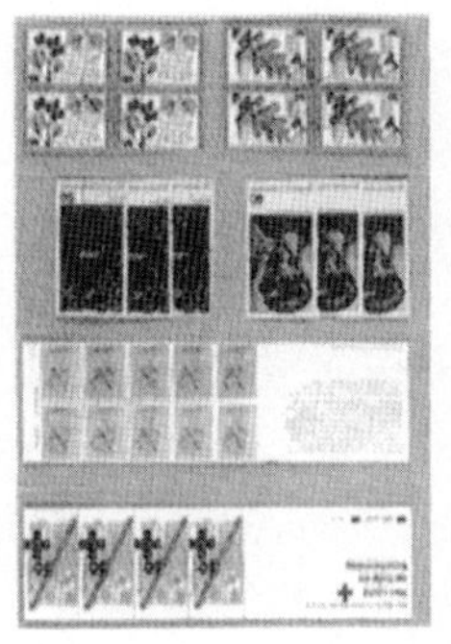

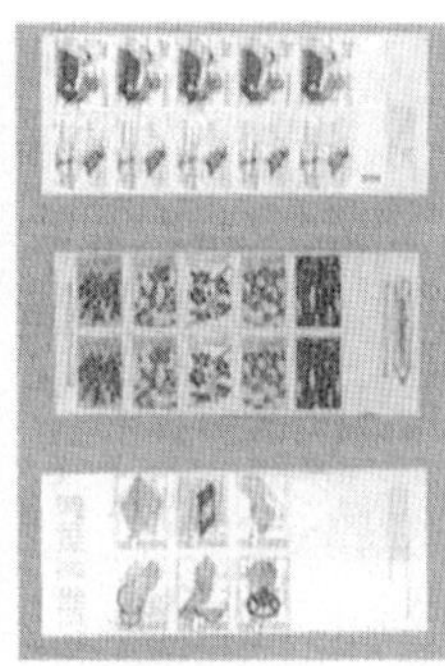

| ITEM | PAGE NO. & COLOUR | NO. OF STRIPS PER PAGE | RETAIL |
|---|---|---|---|
| B4GX-8 | 16 BLACK | 4 | 27.95 |
| B3GX-8 | 16 BLACK | 3 | 27.95 |
| B4GW-8 | 16 WHITE | 4 | 24.95 |
| B3GW-8 | 16 WHITE | 3 | 24.95 |
| B4GX-16 | 32 BLACK | 4 | 39.95 |
| B3GX-16 | 32 BLACK | 3 | 39.95 |
| B4GW-16 | 32 WHITE | 4 | 37.95 |
| B3GW-16 | 32 WHITE | 3 | 37.95 |

Available at your dealer, stationery or bookstore, or contact:

UNITRADE ASSOCIATES

99 Floral Parkway, Toronto, Ont. M6L 2C4

Email: unitrade@rogers.com • Website: www.unitradeassoc.com

Postage and applicable sales taxes are extra.

# Special Offer

## DAVO - Unitrade Associates

SAVE $ 267.95

### CANADA HINGELESS ALBUMS (1851-2017)

This luxurious album bound in navy blue and embossed with the Canada Crest on the cover and spine, is a perfect gift for a stamp collector. With crystal clear protective mounts and plentiful space for your stamps, all ready for immediate insertion. This is a special offer only, buy the complete set and save $ 267.95 !

| | | | |
|---|---|---|---|
| CANADA I | 1851-1969 | $225.95 | complete set |
| II | 1970-1985 | $ 254.50 | |
| III | 1986-1999 | $ 339.95 | Retail |
| IV | 2000-2006 | $ 301.50 | ~~$ 1,704.80~~ |
| V | 2007-2013 | $ 314.95 | |
| VI | 2014-2017 | $ 267.95 | Now $ 1,496.85 |

SAVE $ 267.95

Available at your dealer, stationery or bookstore, or contact:

UNITRADE ASSOCIATES

99 Floral Parkway, Toronto, Ont. M6L 2C4

Email: unitrade@rogers.com - Website: unitradeassoc.com

Postage & applicable sales taxes are extra.

DAVO

# SEMI-POSTAL STAMPS

## OLYMPIC SYMBOLS

B1
"COJO" Symbol

B2
"COJO" Symbol

B3
"COJO" Symbol

Designer: Alois Matanovic.

Lithography (5 colours), panes of 50
Ashton-Potter Limited

**1974, Apr 17** **GT2** **Perf 12.5**

| | | NH–VF | ⊙F | PB | FDC |
|---|---|---|---|---|---|
| **B1** | **8¢ + 2¢ bronze & multicoloured**, HF on back, duller on front | .50 | .50 | 2.25 | 1.00 |
| i | HB on front, duller on back (greenish gum) | 15.00 | 3.00 | 75.00* | — |

Qty: 62,225,000
* Blank (non-inscription) corner block of 4.

| | | NH–VF | ⊙F | PB | FDC |
|---|---|---|---|---|---|
| **B2** | **10¢ + 5¢ silver & multicoloured**, F | .75 | .75 | 3.25 | 1.10 |
| i | HF paper | 3.00 | 1.00 | 14.00 | |

Qty: 26,112,000

| | | NH–VF | ⊙F | PB | FDC |
|---|---|---|---|---|---|
| **B3** | **15¢ + 5¢ gold & multicoloured**, HF | 1.00 | 1.00 | 4.50 | 1.25 |
| i | F | 3.00 | 1.00 | 14.00 | |

Qty: 30,715,000

## WATER SPORTS

B4
Swimming

B5
Rowing

B6
Sailing

Designer: Hal Wallis.

Lithography (4 colours), panes of 50
Canadian Bank Note Company, Limited

**1975, Feb 5** **GT2** **Perf 13.0**

| | | NH–VF | ⊙F | PB | FDC |
|---|---|---|---|---|---|
| **B4** | **8¢ + 2¢ multicoloured**, HF | .50 | .50 | 2.25 | 1.00 |
| ii | red dot on forearm (pos. 21–25) | 1.50 | 1.50 | | |
| i | LF | 3.00 | .75 | 14.00 | |

Qty: 25,300,000

| | | NH–VF | ⊙F | PB | FDC |
|---|---|---|---|---|---|
| **B5** | **10¢ + 5¢ multicoloured**, HF | .75 | .75 | 3.25 | 1.10 |
| i | LF | 3.00 | 1.00 | 14.00 | |

Qty: 18,250,000

| | | NH–VF | ⊙F | PB | FDC |
|---|---|---|---|---|---|
| **B6** | **15¢ + 5¢ multicoloured**, HB | 1.00 | 1.00 | 4.50 | 1.25 |
| i | LF | 3.00 | 1.25 | 14.00 | |

Qty: 21,750,000

B4ii

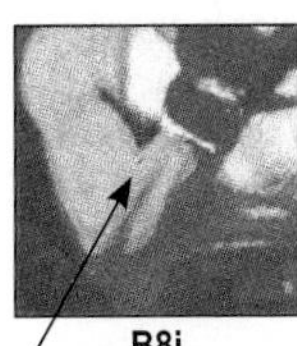
B8i

## COMBAT SPORTS

B7
Fencing

B8
Boxing

B9
Judo

Designer: James Hill.

Lithography (3 colours), panes of 50
Canadian Bank Note Company, Limited

**1975, Aug 6** **GT2** **Perf 13.0**

| | | NH–VF | ⊙F | PB | FDC |
|---|---|---|---|---|---|
| **B7** | **8¢ + 2¢ multicoloured** | .50 | .50 | 2.25 | 1.00 |
| i | imperf. at bottom margin and ½ of bottom stamp in block | 850.00 | — | 1,000.00* | — |

Qty: 25,300,000
* Blank (non-inscription) corner block of 4.

| | | NH–VF | ⊙F | PB | FDC |
|---|---|---|---|---|---|
| **B8** | **10¢ + 5¢ multicoloured** | .75 | .75 | 3.25 | 1.10 |
| i | red dot on bicep (pos. 6–10) | 2.00 | 2.00 | 7.00 | |

Qty: 14,050,000

| | | NH–VF | ⊙F | PB | FDC |
|---|---|---|---|---|---|
| **B9** | **15¢ + 5¢ multicoloured** | 1.00 | 1.00 | 4.50 | 1.25 |

Qty: 14,000,000

## TEAM SPORTS

B10
Basketball

B11
Gymnastics

B12
Soccer

Designer: James Hill.

Lithography (3 colours), panes of 50
Ashton-Potter Limited

**1976, Jan 7** **GT2** **Perf 13.0**

| | | NH–VF | ⊙F | PB | FDC |
|---|---|---|---|---|---|
| **B10** | **8¢ + 2¢ multicoloured**, HF front | .50 | .50 | 2.25 | .90 |
| i | imperf. top margin, block of 4 | 850.00 | — | 950.00* | — |
| ii | F front | 3.00 | .75 | 14.00 | |
| T1 | untagged (error) | 80.00 | 60.00 | | |

Qty: 16,500,000
* Blank (non-inscription) corner block of 4.

| | | NH–VF | ⊙F | PB | FDC |
|---|---|---|---|---|---|
| **B11** | **10¢ + 5¢ multicoloured**, F front | .75 | .75 | 3.25 | 1.10 |
| i | HF front | 3.00 | 1.00 | 14.00 | |
| T1 | untagged (error) | 100.00 | 90.00 | | † |

Qty: 11,000,000
† UR imprint on FDC $400.00

| | | NH–VF | ⊙F | PB | FDC |
|---|---|---|---|---|---|
| **B12** | **20¢ + 5¢ multicoloured**, HF front | 1.25 | 1.25 | 5.25 | 1.50 |
| i | F front | 5.00 | 1.50 | 23.00 | |
| T1 | untagged (error) | 60.00 | — | | |

Qty: 11,500,000

**The surtax of the B1–B12 semi-postals was in support of the 21st Olympic Games, held in Montreal, July 17 to August 1, 1976.**

## CANADIAN LITERACY

B13
Literacy Begins at Home

Designer: Debbie Adams.

Lithography (6 colours), booklet pane of 10
Ashton-Potter Canada Limited

**1996, Sep 9** **FCP, Coated Papers** **Perf 13.0x12.5**

| | | NH–VF | ⊙F | FDC |
|---|---|---|---|---|
| **B13** | **45¢ + 5¢ multicoloured** | 1.50 | .75 | 1.60 |
| a | booklet pane of 10 x B13 (BK193) | 13.50 | 14.00 | |
| **BK193** | pane B13 in cover $15.00 | | | |

Qty: 10,000,000

No. B13 has a die-cut hole representing a missing piece of the literacy puzzle. The 5¢ surcharge was for the benefit of ABC CANADA in support of its family literacy programs.

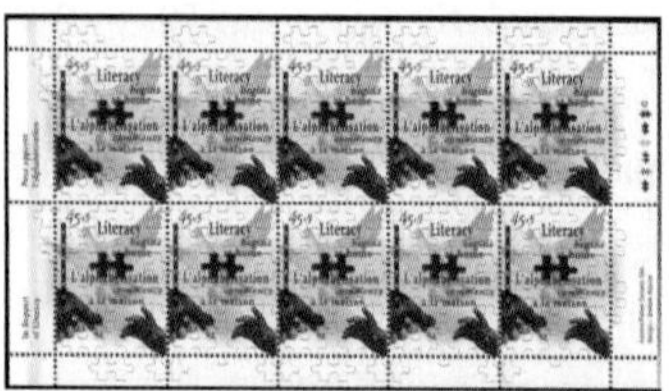

B13a

## MENTAL HEALTH

B14
Figure stepping out of the shadows

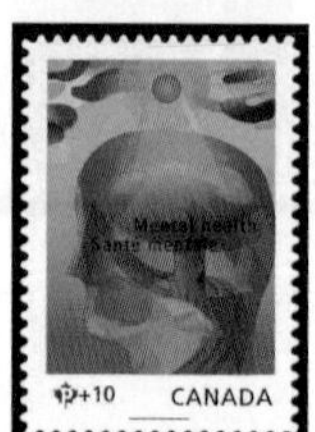

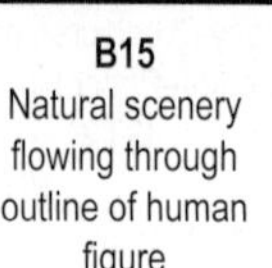

B15
Natural scenery flowing through outline of human figure

B16
Patient on path to recovery

Designer: Paul Haslip (HM&E).

Lithography (6 colours), self-adhesive booklet of 10
Lowe-Martin

**2008, Oct 6** **GT4, TRC Paper**
**Serpentine Die cut 13.2x13.4**

| | | NH–VF | ⊙F | FDC |
|---|---|---|---|---|
| **B14** | **P + 10¢ multicoloured** | 1.90 | 1.00 | 3.25 |
| i | die cut to shape from Quarterly Pack/ Annual Collection | 2.85 | — | |
| a | booklet pane of 10 x (62¢) (B14) (**BK389**) | 19.00 | | |

Qty: 10,000,000 initial print run.

At time of issue, the P stamp was valued at 52¢ + 10¢ donation to the Canada Post Foundation for Mental Health.

Designer: Signals Design Group.

Lithography (7 colours), self-adhesive booklet of 10
Lowe-Martin

**2009, Sep 14** **GT4, TRC Paper**
**Serpentine Die cut 13.2x13.4**

| | | NH–VF | ⊙F | FDC |
|---|---|---|---|---|
| **B15** | **P + 10¢ multicoloured** | 1.90 | 1.00 | 3.30 |
| i | die cut to shape from Quarterly Pack/ Annual Collection | 2.85 | — | |
| a | booklet pane of 10 x (64¢) (B15) (**BK410**) | 19.00 | | |

Qty: 3,750,000

At time of issue, the P stamp was valued at 54¢ + 10¢ donation to the Canada Post Foundation for Mental Health.

Designer: Paprika.

Lithography (7 colours), self-adhesive booklet of 10
Lowe-Martin

**2010, Sep 7** **GT4, TRC Paper**
**Serpentine Die cut 13.2x13.4**

| | | NH–VF | ⊙F | FDC |
|---|---|---|---|---|
| **B16** | **P + 10¢ multicoloured** | 1.90 | 1.00 | 3.35 |
| i | die cut to shape from Quarterly Pack/ Annual Collection | 2.85 | — | |
| a | booklet pane of 10 x (67¢) (B16) (**BK434**) | 19.00 | | |

Qty: 4,000,000

At time of issue, the P stamp was valued at 57¢ + 10¢ donation to the Canada Post Foundation for Mental Health.

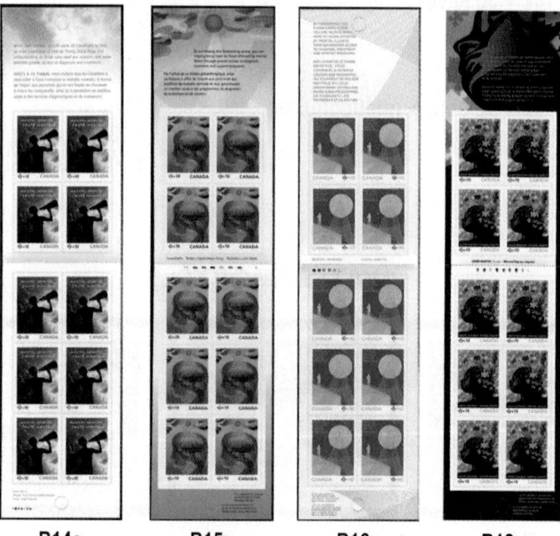

B14a B15a B16a B18a

*Perforated single from water-activated gum souvenir sheet*

*Die cut single from self-adhesive booklet*

B17a B18
Puzzle pieces coming together

Designer: Miriane Mageau; Annue Tardif, Kosta Tsetsekas / Signals.

Lithography (8 colours), water-activated gum souvenir sheet of 2
Lowe-Martin

**2011, Sep 6** **GT4, TRC Paper** **Perf 12.9x13.4**

| | | NH–VF | ⊙F | FDC |
|---|---|---|---|---|
| **B17** | **$1.38 souvenir sheet** of 2 | 4.00 | 4.00 | |
| a | **P + 10¢** multicoloured, single from souvenir sheet | 1.90 | 1.75 | |

Qty: 165,000

Lithography (8 colours), self-adhesive booklet of 10
Lowe-Martin
**GT4, TRC Paper**
**Serpentine Die cut 13.2x13.4**

| | | NH–VF | ⊙F | FDC |
|---|---|---|---|---|
| **B18** | **P + 10¢ multicoloured** | 1.90 | .60 | 3.35 |
| i | die cut to shape from Quarterly Pack | 2.50 | — | |
| a | booklet pane of 10 x (69¢) (B18) (**BK467**) | 19.00 | | |

Qty: 3,750,000

At time of issue, the P stamp was valued at 59¢ + 10¢ donation to the Canada Post Foundation for Mental Health.

B17

## CANADA POST COMMUNITY FOUNDATION

B19
Circle of multi-coloured children's hands forming a heart

B20
*Floating Adrift*, by Ezra Peters

Designer: Debbie Adams.
Lithography (8 colours), self-adhesive booklet of 10
Lowe-Martin
**2012, Sep 17** **GT4, TRC Paper**
**Serpentine Die cut 13.2x13.4**

| | | NH–VF | ⊙F | FDC |
|---|---|---|---|---|
| **B19** | **P + 10¢ multicoloured** | 1.90 | 1.00 | 3.40 |
| i | die cut to shape from Quarterly Pack/ Annual Collection | 2.85 | — | |
| a | booklet pane of 10 x (71¢) (B19) (**BK508**) | 19.00 | | |

Qty: 3,750,000

At time of issue, the P stamp was valued at 61¢ + 10¢ donation to the Canada Post Community Foundation.

Designer: Parable Communications.
Lithography (5 colours), self-adhesive booklet of 10
Lowe-Martin
**2013, Sep 30** **GT4, TRC Paper**
**Serpentine Die cut 13.2x13.4**

| | | NH–VF | ⊙F | FDC |
|---|---|---|---|---|
| **B20** | **63¢ + 10¢ multicoloured** | 1.50 | 1.00 | 3.40 |
| i | die cut to shape from Quarterly Pack/ Annual Collection | 2.25 | — | |
| a | booklet pane of 10 x 73¢ (B20) (**BK560**) | 15.00 | | |

Qty: 3,000,000

63¢ + 10¢ donation to the Canada Post Community Foundation. Illustration by 8-year old Ezra Peters, winner of Canada Post sponsored art competition for kids 15 and under.

B21
Children in a boat

B22
Storytelling under a bed sheet

Designer: Paul Haslip (HM & E Design Communications).
Lithography (6 colours), self-adhesive booklet of 10
Lowe-Martin
**2014, Sep 29** **GT4, TRC Paper** **Serpentine Die cut 13.5**

| | | NH–VF | ⊙F | FDC |
|---|---|---|---|---|
| **B21** | **P + 10¢ multicoloured** | 1.90 | 1.00 | 5.90 |
| i | die cut to shape from Quarterly Pack/ Annual Collection | 2.85 | — | |
| a | booklet pane of 10 x (95¢) (B21) (**BK603**) | 19.00 | | |

Qty: 3,000,000

At time of issue, the P stamp was valued at 85¢ + 10¢ donation to the Canada Post Community Foundation.

Designer: Lionel Gadoury, Kammy Ahuja, Joanna Poon – Context Creative.
Lithography (6 colours), self-adhesive booklet of 10
Lowe-Martin
**2015, Sep 28** **GT4, TRC Paper**
**Serpentine Die cut 13.0x12.6**

| | | NH–VF | ⊙F | FDC |
|---|---|---|---|---|
| **B22** | **P + 10¢ multicoloured** | 1.90 | 1.00 | 5.90 |
| i | die cut to shape from Quarterly Pack/ Annual Collection | 2.85 | — | |
| a | booklet pane of 10 x (95¢) (B22) (**BK631**) | 19.00 | | |

Qty: 1,500,000

At time of issue, the P stamp was valued at 85¢ + 10¢ donation to the Canada Post Community Foundation.

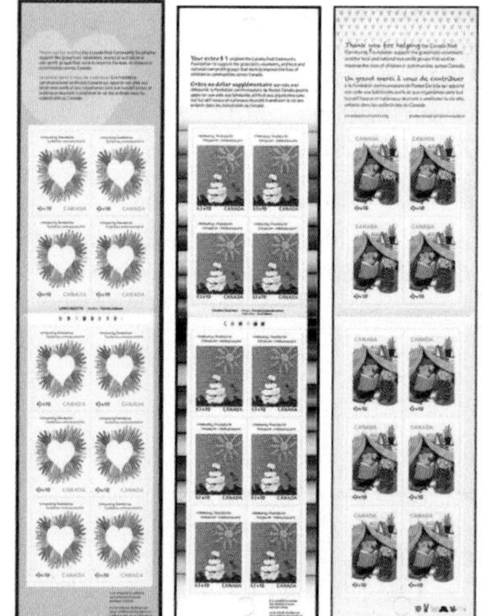
B19a B20a B22a

B21a

Semi-Postal Stamps

## CANADA POST COMMUNITY FOUNDATION

B23 B24

Designer: Andrew Lewis Design.

Lithography (7 colours), self-adhesive booklet of 10
Lowe-Martin

**2016, Sep 26** **GT4, TRC Paper**
**Serpentine Die cut 13.5**

| | | NH–VF | ⊙F | FDC |
|---|---|---|---|---|
| **B23** | **P + 10¢ multicoloured** (blue) | 1.90 | 1.00 | 5.90 |
| **B24** | **P + 10¢ multicoloured** (green) | 1.90 | 1.00 | 5.90 |
| i | horizontal se-tenant pair (B23–B24), die cut to shape from Quarterly Pack/Annual Collection | 5.70 | — | |
| a | booklet pane of 10 x (95¢) (B23–B24) (**BK654**) | 19.00 | | |

Qty: 750,000 of each design

At time of issue, the P stamp was valued at 85¢ + 10¢ donation to the Canada Post Community Foundation.

B25 B26

Designer: Andrew Lewis Design.

Lithography (8 colours), self-adhesive booklet of 10
Lowe-Martin

**2017, Sep 25** **GT4, TRC Paper**
**Serpentine Die cut 13.5**

| | | NH–VF | ⊙F | FDC |
|---|---|---|---|---|
| **B25** | **P + 10¢ multicoloured** (violet) | 1.90 | 1.00 | 5.90 |
| **B26** | **P + 10¢ multicoloured** (green) | 1.90 | 1.00 | 5.90 |
| i | horizontal se-tenant pair (B25–B26), die cut to shape from Quarterly Pack/Annual Collection | 5.70 | — | |
| a | booklet pane of 10 x (95¢) (B25–B26) (**BK677**) | 19.00 | | |

Qty: 800,000 of each design

At time of issue, the P stamp was valued at 85¢ + 10¢ donation to the Canada Post Community Foundation. Microprinted 'CANADA 150' is 'hidden' in the design of each stamp.

B24a

B26a

Semi-Postal Stamps

# AIR MAIL STAMPS

C1
Two winged figures against globe

C2
Mercury, with scroll in hand

C3
C1 Surcharged

C4
C2 Surcharged

Designer: C1: Herman Herbert Schwartz. Picture engraved by Silas Robert Allen.

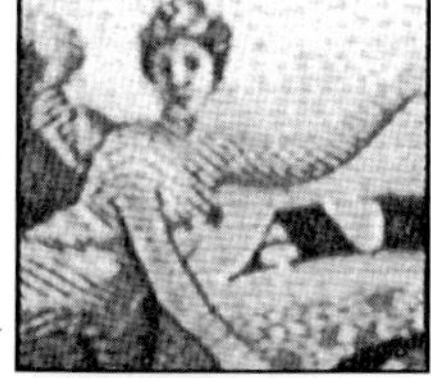
C1i / C3i

C1b

C1c

C1ii

C3b

Canadian Bank Note Company, Limited

**1928, Sep 21** — **Engraved** — **Perf 12**

| | | NH% | ★VF | ★F | ⊙VF | ⊙F | FDC |
|---|---|---|---|---|---|---|---|
| **C1** | **5¢ brown olive** | 100 | 20.00 | 8.00 | 8.00 | 3.50 | 125.00 |
| | plate blocks, plate 1, UL, UR (blocks of 6) | 100 | 175.00 | 100.00 | | | |
| | plate blocks, plate 2, UL (blocks of 6) | 100 | 175.00 | 100.00 | | | |
| a | imperf. pair | 50 | 350.00 | 225.00 | — | — | — |
| | No. C1a plate blocks of 6 | 50 | 1,800.00 | 1,200.00 | | | |
| b | horiz. pair, imperf. vert | 50 | 350.00 | 225.00 | — | — | — |
| | No. C1b plate blocks (blocks of 6) | 50 | 1,800.00 | 1,200.00 | | | |
| c | vert. pair, imperf. horiz. | 50 | 350.00 | 225.00 | — | — | — |
| | No. C1c plate blocks (blocks of 6) | 50 | 1,800.00 | 1,200.00 | | | |
| i | "Swollen breast" variety, Position 4, PL.2 UR | 100 | 120.00 | 60.00 | 100.00 | 50.00 | 175.00† |
| | No. C1i plate blocks, plate 2, UR (blocks of 6) | 100 | 250.00 | 175.00 | | | |
| ii | double paper, in vert. strip of 4 | | | *1,250.00* | | | |
| | double paper, in margin block of 10 | | | *2,500.00* | | | |

Qty: 5,050,000

† Ordinary cover, not FDC. Commercial cover $135.

A shade variety of C1 stated to be "golden olive" (olive sepia on the Stanley Gibbons colour key) has been reported to the editors.

**No. C1 plate proofs**: Three proof sheets (200 on each), no gutter, on India paper: single $200; pair $400.

British American Bank Note Company

**1930, Dec 4** — **Perf 11**

| | | NH% | ★VF | ★F | ⊙VF | ⊙F | FDC |
|---|---|---|---|---|---|---|---|
| **C2** | **5¢ olive brown** | 100 | 80.00 | 30.00 | 35.00 | 20.00 | 300.00 |
| | reversed 1, left margin (blocks of 4)* | 100 | 500.00 | 200.00 | | | |

Qty: 400,000

* Block of 6 (2 x 3) with reversed "1" in left margin of middle row: VF $750.00, F $350.00

Canadian Bank Note Company, Limited

**1932, Feb 22** — **Perf 12**

| | | NH% | ★VF | ★F | ⊙VF | ⊙F | FDC |
|---|---|---|---|---|---|---|---|
| **C3** | **6¢ on 5¢ brown olive** | 100 | 15.00 | 6.00 | 6.00 | 3.00 | 25.00 |
| | plate blocks, plate 1, UL, UR (blocks of 6) | 100 | 150.00 | 100.00 | | | |
| | plate blocks, plate 2, UL (blocks of 6) | 100 | 150.00 | 100.00 | | | |
| a | inverted surcharge | 50 | 300.00 | 150.00 | | | |
| b | double surcharge * | 50 | 1,500.00 | 850.00 | | | |
| | as "b", plate block, plate 1, UR (block of 8) (unique) | | — | *15,000.00* | | | |
| c | triple surcharge | 50 | 500.00 | 200.00 | | | |
| d | pair, one without surcharge | 50 | 1,200.00 | 900.00 | | | |
| i | "Swollen breast" variety, position 4 | 100 | 120.00 | 60.00 | 100.00 | 50.00 | 100.00† |
| | No. C3i plate blocks, plate 2, UR (blocks of 6) | 100 | 250.00 | 175.00 | | | |
| ii | overprint badly shifted | 100 | 125.00 | 95.00 | — | — | — |

Qty: 2,000,000

Counterfeits of the surcharged varieties exist.

* Most known genuine examples of variety C3b are off centre with perforations crowding or cutting design.

† Ordinary cover, not FDC. Commercial cover $135.

British American Bank Note Company

**1932, Jul 12** — **Perf 11**

| | | NH% | ★VF | ★F | ⊙VF | ⊙F | FDC |
|---|---|---|---|---|---|---|---|
| **C4** | **6¢ on 5¢ olive brown** | 100 | 60.00 | 25.00 | 20.00 | 12.00 | 40.00 |
| | reversed "1" in the left margin (block of 4)* | 100 | 300.00 | 120.00 | | | |

Qty: 500,000

* Block of 6 (2 x 3) with reversed "1" in left margin of middle row: VF $450.00, F $250.00

Issued on the occasion of the 1932 Imperial Economic Conference, Ottawa. See also Nos. 192–194.

C5
Daedalus in Flight

Designer: Herman Herbert Schwartz. Based on a painting by Alonzo Earl Foringer. Picture finished by Edwin H. Gunn. Figure engraved by William Adolph. Landscape engraved by Arthur C. Vogel.

Canadian Bank Note Company, Limited

**1935, Jun 1** — **Engraved** — **Perf 12**

| | | NH% | ★VF | ★F | ⊙VF | ⊙F | FDC |
|---|---|---|---|---|---|---|---|
| **C5** | **6¢ red brown** | 50 | 6.00 | 3.00 | 2.00 | 1.25 | 25.00 |
| | plate blocks, plate 1, all (blocks of 6) | 50 | 45.00 | 20.00 | | | |
| a | horiz. pair, imperf. vert. (unique) | — | — | 7,500.00 | — | — | — |
| b | imperf. pair (125 pairs) | 50 | 800.00 | 700.00 | — | — | — |
| | No. C5b in plate block, plate 1 (block of 6) | 50 | 4,125.00 | 2,750.00 | | | |
| i | yellow brown | 50 | 70.00 | 35.00 | 40.00 | 20.00 | |
| | No. C5i plate blocks, plate 1, all (blocks of 6) | 50 | 600.00 | 400.00 | | | |
| ii | "Moulting wing" variety, Pl. 1, LR, pos. 14 | 50 | 150.00 | 60.00 | 70.00 | 35.00 | 110.00* |
| | C5ii, in block with 3 normal | 50 | 200.00 | 80.00 | 90.00 | 45.00 | |
| iii | imperf. gutter block of 4 (10 known) ‡ | 25 | 4,500.00 | 3,000.00 | — | — | — |
| iv | AIR variety † | 50 | 100.00 | 50.00 | 70.00 | 35.00 | 90.00* |
| | C5iv, in block with 3 normal | 50 | 120.00 | 60.00 | 90.00 | 45.00 | |

Qty: 5,000,000

* Any cover, not FDC.

† The AIR variety shows a "shilling stroke" die flaw to the left of AIR, Pl. 1, LL, pos. 10.

‡ There are one each top and bottom gutter blocks of 4 with filing crease down the centre of the gutter and 8 gutter blocks of 8 that are NOT creased in the gutter, from one sheet of 200.

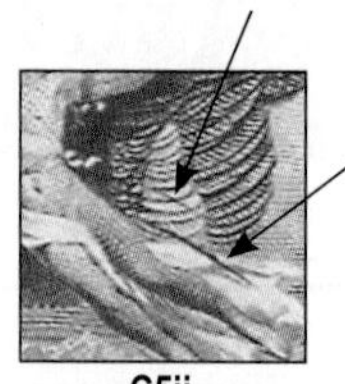

C5ii

C5iv

C6
Monoplane over Mackenzie River, NWT

C7

C8

British Commonwealth Air Training Plan

Designer: C6: Herman Herbert Schwartz. Based on a photograph by Richard N. Hourde.
Picture engraved by Arthur C. Vogel. Border engraved by William H. Maple.
Designer: C7/C8: Herman Herbert Schwartz. Picture finished by Harold Osborn.
Picture engraved by Arthur C. Vogel. Border engraved by Charles H. Milks.

Canadian Bank Note Company, Limited

**1938, Jun 15** — **Engraved** — **Perf 12**

| | | NH% | ★VF | ★F | ⊙VF | ⊙F | FDC |
|---|---|---|---|---|---|---|---|
| **C6** | **6¢ blue** | 50 | 5.50 | 2.75 | .50 | .30 | 20.00 |
| | plate blocks, plate 1, all (blocks of 4) | 50 | 30.00 | 15.00 | | | |
| a | imperf. pair | 50 | 800.00 | 650.00 | — | — | — |
| | No. C6a plate blocks, plate 1 (blocks of 4) | 50 | 3,000.00 | 2,000.00 | | | |

Qty: 29,008,650

**No. C6 plate proofs**: 6¢ blue, imperf., on card * (400) — 200.00 — — — —

* Imperf. plate proofs: pairs – $400, blocks of 4 – $800, gutter blocks of 8 – $2,000, gutter blocks of 4 – $1,200. Two matched sets of imprint blocks of the proof exist. Value $1,250 each imprint block; complete set $5,000.

## WAR ISSUE

**1942–1943** — **Perf 12**

| | | NH% | ★VF | ★F | ⊙VF | ⊙F | FDC |
|---|---|---|---|---|---|---|---|
| **C7** | **6¢ deep blue**, *Jul 1, 1942* | 50 | 9.00 | 4.50 | 2.00 | 1.00 | 15.00 |
| | plate blocks, plate 1, all (blocks of 4) | 50 | 35.00 | 15.00 | | | |
| | plate blocks, plate 2, UL (blocks of 4) | 50 | 650.00 | 400.00 | | | |
| | plate blocks, plate 2, UR, LL, LR (blocks of 4) | 50 | 500.00 | 300.00 | | | |
| a | imperf. pair, 50 pairs recorded | 50 | 800.00 | 650.00 | — | — | — |
| | No. C7a plate blocks | 50 | 3,000.00 | 2,000.00 | | | |
| i | imperf top margin | 50 | — | — | | | |
| | No. C7i UR plate block, unique | — | *6,000.00* | — | | | |

Qty: 14,990,000

Air Mail Stamps

C8i

| | | NH% | ★VF | ★F | ⊙VF | ⊙F | FDC |
|---|---|---|---|---|---|---|---|
| **C8** | **7¢ deep blue**, *Apr 16, 1943* | 50 | 1.50 | 1.00 | .25 | .20 | 10.00 |
| | plate blocks, plates 1–4, all (blocks of 4) | 50 | 8.00 | 4.00 | | | |
| | plate blocks, plate 5, UR (blocks of 4) | 50 | 250.00 | 150.00 | | | |
| | plate blocks, plate 5, LL, LR (blocks of 4) | 50 | 200.00 | 120.00 | | | |
| a | imperf. pair, 50 pairs recorded | 50 | 800.00 | 650.00 | — | — | — |
| | No. C8a plate blocks | 50 | 3,000.00 | 2,000.00 | | | |
| i | imperf. at right margin * | 50 | 1,000.00 | 800.00 | — | — | — |
| | No. C8i plate block, plate 4, LR (unique) | 50 | | 4,000.00 | | | |

Qty: 97,793,000

* Ten copies known from one plate 4, LR pane.

Plate 5 UL plate blocks have yet to be confirmed.

C9

Canada geese near Sudbury, ON

Designer: Herman Herbert Schwartz. Picture engraved by Silas Robert Allen.

Canadian Bank Note Company, Limited

**1946, Sep 16** **Engraved** **Perf 12**

For **O.H.M.S.** overprint see number CO1.
For **G** overprint see number CO2.

C9a

| | | NH% | ★VF | ★F | ⊙VF | ⊙F | FDC |
|---|---|---|---|---|---|---|---|
| **C9** | **7¢ deep blue** | 50 | 1.50 | .75 | .25 | .20 | 10.00 |
| | plate blocks, plates 1, 2, all (blocks of 4) | 50 | 6.00 | 3.00 | | | |
| i | thin transparent ribbed paper * | 50 | 200.00 | 100.00 | — | — | — |
| | No. C9i plate blocks, all | 50 | 1,125.00 | 750.00 | | | |
| ii | major re-entry, double frameline at right † | 50 | 65.00 | 45.00 | 45.00 | 35.00 | 75.00‡ |
| a | booklet pane of 4 x 7¢ (C9as), *Dec 1, 1947* (BK39) | 50 | 3.50 | 3.00 | 3.50 | 2.50 | 75.00 |
| as | single with straight edge, from C9a | 50 | 1.00 | .75 | 1.00 | .70 | 8.00 |

Qty: 72,350,000

* The design shows through on back of this paper.

† Variety C9ii occurs on Plate 2 UR, positions 14, 19, 24, 29 and 34, each is slightly different. Positions 14 and 19 also show slight doubling of left frameline.

‡ Any cover. Commercial cover $90.

## AIR MAIL SPECIAL DELIVERY STAMPS

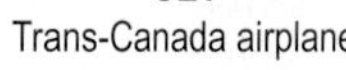

CE1

Trans-Canada airplane

CE2

Trans-Canada airplane

Designer: Herman Herbert Schwartz. Picture finished by Harold Osborn.
Picture engraved by Joseph Keller. Border engraved by Charles H. Milks.

Canadian Bank Note Company, Limited

**1942–1943** **Engraved** **Perf 12**

| | | NH% | ★VF | ★F | ⊙VF | ⊙F | FDC |
|---|---|---|---|---|---|---|---|
| **CE1** | **16¢ bright ultramarine**, *Jul 1, 1942* | 50 | 3.50 | 1.75 | 3.00 | 1.50 | 20.00 |
| | plate blocks, all (blocks of 4) | 50 | 18.00 | 12.00 | | | |
| a | imperf. pair (75 pairs recorded) | 50 | 800.00 | 650.00 | — | — | — |
| | No. CE1a plate blocks, all (blocks of 4) | 50 | 3,000.00 | 2,000.00 | | | |

Qty: 814,841

| | | NH% | ★VF | ★F | ⊙VF | ⊙F | FDC |
|---|---|---|---|---|---|---|---|
| **CE2** | **17¢ bright ultramarine**, *Apr 16, 1943* | 50 | 4.50 | 2.50 | 4.00 | 2.00 | 50.00 |
| | plate blocks, all (blocks of 4) | 50 | 24.00 | 16.00 | | | |
| a | imperf. pair (75 pairs recorded) | 50 | 800.00 | 650.00 | — | — | — |
| | No. CE2a plate blocks, all (blocks of 4) | 50 | 3,000.00 | 2,000.00 | | | |

Qty: 868,689

First issued at the Edmonton main post office at 8:00 a.m. on April 16, 1943. There was no official first day in Ottawa.

CE3
D.C. 4-M Airplane

CE4
D.C. 4-M Airplane

Designer: Herman Herbert Schwartz. Picture engraved by Silas Robert Allen.

Canadian Bank Note Company, Limited

| 1946, Sep 16 | Engraved NH% | ★VF | ★F | ⊙VF | ⊙F | Perf 12 FDC |
|---|---|---|---|---|---|---|
| **CE3 17¢ bright ultramarine**, with Ê | 50 | 7.50 | 4.00 | 7.00 | 3.50 | 25.00 |
| plate blocks, all (blocks of 4) | 50 | 30.00 | 15.00 | | | |

CE3

Qty: 300,000

Incorrect circumflex (Ê) accent on the second E of EXPRÊS. The accent over the second "e" of the French word "Exprês" was circumflexed instead of grave. This error, corrected in the new die, is the first in a Canadian postage stamp.

| 1946, Dec 3 | REVISED ISSUE | | | | | |
|---|---|---|---|---|---|---|
| **CE4 17¢ bright ultramarine**, with È | 50 | 7.50 | 4.00 | 9.00 | 4.50 | 400.00 |
| plate blocks, all (blocks of 4) | 50 | 30.00 | 15.00 | | | |

Qty: 900,000

Corrected grave (È) accent on the second E of EXPRÈS.

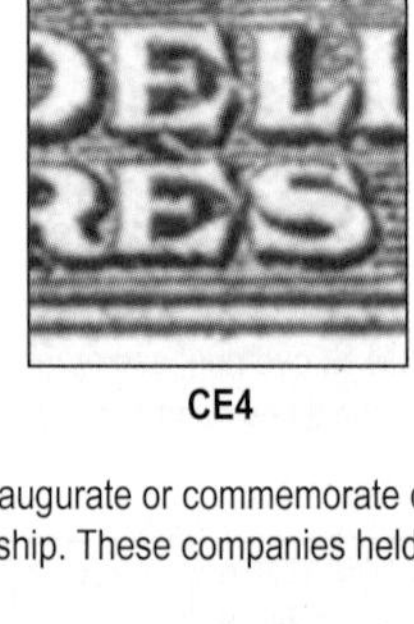


CE4

## AIR POST SEMI-OFFICIAL ISSUES

There were two distinct groups issuing the pioneer or semi-official air mail stamps of Canada. The various Aero Clubs issued their stamps to inaugurate or commemorate certain special flights. And several airplane companies issued stamps to prepay mail carried commercially to areas in Canada not accessible by mail or ship. These companies held contracts with and operated under the strict regulations and control of the Canadian Postal Authorities.

These stamps could only be affixed to the back of covers and usually carried boxed oval cachets giving the dates or points of flight.

As most of these stamps are issued in pairs, sheets, booklets or coils, the prices are given in three categories: single unused, sheet or pane, and on cover. Used singles, removed from covers, may exist. Approximate quantities are shown in parentheses (where known).

Cover prices are for the most common covers used in that period. Premiums will be charged for first flights, special cachets or cancels, etc. **Commercial covers sell for a premium.**

## AIR CLUB AND SPECIAL FLIGHTS

### AERO CLUB OF CANADA Toronto–Ottawa

| 1918, Aug | panes of 2, tête-bêche NH add 100% | (Qty) | Single | Perf 12 Pane | ✉ |
|---|---|---|---|---|---|
| **CLP1 (25¢) red & black**, without numerals of value (Aug. 24) | | (194) | 2,500 | 5,500 | |
| flight: Toronto to Ottawa violet cachet, *Aug 26* | | | | | 3,250 |
| Aug. 26 registered cover | | (26) | | | 5,000 |
| first flight: Ottawa to Toronto normal green cachet, *Aug 27* | | (approx. 35) | | | 4,500 |
| first flight: Ottawa to Toronto black cachet, *Aug 27* | | (2) | | | 5,000 |
| flight: Toronto to Ottawa, *Sep 4/18* | | | | | 4,500 |
| flight: Ottawa to Toronto, *Sep 4/18* | | | | | 4,500 |
| a without red flame | | (6) | 5,000 | | |

Approx. 167 copies of CLP1 were used, thus only approx. 27 mint copies of CLP1 should exist. Flights Aug 26–27. With violet boxed cachet: "Aerial Mail / Aug. 26 or 27, 1918 / Toronto, Canada" as a dispatch cancel or as a receiver. Some flown covers however may not have the violet boxed cancel. Also with green scroll cancel "By Aeroplane / Aug. 26 or 27, 1918 / Toronto or Ottawa, Canada".

**No. CLP1 black essay** on perfed pelure paper, no gum as issued. No red flame. One recorded $7,000.

| | | (Qty) | Single | Pane | ✉ |
|---|---|---|---|---|---|
| **CLP2 25¢ red & black**, with numerals of value, smooth white paper (Aug. 28) | | (2,800) | 650.00 | 1,750 | |
| first flight: Toronto to Ottawa, *Sep 4/18* | | | | | 5,500 |
| first flight: Ottawa to Toronto, *Sep 4/18* | | | | | 5,500 |
| b without red flame | | | 2,500 | | |
| c double red flame, se-tenant with normal | | | 1,500 | 2,500 | |
| ci triple red flame | | | 1,500 | | |
| d wide gutter pair | | | | 2,000 | |
| e as "d", with double perf. in gutter | | | | 2,250 | |
| f narrow gutter pair | | | | 1,900 | |
| g rough, off-white paper | | | 850.00 | 2,000 | |

CLP1

CLP2

CLP1a

CLP1 Essay

Air Mail Stamps

## AERO CLUB OF CANADA
### TORONTO-NEW YORK

CLP3

CLP4

Pilot: Major W.G. Barker, VC

| 1919, Aug 25 | panes of 10 | | | | Perf 12 |
|---|---|---|---|---|---|
| | NH add 75% | (Qty) | Single | Pane | ✉ |
| **CLP3** | **$1 red & blue** * | (3,000) | 500.00 | 6,000 | 925.00 |
| | no gum | | 150.00 | 2,500 | |
| a | thin paper, design showing through as though printed on both sides | | 500.00 | 6,000 | |
| b | white space between sky and red background † | | 500.00 | 5,500 | 925.00 |
| c | red shifted to left, shows white space at left frame and white space between sky and red plate | | 500.00 | | 950.00 |
| e | as "c", on thin paper (design shows through) | | 550.00 | | |

**No. CLP3 proofs**: frame design in red, on card $2,000; frame design in black, on card $2,500.

First Int'l. Air Mail Service from the Leaside Aerodrome, Toronto to Roosevelt Field, Mineola, Long Island, N.Y. Boxed Cachet: Aerial Mail / Aug. 25, 1919 / Toronto, Canada

* Five sheets without gum are known to exist.

† Three complete sheets with full original gum are known to exist.

CLP3 – pane

## GRAND ARMY OF CANADA
### TORONTO–HAMILTON & RETURN

| 1920, May 28 | white wove paper, horiz. strips of 5 | | | | Perf 12 |
|---|---|---|---|---|---|
| | NH add 100% | (Qty) | Single | Pane | ✉ |
| **CLP4** | **$1 black & white,** denomination blocked out | | *20,000* | | |
| | flown: Toronto to Hamilton, *May 28* | | | | *30,000* |
| | flown: Hamilton to Toronto, *May 28* | | | | *30,000* |

Issued on occasion of the Grand Army of Canada Carnival. Beware of forgeries.

Other flights may exist for most issues.
See the *America Airmail Catalogue* for more details.

**Commercial covers sell for a premium.**

## ESTEVAN–WINNIPEG PROMOTIONAL ISSUE

CLP5

| 1924, Oct 1 | pane of 2 | | | | Imperf |
|---|---|---|---|---|---|
| | NH add 100% | (Qty) | Single | Pane | ✉ |
| **CLP5** | **($1) black on red paper** (normal spacing "ew") | (1,028) | 400.00 | 1,750 | 275.00 |
| a | inscriptions inverted | (12) | 3,000 | 6,000 | 3,500 |
| b | without inscriptions | (4) | 7,000 | 14,000 | 7,500 |
| i | wide spacing between "ew" in Saskatchewan | | 400.00 | 1,500 | |
| | Estevan to Winnipeg, *Oct 1* | | | | 300.00 |
| | First flight without CLP5 | (1,400) | | | 75.00 |

Panes of 2 include one each of CLP5 and CLP5i. Pane of 2 with inverted inscriptions on cover (unique) $8,000.00

**No. CLP5 proofs**: black on red, "AIRIAL" error (2 known) *$8,000.*

Publicized coal-bearing area of Estevan in Saskatchewan. Oval cachet: Via aeroplane / Oct. 1, 1924 / Estevan, Sask.

## LONDON (Ont.) to LONDON (England) FLIGHT

CLP6

| 1927, Aug | panes of 4 | | | | Perf 12 |
|---|---|---|---|---|---|
| | NH +100% | (Qty) | Single | Pane | ✉ |
| **CLP6** | **25¢ green & yellow** | (100) | 50,000 | | *100,000* |

Proof in black, sold at auction April 2009 for $50,000.

The "Sir John Carling" trans-Atlantic flight that ended in disaster. The stamp depicts Captain Terrence B. Tully at left and Lieutenant James Medcalf at right with their monoplane flying over a globe where the proposed flight plan is indicated. 100 copies printed, 13 unused copies and 1 cover are known to exist.

## MOOSE JAW FLYING CLUB
### MOOSE JAW–WINNIPEG

CLP7

| 1928, Aug 17 | vertical strip of 5 | | | | Perf 11 |
|---|---|---|---|---|---|
| | NH +75% | (Qty) | Single | Pane | ✉ |
| **CLP7** | **($1) red on white** | (200) | 3,500 | 18,000 | |
| | Flight cover, *Aug 17* | (161) | | | 3,500 |

# PRIVATE COMMERCIAL AIRLINES

## LAURENTIDE AIR SERVICE LTD.

## HAILEYBURY, ONT. – ROUYN / ANGLIERS, QUE.

CL1

CL2

**1924, Aug–Oct** booklets of four panes of 2 **Rouletted**

| | NH +100% | (Qty) | Single | Pane | ✉ |
|---|---|---|---|---|---|
| **CL1** | First issue **(25¢) light green**, rouletted at left, *Aug 30* | (200) | 2,000 | 4,000 | |
| | first flight: Haileybury to Rouyn (or return), *Sep 21* | | | | 3,700 |
| a | complete booklet, plain covers (2 known) | | 16,000 | | |

| | NH +50% | (Qty) | Single | Pane | ✉ |
|---|---|---|---|---|---|
| **CL2** | Second issue **(25¢) green (shades)**, rouletted at top, *Sep 5* | (1,220) | 160.00 | 325.00 | |
| | first flight: Haileybury to Rouyn (or return), *Sep 21* | | | | 2,500 |
| | flight: Angliers to Rouyn, *Oct 1* | | | | 500.00 |
| | flight: Haileybury to Rouyn, *Oct 17* | | | | 450.00 |
| | flight: Three Rivers to Rouyn, *Jan 22/25* | | | | 250.00 |
| | other flights | | | | 275.00 |
| a | complete booklet, front cover green, no printing on back | | 2,000 | | |
| b | as "a", with back cover printed (2nd printing) (Sept. 8) | | 2,000 | | |
| c | Third issue (25¢) as CL2, dark blue green | (2,400) | 200.00 | 400.00 | |
| | flight: Larder Lake to Rouyn, *Jan 22/25* | | | | 400.00 |
| d | complete booklet, dark blue green, back cover printed | | 2,400 | | |

### "CANADA 1924" ADDED

CL3

CL4

panes of 20 (4 x 5) **Perf 11.8**

| | NH +50% | (Qty) | Single | Pane | ✉ |
|---|---|---|---|---|---|
| **CL3** | Fourth issue **(25¢) red**, *Oct 1* | (3,000) | 150.00 | 3,000 | |
| | flight: Haileybury to Rouyn (or return), *Oct 3* | | | | 295.00 |
| | flight: Haileybury to Rouyn (or return), *Oct 24* | | | | 375.00 |
| | flight: Three Rivers to Rouyn, *Jan 22/25* | | | | 295.00 |
| | other flights | | | | 250.00 |
| | Trans Canada Flight cover with postage stamp removed | | | | 125.00 |

booklet pane of 2

| | NH +50% | (Qty) | Single | Pane | ✉ |
|---|---|---|---|---|---|
| **CL4** | Fifth issue **(25¢) red**, rouletted at top, *Oct 2* | (2,100) | 200.00 | 500.00 | |
| | flight: Haileybury to Rouyn (or return), *Oct 3* | | | | 275.00 |
| | flight: Haileybury to Rouyn (or return), *Oct 24* | | | | 375.00 |
| | flight: Three Rivers to Rouyn, *Jan 22/25* | | | | 275.00 |
| a | complete booklet, front cover red, printing on back, 4 panes of 2 | | 3,000 | | |
| b | booklet as "a", top stamp dark red, bottom stamp light red on each pane | | 3,000 | | |
| c | pane of 2, from CL4b | | | 550.00 | |

## NORTHERN AIR SERVICE

## HAILEYBURY, ONT. – ROUYN, QUE.

CL5

**1925, Jun 27** booklets of two panes of 4 **Perf 12**

| | NH +50% | (Qty) | Single | Pane | ✉ |
|---|---|---|---|---|---|
| **CL5** | **25¢ blue** | (4,000) | 175.00 | 1,250 | 175.00 |
| a | tête-bêche pair | | 850.00 | | |
| b | blue dot left of monogram | | 250.00 | | 250.00 |
| c | tête-bêche pair. one with blue dot | | 900.00 | | |
| d | complete booklet (2 panes of 4) | | *2,500* | | |
| e | pane of 4, top 2 stamps with blue dot | | | *1,500* | |
| | Sheet of 20 (5x4) | | | *6,000* | |

Experimental flight without stamp, but with a special cachet, May 18 (value $2,500).

CL5b

## JACK V. ELLIOT AIR SERVICE

## RED LAKE – ROLLING PORTAGE (HUDSON) – SIOUX LOOKOUT, ONT.

CL6

CL7

**1926, Mar 6** sheets of 16, panes of 8 **Perf 11½**

| | NH +50% | (Qty) | Single | Pane | ✉ |
|---|---|---|---|---|---|
| **CL6** | **(25¢) red on yellow background of zig-zag lines** | (2,504) | 60.00 | 600.00 | 85.00 |
| a | imperf. pair (pane of 8) | | 600.00 | 2,400 | — |
| b | tête-bêche gutter pair (sheet of 16) | | 500.00 | 2,500 | |
| i | imperf tête-bêche gutter pair | | 900.00 | — | — |
| c | double impression on imperf. pair (2 known) | | 2,000 | | |
| ci | as "c", bottom stamp with inverted leaves | | 3,000 | (unique) | |
| d | white spot (position 8, LR) | | 125.00 | 600.00 | 150.00 |

**No. CL6 proofs**: tête-bêche pair, top stamp complete, bottom shows zig-zag lines only $2,250.

Unofficial blue Essay $500 (used on cover under CL6).

**CL6** Unofficial essay

**CL7(c)** Sheet of 16

CANADIAN & FOREIGN REVENUE STAMPS • TELEPHONE & TELEGRAPH FRANKS
LIQUOR & TOBACCO STAMPS • DUCK, HUNTING & CONSERVATION STAMPS
CANADIAN SEMI-OFFICIAL AIRMAIL STAMPS & COVERS, etc.

**NEW - 2017 CANADIAN REVENUE STAMP CATALOG** by **E.S.J. van Dam**
Full colour, spiral bound, **NOW 214** pages, over **1200** color photos.
Lists & prices all known Canada & Provinces revenue stamps, Telephone & Telegraph Franks, Duck, Hunting & Conservation stamps, etc. **Prices inc. Air mail postage, insurance** (applicable tax in Canada) to Ontario & Maritimes - $37.25, rest of Canada - $35. to USA - C$40/US$32. Other countries - C$50

**CANADA REVENUE ALBUM** - 449 high quality pages with 4 quality custom gold imprinted binders.
includes tax, shipping, insurance to Canada - $200 Postpaid/insured to USA - C$225
**100 different Canada revenue stamps,** high catalog value - $45 postpaid

shop from about **19,000** Canada & Provinces revenue stamps,
Canada Semi-Official Airmail stamps & covers, Ducks, Telephone & Telegraph franks, etc.

# WWW.CANADAREVENUESTAMPS.COM

Regular illustrated on-line price lists and "***ReveNews***"® newsletters - **FREE** sign up on our website.
Latest full colour newsletters available **FREE** on our website or upon request.
For the largest stock of Canadian revenue stamps contact:

## E. S. J. van Dam Ltd - *since 1970*

P. O. Box 300 - SC, Bridgenorth, Ontario K0L 1H0
phone (705) 292 - 7013
Order Toll Free in North America: PHONE 1 - 866 - evandam (382-6326)

email: erlingvandam@gmail.com

**www.canadarevenuestamps.com**

member
*ARA*
*BNAPS*
*CRS*
*RPSC*
*etc.*

| | | NH% | (Qty) | Single | Pane | ✉ |
|---|---|---|---|---|---|---|
| CL7 | **(25¢) red on yellow background of swastikas** | 50 | (2,000) | 120.00 | 1,000.00 | 250.00 |
| a | imperf. pair | 50 | | 400.00 | — | — |
| b | imperf. pair, one with "AIR SERVICE" inverted | 50 | | 750.00 | | |
| c | vert. tête-bêche gutter pair | 100 | | 650.00 | 3,500 | |
| d | as "c", imperf. | 50 | | 750.00 | 6,000* | |

* Imperforate tête-bêche gutter sheet of 16 includes 4 horizontal pairs of CL7b and 4 CL7 imperf tête-bêche gutter pairs.

## ELLIOT–FAIRCHILD AIR SERVICE
### SERVICE TO RED LAKE AND ROUYN GOLDFIELDS

CL8

**1926, Mar 21** **sheet of 16, panes of 8 (4 x 2)** **Perf 11½**

| | | NH% | (Qty) | Single | Pane | ✉ |
|---|---|---|---|---|---|---|
| CL8 | **(25¢) red on yellow background of swastikas** | 50 | | 50.00 | 450.00 | 250.00 |
| | flight: Rouyn to Halleybury (or return), *May 27* | | | | | 600.00 |
| a | imperf pair | 50 | | 400.00 | — | — |
| b | tête-bêche gutter pair (sheet of 16) | 50 | | 400.00 | 2,000 | |
| c | tall "r" variety (position 2, 4) | | | 70.00 | | |

Five major varieties exist on each of CL6 to CL8 in the lines above and below the words "AIR SERVICE". (1) Upper lines end at right with a "Rosette" on stamps 5 and 7. (2) Both lines end in dashes on stamps 1 and 3. (3) Lines end at right in a dot in top line and dash in lower line on stamps 2 and 4. (4) Both lines start with a dash and end with a dot and "Bent Branch" or "Inverted Leaves" at top of leaves at right in 6th and 8th stamps. A further variety exists on CL8 only, a tall "r" in "Fairchild", stamps 2 and 4. These are all equal printings.

## ELLIOT–FAIRCHILDS AIR SERVICE

CL9

**1926, Apr 7** **panes of 8 (4 x 2)** **Perf 11½**

| | | NH +50% | (Qty) | Single | Pane | ✉ |
|---|---|---|---|---|---|---|
| CL9 | **(25¢) blue on yellow background of swastikas (pane of 8)** | | | 40.00 | 325.00 | 225.00 |
| a | imperf. pair | | | 1,750 | — | — |
| b | horiz. or vert. tête-bêche pair | | | 150.00 | | |
| c | filled-in wing on pos. 1 | | | 100.00 | | |
| d | pane with UR corner stamp inverted | | | | 350.00 | |

**No. CL9 proofs**: (NH +75%)

Red and yellow on white paper, tête-bêche sheet of 16 $5,000, single $300, tête-bêche pair $700. Most sheets cut into gutter tête-bêche pairs. One or two intact.

Black and yellow on white paper, tête-bêche sheet of 16 $5,000, single $300, tête-bêche pair $700. Most sheets cut into gutter tête-bêche pairs. One or two intact.

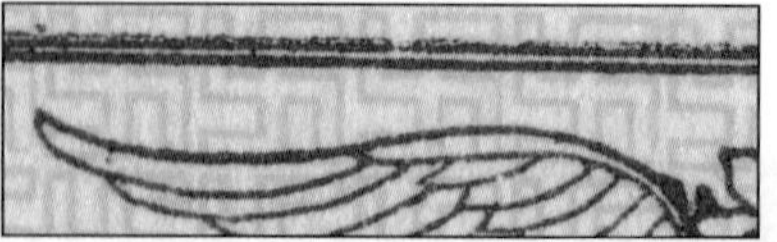

CL9
Above: normal wing
Right: filled-in wing

## ELLIOT–FAIRCHILD AIR TRANSPORT LTD.
### ROUYN – HAILEYBURY

CL10

**1926, Aug 11** **panes of 5 (1 x 5)** **Perf 12**

| | | NH +50% | (Qty) | Single | Pane | ✉ |
|---|---|---|---|---|---|---|
| CL10 | **(25¢) red**, large perfs (shades) | | (2,000) | 80.00 | 400.00 | 225.00 |
| a | fine perfs. | | | 80.00 | 400.00 | 225.00 |
| b | white dot over "O" of ELLIOT, 4th stamp in vert. strip of 5 | | | 95.00 | 400.00 | 275.00 |

**No. CL10 proofs**: Black on white card, single $750.00

## FAIRCHILD AIR TRANSPORT LTD.
### NORTHERN ONTARIO – ROUYN GOLDFIELDS

CL11

CL12

**1926, Oct 19** **panes of 10 (2 x 5)** **Perf 12**

| | | NH +50% | (Qty) | Single | Pane | ✉ |
|---|---|---|---|---|---|---|
| CL11 | **(25¢) deep blue** | | (5,000) | 45.00 | 500.00 | 90.00 |
| a | vertical tête-bêche pair | | | 100.00 | | |

Sheets have 2nd and 4th rows inverted. Vertical pairs have invert top or bottom.

| | | NH +50% | (Qty) | Single | Pane | ✉ |
|---|---|---|---|---|---|---|
| CL12 | **(25¢) ultramarine** | | (5,000) | 50.00 | 550.00 | |
| a | horiz. tête-bêche pair, invert on right | | | 110.00 | | |
| b | horiz. tête-bêche pair, one stamp darker shade | | | 150.00 | 1,500 | |
| c | horiz. tête-bêche pair, invert on left (from CL12e) | | | 750.00 | — | |
| d | vertical tête-bêche pair (from CL12e) | | | 750.00 | — | |
| e | Sheet with all stamps tête-bêche | | (150) | — | 3,000 | |

Normal pane (CL12) has one column of 5 inverted. This pane is also available with one column in a darker shade (CL12b). CL12c and CL12d come from a pane with every stamp tête-bêche with each other (CL12e). Nos. 1, 4, 5, 8 and 9 are inverted, producing 4 pairs as "d" and 1 as "c", or 2 horiz. pairs as "a" and 3 horiz. pairs with invert on left as "c".

CL12 was prepared but not used.

# PATRICIA AIRWAYS AND EXPLORATION CO. LTD.

**Operated between Sioux Lookout and Northern Ontario goldfields, Woman Lake, Pine Ridge, Red Lake, Birch Lake, Ont. and Rouyn, Que.**

## STYLE ONE

CL13

| 1926–1927 | panes of 8 (2 x 4) | | | | Perf 12 |
|---|---|---|---|---|---|
| | NH +50% | (Qty) | Single | Pane | ✉ |
| **CL13** | **(25¢) green and red on yellow paper**, *Jul 1, 1926* | (12,800) | 70.00 | 575.00 | 100.00 |
| a | pair, imperf. between † | | 1,250 | — | 1,250 |
| ai | as "a", red routes double printed, one inverted | | *2,000* | | |
| b | small "t" in "TO" (pos. 8) | (50) | 400.00 | 900.00 | 750.00 |
| c | route inscription in blue-black | (488) | 300.00 | | 400.00 |
| d | as "c", with small "t" in "TO" | | 450.00 | 1,000 | 650.00 |
| e | inscribed "FED" in red ink (only known on cover) | | | | 1,850 |
| f | pale yellow paper | (24) | 150.00 | 1,200.00 | 150.00 |
| g | pale yellow paper, small "t" in "TO" | | 500.00 | | 750.00 |
| h | black overprint "SPECIMEN" | | 3,000 | | |
| i | route inscription ('RED LAKE') inverted (3 types) | | *4,000* | | 2,500 |

**No. CL13 Trial colours**: imperf. panes of 8 on gummed paper as issued; stamp CL13 in trial colours of canary, buff, green and blue. Each colour in pane of 8. One set of 4 panes known. 350.00 6,000

† Horizontal pair imperf between — only 4 covers known.

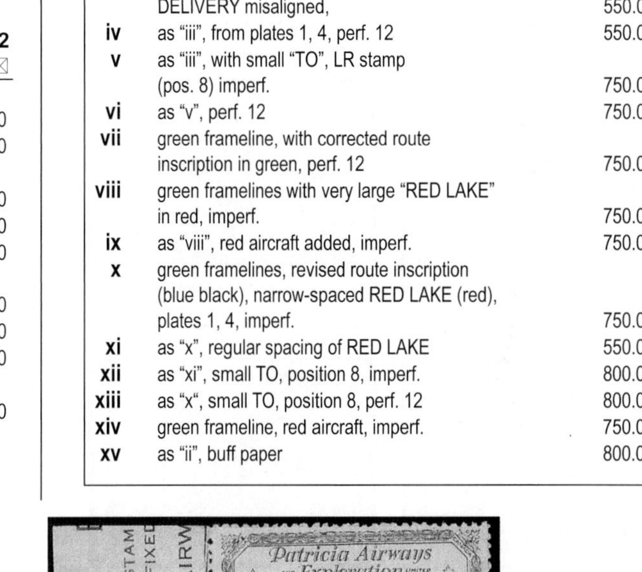

**CL13 Proofs**

Proofs are on white paper unless stated otherwise

| | | Pane | Single |
|---|---|---|---|
| **CL13P** | Proof, green frame only, no inscriptions or airplane, plates 1, 4, imperforate on white paper | 5,000 | 550.00 |
| i | as CL13P, on yellow paper, original gum | 9,500 | 550.00 |
| ii | as CL13P, perf. 12 | | 550.00 |
| iii | as CL13P, with route inscription in blue black, DELIVERY misaligned, | | 550.00 |
| iv | as "iii", from plates 1, 4, perf. 12 | | 550.00 |
| v | as "iii", with small "TO", LR stamp (pos. 8) imperf. | | 750.00 |
| vi | as "v", perf. 12 | | 750.00 |
| vii | green frameline, with corrected route inscription in green, perf. 12 | | 750.00 |
| viii | green framelines with very large "RED LAKE" in red, imperf. | | 750.00 |
| ix | as "viii", red aircraft added, imperf. | | 750.00 |
| x | green framelines, revised route inscription (blue black), narrow-spaced RED LAKE (red), plates 1, 4, imperf. | | 750.00 |
| xi | as "x", regular spacing of RED LAKE | | 550.00 |
| xii | as "xi", small TO, position 8, imperf. | | 800.00 |
| xiii | as "x", small TO, position 8, perf. 12 | | 800.00 |
| xiv | green frameline, red aircraft, imperf. | | 750.00 |
| xv | as "ii", buff paper | | 800.00 |

CL13i

CL13Pii

CL13Piv

CL13Pvi

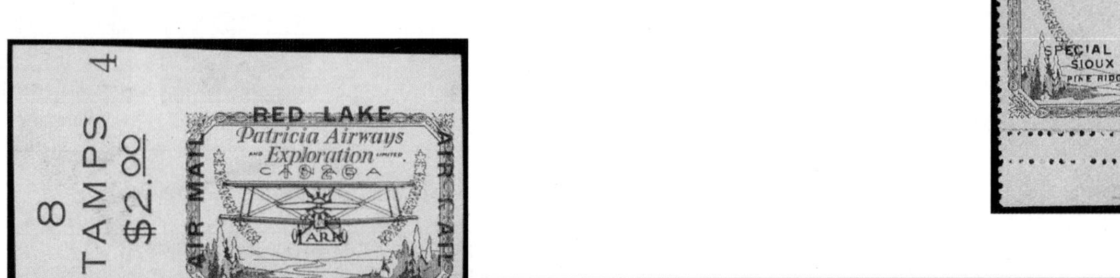


CL13Pviii

CL13Pxiv

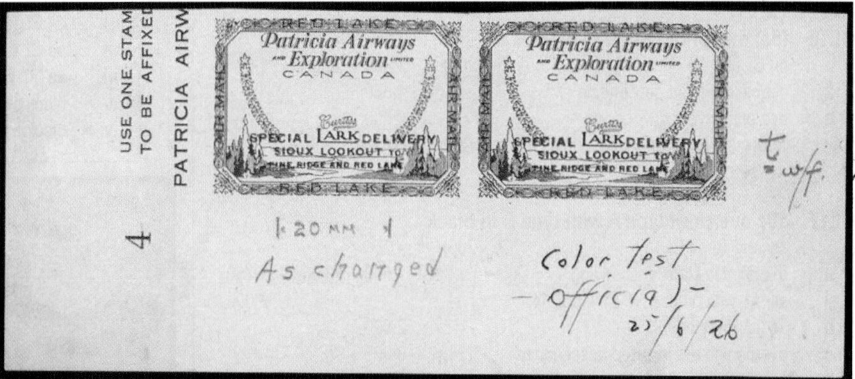


CL13Pxi, CL13Pxii

Air Post Semi-Official

| | 37 mm | 34 mm | |
|---|---|---|---|
| HAILEYBURY<br>and<br>ROUYN<br>10 cents | Special Air Service<br>Sioux Lookout<br>and<br>Red Lake District<br>5 cents | Special Air Service<br>Sioux Lookout<br>and<br>Red Lake District<br>5 cents | RED LAKE |
| (A) | (B) | (C) | (D) |

**These are the four overprints that appear on the three styles of the PATRICIA AIRWAYS AND EXPLORATION stamps**

CL14

CL15

CL16

CL17a

| | | NH +50% (Qty) | Single | Pane | ✉ |
|---|---|---|---|---|---|
| **CL14** | **10¢ overprint type A in red** | | | | |
| | on CL13 | (1,800) | 150.00 | 1,250 | 325.00 |
| a | route inscription in blue-black | (16) | 750.00 | | 850.00 |
| b | small "t" in "TO" (pos. 8) | (2) | 3,000 | | |
| c | overprint inverted | | 500.00 | | |
| d | double overprint, one inverted | | 1,000 | | |
| e | buff paper | | 170.00 | 1,350 | 325.00 |
| f | broken "N" in ROUYN | | 180.00 | 1,350 | 375.00 |
| g | overprint type A in light red | | 150.00 | 1,250 | 325.00 |
| **CL15** | **5¢ overprint type B in black** | | | | |
| | on CL13, ascending | (200) | 275.00 | 2,400 | 375.00 |
| a | overprint in black descending | (8) | 2,500.00 | | 2,900 |
| c | overprint in red descending | (200) | 500.00 | 4,000 | 650.00 |
| d | as "c", malformed "O" in LOOKOUT (Plate 1, position 7) | | 850.00 | 2,650 | 650.00 |
| **CL16** | **(5¢) overprint type D in black** | | | | |
| | on CL13 † | (200) | 1,200 | 10,000 | 1,000 |
| a | double overprint descending | | 1,800 | | |
| b | overprint inverted | | 2,000 | — | — |

† Overprint occurs ascending, descending and inverted descending.

| | | (Qty) | Single | Pane | ✉ |
|---|---|---|---|---|---|
| **CL17** | **10¢ overprint type A with type D in black** | | | | |
| | ascending on CL13 | (200) | *4,500* | | |
| a | overprint in black descending | | 1,500 | 10,000 | 1,750 |
| ai | as "a", with broken "N" in "ROUYN" | | | | 3,000 |
| b | as "a", inverted | | 2,500 | | |
| c | overprint in red inverted descending | (24) | 3,000 | | |

First flight, Aug. 2

Nos. CL14 and CL17 Surcharged in Red "HAILEYBURY / AND / ROUYN / 10 cents" (A).

## STYLE TWO
## Inscribed Woman Lake (Birch Lake)

CL18

**1926, Jul 7 panes of 8 (2 x 4) Perf 12**

| | | NH +50% (Qty) | Single | Pane | ✉ |
|---|---|---|---|---|---|
| **CL18** | **(50¢) black and red on blue paper** | (1,800) | 200.00 | 1,700 | |
| | flight: Sioux Lookout to Woman Lake (or return), *Aug 2* | | | | 300.00 |
| a | imperf. pair (See Proof section) | | 300.00 | — | — |
| b | horiz. pair, imperf. between | | 300.00 | — | — |
| c | variety "OTT" in "LOOKOUT" | | 350.00 | | 750.00 |
| d | as "b", with "OTT" variety | | 600.00 | | |
| e | printed "FED" in green ink | | 2,500 | | 1,500 |
| f | as "e", with "OTT" variety | | 2,850 | | *1,850* |
| g | missing route inscription (Special Del...) | | 2,000 | *16,000* | |

No CL18e is known double "FED", and triple "FED" (one overprint in blue the other two in violet), both unique. Value $5,500.

**CL18 Trial colour**: deep blue paper, perforated 2,000

CL18, CL19 and CL20 exist with a constant variety: small 'v' in 'VIA'. Values: CL18: $350; CL19: $550; CL20: $1550.

Small v

Normal V

**CL18 Proofs**

Proofs are on white paper unless stated otherwise

| | | Single |
|---|---|---|
| **CL18P** | Proof, purple frame, orange airplane, no inscriptions, plate 1, imperforate | 550.00 |
| i | as CL18P, with orange route inscription | 550.00 |
| ii | as CL18P, with orange airplane and all inscriptions | 550.00 |
| iii | as "ii", with "OTT" error | 600.00 |
| iv | black and red on deep blue paper | 1,500.00 |
| v | black and red on greenish yellow paper, perforated | 600.00 |

CL18e

CL18e (double)

CL18e (triple)

CL18g

CL18P

CL18Pii

CL18Pv

CL19

CL20

CL21

CL22a

| | | NH +50% | (Qty) | Single | Pane | ✉ |
|---|---|---|---|---|---|---|
| **CL19** | **10¢ overprint type A in red** on CL18 ascending | | (770) | 350.00 | 2,900 | 900.00 |
| a | overprint in black | | (8) | 1,500.00 | | |
| b | overprint in dark red | | | 350.00 | 2,900 | 900.00 |
| i | missing red route inscription (Special...) | | | *5,500.00* | | |
| ii | missing red border route inscription (Woman Lake & Air Mail...) | | | *5,500.00* | | |
| **CL20** | **5¢ overprint type B in black** on CL18 ascending | | (200) | 1,000 | *8,000* | 1,000 |
| a | as above descending | | (24) | 1,500 | *12,000* | 1,250 |
| b | overprint in red, ascending | | (200) | 1,000 | *8,000* | 1,450 |
| c | overprint in red, descending | | (24) | 1,500 | *12,000* | 1,250 |
| d | as "c", 3rd "O" in LOOKOUT malformed (position 7) | | | 1,500.00 | *9,000* | *2,000* |

| | | NH% | (Qty) | Single | Pane | ✉ |
|---|---|---|---|---|---|---|
| **CL21** | **(5¢) overprint type D** (descending) in black on CL18 | 50 | (24) | 2,500 | | 2,500 |
| i | small "v" in "vIA." (pos. 2) | | | 3,500 | | 4,000 |
| a | overprint in violet ascending | 50 | (16) | 3,500 | | 4,000 |
| ai | as "a", small "v" in "vIA." (pos. 2) | | (2) | 4,500 | | |
| b | overprint in violet, descending | 50 | (16) | 3,500 | *28,000* | 4,000 |
| bi | overprint in violet, horizontal | 50 | | 3,750 | | 4,500 |
| bii | as "b", small "v" in "vIA." (pos. 2) | | (2) | 4,500 | | |
| c | double overprint (ascending) in violet | 50 | | 3,500 | | |

| | | NH +50% | (Qty) | Single | Pane | ✉ |
|---|---|---|---|---|---|---|
| **CL22** | **10¢ overprint type A** with type D ascending in black on CL18 | | (24) | 2,500 | *20,000* | 2,000 |
| i | small "v" in "vIA." (pos. 2) | | | 3,500 | | 2,750 |
| a | CL22 with type D descending | | (24) | 3,500 | *28,000* | 3,500 |
| b | CL22 with type D inverted ascending | | (16) | 2,500 | *20,000* | 2,250 |
| c | CL22 with type D inverted descending | | (16) | 2,500 | *20,000* | 2,750 |
| d | as "a", broken "N" in ROUYN | | | *2,500* | | 2,750 |
| e | as "a", overprint type A in light red | | | *2,500* | | *2,750* |
| f | as "b", broken "N" in ROUYN | | | *2,500* | | *2,750* |

Broken "N" variety exists on type A overprints and adds premium of $20.00 to the listed price.

## STYLE THREE

CL23

**panes of 8 (2 x 4)** — **Rouletted**

| | | NH +75% | (Qty) | Single | Pane | ✉ |
|---|---|---|---|---|---|---|
| **CL23** | **(50¢) green and red on yellow paper**, *May 27, 1927* | | | 750.00 | *6,500* | |
| a | imperf. pair | | | 2,000.00 | 8,000 | |
| b | double rouletted | | | | 1,500 | |
| c | "Grounded Plane" | | | 1,200.00 | — | |

### CL23 Proofs

Proofs are on white paper unless stated otherwise

| | | Pane | Single |
|---|---|---|---|
| CL23P | imperf., green frame on yellow paper, no Curtiss Lark, no routes, third issue, | 3,500 | 350.00 |
| i | basic design with Type D overprint "RED LAKE" in red purple descending to right, ascending to right, inverted descending and ascending to left, overprint in green descending to left and inverted descending to left in se-tenant pairs. Other combinations may exist, full gum, imperf., plate 10 | | 750.00 |
| ii | basic design with inverted airplane, Type D overprint descending to right, imperforate pair | | 750.00 |
| a | Imperf, green frame on yellow paper, No Curtiss Lark, no routes, third issue. | 6,500 | 650.00 |
| b | Imperf, green frame on Buff paper, Plate # 5. No Curtiss Lark, no routes, third issue. | 6,500 | |
| c | Rectangular Perfs., green frame on Light Yellow paper, Plate # 6. No Curtiss Lark, no routes, third issue. Original Gum. Signed "Compliments of A.J. Algate 1927". Only recorded pane with experimental Rectangular Perfs. | 13,500 | |
| d | Rouletted, green frame with red airplane on yellow paper. Plate # 3. Signed, "Compliments of A. J. Algate 1927". Only recorded pane signed by Designer. Original Gum. | 9,500 | |

Air Post Semi-Official

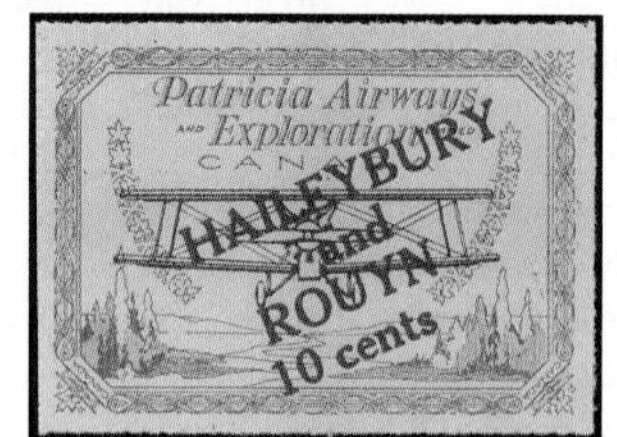

CL24

| | NH +50% | (Qty) | Single | Pane | ✉ |
|---|---|---|---|---|---|
| **CL24** | **10¢ overprint type A** | | | | |
| | in red on CL23 | (800) | 120.00 | 1,000 | 250.00 |

CL25

| | NH +50% | (Qty) | Single | Pane | ✉ |
|---|---|---|---|---|---|
| **CL25** | **5¢ overprint type B in black** | | | | |
| | on CL23 descending | (800) | 60.00 | 500.00 | 175.00 |
| a | overprint in red descending | (1,368) | 40.00 | 350.00 | 175.00 |
| b | overprint in green descending | | 40.00 | 350.00 | 175.00 |
| c | overprint in green ascending | (4,448) | 40.00 | 350.00 | 175.00 |
| d | as "a", 3rd "O" in LOOKOUT malformed (position 7) (red) "O" filled | | 450.00 | 950.00 | 500.00 |
| e | as "b", 3rd "O" in LOOKOUT malformed (position 7) (green) "O" filled | | 450.00 | 950.00 | 500.00 |
| f | as "CL25, 3rd "O" in LOOKOUT malformed (position 7) (black) | | 450.00 | 950.00 | 500.00 |
| g | as "a", on pale yellow paper | | 150.00 | — | — |
| h | as "b", on pale yellow paper | | 150.00 | — | — |
| i | grounded plane variety | | 300.00 | — | — |

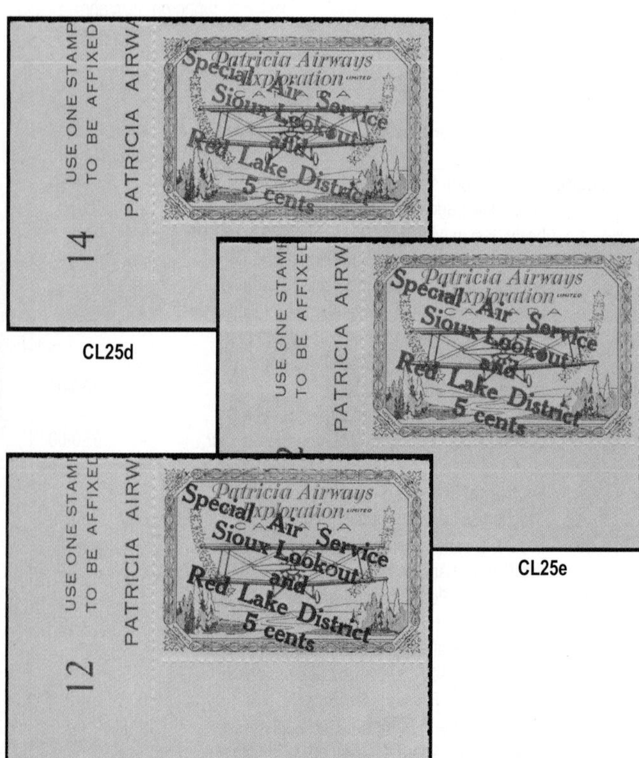

CL25d

CL25e

CL25f

CL26e

| | NH +50% | (Qty) | Single | Pane | ✉ |
|---|---|---|---|---|---|
| **CL26** | **5¢ overprint type C** | | | | |
| | in black on CL23 | (800) | 120.00 | 960.00 | 225.00 |
| a | as above inverted | | 750.00 | | |
| b | horiz. pair, left stamp with additional type D overprint in red | | 750.00 | | |
| c | overprint in red | (800) | 120.00 | 960.00 | 275.00 |
| d | red overprint, inverted | | 750.00 | | |
| e | overprint in green | (800) | 125.00 | 1,000 | 225.00 |
| f | green overprint, inverted | | 750.00 | | |

CL27

| | | (Qty) | Single | Pane | ✉ |
|---|---|---|---|---|---|
| **CL27** | **10¢ overprint type A** in red with 5¢ overprint type B in black on CL23 | (400) | 375.00 | *3,000* | 450.00 |
| a | pair, one stamp missing type B overprint | | 1,500 | | |

CL28

| | | (Qty) | Single | Pane | ✉ |
|---|---|---|---|---|---|
| **CL28** | **10¢ overprint type A** in red with 5¢ overprint type C in black on CL23 | | 150.00 | 1,250 | 300.00 |
| a | with type C overprint inverted | | 600.00 | | |
| b | grounded plane variety | | 500.00 | | 400.00 |
| c | pale yellow paper | | 170.00 | | |

CL29a

| | | (Qty) | Single | Pane | ✉ |
|---|---|---|---|---|---|
| **CL29** | **10¢ overprint type A** with type D in black on CL23 | (400) | 250.00 | 2,000 | 350.00 |
| i | type D ovpt in black inverted descending | incl. | 275.00 | 2,750 | |
| a | type D overprint in purple | | 250.00 | 2,000 | 350.00 |
| ai | type D ovpt in purple inverted descending | incl. | 275.00 | 2,750 | |
| b | type D overprint in green | | 250.00 | 2,000 | 350.00 |
| bi | type D ovpt in green inverted descending | incl. | 275.00 | 2,750 | |
| c | type D overprint inverted, any colour | | 275.00 | 2,200 | 425.00 |

The type D overprint occurs in all 4 orientations in each colour.

CL30di

| | | NH +50% | (Qty) | Single | Pane | ✉ |
|---|---|---|---|---|---|---|
| **CL30** | **(5¢) overprint type D** | | | | | |
| | in black on CL23 † | | (800) | 85.00 | 700.00 | 300.00 |
| a | CL30 with inverted airplane, type D ascending only | | (8) | 3,500 | | |
| b | imperf. pair | | | 350.00 | — | — |
| c | overprint in purple | | (800) | 75.00 | 600.00 | 300.00 |
| di | inverted airplane, purple type D overprint ascending | | | 2,500 | | |
| dii | inverted airplane, purple type D overprint descending | | | 2,500 | | |
| diii | inverted airplane, purple type D overprint inverted | | | 2,500 | | |
| e | purple type D overprint, imperf. pair ‡ | | | 1,500.00 | — | — |
| ei | as "e", inverted airplane (imperf. pair) | | | *7,000* | | |
| f | overprint in green | | (800) | 75.00 | 600.00 | 300.00 |
| g | green type D overprint, imperf. pair ‡ | | | 450.00 | — | — |
| h | double type D overprint, one in green, one in purple | | | 300.00 | | |

† The type D overprint occurs in all 4 orientations in each colour.
‡ Occurs with various combinations of orientations for type D overprint.
"Grounded Plane" variety (the plane is touching the ground) on any PATRICIA AIRWAYS AND EXPLORATION stamp price $300.00 each.
CL30 inverted overprints $200.00, $300 for NH.

Nos. CL31–39 are not assigned.

## WESTERN CANADA AIRWAYS SERVICE

CL40

**1927, May 1** — **sheets of 200, panes of 50** — **Perf 12**

| | | NH +50% | (Qty) | Single | Pane | ✉ |
|---|---|---|---|---|---|---|
| **CL40** | **(10¢) black with pink background** | | | | | |
| | (thick paper) | | (36,600) | 7.00 | 350.00 | 40.00 |
| a | pale rose background | | (10,000) | 9.00 | 450.00 | 40.00 |
| b | dark red background | | (10,000) | 9.00 | 450.00 | 40.00 |
| c | vertical pair, imperf. between | | | 425.00 | — | — |
| d | horizontal pair, imperf. between | | | 425.00 | — | 950.00 |
| e | misplaced perf. variety (extra perfs vertically through centre of stamp) | | | 50.00 | | |
| f | vert. imperf. pair with one-line vert. perf. through middle | | | 600.00 | | |
| g | as "e," with black double printed | | | 250.00 | | |
| h | Plane's skis touch sun | | | 35.00 | — | 80.00 |

Serving Northern Ontario, Manitoba, Saskatchewan, Alberta and the Northwest Territories

Other flights may exist for most issues.
See the *America Airmail Catalogue* for more details.

**Commercial covers sell for a premium.**

## WESTERN CANADA AIRWAYS JUBILEE ISSUE

CL41

**1927, Jul 1** — **sheets of 200, panes of 50** — **Perf 12**

| | | NH +50% | (Qty) | Single | Pane | ✉ |
|---|---|---|---|---|---|---|
| **CL41** | **(10¢) black with orange background** | | | 16.00 | 800.00 | 375.00 |
| a | vert. pair imperf. between | | | 450.00 | — | — |
| b | intense black | | | 20.00 | 1,000 | 375.00 |
| c | misplaced perf. variety (extra perfs vertically through centre of stamp) | | | 75.00 | | |
| d | as "b", vert. pair, imperf. between | | | 475.00 | | |

Sixtieth anniversary of Confederation. Many cachets exist.

## YUKON AIRWAYS AND EXPLORATIONS CO. LTD.

CL42

**sheets of 80 cut into panes of 10 (1 x 10)**

**1927, Nov 11** — **Rouletted horiz.**

| | | NH +50% | (Qty) | Single | Pane | ✉ |
|---|---|---|---|---|---|---|
| **CL42** | **25¢ blue** | | | 45.00 | 500.00 | 65.00 |
| a | "ArRWAYS" variety | | | 200.00 | 750.00 | 550.00 |
| b | double print | | | 500.00 | — | 500.00 |
| i | used on "Whitehorse Star" newspaper | | | — | — | 160.00 |
| c | booklet of 10 panes (3 known) | | | 7,500 | | |
| d | imperf. pair | | (2) | 5,000 | | |
| e | pair, imperf. vertically | | | 2,500 | | |
| f | repair entry in left '2' of '25' | | | 250.00 | | 250.00 |

Sheets of 80 were cut into vertical strips of 10 and assembled into booklets of 10 panes with plain brown covers. Typographed. First flight November 11.
One cross-sheet block of 16 (8x2) with sheet margins on both sides imperf. vertically exists. Value *$20,000.00*

Bright colour rouletted singles in 4 different colours are unofficial reprints. $25 for set of 4.

**No. CL42 Proofs**: reverse die proof, in black, on thick card (99x76mm) $450.
Same, on white wove paper (164x103mm) (6 printed) $4,000.
Same, on matt card (53x27mm) (4 printed) $4,000.
**No. CL42 Trial colour**: pale blue $150.00

CL42e

CL42 proof (53x27mm)

## PATRICIA AIRWAYS LTD.

CL43

| 1928, Mar 5 | panes of 8 (2 x 4) | | Rouletted | |
|---|---|---|---|---|
| | NH +50% (Qty) | Single | Pane | ✉ |
| **CL43** | **(10¢) green & red on yellow paper** | 40.00 | 375.00 | 175.00 |
| a | inverted plane | 2,000 | | |
| b | "grounded plane" variety | 450.00 | | |
| c | imperf. pair | 650.00 | — | — |

No connection with earlier company. Sioux Lookout to various lake areas: Red Lake, Woman Lake, etc.

### CL43 Proofs

Proofs are on white paper unless stated otherwise. (NH +75%)

| | | Single |
|---|---|---|
| CL43P | basic design in black on white card, no airplane | 900.00 |
| i | grounded plane type, airplane in plum shade | 850.00 |
| ii | as "i", triple print airplane in plum shade | 750.00 |
| iii | yellow paper, no airplane | 650.00 |
| iv | as "iii", imperf. | 900.00 |
| | as "iv", imperf. pair | 1,800 |

CL43Pi

CL43Pii

CL43Piii

## BRITISH COLUMBIA AIRWAYS LTD.
### VANCOUVER – VICTORIA. B.C.

CL44

| 1928, Aug 3 | sheets of 220, panes of 55 (5 x 11) | | | Rouletted |
|---|---|---|---|---|
| | NH +25% (Qty) | Single | Pane | ✉ |
| **CL44** | **5¢ ultramarine** | 10.00 | 550.00 | |
| | first flight: Victoria to Vancouver, *Aug 3* | | | 175.00 |
| | flights between Aug 4–25 | | | 275.00 |
| a | "White dot" variety, at left below "R" of "AIR" (pos. 23, 30) | 50.00 | | 200.00 |
| i | spot in left value tablet (pos. 19, 46) | 50.00 | | 200.00 |
| ii | damaged diagonal background (pos. 33, 45) | 50.00 | | |

Lithographed. First flight July 23 with cachet.

## KLONDIKE AIRWAYS LTD.
### OPERATED BETWEEN BASES IN THE YUKON

CL45

| 1928, Oct 4 | panes of 4 (1 x 4) | | Rouletted horiz. | |
|---|---|---|---|---|
| | NH +50% (Qty) | Single | Pane | ✉ |
| **CL45** | **25¢ blue**, shades | 90.00 | 400.00 | 450.00 |
| a | "missing strut" variety | 140.00 | 500.00 | 550.00 |
| b | "malformed strut" variety (pos. 4) | 140.00 | 500.00 | |

First flight, October 4.

Genuinely flown covers demand a significant premium.

## CHERRY RED AIRLINE LTD.
### NORTHERN SASKATCHEWAN

CL46

| 1929, Jul 3 | sheets of 200, panes of 50 | | | | Perf 12 |
|---|---|---|---|---|---|
| | NH +25% | (Qty) | Single | Pane | ✉ |
| **CL46** | **10¢ red & black** | (2,400) | 10.00 | 600.00 | 35.00 |
| a | serif on crossbar of "A" in "AIR" † | | 35.00 | | 60.00 |
| i | "Snow on Wings" caused by minor colour shift | | 20.00 | 1,500. | 60.00 |
| ii | CL46a with "Snow on Wings" variety | | 75.00 | — | 120.00 |
| iii | closed C in CHERRY, pos. 33, first printing | | 75.00 | | 125.00 |

† First printing, on positions 6, 8, 10, 31, 33 and 35; 2nd printing, on positions 8, 10, 33 and 35.

Specimen vertical overprint in Serif lettering $200.00.

Air Post Semi-Official

## COMMERCIAL AIRWAYS LTD.
### NORTHERN ALBERTA AND NORTHWEST TERRITORIES

CL47

**1929–1930** panes of 10 (2 x 5) **Perf 12**

| | | NH +50% (Qty) | Single | Pane | ✉ |
|---|---|---|---|---|---|
| **CL47** | **(10¢) black**, VIA AIR, *May 18, 1929* | (3,000) | 160.00 | 1,750 | 150.00 |
| a | "broken C" in "CIAL" variety, pos. 2 | | 240.00 | | 250.00 |
| c | pane of 10 with rate and record number on side selvedge | | | 1,750 | |
| d | complete booklet, 25 panes of 10 (2 x 5) stapled on left edge | | | | |

**CL47 Proofs**

Proofs are on white paper unless stated otherwise

| | | Sheet | Single | Cpl Set* |
|---|---|---|---|---|
| **CL47P** | basic design in black, on white card | | 400.00 | |
| i | VIA AIR, first issue on thick white card, black, orange, deep carmine, green, violet, lemon yellow, imperforate | 3,000 | 300.00 | 2,000 |
| ii | as "i", on thin white card, light carmine, violet, pale yellow green, mustard yellow, deep orange | | 300.00 | 2,000 |
| iv | "broken C" variety on position 2, colours as "i" | | 600.00 | |
| v | "broken C" variety on position 2, colours as "ii" | | 600.00 | |

*Set of 6 colour singles

CL48

| | | NH +25% (Qty) | Single | Pane | ✉ |
|---|---|---|---|---|---|
| **CL48** | **(10¢) black**, AIR FEE, thick paper, *Jun 2, 1930* | (2,000) | 15.00 | 150.00 | 50.00 |
| a | deep black, thin paper | | 15.00 | 150.00 | 50.00 |
| c | imperf. pair | | 300.00 | — | — |
| d | break in oval (pos. 1) | | 50.00 | | 100.00 |

**CL48 Proof**

| | | Sheet | Single | Cpl Set* |
|---|---|---|---|---|
| **CL48P** | Air Fee issues, imperf. On thick card, black, orange, deep carmine, green, violet, lemon yellow | 3,000 | 300.00 | 2,000 |
| i | break in oval (pos. 1), colours as above | | 350.00 | 2,300 |

*Set of 6 colour singles

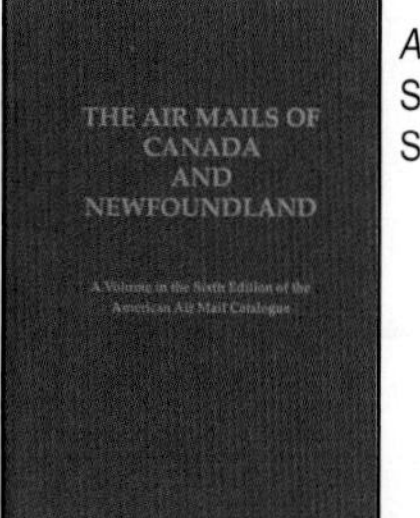


*American Air Mail Catalogue*, Sixth Edition. The American Air Mail Society, 1997 (550 pages)

*The Pioneer and Semi-Official Airmails of Canada*, C.A. Longworth-Dames, 1995 (172 pages)

CL49

CL50

| | | NH +25% (Qty) | Single | Pane | ✉ |
|---|---|---|---|---|---|
| **CL49** | **(10¢) purple**, VIA AIR, *Jul 21, 1930* | (2,000) | 175.00 | 1,750 | 250.00 |
| a | broken "C" in "CIAL" variety | | 250.00 | — | 500.00 |
| b | imperf. pair | | 400.00 | — | — |
| c | imperf. pair, with broken "C" variety | | 500.00 | — | — |
| d | vertical pair, imperf. between | (2) | 1,250 | — | — |
| e | extra row diagonal perfs | | 300.00 | | |
| f | imperf. single on cover | | | | 500.00 |
| **CL50** | **(10¢) orange**, AIR FEE, thick paper, *Dec 6, 1930* | (5,000) | 20.00 | 200.00 | 80.00 |
| a | thin paper | | 20.00 | 200.00 | 80.00 |
| c | imperf. pair | | 300.00 | — | 750.00* |
| d | break in oval (pos. 1) | | 50.00 | | |
| e | as "c" one each CL50d and CL50 | | 350.00 | | |

* single imperf. stamp

CL48d
CL50d

## CANADIAN AIRWAYS LTD.
### NORTHERN ALBERTA, NORTHWEST TERRITORIES, MANITOBA MINING AREAS

CL51

CL52

**1932** sheets of 200, panes of 50 **Perf 12**

| | | NH | (Qty) | Single | Pane | ✉ |
|---|---|---|---|---|---|---|
| **CL51** | **(10¢) orange & blue**, white gum | 25 | | 30.00 | 1,500 | 75.00 |
| a | horizontal pair, imperf. between | 25 | | 650.00 | — | — |
| b | vertical pair, imperf. between | 25 | | 900.00 | — | — |
| c | orange and pale blue, yellow gum | 25 | | 30.00 | 1,500 | 75.00 |
| d | as "c", horizontal pair, imperf. between | 50 | | 800.00 | — | — |
| e | as CL51, vertical shift of orange plate | 50 | | 200.00 | | |

**No. CL51 Proof**: part perforate sheet with vertical shift of orange plate $7,500

| | | NH | (Qty) | Single | Pane | ✉ |
|---|---|---|---|---|---|---|
| **CL52** | **10¢ as "CL51" surcharged "10 cents"** | 25 | | 25.00 | 1,250 | 90.00 |
| a | inverted surcharge | 50 | (100) | 1,000 | — | — |
| b | double surcharge | 50 | | 2,000 | — | — |
| c | pair with invert and normal | 50 | (10) | 2,000 | — | — |

**No. CL52 Essay** of unadopted overprint in violet $1,250

CL52 essay

Air Post Semi-Official

# COLOMBIA SCADTA CONSULAR OVERPRINTS
## Canadian Dispatch for Expedited Airmail Service Within Colombia

The SCADTA Air Mail system (Sociedad Colombo-Alemana de Transportes Aereos) was used throughout the world to expedite delivery of mails to Colombia which would otherwise have taken weeks longer. These overprints on the 1923 airmail stamps of Colombia were available in Canada from the Consulates of Colombia and various agents in the major cities. Covers exist with 1923 unoverprinted SCADTA issue along with Canadian stamps from various Canadian cities (primarily Montreal, Toronto or Vancouver) to various destinations in Colombia.

CLCA1

CLCA2

CLCA3

CLCA4

CLCA6

CLCA7

CLCA8

CLCA9

CLCA10

CLCA11

CFLCA1

Dangerous forgeries exist

| | | NH% | Qty. | Remainders unsold | Sold for use in period | ★ | ⊙ | On Piece | ✉ |
|---|---|---|---|---|---|---|---|---|---|
| **CLCA1** | **5 centavo, orange yellow** | 50 | 125 | 77 | 48 | 450.00 | 300.00 | 1,000.00 | *4,000.00* |
| **CLCA2** | **10 centavo, green** | 50 | 275 | 106 | 169 | 350.00 | 250.00 | | *4,000.00* |
| **a** | double overprint | | | | | | *1,200.00* | | |
| **CLCA3** | **15 centavo, carmine** | 50 | 200 | 179 | 21 | 400.00 | 350.00 | | *10,000.00* |
| **CLCA4** | **20 centavo, grey** | 50 | 225 | 147 | 78 | 375.00 | 275.00 | | |
| **CLCA5** | **30 centavo, blue** | 50 | 1,100 | 678 | 422 | 150.00 | 100.00 | | *3,000.00* |
| a | double overprint | | | | | | | | |
| **CLCA6** | **50 centavo, green** | 50 | 150 | 119 | 31 | 450.00 | 400.00 | | |
| a | inverted overprint | | | | | | *2,000.00* | | |
| **CLCA7** | **60 centavo, brown** | 50 | 150 | 127 | 23 | 450.00 | 400.00 | 1,000.00 | *5,000.00* |
| **CLCA8** | **1 peso, black** | 50 | 150 | 86 | 64 | 450.00 | 400.00 | 1,500.00 | |
| **CLCA9** | **2 peso, red orange** | 50 | 125 | 68 | 56 | 450.00 | 400.00 | 1,500.00 | |
| **CLCA10** | **3 peso, violet** | 50 | 50 | 45 | 5 | 1,200.00 | 1,200.00 | 1,800.00 | |
| **CLCA11** | **5 peso, olive green** | 50 | 50 | 42 | 8 | 1,200.00 | 1,200.00 | 1,800.00 | |
| **CFLCA1** | **20 centavo, registration overprint "R" in red** | 50 | 100 | 93 | 7 | 1,200.00 | 1,200.00 | 1,800.00 | *10,000.00* |
| **a** | with manuscript red "R" overprint (one example known, used on cover) | | | | | | | | *10,000.00* |

The 1929 Gold Dollar issue was also used in a similar manner along with Canadian stamps to Colombia.

All values issued in 1929 and were valid for use until Nov. 30, 1931. Remainders were sold to collectors in the 1930s.

As indicated by the quantities shown, all are scarce to rare. Covers are extremely rare.

Source of "Remainders unsold, Sold in use" quantities: *The Specialized Catalogue of Canadian Airmail Stamps* by Ian C. Morgan, 1934–1935 Edition.

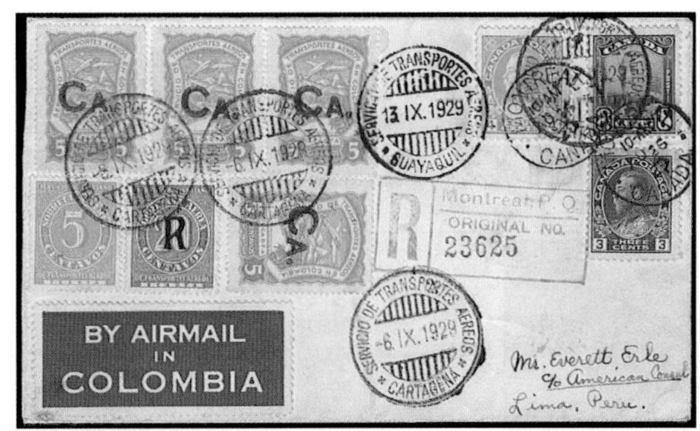

# COMPUTER VENDED POSTAGE

CP1

CP2

CP14

Vending 'kiosk' machines were placed in selected postal outlets commencing mid December 2012 for a 'trial period'. Locations included Toronto, Scarborough, London, Guelph, Mississauga, Richmond Hill, Vancouver, Victoria, Montreal and Longueil. The machines are Wincor-Nixdorf ProPostal 2000 stamp vending kiosks.

Stamps are dispensed singly from rolls of 5,000 (?) that contain the pre-printed design of a multicoloured maple leaf and 'CANADA'. The denomination and barcode are printed at the time of purchase. Two black guideline/corner dash marks may appear on every 16th stamp. Stamps are dispensed in nine different denominations. In March 2013, the kiosks began dispensing the stamps (CP10–CP18) in strips of 4, either with the same value or mixed.

The stamps have tagging on three sides; there is no taggant on the left or upper/lower edges near the barcode/denomination.

Various 'errors' are available, including non-denominated stamps that were given away by post office staff members. Miscuts of varying degrees are known.

Add 50% for on-cover examples cancelled in period.

### *Maple Leaf: First Issue*

Self-adhesive roll

**2012, Dec 12** **GT3** **Die cut**

| Unitrade | | NH–VF | ⊙F | FDC |
|---|---|---|---|---|
| **CP1** | **61¢ multicoloured** | *100.00* | *100.00* | 15.00* |
| **CP2** | **$1.05 multicoloured** | *100.00* | *100.00* | |
| **CP3** | **$1.22 multicoloured** | *no examples reported* | | |
| **CP4** | **$1.29 multicoloured** | *800.00* | — | |
| **CP5** | **$1.80 multicoloured** | *100.00* | *100.00* | |
| **CP6** | **$2.10 multicoloured** | *1,600.00* | — | |
| **CP7** | **$2.95 multicoloured** | *1,800.00* | — | |
| **CP8** | **$3.40 multicoloured** | *2,000.00* | — | |
| **CP9** | **$3.65 multicoloured** | *2,000.00* | — | |

* on-sale date: February 15, 2013.

Guidelines at UL and UR

CP1–CP9 examples with guidelines at UL: multiply by 3; examples with guidelines at UR: multiply by 2. Official First Day Covers with guidelines: UL are 8x; UR are 4x.

Postally used copies are rare. Must be used in period (prior to January 14, 2013). Be aware of 61¢ 'used' stamps removed from first day covers (it is very difficult to soak the stamp without thinning it); the 'used' price is *not* for a FDC-removed stamp.

CP1: First day cover; cancellation (right)

### *Maple Leaf: Second Issue*

Self-adhesive roll

**2013, Jan 14** **GT3** **Die cut**

| Unitrade | | NH–VF | ⊙F | FDC |
|---|---|---|---|---|
| **CP10** | **63¢ multicoloured** | 4.00 | 4.00 | |
| i | second printing | 4.00 | 4.00 | |
| **CP11** | **$1.10 multicoloured** | 6.00 | 6.00 | |
| i | second printing | 6.00 | 6.00 | |
| **CP12** | **$1.26 multicoloured** | 8.00 | 8.00 | |
| i | second printing | 8.00 | 8.00 | |
| **CP13** | **$1.34 multicoloured** | 9.00 | 9.00 | |
| i | second printing | 9.00 | 9.00 | |
| **CP14** | **$1.85 multicoloured** | 11.00 | 11.00 | |
| i | second printing | 11.00 | 11.00 | |
| **CP15** | **$2.20 multicoloured** | 13.00 | 13.00 | |
| i | second printing | 13.00 | 13.00 | |
| **CP16** | **$3.05 multicoloured** | 18.00 | 18.00 | |
| i | second printing | 18.00 | 18.00 | |
| **CP17** | **$3.50 multicoloured** | 21.00 | 21.00 | |
| i | second printing | 21.00 | 21.00 | |
| **CP18** | **$3.75 multicoloured** | 22.00 | 22.00 | |
| i | second printing | 22.00 | 22.00 | |

The second printing appeared during the week of March 25, 2013.

CP10–CP18 (first printing) examples with guidelines at UL: multiply by 5; guidelines at UR: multiply by 3.
CP10–CP18 (second printing) examples with dotted guideline at UR: multiply by 3.

Postally used copies are scarce. Must be used in period. The 'trial period' ended in late July 2013 and kiosk machines were removed from all locations.

### *Second Issue*

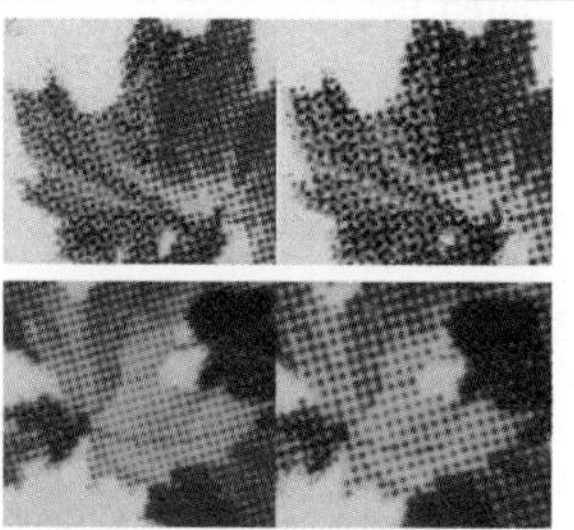

| First printing | Second printing |
|---|---|
| • maple leaf is composed of a pattern of small size dots. | • maple leaf is composed of a pattern of large size dots. |
| • CANADA is silver in colour and shiny. | • CANADA is gray in colour and is flat. |
| • two solid guidelines at the upper left edge or the upper right edge. Rolls either had alternating left and right solid guidelines every 8th label or right guidelines every 16th label. | • a dotted guideline at the upper right edge only. Reprinted rolls either had the dotted guideline every 16th label or none. |

**CP19**
Emily Carr (1871–1945)
*Indian War Canoe (Alert Bay)*, 1912

**CP20**
James Edward Hervey MacDonald (1873–1932)
*The Front of Winter*, 1928

**CP21**
Tom Thomson (1877–1917)
*In the Northland*, 1915

Post office code (first 6 digits):

105341: Vancouver, BC
105260: Edmonton, AB
104965: Richmond Hill, ON
105929: Toronto, ON
106038: Montreal, QC
105856: Vancouver, BC
105937: Vancouver, BC
106011: Toronto, ON

**CP22**
Albert Henry Robinson (1881–1956)
*Winter, Baie-Saint-Paul*, circa 1923

**CP23**
Arthur Lismer (1885–1969)
Little Haven, Nova Scotia, 1930

18-digit code

14-digit code

### *Landscapes by Canadian Painters*

Self-adhesive roll, dispensed in strips of 5 different designs; 18-digit code
Lowe-Martin‡

**2016, Oct 31*** **General Tag†** **Avery Dennison Paper**
**Serpentine Die cut 13.3x13.8**

| Unitrade | | NH–VF | ⊙F § | FDC |
|---|---|---|---|---|
| **CP19** | **multicoloured**, Carr | 5.00 | *8.00* | |
| i | 14-digit code | 1.75 | *4.00* | |
| **CP20** | **multicoloured**, MacDonald | 5.00 | *8.00* | |
| i | 14-digit code | 1.75 | *4.00* | |
| **CP21** | **multicoloured**, Thomson | 5.00 | *8.00* | |
| i | 14-digit code | 1.75 | *4.00* | |
| ii | 18-digit code, w/ partial "11" at bottom left | 10.00 | *15.00* | |
| **CP22** | **multicoloured**, Robinson | 5.00 | *8.00* | |
| i | 14-digit code | 1.75 | *4.00* | |
| **CP23** | **multicoloured**, Lismer | 5.00 | *8.00* | |
| i | 14-digit code | 1.75 | *4.00* | |
| ii | 18-digit code, w/ partial "11" at bottom left | 10.00 | *15.00* | |
| **CP19–23 strip of 5**, 18-digit code | | 25.00 | — | |
| **CP19–23 strip of 5**, 18-digit code, w/ partial "11" on bottom label | | 45.00 | — | |
| **CP19i–23i strip of 5**, 14-digit code♦ | | 8.75 | — | 10.00 |

♦ Strips of 5 with the 14-digit code '10534110310001' were sold to collectors via the National Philatelic Centre.

| Unitrade | | NH–VF | ⊙F § | FDC |
|---|---|---|---|---|
| **CP24** | **$1.20 multicoloured**, Carr | 7.00 | *10.00* | |
| i | 14-digit code | 2.50 | *3.50* | |
| **CP25** | **$1.20 multicoloured**, MacDonald | 7.00 | *10.00* | |
| i | 14-digit code | 2.50 | *3.50* | |
| **CP26** | **$1.20 multicoloured**, Thomson | 7.00 | *10.00* | |
| i | 14-digit code | 2.50 | *3.50* | |
| ii | 18-digit code, w/ partial "11" at bottom left | 17.00 | *20.00* | |
| **CP27** | **$1.20 multicoloured**, Robinson | 7.00 | *10.00* | |
| i | 14-digit code | 2.50 | *3.50* | |
| **CP28** | **$1.20 multicoloured**, Lismer | 7.00 | *10.00* | |
| i | 14-digit code | 2.50 | *3.50* | |
| ii | 18-digit code, w/ partial "11" at bottom left | 17.00 | *20.00* | |
| **CP24–28 strip of 5**, 18-digit code | | 35.00 | — | |
| **CP24–28 strip of 5**, 18-digit code, w/ partial "11" on bottom label | | 45.00 | — | |
| **CP24i–28i strip of 5**, 14-digit code | | 12.50 | — | |
| **CP29** | **$1.80 multicoloured**, Carr | 8.00 | *11.00* | |
| i | 14-digit code | 3.75 | *5.00* | |
| **CP30** | **$1.80 multicoloured**, MacDonald | 8.00 | *11.00* | |
| i | 14-digit code | 3.75 | *5.00* | |
| **CP31** | **$1.80 multicoloured**, Thomson | 8.00 | *11.00* | |
| i | 14-digit code | 3.75 | *5.00* | |
| ii | 18-digit code, w/ partial "11" at bottom left | 20.00 | *25.00* | |
| **CP32** | **$1.80 multicoloured**, Robinson | 8.00 | *11.00* | |
| i | 14-digit code | 3.75 | *5.00* | |

| Unitrade | | NH–VF | ⊙F § | FDC |
|---|---|---|---|---|
| **CP33** | **$1.80 multicoloured**, Lismer | 8.00 | *11.00* | |
| i | 14-digit code | 3.75 | *5.00* | |
| ii | 18-digit code, w/ partial "11" at bottom left | 20.00 | *25.00* | |
| **CP29–33 strip of 5**, 18-digit code | | 40.00 | — | |
| **CP29–33 strip of 5**, 18-digit code, w/ partial "11" on bottom label | | 55.00 | — | |
| **CP29i–33i strip of 5**, 14-digit code | | 18.75 | — | |
| **CP34** | **$2.50 multicoloured**, Carr | 12.50 | *15.00* | |
| i | 14-digit code | 5.00 | *6.00* | |
| **CP35** | **$2.50 multicoloured**, MacDonald | 12.50 | *15.00* | |
| i | 14-digit code | 5.00 | *6.00* | |
| **CP36** | **$2.50 multicoloured**, Thomson | 12.50 | *15.00* | |
| i | 14-digit code | 5.00 | *6.00* | |
| ii | 18-digit code, w/ partial "11" at bottom left | 25.00 | *30.00* | |
| **CP37** | **$2.50 multicoloured**, Robinson | 12.50 | *15.00* | |
| i | 14-digit code | 5.00 | *6.00* | |
| **CP38** | **$2.50 multicoloured**, Lismer | 12.50 | *15.00* | |
| i | 14-digit code | 5.00 | *6.00* | |
| ii | 18-digit code, w/ partial "11" at bottom left | 25.00 | *30.00* | |
| **CP34–38 strip of 5**, 18-digit code | | 60.00 | — | |
| **CP34–38 strip of 5**, 18-digit code, w/ partial "11" at bottom left | | 80.00 | — | |
| **CP34i–38i strip of 5**, 14-digit code | | 25.00 | — | |

* Canada Post says that a machine was functioning in Vancouver, BC as of this date. Collectors believe the machine was not in use until a couple of weeks later, around mid-November. The earliest known coded examples are dated '161119' (Nov. 19/16). Edmonton and Richmond Hill kiosk machines came online around mid-December 2016.

The 14-digit code, introduced to alleviate the problem of the longer 18-digit code being printed over the stamp design, appeared on November 26, 2016. The OFDC used only stamps with the 14-digit code, obviously printed well after the date of release.

‡ Base stamp designs/images were printed at Lowe-Martin in Ottawa, ON, Canada on Avery Dennison Paper. Denomination and numeric codes are printed via direct thermal print at the kiosks.

† one vertical tag bar down right side of stamp.

§ Stamps do not soak off paper without some damage to the stamp — it is recommended to leave any used stamps on paper.

Other labels exist with the "11" on bottom, but these came from misfed or misprinted strips. Only a few are known. The "11" print was removed by Canada Post from labels with the 14-digit code.

Strips of 6, 7, 8 and 10 are known. These are misfed errors. These strips will typically include 1 unprinted single and/or shifted thermal printing.

# SPECIAL DELIVERY STAMPS

E1

E2

E3

E4

E5

American Bank Note Company, Ottawa

**1898, Jun 28** — **Engraved** — **Perf 12**

| | | NH% | ★VF | ★F | ⊙VF | ⊙F | ✉ |
|---|---|---|---|---|---|---|---|
| **E1** | **10¢ blue green** | 300 | 250.00 | 60.00 | 15.00 | 7.50 | 110.00 |
| a | green | 200 | 200.00 | 80.00 | 15.00 | 7.50 | 110.00 |
| b | yellow green | 200 | 250.00 | 110.00 | 25.00 | 15.00 | 110.00 |
| ii | "no shading in value tablet" | 200 | 200.00 | 80.00 | 20.00 | 10.00 | 110.00 |
| iv | deep blue green | 300 | 400.00 | 125.00 | 30.00 | 20.00 | |
| | PB, plate 1 Top* block of 6 | 200 | 1,000.00 | 500.00 | | | |
| | PB, plate 2 Top† block of 4 | 200 | 750.00 | 450.00 | | | |

Qty: 3,667,500

* E1, plate 1 exists with and without the Printing Order Number.

† E1, plate 2 and E2i, plate 1 were 100 subject plates (10 x 10) with imprint above positions 5, 6 and 7. The sheets were guillotined between positions 5 and 6 for distribution to the post office, producing two incomplete UC imprint blocks of 4. UC Left Block shows only "OTTA", with guillotined edge at right; the UC Right Block shows "WA–No. 2–922F" with guillotined edge at left.

**No. E1 Plate proof**: one sheet of 50 + block of 23 stamps on India paper on card. Price $1,000.00 each.

Earliest recorded use July 2, 1898.

**SPECIAL DELIVERY PLATE PROOFS**

The plate proofs of Special Delivery issues are from the ABNC archives auction, September 30, 1990

American Bank Note Company, Ottawa

**1922, Sep** — **Engraved** — **Perf 12**

| | | NH% | ★VF | ★F | ⊙VF | ⊙F | ✉ |
|---|---|---|---|---|---|---|---|
| **E2** | **20¢ carmine**, dry printing, 42½ mm wide | 200 | 150.00 | 60.00 | 12.00 | 7.00 | 40.00 |
| a | scarlet shade, wet printing, 41 mm wide | 200 | 250.00 | 100.00 | 24.00 | 15.00 | 45.00 |
| ii | imperf. at bottom margin, dry printing (1 known) | | — | *4,000.00* | — | — | — |
| | PB, plate 1 TOP (dry) 44 mm wide (block of 4) | 200 | 1,500.00 | 750.00 | | | |
| | PB, plate 1 TOP (wet) 41 mm wide (block of 4) | 200 | 1,500.00 | 750.00 | | | |

Qty: 2,300,000

Sheets of E2 were perforated between panes, not guillotined.

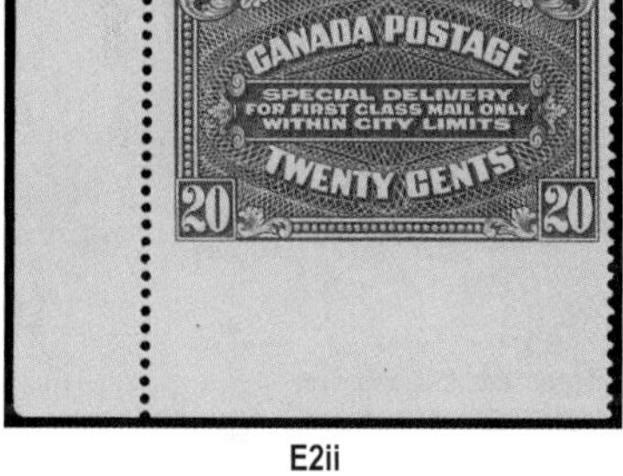
E2ii

## CONFEDERATION ISSUE

Canadian Bank Note Company, Limited

**1927, Jun 29** — **Perf 12**

| | | NH% | ★VF | ★F | ⊙VF | ⊙F | ✉ |
|---|---|---|---|---|---|---|---|
| **E3** | **20¢ orange** | 150 | 60.00 | 20.00 | 30.00 | 12.00 | 95.00*‡ |
| | PB, plate 1, UL, LL (6) | 150 | 350.00 | 125.00 | | | |
| a | imperf pair (250 pairs known) | 100 | 250.00 | 150.00 | — | — | — |
| | PB, imperf. block (6) | 100 | 1,500.00 | 1,000.00 | | | |
| b | horiz. pair, imperf. vert. (250 pairs known) | 100 | 250.00 | 150.00 | — | | — |
| | PB, horiz. pair, imperf. vert. (6) | 100 | 1,500.00 | 1,000.00 | | | |
| c | vert. pair, imperf. horiz. (250 pairs known) | 100 | 250.00 | 150.00 | — | — | — |
| | PB, vert. pair, imperf. horiz. (6) | 100 | 1,500.00 | 1,000.00 | | | |
| iii | top margin single, imperf. between stamp & margin (10 singles known) † | 100 | 1,000.00 | 700.00 | | | |

Qty: 671,400

* For well-centered stamp.

† All known examples show a fold in the margin.

‡ Commercial usage, non-philatelic: $120.00.

Issued to commemorate the 60th anniversary of Confederation. See also Nos. 141–145.

British American Bank Note Company

**Engraved** — **Perf 11**

| | | NH% | ★VF | ★F | ⊙VF | ⊙F | ✉ |
|---|---|---|---|---|---|---|---|
| **E4** | **20¢ henna brown**, *Sep 2, 1930* | 100 | 100.00 | 40.00 | 25.00 | 10.00 | 85.00 |
| | PB, plate 1, centre (4) | 100 | 400.00 | 250.00 | | | |
| | PB, plate 2, UL (4) | 100 | 400.00 | 250.00 | | | |

Qty: 950,000

| | | NH% | ★VF | ★F | ⊙VF | ⊙F | ✉ |
|---|---|---|---|---|---|---|---|
| **E5** | **20¢ henna brown**, *Dec 24, 1932* | 100 | 100.00 | 40.00 | 25.00 | 10.00 | 75.00 |
| | PB, plate 1, UL, UR (4) | 100 | 400.00 | 250.00 | | | |
| a | imperf. pair (75 pairs known) | 100 | 800.00 | 650.00 | — | — | — |
| | PB, imperf. (4) | 100 | 3,000.00 | 2,000.00 | | | |

Qty: 600,000

In this revised design, the bottom tablet reads "CENTS" only in place of "TWENTY CENTS".

Special Delivery

E6

Designer: Herman Herbert Schwartz. Based on a painting by Alonzo Earl Foringer.

Canadian Bank Note Company, Limited

**1935, Jun 1** **Engraved** **Perf 12**

| | | NH% | ★VF | ★F | ⊙VF | ⊙F | ✉ |
|---|---|---|---|---|---|---|---|
| **E6** | **20¢ dark carmine** | 75 | 16.00 | 8.00 | 10.00 | 6.00 | 40.00 |
| | PB, plate 1, UR, dot after "T" of NOTE (6) | 75 | 150.00 | 100.00 | | | |
| | PB, plate 1, UL, no dot after "T" of NOTE (6) | 75 | 150.00 | 100.00 | | | |
| | PB, plate 1, LL, "NO. 1" in side margin (4) | 75 | 100.00 | 60.00 | | | |
| **a** | imperf. pair (75 pairs known)* | 75 | 800.00 | 650.00 | — | — | — |
| | PB, imperf.(6) | 75 | 4,500.00 | 3,000.00 | | | |
| **i** | dot in right 2 | | 80.00 | 40.00 | 80.00 | 40.00 | |

Qty: 883,814

**No. E6 Plate proof**: Sheet of 100 and part sheet of 98, mounted on card. Sheet divided into 2 panes of 50 by a vertical gutter. Twenty gutter pairs exist.

Proof: pair $700; gutter pair $1,500.

E7

E8

E9

Canadian Bank Note Company, Limited

**Engraved** **Perf 12**

| | | NH% | ★VF | ★F | ⊙VF | ⊙F | ✉ |
|---|---|---|---|---|---|---|---|
| **E7** | **10¢ dark green**, *Apr 1, 1939* | 75 | 14.00 | 7.00 | 5.50 | 3.50 | 30.00 |
| | PB, plate 1 (4) | 75 | 60.00 | 40.00 | | | |
| | PB, plate 1, LL, "No. 1" in side margin (4) | 75 | 45.00 | 30.00 | | | |
| **a** | imperf. pair (75 pairs known)* | 75 | 800.00 | 650.00 | — | — | — |
| | PB, imperf. (4) | 75 | 3,000.00 | 2,000.00 | | | |

Qty: 2,305,450

* 1 pane of 50 thought to still be intact.

| | | NH% | ★VF | ★F | ⊙VF | ⊙F | ✉ |
|---|---|---|---|---|---|---|---|
| **E8** | **20¢ dark carmine**, *Jun 15, 1938* | 75 | 50.00 | 25.00 | 42.50 | 27.50 | 50.00 |
| | PB, plate 1, UL, UR (6) | 75 | 325.00 | 250.00 | | | |
| | PB, plate 1, LL, "No. 1" in side margin (4) | 75 | 275.00 | 175.00 | | | |
| **a** | imperf. pair (75 pairs known) | 75 | 800.00 | 650.00 | — | — | — |
| | PB, imperf. (6) | 75 | 4,500.00 | 3,000.00 | | | |

Qty: 200,000

**No. E8 Plate proofs**: Two sheets of 100, divided into 2 panes of 50 by vertical gutter, on card, 20 gutter pairs exist

Proof pair $700; gutter pair $1,500.

E9i

| | | NH% | ★VF | ★F | ⊙VF | ⊙F | ✉ |
|---|---|---|---|---|---|---|---|
| **E9** | **10¢ on 20¢ dark carmine**, *Mar 1, 1939* | 75 | 12.00 | 6.00 | 9.00 | 4.25 | 35.00† |
| **i** | broken "0" in right "10≡" surcharge | 75 | 75.00 | 50.00 | 75.00 | 50.00 | 75.00 |
| | PB, plate 1, UL, UR (6) | 75 | 85.00 | 45.00 | | | |
| | PB, plate 1, LL "No. 1" in side margin (4) | 75 | 60.00 | 30.00 | | | |

Qty: 300,000

† Commercial cover $65.00. Period of use was one month only: 1 March to 1 April.

A 'broken 0' on *left* surcharge, on cover exists, $100.00.

E10

E11

Designer: Herman Herbert Schwartz. Picture engraved by Silas Robert Allen.

## WAR ISSUE

Canadian Bank Note Company, Limited

Engraved — Perf 12

| | | NH% | ★VF | ★F | ⊙VF | ⊙F | ✉ |
|---|---|---|---|---|---|---|---|
| E10 | **10¢ green**, *Jul 1, 1942* | 50 | 6.00 | 2.50 | 2.75 | 1.50 | 15.00 |
| | PB, plate 1 (4) | 50 | 27.50 | 17.50 | | | |
| a | imperf. pair (75 pairs) | 50 | 800.00 | 650.00 | — | — | — |
| | PB, imperf. (4) | 50 | 3,000.00 | 2,000.00 | | | |

Qty: 3,276,404

## PEACE ISSUE

Canadian Bank Note Company, Limited

| | | NH% | ★VF | ★F | ⊙VF | ⊙F | ✉ |
|---|---|---|---|---|---|---|---|
| E11 | **10¢ green**, *Sep 16, 1946* | 50 | 5.00 | 2.00 | 1.75 | 1.10 | 15.00 |
| | PB, plate 1 (4) | 50 | 22.00 | 12.00 | | | |

Qty: 4,500,000

For **O.H.M.S.** overprint see number EO1. For **G** overprint see number EO2.

## REGISTRATION STAMPS

F1

F2

F3

**Usages:**

2¢: domestic (1875–89)
5¢: to USA; to other foreign destinations from 1878 after Canada joined UPU; domestic from May 1889
8¢: to United Kingdom (1876–77)

Covers of F1 (2¢) will include the 3¢ domestic letter rate postage (up to 1 ounce).

British American Bank Note Company

Unused stamps with no gum generally sell for 50–60% of the listed prices.

**1875–1896** — Engraved — Perf 12

| | | NH% | ★VF | ★F | ⊙VF | ⊙F | ✉ |
|---|---|---|---|---|---|---|---|
| F1 | **2¢ orange**, (ERD: *Dec 13, 1875*) | 200 | 150.00 | 75.00 | 9.00 | 3.00 | 55.00 |
| a | vermilion | 200 | 250.00 | 125.00 | 25.00 | 10.00 | 55.00 |
| b | rose carmine (1888) | 200 | 500.00 | 250.00 | 150.00 | 100.00 | 100.00 |
| c | imperf. pair, vermilion (only 1 pair known) | | | | | *4,000.00* | |
| d | perf. 12 x 11½ | 200 | 800.00 | 350.00 | 150.00 | 90.00 | 200.00 |
| i | orange red | 200 | 200.00 | 80.00 | 10.00 | 5.00 | 55.00 |
| ii | imperf. bottom margin | | 4,000.00 | 2,000.00 | | 1,300.00 | |
| iii | burr at UR corner (Pl. 1, pos. 38) | 200 | 600.00 | 300.00 | 150.00 | 90.00 | 200.00 |
| iv | burr to right of T of CENTS (Pl. 1, pos. 22) | 200 | 600.00 | 300.00 | 150.00 | 100.00 | 200.00 |
| v | major re-entry: doubling in right 2, right TWO CENTS, RED of REGISTERED, AMP of STAMP, ANA of CANADA, left TWO CENTS and short transfer below lower left T (Plate 1, pos. 40) | 200 | 600.00 | 300.00 | 150.00 | 100.00 | 200.00 |

Qty: 29,494,350

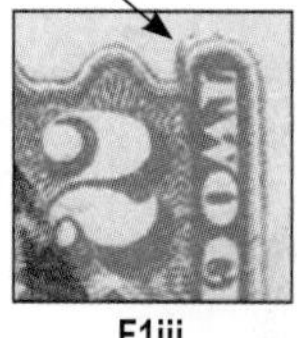
F1iii

F1iv

F1v

| | | NH% | ★VF | ★F | ⊙VF | ⊙F | ✉ |
|---|---|---|---|---|---|---|---|
| F2 | **5¢ dark green** (ERD: *Jan 12, 1876*) | 200 | 200.00 | 100.00 | 8.00 | 3.00 | 60.00 |
| a | blue green, *1888* | 200 | 220.00 | 110.00 | 8.00 | 3.00 | 60.00 |
| b | yellow green | 200 | 320.00 | 160.00 | 10.00 | 5.00 | 60.00 |
| c | imperf. pair (200 pairs recorded) | 100 | 1,500.00 | 900.00 | — | — | — |
| d | perf. 12 x 11½ | 200 | 3,000.00 | 1,250.00 | 400.00 | 200.00 | 600.00 |
| i | green | 200 | 200.00 | 100.00 | 8.00 | 3.00 | |
| ii | major re-entry in "N" of CANADA, and "S" of REGISTERED, and "ER" of LETTER (Pl. 2, pos. 77) | 200 | 500.00 | 250.00 | 150.00 | 100.00 | 200.00 |
| iii | missing right frameline (Pl. 3) | | | | | | |
| iv | misplaced entry (Pl. 2, pos. 85) | | | | | | |

Qty: 12,374,315

F2iii

| | | NH% | ★VF | ★F | ⊙VF | ⊙F | ✉ |
|---|---|---|---|---|---|---|---|
| F3 | **8¢ dull blue**, (ERD: *Mar 2, 1876*) | 500 | 900.00 | 350.00 | 450.00 | 225.00 | 20,000.00* |
| a | bright blue | 500 | 1,000.00 | 400.00 | 500.00 | 250.00 | 20,000.00* |
| ii | horiz. guide line through "I" of EIGHT at left (pos. 33) | 500 | 1,250.00 | 550.00 | 700.00 | 350.00 | — |
| iii | horiz. guide lines through "E" and "T" of CENTS at right (pos. 32) | 500 | 1,250.00 | 550.00 | 700.00 | 350.00 | — |

Qty: 78,971

* Price shown is for a VF cover with correct usage during 1876–1877 period.

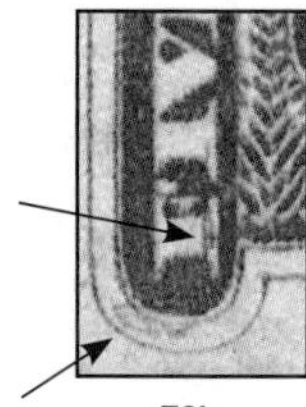
F2iv

F1–F3 plate blocks: sum of singles plus 50%.

Plate proofs: 2¢ - $1,500; 5¢ - $1,000; 8¢ - $2,500.

Special Delivery

# POSTAGE DUE STAMPS

Cover prices for J1–J20 are for single usages, with a postmark, tied to cover. Pen or crayon cancels and uncancelled stamps are valued at 60% less.

## FIRST POSTAGE DUE ISSUE

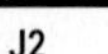

J1 J2

J3 J4 J5

(NH +100% unless marked)
Initial printings were by the "wet" printing method; the 1928 printings by the "dry" method.

American Bank Note Company, Ottawa

**1906–1928** **Engraved** **Perf 12**

| | | | NH% | ★VF | ★F | ⊙VF | ⊙F | ⊠ |
|---|---|---|---|---|---|---|---|---|
| **J1** | | **1¢ violet**, *Jul 1, 1906* | | 40.00 | 10.00 | 6.50 | 3.25 | 30.00 |
| | a | thin paper, *1924* | | 75.00 | 30.00 | 10.50 | 6.25 | — |
| | b | imperf. pair (w/o gum) (100 pairs) | (—) | 500.00 | 350.00 | — | — | — |
| | c | reddish violet, *1928* | | 40.00 | 10.00 | 6.50 | 3.25 | — |
| | i | pyramid guide, block of 4 | | 900.00 | — | 350.00 | | |
| | ii | R-gauge, block of 4 | | 900.00 | — | 400.00 | | |
| Qty: 18,870,000 | | | | | | | | |
| **J2** | | **2¢ violet**, *Jul 1, 1906* | | 40.00 | 10.00 | 1.40 | .75 | 20.00 |
| | a | thin paper, *1924* | | 75.00 | 30.00 | 14.00 | 7.50 | |
| | b | imperf. pair (w/o gum) (100 pairs) | (—) | 500.00 | 350.00 | — | — | — |
| | c | reddish violet, *1928* | | 40.00 | 10.00 | 1.40 | .75 | — |
| Qty: 44,178,000 | | | | | | | | |
| **J3** | | **4¢ reddish violet**, *Jul 3/28* | | 100.00 | 30.00 | 30.00 | 15.00 | 60.00 |
| Qty: 14,487,000 | | | | | | | | |
| **J4** | | **5¢ violet**, *Jul 1, 1906* | | 40.00 | 10.00 | 2.50 | 1.25 | * |
| | a | thin paper, reddish violet, *1924* | | 50.00 | 15.00 | 10.00 | 6.25 | — |
| | b | imperf. pair (w/o gum) (100 pairs) | (—) | 500.00 | 350.00 | — | — | — |
| | c | reddish violet, *1928* | | 40.00 | 10.00 | 2.50 | 1.25 | — |
| | ii | pyramid guide, block of 4 | (50) | 500.00 | 350.00 | | | |
| | iii | as J4a, pyramid guide, block of 4 | (50) | 300.00 | 200.00 | | | |
| | iv | R-Gauge, block of 4 | | 500.00 | 350.00 | | | |
| Qty: 13,000,000 | | | | | | | | |
| **J5** | | **10¢ reddish violet**, *Jul 3/28* | | 140.00 | 40.00 | 17.50 | 9.50 | * |
| Qty: 1,000,000 | | | | | | | | |
| **Nos. J1–J5** | | (5) Set | (100) | 360.00 | 100.00 | 57.90 | 30.00 | |

* No specific domestic single usage.

**Nos. J1–J5 Plate blocks**: All imprint pieces are scarce. Minimum value is double the total of the stamps in the piece.

For lathework on Postage Due stamps see the end of the "Admiral" section.

## SECOND POSTAGE DUE ISSUE

The only inscription is the numeral "1" in top margin. The perforation between columns 5 and 6 usually extends through the number.

J6 J7

J8 J9 J10

(NH +100%)

British American Bank Note Company

**1930–1932** **Engraved** **Perf 11**

| **(PB size)** | | | ★VF | ★F | ⊙VF | ⊙F | ⊠ |
|---|---|---|---|---|---|---|---|
| **J6** | | **1¢ dark violet** | 20.00 | 7.00 | 6.00 | 3.00 | 30.00 |
| | i | dull violet | 20.00 | 7.00 | 6.00 | 3.00 | 30.00 |
| (4) | | pl. 1(top) inverted | 300.00 | 200.00 | | | |
| Qty: 5,334,000 | | | | | | | |
| **J7** | | **2¢ dark violet** | 10.00 | 5.00 | 1.50 | .75 | 25.00 |
| | i | dull violet | 10.00 | 5.00 | 1.50 | .75 | 25.00 |
| (4) | | pl. 1(top) | 225.00 | 150.00 | | | |
| Qty: 10,758,000 | | | | | | | |
| **J8** | | **4¢ dark violet** | 20.00 | 8.00 | 7.50 | 2.50 | 30.00 |
| | i | dull violet | 20.00 | 8.00 | 7.50 | 2.50 | 30.00 |
| (4) | | pl. 1(top) inverted | 375.00 | 250.00 | | | |
| Qty: 2,443,000 | | | | | | | |
| **J9** | | **5¢ dark violet** | 30.00 | 10.00 | 9.00 | 4.50 | * |
| | i | dull violet | 30.00 | 10.00 | 9.00 | 4.50 | * |
| (4) | | pl. 1(top) | 375.00 | 250.00 | | | |
| (4) | | pl. 1(bottom) | 450.00 | 300.00 | | | |
| Qty: 523,000 | | | | | | | |
| **J10** | | **10¢ dark violet** | 160.00 | 70.00 | 15.00 | 7.50 | * |
| | i | dull violet | 160.00 | 70.00 | 15.00 | 7.50 | * |
| (4) | | pl. 1(top) | 750.00 | 500.00 | | | |
| | a | vert. pair, imperf. horiz. | 2,500.00 | 1,500.00 | — | | |
| (4) | | J10a in PB† | | *6,000.00* | | | |
| Qty: 309,000 | | | | | | | |
| **Nos. J6–J10** | | (5) Set | 250.00 | 100.00 | 39.00 | 18.25 | |

Only one sheet of 100 of the imperf. variety exists, and as the vertical perforations are positioned at a slight diagonal angle, most pairs are badly off-centre. Only 10 VF pairs exist from rows 3 and 4; off-centre VG pairs $750.

† The imperf. horiz plate block is unique. * No specific domestic single usage.

**TYPICAL DOMESTIC SINGLE USAGES OF THE POSTAGE DUE STAMPS (1906–1965)**

**Issues: A:** 1906–1928; **B:** 1930–1932; **C:** 1933–1934; **D:** 1935–1965

| Rate | Issue | Rating |
|---|---|---|
| 1¢ | A, B, C, D | Redirection of a local first class letter to a non local address |
| | | Undeliverable third class printed matter returned to sender |
| 2¢ | A, B, C, D | Shortpaid (local or forward) first class letters and post cards |
| | D | Undeliverable third class printed matter returned to sender |
| 3¢ | D | Undeliverable third class printed matter returned to sender |
| 4¢ | A, B, C, D | Upaid local first class letters |
| | A, B | Upaid forward first class letters |
| | A, B, C, D | Unpaid post cards |
| | B, C, D | Business reply envelopes and post cards |
| 5¢ | D | Business reply envelopes and post cards |
| 6¢ | D | Business reply envelopes |
| | D | Unpaid third class printed matter |
| 10¢ | D | Unpaid forward first class letters |

## THIRD POSTAGE DUE ISSUE

J11 J12 J13 J14

J11–J14 PLATE BLOCKS: "PLATE NO. 1" appears in the upper and lower margins.

(NH +100%)

British American Bank Note Company

**1933–1934** **Engraved** **Perf 11**

| | | ★VF | ★F | ⊙VF | ⊙F | ✉ |
|---|---|---|---|---|---|---|
| **J11** | **1¢ dark violet**, *May 5, 1934* | 25.00 | 10.00 | 9.00 | 5.00 | 30.00 |
| | plate block | 115.00 | 60.00 | | | |
| a | imperf. pair (100 pairs) | 500.00 | 350.00 | — | — | — |
| | plate block | 2,250.00 | 1,500.00 | | | |
| Qty: 2,070,000 | | | | | | |
| **J12** | **2¢ dark violet**, *Dec 20, 1933* | 15.00 | 6.00 | 1.75 | .95 | 25.00 |
| | plate block | 90.00 | 50.00 | | | |
| Qty: 4,390,000 | | | | | | |
| **J13** | **4¢ dark violet**, *Dec 12, 1933* | 25.00 | 10.00 | 11.00 | 5.50 | 30.00 |
| | plate block | 100.00 | 60.00 | | | |
| Qty: 1,900,000 | | | | | | |
| **J14** | **10¢ dark violet**, *Dec 20, 1933* | 50.00 | 20.00 | 10.00 | 5.00 | * |
| | plate block | 225.00 | 150.00 | | | |
| Qty: 500,000 | | | | | | |
| **Nos. J11–J14** (4) Set | | 115.00 | 44.00 | 30.75 | 15.95 | |

* No specific domestic single usage.

## FOURTH POSTAGE DUE ISSUE

J15 J16 J16B J17 J18 J19 J20

Plate Blocks are listed after J20

(NH +50%)

Canadian Bank Note Company, Limited

**1935–1965** **Engraved** **Perf 12**

| | | ★VF | ★F | ⊙VF | ⊙F | ✉ |
|---|---|---|---|---|---|---|
| **J15** | **1¢ dark violet**, *Oct 14, 1935* | .40 | .20 | .25 | .20 | 20.00 |
| a | imperf. pair (100 pairs) | 300.00 | 150.00 | — | — | — |
| b | red violet, *1940* | 3.00 | 1.50 | .75 | .45 | — |
| ii | HB paper | 20.00 | 10.00 | 6.00 | 4.00 | — |
| Qty: 51,429,000 | | | | | | |
| **J16** | **2¢ dark violet**, *Sep 9, 1935* | .40 | .20 | .25 | .20 | 15.00 |
| ii | reverse offset | 200.00 | | | | |
| a | imperf. pair (100 pairs) | 300.00 | 150.00 | — | — | — |
| c | red violet | 3.00 | 1.50 | .75 | .45 | — |
| i | HB paper | 20.00 | 10.00 | 5.00 | 3.50 | — |
| Qty: 93,710,000 | | | | | | |
| **J16B** | **3¢ dark violet**, *Apr 1965* | 2.50 | 2.25 | 2.00 | 1.50 | 60.00 |
| Qty: 3,020,000 | | | | | | |
| **J17** | **4¢ dark violet**, *Jul 2, 1935* | .40 | .30 | .25 | .20 | 20.00 |
| a | imperf. pair (100 pairs) | 300.00 | 150.00 | — | — | — |
| b | red violet | 2.50 | 1.25 | .75 | .45 | — |
| Qty: 61,502,000 | | | | | | |
| **J18** | **5¢ dark violet**, *Aug 11, 1948* | .50 | .45 | .50 | .40 | 30.00 |
| a | red violet | 4.00 | 2.00 | 1.50 | 1.00 | — |
| Qty: 20,666,000 | | | | | | |
| **J19** | **6¢ dark violet**, *Jan 16, 1957* | 2.50 | 2.20 | 2.20 | 1.90 | 25.00 |
| i | HB paper | 20.00 | 10.00 | 6.00 | 4.00 | — |
| Qty: 9,500,000 | | | | | | |
| **J20** | **10¢ dark violet**, *Sep 16, 1935* | .50 | .35 | .25 | .20 | 20.00 |
| a | imperf. pair (100 pairs) | 300.00 | 150.00 | — | — | — |
| b | red violet | 2.50 | 1.25 | .75 | .50 | — |
| Qty: 65,963,000 | | | | | | |
| **Nos. J15–J20, J16B** (7) Set | | 7.20 | 5.95 | 5.45 | 3.20 | |

Most of the imperf. pairs have slightly disturbed gum due to poor storage. Specimens with perfect gum are scarce.

**PLATE BLOCKS (1935–1965)**

On this issue, inscriptions appear in the Upper Centre and Lower Centre margins as follows:

**UC Left**: above stamps 3, 4 and 5, starting above left edge of stamp 3.

**UC Right**: above stamps 6, 7 and 8, starting above centre of stamp 6.

**LC Left**: below stamps 93, 94 and 95, starting below left edge of stamp 93.

**LC Right**: below stamps 96, 97 and 98, starting below centre of stamp 96.

A fifth inscription, with the plate number and order number (No. 1 501, etc.), appears in the LL side margin, reading up.

Premiums: VF +50%, NH +50%

| | | ★F | | |
|---|---|---|---|---|
| | Pl No | Block of 10 | Block of 6 | LL Block of 4 |
| **J15** | 1 | 5.00 | 4.00 | 2.50 |
| a | imperf. block | | 1,250 | |
| b | 1 | 27.50 | 20.00 | 12.00 |
| ii | 1 hibrite | 300.00 | 200.00 | 150.00 |
| **J16** | 1 | 5.00 | 4.00 | 2.50 |
| a | imperf. block | | 1,250 | |
| | 2 | 10.00 | 8.00 | 5.00 |
| i | 1 hibrite | 300.00 | 200.00 | 150.00 |
| c | | 27.50 | 20.00 | 12.00 |
| **J16B** | 1 | 40.00 | 30.00 | 20.00 |
| **J17** | 1 | 6.00 | 5.00 | 3.00 |
| a | imperf. block | | 1,250 | |
| b | | 27.50 | 20.00 | 12.00 |
| **J18** | 1 | 8.00 | 6.50 | 4.00 |
| a | 1 | 40.00 | 30.00 | 20.00 |
| **J19** | 1 | 30.00 | 25.00 | 15.00 |
| i | 1 hibrite | 300.00 | 200.00 | 150.00 |
| **J20** | 1 | 7.00 | 5.50 | 3.50 |
| a | imperf. block | | 1,250 | |
| b | 1 | 35.00 | 25.00 | 17.50 |

## CENTENNIAL POSTAGE DUES (aka "Red Dues")

Cover prices for J21–J40 are for single usages with a postmark, tied to cover. Pen or crayon cancels and uncancelled stamps are valued much lower.

In keeping with established Canadian philatelic practice, we have arranged the "Centennial" series into four groupings. However, the original Scott numbering system has been retained for consistency.

| Centennial Postage Dues | | | | |
|---|---|---|---|---|
| | First Issue 1967 | Second Issue 1969 | Third Issue 1973–1974 | Fourth Issue 1977–1978 |
| Perforation | 12 | | | 12½x12 |
| Stamp size | 25x21½mm | 24x20½mm | | |
| Image size | 20x17mm | 19½x15¾mm | | |
| Gum | Dex | | PVA | |

### "FIRST ISSUE"

J21

J22

J23

J24

J25

J26

J27

Stamp size: 25x21½mm; Design size: 20x17mm

Canadian Bank Note Company, Limited

**1967, Feb 8** — **DF Paper, Dex gum** — **Perf 12**

| | | NH–VF | ⊙VF | PB | ✉ |
|---|---|---|---|---|---|
| **J21** | **1¢ carmine rose** | .25 | .25 | 10.00 | 15.00 |
| **J22** | **2¢ carmine rose** | .30 | .30 | 1.75 | 15.00 |
| i | very dull paper | 1.00 | 1.00 | 6.00 | — |
| ii | F paper | 10.00 | 2.00 | 60.00† | — |
| **J23** | **3¢ carmine rose** | .30 | .30 | 1.75 | 50.00 |
| i | very dull paper | 1.00 | 1.00 | 6.00 | — |
| **J24** | **4¢ carmine rose** | .40 | .40 | 3.50 | * |
| i | very dull paper | 1.50 | 1.50 | 8.00 | — |
| **J25** | **5¢ carmine rose** | 2.00 | 2.00 | 12.00 | 25.00 |
| i | very dull paper | 2.50 | 2.50 | 17.50 | — |
| **J26** | **6¢ carmine rose** | .40 | .40 | 3.50 | 20.00 |
| i | very dull paper | .50 | .50 | 3.50 | — |
| **J27** | **10¢ carmine rose** | .50 | .40 | 3.50 | 15.00 |
| i | very dull paper | .50 | .50 | 3.50 | — |
| **Nos. J21–J27** (7) Set | | 4.15 | 4.05 | 36.00 | |

* No specific domestic single usage.

† Blank corner block of 4.

### "SECOND ISSUE"

J28

J31

J32a

J34i

J35

J36

Stamp size: 24x20½mm; Design size: 19½x15¾mm

Canadian Bank Note Company, Limited

**1969** — **DF Paper, Dex gum** — **Perf 12**

| | | NH–VF | ⊙VF | PB | ✉ |
|---|---|---|---|---|---|
| **J28** | **1¢ carmine rose** | .60 | .50 | 3.50 | * |
| **J31** | **4¢ carmine rose** | .50 | .40 | 2.50 | * |
| **J32a** | **5¢ carmine rose** | 20.00 | 20.00 | 100.00 | 50.00 |
| **J34i** | **8¢ carmine rose** | .50 | .25 | 2.75 | 25.00 |
| ii | HB | 1.50 | 1.50 | 10.00 | — |
| **J35** | **10¢ carmine rose** | .75 | .25 | 3.00 | 15.00 |
| **J36** | **12¢ carmine rose** | 1.00 | .75 | 6.00 | 15.00 |
| iii | HB | 1.75 | 1.75 | 11.00 | — |
| **Nos. J28, J31, J32a, J34i, J35 J36** (6) Set | | 23.35 | 22.05 | 117.75 | |

* No specific domestic single usage.

This issue was printed on plain paper with dextrine gum.

Issue months: Jan: 8¢, 12¢; Feb: 5¢; Apr: 4¢, 10¢; Dec: 1¢

**TYPICAL DOMESTIC SINGLE USAGES OF THE POSTAGE DUE STAMPS (1967–1978)**

**Issues: E:** 1967; **F:** 1969; **G:** 1973–1974; **H:** 1977–1978

| Rate | Issue | Rating |
|---|---|---|
| 1¢ | E | Redirection of a local first class letter to a non local address |
| 2¢ | E, G | Shortpaid (local or forward) first class letters and post cards |
| 3¢ | E | Undeliverable third class printed matter returned to sender |
| 5¢ | E | Business reply post cards |
| | E, F | Undeliverable third class printed matter returned to sender |
| 6¢ | E | Business reply envelopes |
| | E | Unpaid third class printed matter |
| | E, G | Undeliverable third class printed matter returned to sender |
| 8¢ | F | Business reply envelopes and post cards |
| | G | Undeliverable third class printed matter returned to sender |
| 10¢ | E | Unpaid forward first class letters |
| | E, F | Unpaid third class printed matter |
| | G, H | Undeliverable third class printed matter returned to sender |
| 12¢ | F | Unpaid first class letters and post cards |
| | F, G | Unpaid third class printed matter |
| | H | Undeliverable third class printed matter returned to sender |
| 16¢ | G | Unpaid first class letters and post cards |
| 20¢ | H | Unpaid third class printed matter |
| 24¢ | H | Unpaid first class letters and post cards |
| 50¢ | H | "Request for Additional Delivery" fee |

## "THIRD ISSUE"

J28i

J29

J30

J31i

J33

J34

J35i

J36i

J37

Stamp size: 24x20½mm; Design size: 19½x15¾mm; Imprints at top or bottom.
Canadian Bank Note Company, Limited

**1973–1974** **DF Paper, PVA gum** **Perf 12**

| | | NH–VF | ⊙VF | PB | ⊠ |
|---|---|---|---|---|---|
| J28i | **1¢ carmine rose**, DF paper | 2.00 | † | 10.00 | * |
| ii | ribbed-effect paper | .50 | .35 | 2.50 | — |
| iii | HB paper | 10.00 | 3.00 | 50.00 | — |
| J29 | **2¢ carmine rose**, DF paper | .30 | .25 | 2.00 | 15.00 |
| i | ribbed-effect paper | .50 | .25 | 2.50 | — |
| ii | HB paper | 20.00 | 4.00 | 100.00 | — |
| J30 | **3¢ carmine rose**, DF paper | .30 | .25 | 2.00 | * |
| i | ribbed-effect paper | .50 | .50 | 2.50 | — |
| ii | HB paper | 10.00 | 4.00 | 50.00 | — |
| J31i | **4¢ carmine rose**, DF paper | 5.00 | † | 25.00 | * |
| ii | ribbed-effect paper | .50 | .25 | 2.50 | — |
| iii | HB paper | 5.00 | 4.00 | 25.00 | — |
| b | printed on gum side, HB paper | 2,000.00 | — | — | — |
| J33 | **6¢ carmine rose**, DF paper | .30 | .25 | 1.50 | 15.00 |
| i | LF paper | .50 | .50 | 2.50 | — |
| ii | HB paper | 10.00 | 4.00 | 50.00 | — |
| iii | ribbed-effect paper | .50 | .25 | 2.50 | — |
| J34 | **8¢ carmine rose**, DF paper | .30 | † | 1.50 | 15.00 |
| iii | LF paper | 1.00 | 1.00 | 5.00 | — |
| J35i | **10¢ carmine rose**, DF paper | .30 | † | 1.50 | 15.00 |
| ii | LF paper | 1.00 | 1.00 | 5.00 | — |
| iii | ribbed-effect paper, strongly speckled MF | 15.00 | 10.00 | 75.00 | — |
| J36i | **12¢ carmine rose**, DF paper | .50 | † | 2.50 | 15.00 |
| ii | LF paper | 5.00 | 1.50 | 25.00 | — |
| J37 | **16¢ carmine rose**, DF paper | 5.00 | 4.00 | 25.00 | 15.00 |
| i | LF paper | .50 | .35 | 2.50 | — |
| ii | nick above last A of Canada (col 9) | 5.00 *EP* | 3.00 | 15.00 | |
| iii | line to left of 1 of 16 (col 4) | 5.00 *EP* | 3.00 | | |
| **Nos. J28i, J29, J30, J31i, J33, J34, J35i, J36i, J37** (9) Set | | 14.00 | | 71.00 | |

† The "Second" and "Third" issues are indistinguishable once the gum is removed.
* No specific domestic single usage.

Issue months: 1973: 2¢, 6¢, 10¢, 12¢;
Jan 74: 1¢, 3¢, 4¢, 8¢, 16¢

J37ii

J37iii

## "FOURTH ISSUE"

J28a

J31a

J32

J34a

J35a

J36a

J38

J39

J40

Stamp size: 24x20½mm; Design size: 19½x15¾mm; Imprints at sides.
Canadian Bank Note Company, Limited

**1977–1978** **DF Paper, PVA gum** **Perf 12.5x12.0**

| | | NH–VF | ⊙VF | PB | ⊠ |
|---|---|---|---|---|---|
| J28a | **1¢ carmine rose** | .25 | .25 | .50 | * |
| ai | white mark in front of A (pos 22) | 20.00 *EP* | 20.00 | | |
| J31a | **4¢ carmine rose** | .25 | .25 | .50 | * |
| J32 | **5¢ carmine rose** | .25 | .25 | .75 | * |
| J34a | **8¢ carmine rose** | .50 | .25 | 3.00 | * |
| J35a | **10¢ carmine rose**, DF paper | .30 | .25 | 1.50 | 20.00 |
| iii | LF paper | .30 | .25 | 1.50 | 20.00 |
| J36a | **12¢ carmine rose** | 2.00 | 1.00 | 15.00 | 20.00 |
| J38 | **20¢ carmine rose** | .60 | .50 | 3.00 | 20.00 |
| J39 | **24¢ carmine rose** | .75 | .50 | 3.50 | 20.00 |
| J40 | **50¢ carmine rose** | 1.25 | 1.00 | 6.00 | *† |
| **Nos. J28a, J31a, J32, J34a, J35a, J36a, J38, J39, J40** (9) Set | | 5.75 | 3.85 | 33.75 | |

* No specific domestic single usage.
† A properly rated, single use cover sold in Oct '04 for $150.00.

Issue dates: Sep 77: 10¢, 12¢; Dec 9/77: 1¢, 4¢, 5¢, 20¢, 24¢, 50¢; Jun 28/78: 8¢

J28ai

**The usage of postage due stamps was discontinued as of January 1, 1982.**

Postage Due

## WAR TAX STAMPS

MR1

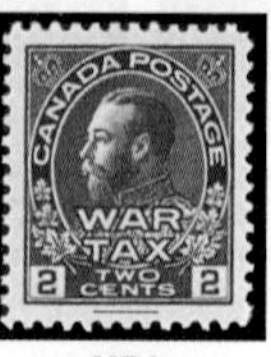
MR2

American Bank Note Company, Ottawa

| 1915, Apr 15 | Engraved | NH% | ★VF | ★F | ⊙VF | ⊙F | Perf 12 ✉ |
|---|---|---|---|---|---|---|---|
| MR1 | **1¢ green** | 200 | 40.00 | 10.00 | .50 | .20 | 2.00 |
| MR2 | **2¢ carmine** | 200 | 40.00 | 10.00 | .50 | .20 | 5.00 |
| a | rose carmine | 200 | 50.00 | 10.00 | .75 | .30 | 5.00 |
| xx | No. MR2, precancelled [2 styles] | | | | | 50.00 | |

MR2B MR2Bi

MR2C MR2Ci

MR2D

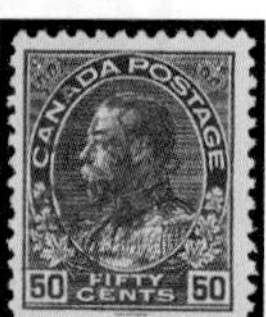
MR2Di

| No. | Description | NH% | ★VF | ★F | ⊙VF | ⊙F | ✉ |
|---|---|---|---|---|---|---|---|
| MR2B | **5¢ blue**, overprinted WAR TAX in black | 300 | 400.00 | 150.00 | 250.00 | 100.00 | *500.00* |
| i | overprinted INLAND REVENUE WAR TAX* | 300 | 300.00 | 120.00 | 150.00 | 40.00 | |
| MR2C | **20¢ olive green**, overprinted WAR TAX in black | 300 | 180.00 | 80.00 | 150.00 | 40.00 | *500.00* |
| i | overprinted INLAND REVENUE WAR TAX* | 300 | 200.00 | 90.00 | 150.00 | 40.00 | |
| MR2D | **50¢ black**, overprinted WAR TAX in red | 300 | 500.00 | 180.00 | 300.00 | 80.00 | *500.00* |
| i | overprinted INLAND REVENUE WAR TAX* | 300 | 500.00 | 180.00 | 200.00 | 60.00 | |

The 5¢ to 50¢ values were overprinted "WAR / TAX" in two lines and released on February 12, 1915. These were intended for fiscal use, the tax on postal matter being only 1¢. A few were postally used.

* Overprinted "INLAND / REVENUE / WAR / TAX" in 4 diagonal lines.

For lathework on Admiral War Tax stamps see the end of the "Admiral" section.

MR3

MR4

MR5

American Bank Note Company, Ottawa

| 1915–1916 | Engraved | NH% | ★VF | ★F | ⊙VF | ⊙F | Perf 12 ✉ |
|---|---|---|---|---|---|---|---|
| MR3 | **2¢ + 1¢ carmine** (Die I), *Jan 1, 1916* | 200 | 60.00 | 15.00 | .25 | .20 | 2.00 |
| a | carmine (Die II), *Aug 22, 1916* | 200 | 400.00 | 150.00 | 6.00 | 3.50 | 10.00 |
| b | rose red (Die I) (ERD: *Jun 23, 1916*) | 200 | 75.00 | 20.00 | .50 | .25 | 2.00 |
| xx | No. MR3, precancelled [2 styles] | | | | | 200.00 | |
| MR4 | **2¢ + 1¢ brown** (Die II), *Aug 29, 1916* | 200 | 40.00 | 10.00 | .25 | .20 | 1.50 |
| a | brown (Die I), *Sep 16, 1916* | 200 | 1,350.00 | 400.00 | 14.00 | 8.00 | 20.00 |
| b | imperf. pair (Die I), issued without gum (shades) | — | 275.00 | 175.00 | — | — | — |
| c | imperf. pair (Die II), issued without gum (50 pairs) | — | 3,000.00 | 1,500.00 | — | — | — |
| i | yellow brown (Die II) | 200 | 40.00 | 10.00 | .25 | .20 | 1.50 |
| ii | as "i", horiz. pair, imperf. vert. (Die I) | * | 750.00 | 375.00 | — | — | — |
| iii | as "MR4", horiz. pair, imperf. vert. (Die I) | * | 750.00 | 375.00 | — | — | — |
| iv | vert. pair, imperf. horiz. (Die I) | * | 750.00 | 375.00 | — | — | — |
| xx | No. MR4, precancelled [11 styles] | | | | | 20.00 | |

* issued without gum

| No. | Description | NH% | ★VF | ★F | ⊙VF | ⊙F | ✉ |
|---|---|---|---|---|---|---|---|
| MR5 | **2¢ + 1¢ carmine**, perf. 12 x 8 (ERD: *Jul 27, 1916*) | 200 | 80.00 | 30.00 | 40.00 | 25.00 | 50.00 |
| i | bright rose red (Die I) | 200 | 125.00 | 60.00 | 60.00 | 30.00 | 50.00 |

**Die I**

A single coloured line between 2 white lines below the large letter T.

**Die II**

The right half of the coloured line is replaced by 2 short diagonal lines and 5 small dots.

War Tax Stamps

## COIL STAMPS

MR6

MR7

American Bank Note Company, Ottawa

| 1916 | | Engraved NH% | ★VF | ★F | ⊙VF | ⊙F | Perf 8 vert ✉ |
|---|---|---|---|---|---|---|---|
| MR6 | **2¢ + 1¢ carmine** (Die I), *Mar 1916* | 200 | 200.00 | 80.00 | 15.00 | 6.00 | 20.00 |
| | pair | 200 | 400.00 | 160.00 | 150.00 | 50.00 | 75.00† |
| | strip of 4 | 200 | 800.00 | 320.00 | 300.00 | 100.00 | |
| i | paste-up pair | 200 | 450.00 | 180.00 | | | |
| ii | rose carmine (Die I) | 200 | 225.00 | 100.00 | 15.00 | 6.00 | 20.00 |
| | pair | 200 | 450.00 | 200.00 | 150.00 | 50.00 | 75.00† |
| | strip of 4, rose carmine | 200 | 900.00 | 400.00 | 300.00 | 100.00 | |
| iii | paste-up pair | 200 | 500.00 | 220.00 | | | |

† Commercial cover.

| | | NH% | ★VF | ★F | ⊙VF | ⊙F | ✉ |
|---|---|---|---|---|---|---|---|
| MR7 | **2¢ + 1¢ brown** (Die II), *Dec 1916* | 200 | 70.00 | 20.00 | 3.00 | 1.00 | 15.00 |
| | pair | 200 | 140.00 | 40.00 | 20.00 | 10.00 | |
| | strip of 4 | 200 | 280.00 | 80.00 | 40.00 | 20.00 | |
| i | paste-up pair | 200 | 160.00 | 50.00 | | | |
| a | brown (Die I) | 200 | 250.00 | 125.00 | 10.00 | 5.00 | 20.00 |
| | pair | 200 | 500.00 | 250.00 | 100.00 | 50.00 | |
| | strip of 4, brown (Die I) | 200 | 1,000.00 | 500.00 | 200.00 | 100.00 | |
| ii | paste-up pair | 200 | 550.00 | 225.00 | | | |
| iii | yellow brown (Die I) | 200 | 250.00 | 125.00 | 10.00 | 6.00 | 18.00 |
| | pair | 200 | 500.00 | 250.00 | 100.00 | 50.00 | |
| | strip of 4, yellow brown (Die I) | 200 | 1,000.00 | 500.00 | 200.00 | 100.00 | |
| iv | paste-up pair | 200 | 600.00 | 250.00 | | | |
| v | paste-up pair, I and II se-tenant | 200 | — | 550.00 | | | |



War Tax Stamps

# PERFORATED OFFICIAL STAMPS

The Department of Finance began perforating regular issue postage stamps "OHMS" (On His Majesty's Service) in 1923, for use by its provincial offices. In 1935, the Post Office Department became responsible for perforating official stamps supplied to government offices, and after June 30, 1939, all postage stamps for use by the government had to be perforated OHMS. The perforating of postage stamps for use on official government mail continued until 1949.

There are eight different orientations of the OHMS perforation relative to the postage stamp. Values for different orientations can vary from a few cents to many dollars. This catalogue lists only the most common variety in each case. For a complete listing and pricing of the many varieties, reference should be made to a more specialized catalogue of perforated official stamps.

The numbers for perforated official stamps are from the 10th edition of *The Catalogue and Guidebook of Canadian Official Stamps*, published by J & M Publishing Co. Ltd., with the permission of the publisher.

Used prices only are given for the large OHMS perforated stamps. Mint stamps are almost non-existent. Coil stamps exist with OHMS but are not listed. VF stamps must have no damaged perforations caused by the positioning of the perfin.

There is a "missing pin in S" variety that can be found on most of the 5-hole OHMS. Premium of 20% for this variety over the listed "normal" prices.

Plate blocks exist. Value add 50% to the sum of value listed for singles in the block.

## LARGE OHMS

### 5 HOLES IN VERTICAL BARS OF H
### ADMIRAL ISSUE
### 1912–1925

| | Used: VF | F |
|---|---|---|
| **OA104** 1c green | 100.00 | 50.00 |
| **OA105** 1¢ yellow, Die I | 80.00 | 40.00 |
| d 1¢ yellow, Die II | 90.00 | 45.00 |
| **OA106** 2¢ carmine | 80.00 | 40.00 |
| **OA107** 2¢ green | 60.00 | 30.00 |
| a 2¢ green, thin paper | 70.00 | 35.00 |
| **OA108** 3¢ brown | 80.00 | 40.00 |
| **OA109** 3¢ carmine Die I | 70.00 | 35.00 |
| c 3¢ carmine, Die II | 100.00 | 50.00 |
| **OA110** 4¢ olive bistre | 180.00 | 90.00 |
| **OA111** 5¢ dark blue | 120.00 | 60.00 |
| **OA112** 5¢ violet | 100.00 | 50.00 |
| a 5¢ violet, thin paper | 120.00 | 60.00 |
| **OA113** 7¢ yellow ochre | 160.00 | 80.00 |
| **OA114** 7¢ red brown | 120.00 | 60.00 |
| **OA115** 8¢ blue | 200.00 | 100.00 |
| **OA116** 10¢ plum | 120.00 | 60.00 |
| **OA117** 10¢ blue | 110.00 | 55.00 |
| **OA118** 10¢ bistre brown | 60.00 | 30.00 |
| **OA119** 20¢ olive green | 120.00 | 60.00 |
| **OA120** 50¢ black brown | 160.00 | 80.00 |
| a 50¢ black | 220.00 | 110.00 |
| **OA122** $1 orange | 180.00 | 90.00 |
| **OA129** 3¢ brown | 600.00 | 300.00 |
| **OA135** 3¢ yellow brown | 700.00 | 350.00 |
| All 25 above | 4,000.00 | 2,000.00 |

### CONFEDERATION & HISTORICAL ISSUES
### 1927

| | VF | F |
|---|---|---|
| **OA141** 1¢ Sir John A. Macdonald | 150.00 | 75.00 |
| **OA142** 2¢ Fathers of Confederation | 200.00 | 100.00 |
| **OA143** 3¢ Parliament Buildings | 200.00 | 100.00 |
| **OA144** 5¢ Sir Wilfred Laurier | 150.00 | 75.00 |
| **OA145** 12¢ Map of Canada | 500.00 | 250.00 |
| **OA146** 5¢ Thomas D'Arcy McGee | 160.00 | 80.00 |
| **OA147** 12¢ Macdonald & Laurier | 500.00 | 250.00 |
| **OA148** 20¢ Baldwin & Lafontaine | 400.00 | 200.00 |
| **OA141–OA148** (8) | 2,260.00 | 1,130.00 |

### SCROLL ISSUE
### 1928

| | Used: VF | F |
|---|---|---|
| **OA149** 1¢ orange | 90.00 | 45.00 |
| **OA150** 2¢ green | 50.00 | 25.00 |
| **OA151** 3¢ dark carmine | 180.00 | 90.00 |
| **OA152** 4¢ bistre | 220.00 | 110.00 |
| **OA153** 5¢ violet | 80.00 | 40.00 |
| **OA154** 8¢ blue | 200.00 | 100.00 |
| **OA155** 10¢ Mt. Hurd | 70.00 | 35.00 |
| **OA156** 12¢ Quebec Bridge | 550.00 | 275.00 |
| **OA157** 20¢ Harvesting | 120.00 | 60.00 |
| **OA158** 50¢ Bluenose | 900.00 | 450.00 |
| **OA159** $1 Parliament Buildings | 700.00 | 350.00 |
| **OA149–OA159** (11) Set | 3,160.00 | 1,580.00 |

### LEAF ISSUE
### 1930

| | VF | F |
|---|---|---|
| **OA162** 1¢ orange | 70.00 | 35.00 |
| **OA163** 1¢ deep green, Die II | 50.00 | 25.00 |
| b 1¢ deep green, Die I | 60.00 | 30.00 |
| **OA164** 2¢ dull green | 200.00 | 100.00 |
| **OA165** 2¢ deep red, Die I | 70.00 | 35.00 |
| a 2¢ deep red, Die II | 60.00 | 30.00 |
| **OA166** 2¢ dark brown, Die II | 60.00 | 30.00 |
| b 2¢ dark brown, Die I | 80.00 | 40.00 |
| **OA167** 3¢ deep red | 50.00 | 25.00 |
| **OA168** 4¢ yellow bistre | 160.00 | 80.00 |
| **OA169** 5¢ dull violet | 80.00 | 40.00 |
| **OA170** 5¢ dull blue | 70.00 | 35.00 |
| **OA171** 8¢ dark blue | 150.00 | 75.00 |
| **OA172** 8¢ red orange | 140.00 | 70.00 |
| **OA173** 10¢ Library of Parliament | 50.00 | 25.00 |
| **OA174** 12¢ Quebec Citadel | 400.00 | 200.00 |
| **OA175** 20¢ Harvesting Wheat | 100.00 | 50.00 |
| **OA176** 50¢ Grand Pre | 350.00 | 175.00 |
| **OA177** $1 Mt. Edith Cavell | 500.00 | 250.00 |
| **OA162–OA177** (16) Set | 2,500.00 | 1,250.00 |
| all 19 above | 2,700.00 | 1,350.00 |

### DEFINITIVES
### 1931–1932

| | VF | F |
|---|---|---|
| **OA184** 3¢ Admiral Provisional, Perf. 12 x 8 | 200.00 | 100.00 |
| **OA190** 10¢ Georges Etienne Cartier | 100.00 | 50.00 |
| **OA191** 3¢ on 2¢ surcharge, Die II | 80.00 | 40.00 |
| a as above, Die I | 100.00 | 50.00 |
| **OA184–OA191a** (4) | 480.00 | 240.00 |

### IMPERIAL ECONOMIC CONFERENCE
### 1932

| | Used: VF | F |
|---|---|---|
| **OA192** 3¢ King George V | 80.00 | 40.00 |
| **OA193** 5¢ Prince of Wales | 150.00 | 75.00 |
| **OA194** 13¢ Britannia | 500.00 | 250.00 |
| **OA192–OA194** (3) | 730.00 | 365.00 |

### MEDALLION ISSUE
### 1932

| | VF | F |
|---|---|---|
| **OA195** 1¢ dark green | 50.00 | 25.00 |
| **OA196** 2¢ black brown | 50.00 | 25.00 |
| **OA197** 3¢ deep red | 50.00 | 25.00 |
| **OA198** 4¢ ochre | 180.00 | 90.00 |
| **OA199** 5¢ dark blue | 80.00 | 40.00 |
| **OA200** 8¢ red orange | 200.00 | 100.00 |
| **OA201** 13¢ Quebec Citadel | 180.00 | 90.00 |
| **OA195–OA201** (7) | 790.00 | 395.00 |

### COMMEMORATIVES
### 1933, 1934

| | VF | F |
|---|---|---|
| **OA202** 5¢ UPU Meeting | 180.00 | 90.00 |
| **OA203** 20¢ Grain Exhibition | 300.00 | 150.00 |
| **OA204** 5¢ Royal William | 180.00 | 90.00 |
| **OA208** 3¢ Jacques Cartier | 240.00 | 120.00 |
| **OA209** 10¢ Loyalists | 320.00 | 160.00 |
| **OA210** 2¢ New Brunswick | 300.00 | 150.00 |
| **OA202–OA210** (6) | 1,520.00 | 760.00 |

### SILVER JUBILEE ISSUE
### 1935

| | VF | F |
|---|---|---|
| **OA211** 1¢ Princess Elizabeth | 140.00 | 70.00 |
| **OA212** 2¢ Duke of York | 150.00 | 75.00 |
| **OA213** 3¢ King George V and Queen Mary | 180.00 | 90.00 |
| **OA214** 5¢ Prince of Wales | 200.00 | 100.00 |
| **OA215** 10¢ Windsor Castle | 500.00 | 250.00 |
| **OA216** 13¢ Royal Yacht Britannia | 600.00 | 300.00 |
| **OA211–OA216** (6) | 1,770.00 | 885.00 |

### PICTORIAL ISSUE
### 1935

| | VF | F |
|---|---|---|
| **OA217** 1¢ green | 50.00 | 25.00 |
| **OA218** 2¢ brown | 100.00 | 50.00 |
| **OA219** 3¢ dark carmine | 80.00 | 40.00 |
| **OA220** 4¢ yellow | 160.00 | 80.00 |
| **OA221** 5¢ blue | 100.00 | 50.00 |
| **OA222** 8¢ deep orange | 160.00 | 80.00 |
| **OA223** 10¢ R.C.M.P. | 160.00 | 80.00 |
| **OA224** 13¢ Charlottetown Conf. | 160.00 | 80.00 |
| **OA225** 20¢ Niagara Falls | 180.00 | 90.00 |
| **OA226** 50¢ Victoria, B.C. | 80.00 | 40.00 |
| **OA227** $1 Champlain Monument | 400.00 | 200.00 |
| **OA217–OA227** (11) Set | 1,630.00 | 820.00 |

| | | Used: VF | F |
|---|---|---|---|

## KING GEORGE VI
### 1937

| | | VF | F |
|---|---|---|---|
| **OA231** | 1¢ green | 8.00 | 4.00 |
| **OA232** | 2¢ brown | 10.00 | 5.00 |
| **OA233** | 3¢ carmine | 8.00 | 4.00 |
| **OA234** | 4¢ yellow | 30.00 | 15.00 |
| **OA235** | 5¢ blue | 20.00 | 10.00 |
| **OA236** | 8¢ orange | 50.00 | 25.00 |
| **OA237** | 3¢ Coronation | 160.00 | 80.00 |
| **OA240** | 3¢ carmine, coil | 240.00 | 120.00 |
| **OA231–OA240** (8) | | 526.00 | 263.00 |

## PICTORIAL ISSUE
### 1938

| | | VF | F |
|---|---|---|---|
| **OA241** | 10¢ dark carmine | 60.00 | 30.00 |
| **a** | 10¢ carmine rose | 50.00 | 25.00 |
| **OA242** | 13¢ Halifax Harbour | 60.00 | 30.00 |
| **OA243** | 20¢ Fort Garry | 90.00 | 45.00 |
| **OA244** | 50¢ Vancouver Harbour | 220.00 | 110.00 |
| **OA245** | $1 Chateau de Ramesay | 440.00 | 220.00 |
| **OA241–OA245** (6) | | 920.00 | 460.00 |

## ROYAL VISIT
### 1939

| | | VF | F |
|---|---|---|---|
| **OA246** | 1¢ Princesses | 180.00 | 90.00 |
| **OA247** | 2¢ War Memorial | 180.00 | 90.00 |
| **OA248** | 3¢ King George VI and Queen Elizabeth | 180.00 | 90.00 |
| **OA246–OA248** (3) | | 540.00 | 270.00 |

## AIR MAIL ISSUES
### 1928–1938

| | | VF | F |
|---|---|---|---|
| **OAC1** | 5¢ brown olive | 400.00 | 200.00 |
| **OAC2** | 5¢ olive brown | 700.00 | 350.00 |
| **OAC3** | 6¢ on 5¢ brown olive | 600.00 | 300.00 |
| **OAC4** | 6¢ on 5¢ olive brown | 700.00 | 350.00 |
| **OAC5** | 6¢ red brown | 600.00 | 300.00 |
| **OAC6** | 6¢ blue | 60.00 | 30.00 |
| **OAC1–OAC6** (6) | | 3,060.00 | 1,530.00 |

## SPECIAL DELIVERY ISSUES
### 1898–1939

| | | VF | F |
|---|---|---|---|
| **OAE1** | 10¢ blue green | 750.00 | 375.00 |
| **OAE2** | 20¢ carmine | 650.00 | 325.00 |
| **OAE3** | 20¢ orange | 700.00 | 350.00 |
| **OAE4** | 20¢ henna brown "Twenty Cents" | 500.00 | 250.00 |
| **OAE5** | 20¢ henna brown "Cents" | 450.00 | 225.00 |
| **OAE6** | 20¢ dark carmine | 500.00 | 250.00 |
| **OAE7** | 10¢ dark green | 100.00 | 50.00 |
| **OAE8** | 20¢ Coat of Arms | 400.00 | 200.00 |
| **OAE9** | 10¢ on 20¢ dark carmine | 350.00 | 175.00 |
| **OAE1–OAE9** (9) | | 4,400.00 | 2,200.00 |

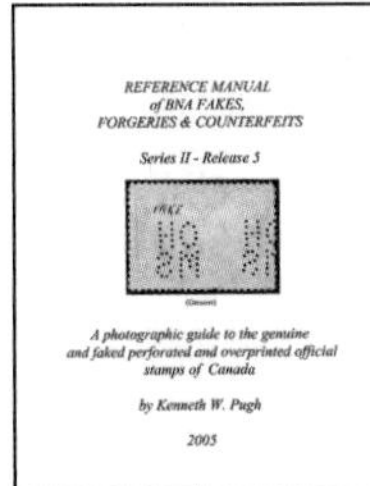

*Reference Manual of BNA Fakes, Forgeries and Counterfeits Series II - Release 5. A photographic guide to the genuine and faked perforated and overprinted official stamps of Canada,* Ken Pugh, 2005

Premiums: VF +50%, NH +50% — Mint — Used

## SMALL OHMS

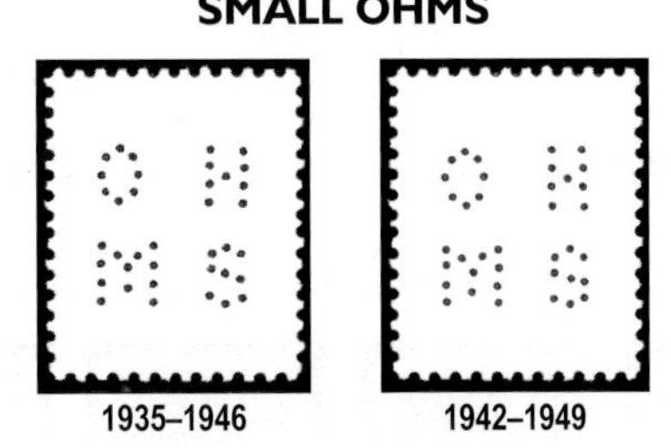

1935–1946 1942–1949

## 4 HOLES IN VERTICAL BARS OF H

Two types of 4-hole OHMS perfins exist:

1935–1946: identified by a narrow "O" and an extended seventh pin from the top of the "S". There are 10 dies used for this type.

1942–1949: identified by a wide "O" and the seventh pin from the top of the "S" not extended on seven of the 10 dies.

Some stamps exist with both types. These are indicated with a ‡. Pricing differences have not yet been established.

## PICTORIAL ISSUE
### 1935

| | | Mint | Used |
|---|---|---|---|
| **O223** | 10¢ R.C.M.P. | 160.00 | 80.00 |
| **O224** | 13¢ Charlottetown Conference | 160.00 | 80.00 |
| **O225** | 20¢ Niagara Falls | 180.00 | 90.00 |
| **O226** | 50¢ Victoria, B.C. | 180.00 | 60.00 |
| **O223–O226** (4) | | 680.00 | 310.00 |

## KING GEORGE VI
### 1937

| | | Mint | Used |
|---|---|---|---|
| **O231** | 1¢ green | 2.00 | .20 |
| **O232** | 2¢ brown | 2.50 | .20 |
| **O233** | 3¢ carmine | 2.50 | .20 |
| **O234** | 4¢ yellow | 10.00 | 3.50 |
| **O235** | 5¢ blue | 4.00 | .25 |
| **O236** | 8¢ orange | 20.00 | 8.00 |
| **O237** | 3¢ Coronation | 100.00 | 85.00 |
| **O239** | 2¢ brown, coil | 180.00 | 120.00 |
| **O240** | 3¢ carmine, coil | 150.00 | 100.00 |
| **O231–O240** (9) | | 471.00 | 317.35 |

## PICTORIAL ISSUE
### 1938

| | | Mint | Used |
|---|---|---|---|
| **O241** | 10¢ dark carmine | 10.00 | .50 |
| **a** | 10¢ carmine rose | 70.00 | 6.00 |
| **O242** | 13¢ Halifax Harbour | 15.00 | 2.50 |
| **O243** | 20¢ Fort Garry | 45.00 | 3.00 |
| **O244** | 50¢ Vancouver Harbour | 75.00 | 15.00 |
| **O245** | $1 Chateau de Ramesay | 160.00 | 60.00 |
| **i** | analine violet | 160.00 | 60.00 |
| **O241–O245i** (7) | | 535.00 | 147.00 |

## ROYAL VISIT
### 1939

| | | Mint | Used |
|---|---|---|---|
| **O246** | 1¢ Princesses | 125.00 | 80.00 |
| **O247** | 2¢ War Memorial | 125.00 | 80.00 |
| **O248** | 3¢ King George VI & Queen Elizabeth | 125.00 | 80.00 |
| **O246–O248** (3) | | 375.00 | 240.00 |

Premiums: VF +50%, NH +50% — Mint — Used

## WAR ISSUE
### 1942–1943

| | | Mint | Used |
|---|---|---|---|
| **O249** | 1¢ green ‡ | .50 | .20 |
| **O250** | 2¢ brown ‡ | .70 | .20 |
| **O251** | 3¢ dark carmine | 2.00 | .60 |
| **O252** | 3¢ rose violet ‡ | .95 | .20 |
| **O253** | 4¢ Grain Elevators | 3.50 | 1.25 |
| **O254** | 4¢ dark carmine ‡ | .80 | .20 |
| **O255** | 5¢ deep blue ‡ | 1.50 | .20 |
| **O256** | 8¢ Farm Scene ‡ | 10.00 | 3.50 |
| **O257** | 10¢ Parliament Buildings ‡ | 6.00 | .30 |
| **O258** | 13¢ Ram Tank | 7.00 | 6.00 |
| **O259** | 14¢ Ram Tank ‡ | 9.00 | 1.50 |
| **O260** | 20¢ Corvette ‡ | 12.50 | 1.25 |
| **O261** | 50¢ Munitions ‡ | 50.00 | 8.00 |
| **O262** | $1 Destroyer ‡ | 150.00 | 50.00 |
| **Nos. O249–O262** (14) Set | | 254.95 | 73.40 |

## PEACE ISSUE
### 1946

| | | Mint | Used |
|---|---|---|---|
| **O268** | 8¢ Farm Scene ‡ | 30.00 | 10.00 |
| **O269** | 10¢ Great Bear Lake ‡ | 4.00 | .50 |
| **O270** | 14¢ Hydroelectric Plant ‡ | 5.00 | 1.00 |
| **O271** | 20¢ Combine ‡ | 6.00 | 1.00 |
| **O272** | 50¢ Lumbering ‡ | 40.00 | 8.50 |
| **O273** | $1 Train Ferry ‡ | 90.00 | 30.00 |
| **O268–O273** (6) | | 175.00 | 51.00 |

## KING GEORGE VI WITH "POSTES-POSTAGE"
### 1949

| | | Mint | Used |
|---|---|---|---|
| **O285** | 2¢ sepia | 1.00 | 1.00 |
| **O286** | 3¢ rose violet | 1.00 | 1.00 |

## AIR MAIL ISSUES
### 1928–1946

| | | Mint | Used |
|---|---|---|---|
| **OC1** | 5¢ Allegory of Flight | 30.00 | 15.00 |
| **OC5** | 6¢ Daedalus in Flight | 300.00 | 125.00 |
| **OC6** | 6¢ Steamer & Monoplane ‡ | 4.00 | 1.50 |
| **OC7** | 6¢ R.C.A.F. Training Plane ‡ | 4.00 | 2.00 |
| **OC8** | 7¢ R.C.A.F. Training Plane ‡ | 4.00 | .50 |
| **OC9** | 7¢ Canada Goose ‡ | 3.00 | .75 |
| **i** | major re-entry, double frameline at right | 50.00 | 35.00 |
| **OC1–OC9** (6) | | 345.00 | 144.75 |

## AIR MAIL SPECIAL DELIVERY ISSUE
### 1942–1947

| | | Mint | Used |
|---|---|---|---|
| **OCE1** | 16¢ bright ultramarine | 30.00 | 25.00 |
| **OCE2** | 17¢ bright ultramarine ‡ | 20.00 | 20.00 |
| **OCE3** | 17¢ incorrect accent (Ê) ‡ | 50.00 | 45.00 |
| **OCE4** | 17¢ corrected die (É) ‡ | 100.00 | 100.00 |
| **OCE1–OCE4** (4) | | 200.00 | 190.00 |

## SPECIAL DELIVERY ISSUES
### 1933–1946

| | | Mint | Used |
|---|---|---|---|
| **OE5** | 20¢ henna brown | 750.00 | 500.00 |
| **OE6** | 20¢ dark carmine | 350.00 | 200.00 |
| **OE7** | 10¢ dark green ‡ | 20.00 | 9.00 |
| **OE9** | 10¢ on 20¢ dark carmine | 400.00 | 250.00 |
| **OE10** | 10¢ green (1942) ‡ | 20.00 | 12.00 |
| **OE11** | 10¢ green (1946) ‡ | 12.00 | 8.00 |
| **OE5–OE11** (6) | | 1,552.00 | 979.00 |

‡ 2 types; see note at beginning of 4-Hole listing

# OVERPRINTED OFFICIAL STAMPS

In 1949, the practice of perforating stamps for official government use was discontinued and the Post Office began overprinting "O.H.M.S." on stamps supplied to government offices. The "O.H.M.S." overprint was used for only one year, being replaced by the single letter "G" in 1950. Government offices ceased using "official stamps" at the end of 1963.

## OVERPRINTED "O.H.M.S." IN BLACK

### KING GEORGE VI, WAR ISSUE

O1

O2

O3

O4

1949–1950

| NH+50% | | ★VF | ★F | ⊙VF | ⊙F | ✉ | Plate No. | | ★F PLATE BLOCKS, VF + 50% UL | UR | LL | LR |
|---|---|---|---|---|---|---|---|---|---|---|---|---|
| **O1** | **1¢ green** | 3.00 | 1.75 | 2.50 | 1.75 | 10.00 | O1 | 30 | 11.00 | 11.00 | 140.00 | 150.00 |
| a | no period after "S" | 200.00 | 125.00 | 150.00 | 100.00 | 160.00 | O1 | 31 | 160.00 | 160.00 | 15.00 | 15.00 |
| i | narrow spacing, strip of 3 | 20.00 | 15.00 | 20.00 | 15.00 | | O1i | | 40.00† | — | 40.00† | — |
| **O2** | **2¢ brown** | 10.00 | 7.00 | 10.00 | 7.00 | 30.00 | O2 | 4 | 125.00 | 125.00 | 150.00 | 125.00 |
| a | no period after "S" (Pl. 4 LL, pos. 52) | 300.00 | 150.00 | 200.00 | 125.00 | 250.00 | O2a | | | | 500.00‡ | — |
| i | narrow spacing, strip of 3 | 100.00 | 70.00 | 100.00 | 70.00 | | O2i | | 200.00† | — | 200.00† | — |
| **O3** | **3¢ rose violet** | 3.00 | 1.75 | 1.75 | 1.50 | 10.00 | O3 | 32 | 11.00 | 11.00 | 12.00 | 100.00 |
| | | | | | | | O3 | 34 | 150.00 | 11.00 | 12.00 | 11.00 |
| i | narrow spacing, strip of 3 | 20.00 | 14.00 | 20.00 | 14.00 | | O3i | | 40.00† | — | 40.00† | — |
| **O4** | **4¢ dark carmine** | 4.00 | 2.00 | 1.00 | .75 | 10.00 | O4 | 49 | 20.00 | 1,500.00 | 40.00 | 250.00 |
| i | narrow spacing, strip of 3 | 27.50 | 18.00 | 27.50 | 18.00 | | O4 | 50 | 90.00 | 20.00 | 500.00 | 30.00 |
| | | | | | | | O4i | | 60.00† | — | 60.00† | — |

† Narrow spacing, blank corner block of 6
‡ Vertical plate block of 10 (2 x 5)

No. O5 is not assigned.

### PEACE ISSUE

O6

O7

O8

O9

O10

1949–1950

| NH+50% | | ★VF | ★F | ⊙VF | ⊙F | ✉ | Plate No. | | ★F PLATE BLOCKS, VF + 50% UL | UR | LL | LR |
|---|---|---|---|---|---|---|---|---|---|---|---|---|
| **O6** | **10¢ Great Bear Lake** | 6.00 | 2.25 | .90 | .75 | 20.00 | O6 | 1,2 | 30.00 | 22.50 | 35.00 | 22.50 |
| a | no period after "S" (pos. 47) | 100.00 | 65.00 | 90.00 | 60.00 | 110.00 | O6a | 1 | — | — | 175.00 | — |
| | | | | | | | O6a | 2 | — | — | 225.00 | — |
| **O7** | **14¢ Hydroelectric Plant** | 10.00 | 3.25 | 3.25 | 2.80 | 20.00 | O7 | 1 | 35.00 | 35.00 | 50.00 | 40.00 |
| a | no period after "S" (pos. 47) | 150.00 | 100.00 | 120.00 | 75.00 | | O7a | 1 | — | — | 150.00 | — |
| **O8** | **20¢ Combine** | 24.00 | 15.00 | 4.25 | 3.75 | 20.00 | O8 | 1 | 85.00 | 85.00 | 100.00 | 85.00 |
| | | | | | | | O8 | 2 | 100.00 | 120.00 | 120.00 | 100.00 |
| a | no period after "S", (pos. 47) | 160.00 | 110.00 | 120.00 | 80.00 | | O8a | 1 | — | — | 150.00 | — |
| | | | | | | | O8a | 2 | — | — | 200.00 | — |
| **O9** | **50¢ Lumbering** | 220.00 | 160.00 | 150.00 | 125.00 | 260.00 | O9 | 1 | 1,200.00 | 1,200.00 | — | 1,200.00 |
| a | no period after "S" (pos. 47) | 900.00 | 600.00 | 750.00 | 500.00 | | O9a | 1 | — | — | 1,600.00 | — |
| **O10** | **$1 Train Ferry** | 80.00 | 50.00 | 60.00 | 35.00 | 150.00 | O10 | 1 | 350.00 each | | | |
| a | no period after "S" (pos. 47) | *6,000.00* | *4,000.00* | *5,000.00* | *3,000.00* | | O10a | 1 | — | — | *9,000.00* | — |

"No period after S" variety occurs on Plates 1 and 2, in LL position 47 on some O6, O7, O8, on all O9 and on a very few copies of O10. A certificate of authenticity is recommended for No. O10a.

| | ★VF | ★F | ⊙VF | ⊙F |
|---|---|---|---|---|
| **Nos. O1–O10 (9)** Set | 360.00 | 243.00 | 233.65 | 178.30 |

Overprinted Officials

## NATURAL RESOURCES

O11

| 1950, NH+50% | | ★VF | ★F | ⊙VF | ⊙F | ✉ | | Plate No. | UL | UR | LL | LR |
|---|---|---|---|---|---|---|---|---|---|---|---|---|
| **O11** | **50¢ Oil Wells** | 40.00 | 20.00 | 20.00 | 12.00 | 120.00 | O11 | 1 | 175.00 | 175.00 | 175.00 | 175.00 |

## KING GEORGE VI "POSTES-POSTAGE"

O12

O13

O14

O15

O15A

| 1950 NH+50% | | ★VF | ★F | ⊙VF | ⊙F | ✉ | ★F PLATE BLOCKS, VF + 50% | Plate No. | UL | UR | LL | LR |
|---|---|---|---|---|---|---|---|---|---|---|---|---|
| **O12** | **1¢ green** | .75 | .30 | .50 | .30 | 10.00 | O12 | 1 | 10.00 | 75.00 | 4.00 | 4.00 |
| | | | | | | | O12 | 2 | 15.00 | 75.00 | 4.00 | 4.00 |
| i | narrow spacing, strip of 3 | 15.00 | 9.00 | 15.00 | 9.00 | | O12i | | 27.50† | — | 27.50† | — |
| **O13** | **2¢ sepia** | 1.50 | .90 | 1.20 | .90 | 10.00 | O13 | 1,2 | 6.00 | 5.00 | 6.00 | 5.00 |
| **O14** | **3¢ rose violet** | 1.50 | .95 | .85 | .65 | 10.00 | O14 | 1,2 | 6.50 | 6.50 | 6.50 | 6.50 |
| **O15** | **4¢ dark carmine** | 1.50 | .95 | .25 | .20 | 10.00 | O15 | 2 | 6.50 | 6.50 | 900.00 | 400.00 |
| | | | | | | | O15 | 3 | 6.50 | 6.50 | 600.00 | 400.00 |
| | | | | | | | O15 | 4 | 7.50 | 7.50 | 10.00 | 15.00 |
| | | | | | | | O15 | 6 | 6.50 | 7.50 | 6.50 | 15.00 |
| | | | | | | | O15 | 6 cracked plate | | | 30.00 | |
| b | no period after "S" (pos. 52) | 350.00 | 200.00 | 250.00 | 150.00 | | O15b | | | | 750.00‡ | |
| i | narrow spacing, strip of 3 | 35.00 | 20.00 | 35.00 | 20.00 | | O15i | | 50.00† | — | 50.00† | — |
| **O15A** | **5¢ deep blue** | 2.50 | 1.50 | 2.25 | 1.50 | 9.00 | O15A | 1 | 12.00 | 12.00 | 50.00 | 30.00 |
| | | | | | | | O15A | 2 | 12.00 | 12.00 | 50.00 | 18.00 |
| c | no period after "S" | 100.00 | 65.00 | 80.00 | 60.00 | 130.00 | | | | | | |
| i | narrow spacing, strip of 3 | 55.00 | 40.00 | 50.00 | 35.00 | — | O15Ai | | 100.00† | — | 100.00† | — |

Note: O15Ac exists on plates 1 and 2 in LL position 52, on plates 1 and 2, in UL position 78.
† Narrow spacing, blank corner block of 6, plate 1 or 2.
‡ Vertical plate block of 10 (2 x 5).

CO1

EO1

## AIR MAIL

| 1946 NH+50% | | ★VF | ★F | ⊙VF | ⊙F | ✉ | ★F PLATE BLOCKS, VF + 50% | Plate No. | UL | UR | LL | LR |
|---|---|---|---|---|---|---|---|---|---|---|---|---|
| **CO1** | **7¢ Canada Goose** | 12.00 | 8.00 | 6.50 | 5.00 | 30.00 | CO1 | 1,2 | 50.00 | 50.00 | 52.50 | 52.50 |
| a | no period after "S" (pos. 47) | 150.00 | 90.00 | 100.00 | 60.00 | 130.00 | CO1a | 1 | — | — | 160.00 | — |
| | | | | | | | CO1a | 2 | — | — | 190.00 | — |
| i | major re-entry, double frameline at right | 100.00 | 60.00 | 60.00 | 35.00 | 90.00 | CO1i | 1 | — | 200.00 | — | — |

## SPECIAL DELIVERY

| 1950, NH+50% | | | | | | | | | | | | |
|---|---|---|---|---|---|---|---|---|---|---|---|---|
| **EO1** | **10¢ green** | 16.00 | 10.00 | 16.00 | 10.00 | 90.00 | EO1 | 1 | 60.00 | 60.00 | 60.00 | 60.00 |

**Nos. O1–O15A, CO1, EO1 (17)**

| Set of "O.H.M.S." overprints | 435.75 | 275.60 | 296.20 | 221.85 |
|---|---|---|---|---|

## OVERPRINTED "G" IN BLACK

| G | G | G | G | G |
|---|---|---|---|---|
| (a) 3mm high | (b) 3.75mm high | (c) Flying G | (d) Fishhook G | Blunt G |

## KING GEORGE VI, "POSTES-POSTAGE"

O16

O17

O18

O19

O20

| 1950 NH+50% | | ★VF | ★F | ⊙VF | ⊙F | ✉ | | Plate No. | ★F PLATE BLOCKS, VF + 50% UL | UR | LL | LR |
|---|---|---|---|---|---|---|---|---|---|---|---|---|
| **O16** | **1¢ green** (a) | 1.00 | .30 | .25 | .20 | 8.00 | O16 | 1,2 | 4.00 each | | | |
| | | | | | | | O16 | 4 | 7.00 | 9.00 | 12.00 | 8.00 |
| | | | | | | | O16 | 5 | 4.00 | 4.00 | 4.00 | 4.00 |
| | | | | | | | O16 | 6 | 5.00 | 5.00 | 7.00 | 4.00 |
| | | | | | | | O16 | 7 | 15.00 | 100.00 | 15.00 | 12.00 |
| | | | | | | | O16 | 8 | 7.50 each | | | |
| **O17** | **2¢ sepia** (a) | 2.00 | .95 | 1.25 | .90 | 8.00 | O17 | 1,2 | 10.00 | 8.00 | 9.00 | 8.00 |
| **O18** | **3¢ rose violet** (a) | 2.00 | .95 | .25 | .20 | 8.00 | O18 | 3 | 8.00 | 8.00 | 8.00 | 8.00 |
| | | | | | | | O18 | 4 | 8.00 each | | | |
| | | | | | | | O18 | 6 | 10.00 | 15.00 | 10.00 | 12.00 |
| | | | | | | | O18 | 7 | 9.00 | 8.00 | 8.00 | 8.00 |
| | | | | | | | O18 | 8,10 | 8.00 each | | | |
| **O19** | **4¢ dark carmine** (a) | 2.00 | .95 | .25 | .20 | 8.00 | O19 | 4 | 8.00 | 8.00 | 8.00 | 8.00 |
| | | | | | | | O19 | 6 | 8.00 | 10.00 | 15.00 | 10.00 |
| | | | | | | | O19 | 6 hairlines | | | 30.00 | |
| | | | | | | | O19 | 8 | 8.00 each | | | |
| | | | | | | | O19 | 9 | 10.00 | 10.00 | 11.00 | 11.00 |
| | | | | | | | O19 | 11 | 12.00 | 11.00 | 15.00 | 15.00 |
| **O20** | **5¢ deep blue** (a) | 3.00 | 1.20 | 1.25 | 1.00 | 8.00 | O20 | 1 | 17.50 each | | | |
| i | misplaced "G" | | | | | | O20 | 2 | 15.00 each | | | |
| | (in front of king"s head) | 125.00 | 75.00 | | | | O20 | 3 | 20.00 each | | | |

## PEACE / NATURAL RESOURCES

O21

O22

O23

O24

O25

O26

O27

| 1950–1951 NH+50% | | ★VF | ★F | ⊙VF | ⊙F | ✉ | | Plate No. | ★F PLATE BLOCKS, VF + 50% UL | UR | LL | LR |
|---|---|---|---|---|---|---|---|---|---|---|---|---|
| **O21** | **10¢ Great Bear Lake** (b) | 6.00 | 1.75 | .70 | .50 | 14.00 | O21 | 1,2 | 16.00 | 30.00 | 16.00 | 16.00 |
| **O22** | **14¢ Hydroelectric Plant** (b) | 12.00 | 6.00 | 3.00 | 2.50 | 15.00 | O22 | 1 | 37.50 each | | | |
| **O23** | **20¢ Combine** (b) | 20.00 | 12.00 | 1.50 | 1.25 | 18.00 | O23 | 1,2 | 100.00 each | | | |
| **O24** | **50¢ Oil Wells** (b) | 12.00 | 8.00 | 7.25 | 6.75 | 125.00 | O24 | 1 | 65.00 each | | | |
| **O25** | **$1 Train Ferry** | 80.00 | 40.00 | 100.00 | 50.00 | 150.00 | O25 | 1 | 350.00 each | | | |

| | ★VF | ★F | ⊙VF | ⊙F |
|---|---|---|---|---|
| **Nos. O16–O25 (10)** Set | 140.00 | 72.10 | 115.45 | 63.50 |

| 1950–1951 NH+50% | | ★VF | ★F | ⊙VF | ⊙F | ✉ | Plate No. | | ★F PLATE BLOCKS, VF + 50% UL | UR | LL | LR |
|---|---|---|---|---|---|---|---|---|---|---|---|---|
| **O26** | **10¢ Fur – Drying Skins** (b) | 2.00 | 1.00 | .30 | .25 | 12.00 | **O26** | 1,2 | 9.00 each | | | |
| a | pair, one without "G" (pos. 31)* | 850.00 | 600.00 | 750.00 | 500.00 | 1,200.00‡ | **O26a** | | 1,200.00† | | | |
| **O27** | **$1 Fisherman** (b) | 80.00 | 40.00 | 80.00 | 40.00 | 175.00 | **O27** | 1 | 350.00 each | | | |

* Certificates of authenticity highly recommended on variety O26a.
‡ Commercial cover.
† Value is for plate block of 14 (2 x 7)

## DEFINITIVES

O28

O29

O30

O31

O32

| 1951–1953 NH+50% | | ★VF | ★F | ⊙VF | ⊙F | ✉ | Plate No. | | ★F PLATE BLOCKS, VF + 50% UL | UR | LL | LR |
|---|---|---|---|---|---|---|---|---|---|---|---|---|
| **O28** | **2¢ olive green** (a) | .70 | .50 | .25 | .20 | 7.00 | **O28** | 3,4 | 3.00 | 3.00 | 3.50 | 3.50 |
| | | | | | | | **O28** | 7 | 4.00 | each | | |
| **O29** | **4¢ orange vermilion** (a) | 1.00 | .70 | .25 | .20 | 7.00 | **O29** | 17,18 | 8.00 | 5.00 | 5.00 | 5.00 |
| **O30** | **20¢ Pulp & Paper** (b) | 4.00 | 2.00 | .25 | .20 | 15.00 | **O30** | 1,2 | 16.00 | each | | |
| **O31** | **7¢ Canada Goose** (b) | 4.25 | 3.00 | 1.75 | 1.25 | 16.00 | **O31** | 1,2 | 17.50 | each | | |
| **O32** | **$1 Totem Pole** (b) | 12.00 | 6.00 | 10.00 | 5.00 | 75.00‡ | **O32** | 1,2 | 50.00 | each | | |

‡ Single usage only, in time period.

## QUEEN ELIZABETH II "KARSH" PORTRAIT

O33

O34

O35

O36

O37

| 1953 NH+50% | | ★VF | ★F | ⊙VF | ⊙F | ✉ | Plate No. | | ★F PLATE BLOCKS, VF + 50% UL | UR | LL | LR |
|---|---|---|---|---|---|---|---|---|---|---|---|---|
| **O33** | **1¢ violet brown** | .50 | .30 | .25 | .20 | 10.00 | **O33** | 1,2 | 2.00 | each | | |
| **O34** | **2¢ green** | .50 | .30 | .25 | .20 | 10.00 | **O34** | 1,2 | 7.50 | each | | |
| | | | | | | | **O34** | 3,4 | 2.00 | each | | |
| **O35** | **3¢ carmine rose** | .50 | .30 | .25 | .20 | 10.00 | **O35** | 1 | 2.00 | each | | |
| | | | | | | | **O35** | 2 | 7.50 | each | | |
| | | | | | | | **O35** | 3 | 2.00 | each | | |
| **O36** | **4¢ violet** | .60 | .40 | .25 | .20 | 10.00 | **O36** | 1 | 7.50 | each | | |
| | | | | | | | **O36** | 2,4 | 2.75 | each | | |
| **O37** | **5¢ ultramarine** | .60 | .40 | .25 | .20 | 10.00 | **O37** | 1.2 | 2.75 | each | | |

Minor shifts of the 'G' are known.

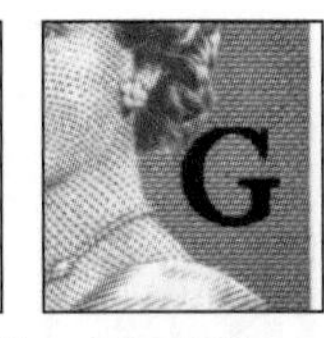

Minor shifts of 'G' overprint

## DEFINITIVES

O38

O39

1953–1955

| NH+50% | | ★VF | ★F | ⊙VF | ⊙F | ✉ | Plate No. | | UL | UR | LL | LR |
|---|---|---|---|---|---|---|---|---|---|---|---|---|
| **O38** | **50¢ Textile Industry** | 6.00 | 4.00 | 1.75 | 1.50 | 22.00 | O38 | 1 | 30.00 | each | | |
| i | cracked plate | | | | | | O38 | 2 | 35.00 | each | | |
| | (Pl. 1: LL36, LL41, LL47 & UL40) | 40.00 | 30.00 | 30.00 | 20.00 | 75.00 | O38i | 1 position 41, 47 | — | | 60.00 | — |
| ii | blunt "G" overprint | 250.00 | 200.00 | 200.00 | 150.00 | 250.00 | O38i | 1 LL pos. 36, PB of 6 (2 x 3) | | | 90.00 | — |
| **O39** | **10¢ Inuk & Kayak** | 1.50 | .80 | .25 | .20 | 12.00 | O39 | 1,2 | 6.00 | each | | |
| | | | | | | | O39 | 3,4 | 9.00 | each | | |

★F PLATE BLOCKS, VF + 50%

O38i: Pos. 41, LL pane — left vertical frame line retouched with engraver's slip along left edge of design at bottom.
O38i: Pos. 47, LL pane — bottom frame line retouched with engraver's slip from below last A in CANADA to the T of POSTAGE.
Both O38i varieties (pos. 41 and 47) occur together on the same plate block, plate 1, LL.

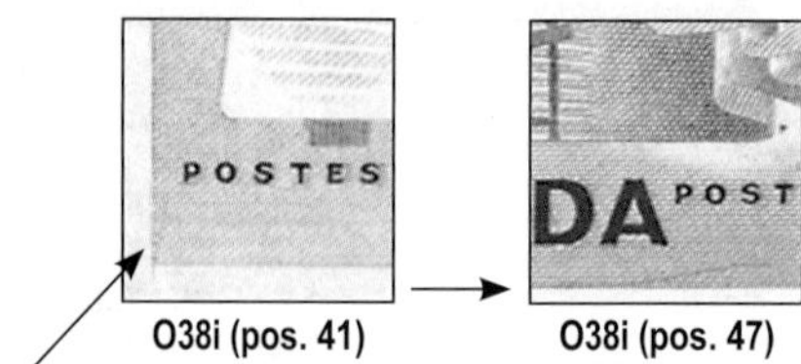
O38i (pos. 41) O38i (pos. 47)

## QUEEN ELIZABETH II "WILDING" PORTRAIT

O40

O41

O43

O44

O45

1955–1956

| NH+50% | | ★VF | ★F | ⊙VF | ⊙F | ✉ | Plate No. | | UL | UR | LL | LR |
|---|---|---|---|---|---|---|---|---|---|---|---|---|
| **O40** | **1¢ violet brown**, Ribbed (horiz) | 1.00 | .30 | .50 | .30 | 4.00 | O40 | 4,5 | 3.00 each | | | |
| i | wide spacing strip of 3 | 45.00 | 30.00 | 45.00 | 30.00 | | O40 | 8n | 10.00 each | | | |
| ii | misplaced overprint (over mouth) | 50.00 | 40.00 | — | — | | | | | | | |
| iii | Ribbed (vert) | 2.50 | 1.75 | 1.50 | 1.00 | | | | | | | |
| **O41** | **2¢ green**, Ribbed (horiz) | 1.00 | .30 | .25 | .20 | 4.00 | O41 | 1,2,5,6 | 3.00 each | | | |
| i | wide spacing strip of 3 | 30.00 | 20.00 | 30.00 | 20.00 | | O41 | 7,8 | 6.00 each | | | |
| ii | Ribbed (vert) | 2.50 | 1.75 | 1.50 | 1.00 | | | | | | | |
| No. O42 is not assigned. | | | | | | | | | | | | |
| **O43** | **4¢ violet**, Ribbed (horiz) | 2.00 | .95 | .25 | .20 | 4.00 | O43 | 1,2 | 8.00 each | | | |
| i | wide spacing strip of 3 | 30.00 | 20.00 | 30.00 | 20.00 | | | | | | | |
| ii | Ribbed (vert) | 5.00 | 3.00 | 1.50 | 1.00 | | | | | | | |
| **O44** | **5¢ bright blue**, Ribbed (horiz) | 1.00 | .40 | .25 | .20 | 5.00 | O44 | 1,2,5,7 | 3.00 each | | | |
| i | wide spacing strip of 3 | 18.00 | 12.00 | 18.00 | 12.00 | | O44 | 10,11 | 3.50 each | | | |
| ii | Ribbed (vert) | 2.50 | 1.75 | 1.50 | 1.00 | | | | | | | |

★F PLATE BLOCKS, VF + 50%

Plate blocks of the ribbed vertically Widling official stamps (O40iii, O41ii, O43ii, and O44ii) have not been reported.

## INDUSTRY DEFINITIVE

| | | ★VF | ★F | ⊙VF | ⊙F | ✉ | Plate No. | | UL |
|---|---|---|---|---|---|---|---|---|---|
| **O45** | **20¢ Paper Industry** | 2.50 | 1.50 | .30 | .20 | 14.00 | O45 | 1,2,2n | 10.00 each |

O40ii

## TYPE C — FLYING "G" OVERPRINT

**1961–1962**

| NH+50% | | ★VF | ★F | ⊙VF | ⊙F | ✉ | ★F PLATE BLOCKS, VF + 50% Plate No. | | UL | UR | LL | LR |
|---|---|---|---|---|---|---|---|---|---|---|---|---|
| **O38a** | **50¢ Textile Industry** | 6.00 | 4.00 | 3.00 | 2.00 | 25.00 | O38a | 1 | 35.00 | each | (Flying G) | |
| | | | | | | | O38a | 2 | 375.00 | each | (Flying G) | |
| i | fishhook "G", Pl. 1 or 2, UR pos. 5 | 500.00 | 400.00 | 400.00 | 300.00 | — | O38ai | 1,2 | — | 500.00(Fishhook G) | | |
| ii | cracked plate | | | | | | O38aii | 1 position 41, 47 | | — | 60.00 | — |
| | (Pl. 1: LL36, LL41, LL47 & UL40) | 40.00 | 30.00 | 30.00 | 20.00 | 75.00 | O38aii | 1 LL position 36, | | | | |
| | | | | | | | | PB of 6 (2 x 3) | | | 90.00 | — |
| **O39a** | **10¢ Inuk & Kayak** | 2.25 | 1.60 | 1.75 | 1.00 | 10.00 | O39a | 3,4 | 15.00 | each | (Flying G) | |
| **O45a** | **20¢ Paper Industry** | 7.50 | 5.00 | .80 | .50 | 18.00 | O45a | blank | 45.00 | each | (Flying G) | |
| | | | | | | | O45a | 2n | 250.00 | each | (Flying G) | |
| i | raised "High Flying G" | | | | | | O45ai | UR, LR block of 4 (High Flying G) | | | | 75.00 |
| | in right margin pair | 20.00 | 15.00 | — | — | — | O45aii | LR block of 4 (Blunt G) | | | | 175.00 |
| ii | blunt "G" (pos. 49 or 7) | 100.00 | 75.00 | 75.00 | 50.00 | — | O45aii | UL block of 4 (pos. 7, Blunt G) | | | | 175.00 |

## QUEEN ELIZABETH II "CAMEO" PORTRAIT

O46

O47

O48

O49

O47iii

**1963**

| NH+50% | | ★VF | ★F | ⊙VF | ⊙F | ✉ | ★F PLATE BLOCKS, VF + 50% Plate No. | | UL | UR | LL | LR |
|---|---|---|---|---|---|---|---|---|---|---|---|---|
| **O46** | **1¢ deep brown** | 1.00 | .70 | 1.00 | .70 | 24.00‡ | O46 | blank | 4.50 each | | | |
| a | double "G" | 1,000.00 | — | — | — | — | O46a | blank | 4,000.00 | | | |
| **O47** | **2¢ green** | 1.00 | .70 | 1.00 | .70 | 24.00‡ | O47 | blank | 4.50 each | | | |
| a | pair, one without "G" | 1,500.00 | — | — | — | — | O47a | blank | 3,000.00 | 3,000.00 | — | — |
| i | blunt "G", pos. 39 and 91 | 50.00 | 40.00 | 35.00 | 25.00 | — | | | | | | |
| | O47i (pos. 39) in right margin pos. block of 9 (3 x 3) | 67.50 | 45.00 | — | — | — | O47i | block of 8, pos. 39 | | 100.00 (blank) | | |
| | O47i (pos. 91) in LL blank corner block of 4 | 60.00 | 40.00 | — | — | — | O47i | block of 4, pos. 91 | | | 60.00 | |
| ii | wide spacing "G" in vert. pair (NH+25%) | 800.00 | — | — | — | — | O47ii | blank | 2,000.00 | 2,000.00 | — | — |
| iii | shifted "G", badly misplaced | 125.00 | — | — | — | — | O47iii | blank (4) | — | — | 450.00 | 450.00 |
| **O48** | **4¢ carmine** | 1.10 | .75 | 1.00 | .75 | 60.00‡ | O48 | blank | 10.00 each | | | |
| i | blunt "G", position 91 | 50.00 | 40.00 | 35.00 | 25.00 | — | O48i | | — | — | 60.00 | — |
| **O49** | **5¢ violet blue** | 1.00 | .70 | .70 | .50 | 24.00‡ | O49 | blank | 3.50 each | | | |

‡ Single usage only, in time period.

CO2

EO2

## AIR MAIL

**1950**

| NH+50% | | ★VF | ★F | ⊙VF | ⊙F | ✉ | ★F PLATE BLOCKS, VF + 50% Plate No. | | UL | UR | LL | LR |
|---|---|---|---|---|---|---|---|---|---|---|---|---|
| **CO2** | **7¢ Canada Goose** | 18.00 | 12.00 | 18.00 | 12.00 | 40.00 | CO2 | 1,2 | 80.00 | 80.00 | 90.00 | 90.00 |
| i | major re-entry, double frameline at right | 75.00 | 50.00 | 50.00 | 40.00 | 100.00 | | | | | | |

## SPECIAL DELIVERY

**1950, NH+50%**

| | | ★VF | ★F | ⊙VF | ⊙F | ✉ | Plate No. | | UL | |
|---|---|---|---|---|---|---|---|---|---|---|
| **EO2** | **10¢ green** | 24.00 | 16.00 | 24.00 | 16.00 | 100.00 | EO2 | 1 | 90.00 | each |

| | ★VF | ★F | ⊙VF | ⊙F |
|---|---|---|---|---|
| **Nos. O16–O49, CO2, EO2** (35) Set of "G" overprints | 324.75 | 183.10 | 324.00 | 182.55 |

## OFFICIALLY SEALED STAMPS

OX1

OX2, OX3

OX4

**1879–1913** **Engraved** **Perf 12**

| | | NH% | ★VF | ★F | ⊙VF | ⊙F | ✉ |
|---|---|---|---|---|---|---|---|
| **OX1** | **yellow brown**, *1879* | 400 | 750.00 | 150.00 | 250.00† | 100.00† | 2,600.00† |
| **OX2** | **Victoria, bluish paper**, *1902* | 300 | 800.00 | 400.00 | 450.00† | 300.00† | 4,000.00† |
| a | imperf. pair, without gum (25 pairs) | — | *6,500.00* | *4,000.00* | — | — | |
| **OX3** | **Victoria, white paper**, *1907* | 200 | 200.00 | 75.00 | 90.00† | 30.00† | 3,200.00† |
| **OX4** | **brown black**, *1913* | 200 | 200.00 | 50.00 | 60.00† | 25.00† | 3,000.00† |

VF-NH examples of OX1 are EXTREMELY rare (if they indeed exist).

† Used copies are generally creased, as the Dead Letter Office used these stamps to re-seal opened envelopes. Must be tied by a postmark any type. Untied seals are worth 60% less and require a certificate of authenticity.

Plate Blocks of Nos. OX1–OX4 are rare. Value 3 times sum of singles in block.

### OFFICIALLY SEALED PLATE PROOFS

| | | |
|---|---|---|
| **OX1P** | brown on india card | 600.00 |
| **OX2P** | black on india card | 1,000.00 |
| **OX4P** | brown black on india card | 800.00 |

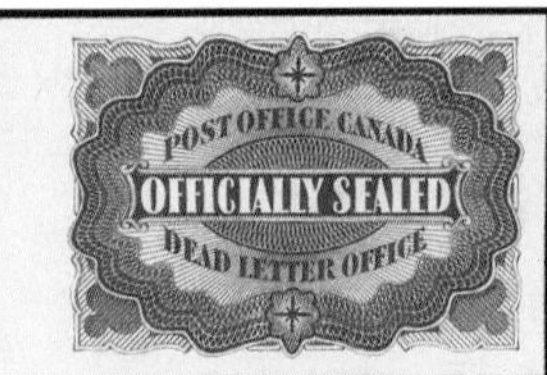

OX1P

OX2P

OX4P

## PRISONER OF WAR FREE FRANKS

Valid for postage in Canada on parcels up to 20 lbs. Used by prisoners of war interned in Canada during World War II. Printed black on red, gummed paper.

PWF2

PWF4

### SECRETARY OF STATE ISSUES

**NO INSCRIPTION AT TOP OF CANADA**

**1940–1941**
**Imperforate**

| | | NH% | Qty | ★VF | ⊙VF | ✉ |
|---|---|---|---|---|---|---|
| **PWF1** | "P/W" in large type, *Feb 1940* | 100 | 2,000 | 600.00 | 700.00 | 1,200.00 |
| **PWF2** | "P/W" in small type, *Feb 1941* | 100 | 2,000 | 600.00 | 700.00 | 1,200.00 |

### DEPARTMENT OF NATIONAL DEFENSE ISSUES

**INSCRIPTION AT TOP OF CANADA**

**1943–1946**

| | | NH% | Qty | ★VF | ⊙VF | ✉ |
|---|---|---|---|---|---|---|
| **PWF3** | Imperf., "...5M—5-43 (2)" at UR, *Jun 1943* | 100 | 5,000 | 500.00 | 425.00 | 1,000.00 |
| **PWF4** | rouletted, "5M—11-44..." at UR, *Nov 1944* | 100 | 5,000 | 400.00 | 450.00 | 500.00 |
| a | vert. pane of 5 | 100 | | 2,200.00 | | |
| **PWF5** | perf 12½, "1M—7-45..." at UR, Jul 1945 | 100 | 1,000 | 900.00 | 950.00 | 1,350.00 |
| a | vert. strip of 5 | 100 | | 5,000.00 | | |
| **PWF6** | rouletted, "5M—3-46..." at UR, Mar 1946 | 50 | 5,000 | 50.00 | 250.00 | 600.00 |
| a | vert. pane of 5 | 50 | | 275.00 | | |

Values for used copies are for those with contemporary cancels.

The numbers for Prisoner of War Free Franks are from *The Canadian Revenue Stamp Catalogue*, by E.S.J. Van Dam, with the author's permission. Values current retail prices. Values on cover are for basic stamp on piece; complete covers and unusual usages are valued higher.

# PICTURE POSTAGE™

Picture Postage™, introduced in April 2000, allows you to customize your mail and create personalized stamps using your favourite photos. The general public can order their own personalized Picture Postage™ stamps and tens of thousands (or perhaps hundreds of thousands) of different designs have been created over the years. It would be impossible for this catalogue to know, and then list, these personalized stamps.

Only Picture Postage™ stamps created by Canada Post, and sold to collectors in mint (unused) condition through Canada Post outlets or direct from Canadian Bank Note (CBN), are listed here. These stamps were available to the general public via mail order, on-line, selected post offices across the country, and/or CBN in full panes only (individual stamps were not sold by Canada Post).

Four types of panes of 21 are known: Type 1: CBN barcode and product number on front; no Canada Post UPC on back.
Type 2: CBN barcode and product number on front with Canada Post UPC on back.
Type 3: only Canada Post UPC on back.
Type 4: Canada Post UPC on front only.

Pane types 1 and 2

Pane type 3

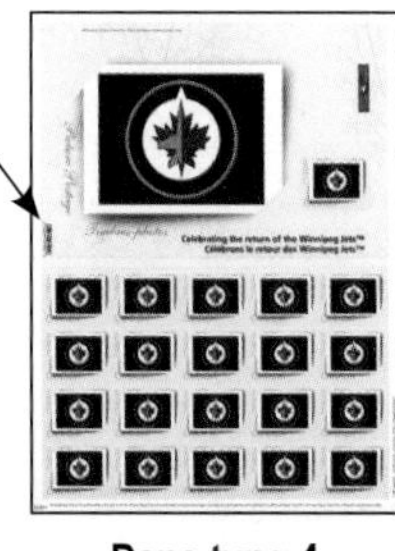
Pane type 4

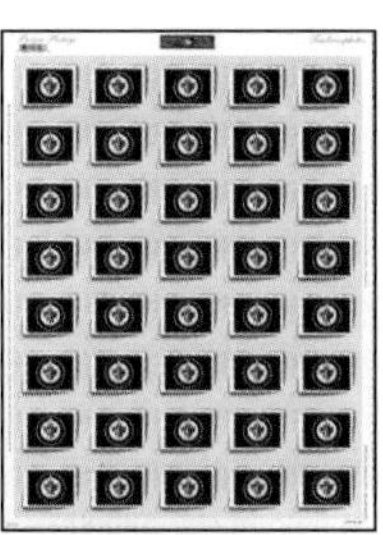
Pane of 40

**Outer frame pane printing dates (lower left corner of pane)**
The distribution of A, B, C panes is not known.

Lithography (outer frame, 6 colours), Laser (inner image)
Self-adhesive panes of 20+1
Canadian Bank Note Company

**2011** **GT4, TRC Paper**
**Serpentine Die cut 12.7x13.0**

## Diwali

PP1
Candle

PP2
Lotus flower

| 2011, Sep 12* | | NH–VF | ⊙F | ✉ |
|---|---|---|---|---|
| PP1 | candle | 2.25 | *3.50* | *15.00* |
| | pane of 21 (Type 1, 10060439, 12 2006) | 50.00 | | |
| | pane of 21 (Type 2, 10060748, 12 2006) | 50.00 | | |
| | pane of 21 (Type 3, 09 2011) | 35.00 | | |
| PP2 | Lotus flower | 2.25 | *3.50* | *15.00* |
| | pane of 21 (Type 1, 10060440, 12 2006) | 50.00 | | |
| | pane of 21 (Type 2, 10060747, 12 2006) | 50.00 | | |
| | pane of 21 (Type 3, 09 2011) | 35.00 | | |

Initial qty: 1,050 panes of each design (22,050 stamps of each)

* Initial on sale date. Original selling price was $17.90 per pane of 21 stamps. At time of issue the postage value was 59¢.

## Eid

PP3
Calligraphy

PP4
The Feast

| 2011, Oct 18* | | NH–VF | ⊙F | ✉ |
|---|---|---|---|---|
| PP3 | calligraphy | 2.25 | *3.50* | *15.00* |
| | pane of 21 (Type 2, 10060951, 12 2006) | 70.00 | | |
| | pane of 21 (Type 2, 09 2011) | 70.00 | | |
| | pane of 21 (Type 3, 09 2011) | 35.00 | | |
| PP4 | The Feast | 2.25 | *3.50* | *15.00* |
| | pane of 21 (Type 2, 10060950, 12 2006) | 70.00 | | |
| | pane of 21 (Type 2, 09 2011) | 70.00 | | |
| | pane of 21 (Type 3, 09 2011) | 35.00 | | |

Initial qty: 600 panes of each design (12,600 stamps of each)

* Initial on sale date. Original selling price was $17.90 per pane of 21 stamps. At time of issue the postage value was 59¢.

NH-VF prices are for stamps on original backing paper, ***as issued***.
Used, and on cover prices are for stamps used in-period.

## Hanukkah

PP5
Dreidel

PP6
Menorah

| 2011, Nov 16* | | NH–VF | ⊙F | ✉ |
|---|---|---|---|---|
| **PP5** | **dreidel** | 2.25 | *3.50* | *15.00* |
| | pane of 21 (Type 3, 12 2006) | 70.00 | | |
| | pane of 21 (Type 3, 09 2011) | 35.00 | | |
| **PP6** | **Menorah** | 2.25 | *3.50* | *15.00* |
| | pane of 21 (Type 3, 09 2011) | 35.00 | | |

Initial qty: 1,300 panes of each design (27,300 stamps of each)

* Initial on sale date (originally announced as Nov 7). Original selling price was $17.90 per pane of 21 stamps. At time of issue the postage value was 59¢.

## Winnipeg Jets

PP7
Primary logo

PP8
Secondary logo

PP9
"First goal" by #80 Nik Antropov

Lithography (both outer frame *and* inner image, 6 colours),

| 2011, Nov 10 | | NH–VF | ⊙F | ✉ |
|---|---|---|---|---|
| **PP7** | **primary logo** (single from pane of 21) | 2.50 | *3.50* | *15.00* |
| | pane of 21 (Type 4, 09 2011) | 50.00 | | |
| Initial qty: 5,000 panes of 21. Sold for $24.95 per pane. | | | | |
| a | **primary logo** (single from pane of 40, dated 12 2008)† | 5.00 | *7.00* | *25.00* |
| ai | vertical scratch (pos. 26) | 15.00 | *20.00* | *40.00* |
| | pane of 40 | *200.00* | | |
| Initial qty: 1,000 panes of 40. Sold for $34.95 per pane. | | | | |
| **PP8** | **secondary logo** | 2.50 | *3.50* | *15.00* |
| | pane of 21 (Type 4, 09 2011) | 50.00 | | |
| Initial qty: 5,000 panes. Sold for $24.95 per pane. | | | | |
| **PP9** | **first goal** | 4.00 | *6.00* | *20.00* |
| | pane of 21 (Type 4, 09 2011) | 75.00 | | |
| Qty: 10,000 panes of 21 ('limited edition', numbered on front). Sold for $34.95 per pane. | | | | |

† the stamps from the pane of 40 (PP7a) had only the outer frame printed by lithography; the inner image was laser printed. The quality of print of the inner image is quite different between the pane of 21 and pane of 40 stamps.

At time of issue the postage value was 59¢ for all three Winnipeg Jets stamps.

For non-denominated postal card of the primary logo design, see UXnnn.

**Left: detail of PP7 (lithography)**
**Right: detail of PP7a (laser)**

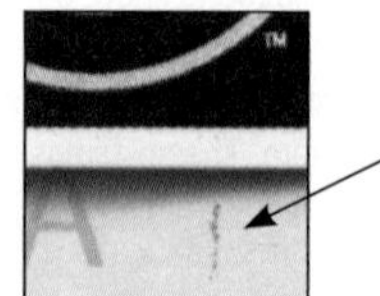

**PP7ai**

PP10
Torbay, NL

PP11
Victoria, BC

PP12
Royal Conservatory

| 2012 | | NH–VF | ⊙F | ✉ |
|---|---|---|---|---|
| **PP10** | **Torbay, NL 250th**, *Jun 8* | 8.00 | *8.00* | *25.00* |
| | pane of 21 | 100.00 | | |
| | pane of 40 | 200.00 | | |
| **PP11** | **Victoria, BC 150th**, *Aug 2* | 8.00 | *8.00* | *25.00* |
| | pane of 21 | 100.00 | | |
| | pane of 40 | 200.00 | | |
| **PP12** | **Royal Conservatory**, *Sep 19* | 10.00 | *10.00* | *25.00* |
| | pane of 21 | 200.00 | | |
| | pane of 40 | 400.00 | | |

Very similar designs of these three stamps (PP10–PP12) were used on Commemorative Envelopes (S90–S92). Mint panes were made available to collectors with very little fanfare (they could only be ordered directly from Canadian Bank Note).

## "STICK 'N TIC" LABELS

**1983–1984** **Die cut**

| | | Unused | Used | ✉ |
|---|---|---|---|---|
| **1-ST** | 1983 Experimental label | 6.00 | 6.00 | 20.00 |
| **2-ST** | 1984 Experimental label | 6.00 | 6.00 | 20.00 |

These labels were introduced on an experimental basis to speed up automatic sorting during the busy Christmas mail season. The 1983 experiment was conducted in Winnipeg only, and covers must bear a Winnipeg postmark during the period of late-November to December 1983. The 1984 experiment was expanded to other major cities across Canada.

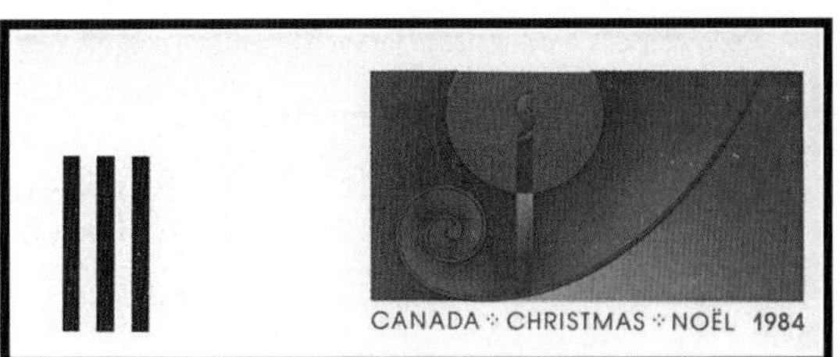

2-ST

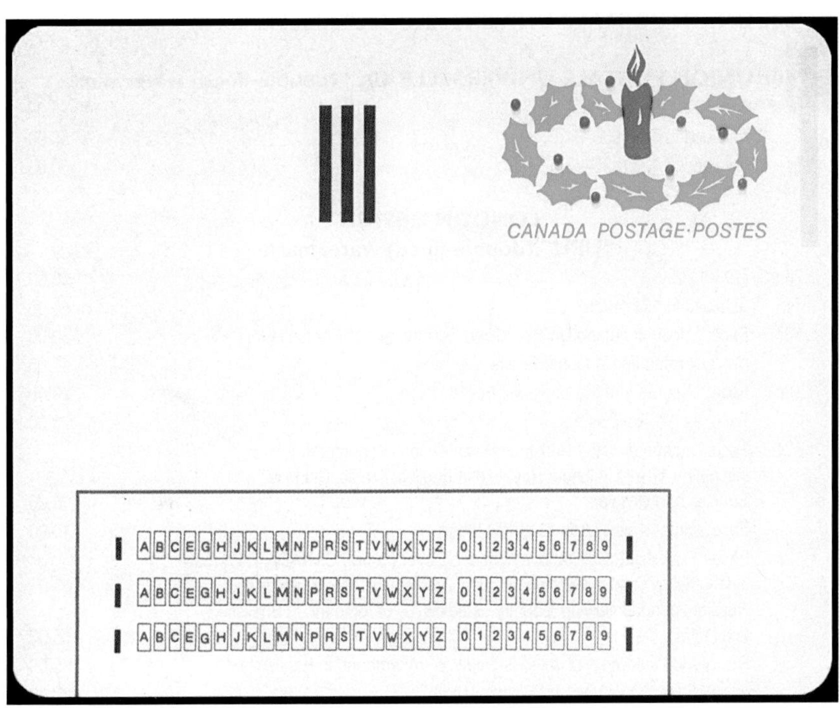

1-ST

## UNITED NATIONS STAMPS IN CANADIAN DENOMINATIONS

British American Bank Note Co. Ltd.

**1967, April 28** **Perf 11**

| UN | | Mint | Used | ✉ |
|---|---|---|---|---|
| 170 | **4¢ Peace** (4,000,000) | .25 | .25 | |
| 171 | **5¢ Justice** (4,000,000) | .25 | .25 | |
| 172 | **8¢ Pavilion** (3,000,000) | .25 | .25 | |
| 173 | **10¢ Fraternity** (3,000,000) | .25 | .25 | |
| 174 | **15¢ Truth** (3,000,000) | .25 | .25 | |

Combination FDC $3.00 [Total FDC quantity of all 5 values: 901,625]
Expo 67 UN Souvenir folder (set of singles plus UN Scott 105) $10.00 [15,000]

For use at the United Nations Pavilion at Expo '67 (Apr 28–Oct 29) in Montreal, the first time the United Nations Postal Administration had arranged to establish a United Nations postal station outside of United Nations territory.

Denominations expressed in Canadian currency. They were valid for postage only on mail posted at the UN Pavilion during the fair.

Last day of sale: Oct 29, 1967.

UN 170

JUSTICE · UNITED NATIONS · NATIONS UNIES · JUSTITIA · 5 JUSTICE 5

UN 171

UN 172

UN 173

UN 174

**Rates:**

4¢: local letter
5¢: domestic forward letter, USA
8¢: air letters to USA
10¢: air postcard to all countries
15¢: air letters to Great Britain, Republic of Ireland, Europe, Bermuda, Mexico, Central and South America, West Indies

# REPLY COUPONS SOLD BY CANADA

Reply coupons are purchased (or exchanged) at a post office to prepay (or receive) the minimum postage of a basic reply by surface or air (since 1991) mail.

Rome design

Uncut blocks of four are known of numbers: 1, 6, 9, 10, 11, 13

London design

Vienna design

Lausanne design

## INTERNATIONAL REPLY COUPONS

International Reply Coupons are issued by the Universal Postal Union. The last day of sale of International Reply Coupons in Canada was 2017.10.13.

| No. | | | Value |
|---|---|---|---|
| | | **ROME DESIGN** | |
| | | **"25c UNION POSTALE UNIVERSELLE 25c" (double-lined) watermark** | |
| 1 | 6¢ | (1907) | 25.00 |
| | | **"50c UNION POSTALE UNIVERSELLE 50c" (double-lined) watermark** | |
| 2 | 9¢ | (1925) | 50.00 |
| | | **"40c UNION POSTALE UNIVERSELLE 40c" (double-lined) watermark** | |
| 3 | 9¢ | | 25.00 |
| 4 | 9¢ | revalued to 7¢ (1930–34) | 50.00 |
| 5 | 9¢ | revalued to 12¢ (1934–35) | 50.00 |
| | | **LONDON DESIGN** | |
| | | **"UPU" (double-lined) watermark** | |
| 6 | 7¢ | (1930) | 50.00 |
| 7 | 7¢ | revalued to 12¢ (1935) | 50.00 |
| 8 | 12¢ | Face: "...country of the Union..." Rev: German text in Roman letters | 30.00 |
| a | | Rev.: German text in Gothic letters | 15.00 |
| 9 | 12¢ | Face: "...country of the Universal Postal Union..." | 10.00 |
| a | | Face: as "9"; Rev.: as "8a" | 20.00 |
| 10 | 12¢ | Face: "...country of the Universal Postal Union..."; printer's inscription 17 mm in length Rev: text in English, Arabic, Chinese, Spanish and Russian. | 5.00 |
| a | | Face: printer's inscription 13 mm in length | 10.00 |
| 11 | 12¢ | Face: "FORMULE C22" above right circle over frame; "CANADA" 14½ mm in length Rev.: text in German, English, Arabic, Chinese, Spanish and Russian; period following "country" is below "u" of "amount" in English text (1954) | 5.00 |
| a | | Rev: period following "country" is below "n" of "amount" in English text | 5.00 |
| b | | as "a", Face: "CANADA" 15½ mm in length | 10.00 |
| 12 | 12¢ | revalued to 15¢ (1959) | 10.00 |
| 13 | 15¢ | as "11a" (1959) | 5.00 |
| 14 | 15¢ | Face: "C22" above right circle over frame. Rev: Arabic text in large characters (printed by typography) | 3.00 |
| a | | printed by lithography | 10.00 |
| b | | Rev: Arabic text in small characters (printed by combination of typography and lithography) | 15.00 |
| | | **VIENNA DESIGN** | |
| | | **Multiple "UPU" watermark** | |
| 15 | 15¢ | Face: "CANADA" 11½ mm in length (1966) | 15.00 |
| a | | Face: "CANADA" 12½ mm in length | 3.00 |
| 16 | 22¢ | Rev: text in German "...Gesamtwert der Taxe..." (1971) | 3.00 |
| a | | Rev: text in German "...Gesamtwert der Gebuhr..." | 15.00 |
| b | | as "16", break at the foot of "D" in "CANADA" | 10.00 |
| 17 | 22¢ | revalued to 25¢ (1974) Rev: text in German "...Gesamtwert der Taxe..." | 7.50 |
| a | | Rev: text in German "...Gesamtwert der Gebuhr..." | 15.00 |
| | | **LAUSANNE DESIGN** | |
| | | **Multiple "UPU" watermark** | |
| 18 | | no value; Rev: text in English " ...the minimum postage for an unregistered letter sent by surface..." (1975) | 5.00 |
| a | | vertical watermark | 5.00 |
| 19 | | no value; as "18" except "(date facultative)" and dotted circle in left square omitted | 5.00 |
| a | | vertical watermark | 5.00 |
| 20 | | no value; Rev: text in English "...the minimum postage for a priority item or an unregistered letter sent by air..."; vertical watermark | 5.00 |
| 21 | | as "20", date "9.1992" printed at the lower left margin of the coupon | 7.00 |
| 22 | | as "20", date "8.1993" printed at the lower left margin of the coupon | 7.00 |

Beijing design (23)

Bucharest design (24)

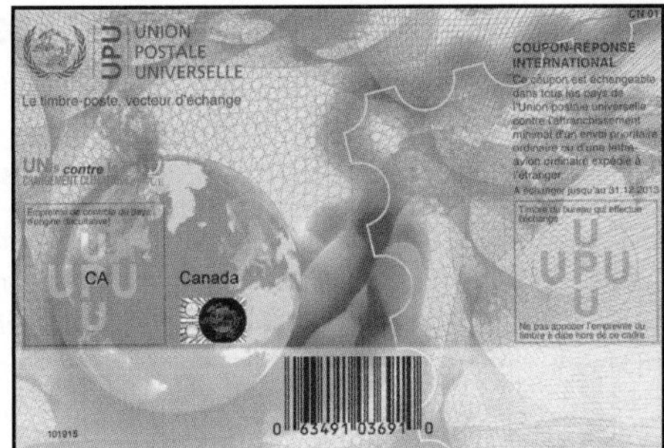


Nairobi design (25)

Water for Life (26)

| | | Value |
|---|---|---|
| | **Multiple UPU Cross and 8-pointed Star watermark** | |
| 23 | no value; Beijing design; expiry date 31.12.2006 (date under barcode starts CA 20011119...) | 7.00 |
| a | revised (date under barcode starts CA 20040315...) | 7.00 |
| b | revised (date under barcode starts CA 20050407...) | 7.00 |
| 24 | no value; Bucharest design; expiry date 31.12.2009 (CA 20060626...) | 7.00 |
| a | revised (date under barcode starts CA 20070419...) | 7.00 |
| | **No watermark** | |
| 25 | no value; Nairobi design; flrsc. ink security print; expiry date 31.12.2013 | 7.00 |
| 26 | no value; "Water for Life"; flrsc. ink security print; expiry date 31.12.2017 | 8.50 |

## IMPERIAL AND COMMONWEALTH REPLY COUPONS

Imperial and Commonwealth Reply Coupons were administered by the British Post Office. On July 1, 1971, the sale of Commonwealth Reply Coupons was discontinued in Canada. They are no longer valid on redemption.

Imperial design

### IMPERIAL

| | | | |
|---|---|---|---|
| | | **Multiple Crown and GVR (vertical) watermark** | |
| 1 | 5¢ | "This coupon ... It is valid for six months exclusive of the month of issue." (1927) | 15.00 |
| 2 | 5¢ | "This coupon ... to a destination within the Empire." | 50.00 |
| | | **Multiple Crown and GVR (double-lined) watermark** | |
| 3 | 5¢ | "This coupon ... to a destination within the Empire" | 25.00 |
| | | **Multiple Crown and GVIR (double-lined) watermark** | |
| 4 | 5¢ | as "3" | 25.00 |
| 5 | 5¢ | "This coupon ... Exceptionally the exchange value in India is 2½ annas." | 25.00 |
| 6 | 5¢ | as "5" with Burma added to inscription | 50.00 |
| 7 | 5¢ | as "5" with Pakistan added to inscription | 15.00 |

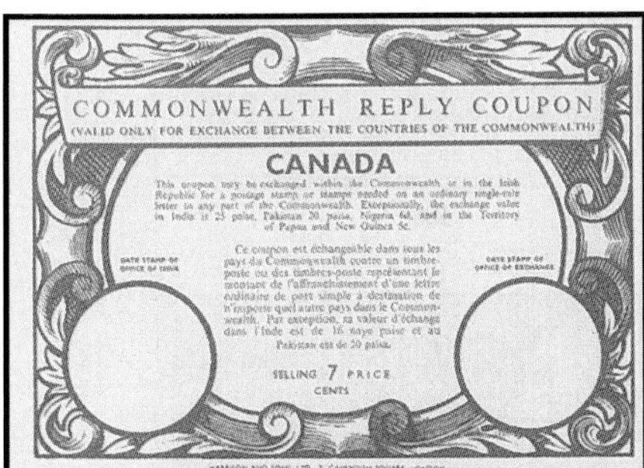


Commonwealth design

#9 is known overprinted "SPECIMEN"

### COMMONWEALTH

| | | | |
|---|---|---|---|
| | | **Multiple Crown and GVIR (double-lined) watermark** | |
| 8 | 5¢ | "This coupon ... in India is 2½ annas and in Pakistan 1 anna 9 pies." (1953) | 20.00 |
| 9 | 6¢ | as "8" (1954) | 5.00 |
| 10 | 6¢ | "This coupon ... in India and Pakistan is 2½ annas." (1956) | 10.00 |
| | | **Multiple Crown and EIIR (double-lined) watermark** | |
| 11 | 6¢ | as "10" (1957) | 3.00 |
| 12 | 6¢ | "This coupon ... in India is 16 naye paise and in Pakistan 2½ annas." (1961) | 3.00 |
| 13 | 6¢ | "This coupon ... on a single-rate letter ... in India is 16 naye paise and in Pakistan 20 Paisa." | 3.00 |
| a | | break in oval frameline to right of left circle | 10.00 |
| 14 | 6¢ | "This coupon ... on an ordinary rate letter ..." | 3.00 |
| a | | break in oval frameline to right of left circle | 20.00 |
| 15 | 6¢ | "This coupon ... on an ordinary single-rate letter ..."; printer's inscription: "St. Martin's Lane" | 15.00 |
| a | | printer's inscription: "7, Cavendish Square" | 3.00 |
| b | | as "15", watermark inverted | 50.00 |
| 16 | 6¢ | "This coupon ... in India is 16 paise, Pakistan 20 paisa and in Territory of Papua and New Guinea 5d." | 3.00 |
| | | **Unwatermarked** | |
| 17 | 7¢ | "This coupon ... in India is 25 paise ..." (1968) | 3.00 |
| 18 | 7¢ | "This coupon ... in India is 20 paise ..."; French text: "... valeur d'échange dans l'Inde est de 16 naye paise ..." (1969) | 3.00 |
| 19 | 7¢ | English text as "18"; French Text: "...valeur d'échange est de 20 paise aux Indes,..." (1970) | 3.00 |

# CANADA POST UNCUT PRESS SHEETS

| Unitrade # | Description | Issue date | Panes | Post office price | (signed) | Quantity Issued Unsigned | Signed | Value Unsigned | Signed | Size(mm) |
|---|---|---|---|---|---|---|---|---|---|---|
| **1591–94iv** | Birds I (45¢) | *Jan 9, 1996* | 5 | $27.00 | $69.00 | 9,000 | 1,000 | 175.00 | 500.00 | 610x637 |
| **1605z** | Historic Land Vehicles V | *Jun 8, 1996* | 3 | $20.00 | | 25,000 | – | 50.00 | – | 447x625 |
| **1630aiv** | Lunar New Year – Year of the Ox | *Feb 7, 1997* | 12 | $20.00 | | 15,000 | – | 225.00 | – | 570x540 |
| **1631–34i** | Birds II (45¢) | *Jan 10, 1997* | 6 | $54.00 | $89.95 | 8,500 | 1,500 | 100.00 | 200.00 | 570x340 |
| **1708ai** | Lunar New Year – Year of the Tiger | *Jan 8, 1998* | 12 | $24.95 | | 30,000 | – | 85.00 | – | 550x602 |
| **1710–13i** | Birds III (45¢) [two types exist] | *Mar 13, 1998* | 6 | $54.00 | $89.95 | 8,500 | 1,500 | 100.00 | 200.00 | 570x340 |
| **1736–37i** | RCMP 125th Anniversary | *Jul 3, 1998* | 10 | $24.95 | | 25,000 | – | 75.00 | – | 698x690 |
| **1768ii** | Lunar New Year – Year of the Rabbit | *Jan 8, 1999* | 12 | $24.95 | | 30,000 | – | 75.00 | – | 580x566 |
| **1770–73i** | Birds IV (46¢) | *Feb 24, 1999* | 6 | $55.20 | $89.95 | 5,000 | 1,500 | 100.00 | 150.00 | 650x530 |
| **1812ii** | Millennium Dove (hologram) | *Oct 12, 1999* | 9 | $79.99 | | – | 30,000 | – | 130.00 | 690x437 |
| **1837ii** | Lunar New Year – Year of the Dragon | *Jan 5, 2000* | 12 | $24.95 | | 50,000 | – | 65.00 | – | 660x640 |
| **1839–42i** | Birds V (46¢) | *Mar 1, 2000* | 6 | $55.20 | | ? | ? | 100.00 | 150.00 | 650x530 |
| **1884ii** | Lunar New Year – Year of the Snake | *Jan 5, 2001* | 12 | $24.95 | | 35,000 | – | 60.00 | – | 640x627 |
| **1886–89i** | Birds VI (47¢) | *Feb 1, 2001* | 6 | $56.40 | $89.95 | 1,500 | 800 | 200.00 | 300.00 | 650x530 |
| **1934ii** | Lunar New Year – Year of the Horse | *Jan 3, 2002* | 12 | $26.95 | | 35,000 | – | 75.00 | – | 600x581 |
| **1970ii** | Lunar New Year – Year of the Ram | *Jan 3, 2003* | 12 | $26.95 | | 35,000 | – | 75.00 | – | 760x582 |
| **2016ii** | Lunar New Year – Year of the Monkey | *Jan 8, 2004* | 12 | $26.95 | | 35,000 | – | 75.00 | – | 600x580 |
| **2084ii** | Lunar New Year – Year of the Rooster | *Jan 7, 2005* | 12 | $26.95 | | 25,000 | – | 75.00 | – | 580x600 |
| **2141ii** | Lunar New Year – Year of the Dog | *Jan 6, 2006* | 12 | $26.95 | | 20,000 | – | 75.00 | – | 580x700 |
| **2158–59i** | Canadian Forces Snowbirds | *Jun 28, 2006* | 4+6 | $38.75 | | – | 1,000 | – | 250.00 | 560x485 |
| **2202ii** | Lunar New Year – Year of the Pig | *Jan 5, 2007* | 12 | $26.95 | | 15,000 | – | 125.00 | – | 540x580 |
| **2215–18i** | Royal Architectural Institute of Canada | *May 9, 2007* | 9 | | $37.44 | – | 2,000 | – | 100.00 | 649x598 |
| **2238i** | Beneficial Insects | *Oct 12, 2007* | 8 | | $28.00 | – | 2,500 | – | 60.00 | 616x485 |
| **2258ii** | Lunar New Year 2 – Year ot the Rat | *Jan 8, 2008* | 12 | $26.96 | | 15,000 | – | 125.00 | – | 360x610 |
| **2271i** | Yousuf Karsh | *May 21, 2008* | 6+2 | | $35.12 | – | 3,000 | – | 75.00 | 484x650 |
| **2297ii** | Lunar New Year 2 – Year of the Ox | *Jan 8, 2009* | 12 | $28.95 | | 25,000 | – | 75.00 | – | 360x610 |
| **2323ci** | International Year of Astronomy | *Apr 2, 2009* | 14 | $19.95 | | 7,500 | – | 100.00 | – | 482x650 |
| **2349ii** | Lunar New Year 2 – Year of the Tiger | *Jan 8, 2010* | 12 | $28.95 | | 25,000 | – | 60.00 | – | 360x610 |
| **2405i** | Blue Whale | *Oct 4, 2010* | 9 | $180.00 | | 1,000 | – | 425.00 | – | 560x476 |
| **2410i** | Beneficial Insects | *Oct 19, 2010* | 8 | | $30.00 | – | 5,000 | – | 60.00 | 616x483 |

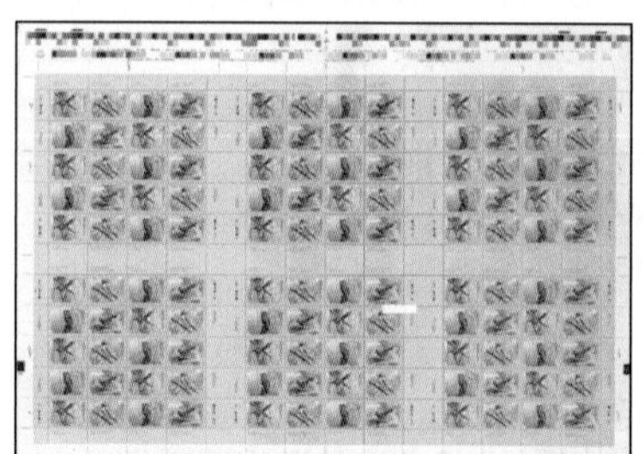

**1713i**

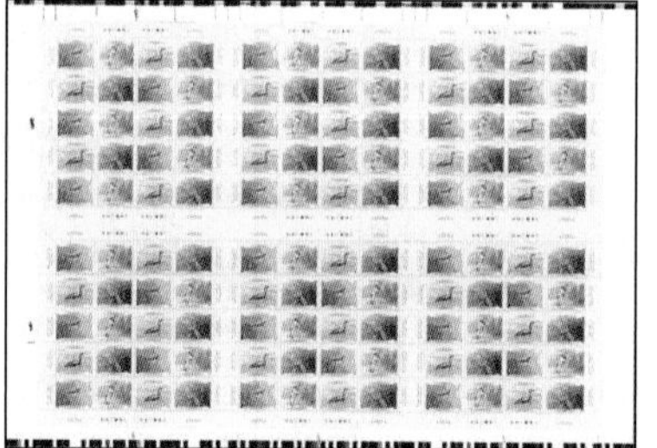

**1842i**

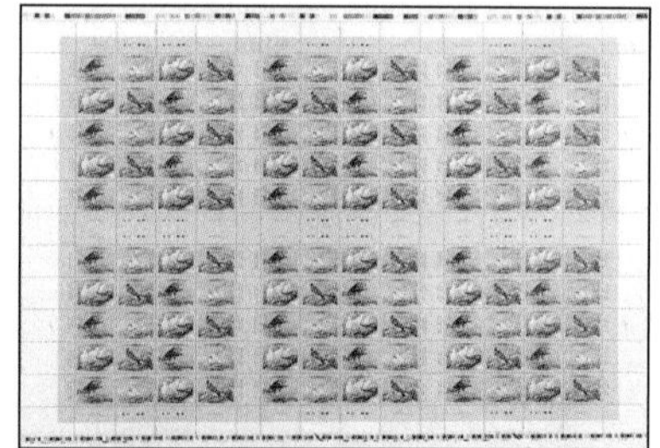

**1889i**

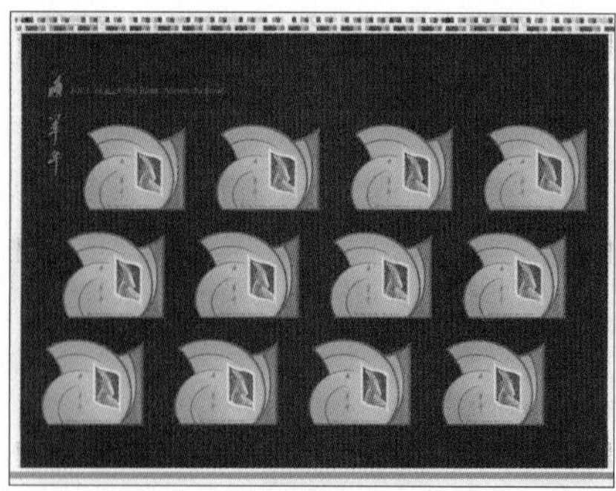

**1970ii**

**2016ii**

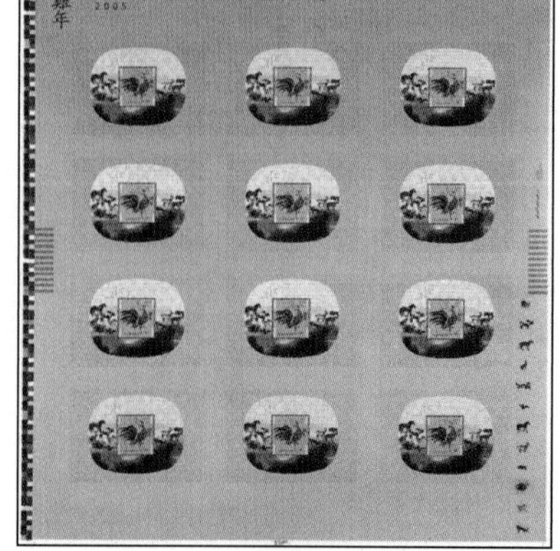

**2084ii**

| Unitrade # | Description | Issue date | Panes | Post office price | (signed) | Quantity Issued Unsigned | Signed | Value Unsigned | Signed | Size(mm) |
|---|---|---|---|---|---|---|---|---|---|---|
| **2417ii** | Lunar New Year 2 – Year of the Rabbit | *Jan 7, 2011* | 12 | $29.95 | | 20,000 | – | 60.00 | – | 360x610 |
| **2436i** | Art Canada: Daphne Odjig | *Feb 21, 2011* | 2+4 | $32.36 | | 1,500 | – | 60.00 | – | 483x510 |
| **2471i** | Architecture: Art Deco | *Jun 9, 2011* | 18 | $53.10 | | 1,500 | – | 160.00 | – | 482x650 |
| **2496ii** | Lunar New Year 2 – Year of the Dragon | *Jan 10, 2012* | 12 | $29.95 | | 15,000 | – | 80.00 | – | 360x610 |
| **2522i** | Art Canada: Joe Fafard | *Feb 23, 2012* | 2+4 | $33.36 | | 1,500 | – | 60.00 | – | 510x483 |
| **2535ii** | Titanic | *Apr 5, 2012* | 12 | $26.95 | | 5,000 | – | 90.00 | – | 650x483 |
| **2540ai** | Queen Elizabeth II Diamond Jubilee | *May 7, 2012* | 8+4 | $80.00 | | – | 2,500 | – | 200.00 | 570x508 |
| **2600ii** | Lunar New Year 2 – Year of the Snake | *Jan 8, 2013* | 12 | $29.95 | | 15,000 | – | 60.00 | – | 360x610 |
| **2642i** | Chinatown Gates | *May 1, 2013* | 5 | $25.20 | | 2,500 | – | 70.00 | – | 560x360 |
| **2646i** | Motorcycles | *Jun 5, 2013* | 12 | $17.99 | | 5,000 | – | 42.00 | – | 616x482 |
| **2677i** | Superman | *Sep 10, 2013* | 6 | $24.95 | | 7,500 | – | 55.00 | – | 482x650 |
| **2700ii** | Lunar New Year 2 – Year of the Horse | *Jan 13, 2014* | 12 | $29.95 | | 13,000 | – | 60.00 | – | 360x610 |
| **2746ii** | Empress of Ireland | *May 29, 2014* | 12 | $30.00 | | 5,000 | – | 60.00 | – | 650x482 |
| **2748i** | Haunted Canada I | *Jun 13, 2014* | 8 | $34.00 | | 5,000 | – | 68.00 | – | 650x480 |
| **2772i** | Great Canadian Comedians | *Aug 29, 2014* | 4 | $19.95 | | 7,500 | – | 68.00 | – | 615x482 |
| **2802ii** | Lunar New Year 2 – Year of the Ram | *Jan 8, 2015* | 12 | $30.00 | | 11,000 | – | 60.00 | – | 360x610 |
| **2808iii** | Canada Flag | *Feb 15, 2015* | 20+3 | $115.00 | | – | 1,000 | – | 275.00 | 616x483 |
| **2823i** | Dinos of Canada I | *Apr 13, 2015* | 8 | $34.00 | | 5,000 | – | 68.00 | – | 610x360 |
| **2838i** | Weather Wonders | *Jun 18, 2015* | 6 | $25.50 | | 5,000 | – | 51.00 | – | 615x485 |
| **2853i** | The Franklin Expedition | *Aug 6, 2015* | 12 | $30.00 | | 5,000 | – | 60.00 | – | 484x650 |
| **2860i** | Haunted Canada II | *Sep 14, 2015* | 8 | $34.00 | | 2,000 | – | 68.00 | – | 615x482 |
| **2885ii** | Lunar New Year 2 – Year of the Monkey | *Feb 1, 2016* | 12 | $30.00 | | 8,000 | – | 60.00 | – | 360x610 |
| **2912ii** | Star Trek [TV series 50th anniversary] | *May 5, 2016* | 6 | $44.10 | | 10,000 | – | 90.00 | – | 483x650 |
| **2922i** | Star Trek (lenticular) | *May 5, 2016* | 12 | $120.00 | | 2,000 | – | 240.00 | – | 425x630 |
| **2923i** | Dinos of Canada II | *May 26, 2016* | 7 | $30.60 | | 2,500 | – | 62.00 | – | 648x481 |
| **2935i** | Haunted Canada III | *Sep 8, 2016* | 8 | $34.00 | | 2,000 | – | 68.00 | – | 615x482 |
| **2960ii** | Lunar New Year 2 – Year of the Rooster | *Jan 9, 2017* | 12 | $30.00 | | 8,000 | – | 60.00 | – | 360x610 |
| **2983i** | Star Trek [Captains] | *Apr 27, 2017* | 6 | $44.10 | | 5,000 | – | 90.00 | – | 483x650 |
| **2992i** | Formula 1 in Canada | *May 16, 2017* | 5 strips | $21.25 | | 2,000 | – | 45.00 | – | 358x608 |
| **3098ii** | Queen Elizabeth II Coronation | *Apr 20, 2018* | 12 | $102.00 | | 1,000 | – | 205.00 | – | 620x520 |

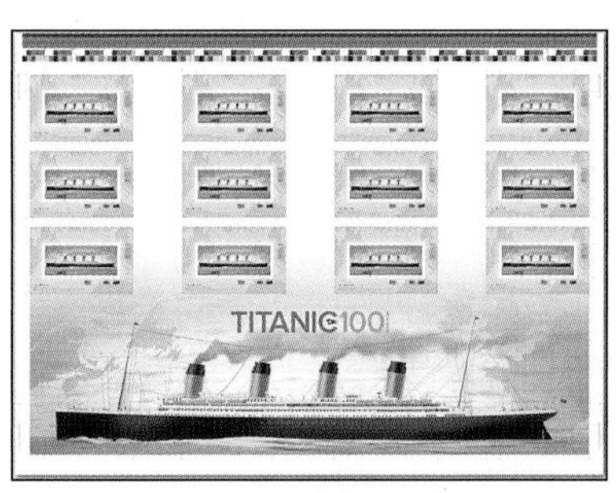

**2535ii**

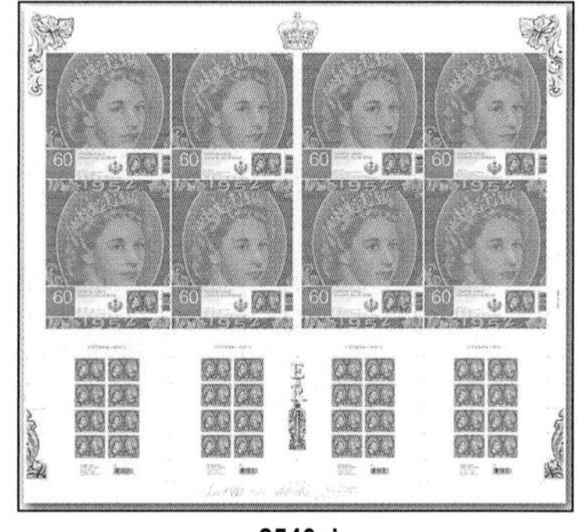
**2540ai**

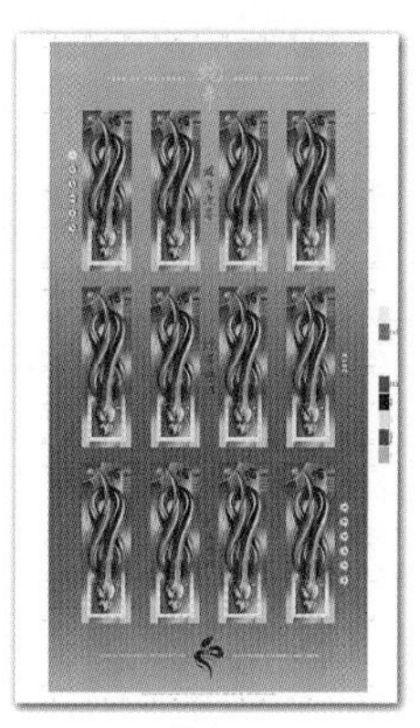
**2600ii**

**2642i**

**2677i**

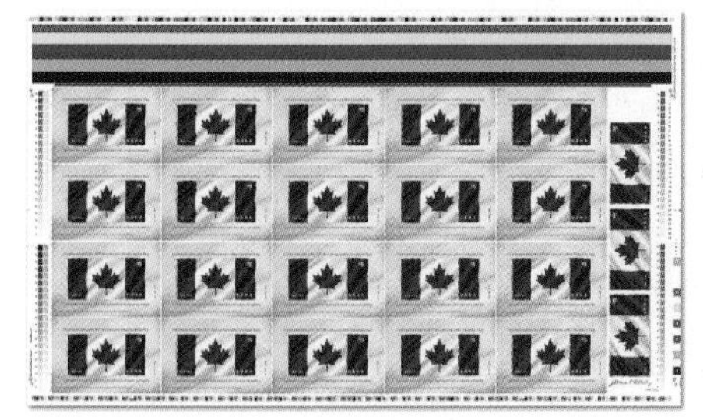
**2808iii**

## Uncut press sheet gutter combinations

Used pieces reflect items used "in period".

Some collectors may prefer to cut up their press sheets into smaller units for display and/or storage purposes. Remember that you are sacrificing one or more uncut press sheets to obtain the gutter combinations listed here.

| Unitrade # | VF NH | VF used |
|---|---|---|
| **1591–94** Birds of Canada - I (from press sheet) | | |
| horizontal gutter of 6 | $75.00 | $90.00 |
| pane of 12 from press sheet (side margins) | $40.00 | $50.00 |
| **1631–34** Birds of Canada - II (from press sheet) | | |
| vertical gutter pair (4 diff possible) | $4.00 | $4.00 |
| horizontal gutter pair (4 diff possible) | $4.00 | $4.00 |
| small cross-gutter of 8 | $25.00 | $30.00 |
| large cross-gutter of 16 | $35.00 | $45.00 |
| set of plate blocks from press sheet | $35.00 | $45.00 |
| **1708a** Year of Tiger press sheet | | |
| single S/S from press sheet (square margins, 12 diff possible) | $7.00 | $8.00 |
| vert. or horiz. pair of S/S from press sheet (square margins, 6 diff possible) | $14.00 | $16.00 |
| **1710–13** Birds of Canada - III (from press sheet) | | |
| vertical gutter pair (4 diff possible) | $4.00 | $4.00 |
| horizontal gutter pair (4 diff possible) | $4.00 | $4.00 |
| small cross-gutter of 8 | $20.00 | $25.00 |
| large cross-gutter of 16 | $30.00 | $40.00 |
| T1 set of plate blocks from press sheet | $30.00 | $40.00 |
| T2 set of plate blocks from press sheet | $45.00 | $60.00 |
| **1768** Year of Rabbit press sheet | | |
| single S/S from press sheet (square margins, 2 diff possible) | $12.00 | $15.00 |
| vertical pair of S/S from press sheet (square margins, unique in sheet) | $30.00 | $35.00 |
| single S/S from press sheet (irregular margins, 10 diff possible) | $8.00 | $10.00 |
| **1770–73** Birds of Canada - IV (from press sheet) | | |
| vertical gutter pair (4 diff possible) | $4.00 | $4.00 |
| horizontal gutter pair (4 diff possible) | $4.00 | $4.00 |
| small cross-gutter of 8 | $20.00 | $25.00 |
| large cross-gutter of 16 | $30.00 | $40.00 |
| set of plate blocks from press sheet | $35.00 | $45.00 |
| **1812** Millennium press sheet | | |
| vert. or horiz. pair of S/S from press sheet (square margins, 6 diff possible) | $50.00 | --- |
| **1837** Year of Dragon press sheet | | |
| single S/S from press sheet (square margins, 12 diff possible) | $6.00 | $7.00 |
| vert. or horiz. pair of S/S from press sheet (square margins, 6 diff possible) | $12.00 | $14.00 |
| **1839–42** Birds of Canada - V (from press sheet) | | |
| vertical gutter pair (4 diff possible) | $4.00 | $4.00 |
| horizontal gutter pair (4 diff possible) | $4.00 | $4.00 |
| small cross-gutter of 8 | $20.00 | $25.00 |
| large cross-gutter of 16 | $30.00 | $40.00 |
| set of plate blocks from press sheet | $35.00 | $45.00 |

2159i

| Unitrade # | VF NH | VF used |
|---|---|---|
| **1886–89** Birds of Canada - VI (from press sheet) | | |
| vertical gutter pair (4 diff possible) | $5.00 | $5.00 |
| horizontal gutter pair (4 diff possible) | $5.00 | $5.00 |
| small cross-gutter of 8 | $30.00 | $35.00 |
| large cross-gutter of 16 | $40.00 | $50.00 |
| set of plate blocks from press sheet | $45.00 | $55.00 |
| **1934** Year of Horse press sheet | | |
| single S/S from press sheet (square margins, 12 diff possible) | $7.00 | $8.00 |
| vert. or horiz. pair of S/S from press sheet (square margins, 6 diff possible) | $14.00 | $16.00 |
| **1970** Year of Ram press sheet | | |
| single S/S from press sheet (square margins, 12 diff possible) | $7.00 | $8.00 |
| vert. or horiz. pair of S/S from press sheet (square margins, 6 diff possible) | $14.00 | $16.00 |
| **2084** Year of Rooster press sheet | | |
| single S/S from press sheet (square margins) | $7.00 | $8.00 |
| vert. or horiz. pair of S/S from press sheet (square margins) | $14.00 | $16.00 |
| **2141** Year of Dog press sheet | | |
| single S/S from press sheet (square margins, 12 diff possible) | $7.00 | $8.00 |
| vert. or horiz. pair of S/S from press sheet (square margins, 6 diff possible) | $14.00 | $16.00 |
| **2158–59** Snowbirds (more than one sheet must be broken to make all combinations) | | |
| #2158 vert double gutter pair (4x per sheet) | $15.00 | $17.00 |
| #2158 vertical single gutter w/ 2159 (2x) | $20.00 | $23.00 |
| #2158 w/ two vertical labels (1x) | $10.00 | $12.00 |
| #2158 vert single gutter pair (1x) | $20.00 | $23.00 |
| #2158 vertical part-perf double gutter pair (3x) | $15.00 | $17.00 |
| #2158 w/ 2159, cross gutter of four (1x) | $35.00 | $40.00 |
| #2158 vertical strip of 3 A198w/ 2 labels a 2158 (1x) | $10.00 | $12.00 |
| #2159 vert double gutter pair (4x per sheet) | $15.00 | $17.00 |
| #2159 vertical single gutter w/ 2158 (1x) | $25.00 | $28.00 |
| #2159 w/ two vertical labels (2x) | $10.00 | $12.00 |
| #2159 vert single gutter pair 1x) | $20.00 | $23.00 |
| #2159 vertical part-perf double gutter pair (3x) | $15.00 | $17.00 |
| #2159 w/ 2158, horizontal gutter pair (12x) | $10.00 | $12.00 |
| #2159 cross gutter block of four w/ 2159 (vert dbl gutter) (1x) | $40.00 | $45.00 |
| #2159 cross gutter block of four w/ 2159 (vert sgl gutter) (1x, incl. horiz. pair from s/s) | $40.00 | $45.00 |
| **2202** Year of Pig press sheet | | |
| single S/S from press sheet (square margins, 12 diff possible) | $15.00 | $18.00 |
| vert. or horiz. pair of S/S from press sheet (square margins, 6 diff possible) | $30.00 | $35.00 |
| **2215–18** Architecture press sheet | | |
| horizontal gutter pair (#2215 w/ 2 labels) | $4.00 | $5.00 |
| horizontal gutter pair (#2216 w/ 2 labels) | $4.00 | $5.00 |
| horizontal gutter pair (#2217 w/ 2 labels) | $4.00 | $5.00 |
| horizontal gutter pair (#2218 w/ 2 labels) | $4.00 | $5.00 |
| vertical gutter pair, #2218 w/ #2215 | $4.00 | $5.00 |
| "small" cross gutter of 4 (2 #2215 and 2 # 2218, w/ 4 labels) | $25.00 | $30.00 |
| "large" cross-gutter block of 8 (2 each of #2215 - 8, w/ 8 labels) | $35.00 | $40.00 |
| set of four corner plate blocks | $40.00 | $45.00 |

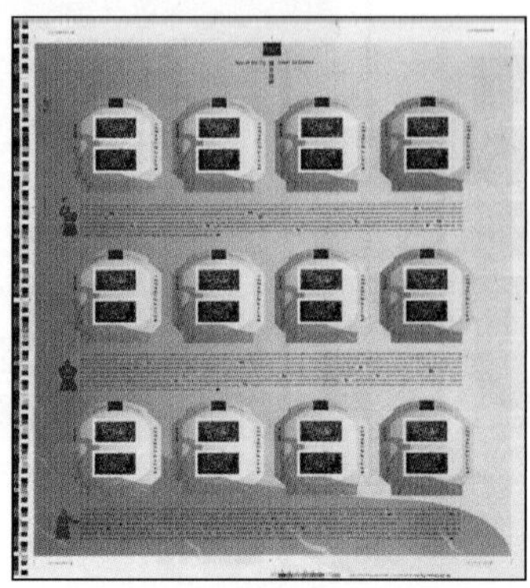
2202ii

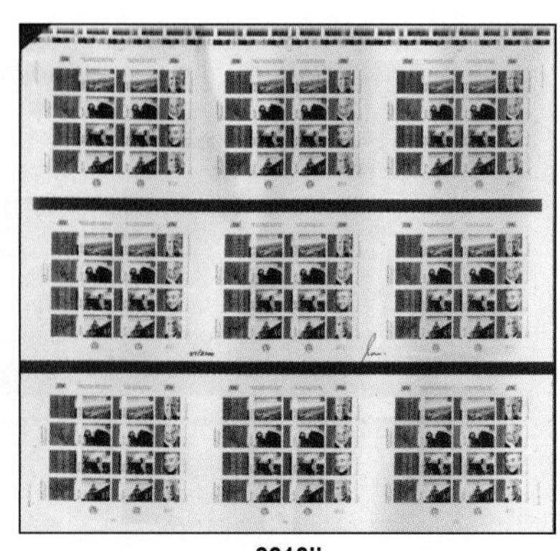
2218ii

| Unitrade # | VF NH | VF used |
|---|---|---|
| **2234–38** Beneficial insects press sheet (stamps orientated horizontally) | | |
| horiz gutter pair, #2234 w/ #2235 | $1.00 | $1.50 |
| horiz gutter pair, #2234 w/ #2237 | $1.00 | $1.50 |
| vertical gutter pair, #2234 w/ #2238 | $2.00 | $3.00 |
| "small" cross-gutter block w/ 2 x #2234, 2237 and 2238 | $15.00 | $20.00 |
| "large" cross-gutter block w/ 8 x #2234, 4 x 2237 and 4 x 2238 | $20.00 | $25.00 |
| horiz gutter pair, #2235 w/ #2238 | $1.25 | $1.75 |
| horiz gutter, #2236 w/ 2234 | $1.25 | $1.75 |
| vertical gutter, #2236 w/ 2235 | $2.00 | $3.00 |
| "small" cross-gutter block w/ #2234, 2235, 2236 and 2238 | $15.00 | $20.00 |
| "large" cross-gutter block w/ 4 x each #2234–2236 and 2237 | $20.00 | $25.00 |
| horiz gutter pair, #2237 w/ #2236 | $1.00 | $1.50 |
| vertical gutter pair, #2237 w/ #2234 | $1.00 | $1.50 |
| "small" cross-gutter block w/ #2234, 2235, 2236 and 2238 | $15.00 | $20.00 |
| "large" cross-gutter block w/ 4 x each #2234–2236 and 2238 | $20.00 | $25.00 |
| horiz gutter, #2238 w/ #2234 | $1.00 | $1.50 |
| **2258** Year of the Rat press sheet | | |
| single S/S from press sheet (square margins, 12 diff possible) | $12.00 | $15.00 |
| vert. or horiz. pair of S/S from press sheet (square margins, 6 diff possible) | $24.00 | $28.00 |
| **2270–71** Yousuf Karsh press sheet | | |
| horiz pair w/ gutter, #2270 | $4.00 | $5.00 |
| small cross gutter block of 4 #2270 | $12.00 | $15.00 |
| large cross gutter block of 16 #2270 | $25.00 | $30.00 |
| single souvenir sheet, #2271 | $10.00 | $12.00 |
| horiz. pair of S/S, #2271 | $20.00 | $25.00 |
| vertical pair of S/S, #2271 | $20.00 | $25.00 |
| vertical unit, #2271 and 4 x #2270 | $25.00 | $30.00 |
| **2297** Year of the Ox press sheet | | |
| single S/S from press sheet (square margins, 12 diff possible), #2297 | $8.00 | $9.00 |
| vert. or horiz. pair of S/S from press sheet (square margins, 6 diff possible), #2297 | $16.00 | $18.00 |
| **2323** International Year of Astronomy press sheet | | |
| horiz pair of S/S, #2323c | $15.00 | $18.00 |
| vertical pair of S/S, #2323c | $15.00 | $18.00 |
| corner block of 3 S/S, any corner, #2323c | $25.00 | $30.00 |
| Note: S/S in press sheet are very slightly smaller than those issued individually | | |
| **2349** Year of the Tiger press sheet | | |
| single S/S from press sheet (square margins, 12 diff possible), #2349 | $8.00 | $9.00 |
| vert. or horiz. pair of S/S from press sheet (square margins, 6 diff possible), #2349 | $16.00 | $18.00 |
| **2405** Blue Whale press sheet | | |
| horiz pair w/ gutter, #2405 | $60.00 | $70.00 |
| vert. pair w/ gutter, #2405 | $60.00 | $70.00 |
| cross gutter of 4, #2405 | $125.00 | $150.00 |
| corner block of 4, any corner, #2405 | $125.00 | $150.00 |
| single w/ edge margin (horiz. or vert.), #2405 | $25.00 | $27.00 |

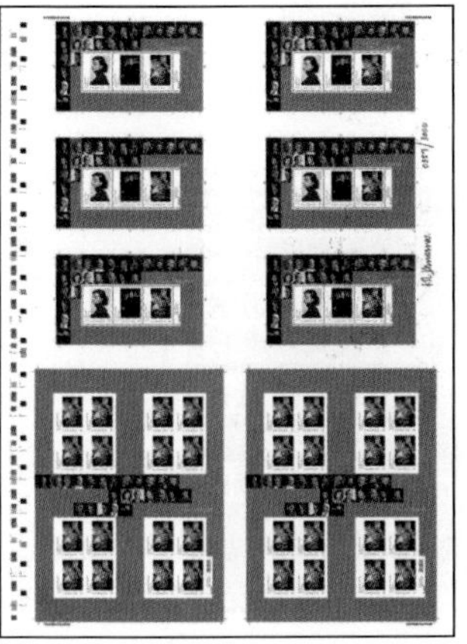
2271i

2323ci

| Unitrade # | VF NH | VF used |
|---|---|---|
| **2406–10** Beneficial insects press sheet (stamps orientated horizontally) | | |
| horiz gutter pair #2406 w/ #2408 | $1.25 | $1.75 |
| horiz gutter #2407 w/ #2410 | $1.25 | $1.75 |
| vertical gutter $2407 w/ #2406 | $2.00 | $3.00 |
| "small" cross-gutter block w/ #2410, 2406, 2407 and 2408 | $12.00 | $15.00 |
| "large" cross-gutter block w/ 4 x each # 2406, 2407, 2408 and 2410 | $15.00 | $20.00 |
| "large" cross-gutter block w/ 4 x each #2406, 2407, 2409 and 2410 | $15.00 | $20.00 |
| horiz gutter pair #2408 w/ #2410 | $1.00 | $1.50 |
| horiz gutter pair #2410 w/ #2409 | $1.00 | $1.50 |
| horiz gutter pair #2409 w/ #2407 | $1.00 | $1.50 |
| vertical gutter pair #2409 w/ #2410 | $1.00 | $1.50 |
| "small" cross-gutter block w/ #2406, 2407, 2409 and 2410 | $12.00 | $15.00 |
| horiz gutter pair #2410 w/ #2406 | $1.00 | $1.50 |
| vertical gutter pair #2410 w/ #2408 | $2.00 | $3.00 |
| "small" cross-gutter block w/ 2 x #2409, 2408 and 2410 | $12.00 | $15.00 |
| "large" cross-gutter block w/ 4 x #2409, 4 x 2408 and 8 x 2410 | $15.00 | $20.00 |
| **2417** Year of the Rabbit press sheet | | |
| single S/S from press sheet (square margins, 12 diff possible), #2417 | $8.00 | $9.00 |
| vert. or horiz. pair of S/S from press sheet (square margins, 6 diff possible), #2417 | $16.00 | $18.00 |
| **2436/7** Arts Canada - Daphne Odjig | | |
| #2436, horizontal pair w/ gutter | $6.00 | $8.00 |
| #2436, horizontal blocks of 4 w/ gutter | $15.00 | $20.00 |
| #2436 plate block of 4 w/ wider margin (4 diff. possible) | $9.00 | $11.00 |
| #2437, vertical pair of SS, w/ gutter | $20.00 | $24.00 |
| #2437, horizontal pair of SS, w/ gutter | $20.00 | $24.00 |
| #2436 horiz strip of 4 and #2437, w/ gutter | $20.00 | $24.00 |
| **2471** Architecture / Art Deco | | |
| vertical pair of SS | $20.00 | $24.00 |
| horizontal pair of SS | $20.00 | $24.00 |
| **2495** Year of the Dragon press sheet: | | |
| single S/S from press sheet (square margins, 1 version only) | $8.00 | $10.00 |
| vert. or horiz. pair of S/S from press sheet (square margins) | $16.00 | $20.00 |
| **2522/3** Arts Canada - Joe Fafard | | |
| #2522, horizontal pair w/ gutter | $6.00 | $8.00 |
| #2522, horizontal pair of blocks of 4 w/ gutter | $20.00 | $25.00 |
| #2523, vertical pair of SS (2 diff possible) | $20.00 | $24.00 |
| #2523, horizontal pair of SS (2 diff possible) | $20.00 | $24.00 |
| #2522 strip of four and #2523 w/ gutter (2 diff possible) | $20.00 | $24.00 |

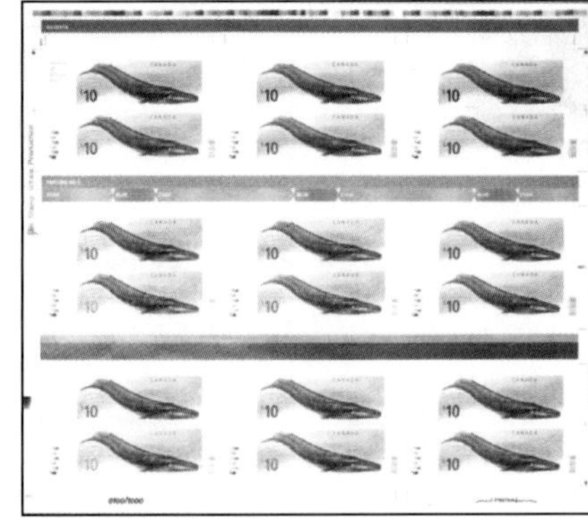
2405i

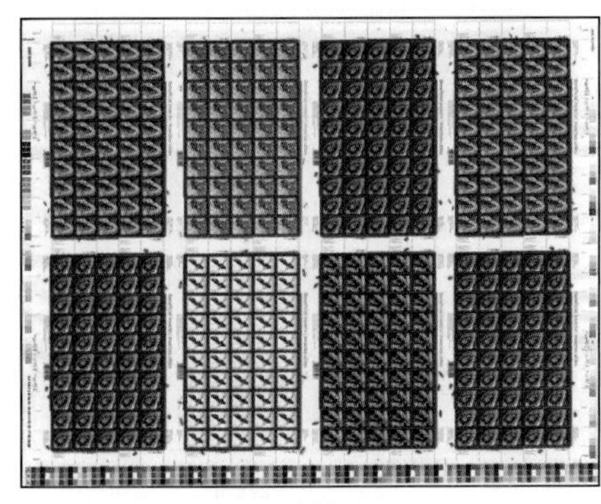
2410i

| Unitrade # | VF NH | VF used |
|---|---|---|
| **2535, 2535iii** $1.80 Titanic | | |
| #2535, single S/S from press sheet (white, square, margins) | $6.00 | $8.00 |
| 2523, vertical pair of SS | $10.00 | $13.00 |
| 2523, horizontal pair of SS | $10.00 | $13.00 |
| #2535iii, single S/S from press sheet w/ missing colour stars white, square, margins) | $20.00 | $24.00 |
| #2523 + #2535iii, vertical pair of SS | $30.00 | $36.00 |
| #2523iii, horizontal pair of SS | $45.00 | $50.00 |
| **2600** Year of the Snake press sheet: | | |
| single S/S from press sheet (square margins, 12 diff possible), | $8.00 | $10.00 |
| vert. or horiz. pair of S/S from press sheet (square margins, 6 different possible) | $16.00 | $20.00 |
| **2642** Chinatown Gates press sheet: | | |
| single S/S from press sheet (square margins, 5 diff possible) | $20.00 | $24.00 |
| vert. or horiz. pair of S/S from press sheet (square margins, 6 different possible) | $50.00 | $60.00 |
| **2646i** Motorcycles press sheet (no symmetric pairs / blocks possible due to layout) | | |
| **2677** Superman press sheet: | | |
| single S/S from press sheet (square margins, 6 diff possible), | $15.00 | $20.00 |
| vert. or horiz. pair of S/S from press sheet (square margins, 6 different possible) | $30.00 | $40.00 |
| **2700** Year of the Horse press sheet: | | |
| single S/S from press sheet (square margins, no horse legs in top margin), | $10.00 | $12.00 |
| single S/S from press sheet (square margins, horse legs in top margin), | $8.00 | $10.00 |
| vert. or horiz. pair of S/S from press sheet (square margins, 6 different possible) | $16.00 | $20.00 |
| **2746** $2.50 Empress of Ireland press sheet: | | |
| single S/S from press sheet (square margins; 12 diff possible) | $8.00 | $10.00 |
| vertical pair of S/S from press sheet (square margins, 8 diff possible) | $16.00 | $20.00 |
| horizontal pair of S/S from press sheet (square margins, 9 diff possible) | $16.00 | $20.00 |
| **2748** Haunted Canada I press sheet | | |
| single S/S cut from pane | $9.00 | $11.00 |
| vertical pair of S/S | $20.00 | $25.00 |

| Unitrade # | VF NH | VF used |
|---|---|---|
| **2772** Great Canadian Comedians press sheet | | |
| horizontal gutter pair | $7.50 | $9.00 |
| vertical gutter pair | $7.50 | $9.00 |
| cross-gutter block of 4 | $30.00 | $35.00 |
| single S/S cut from pane | $12.50 | $13.00 |
| horizontal pair of S/S | $25.00 | $30.00 |
| vertical pair of S/S | $25.00 | $30.00 |
| **2802** Year of the Ram press sheet: | | |
| single S/S from press sheet (square margins, 12 diff possible), | $8.00 | $10.00 |
| vertical pair of S/S from press sheet (square margins, 8 different possible) | $16.00 | $20.00 |
| horizontal pair of S/S from press sheet (square margins, 9 different possible) | $16.00 | $20.00 |
| **2808iii** Canada's Flag press sheet (used S/S must have the backing attached) | | |
| single S/S (horizontal fabric pattern) (w/ larger margin than on issued single S/S) | $13.00 | $15.00 |
| as above, vertical pair of S/S | $25.00 | $30.00 |
| as above, horizontal pair of S/S | $25.00 | $30.00 |
| single S/S (vertical fabric pattern) | $40.00 | $50.00 |
| as above, horizontal pair of S/S | $80.00 | $100.00 |
| **2823** Dinosaurs press sheet: | | |
| single S/S from press sheet (square margins, 8 diff possible), | $12.00 | $15.00 |
| vertical pair of S/S from press sheet (square margins, 6 different possible) | $24.00 | $30.00 |
| **2838** Weather Wonders press sheet | | |
| single S/S cut from pane | $11.00 | $13.00 |
| #2838b + 2838a, horizontal gutter pair | $5.00 | $6.50 |
| #2838c + label; horizontal gutter pair | $3.00 | $5.00 |
| #2838e + 2838d, horizontal gutter pair | $5.00 | $6.50 |
| #2838d + 2838a, vertical gutter pair | $5.00 | $6.50 |
| #2838e + 2838b, vertical gutter pair | $5.00 | $6.50 |
| horizontal pair of S/S | $22.00 | $25.00 |
| vertical pair of S/S | $22.00 | $25.00 |
| **2853** Franklin Expedition press sheet | | |
| single S/S cut from pane | $6.00 | $7.00 |
| vertical pair of S/S | $14.00 | $16.00 |
| horizontal pair of S/S (w/ wide gutter) | $14.00 | $16.00 |

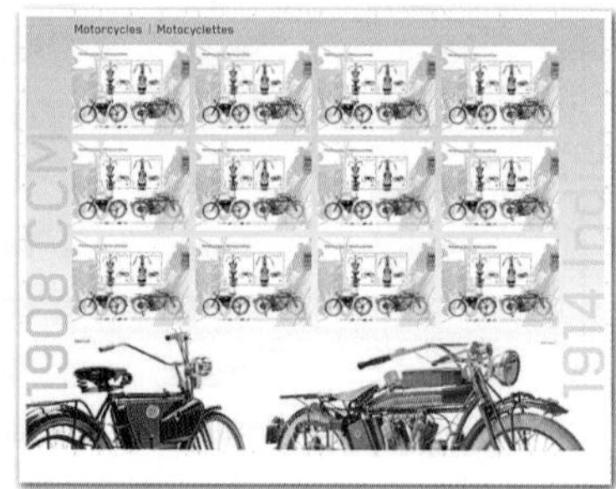


2646i

2772i

2748i

2823i

| Unitrade # | VF NH | VF used |
|---|---|---|
| **2860** Haunted Canada II | | |
| single S/S cut from pane | $9.00 | $11.00 |
| vertical pair of S/S | $20.00 | $25.00 |
| **2885** Year of Monkey press sheet | | |
| single S/S | $9.00 | $11.00 |
| vertical pair of S/S | $20.00 | $24.00 |
| horizontal pair of S/S | $20.00 | $24.00 |
| (background design is the same on each S/S in press sheet) | | |
| **2912i** Star Trek press sheet (with set of 5 different values) | | |
| single S/S cut from press sheet | $16.00 | $18.00 |
| horizontal pair of S/S (3 diff possible) | $35.00 | $40.00 |
| vertical pair of S/S (4 diff possible) | $35.00 | $40.00 |
| **2922** Star Trek press sheet (lenticular 2 x $5.00) | | |
| used S/S must have the backing attached | | |
| single S/S cut from press sheet (w/ wider margins) | $22.00 | $25.00 |
| horizontal pair of S/S | $45.00 | $50.00 |
| vertical pair of S/S | $45.00 | $50.00 |
| (the thick plastic makes it difficult to separate the S/Ss cleanly) | | |
| **2923** Dinosaurs press sheet | | |
| single S/S cut from pane | $8.00 | $9.00 |
| vertical pair of S/Ss | $18.00 | $20.00 |
| #2923a single (margins all-round) | $5.00 | $6.00 |
| #2923a pair, vertical gutter | $4.00 | $5.00 |
| #2923d+b, vertical gutter pair | $4.00 | $5.00 |
| #2923e+c, vertical gutter pair | $4.00 | $5.00 |
| **2935i** Haunted Canada III | | |
| single S/S cut from pane | $8.00 | $10.00 |
| vertical pair of S/S | $18.00 | $20.00 |
| #2935a, vertical gutter pair | $4.00 | $5.00 |
| #2935d+b, vertical gutter pair | $4.00 | $5.00 |
| #2935e+c, vertical gutter pair | $4.00 | $5.00 |

| Unitrade # | VF NH | VF used |
|---|---|---|
| **2960ii** Year of Rooster press sheet | | |
| single S/S | $8.00 | $10.00 |
| vertical pair of S/S | $18.00 | $20.00 |
| horizontal pair of S/S | $18.00 | $20.00 |
| (background design is the same on each S/S in press sheet) | | |
| **2983ii** Star Trek II press sheet (with set of 5 different values) | | |
| single S/S cut from press sheet | $16.00 | $18.00 |
| horizontal pair of S/S (3 diff possible) | $35.00 | $40.00 |
| vertical pair of S/S (4 diff possible) | $35.00 | $40.00 |
| #2983a, vertical gutter pair | $6.00 | $7.00 |
| #2983c+a, vertical gutter pair | $6.00 | $7.00 |
| #2983b+e, vertical gutter pair | $10.00 | $12.00 |
| #2983e+a, horizontal gutter pair | $8.00 | $10.00 |
| #2983b+d, horizontal gutter pair | $8.00 | $10.00 |
| **2992i** 50th Anniv. Grand Prix | | |
| (Stewart) horizontal pair | $5.00 | $6.00 |
| (Villeneuve) horizontal pair | $5.00 | $6.00 |
| (Senna) horizontal pair | $5.00 | $6.00 |
| (Schumacher) horizontal pair | $5.00 | $6.00 |
| (Hamilton) horizontal pair | $5.00 | $6.00 |
| Stewart + Senna vertical gutter pair | $3.00 | $4.00 |
| Villeneuve + Schumacher vertical gutter pair | $3.00 | $4.00 |
| Schumacher + Hamilton vertical gutter pair | $3.00 | $4.00 |
| Stewart + Villeneuve horizontal gutter pair | $5.00 | $6.00 |
| Senna + Schumacher horizontal gutter pair | $5.00 | $6.00 |
| Stewart + Villeneuve + Senna + Schumacher cross-gutter block | $10.00 | $12.00 |

2912ii

2923i

# CANADA POST SOUVENIR ARTICLES

This list includes only items produced by Canada Post which were available to the public.

## SOUVENIR CARDS "CANADIAN HISTORY IN POSTAGE STAMPS"

Numbers 1–10 had the stamps affixed to the card. Later cards were issued with the stamps provided loose.

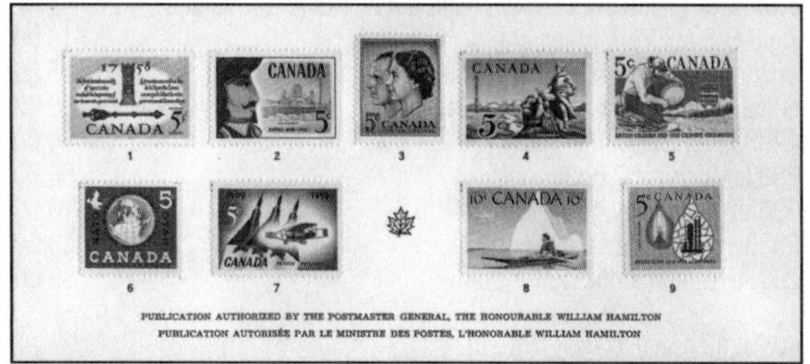

1 (1959)

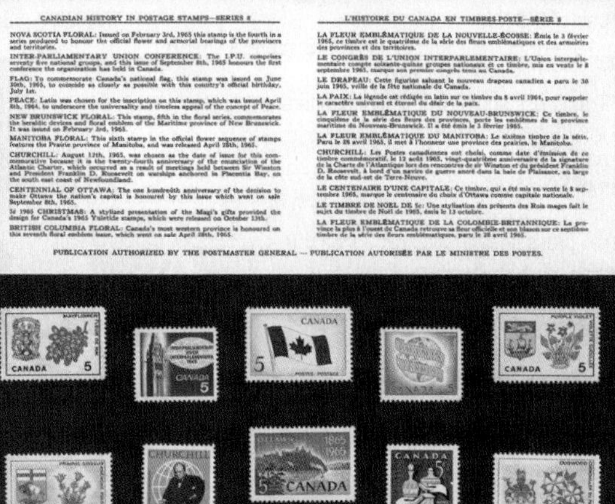

8 (1966)

6 (1964)

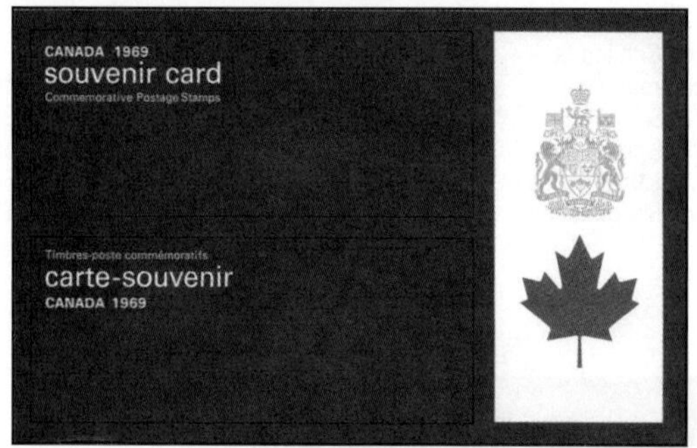


11 (1969)

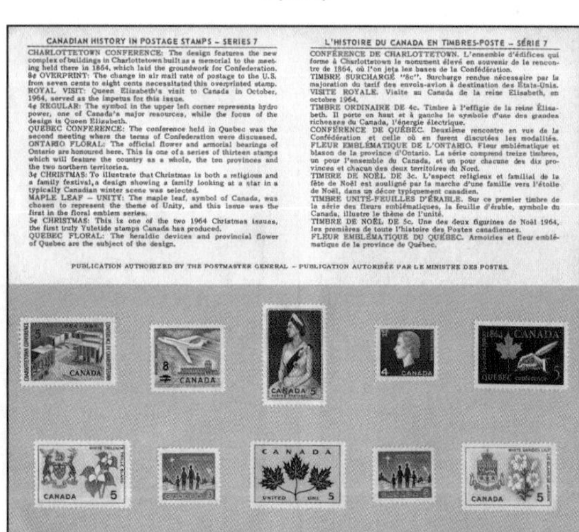

7 (1965)

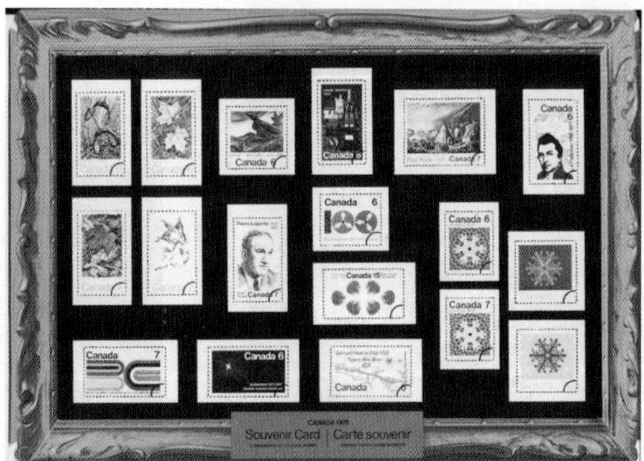


14 (1972)

10 (1968)

| No. | Year | Value |
|---|---|---|
| 1 | 1959 | 30.00 |
| 2 | 1960 | 20.00 |
| 3 | 1961 | 20.00 |
| a | "over/verso" in lower margin | 10.00 |
| 4 | 1962 | 10.00 |
| 5 | 1963 | 7.50 |
| a | "SPECIMEN" handstamp on each stamp | 200.00 |
| 6 | 1964 | 7.50 |
| 7 | 1965 | 7.50 |
| 8 | 1966 | 7.50 |
| 9 | 1967 | 5.00 |
| 10 | 1968 | 5.00 |
| 11 | 1969 | 10.00 |
| 12 | 1970 | 22.50 |
| 13 | 1971 | 7.50 |
| 14 | 1972 | 15.00 |

# ANNUAL COLLECTIONS

The annual Souvenir Collection of the Postage Stamps of Canada includes all the year's stamp issues in a book describing the stamps.

15 (1972)

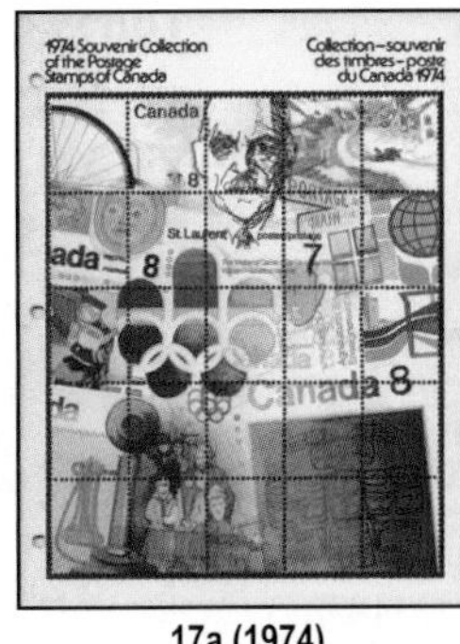
17a (1974)

19 (1976)

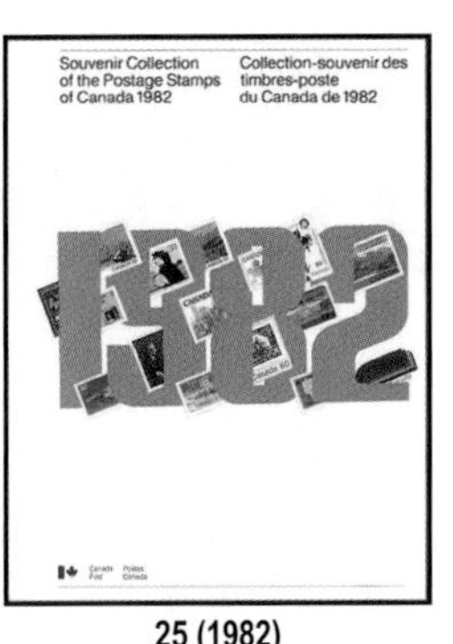
25 (1982)

30 (1987)

32 (1989)

35 (1992)

37 (1994)

38 (1995)

47 (2004)

49 (2006)

51 (2008)

54 (2011)

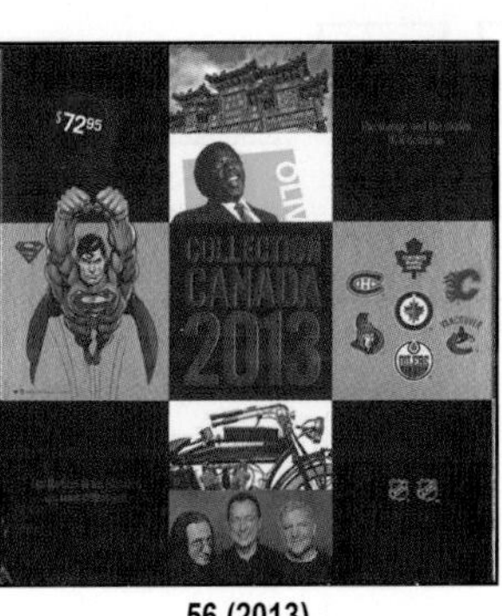

56 (2013)

| No. | Year | Value | No. | Year | Value | No. | Year | Value | No. | Year | Value | No. | Year | Value |
|---|---|---|---|---|---|---|---|---|---|---|---|---|---|---|
| 15 | 1972 | 25.00 | 25 | 1982 | 45.00 | 32 | 1989 | 50.00 | 41 | 1998 | 95.00 | 51 | 2008 | 120.00 |
| 16 | 1973 | 12.50 | 26 | 1983 | 55.00 | a | Hardcover | 70.00 | 42 | 1999 | 85.00 | 52 | 2009 | 120.00 |
| 17 | 1974 | 250.00 | 27 | 1984 | 40.00 | 33 | 1990 | 55.00 | 43 | 2000 | 85.00 | 53 | 2010 | 125.00 |
| a | 3-hole punch | 250.00 | 28 | 1985 | 45.00 | 34 | 1991 | 55.00 | 44 | 2001 | 90.00 | 54 | 2011 | 110.00 |
| 18 | 1975 | 85.00 | 29 | 1986 | 45.00 | 35 | 1992 | 85.00 | 45 | 2002 | 100.00 | 55 | 2012 | 134.00 |
| 19 | 1976 | 85.00 | a | Hardcover | 100.00 | 36 | 1993 | 80.00 | 46 | 2003 | 100.00 | 56 | 2013 | 146.00 |
| 20 | 1977 | 40.00 | 30 | 1987 | 45.00 | 37 | 1994 | 70.00 | 47 | 2004 | 110.00 | 57 | 2014 | 166.00 |
| 21 | 1978 | 30.00 | a | Hardcover | 65.00 | 38 | 1995 | 80.00 | 48 | 2005 | 110.00 | 58 | 2015 | 166.00 |
| 22 | 1979 | 30.00 | b | Employee* | 10.00 | 39 | 1996 | 80.00 | 49 | 2006 | 115.00 | 59 | 2016 | 166.00 |
| 23 | 1980 | 30.00 | 31 | 1988 | 45.00 | 40 | 1997 | 90.00 | 50 | 2007 | 115.00 | 60 | 2017 | 180.00 |
| 24 | 1981 | 30.00 | a | Hardcover | 70.00 | | | | | | | | | |

** (30b) Special employee edition (softcover); presented to Canada Post Employees; no stamps*

# SEMI-ANNUAL and QUARTERLY PACKS

These were sold at face value (i.e. no premium) on a semi-annual basis (1974–1992) and quarterly basis thereafter.

## 1973

Jan–Jun ($ 2.13)

## 1973–74

Definitives ($ 4.56)

## 1974

Jan–Jun ($ 1.72) | Jul–Dec ($ 1.42)

## 1975

Jan–Jun ($ 5.20) | Jul–Dec ($ 1.62)

## 1976

Jan–Jun ($ 5.64) | Jul–Dec ($ 1.64)

## 1977

Jan–Jun ($ 1.34) | Jul–Dec ($ 2.64)

## 1978

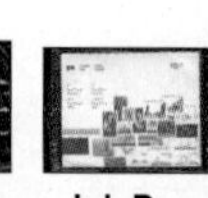

Jan–Jun ($ 3.51) | Jul–Dec ($ 5.01)

## 1979

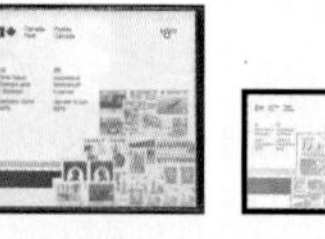
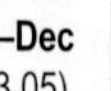

Jan–Jun ($ 8.25) | Jul–Dec ($ 3.05)

## 1980

Jan–Jun ($ 2.75) | Jul–Dec ($ 4.12)

## 1981

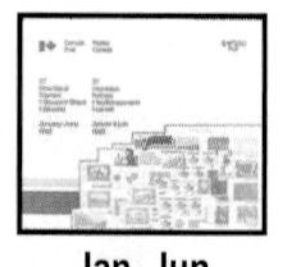

Jan–Jun ($ 3.08) | Jul–Dec ($ 2.51)

## 1982

Jan–Jun ($ 13.30) | Jul–Dec ($ 4.06)

## 1983

Jan–Jun ($ 15.71) | Jul–Dec ($ 5.86)

## 1984

Jan–Jun ($ 6.08) | Jul–Dec ($ 9.15)

## 1985

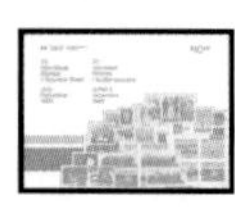

Jan–Jun ($ 7.84) | Jul–Dec ($ 10.49)

## 1986

Jan–Jun ($ 10.83) | Jul–Dec ($ 8.55)

## 1987

Jan–Jun ($ 11.88) | Jul–Dec ($ 6.49)

## 1988

Jan–Jun ($ 9.83) | Jul–Dec ($ 7.93)

## 1989

Jan–Jun ($ 12.25) | Jul–Dec ($ 8.37)

## 1990

Jan–Jun ($ 15.25) | Jul–Dec ($ 9.37)

## 1991

Jan–Jun ($ 10.46) | Jul–Dec ($ 14.47)

## 1992

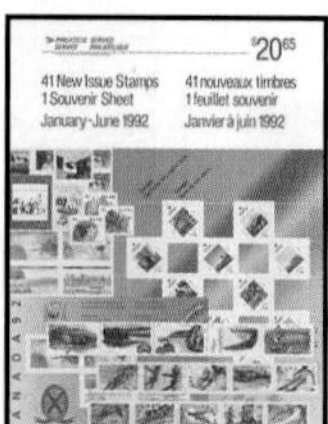

Jan–Jun ($ 20.65) | Jul–Dec ($ 11.03)

## 1993

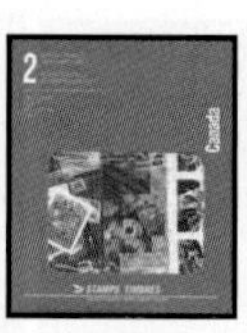
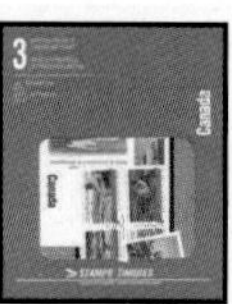
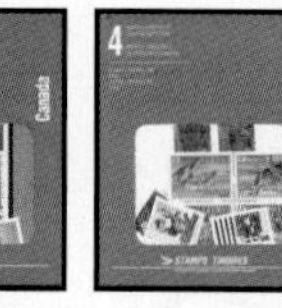

Jan–Mar ($ 5.89) | Apr–Jun ($ 15.05) | Jul–Sep ($ 10.01) | Oct–Dec ($ 5.60)

## 1994

Jan–Mar ($ 8.08) | Apr–Jun ($ 13.35) | Jul–Sep ($ 8.87) | Oct–Dec ($ 3.91)

## 1995

Jan–Jun ($ 19.98) | Jul–Sep ($ 13.36) | Oct–Dec ($ 8.12)

## 1996

Jan–Mar ($ 8.60) | Apr–Jun ($ 11.54) | Jul–Sep ($ 8.60) | Oct–Dec ($ 5.92)

## 1997

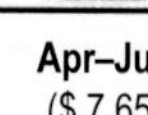

Jan–Mar ($ 4.05) | Apr–Jun ($ 7.65) | Jul–Sep ($ 4.95) | Oct–Dec ($ 12.12)

## 1998

Jan–Mar ($ 7.20)

Apr–Jun ($ 9.90)

Jul–Sep ($ 13.50)

Oct–Dec ($ 8.47)

## 1999

Jan–Mar ($ 10.54)

Apr–Jun ($ 6.11)

Jul–Sep ($ 13.83)

Oct–Dec ($ 3.80)

## 2000

Jan–Mar ($ 6.47)

Apr–Jun ($ 12.59)

Jul–Sep ($ 5.09)

Oct–Dec ($ 5.18)

## 2001

Jan–Mar ($ 15.20)

Apr–Jun ($ 10.60)

Jul–Sep ($ 6.22)

Oct–Dec ($ 4.94)

## 2002

Jan–Mar ($ 15.20)

Apr–Jun ($ 15.74)

Jul–Sep ($ 3.84)

Oct–Dec ($ 8.62)

## 2003

Jan–Mar ($ 9.10)

Apr–Jun ($ 11.90)

Jul–Sep ($ 3.84)

Oct–Dec ($ 11.31)

## 2004

Jan–Mar ($ 18.82)

Apr–Jun ($ 8.15)

Jul–Sep ($ 2.94)

Oct–Dec ($ 10.77)

## 2005

Jan–Mar ($ 18.10)

Apr–Jun ($ 8.85)

Jul–Sep ($ 4.00)

Oct–Dec ($ 8.30)

## 2006

Jan–Mar ($ 16.06)

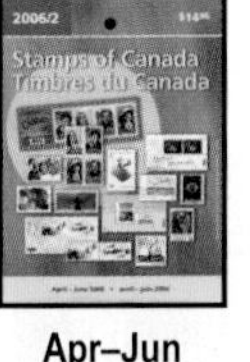
Apr–Jun ($ 14.96)

Jul–Sep ($ 8.16)

Oct–Dec ($ 10.03)

## 2007

Jan–Mar ($ 21.11)

Apr–Jun ($ 8.81)

Jul–Sep ($ 7.28)

Oct–Dec ($ 8.56)

## 2008

Jan–Mar ($ 17.86)

Apr–Jun ($ 16.04)

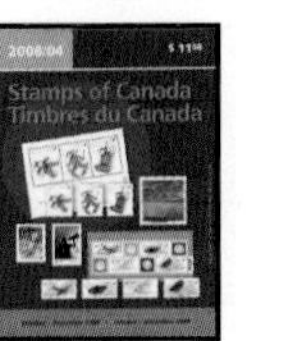
Jul–Sep ($ 2.60)

Oct–Dec ($ 11.98)

## 2009

Jan–Mar ($ 31.50)

Apr–Jun ($ 7.58)

Jul–Sep ($ 11.98)

Oct–Dec ($ 18.58)

## 2010

Jan–Mar ($ 29.99) | Apr–Jun ($ 21.08) | Olympics ($ 8.73)

Jul–Sep ($ 9.78) | Oct–Dec ($ 17.79)

## 2011

Jan–Mar ($ 34.15) | Apr–Jun ($ 19.47)

Jul–Sep ($ 22.05) | Oct–Dec ($ 7.92)

## 2012

Jan–Mar ($ 42.35) | Apr–Jun ($ 28.61)

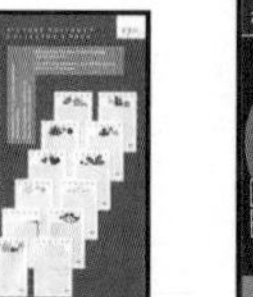

Jul–Sep ($ 26.23) | Oct–Dec ($ 12.05) | Picture Postage ($ 7.32)

## 2013

Jan–Mar ($ 54.41) | Apr–Jun ($ 22.68)

Jul–Sep ($ 33.49) | Oct–Dec ($ 10.31)

## 2014

Jan–Mar ($ 18.11) | Apr–Jun ($ 80.87)

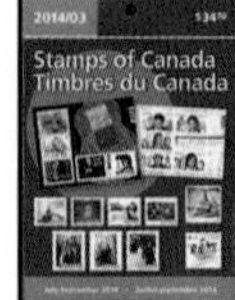

Jul–Sep ($ 34.70) | Oct–Dec ($ 33.75)

## 2015

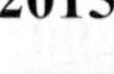

Jan–Mar ($ 25.35) | Apr–Jun ($ 43.95)

Jul–Sep ($ 36.75) | Oct–Dec ($ 30.95)

## 2016

Jan–Mar ($ 27.85) | Apr–Jun ($ 49.40)

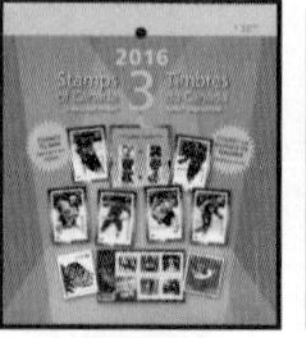

Jul–Sep ($ 39.90) | Oct–Dec ($ 9.95)

## 2017

Jan–Mar ($ 34.65) | Apr–Jun ($ 44.65)

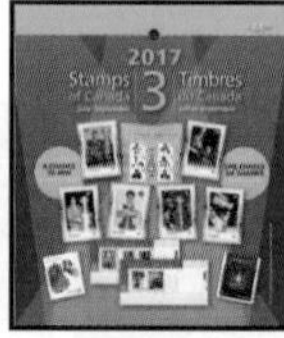

Jul–Sep ($ 44.60) | Oct–Dec ($ 21.75)

## 2018

Jan–Mar ($ 62.50)

Apr–Jun ($ 15.30)

## "Stuck on Stamps!"

**For Kids** ($ 5.95 each)

### 2012

### 2013

### 2014

### 2015

### 2016

## THEMATIC COLLECTIONS

| No. | | Description | Value |
|---|---|---|---|
| 1 | 1967 | Centennial Stamp Case | 12.50 |
| 2 | 1970 | Expo 70 | 20.00 |
| 3 | 1970 | The Group of Seven | 5.00 |
| 4 | 1970 | Children Look at Christmas | 15.00 |
| 5 | 1971 | The Four Seasons | 3.00 |
| 6 | 1973 | RCMP | 3.50 |
| 7 | 1974 | 1972-1974 Definitives | 22.50 |
| 8 | 1975 | Olympic Stamp Souvenir Case | 30.00 |
| 9 | 1975 | Olympic Stamp Souvenir Collection, Volume 1 | 35.00 |
| 10 | 1976 | Olympic Stamp Souvenir Collection, Volume 2 | 35.00 |
| 11 | 1976 | Indians of Canada | 20.00 |
| 12 | 1978 | XI Commonwealth Games | 5.00 |
| 13 | 1978 | Ships of Canada | 17.50 |
| 14 | 1979 | Canadian Flying Boats | 5.00 |
| 15 | 1980 | Singing Songs of the Spirit | 20.00 |
| 16 | 1980 | Canadian Military Aircraft | 5.00 |
| 17 | 1981 | Endangered Wildlife | 7.50 |
| 18 | 1982 | Transport and Training Aircraft | 5.00 |
| 19 | 1982 | Wildflowers and Trees | 7.50 |
| 20 | 1982 | Canadian Bush Aircraft | 7.50 |
| 21 | 1983 | Airborne | 30.00 |
| 22 | 1983 | Canadian Locomotives 1836–1860 | 6.00 |
| 23 | 1984 | Jacques Cartier (1534–1984) | 12.50 |
| 24 | 1984 | Document Official – Jacques Cartier | 30.00 |
| 25 | 1984 | Jacques Cartier's First Voyage to Canada (post card) | 7.50 |
| 26 | 1984 | St. Lawrence Seaway (souvenir card) | 7.50 |
| 27 | 1984 | Papal Visit | 5.00 |
| 28 | 1984 | Lighthouses of Canada | 5.00 |
| 29 | 1984 | Canadian Locomotives 1860–1905 | 6.00 |
| 30 | 1985 | Banff National Park | 6.00 |
| 31 | 1985 | Lighthouses of Canada | 5.00 |
| 32 | 1985 | Canadian Locomotives 1906–1925 | 6.00 |
| 33 | 1985 | Canadian Forces | 5.00 |
| 34 | 1986 | Birds of Canada | 5.00 |
| 35 | 1986 | Canadian Locomotives 1925–1945 | 6.00 |
| 36 | 1987 | The Heart of Town (CAPEX 87) | 10.00 |
| 37 | 1987 | CAPEX 87 Souvenir Sheets | 10.00 |
| 38 | 1988 | Catching the Spirit | 10.00 |
| 39 | 1988 | Butterflies of Canada | 6.00 |
| 40 | 1988 | Dogs of Canada | 6.00 |
| | i | block of 4 with two stamps the same (must be sealed) | 18.00 |
| 41 | 1989 | Mushrooms of Canada | 6.00 |
| 42 | 1989 | Our World: International Images of Nature (Vol. 1) | 25.00 |
| 43 | 1989 | Second World War – 1939 | 10.00 |
| 44 | 1990 | Norman Bethune | 15.00 |
| 45 | 1990 | Dolls of Canada | 15.00 |
| 46 | 1990 | Legendary Creatures | 35.00 |
| 47 | 1990 | Our World: International Images of Nature (Vol. 2) | 30.00 |
| 48 | 1990 | Second World War – 1940 | 10.00 |
| 49 | 1991 | Public Gardens | 15.00 |
| 50 | 1991 | Canadian Small Craft | 15.00 |
| 51 | 1991 | Folktales | 15.00 |
| 52 | 1991 | Our World: International Images of Nature (Vol. 3) | 25.00 |
| 53 | 1991 | A visit from Santa Claus | 10.00 |
| 54 | 1991 | Second World War – 1941 | 10.00 |
| 55 | 1992 | Struggle and Triumph/Canada and the Olympics | 15.00 |
| 56 | 1992 | Living the Landscape | 40.00 |
| 57 | 1992 | Legendary Heroes | 15.00 |
| 58 | 1992 | Second World War – 1942 | 10.00 |
| 59 | 1992 | The Christmas Lamb | 10.00 |
| 60 | 1993 | Folk Songs | 15.00 |
| 61 | 1993 | The Dinosaurs | 25.00 |
| 62 | 1993 | Christmas – Ho-Ho-Ooh | 10.00 |
| 63 | 1993 | Second World War – 1943 | 10.00 |
| 64 | 1994 | XV Commonwealth Games | 15,00 |
| 65 | 1994 | Public Service Vehicles | 7.50 |
| 66 | 1994 | Second World War – 1944 | 10.00 |
| 67 | 1995 | Second World War – 1945 | 10.00 |
| 68 | 1995 | Farm and Frontier Vehicles | 7.50 |
| 69 | 1995 | Living Earth Nature's Collection | 35.00 |
| 70 | 1996 | 45¢ Polar Bear Stamp, $2 Coin and $2 Bank Note Set* | 75.00 |
| 71 | 1996 | Industrial and Commercial Vehicles | 7.50 |
| 72 | 1996 | Historic Land Vehicles Pane of 25 collection | 10.00 |
| 73 | 1996 | Historic Land Vehicles Souvenir Sheet collection | 37.50 |
| 74 | 1997 | Year of the Ox pack | 25.00 |
| 75 | 1997 | The Supernatural | 15.00 |
| 76 | 1997 | Series of the Century Stamp and Coin Set* | 45.00 |
| 77 | 1997 | John Cabot (Caboto) Stamp and Coin Set* | 80.00 |

Back-of-the-Book

| No. | | Description | Value |
|---|---|---|---|
| 78 | 1998 | Year of the Tiger pack | 15.00 |
| 79 | 1998 | Year of the Tiger Stamp and Coin Set* | 500.00 |
| 80 | 1998 | Grizzly Bear | 145.00 |
| 81 | 1998 | RCMP Stamp and Coin Set* | 75.00 |
| 82 | 1998 | Circus Juggling Kit | 15.00 |
| 83 | 1998 | Loon Stamp and Coin Set* | 40.00 |
| 84 | 1998 | Polar Bear Stamp and Coin Set* | 45.00 |
| 85 | 1999 | Year of the Rabbit pack | 15.00 |
| 86 | 1999 | Year of the Rabbit Stamp and Coin Set* | 135.00 |
| 87 | 1999 | Celebration of the Seas | 25.00 |
| 88 | 1999 | The Millennium Collection | 120.00 |
| 89 | 1999 | The Official Millennium Keepsake | 22.50 |
| 90 | 1999 | Nunavut Stamp and Coin Set* | 50.00 |
| 91 | 2000 | Year of the Dragon pack | 15.00 |
| 92 | 2000 | Year of the Dragon Stamp and Coin Set* | 175.00 |
| 93 | 2000 | NHL All-Stars Stamp Cards | 25.00 |
| 94 | 2000 | Tall Ships Stamp and Coin Set* | 40.00 |
| 95 | 2000 | $1 Loon Stamp and 2000 Coin Set* | 37.50 |
| 96 | 2000 | $2 Polar Bear Stamp and 2000 Coin Set* | 40.00 |
| 97 | 2000 | Heart of the Dragon Gold Stamp Set* | 585.00 |
| 98 | 2001 | Year of the Snake pack | 15.00 |
| 99 | 2001 | Year of the Snake Stamp and Coin Set* | 142.50 |
| 100 | 2001 | NHL All-Stars Stamp Cards | 30.00 |
| 101 | 2001 | NHL All-Stars Stamp and Medallion Set | |
| | a | Jean Béliveau | 22.50 |
| | b | Eddie Shore | 22.50 |
| | c | Bobby Hull | 22.50 |
| | d | Terry Sawchuk | 22.50 |
| | e | Denis Potvin | 22.50 |
| | f | Syl Apps | 22.50 |
| 102 | 2001 | NHL Commemorative Set (with hockey puck and plaque) | 135.00 |
| 103 | 2001 | Living Earth 2 Nature's Collection | 30.00 |
| 104 | 2001 | World Figure Skating Stamp and Medallion Set* | |
| | a | Singles | 27.50 |
| | b | Pairs and Ice Dance | 27.50 |
| 105 | 2001 | Three Pence Beaver Commemorative Set* | 60.00 |
| 106 | 2001 | Blue Jays Stamp and Medallion Set* | 27.50 |
| 107 | 2001 | Trudeau Commemorative Tribute | 52.50 |
| 108 | 2002 | Year of the Horse pack | 20.00 |
| 109 | 2002 | Year of the Horse Stamp and Coin Set* | 150.00 |
| 110 | 2002 | NHL All-Stars Stamp Cards | 30.00 |
| 111 | 2002 | NHL All-Stars Stamp and Medallion Set | |
| | a | Tim Horton | 22.50 |
| | b | Howie Morenz | 22.50 |
| | c | Red Kelly | 22.50 |
| | d | Guy Lafleur | 22.50 |
| | e | Glenn Hall | 22.50 |
| | f | Phil Esposito | 22.50 |

| No. | | Description | Value |
|---|---|---|---|
| 112 | 2002 | NHL Commemorative Set (with pin and hockey puck) | 135.00 |
| 113 | 2002 | Olympic Presentation Folder* | 82.50 |
| 114 | 2002 | Corals Joint Presentation Pack | 15.00 |
| 115 | 2003 | Year of the Ram pack | 20.00 |
| 116 | 2003 | Year of the Ram Stamp and Coin Set* | 150.00 |
| 117 | 2003 | NHL All-Star Stamp Cards | 80.00 |
| 118 | 2003 | NHL Heritage Stamp & Jersey Sets | |
| | a | Frank Mahovlich | 15.00 |
| | b | Serge Savard | 15.00 |
| | c | Mike Bossy | 15.00 |
| | d | Raymond Bourque | 15.00 |
| | e | Stan Mikita | 15.00 |
| | f | Bill Durnan | 15.00 |
| 119 | 2003 | NHL All-Stars Commemorative Set (with hockey puck and wafer) | 135.00 |
| 120 | 2003 | QE II Coronation Stamp and Coin Set* | 50.00 |
| 121 | 2003 | $5 Moose Stamp and Coin Set* | 175.00 |
| 122 | 2004 | Year of the Monkey pack | 20.00 |
| 123 | 2004 | Year of the Monkey Stamp and Coin Set* | 160.00 |
| 124 | 2004 | NHL All-Star Stamp Cards | 20.00 |
| 125 | 2004 | NHL Heritage Stamp & Jersey Sets | |
| | a | Larry Robinson | 20.00 |
| | b | Ted Lindsay | 20.00 |
| | c | Brad Park | 20.00 |
| | d | Marcel Dionne | 20.00 |
| | e | Johnny Bower | 20.00 |
| | f | Milt Schmidt | 20.00 |
| 126 | 2004 | NHL All-Stars Commemorative Set (with hockey puck and water) | 135.00 |
| 127 | 2004 | Living Earth 3 Nature's Collection | 30.00 |
| 128 | 2004 | $8 Grizzly Stamp and Coin Set* | 100.00 |
| 129 | 2004 | Otto Sverdrup Joint Presentation Pack | 16.50 |
| 130 | 2004 | $1 Loon Stamp and Coin Set* | 50.00 |
| 131 | 2004 | $2 Polar Bear Stamp and Coin Set* | 60.00 |
| 132 | 2004 | St. Croix Island Joint Presentation Pack | 20.00 |
| 133 | 2004 | St. Croix Island Treasure Chest* | 200.00 |
| 134 | 2004 | Open Championship (Golf) Stamp and Coin Set* | 40.00 |
| 135 | 2004 | Open Championship (Golf) Commemorative Frame* | 100.00 |
| 136 | 2005 | Year of the Rooster pack | 20.00 |
| 137 | 2005 | Year of the Rooster Stamp and Coin Set* | 160.00 |
| 138 | 2005 | NHL All-Stars Stamp Cards | 20.00 |
| 139 | 2005 | NHL All-Stars Commemorative Set (with hockey puck and wafer) | 135.00 |
| 140 | 2005 | Fishing Flies Collector's Frame | 80.00 |
| 141 | 2005 | Deer Stamp and Coin Set* | 100.00 |
| 142 | 2005 | Walrus Stamp and Coin Set* | 100.00 |
| 143 | 2006 | Year of the Dog pack | 20.00 |
| 144 | 2006 | Year of the Dog Stamp and Coin Set* | 170.00 |

| No. | | Description | Value |
|---|---|---|---|
| 145 | 2006 | Falcon Stamp and Coin Set* | 100.00 |
| 146 | 2006 | Horse Stamp and Coin Set* | 100.00 |
| 147 | 2006 | Snowbirds Stamp and Coin Set* | 120.00 |
| 148 | 2007 | Year of the Pig pack | 20.00 |
| 149 | 2007 | Year of the Pig Stamp and Coin Set* | 170.00 |
| 150 | 2007 | International Polar Year | 75.00 |
| 151 | 2008 | Year of the Rat pack | 20.00 |
| 152 | 2008 | Year of the Rat Stamp and Coin Set* | 170.00 |
| 153 | 2008 | Royal Canadian Mint Stamp and Coin Set* | 90.00 |
| 154 | 2008 | The Royal Candian Mint, 100 Years of History | |
| | a | English edition book | 150.00 |
| | b | French edition book | 150.00 |
| 155 | 2008 | Founding of Quebec City Joint Presentation Pack | 26.00 |
| 156 | 2008 | France-Quebec joint Souvenir Sheet Folder | 30.00 |
| 157 | 2008 | as 156, Souvenir Sheet pack (incl. six s/s folders) | 68.00 |
| 158 | 2008 | Engraved in our memory | 80.00 |
| 159 | 2009 | Year of the Ox Stamp and Coin Set* | 170.00 |
| 160 | 2009 | Vancouver 2010 Bronze Collectors Set* | 100.00 |
| 161 | 2009 | Vancouver 2010 Silver Collectors Set* | 100.00 |
| 162 | 2010 | The Canadiens 100th Anniversary Pack | 30.00 |
| 163 | 2010 | Montreal Canadiens 100th Anniversary Collector Set | 225.00 |
| 164 | 2010 | Vancouver 2010 Gold Collectors Set* | 100.00 |
| 165 | 2010 | Blue Whale Stamp and Coin Set* | 160.00 |
| 166 | 2010 | Canadian Navy Stamp and Coin Set* | 80.00 |
| 167 | 2011 | Royal Wedding Keepsake Kit | 10.00 |
| 168 | 2011 | Miss Supertest III Collectible folder | 40.00 |

| No. | | Description | Value |
|---|---|---|---|
| | | QE II Diamond Jubilee Keepsake Folders | |
| 169 | 2012 | Volume 1 (1952–1962) | 12.00 |
| 170 | 2012 | Volume 2 (1963–1972) | 12.00 |
| 171 | 2012 | Volume 3 (1973–1982) | 12.00 |
| 172 | 2012 | Volume 4 (1983–1992) | 12.00 |
| 173 | 2012 | Volume 5 (1993–2002) | 16.00 |
| 174 | 2012 | Volume 6 (2003–2012) | 12.00 |
| 175 | 2012 | Titanic Collector's Set | 215.00 |
| 176 | 2012 | Calgary Stampede Stamp and Coin Set* | 55.00 |
| | 2012 | CFL Teams Stamp and Coin Sets*: | |
| 177 | | BC Lions | 52.00 |
| 178 | | Edmonton Eskimos | 52.00 |
| 179 | | Calgary Stampeders | 52.00 |
| 180 | | Saskatchewan Roughriders | 52.00 |
| 181 | | Winnipeg Blue Bombers | 52.00 |
| 182 | | Hamilton Tiger-Cats | 52.00 |
| 183 | | Toronto Argonauts | 52.00 |
| 184 | | Montréal Alouettes | 52.00 |
| 185 | 2012 | Ultimate CFL Fan Set | 300.00 |
| 186 | 2013 | Chinatown Gates Collection | 180.00 |
| 187 | 2013 | Superman Stamp and Coin Set* | 60.00 |
| | 2013 | NHL Team Jerseys Stamp and Coin Sets*: | |
| 188 | | Vancouver Canucks | 60.00 |
| 189 | | Edmonton Oilers | 60.00 |
| 190 | | Calgary Flames | 60.00 |
| 191 | | Winnipeg Jets | 60.00 |
| 192 | | Toronto Maple Leafs | 60.00 |
| 193 | | Ottawa Senators | 60.00 |
| 194 | | Montreal Canadiens | 60.00 |
| 195 | 2013 | NHL Collector's Album | 200.00 |
| 196 | 2014 | Empress of Ireland | 200.00 |
| 197 | 2014 | Haunted Canada | 60.00 |
| 198 | 2014 | Argos – Ultimate CFL Fan Set | 300.00 |
| 199 | 2014 | Beaver Stamp and Coin Set* | 200.00 |
| 200 | 2014 | Puffin Stamp and Coin Set* | 220.00 |
| 201 | 2014 | NHL Collector's Album | 200.00 |
| 202 | 2014 | Burrowing Owl Stamp and Coin Set* | 220.00 |
| 203 | 2014 | Black Bear Stamp and Coin Set* | 200.00 |
| 204 | 2014 | Mountain Goat Stamp and Coin Set* | 200.00 |
| 205 | 2015 | Haunted Canada | 60.00 |
| 206 | 2015 | White-tailed Deer Stamp and Coin Set* | 200.00 |
| 207 | 2015 | NHL Collector's Album | 200.00 |
| 208 | 2016 | Star Trek Stamp and Coin Set* | 70.00 |
| 209 | 2016 | Haunted Canada | 64.00 |
| 210 | 2016 | NHL Collector's Album | 200.00 |
| 211 | 2017 | NHL Collector's Album | 200.00 |

* Joint Royal Canadian Mint / Canada Post stamp and coin product.

## PHILATELIC EXHIBITION CARDS AND ITEMS PRODUCED BY CANADA'S POSTAGE STAMP PRINTERS

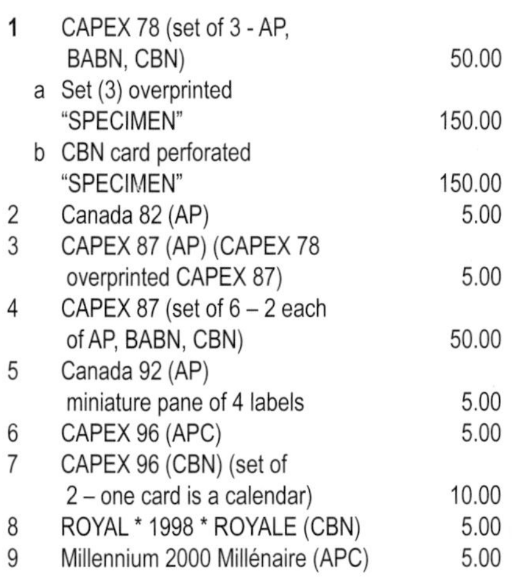

| No. | Description | Value |
|---|---|---|
| 1 | CAPEX 78 (set of 3 - AP, BABN, CBN) | 50.00 |
| a | Set (3) overprinted "SPECIMEN" | 150.00 |
| b | CBN card perforated "SPECIMEN" | 150.00 |
| 2 | Canada 82 (AP) | 5.00 |
| 3 | CAPEX 87 (AP) (CAPEX 78 overprinted CAPEX 87) | 5.00 |
| 4 | CAPEX 87 (set of 6 – 2 each of AP, BABN, CBN) | 50.00 |
| 5 | Canada 92 (AP) miniature pane of 4 labels | 5.00 |
| 6 | CAPEX 96 (APC) | 5.00 |
| 7 | CAPEX 96 (CBN) (set of 2 – one card is a calendar) | 10.00 |
| 8 | ROYAL * 1998 * ROYALE (CBN) | 5.00 |
| 9 | Millennium 2000 Millénaire (APC) | 5.00 |

AP - Ashton-Potter Limited
BABN - British American Bank Note
CBN - Canadian Bank Note
APC – Ashton Potter Canada Ltd.
Quantities issued:
No. 1 – 10,000 sets of 3
No. 1a – 200 sets of 3
No. 1b – 25 cards only

Philatelic Exhibition Cards – 2 (Canada 82)

## THEMATIC POST CARDS

| No. | Description | Price |
|---|---|---|
| **1** | National Postal Museum Classic Stamps (5), without postage indicia† | 3.00 |
| **2** | National Postal Museum Mail Transportation (5), without postage indicia† | 3.00 |
| 3 | Canada 82 (5) | 3.00 |
| 4 | Scouting – 75th Anniversary | 2.50 |
| 5 | Canadian Locomotives 1836–1860 (4) | 2.50 |
| **6** | Tall Ships Visit | 2.50 |
| 7 | Tall Ships Visit Maximum Card | 2.50 |
| 8 | Papal Visit (2) | 1.25 |
| 9 | Lighthouses of Canada (4) | 2.50 |
| 10 | Canadian Locomotives 1860-1905 (4) | 2.50 |
| 11 | Canadian in Space Maximum Card | 2.50 |
| 12 | The Last Spike Maximum Card | 2.50 |
| 13 | CAPEX '87 (4) | 2.50 |
| 14 | Dolls of Canada (4) | 2.50 |
| 15 | Public Gardens (5) | 2.50 |
| 16 | Canada 92 (5) | 2.50 |
| 17 | Historic Hotels (5) | 4.00 |
| 18 | XV Commonwealth Games (6) | 5.00 |
| 19 | Comic Book Superheroes (5) | 4.50 |
| 20 | Historic Land Vehicles Maximum Cards (25) | 50.00 |
| 21 | Québec en fleurs | 1.50 |
| 22 | Canadian Museum Association (6) | 8.00 |

† See UX109Ca (postal cards) for these with postage indicia.

## INTERNATIONAL PHILATELIC EXHIBITION CARDS

| No. | Exhibition | Price |
|---|---|---|
| **1** | WIPA 1981 | 10.00 |
| 2 | ESSEN 82 | 10.00 |
| 3 | PHILEX FRANCE 82 | 10.00 |
| 4 | HAMBURG 84 | 5.00 |
| 5 | AUSIPEX 84 | 5.00 |
| 6 | ITALIA 85 | 5.00 |
| 7 | AMERIPEX 86 | 5.00 |
| 8 | STOCKHOLMIA 86 | 5.00 |
| 9 | CAPEX 87 | 5.00 |
| 10 | HAFNIA 87 | 5.00 |
| 11 | FINLANDIA 88 | 5.00 |
| 12 | PHILEX FRANCE 89 | 5.00 |
| 13 | WORLD STAMP EXPO 89 | 5.00 |
| 14 | STAMP WORLD LONDON 90 | 2.50 |
| 15 | NEW ZEALAND 1990 | 2.50 |
| 16 | PHILA NIPPON 91 | 2.50 |
| 17 | CANADA 92 † | 5.00 |
| 18 | GRANADA 92 | 2.50 |
| 19 | WORLD COLUMBIAN STAMP EXPO 92 | 2.50 |
| 20 | PORTUGAL 98 | 7.50 |

**International Philatelic Exhibition Cards - 1 (WIPA 1981)**

† Card measures approximately 150 mm x 105 mm to the standard size of 150 mm x 200 mm
Cards which are postmarked at the exhibition are valued at twice the listed price.

## FRAMEABLE PRINTS

| No. | Description | Price |
|---|---|---|
| **1** | 1984 Tall Ships Visit | 20.00 |
| 2 | 1988 "The Young Reader" | 30.00 |
| 3 | 1988 Tahltan Bear Dog | 30.00 |
| 4 | 1996 Birds of Canada | |
| a | 10" x 8" – set of 4 | 25.00 |
| b | 24" x 20" – set of 4 | 150.00 |
| 5 | 1996 Christmas (45¢ design) | 125.00 |
| 6 | NHL All-Stars Lithographs (2001) | |
| a | Jean Béliveau | 20.00 |
| b | Eddie Shore | 20.00 |
| c | Bobby Hull | 20.00 |
| d | Terry Sawchuk | 20.00 |
| e | Denis Potvin | 20.00 |
| f | Syl Apps | 20.00 |
| 7 | NHL All-Stars Lithographs - Autographed | |
| a | Jean Béliveau | 135.00 |
| b | Bobby Hull | 135.00 |
| c | Denis Potvin | 135.00 |
| 8 | World Figure Skating Prints | |
| a | Ice Dance | 67.50 |
| b | Pairs | 67.50 |
| c | Men's Singles | 67.50 |
| d | Women's Singles | 67.50 |
| 9 | Year of the Horse | 90.00 |
| 10 | NHL All-Stars Lithographs (2002) | |
| a | Tim Horton | 20.00 |
| b | Howie Morenz | 20.00 |
| c | Red Kelly | 20.00 |
| d | Guy Lafleur | 20.00 |
| **e** | Glenn Hall | 20.00 |
| f | Phil Esposito | 20.00 |
| 11 | NHL All-Stars Lithographs - Autographed | |
| a | Red Kelly | 135.00 |
| b | Guy Lafleur | 135.00 |
| c | Glenn Hall | 135.00 |
| d | Phil Esposito | 135.00 |
| 12 | Tulips | |
| a | Monte Carlo and Ottawa | 22.50 |
| b | City of Vancouver and The Bishop | 22.50 |
| 13 | Year of the Ram | 90.00 |
| 14 | NHL All-Stars Lithographs (2003) | |
| a | Frank Mahovlich | 20.00 |
| b | Serge Savard | 20.00 |
| c | Mike Bossy | 20.00 |
| d | Raymond Bourque | 20.00 |
| e | Stan Mikita | 20.00 |
| f | Bill Durnan | 20.00 |
| 15 | NHL All-Stars Lithographs – Autographed | |
| a | Frank Mahovlich | 135.00 |
| b | Serge Savard | 135.00 |
| c | Mike Bossy | 135.00 |
| d | Raymond Bourque | 135.00 |
| e | Stan Mikita | 135.00 |
| 16 | Year of the Monkey | 90.00 |
| 17 | NHL All-Stars Lithographs (2004) | |
| a | Larry Robinson | 20.00 |
| b | Ted Lindsay | 20.00 |
| c | Brad Park | 20.00 |
| **d** | Marcel Dionne | 20.00 |
| e | Johnny Bower | 20.00 |
| f | Milt Schmidt | 20.00 |
| 18 | NHL All-Stars Lithographs – Autographed | |
| a | Larry Robinson | 135.00 |
| b | Ted Lindsay | 135.00 |
| c | Brad Park | 135.00 |
| d | Marcel Dionne | 135.00 |
| e | Johnny Bower | 135.00 |
| f | Milt Schmidt | 135.00 |
| 19 | NHL All-Stars Lithographs (2005) | |
| a | Henri Richard | 20.00 |
| b | Allan Stanley | 20.00 |
| c | Bryan Trottier | 20.00 |
| d | Grant Fuhr | 20.00 |
| e | Pierre Pilote | 20.00 |
| f | John Bucyk | 20.00 |
| 20 | NHL All-Stars Lithographs - Autographed | |
| a | Henri Richard | 135.00 |
| b | Allan Stanley | 135.00 |
| c | Bryan Trottier | 135.00 |
| d | Grant Fuhr | 135.00 |
| e | Pierre Pilote | 135.00 |
| f | John Bucyk | 135.00 |
| 21 | NHL All-Stars Laminated Vertical Print (2005) | 30.00 |
| 22 | NHL All-Stars Laminated Vertical Print - Autographed | 105.00 |
| 23 | Fishing Flies Prints | |
| a | Alevin | 22.50 |
| b | Jock Scott | 22.50 |
| c | Mickey Finn | 22.50 |
| d | P.E.I. Fly | 22.50 |
| **24** | Fishing Flies Prints - Autographed | |
| a | Alevin | 135.00 |
| b | Jock Scott | 135.00 |
| c | Mickey Finn | 135.00 |
| d | P.E.I. Fly | 135.00 |
| 25 | Montreal Canadiens Lenticular Souvenir Sheet Enlargement (2010) | 115.00 |

**Products with stamp reproductions, such as clothing, coasters, playing cards, and plates, are not listed as they do not include actual stamps with the product.**

## SPECIAL EVENT COVERS, CUSTOM and COMMEMORATIVE ENVELOPES PRODUCED BY CANADA POST

Special event covers produced by Canada Post to commemorate or promote events of national or international importance.

Most of the covers were available by mail order through the National Philatelic Centre (NPC) in Antigonish (formerly known as the Philatelic Service (PS) in Ottawa) or at selected postal outlets where philatelic products were sold. A few were exclusive (X) in availablilty and therefore not offered to philatelists.

S01

S07A

S11

S12a

S16

S23

| Cat# | Issue date | Unitrade # | Description | Source | Qty | Value |
|---|---|---|---|---|---|---|
| **S01** | *Jul 17, 1976* | 682 | 1976 Olympic Games - Event cancellations | | | |
| a | | | Series A, Team sports (set of 5 covers) | PS | | 5.00 |
| b | | | Series B, Tradition (set of 5 covers) | PS | | 5.00 |
| c | | | Series C, Combat and Cycling (set of 5 covers) | PS | | 5.00 |
| d | | | Series D, Water and Equestrian (set of 5 covers) | PS | | 5.00 |
| e | | | Series E, Individual Sports (set of 5 covers) | PS | | 5.00 |
| **S02** | *Aug 1, 1976* | 681–683 | 1976 Olympic Games - Event cancellation, Closing Ceremony | PS | | 2.00 |
| **S02A** | *Jan 25/1981* | 878 | Canadian Postal Users' Conference | X | | 15.00 |
| **S03** | *Sep 1, 1981* | 883–884 | SPRINT 81 | X | | 25.00 |
| **S04** | *Oct 16, 1981* | 890–893 | Canada Post Corporation Proclamation Day | X | | 10.00 |
| **S05** | *Nov 16, 1981* | one of 900/901/902 | Gift Suggestions from Canada Post | X | | 15.00 |
| **S06** | *Nov 3, 1982* | 973 | Gift Suggestions from Canada Post | X | | 15.00 |
| **S06A** | *Dec 15, 1982* | 439/893/654 | Marconi's First Wireless Message in 1902 | X | | 25.00 |
| **S07** | *Sep 1984* | 1030 | Papal Visit - Event cancellations (set of 11 covers) | PS | | 27.50 |
| **S07A** | *Apr 5, 1990* | 1270 | A Coat of Many Colours | X | | 20.00 |
| **S08** | *Jul 3, 1990* | 1270 | Toronto '96 | X | | 25.00 |
| **S09** | *Sep 5, 1990* | 1287 | Weather Observing | X | | 20.00 |
| **S10** | *Sep 27, 1990* | 1166i | 59th General Assembly Session of INTERPOL | X | | 20.00 |
| **S11** | *Oct 1, 1991* | 1336–1337 | October - Stamp Month: Ronald McDonald Children's Charities of Canada | NPC | 60,000 | 2.50 |
| **S12** | *Jun 6, 1992* | 1388 | The 1992 Mount Logan Expedition | NPC | 12,000 | 2.00 |
| a | | | autographed by the climb team | NPC | 120 | 75.00 |
| [S13 became PNC1 in the 2013 Unitrade catalogue] | | | | | | |
| **S14** | *May 15, 1994* | 1506 | Royal Canadian Electrical and Mechanical Engineers (1944–1994) | X | 3,000 | 20.00 |
| **S15** | *Oct 4, 1994* | 1518–1520 | 40th Commonwealth Parliamentary Conference | X | | 20.00 |
| **S16** | *Feb 26, 1995* | 614/1359c | Royal Canadian Mounted Police – 1995 Centennial Patrol of the Yukon | X | 2,500 | 20.00 |
| **S17** | *Apr 7, 1995* | 1531 | Official Opening - Iqaluit Retail Postal Outlet | X | | 20.00 |
| **S18** | *May 3, 1995* | 1546 | Navy League (1895–1995) | X | | 20.00 |
| **S19** | *Jun 25, 1995* | 1546 | International Association for the Protection of Industrial Property Congress | X | | 20.00 |
| **S20** | *Feb 15, 1996* | 1596 | Pratt & Whitney Canada | X | | 20.00 |
| **S21** | *Jun 8, 1996* | | CAPEX 96 Prepaid Telephone Card FDC - Historic Land Vehicles | | | |
| a | | 1605y | 45¢ Bricklin SV-1 Sports Car | NPC | | 50.00 |
| b | | 1604e | 90¢ White Model WA 122 Tractor-Trailer | NPC | | 50.00 |
| **S22** | *Jun 13, 1996* | | CAPEX 96 Prepaid Telephone Card FDC - Klondike Gold Rush | | | |
| a | | 1606a | 45¢ Klondike Gold Strike | NPC | | 50.00 |
| b | | 1606b | 45¢ Klondike Fever | NPC | | 50.00 |
| c | | 1606c | 45¢ Gold Rush Law and Order | NPC | | 50.00 |
| d | | 1606d | 45¢ Boom Times in Dawson | NPC | | 50.00 |
| e | | 1606e | 45¢ Klondike Bonanza | NPC | | 50.00 |
| **S23** | *Dec 17, 1996* | 1604e | Labatt (1847–1997) | X | | 50.00 |

S24b

S29

S36

S39

S44

S62

| Cat# | Issue date | Unitrade # | Description | Source | Qty | Value |
|---|---|---|---|---|---|---|
| S24 | *Apr 23, 1997* | 1361c | Lester B Pearson (1897–1972) | | | |
| a | | | Diplomat | NPC | 3,800 | 10.00 |
| b | | | Nobel Peace Prize Winner | NPC | 3,800 | 10.00 |
| c | | | Prime Minister of Canada | NPC | 3,800 | 10.00 |
| S25 | *Jun 11, 1997* | 1607 | Canadian Postal Museum Opening | NPC | 7,500 | 1.50 |
| pf | | | with presentaion folder picturing a panel of ornate lock boxes | X | | 5.00 |
| S26 | *Aug 15, 1998* | one of 1595–1598 | Festival of the Future | NPC | 5,000 | 5.00 |
| S27 | *Aug 25, 1997* | 1361c | Leduc No. 1 Well | NPC | 5,000 | 5.00 |
| S28 | *Nov 2, 1997* | 1638 | The Ursulines of Trois-Rivières (1697–1997) | NPC | 5,000 | 5.00 |
| S29 | *Mar 7, 1998* | 1659/1660 | 1948 Olympic Winter Games - St. Moritz | NPC | 6,000 | 10.00 |
| S30 | *May 13, 1998* | 1360viii | Canada House | NPC | 5,000 | 5.00 |
| S31 | *Jun 22, 1998* | 1361c | Royal Canadian Mint (1908–1998) | NPC | 5,000 | 10.00 |
| S32 | *Sep 23, 1998* | 1755d–f | Heritage Canada Foundation (1973–1998) | X | 4,500 | 15.00 |
| S33 | *Oct 29, 1998* | 1722 | The Canadian National Institute for the Blind | NPC | 5,000 | 3.00 |
| S34 | *Nov 19, 1998* | 1697 | Louis de Buade, Comte de Frontenac (1620–1698) | NPC | 5,000 | 3.00 |
| S35 | *Jun 7, 1999* | 1785 | Heritage Club of Canada Post (1989–1999) | NPC | 27,000 | 7.50 |
| S36 | *Jun 24, 1999* | 1695 | Saskatchewan Wheat Pool (1924–1999) | NPC | 7,000 | 5.00 |
| S37 | *Jun 30, 1999* | 1695 | National Capital Commission (1899–1999) | NPC | 5,000 | 5.00 |
| S38 | *Oct 2, 1999* | 1695 | Halifax (1749–1999) | NPC | 5,000 | 5.00 |
| S39 | *Dec 27, 1999* | 1695 | Jam des neiges | NPC | 5,000 | 7.50 |
| S40 | *May 29, 2000* | 1695 | Michel Sarrazin | NPC | 5,000 | 3.00 |
| S41 | *Jun 21, 2000* | 1784 | National Aboriginal Day | NPC | 7,000 | 3.00 |
| S42 | *Jul 15, 2000* | 1695 | Bracebridge (1875–2000) | NPC | 5,000 | 3.00 |
| S43 | *Sep 29, 2000* | 1695 | Fulbright Educational Exchange Program (1990–2000) | NPC | 5,000 | 3.00 |
| S44 | *Apr 13, 2001* | one of 1885a–f | International Postal Hockey Tournament | NPC | 12,000 | 3.00 |
| S45 | *May 3, 2001* | 1683 | Royal Canadian Army Services Corps (1901–2001) | NPC | 7,500 | 3.00 |
| S46 | *May 18, 2001* | 1878 | The Canadian Medical Protective Association (1901–2001) | NPC | 10,000 | 3.00 |
| S47 | *Jan 12, 2002* | 1918a | Toronto Maple Leafs (1927 - 2002) | NPC | 20,000 | 6.00 |
| v1 | | | cancellation only – stamp missing | | | 50.00 |
| S48 | *Apr 23, 2002* | 1927 | Guelph (1827–2002) | NPC | 14,000 | 4.00 |
| S49 | *May 1, 2002* | 1927 | Le Courrier de Saint-Hyacinthe (1852–2002) | NPC | 12,000 | 4.00 |
| S50 | *Nov 13, 2002* | 1931 | Toronto Station K | X | | 15.00 |
| S51 | *Dec 15, 2002* | 1964 | Marconi's First Wireless Message (1902–2002) | NPC | 10,000 | 4.00 |
| S52 | *Feb 17, 2003* | 1927 | Les Affaires (1928–2003) | NPC | 12,000 | 4.00 |
| S53 | *Apr 26, 2003* | 1932 | Canadian Military Engineers (1903–2003) | NPC | 12,000 | 4.00 |
| S54 | *May 30, 2003* | 1940 | The Royal Philatelic Society of Canada – 75th Annual Convention | NPC | 12,000 | 4.00 |
| S55 | *Jun 7, 2003* | 1927 | Lunenburg (1753–2003) | NPC | 12,000 | 6.00 |
| S56 | *Jul 1, 2003* | 1964 | Canadian Military Communications (1903–2003) | NPC | 12,000 | 4.00 |
| S57 | *Jul 14, 2003* | 1983 | The Granby Zoo (1953–2003) | NPC | 12,000 | 4.00 |
| S58 | *Nov 21, 2003* | 1927 | Mail – Rail – Retail: Connecting Canadians | X | | 15.00 |
| S59 | *Apr 1, 2004* | 2008 | Henry Birks and Sons (1879–2004) | NPC | 12,000 | 4.00 |
| S60 | *Apr 24, 2004* | 2008 | La Société philatélique de Québec (1929–2004) | NPC | 12,000 | 4.00 |
| S61 | *Jun 14, 2004* | 2008 | The Royal College of Physicians and Surgeons of Canada (1929–2004) | NPC | 12,000 | 4.00 |
| S62 | *Jun 19, 2004* | 2010 | Mahone Bay (1754–2004) | NPC | 12,000 | 4.00 |
| S63 | *Jun 24, 2004* | 2008 | Canadian Forces Health Services (1904–2004) | NPC | 12,000 | 4.00 |
| S64 | *Oct 1, 2004* | 2008 | National Philatelic Centre (1984–2004) | X | | 15.00 |

S47

S57

S58

S67

S70

S71

S72

S76

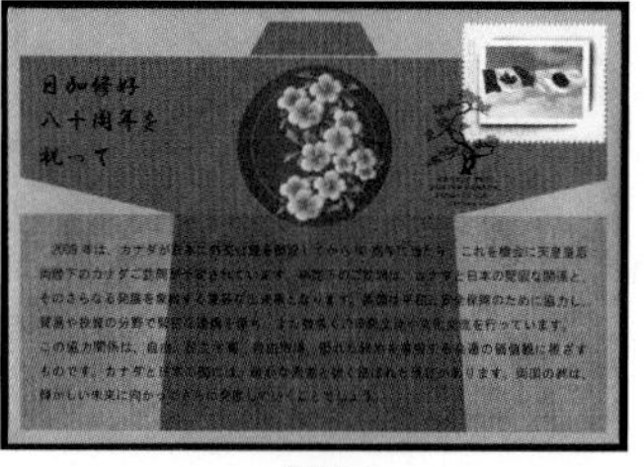
S81

| Cat# | Issue date | Unitrade # | Description | Source | Qty | Value |
|---|---|---|---|---|---|---|
| **S65** | *Nov 4, 2004* | 2008 | The Royal Canadian Geographical Society (1929–2004) | NPC | 12,000 | 4.00 |
| **S66** | *May 8, 2005* | 2075 | Canada's War Brides | NPC | 10,000 | 5.00 |
| **S67** | *May 26, 2005* | 2108 | The Royal Regiment of Canadian Artillery | NPC | 10,000 | 5.00 |
| **S68** | *May 27, 2005* | 2072 | London (1855–2005) | NPC | 10,000 | 5.00 |
| **S69** | *May 28, 2006* | 2155 | Benjamin Franklin (1706–2006) | NPC | 10,000 | 5.00 |
| **S70** | *Oct 12, 2006* | 2064† | Hungarian Immigration (1956–2006) | NPC | 10,000 | 5.00 |
| **S71** | *Oct 16, 2006* | 2063† | Canada Post Corporation (1981–2006) | NPC | 72,500 | 5.00 |
| **pf** | | | with blue presentation folder picturing silver silhouttes of three letter carriers | X | | 7.50 |
| **S72** | *Feb 8, 2007* | 2063† | Purdy's Chocolates (1907–2007) | NPC | 10,000 | 15.00 |
| **S73** | *Apr 28, 2007* | 2063 | Shoppers Drug Mart - Celebrating 1000 Stores | X | | 15.00 |
| **S74** | *Aug 1, 2007* | 2064† | 100 Years of Scouting | NPC | 15,000 | 5.00 |
| **S75** | *Sep 10, 2007* | 2064† | Glenn Gould | NPC | 10,000 | 5.00 |
| **S76** | *Nov 2, 2007* | 2239 | Santa Letter-writing Program | NPC | 10,000 | 5.00 |
| **pf** | | | mounted in a dark blue presentation folder embossed with Canada Post's Mark of Commitment symbol | X | | 7.50 |
| **S77** | *Apr 21, 2008* | 2266 | Montreal Association for the Blind (1908–2008) | NPC | 11,000 | 5.00 |
| **S78** | *Apr 29, 2008* | 2064† | Public Service Commission of Canada (1908–2008) | NPC | 13,000 | 5.00 |
| **S79** | *Jun 20, 2008* | 2064† | St. John Ambulance (1883–2008) | NPC | 10,000 | 5.00 |
| **S80** | *Oct 1, 2008* | 2064† | Christmas Seal (1908–2008) | NPC | 10,000 | 5.00 |
| **S81** | *Jul 8, 2009* | 2064† | Canada/Japan Diplomatic Relations (1929–2009) | NPC | 10,000 | 6.00 |
| **S82** | *Jan 10, 2010* | 485 in 2064† | *Le Devoir* (1910–2010) | NPC | 10,000 | 6.00 |
| **S83** | *Jun 4, 2010* | 2064† | Winnipeg Mail Processing Plant | X | 3,700 | 15.00 |
| **S84** | *Jul 6, 2010* | 2064† | Saskatchewan Roughriders (1910–2010) | NPC | 20,000 | 6.00 |
| **S85** | *Oct 2, 2010* | 2064† | St. Thomas University (1910–2010) | NPC | 10,000 | 6.00 |
| **S86** | *May 3, 2011* | 2064† | Canadian Forces Postal Service (1911–2011) | NPC | 10,000 | 6.00 |
| **S87** | *May 9, 2011* | 2064† | University of Regina (1911–2011) | NPC | 10,000 | 6.00 |
| **S88** | *Jun 1, 2011* | 2064† | Wilfrid Laurier University (1911–2011) | NPC | 10,000 | 6.00 |
| **S89** | *Sep 26, 2011* | 2064† | Montreal Museum of Fine Arts | NPC | 10,000 | 6.00 |
| **S90** | *Jun 8, 2012* | 2064† | Town of Torbay (1762–2012) | NPC | 10,000 | 6.00 |
| **S91** | *Aug 2, 2012* | 2064† | City of Victoria (1862–2012) | NPC | 10,000 | 6.00 |
| **S92** | *Sep 19, 2012* | 2064† | The Royal Conservatory (1887–2012) | NPC | 8,000 | 6.00 |
| **S93** | *Feb 22, 2013* | 2586† | Olds College (1913–2013) | NPC | 8,000 | 6.00 |
| **S94** | *Apr 22, 2013* | 2587† | Service de sécurité incendie de Montréal (1863–2013) | NPC | 8,000 | 6.00 |

| Cat# | Issue date | Unitrade # | Description | Source | Qty | Value |
|---|---|---|---|---|---|---|
| **S95** | *May 6, 2013* | 2587† | Louisbourg (1713–2013) | NPC | 8,000 | 6.00 |
| **S96** | *May 26, 2013* | 2587† | The 49th Field Artillery Regiment (1913–2013) | NPC | 8,000 | 6.00 |
| **S97** | *May 30, 2013* | 2586† | 4-H Canada (1913–2013) | NPC | 10,000 | 6.00 |
| **S98** | *Jun 4, 2013* | 2586† | The Canadian Heraldic Authority (1988–2013) | NPC | 8,000 | 6.00 |
| **S99** | *Oct 19, 2013* | 2586† | Royal 22e Régiment (1914–2014) | NPC | 8,000 | 6.00 |
| **S100** | *Mar 17, 2014* | 2586† | Princess Patricia's Canadian Light Infantry (1914–2014) | NPC | 8,000 | 6.00 |
| **S101** | *Jun 8, 2014* | 2586† | Art Gallery of Hamilton (1914–2014) | NPC | 8,000 | 6.00 |
| **S102** | *Aug 7, 2014* | 2586† | Le Régiment de Hull (1914–2014) | NPC | 8,000 | 6.00 |
| **S103** | *Sep 1, 2014* | 2587† | Charlottetown Conference (1864–2014) | NPC | 8,000 | 6.00 |
| **S104** | *Sep 2, 2014* | 2586† | Royal Montreal Regiment (1914–2014) | NPC | 8,000 | 6.00 |
| **S105** | *Oct 10, 2014* | 2587† | Québec Conference (1864–2014) | NPC | 8,000 | 6.00 |
| **S106** | *Apr 2, 2016* | 2586† | The Brockville Rifles | NPC | | 6.00 |
| **S107** | *Apr 2, 2016* | 2586† | 31 Combat Engineer Regiment (The Elgins) | NPC | | 6.00 |
| **S108** | *Apr 2, 2016* | 2586† | The Grey and Simcoe Foresters | NPC | | 6.00 |
| **S109** | *Apr 2, 2016* | 2586† | The Lorne Scots (Peel, Dufferin and Halton Regiment) | NPC | | 6.00 |
| **S110** | *Jun 6, 2016* | 2586† | National Research Council of Canada | NPC | | 6.00 |
| **S111** | *Sep 10, 2016* | 2586† | The Royal Highland Fusiliers of Canada | NPC | | 6.00 |
| **S112** | *Sep 10, 2016* | 2586† | The Ontario Regiment (RCAC) | NPC | | 6.00 |
| **S113** | *Sep 10, 2016* | 2586† | The Queen's York Rangers (1st American Regiment) (RCAC) | NPC | | 6.00 |
| **S114** | *Sep 10, 2016* | 2586† | 42nd Field Artillery Regiment (Lanark and Renfrew Scottish), RCA | NPC | | 6.00 |
| **S115** | *Sep 10, 2016* | 2586† | 56th Field Artillery Regiment, RCA | NPC | | 6.00 |
| **S116** | *Sep 10, 2016* | 2586† | The Sherbrooke Hussars | NPC | | 6.00 |
| **S117** | *Oct 16, 2016* | 2586† | Southern Alberta Institute of Technology | NPC | | 6.00 |
| **S118** | *Feb 8, 2018* | 2586† | The War Amps, 100th Anniversary | NPC | | 6.00 |
| **S119** | *Mar 21, 2018* | 2586† | CNIB, 100th Anniversary | NPC | | 6.00 |

† These Commemorative envelopes have the Picture Postage™ design printed on the envelope.

## PHILATELIC/NUMISMATIC COVERS PRODUCED BY CANADA POST

PNC1

PNC2

PNC3

PNC4

PNC5

| Cat# | Issue date | Unitrade # | Description | Source | Qty | Value |
|---|---|---|---|---|---|---|
| **PNC1** | *Apr 16, 1993* | 1460 | Stanley Cup (1893–1993) issue with a proof silver dollar coin | NPC | 30,000 | 60.00 |
| **PNC2** | *Apr 29, 2011* | 2465a | Royal Wedding issue with a nickel plated steel 25-cent coin | NPC | 10,000 | 65.00 |
| **PNC3** | *Apr 5, 2012* | 2535i | Titanic (1912–2012) issue with a cupronickel 25-cent coin | NPC | 10,000 | 55.00 |
| **PNC4** | *May 7, 2012* | 2540 | Queen Elizabeth II Diamond Jubilee (1952–2012) issue with a silver-plated copper 50-cent coin | NPC | 10,000 | 55.00 |
| **PNC5** | *May 8, 2013* | 2644 | Coronation of Queen Elizabeth II (1953–2013) issue with a cupronickel 25-cent coin | NPC | 10,000 | 55.00 |

# STAMP SPONSORSHIP PRODUCTS (1990–1993)

The Stamp Sponsorship Program permitted corporate entities and organizations to partner with Canada Post Corporation and sponsor a specific commemorative stamp issue. Sponsors share the prestige of participation, and being identified with Canada Post products increases their profile further.

This section lists products offered by either Canada Post or the sponsor that reproduces the artwork or the image of the stamp issue with the name or trademark of the sponsor identified on the product. Images in this section are 20%.

OFDC cat. no. refers to *The New Specialized Catalogue of Canada Post Official First Day Covers*, Third Edition, 2007 by Andrew Chung FRPSC and R.F. Narbonne FRPSC OTB.

| Scott Number | Issue | Sponsor | Description of product(s) | Value |
|---|---|---|---|---|
| 1278 | Canada Day – The Canadian Flag | The Canadian Chamber of Commerce | OFDC printed with the logo of The Canadian Chamber of Commerce (cat. no. 338a) | 25.00 |
| 1283a – 1286b | Canadian Forests | Petro-Canada | four different panes of 4; one pane in a matching envelope with a business reply post card to receive a Scouts Canada Certificate of Participation and a postmarked set of the four stamps | |
| | | | • Acadian Forest pane of 4 with matching envelope | 15.00 |
| | | | • Great Lakes-St. Lawrence Forest pane of 4 with matching envelope | 15.00 |
| | | | • Coast Forest pane of 4 with matching envelope | 15.00 |
| | | | • Boreal Forest pane of 4 with matching envelope | 15.00 |
| | | | • Certificate of Participation and a postmarked set of the four stamps | 15.00 |

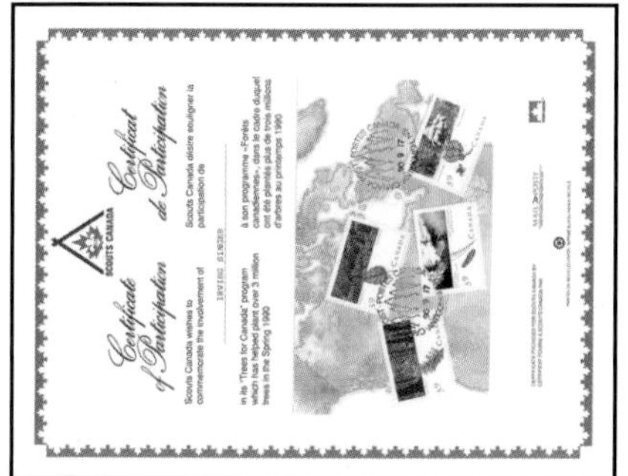


| Scott Number | Issue | Sponsor | Description of product(s) | Value |
|---|---|---|---|---|
| 1289 – 1292 | Legendary Creatures | McDonald's | set of two folders depicting the Sasquatch/Werewolf and the Kraken/Ogopogo with a postmarked pair of the stamps relating to the folder | |
| | | | • Sasquatch/Werewolf folder in English with a postmarked pair of the stamps | 7.50 |
| | | | • Sasquatch/Werewolf folder in French with a postmarked pair of the stamps | 10.00 |
| | | | • Kraken/Ogopogo folder in English with a postmarked pair of the stamps | 7.50 |
| | | | • Kraken/Ogopogo folder in French with a postmarked pair of the stamps | 10.00 |
| | | | • OFDC printed with the logo of McDonald's (cat. no. 343a) | 10.00 |

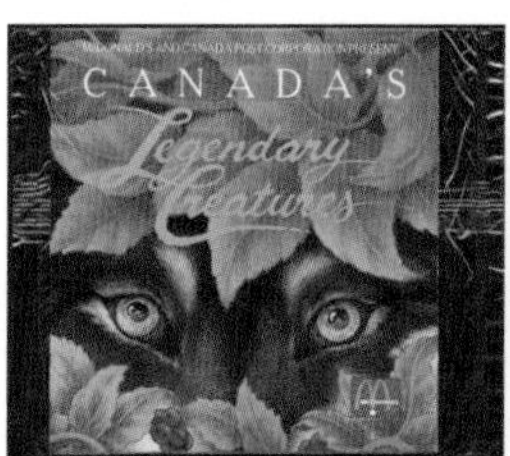

| Scott Number | Issue | Sponsor | Description of product(s) | Value |
|---|---|---|---|---|
| 1311 – 1315 | Public Gardens | Environment Canada | "Green Plan/Environment Week" slogan cancellation installed at Alta Vista (Ottawa) Mail Processing Plant | 2.00 |
| 1336 + 1337 | Folktales | McDonald's | set of two folders depicting Buried Treasure and Warm Wind Chinook with a postmarked single of the stamp relating to the folder | |
| | | | • Buried Treasure folder in English with a postmarked single of the stamp | 5.00 |
| | | | • Buried Treasure folder in French with a postmarked single of the stamp | 7.50 |
| | | | • Warm Wind Chinook folder in English with a postmarked single of the stamp | 5.00 |
| | | | • Warm Wind Chinook folder in French with a postmarked single of the stamp | 7.50 |

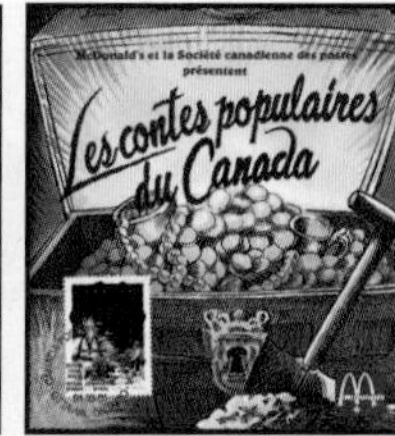

| Scott Number | Issue | Sponsor | Description of product(s) | Value |
|---|---|---|---|---|
| 1343 | Basketball | TSN/RDS | no products known | |

| Scott Number | Issue | Sponsor | Description of product(s) | Value |
|---|---|---|---|---|
| 1399 – 1403 | Olympic Winter Games | Kraft General Foods | post card – "Priority Courier Brings You the Miracle Whip Olympic Mailbag" | 2.00 |
| | | | OFDC printed with the Miracle Whip pictorial postmark (cat. no. 372a) | 25.00 |
| 1414 – 1418 | Olympic Summer Games | Kraft General Foods | post cards – "Go Canada" set of four post cards with recipes by Danny Foster, Paige Gordon, Curt Harnett and Curtis Hibbert | 8.00 |
| | | | place mats – set of five place mats with a postmarked single of one of the five stamps | 50.00 |
| | | | OFDC printed with the Miracle Whip pictorial postmark (cat. no. 379a) | 25.00 |
| 1434 | Legendary Heroes | Laura Secord | Laura Secord note card and stamped envelope | 2.50 |
| | | | gift pack of five note cards and five stamped envelopes | 12.50 |
| | | | OFDC printed with the Laura Secord pictorial postmark (cat. no. 383a) | 25.00 |
| 1436 – 1440 | Canadian Minerals | The Mining Association of Canada | no products known | |
| 1467 – 1471 | Historic Hotels | Canadian Pacific Hotels & Resorts | set of five note cards and five envelopes | 25.00 |
| | | | gift pack of three different or identical note cards and envelopes | 15.00 |
| | | | OFDC printed with the Canadian Pacific Hotels & Resorts pictorial postmark (cat. no. 399a) | 25.00 |
| 1495 – 1498 | The Age of Dinosaurs | McDonald's | folder with a postmarked pair of the stamps | 7.50 |

# FEDERAL WILDLIFE HABITAT CONSERVATION

Beginning in 1985, the Migratory Bird Regulations have required that the current habitat conservation stamp be purchased and affixed to a hunting license before hunting. One stamp design is issued each year in a booklet format consisting of a single pane of one stamp. Sheets of 16 have also been issued for all years except 1985. Unsold stamps, and licenses bearing stamps, are destroyed each year by Canada Post and the Canadian Wildlife Service. "On license" prices are for nice clean undamaged complete licenses.
Note: The Federal Wildlife Habitat Conservation stamps are numbered according to *The Canadian Revenue Stamp Catalogue*, by E.S.J. van Dam, with the author's permission.

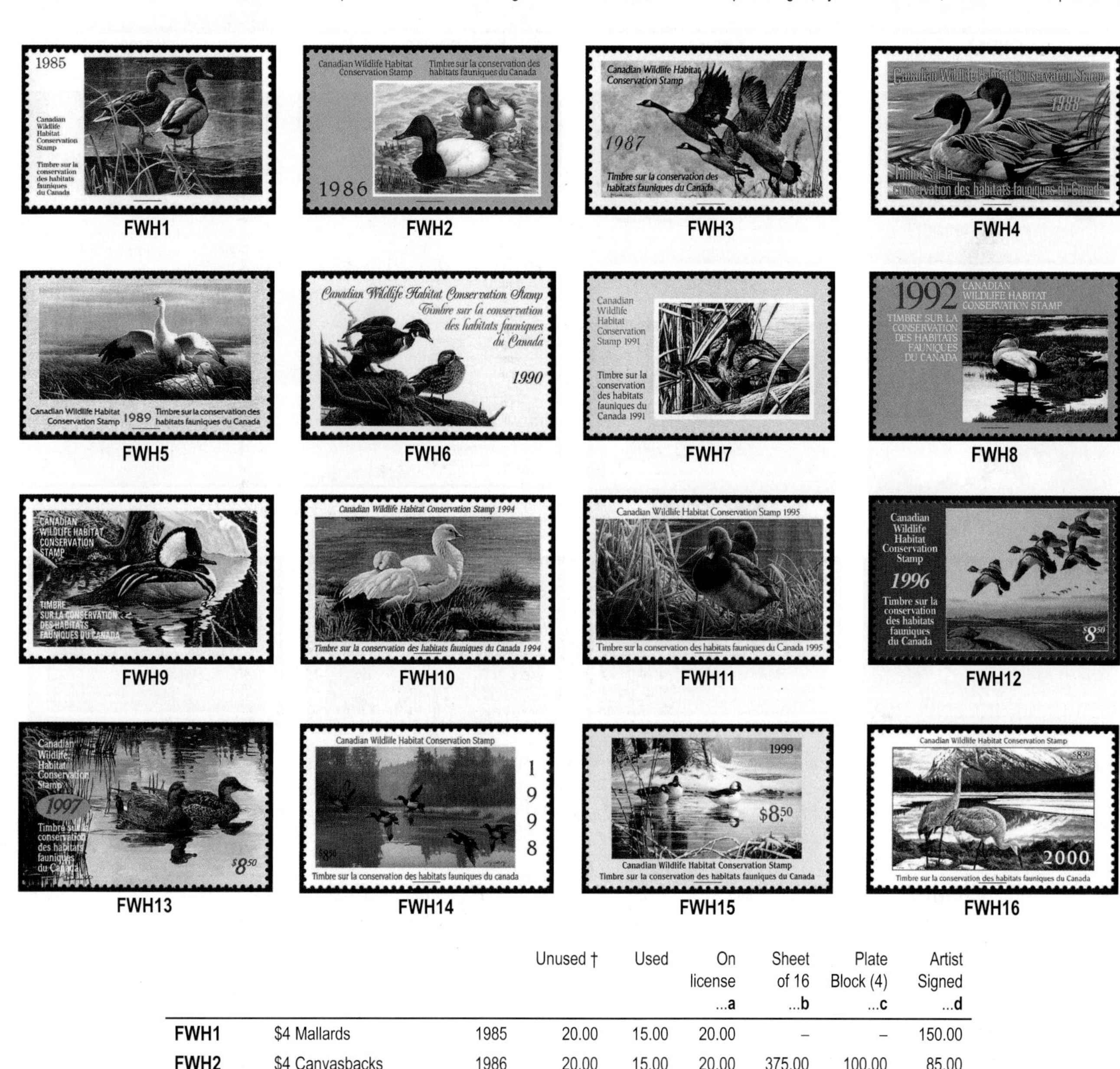


FWH1 FWH2 FWH3 FWH4

FWH5 FWH6 FWH7 FWH8

FWH9 FWH10 FWH11 FWH12

FWH13 FWH14 FWH15 FWH16

| | | | Unused † | Used | On license ...a | Sheet of 16 ...b | Plate Block (4) ...c | Artist Signed ...d |
|---|---|---|---|---|---|---|---|---|
| **FWH1** | $4 Mallards | 1985 | 20.00 | 15.00 | 20.00 | – | – | 150.00 |
| **FWH2** | $4 Canvasbacks | 1986 | 20.00 | 15.00 | 20.00 | 375.00 | 100.00 | 85.00 |
| **FWH3** | $6.50 Canada Geese | 1987 | 20.00 | 10.00 | 20.00 | 375.00 | 100.00 | 100.00 |
| **FWH4** | $6.50 Pintails | 1988 | 20.00 | 10.00 | 20.00 | 325.00 | 85.00 | 85.00 |
| **FWH5** | $7.50 Snow Geese | 1989 | 20.00 | 10.00 | 20.00 | 325.00 | 85.00 | 75.00 |
| **FWH6** | $7.50 Wood Ducks | 1990 | 25.00 | 15.00 | 20.00 | 375.00 | 100.00 | 70.00 |
| **FWH7** | $8.50 Black Duck | 1991 | 30.00 | – | 20.00 | 400.00 | 100.00 | 70.00 |
| **FWH8** | $8.50 Eider Duck | 1992 | 30.00 | – | 20.00 | 375.00 | 100.00 | 60.00 |
| **FWH9** | $8.50 Hooded Merganser | 1993 | 20.00 | – | 20.00 | 325.00 | 85.00 | 60.00 |
| **FWH10** | $8.50 Ross' Geese | 1994 | 25.00 | – | 20.00 | 375.00 | 100.00 | 60.00 |
| **FWH11** | $8.50 Redheads | 1995 | 20.00 | – | 20.00 | 325.00 | 85.00 | 60.00 |
| **FWH12** | $8.50 Goldeneyes | 1996 | 25.00 | – | 20.00 | 400.00 | 115.00 | 60.00 |
| **FWH13** | $8.50 Gadwalls | 1997 | 50.00 | – | 25.00 | 800.00 | 225.00 | 60.00 |
| **FWH14** | $8.50 Ringnecked Ducks | 1998 | 50.00 | – | 25.00 | 800.00 | 225.00 | 60.00 |
| **FWH15** | $8.50 Bufflehead Ducks | 1999 | 25.00 | – | 25.00 | 400.00 | 115.00 | 60.00 |
| **FWH16** | $8.50 Sandhill Cranes | 2000 | 30.00 | – | 25.00 | 480.00 | 135.00 | 60.00 |

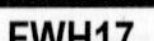
FWH17

FWH18

FWH19

FWH20

FWH21

FWH22

FWH23

FWH24

FWH26

FWH25

FWH27

FWH28

FWH29

| | | | Unused † | Used | On license ...a | Sheet of 16 ...b | Plate Block (4) ...c | Artist Signed ...d |
|---|---|---|---|---|---|---|---|---|
| **FWH17** | $8.50 Harlequin Duck | 2001 | 50.00 | – | 25.00 | 800.00 | 225.00 | 60.00 |
| **FWH18** | $8.50 King Eider Duck | 2002 | 45.00 | – | 25.00 | 720.00 | 200.00 | 60.00 |
| **FWH19** | $8.50 Northern Shovelers | 2003 | 40.00 | – | 25.00 | 640.00 | 180.00 | 60.00 |
| **FWH20** | $8.50 Mallards | 2004 | 35.00 | – | 25.00 | 560.00 | 160.00 | 60.00 |
| **FWH21** | $8.50 Harlequin Ducks | 2005 | 50.00 | – | 25.00 | 800.00 | 225.00 | 60.00 |
| **FWH22** | $8.50 Brant Goose | 2006 | 50.00 | – | 25.00 | 800.00 | 225.00 | 60.00 |
| **FWH23** | $8.50 Wilson's Snipe | 2007 | 30.00 | – | 25.00 | 480.00 | 135.00 | 60.00 |
| **FWH24** | $8.50 Ruddy Ducks | 2008 | 30.00 | – | 25.00 | 480.00 | 135.00 | 60.00 |
| **FWH25** | $8.50 Lesser Scaup | 2009 | 35.00 | – | 25.00 | 560.00 | 180.00 | 100.00 |
| **FWH26** | $25.00 souvenir sheet | 2009 | 70.00 | – | – | – | – | – |
| **FWH27** | $8.50 Green-winged Teal | 2010 | 25.00 | – | 25.00 | 400.00 | 115.00 | 50.00 |
| **FWH28** | $8.50 American Wigeon | 2011 | 25.00 | – | 25.00 | 400.00 | 115.00 | 50.00 |
| **FWH29** | $8.50 Blue-winged Teal | 2012 | 20.00 | – | 25.00 | 325.00 | 85.00 | 50.00 |

*The Canadian Revenue Stamp Catalogue,*
E.S.J. van Dam, 2017.

FWH30

FWH31

FWH32

FWH33

FWH34

FWH35

| | | | Unused † | Used | On license ...a | Sheet of 16 ...b | Plate Block (4) ...c | Artist Signed ...d |
|---|---|---|---|---|---|---|---|---|
| **FWH30** | $8.50 Long-tailed Duck | 2013 | 20.00 | – | 25.00 | 325.00 | 85.00 | 40.00 |
| **FWH31** | $8.50 Cinnamon Teal | 2014 | 20.00 | – | 25.00 | 325.00 | 85.00 | 35.00 |
| **FWH32** | $8.50 Mourning Doves | 2015 | 20.00 | – | 25.00 | 325.00 | 85.00 | 30.00 |
| **FWH33** | $8.50 Surf Scoters | 2016 | 20.00 | – | 25.00 | 325.00 | 85.00 | 30.00 |
| **FWH34** | $8.50 Canada Geese | 2017 | 20.00 | – | 25.00 | 325.00 | 85.00 | 30.00 |
| **FWH35** | $8.50 Wood Duck | 2018 | 20.00 | – | 25.00 | 325.00 | 85.00 | 30.00 |

## QUEBEC WILDLIFE HABITAT CONSERVATION

The Quebec Minister of Fish and Game has authorized the Quebec Wildlife Foundation to raise revenue for the conservation of wildlife habitat in Quebec by issuing the first in an annual series of Wildlife conservation Stamps. These stamps must be affixed to permits of outfitters or provincial park authorities to validate the annual licence fee.

QW1 / DQ-1

QW2 / DQ-3

QW3 / DQ-5

QW4 / DQ-7

QW5 / DQ-9

| Van Dam | FFQ | | Year | Booklet | Sheet (4) | Imperforate | | | FDC | |
|---|---|---|---|---|---|---|---|---|---|---|
| | | | | | | Block of 4 | Single | Qty | | Qty |
| **QW1** | **DQ-1** | Ruffed Grouse | 1988 | $ 90.00 | $ 300.00 | $ 2,250.00 | — | 100 | $ 500.00 | 96 |
| **QW2** | **DQ-3** | Black Ducks | 1989 | 25.00 | 100.00 | 500.00 | — | 150 | 150.00 | 200 |
| **QW3** | **DQ-5** | Common Loons | 1990 | 25.00 | 75.00 | 500.00 | — | 150 | 125.00 | 200 |
| **QW4** | **DQ-7** | Common Goldeneyes | 1991 | 25.00 | 75.00 | 500.00 | — | 175 | 125.00 | 200 |
| **QW5** | **DQ-9** | Lynx | 1992 | 20.00 | 65.00 | 650.00 | — | 200 | 125.00 | 200 |
| **QW5s** | **DQ-9b** | "Canada 92 + $3.50" overprint | | 30.00 | 650.00 | — | — | — | 150.00 | 200 |

*Add $5 for artist signed single*

QW6 / DQ-11

QW7 / DQ-13

QW8 / DQ-15

QW9 / DQ-17

QW10 / DQ-22

QW11 / DQ-25

QW12 / DQ-28

QW13A / DQ-31

QW14 / DQ-34

QW15 / DQ-37

QW16A / DQ-40

QW17 / DQ-43

QW18 / DQ-46

QW19 / DQ-49

| Van Dam | FFQ | | Year | Booklet | Sheet (4) | Imperforate | | | FDC | |
|---|---|---|---|---|---|---|---|---|---|---|
| | | | | | | Block of 4 | Single | Qty | | Qty |
| **QW6** | **DQ-11** | Peregrine Falcon | 1993 | 20.00 | 65.00 | 500.00 | — | 275 | 110.00 | 200 |
| **QW7** | **DQ-13** | Belugas | 1994 | 25.00 | 60.00 | 375.00 | — | 300 | 80.00 | 325 |
| **QW8** | **DQ-15** | Moose | 1995 | 20.00 | 60.00 | 300.00 | — | 300 | 110.00 | 325 |
| **QW9** | **DQ-17** | Great Blue Heron | 1996 | 30.00 | 75.00 | 300.00 | — | 325 | 80.00 | 325 |
| **QW9A** | **DQ-19** | "WWF + $2.50" surcharge | | 25.00 | — | — | 100.00 | 500 | 100.00 | 250 |
| **QW9B** | **DQ-20** | Capex 1996 show surcharge | | 25.00 | 100.00 | — | — | — | 100.00 | |
| **QW10** | **DQ-22** | Snowy Owl | 1997 | 25.00 | 100.00 | 150.00 | — | 325 | 75.00 | 325 |
| **QW10A** | **DQ-24** | "WWF + $2.50" surcharge | | 35.00 | — | — | 100.00 | 500 | 95.00 | 250 |
| **QW11** | **DQ-25** | Snow Goose | 1998 | 100.00 | 175.00 | 500.00 | — | 300 | 125.00 | 325 |
| **QW11A** | **DQ-27** | "WWF + $2.50" surcharge | | 100.00 | — | — | 250.00 | 500 | 150.00 | 250 |
| **QW12** | **DQ-28** | River Otter | 1999 | 60.00 | 65.00 | 150.00 | — | 300 | 75.00 | 325 |
| **QW12A** | **DQ-30** | "WWF + $2.50" surcharge | | 75.00 | — | — | 100.00 | 500 | 80.00 | 250 |
| **QW13** | **DQ-31** | Atlantic Puffin and Wood Turtle (2) | 2000 | 50.00 | 65.00 | 150.00 | — | 300 | 75.00 | 325 |
| **QW13A** | **DQ-33** | "WWF + $2.50" surcharge | | 50.00 | — | — | 150.00 | 500 | 75.00 | 250 |
| **QW14** | **DQ-34** | Blue Jay | 2001 | 25.00 | 65.00 | 150.00 | — | 300 | 75.00 | 325 |
| **QW14A** | **DQ-36** | "WWF + $2.50" surcharge | | 45.00 | — | — | 55.00 | 500 | 75.00 | 250 |
| **QW15** | **DQ-37** | Caribous | 2002 | 50.00 | 65.00 | 150.00 | — | 325 | 50.00 | 350 |
| **QW15A** | **DQ-39** | "WWF + $2.50" surcharge | | 75.00 | — | — | 100.00 | 500 | 75.00 | 400 |
| **QW16** | **DQ-40** | Arctic Fox | 2003 | 50.00 | 65.00 | 150.00 | — | 325 | 50.00 | 350 |
| **QW16A** | **DQ-42** | "WWF + $2.50" surcharge | | 50.00 | — | — | 100.00 | 500 | 75.00 | 400 |
| **QW17** | **DQ-43** | Musk Oxen | 2004 | 25.00 | 60.00 | 150.00 | — | 325 | 50.00 | 350 |
| **QW17A** | **DQ-45** | "WWF + $2.50" surcharge | | 45.00 | — | — | 50.00 | 500 | 75.00 | 400 |
| **QW18** | **DQ-46** | Hare | 2005 | 20.00 | 60.00 | 150.00 | — | 325 | 50.00 | 350 |
| **QW18A** | **DQ-48** | "WWF + $2.50" surcharge | | 25.00 | — | — | 50.00 | 500 | 75.00 | 400 |
| **QW19** | **DQ-49** | Western Chorus Frog | 2006 | 20.00 | 60.00 | 150.00 | — | 325 | 50.00 | 350 |
| **QW19A** | **DQ-51** | "WWF + $2.50" surcharge | | 25.00 | — | — | 50.00 | 500 | 75.00 | 400 |

QW20 / DQ-52 QW21 / DQ-56 QW22 / DQ-59 QW23 / DQ-62 QW24 / DQ-65

QW25 / DQ-68 QW26 / DQ-72 QW27 / DQ-75 QW28 / DQ-78 QW29 / DQ-81

QW30 / DQ-84

QW31 / DQ-87

| Van Dam | FFQ | | Year | Booklet | Sheet (4) | Imperforate | | | FDC | |
|---|---|---|---|---|---|---|---|---|---|---|
| | | | | | | Block of 4 | Single | Qty | | Qty |
| **QW20** | **DQ-52** | Loggerhead Shrike | | 20.00 | 60.00 | 150.00 | — | 325 | 50.00 | 350 |
| **QW20A** | **DQ-55** | "WWF + $2.50" surcharge | 2007 | 25.00 | — | — | 50.00 | 500 | 75.00 | 400 |
| | **DQ-54** | 20th anniversary | | — | — | — | 100.00 | 350 | | |
| **QW21** | **DQ-56** | Polar Bears | 2008 | 50.00 | 60.00 | 150.00 | — | 300 | 50.00 | 350 |
| **QW21A** | **DQ-58** | "WWF + $2.50" surcharge | | 25.00 | — | — | 50.00 | 500 | 75.00 | 400 |
| **QW22** | **DQ-59** | Snow Geese | 2009 | 20.00 | 60.00 | 150.00 | — | 300 | 50.00 | 350 |
| **QW22A** | **DQ-61** | "WWF + $2.50" surcharge | | 25.00 | — | — | 50.00 | 500 | 75.00 | 400 |
| **QW23** | **DQ-62** | Cerulean Warbler | 2010 | 20.00 | 60.00 | 150.00 | — | 300 | 50.00 | 300 |
| **QW23A** | **DQ-64** | "WWF + $2.50" surcharge | | 25.00 | — | — | 50.00 | 500 | 75.00 | 300 |
| **QW24** | **DQ-65** | Red-headed Woodpecker | 2011 | 20.00 | 60.00 | 150.00 | — | 300 | 50.00 | 300 |
| **QW24A** | **DQ-67** | "WWF + $2.50" surcharge | | 25.00 | — | — | 50.00 | 500 | 75.00 | 300 |
| **QW25** | **DQ-68** | White-tailed deer | | 20.00 | 60.00 | 150.00 | — | 300 | 50.00 | 300 |
| **QW25A** | **DQ-71** | "WWF + $2.50" surcharge | 2012 | 25.00 | — | — | 50.00 | 300 | 75.00 | 300 |
| | **DQ-70** | 25th anniversary | | — | — | — | 100.00 | 300 | | |
| **QW26** | **DQ-72** | Pine Marten | 2013 | 20.00 | 60.00 | 150.00 | — | 300 | 50.00 | 300 |
| **QW26A** | **DQ-74** | "WWF + $2.50" surcharge | | 25.00 | — | — | 50.00 | 300 | 75.00 | 300 |
| **QW27** | **DQ-75** | American Woodcock | 2014 | 20.00 | 60.00 | 150.00 | — | 300 | 50.00 | 300 |
| **QW27A** | **DQ-77** | "WWF + $2.50" surcharge | | 25.00 | — | — | 50.00 | 300 | 75.00 | 300 |
| **QW28** | **DQ-78** | Northern Harrier | 2015 | 20.00 | 60.00 | 150.00 | — | 300 | 50.00 | 300 |
| **QW28A** | **DQ-80** | "WWF + $2.50" surcharge | | 25.00 | — | — | 50.00 | 300 | 75.00 | 300 |
| **QW29** | **DQ-81** | Grey Wolf | 2016 | 20.00 | 60.00 | 150.00 | — | 300 | 50.00 | 300 |
| **QW29A** | **DQ-83** | "WWF + $2.50" surcharge | | 25.00 | — | — | 50.00 | 300 | 75.00 | 300 |
| **QW30** | **DQ-84** | Black Bears | | 20.00 | 60.00 | 150.00 | — | 300 | 50.00 | 300 |
| **QW30A** | **DQ-86** | "WWF + $2.50" surcharge | 2017 | 25.00 | — | — | 50.00 | 300 | 75.00 | 300 |
| | **DQ-86FS** | 30th anniversary | | — | — | — | 100.00 | 300 | — | — |
| **QW31** | **DQ-87** | Brook Trout | 2018 | 20.00 | 60.00 | 150.00 | — | 300 | 50.00 | 300 |
| **QW31A** | **DQ-89** | "WWF + $2.50" surcharge | | 25.00 | — | — | 50.00 | 300 | 75.00 | 300 |

# FOUR-RING NUMERAL CANCELS

## RARITY FACTORS FOR USAGE ON THE 1859 ISSUES

**Rarity Scale**

| | |
|---|---|
| RF 1 | Common |
| RF 2 to 3 | Scarce |
| RF 4 to 5 | Very Scarce |
| RF 6 to 7 | Rare |
| RF 8 to 9 | Very Rare |
| RF 10 | Extremely Rare |

| NO. | TOWN | RF | NOTES |
|---|---|---|---|
| 1 | Barrie, U.C. | 7 | Generally struck faintly |
| 2 | Belleville, U.C. | 4 | RF7 on cover |
| | blue strike | 3 | RF6 on cover |
| 3 | Berlin, C.W. | 5 | Now Kitchener, Ont. |
| 4 | Bowmanville, U.C. | 6 | |
| 5 | Brantford, U.C. | 3 | |
| | blue Strike | 7 | Common in "Pence" period |
| 6 | Not used | | To avoid confusion with "No. 9" |
| 7 | Collingwood, U.C. | 4 | Always struck faintly |
| 8 | Chatham, U.C. | 4 | |
| 9 | Not used | | To avoid confusion with "No. 6" |
| 10 | Cobourg, U.C. | 5 | |
| 11 | Cornwall, C.W. | 2 | |
| 12 | Dundas, U.C. | 8 | Generally struck faintly |
| 13 | Galt, U.C. | 7 | Two types known |
| 14 | Goderich, U.C. | 7 | Generally struck faintly |
| 15 | Guelph, U.C. | 8 | |
| 16 | Hamilton, U.C. | 10 | Hammer lost in 1858, now known on "1859s" |
| 17 | Ingersoll, C.W. | 4 | |
| 18 | Kingston, C.W. | 2 | |
| 19 | London, U.C. | 4 | |
| | blue strike | 10 | Only 2 strikes known |
| 20 | Melbourne, L.C. | 6 | RF8 on cover |
| 21 | Montreal, L.C. | 1 | Three types known |
| 22 | Napanee, U.C. | 4 | |
| | green strike | 8 | |
| 23 | Niagara, U.C. | 4 | |
| 24 | Oakville, C.W. | 4 | |
| 25 | Oshawa, U.C. | 5 | |
| | red strike | 7 | Always struck faintly |
| 26 | Owen Sound, U.C. | 6 | Generally struck faintly |
| 27 | Ottawa, U.C. | 2 | Two types known |
| 28 | Paris, C.W. | 4 | |
| 29 | Perth, U.C. | 4 | |
| 30 | Peterboro, C.W. | 2 | RF5 on cover |
| 31 | Picton, U.C. | 4 | |
| | green strike | 6 | |
| 32 | Port Dover, U.C. | 7 | |
| 33 | Port Hope, U.C. | 7 | |
| 34 | Sarnia, C.W. | 3 | Two types, early strikes are "Port Sarnia" |
| | blue strike | 10 | Only 1 strike known |
| 35 | Prescott, U.C. | 5 | |
| 36 | Preston, C.W. | 8 | |
| 37 | Quebec, L.C. | 3 | Two types known |
| 38 | St. Catharines, U.C. | 8 | |
| 39 | St. Johns, C.E. | 5 | Previously misidentified as "St. Hyacinthe" |
| 40 | St. Thomas, U.C. | 5 | |
| 41 | Sandwich, U.C. | 8 | Generally struck faintly |
| 42 | Sherbrooke, L.C. | 4 | |
| 43 | Simcoe, U.C. | 9 | |
| 44 | Smith's Falls, U.C. | 7 | Always struck faintly |
| | dark blue strike | 8 | Always struck faintly |
| 45 | Stanstead, L.C. | 6 | |
| | blue strike | 6 | |
| 46 | Stratford, U.C. | 8 | |
| 47 | Three Rivers, C.E. | 4 | |
| 48 | Thorold, U.C. | 10 | Only 1 strike known |
| 49 | Whitby, C.W. | 5 | |
| | blue strike | 3 | |
| 50 | Windsor, C.W. | 4 | Generally struck faintly |
| 51 | Brockville, C.W. | 3 | RF5 on cover. Replaces No. 6 |
| 52 | Clifton, C.W. | 5 | Replaces No. 9 |
| 516 | Montreal, L.C. | 7 | RF10 on 5¢ "Beaver" (none known) |
| 627 | Ottawa, C.W. | 9 | Used late 1859 period. (Legislative Senate |

# TWO-RING NUMERAL CANCELS

## RARITY FACTORS (RF) FOR USAGE ON LARGE QUEENS (LQ) AND SMALL QUEENS (SQ)

**Rarity Scale**

| | |
|---|---|
| RF 1 | Common |
| RF 2 to 3 | Scarce |
| RF 4 to 5 | Very Scarce |
| RF 6 to 7 | Rare |
| RF 8 to 9 | Very Rare |
| RF 10 | Extremely Rare |

| NO. | CITY/TOWN | LQ PERIOD | SQ PERIOD | COMMENTS |
|---|---|---|---|---|
| 1 | Montreal | 2 | 3 | Two blue strikes known |
| 2 | Toronto | 2 | 8 | Very rare in S.Q. period |
| 3 | Quebec | 1 | 1 | Known in red in mid-1870s |
| 4 | Halifax | 3 | 7 | S.Q. covers are RF9 |
| 4 | Watsons Corners | — | 8 | Larger than "Halifax 4" |
| 5 | Hamilton | 1 | 2 | Known in red, RF10 |
| 6 | London | 1 | 4 | Cut-out portion below "6" |
| 7 | St. John | 1 | 1 | Commonest of all two-ring cancels |
| 8 | Ottawa | 5 | 10 | Only one cover known |
| 9 | Kingston | 3 | 10 | L.Q. covers are RF6 |
| 10 | Sydney | 3 | 3 | Known in blue, RF6 |

| NO. | CITY/TOWN | LQ PERIOD | SQ PERIOD | COMMENTS |
|---|---|---|---|---|
| 11 | Fredericton | 2 | 2 | Possibly two hammers used |
| 12 | St. Catharines | 2 | 2 | With "St. Catharines West" CDS, 1870s |
| 13 | Belleville | 1 | 2 | Known in blue on "L.Q.s", RF8 |
| 14 | Guelph | 2 | 4 | Used for over ten years |
| 15 | Brantford | 2 | 3 | Possibly exists in blue |
| 16 | Brockville | 8 | 7 | Most strikes are poor |
| 17 | Not Known | 10 | 8 | One L.Q. cover known |
| 18 | Yarmouth | 3 | 7 | Most strikes are poor |
| 19 | Peterborough | 10 | 8 | One L.Q. cover known |
| 20 | Not Identified | 10 | 10 | Estimated 3 strikes known |
| 21 | Goderich | 3 | 3 | L.Q. covers are RF6 |
| 22 | Galt | 9 | 7 | One undated L.Q. Circular known |
| 23 | Woodstock | 5 | 5 | (Ontario) |
| 24 | Stratford | 4 | 5 | Most strikes are poor |
| 25 | New Glasgow | 3 | 3 | Covers are RF4 |
| 26 | Windsor | 5 | 5 | (Ontario), see No. 43 |
| 27 | Ingersoll | 3 | 4 | Used until 1870, revived late 1875 |
| 28 | Sarnia | 5 | 4 | |
| 29 | Cobourg | 2 | 5 | Replaced by fancy corks, 1871 |
| 30 | Pictou | 7 | 5 | All strikes seen are faint |
| 31 | Oshawa | 7 | 8 | Most strikes are faint |
| 32 | Barrie | 5 | 7 | Blue strikes on "L.Q.s" RF3 |
| 33 | Sherbrooke | 6 | 7 | Known in blue, RF10 |
| 34 | Chatham | 8 | 8 | L.Q. covers are rare |
| 35 | Lindsay | 2 | 4 | Replaced by fancy leafs, 1870s |
| 36 | St. Johns | 6 | 5 | L.Q. covers rare, RF8 |
| 37 | Amherst | 8 | 5 | Many strikes illegible |
| 38 | Bowmanville | 6 | 3 | L.Q. covers are RF8 |
| 39 | Whitby | 6 | 8 | Two hammers, slim & wide numbers |
| 40 | Cornwall | 7 | 2 | Over 60 years usage, two provinces |
| 40 | St. Regis | — | — | Used at Quebec Indian Reserve, 1930s |
| 41 | St. Marys | 3 | 1 | Used for over 30 years |
| 42 | Acton Vale | 9 | 8 | Any cover, RF10 |
| 43 | Windsor | 4 | 3 | (Nova Scotia), see No. 26 |
| 44 | Owen Sound | 4 | 5 | Many strikes are faint |
| 45 | Perth | 5 | 3 | Many strikes are faint |
| 46 | Dundas | 5 | 3 | Many strikes on 6¢ L.Q. |
| 47 | Napanee | 4 | 4 | Any cover, RF6 |
| 48 | Simcoe | 6 | 5 | Any cover, RF8 |
| 49 | Prescott | 5 | 5 | Any cover, RF7 |
| 50 | St. Andrews | 10 | 4 | Extremely rare on any "L.Q." |
| 51 | Picton | 4 | 7 | S.Q. covers, RF9 |
| 52 | St. Hyacinthe | 4 | 3 | Known in red, RF10 |
| 53 | Three Rivers | 5 | 4 | S.Q. strikes mostly on early shades |
| 54 | Truro | 3 | 5 | Many strikes are faint |
| 55 | Berlin | 5 | 4 | L.Q. covers, RF7 |
| 56 | Brampton | 6 | 3 | L.Q. covers, RF8 |
| 57 | Paris | 6 | 8 | Cork or wood strikes known |
| 58 | St. Thomas | 7 | 3 | Blue strikes known in 1873 |
| 59 | Clinton | 7 | 4 | Any cover, RF8 |
| 60 | Newmarket | 5 | 10 | Extremely rare on any "S.Q." |

## SQUARED CIRCLE POSTMARKS

It is not within the scope of this catalogue to go much beyond an introductory listing of the Squared Circle Postmarks of Canada and their rarity factors. For a much more detailed listing and analysis of hammer types, please refer to Hansen and Moffatt, *The Squared Circle Postmarks of Canada* (1981) and *The Squared Circle Cancellations of Canada* (2001), edited by John S. Gordon.

Type A

Type B

**RARITY FACTORS (RF)**

| RF | STRIKES |
|---|---|
| 1 | 850 plus |
| 2 | 235–849 |
| 3 | 112–234 |
| 4 | 77–111 |
| 5 | 56–76 |
| 6 | 34–55 |
| 7 | 21–33 |
| 8 | 11–20 |
| 9 | 6–10 |
| 10 | 0–5 |

**PRECURSORS**

| Post Office or Hammer | RF |
|---|---|
| Ottawa 1880–1881 (Type A)* | 5 |
| Halifax | 2 |
| Hamilton | 2 |
| London | 2 |
| Montreal I | 7 |
| Montreal II | 4 |
| Montreal III | 5 |
| Montreal IV | 6 |
| Montreal V | 8 |
| Ottawa | 2 |
| St. John N.B. | 2 |
| Seaforth | 4 |
| Toronto | 1 |
| Winnipeg | 2 |
| St. John's, NFLD. | 4 |

*All other are Type B

*The Squared Circle Postmarks of Canada*, Dr. W.G. Moffatt and Glenn Hansen, 1981.

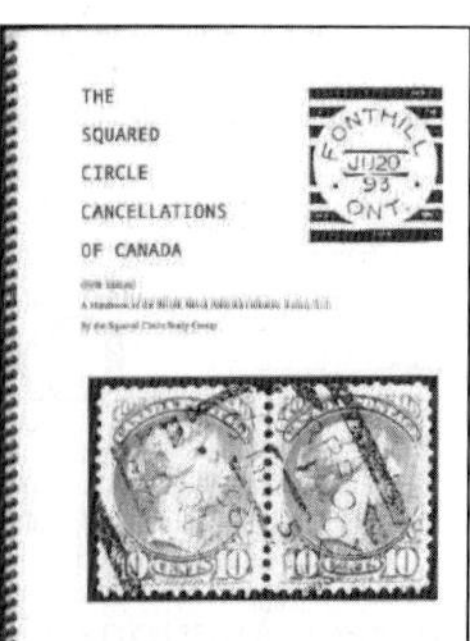

*The Squared Circle Cancellations of Canada*, Fifth Edition. John S. Gordon (Editor), 2001.

## SQUARED CIRCLE CANCELS

Type I

Type II

| Post Office or Hammer | RF |
|---|---|
| **TYPE I** | |
| Aldergrove, B.C. | 6 |
| Beaverton, Ont. | 2 |
| Beeton, Ont. | 6 |
| Brockville, Ont | 1 |
| Byng Inlet North, Ont. | 8 |
| Coleman, Ont | 10 |
| Cumberland, Ont. | 3 |
| Dutton, Ont. | 2 |
| Grimsby, Ont. | 1 |
| London, Ont. State 1 | 1 |
| London, Ont. State 2 | 1 |
| London, East, Ont. | 1 |
| Masonville, Que. | 3 |
| Montreal, Canada* | 10 |
| Mount Forest, Ont. | 1 |
| New Germany, Ont. | 5 |
| Ottawa, Canada | 2 |
| Point St. Charles, Que. | 3 |
| Rat Portage, Ont. | 2 |
| St. Ann's, Ont. | 4 |
| St. Hilarion, Que. | 7 |
| Shannonville, Que. | 3 |
| Springhill Mines, N.S. | 8 |
| Terrebonne, Que. | 2 |
| Three Rivers, Que. | 1 |
| Westville, N.S. | 2 |
| **MARITIMES TYPE II** | |
| Annapolis, N.S. | 1 |
| Antigonish, N.S. | 2 |
| Arichat, N.S. | 3 |
| Baddock, N.S. | 3 |
| Canning, N.S. | 2 |
| Canso, N.S. | 3 |
| Freeport,N.S. | 6 |
| Great Village,N.S. | 5 |
| Halifax, N.S. I (Canada) | 1 |
| Halifax, N.S. II (Canada) | 1 |
| Kentville, N.S. | 2 |
| Lunenberg, N.S. | 2 |
| Maccan, N.S. | 3 |
| Maitland, N.S. | 9 |
| Newport, N.S. | 3 |
| Newport Landing, N.S. | 3 |
| Noel, N.S. | 8 |
| Northport, N.S. | 3 |
| North Sydney, N.S. | 2 |
| Pictou, N.S. | 1 |
| Port Maitland, N.S. | 3 |
| Port Williams, N.S. | 2 |
| Springhill, N.S. | 2 |
| Stellarton, N.S. | 2 |
| Sydney, N.S. I | 2 |
| Sydney, N.S. II* | 10 |
| Truro, N.S. | 1 |
| Whycocmagh, N.S. | 3 |

| Post Office or Hammer | RF |
|---|---|
| Windsor, N.S. | 1 |
| Wolfville, N.S. | 4 |
| Yarmouth, N.S. | 1 |
| Baie Verte, N.B. | 3 |
| Butternut Ridge, N.B. | 4 |
| Clifton, N.B. | 6 |
| Fredericton, N.B. | 1 |
| Indiantown, N.B. | 2 |
| Milltown, N.B. | 3 |
| Newcastle Creek, N.B. | 6 |
| Petitcodiac, N.B. | 3 |
| River Louison, N.B. | 3 |
| Rothesay, N.B. | 3 |
| Sackville, N.B. | 2 |
| St. John, N.B. Canada I | 1 |
| St. John, N.B. Canada II | 1 |
| St. John, N.B. Canada III | 1 |
| Shediac, N.B. | 2 |
| Woodstock, N.B. | 2 |
| Charlottetown, P.E.I. | 1 |
| Georgetown, P.E.I. | 2 |
| Summerside, P.E.I. | 2 |
| **QUEBEC TYPE II** | |
| Acton Vale, Que. | 3 |
| Aylmer (East), Que. | 2 |
| Belle Rive, Montreal | 3 |
| Clarenceville, Que. | 3 |
| Danville, Que. | 2 |
| Eastman, Que. | 3 |
| Farnham, Que. | 2 |
| Granby, Que | 2 |
| Hochelaga, Que. (Montreal) | 4 |
| Hull, Que. I | 2 |
| Hull, Que. II | 1 |
| Iberville, Que. | 2 |
| Laurentides, Que. | 2 |
| Lennoxville, Que. | 6 |
| Levis, Que. | 2 |
| Lotbiniere, Que. | 3 |
| Magog, Que. | 2 |
| Matane, Que. | 8 |
| Melbourne, Que. | 3 |
| Montreal, Que. I | 2 |
| Montreal, Que. II | 10 |
| Notre Dame St. West, Montreal | 5 |
| Point-a-Pic, Que. | 8 |
| Quebec, Que. (Canada) | 1 |
| Richmond, Que. | 6 |
| Riviere du Loup Station, Que. | 2 |
| Ste. Anne de Beaupre, Que. | 3 |
| Ste. Cunegonde, Que. (Montreal) | 1 |
| St. Gabriel de Montreal, Que. | 10 |
| St. Gregoire, Que. | 3 |
| St. Hyacinthe, Que. | 1 |
| St. Johns, Que.* | 10 |

| Post Office or Hammer | RF |
|---|---|
| St. Polycarpe, Que. | 4 |
| Sherbrooke, Que. I | 1 |
| Sherbrooke, Que. II | 10 |
| Stanstead, Que. | 6 |
| Sutton, Que. | 6 |
| Victoriaville, Que. | 2 |
| Waterloo, Que. | 2 |
| Windsor Mills, Que. | 4 |
| **ONTARIO TYPE II** | |
| Acton, Ont. I | 9 |
| Acton, Ont. II | 2 |
| Alma, Ont. State 1 | 9 |
| Alma, Ont. State 2 | 3 |
| Almonte, Ont. | 1 |
| Angus, Ont. | 4 |
| Arnprior, Ont. | 1 |
| Athens, Ont. | 2 |
| Aurora, Ont. | 2 |
| Aylmer West, Ont. | 2 |
| Beamsville, Ont. | 2 |
| Belleville, Ont. I | 2 |
| Belleville, Ont. II | 1 |
| Belleville, Ont III | 1 |
| Berlin, Ont. | 3 |
| Bleecker St. Toronto | 2 |
| Bleeker St. Toronto | 5 |
| Blue Vale, Ont. | 6 |
| Byth, Ont. | 8 |
| Bobcaygeon, Ont. State 1 | 1 |
| Bobcaygeon, Ont. State 2 | 7 |
| Bowmanville, Ont. | 3 |
| Bracebridge, Ont. | 2 |
| Brampton, Ont. | 2 |
| Brantford, Ont. | 1 |
| Burford, Ont. | 2 |
| Cache Bay, Ont. | 5 |
| Cardinal, Ont. | 2 |
| Cheltenham, Ont. | 3 |
| Chesley, Ont. | 3 |
| Chesterville, Ont. | 2 |
| Cobden, Ont. | 2 |
| Cobourg, Ont. | 2 |
| Comber, Ont. | 4 |
| Cornwall, Ont. | 1 |
| Dundas, Ont. | 1 |
| Dunnville, Ont. | 1 |
| Durham, Ont. | 3 |
| Flesherton, Ont. | 2 |
| Fonthill, Ont. | 10 |
| Forest, Ont. | 7 |
| Formosa, Ont. I* | 10 |
| Formosa, Ont. II State 1 | 10 |
| Formosa, Ont II State 2 | 10 |
| Fort William West, Ont. | 7 |
| Galt, Ont. | 2 |

| Post Office or Hammer | RF |
|---|---|
| Georgetown, Ont. | 1 |
| Glammis, Ont. | 3 |
| Glencoe, Ont. | 2 |
| Goderich, Ont. | 1 |
| Gore Bay, Ont. | 2 |
| Grafton, Ont. | 3 |
| Gravenhurst, Ont. | 2 |
| Guelph, Ont. | 1 |
| Hagersville, Ont. | 2 |
| Hamilton, Ont. (Canada) | 1 |
| Harriston, Ont. | 2 |
| Hawkesbury, Ont. | 3 |
| Humberstone, Ont. | 3 |
| Huntsville, Ont. | 2 |
| Ingersoll, Ont. | 1 |
| International Bridge, Ont. | 4 |
| Iroquois, Ont. | 2 |
| Kincardine, Ont. | 3 |
| Kingston, Ont. I (Canada) | 2 |
| Kingston, Ont. II (Canada) | 1 |
| Kingston, Ont. III (Canada) | 10 |
| Kingsville, Ont. | 10 |
| Lakefield, Ont. | 2 |
| Lambton Mills, Ont. | 8 |
| Lanark, Ont. | 2 |
| Leamington, Ont. | 1 |
| Lindsay, Ont. | 1 |
| Listowel, Ont. | 2 |
| Little Current, Ont. | 2 |
| London, Ont. | 1 |
| L'Orignal, Ont. | 2 |
| Lucknow, Ont. | 2 |
| Manitowaning, Ont. | 2 |
| Markdale, Ont. I | 4 |
| Markdale, Ont. II | 6 |
| Markdale, Ont. III | 2 |
| Marmora, Ont. | 2 |
| Martintown, Ont. | 3 |
| Mattawa, Ont. | 2 |
| Merrickville, Ont. | 2 |
| Merritton, Ont. | 2 |
| Mill Brook, Ont. | 6 |
| Milton West, Ont. | 2 |
| Mitchell, Ont. | 2 |
| Mount Brydges, Ont. | 1 |
| Nassagaweya, Ont. | 8 |
| Newmarket, Ont. | 2 |
| Niagara, Ont. | 2 |
| Niagara Falls South, Ont. | 2 |
| North Bay, Ont. | 1 |
| Orangeville, Ont. | 4 |
| Orillia, Ont. | 2 |
| Oshawa, Ont. | 2 |
| Owen Sound, Ont. | 1 |
| Oxford Mills, Ont. | 3 |
| Paisley, Ont. | 2 |
| Palmerston, Ont. | 10 |
| Paris, Ont. | 1 |
| Paris Station, Ont. | 2 |
| Parliament Street, Toronto | 6 |
| Pembroke, Ont. | 2 |
| Perth, Ont. | 1 |
| Peterborough, Ont. | 1 |
| Petrolia, Ont. | 1 |
| Picton, Ont. | 1 |
| Ponypool, Ont. | 8 |
| Port Arthur, Ont. | 1 |
| Port Dover, Ont. | 5 |

| Post Office or Hammer | RF |
|---|---|
| Port Hope, Ont. | 1 |
| Port Perry, Ont. | 2 |
| Powassan, Ont. | 2 |
| Prescott, Ont. | 1 |
| Queen St. East, Toronto | 2 |
| Ripley, Ont. | 3 |
| Rockton, Ont. | 3 |
| Rodney 2 | |
| Roseneath, Ont. | 3 |
| Rosseau, Ont. | 4 |
| St. Thomas, Ont. | 1 |
| Sarnia, Ont. | 1 |
| Sault Ste. Marie, Ont. | 1 |
| Screiber, Ont. State 1 | 4 |
| Screiber, Ont. State 2 | 3 |
| Seely's Bay, Ont. | 3 |
| Shakespeare, Ont. | 2 |
| Simcoe, Ont. | 7 |
| Smiths Falls, Ont. | 1 |
| Spadina Ave., Toronto | 2 |
| Stirling, Ont. | 2 |
| Stouffville, Ont. | 2 |
| Strachan Avenue, Toronto | 2 |
| Strathroy, Ont. | 2 |
| Sudbury, Ont. | 2 |
| Sutton West, Ont. | 2 |
| Tara, Ont. | 2 |
| Tavistock, Ont. | 2 |
| Teeswater, Ont. | 3 |
| Thamesford, Ont. | 2 |
| Thornbury, Ont. | 2 |
| Thornhill, Ont. | 3 |
| Tillsonburg, Ont. | 1 |
| Toronto, Ont. (Canada) | 1 |
| Vienna, Ont. | 3 |
| Wallaceburg, Ont. | 2 |
| Warkworth, Ont. | 2 |
| Waterdown, Ont. | 9 |
| Waterford, Ont. | 2 |
| Waterloo, Ont. | 1 |
| Watford, Ont. | 4 |
| Wellington, Ont. | 2 |
| Weston, Ont. | 3 |
| Whitby, Ont. | 2 |
| Wiarton, Ont. | 5 |
| Williamstown, Ont. | 2 |
| Windsor, Ont. | 1 |
| Wingham, Ont. State 1 | 8 |
| Wingham, Ont. State 2 | 1 |
| Winona, Ont. | 2 |
| Woodstock, Ont. | 2 |
| Woodville, Ont. | 3 |
| Wooler, Ont. | 3 |
| York Street, Toronto | 1 |

## WESTERN PROVINCES TYPE II

| Post Office or Hammer | RF |
|---|---|
| Birtle, Man. | 2 |
| Brandon, Man. | 1 |
| Deloraine, Man. | 2 |
| Elkhorn, Man. | 2 |
| Gretna, Man. | 3 |
| Hartney, Man. | 2 |
| McGregor Station, Man. | 2 |
| Manitou, Man. | 3 |
| Minnedosa, Man. | 2 |
| Morden, Man. | 2 |
| Neepawa, Man. | 1 |
| Pipestone, Man. | 4 |
| Portage La Prairie, Man. | 2 |
| St. Boniface, Man. | 3 |
| Selkirk, Man. | 2 |
| Souris, Man. | 3 |
| Winnipeg, Man. I | 1 |
| Winnipeg, Man. II | 1 |
| Winnipeg, Man. III (Canada) | 1 |
| Winnipeg, Man. IV | 7 |
| Estevan, Assa. | 6 |
| Grenfell, Assa. | 3 |
| Maple Creek, Assa. | 2 |
| Moose Jaw, Assa. | 2 |
| Regina, Assa. | 2 |
| Wolseley, Assa. I | 8 |
| Wolseley, Assa. II | 3 |
| Prince Albert, Sask. | 2 |
| Calgara, Alta. I | 1 |
| Calgary, Alta. II | 10 |
| Edmonton, Alta. | 2 |
| Innisfail, Alta. | 3 |
| Lethbridge, Alta. | 2 |
| MacLeod, Alta. | 2 |
| Medicine Hat, Alta. | 2 |
| Red Deer, Alta. | 2 |
| Ashcroft Station, B.C. | 7 |
| Donald, B.C. | 3 |
| Golden, B.C. | 4 |
| Kamloops, B.C. | 3 |
| Kaslo, B.C. | 2 |
| Mission City, B.C. | 9 |
| Nanaimo, B.C. State 1 | 2 |
| Nanaimo, B.C. State 2 | 1 |
| Revelstoke, B.C. | 10 |
| Rossland, B.C. | 5 |
| Sandon, B.C. | 4 |
| Union, B.C. | 3 |
| Vancouver, B.C. | 2 |
| Vernon, B.C. | 2 |
| Victoria, B.C. I | 1 |
| Victoria, B.C. II | 1 |
| Victoria, B.C. III | 1 |

## R.P.O.s TYPE II

| Post Office or Hammer | RF |
|---|---|
| Que. Camp. M.C. Local (No. 5) | 3 |
| Que. Camp M.C. Local State 1 (No. 20) | 5 |
| Que. Camp M.C. Local II State 2 | 4 |
| Que. Camp M.C. Local II State 3 | 5 |
| Que. Camp M.C. Local II State 4 | 6 |
| Que. Camp M.C. Local II State 5 | 6 |
| Que. Camp M.C. Local II State 6 | 3 |
| Napinka Winnipeg M.C. I | 2 |
| Napinka Winnipeg M.C. II | 3 |
| Souris Winnipeg M.C. I | 2 |
| Souris Winnipeg M.C. II | 2 |

## FOREIGN TYPE II

| Post Office or Hammer | RF |
|---|---|
| Honolulu, H'I. | 2 |

*Cancel only known in proof book at the National Postal Museum.

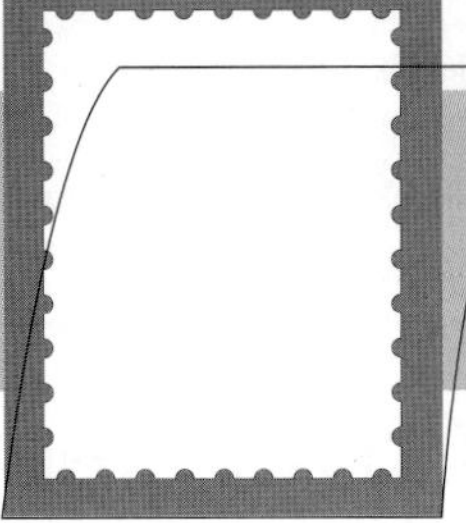

## (TOP OPENING)

A complete line of quality stamp mounts made solely for Unitrade.
Easy-to-Use UNI-SAFE mounts are available for all sizes of stamps.
Protect your stamps with UNI-SAFE "S" mounts.

| Size | | Pcs. | Reference No. Black | Clear | Price |
|---|---|---|---|---|---|
| 24 | CAN. U.S. G.B. HORIZ. COMM | 20 | S1024 | S2024 | |
| 26 | CAN. U.S. G.B. REG. COMM. | 20 | S1026 | S2026 | |
| 27 | U.S. U.N. FOREIGN | 20 | S1027 | S2027 | 8.50 |
| 29 | ISRAEL, SWITZ., FOREIGN | 20 | S1029 | S2029 | |
| 31 | CAN. U.S. JUMBO | 20 | S1031 | S2031 | |
| 33 | CAN. U.S. U.N. | 20 | S1033 | S2033 | |
| 36 | CAN. & FOREIGN | 20 | S1036 | S2036 | |
| 39 | U.N. & JUMBO | 20 | S1039 | S2039 | |
| 41 | CAN. U.S. VERT. COMM. | 20 | S1041 | S2041 | |
| 44 | CAN. REG. BLOCKS | 20 | S1044 | S2044 | 10.95 |
| 48 | CAN. BLOCKS | 20 | S1048 | S2048 | |
| 51 | U.S. JUMBO | 20 | S1051 | S2051 | |
| 55 | U.S. SMALL PLATE BLOCKS | 20 | S1055 | S2055 | |
| 57 | CAN. U.S. REG. PL. BL. | 10 | S1057 | S2057 | |
| 63 | CAN. HORIZ. COMM. | 10 | S1063 | S2063 | |
| 66 | CAN. ISRAEL JUMBO PL. BL. | 10 | S1066 | S2066 | |
| 70 | U.S. ISRAEL PL. BL. | 10 | S1070 | S2070 | |
| 78 | SOUV. SHEETS | 10 | S1078 | S2078 | |
| 84 | ISRAEL AND U.N. BLOCKS | 10 | S1084 | S2084 | |
| 86 | ISRAEL AND U.N. BLOCKS | 10 | S1086 | S2086 | 9.95 |
| 120 | BLOCKS | 7 | S1120 | S2120 | |
| 150 | BLOCKS | 5 | S1150 | S2150 | |
| 148/105 | BLOCKS & SOUV. SHEETS | 10 | S1148 | S2148 | |
| 160/120 | BLOCKS & SOUV. SHEETS | 10 | S1160 | S2160 | |
| 165/93 | F.D.C. | 10 | S1165 | S2165 | |
| 165/95 | F.D.C. | 10 | S1195 | S2195 | |
| 143/ 130 | | 7 | S1143 | S2143 | |
| 168/231 | SOUVENIR SHEETS | 3 | S1168 | S2168 | 10.95 |
| 175/123 | SOUVENIR SHEETS | 5 | S1175 | S2175 | 10.95 |
| 184/185 | SOUVENIR SHEETS | 3 | S1184 | S2184 | 10.95 |
| 186/143 | SOUVENIR SHEETS | 5 | S1186 | S2186 | 9.95 |
| 187/180 | SOUVENIR SHEETS | 3 | S1187 | S2187 | 9.95 |
| 193/158 | LARGE SIZE | 05 | S1193 | S2193 | 10.95 |
| 210/170 | LG. SOUV. SHEETS | 05 | S1210 | S2210 | 9.95 |
| 217/170 | LG. SOUV. SHEETS | 03 | S1217 | S2217 | 10.95 |
| 264/108 | SOUV. SHEETS | 05 | S1264 | S2264 | 10.95 |
| 297/210 | SOUV. SHEETS | 05 | S1297 | S2297 | 19.95 |
| ASST'D | ASSORTED SIZES | 12 | S1000 | S2000 | 9.95 |

| Size | | Ref.# Black | Ref.# Clear | Price |
|---|---|---|---|---|
| 26/22 | CANADA HORIZONTAL REGULAR ISSUES | S1301 | S2301 | |
| 21/24 | EUROPEAN ISSUES | S1302 | S2302 | 2.95 |
| 22/26 | CANADA VERTICAL REGULAR ISSUES | S1303 | S2303 | |
| 40/26 | CANADA HORIZONTAL COMMEMS. | S1304 | S2304 | |
| 44/27 | EUROPEAN ISSUES | S1305 | S2305 | 2.95 |
| 25.5/28 | CHAMPIONS OF LIBERTY | S1306 | S2306 | |
| 24.5/29 | SMALL U.N. AND FOREIGN | S1307 | S2307 | |
| 41/30 | EUROPEAN ISSUES | S1308 | S2308 | 2.95 |
| 50/31 | CANADA HIGH VALUE REGULAR ISSUES | S1309 | S2309 | |
| 27.5/33 | U.N. AND FOREIGN | S1310 | S2310 | |
| 26/40 | CANADA VERTICAL COMMEMS | S1311 | S2311 | 2.95 |
| 26/43 | EUROPEAN ISSUES | S1312 | S2312 | 2.95 |
| 57/55 | U.S. REG. PL. BLCKS & FOREIGN ART STMPS | S1313 | S2313 | 9.95 |
| 106/55 | 3c & 4c COMMEM. PLATE BLOCKS | S1314 | S2314 | 9.95 |
| 105/57 | COMMEM. PLATE BLOCKS | S1315 | S2315 | 9.95 |
| 127/70 | COMMEM. PLATE BLOCKS | S1317 | S2317 | 9.95 |
| ASST'D Special Sizes for complete set of 1995 CND stamps | | S1995 | S2995 | 9.95 |

HAWID MOUNTS & TONGS special Pack
(50 pcs.) Sizes 24, 26, 27.5, 30, 33, 35, 41, 44, 48 & 55
** With 1 pair of round ended tong

Available as:

| | | |
|---|---|---|
| #1997 | Black Mounts with Stamp Tong | 16.95 |
| #2997 | Clear Mounts with Stamp Tong | 16.95 |

Available at your dealer, stationery or bookstore, or contact:
UNITRADE ASSOCIATES
99 Floral Parkway, Toronto, Ont. M6L 2C4
Email: unitrade@rogers.com • Website: www.unitradeassoc.com
Postage and applicable sales taxes are extra.

# UNITRADE ASSOCIATES

## UNI-SAFE ACETATE COVER HOLDERS

Made in Canada, these popular holders are excellent for covers and postal stationery.

***Available in two styles:***
***Side-open or Top-open***

**Side-Open, sizes start from ....**

(#U403A SMALL, 5-3/16 x 3-3/8") per 100 at $33.50

to sizes in...

(#U403D LARGE covers, size 8 x 5") per 100 at $48.50

**Top-Open, sizes start from ....**

(**#U405A** SMALL, size 4-1/4x 3") per 100 at $27.95

**to sizes in...**

(**#U405D** JUMBO, size 8 x 5-1/4") per 100 at $48.95

## Lightweight Cover Sleeves

Made of light gauge acetate – super clear.
***Available in two styles:***
***Side-open or Top-open***

**Side-Open, sizes start from ....**

(**#U303A** SMALL with white insert, 5-3/16 x 3-3/8") ***per 100 $30.50***

**To Sizes in ...**

(**#U303D** LARGE cover, size 8 x 5") ***per 100 $30.50***

**Top-Open, sizes start from ....**

(**#U305A** SAMLL, size 4-1/4 x 3") ***per 100 $30.50***

**To Sizes in ...**

(**#U305D** JUMBO, size 8 x 51/4") ***per 100 $30.50***

## Uni-safe Poly Cover & Postcard Holders

Made in China, these are the most inexpensive method of storing postcards or covers available today. Made of 3 mil polyethylene

| ITEM | DESCRIPTION PER 100 | |
|---|---|---|
| U406 | (Postcards), Size 6-1/4 x 4" | $4.50 |
| U406A | (Postcards), Size 5-5/8 X 3-5/8" | $4.50 |
| U407 | (No. 6 envelopes), Size 7-3/8 x 4-1/8" | $5.00 |
| U408 | Large , Size 8-1/4 x 4" | $5.00 |
| U408A | (Official Canada Post Covers) 8 x 4-1/2" | $5.50 |
| U509 | Extra Large Size 9 X 5-1/4" | $6.50 |
| U510 | #10 Envelopes Size 4-3/4 x 10" | $6.50 |

**UNITRADE ASSOCIATES**

99 FLORAL PARKWAY, TORONTO, ONTARIO, M6L 2C4
PHONE: 416.242.5900 FAX: 416. 242.6115
EMAIL: unitrade@rogers.com
WEBSITE: www.unitradeassoc.com

# NATIONAL CHRISTMAS SEALS

Acknowledgements: The *Green's Catalog of the Tuberculosis Seals of the World* numbering system is used with permission granted by The Christmas Seal & Charity Stamp Society in the United States of America.

Contributors: Cliff A. Beattie
Andrew Chung FRPSC
Robert D. Vogel

In 1927, it was agreed that the Christmas Seal campaign was to be the official method for tuberculosis associations to appeal to the public for funds across Canada. The Canadian Tuberculosis Association, now known as The Lung Association, introduced the first national seal.

Adopted in 1902, the red, double-barred cross is an emblem recognized universally in the fight againt TB. The cross resembles the Lorraine cross.

This catalogue presents a basic listing of seals only. To learn more, refer to *The National Christmas Seals of Canada, 1927–2008*, authored by the contributors of this section.

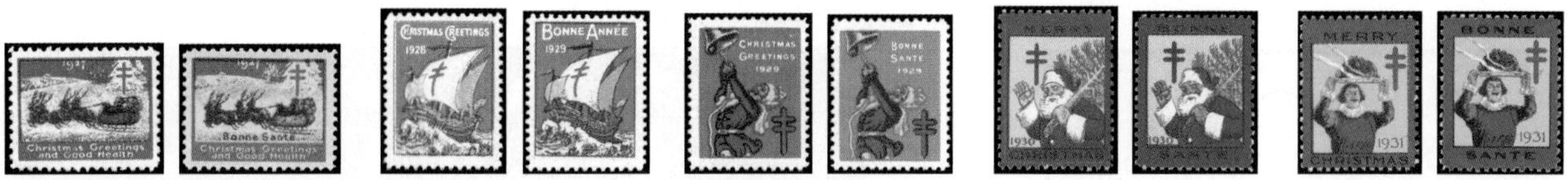

1 2 3 4 5 6 7 8 9 10

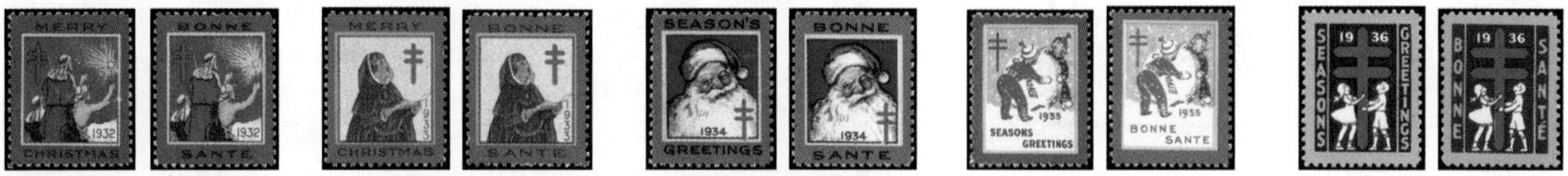

11 12 13 14 15 16 17 18 19 20

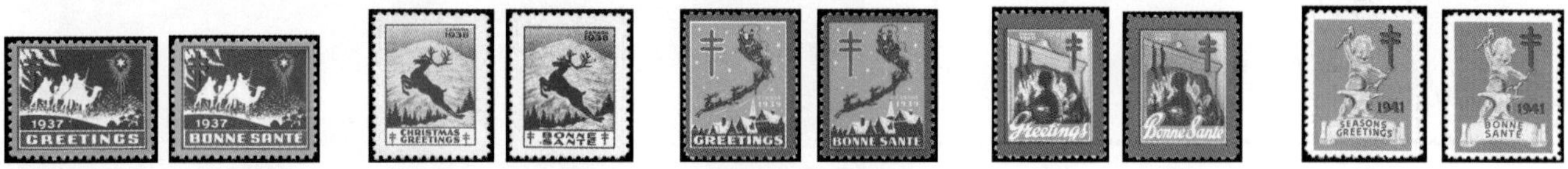

21 22 23 24 25 26 27 28 29 30

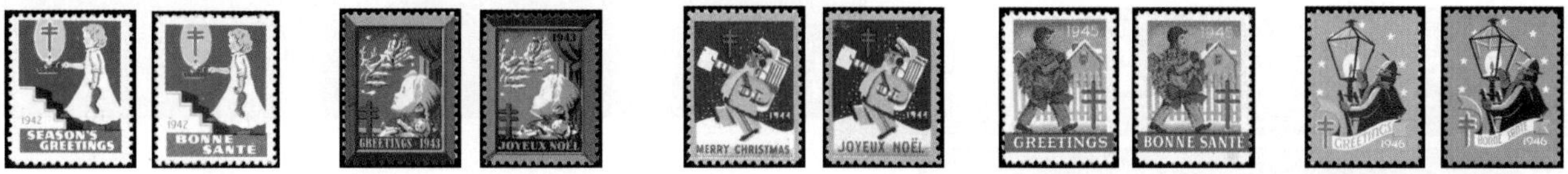

31 32 33 34 35 36 37 38 39 40

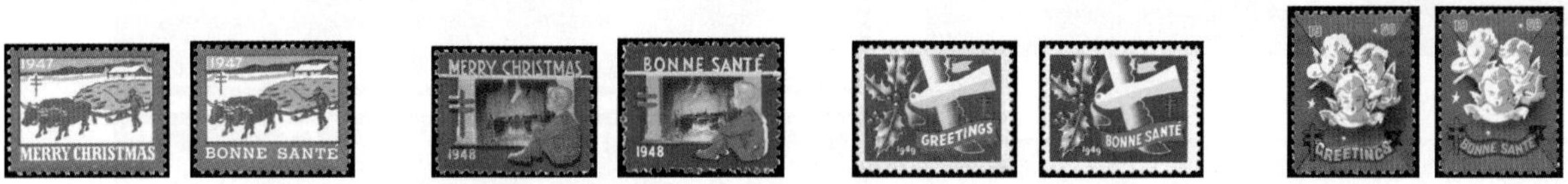

41 42 43 44 45 46 47 48

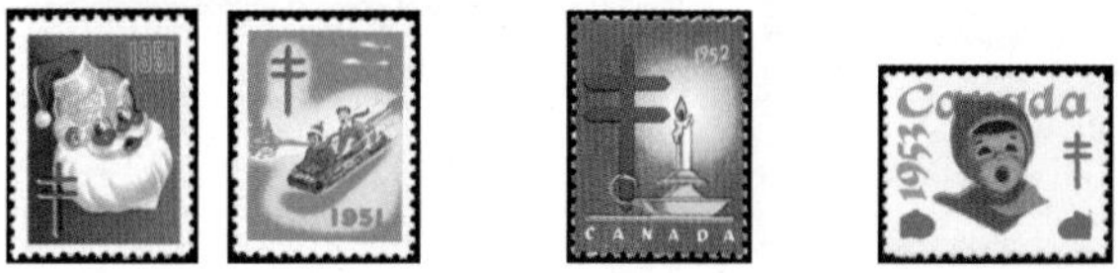

49 50 51 52

| | English Seal | | | French Seal | | |
|---|---|---|---|---|---|---|
| Year | No. | ★VF | Pane (100) | No. | ★VF | Pane (100) |
| 1927 | **1** | 3.00 | 250.00 | **2** | 4.00 | 600.00 |
| 1928 | **3** | 3.00 | 150.00 | **4** | 4.00 | 300.00 |
| 1929 | **5** | 3.00 | 100.00 | **6** | 4.00 | 150.00 |
| 1930 | **7** | 1.50 | 75.00 | **8** | 2.00 | 100.00 |
| 1931 | **9** | 1.50 | 75.00 | **10** | 2.00 | 100.00 |
| 1932 | **11** | 1.50 | 75.00 | **12** | 2.00 | 100.00 |
| 1933 | **13** | 1.50 | 100.00 | **14** | 2.00 | 150.00 |
| 1934 | **15** | 1.50 | 75.00 | **16** | 2.00 | 100.00 |
| 1935 | **17** | 1.00 | 75.00 | **18** | 2.00 | 100.00 |
| 1936 | **19** | 1.00 | 75.00 | **20** | 2.00 | 100.00 |
| 1937 | **21** | 1.00 | 75.00 | **22** | 2.00 | 100.00 |
| 1938 | **23** | 1.00 | 50.00† | **24** | 2.00 | 75.00* |
| 1939 | **25** | 1.00 | 50.00* | **26** | 2.00 | 75.00* |
| | **25i** | 2.00 | 75.00* | | | |
| 1940 | **27** | 0.75 | 50.00* | **28** | 1.00 | 75.00* |

† issued in panes of 100 and a complete booklet of 5 panes of 20 seals ($50.00)
* issued only in a booklet of 5 panes of 20.
[Individual booklet panes of 20 seals – $10.00; 25i: $15.00]

| | English Seal | | | French Seal | | |
|---|---|---|---|---|---|---|
| Year | No. | ★VF | Pane (100) | No. | ★VF | Pane (100) |
| 1941 | **29** | 0.75 | 40.00 | **30** | 1.00 | 50.00 |
| 1942 | **31** | 0.75 | 30.00 | **32** | 1.00 | 40.00 |
| 1943 | **33** | 0.75 | 30.00 | **34** | 1.00 | 40.00 |
| 1944 | **35** | 0.75 | 25.00 | **36** | 1.00 | 35.00 |
| 1945 | **37** | 0.50 | 25.00 | **38** | 1.00 | 35.00 |
| 1946 | **39** | 0.50 | 25.00 | **40** | 1.00 | 35.00 |
| 1947 | **41** | 0.50 | 25.00 | **42** | 1.00 | 35.00 |
| 1948 | **43** | 0.50 | 25.00 | **44** | 1.00 | 35.00 |
| 1949 | **45** | 0.50 | 25.00 | **46** | 1.00 | 35.00 |
| 1950 | **47** | 0.50 | 25.00 | **48** | 1.00 | 35.00 |
| 1951 | **49** | 0.50 | 25.00 | **50** | 1.00 | 35.00 |
| 1952 | **51** | 0.50 | 25.00 | | | |
| 1953 | **52** | 0.50 | 25.00 | | | |

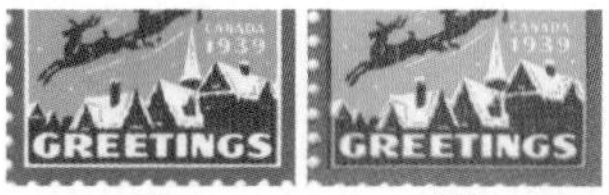

**25** white frameline **25i** no frameline

53

54

55

56

57

58

59

60

61

64

63

62

| Year | No. | Full pane ★VF | Pane size |
|---|---|---|---|
| 1954 | **53** | 25.00 | (100) |
| 1955 | **54** | 25.00 | (100) |
| 1956 | **55** | 25.00 | (100) |
| 1957 | **56** | 25.00 | (100) |
| 1958 | **57** | 25.00 | (100) |
| | | 35.00 | (50) |
| 1959 | **58** | 25.00 | (50) |
| | | 25.00 | (90) |
| 1960 | **59** | 10.00 | (60) |
| | | 25.00 | (50) |
| | | 25.00 | (80) |
| 1961 | **60** | 10.00 | (80) |
| | | 37.50 | (100) |
| 1962 | **61** | 10.00 | (80) |
| | | 37.50 | (50) |
| | | 15.00 | (100) |
| 1963 | **62** | 10.00 | (80) |
| | | 15.00 | (100) |
| 1964 | **63** | 10.00 | (80) |
| | | 15.00 | (100) |
| 1965 | **64** | 10.00 | (100) |

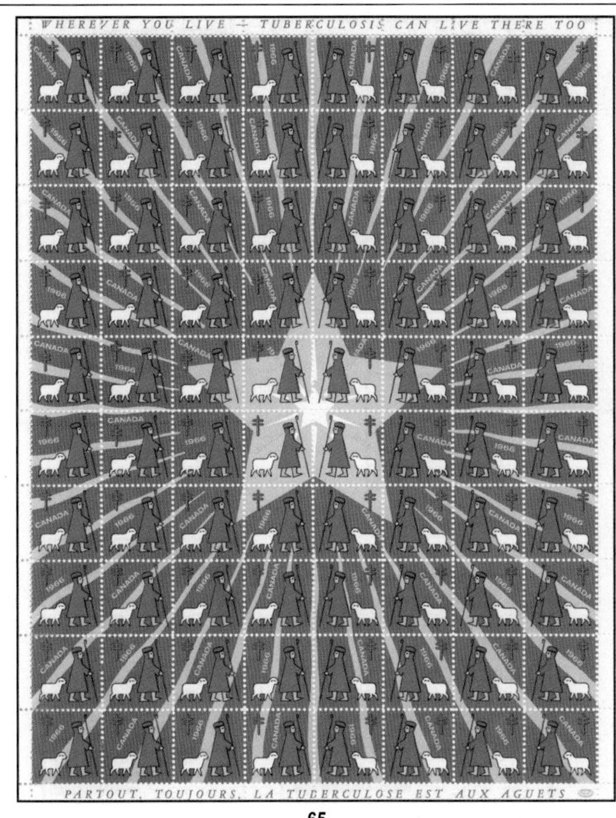

65

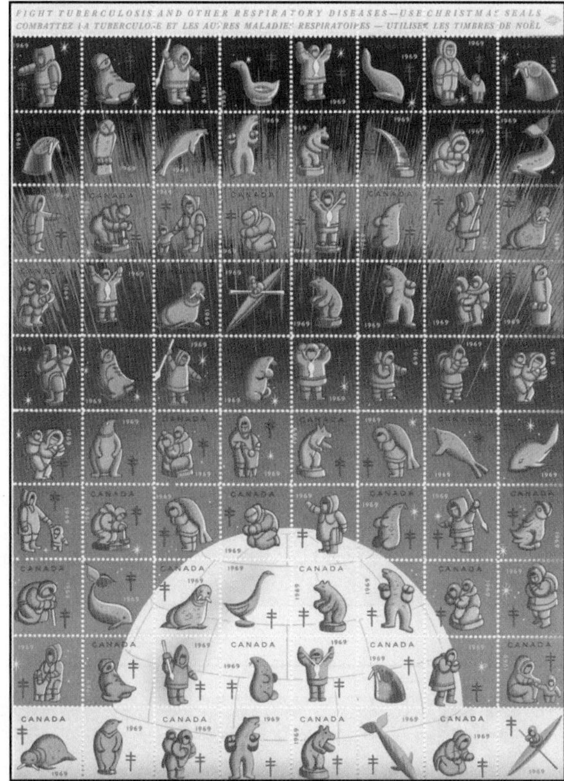

68

66

69

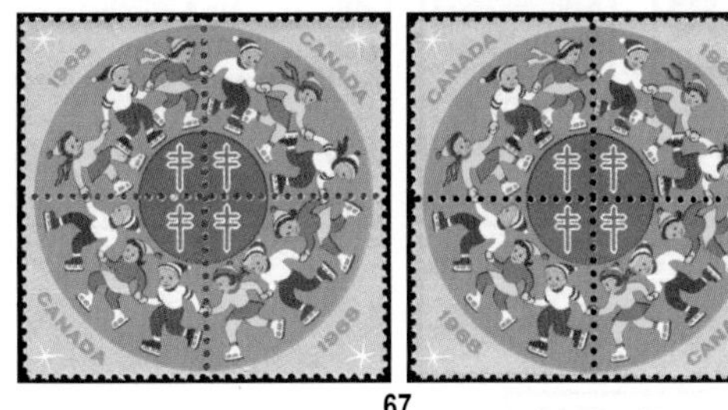

67

70

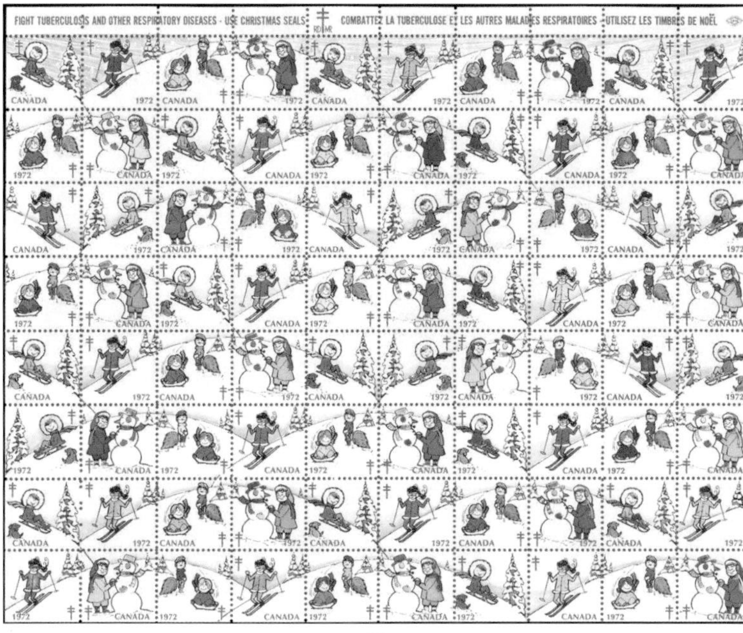

71

*The National Christmas Seals of Canada 1927–2008*, Beattie/Chung/Vogel, 2009

| Year | No. | Full pane ★VF | Pane size |
|---|---|---|---|
| 1966 | **65** | 10.00 | (80) |
| 1967 | **66** | 10.00 | (100) |
| 1968 | **67** | 10.00 | (80) |
| 1969 | **68** | 10.00 | (80) |
| 1970 | **69** | 7.50 | (70) |
| 1971 | **70** | 7.50 | (80) |
| 1972 | **71** | 7.50 | (80) |

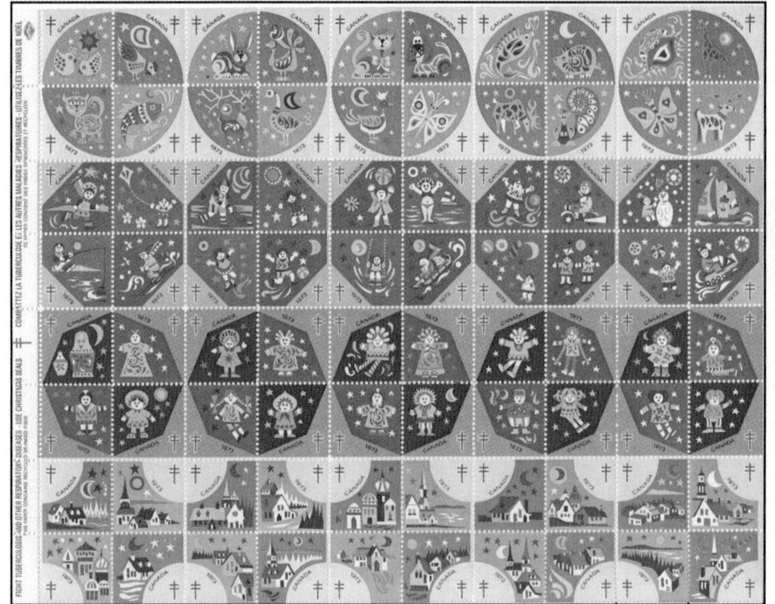
72

73 74 76 77 78

80 81

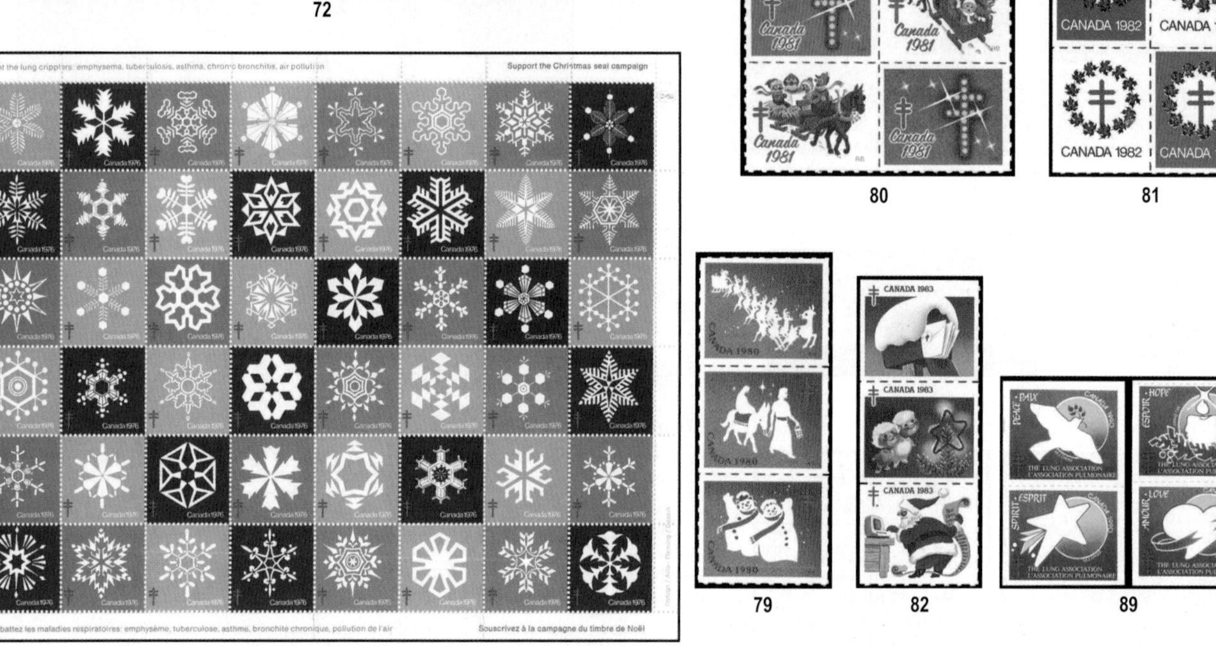
75 79 82 89

83

84

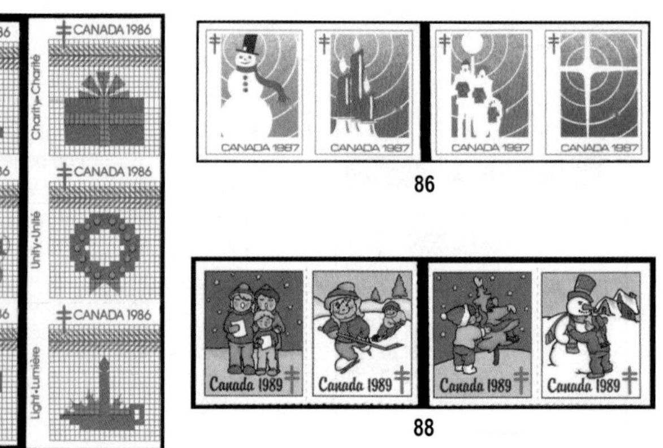
85 86 88

87

| Year | No. | Full pane ★VF | Pane size |
|---|---|---|---|
| 1973 | **72** | 7.50 | (80) |
| 1974 | **73** | 7.50 | (80) |
| 1975 | **74** | 7.50 | (60) |
| 1976 | **75** | 10.00 | (48) |
| 1977 | **76** | 7.50 | (60) |
| 1978 | **77** | 7.50 | (60) |
| 1979 | **78** | 7.50 | (60) |
| 1980 | **79** | 7.50 | (60) |
| 1981 | **80** | 7.50 | (60) |
| 1982 | **81** | 3.00 | (24) |
| 1983 | **82** | 3.00 | (24) |
| 1984 | **83** | 3.00 | (24) |
| 1985 | **84** | 3.00 | (24) |
| 1986 | **85** | 3.00 | (24) |
| 1987 | **86** | 3.00 | (24) |
| 1988 | **87** | 3.00 | (24) |
| 1989 | **88** | 3.00 | (24) |
| 1990 | **89** | 2.00 | (24) |

90

91

92

93

94

95

96

97

99

98

100

102

103

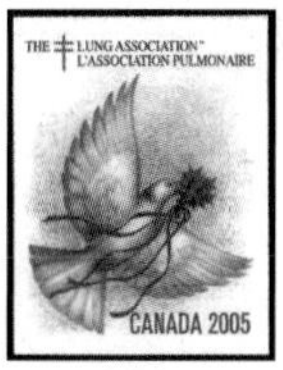

104

105

101

106

107

108

109

110

111

112

| Year | Full pane No. | ★VF | Pane size | Year | Full pane No. | ★VF | Pane size |
|---|---|---|---|---|---|---|---|
| 1991 | **90** | 2.00 | (15) | 2004 | **103x1** | 1.00 | (10) |
| 1992 | **91** | 2.00 | (15) | | **103x2*** | 5.00 | (10) |
| 1993 | **92** | 2.00 | (15) | 2005 | **104x1** | 1.00 | (10) |
| 1994 | **93** | 2.00 | (15) | | **104x2*** | 5.00 | (10) |
| 1995 | **94** | 2.00 | (10) | 2006 | **105x1** | 1.00 | (10) |
| 1996 | **95** | 2.00 | (10) | | **105x2*** | 5.00 | (10) |
| 1997 | **96** | 2.00 | (10) | 2007 | **106*** | 1.00 | (12) |
| 1998 | **97** | 2.00 | (10) | 2008 | **107*** | 1.00 | (10) |
| 1999 | **98** | 2.00 | (10) | 2009 | **108*** | 1.00 | (10) |
| 2000 | **99** | 1.00 | (10) | 2010 | **109*** | 1.00 | (10) |
| 2001 | **100** | 1.00 | (10) | 2011 | **110*** | 1.00 | (10) |
| 2002 | **101** | 1.00 | (10) | 2012 | **111*** | 1.00 | (10) |
| 2003 | **102** | 1.00 | (10) | 2013 | **112*** | 1.00 | (10) |

* self-adhesive

113

114

115

116

| Year | Full pane No. | ★VF | Pane size |
|---|---|---|---|
| 2014 | **113***| 1.00 | (10) |
| 2015 | **114*** | 1.00 | (10) |
| 2016 | **115*** | 1.00 | (10) |
| 2017 | **116a*** | 5.00 | (10[1]) |
| | **116b*** | 3.00 | (30[2]) |
| | **116c*** | 4.00 | (36[2]) |

* self-adhesive

[1] issued only in Manitoba; 6 different designs depicted out of 7.

[2] issued throughout Canada except Manitoba and Quebec; 7 different designs.

# UNITRADE ASSOCIATES

**2 Toned Binders, with matching slipcases!!**

## U/A-MAX

Made to fit 4 ring, 9" x 12" pages and MAX page sizes for both Stamp and Coin collecting.

Relieur fabriqué pour contenir les pages 8½" x 11" à 4 trous et les pages de style MAX pour les collections de timbres ou de monnaies.

*$35.95 Retail*

## U/A-U283N (New COMBI)

Made to fit all 3 ring, 8 1/2" x 11" pages for both Stamp and Coin collecting.

Relieur fabriqué pour contenir les pages 8½" x 11" à trois trous pour les collections de timbres ou de monnaies.

*$29.95 Retail*

**Colours available: Blue, Black, Burgundy, and Green**

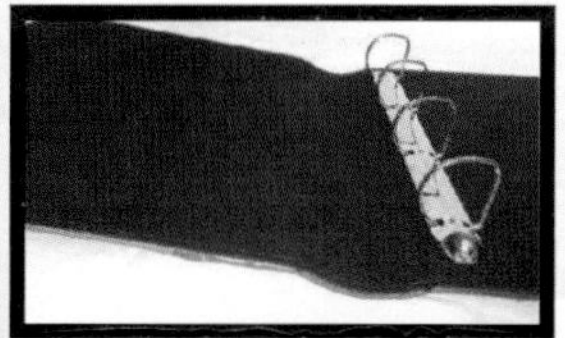

**NEW MAX** FLEXO STOCK SHEETS to fit the MAX 4 Ring Binders, available in Black @ $13.50 and Clear @ $10.95

| | | | |
|---|---|---|---|
| Order No. | SFMAX/1S or 1C | 1 Strip | Black or Clear 5 pages |
| Order No. | SFMAX/2S or 2C | 2 Strips | Black or Clear 5 pages |
| Order No. | SFMAX/3S or 3C | 3 Strips | Black or Clear 5 pages |
| Order No. | SFMAX/4S or 4C | 4 Strips | Black or Clear 5 pages |

**CLEAR ONLY retail $10.95**

| | | | |
|---|---|---|---|
| Order No. | SFMAX/5S | 5 Strips | Black, 5 pages |
| Order No. | SFMAX/6S | 6 Strips | Black, 5 pages |
| Order No. | SFMAX/7S | 7 Strips | Black, 5 pages |
| Order No. | SFMAX/8S | 8 Strips | Black, 5 pages |

email: unitrade@rogers.com
Fax: 416.242.6115
www.unitradeassoc.com

# UNI-SAFE "G" STAMP MOUNTS

## (SPLIT-BACK)

A complete line of quality mounts made solely for Unitrade. Easy-to-Use UNI-SAFE mounts are available for all sizes of stamps. Protect your stamps with UNI-SAFE "G" mounts.

| Size | | No. Pcs. | Ref. # Black | Ref. # Clear | Price |
|---|---|---|---|---|---|
| 20 | MINI STAMPS | 20 | G1020 | G2020 | 8.50 |
| 22 | CND., U.S., G.B. DEF. | 20 | G1022 | G2022 | 8.50 |
| 24 | CDN., U.S., G.B. | | | | |
| | HORIZ. COMM. | 20 | G1024 | G2024 | 8.50 |
| 25 | CAN., U.S. REG., | | | | |
| | COMM. ISSUES | 20 | G1025 | G2025 | 8.50 |
| 27 | U.S. FAM. AMER, U.N. | 20 | G1027 | G2027 | 8.50 |
| 28 | U.S., FOREIGN ISSUES | 20 | G1028 | G2028 | 8.50 |
| 29 | CAN, US ISSUES | 20 | G1029 | G2029 | 8.50 |
| 30 | CAN. INDIANS, CHRISTMAS | 20 | G1030 | G2030 | 8.50 |
| 31 | CAN., U.S. JUMBO | 20 | G1031 | G2031 | 8.50 |
| 33 | CAN. KREIGHOFF, U.N. | 20 | G1033 | G2033 | 8.50 |
| 36 | CAN. JUMBO COMM. | 20 | G1036 | G2036 | 10.95 |
| 39 | CAN. VERT. COMM. | 20 | G1039 | G2039 | 10.95 |
| 40 | U.S. SEMI-JUMBO | 20 | G1040 | G2040 | 10.95 |
| 41 | CAN., U.S., ISRAEL | | | | |
| | VERT. COMM. | 20 | G1041 | G2041 | 10.95 |
| 44 | CAN. REG. BL. OF 4 | 20 | G1044 | G2044 | 10.95 |
| 48 | CAN. BLOCK, GUTTER PAIR | 20 | G1048 | G2048 | 10.95 |
| 50 | CAN. BLOCK & JUMBO | 20 | G1050 | G2050 | 10.95 |
| 51 | CAN. BLOCK | 20 | G1051 | G2051 | 10.95 |
| 52 | CAN. U.S. HORIZ. | | | | |
| | COMM. BLOCK | 20 | G1052 | G2052 | 10.95 |
| 55 | U.S. LARGE | 20 | G1055 | G2055 | 10.95 |
| 57 | CAN., U.S. REG. PL. BLOCKS | 10 | G1057 | G2057 | 9.95 |
| 59 | VARIOUS BLOCKS | 10 | G1059 | G2059 | 9.95 |
| 61 | CN. HORIZ. COMM. PL. BL. | 10 | G1061 | G2061 | 9.95 |
| 63 | U.S. JUMBO COMM. | 10 | G1063 | G2063 | 9.95 |
| 66 | CAN. JUMBO PL. BL. | 10 | G1066 | G2066 | 9.95 |
| 68 | CAN. XMAS PL. BL. | 10 | G1068 | G2068 | 9.95 |
| 70 | JUMBO COMM. PL. BL. | 10 | G1070 | G2070 | 9.95 |
| 74 | CAN. PL. BL. | 10 | G1074 | G2074 | 9.95 |
| 79 | VARIOUS BLOCKS | 10 | G1079 | G2079 | 9.95 |
| 80 | U.S. VERT. PL. BL. | 10 | G1080 | G2080 | 9.95 |

| Size | | No. Pcs. | Ref. # Black | Ref. # Clear | Price |
|---|---|---|---|---|---|
| 100 | U.N. MARGIN BL. | 7 | G1100 | G2100 | 9.95 |
| 105 | U.S. STRIPS | 7 | G1105 | G2105 | 9.95 |
| 107 | U.S. STRIPS WIDE | 7 | G1107 | G2107 | 9.95 |
| 111 | U.S. PL. # STRIPS | 7 | G1111 | G2111 | 9.95 |
| 120 | VARIOUS BLOCKS | 10 | G1120 | G2120 | 9.95 |
| 127 | U.S. JUMBO COMM. | 7 | G1127 | G2127 | 9.95 |
| 137 | GR. BR. CORON. | 7 | G1137 | G2137 | 9.95 |
| 150 | SOUV. SHEETS | 5 | G1150 | G2150 | 9.95 |
| 158 | SOUV. SHEETS | 5 | G1158 | G2158 | 9.95 |
| 165/95 | F.D.C. | 10 | G1165 | G2165 | 9.95 |
| 187/144 | SOUV. SHEETS | 5 | G1187 | G2187 | 9.95 |
| ASST'D | ASSORTIMENT | 12 | G1000 | G2000 | 9.95 |
| 204/153 | SOUV. SHEETS | 5 | G1204 | G2204 | 10.95 |
| 264/171 | SOUV. SHEETS | 3 | G1264 | G2264 | 10.95 |
| 265/231 | SOUV. SHEETS | 5 | G1265 | G2265 | 19.95 |
| 50/31 | CANADA HIGH | | | | |
| | VALUE REGULAR ISSUES | 45 | G1301 | G2301 | 2.95 |
| 31/50 | SAME VERTICAL | 40 | G1302 | G2302 | 2.95 |
| 41/31 | U.S. HORIZONTAL | | | | |
| | SEMI-JUMBO | 45 | G1303 | G2303 | 2.95 |
| 31/41 | SAME VERTICAL | 45 | G1304 | G2304 | 2.95 |
| 25/22 | CANADA HORIZONTAL | | | | |
| | REGULAR ISSUES | 45 | G1305 | G2305 | 2.95 |
| 22/25 | SAME VERTICAL | 45 | G1306 | G2306 | 2.95 |
| 40/25 | CANADA HORIZONTAL | | | | |
| | COMMEMS. | 45 | G1307 | G2307 | 2.95 |
| 25/40 | CANADA VERTICAL | | | | |
| | COMMEMS. | 45 | G1308 | G2308 | 2.95 |
| 25/27 | U.S. FAMOUS AMERICANS | 40 | G1309 | G2309 | 2.95 |
| 33/27 | UNITED NATIONS | 40 | G1310 | G2310 | 2.95 |
| 40/27 | UNITED NATIONS | 45 | G1311 | G2311 | 2.95 |
| 57/55 | CANADIAN REG. ISSUE | | | | |
| | PLATE BLOCKS | 30 | G1312 | G2312 | 9.95 |
| 106/55 | CANADIAN HORIZ. | | | | |
| | COMMEMS. PLATE BLOCK | 25 | G1313 | G2313 | 9.95 |
| 105/57 | CANADIAN VERT. | | | | |

# POSTAL STATIONERY

Stationery items regularly issued by the Canadian Post Office (including items precancelled by the security printer) are listed. Stamp impressions known to have been used on various types of Special Order envelopes follow the listings for the regularly issued envelopes. Values are for unused Entires in fine condition, and for used examples cancelled while current. "Cut squares" are worth 10%, and "fronts only" are valued at 30%.

## ENVELOPES

### PROVINCE OF CANADA

### Queen Victoria

**1860–1864. Embossed. Printed by Geo. F. Nesbitt of New York on white or cream laid paper, batonne lines 18 mm apart. Watermarked "CaPOD"**

U1

U2

| | | | Unused | Used |
|---|---|---|---|---|
| U1 | | **5¢ red** | 125.00 | 250.00 |
| | a | pointed flap, *1864* | 200.00 | 450.00 |
| U2 | | **10¢ dark brown** | 100.00 | 2,100.00 |

### DOMINION OF CANADA

**1877. Embossed.**
**Printed by American Bank Note Company on white to cream laid paper, batonne lines 18 mm apart**

U3

U7

| | | | Unused | Used |
|---|---|---|---|---|
| U3 | | **1¢ blue**, size 140 mm x 80 mm | 2.50 | 4.50 |
| | a | rounded flap | 65.00 | 100.00 |
| U4 | | **3¢ red**, size 140 mm x 80 mm | 3.00 | 4.00 |
| | a | as "U4" but rounded flap | 60.00 | 85.00 |
| | b | size 150 mm x 86 mm | 7.00 | 6.00 |
| | c | as "b", rounded flap | 650.00 | 500.00 |

**1887–1891. Batonne lines 24 mm to 27 mm apart**

| | | | Unused | Used |
|---|---|---|---|---|
| U5 | | **1¢ blue**, size 140 mm x 80 mm | 1.50 | 3.50 |
| | a | wove paper | 600.00 | 600.00 |
| | b | watermarked "Old Berkshire Mills 1881" | — | 2,000.00 |
| U6 | | **3¢ red**, size 140 mm x 80 mm | 1.50 | 3.50 |
| | a | watermarked "Old Berkshire Mills 1881" | — | 2,000.00 |
| | b | size 150 mm x 86 mm | 2.00 | 2.00 |
| | c | as "b", watermarked "C.P.co" | — | 2,250.00 |
| | d | as "b", thick paper | 40.00 | 50.00 |
| | e | as "b", wove paper | 200.00 | 175.00 |

**1895. Embossed.**
**Printed by BABNC on white to cream laid paper, batonne lines**

| | | | Unused | Used |
|---|---|---|---|---|
| U7 | | **2¢ green**, size 150 mm x 86 mm | .50 | 40.00 |

The used value is for copies postmarked before Jan. 1, 1899 with no added stamps. The value otherwise is $10.00 (for domestic use).

**1898. Embossed.**
**Printed by Printing & Stationery Dept., Ottawa (PSPO), on white to cream wove paper**

U8

U9

U10

| | | | Unused | Used |
|---|---|---|---|---|
| U8 | | **3¢ red**, size 150 mm x 88 mm | 1.00 | 2.00 |
| | a | with Return Notice | 12.00 | 22.00 |

**1898. Embossed.**
**Printed by PSDO on white to cream wove paper**

| | | | Unused | Used |
|---|---|---|---|---|
| U9 | | **1¢ green**, size 150 mm x 86 mm | 1.00 | 2.50 |
| | a | size 152 mm x 90 mm | 25.00 | 35.00 |
| U10 | | **2¢ violet** | 4.00 | 50.00 |
| U11 | | **2¢ red**, size 150 mm x 86 mm | 1.25 | 1.50 |
| | a | with Return Notice | 20.00 | 15.00 |
| | b | size 152 mm x 90 mm | 2.50 | 2.50 |

**1899. Surcharges. Type "A" unless otherwise noted**

Type A Type B

| | | | Unused | Used |
|---|---|---|---|---|
| U12 | | **2¢ on 3¢** (U4), size 140 mm x 80 mm | 3.00 | 12.00 |
| | a | surcharged on U4a, size 140 mm x 80 mm, rounded flap | 350.00 | |
| | b | surcharged on U4b, size 150 mm x 86 mm | 10.00 | 12.00 |
| U13 | | **2¢ on 3¢** (U6), size 140 mm x 80 mm | 3.50 | 5.00 |
| | a | surcharged on U6e, wove paper | 350.00 | 450.00 |
| | b | surcharged on U6b, size 150 mm x 86 mm | 3.50 | 7.50 |
| | c | surcharged on U6d, thick paper | 65.00 | — |
| | d | surcharge "B" on U6 | 20.00 | 30.00 |
| U14 | | **2¢ on 3¢** (U8) | .75 | 1.00 |
| | a | surcharge "B" on U8 | 35.00 | 35.00 |
| | b | surcharged on U8a, Return Notice | .75 | 1.75 |
| | c | surcharged "B" on U8a | 15.00 | 20.00 |

**One-Cent (1¢)**

**Die 1:** Long bar in "G", thin letters
**Die 2:** Short bar in "G", thick letters, top bar of "E" in "ONE" shorter than bottom bar
**Die 3:** As Die 2, top bar of "E" in "ONE" is longer, "E" in "CENT" raised

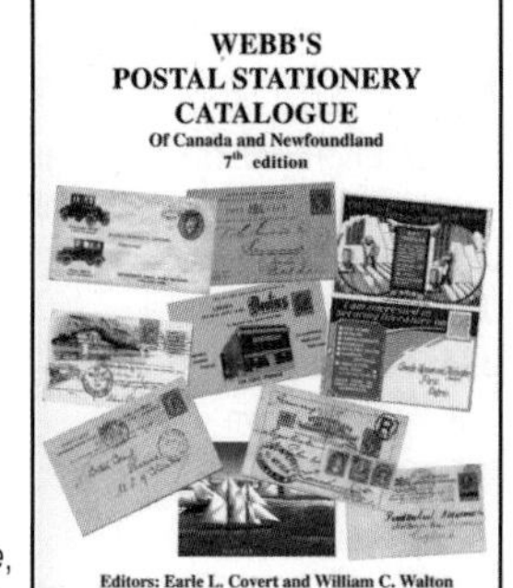


*Webb's Postal Stationery Catalogue*, Earle L. Covert and William C. Walton, 2001.

Two-Cent (2¢)

**Die 1**: Thin lettering, bottom left of bust points between "WO", bar of "G" is long, panel lines above "CENTS" extended, intersecting a loop. border loops are even and join the frame
**Die 2**: Lettering is thick and bar of "G" is short, border loops are high, even, and join the frame, "D" of "CANADA" is low
**Die 3**: Border loops are flat, "D" is normal, lettering is thick
**Die 4**: Bottom left of bust points at "O", panel lines meet at a junction, loops are uneven and seldom join frame
**Die 5**: As Die 4, panel ines and border loops as Die 2
**Die 6**: As Die 5, centre bar of "E" very thick bar of "G" is long with a vertical serif

## King Edward VII

**1905. Embossed.**
**White to cream wove paper. Size 152 mm x 88 mm**

U15

U19

| | | Unused | Used |
|---|---|---|---|
| U15 | **1¢ green**, Die 1 | 2.50 | 2.50 |
| a | Die 2 | 1.75 | 2.00 |
| b | Die 3 | 2.50 | 2.50 |
| U16 | **2¢ red**, Die 1 | 2.00 | 2.00 |
| a | Die 2 | 3.00 | 2.50 |
| b | Die 3 | 6.00 | 6.00 |
| c | Die 4 | 2.50 | 2.50 |
| d | Die 5 | 25.00 | 25.00 |
| e | Die 6 | 60.00 | 40.00 |

**Die 1**: Numerals of value are larger than "CENT" or "CENTS"; 3¢ value has a flat top
**Die 2**: Same as 3¢ (Die 1) but loops at border are deeper or more round
**Die 3**: Numerals of value and "CENT" or "CENTS" are same height, top of "3" is more round,
hair lines are deeply engraved
**Die 4**: Numerals of value are same as Die 1, printing is perfectly flat with no embossing
**Die 5**: As Die 4, lines of the head and beard show colour

## King George V

**1916. Embossed. Die 1. White to cream wove paper. Size 152 mm x 88 mm**

| | | | |
|---|---|---|---|
| U17 | **1¢ green** | 1.25 | 1.25 |
| U18 | **1¢ orange** | 3.00 | 2.50 |
| U19 | **2¢ red** | 2.00 | 2.00 |
| U20 | **2¢ green** | 1.50 | 3.00 |
| U21 | **3¢ brown** | 2.00 | 2.50 |
| a | Die 2 | 2.00 | 3.50 |

---

**For subsequent regular issues available to the public (until 2001) only two standard size envelopes were used. These are the #8 envelope (165 mm x 92 mm) and the #10 envelope (241 mm x 105 mm).**

---

**1922. Engraved. Die 4. Typographed by Dominion Envelope Co. on white to cream wove paper. Unembossed, with vertical side seams. Size #10**

| | | | |
|---|---|---|---|
| U22 | **1¢ orange** | 10.00 | 20.00 |
| U23 | **2¢ green** | 12.00 | 20.00 |
| U24 | **3¢ brown** | 7.00 | 20.00 |
| a | olive brown | 20.00 | 30.00 |

| | | Unused | Used |
|---|---|---|---|
| | **1923. Heavily Embossed. Die 3. White to cream wove paper** | | |
| U25 | **1¢ orange**, #8 | .75 | 1.50 |
| a | same, #10 | 1.50 | 2.00 |
| b | same, #10 precancelled with horizontal bars | | 150.00 |
| U26 | **1¢ green**, #8 | 4.50 | 4.50 |
| a | same, #10 | 10.00 | 12.00 |
| b | as U26 (#8) precancelled with horizontal bars | | 200.00 |
| c | as U26a (#10) precancelled with horizontal bars | | 200.00 |
| U27 | **2¢ green**, #8 | 1.00 | .75 |
| a | Return Notice, English | 3.50 | 3.75 |
| b | Return Notice, French | 40.00 | 40.00 |
| c | #10 | 1.25 | 1.25 |
| U28 | **2¢ red**, shades #8 | 1.00 | .75 |
| a | same, #10 | 1.50 | 1.75 |
| U29 | **2¢ brown**, #8 | 15.00 | 20.00 |
| U30 | **3¢ brown**, #8 | 6.00 | 5.00 |
| a | same, #10 | 7.50 | 12.00 |
| U31 | **3¢ red**, #8 | .50 | .75 |
| a | carmine, #8 | 5.00 | 5.00 |
| b | red #8, Return Notice, 1st printing, 36 dots in bottom line | 30.00 | 20.00 |
| c | as "b", 2nd printing, 27 dots in bottom line | 5.00 | 6.00 |
| d | red #10 | 5.00 | 6.00 |
| U32 | **10¢ brown**, #8, Registered letter | 6.00 | 50.00 |

**1926. Surcharged "2 CENTS" in black, 23 mm or 25 mm long**

| | | | |
|---|---|---|---|
| U33 | **2¢ on 3¢ brown** (U21), 23 mm | 40.00 | 65.00 |
| a | length 25 mm surcharged on U21 | 250.00 | — |
| b | length 23 mm surcharged on U21a | 50.00 | 75.00 |
| c | length 25 mm surcharged on U21a | 75.00 | 100.00 |
| U34 | **2¢ on 3¢ brown** (U24), 23 mm | 6.00 | 15.00 |
| a | surcharged on U24a | 35.00 | 45.00 |
| U35 | **2¢ on 3¢ brown** (U30), 23 mm | 12.00 | 15.00 |
| a | surcharged on U30a | 7.50 | 15.00 |
| U36 | **2¢ on 3¢ red** (U31), 23 mm | 1.25 | 2.00 |
| a | surcharged on U31b | 150.00 | 150.00 |
| b | surcharged on U31c | 2.50 | 3.00 |
| c | length 25 mm surcharged on U31 | 12.00 | 15.00 |
| d | length 25 mm surcharged on U31c | 25.00 | 50.00 |
| e | length 23 mm surcharged on U31d | 2.50 | 3.50 |
| f | 2¢ on 3¢ carmine (U31a), 23 mm | 25.00 | 35.00 |

**1931. Line Die. White to cream wove paper.**
**Head with shaded hair. Die 5**

U39

| | | | |
|---|---|---|---|
| U37 | **1¢ green**, #8 | 2.50 | 3.00 |
| a | same, #10 | 4.50 | 7.50 |
| b | same, #10 precancelled with horizontal lines | | 200.00 |
| U38 | **1¢ orange**, #10, manilla, *1927* | 6.00 | 25.00 |
| U39 | **2¢ brown**, #8 | 4.00 | 3.00 |
| a | same, #10 | 4.00 | 5.00 |
| U40 | **3¢ red**, #8 | 3.00 | .75 |
| a | same, #10 | 3.50 | 4.50 |

| | | Unused | Used |
|---|---|---|---|

1931. 1¢ Die 5 added to envelopes with 2¢ Die 3

U41

| | | Unused | Used |
|---|---|---|---|
| U41 | **2¢ red + 1¢ green**, #8 | 2.00 | 2.50 |
| a | same, #10 | 2.00 | 5.00 |
| b | 2¢ red + two 1¢ green | 70.00 | |

1932. Engraved Die.
Typographed by PSDO on white wove paper

U43

| | | Unused | Used |
|---|---|---|---|
| U42 | **1¢ green**, #8 | 1.50 | 1.50 |
| a | same, #10 | 5.00 | 3.00 |
| U43 | **2¢ brown**, #8 | 2.00 | 1.25 |
| U44 | **3¢ red**, #8 | .75 | .50 |
| a | same, #10 | 2.50 | 3.00 |

1933. Surcharged. Typographed by PSDO

| | | Unused | Used |
|---|---|---|---|
| U45 | **3¢ on 2¢ red** (U28a), #10 | 4.00 | 125.00 |

1933. Engraved Die. Typographed by PSDO

U48

| | | Unused | Used |
|---|---|---|---|
| U46 | **1¢ green**, #8 | 1.25 | .50 |
| a | same, #10 | 3.00 | 1.50 |
| U47 | **2¢ brown**, #8 | 1.50 | 1.00 |
| a | same, #10 | 7.50 | 10.00 |
| U48 | **3¢ red**, #8 | 1.25 | .75 |
| a | same, #10 | 3.00 | 3.00 |

## King George VI

1938–1949. Typographed. "19" and "38" appear in the lower corners but can be hard to detect. Large coloured dot in "A" of "POSTAGE". The veins in leaf are full, extending to borders of leaf.

U53

U54

| | | Unused | Used |
|---|---|---|---|
| U49 | **1¢ blue green**, #8 | .50 | .25 |
| a | same, #10 | .50 | .25 |
| U50 | **1¢ yellow green**, #8 | 1.00 | .75 |
| a | same, #10 | 1.50 | 1.50 |
| U51 | **2¢ brown**, (shades), #8 | 2.50 | 1.50 |
| a | same, #10 | 4.00 | 5.00 |
| U53 | **3¢ red**, #8 | 2.00 | .75 |
| a | same, #10 | 3.00 | 3.50 |
| U54 | **3¢ purple** (shades), #8 | 2.00 | 1.25 |
| a | same, #10 | 4.00 | 4.50 |

1943. Various 2¢ Envelopes with 1¢ (as U49) added

| | | Unused | Used |
|---|---|---|---|
| U56 | **2¢ brown (U47) + 1¢ green**, #8 | 15.00 | 18.00 |
| a | U47a revalued, #10 | 17.00 | 30.00 |
| U57 | **2¢ brown (U51) + 1¢ green**, #8 | 1.00 | .75 |
| a | U51a revalued, #10 | 1.25 | 4.00 |

1943. Offset. "19" and "43" appear in lower corners.
A very small dot in "A" of "POSTAGE".
Veins of leaf are weak, falling short of borders.

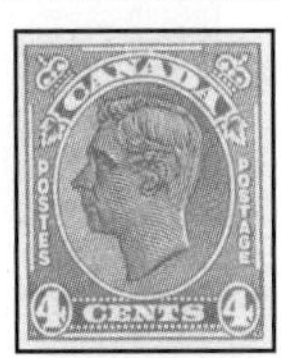

Offset

Typographed

| | | Unused | Used |
|---|---|---|---|
| U59 | **1¢ pale green**, #8 | 30.00 | 20.00 |
| a | same, #10 | 12.00 | 12.00 |
| U60 | **2¢ grey brown**, #8 | 4.50 | 5.50 |
| a | same, #10 | 10.00 | 10.00 |
| U61 | **2¢ olive green**, #8 | 1.00 | .75 |
| a | same, #10 | 2.00 | 1.00 |
| U62 | **2¢ bistre**, #8 | .50 | .25 |
| a | same, #10 | 1.75 | .75 |
| U63 | **3¢ light mauve**, #8 | 1.25 | .75 |
| a | same, #10 | 2.75 | 3.00 |
| b | watermarked "Victory Bond", #8 | 70.00 | 75.00 |
| U64 | **3¢ purple**, typographed, #8 | 20.00 | 20.00 |
| a | same, #10 | 27.50 | 27.50 |
| b | **3¢ purple**, three-quarters on top of 4¢ red, #8 | 500.00 | — |
| U65 | **4¢ red**, typographed, #8 | .75 | .35 |
| a | same, #10 | 1.00 | .75 |
| b | "hole in forehead" variety, #8 | 20.00 | — |
| U66 | **4¢ pale rose**, #8 | 4.00 | 2.00 |
| a | same, #10 | 10.00 | 10.00 |
| U67 | **4¢ orange**, #8 | .50 | .35 |
| a | same, #10 | 1.00 | 1.25 |
| b | "hole in forehead" variety, #8 | 15.00 | 15.00 |

The values for U63b are for copies showing a large portion of the watermark. Copies showing only one or two letters are valued at 50%.

U70

U72

1951–1954. Surcharges.

| | | Unused | Used |
|---|---|---|---|
| U68 | **2¢ on 1¢ blue green** (U49a), #10 | — | 75.00 |
| U69 | **2¢ on 1¢ yellow green** (U50), #8 | 17.00 | 7.50 |
| a | surcharged on U50a, #10 | 17.00 | 7.50 |

Postal Stationery

| | | Unused | Used |
|---|---|---|---|
| U70 | **2¢ on 1¢ pale green** (U59), #8 | .50 | .75 |
| a | surcharged on U59a, #10 | 8.00 | 3.00 |
| U71 | **5¢ on 3¢ purple** (U54), typographed, #8 | — | 60.00 |
| a | surcharged on U54a | — | 60.00 |
| b | surcharged on U64a | 60.00 | 60.00 |
| U72 | **5¢ on 3¢ light mauve** (U63), offset, #8 | 1.00 | 1.00 |
| a | surcharged on U63a, #10 | 3.00 | 5.00 |
| b | surcharged on U63b, watermarked "Victory Bond", #8 | 150.00 | 150.00 |

## Queen Elizabeth II

**1953. Die dated "1953" in lower right corner. White wove paper. Gum varieties exist.**

U73

U76

| | | | |
|---|---|---|---|
| U73 | **2¢ green**, #8 | .35 | .25 |
| a | same, #10 | .35 | .25 |
| U74 | **4¢ purple**, #8 | .35 | .25 |
| a | same, #10 | .75 | 1.00 |
| b | Return Notice, #8 | 3.50 | 2.00 |
| c | Return Notice, #10 | 3.50 | 4.00 |
| U75 | **5¢ blue**, #8 | .35 | .25 |
| a | same, #10 | .35 | .25 |
| b | Return Notice, #8 | 3.50 | 1.00 |
| c | Return Notice, #10 | 3.50 | 4.00 |

**1954. Die dated "1954" in lower right corner. White wove paper. Two types of knife**

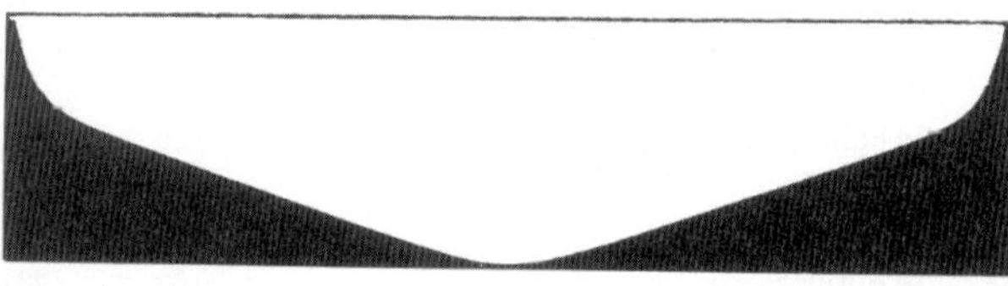
Knife 1

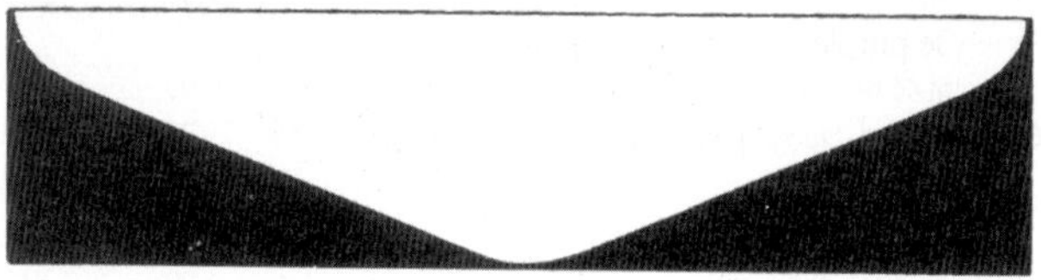
Knife 2

| | | Unused | Used |
|---|---|---|---|
| U76 | **2¢ green**, #8, knife 1 (flap 20 mm deep, 20 mm from the edge) | 10.00 | 12.00 |
| a | as U76, knife 2 (flap 16 mm deep, 20 mm from the edge) | 12.00 | 20.00 |

**1962–64. Die dated "1961" at right side. White wove paper**

U79

U81 surcharge

| | | Unused | Used |
|---|---|---|---|
| U77 | **2¢ green**, #8 | 1.00 | .50 |
| a | same, #10 | 1.25 | .50 |
| U78 | 4¢ purple, #8 | 1.00 | .50 |
| a | same, #10 | 1.50 | .75 |
| U79 | **5¢ blue**, #8 | 1.25 | .35 |
| a | same, #10 | 1.50 | .75 |
| U80 | **3¢ on 2¢ green** (U73), #8 | 5.00 | 85.00† |
| a | surcharged on U73a, #10 | 65.00 | 130.00 |

† Used in period only.

| | | | |
|---|---|---|---|
| U81 | **3¢ on 2¢ green** (U77), #8 | .75 | .50 |
| a | surcharged on U77a, #10 | .75 | 1.00 |

**1963–1966. Hair consists of dots. White wove paper**

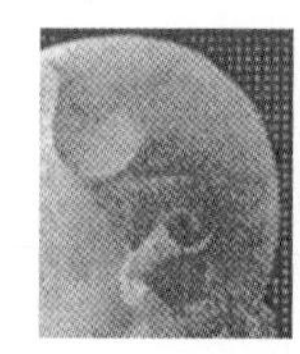

U82

U85

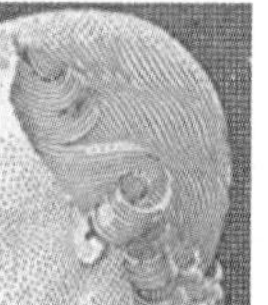

| | | | |
|---|---|---|---|
| U82 | **3¢ purple**, #8 | 1.00 | .50 |
| a | same, #10 | 1.00 | 1.00 |
| U83 | **4¢ red**, #8, stamp size 24 mm x 21 mm | 1.50 | 1.25 |
| a | same, #10 | 1.50 | 1.50 |
| b | stamp size 25 mm x 21 mm, #8 | 5.00 | 2.50 |
| c | as "b", #10 | 6.00 | 2.75 |
| U84 | 5¢ blue, #8 | 1.25 | .50 |
| a | same, #10 | 2.50 | 2.50 |

**1964–1966. Hair consists of lines. White wove paper**

| | | | |
|---|---|---|---|
| U85 | **3¢ purple**, #8, stamp size 23 mm x 19 mm | 1.50 | 1.50 |
| a | same, #10 | 10.00 | 4.00 |
| b | stamp size 25 mm x 21 mm, #8 | 10.00 | 4.00 |
| c | as "b", #10 | 25.00 | 7.00 |
| d | pointed flap, stamp size 23 mm x 19 mm, inspection notice 36 mm, #10 | 35.00 | 70.00 |
| e | as "d", inspection notice 41 mm | 75.00 | 55.00 |
| U86 | **5¢ blue**, #8 | 2.00 | .35 |
| a | same, #10 | 2.50 | .50 |

**1967–1972. Centennial issue**

Type A: Plain white paper.
Type B: Inside of envelope printed all over with "Canada Post Postes".
Type C: As "B", with bilingual apartment notice under flap.

U89

U89d

| | | | |
|---|---|---|---|
| U87 | **3¢ purple**, #8 (A) | 1.50 | 4.00 |
| a | same, #10 (A) | 2.00 | 2.00 |
| b | precancelled, #8 (A) | 2.50 | 6.00 |
| c | as "b", #10 (A) | 3.00 | 3.00 |
| U88 | **4¢ red**, #8 (A) | 3.50 | 2.50 |
| a | same, #10 (A) | 5.00 | 6.00 |
| b | size #8 (B) | 1.00 | 1.50 |
| c | size #10 (B) | 1.25 | 1.50 |
| U89 | **5¢ blue**, #8 (A), shades | 1.50 | .75 |
| a | same, #10 (A) | 3.00 | 2.75 |
| b | size #8, (B) | 1.50 | .50 |
| c | size #10, (B) | 2.00 | 2.25 |
| d | precancelled, #8 (A) | 1.00 | 1.25 |
| e | as "a", precancelled | 1.00 | 1.25 |

| | | Unused | Used |
|---|---|---|---|
| U90 | **6¢ orange**, #8 (B) | .75 | .25 |
| a | same, #10 (B) | .75 | 1.00 |
| U91 | **6¢ black**, #8 (B), stamp size 25 mm x 20 mm | .35 | .25 |
| a | same, #10 (B) | .35 | .25 |
| b | size #8, (C) | 5.00 | 5.00 |
| c | size #10, (C) | 5.50 | 5.00 |
| d | 6¢ black precancelled, #8 (A), stamp size 20 mm x 16 mm | .50 | 1.00 |
| e | same, #10 (A) | .50 | 1.00 |
| f | as U91D, tagged | .50 | .50 |
| g | as "e", tagged | .50 | .75 |
| U92 | **7¢ green**, #8 (C) | .50 | .75 |
| a | same #10 (C) | .50 | .75 |
| U93 | **8¢ slate**, #8 (C) | .25 | .25 |
| a | same, #10 (C) | .50 | .25 |
| b | size #8 (C), tagged | .25 | .25 |
| c | as "a", tagged | .50 | .25 |

### 1969–1971. Various issues surcharged

Type A Type B Type C

Type A: Gasparo Printing. The vertical stroke runs entirely through the "¢".
Type B: International Printing. The vertical stroke is at top and bottom of "¢" only.
Type C: Red Maple Leaf.
All listings are Type A unless otherwise noted

| | | Unused | Used |
|---|---|---|---|
| U94 | **5¢ on 3¢ purple** (U82a), #10 | 150.00 | 200.00 |
| U95 | **5¢ on 3¢ purple** (U85), #8 | 60.00 | 60.00 |
| a | surcharged on U85a, #10 | — | 70.00 |
| b | surcharged on U85b, #8 | 18.00 | 25.00 |
| c | surcharged on U85c, #10 | 100.00 | 90.00 |
| d | 5¢ on 3¢ purple (U87), #8 | 20.00 | 20.00 |
| e | surcharged on U87a, #10 | 45.00 | 40.00 |
| f | surcharged on U87b, #8 | 1.00 | 1.50 |
| g | surcharged on U87c, #10 | 1.50 | 2.00 |
| U95A | **6¢ on 4¢ purple** (U78a), #10 | 250.00 | 250.00 |
| U96 | **6¢ on 4¢ red** (U83), #8 | — | 60.00 |
| a | surcharged on U83a, #10 | — | 75.00 |
| b | surcharged on U83b, #8 | 90.00 | 60.00 |
| c | surcharged on U83c, #10 | 65.00 | 65.00 |
| U97 | **6¢ on 4¢ red** (U88), #8 | 50.00 | 40.00 |
| a | surcharged on U88a, #10 | — | 40.00 |
| b | surcharged on U88b, #8 | 1.00 | .75 |
| c | surcharged on U88c, #10 | 1.00 | 1.00 |
| d | surcharged on U88c, #10 (B) | 10.00 | 10.00 |
| U98 | **6¢ on 5¢ blue** (U84a), #10 | 110.00 | 110.00 |
| U100 | **6¢ on 5¢ blue** (U86), #8 | 40.00 | 30.00 |
| a | surcharged on "U86a," #10 | 50.00 | 45.00 |
| U101 | **6¢ on 5¢ blue** (U89), #8 | — | 40.00 |
| a | surcharged on U89a, #10 | — | 50.00 |
| b | surcharged on U89b, #8 | 1.00 | 1.00 |
| c | surcharged on U89c, #10 | 1.00 | 1.00 |
| d | surcharged on U89b, #8 (B) | 4.50 | 3.00 |
| e | surcharged on U89c, #10 (B) | 5.00 | 3.50 |
| f | surcharged on U89d, #8 | 200.00 | 150.00 |
| g | surcharged on U89e, #10 | 200.00 | 150.00 |
| h | surcharged on U79, #8 | — | 200.00 |
| i | surcharged on U79a, #10 | — | 200.00 |
| U102 | **6¢ on 5¢ blue**, #8 (C) | .75 | .75 |
| a | same, #10 (C) | .75 | 2.00 |

### 1975–1979. New Design

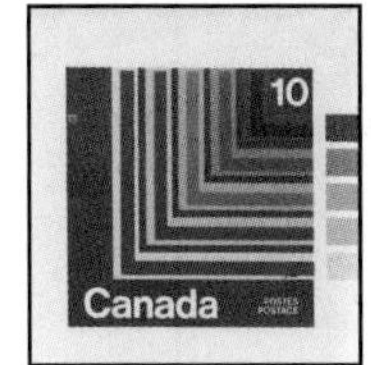


U105

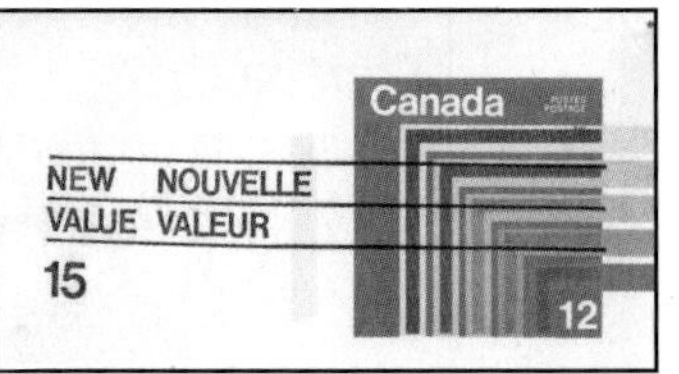


U108

| | | Unused | Used |
|---|---|---|---|
| U103 | **6¢ red**, #8 | .75 | 1.00 |
| a | same, #10 | .50 | .75 |
| U104 | **8¢ blue**, #8 | .50 | .35 |
| a | same, #10 | .50 | .50 |
| U105 | **10¢ red & blue**, #8, no postal code information | .50 | .50 |
| a | same, #10 | .50 | .50 |
| b | size #8, with postal code information | .50 | .50 |
| c | size #10, with postal code information | .50 | .65 |
| U106 | **12¢ blue & green**, #8 with postal code information | .50 | .35 |
| a | same, #10 | .50 | .60 |
| b | size #10, no postal code information | 10.00 | 15.00 |
| U107 | **14¢ purple & blue**, #8 | .50 | .35 |
| a | same, #10 | .50 | .60 |
| U108 | **15¢ on 12¢ blue & green** (U106) #8 | 1.00 | 5.00 |
| a | surcharged on U106a, #10, with postal code information | 2.00 | 5.00 |
| b | surcharged on U106b, as "a", no postal code information | 1.00 | 5.00 |
| U109 | **17¢ on 14¢ purple & blue** (U107), #8 | .50 | .50 |
| U110 | **15¢ green & brown**, #8 | .45 | 8.00 |
| a | same, #10 | .45 | 8.00 |
| U111 | **17¢ brown & blue**, #8 | .45 | .45 |
| a | same, #10, blue printing on back | .75 | 1.00 |
| b | as "a", brown printing on back | .45 | .50 |
| c | as "b", brown colour missing | 75.00 | — |

### 1982–1989. Transportation

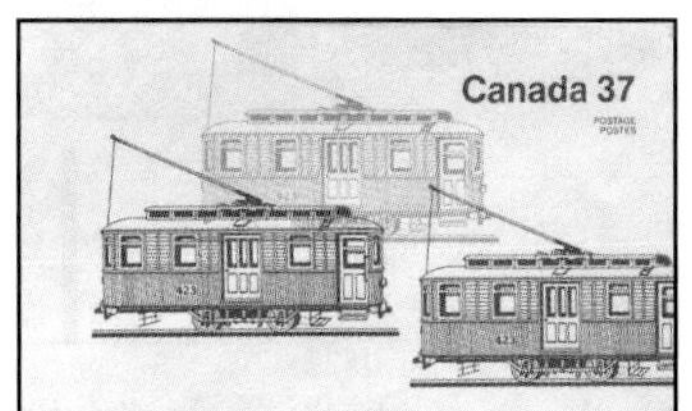


U122

| | | Unused | Used |
|---|---|---|---|
| U112 | **30¢ olive**, #8 (Trains) | 1.00 | 1.00 |
| U113 | **30¢ blue green**, #10 (Ships) | 1.00 | 1.00 |
| U114 | **32¢ sepia**, #8 (Trains), 4452 Kg on back | 1.00 | 1.00 |
| a | **32¢ sepia**, #8 (Trains), 44,545 Kg on back | 1.00 | 2.00 |
| U115 | **32¢ blue**, #10 (Ships), 202 Ft on back | 1.00 | 1.00 |
| a | **32¢ blue**, #10 (Ships), 61.5 M on back | 1.00 | 2.00 |
| U116 | **34¢ olive and yellow**, #8 (Rail Cars) | 1.00 | 1.00 |
| U117 | **34¢ purple and orange**, #10 (Ocean Liners) | 1.00 | 1.00 |
| U118 | **34¢ on 32¢**, (U114a), #8 | 2.00 | 2.00 |
| U119 | **34¢ on 32¢**, (U115a), #10 | 2.00 | 2.00 |
| U120 | **36¢ blue and grey**, #8 (Rail Cars) | 1.00 | 1.00 |
| U121 | **36¢ purple and green**, #10 (Ocean Liners) | 1.00 | 1.00 |
| U122 | **37¢ mauve**, #8 (Street Cars) | 1.00 | 1.00 |
| U123 | **37¢ brown**, #10 (Steamers) | 1.00 | 1.00 |
| U124 | **38¢ brown**, #8 (Street Cars) | 1.00 | 1.00 |
| U125 | **38¢ blue and tan**, #10 (Steamers) | 1.00 | 1.00 |

## 1990–1991. Post Office Artifacts

U126

| | | Unused | Used |
|---|---|---|---|
| U126 | **39¢ multicoloured**, #8 (Scales) | 1.00 | .50 |
| U127 | **39¢ multicoloured**, #10 (Scales) | 1.00 | .50 |
| U128 | **40¢ multicoloured**, #8 (Scales) | 1.00 | .50 |
| U129 | **40¢ multicoloured**, #10 (Scales) | 1.00 | .50 |
| U130 | **42¢ multicoloured**, #8 (Scales) | 1.00 | .50 |
| U131 | **42¢ multicoloured**, #10 (Scales) | 1.00 | .50 |

## 1991–1992. Colonial Postage Stamps

U132

| | | Unused | Used |
|---|---|---|---|
| U132 | **40¢ multicoloured**, #8 (New Brunswick) | 1.00 | 4.00 |
| U133 | **40¢ multicoloured**, #8 (Newfoundland) | 1.00 | 4.00 |
| U134 | **42¢ multicoloured**, #8 (Vancouver) | 1.00 | 4.00 |
| U135 | **40¢ multicoloured**, #10 (Nova Scotia) | 1.00 | 4.00 |
| U136 | **40¢ multicoloured**, #10 (Prince Edward Island) | 1.00 | 4.00 |
| U137 | **42¢ multicoloured**, #10 (British Columbia) | 1.00 | 4.00 |

## 1992–1995. Provincial Capital Cities

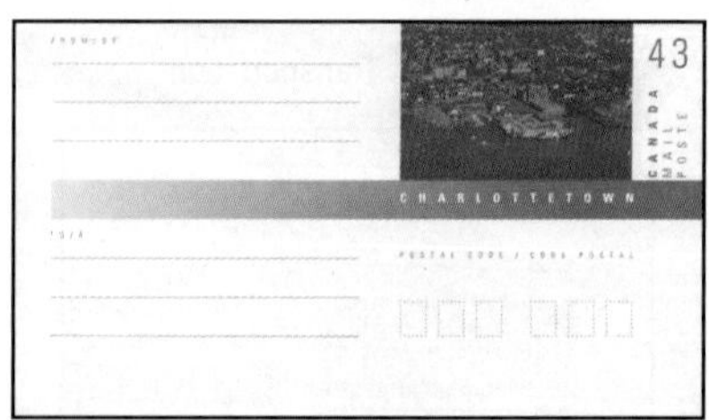


U138

| | | Unused | Used |
|---|---|---|---|
| U138 | **43¢ multicoloured**, #8 (Charlottetown) | 1.00 | 1.00 |
| U139 | **43¢ multicoloured**, #10 (Victoria) | 1.00 | 1.00 |
| U140 | **43¢ multicoloured**, #8 (St. John's) | 1.00 | 1.00 |
| U141 | **43¢ multicoloured**, #10 (Toronto) | 1.00 | 1.00 |
| U142 | **43¢ multicoloured**, #8 (Regina) | 1.00 | 1.40 |
| U143 | **43¢ multicoloured**, #10 (Halifax) | 1.00 | 1.00 |
| U144 | **43¢ multicoloured**, #8 (Yellowknife) | 1.00 | 1.00 |
| U145 | **43¢ multicoloured**, #10 (Winnipeg) | 1.00 | 1.00 |
| U146 | **43¢ multicoloured**, #8 (Whitehorse) | 1.00 | 4.00 |
| U147 | **43¢ multicoloured**, #10 (Fredericton) | 1.00 | 4.00 |
| U148 | **45¢ multicoloured**, #8 (Edmonton) | 1.00 | 1.00 |
| U149 | **45¢ multicoloured**, #10 (Quebec) | 1.00 | 1.00 |

**STATIONERY USED PRICING PREMIUMS**

Nice, clean, commercially used in-period, full envelope entires (i.e. not trimmed with an electric letter opener) will command a premium (typically more than an unused copy).

## 1996–2002. Birds of Canada

U154

| | | Unused | Used |
|---|---|---|---|
| U150 | **45¢ multicoloured**, #8 (Pileated woodpecker) | .85 | .35 |
| U151 | **45¢ multicoloured**, #10 (Atlantic puffin) | .85 | .35 |
| U152 | **45¢ multicoloured**, #8 (Ruby-throated hummingbird) | .85 | .35 |
| U153 | **45¢ multicoloured**, #10 (American kestrel) | .85 | .35 |
| U154 | **45¢ multicoloured**, #8 (Western grebe) | .85 | .35 |
| U155 | **45¢ multicoloured**, #10 (Mountain bluebird) | .85 | .35 |
| U156 | **45¢ multicoloured**, #8 (Gray-crowned rosy finch) | .85 | .35 |
| U157 | **45¢ multicoloured**, #10 (Eastern screech owl) | .85 | .35 |
| U158 | **46¢ multicoloured**, #8 (Hairy woodpecker) | .85 | .35 |
| a | straight edge seam, numeral in yellow | .90 | .40 |
| b | straight edge seam, numeral in white | .90 | .40 |
| U159 | **46¢ multicoloured**, #10 (Great crested flycatcher) | .85 | .35 |
| a | straight edge seam, numeral in blue green | .90 | .40 |
| b | straight edge seam, numeral in white | .90 | .40 |
| U160 | **46¢ multicoloured**, #8 (Canada warbler) | .85 | .35 |
| U161 | **46¢ multicoloured**, #10 (Blue jay) | .85 | .35 |
| U162 | **47¢ multicoloured**, #8 (Lapland Longspur), bar code ends in 01818 | .85 | .35 |
| a | bar code ends in 01830 | .85 | .60 |
| U163 | **47¢ multicoloured**, #10 (Golden Eagle), bar code ends in 01820 | .85 | .35 |
| a | bar code ends in 01831 | .85 | .60 |

## 1997. Scenic Highways (Window envelopes)

U164

| | | Unused | Used |
|---|---|---|---|
| U164 | **45¢ multicoloured**, #8 (Ontario Wine Route) | .85 | 8.00 |
| U165 | **45¢ multicoloured**, #10 (Ontario Wine Route) | .85 | 8.00 |
| U166 | **45¢ multicoloured**, #8 (Sea to Sky Highway, BC) | .85 | 8.00 |
| U167 | **45¢ multicoloured**, #10 (Sea to Sky Highway, BC) | .85 | 8.00 |

### Envelope Varieties

Same errors commonly occur on Canadian envelopes. These are not listed separately under each envelope type for which they are known, however, approximate price ranges are given below for these errors. Price depends on the general price and printing quality for envelopes of the same era.

| | |
|---|---|
| Albinos | $75.00–100.00 |
| Stamp inside envelope | $50.00–75.00 |
| Stamp impression in wrong place on envelope | $50.00–75.00 |
| Double or multiple impressions | $50.00–75.00 |
| Complete extra stamp impression | $50.00–75.00 |
| Surcharge on albino envelope | $50.00–75.00 |
| Misplaced or double surcharge | $10.00–50.00 |
| Offset impression (extra or inside the envelope) | $25.00–75.00 |
| Double envelope folding variety | $50.00–75.00 |

| | | Unused | Used |
|---|---|---|---|

### 2002–2006. Birds of Canada (self-adhesive flap)

Various printing dates appear on the back of these envelopes. The dates are either beside the UPC barcode or under the flap.

**U168** **domestic lettermail rate**, multicoloured #8 (American Goldfinch), no date — 1.75 — .35

| | | Unused | Used | | | Unused | Used |
|---|---|---|---|---|---|---|---|
| a | 2002-02-25 | 1.75 | .35 | f | 2004.07.02 | 1.75 | .35 |
| b | 2002-04-04 | 1.75 | .35 | g | 2004.11.02 | 1.75 | .35 |
| c | April 2002 | 1.75 | .35 | h | 2004.12.02 | 1.75 | .35 |
| d | 2002-11-01 | 1.75 | .35 | i | 2005.4.22 | 1.75 | .35 |
| e | 2003.02.03 | 1.75 | .35 | | | | |

**U169** **domestic lettermail rate**, multicoloured #10 (Scarlet Tanger), no date — 1.75 — .35

| | | Unused | Used | | | Unused | Used |
|---|---|---|---|---|---|---|---|
| a | 2002-02-25 | 1.75 | .35 | h | 2004.03.15 | 1.75 | .35 |
| b | 2002-04-04 | 1.75 | .35 | i | 2004.12.29 | 1.75 | .35 |
| c | April 2002 | 1.75 | .35 | j | 2005.03.11 | 1.75 | .35 |
| d | 2002-11-01 | 1.75 | .35 | k | 2005.08.05 | 1.75 | .35 |
| e | 2003.02.03 | 1.75 | .35 | l | 2005.10.01 | 1.75 | .35 |
| f | 2003.10.15 | 1.75 | .35 | m | 2006.01.13 | 1.75 | .35 |
| g | 2003.11.17 | 1.75 | .35 | n | 2006.06.16 | 1.75 | .35 |

### 2001. Roses Envelopes

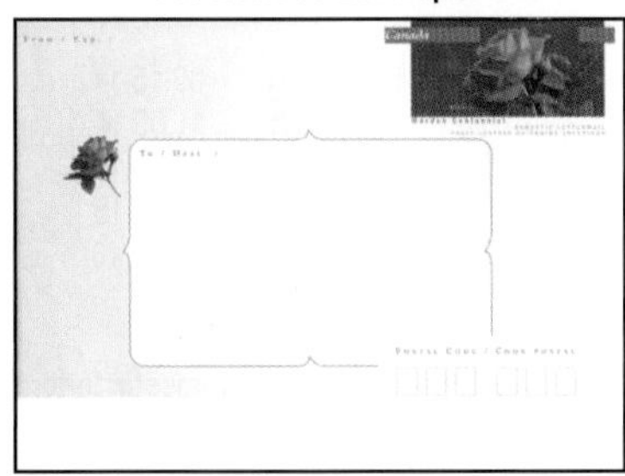

U170

(issued as part of a letter-writing kit, with 12 envelopes – three of each type – and 24 sheets of paper). The envelopes have no printed denomination (domestic lettermail) and are 191 mm x 137 mm.

| | | Unused | Used |
|---|---|---|---|
| **U170** | **Morden Centennial** | 2.50 | 2.50 |
| **U171** | **Champlain** | 2.50 | 2.50 |
| **U172** | **Canadian White Star** | 2.50 | 2.50 |
| **U173** | **Agnes** | 2.50 | 2.50 |

### 2003–2004. Tulips (self-adhesive flap)

U174

Printing dates appear under flap.

**U174** **domestic lettermail rate**, #8 (The Bishop Tulip)

| | | Unused | Used |
|---|---|---|---|
| a | 2003.04.04 | 1.75 | .35 |
| b | 2003.11.17 | 1.75 | .35 |
| c | 2005.01.21 | 1.75 | .35 |

**U175** **domestic lettermail rate**, #10 (Ottawa Tulip)

| | | Unused | Used | | | Unused | Used |
|---|---|---|---|---|---|---|---|
| a | 2003.04.04 | 1.75 | .35 | d | 2005.03.14 | 1.75 | .35 |
| b | 2004.03.15 | 1.75 | .35 | e | 2005.12.23 | 1.75 | .35 |
| c | 2004.12.29 | 1.75 | .35 | | | | |

### 2007–2008. Flowers [PERMANENT™ logo] (self-adhesive flap)

The indicium on the initial 2006 printings of size 8 envelopes is larger than subsequent printings.

Size 8, printing dates appear beside the UPC bar code.

**U176** **domestic lettermail rate**, red bergamot blossom (Sc. 2128)

| | | Unused | Used | | | Unused | Used |
|---|---|---|---|---|---|---|---|
| a | 2006.12.01 | 1.75 | .35 | d | 2007.13.07* | 1.75 | .35 |
| b | 2007.26.01 | 1.75 | .35 | e | 2007.13.11* | 1.75 | .35 |
| c | 2007.05.18 | 1.75 | .35 | f | 2008.02.19* | 1.75 | .35 |
| | | | | g | 2008.07.18* | 1.75 | .35 |

U178

Indicia with "Postage paid ..."

**U177** **domestic lettermail rate**, yellow lady's slipper (Sc. 2129/2132)

| | | Unused | Used | | | Unused | Used |
|---|---|---|---|---|---|---|---|
| a | 2006.12.01 | 1.75 | .35 | d | 2007.13.07* | 1.75 | .35 |
| b | 2007.26.01 | 1.75 | .35 | e | 2007.13.11* | 1.75 | .35 |
| c | 2007.05.18 | 1.75 | .35 | f | 2008.02.19* | 1.75 | .35 |
| | | | | g | 2008.07.18* | 1.75 | .35 |

**U178** **domestic lettermail rate**, pink fairy slipper (Sc. 2130/2133)

| | | Unused | Used | | | Unused | Used |
|---|---|---|---|---|---|---|---|
| a | 2006.12.01 | 1.75 | .35 | d | 2007.13.07* | 1.75 | .35 |
| b | 2007.26.01 | 1.75 | .35 | e | 2007.13.11* | 1.75 | .35 |
| c | 2007.05.18 | 1.75 | .35 | f | 2008.02.19* | 1.75 | .35 |
| | | | | g | 2008.07.18* | 1.75 | .35 |

**U179** **domestic lettermail rate**, himalayan blue poppy (Sc. 2131/2134)

| | | Unused | Used | | | Unused | Used |
|---|---|---|---|---|---|---|---|
| a | 2006.12.01 | 1.75 | .35 | d | 2007.13.07* | 1.75 | .35 |
| b | 2007.26.01 | 1.75 | .35 | e | 2007.13.11* | 1.75 | .35 |
| c | 2007.05.18 | 1.75 | .35 | f | 2008.02.19* | 1.75 | .35 |
| | | | | g | 2008.07.18* | 1.75 | .35 |

Size 10, printing dates appear under flap.

**U180** **domestic lettermail rate**, red bergamot blossom (Sc. 2128)

| | | Unused | Used | | | Unused | Used |
|---|---|---|---|---|---|---|---|
| a | 2006.12.01 | 1.75 | .35 | e | 2007.13.11* | 1.75 | .35 |
| b | 2007.01.26 | 1.75 | .35 | f | 2008.02.14* | 1.75 | .35 |
| c | 2007.05.18 | 1.75 | .35 | g | 2008.07.18* | 1.75 | .35 |
| d | 2007.13.07* | 1.75 | .35 | | | | |

**U181** **domestic lettermail rate**, yellow lady's slipper (Sc. 2129/2132)

| | | Unused | Used | | | Unused | Used |
|---|---|---|---|---|---|---|---|
| a | 2006.12.01 | 1.75 | .35 | e | 2007.13.11* | 1.75 | .35 |
| b | 2007.01.26 | 1.75 | .35 | f | 2008.02.14* | 1.75 | .35 |
| c | 2007.05.18 | 1.75 | .35 | g | 2008.07.18* | 1.75 | .35 |
| d | 2007.13.07* | 1.75 | .35 | | | | |

**U182** **domestic lettermail rate**, pink fairy slipper (Sc. 2130/2133)

| | | Unused | Used | | | Unused | Used |
|---|---|---|---|---|---|---|---|
| a | 2006.12.01 | 1.75 | .35 | e | 2007.13.11* | 1.75 | .35 |
| b | 2007.01.26 | 1.75 | .35 | f | 2008.02.14* | 1.75 | .35 |
| c | 2007.05.18 | 1.75 | .35 | g | 2008.07.18* | 1.75 | .35 |
| d | 2007.13.07* | 1.75 | .35 | | | | |

**U183** **domestic lettermail rate**, himalayan blue poppy (Sc. 2131/2134)

| | | Unused | Used | | | Unused | Used |
|---|---|---|---|---|---|---|---|
| a | 2006.12.01 | 1.75 | .35 | e | 2007.13.11* | 1.75 | .35 |
| b | 2007.01.26 | 1.75 | .35 | f | 2008.02.14* | 1.75 | .35 |
| c | 2007.05.18 | 1.75 | .35 | g | 2008.07.18* | 1.75 | .35 |
| d | 2007.13.07* | 1.75 | .35 | | | | |

### 2007–2008. Tourist Attractions [PERMANENT™ logo] (self-adhesive flap)

10 designs feature: Agawa Canyon (Sc. 1952c), Icefields Parkway (1952b), Northern Lights (1953a), Auyuittuq National Park (1904d), Canadian Tulip Festival (1904c), Peggy's Cove (1953e), Signal Hill Historic Site (1904e), Sugar Bushes (1903d), The Forks National Historic Site (1904a), White Pass & Yukon Route Railway (1903c).

U202

Indicia with "Postage paid ..."

Size 8, printing dates appear beside the UPC bar code.

**U184–193** **domestic lettermail rate**

| | | Unused | Used | | | Unused | Used |
|---|---|---|---|---|---|---|---|
| a | 2006.12.01 | 1.75 | .35 | d | 2007.13.07* | does this exist? | |
| b | 2007.26.01 | 1.75 | .35 | e | 2007.15.10* | 1.75 | .35 |
| c | 2007.05.18 | 1.75 | .35 | f | 2007.15.12* | 1.75 | .35 |

* indicia include "Postage paid - Port payé" under stamp image

Size 10, printing dates appear under flap.

**U194–203 domestic lettermail rate**

| | | | | | | | |
|---|---|---|---|---|---|---|---|
| a | 2006.12.01 | 1.75 | .35 | e | 2007.11.16* | 1.75 | .35 |
| b | 2007.01.26 | 1.75 | .35 | f | 2008.02.15* | 1.75 | .35 |
| c | 2007.05.18 | 1.75 | .35 | g | 2008.07.18* | 1.75 | .35 |
| d | 2007.13.07* | 1.75 | .35 | | | | |

U205

U212

U226

**2009. Gardens [PERMANENT™, domestic lettermail] (self-adhesive flap)**

4 designs feature: Shade (Sc. 2145a), Flower (Sc. 2145b), Water (Sc. 2145c), Rock (Sc. 2145d)

Size 8

**U204–207**

| | | | |
|---|---|---|---|
| a | 01.19.09 | 1.75 | .35 |
| b | 04.04.09 | 1.75 | .35 |
| c | 04.04.10 | 1.75 | .35 |
| d | 10.29.10 | 1.75 | .35 |
| e | 12.12.10 | 1.75 | .35 |
| f | 6.6.11 | 1.75 | .35 |

Size 10

**U208–211**

| | | | |
|---|---|---|---|
| a | 01.19.09 | 1.75 | .35 |
| b | 04.04.09 | 1.75 | .35 |
| c | 07.14.09 | 1.75 | .35 |
| d | 04.04.10 | 1.75 | .35 |
| e | 10.27.10 | 1.75 | .35 |
| f | 12.12.10 | 1.75 | .35 |
| g | 6.6.11 | 1.75 | .35 |

**2009. Orchids [PERMANENT™, domestic lettermail] (self-adhesive flap)**

4 designs feature: Dragon's Mouth (Sc. 1787), Round-leaved (Sc. 1788), Purple-fringed (Sc. 1789), Greater Yellow Lady's Slipper (Sc. 1790)

Size 8

**U212–215**

| | | | |
|---|---|---|---|
| a | 01.19.09 | 1.75 | .35 |
| b | 04.04.09 | 1.75 | .35 |
| c | 04.04.10 | 1.75 | .35 |
| d | 10.29.10 | 1.75 | .35 |
| e | 12.12.10 | 1.75 | .35 |
| f | 6.6.11 | 1.75 | .35 |

Size 10

**U216–219**

| | | | |
|---|---|---|---|
| a | 01.19.09 | 1.75 | .35 |
| b | 04.04.09 | 1.75 | .35 |
| c | 07.14.09 | 1.75 | .35 |
| d | 04.04.10 | 1.75 | .35 |
| e | 10.27.10 | 1.75 | .35 |
| f | 12.12.10 | 1.75 | .35 |
| g | 6.6.11 | 1.75 | .35 |

**2009. Fishing Flies [PERMANENT™, domestic lettermail] (self-adhesive flap)**

10 designs feature: Coquihalla Orange (Sc. 1715), Steelhead Bee (Sc. 1716), Dark Montréal (Sc. 1717), Lady Amherst (Sc. 1718), Coho Blue (Sc. 1719), Cosseboom Special (Sc. 1720), Alevin (Sc. 2087a/2088a), Jock Scott (Sc. 2087b/2088b), Mickey Finn (Sc. 2087d/2088c), P.E.I. Fly (Sc. 2087c/2088d)

Size 8

**U220–229**

| | | | |
|---|---|---|---|
| a | 01.19.09 | 1.75 | .35 |
| b | 04.04.09 | 1.75 | .35 |
| c | 04.04.10 | 1.75 | .35 |
| d | 10.29.10 | 1.75 | .35 |
| e | 12.12.10 | 1.75 | .35 |
| f | 6.6.11 | 1.75 | .35 |

Size 10

**U230–239**

| | | | |
|---|---|---|---|
| a | 01.19.09 | 1.75 | .35 |
| b | 04.04.09 | 1.75 | .35 |
| c | 07.14.09 | 1.75 | .35 |
| d | 04.04.10 | 1.75 | .35 |
| e | 10.29.10 | 1.75 | .35 |
| f | 12.12.10 | 1.75 | .35 |
| g | 6.6.11 | 1.75 | .35 |

**2011. Royal Wedding (self-adhesive flap)**

**U240** **multicoloured**, size 10 1.75 .35

**2012. Flowers [PERMANENT™, domestic lettermail] (self-adhesive flap)**

10 designs feature: Daffodils - Yellow (Sc. 2092), White (Sc. 2093); Lilacs - White (Sc. 2207), Pale purple (Sc. 2208); Peonies - Elgin (Sc. 2261), Coral 'n Gold (Sc. 2262); Rhododendrons - white (Sc. 2319), pink (Sc. 2320); African Violets - red (Sc. 2377), purple (Sc. 2379)

Size 10, printing dates appear under flap.

**U241–250**

| | | | | | | | |
|---|---|---|---|---|---|---|---|
| a | 9.28.11 | 1.75 | .50 | e | 05.09.14 | 1.75 | .50 |
| b | 6.22.12 | 1.75 | .50 | f | 05.15.15 | 1.75 | .50 |
| c | 08.24.12 | 1.75 | .50 | g | 11.25.15 | 1.75 | .50 |
| d | 06.06.13 | 1.75 | .50 | h | 05.10.16 | 1.75 | .50 |

The date '03.22.13' has been reported; confirmation is requested.

**2012. Animals [PERMANENT™, domestic lettermail] (self-adhesive flap)**

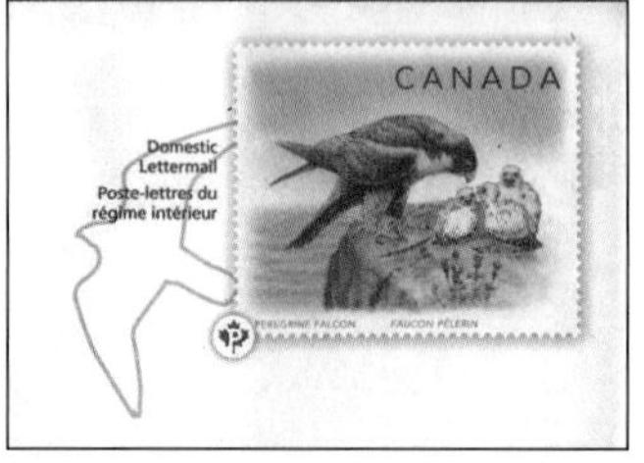

9 designs feature: Loon (Sc. 1687); Polar Bear (Sc. 1690); White-tailed Deer (Sc. 1688); Atlantic Walrus (Sc. 1689); Peregrin Falcon (Sc. 1691); Sable Island Horse (Sc. 1692); Moose (Sc. 1693); Grizzly Bear (Sc. 1694); Blue Whale (Sc. 2405)

Size 10, printing dates appear under flap.

**U251–259**

| | | | | | | | |
|---|---|---|---|---|---|---|---|
| a | 9.28.11 | 1.75 | .50 | g | 05.15.14 | 1.75 | .50 |
| b | 6.15.12 | 1.75 | .50 | h | 11.05.14 | 1.75 | .50 |
| c | 8.17.12 | 1.75 | .50 | i | 04.15.15 | 1.75 | .50 |
| d | 12.17.12 | 1.75 | .50 | j | 11.25.15 | 1.75 | .50 |
| e | 03.22.13 | 1.75 | .50 | k | 05.10.16 | 1.75 | .50 |
| f | 06.06.13 | 1.75 | .50 | | | | |

**2012. Animals [PERMANENT™, domestic lettermail]**

8 designs feature: Arctic Hare (Sc. 2426); Red Fox (Sc. 2427); Canada Geese (Sc. 2428); Polar Bear (Sc. 2429); Racoons (Sc. 2506); Caribou (Sc. 2507); Loon (Sc. 2508); Moose (Sc. 2509). Monarch size.

**U260–267** 1.75 .50

U268–71

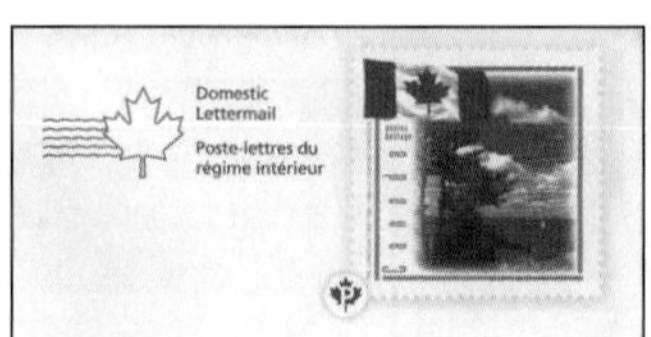

U272

**2012. Write me back [PERMANENT™, domestic lettermail]**

4 designs using a Picture Postage™ frame, with designs extending outside of the 'stamp': Frog, Ladybug, Goose, Flower. Each design sold in a set of two different-sized envelopes, one for use as a reply to the original sender.

**U268–271**

| | | | |
|---|---|---|---|
| a | 5"x6.5" | 4.00 | 2.50 |
| b | 4.375"x5.75" (reply) | 4.00 | 2.50 |

**2014. Canada Flag**

**U272** Based on Sc. 1546; Size 10, printing dates appear under flap.

| | | | |
|---|---|---|---|
| a | 09.15.14 | 2.25 | .50 |
| b | 04.15.15 | 2.25 | .50 |
| c | 10.14.15 | 2.25 | .50 |
| d | 05.10.16 (maple leaf and waves at left are red) | 2.25 | .50 |

Postal Stationery

## SPECIAL ORDER ENVELOPES

The following is a list of stamp impressions known to have been used on various types of envelopes prepared for use by private businesses or government departments which differ in some basic way from regular issue envelopes.

The value shown is for the most common item for each stamp impression. Some envelopes in unusual size, style, etc. can demand a considerable premium.

For more detailed information see Webb's *Postal Stationery Catalogue of Canada & Newfoundland*.

| | | Unused | Used |
|---|---|---|---|
| | **1894. Queen Victoria As Illustration U3** | | |
| UO1 | **1¢ blue** | 15.00 | 75.00 |
| UO2 | **3¢ red** | 25.00 | 90.00 |
| | **1923–1931. King George V As Illustration U19** | | |
| UO3 | **1¢ orange**, not embossed | 6.00 | 4.00 |
| a | precancelled | 10.00 | 5.00 |
| UO4 | **1¢ green**, not embossed | — | 12.00 |
| a | precancelled | 18.00 | 6.00 |
| UO5 | **2¢ green**, not embossed | 4.00 | 5.00 |
| a | precancelled | 45.00 | — |
| UO6 | **2¢ green**, embossed | 60.00 | 25.00 |
| UO7 | **2¢ red**, not embossed | 6.00 | 3.00 |
| UO8 | **2¢ brown**, not embossed | 12.00 | 5.00 |
| UO9 | **3¢ brown**, not embossed | 25.00 | 26.00 |
| UO10 | **3¢ red** (shades), not embossed | 7.50 | 4.00 |
| UO11 | **2¢ on 3¢ red**, surcharged | 35.00 | 40.00 |
| | **1924–1931. King George V, head with shaded hair As Illustration U39** | | |
| UO12 | **1¢ orange** | 22.50 | 25.00 |
| a | precancelled | — | 50.00 |
| UO13 | **1¢ green** | 40.00 | 40.00 |
| UO14 | **2¢ green** | 10.00 | 7.50 |
| UO15 | **2¢ red** | 12.00 | 8.00 |
| UO16 | **2¢ brown** | 15.00 | 10.00 |
| UO17 | **3¢ brown** | — | 80.00 |
| UO18 | **3¢ red** | 12.00 | 9.00 |
| UO19 | **2¢ on 3¢ red**, surcharged | — | 40.00 |
| UO20 | **2¢ green + 2¢ green** stamp impression added (O.H.M.S.) | 40.00 | 60.00 |
| | **1932. The Arch Issue As illustration U43** | | |
| UO21 | **1¢ green** | 3.50 | 3.00 |
| a | precancelled | 9.00 | 3.50 |
| UO22 | **2¢ brown** | 4.50 | 3.50 |
| UO23 | **2¢ green**, precancelled | — | 90.00 |
| UO24 | **3¢ red** | 5.00 | 3.00 |
| | **1933. The Medallion Issue As illustration U48** | | |
| UO25 | **1¢ green** | 6.00 | 2.50 |
| a | precancelled | 4.50 | 3.00 |
| UO26 | **2¢ brown** | 5.00 | 3.50 |
| UO27 | **3¢ red** | 6.00 | 5.00 |
| | **1938–1951. King George VI As illustration U53** | | |
| UO28 | **1¢ green** | 4.00 | 2.00 |
| a | precancelled | 6.00 | 2.50 |
| UO29 | **2¢ brown** (shades) | 12.00 | 3.00 |
| UO30 | **2¢ green** (shades) | 7.50 | 5.00 |
| a | precancelled | — | 10.00 |
| UO31 | **3¢ red** | 2.00 | 1.75 |
| UO32 | **3¢ brown** | 15.00 | 8.00 |
| UO33 | **3¢ purple** | 4.00 | 1.50 |
| UO34 | **4¢ red** | 6.00 | 1.25 |
| UO35 | **4¢ orange** | — | 12.00 |

| | | Unused | Used |
|---|---|---|---|
| UO36 | **2¢ on 1¢ green**, surcharged | — | 75.00 |
| UO36A | **5¢ on 4¢ orange**, surcharged | 150.00 | 125.00 |
| UO37 | **2¢ brown + 1¢ green** stamp impression added | — | 45.00 |
| UO38 | **2¢ brown + 2¢ brown** stamp impression added | 110.00 | 90.00 |
| UO39 | **3¢ red + 1¢ green** stamp impression added | 60.00 | 40.00 |
| | **1954–1955. The First Karsh Issue (EIIR) As illustration U73** | | |
| UO40 | **4¢ purple** | 17.50 | 15.00 |
| UO41 | **5¢ blue** | 15.00 | 12.00 |
| | **1955. The Wilding Issue (EIIR) As illustration U76** | | |
| UO42 | **2¢ green** | 8.00 | 7.50 |
| UO43 | **4¢ purple** | 4.00 | 2.00 |
| UO44 | **5¢ blue** | 4.50 | 2.00 |
| UO45 | **2¢ green + 1¢ brown stamp** impression added | 10.00 | 12.00 |
| UO46 | **2¢ green (U73) + 1¢ brown** stamp impression added | 15.00 | 20.00 |
| UO47 | **4¢ purple (2-bar obliteration) + 2¢ green** stamp impression added | 90.00 | 50.00 |
| | **1962. The Second Karsh Issue (EIIR) As illustration U79** | | |
| UO48 | **2¢ green** | 15.00 | 10.00 |
| UO49 | **4¢ purple** | 8.00 | 8.00 |
| UO50 | **5¢ blue** | 12.00 | 10.00 |
| | **1963. The Cameo Issue (EIIR). Hair consists of dots As illustration U82** | | |
| UO51 | **3¢ purple** | — | 45.00 |
| UO52 | **4¢ red** | 5.00 | 3.00 |
| | **1964. Hair consists of lines** | | |
| UO53 | **3¢ purple** | 12.00 | 30.00 |
| UO54 | **5¢ blue** | 5.00 | 4.50 |
| | **1967–1973. The Centennial Issue As illustration U89** | | |
| UO55 | **3¢ purple** | 25.00 | 40.00 |
| UO56 | **4¢ red** | 10.00 | 18.00 |
| UO57 | **5¢ blue** | 12.00 | 20.00 |
| a | precancelled | — | 50.00 |
| UO58 | **6¢ orange** | 12.00 | 18.00 |
| UO59 | **6¢ black** | 7.50 | 10.00 |
| a | precancelled | 6.00 | 10.00 |
| UO60 | **7¢ green** | 70.00 | — |
| UO61 | **8¢ slate** | 1.50 | 2.50 |
| UO62 | **8¢ slate**, stamp size 21 mm x 16.5 mm | 11.00 | 12.00 |
| UO63 | **8¢ Alaskan Highway**, purple | 7.00 | 10.00 |
| UO64 | **8¢ Alaskan Highway**, black | 400.00 | 600.00 |
| | **1975–1979. The Fisher Issue As illustration U105** | | |
| UO65 | **10¢ red & blue** | — | 2.00 |
| UO66 | **12¢ green & blue** | — | 2.00 |
| UO67 | **14¢ purple & blue** | — | 2.00 |
| UO68 | **17¢ brown & blue** | 5.00 | 2.00 |
| | **1982. The Transportation Issue As illustration U122** | | |
| UO69 | **30¢ olive** | 2.00 | 1.50 |

**1991–1994. Same designs as the current postage stamps, but without value** "Postes/Postage" is replaced with "Postage paid/Port payé" to the lower left of the stamp impression.

| | | Unused | Used |
|---|---|---|---|
| UO70 | **as Flag stamp** No. 1192 with no value shown | 3.00 | 5.00 |
| UO71 | **as Manitoba** commemorative stamp No. 1562 with no value shown | 25.00 | 25.00 |

Postal Stationery

| | | Unused | Used |
|---|---|---|---|
| | **1998. Same design as the Year of the Tiger commemorative stamp** | | |
| **UO72** | **45¢ multicoloured** No. 1708 | 4.50 | 3.00 |
| | **2000. Same design as the IMAX commemorative stamp in the Millennium Collection** | | |
| **UO73** | **46¢ multicoloured** No. 1818a | 6.00 | 6.00 |
| | **2000. Same design as the Year of the Dragon commemorative stamp** | | |
| **UO74** | **46¢ multicoloured** No. 1836 | 2.00 | 2.00 |
| | **2001. Same design as the Year of the Snake commemorative stamp** | | |
| **UO75** | **47¢ multicoloured** No. 1883 | 2.00 | 2.00 |
| | **2008. Same design as the Mental Health semi-postal stamp** | | |
| **UO76** | **multicoloured** No. B14 with no value shown | 5.00 | 5.00 |
| | **2011. Same design as the Holly Christmas stamp** | | |
| **UO77** | **P multicoloured** No. 2491 | – | 10.00 |

Used by Canada Post for mailing of Christmas cards to Venture One customers.

## ELECTION ENVELOPES

Envelopes especially printed for use by various election officials for specific types of election business showing different form numbers, printing dates and quantities in the upper left corner. All are size #10 envelopes.

| | | Unused | Used |
|---|---|---|---|
| | **1925. King George V**<br>**As Illustration U17** | | |
| **UE1** | **3¢ red** | 6.00 | 3.00 |
| | **1931. King George V, head with shaded hair**<br>**As Illustration U39** | | |
| **UE2** | **2¢ green** | 15.00 | 5.00 |
| **UE3** | **2¢ green + 1¢ green** stamp impression added | 15.00 | 10.00 |
| **UE4** | **2¢ red + 1¢ red** stamp impression added | 7.50 | 4.00 |
| | **1933. The Medallion Issue**<br>**As illustration U48** | | |
| **UE5** | **3¢ red** | 12.00 | 3.00 |
| | **1940. Kimg George VI**<br>**As illustration U53** | | |
| **UE6** | **3¢ red** | 10.00 | 5.00 |
| **UE7** | **4¢ red** | 10.00 | 5.00 |
| **UE8** | **4¢ orange** | 20.00 | 15.00 |
| **UE9** | **3¢ red (U39) + 1¢ green** stamp impression added | 200.00 | 200.00 |
| **UE10** | **3¢ red (U46) + 1¢ green** stamp impression added | 150.00 | 50.00 |
| **UE11** | **3¢ red (U53) + 1¢ green** stamp impression added | 10.00 | 3.00 |
| **UE12** | **5¢ on 4¢ red**, surcharged | 30.00 | 16.00 |
| **UE13** | **5¢ on 4¢ orange**, surcharged | 50.00 | 20.00 |
| | **1957–1963. The Wilding Issue (EIIR)**<br>**As illustration U76** | | |
| **UE14** | **5¢ blue** | 4.00 | 2.00 |
| | **1963–1965. The Second Karsh Issue (EIIR)**<br>**As illustration U79** | | |
| **UE15** | **5¢ blue** | 4.00 | 2.00 |
| | **1968. The Cameo Issue (EIIR). Hair consists of lines**<br>**As illustration U82** | | |
| **UE16** | **5¢ blue** | 30.00 | 27.50 |
| **UE17** | **6¢ on 5¢ blue**, surcharged | 200.00 | 200.00 |
| | **1972–1974. The Centennial Issue**<br>**As illustration U89** | | |
| **UE18** | **6¢ black** | 15.00 | 2.00 |
| **UE19** | **8¢ slate** | 15.00 | 2.00 |

Postal Stationery

## REGULAR AND SPECIAL ORDER LETTER SHEETS

UD1

UD5

| | | Unused | Used |
|---|---|---|---|
| | **1893–1895. Rosette under numerals.**<br>**(Special order for CPR mailings)** | | |
| **UD1** | **1¢ black** | 90.00 | 65.00 |

UD2

UD3

| | | Unused | Used |
|---|---|---|---|
| | **1973. Floral domestogrammes (Regular Issue)** | | |
| **UD2** | **8¢ multicoloured**, "Postage/Poste" below stamp | .75 | 10.00 |
| a | set of 12 | 10.00 | |
| **UD3** | **8¢ multicoloured**, "Postage/Postes" below stamp | 1.00 | 20.00 |
| a | set of 12 | 13.00 | |

Values for First Day cancelled copies of UD2 and UD3 are the same as for unused copies.

| | | Unused | Used |
|---|---|---|---|
| | **1973. Centennial (Regular Issue)** | | |
| **UD5** | **8¢ slate**, 185 mm x 257 mm | 15.00 | — |
| **UD6** | **8¢ slate**, 203 mm x 343 mm | 15.00 | — |

## POST BANDS AND WRAPPERS

Wrappers (W) are 152-203 mm x 336–381 mm and include the following: "This wrapper to be used only by publishers and for the sole purpose of mailing second class matter to the United States."

Post Bands (PB) are 121 mm x 241–279 mm and were sold to the public.

Used copies of post bands and wrappers usually have roller or smudge cancels. For copies with clean dated postmarks add 50%. Precancel types on the post bands and wrappers are illustrated in the section on the post cards.

**1875. Scrollwork around numerals, scallops around inner oval, cream paper**

PB1

PB2

PB3

| | | Unused | Used |
|---|---|---|---|
| **PB1** | **1¢ dark blue**, 127 mm x 241 mm | 4.00 | 8.00 |
| a | stamp at left, size 125 mm x 291 mm | 125.00 | |
| b | 1880, size 127 mm x 279 mm | 4.00 | 7.00 |
| | **1882. Shield-like ornament under numerals,**<br>**cream to pale buff paper** | | |
| **PB2** | **1¢ blue**, shades | 3.50 | 6.00 |
| a | stitch watermark | 15.00 | 15.00 |
| b | violet blue colour | 4.00 | 6.00 |

**1887. Scrollwork around numerals, no scallops, sharper lines in face and neck, white to manilla paper**

| | | Unused | Used |
|---|---|---|---|
| PB3 | **1¢ blue**, shades | 1.50 | 3.50 |
| a | thin cream tissue | 3.50 | 8.00 |
| b | stitch watermark | 15.00 | 15.00 |
| c | part of design at left | 35.00 | — |

**1892. Rosette under numerals, cream to light brown paper**

PB5

| | | Unused | Used |
|---|---|---|---|
| PB4 | **1¢ blue** | 3.00 | 4.50 |
| a | stitch watermark | 15.00 | 15.00 |
| PB5 | **1¢ black**, hard brown wove paper | 3.00 | 4.50 |
| a | cream paper | 3.00 | 6.00 |
| b | stitch watermark | 15.00 | — |

**1898. Maple Leaf issue**
**Paper in various shades**

PB6

PB7

W11

| | | Unused | Used |
|---|---|---|---|
| PB6 | **1¢ green**, cream paper | 2.00 | 3.75 |
| a | 1¢ green, greenish brown paper | 3.50 | 6.00 |

**1903. King Edward VII**
**Various shades of paper**

| | | Unused | Used |
|---|---|---|---|
| PB7 | **1¢ green** | 2.00 | 3.75 |
| a | hard oily buff wove paper | 4.50 | 6.00 |
| W8 | **1¢ green**, 152 mm x 330 mm | 3.80 | 6.00 |
| a | size 165 mm x 381 mm | 5.00 | 7.00 |
| W9 | **2¢ carmine** | 8.00 | 45.00 |
| W10 | **3¢ slate violet** | 75.00 | 120.00 |
| W11 | **1¢ on 2¢ carmine** | 4.00 | 20.00 |
| W12 | **1¢ on 3¢ slate violet** | 50.00 | 80.00 |

W10, W12: used values are for large pieces bearing complete inscription and stamp impression. Clean undamaged entires, substantially higher.

**1912. King George V**
**Manila paper**

PB13

For description of Dies I, II and III see note above post card UX26.

| | | Unused | Used |
|---|---|---|---|
| PB13 | **1¢ green**, wove paper, Die II | 2.50 | 3.50 |
| a | laid paper, Die II | 1.50 | 2.50 |
| W14 | **1¢ green**, wove paper, Die I | 2.00 | 4.00 |
| a | laid paper, Die I | 2.50 | 5.00 |
| b | as "W14", Die II | — | 150.00 |
| c | Die Ia | 150.00 | 150.00 |
| PB15 | **1¢ orange**, laid paper, Die II | 3.50 | 5.00 |
| a | wove paper, Die II | 1.00 | 2.00 |
| b | as "a", Die III | 20.00 | 20.00 |
| W16 | **1¢ orange**, Die I | 5.00 | 10.00 |
| a | same, Die III | 3.50 | 7.00 |

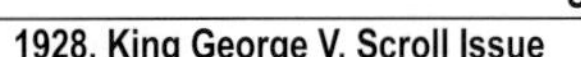

**1928. King George V. Scroll Issue**

PB17

PB21

| | | Unused | Used |
|---|---|---|---|
| PB17 | **1¢ orange** | 1.50 | 3.00 |
| W18 | **1¢ orange** | 2.50 | 6.00 |

**1930–1932. King George V. Arch Issue**

| | | Unused | Used |
|---|---|---|---|
| PB19 | **1¢ orange**, manila | 13.00 | 17.00 |
| W20 | **1¢ orange**, manila | 15.00 | 27.00 |
| PB21 | **1¢ green**, kraft | 2.50 | 3.50 |
| a | manila | 5.00 | 6.00 |
| W22 | **1¢ green**, kraft | 2.50 | 3.50 |
| a | manila | 6.00 | 8.00 |

**1932. King George V. Medallion Issue**

PB23

W25

| | | Unused | Used |
|---|---|---|---|
| PB23 | **1¢ green**, grey kraft | 3.00 | 4.00 |
| a | kraft | 6.00 | 9.00 |
| W24 | **1¢ green**, grey kraft | 4.00 | 8.00 |
| a | kraft | 7.00 | 12.00 |

**1935. King George V. Front Face**

| | | Unused | Used |
|---|---|---|---|
| W25 | **1¢ green** | 10.00 | 20.00 |

**1935. King George V. Profile Head**

PB26

PB28

| | | Unused | Used |
|---|---|---|---|
| PB26 | **1¢ green** | 1.50 | 2.50 |
| W27 | **1¢ green**, green kraft | 4.00 | 8.00 |
| a | brown kraft | 5.00 | 9.00 |

**1938–1943. King George VI**

| | | Unused | Used |
|---|---|---|---|
| PB28 | **1¢ green** | .25 | .50 |
| a | precancelled (Type A) | — | 2.00 |
| W29 | **1¢ green**, green kraft | 5.00 | 9.00 |
| a | brown kraft | 3.00 | 5.00 |
| PB30 | **2¢ olive green**, cream paper, Die dated 1943 | .75 | 1.00 |
| a | precancelled (Type A) | — | 10.00 |
| W31 | **2¢ olive green** | 2.50 | 7.00 |

Note: Precancel types are illustrated in the Post Card section.

### 1954. Queen Elizabeth II

PB33

| | | Unused | Used |
|---|---|---|---|
| PB32 | **1¢ brown** | 1.00 | 3.00 |
| PB33 | **2¢ green** | .75 | 1.25 |
| a | precancelled (Type A) | — | 5.00 |
| W34 | **2¢ green** | 3.00 | 25.00 |

### 1960. Queen Elizabeth II

PB36

PB38

| | | Unused | Used |
|---|---|---|---|
| PB36 | **1¢ brown** | .50 | 2.50 |
| PB37 | **2¢ green** | .50 | 1.00 |
| a | precancelled (Type C) | .75 | 1.50 |

### 1964. Queen Elizabeth II

| | | Unused | Used |
|---|---|---|---|
| PB38 | **2¢ green** | .50 | 25.00 |
| a | precancelled (5 printed green lines) | 8.50 | 25.00 |

## AIR LETTERS

All Air Letters are printed on pale grey to blue grey paper. The paper was watermarked until 1957 when the use of watermarked paper was discontinued. Because of the wide distance between watermarks, examples of early issues can be found showing only small portions of the watermark, or none at all.

### 1947. King George VI

Type A The sheet folds into 3 panels
Type B The sheet folds into 4 panels

**Printed by Le Comptoir National.**
**Rounded ends on the top and side flaps.**
**Letters in the tablet box and on the back (enclosure note) are without serifs.**

UA1

| | | Unused | Used |
|---|---|---|---|
| UA1 | **10¢ blue**, square corners at bottom of the sheet (A) | 35.00 | 55.00 |
| a | rounded corners at bottom of the sheet (A) | 7.00 | 20.00 |

**Printed by Globe Envelope Ltd.**
**Straight ends on the top and side flaps.**
**Serif letters in the tablet box and on the back (enclosure note)**

| | | Unused | Used |
|---|---|---|---|
| UA2 | **10¢ blue** (A) | 3.50 | 12.00 |
| a | **10¢ blue**, error "second fold her" (A) | 25.00 | 35.00 |
| UA3 | **15¢ carmine** (A) | 10.00 | 30.00 |

**1948. Printed by Le Comptoir National.**
**Rounded ends on the top and side flaps.**
**Serif letters in the tablet box and**
**sans serif letters on the back (enclosure note).**

| | | Unused | Used |
|---|---|---|---|
| UA4 | **10¢ blue**, 47 mm wide tablet box (B) | 5.00 | 12.00 |
| UA5 | **10¢ blue**, 45 mm wide tablet box (B) | 3.50 | 12.00 |

**1949. Printed by Globe Envelope Ltd.**
**Straight ends on the top and side flaps.**
**Serif letters on front and back.**
**The "P" is below "AI" of "AIR" in the tablet box.**

| | | Unused | Used |
|---|---|---|---|
| UA6 | **10¢ blue**, (B) | 4.50 | 10.00 |
| UA7 | **15¢ carmine**, (B) | 5.00 | 30.00 |

**1949. Printed by Barber-Ellis Co. As UA6, UA7**
**except the "P" is directly below the "AI" of "AIR".**

| | | Unused | Used |
|---|---|---|---|
| UA8 | **10¢ blue**, (B) | 6.00 | 10.00 |
| UA9 | **15¢ carmine**, (B) | 8.00 | 40.00 |

**1950–1953. Plane over Landscape issue.**
**Undated sheets.**
**Horizontal line below the plane is almost straight**

UA10

UA18

| | | Unused | Used |
|---|---|---|---|
| UA10 | **10¢ blue** | 3.50 | 7.50 |
| UA11 | **15¢ carmine** | 6.00 | 20.00 |

**Horizontal line below the plane is very wavy.**
**Undated sheets**

| | | Unused | Used |
|---|---|---|---|
| UA12 | **10¢ blue** | 3.00 | 7.00 |
| UA13 | **15¢ carmine** | 3.50 | 25.00 |

**Straight horizontal line. Sheets dated "52"**

| | | Unused | Used |
|---|---|---|---|
| UA14 | **10¢ blue**, the size of "52" is 2.5 mm x 1.5 mm | 3.00 | 6.00 |
| UA15 | **10¢ blue**, the size of "52" is 3mm x 2 mm | 8.00 | 10.00 |
| UA16 | **15¢ carmine**, the size of "52" is 2.5 mm x 1.5 mm | 3.50 | 15.00 |
| UA17 | **15¢ carmine**, the size of "52" is 3mm x 2 mm | 10.00 | 25.00 |

**1953. Plane over Globe issue.**
**"AEROGRAMME etc." in upper left corner**

| | | Unused | Used |
|---|---|---|---|
| UA18 | **10¢ blue** | 1.50 | 3.00 |

**1955–1958. Now "AEROGRAMME etc." in lower left corner**

| | | Unused | Used |
|---|---|---|---|
| UA19 | **10¢ blue**, solid address lines. "First fold here" to the left of the guide line | 12.00 | 15.00 |
| UA20 | **10¢ blue**, as before. except "First fold here" to the right of the guide line | 2.50 | 4.00 |
| a | unwatermarked | 8.00 | 10.00 |
| UA21 | **10¢ blue**, address lines dotted, unwatermarked | 1.75 | 2.50 |
| a | watermarked | 150.00 | 100.00 |

**1960–1966. "CANADA" and**
**a maple leaf above a plane**

UA22

| | | Unused | Used |
|---|---|---|---|
| UA22 | **10¢ red, black and grey**, 4 dotted address lines | 2.00 | 3.00 |
| UA23 | **10¢ red, black and grey**, 5 dotted address lines, rounded flap join | 2.50 | 5.00 |
| a | square flap join | 10.00 | 15.00 |

Postal Stationery

| | | Unused | Used |
|---|---|---|---|

**1966. Stylized plane and maple leaf. "expo 67" and Centennial emblem on back.**

UA24

| | | Unused | Used |
|---|---|---|---|
| UA24 | **10¢ red, black and grey**, dotted line at "First fold here" | 1.50 | 2.50 |
| UA25 | **10¢ red, black and grey**, without dotted line at "First fold here" | 300.00 | 150.00 |

**1967–1968. Without the Expo and Centennial emblems on back.**

| | | Unused | Used |
|---|---|---|---|
| UA26 | **10¢ red, black and grey**, sender's address lines 52 mm long | 1.50 | 3.00 |
| UA27 | **10¢ red, black and grey**, (shades) sender's address line 67 mm long | 1.50 | 2.50 |

**1971–1972. Value in maple leaf, with a goose on the front**

UA28

| | | Unused | Used |
|---|---|---|---|
| UA28 | **15¢ blue and red**, without decorative panel on the back | 2.50 | 4.00 |

**With decorative panel on back**

| | | Unused | Used |
|---|---|---|---|
| UA29 | **15¢ blue and red**, angled flap corners | 2.75 | 4.00 |
| UA30 | **15¢ blue and red**, rounded flap corners, no dots before or after "to open" | 3.50 | 7.50 |
| a | as previous, tagged | 100.00 | — |
| UA31 | **15¢ blue and red**, rounded flap corners, dots before and after "to open" | 1.25 | 3.00 |
| a | as previous, tagged | 1.50 | 3.50 |

**1972–1975. With the goose now on the back**

| | | Unused | Used |
|---|---|---|---|
| UA32 | **15¢ blue and red**, tagged to the left of the value | 1.00 | 10.00 |
| a | tagged to the right of the value | .75 | 10.00 |
| UA33 | **20¢ blue and red** | 1.25 | 15.00 |

**1973. Floral Aerogrammes**

UA34 UA35

| | | Unused | Used |
|---|---|---|---|
| UA34 | **15¢ multicoloured flowers** of the provinces. "Postage/Poste" below stamp | .75 | 15.00 |
| a | set of 12 | 10.00 | |
| UA35 | **15¢ multicoloured flowers**. Corrected to "Postage/Postes" below stamp | 1.50 | 25.00 |
| a | set of 12 | 20.00 | |

Values for First Day cancelled copies of UA34 and UA35 are the same as for unused copies.

**1976–1982. Maple leaf to the left of the value. Reproductions of paintings on the back.**

UA36

| | | Unused | Used |
|---|---|---|---|
| UA36 | 25¢ blue and red, Prairie sky | .80 | 15.00 |
| UA37 | 25¢ blue and red, Shoreline landscape | .80 | 15.00 |
| UA38 | 30¢ blue and red, Arctic sky | .80 | 15.00 |
| UA39 | 30¢ blue and red, Farmland | .80 | 15.00 |
| a | blue colour missing | 90.00 | |
| UA40 | 35¢ blue and red, Fishing village | .80 | 15.00 |
| UA41 | 60¢ blue and red, Mountains | .80 | 15.00 |

**1983–1987. Aircraft**

UA42

| | | Unused | Used |
|---|---|---|---|
| UA42 | **64¢ blue and red**, back text at the top | 1.25 | 20.00 |
| UA43 | **64¢ blue and red**, back text at the bottom | 1.25 | 20.00 |
| UA44 | **68¢ grey**, umber and red | 1.25 | 20.00 |
| UA45 | **72¢ blue**, violet and red | 1.50 | 20.00 |
| UA46 | **74¢ blue**, grey and red | 1.50 | 20.00 |
| UA47 | **76¢ grey green**, light grey and red | 1.60 | 20.00 |

**1989–1995. Motorless flight**

UA49

| | | Unused | Used |
|---|---|---|---|
| UA48 | **78¢ multicoloured**, balloons | 1.60 | 20.00 |
| UA49 | **80¢ multicoloured**, balloons | 1.60 | 20.00 |
| UA50 | **84¢ multicoloured**, glider | 1.70 | 20.00 |
| UA51 | **86¢ light mauve**, yellow and red | 1.70 | 20.00 |
| a | violet, yellow and red (printed in Australia by LM) | 10.00 | 15.00 |
| UA52 | **88¢ multicoloured**, kite | 1.70 | 20.00 |
| UA53 | **90¢ multicoloured**, parachute | 1.80 | 20.00 |

**1996. Birds**

| | | Unused | Used |
|---|---|---|---|
| UA54 | **90¢ multicoloured**, Harlequin duck | 1.80 | 20.00 |

## POSTAL CARDS

Reply cards are considered "used" when the message portion is used and the attached reply portion is unused. Attached cards with both sections used are very rare. Separate used message portions are usually valued at one-third the used price. Separate used reply portions are valued from two-thirds to full used price. Many postal cards were made available in large sheets and these were later privately rouletted or perforated. Rouletted cards are listed only if they were regularly issued in that form.

### 1871. "BRITISH AMERICAN BANK NOTE CO., MONTREAL & OTTAWA" printed at bottom. Engraved

UX1

UX3

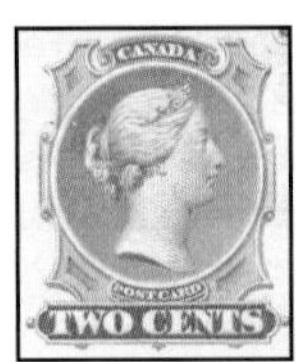
UX4

| | | Unused | Used |
|---|---|---|---|
| UX1 | **1¢ blue**, shades | 3.50 | 2.00 |

Many re-entries exist.

### 1876. "BRITISH AMERICAN BANK NOTE CO., MONTREAL" printed at bottom

| | | Unused | Used |
|---|---|---|---|
| UX2 | **1¢ blue**, shades | 3.00 | 1.25 |

Many re-entries exist.

### 1877. To United Kingdom.

| | | Unused | Used |
|---|---|---|---|
| UX3 | **2¢ green**, shades | 5.00 | 45.00 |

### 1879. Universal Postal Union

| | | Unused | Used |
|---|---|---|---|
| UX4 | **2¢ yellow green**, shades | 1.25 | 15.00 |
| a | blue green | 4.00 | 15.00 |
| b | pale olive green | 4.00 | 16.00 |
| c | smooth thin card | 5.00 | 16.00 |

### 1882. Shieldlike ornament below numerals Typographed

UX5

UX7

UX11

| | | Unused | Used |
|---|---|---|---|
| UX5 | **1¢ blue**, shades | 4.50 | 1.50 |
| a | ultramarine | 4.50 | 1.75 |
| b | blue violet | 4.50 | 1.75 |
| c | lilac | 5.00 | 2.00 |
| d | grey | 5.50 | 2.25 |
| e | bistre | 8.00 | 3.50 |
| f | slate green | 8.00 | 3.50 |
| UY6 | **1¢ + 1¢ slate**, reply | 7.00 | 20.00 |
| a | stamp at left | 12.00 | 40.00 |

### 1887. Scroll work around numerals

| | | Unused | Used |
|---|---|---|---|
| UX7 | **1¢ blue** | 2.00 | 1.50 |
| a | lilac | 4.00 | 2.00 |
| b | slate blue | 4.00 | 2.00 |
| c | slate green | 4.00 | 1.75 |
| d | grey | 3.00 | 2.00 |
| UY8 | **1¢ + 1¢ slate green**, reply | 4.00 | 7.00 |
| a | olive green | 5.00 | 20.00 |
| b | reply on back of message card | 60.00 | |

### 1891. Rosette under numerals

| | | Unused | Used |
|---|---|---|---|
| UX9 | **1¢ ultramarine**, shades | 3.00 | 2.50 |
| a | blue, shades | 3.00 | 2.50 |
| b | straw card | 7.00 | 7.00 |
| UY10 | **1¢ + 1¢ slate green**, reply | 5.00 | 15.00 |
| a | reply on back of message card | 60.00 | |

Note: The reply portion is scroll work type.

### 1893–1896. Rosette under numerals.

| | | Unused | Used |
|---|---|---|---|
| UX11 | **1¢ black**, 127 mm x 76 mm | 5.00 | 5.00 |
| a | olive black | 7.00 | 6.00 |
| UY12 | **1¢ + 1¢ black**, reply, 127 mm x 76 mm | 4.00 | 12.00 |
| a | yellow straw card | 10.00 | 16.00 |
| b | olive black | 5.00 | 13.00 |
| c | reply one-third on back of message card | 60.00 | 60.00 |
| d | reply on back of message card | | 60.00 |
| UX13 | **1¢ black**, 152 mm x 92 mm | 2.00 | 1.50 |
| UX14 | **1¢ black**, 140 mm x 86 mm | 2.00 | 1.50 |
| a | yellowish or brown straw card | 3.00 | 2.00 |

### 1896. UPU Issue. Bilingual inscriptions with Royal Arms over Canada. Engraved and printed by BABNC, Ottawa.

UX15

UX16

| | | Unused | Used |
|---|---|---|---|
| UX15 | **2¢ vermilion** | 2.00 | 35.00 |

### 1897. Queen Victoria Jubilee Typographed

| | | Unused | Used |
|---|---|---|---|
| UX16 | **1¢ black** | .75 | 1.25 |
| a | stamp impression doubled | 50.00 | |

### 1897–1898. Maple Leaf Issue

UX17

UX22

UX25

| | | Unused | Used |
|---|---|---|---|
| UX17 | **1¢ green** | .35 | .50 |
| a | thick soft card | 2.50 | 1.50 |
| b | yellow straw card | 3.50 | 2.50 |
| UX18 | **1¢ rose carmine**, 83 mm inscription | 1.25 | 3.00 |
| a | 75 mm inscription and taller | 700.00 | 450.00 |
| UY19 | **1¢ + 1¢ black**, reply | 3.00 | 5.00 |
| a | yellow straw card | 5.00 | 7.50 |
| b | reply on back of message card | 75.00 | 75.00 |
| UX20 | **2¢ orange**, UPU Type 17 | 3.00 | 35.00 |
| UX21 | **2¢ blue**, UPU Type 17 | 3.00 | 30.00 |

### 1903–1904. King Edward VII

| | | Unused | Used |
|---|---|---|---|
| UX22 | **1¢ green** | .35 | .50 |
| a | yellowish straw card | 2.50 | 1.50 |
| UX23 | **1¢ rose** | 10.00 | 3.00 |
| UY24 | **1¢ + 1¢ black**, reply | .50 | 5.00 |
| a | reply on back of message card | 100.00 | 100.00 |
| b | soft thin card | | 30.00 |
| UX25 | **2¢ blue**, UPU Type 17 | 3.00 | 30.00 |

### Inscriptions Common to Cards

| Type | |
|---|---|
| 1 | No inscription |
| 2 | Horizontal line below stamp |
| 3 | Lines forming "L" for address area |
| 4 | "The space below … ," L'espace ci-dessous … , below stamp |
| 5 | Straight line "CANADA POST CARD" top centre of card |
| 6 | As Type 5, with second line: "The address to be …" |
| 7 | Bilingual "CANADA/POST CARD" top centre |
| 8 | As Type 7, additional lines: "The address …" and "Cote reserve a … |
| 9 | "CANADA/BUSINESS REPLY CARD" 2 lines top left |
| 10 | As Type 9, additional line: "CARTE REPONSE D'AFFAIRES" |
| 11 | Three lines, "CANADA/BUSINESS REPLY CARD/The address only …" |
| 12 | Two lines, "CANADA POST CARD/(REPLY)" |
| 13 | As Type 12, with third line, "The address to be …" |
| 14 | Two lines, "CANADA/REPLY POST CARD-CARTE POSTALE REPONSE" |
| 15 | Five lines, "CANADA/BUSINESS REPLY CARD/CARTE REPONSE D'AFFAIRES/The address … / Cote reserve a …" |
| 16 | As Type 14, with 2 additional lines, "The address only … /Cote reserve a …" |
| 17 | "UNIVERSAL POSTAL UNION," as UX15 |
| 18 | "POST CARD/CARTE POSTALE". |
| 19 | "CANADA/REPLY-PAID CARD-CARTE POSTALE AVEC REPONSE PAYEE". |

### 1912–1929. King George V. Admiral Issue

**Die I:** Lower leaf on left side, upper right tip just extends into white oval. Five braids in epaulet on left shoulder.
**Die Ia:** As Die I, but white line on collar curves upward around the neck.
**Die II:** Leaf extends across oval and slightly beyond. Four blurred braids.
**Die III:** Diagonal lines have been added to the upper background and above shoulder.

UX26

| | | Unused | Used |
|---|---|---|---|
| **UX26** | **½¢ blue**, Type 9 | 2.00 | 12.00 |
| a | Type 10 | 2.00 | 30.00 |
| b | Type 11 | .50 | 7.50 |
| c | Type 15 | 1.00 | 15.00 |
| d | as "c", mimeo | 30.00 | |
| **UX27** | **1¢ green**, Type 2 | 2.00 | 3.50 |
| a | same, mimeo | 4.00 | 4.00 |
| b | Type 3, lines in black, Die Ia | 110.00 | 100.00 |
| c | Type 3, lines in green, Die Ia | | 500.00 |
| d | as "c", Die II | | 300.00 |
| e | Type 4 (known only with railway views) | 125.00 | 65.00 |
| f | Type 6, Die Ia | 80.00 | 80.00 |
| g | as "f", inscription inverted | 100.00 | |
| h | as "f", Die II | 1.00 | 1.00 |
| j | as "h," mimeo | 2.00 | 2.00 |
| k | Type 8 | .35 | .35 |
| l | as "k", mimeo | 2.50 | 3.50 |
| **UX28** | **1¢ carmine**, Type 3, Die Ia | 13.00 | 15.00 |
| a | Type 4, Die Ia | 7.00 | 7.00 |
| b | as "a", Die II | 18.00 | 16.00 |
| c | as "b", inscription inverted | 250.00 | |

Standard Precancel A

UX33

UX36

| | | Unused | Used |
|---|---|---|---|
| **UX29** | **1¢ orange**, Type 1, Die II | 15.00 | 8.00 |
| a | Type 1, Die III | 20.00 | 10.00 |
| b | Die II, precancelled (Type A) | | 80.00 |
| c | Die III, precancelled (Type A) | | 40.00 |
| d | Type 2 | 4.00 | 4.00 |
| e | Type 5, shades | .50 | .50 |
| f | Type 6 "Canada Post Card", 83 mm long | .35 | .35 |
| g | as "f", precancelled (Type A) | | 150.00 |
| h | as "f", mimeo | 5.00 | 7.50 |
| j | Type 7 | 3.00 | 4.00 |
| k | Type 8, "Post Card etc.", 63 mm long | 2.00 | 1.50 |
| l | as "k", 69 mm long | 100.00 | 75.00 |
| m | as "k", mimeo | 4.00 | 4.50 |
| **UY30** | **1¢ orange + ½¢ blue**, reply, types 5 & 9 | 75.00 | 80.00 |
| a | Types 6 & 11 | 4.00 | 5.00 |
| b | Types 8 & 15, "Post Card etc.", 63 mm | 5.00 | 7.50 |
| c | as "b", 69 mm | 135.00 | 95.00 |
| **UY31** | **1¢ orange + 1¢ orange**, reply, Types 5 & 12 | 10.00 | 20.00 |
| a | Types 6 & 13 | 5.00 | 14.00 |
| b | as "a", mimeo | 15.00 | 20.00 |
| c | Types 7 & 14 | 25.00 | 40.00 |
| d | Types 8 & 16 | 10.00 | 20.00 |
| **UY32** | **1¢ black + 1¢ black**, repl, Types 6 & 13 | 3.00 | 15.00 |
| a | Types 8 & 16 | 3.50 | 15.00 |
| **UX33** | **2¢ carmine**, Type 2 | 3.00 | 3.50 |
| a | Type 3, Die I | 8.00 | 9.00 |
| b | as "a", Die Ia | 8.00 | 10.00 |
| c | as "a", Die II | 35.00 | 25.00 |
| d | type 6, Die I | 7.50 | 4.00 |
| e | as "d", Die II, shades | .75 | .60 |
| f | as "e", mimeo | 1.50 | .60 |
| g | Type 8, Die I | 125.00 | 40.00 |
| h | as "g", Die II, shades | 2.50 | 2.00 |
| j | as "h", mimeo | 4.00 | 4.50 |
| k | Type 6, 1917 Confederation, English | 4.00 | 6.00 |
| l | Type 8, 1917 Confederation, Bilingual | 17.00 | 20.00 |
| **UX34** | **2¢ green**, Type 1, Die II | 10.00 | 10.00 |
| a | Die III | 15.00 | 8.50 |
| b | Type 2 | 2.00 | 2.00 |
| c | Type 5, shades | .75 | .50 |
| d | Type 6 | .35 | .25 |
| e | as "d," mimeo | 9.00 | 7.00 |
| f | Type 7 | 5.00 | 6.00 |
| g | Type 8 | .75 | 1.00 |
| **UX35** | **2¢ blue**, type 17 | 4.00 | 350.00 |
| **UX36** | **6¢ on 2¢ blue**, type 17 | 4.00 | 550.00 |

UX35, UX36: used prices are for copies properly used to pay the UPU post card rates. The 6¢ UPU rate was in effect from October 1921 to September 1925. For use to North American destinations or used out of period, the used price of either card is $25.00.

For Admiral issue cards, the term "mimeo" is used to refer to cards printed on a soft porous stock, used primarily in the early 1920s. Beginning in 1932, cards were printed on a similar stock, in part for use with mimeograph machines.

### 1928. King George V. Scroll Issue

UX37 Standard Precancel B UX48a

| | | Unused | Used |
|---|---|---|---|
| **UX37** | **½¢ blue**, Type 9 | 2.00 | 15.00 |
| a | Type 10 | 3.00 | 15.00 |
| **UX38** | **1¢ orange**, Type 1 | 8.00 | 4.00 |
| a | same, precancelled, Type A | | 50.00 |
| b | Type 5 | 10.00 | 20.00 |
| **UY39** | **1¢ orange + ½¢ blue**, reply, Types 5 & 9 | 3.00 | 6.00 |
| a | reply on back of message card | 200.00 | |
| b | Types 7 & 10 | 10.00 | 12.00 |
| **UX40** | 2¢ green, Type 1 | 5.00 | 4.50 |

### 1930. King George V. Arch or Leaf Issue

**Die I:** Lines of shading behind King's head are horizontal.
**Die II:** The lines are slanting.

| | | Unused | Used |
|---|---|---|---|
| **UX41** | **½¢ blue**, Type 9, Die II | 2.00 | 10.00 |
| a | Type 10, Die I | 5.00 | 15.00 |
| b | as "a", Die II, round "O" | 5.00 | 16.00 |
| c | as "b", oval "O" | 4.00 | 15.00 |
| **UX42** | **1¢ orange**, Type 1,Die I | 40.00 | 25.00 |
| a | Type 1, Die II | 4.00 | 4.00 |
| b | Type 5, Die I | 4.00 | 4.00 |
| c | as "b", Die II | 4.00 | 4.00 |
| d | Type 7, Die I | 7.50 | 4.00 |
| e | as "d", Die II | 4.00 | 5.00 |
| **UX43** | **1¢ green**, Type 1 | 9.00 | 4.00 |
| a | same, precancelled, (Type B) | | 30.00 |
| b | Type 5 | .50 | .35 |
| c | as "b", mimeo | 15.00 | 13.00 |
| d | as "c", rouletted | 35.00 | 20.00 |
| e | Type 7 | 1.00 | 1.25 |
| **UY44** | **1¢ orange + ½¢ blue**, reply, Types 5 & 9, Die I | 6.00 | 30.00 |
| a | Die II | 20.00 | 40.00 |
| b | Types 7 & 10 Die II, ¢ round "O" | | 375.00 |
| **UY45** | **1¢ green + ½¢ blue**, reply, Types 5 & 9 | 10.00 | 22.00 |
| **UY46** | **1¢ orange + 1¢ orange**, reply, Types 5 & 12 | 15.00 | 30.00 |
| a | Types 7 & 14 | 15.00 | 40.00 |
| **UY47** | **1¢ green + 1¢ green**, reply, Types 5 & 12 | 5.00 | 10.00 |
| a | Types 7 & 14 | 6.00 | 20.00 |
| **UX48** | **2¢ green**, Type 1 | 35.00 | 35.00 |
| a | Type 5, Die I | 5.00 | 6.00 |
| b | as "a", Die II | 2.00 | 3.50 |
| c | Type 7 | 5.00 | 8.00 |
| **UX49** | **2¢ red**, Type 1 | 40.00 | 20.00 |
| a | Type 5 | 2.00 | 3.50 |
| b | Type 7 | 5.00 | 9.00 |
| **UX50** | **2¢ brown**,Type 1 | 5.00 | 3.00 |
| a | Type 5 | .75 | .50 |
| b | as "a", divided back, with view | 4.00 | 8.00 |
| c | Type 7 | 2.00 | 2.50 |
| d | as "c", divided back, with view | 5.00 | 10.00 |
| i | set of 70 views (61 x UX50b, 9 x UX50d) | 475.00 | |

Prices for UX50b and UX50d are for common views. A few cards are considerably scarcer.

For illustration of "Scroll" and "Arch' issues, please refer to Post Bands and Wrappers section.

### 1933–1934. King George V. Medallion Issue

UX55 UX57

| | | Unused | Used |
|---|---|---|---|
| **UX51** | **½¢ blue**, Type 9 | 2.00 | 10.00 |
| a | Type 10 | 3.00 | 20.00 |
| **UX52** | **1¢ green**, Type 1 | 3.00 | 3.00 |
| a | same, precancelled, (Type B) | | 20.00 |
| b | Type 5 | .75 | .50 |
| c | as "b", mimeo | 7.50 | 6.00 |
| d | as "c", rouletted | 12.00 | 12.00 |
| e | Type 7 | 4.00 | 5.00 |
| **UY53** | **1¢ green + ½¢ blue**, reply, Types 5 & 9 | 6.00 | 10.00 |
| a | Types 7 & 10 | 20.00 | 27.50 |
| **UY54** | **1¢ green + 1¢ green**, reply, Types 5 & 12 | 6.00 | 15.00 |
| a | Types 7 & 14 | 12.00 | 90.00 |
| **UX55** | **2¢ brown**, Type 1 | 5.00 | 5.00 |
| a | Type 5 | .75 | .50 |
| b | Type 7 | 6.00 | 6.00 |

### 1935. King George V. Front Face

| | | Unused | Used |
|---|---|---|---|
| **UX56** | **½¢ blue**, Type 9, 2nd line, 42 mm, no period | 5.00 | 10.00 |
| a | same, 2nd line 39 mm, with period | 20.00 | 25.00 |
| **UX57** | **1¢ green**, Type 1 | 8.00 | 10.00 |
| a | Type 5 | 3.50 | 5.00 |
| b | Type 7 | 5.00 | 15.00 |
| **UY58** | **1¢ green + ½¢ blue**, reply, Types 5 & 9 | 10.00 | 15.00 |
| **UY59** | **1¢ green + 1¢ green**, reply, Types 5 & 12 | 7.00 | 15.00 |
| a | Types 7 & 14 | 13.00 | 90.00 |
| **UX60** | **2¢ brown**, Type 1 | 5.00 | 10.00 |
| a | Type 5 | 7.00 | 6.00 |
| b | Type 7 | 8.00 | 15.00 |

### 1935. King George V. Profile Head

UX61

| | | Unused | Used |
|---|---|---|---|
| **UX61** | **½¢ blue**, Type 9, 2nd line 42 mm, no period | 5.00 | 12.00 |
| a | same, 2nd line 39 mm, with period | 6.00 | 22.00 |
| b | Type 10 | 2.00 | 20.00 |
| **UX62** | **1¢ green**, Type 1 | 2.00 | 2.00 |
| a | same, precancelled, (Type A) | | 40.00 |
| b | Type 5 | .75 | .25 |
| c | as "b", mimeo | 2.50 | 3.00 |
| d | as "c", rouletted | 40.00 | 15.00 |
| e | Type 7 | 1.75 | 2.25 |
| **UY63** | **1¢ green + ½¢ blue**, reply, Types 5 & 9 | 3.00 | 4.00 |
| a | Types 7 & 10 | 3.50 | 12.00 |
| **UY64** | **1¢ green + 1¢ green**, reply, Types 5 & 12 | 40.00 | 50.00 |
| a | Types 7 & 14 | 10.00 | 90.00 |
| **UX65** | **2¢ brown**, Type 1 | 4.00 | 4.00 |
| a | Type 5 | .60 | .35 |
| b | Type 7 | 2.50 | 3.00 |

1938–1953. KING GEORGE VI. Die dated "19-38" or "19-43" in lower corners. See "Envelopes" section for descriptions of the offset and typographed dies.

UX66

| | | Unused | Used |
|---|---|---|---|
| UX66 | **1¢ green**, Type 1 offset | .30 | .25 |
| a | Type 1, precancelled, (Type A) | | 5.00 |
| b | Type 1, stamp on both sides | 60.00 | |
| c | Type 5, typographed | .30 | .25 |
| d | Type 5, offset, heading 83 mm or 81½ mm long | 10.00 | 4.00 |
| e | as "c", mimeo | .75 | .50 |
| f | as "d", mimeo, rouletted | 1.00 | .75 |
| g | Type 7, typographed | .35 | .40 |
| h | as "g", mimeo, rouletted | 200.00 | 150.00 |
| UY67 | **1¢ green + 1¢ green**, reply, Types 5 & 12, black inscription | 1.50 | 1.75 |
| a | Types 5 & 12, green inscription | 3.50 | 5.00 |
| b | Types 7 & 14, black inscription | 3.50 | 5.00 |
| c | as "b", green inscription | 25.00 | 60.00 |
| UX68 | **2¢ light brown**, Type 1 | 3.00 | 3.50 |
| a | one-half stamp impression only | | 50.00 |
| b | Type 5 | .50 | .25 |
| c | Type 7 | 1.00 | 1.25 |
| UX69 | **2¢ black brown**, Type 1, dated 1938 | 3.50 | 3.00 |
| a | same, mimeo | 5.00 | 5.00 |
| b | as "a", rouletted | 7.00 | 8.00 |
| UX70 | **2¢ sepia**, Type 1, dated 1943 | 35.00 | 25.00 |
| a | same, precancelled, (Type A) | | 17.50 |
| UY71 | **2¢ sepia + 2¢ sepia**, reply, types 5 & 12 | 6.00 | 8.00 |
| a | Types 7 & 14 | 10.00 | 30.00 |

UX72

| | | Unused | Used |
|---|---|---|---|
| UX72 | **2¢ on 1¢ green, Type 1**, surcharge on UX66 | 5.00 | 4.00 |
| a | surcharge inverted at LL | 45.00 | |
| b | Type 5, mimeo, rouletted, surcharged on UX66e | 5.00 | 7.00 |
| UY73 | **2¢ on 1¢ green + 2¢ on 1¢ green** (UY67a), reply, Types 5 & 12 | 3.00 | 7.50 |
| a | Types 7 & 14 surcharged on UY67c | 5.00 | 12.00 |
| b | Types 5 & 12 surcharged on UY67 | | 120.00 |
| UX74 | **2¢ dark olive green**, Type 1, dated 1938 | .35 | .25 |
| a | mimeo | 5.00 | 5.00 |
| b | as "a", rouletted | 7.50 | 8.00 |
| UX75 | **2¢ olive green**, Type 1, dated 1943 | 3.00 | 1.50 |
| a | same, precancelled, (Type A) | | 5.00 |
| UY76 | **2¢ olive green + 2¢ olive green**, reply, Types 5 & 12 | 7.50 | 10.00 |
| a | Types 7 & 14 | 7.50 | 14.00 |
| UX77 | **3¢ brown**, Type 1 | 16.00 | 12.00 |
| a | Type 5 | 12.00 | 8.00 |
| b | Type 7 | 12.00 | 12.00 |
| UX78 | **3¢ mauve**, Type 1, typographed | .35 | .35 |
| a | dark mauve, thin card | 2.00 | 2.50 |
| b | Type 5, typographed | .35 | .25 |
| c | Type 7, typographed | .75 | 1.00 |
| UX79 | **3¢ pale mauve**, Type 1, offset | 2.50 | 2.00 |
| UX80 | **4¢ purple**, Type 1 | .75 | .75 |

UX81

UX82

| | | Unused | Used |
|---|---|---|---|
| UX81 | **4¢ on 3¢ mauve**, Type 1, surcharge "B" on UX78 | 1.00 | 1.25 |
| a | dark mauve, thin card, surcharge on UX78a | 5.00 | 6.00 |
| b | Type 5 on UX78b | 65.00 | 65.00 |
| c | Type 7 on UX78c | 150.00 | 130.00 |
| d | Type 1 on UX79 | 50.00 | 50.00 |
| UX82 | **4¢ on 3¢ pale mauve**, Type 1, surcharge "A" on UX79 | 4.00 | 4.00 |

1953. Queen Elizabeth II. "1953" in lower right corner of stamp

UX83

UX83a

UX86

| | | Unused | Used |
|---|---|---|---|
| UX83 | **2¢ green**, Type 1 | .75 | .50 |
| a | same, precancelled, Type A | | 3.00 |
| b | mimeo | 6.00 | 7.00 |
| c | as "b", rouletted | 30.00 | 30.00 |
| UY84 | **2¢ green + 2¢ green**, reply, Types 5 & 12 | 5.00 | 20.00 |
| a | Types 7 & 14 | 2.50 | 5.00 |
| UX85 | **4¢ purple**, Type 1 | 2.00 | 2.00 |
| UX86 | **4¢ on 3¢ carmine**, Type 1 (surcharge on card similar to "UX83") | 4.00 | 3.00 |

1954. Queen Elizabeth II. "1954" in lower right corner of stamp

UX88

UX90

| | | Unused | Used |
|---|---|---|---|
| UX87 | **2¢ green**, Type 1 | .50 | .35 |
| a | mimeo | 2.00 | 2.00 |
| b | as "a", rouletted | 10.00 | 2.50 |
| UX88 | **4¢ purple**, Type 1 | 1.00 | .50 |

1955. Queen Elizabeth II. Design as before with "1955" in lower right corner

| | | Unused | Used |
|---|---|---|---|
| UX89 | **2¢ green**, Type 1 | .50 | .25 |
| a | same, mimeo | 2.00 | 2.00 |
| b | as "a", rouletted | 7.50 | 3.00 |
| UX90 | **4¢ purple**, Type 1 | .35 | .25 |

## 1960–1964. Queen Elizabeth II.
### "1960" on lower right side of stamp

UX94

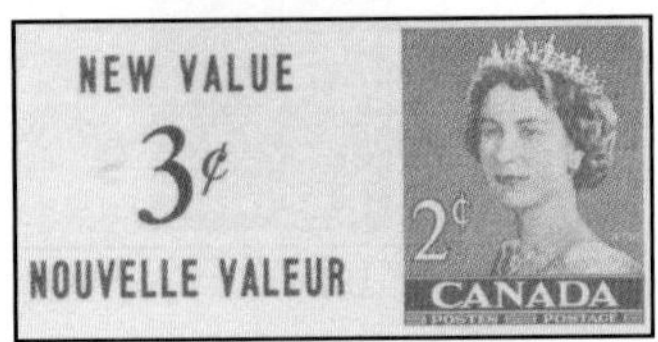

UX95

| | | Unused | Used |
|---|---|---|---|
| **UX92** | **2¢ green**, Type 1 | .50 | .25 |
| a | same, precancelled (Type C) | | 6.00 |
| b | mimeo | 2.00 | 1.50 |
| c | as "b", rouletted | 2.50 | 2.50 |
| **UY93** | **2¢ green +2¢ green**, reply, Types 7 & 14 | 1.30 | 4.00 |
| **UX94** | **4¢ purple**, Type 1 | .50 | .50 |
| **UX95** | **3¢ on 2¢ green**, Type 1 | .75 | 1.00 |
| a | same, precancelled, (Type C) | 12.00 | 10.00 |

### 1964. Queen Elizabeth II. Cameo Issue

UX96

UX96d

| | | Unused | Used |
|---|---|---|---|
| **UX96** | **3¢ violet**, Type 1 | 1.00 | .50 |
| a | mimeo | 2.50 | 2.00 |
| b | as "a", rouletted | 17.50 | 10.00 |
| c | precancelled | 3.00 | 2.50 |
| d | as "a", precancelled | 5.00 | 5.00 |
| e | as "b", precancelled | 20.00 | 8.00 |
| f | Type 18, precancelled | 2.50 | 2.00 |
| g | as "f", mimeo | 2.50 | 2.00 |
| h | as "g", rouletted | 25.00 | 16.00 |
| **UY97** | **3¢ violet + 3¢ violet**, reply, Types 14 & 19 | 1.50 | 20.00 |
| a | same, precancelled | 2.00 | 25.00 |
| **UX98** | **4¢ red**, Type 1 | .50 | .50 |
| a | Type 18 | 2.50 | 2.00 |

Starting with this issue, the Post Office introduced a policy of precancelling with five thin lines in the stamp colour during the printing process. Unless cards have not passed through the mail, used cards will show some evidence of usage, such as address, etc.

### 1967–1973. Queen Elizabeth II. Centennial Issue

UX99a

| | | Unused | Used |
|---|---|---|---|
| **UX99** | **3¢ violet**, Type 18, precancelled | .50 | .75 |
| a | mimeo, precancelled | 2.00 | 2.50 |
| b | as "a", rouletted | 22.00 | 25.00 |
| **UY100** | **3¢ violet + 3¢ violet**, reply, Types 14 & 19, precancelled | 3.00 | 30.00 |
| **UX101** | **4¢ red**, Type 18 | .75 | .75 |
| **UX102** | **5¢ blue**, Type 18, precancelled | .35 | .40 |
| a | same, mimeo | 2.00 | 2.50 |
| b | as "a", rouletted | 8.00 | 12.00 |
| **UX103** | **6¢ orange**, Type 18 | .50 | .50 |
| **UX104** | **6¢ black**, Type 18, stamp size 24 mm x 19 mm | .30 | .50 |
| **UX104A** | **6¢ black**, stamp size 20 mm x 16 mm, precancelled | .30 | 1.00 |
| a | same, mimeo | 10.00 | 10.00 |
| b | as "a", rouletted | 7.00 | 15.00 |
| **UX105** | **7¢ green**, Type 18 | .35 | 1.00 |
| **UX106** | **8¢ slate**, Type 18, size 140 mm x 86 mm | .25 | .30 |
| a | same, size 140 mm x 89 mm | .50 | .35 |
| b | as "a", tagged | .25 | .30 |

### 1969-1971. Various Issues Surcharged.

Three styles of surcharges were used.
Style A: Gasparo printing, 5¢ has sloping back "5", 4 mm high, 6¢ "c" of "¢" is shallow.
Style B: British American Bank Note Co. printing, 5¢ has straight back "5", 5 mm high, 6¢ has a bolder "6" and the "c" of "¢" is more rounded.
Style C: Red Maple Leaf
All listings are Style A, unless shown otherwise.

UX109

| | | Unused | Used |
|---|---|---|---|
| **UX107** | **5¢ on 3¢ violet**, on "UX96c", Style B | | 10.00 |
| a | surcharged on "UX96f", Style B | 25.00 | 17.50 |
| b | surcharged on "UX96f" | | 75.00 |
| c | surcharged on "UX96g" | 50.00 | 50.00 |
| d | surcharged on "UX99" | .75 | 1.00 |
| e | surcharged on "UX99a" | 1.00 | 4.00 |
| f | surcharged on "UX99", Style B | 15.00 | 15.00 |
| g | surcharged on "UX99a", Style B | 15.00 | 15.00 |
| h | surcharged on "UX99b", Style B | 45.00 | 50.00 |
| j | surcharged on "UX96h", Style B | | 120.00 |
| k | surcharged on "UX96d", Style A | 100.00 | — |
| **UX108** | **6¢ on 4¢ red**, on "UX98a" | | 120.00 |
| a | surcharged on "UX98", Style B | | 75.00 |
| b | surcharged on "UX98a", Style B | 50.00 | 50.00 |
| c | surcharged on "UX101" | .50 | .60 |
| d | surcharged on "UX101", Style B | 20.00 | 7.50 |
| **UX109** | **6¢ on 5¢ blue**, on "UX102", surcharged C | .35 | .40 |
| a | surcharged on "UX102a", Style C | .45 | .50 |
| b | surcharged on "UX102b", Style C | 3.00 | 3.00 |

### 1971–1974 Pictorial Issues.
### Matching views and stamp designs

See Webb's Postal Stationery Catalogue for details of all 115 cards included in UX109A, B, C.

| | | Unused | Used |
|---|---|---|---|
| **UX109A** | **7¢ multicoloured views**, *1971* | 1.25 | 12.00 |
| a | set of 15 | 20.00 | |

Values for UX109A are for non-philatelic copies used in 1971. These were sold in 3 sets of 5 cards each. Cards are titled (in English only) but not numbered.

| | Unused | Used |
|---|---|---|
| **UX109B 8¢ multicoloured views**, *1972* | .75 | 4.00 |
| a set of 90 | 70.00 | |

Text is bilingual. Cards are numbered in units of 5, grouped by province (all 5 cards in a unit all have the same number). Cards in the three Ontario series are tagged; the rest are untagged.

| | | |
|---|---|---|
| **UX109C 8¢ postal museum cards**, *1974* | 1.00 | 4.00 |
| a set of 10 | 10.00 | |

Text is bilingual. Unstamped cards were also sold in the Postal Museum (not listed or valued here).

Values for First Day cancelled copies of UX109B and UX109C are the same as for unused copies.

**1975–1979. New Design**

UX110

| | | |
|---|---|---|
| **UX110 6¢ red**, Type 18 | .40 | 1.00 |
| a same, rouletted | 3.50 | 9.00 |
| **UX111 8¢ blue**, Type 18 | .40 | .75 |
| **UX112 10¢ red & blue**, Type 18 | .45 | 1.00 |
| a same, rouletted | 5.00 | 25.00 |
| **UX113 12¢ blue & green**, Type 18 | .45 | 1.00 |
| a same, rouletted | 3.00 | 25.00 |
| **UX114 14¢ purple & brown**, Type 18 | .50 | 1.50 |
| **UX115 15¢ green & brown**, Type 18 | .45 | 1.50 |
| a same, rouletted | 5.00 | 25.00 |
| **UX116 17¢ blue & brown**, Type 18 | .45 | 2.00 |

**1982–1985. Transportation**

UX117

| | | |
|---|---|---|
| **UX117 30¢ red** (Stagegoach), Type 18, one line | .60 | 4.00 |
| a dark red colour missing, including value | 50.00 | |
| **UX118 32¢ brown** (Stagecoach), Type 18, one line | .65 | 5.00 |
| **UX119 34¢ Model T Ford**, Type 18, one line | .70 | 5.00 |

UX120

| | Unused | Used |
|---|---|---|

**1997–1999. Pictorial issues.**
**Same design as the 45¢ Flag definitive (Sc. 1361), but without value**

"Postes/Postage" is replaced with "postage paid port payé" to the left of the stamp impression.

| | | |
|---|---|---|
| **UX120 Flag and Office Building**, (Sc. 1361/1362 design) | | |
| address side printed in black | 4.00 | 2.00 |
| a address side printed in brown | 6.00 | 6.00 |

Initially (Jul 7/97) three sets of five and one set of ten different cards were available through the Philatelic Agency in Antigonish. Another set of 10 was released Nov 3/97. Additional cards appeared in 1998, and new views continue to be issued. These can be found in selected card shops and Post Offices, often primarily in a restricted region. Some views that didn't appear in the original sets were also sold through the Philatelic Agency. Cards in the tourist shops are supplied directly by "The Postcard Factory", Markham Ontario. To date 85 different views are known on cards with wide white borders surrounding the views (one of these was prepared to private order for the African Lion Safari, Cambridge, ON).

All of these except the private order card are known with the text on the address side printed in black, and more than 40 of these same views are known with the text printed in brown. All 84 "regular issue" cards later appeared with an added bar code sticker, and most of the cards were then re-issued with minor typesetting changes and individual printed bar codes. Starting in 2001, a new series of borderless views has appeared, address side printed in black, with the same "stamp" design as was used on the earlier cards. So far, over 50 different "borderless" views have been recorded. In 2005 and 2006 three slightly modified versions of this indicium were introduced. Approximately 150 of the post card views are known with one or both of the modified versions of the indicium. The prices above are for the more common views. By 2016, some 1400+ varieties exist from 300+ different views.

**1998. Pictorial issues.**
**Matching views and stamp designs**

UX122

Same design as 1996 (3) and 1998 (2) Birds of Canada commemoratives (Sc. 1592–94, 1711–12), but without value

| | | |
|---|---|---|
| **UX122** single card, multicoloured | 2.00 | 1.75 |
| a set of 5 different birds | 10.00 | — |

**1999. XIII Pan American Game**

Same design as the XIII Pan American Game commemoratives (Sc. 1801–04), but without value.

| | | |
|---|---|---|
| **UX123** View of Winnipeg and enlarged matching stamp | 2.00 | 2.00 |
| a set of 4 different views of Winnipeg | 10.00 | — |

**1999. Francophone Summit issue**

Same design as the 1995 La Francophonie commemorative (Sc. 1589), but without value. "Postes/Postage" is replaced with "port payé/postage paid" to the left of the stamp impression.

| | | |
|---|---|---|
| **UX124 multicoloured** | 7.50 | 7.50 |

**1999. Millennium pictorial issue**

UX125

Same design as the 55¢ Dove of Peace commemorative (Sc. 1813) in the Millennium Keepstake.

| | | |
|---|---|---|
| **UX125 multicoloured** | 8.00 | 8.00 |

This card was only available in a purchase of the Millennium Keepstake metal box, which included stamps.

Postal Stationery

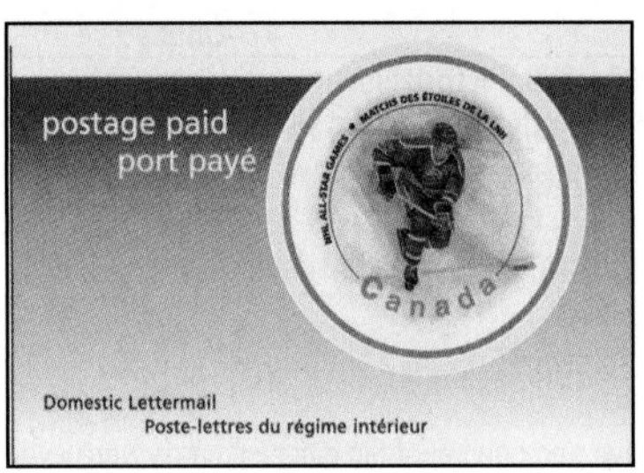

UX127

UX128

UX129

UX130

UX132

UX133

UX134

UX136

UX138

| | Unused | Used |
|---|---|---|

**2000. Tall Ships Visit to Halifax**

There are two different stamp impressions (Sc. 1864–65), each used on two different cards.

| | | Unused | Used |
|---|---|---|---|
| **UX126** | single card, multicoloured | 2.50 | 2.50 |
| a | set of four different views | 10.00 | — |

**2001. Canadian National Hockey teams card**

Cards purchased were to be sent, as an indication of support for the Canadian hockey teams at the 2002 Olympics, to an address that was preprinted on the cards (Goodyear Drive for Gold). $1 of the $2 purchase price was sent to the Canadian Hockey Association. Features the Wayne Gretzky commemorative stamp (Sc.1838a).

| | | Unused | Used |
|---|---|---|---|
| **UX127** | **multicoloured** | 5.00 | — |

**2001 (or 2002?). Tourist Attractions**

The stamp impressions match the pictures on the cards and adhesives issued in 2001 (Sc. 1903a–e, 1904a–e).

| | | Unused | Used |
|---|---|---|---|
| **UX127A** | single card, multicoloured | 4.00 | 1.50 |
| a | set of ten different views | 40.00 | — |

**2002. Tulips**

Features the Tulip commemoratives (Sc. 1946a–d).

| | | Unused | Used |
|---|---|---|---|
| **UX128** | single card, multicoloured | 4.00 | 1.50 |
| a | set of four different views | 16.00 | — |

**2002. Tourist Attractions**

The stamp impressions match the pictures on the cards and adhesives issued in 2002 (Sc. 1952a–e, 1953a–e).

| | | Unused | Used |
|---|---|---|---|
| **UX129** | single card, multicoloured | 4.00 | 1.50 |
| a | set of ten different views | 40.00 | — |

**2003. Tourist Attractions**

The stamp impressions match the pictures on the cards and adhesives issued at the same time (Sc. 1989a–e, 1990a–e).

| | | Unused | Used |
|---|---|---|---|
| **UX130** | single card, multicoloured | 4.00 | 1.50 |
| a | set of ten different views | 40.00 | — |

**2003. Canada Can**

Tin can containing a T-shirt, desktop flag and postcard featuring the Canada Flag commemorative of 1965 (Sc. 439). The "Canada Can" sold for $19.95

| | Unused | Used |
|---|---|---|
| **UX131 multicoloured** | 10.00 | 10.00 |

There is a picture of the 1965 stamp on the front of the card. See also UX145 for PostCard Factory style postcards with same stamp indicia.

**2003. Anne of Green Gables**

Features the Anne of Green Gables stamps first issued in 1975 (Sc. 658).

| | Unused | Used |
|---|---|---|
| **UX132 multicoloured** | 4.00 | 1.50 |

**2003. Cycling Can**

Tin can containing a T-shirt, water bottle and postcard featuring the World Road Cycling Championships commemorative issued at same time (Sc. 1998).The can sold for $19.95.

| | Unused | Used |
|---|---|---|
| **UX133 multicoloured**, *Sep 8* | 4.00 | 1.50 |

This card was also sold separately, not just in the Cycling can.

**2004. Year of the Monkey**

Year of the Monkey commemoratives (Sc. 2015–2016i) issued January 8, 2004.

| | Unused | Used |
|---|---|---|
| **UX134 multicoloured**, design from 49¢ stamp | 4.00 | 1.50 |
| **UX135 multicoloured**, design from $1.40 stamp | 4.00 | 1.50 |

**2004. Canada Celebration Pack**

Tin can containing a T-shirt, 25¢ coin, water bottle, two pocket "fanny pack", and postcard.The can sold for $19.95. The postcard was kept in the fanny pack; as such, most cards are bent. Features red Maple Leaf (Sc. 2009/2013).

| | Unused | Used |
|---|---|---|
| **UX136 multicoloured** | 10.00 | 10.00 |

**2004. Tourist Attractions**

| | Unused | Used |
|---|---|---|
| **UX137 Quebec Winter Carnival** (as Sc. 2019), *Jan 29* | 4.00 | 1.50 |
| **UX138 St. Joseph's Oratory** (as Sc. 2020), *Apr 2* | 4.00 | 1.50 |
| **UX139 Montreal Jazz Festival** (as Sc. 2021), *Jun 1* | 4.00 | 1.50 |
| **UX140 Lac St. Jean** (as Sc. 2022), *Jun 18* | 4.00 | 1.50 |
| **UX141 Canadian National Exhibition** (as Sc. 2023), *Jul 19* | 4.00 | 1.50 |

UX142

UX143

UX145

UX150

UX153

UX161

UX163

UX166

UX174

| | Unused | Used |
|---|---|---|
| **2004. PostCard Factory — Maple Leaf Design** | | |
| Similar to UX120 series featuring Maple Leaf definitive design (Sc. 2008). | | |
| **UX142 multicoloured** | 5.00 | 2.00 |
| More than 250 different post card views are known with this indicium. | | |
| **2005. Year of the Rooster** (Jan 7/05) | | |
| **UX143 multicoloured** (as Sc. 2083) | 4.00 | 1.50 |
| **UX144 multicoloured** (as Sc. 2084i) | 4.00 | 1.50 |
| **2005. PostCard Factory — Maple Leaf Flag Design** | | |
| Similar to UX120 series featuring Maple Leaf flag commemorative (Sc. 439). | | |
| **UX145 multicoloured** | 4.00 | 2.00 |
| Forty different post card views are known with this indicium. | | |
| **2005. Flowers** (Feb 1/05) | | |
| **UX146 Red Calla Lily** (as Sc. 2072), *Feb 1* | 4.00 | 1.50 |
| **UX147 Yellow Calla Lily** (as Sc. 2073/2081), *Feb 1* | 4.00 | 1.50 |
| **UX148 Blue Iris** (as Sc. 2074/2082), *Feb 1* | 4.00 | 1.50 |
| **2005. Fishing Flies** (Feb 4/05) | | |
| **UX149 Alevin** (as Sc. 2087a/2088a) | 4.00 | 1.50 |
| **UX150 Jock Scott** (as Sc. 2087b/2088b) | 4.00 | 1.50 |
| **UX151 Mickey Finn** (as Sc. 2087d/2088c) | 4.00 | 1.50 |
| **UX152 P.E.I. Fly** (as Sc. 2087c/2088d) | 4.00 | 1.50 |
| **2005. Daffodils** (Mar 10/05) | | |
| **UX153 Yellow Daffodil** (as Sc. 2091a/2092) | 4.00 | 1.50 |
| **UX154 White Daffodil** (as Sc. 2091b/209e) | 4.00 | 1.50 |
| **2005. Flag Over...** (May 13/05) | | |
| **UX155 Toronto, ON** (as Sc. 2080) | 4.00 | 1.50 |
| **UX156 Mont-Saint-Hilaire, QC** (as Sc. 2079) | 4.00 | 1.50 |
| **UX157 Shannon Falls, BC** (as Sc. 2078) | 4.00 | 1.50 |
| **UX158 Saskatoon, SK** (as Sc. 2076) | 4.00 | 1.50 |
| **UX159 Durrell, NL** (as Sc. 2077) | 4.00 | 1.50 |

| | Unused | Used |
|---|---|---|
| **2006. Year of the Dog** (Jan 6/06) | | |
| **UX160 multicoloured** (as Sc. 2140) | 4.00 | 1.50 |
| **UX161 multicoloured** (as Sc. 2141i) | 4.00 | 1.50 |
| **2006. Canadians in Hollywood** (May 26/06) | | |
| **UX162 Fay Wray** (as Sc. 2153b/2154c) | 4.00 | 1.50 |
| **UX163 John Candy** (as Sc. 2153a/2154a) | 4.00 | 1.50 |
| **UX164 Lorne Greene** (as Sc. 2153c/2154d) | 4.00 | 1.50 |
| **UX165 Mary Pickford** (as Sc. 2153d/2154b) | 4.00 | 1.50 |
| In April 2005, before the cards were released generally, Canada Post used copies of the Fay Wray card for a mailing to US customers to publicize the international stamp show in Washington, DC. | | |
| **2006. Snowbirds** (Jun 28/06) | | |
| **UX166 Pilot and planes** (as Sc. 2158) | 4.00 | 1.50 |
| **UX167 Three planes in flight** (as Sc. 2159) | 4.00 | 1.50 |
| **2006. Duck Decoys** (Aug 3/06) | | |
| **UX168 blue** (as Sc. 2163) | 4.00 | 1.50 |
| **UX169 yellow** (as Sc. 2164) | 4.00 | 1.50 |
| **UX170 orange** (as Sc. 2165) | 4.00 | 1.50 |
| **UX171 green** (as Sc. 2166) | 4.00 | 1.50 |
| **2007. Year of the Pig** (Jan 5/07) | | |
| **UX172 multicoloured** (as Sc. 2201) | 4.00 | 1.50 |
| **UX173 multicoloured** (as Sc. 2202i) | 4.00 | 1.50 |
| **2007. Lilacs** (Mar 1/07) | | |
| **UX174 white lilac** (as Sc. 2206a/2207) | 4.00 | 1.50 |
| **UX175 pale purple lilac** (as Sc. 2206b/2208) | 4.00 | 1.50 |
| **2007. Canadian Recording Artists** (Jun 29/07) | | |
| **UX176 Gordon Lightfoot** (as Sc. 2221a/2222a) | 4.00 | 1.50 |
| **UX177 Joni Mitchell** (as Sc. 2221b/2222b) | 4.00 | 1.50 |
| **UX178 Anne Murray** (as Sc. 2221c/2222c) | 4.00 | 1.50 |
| **UX179 Paul Anka** (as Sc. 2221d/2222d) | 4.00 | 1.50 |

UX180

UX186

UX188

UX194

UX200

UX203

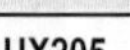
UX205

UX211

UX217

| | Unused | Used |
|---|---|---|
| **2008. Year of the Rat** (Jan 8/08) | | |
| **UX180 multicoloured** (as Sc. 2257) | 4.00 | 1.50 |
| **UX181 multicoloured** (as Sc. 2258i) | 4.00 | 1.50 |
| **2008. Peonies** (Mar 3/08) | | |
| **UX182 pink flower** (as Sc. 2260a/2261) | 4.00 | 1.50 |
| **UX183 red flower** (as Sc. 2260b/2262) | 4.00 | 1.50 |
| **2008. Art Canada: Yousuf Karsh** (May 21/08) | | |
| **UX184 Karsh** (as Sc. 2270) | 4.00 | 1.50 |
| **UX185 Hepburn** (as Sc. 2271a/2272) | 4.00 | 1.50 |
| **UX186 Churchill** (as Sc. 2271b/2273) | 4.00 | 1.50 |
| **UX187 Karsh** (as Sc. 2270 with s/s on reverse) | 4.00 | 1.50 |
| **2008. Anne of Green Gables** (Jun 20/08) | | |
| **UX188 Anne of Green Gables** (as Sc. 2276a/2277) | 4.00 | 1.50 |
| **UX189 Gables' house** (as Sc. 2276b/2278) | 4.00 | 1.50 |
| **2008. Legends of Hollywood: The Sequel** (Jun 30/08) | | |
| **UX190 Norma Shearer** (as Sc. 2279a/2280c) | 4.00 | 1.50 |
| **UX191 Chief Dan George** (as Sc. 2279b/2280b) | 4.00 | 1.50 |
| **UX192 Marie Dressler** (as Sc. 2279c/2280a) | 4.00 | 1.50 |
| **UX193 Raymond Burr** (as Sc. 2279d/2280d) | 4.00 | 1.50 |
| **2009. Year of the Ox** (Jan 8/09) | | |
| **UX194 multicoloured** (as Sc. 2296) | 4.00 | 1.50 |
| **UX195 multicoloured** (as Sc. 2297i) | 4.00 | 1.50 |
| **2009. Olympic Sporting Events** (Jan 12/09) | | |
| **UX196 Ice Sled Hockey** (as Sc. 2299e/2301) | 4.00 | 1.50 |
| **UX197 Snowboarding** (as Sc. 2299c/2304) | 4.00 | 1.50 |
| **UX198 Bobsledding** (as Sc. 2299b/2302) | 4.00 | 1.50 |
| **UX199 Curling** (as Sc. 2299a/2303) | 4.00 | 1.50 |
| **UX200 Freestyle Skiing** (as Sc. 2299d/2300) | 4.00 | 1.50 |
| **2009. Olympic Emblems and Mascots** (Jan 12/09) | | |
| **UX201 Miga** (as Sc. 2305c/2308/2311) | 4.00 | 1.50 |
| **UX202 Sumi** (as Sc. 2305d/2309/2312) | 4.00 | 1.50 |
| **UX203 Quatchi** (as Sc. 2305e/2310/2313) | 4.00 | 1.50 |

The postage stamps were not released until Feb 12/09, a month *after* the postal cards had been issued.

| | Unused | Used |
|---|---|---|
| **2009. Rhododendrons** (Mar 13/09) | | |
| **UX204 white flower** (as Sc. 2318a/2319) | 4.00 | 1.50 |
| **UX205 pink flower** (as Sc. 2318b/2320) | 4.00 | 1.50 |
| **2009. Canadian Recording Artists** (Jul 2/09) | | |
| **UX206 Robert Charlebois** (as Sc. 2333a/2334d) | 4.00 | 1.50 |
| **UX207 Édith Butler** (as Sc. 2333b/2334c) | 4.00 | 1.50 |
| **UX208 Stompin' Tom Connors** (as Sc. 2333c/2334b) | 4.00 | 1.50 |
| **UX209 Bryan Adams** (as Sc. 2333d/2334a) | 4.00 | 1.50 |
| **2009. Roadside Attractions** (Jul 6/09) | | |
| **UX210 Mr. PG** (as Sc. 2335a/2336a) | 4.00 | 1.50 |
| **UX211 Watson Lake** (as Sc. 2335b/2336b) | 4.00 | 1.50 |
| **UX212 Inukshuk** (as Sc. 2335c/2336d) | 4.00 | 1.50 |
| **UX213 Pysanka** (as Sc. 2335d/2336d) | 4.00 | 1.50 |
| **2010. Year of the Tiger** (Jan 8/10) | | |
| **UX214 multicoloured** (as Sc. 2348) | 4.00 | 1.50 |
| **UX215 multicoloured** (as Sc. 2349i) | 4.00 | 1.50 |
| **2010. Flag over Mills** (Jan 11/10) | | |
| **UX216 Watson's Mill** (as Sc. 2350a/2351) | 4.00 | 1.50 |
| **UX217 Keremeos Grist Mill** (as Sc. 2350b/2352) | 4.00 | 1.50 |
| **UX218 Stone Mill** (as Sc. 2350c/2353) | 4.00 | 1.50 |
| **UX219 Riordon Grist Mill** (as Sc. 2350d/2354) | 4.00 | 1.50 |
| **UX220 Cornell Mill** (as Sc. 2350e/2355) | 4.00 | 1.50 |
| **2010. Vancouver Olympic Winter Games** (Jan 12/10) | | |
| **UX221 Whistler, BC** (as Sc. 2366a/2367) | 4.00 | 1.50 |
| **UX222 Vancouver, BC** (as Sc. 2366b/2368) | 4.00 | 1.50 |
| **2010. African Violets** (Mar 3/10) | | |
| **UX223 red flowers** (as Sc. 2376a/2377) | 4.00 | 1.50 |
| **UX224 purple flowers** (as Sc. 2376b/2378) | 4.00 | 1.50 |
| **2010. Rotary International** | | |
| **UX225 multicoloured** (as Sc. 2394), *Jun 18/10* | 4.00 | 1.50 |

Postal Stationery

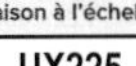
UX225

UX230

UX233

UX239

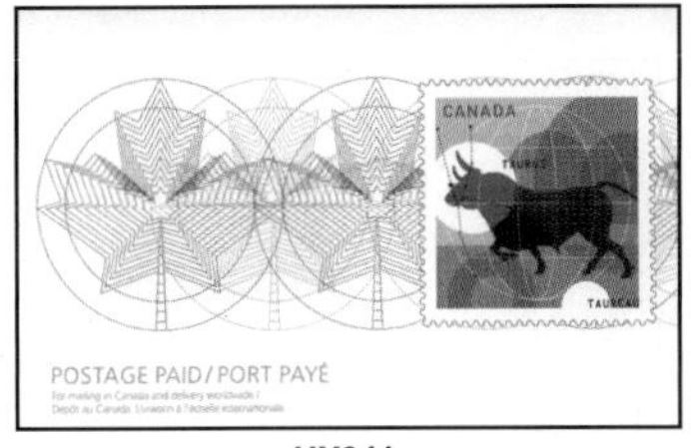

UX241

UX244

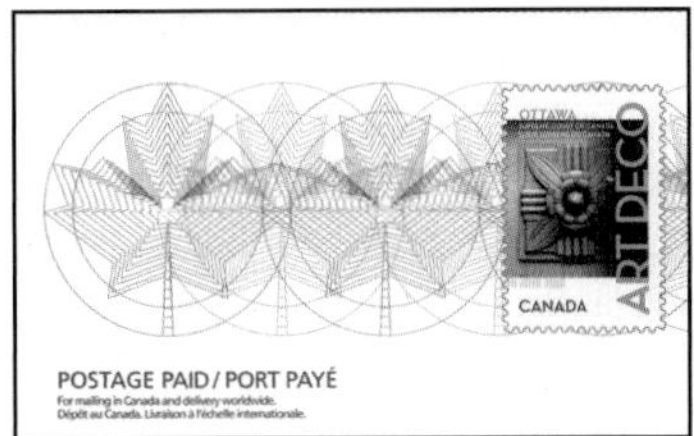

UX249

UX251

UX253

| | Unused | Used |
|---|---|---|
| **2010. Roadside Attractions** (Jul 5/10) | | |
| **UX226 Coffee Pot** (as Sc. 2397a/2398) | 4.00 | 1.50 |
| **UX227 Happy Rock** (as Sc. 2397b/2399) | 4.00 | 1.50 |
| **UX228 Wawa Goose** (as Sc. 2397c/2400) | 4.00 | 1.50 |
| **UX229 Puffin** (as Sc. 2397d/2401) | 4.00 | 1.50 |
| **2011. Year of the Rabbit** (Jan 7/11) | | |
| **UX230 multicoloured** (as Sc. 2416) | 4.00 | 1.50 |
| **UX231 multicoloured** (as Sc. 2417i) | 4.00 | 1.50 |
| **2011. Baby Wildlife** (Jan 17/11) | | |
| **UX232 Arctic Hare** (as Sc. 2425) | 4.00 | 1.50 |
| **UX233 Red Fox** (as Sc. 2433) | 4.00 | 1.50 |
| **UX234 Canada Geese** (as Sc. 2433) | 4.00 | 1.50 |
| **UX235 Polar Bear** (as Sc. 2433) | 4.00 | 1.50 |
| **2011. Black History** (Feb 1/11) | | |
| **UX236 multicoloured**, Carrie Best (as Sc. 2433) | 4.00 | 1.50 |
| **UX237 multicoloured**, Ferguson Jenkins (as Sc. 2434) | 4.00 | 1.50 |
| **2011. Sunflowers** (Mar 3/11) | | |
| **UX238 red sunflower** (as Sc. 2440a, 2443) | 4.00 | 1.50 |
| **UX239 yellow sunflower** (as Sc. 2440b, 2444) | 4.00 | 1.50 |
| **2011. Signs of the Zodiac** | | |
| **UX240 Aries** (as Sc. 2449), *Mar 21/11* | 4.00 | 1.50 |
| **UX241 Taurus** (as Sc. 2450), *Apr 21/11* | 4.00 | 1.50 |
| **UX242 Gemini** (as Sc. 2451), *May 20/11* | 4.00 | 1.50 |
| **UX243 Cancer** (as Sc. 2452), *Jun 22/11* | 4.00 | 1.50 |
| **2011. Royal Wedding** | | |
| **UX244 multicoloured** (as Sc. 2464/66), *Apr 29/11* | 4.00 | 1.50 |
| **2011. Parks Canada Centennial** | | |
| **UX245 multicoloured** (as Sc. 2470), *May 19/11* | 4.00 | 1.50 |

| | Unused | Used |
|---|---|---|
| **2011. Architecture: Art Deco** (Jun 9/11) | | |
| **UX246 Vancouver** (as Sc. 2471a/2472) | 4.00 | 1.50 |
| **UX247 Montréal** (as Sc. 2471b/2473) | 4.00 | 1.50 |
| **UX248 Toronto** (as Sc. 2471c/2474) | 4.00 | 1.50 |
| **UX249 Ottawa** (as Sc. 2471d/2475) | 4.00 | 1.50 |
| **UX250 Regina** (as Sc. 2471e/2476) | 4.00 | 1.50 |
| **2011. Royal Wedding Day** | | |
| **UX251 multicoloured** (as Sc. 2477a/2478), *Jun 22/11* | 4.00 | 1.50 |
| **2011. Recording Artists** (Jun 30/11) | | |
| **UX252 Reno** (as Sc. 2479/a/2483c) | 4.00 | 1.50 |
| **UX253 Cockburn** (as Sc. 2480/a/2483a) | 4.00 | 1.50 |
| **UX254 Robertson** (as Sc. 2481/a/2483d) | 4.00 | 1.50 |
| **UX255 McGarrigle sisters** (as Sc. 2482/a/2483b) | 4.00 | 1.50 |
| **2011. Roadside Attractions** (Jul 7/11) | | |
| **UX256 Lobster** (as Sc. 2484a/2485a) | 4.00 | 1.50 |
| **UX257 Blueberry** (as Sc. 2484b/2485b) | 4.00 | 1.50 |
| **UX258 Potato** (as Sc. 2484c/2485c) | 4.00 | 1.50 |
| **UX259 Squid** (as Sc. 2484d/2485d) | 4.00 | 1.50 |
| **2011. Supertest III** (Aug 8/11) | | |
| **UX260 front view** (as Sc. 2486a/2487) | 4.00 | 1.50 |
| **UX261 side view** (as Sc. 2486b) | 4.00 | 1.50 |
| **2011. Winnipeg Jets** (Nov 10/11) | | |
| **UX262 Winnipeg Jets logo** (as Picture Postage PP7) | 4.00 | 1.50 |
| **2012. Year of the Dragon** (Jan 10/12) | | |
| **UX263 multicoloured** (as Sc. 2495) | 4.00 | 1.50 |
| **UX264 multicoloured** (as Sc. 2496i/2497) | 4.00 | 1.50 |
| **2012. Diamond Jubilee** | | |
| **UX265 Coronation issue** (as Sc. 330), *Jan 16/12* | 4.00 | 1.50 |
| **UX266 Royal Visit issue** (as Sc. 471), *Feb 6/12* | 4.00 | 1.50 |
| **UX267 Silver Jubilee issue** (as Sc. 704), *Mar 6/12* | 4.00 | 1.50 |
| **UX268 Karsh design** (as Sc. 1168), *Apr 10/12* | 4.00 | 1.50 |

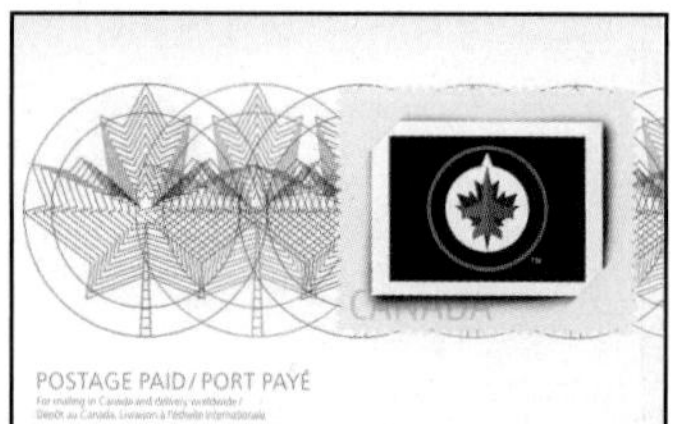

UX262

UX267

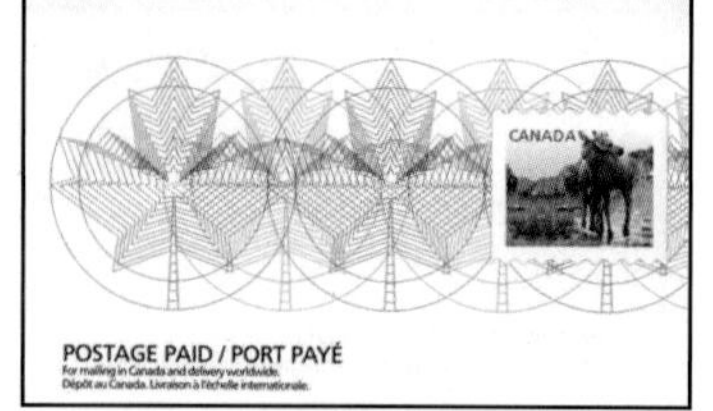

UX279

UX281

UX283

UX287

| | Unused | Used |
|---|---|---|
| **UX269 Golden Jubilee issue** (as Sc. 1932), *May 7/12* | 4.00 | 1.50 |
| **UX270 Diamond Jubilee issue** (as Sc. 2519), *Jun 1/12* | 4.00 | 1.50 |
| **2012. Canadian Pride** (Jan 16/12) | | |
| **UX271 Coast Guard ship** (as Sc. 2499) | 4.00 | 1.50 |
| **UX272 Van** (as Sc. 2500) | 4.00 | 1.50 |
| **UX273 Olympic athlete** (as Sc. 2501) | 4.00 | 1.50 |
| **UX274 Bobsled** (as Sc. 2502) | 4.00 | 1.50 |
| **UX275 Inuit child** (as Sc. 2503) | 4.00 | 1.50 |
| **2012. Baby Wildlife** (Jan 16/12) | | |
| **UX276 Racoons** (as Sc. 2506) | 4.00 | 1.50 |
| **UX277 Caribou** (as Sc. 2507) | 4.00 | 1.50 |
| **UX278 Loons** (as Sc. 2508) | 4.00 | 1.50 |
| **UX279 Moose** (as Sc. 2509) | 4.00 | 1.50 |
| **2012. Art Canada: Joe Fafard** (Feb 23/12) | | |
| **UX280 cow** (as Sc. 2522) | 4.00 | 1.50 |
| **UX281 man sitting** (as Sc. 2524) | 4.00 | 1.50 |
| **UX282 horses** (as Sc. 2525) | 4.00 | 1.50 |
| **2012. Daylilies** (Mar 1/12) | | |
| **UX283 orange daylily** (as Sc. 2529) | 4.00 | 1.50 |
| **UX284 purple daylily** (as Sc. 2530) | 4.00 | 1.50 |
| **2012. Titanic** (Apr 5/12) | | |
| **UX285 bow** (as Sc. 2531–32/2536–37) | 4.00 | 1.50 |
| **UX286 stern** (as Sc. 2533–34) | 4.00 | 1.50 |
| **UX287 full ship, side view** (as Sc. 2535/2538) | 4.00 | 1.50 |
| **2012. Franklin the Turtle** (May 11/12) | | |
| **UX288 Beaver** (as Sc. 2542) | 4.00 | 1.50 |
| **UX289 Harriet** (as Sc. 2543) | 4.00 | 1.50 |
| **UX290 Snail** (as Sc. 2544) | 4.00 | 1.50 |
| **UX291 Bear** (as Sc. 2545) | 4.00 | 1.50 |
| **2012. Calgary Stampede** (May 17/12) | | |
| **UX292 horse** (as Sc. 2457) | 4.00 | 1.50 |
| **UX293 belt buckle** (as Sc. 2548) | 4.00 | 1.50 |
| **2012. Summer Olympics** (Jun 27/12) | | |
| **UX294 rowers** (as Sc. 2556) | 4.00 | 1.50 |
| **2012. Signs of the Zodiac** (Jul 23/12) | | |
| **UX295 Leo** (as Sc. 2453) | 4.00 | 1.50 |
| **UX296 Virgo** (as Sc. 2454) | 4.00 | 1.50 |
| **UX297 Libra** (as Sc. 2455) | 4.00 | 1.50 |
| **UX298 Scorpio** (as Sc. 2456) | 4.00 | 1.50 |

| | Unused | Used |
|---|---|---|
| **2012. 100th Grey Cup Game** (Aug 16/12) | | |
| **UX299 Grey Cup** (as Sc. 2568) | 4.00 | 1.50 |
| **UX300 British Columbia Lions** (as Sc. 2569) | 4.00 | 1.50 |
| **UX301 Edmonton Eskimos** (as Sc. 2570) | 4.00 | 1.50 |
| **UX302 Calgary Stampeders** (as Sc. 2571) | 4.00 | 1.50 |
| **UX303 Saskatchewan Roughriders** (as Sc. 2572) | 4.00 | 1.50 |
| **UX304 Winnipeg Blue Bombers** (as Sc. 2573) | 4.00 | 1.50 |
| **UX305 Hamilton Tiger-Cats** (as Sc. 2574) | 4.00 | 1.50 |
| **UX306 Toronto Argonauts** (as Sc. 2575) | 4.00 | 1.50 |
| **UX307 Montreal Alouettes** (as Sc. 2576) | 4.00 | 1.50 |
| **2013. Year of the Snake** (Jan 8/13) | | |
| **UX308 multicoloured** (as Sc. 2599) | 4.00 | 1.50 |
| **UX309 multicoloured** (as Sc. 2600i/2601) | 4.00 | 1.50 |
| **2013. Baby Wildlife** (Jan 14/13) | | |
| **UX310 Woodchucks** (as Sc. 2604) | 4.00 | 1.50 |
| **UX311 Porcupine** (as Sc. 2605) | 4.00 | 1.50 |
| **UX312 Fawn** (as Sc. 2606) | 4.00 | 1.50 |
| **UX313 Black bear** (as Sc. 2607) | 4.00 | 1.50 |
| **2013. Canadian Pride** (Jan 14/13) | | |
| **UX314 Chairs on dock** (as Sc. 2612) | 4.00 | 1.50 |
| **UX315 Hay bale** (as Sc. 2613) | 4.00 | 1.50 |
| **UX316 Sailboat** (as Sc. 2614) | 4.00 | 1.50 |
| **UX317 'Living flag'** (as Sc. 2615) | 4.00 | 1.50 |
| **UX318 Fishing hut** (as Sc. 2616) | 4.00 | 1.50 |
| **2013. Signs of the Zodiac** (Feb 20/13) | | |
| **UX319 Sagittarius** (as Sc. 2457) | 4.00 | 1.50 |
| **UX320 Capricorn** (as Sc. 2458) | 4.00 | 1.50 |
| **UX321 Aquarius** (as Sc. 2459) | 4.00 | 1.50 |
| **UX322 Pisces** (as Sc. 2460) | 4.00 | 1.50 |
| **2013. Magnolias** (Mar 4/13) | | |
| **UX323 Yellow Bird** (as Sc. 2624) | 4.00 | 1.50 |
| **UX324 Eskimo** (as Sc. 2625) | 4.00 | 1.50 |
| **2013. Canadian Photography** (Mar 22/13) | | |
| **UX325 Hot Properties #1** (as Sc. 2628) | 4.00 | 1.50 |
| **UX326 Louis-Joseph Papineau** (as Sc. 2629) | 4.00 | 1.50 |
| **UX327 The Kitchen Sink** (as Sc. 2630) | 4.00 | 1.50 |
| **UX328 Andor Pasztor** (as Sc. 2631) | 4.00 | 1.50 |
| **UX329 Koo-tuck-tuck** (as Sc. 2632) | 4.00 | 1.50 |
| **UX330 Basic Camera Shop** (as Sc. 2633) | 4.00 | 1.50 |
| **UX331 Yousuf Karsh** (as Sc. 2634) | 4.00 | 1.50 |

UX332–UX339 (packaged set)

UX340

UX344–UX347 (packaged set)

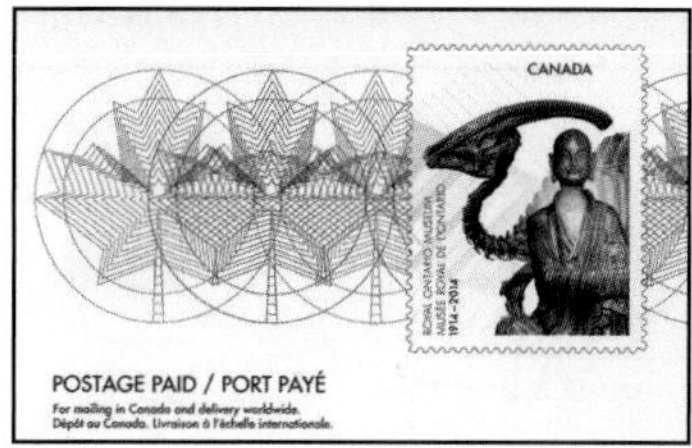

UX378



UX380

UX388

| | Unused | Used |
|---|---|---|
| **2013. Chinatown Gates** (May 1/13) | | |
| **UX332 Toronto** (as Sc. 2643a) | 4.00 | 1.50 |
| **UX333 Montreal** (as Sc. 2643b) | 4.00 | 1.50 |
| **UX334 Winnipeg** (as Sc. 2643c) | 4.00 | 1.50 |
| **UX335 Edmonton** (as Sc. 2643d) | 4.00 | 1.50 |
| **UX336 Vancouver** (as Sc. 2643e) | 4.00 | 1.50 |
| **UX337 Ottawa** (as Sc. 2643f) | 4.00 | 1.50 |
| **UX338 Mississauga** (as Sc. 2643g) | 4.00 | 1.50 |
| **UX339 Victoria** (as Sc. 2643h) | 4.00 | 1.50 |
| **2013. Motorcycles** (Jun 5/13) | | |
| **UX340 1908 CCM** (as Sc. 2647) | 4.00 | 1.50 |
| **UX341 1914 Indian** (as Sc. 2648) | 4.00 | 1.50 |
| **2013. Stella** (Jul 5/13) | | |
| **UX342 Hanging from tree** (as Sc. 2653) | 4.00 | 1.50 |
| **UX343 Reading book** (as Sc. 2654) | 4.00 | 1.50 |
| **2013. Canadian Recording Artists** (Jul 19/13) | | |
| **UX344 The Tragically Hip** (as Sc. 2656) | 4.00 | 1.50 |
| **UX345 Rush** (as Sc. 2657) | 4.00 | 1.50 |
| **UX346 Beau Dommage** (as Sc. 2658) | 4.00 | 1.50 |
| **UX347 The Guess Who** (as Sc. 2659) | 4.00 | 1.50 |
| **2013. NHL Team Jerseys** (Sep 3/13) | | |
| **UX348 Vancouver Canucks** (as Sc. 2670) | 4.00 | 1.50 |
| **UX349 Montreal Canadiens** (as Sc. 2671) | 4.00 | 1.50 |
| **UX350 Edmonton Oilers** (as Sc. 2672) | 4.00 | 1.50 |
| **UX351 Ottawa Senators** (as Sc. 2673) | 4.00 | 1.50 |
| **UX352 Calgary Flames** (as Sc. 2674) | 4.00 | 1.50 |
| **UX353 Winnipeg Jets** (as Sc. 2675) | 4.00 | 1.50 |
| **UX354 Toronto Maple Leafs** (as Sc. 2676) | 4.00 | 1.50 |
| **2013. Superman** (Sep 10/13) | | |
| **UX355 Superman #1 (1939)** (as Sc. 2679) | 4.00 | 1.50 |
| **UX356 Superman #32 (1945)** (as Sc. 2680) | 4.00 | 1.50 |
| **UX357 Superman #233 (1971)** (as Sc. 2681) | 4.00 | 1.50 |
| **UX358 Superman #204 (2004)** (as Sc. 2682) | 4.00 | 1.50 |
| **UX359 Superman Annual #1 (2012)** (as Sc. 2683) | 4.00 | 1.50 |
| **2013. Superman** (Sep 10/13) | | |
| **UX360 1939** (as BK555) | 4.00 | 1.50 |
| **UX361 1939/train** (as BK556) | 4.00 | 1.50 |
| **UX362 1986** (as BK557) | 4.00 | 1.50 |
| **UX363 2004** (as BK558) | 4.00 | 1.50 |
| **UX364 2012** (as BK559) | 4.00 | 1.50 |

| | Unused | Used |
|---|---|---|
| **2014. Year of the Horse** (Jan 13/14) | | |
| **UX365 multicoloured** (as Sc. 2699) | 4.00 | 1.50 |
| **UX366 multicoloured** (as Sc. 2700i/2701) | 4.00 | 1.50 |
| **2014. Baby Wildlife** (Mar 31/14) | | |
| **UX367 Beavers** (as Sc. 2711) | 5.00 | 2.00 |
| **UX368 Burrowing Owl** (as Sc. 2710) | 5.00 | 2.00 |
| **UX369 Mountain Goat** (as Sc. 2712) | 5.00 | 2.00 |
| **UX370 Puffin** (as Sc. 2713) | 5.00 | 2.00 |
| **UX371 Wapiti** (as Sc. 2714) | 5.00 | 2.00 |
| **2014. UNESCO** (Mar 31/14) | | |
| **UX372 Gros Morne** (as Sc. 2719) | 5.00 | 2.00 |
| **UX373 Nahanni** (as Sc. 2720) | 5.00 | 2.00 |
| **UX374 Joggins** (as Sc. 2721) | 5.00 | 2.00 |
| **UX375 Miguasha** (as Sc. 2722) | 5.00 | 2.00 |
| **UX376 Rocky Mountain** (as Sc. 2723) | 5.00 | 2.00 |
| **2014. Royal Ontario Museum** (Apr 14/14) | | |
| **UX377 Cat** (as Sc. 2725) | 5.00 | 2.00 |
| **UX378 Statue** (as Sc. 2726) | 5.00 | 2.00 |
| **UX379 Museum exterior** (as BK580) | 5.00 | 2.00 |
| **2014. Roses** (Apr 23/14) | | |
| **UX380 Konrad Henkel** (as Sc. 2730) | 5.00 | 2.00 |
| **UX381 Maid of Honour** (as Sc. 2731) | 5.00 | 2.00 |
| **2014. UNESCO** (May 16/14) | | |
| **UX382 Lunenburg** (as Sc. 2740) | 5.00 | 2.00 |
| **UX383 Buffalo Jump** (as Sc. 2741) | 5.00 | 2.00 |
| **UX384 Grand Pré** (as Sc. 2742) | 5.00 | 2.00 |
| **UX385 SGang Gwaay** (as Sc. 2743) | 5.00 | 2.00 |
| **UX386 Rideau Canal** (as Sc. 2744) | 5.00 | 2.00 |
| **2014. Empress of Ireland** (May 29/14) | | |
| **UX387 Frontal view, map** (as Sc. 2747) | 5.00 | 2.00 |
| **UX388 Full side view** (as Sc. 2746) | 5.00 | 2.00 |
| **2014. Haunted Canada** (Jun 13/14) | | |
| **UX389 Ghost Bride** (as Sc. 2749) | 5.00 | 2.00 |
| **UX390 Fiery Ships** (as Sc. 2750) | 5.00 | 2.00 |
| **UX391 Phantom Train** (as Sc. 2751) | 5.00 | 2.00 |
| **UX392 Count of Frontenac** (as Sc. 2752) | 5.00 | 2.00 |
| **UX393 Fort George** (as Sc. 2753) | 5.00 | 2.00 |

UX394–UX400 (packaged set)

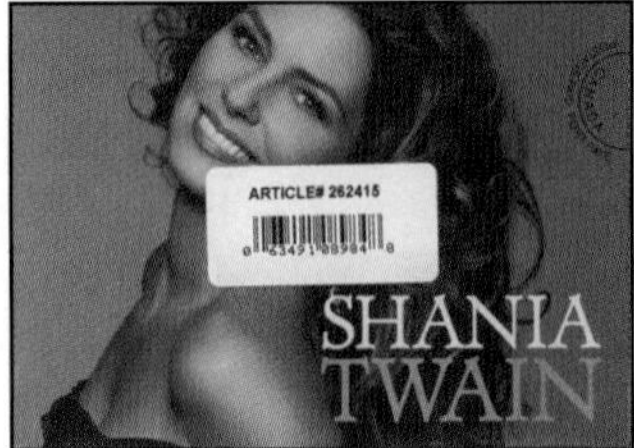

UX401–UX405 (packaged set)

UX406–UX412 (packaged set)

UX413

UX417

UX419

| | Unused | Used |
|---|---|---|
| **2014. Canadian Photography** (Jul 7/14) | | |
| **UX394 Bogner's Grocery** (as Sc. 2758) | 5.00 | 2.00 |
| **UX395 St. Joseph's Convent School** (as Sc. 2759) | 5.00 | 2.00 |
| **UX396 La ville de Québec en hiver** (as Sc. 2760) | 5.00 | 2.00 |
| **UX397 Untitled** (as Sc. 2761) | 5.00 | 2.00 |
| **UX398 Unidentified Chinese Man** (as Sc. 2762) | 5.00 | 2.00 |
| **UX399 Sitting Bull and Buffalo Bill** (as Sc. 2763) | 5.00 | 2.00 |
| **UX400 Railcuts: #1** (as Sc. 2764) | 5.00 | 2.00 |
| **2014. Canadian Country Artists** (Jul 31/14) | | |
| **UX401 Hank Snow** (as Sc. 2766) | 5.00 | 2.00 |
| **UX402 Renée Martel** (as Sc. 2767) | 5.00 | 2.00 |
| **UX403 Shania Twain** (as Sc. 2768) | 5.00 | 2.00 |
| **UX404 Tommy Hunter** (as Sc. 2769) | 5.00 | 2.00 |
| **UX405 k.d. lang** (as Sc. 2770) | 5.00 | 2.00 |
| **2014. NHL Zambonis** (Oct 3/14) | | |
| **UX406 Winnipeg Jets** (as Sc. 2779) | 5.00 | 2.00 |
| **UX407 Ottawa Senators** (as Sc. 2780) | 5.00 | 2.00 |
| **UX408 Toronto Maple Leafs** (as Sc. 2781) | 5.00 | 2.00 |
| **UX409 Montreal Canadiens** (as Sc. 2782) | 5.00 | 2.00 |
| **UX410 Vancouver Canucks** (as Sc. 2783) | 5.00 | 2.00 |
| **UX411 Calgary Flames** (as Sc. 2784) | 5.00 | 2.00 |
| **UX412 Edmonton Oilers** (as Sc. 2785) | 5.00 | 2.00 |
| **2014. Wait For Me Daddy** (Oct 4/14) | | |
| **UX413 Running to daddy** (as Sc. 2795) [barcode 09052 3] | 5.00 | 2.00 |
| **UX414 Family by train** (as Sc. 2795) [barcode 09095 0] | 5.00 | 2.00 |
| **2015. Year of the Ram** (Jan 8/15) | | |
| **UX415 multicoloured (red)** (as Sc. 2801) | 5.00 | 2.00 |
| **UX416 multicoloured (green)** (as Sc. 2802i/2803) | 5.00 | 2.00 |
| **2015. Canada Flag** (Feb 15/15) | | |
| **UX417 multicoloured** (as Sc. 2807) | 5.00 | 2.00 |
| **2015. Pansies** (Mar 2/15) | | |
| **UX418 Delta Premium Pure Light Blue** (as Sc. 2812) | 5.00 | 2.00 |
| **UX419 Midnight Glow** (as Sc. 2813) | 5.00 | 2.00 |
| **2015. Canadian Photography** (Apr 8/15) | | |
| **UX420 Angels** (as Sc. 2816) | 5.00 | 2.00 |
| **UX421 Southam Sisters** (as Sc. 2817) | 5.00 | 2.00 |
| **UX422 Friends and Family** (as Sc. 2818) | 5.00 | 2.00 |
| **UX423 Isaac's First Swim** (as Sc. 2819) | 5.00 | 2.00 |
| **UX424 Shoeshine Stand** (as Sc. 2820) | 5.00 | 2.00 |
| **UX425 Alex Colville** (as Sc. 2821) | 5.00 | 2.00 |
| **UX426 La Voie Lactée** (as Sc. 2822) | 5.00 | 2.00 |

| | Unused | Used |
|---|---|---|
| **2015. UNESCO** (July 3/15) | | |
| **UX427 Dinosaur** (as Sc. 2845) * | *500.00* | |
| **UX428 Red Bay** (as Sc. 2846) | 5.00 | 2.00 |
| **UX429 Wood Buffalo** (as Sc. 2847) | 5.00 | 2.00 |
| **UX430 Waterton-Glacier** (as Sc. 2848) | 5.00 | 2.00 |
| **UX431 Kluane** (as Sc. 2849) | 5.00 | 2.00 |

* the Dinosaur Provincial Park postal card was recalled on July 7, 2015 due to an incorrect image being used. Less than 25 have been reported sold to collectors.

| | Unused | Used |
|---|---|---|
| **2015. UNESCO** (August 21/15) | | |
| **UX432 Dinosaur** (as Sc. 2858) * | 5.00 | 2.00 |

* corrected image of Dinosaur Provincial Park, replacing UX427.

| | Unused | Used |
|---|---|---|
| **2015. Haunted Canada** (Sep 14/15) | | |
| **UX433 Brakeman Ghost** (as Sc. 2861) | 5.00 | 2.00 |
| **UX434 Marie-Josephte Corriveau** (as Sc. 2862) | 5.00 | 2.00 |
| **UX435 Halfiax Citadel** (as Sc. 2863) | 5.00 | 2.00 |
| **UX436 Red River** (as Sc. 2864) | 5.00 | 2.00 |
| **UX437 Caribou Hotel** (as Sc. 2865) | 5.00 | 2.00 |
| **2016. Year of the Monkey** (Jan 11/16; Feb 1/16) | | |
| **UX438 multicoloured (red)** (as Sc. 2884/2886) | 5.00 | 2.00 |
| **UX439 multicoloured (beige)** (as Sc. 2885i/2887) | 5.00 | 2.00 |
| **2016. Hydrangeas** (Mar 1/16) | | |
| **UX440 Hydrangeas macrophylla** (as Sc. 2899) | 5.00 | 2.00 |
| **UX441 Hydrangeas arborescens** (as Sc. 2900) | 5.00 | 2.00 |
| **2016. Canadian Photography** (Apr 13/16) | | |
| **UX442 Toronto** (as Sc. 2904) | 5.00 | 2.00 |
| **UX443 Window** (as Sc. 2905) | 5.00 | 2.00 |
| **UX444 Freighter's Boat** (as Sc. 2906) | 5.00 | 2.00 |
| **UX445 Victoria Bridge** (as Sc. 2907) | 5.00 | 2.00 |
| **UX446 Sans titre 0310** (as Sc. 2908) | 5.00 | 2.00 |
| **UX447 Mt. Habel** (as Sc. 2909) | 5.00 | 2.00 |
| **UX448 Grey Owl** (as Sc. 2910) | 5.00 | 2.00 |
| **2016. Star Trek** (May 5/16) [yellow tagging bar at right of stamp indicia] | | |
| **UX449 Kirk** (as Sc. 2917) | 5.00 | 2.00 |
| a pink tagging bar* | | |
| i doubled image: UX449 and UX453 (inverted to each other) | | |
| **UX450 Spock** (as Sc. 2920) | 5.00 | 2.00 |
| a pink tagging bar* | | |
| **UX451 Scott** (as Sc. 2918) | 5.00 | 2.00 |
| a pink tagging bar* | | |
| **UX452 McCoy** (as Sc. 2921) | 5.00 | 2.00 |
| a pink tagging bar* | | |

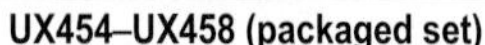
UX454–UX458 (packaged set)

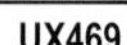
UX469

UX475

| | Unused | Used |
|---|---|---|
| **UX453 U.S.S. Enterprise** (as Sc. 2915) | 5.00 | 2.00 |
| a pink tagging bar* | | |

* from Canada Post mailing promoting World Stamp Show NY2016; may exist with English or French announcement.

**2016. Birds of Canada** (Jul 12/16)

| | Unused | Used |
|---|---|---|
| **UX454 Sharp-tailed grouse** (as Sc. 2930) | 5.00 | 2.00 |
| **UX455 Great horned owl** (as Sc. 2931) | 5.00 | 2.00 |
| **UX456 Atlantic puffin** (as Sc. 2932) | 5.00 | 2.00 |
| **UX457 Common raven** (as Sc. 2933) | 5.00 | 2.00 |
| **UX458 Rock ptarmigan** (as Sc. 2934) | 5.00 | 2.00 |

**2016. Haunted Canada** (Sep 8/16)

| | Unused | Used |
|---|---|---|
| **UX459 Bell Island Hag** (as Sc. 2936) | 5.00 | 2.00 |
| **UX460 Dungarvon Whooper** (as Sc. 2937) | 5.00 | 2.00 |
| **UX461 Lady in White** (as Sc. 2938) | 5.00 | 2.00 |
| **UX462 Winter Garden Theatre** (as Sc. 2939) | 5.00 | 2.00 |
| **UX463 Phantom Bell Ringers** (as Sc. 2940) | 5.00 | 2.00 |

**2017. Year of the Rooster** (Jan 9/17)

| | Unused | Used |
|---|---|---|
| **UX464 rooster facing left** (as Sc. 2959/2961) | 5.00 | 2.00 |
| **UX465 rooster facing right** (as Sc. 2960i/2962) | 5.00 | 2.00 |

**2017. UNESCO** (Jan 16/17)

| | Unused | Used |
|---|---|---|
| **UX466 Old Québec** (as Sc. 2965) | 5.00 | 2.00 |
| **UX467 Mistaken Point** (as Sc. 2967) | 5.00 | 2.00 |
| **UX468 L'Anse aux Meadows** (as Sc. 2968) | 5.00 | 2.00 |

See UX432 and UX428 for the designs of Dinosaur National Park and Red Bay Basque Whaling station.

**2016. Daisies** (Mar 1/17)

| | Unused | Used |
|---|---|---|
| **UX469 purple** (as Sc. 2979) | 5.00 | 2.00 |
| **UX470 yellow** (as Sc. 2980) | 5.00 | 2.00 |

**2017. Star Trek** (May 5/16)

| | Unused | Used |
|---|---|---|
| **UX471 The Wrath of Kkan** (as Sc. 2986) | 5.00 | 2.00 |
| **UX472 The Next Generation** (as Sc. 2987) | 5.00 | 2.00 |
| **UX473 Deep Space Nine** (as Sc. 2988) | 5.00 | 2.00 |
| **UX474 Voyager** (as Sc. 2989) | 5.00 | 2.00 |
| **UX475 Enterprise** (as Sc. 2990) | 5.00 | 2.00 |

**2017. Canadian Photography** (Jul 4/17)

| | Unused | Used |
|---|---|---|
| **UX476 Blind Violinist** (as Sc. 3012) | 5.00 | 2.00 |
| **UX477 Enlacées** (as Sc. 3013) | 5.00 | 2.00 |
| **UX478 Ontario** (as Sc. 3014) | 5.00 | 2.00 |
| **UX479 Centre Block** (as Sc. 3015) | 5.00 | 2.00 |
| **UX480 Macdonald** (as Sc. 3016) | 5.00 | 2.00 |

**2017. Birds of Canada** (Aug 1/17)

| | Unused | Used |
|---|---|---|
| **UX481 Osprey** (as Sc. 3018) | 5.00 | 2.00 |
| **UX482 Gyrfalcon** (as Sc. 3019) | 5.00 | 2.00 |
| **UX483 Blue jay** (as Sc. 3020) | 5.00 | 2.00 |
| **UX484 Great gray owl** (as Sc. 3021) | 5.00 | 2.00 |
| **UX485 Common loon** (as Sc. 3022) | 5.00 | 2.00 |

**2018. Year of the Dog** (Jan 15/18)

| | Unused | Used |
|---|---|---|
| **UX486 multicoloured (short-legged)** (as Sc. 3052/3054) | 5.00 | 2.00 |
| **UX487 multicoloured (long-legged)** (as Sc. 3053i/3055) | 5.00 | 2.00 |

**2018. From Far and Wide** (Jan 15/18)

| | Unused | Used |
|---|---|---|
| **UX488 St. John's, NL** (as Sc. 3071) | 5.00 | 2.00 |
| **UX489 MacMillan Provincial Park, BC** (as Sc. 3072) | 5.00 | 2.00 |
| **UX490 Prince Edward Island Park, PE** (as Sc. 3073) | 5.00 | 2.00 |
| **UX491 Hopewell Rocks, NB** (as Sc. 3074) | 5.00 | 2.00 |
| **UX492 I'lle-Bonaventure, QC** (as Sc. 3075) | 5.00 | 2.00 |
| **UX493 Pisew Falls, MB** (as Sc. 3070) | 5.00 | 2.00 |
| **UX494 Point Pelee, ON** (as Sc. 3076) | 5.00 | 2.00 |
| **UX495 Naats'ihch'oh Park, NT** (as Sc. 3077) | 5.00 | 2.00 |
| **UX496 Arctic Bay, NU** (as Sc. 3078) | 5.00 | 2.00 |

## SPECIAL ORDER POSTAL CARDS

**2017. Canada Post: 'Canada 150 stamps' announcement**

| | Unused | Used |
|---|---|---|
| **UXO1 grey and red**, English text | | *10.00* |
| a French text | | *15.00* |
| **UXO2 $1.20 grey and red**, English text | | *25.00* |
| a French text | | *50.00* |
| **UXO3 $2.50 grey and red**, English text | | *50.00* |
| a French text | | *100.00* |

UXO1–3 announced the 'Canada 150' stamps and collectibles to be released June 1. Cards were mailed to subscribers of Canada Post's *Details* magazine. Used examples will have a printed name and address, and typically a barcode on the reverse side dated in late April; they will not necessarily be cancelled.

**2017. Canada Post: Holiday Season Greeting**

| | Unused | Used |
|---|---|---|
| **UXO4 multicoloured** (as Sc. 3047), English text | | *10.00* |
| a French text | | *15.00* |

Cards were mailed to subscribers of Canada Post's *Details* magazine.

## LETTER CARDS

**1893–1897. Queen Victoria**

**Printed by the British American Bank Note Company**

There are two settings used for these issues:

| DA<br>CARD | DA<br>CARD |
|---|---|
| **Setting 1** | **Setting 2** |

**Setting 1:**"A" of "CARD" aligns under the centre of the last "A" in "CANADA".
**Setting 2:**"A" of "CARD" aligns under the right leg of the last "A" in "CANADA".

There are also two perforation types:

**Perf. A** **Perf. B**

**Perf. A:** 12 x 12, the horizontal perforations extend beyond the vertical perforations.
**Perf. B:** 12½ x 11¼, the horizontal perforations end at the vertical perforation lines.

| | | Unused | Used |
|---|---|---|---|
| **UL1** | **1¢ black**, setting 2, perforation A (1895) | 2.00 | 4.00 |
| a | as above, perforation B (1897?) | 150.00 | 175.00 |
| **UL2** | **2¢ green**, setting 1, perforation A (1895) | 10.00 | 12.00 |
| a | as above, setting 2, (1895) | 3.00 | 6.00 |
| b | as "a", perforation B (1897?) | 500.00 | 250.00 |

UL3

UL4

| | | Unused | Used |
|---|---|---|---|
| **UL3** | **3¢ carmine** (shades), setting 1, perforation A (1893) | 1.00 | 1.50 |
| a | as above, setting 2 (1897?) | 5.00 | 8.00 |
| b | as "a", perforation B (1897?) | 30.00 | 60.00 |

**1898–1902. Maple Leaf issue**

**Printed by the American Bank Note Company**

There are considerable variations in the card stock used for this issue. The thin glazed stock is a distinctive surfaced stock.

| | | Unused | Used |
|---|---|---|---|
| **UL4** | **1¢ black** | 2.00 | 3.00 |
| **UL5** | **1¢ green** (1900) | 4.00 | 5.00 |
| a | as above, thin glazed stock (1902?) | 5.00 | 20.00 |
| **UL6** | **2¢ green** | 2.00 | 4.00 |
| **UL7** | **2¢ carmine** (1900) | 3.00 | 4.00 |
| a | as above, thin glazed stock (1902) | 5.00 | 20.00 |
| **UL8** | **3¢ carmine** | 3.00 | 8.00 |

**1899. Revalued issues**

| 2c | 2c |
|---|---|
| **Type A** | **Type B** |

Copies surcharged with a handstamp in black or violet. Surcharge Types A and B are the same as used on envelopes. Other distinct types exist.

**Surcharges on B.A.B.N.C. issues**

| | | Unused | Used |
|---|---|---|---|
| **UL9** | **2¢ on 3¢** (UL3), type A | 2.00 | 3.00 |
| a | surcharge type A on UL3a | 2.00 | 3.00 |
| b | surcharge type A on UL3b | 80.00 | 120.00 |
| c | surcharge type B on UL3 | 25.00 | 30.00 |

**Surcharges on the Maple Leaf issue**

| | | Unused | Used |
|---|---|---|---|
| **UL10** | **2¢ on 3¢** (UL8), type A | 1.00 | 2.00 |
| a | as above, surcharge type B | 25.00 | 30.00 |

Stitch watermarks exist on Ul1, UL4, UL6 and UL9. Value $15–$20.

**2000. Lettersheet (Regular Issue)**

UL11

| | | Unused | Used |
|---|---|---|---|
| **UL11** | **46¢ multicoloured**, Valentine greeting | 6.00 | 12.50 |

Postal Stationery

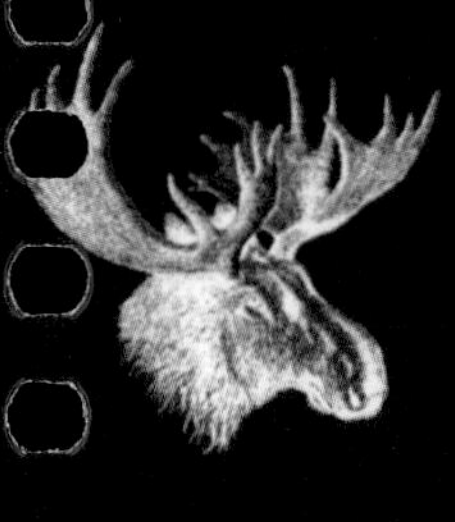

# BRITISH COLUMBIA & VANCOUVER ISLAND

## QUEEN VICTORIA

1

2

2a

1860 Typographed Unwatermarked
OG +150% Imperforate

| | | ★VF | ★F | ⊙VF | ⊙F | ✉ |
|---|---|---|---|---|---|---|
| 1 | **2½d dull rose**, imperf. | 24,000.00 | 12,000.00 | | | |

| | | ★F | ★VG | ⊙F | ⊙VG | ✉ |
|---|---|---|---|---|---|---|
| 2 | **2½d dull rose**, perf. 14 | 400.00 | 200.00 | 350.00 | 150.00 | 1,250 |
| a | 2½d pale dull rose | 400.00 | 200.00 | 350.00 | 150.00 | 1,250 |

No. 1 was never placed in use.

# VANCOUVER ISLAND

## QUEEN VICTORIA

3, 5

4, 6

1865, Sep 19 Watermarked Crown and C.C.
OG +150% Imperforate

| | | ★VF | ★F | ⊙VF | ⊙F | ✉ |
|---|---|---|---|---|---|---|
| 3 | **5¢ rose** | 50,000.00 | 20,000.00 | 15,000.00 | 5,000.00 | 20,000 |

A certificate of authenticity is recommended for #3.

| | | ★VF | ★F | ⊙VF | ⊙F | ✉ |
|---|---|---|---|---|---|---|
| 4 | **10¢ blue** | 3,000.00 | 1,500.00 | 1,500.00 | 1,000.00 | |

Perf 14

| | | ★F | ★VG | ⊙F | ⊙VG | ✉ |
|---|---|---|---|---|---|---|
| 5 | **5¢ rose** | 500.00 | 250.00 | 400.00 | 200.00 | 800.00 |
| i | inverted watermark | 1,400.00 | 700.00 | 1,000.00 | 500.00 | |
| 6 | **10¢ blue** | 500.00 | 250.00 | 400.00 | 200.00 | |
| i | inverted watermark | 800.00 | 400.00 | 800.00 | 400.00 | |

# BRITISH COLUMBIA

## SEAL OF BRITISH COLUMBIA

7

1865, Nov 1 Watermarked Crown and CC
OG +100% Perf 14

| | | ★VF | ★F | ★VG | ⊙F | ⊙VG | ✉ |
|---|---|---|---|---|---|---|---|
| 7 | **3d blue** (1867) | 200.00 | 100.00 | 40.00 | 160.00 | 80.00 | 350.00 |
| i | inverted watermark | 600.00 | 300.00 | 150.00 | 300.00 | 150.00 | |
| a | pale blue (1865) | 300.00 | 135.00 | 70.00 | 200.00 | 85.00 | 350.00 |

On November 19, 1866, British Columbia and Vancouver Island were consolidated as one territory, and the current stamps of each were valid throughout the entire colony.

## SURCHARGES

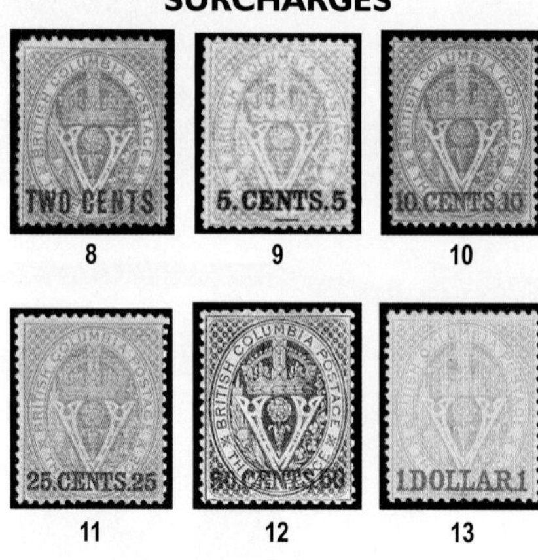
8 9 10
11 12 13

1867–1871 Perf 14
OG +100%

| | | ★F | ★VG | ⊙F | ⊙VG | ✉ |
|---|---|---|---|---|---|---|
| 8 | **2¢ on 3d brown** (black) | 100.00 | 60.00 | 150.00 | 100.00 | 1,200 |
| 9 | **5¢ on 3d bright red** (black) | 250.00 | 150.00 | 300.00 | 200.00 | 600.00 |
| 10 | **10¢ on 3d lilac rose** (blue) | 1,800.00 | 1,200.00 | | | |
| 11 | **25¢ on 3d orange** (violet) | 300.00 | 200.00 | 300.00 | 200.00 | 900.00 |
| i | inverted watermark | 700.00 | 350.00 | 700.00 | 350.00 | |
| 12 | **50¢ on 3d violet** (red) | 900.00 | 600.00 | 1,600.00 | 900.00 | |
| i | inverted watermark | 1,500.00 | 1,000.00 | | | |
| 13 | **$1 on 3d green** (green) | 1,500.00 | 1,000.00 | | | |

Nos. 10 and 13 were never placed in use.

## SURCHARGES

14 15
16 17 18

1869, March Perf 12½
OG +100%

| | | ★F | ★VG | ⊙F | ⊙VG | ✉ |
|---|---|---|---|---|---|---|
| 14 | **5¢ on 3d bright red** (black) | 2,000.00 | 1,350.00 | 1,800.00 | 1,200.00 | |
| 15 | **10¢ on 3d lilac rose** (blue) | 1,200.00 | 800.00 | 1,200.00 | 800.00 | |
| 16 | **25¢ on 3d orange** (violet) | 750.00 | 500.00 | 750.00 | 500.00 | 1,600 |
| 17 | **50¢ on 3d violet** (red) | 1,200.00 | 800.00 | 1,000.00 | 650.00 | 5,000 |
| 18 | **$1 on 3d green** (green) | 1,800.00 | 1,200.00 | 2,200.00 | 1,500.00 | |

**Grading of Perforated British Columbia Stamps:** Due to very close spacing of stamps in sheets, virtually all stamps show perfs touching or cutting outer framelines. F will have balanced margins with perfs cutting or touching the same on each side.

**On July 20, 1871, British Columbia joined the Dominion of Canada.**

# BRITISH COLUMBIA NUMERAL CANCELS

## RARITY FACTORS



**Rarity Scale**

| | |
|---|---|
| RF 1 | Common |
| RF 2 to 3 | Scarce |
| RF 4 to 5 | Very Scarce |
| RF 6 to 7 | Rare |
| RF 8 to 9 | Very Rare |
| RF 10 | Extremely Rare |

| NUMBER | TOWN | FACTOR | COMMENTS |
|---|---|---|---|
| 1 | New Westminster | 3 | In black |
| 1 | New Westminster | 5 | In red |
| 1 | New Westminster | 8 | In blue |
| 2 | Douglas | 8 | May exist in blue |
| 3 | Hope | 9 | |
| 4 | Yale | 6 | |
| 4 | Yale | 8 | In red |
| 4 | Yale | 9 | In blue |
| 5 | Unknown origin | 10 | |
| 7 | Lytton | 7 | |
| 8 | Clinton | 8 | |
| 9 | Seymour | 9 | |
| 10 | William's Creek | 4 | Renamed Caribou after Confederation |
| 12 | Ashcroft | 10 | (believed) |
| 13 | Quesnellemouth | 7 | |
| 14 | French Creek | 10 | |
| 15 | Lillooet | 7 | (believed) |
| 16 | Lake La Hache | 10 | (believed) |
| 19 | Unknown origin | 10 | |
| 20 | Soda Creek | 8 | |
| 21 | Unknown origin | 10 | |
| 22 | Van Winkle | 8 | (believed) |
| 23 | Unknown origin | 10 | |
| 26 | Langley | 7 | |
| 27 | Spence's Bridge | 7 | Only known on Canadian stamps |
| 28 | Burrard Inlet | 8 | |
| 29 | Unknown origin | 9 | |
| 30 | Unknown origin | 10 | Only known on Canadian stamps |
| 32 | Unknown origin | 10 | |
| 33 | Ladner | 10 | RF 7 on Canadian stamps |
| 34 | Unknown origin | 9 | |
| 35 | Victoria | 2 | In black |
| 35 | Victoria | 1 | In blue |
| 36 | Nanaimo | 6 | In black. RF 10 on Canadian stamps. |
| 36 | Nanaimo | 10 | In blue |

Numbers not listed may exist but have not yet been confirmed by the editors.
Forgeries on some rarer numbers exist.
Additional information is solicited.

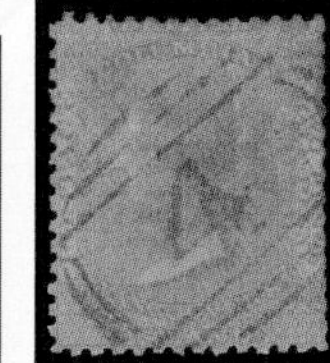

# NEW BRUNSWICK

Covers of the New Brunswick Pence Issue should have a certificate of authenticity. Clean covers demand a premium.

## PENCE ISSUE

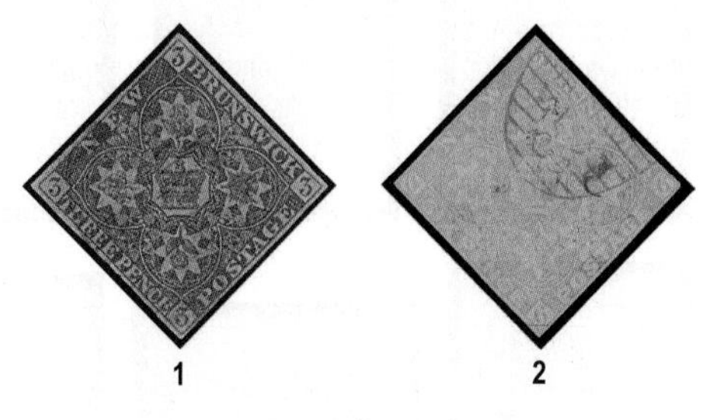

1 2

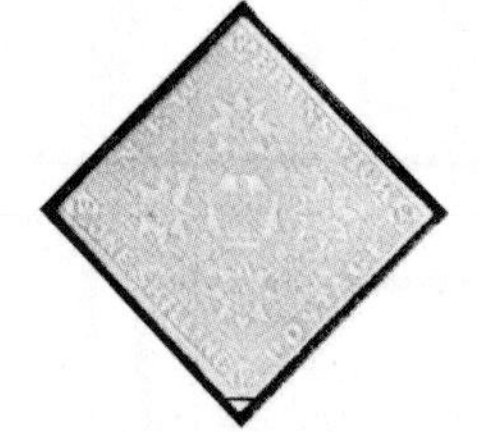

3, 4

**1851, Sep** **Engraved** **Imperforate**
**OG +100%** **Blue paper**

| | | ★VF | ★F | ⊙VF | ⊙F | ✉ |
|---|---|---|---|---|---|---|
| **1** | **3d red** | 5,000.00 | 2,000.00 | 700.00 | 350.00 | 800.00 |
| a | dark red | 6,000.00 | 2,250.00 | 800.00 | 400.00 | 1,000 |
| b | half used as 1½d on cover | | | | | 6,000 |
| i | watermarked | | | 1,500.00 | 900.00 | |
| ii | vert. line thru left value tablet | 6,500.00 | 3,000.00 | 1,000.00 | 500.00 | |
| **2** | **6d olive yellow** | 7,500.00 | 3,000.00 | 1,600.00 | 800.00 | 2,000 |
| a | orange yellow | 7,500.00 | 3,000.00 | 1,600.00 | 800.00 | 2,000 |
| b | half used as 3d on cover | | | | | 5,000 |
| c | quarter used as 1½d on cover | | | | | 60,000 |
| d | mustard yellow | 10,000.00 | 4,000.00 | 1,800.00 | 900.00 | 2,500 |
| **3** | **1/- bright red violet** | 30,000.00 | 13,500.00 | 8,000.00 | 4,000.00 | 15,000 |
| a | half used as 6d on cover | | | | | 30,000 |
| b | quarter used as 3d on cover | | | | | 45,000 |
| **4** | **1/- dull violet** | 35,000.00 | 15,000.00 | 10,000.00 | 5,000.00 | 20,000 |
| a | half used as 6d on cover | | | | | 30,000 |
| b | quarter used as 3d on cover | | | | | 45,000 |

Reprints of 3d, 6d and shilling values exist on stout white paper. Set of 3, $400.00. Only 3 sheets of each value were thought to have been reprinted.

1ii

## CHARLES CONNELL

5

**1860, May 15** **Perf 12**
**OG +100%**

| | | ★VF | ★F | ⊙VF | ⊙F | ✉ |
|---|---|---|---|---|---|---|
| **5** | **5¢ brown** | 20,000.00 | 8,000.00 | — | — | — |

This stamp was never issued. Postmaster Charles Connell had decided to use his portrait on the most commonly-used stamp, rather than that of Queen Victoria. No. 8 was issued in its place. One pair exists, unused, value $35,000. Most examples have perforation faults. Beware of forgeries made from plate proofs. A certificate is recommended.

## CENTS ISSUE

6
Locomotive

7 Queen Victoria · 8 Queen Victoria · 9 Queen Victoria

10 Steamship · 11 Prince of Wales

**1860, May 15** **White paper** **Perf 12**

Most unused examples of Nos. 6, 7 and 8 are without gum; prices are for Original Gum copies.

| | | NH% | ★VF | ★F | ⊙VF | ⊙F | ✉ |
|---|---|---|---|---|---|---|---|
| **6** | **1¢ red lilac** | 200 | 60.00 | 20.00 | 50.00 | 20.00 | 300.00 |
| a | brown violet | 200 | 125.00 | 50.00 | 90.00 | 40.00 | 350.00 |
| b | horiz. pair, imperf. vert. (w/o gum) | | 1,000.00 | 650.00 | | | |
| **7** | **2¢ orange**, *1863* | 400 | 25.00 | 7.50 | 25.00 | 7.50 | 800.00 |
| a | vert. pair, imperf. horiz. (no gum) | — | 950.00 | 600.00 | | | |
| b | deep orange | 400 | 30.00 | 8.50 | 30.00 | 8.50 | 800.00 |
| c | yellow orange | 400 | 30.00 | 8.50 | 30.00 | 8.50 | 800.00 |
| **8** | **5¢ yellow green** | 300 | 35.00 | 7.50 | 30.00 | 7.50 | 35.00 |
| a | blue green | 300 | 40.00 | 7.50 | 30.00 | 7.50 | 35.00 |
| b | olive green | 400 | 225.00 | 75.00 | 50.00 | 22.50 | 35.00 |
| i | "elongated earring" variety (pos. 60) | 300 | 150.00 | 100.00 | 150.00 | 100.00 | 300.00 |
| **9** | **10¢ vermilion** | 200 | 75.00 | 35.00 | 60.00 | 30.00 | 125.00 |
| a | half used as 5¢ on cover | | | | | | 1,000 |
| b | double impression | | | | | | |
| **10** | **12½¢ blue** | 200 | 125.00 | 60.00 | 100.00 | 50.00 | 350.00 |
| i | stitch watermark | | | | | | |
| **11** | **17¢ black** | 200 | 75.00 | 35.00 | 80.00 | 40.00 | 8,000 |

Cover prices for Nos. 6 and 7 are for combination with other stamps of any franking. The gum on No. 11 typically shows offset from another sheet.

**On July 1, 1867 New Brunswick joined the Dominion of Canada.**

## NEW BRUNSWICK PLATE PROOFS

All New Brunswick proofs are on India paper unless noted otherwise.
Four types of SPECIMEN overprints were used on New Brunswick stamps:

Type A: 23 mm x 3 mm, serif lettering
Type B: 21 mm x 3 mm, thin sans serif lettering, dot after N (50 in each sheet of 100 - columns 1-4 & 6)
Type C: 21 mm x 3 mm, thick sans serif lettering, dot after N (40 in each sheet of 100 - columns 7-10)
Type D: 22 mm x 3 mm, thin sans serif lettering, no dot after N (10 in each sheet of 100 - ONLY column 5)

**Multiples with se-tenant specimen types are worth a premium: 2 Types + 25%; 3 Types + 100%. Imprint blocks of 4 of Proofs sell for 5 times single price. Prices are for proofs in Very Fine condition.**

The approximate thickness of different papers is shown in parentheses.

| No. | Description | Price |
|---|---|---|
| 1P | 3d black on thin card | 3,000.00 |
| 2P | 6d black on thin card | 500.00 |
| 3P | 1/- black on thin card | 800.00 |
| 5P | 5¢ Connell, brown | 300.00 |
| i | brown, wove paper (.0025") | 350.00 |
| ii | light brown, thick bond paper (.0045") | 600.00 |
| iii | dark red brown, (D) red, Type A | 400.00 |
| iv | as iii, (V) red, Type B | 250.00 |
| v | as iv, Type C | 250.00 |
| vi | as iv, Type D | 600.00 |
| vii | as 5P, major re-entry (pos. 60) | 600.00 |
| viii | as 5P, major re-entry (pos. 13) | 600.00 |
| ix | as 5P, major re-entry (pos. 61) | 600.00 |

Numerous other re-entries exist.

| No. | Description | Price |
|---|---|---|
| 5TC | orange, no specimen | 500.00 |
| i | compound die proof of 5¢ Connell and 10¢ Victoria* | *7,500.00* |

* These exist in various colours. Orange, violet, blue, green, brown and black seen by editors. Singles, cut from the compound proofs, in any colour ... value $2,000 with wide margins, $1,200 with close but clear margins.

| No. | Description | Price |
|---|---|---|
| 6P | 1¢ dark violet | 125.00 |
| i | dark violet brown | 100.00 |
| ii | as i, (D) red, Type A | 150.00 |
| iii | as i, (H) red, Type B | 100.00 |
| iv | as iii, Type C | 100.00 |
| v | as iii, Type D | 200.00 |
| 6TC | reddish orange | 200.00 |
| i | light rose, bond paper (.004") | 250.00 |
| ii | rose red, bond paper (.004") | 250.00 |
| 7P | 2¢ reddish orange | 50.00 |
| i | orange | 50.00 |
| 7TC | rose | 75.00 |
| i | dark green | 90.00 |
| ii | slate black | 120.00 |
| iii | deep orange, wove paper (.0035") | 100.00 |
| 8P | 5¢ green (shades) | 60.00 |
| i | green, (D) black, Type A | 100.00 |
| ii | yellow green, (V) red, Type B | 50.00 |
| iii | as ii, Type C | 50.00 |
| iv | as ii, Type D | 125.00 |
| 8TC | orange (shades) | 60.00 |
| i | black, (V) red, Type B | 125.00 |
| ii | as i, Type C | 125.00 |
| iii | as i, Type D | 250.00 |
| iv | black, diagonal Type A | 200.00 |

| No. | Description | Price |
|---|---|---|
| 9P | 10¢ red | 60.00 |
| i | vermilion | 50.00 |
| ii | reddish brown, (D) black, Type A | 100.00 |
| iii | reddish brown, (V) green, Type B | 50.00 |
| iv | as iii, Type C | 50.00 |
| v | as iii, Type D | 150.00 |
| 9TC | orange, no specimen | 300.00 |
| i | black (stamp size die proof) | 1,000.00 |
| 10P | 12½¢ dark blue (shades) | 80.00 |
| i | dark blue, (D) red, Type A | 100.00 |
| ii | dark blue, (H) red, Type B | 70.00 |
| iii | as ii, Type C | 70.00 |
| iv | as ii, Type D | 150.00 |
| v | dark blue, "SPECIMEN" (18 mm x 3 mm, with serifs) | |
| 10TC | reddish orange | 80.00 |
| i | orange (shades) | 80.00 |
| ii | black | 125.00 |
| iii | black, (H) red, Type B | 125.00 |
| iv | as iii, Type C | 125.00 |
| v | as iii, Type D | 250.00 |
| 11P | 17¢ black | 70.00 |
| i | black, (D) red, Type A | 150.00 |
| ii | black, (V) red, Type B | 50.00 |
| iii | as ii, Type C | 50.00 |
| iv | as ii, Type D | 150.00 |
| 11TC | reddish orange | 90.00 |

**5Pvii**
Heavy doubling, particularly in left 5's

**5Pviii**
Heavy doubling overall

**5Pix**
Heavy doubling in top half of stamp

**5TCi**

**5P**

**6P**

**7P**

**8Pii**

**9P**

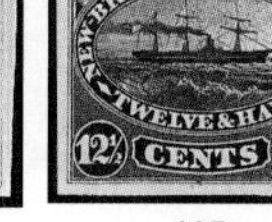
**10P**

**11P**

**11Pii**

*The Postage Stamps of New Brunswick and Nova Scotia*, Nicholas Argenti, 1976

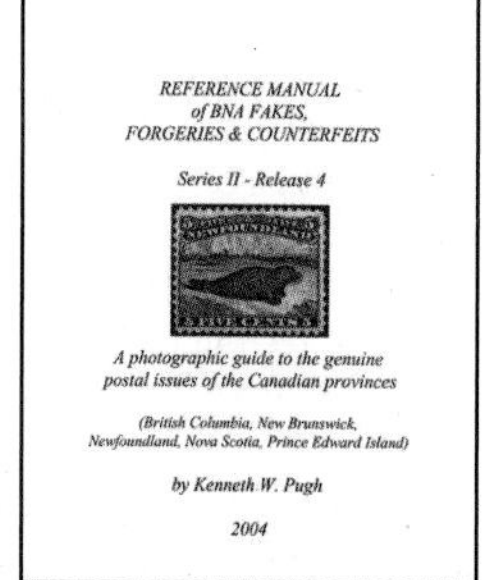

*Reference Manual of BNA Fakes, Forgeries and Counterfeits Series II - Release 4*, Ken Pugh, 2004

# NUMERAL CANCELS OF NEW BRUNSWICK

## RARITY FACTORS

**Rarity Scale**

| | |
|---|---|
| RF 1 | Common |
| RF 2 to 3 | Scarce |
| RF 4 to 5 | Very Scarce |
| RF 6 to 7 | Rare |
| RF 8 to 9 | Very Rare |
| RF 10 | Extremely Rare |

| NO. | TOWN (Earliest) | N.B. Pence | N.B. Cents | Large Queen | Small Queen | Comments |
|---|---|---|---|---|---|---|
| 1 | Saint John (1853) | 4 | 3 | 10 | 7 | |
| 2 | Andover (c1850s) | 9 | 9 | – | – | |
| 2 | Tracey's Mills (1868) | – | – | 8 | 9 | |
| 3 | Baie Verte (1860) | 9 | 9 | – | – | |
| 3 | Woodstock (1868) | – | – | 7 | 3 | |
| 3 | Little Ridge (c1894) | – | – | – | 10 | |
| 4 | Bathurst (1860) | 10 | 10 | 10 | 10 | |
| 5 | Bend [of Petitcodiac] | 8 | 9 | – | – | |
| 5 | W.O. Brookvale (1869) | – | – | 10 | 9 | |
| 6 | Campbellton | 10 | 10 | – | – | |
| 6 | Westmoreland Point (1880) | – | – | 9 | 7 | |
| 7 | Campobello (1855) | 9 | 10 | – | – | |
| 7 | W.O. Waterville (1869) | – | – | – | 10 | |
| 8 | Chatham | 7 | 8 | – | – | |
| | as above but in blue | 5 | 10 | – | – | |
| 8 | W.O. Upper Wicklow (1860) | – | 8 | 10 | 10 | |
| 9 | Colebrooke | – | – | – | – | Became Grand Falls in 1856 |
| 9 | Grand Falls (1863) | – | 4 | 8 | 3 | |
| 10 | Dalhousie (1859) | 7 | 8 | – | – | |
| 10 | White's Cove (1865) | – | 8 | 8 | 8 | |
| | as above but in red | – | – | – | 8 | |
| 11 | Dorchester (1851) | 6 | – | – | – | |
| 11 | Upper Woodstock (1869) | – | – | – | 5 | |
| 12 | Edmunston (1854) | 6 | 10 | – | 9 | |
| 13 | Fredericton (1855) | 4 | 1 | 5 | – | |
| 14 | Gagetown (1857) | 8 | 7 | – | – | |
| 14 | Upper Maugerville (1898) | – | – | – | 7 | |
| 15 | Hampton Ferry (1854) | 8 | – | – | 9 | |
| 16 | Harvey (1860) | 9 | 9 | – | – | |
| 16 | Penobsquis (1868) | – | – | 8 | 6 | |
| 17 | Hillsborough (1855) | 9 | 7 | – | – | |
| 17 | Hopewell The Cape (1897) | – | – | – | 10 | |
| 18 | Kingston (1859) | 10 | 8 | 7 | 9 | |
| 19 | Memramcook (1859) | 10 | – | 6 | 4 | |
| 20 | Milltown (1856) | 9 | 9 | – | – | |
| 20 | Wickham (1871) | – | – | – | 5 | Changed from W.O. to P.O. in 1875 |
| 21 | Newcastle (1860) | 8 | 7 | – | – | |
| 21 | W.O. Victoria (1865) | – | 8 | 8 | 6 | |
| 22 | Oromocto | 10 | – | 9 | 7 | |
| 23 | Richibucto (1857) | 6 | 9 | 9 | 9 | |
| 24 | Sackville (1858) | 8 | 9 | – | – | No post Confederation use recorded |
| 25 | Salisbury (1856) | 8 | 10 | – | – | No post Confederation use recorded |
| 26 | Shediac (1854) | 5 | 9 | – | – | |
| 26 | W.O. Upper Gagetown (1868) | – | – | 7 | 4 | |
| 27 | St. Andrews | 7 | – | – | – | |
| 27 | Upper Sackville (1890) | – | – | – | 7 | |
| 28 | St. George (1854) | 8 | 10 | – | – | No post Confederation use recorded |
| 29 | St. Martins (1858) | 9 | – | – | – | No post Confederation use recorded |
| 30 | St. Stephen (1853) | 7 | 10 | 10 | 5 | |
| 31 | Sussex | 10 | – | – | 10 | |
| 32 | Webster's Creek | – | 10 | – | – | |
| 32 | Winding Ledges (1889) | – | – | – | 2 | |
| 33 | Upper Mills (1864) | – | 9 | – | – | |
| 33 | W.O. Wicklow (1870) | – | – | 10 | 7 | |
| 34 | Woodstock (1854) | 7 | 9 | – | – | |
| 35 | Sheffield | 8 | – | – | – | |
| 35 | Upper Peel (c1894) | – | – | 10 | 10 | |
| 36 | Not known | | | | | |
| 37 | New Mills | 10 | – | – | – | |
| 38 | Ossekeag (1863) | – | 10 | – | – | |
| 39 | Indiantown (1866) | – | 6 | 9 | – | |

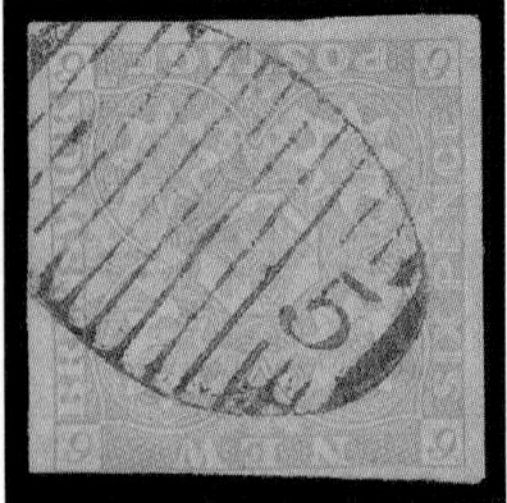

# NOVA SCOTIA

Covers of the Nova Scotia Pence Issue should have a certificate of authenticity. Clean covers demand a premium.

## PENCE ISSUE

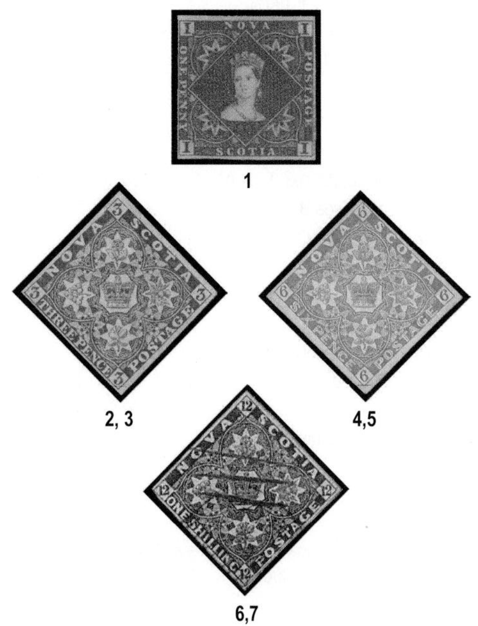

1 — 2, 3 — 4,5 — 6,7

**1851–1857** **Engraved Blue Paper** **Imperforate**
**OG +100%**

| No. | Description | ★VF | ★F | ⊙VF | ⊙F | ✉ |
|---|---|---|---|---|---|---|
| 1 | **1d red brown**, *May 12, 1853* | 3,000.00 | 1,500.00 | 700.00 | 350.00 | 2,000 |
| a | half used as ½d on cover | | | | | *75,000* |

Fresh entries have been documented on pos. 19, 49 and 80, showing in all four corners and some lettering.

| No. | Description | ★VF | ★F | ⊙VF | ⊙F | ✉ |
|---|---|---|---|---|---|---|
| 2 | **3d blue**, *Sep 1, 1851* | 1,600.00 | 800.00 | 300.00 | 150.00 | 400.00 |
| a | half used as 1½d on cover | | | | | *5,000* |
| b | pale blue, *1857* | 1,600.00 | 800.00 | 350.00 | 175.00 | 400.00 |
| c | as "b", half used as 1½d on cover | | | | | |
| i | bright blue | 1,800.00 | 900.00 | 300.00 | 150.00 | 400.00 |
| 3 | **3d dark blue**, on blued paper, *1857* | 2,200.00 | 1,100.00 | 400.00 | 200.00 | 500.00 |
| a | half used as 1½d on cover | | | | | *6,000* |

No. 2/3: Fresh entries have been documented on pos. 9 (in THREE PENCE) and pos. 12.

| No. | Description | ★VF | ★F | ⊙VF | ⊙F | ✉ |
|---|---|---|---|---|---|---|
| 4 | **6d yellow green**, *Sep 1, 1851* | 7,500.00 | 3,000.00 | 1,200.00 | 500.00 | 2,000 |
| a | half used as 3d on cover | | | | | *6,000* |
| 5 | **6d dark green**, *1857* | 12,500.00 | 5,000.00 | 3,000.00 | 1,000.00 | 4,000 |
| a | half used as 3d on cover | | | | | *8,000* |
| b | quarter used as 1½d on cover | | | | | *60,000* |
| 6 | **1/– reddish violet**, *1857* | 30,000.00 | 16,000.00 | 7,000.00 | 3,500.00 | 20,000 |
| a | half used as 6d on cover | | | | | *50,000* |
| b | deep purple | 32,500.00 | 18,000.00 | 9,000.00 | 4,500.00 | 20,000 |
| i | watermarked "T.H. Saunders" | *40,000.00* | 20,000.00 | 12,000.00 | 6,000.00 | |

No. 6/7: Fresh entries have been documented on pos. 1 and 11.

| No. | Description | ★VF | ★F | ⊙VF | ⊙F | ✉ |
|---|---|---|---|---|---|---|
| 7 | **1/– dull violet** | 35,000.00 | 13,500.00 | 9,000.00 | 4,000.00 | 20,000 |
| a | half used as 6d on cover | | | | | *60,000* |
| b | quarter used as 3d on cover | | | | | *125,000* |
| i | watermarked "T.H. Saunders" | 40,000.00 | 20,000.00 | 12,000.00 | 6,000.00 | |

Reprints are on thin hard white paper: 1p in brown, 3p in blue, 6p in dark green and 1/– in violet black. Price: $500.00 per set.

## QUEEN VICTORIA

8 — 9 — 10 — 11 — 12 — 13

**1860–1863** **White or yellowish paper** **Perf 12**

Inscription blocks of four of 8–9 and 11–13 are valued at 6 times normal stamps.

| No. | Description | NH% | ★VF | ★F | ⊙VF | ⊙F | ✉ |
|---|---|---|---|---|---|---|---|
| 8 | **1¢ black** | 100 | 20.00 | 5.00 | 10.00 | 5.00 | 150.00 |
| a | white paper | 100 | 20.00 | 5.00 | 10.00 | 5.00 | 150.00 |
| b | half used as ½¢ on cover | | | | | | 12,000 |
| c | horiz. pair, imperf. vert | 100 | 500.00 | 250.00 | | | |
| i | stitch watermark | | 350.00 | 175.00 | 300.00 | 150.00 | |

Numerous minor re-entries exist, mainly on bottom framelines.

| No. | Description | NH% | ★VF | ★F | ⊙VF | ⊙F | ✉ |
|---|---|---|---|---|---|---|---|
| 9 | **2¢ lilac** | 100 | 20.00 | 6.00 | 15.00 | 6.00 | 90.00 |
| a | yellowish paper | 100 | 20.00 | 6.00 | 15.00 | 6.00 | |
| b | half used as 1¢ on cover | | | | | | 5,000 |
| c | greyish purple | 100 | 25.00 | 7.00 | 18.00 | 7.00 | |
| 10 | **5¢ blue** (OG +100%) | 300 | 600.00 | 250.00 | 15.00 | 5.00 | 50.00 |
| a | yellowish paper | 300 | 600.00 | 250.00 | 15.00 | 5.00 | |
| b | half used as 2½¢ on cover | | | | | | — |
| c | dark blue | 300 | 600.00 | 250.00 | 15.00 | 5.00 | |

Numerous minor re-entries exist.

| No. | Description | NH% | ★VF | ★F | ⊙VF | ⊙F | ✉ |
|---|---|---|---|---|---|---|---|
| 11 | **8½¢ green** | 100 | 20.00 | 5.00 | 30.00 | 10.00 | 1,500 |
| a | white paper | 100 | 20.00 | 5.00 | 30.00 | 10.00 | 1,500 |
| i | yellow green | 100 | 25.00 | 5.50 | 30.00 | 10.00 | 1,500 |
| ii | unshaded "E" (pos. 94) | 100 | 50.00 | 25.00 | 50.00 | 25.00 | |
| 12 | **10¢ vermilion** | 100 | 20.00 | 7.00 | 15.00 | 7.00 | 125.00 |
| a | yellowish paper | 100 | 20.00 | 7.00 | 15.00 | 7.00 | 125.00 |
| b | half used as 5¢ on cover | | | | | | 1,500 |
| i | stitch watermark | | 250.00 | 125.00 | 150.00 | 75.00 | |
| 13 | **12½¢ black** | 100 | 60.00 | 20.00 | 50.00 | 20.00 | 500.00 |
| a | white paper | 100 | 60.00 | 20.00 | 50.00 | 20.00 | 500.00 |

Numerous minor re-entries exist on top framelines.

**On July 1, 1867 Nova Scotia joined the Dominion of Canada.**

## NOVA SCOTIA PLATE PROOFS

All Nova Scotia proofs are on India paper unless noted otherwise. All SPECIMEN overprints are diagonal. Four types of SPECIMEN overprints were used on Nova Scotia stamps.

Type A: 23 mm x 3 mm, serif lettering
Type B: 21 mm x 3 mm, thin sans serif lettering (52 in each sheet of 100)
Type C: 21 mm x 3 mm, thick sans serif lettering (40 in each sheet of 100)
Type D: 23 mm x 3 mm, thin sans serif lettering. (8 in each sheet of 100)
Type D comes only from positions 11–14 and 61–64.

**Multiples with se-tenant specimen types are worth a premium: 2 Types + 25%; 3 Types + 100%. Imprint blocks of 4 of Proofs sell for 5 times single price. Prices are for proofs in Very Fine condition.**

| | | |
|---|---|---|
| **1P** | 1d black on thin card | 650.00 |
| **2P** | 3d black on thin card | 3,000.00 |
| **4P** | 6d black on thin card | 400.00 |
| **6P** | 1/- black on thin card | 850.00 |
| **8P** | 1¢ black | 60.00 |
| **i** | black, (D) red, Type A | 60.00 |
| **ii** | as i, Type B | 50.00 |
| **iii** | as i, Type C | 50.00 |
| **iv** | as i, Type D | 130.00 |
| **v** | black, (D) gold, Type B | 400.00 |
| **8TC** | vermilion | 125.00 |
| **i** | vermilion, (D) green, Type A | 100.00 |
| **ii** | as i, Type B | 60.00 |
| **iii** | as i, Type C | 60.00 |
| **iv** | as i, Type D | 180.00 |
| **v** | green (shades) | 120.00 |
| **vi** | dark green, (D) red, Type A | 100.00 |
| **vii** | as vi, Type B | 60.00 |
| **viii** | as vi, Type C | 60.00 |
| **ix** | as vi, Type D | 180.00 |
| **x** | dark violet | 120.00 |
| **xi** | orange | 100.00 |
| **9P** | 2¢ lilac (shades) | 100.00 |
| **9TC** | grey | 90.00 |
| **i** | orange | 90.00 |
| **ii** | dark slate violet | 90.00 |
| **iii** | as ii, (D) red, Type A | 50.00 |
| **10P** | 5¢ blue | 60.00 |
| **i** | blue, (D) red, Type A | 75.00 |
| **ii** | as i, Type B | 50.00 |
| **iii** | as i, Type C | 50.00 |
| **iv** | as i, Type D | 150.00 |
| **10TC** | black | 100.00 |
| **i** | black, (D) red, Type A | 150.00 |
| **ii** | as i, Type B | 100.00 |
| **iii** | as i, Type C | 100.00 |
| **iv** | as i, Type D | 200.00 |
| **v** | black, (D) gold, Type C | 500.00 |
| **vi** | as v, Type D | 500.00 |
| **vii** | orange | 100.00 |
| **viii** | as i, (D) green, Type C | 500.00 |
| **11P** | 8½¢ light bluish green (shades) | 50.00 |
| **i** | dark green | 75.00 |
| **ii** | dark green, (D) red, Type A | 90.00 |
| **iii** | as ii, Type C | 200.00 |
| **iv** | as ii, Type B | 200.00 |
| **v** | as ii, Type D | 500.00 |
| **11TC** | black | 75.00 |
| **i** | black, (D) red, Type B | 75.00 |
| **ii** | as i, Type C | 75.00 |
| **iii** | as i, Type D | 150.00 |
| **iv** | vermilion, (D) green, Type B | 75.00 |
| **v** | as iv, Type C | 75.00 |
| **vi** | as iv, Type D | 150.00 |
| **vii** | orange | 100.00 |
| **12P** | 10¢ vermilion (shades) | 60.00 |
| **i** | vermilion, (D) green, Type B | 50.00 |
| **ii** | as i, Type C | 50.00 |
| **iii** | as i, Type D | 150.00 |
| **iv** | vermilion, (D) red, Type C | 250.00 |
| **v** | vermilion, (D) black, Type A | 150.00 |
| **12TC** | black | 100.00 |
| **i** | black, (D) red, Type A* | 150.00 |
| **ii** | as i, Type B | 80.00 |
| **iii** | as i, Type C | 80.00 |
| **iv** | as i, Type D | 500.00 |
| **v** | black, (D) gold, Type B | 400.00 |
| **vi** | as v, Type C | 400.00 |
| **vii** | as v, Type D (only 8 exist) | 1,500.00 |
| **viii** | dull red | 90.00 |
| **ix** | scarlet | 90.00 |
| **x** | yellow brown | 150.00 |
| **xi** | green | 120.00 |
| **xii** | blue (shades) | 150.00 |
| **xiii** | orange | 120.00 |

* Examples are known with SPECIMEN almost faded out ... same value.

| | | |
|---|---|---|
| **13P** | 12½¢ black | 60.00 |
| **i** | black, (D) red, Type B | 50.00 |
| **ii** | as i, Type C | 50.00 |
| **iii** | as i, Type D | 150.00 |
| **13TC** | vermilion | 100.00 |
| **i** | vermilion, (D) green, Type A | 60.00 |
| **ii** | as i, Type B | 100.00 |
| **iii** | as i, Type C | 100.00 |
| **iv** | as i, Type D | 350.00 |
| **v** | green (shades) | 120.00 |
| **vi** | green, (D) red, Type B | 60.00 |
| **vii** | as vi, Type C | 60.00 |
| **viii** | as vi, Type D | 150.00 |
| **ix** | orange | 100.00 |
| **x** | vermilion, (D) black, Type A | 100.00 |

Proofs 8TCv, 8TCvii, 10TC and 12TCi exist with laid lines (others may also exist).

8Piii 8TCii 8TCv 8TCx 8TCxi 10P

12P 12TC 12TCxiii 13Pii 13TC 13TCv

Nova Scotia

# PRINCE EDWARD ISLAND

Prince Edward Island covers valued at $250 or higher should have certificates of authenticity.
Cover values shown are for Fine condition.

## QUEEN VICTORIA

1 2 3

**1861, Jan 1** — **Yellowish paper** — **Typographed** — **Perf 9**
**OG +100%, NH +100%**

| | | ★VF | ★F | ⊙VF | ⊙F | ✉ |
|---|---|---|---|---|---|---|
| **1** | **2d dull rose** | 1,000.00 | 350.00 | 400.00 | 175.00 | 650.00 |
| a | deep rose | 1,200.00 | 400.00 | 450.00 | 200.00 | 750.00 |
| b | rouletted* | | | *35,000.00* | *20,000.00* | |
| c | horiz. pair, imperf. between (unique) | — | 7,500 | — | — | — |
| d | diagonal half used as 1d on cover | | | | | 10,000 |

* Certificate of authenticity is recommended; reportedly only 3 used copies known.

| | | ★VF | ★F | ⊙VF | ⊙F | ✉ |
|---|---|---|---|---|---|---|
| **2** | **3d blue** | 2,000.00 | 800.00 | 900.00 | 450.00 | 1,500 |
| a | diagonal half used as 1½d on cover | | | | | 10,000 |
| b | double impression | 6,000.00 | 3,000.00 | | | |
| **3** | **6d yellow green** | 2,750.00 | 1,250.00 | 1,500.00 | 750.00 | 4,000 |

## QUEEN VICTORIA

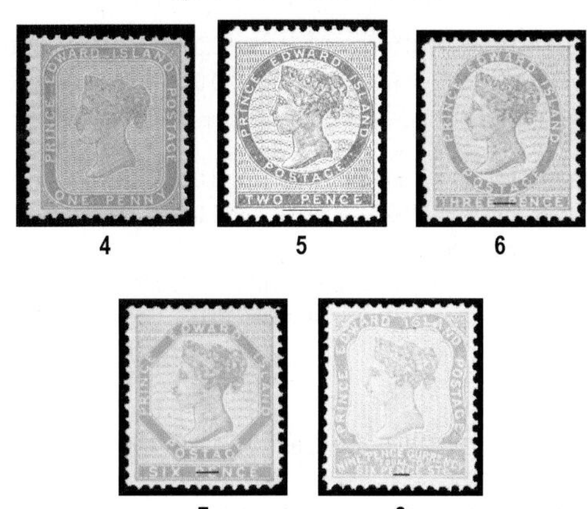

4 5 6
7 8

**1862–1865** — **White or yellowish paper** — **Perf 11½–12**

| | | NH% | ★VF | ★F | ⊙VF | ⊙F | ✉ |
|---|---|---|---|---|---|---|---|
| **4** | **1d yellow orange** | 100 | 60.00 | 20.00 | 40.00 | 20.00 | 325.00 |
| a | brown orange, perf. 11 x 11 | 100 | 70.00 | 30.00 | 40.00 | 20.00 | 350.00 |
| b | imperf. pair | 100 | 225.00 | 150.00 | — | — | — |
| c | half used as ½d on cover | | | | | | *7,500* |
| d | compound perf. 11 x 11½–12 | 100 | 250.00 | 125.00 | 90.00 | 45.00 | |
| i | orange buff | 100 | 60.00 | 20.00 | 40.00 | 20.00 | 325.00 |
| ii | yellow | 100 | 60.00 | 20.00 | 40.00 | 20.00 | 325.00 |
| iii | yellowish paper | 100 | 350.00 | 300.00 | | | |
| iv | horiz. pair, imperf. vert. | 100 | 500.00 | 350.00 | | | |
| v | imperf. bottom margin | | | | | | |

**Compound perfs** are typically perf. 11 on the top and bottom, perf. 11½ on one side and perf. 12 on the other side.

**1862–1865** — **White or yellowish paper** — **Perf 11½–12**

| | | NH% | ★VF | ★F | ⊙VF | ⊙F | ✉ |
|---|---|---|---|---|---|---|---|
| **5** | **2d rose**, printed in sheets of 60 (10 x 6) | 100 | 12.00 | 6.00 | 10.00 | 5.00 | 125.00 |
| a | yellowish paper | 100 | 30.00 | 10.00 | 10.00 | 5.00 | 125.00 |
| b | imperf. pair | 100 | 150.00 | 75.00 | — | — | — |
| c | horiz. pair, imperf. vert. | 100 | 350.00 | 200.00 | — | — | — |
| d | vert. pair, imperf. horiz. | 100 | 500.00 | 300.00 | — | — | — |
| e | diagonal half used as 1d on cover | | | | | | *5,000* |
| f | "TWC" for "TWO", (pos. 54) | 100 | 100.00 | 50.00 | 100.00 | 50.00 | |
| g | compound perf. 11 x 11½–12 | 100 | 300.00 | 180.00 | 130.00 | 100.00 | 350.00 |
| i | deep rose | 100 | 15.00 | 7.00 | 12.00 | 6.00 | 125.00 |
| iii | horiz. pair, double perf. between | 100 | — | 400.00 | — | — | — |
| iv | as "f", in block with 3 normals | 100 | 125.00 | 80.00 | | | |
| v | imperf. left margin | 100 | 250.00 | 150.00 | | | |
| vi | as "d" with perf. at bottom | 100 | 350.00 | 200.00 | | | |
| vii | imperf. bottom margin | 100 | 250.00 | 150.00 | | | |
| viii | imperf. left and bottom margins | 100 | 600.00 | 350.00 | | | |
| **6** | **3d blue** | 100 | 20.00 | 8.00 | 20.00 | 7.00 | 60.00 |
| a | yellowish paper | 100 | 50.00 | 16.00 | 20.00 | 7.00 | 60.00 |
| b | imperf. pair | 100 | 150.00 | 75.00 | — | — | — |
| c | vert. pair, imperf. horiz. | 100 | 300.00 | 150.00 | — | — | — |
| d | horiz. pair, imperf. vert. | 100 | 300.00 | 150.00 | — | — | — |
| e | diagonal half used as 1½d on cover | | | | | | — |
| f | compound perf. 11 x 11½–12 | 100 | 280.00 | 140.00 | 70.00 | 35.00 | 150.00 |
| g | imperf. gutter pair | 100 | — | 1,250.00 | — | — | — |
| iv | imperf. bottom margin | 100 | 400.00 | 250.00 | | | |
| h | imperf. tête-bêche gutter pair (all are creased in margin) | | | 3,000.00 | | | |
| **7** | **6d yellow green** | 200 | 160.00 | 80.00 | 120.00 | 60.00 | 600.00 |
| a | blue green | 200 | 160.00 | 80.00 | 120.00 | 60.00 | 600.00 |
| c | diagonal half used as 3d on cover | | | | | | *9,000* |
| d | compound perf. 11 x 11½–12 | 150 | 375.00 | 175.00 | 300.00 | 150.00 | |
| ii | imperf. left margin | 100 | 500.00 | 300.00 | | | |

No. 7: 6d "reprint" die proofs exist in 10 colours: vermilion, light brown, yellow green, yellow, blue green, light blue, dark blue, dark brown, purple and magenta. Value $20 each.

| | | NH% | ★VF | ★F | ⊙VF | ⊙F | ✉ |
|---|---|---|---|---|---|---|---|
| **8** | **9d violet** | 150 | 120.00 | 60.00 | 100.00 | 50.00 | 750.00 |
| a | imperf. pair | 100 | 500.00 | 200.00 | | | |
| b | horiz. pair, imperf. vert. | | 600.00 | 240.00 | | | |
| c | diagonal half used as 4½d on cover | | | | | | *7,500* |
| d | perf. 11 | 150 | 150.00 | 75.00 | 100.00 | 50.00 | 1,500 |
| i | red violet | 150 | 120.00 | 60.00 | 100.00 | 50.00 | |
| ii | blue violet | 150 | 120.00 | 60.00 | 100.00 | 50.00 | |

## QUEEN VICTORIA

9

10

**1868–1870**

| | | NH% | ★VF | ★F | ⊙VF | ⊙F | ✉ |
|---|---|---|---|---|---|---|---|
| 9 | **4d black** | 100 | 12.00 | 6.00 | 25.00 | 15.00 | 250.00 |
| a | yellowish paper | 100 | 20.00 | 10.00 | 27.50 | 17.50 | 250.00 |
| b | horiz. pair, imperf. vert. | 100 | 250.00 | 150.00 | — | — | — |
| c | diagonal half used as 2d on cover | | | | | | *3,000* |
| d | imperf. pair | 100 | 150.00 | 90.00 | — | — | — |
| e | horiz. pair, imperf. between | 100 | 200.00 | 120.00 | — | — | — |
| f | compound perf. 11 x 11½-12 | 100 | 300.00 | 150.00 | 200.00 | 100.00 | 400.00 |
| ii | shading variety* (pos. 7) | 100 | 40.00 | 20.00 | 60.00 | 30.00 | 300.00 |
| iii | imperf. bottom margin** | 100 | — | 150.00 | — | — | — |
| iv | imperf. right margin | 100 | | 150.00 | | | |
| v | "FOUP" variety (pos. 19) | 100 | 40.00 | 20.00 | 60.00 | 30.00 | |
| g | horiz. strip of 3, imperf. between | 100 | 1,500.00 | 600.00 | | | |
| vii | gutter block of 8 | 100 | 2,000.00 | 1,200.00 | | | |
| viii | imperf left margin | 100 | 250.00 | 150.00 | | | |

* Break in horizontal shading line in front of the Queen's nose, resulting in "2 dots" instead of a line.

**1870, Jun 1** **Engraved** **Perf 12**

| | | NH% | ★VF | ★F | ⊙VF | ⊙F | ✉ |
|---|---|---|---|---|---|---|---|
| 10 | **4½d brown** | 200 | 100.00 | 40.00 | 100.00 | 40.00 | 3,000 |
| i | yellow brown | 200 | 100.00 | 40.00 | 100.00 | 40.00 | 3,000 |
| ii | wide gutter block | 200 | 750.00 | 400.00 | — | — | — |
| iii | imperf. bottom margin** | 200 | — | 150.00 | — | — | — |

** All known examples of 9iii and 10iii are badly off centre.

#10 plate imprint blocks of 8 value at the sum of the catalogue value of the singles plus 50%.

## QUEEN VICTORIA "CENTS" ISSUE

11 12 13

14 15 16

**1872, Jan 1** **Typographed** **Perf 12, 12½**

| | | NH% | ★VF | ★F | ⊙VF | ⊙F | ✉ |
|---|---|---|---|---|---|---|---|
| 11 | **1¢ brown orange** perf. 11½-12 | 100 | 10.00 | 4.00 | 10.00 | 6.50 | 200.00 |
| a | imperf. pair | 100 | 300.00 | 150.00 | | | |
| b | perf. 12½-13 | 100 | 12.00 | 5.00 | 12.50 | 8.00 | 200.00 |
| c | orange, perf. 11½-12 x 12½-13 | 100 | 90.00 | 45.00 | 70.00 | 35.00 | 200.00 |
| i | yellow orange | 100 | 10.00 | 4.00 | 10.00 | 6.50 | 200.00 |
| iii | orange, perf. 12½-13 | 100 | 25.00 | 12.50 | 25.00 | 12.50 | 200.00 |
| v | imperf. bottom margin | 100 | — | 200.00 | — | — | — |
| vi | imperf. right margin | 100 | — | 200.00 | — | — | — |
| vii | imperf. right and bottom margins (corner) | 100 | | 500.00 | | | |
| 12 | **2¢ ultramarine**, perf. 12 x 12 | 200 | 60.00 | 20.00 | 80.00 | 30.00 | 1,000* |
| a | imperf. pair | 100 | 600.00 | 250.00 | — | — | — |
| b | diagonal half used as 1¢ on cover | | | | | | *6,500* |

* No. 12 on cover should be in pair or in combination with other stamps.

| | | NH% | ★VF | ★F | ⊙VF | ⊙F | ✉ |
|---|---|---|---|---|---|---|---|
| 13 | **3¢ rose**, perf. 11½-12 | 200 | 50.00 | 20.00 | 32.00 | 16.00 | 75.00 |
| a | imperf. pair | 100 | 750.00 | 375.00 | — | — | — |
| b | diagonal half used as 1½¢ cover | | | | | | — |
| c | horiz. or vert. pair, imperf. between | 100 | 350.00 | 200.00 | — | — | — |
| i | dot between "PRINCE EDWARD" † | 100 | 80.00 | 40.00 | 60.00 | 40.00 | 150.00 |
| d | perf. 12½-13 | 100 | 40.00 | 15.00 | 30.00 | 15.00 | 60.00 |
| iii | as d, with dot | 100 | 80.00 | 40.00 | 60.00 | 25.00 | 150.00 |
| e | perf. 11½-12 x 12½-13 | 100 | 100.00 | 50.00 | 70.00 | 35.00 | 60.00 |
| v | as e, with dot | 100 | 80.00 | 40.00 | 60.00 | 40.00 | 150.00 |

† Several positions on pane.

| | | NH% | ★VF | ★F | ⊙VF | ⊙F | ✉ |
|---|---|---|---|---|---|---|---|
| 14 | **4¢ green**, perf. 12 | 100 | 20.00 | 8.00 | 20.00 | 10.00 | 300.00 |
| a | imperf. pair | 100 | 750.00 | 375.00 | — | — | — |
| b | diagonal half used as 2¢ on cover | | | | | | *7,000* |
| i | yellow green | 100 | 16.00 | 8.00 | 20.00 | 10.00 | 20.00 |
| iii | imperf. at bottom margin | 100 | — | 300.00 | — | — | — |
| 15 | **6¢ black**, perf. 12 | 100 | 10.00 | 5.00 | 17.50 | 10.00 | 300.00 |
| a | horiz. pair, imperf. between* | 100 | 350.00 | 175.00 | — | — | — |
| b | half used as 3¢ on cover | | | | | | *3,000* |
| c | perf. 12½-13 | 100 | 200.00 | 100.00 | 250.00 | 125.00 | 300.00 |
| i | imperf. at left margin | 100 | 300.00 | 200.00 | — | — | — |
| 16 | **12¢ violet**, perf. 12 | 100 | 10.00 | 5.00 | 40.00 | 20.00 | 2,500 |
| a | imperf. pair | 100 | 750.00 | 375.00 | — | — | — |
| b | half used as 6¢ on cover | | | | | | — |

* Perforations around horizontal pair (15a) measure 12.4 x 12.2.

Reprint plate proofs exist in black on thick paper for the 2d (#5), 4d (#9), 3¢ (#13) and 12¢ (#16). Value $30 each.

**In July 1873 Prince Edward Island joined the Dominion of Canada.**

# NEWFOUNDLAND

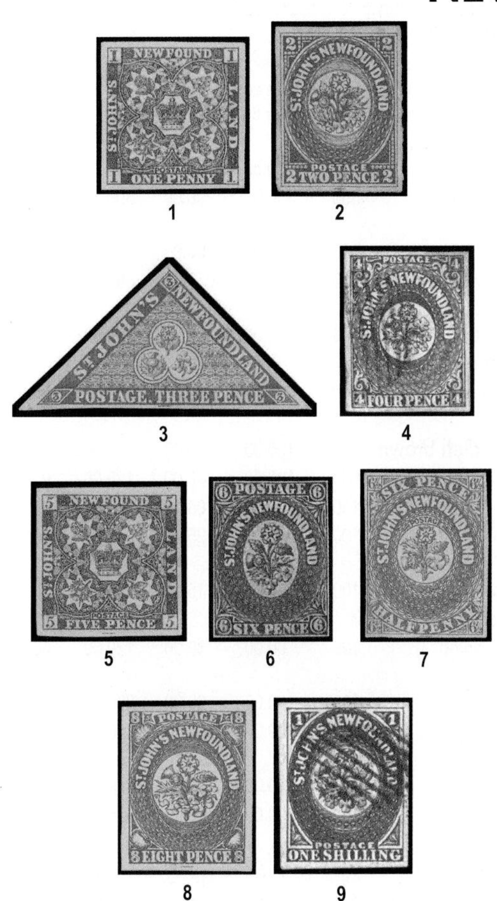

1 2 3 4 5 6 7 8 9

**1857** **Thick porous wove paper with mesh**
**Engraved** **Imperforate**

| No. | | NH% | ★VF | ★F | ⊙VF | ⊙F | ✉ |
|---|---|---|---|---|---|---|---|
| 1 | **1d brown violet**, (22 mm x 22.5 mm) | | | | | | |
| | dry printing | 200 | 160.00 | 80.00 | 300.00 | 180.00 | 7,500 |
| a | half used as ½d on cover | | | | | | 25,000 |
| i | major re-entry (pos. 25) | 200 | 400.00 | 250.00 | 600.00 | 350.00 | |

1i
Strong line through NEWFOUND and both upper numeral boxes

| No. | | NH% | ★VF | ★F | ⊙VF | ⊙F | ✉ |
|---|---|---|---|---|---|---|---|
| 2 | **2d scarlet** | | | | | | |
| | **vermilion** † | — | 25,000.00 | 12,500.00 | 12,000.00 | 6,000.00 | 15,000 |
| a | vert. half used as 1d on cover | | | | | | 30,000 |
| i | line through bottom "2s" | — | 27,500.00 | 13,500.00 | 12,000.00 | 6,000.00 | |

† No. 2: for mint copies with original gum add 100%.

| No. | | NH% | ★VF | ★F | ⊙VF | ⊙F | ✉ |
|---|---|---|---|---|---|---|---|
| 3 | **3d green** | — | 1,200.00 | 500.00 | 800.00 | 450.00 | 3,000 |
| 4 | **4d scarlet** | | | | | | |
| | **vermilion** † | — | 15,000.00 | 7,500.00 | 7,000.00 | 4,000.00 | 6,500 |
| a | half used as 2d on cover | | | | | | 30,000 |

† No. 4: for mint copies with original gum add 100%.

| No. | | NH% | ★VF | ★F | ⊙VF | ⊙F | ✉ |
|---|---|---|---|---|---|---|---|
| 5 | **5d brown violet**, (22 mm x 22.5 mm) | | | | | | |
| | dry printing | 200 | 450.00 | 200.00 | 600.00 | 300.00 | 12,000 |
| i | re-entry (pos. 34) | | | | | | |
| 6 | **6d scarlet** | | | | | | |
| | **vermilion** † | — | 30,000.00 | 12,000.00 | 7,000.00 | 3,500.00 | 25,000 |
| i | half used as 3d | | — | — | — | — | 25,000 |

† No. 6: for mint copies with original gum add 100%.

| No. | | NH% | ★VF | ★F | ⊙VF | ⊙F | ✉ |
|---|---|---|---|---|---|---|---|
| 7 | **6½d scarlet** | | | | | | |
| | **vermilion** † | — | 6,000.00 | 3,000.00 | 5,500.00 | 2,750.00 | 9,000 |

† No. 7: for mint copies with original gum add 100%.

| No. | | NH% | ★VF | ★F | ⊙VF | ⊙F | ✉ |
|---|---|---|---|---|---|---|---|
| 8 | **8d scarlet** | | | | | | |
| | **vermilion** | 200 | 500.00 | 250.00 | 800.00 | 500.00 | 25,000 |
| a | half used as 4d on cover | | | | | | 7,500 |
| 9 | **1/– scarlet** | | | | | | |
| | **vermilion** † | — | 35,000.00 | 15,000.00 | 14,000.00 | 7,000.00 | 35,000 |
| a | half used as 6d on cover | | | | | | 25,000 |

† No. 9: for mint copies with original gum add 100%.

| No. | | NH% | ★VF | ★F | ⊙VF | ⊙F | ✉ |
|---|---|---|---|---|---|---|---|
| 10 | **1/– orange**, *1860* | — | 32,500.00 | — | — | — | — |

The 1/– orange (Sc# 10) exists on vertical laid and horizontal laid paper. Many authorities consider these to be a proof. Beware of forgeries of this issue.

11 11A 12 12A 13 15

**1860** **Thin to thick wove paper, no mesh** **Imperforate**

| No. | | NH% | ★VF | ★F | ⊙VF | ⊙F | ✉ |
|---|---|---|---|---|---|---|---|
| 11 | **2d orange** † | — | 600.00 | 300.00 | 600.00 | 350.00 | |
| i | watermarked | — | 800.00 | 500.00 | 750.00 | 500.00 | |
| ii | line through bottom "2s" | — | 800.00 | 500.00 | 750.00 | 500.00 | |
| iii | as "ii", watermarked | — | 1,000.00 | 650.00 | 900.00 | 600.00 | |

† No 11: for mint copies with original gum add 100%.

| No. | | NH% | ★VF | ★F | ⊙VF | ⊙F | ✉ |
|---|---|---|---|---|---|---|---|
| 11A | **3d green** | 200 | 120.00 | 60.00 | 150.00 | 75.00 | 2,500 |
| i | watermarked | 200 | 200.00 | 100.00 | 200.00 | 100.00 | |

Newfoundland

| No. | | NH% | ★VF | ★F | ⊙VF | ⊙F | ✉ |
|---|---|---|---|---|---|---|---|
| **12** | **4d orange †** | — | 4,000.00 | 2,000.00 | 1,800.00 | 900.00 | 9,000 |
| **b** | half used as 2d on cover | | | | | | *20,000* |
| **i** | watermarked | — | 5,000.00 | 2,500.00 | 2,400.00 | 1,200.00 | |

† No. 12: for mint copies with original gum add 100%.

| No. | | NH% | ★VF | ★F | ⊙VF | ⊙F | ✉ |
|---|---|---|---|---|---|---|---|
| **12A** | **5d violet brown**, (22.5 mm x 22 mm) dry printing | 100 | 120.00 | 60.00 | 200.00 | 100.00 | 10,000 |
| **i** | watermarked | 100 | 200.00 | 100.00 | 300.00 | 150.00 | |
| **ii** | venetian red | 100 | 250.00 | 150.00 | 350.00 | 175.00 | |
| **13** | **6d orange †** | — | 5,000.00 | 2,500.00 | 1,600.00 | 800.00 | 17,500 |
| **i** | watermarked | — | 7,000.00 | 3,500.00 | 1,800.00 | 900.00 | |

† No. 13: for mint copies with original gum add 100%.

No. 14 is not assigned.

| No. | | NH% | ★VF | ★F | ⊙VF | ⊙F | ✉ |
|---|---|---|---|---|---|---|---|
| **15** | **1/– orange †** | — | 40,000.00 | 15,000.00 | 15,000.00 | 6,000.00 | * |
| **b** | half used as 6d on cover | | | | | | *20,000* |
| **ii** | watermarked | — | 50,000.00 | 18,500.00 | 18,000.00 | 8,000.00 | * |
| **iii** | laid paper | — | 30,000.00 | 20,000.00 | | | |

† No. 15: for mint copies with original gum add 100%.
* No singles known on cover.

The watermark is the papermaker's "STACEY WISE 1858" in large capitals. A 6½d orange exists and is considered to be a proof by most authorities.

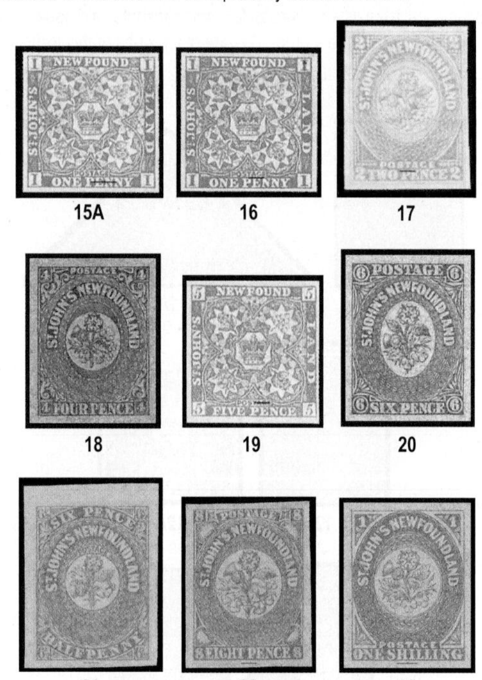

15A 16 17

18 19 20

21 22 23

**1861–1862 Wet printing Imperforate**

**1st printing on soft paper; 2nd printing on hard paper**

| No. | | NH% | ★VF | ★F | ⊙VF | ⊙F | ✉ |
|---|---|---|---|---|---|---|---|
| **15A** | **1d violet brown** | 300 | 200.00 | 120.00 | 300.00 | 240.00 | |
| **c** | chocolate brown | 300 | 250.00 | 150.00 | 360.00 | 300.00 | |
| **ii** | watermarked | 300 | 400.00 | 200.00 | 450.00 | 360.00 | |
| **iii** | major re-entry (pos. 25) | 300 | 500.00 | 350.00 | 650.00 | 400.00 | |
| **iv** | major re-entry in NEWFOUND | | | | | | |

**15Aiv**
Angled line of doubling can be seen through NEWFOUN and in the upper left numeral box

| No. | | NH% | ★VF | ★F | ⊙VF | ⊙F | ✉ |
|---|---|---|---|---|---|---|---|
| **16** | **1d reddish brown †** | — | 16,000.00 | 8,000.00 | | | |
| **i** | watermarked * | — | 35,000.00 | | | | |

No.16 was prepared but never issued. Design size is 21.75x21.75mm.
† No. 16: for mint copies with original gum add 100%
* One example of 16i is known; price is for original gum.

| No. | | NH% | ★VF | ★F | ⊙VF | ⊙F | ✉ |
|---|---|---|---|---|---|---|---|
| **17** | **2d rose** | 300 | 200.00 | 130.00 | 200.00 | 150.00 | |
| **i** | watermarked | 300 | 350.00 | 200.00 | 300.00 | 225.00 | |
| **ii** | line through bottom "2s" | 300 | 375.00 | 260.00 | 400.00 | 280.00 | |
| **iii** | as "ii", watermarked | 300 | 500.00 | 350.00 | 500.00 | 350.00 | |
| **18** | **4d rose** | 100 | 50.00 | 30.00 | 100.00 | 50.00 | 7,500 |
| **a** | half used as 2d on cover | | | | | | — |
| **ii** | watermarked | 100 | 80.00 | 40.00 | 150.00 | 75.00 | |
| **19** | **5d reddish brown** | 100 | 100.00 | 50.00 | 100.00 | 70.00 | 9,000 |
| **a** | orange brown | 100 | 120.00 | 60.00 | 125.00 | 90.00 | |
| **b** | chocolate brown | 100 | 160.00 | 80.00 | 200.00 | 100.00 | |
| **i** | watermarked | 100 | 250.00 | 125.00 | 250.00 | 125.00 | |
| **20** | **6d rose** | 100 | 30.00 | 15.00 | 80.00 | 40.00 | 8,000 |
| **a** | half used as 3d on cover | | | | | | *14,000* |
| **ii** | watermarked | 100 | 60.00 | 30.00 | 120.00 | 60.00 | |
| **21** | **6½d rose** | 100 | 120.00 | 60.00 | 200.00 | 140.00 | *12,000* |
| **i** | watermarked | 100 | 200.00 | 100.00 | 300.00 | 210.00 | |
| **22** | **8d rose** | 100 | 120.00 | 60.00 | 375.00 | 275.00 | |
| **i** | watermarked | 100 | 200.00 | 100.00 | 525.00 | 400.00 | |
| **23** | **1/– rose** | 100 | 60.00 | 30.00 | 160.00 | 120.00 | |
| **a** | half used as 6d on cover | | | | | | *20,000* |
| **i** | watermarked | 100 | 100.00 | 50.00 | 240.00 | 180.00 | |

**Beware of false cancellations on the first three issues.**

**Most Newfoundland stamps have some gum wrinkles due to humidity in both England (where a lot of them were printed) and in Newfoundland.**

**24** Codfish
**25** Harp seal
**26** Harp Seal
**27** Prince Albert
**28** Queen Victoria
**29** Queen Victoria
**30** Ship
**31** Queen Victoria

**1865–1894** (OG +100% #24, 24a, 25, 26, 27, 27a, 28a) **Perf 12**

**Nos 24, 26, 27, 28, 29, 31a on stout white paper**
**Nos. 24a, 25, 27a, 28a, 30, 31 on thin yellowish paper**

| No. | Description | NH% | ★VF | ★F | ⊙VF | ⊙F | ✉ |
|---|---|---|---|---|---|---|---|
| 24 | **2¢ green**, *1870* | 500 | 150.00 | 50.00 | 50.00 | 20.00 | 500.00 |
| | plate blocks of 6 $400.00 | | | | | | |
| a | thin yellowish paper | 500 | 250.00 | 100.00 | 100.00 | 40.00 | 700.00 |
| | plate blocks of 6 $500.00 | | | | | | |
| b | half used as 1¢ on cover | | | | | | *5,000* |
| 25 | **5¢ brown** | — | 800.00 | 400.00 | 600.00 | 300.00 | 900.00 |
| a | half used as 2¢ on cover | | | | | | 8,500 |
| i | major re-entry (pos. 14) | | | | | | |
| ii | misplaced entry (pos. 95) | | | | | | |
| 26 | **5¢ black**, *1868* | 500 | 600.00 | 300.00 | 400.00 | 200.00 | 750.00 |
| i | half used as 2¢ on cover | | | | | | 6,500 |
| ii | major re-entry (pos. 14) | | | | | | |
| iii | misplaced entry (pos. 95) | | | | | | |

Numerous re-entries show in NEWFOUNDLAND on the 5¢ value (Sc. 25 and 26).

| No. | Description | NH% | ★VF | ★F | ⊙VF | ⊙F | ✉ |
|---|---|---|---|---|---|---|---|
| 27 | **10¢ black** | 200 | 500.00 | 200.00 | 80.00 | 40.00 | 300.00 |
| a | thin yellowish paper | 200 | 600.00 | 225.00 | 150.00 | 75.00 | 400.00 |
| b | half used as 5¢ on cover | | | | | | 5,000 |
| i | major re-entry in FOUND (pos 8) (directly below imprint) | 200 | | 500.00 | | 125.00 | |
| 28 | **12¢ pale red brown**, *1870* | 200 | 120.00 | 40.00 | 60.00 | 30.00 | 200.00 |
| | plate blocks of 6 $500.00 | | | | | | |
| a | thin yellowish paper | 500 | 800.00 | 300.00 | 250.00 | 110.00 | 300.00 |
| b | half used as 6¢ on cover | | | | | | 5,000 |
| i | chin strap variety (pos. 68) | 200 | 200.00 | 100.00 | 150.00 | 75.00 | — |
| ii | gash on nose (pos. 95) | 200 | 200.00 | 100.00 | 150.00 | 75.00 | — |
| iii | re-entry in U and E (pos. 25) | | | | | | |
| iv | re-entry in U and E (pos. 24) | | | | | | |

28i / 29i

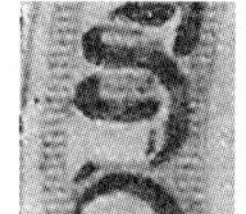

28iii / 29ii

28iv / 29iii

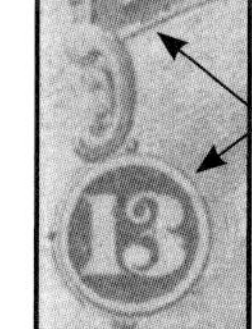

30i

| No. | Description | NH% | ★VF | ★F | ⊙VF | ⊙F | ✉ |
|---|---|---|---|---|---|---|---|
| 29 | **12¢ brown**, unwatermarked medium white paper *1894* | 200 | 100.00 | 40.00 | 60.00 | 30.00 | 250.00 |
| | plate blocks of 6 $500.00 | | | | | | |
| i | chin strap variety (pos. 68) | 200 | 200.00 | 100.00 | 150.00 | 75.00 | — |
| ii | re-entry in U and E (pos. 25) | | | | | | |
| iii | re-entry in U and E (pos. 24) | | | | | | |
| 30 | **13¢ orange** | 200 | 300.00 | 120.00 | 150.00 | 75.00 | 750.00 |
| i | major re-entry (pos. 18) | | | | | | |
| | plate blocks of 6 $2,500.00 | | | | | | |
| 31 | **24¢ blue** on thin, crisp, transluscent paper | 200 | 100.00 | 40.00 | 50.00 | 25.00 | 600.00 |
| | plate blocks of 6 $500.00 | | | | | | |
| a | stout white paper, *1870* | — | 500.00 | 250.00 | 400.00 | 200.00 | |
| i | major re-entry (pos. 9) | 200 | 500.00 | 250.00 | | | |

31i
In and above right numeral oval, and vertical lines on either side of portrait

32 32A 33
Edward, Prince of Wales — Queen Victoria

34 35 36

**1868–1894** **Perf 12**

| No. | Description (OG +100% #32–34) | NH% | ★VF | ★F | ⊙VF | ⊙F | ✉ |
|---|---|---|---|---|---|---|---|
| 32 | **1¢ violet** | 400 | 120.00 | 40.00 | 80.00 | 40.00 | 600.00 |
| 32A | **1¢ brown lilac**, *1871* | 500 | 160.00 | 60.00 | 100.00 | 50.00 | 600.00 |

In No. 32A (re-engraved), the top of the letters "N" and "F" are about ½ mm from the ribbon with "ONE CENT", and the white oval frame line is unbroken by the ribbon.
In No. 32 the letters are fully 1 mm from the scroll. There are many other minor differences in the engraving.

| No. | Description | NH% | ★VF | ★F | ⊙VF | ⊙F | ✉ |
|---|---|---|---|---|---|---|---|
| 33 | **3¢ vermilion**, *1870* | 500 | 600.00 | 250.00 | 250.00 | 125.00 | 500.00 |
| i | misplaced entry (pos. 55) | | | | | | |
| ii | "tumbling stones", pos. 11 | | | | | 200.00 | |
| 34 | **3¢ blue**, *1873* | 500 | 500.00 | 200.00 | 100.00 | 50.00 | 250.00 |
| i | misplaced entry (pos. 55) | | | | | | |
| ii | "tumbling stones", pos. 11 | | | | | 150.00 | |
| | plate block of 6 $5,000.00 | | | | | | |
| 35 | **6¢ dull rose**, *1870* | 200 | 50.00 | 15.00 | 25.00 | 10.00 | 90.00 |
| i | "falling rocks" | | | | | | |
| | plate blocks of 6 $300.00 | | | | | | |
| a | bright rose, *1874* | 200 | 70.00 | 25.00 | 30.00 | 15.00 | 90.00 |
| 36 | **6¢ carmine lake**, *1894* | 200 | 70.00 | 25.00 | 30.00 | 12.50 | 90.00 |
| i | "falling rocks" | | | | | | |
| | plate blocks of 6 $350.00 | | | | | | |

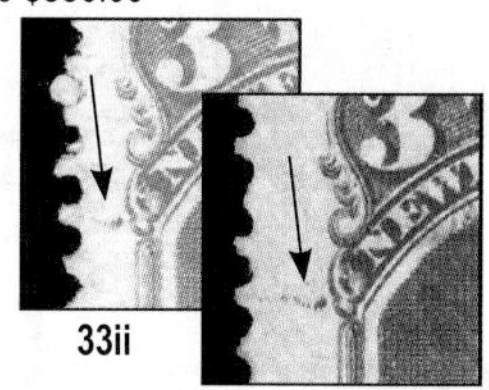

33ii 34ii

35i / 36i

37 Edward, Prince of Wales — 38 Codfish — 39 Queen Victoria — 40 Harp seal

**1876–1879** **Rouletted**

| No. | Description | NH% | ★VF | ★F | ⊙VF | ⊙F | ✉ |
|---|---|---|---|---|---|---|---|
| 37 | **1¢ brown lilac**, *1877* | 300 | 200.00 | 100.00 | 70.00 | 30.00 | 600.00 |
| 38 | **2¢ green**, *1879* | 300 | 300.00 | 150.00 | 70.00 | 30.00 | 600.00 |

**1876–1879** **Rouletted**

| | NH% | ★VF | ★F | ⊙VF | ⊙F | ✉ |
|---|---|---|---|---|---|---|
| **39** **3¢ blue**, *1877* | 300 | 600.00 | 250.00 | 20.00 | 10.00 | 100.00 |
| i misplaced entry (pos. 55) | | | | | | |

Numerous re-entries exist, some major.

**33i/34i/39i**
Shows in all four corners and in top margin, as well as CENTS

| | NH% | ★VF | ★F | ⊙VF | ⊙F | ✉ |
|---|---|---|---|---|---|---|
| **40** **5¢ blue** | 200 | 400.00 | 150.00 | 20.00 | 10.00 | 75.00 |
| i major re-entry (pos. 14) | | | | | | |
| ii misplaced entry (pos. 95) plate blocks of 6 $3,000.00 | | | | | | |

Numerous re-entries show in NEWFOUNDLAND.

| | NH% | ★VF | ★F | ⊙VF | ⊙F | ✉ |
|---|---|---|---|---|---|---|
| **Nos. 37–40** (4) Set | 200 | 1,500.00 | 650.00 | 180.00 | 80.00 | |

**25i / 26ii / 40i**
Sloppy looking marks in NEWFOUNDLAND

**25ii / 26iii / 40ii**
Evidence in DLAND and particularly in and below CENTS

41 42 43
Edward, Prince of Wales

44 45 46
Codfish

47 48 49
Queen Victoria

51 52 53
Harp seal

54 55

**1880–1896** **Perf 12**

| | NH% | ★VF | ★F | ⊙VF | ⊙F | ✉ |
|---|---|---|---|---|---|---|
| **41** **1¢ violet brown** | 300 | 90.00 | 30.00 | 16.00 | 8.00 | 60.00 |
| plate blocks of 4 $500.00 | | | | | | |
| **42** **1¢ grey brown**, *1880* | 300 | 90.00 | 30.00 | 16.00 | 8.00 | 60.00 |
| plate blocks of 4 $500.00 | | | | | | |
| **43** **1¢ brown**, *1896* | 200 | 200.00 | 80.00 | 100.00 | 40.00 | 300.00 |
| plate blocks of 4 $1,250.00 | | | | | | |

No. 43 is a re-issue for postal purposes. The colour is generally brighter than the original

| | NH% | ★VF | ★F | ⊙VF | ⊙F | ✉ |
|---|---|---|---|---|---|---|
| **44** **1¢ deep green**, *1887* | 200 | 40.00 | 8.00 | 6.00 | 3.00 | 25.00 |
| plate blocks of 8 $300.00 | | | | | | |
| a grey green | 200 | 50.00 | 12.00 | 8.00 | 4.00 | 25.00 |
| plate blocks of 8 $300.00 | | | | | | |
| **45** **1¢ green**, *1896* | 200 | 40.00 | 8.00 | 6.00 | 3.00 | 25.00 |
| plate blocks of 8 $250.00 | | | | | | |
| a yellow green | 200 | 50.00 | 12.00 | 8.00 | 4.00 | 25.00 |

No.45 is a re-issue for postal purposes. The colour is generally brighter than the original

| | NH% | ★VF | ★F | ⊙VF | ⊙F | ✉ |
|---|---|---|---|---|---|---|
| **46** **2¢ yellow green**, *1882* | 300 | 100.00 | 25.00 | 18.00 | 12.00 | 125.00 |
| i deep yellow green | 300 | 150.00 | 50.00 | 30.00 | 20.00 | |
| plate blocks of 4 $800.00 | | | | | | |
| **47** **2¢ green**, *1896* | 200 | 180.00 | 50.00 | 40.00 | 20.00 | 150.00 |
| plate blocks of 4 $1,000.00 | | | | | | |

No. 47 is a re-issue for postal purposes. The colour is generally brighter than the original.

| | NH% | ★VF | ★F | ⊙VF | ⊙F | ✉ |
|---|---|---|---|---|---|---|
| **48** **2¢ red orange** | 200 | 60.00 | 20.00 | 12.50 | 7.50 | 60.00 |
| a imperf. pair | 200 | 400.00 | 250.00 | — | — | — |
| i half used as 1¢ | — | — | — | — | — | 500.00 |
| b orange, *1887* | 200 | 60.00 | 20.00 | 12.50 | 7.00 | 60.00 |
| plate blocks of 4 $400.00 | | | | | | |
| **49** **3¢ blue**, *1896* | 300 | 100.00 | 25.00 | 10.00 | 5.00 | 40.00 |
| plate blocks of 4 $1,000.00 | | | | | | |
| a pale blue | 300 | 160.00 | 50.00 | 10.00 | 5.00 | 40.00 |
| b deep blue | 300 | 120.00 | 30.00 | 10.00 | 5.00 | 40.00 |

No. 50 is not assigned.

| | NH% | ★VF | ★F | ⊙VF | ⊙F | ✉ |
|---|---|---|---|---|---|---|
| **51** **3¢ umber brown**, *1887* | 200 | 100.00 | 25.00 | 6.00 | 3.00 | 20.00 |
| a brown | 200 | 100.00 | 25.00 | 7.50 | 4.00 | 30.00 |
| ii vert. pair, double perf. between | 150 | — | 250.00 | — | — | — |
| plate blocks of 4 $750.00 | | | | | | |
| **52** **3¢ violet brown**, *1896* | 200 | 180.00 | 60.00 | 120.00 | 40.00 | 200.00 |
| plate blocks of 4 $1,250.00 | | | | | | |

No. 52 is a re-issue for postal purposes. The colour is generally brighter than the original.

Newfoundland

| | | NH% | ★VF | ★F | ⊙VF | ⊙F | ✉ |
|---|---|---|---|---|---|---|---|
| 53 | **5¢ pale blue** | 400 | 600.00 | 200.00 | 20.00 | 10.00 | 75.00 |
| i | major re-entry in WFOUN | | | | | | |
| 54 | **5¢ dark blue**, *1887* | 200 | 300.00 | 100.00 | 16.00 | 8.00 | 50.00 |
| i | major re-entry in WFOUN | | | | | | |
| 55 | **5¢ bright blue**, *1894* | 200 | 100.00 | 30.00 | 8.00 | 4.00 | 35.00 |
| i | major re-entry in WFOUN<br>plate blocks of 4 $600.00 | | | | | | |

Numerous re-entries exist on all 5¢ values (Sc 53–55) in upper left corner vertical lines.

53i

59ii

56 57 58 59
Newfoundland dog — Schooner

**1887–1898** Perf 12

| | | NH% | ★VF | ★F | ⊙VF | ⊙F | ✉ |
|---|---|---|---|---|---|---|---|
| 56 | **½¢ rose red**, *1888*<br>plate blocks of 8 $150.00 | 200 | 20.00 | 6.00 | 10.00 | 5.00 | 2,000* |
| a | deep rose red | 200 | 30.00 | 10.00 | 12.00 | 6.00 | 2,000* |

Numerous re-entries exist in HALF CENT, 1/2, and right and left portrait ovals.

| | | NH% | ★VF | ★F | ⊙VF | ⊙F | ✉ |
|---|---|---|---|---|---|---|---|
| 57 | **½¢ orange red**, *'96*<br>plate blocks of 8 $800.00 | 200 | 120.00 | 60.00 | 60.00 | 30.00 | 2,500* |

No. 57 is a re-issue for postal purposes. The colour is generally brighter than the original.
* Single usage in period. Covers with multiples sell for much less.
Numerous re-entries exist in HALF CENT, 1/2, and right and left portrait ovals.

| | | NH% | ★VF | ★F | ⊙VF | ⊙F | ✉ |
|---|---|---|---|---|---|---|---|
| 58 | **½¢ black**, *1894*<br>plate blocks of 8 $150.00 | 200 | 20.00 | 8.00 | 10.00 | 5.00 | 2,000* |
| i | grey black (1898) | 200 | 25.00 | 9.00 | 12.00 | 6.00 | 2,000* |

Numerous re-entries exist in HALF CENT, 1/2, and right and left portrait ovals.

| | | NH% | ★VF | ★F | ⊙VF | ⊙F | ✉ |
|---|---|---|---|---|---|---|---|
| 59 | **10¢ black**, *1894*<br>plate blocks of 6 $1,000.00 | 200 | 200.00 | 80.00 | 80.00 | 40.00 | 350.00 |
| i | line through "CE" of "CENTS" | 200 | 250.00 | 100.00 | 120.00 | 60.00 | 500.00 |
| ii | two lines through "CE" of "CENTS" | 200 | 400.00 | 150.00 | 200.00 | 100.00 | 600.00 |

* Single usage in period.

## QUEEN VICTORIA

60
Queen Victoria

**1890** Perf 12

| | | NH% | ★VF | ★F | ⊙VF | ⊙F | ✉ |
|---|---|---|---|---|---|---|---|
| 60 | **3¢ slate** | 200 | 50.00 | 15.00 | 2.00 | .75 | 10.00 |
| a | grey lilac | 200 | 50.00 | 15.00 | 2.00 | .75 | 10.00 |
| b | brown lilac | 200 | 75.00 | 25.00 | 2.00 | .75 | 10.00 |
| c | lilac | 200 | 60.00 | 20.00 | 2.00 | .75 | 10.00 |
| d | slate violet | 200 | 100.00 | 40.00 | 5.00 | 2.00 | 20.00 |
| e | vert. pair, imperf. horiz. | 200 | 1,000.00 | 600.00 | — | — | — |
| i | red tinted paper* | | 75.00 | 35.00 | 15.00 | 10.00 | |

Top or Bottom Plate Block of 4 $350 each.
* Only comes with disturbed gum or no gum, NH not known.

## DISCOVERY OF NEWFOUNDLAND

61 Queen Victoria — 62 John Cabot — 63 Cape Bonavista — 64 Caribou Hunting

65 Mining — 66 Logging — 67 Fishing

68 Cabot's Ship, *Matthew* — 69 Willow Ptarmigan — 70 Seals

71 Salmon Fishing — 72 Colony Seal — 73 Iceberg — 74 King Henry VII

**1897, Jun 24** Perf 12

| | | NH% | ★VF | ★F | ⊙VF | ⊙F | ✉ |
|---|---|---|---|---|---|---|---|
| 61 | **1¢ deep green** | 100 | 2.50 | 1.75 | 2.50 | 1.75 | 10.00 |
| i | thin oily paper | 100 | 90.00 | 60.00 | | | |
| 62 | **2¢ carmine lake** | 100 | 3.00 | 2.25 | 2.00 | 1.50 | 10.00 |
| i | half used as 1¢ | — | — | — | — | — | 500.00 |
| ii | major re-entry (both 2's and lower letters) (pos. 76) | | | | | | |

62ii

| | | NH% | ★VF | ★F | ⊙VF | ⊙F | ✉ |
|---|---|---|---|---|---|---|---|
| 63 | **3¢ ultramarine** | 100 | 6.00 | 3.25 | 2.00 | 1.50 | 15.00 |
| i | half used as 1½¢ | — | — | — | — | — | 500.00 |
| 64 | **4¢ olive green** | 100 | 8.00 | 5.00 | 4.00 | 3.00 | 30.00 |
| 65 | **5¢ violet** | 100 | 15.00 | 7.50 | 4.00 | 3.00 | 30.00 |
| 66 | **6¢ red brown** | 100 | 8.00 | 5.25 | 4.50 | 3.50 | 30.00 |
| i | half used as 3¢ | — | — | — | — | — | 500.00 |
| 67 | **8¢ red orange** | 100 | 35.00 | 15.00 | 20.00 | 10.00 | 60.00 |
| 68 | **10¢ black brown** | 100 | 35.00 | 15.00 | 10.00 | 5.00 | 60.00 |
| 69 | **12¢ dark blue** | 100 | 40.00 | 15.00 | 20.00 | 10.00 | 60.00 |
| i | major misplaced entry | | | | | | |

69i
In left margin near upper left scroll.

| | | NH% | ★VF | ★F | ⊙VF | ⊙F | ✉ |
|---|---|---|---|---|---|---|---|
| 70 | **15¢ scarlet** | 100 | 30.00 | 15.00 | 18.00 | 9.00 | 60.00 |
| 71 | **24¢ grey violet** | 100 | 40.00 | 20.00 | 16.00 | 8.00 | 60.00 |
| 72 | **30¢ slate** | 100 | 90.00 | 35.00 | 70.00 | 35.00 | 150.00 |
| 73 | **35¢ red** | 200 | 160.00 | 75.00 | 80.00 | 40.00 | 350.00 |
| 74 | **60¢ black** | 100 | 25.00 | 12.50 | 16.00 | 8.00 | 75.00 |
| **Nos. 61–74** (14) Set | | 100 | 497.50 | 227.50 | 269.00 | 139.25 | |

**Nos. 61–74** (14) Set with diagonal "SPECIMEN" overprints $1,500

Issued to commemorate the 400th anniversary of John Cabot's discovery of Newfoundland in 1497 and the 60th anniversary of the accession of Queen Victoria.

**Essays on 60¢ black**

74E-1 TWO/ 2/ CENTS in red. Value $1,500

74E-2 TWO/ 2/ CENTS in red, doubled. Value $1,500

## SURCHARGES on 60a

75–77
Queen Victoria

A 

B 

C

Surcharge types

75–77 800 blocks of 50 were overprinted on remainder stock. Centering on this issue is generally very poor.

**1897, Oct** **Perf 12**

| | | NH% | ★VF | ★F | ⊙VF | ⊙F | ✉ |
|---|---|---|---|---|---|---|---|
| 75 | **1¢ on 3¢ grey lilac (60a) (A)** | 200 | 125.00 | 60.00 | 75.00 | 25.00 | 90.00 |
| a | double surcharge, one diagonal | — | 2,000.00 | 1,000.00 | — | — | — |
| b | vert. pair, "ONE CENT" and lower bar omitted on bottom stamp | — | — | 6,000.00 | — | — | — |

Qty: 40 of 50 in the overprint setting are this type = 80 in sheet of 100 = 32,000 (all types included)

| | | NH% | ★VF | ★F | ⊙VF | ⊙F | ✉ |
|---|---|---|---|---|---|---|---|
| 76 | **1¢ on 3¢ grey lilac (60a) (B)** | 200 | 400.00 | 150.00 | 300.00 | 125.00 | 350.00 |
| i | 2 mm space between "ONE" and "CENT" | 200 | 800.00 | 300.00 | 800.00 | 300.00 | 750.00 |
| ii | double surcharge, one diagonal | — | 3,500. | 2,000 | — | — | — |
| iii | as "ii", 2 mm space between "ONE" and "CENT" | — | — | 2,000. | — | — | — |

Nos. 75, 76 bottom plate blocks of 4 $1,200 each

Qty: 8 of 50 in the overprint setting are this type = 16 in sheet of 100 = 6,400 (all types included)

| | | NH% | ★VF | ★F | ⊙VF | ⊙F | ✉ |
|---|---|---|---|---|---|---|---|
| 77 | **1¢ on 3¢ grey lilac (60a) (C)** | 200 | 1,250.00 | 750.00 | 1,000.00 | 600.00 | 2,000 |
| a | block of 4, #76–77, 2x#75 | | | | | | |
| i | double surcharge, one diagonal | — | 7,000.00 | 3,500.00 | — | — | — |

Qty: 2 of 50 in the overprint setting are this type = 4 in sheet of 100 = 1,600 (all types included)

**Nos. 75–77** bottom plate block of 20: $4,000 each

**Nos. 75–77** Values for blocks showing two or three of the 1¢ on 3¢ surcharges: 2 different, add 25%; for all three, add 50% to the total catalogue value of the singles in the block.

**Nos. 75–77** Examples surcharged in red (or red and black) are proofs. Beware of forgeries.

| | # 75 | # 76 | # 77 |
|---|---|---|---|
| Red and black overprint | $2,000 | $6,000 | $12,500 |
| Red only overprint | $2,000 | $6,000 | $12,500 |

**Type A**
Red and black ovpt

**Type A**
Red ovpt

**Type B**
Red and black ovpt

**Type B**
Red ovpt

## ROYAL FAMILY

78
King Edward VIII as child

79
Queen Victoria

80
Queen Victoria

81
King Edward VII

82
King Edward VII

83
Queen Alexandra

84
Duchess of York

85
Duke of York

**1897–1901** **Engraved** **Perf 12**

| | | NH% | ★VF | ★F | ⊙VF | ⊙F | ✉ |
|---|---|---|---|---|---|---|---|
| 78 | **½¢ olive green** | 100 | 6.00 | 2.50 | 4.00 | 2.00 | 750.00* |
| a | imperf. pair | 100 | 750.00 | 450.00 | — | — | — |

* Single use. Multiples on cover worth much less.

| | | NH% | ★VF | ★F | ⊙VF | ⊙F | ✉ |
|---|---|---|---|---|---|---|---|
| 79 | **1¢ carmine rose** | 100 | 8.00 | 3.50 | 7.00 | 3.50 | 75.00 |
| i | thick paper | 100 | 300.00 | 150.00 | — | — | — |

| No. | | NH% | ★VF | ★F | ⊙VF | ⊙F | ✉ |
|---|---|---|---|---|---|---|---|
| 80 | **1¢ yellow green,** *1898* | 100 | 8.00 | 3.00 | .50 | .25 | 10.00 |
| | inscription blocks, plate 2, UR $500, plate 3, UL $500.00 | | | | | | |
| a | deep green | 100 | 10.00 | 4.00 | .50 | .25 | 7.50 |
| b | vert. pair, imperf. horiz.* | 100 | 500.00 | 250.00 | — | — | — |

* Most examples of 80b are off centre.

| No. | | NH% | ★VF | ★F | ⊙VF | ⊙F | ✉ |
|---|---|---|---|---|---|---|---|
| 81 | **2¢ orange** | 100 | 10.00 | 4.00 | 6.00 | 3.50 | 25.00 |
| a | imperf. pair | — | | | 650.00 | | |
| i | misplaced entry (pos. 1) | | | | | | |
| ii | major re-entry (pos. 91) | | | | | | |
| 82 | **2¢ vermilion**, *1898* | 100 | 18.00 | 7.50 | 1.00 | .60 | 15.00 |
| | inscription block, plate 2, UR $400.00 | | | | | | |
| a | imperf. pair | 100 | 600.00 | 300.00 | — | — | — |
| b | pair, imperf. between | 100 | 800.00 | 400.00 | — | — | — |
| i | misplaced entry (pos. 1) | | | | | | |
| ii | major re-entry (pos. 91) | | | | | | |

81i / 82i

In NEWFOUNDLAND and right margin.

81ii / 82ii

In NEWFOUNDLAND

| No. | | NH% | ★VF | ★F | ⊙VF | ⊙F | ✉ |
|---|---|---|---|---|---|---|---|
| 83 | **3¢ orange** | 100 | 45.00 | 15.00 | 1.00 | .60 | 15.00 |
| | inscription blocks: plate 3, UL $500.00; plate 4, UR $500.00 | | | | | | |
| a | vert. pair, imperf. horiz. | 100 | 600.00 | 400.00 | — | — | — |
| b | imperf. pair | 100 | 600.00 | 300.00 | — | — | — |
| c | red orange on thin bluish paper | 100 | 75.00 | 30.00 | 4.00 | 2.00 | 25.00 |
| | No. 83c, inscription blocks plate 4, UR $600.00 | | | | | | |
| i | major re-entry in '3 THREE CENTS 3' | | | | | | |
| 84 | **4¢ violet**, *1901* | 100 | 60.00 | 20.00 | 6.00 | 4.00 | 6.00 |
| | bottom plate block of 4 $400.00 | | | | | | |
| a | imperf. pair | 100 | 1,000.00 | 600.00 | — | — | — |
| 85 | **5¢ blue**, *1899* | 100 | 75.00 | 25.00 | 4.00 | 2.75 | 50.00 |
| | bottom plate block of 4 $300.00 | | | | | | |
| i | major re-entry (pos. 1) | | | | | | |
| **Nos. 78–85** | (8) Set | 100 | 230.00 | 80.50 | 33.50 | 19.20 | |

85i

In POSTAGE and FIVE CENTS.

## MAP OF NEWFOUNDLAND

86

**1908, Sep** **Perf 12**

| No. | | NH% | ★VF | ★F | ⊙VF | ⊙F | ✉ |
|---|---|---|---|---|---|---|---|
| 86 | **2¢ rose carmine** | 100 | 90.00 | 30.00 | 5.00 | 2.00 | 100.00 |
| | used on post card | — | — | — | — | — | 40.00 |

**Nos. 78–86** (47 varieties comprise a full set)

Set of all types of SPECIMEN overprints (47 different): $1,850.00. Single SPECIMEN (any type) $50.00.

## JOHN GUY ISSUE
### Lithographed

87 King James I

88 Coat-of-Arms

89 John Guy

90 Guy's ship, *Endeavour*

91 View of Cupids

92 Lord Bacon

93 View of Mosquito

94 Logging Camp

95 Paper mills

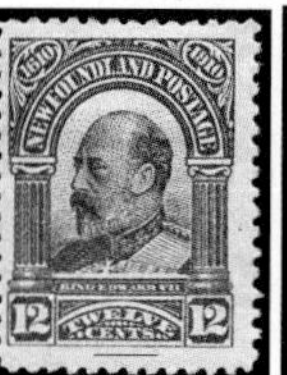

96 King Edward VII

97 King George V

**1910, Aug 15** **Lithographed**

**NH +200%**

| No. | | (Perf) | ★VF | ★F | ⊙VF | ⊙F | ✉ |
|---|---|---|---|---|---|---|---|
| 87 | **1¢ deep green** | (12 x 11) | 3.00 | 1.50 | 1.50 | 1.00 | 6.00 |
| a | new perf. | (12 x 12) | 6.00 | 3.00 | 2.50 | 2.00 | 9.00 |
| b | new perf. | (12 x 14) | 9.00 | 4.50 | 3.00 | 1.50 | 9.00 |
| c | horiz. pair, imperf. between | (12 x 11) | 500.00 | 250.00 | — | — | — |
| d | vert. pair, imperf. between | (12 x 11) | 600.00 | 300.00 | — | — | — |
| e | horiz. pair, imperf. between | (12 x 12) | 600.00 | 300.00 | — | — | — |
| f | vert. pair, imperf. between | (12 x 12) | 600.00 | 300.00 | — | — | — |
| g | horiz. pair, imperf. between | (12 x 14) | 1,000.00 | 600.00 | — | — | — |
| h | compound | (12x12x12x11) | | | | | |
| iii | "NFW" var. | (12 x 12) | 80.00 | 60.00 | 70.00 | 50.00 | 110.00 |

| NH +200% | | (Perf) | ★VF | ★F | ⊙VF | ⊙F | ✉ |
|---|---|---|---|---|---|---|---|
| iv | "NFW" var. | (12 x 14) | 80.00 | 55.00 | 65.00 | 45.00 | 110.00 |
| vi | as "e", "NFW" var. | (12 x 12) | 1,000.00 | 750.00 | 600.00 | — | — |
| vii | as "g", "NFW" var. | (12 x 14) | 1,000.00 | 750.00 | — | — | — |
| ix | "Jamrs" variety (damaged "e" in "James") | (12 x 11) | 70.00 | 45.00 | 50.00 | 40.00 | 100.00 |
| x | as "ix" | (12 x 12) | 70.00 | 45.00 | 50.00 | 40.00 | 100.00 |
| xi | as "ix" | (12 x 14) | 70.00 | 45.00 | 50.00 | 40.00 | 100.00 |
| xii | "NFW" var. | (12 x 11) | 75.00 | 50.00 | 60.00 | 40.00 | 100.00 |
| xiii | as "c", "NFW" var. | (12 x 11) | 1,000.00 | 750.00 | — | — | — |
| xiv | "ONE'CENT" variety | (12 x 11) | 70.00 | 45.00 | 50.00 | 40.00 | 100.00 |
| xv | as "xiv" | (12 x 12) | 70.00 | 45.00 | 50.00 | 40.00 | 100.00 |
| xvi | as "xiv" | (12 x 14) | 70.00 | 45.00 | 50.00 | 40.00 | 100.00 |
| xvii | "E-W" joined | (12 x 11) | 70.00 | 45.00 | 50.00 | 40.00 | |
| xviii | as "xvii" | (12 x 12) | 70.00 | 45.00 | 50.00 | 40.00 | |
| xix | as "xvii" | (12 x 14) | 70.00 | 45.00 | 50.00 | 40.00 | |
| xxi | as "h", with "NFW" var. | (12x12x12x11) | | | *1,000.00* | | |

Qty: 3,005,000 (all types included)

"NFW" variety is from position 41; damaged 'e' variety is from position 42; ONE'CENT variety is from position 52. "E-W" joined variety is from position 10.

87iii–vii / xii–xiii
'NFW' variety

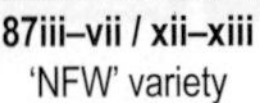

87ix / x / xi
'JAMRS' variety

87xiv / xv / xvi
'ONE'CENT' variety

87xvii / xviii / xix
'E-W' joined variety

| | | (Perf) | ★VF | ★F | ⊙VF | ⊙F | ✉ |
|---|---|---|---|---|---|---|---|
| **88** | **2¢ carmine** | (12 x 12) | 18.00 | 10.00 | 1.50 | 1.00 | 10.00 |
| a | new perf. | (12 x 14) | 10.00 | 5.00 | 1.25 | .75 | 10.00 |
| b | horiz. pair, imperf. between | (12 x 14) | 1,000.00 | 600.00 | — | — | — |
| c | new perf. | (11.8 x 11.4) | 1,000.00 | 500.00 | 450.00 | 300.00 | |

Qty: 5,005,000 (all types included)

| | | (Perf) | ★VF | ★F | ⊙VF | ⊙F | ✉ |
|---|---|---|---|---|---|---|---|
| **89** | **3¢ brown olive** | (12 x 12) | 40.00 | 15.00 | 20.00 | 10.00 | 75.00 |

Qty: 55,000

| | | (Perf) | ★VF | ★F | ⊙VF | ⊙F | ✉ |
|---|---|---|---|---|---|---|---|
| **90** | **4¢ dull violet** | (12 x 12) | 40.00 | 15.00 | 20.00 | 10.00 | 50.00 |
| i | imperf right margin (single) | | 600.00 | 400.00 | — | — | — |

Qty: 55,000

| | | (Perf) | ★VF | ★F | ⊙VF | ⊙F | ✉ |
|---|---|---|---|---|---|---|---|
| **91** | **5¢ ultramarine** | (14 x 12) | 40.00 | 15.00 | 6.00 | 3.25 | 30.00 |
| a | new perf. | (12 x 12) | 50.00 | 25.00 | 10.00 | 5.00 | 30.00 |

Qty: 535,000

NH +200% (Perf) ★VF ★F ⊙VF ⊙F ✉

6 Cents:

Type I "Z" of "COLONIZATION" backwards
Type II "Z" of "COLONIZATION" normal

92
Type I

92A
Type II

92i/92Ai/92Aii
Top: Pos. 10; Bottom: Pos. 17

| | | (Perf) | ★VF | ★F | ⊙VF | ⊙F | ✉ |
|---|---|---|---|---|---|---|---|
| **92** | **6¢ claret**, Type I ("Z" backwards) | (12 x 12) | 140.00 | 60.00 | 90.00 | 55.00 | 300.00 |
| i | "WF" joined* | (12 x 12) | 400.00 | 200.00 | 350.00 | 175.00 | |
| ii | imperf. left margin | (12 x 12) | 500.00 | 300.00 | — | — | |

Qty: 15,000

| | | (Perf) | ★VF | ★F | ⊙VF | ⊙F | ✉ |
|---|---|---|---|---|---|---|---|
| **92A** | **6¢ claret**, Type II | (12 x 12) | 80.00 | 35.00 | 50.00 | 35.00 | 100.00 |
| b | imperf. pair (50) | | 600.00 | 400.00 | — | — | — |
| i | "WF" joined* | (12 x 12) | 300.00 | 150.00 | 200.00 | 100.00 | |
| ii | as "i", imperf. pr. (NH+50%) | | 1,000.00 | 650.00 | | | |
| iii | imperf. pr. wmkd paper (NH+50%) | | 800.00 | | | | |

Qty: 10,000; 92ii: 20 examples from two sheets thought to exist.

* Position 10 and 17, pos. 17 also has a damaged "L" in NEWFOUNDLAND.

| | | ★VF | ★F | ⊙VF | ⊙F | ✉ |
|---|---|---|---|---|---|---|
| **93** | **8¢ pale brown** | 110.00 | 40.00 | 75.00 | 40.00 | 300.00 |
| i | "MCSQUITO" variety | 900.00 | 600.00 | 600.00 | 400.00 | |

Qty: 15,000

93i

| | | ★VF | ★F | ⊙VF | ⊙F | ✉ |
|---|---|---|---|---|---|---|
| **94** | **9¢ olive green** | 110.00 | 40.00 | 75.00 | 40.00 | 300.00 |

Qty: 15,000

| | | ★VF | ★F | ⊙VF | ⊙F | ✉ |
|---|---|---|---|---|---|---|
| **95** | **10¢ violet black** | 110.00 | 40.00 | 75.00 | 35.00 | 300.00 |

Qty: 15,000

| | | ★VF | ★F | ⊙VF | ⊙F | ✉ |
|---|---|---|---|---|---|---|
| **96** | **12¢ lilac** | 110.00 | 40.00 | 75.00 | 40.00 | 350.00 |
| a | imperf. pair (100) | 600.00 | 400.00 | — | — | — |

Qty: 15,000

| | | ★VF | ★F | ⊙VF | ⊙F | ✉ |
|---|---|---|---|---|---|---|
| **97** | **15¢ grey black** | 110.00 | 40.00 | 85.00 | 50.00 | 650.00 |

Qty: 15,000

| | | ★VF | ★F | ⊙VF | ⊙F | ✉ |
|---|---|---|---|---|---|---|
| **Nos. 87–97** | (12) set | 909.00 | 351.50 | 574.00 | 320.25 | — |

**Nos. 87–97**: Plate proof pairs (on thick gummed paper) of any value NH+50%
250.00 150.00

Cover prices are for single usage.
Issued to commemorate the 300th anniversary of the colonization of Newfoundland.

## JOHN GUY ISSUE
### Engraved

98 Lord Bacon | 99 Mosquito | 100 Logging

101 Paper mills | 102 King Edward VII | 103 King George V

**1911, Feb 7** **Engraved** **Perf 14**

| | | NH% | ★VF | ★F | ⊙VF | ⊙F | ✉ |
|---|---|---|---|---|---|---|---|
| **98** | **6¢ brown violet** | 150 | 50.00 | 20.00 | 35.00 | 18.00 | 100.00 |
| **a** | imperf. pair (with and w/o gum) | 50 | 400.00 | 350.00 | — | — | — |
| **b** | horiz. pair, imperf. btwn | | *1,500.00* | *1,000.00* | — | — | — |
| Qty: 22,500 | | | | | | | |
| **99** | **8¢ bistre brown** | 150 | 100.00 | 50.00 | 90.00 | 40.00 | 250.00 |
| **a** | imperf. pair (with and w/o gum) | 50 | 400.00 | 350.00 | — | — | — |
| **b** | horiz. pair, imperf. btwn | | 1,500.00 | 1,000.00 | — | — | — |
| Qty: 15,000 | | | | | | | |
| **100** | **9¢ olive green** | 150 | 100.00 | 50.00 | 80.00 | 35.00 | 250.00 |
| **a** | imperf. pair (with and w/o gum) | 50 | 400.00 | 350.00 | — | — | — |
| **b** | horiz. pair, imperf. btwn | | 1,500.00 | 1,000.00 | — | — | — |
| **ii** | watermarked | 100 | 1,000.00 | 500.00 | 1,000.00 | 500.00 | |
| Qty: 15,000 | | | | | | | |
| **101** | **10¢ violet black** | 150 | 130.00 | 60.00 | 120.00 | 60.00 | 350.00 |
| **a** | imperf. pair (with and w/o gum) | 50 | 400.00 | 350.00 | — | — | — |
| **b** | horiz. pair, imperf. btwn | | 1,500.00 | 1,000.00 | — | — | — |
| Qty: 15,000 | | | | | | | |
| **102** | **12¢ red brown** | 150 | 100.00 | 50.00 | 100.00 | 50.00 | 300.00 |
| **a** | imperf. pair (with and w/o gum) | 50 | 400.00 | 350.00 | — | — | — |
| **b** | horiz. pair, imperf. btwn | | *1,500.00* | *1,000.00* | — | — | — |
| Qty: 15,000 | | | | | | | |
| **103** | **15¢ slate green** | 150 | 100.00 | 50.00 | 100.00 | 50.00 | 750.00 |
| **a** | imperf. pair (with and w/o gum) | 50 | 400.00 | 350.00 | — | — | — |
| **b** | horiz. pair, imperf. between | | *1,500.00* | *1,000.00* | — | — | — |
| **i** | watermarked | 100 | 1,250.00 | 600.00 | 1,250.00 | 500.00 | |
| **ii** | as "a", watermarked | 50 | 600.00 | 400.00 | | | |
| Qty: 15,000 | | | | | | | |
| **Nos. 98–103** | (6) engraved | 150 | 580.00 | 280.00 | 525.00 | 253.00 | — |

**99b**

## ROYAL FAMILY ISSUE
### CORONATION OF KING GEORGE V

104 Queen Mary | 105 King George V | 106 Prince of Wales | 107 Prince Albert

108 Princess Mary | 109 Prince Henry | 110 Prince George | 111 Prince John

112 Queen Alexandra | 113 Duke of Connaught | 114 Colony Seal

**1911, Jun 19** **Perf 13½x14; 14x14**

| | | NH% | ★VF | ★F | ⊙VF | ⊙F | ✉ |
|---|---|---|---|---|---|---|---|
| **104** | **1¢ yellow green** | 150 | 5.00 | 1.75 | .30 | .20 | 2.00 |
| **a** | imperf. pair, w/o gum | — | 450.00 | 250.00 | — | — | — |
| **b** | blue green | 150 | 6.00 | 3.00 | .30 | .20 | 2.00 |
| **105** | **2¢ carmine** | 150 | 5.00 | 2.50 | 1.50 | .20 | 1.50 |
| **a** | imperf. pair, w/o gum | — | 450.00 | 250.00 | — | — | — |
| **b** | rose red (war-time printing, blurred impression) | 150 | 10.00 | 6.00 | 1.50 | .30 | 2.00 |
| **106** | **3¢ red brown** | 150 | 50.00 | 20.00 | 25.00 | 20.00 | 30.00 |
| **107** | **4¢ violet** | 150 | 60.00 | 20.00 | 18.00 | 13.00 | 25.00 |
| **108** | **5¢ ultramarine** | 150 | 35.00 | 12.50 | 2.50 | 1.40 | 6.00 |
| **a** | imperf. pair, w/o gum | — | 450.00 | 250.00 | — | — | — |
| **109** | **6¢ black** | 150 | 40.00 | 16.50 | 30.00 | 16.50 | 25.00 |
| **i** | major re-entry | | | | | | |
| **ii** | re-entry above FOUND | | | | | | |

**109i**

Lines in bottom of NEWFOUNDLAND POSTAGE

| | | NH% | ★VF | ★F | ⊙VF | ⊙F | ✉ |
|---|---|---|---|---|---|---|---|
| **110** | **8¢ blue** (aniline blue paper) | 150 | 110.00 | 50.00 | 90.00 | 50.00 | 225.00 |
| **a** | peacock blue | 150 | 125.00 | 55.00 | 95.00 | 55.00 | 225.00 |
| **i** | re-entry above FOUND | | | | | | |

| | NH% | ★VF | ★F | ⊙VF | ⊙F | ✉ |
|---|---|---|---|---|---|---|
| **111 9¢ blue violet** | 150 | 50.00 | 20.00 | 27.50 | 20.00 | 75.00 |
| i strong re-entry | | | | | | |

Similar re-entries occur on numerous plate positions, with some being stronger than others and showing marks in the lettering.

111i
Top of band above NEWFOUNDLAND

| | NH% | ★VF | ★F | ⊙VF | ⊙F | ✉ |
|---|---|---|---|---|---|---|
| **112 10¢ dark green** | 150 | 80.00 | 30.00 | 50.00 | 27.50 | 50.00 |
| **113 12¢ plum** | 150 | 60.00 | 27.50 | 50.00 | 27.50 | 50.00 |
| a imperf. pair, w/o gum | — | 600.00 | | | | |
| i imperf. at right margin, single (10 known) | 50 | 500.00 | 300.00 | — | — | — |
| ii re-entry | | | | | | |

113i

113ii
Top framelines and some letters

| | NH% | ★VF | ★F | ⊙VF | ⊙F | ✉ |
|---|---|---|---|---|---|---|
| **114 15¢ magenta** | 150 | 50.00 | 27.50 | 50.00 | 27.50 | 100.00 |
| a imperf. pair, w/o gum | — | 200.00 | 120.00 | — | — | — |
| **Nos. 104–114** (11) Set | 150 | 536.00 | 228.25 | 344.80 | 203.80 | |

**Nos. 104–114** Set of 11 plate proofs in black on card $1,500.00.
Issued on the occasion of the Coronation of King George V.

## TRAIL OF THE CARIBOU ISSUE

115
Suvla Bay

116
Ubique

117
Gueudecourt

118
Beaumont Hamel

119
Ubique

120
Monchy

121
Ubique

122
Steenbeck

123
Ubique

124
Langemarck

125
Cambrai

126
Combles

**1919, Jan 2** **Perf 14**

Two perforation heads were used: 14 x 13.9 and 14.1 x 14.1.

| | NH% | ★VF | ★F | ⊙VF | ⊙F | ✉ |
|---|---|---|---|---|---|---|
| **115 1¢ green** | 100 | 4.00 | 1.50 | .50 | .20 | 1.00 |
| a imperf. pair (w/o gum) | — | 350.00 | 200.00 | — | — | — |
| **116 2¢ scarlet** | 100 | 4.00 | 1.75 | .75 | .45 | 1.00 |
| a imperf. pair (w/o gum) | — | 350.00 | 200.00 | — | — | — |
| b carmine red | | 6.00 | 3.00 | 1.00 | .55 | 1.50 |
| **117 3¢ red brown** | 100 | 5.00 | 2.00 | .50 | .20 | .75 |
| a imperf. pair, red brown (w/o gum) | — | 350.00 | 200.00 | — | — | — |
| b brown | 100 | 5.00 | 2.00 | .50 | .20 | .75 |
| c imperf. pair, brown (w/o gum) | — | 350.00 | 200.00 | — | — | — |
| ii deep brown | 100 | 5.00 | 2.00 | .60 | .30 | .75 |

Nos. 115–117: centre inscription blocks
Pl. 1, CL – $300.00; Pl. 2, CR – $250.00; Pl. 3, CL – $250.00

| | NH% | ★VF | ★F | ⊙VF | ⊙F | ✉ |
|---|---|---|---|---|---|---|
| **118 4¢ violet** | 100 | 7.00 | 3.25 | 2.00 | 1.25 | 4.00 |
| a imperf. pair (w/o gum) | — | 350.00 | 200.00 | — | — | — |
| b mauve | 100 | 8.50 | 4.25 | 2.00 | 1.25 | 4.00 |
| **119 5¢ ultramarine** | 100 | 15.00 | 6.50 | 2.00 | 1.25 | 3.00 |
| a imperf. pair (w/o gum) | — | 350.00 | 200.00 | — | — | — |
| **120 6¢ grey** | 100 | 30.00 | 15.00 | 30.00 | 15.00 | 25.00 |
| a imperf. pair (w/o gum) | — | 350.00 | 200.00 | — | — | — |
| **121 8¢ magenta** | 100 | 35.00 | 15.00 | 25.00 | 12.50 | 20.00 |
| a imperf. pair (w/o gum) | — | 350.00 | 200.00 | — | — | — |
| **122 10¢ dark green** | 100 | 30.00 | 10.00 | 8.00 | 3.50 | 8.00 |
| a imperf. pair (w/o gum) | — | 350.00 | 200.00 | — | — | — |
| **123 12¢ orange** | 100 | 100.00 | 40.00 | 65.00 | 27.50 | 45.00 |
| a imperf. pair (w/o gum) | — | 350.00 | 200.00 | — | — | — |
| **124 15¢ dark blue** | 100 | 60.00 | 25.00 | 60.00 | 30.00 | 55.00 |
| a imperf. pair (w/o gum) | — | 350.00 | 200.00 | — | — | — |
| b Prussian blue* | 100 | 400.00 | 250.00 | 200.00 | 150.00 | 250.00 |

*Certificates recommended to verify shade.

| | NH% | ★VF | ★F | ⊙VF | ⊙F | ✉ |
|---|---|---|---|---|---|---|
| **125 24¢ bistre** | 100 | 60.00 | 30.00 | 60.00 | 30.00 | 50.00 |
| a imperf. pair (w/o gum) | — | 350.00 | 200.00 | — | — | — |
| **126 36¢ olive green** | 100 | 50.00 | 25.00 | 50.00 | 25.00 | 50.00 |
| a imperf. pair (w/o gum) | — | 350.00 | 200.00 | — | — | — |
| **Nos. 115–126** (12) | 100 | 400.00 | 175.00 | 303.75 | 146.85 | — |
| **Nos. 115a–126i** set of 12 imperf. pairs, w/o gum | — | 4,200.00 | 2,400.00 | | | |

Issued to honour the services and memory of the Newfoundland contingent in World War I. The places where action took place are inscribed on the various denominations, with "Ubique" representing all battle scenes.

## SURCHARGES

127 Colony seal — 128 Seals — 129 Seals — 130 Iceberg

| **1920** | **Sheets of 25** | | | | **Perf 12** |
|---|---|---|---|---|---|
| **NH +100%** | **★VF** | **★F** | **⊙VF** | **⊙F** | ✉ |
| **127 2¢ on 30¢ slate (72)** | 8.00 | 5.00 | 7.50 | 5.00 | 120.00 |
| a inverted surcharge (qty: 50) | 2,000.00 | 1,000.00 | | | *6,000* |
| i surcharge in red | 2,000.00 | 1,250.00 | — | — | — |
| ii seriously misplaced surcharge | 600.00 | 400.00 | — | — | |
| iii pair, one without surcharge | | *5,000.00* | | | |
| **128 3¢ on 15¢ scarlet, (70)** | | | | | |
| **Type I** (bars 10½ mm apart) | 300.00 | 200.00 | 350.00 | 225.00 | 500.00 |
| a inverted surcharge | 4,500.00 | 2,500.00 | | | |
| i raised "E" variety | 400.00 | 250.00 | 400.00 | 250.00 | |

A THREE CENTS surcharge (in red or black) essay on the 6¢ red brown Logging stamp (Scott 66) exists, prepared in 1920. Mint value $1,000 (VF) and $800 (F).

| | **★VF** | **★F** | **⊙VF** | **⊙F** | ✉ |
|---|---|---|---|---|---|
| **129 3¢ on 15¢ scarlet, (70)** | | | | | |
| **Type II** (bars 13½ mm apart) | 25.00 | 15.00 | 15.00 | 10.00 | 30.00 |
| i raised "E" variety | 50.00 | 30.00 | 40.00 | 25.00 | |
| **130 3¢ on 35¢ red (73)** | 16.00 | 10.00 | 12.00 | 8.00 | 30.00 |
| a lower bar omitted | 200.00 | 140.00 | 200.00 | 140.00 | |
| block of 4 most of 1 bar and part of 1 bar missing | 300.00 | 200.00 | | | |
| i inverted surcharge* | 3,000.00 | 2,000.00 | | | |
| ii "THREE" omitted† | 2,000.00 | 1,200.00 | 2,000.00 | 1,200.00 | |
| iii raised "E" variety | 40.00 | 24.00 | 40.00 | 24.00 | |

* The existence of number 130i has been questioned by some experts.

† On number 130ii the "THREE" is never completely missing.

Surcharges are in black. Those in different colours are either essays or trial colour proofs. There are many minor broken bar or letter varieties.

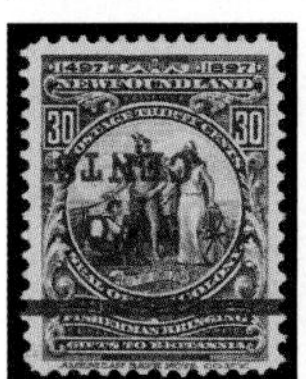

127a

127ii

130a

130ii

128a

THREE CENTS on 6¢ Logging (Sc. 66)

## PICTORIAL ISSUE

131 Twin Hills, Tor's Cove

132 South West Arm, Trinity

133 War Memorial

134 Humber River

135 Coast of Trinity

136 Upper Steadies, Humber River

137 Quidi Vidi

138 Caribou Crossing

139 Humber River Canyon

140 Shell Bird Island

141 Mt. Moriah

142 Little Rapids

143 Placentia

144 Topsail Falls

**1923–1924** **Engraved** **Perf 14x14; 13½x14**

Three perforation heads were used: comb perf. 13.8 x 14 on all values, line perf. 13.7 and 14 and combinations of these two on all values except the 6¢, 8¢, 9¢ and 11¢.

| | **NH%** | **★VF** | **★F** | **⊙VF** | **⊙F** | ✉ |
|---|---|---|---|---|---|---|
| **131 1¢ grey green** | 100 | 2.50 | 1.50 | .40 | .25 | 2.50 |
| a booklet pane of 8 | 75 | 700.00 | 500.00 | 450.00 | 300.00 | |
| b imperf. pair (with and without gum) | 50 | 250.00 | 175.00 | — | — | |
| i booklet pane with cutting lines in middle of tab | 75 | 800.00 | 550.00 | | | |
| **132 2¢ carmine** | 100 | 2.50 | 1.50 | .35 | .20 | 2.50 |
| a booklet pane of 8 | 75 | 450.00 | 350.00 | 275.00 | 135.00 | |
| b imperf. pair (with and without gum) | 50 | 250.00 | 175.00 | — | — | |
| i booklet pane with cutting lines in middle of tab | 75 | 600.00 | 500.00 | | | |
| **133 3¢ brown** | 100 | 3.50 | 1.50 | .35 | .20 | 3.00 |
| inscription blocks, plate 2, UL, LL $100.00 | | | | | | |
| a imperf. pair (without gum) | | 500.00 | 350.00 | | | |
| **134 4¢ brown violet** | 100 | 4.00 | 2.00 | 2.50 | 1.75 | 5.00 |
| a imperf. pair (with or without gum) | 50 | 300.00 | 200.00 | — | — | |
| **135 5¢ ultramarine** | 100 | 10.00 | 5.00 | 3.00 | 2.00 | 7.50 |
| a imperf. pair (with or without gum) | 50 | 300.00 | 200.00 | — | — | |

| No. | | NH% | ★VF | ★F | ⊙VF | ⊙F | ✉ |
|---|---|---|---|---|---|---|---|
| 136 | **6¢ grey black** | 100 | 9.00 | 4.00 | 9.00 | 4.00 | 15.00 |
| a | imperf. pair (without gum) | — | 300.00 | 200.00 | — | — | — |
| 137 | **8¢ dull violet** | 100 | 7.00 | 3.25 | 7.00 | 3.00 | 15.00 |
| a | imperf. pair (without gum) | — | 300.00 | 200.00 | — | — | — |
| 138 | **9¢ slate green** | 100 | 60.00 | 30.00 | 40.00 | 26.00 | 70.00 |
| a | imperf. pair (without gum) | — | 300.00 | 200.00 | — | — | — |
| 139 | **10¢ dark violet** | 100 | 6.00 | 3.75 | 4.00 | 2.00 | 10.00 |
| a | imperf. pair (without gum) | — | 300.00 | 200.00 | — | — | — |
| b | purple | 100 | 7.00 | 4.50 | 4.00 | 2.00 | |
| 140 | **11¢ olive green** | 100 | 10.00 | 6.50 | 10.00 | 6.50 | 25.00 |
| a | imperf. pair (with and without gum) | 50 | 300.00 | 200.00 | — | — | — |
| 141 | **12¢ lake** | 100 | 10.00 | 6.25 | 10.00 | 6.25 | 20.00 |
| a | imperf. pair (without gum) | — | 300.00 | 200.00 | — | — | — |
| 142 | **15¢ deep blue** | 100 | 12.50 | 7.50 | 11.00 | 7.00 | 25.00 |
| a | imperf. pair (without gum) | — | 250.00 | 160.00 | — | — | — |
| 143 | **20¢ red brown** | 100 | 18.00 | 10.00 | 10.00 | 6.00 | 35.00 |
| 144 | **24¢ black brown** | 100 | 120.00 | 50.00 | 75.00 | 45.00 | 150.00 |
| **Nos. 131–144** | (14) Set | 100 | 275.00 | 132.75 | 186.60 | 110.15 | |

## PICTORIAL ISSUE — I

145 Map of Newfoundland | 146 Steamship "Caribou" | 147 King George V and Queen Mary | 148 Prince of Wales

149 Express Train | 150 Newfoundland Hotel | 151 Heart's Content

152 Cabot Tower | 153 War Memorial | 154 General Post Office | 155 Cabot Tower

156 First Nonstop Transatlantic Flight | 157 Colonial Building, St. John's | 158 General Post Office | 159 Grand Falls

**1928, Jan 3** **Engraved, Unwatermarked**

**Perf 14x14; 13½x14; 13x13½**

Three perforation heads were used: comb perf. 14 x 13.9, comb perf. 13.5 x 12.75 and line perf. 13.7 to 14 or compound.

See also 163–171, 172–182

| NH +100% | | | ★VF | ★F | ⊙VF | ⊙F | ✉ |
|---|---|---|---|---|---|---|---|
| 145 | **1¢ deep green** | | 2.00 | 1.25 | 1.00 | .65 | 1.00 |
| i | major misplaced entry (pos. 60) | | | | | | |

Numerous re-entries exist over the entire design, some upwards, some downwards, some both; some are quite major.

145i

NEWFOUNDLAND & LABRADOR shifted a full 2.0mm above normal design (also NEWFOUNDLAND at bottom of stamp)

| | | | ★VF | ★F | ⊙VF | ⊙F | ✉ |
|---|---|---|---|---|---|---|---|
| 146 | **2¢ deep carmine** | — | 4.00 | 2.00 | 1.00 | .60 | 1.00 |
| a | imperf. pair | | 375.00 | 250.00 | — | — | — |
| | inscription blocks, plates 2, 3, LL $80.00 | | | | | | |
| i | lathework in bottom margin | | 65.00 | 35.00 | | | |
| 147 | **3¢ brown** | | 4.00 | 2.00 | .75 | .45 | 1.00 |
| | inscription blocks, plate 2, LL $60.00; plate 3, UR $60.00 | | | | | | |
| i | re-entry of UR corner and/or LL corner | | | | | | |
| ii | lathework in lower margin | | 100.00 | 50.00 | | | |
| 148 | **4¢ lilac rose** | | 5.00 | 2.50 | 2.50 | 1.75 | 10.00 |
| a | rose purple, *1929* | | 8.00 | 4.00 | 2.75 | 2.00 | 10.00 |
| 149 | **5¢ slate green** | | 12.00 | 6.00 | 6.00 | 3.50 | 10.00 |
| 150 | **6¢ ultramarine** | | 8.00 | 4.00 | 8.00 | 4.00 | 10.00 |
| 151 | **8¢ light red brown** | | 10.00 | 5.00 | 6.25 | 4.25 | 15.00 |
| 152 | **9¢ myrtle green** | | 10.00 | 4.00 | 10.00 | 5.50 | 15.00 |
| 153 | **10¢ dark violet** | | 12.00 | 6.00 | 7.00 | 4.50 | 15.00 |
| 154 | **12¢ brown carmine** | | 8.00 | 4.00 | 8.00 | 3.50 | 20.00 |
| 155 | **14¢ red brown** | | 17.00 | 8.50 | 10.00 | 4.50 | 25.00 |
| 156 | **15¢ dark blue** | | 15.00 | 6.00 | 10.00 | 6.00 | 20.00 |
| i | major re-entry (pos. 20) | | | | | | |
| ii | lathework in lower margin | | 60.00 | 30.00 | | | |
| iii | major re-entry in LR corner (all letters and 15) (pos. 19) | | | | | | |

156i

In NEWFOUNDLAND POSTAGE and both 15's

156iii

| | ★VF | ★F | ⊙VF | ⊙F | ✉ |
|---|---|---|---|---|---|
| **157 20¢ grey black** | 18.00 | 8.00 | 9.50 | 4.00 | 20.00 |
| **158 28¢ grey green** | 50.00 | 20.00 | 40.00 | 20.00 | 70.00 |
| **159 30¢ olive brown** | 25.00 | 10.00 | 10.00 | 6.00 | 20.00 |
| **Nos. 145–159** (15) Set | 200.00 | 83.25 | 130.00 | 69.20 | — |

## SURCHARGE on 136

160

Humber River

**1929, Aug 23** **Sheets of 25** **Perf 14x13½**

| NH +100% | | ★VF | ★F | ⊙VF | ⊙F | ✉ |
|---|---|---|---|---|---|---|
| | Type I: space of 5 mm between "CENTS" and bar. Type II: space of 3 mm between "CENTS" and bar. | | | | | |
| **160** | **3¢ on 6¢ grey black (136), Type II, red surcharge** | 6.00 | 2.00 | 8.00 | 4.00 | 50.00 |
| a | inverted surcharge, Type II (75 printed) | 1,400.00 | 1,000.00 | — | — | — |
| i | black surcharge, Type I | 1,750.00 | 1,250.00 | — | — | — |
| ii | black surcharge, Type II | 1,750.00 | 1,250.00 | — | — | — |
| iii | "C" of CENTS below the "T" of THREE (pos. 1, 15, 23) | 50.00 | 30.00 | 20.00 | 15.00 | 60.00 |
| iv | re-entry in NEWFOUN | | | | | |

No. 136 surcharged in red.

Numerous other re-entries exist, some major.

160a

160i

160ii

160iv

Re-entry in NEWFOUN

Nos. 161–162 are not assigned.

## PICTORIAL ISSUE — 2

163
Map of Newfoundland

164
Steamship "Caribou"

165
King George V and Queen Mary

166
Prince of Wales

167
Express Train

168
Newfoundland Hotel

169
War Memorial

170
First Nonstop Transatlantic Flight

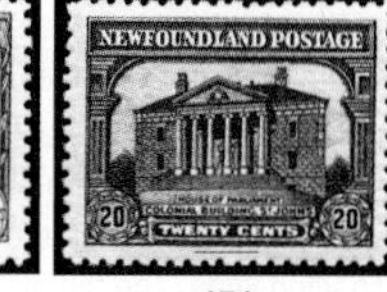

171
Colonial Building, St. John's

**1929–1931** **Re-engraved, Unwatermarked**

**Perf 13½ to 14**

Four perforation heads were used: comb perf. 14 x 13.9, comb perf. 13.6 x 13.5, comb perf. 13.6 x 13.8 and line perf. 13.7 to 14 or compound.

See also 145–159, 172–182

| NH +100% | | ★VF | ★F | ⊙VF | ⊙F | ✉ |
|---|---|---|---|---|---|---|
| **163** | **1¢ green** | 3.00 | 1.50 | 1.00 | .50 | 1.50 |
| a | double impression | 600.00 | 300.00 | | | |
| b | vert. pair, imperf. between | 270.00 | 180.00 | | | |
| c | imperf. pair, with and w/o gum | 160.00 | 100.00 | | | |
| i | imperf. right margin, single | 200.00 | 150.00 | | | |
| ii | imperf. bottom margin, single | 200.00 | 150.00 | | | |
| iii | horiz. pair, imperf. between | 400.00 | | | | |
| **164** | **2¢ deep carmine** | 3.00 | 1.50 | 1.00 | .50 | 1.50 |
| | inscription blocks, plate 2, 3, LL $80 | | | | | |
| a | imperf. pair, pale carmine on cream paper | 200.00 | 120.00 | | | |
| b | imperf. pair, dark carmine on white paper, w/o gum | 200.00 | 120.00 | | | |
| i | imperf. at top margin | 300.00 | 200.00 | | | |
| **165** | **3¢ deep red brown** | 3.00 | 1.50 | 1.00 | .50 | 1.50 |
| | inscription blocks, plate 2, 3, UR $80. | | | | | |
| a | imperf. pair, with and w/o gum | 200.00 | 120.00 | | | |
| i | imperf. between stamp and bottom margin | 300.00 | 200.00 | | | |
| **166** | **4¢ magenta** | 5.00 | 2.50 | 2.00 | 1.25 | 5.00 |
| a | imperf. pair | 240.00 | 160.00 | | | |
| i | imperf. at right margin | 300.00 | 200.00 | | | |
| **167** | **5¢ slate green** | 10.00 | 5.00 | 4.00 | 1.25 | 10.00 |

| NH +100% | ★VF | ★F | ⊙VF | ⊙F | ✉ |
|---|---|---|---|---|---|
| **168 6¢ ultramarine** | 14.00 | 7.00 | 12.00 | 8.00 | 15.00 |
| **169 10¢ dark violet** | 12.00 | 6.00 | 4.00 | 1.75 | 10.00 |
| **170 15¢ deep blue** | 70.00 | 35.00 | 50.00 | 35.00 | 50.00 |
| **171 20¢ grey black** | 100.00 | 50.00 | 35.00 | 22.50 | 40.00 |
| i imperf. at top margin | 600.00 | 400.00 | | | |
| **Nos. 163–171** (9) Set | 220.00 | 110.00 | 110.00 | 71.25 | |

## DIFFERENCES BETWEEN ORIGINAL AND RE-ENGRAVED PRINTINGS

**1¢** On No. 145 the lines of the engraving are thinner and the impression is clearer than on No. 163. On the former, "C. BAULD" is above "C. NORMAN". On the latter these words are transposed.

**2¢** On the original the "D" of "NEWFOUNDLAND" is 1 mm from the right scroll and the flag at the stern is lower than the top of the boat davit. On the 1929 stamp the "D" is ½ mm from the scroll and the flag rises above the davits.

**3¢** On the original the pearls at the top of the crown, the jewels of the tiara and the pillars flanking the portraits are all unshaded. On the re-engraving there are small curved lines inside the pearls, the jewels are in solid colour and the pillars have vertical shading lines. The tablets with "THREE" and "CENTS" have a background of crossed lines (vertical and horizontal) on the original and one of the horizontal lines only on the re-engraving.

**4¢** On the 1928 stamp the figures "4" have horizontal and diagonal crossed line shading and there are six circles at each side of the portrait. On the 1929 version the "4s" have horizontal-line shading only and there are five roses at each side of the portrait.

**5¢** The crossbars of the telegraph pole touch the left frame on the 1929 stamp but just clear it on the original. On the original the foliate ornaments beside and below the figures "5" end in small scrolls and a small spur. These spurs are omitted from the re-engraved stamp.

**6¢** On the re-engraving the column at the right and left have heavy wavy outlines on the inner sides and there is no period after "JOHN'S". The numerals in the lower corners are 1½ mm wide rather than 1 mm.

**8¢** The impression of the original is clear while that of the re-engraving is slightly blurred. The 1928 stamp has three horizontal lines above "EIGHT CENTS" and four berries on the laurel branch at the right. The re-engraving has two horizontal lines and three berries.

**10¢** On the re-engraving there is no period after "ST. JOHN'S". The letters of "TEN CENTS" are slightly larger and the numerals "10" slightly smaller than the original. Inside the "0" of "10" at the right there are two vertical lines instead of three. The clouds are fainter in 1929 and the cross upheld by the figure on the monument is more distinct. On the original the torch at the left terminates in a single tongue of flame while the re-engraving has two tongues of flame.

**15¢** On the original the "N" of "NEWFOUNDLAND" is 1½ mm from the left frame, the "L" of "LEAVING" is under the first "A" of "AIRPLANE" and the apostrophe in "JOHN'S" breaks the first line above it. On the re-engraving the "N" of "NEWFOUNDLAND" is 1 mm from the left frame, the "L" of "LEAVING" is below the "T" of "FIRST" and the apostrophe in "JOHN'S" does not touch the line above it.

**20¢** On the original the points of the "W" of "NEWFOUNDLAND" are truncated and the "O" is wide and nearly round. The columns at the sides have a shading of evenly spaced horizontal lines at their inner sides. On the re-engraving the points of the "W" form sharp angles and the "O" is narrower and has a small opening. The columns' shading appears almost solid.

**30¢** The size of the original is 19¼ x 24½ mm with three strong and two faint vertical lines at the outer side of the right column and a faint period after "FALLS". The re-engraving is 19 x 25 mm with two strong vertical lines and a fragment of a lower end of a faint one. There is a clear period after "FALLS" and a great many of the small lines of the design have been deepened making the whole stamp appear darker.



## PICTORIAL ISSUE — 3

**172**
Map of Newfoundland

**173**
Steamship "Caribou"

**174**
King George V and Queen Mary

**175**
Prince of Wales

**176**
Express Train

**177**
Newfoundland Hotel

**178**
Heart's Content

**179**
War Memorial

**180**
First Nonstop Transatlantic Flight

**181**
Colonial Building, St. John's

**182**
Grand Falls

**1931, Jan 3 — Re-engraved — Perf 13½x14**
**Watermarked "Coat-of-Arms"**

Two perforating heads were used: comb perf. 13.4 x 13.4 for the 1¢ and comb perf. 13.6 x 13.8 for the other values.

See also 145–159, 163–171

| NH +100% | ★VF | ★F | ⊙VF | ⊙F | ✉ |
|---|---|---|---|---|---|
| **172 1¢ green** | 4.00 | 2.00 | 2.00 | 1.00 | 2.50 |
| a horiz. pair, imperf. between | 600.00 | 400.00 | — | — | — |
| i perf. 14 | 450.00 | 300.00 | 400.00 | 300.00 | |
| **173 2¢ red** | 10.00 | 5.00 | 2.00 | 1.25 | 2.00 |
| **174 3¢ red brown** | 5.00 | 2.50 | 2.00 | 1.00 | 3.00 |
| inscription blocks, plate 3, UR $100. | | | | | |
| **175 4¢ rose** | 6.00 | 3.00 | 4.00 | 1.50 | 10.00 |
| **176 5¢ greenish grey** | 15.00 | 10.00 | 10.00 | 7.00 | 15.00 |
| **177 6¢ ultramarine** | 25.00 | 15.00 | 25.00 | 16.50 | 30.00 |
| **178 8¢ light red brown** | 30.00 | 15.00 | 25.00 | 16.50 | 25.00 |
| i inverted watermark | 75.00 | 45.00 | | | |
| **179 10¢ dark violet** | 20.00 | 10.00 | 12.00 | 7.00 | 15.00 |
| **180 15¢ deep blue** | 55.00 | 30.00 | 40.00 | 30.00 | 35.00 |
| **181 20¢ grey black** | 75.00 | 40.00 | 25.00 | 15.00 | 20.00 |
| **182 30¢ olive brown** | 55.00 | 27.50 | 35.00 | 25.00 | 30.00 |
| **Nos. 172–182** (11) Set | 300.00 | 160.00 | 182.00 | 121.75 | |

As the "Coat-of-Arms" watermark does not show on every stamp in the sheet, pairs are found one with and one without watermark.

Number 180 (15¢) was gummed after perforating.

## DEFINITIVE ISSUE
## PERKINS BACON PRINTINGS

See 253–266 for Waterlow Printings

183
Codfish

184
Codfish

185
King George V

186
King George V

187
Queen Mary

188
Prince of Wales

189
Prince of Wales

190
Caribou

191
Caribou

192
Princess Elizabeth

193
Salmon Leaping

194
Newfoundland Dog

195
Harp Seal Pup

196
Cape Race

197
Sealing Fleet

198
Fishing Fleet

199
Fishing Fleet

**1932–1937 Engraved, Watermarked Arms**
**Comb perf. 13½, line perf. 14;Perfs. 13¾, 14 and 14¼ also exist**

See also 253–266 for Waterlow Printings

The Perkins printings (20.4 mm) are slightly smaller than the Waterlow printings (21.0 mm).

| | | NH% | ★VF | ★F | ⊙VF | ⊙F | ✉ |
|---|---|---|---|---|---|---|---|
| **183** | **1¢ green** | 50 | 4.00 | 2.00 | .75 | .35 | 1.50 |
| | inscription blocks, plates 1, 2, UL $40.00 | | | | | | |
| a | booklet pane of 4, perf. 13 | 50 | 100.00 | 70.00 | | | |
| b | imperf. pair* | 50 | 300.00 | 200.00 | — | — | — |
| c | vert. pair, imperf. between (perf. 13.3) | 50 | 250.00 | 150.00 | — | — | — |
| ii | line perf. 13.2 | 50 | 15.00 | 10.00 | 12.00 | 8.00 | 25.00 |
| iii | horiz. pair, imperf. vert., perf. 13.3 horiz. | 50 | 350.00 | 275.00 | — | — | — |
| iv | imperf. bottom margin, single perf. 13.3 | 50 | 250.00 | 150.00 | | | |

* 183b exists with and without gum.

| | | NH% | ★VF | ★F | ⊙VF | ⊙F | ✉ |
|---|---|---|---|---|---|---|---|
| **184** | **1¢ grey black** | 50 | 1.00 | .50 | .25 | .20 | .75 |
| | inscription blocks: plates 1, 2, UL $35.00; plate 3, UL $40.00; plates 4, 5, UR $40.00; plate 6, UL $100.00 | | | | | | |
| a | booklet pane of 4, perf. 13½ | 50 | 75.00 | 50.00 | | | |
| b | booklet pane of 4, perf. 14 | 50 | 90.00 | 60.00 | | | |
| c | imperf. pair* | 50 | 60.00 | 40.00 | — | — | — |
| | as 'c', plate 4 UR (ungummed) $400.00 | | | | | | |
| i | line perf. 14 | 50 | 12.00 | 8.00 | 12.00 | 8.00 | 25.00 |
| ii | line perf. 14, small holes | 50 | 20.00 | 14.00 | 20.00 | 14.00 | 30.00 |
| iii | inverted watermark | 50 | 40.00 | 20.00 | | | |
| iv | lathework in left margin | 50 | 250.00 | 150.00 | | | |

* 184c exists with and without gum.

| | | NH% | ★VF | ★F | ⊙VF | ⊙F | ✉ |
|---|---|---|---|---|---|---|---|
| **185** | **2¢ rose** | 50 | 3.00 | 1.50 | .50 | .20 | 1.50 |
| c | imperf. pair | 50 | 300.00 | 200.00 | — | — | — |
| ii | line perf. 13 | 50 | 20.00 | 10.00 | 15.00 | 8.00 | 25.00 |
| iii | imperf. top margin | 50 | 100.00 | 70.00 | — | — | |
| a | booklet pane of 4, perf. 13½ | 50 | 45.00 | 30.00 | 45.00 | 30.00 | |
| b | booklet pane of 4, perf. 13.2 | 50 | 60.00 | 40.00 | | | |
| bi | pane with imperf. top margin & triple perf. between top row and second row | 50 | 600.00 | 400.00 | | | |
| bii | pane with imperf. top margin & double perf. between top row and second row | 50 | — | 400.00 | — | — | |
| | inscription blocks plates 1, 2, UL $40.00 | | | | | | |
| | inscription blocks plate 3, UL $75.00 | | | | | | |

| | | NH% | ★VF | ★F | ⊙VF | ⊙F | ✉ |
|---|---|---|---|---|---|---|---|
| **186** | **2¢ green, Die I*** | 50 | 1.50 | 1.25 | .35 | .20 | .75 |
| | inscription blocks, plates 1, 2, UL $35.00 | | | | | | |
| | inscription blocks, plates 3, 4, UL $40.00 | | | | | | |
| a | booklet pane of 4, perf. 13½ | 50 | 33.00 | 22.00 | | | |
| b | booklet pane of 4, perf. 14 | 50 | 45.00 | 30.00 | | | |
| c | imperf. pair, Die I* (with or without gum) | 50 | 60.00 | 40.00 | — | — | — |
| | as 'c', plate 4 UL $500.00 | | | | | | |
| d | horiz. pair, imperf. between, perf. 14¼ x 14¼ | 50 | 200.00 | 140.00 | — | — | — |
| i | line perf. 14 | 50 | 12.00 | 8.00 | 12.00 | 8.00 | 25.00 |
| ii | Die II, perf. 13½* | 50 | 1.75 | 1.50 | .50 | .20 | .75 |
| ai | booklet pane of 4, Die II, perf. 13½ | 50 | 35.00 | 25.00 | | | |
| iii | imperf. pair, Die II* | 50 | 60.00 | 40.00 | — | — | — |
| | as 'iii', plate 4 UL $500.00 | | | | | | |
| iv | double printed | 50 | 300.00 | 200.00 | | | |
| v | pair, one w/o watermark | 50 | 100.00 | 75.00 | — | — | — |
| vi | offset image on gum side | 50 | 100.00 | 75.00 | | | |
| vii | bisect used from Curling, NF | | — | — | — | — | 100.00 |
| viii | horizontal strip of 20, 2 rows imperf. | 50 | 1,500.00 | 1,000.00 | — | — | |
| ix | double perforated | 50 | 200.00 | 150.00 | | | |

* Die I displays a dot in the letter "O" of the word TWO; Die II does not have the dot in the letter "O". 186iii exists with and without gum.

**First Day Covers**

| | | | | | | | | |
|---|---|---|---|---|---|---|---|---|
| 183 | Jan 2/32 | $5.00 | 189 | Aug 15/32 | $7.50 | 195 | Jan 2/32 | $15.00 |
| 184 | Aug 15/32 | $5.00 | 190 | Jan 2/32 | $7.50 | 196 | Jan 2/32 | $15.00 |
| 185 | Jan 2/32 | $5.00 | 191 | Aug 15/32 | $5.00 | 197 | Jan 2/32 | $15.00 |
| 186 | Aug 15/32 | $7.50 | 192 | Jan 2/32 | $30.00 | 198 | Jan 2/32 | $50.00 |
| 187 | Jan 2/32 | $5.00 | 193 | Jan 2/32 | $5.00 | 199 | Jan 1/38 | $40.00 |
| 188 | Jan 2/32 | $5.00 | 194 | Jan 2/32 | $15.00 | | | |

| No. | | NH% | ★VF | ★F | ⊙VF | ⊙F | ✉ |
|---|---|---|---|---|---|---|---|
| **187** | **3¢ orange brown** | 50 | 1.50 | 1.25 | .50 | .20 | .75 |
| | inscription blocks, plate 1, UL $35.00 | | | | | | |
| | inscription blocks, plate 2, UL $30.00 | | | | | | |
| | inscription blocks, plate 3, UL $35.00 | | | | | | |
| a | booklet pane of 4, perf. 13½ | 50 | 75.00 | 50.00 | | | |
| b | booklet pane of 4, perf. 14 | 50 | 90.00 | 60.00 | | | |
| c | booklet pane of 4, perf. 13.2 | 50 | 100.00 | 70.00 | | | |
| d | imperf. pair (with or without gum) | 50 | 120.00 | 80.00 | — | — | — |
| e | vertical pair, imperf. between perf. 13.3 | 50 | 400.00 | 250.00 | — | — | — |
| i | line perf. 13 | 50 | 20.00 | 10.00 | 15.00 | 8.00 | 25.00 |
| ii | line perf. 14 | 50 | 15.00 | 10.00 | 15.00 | 10.00 | 25.00 |
| iv | imperf. between single and top margin | 50 | 150.00 | 100.00 | — | — | — |
| v | imperf. between single and bottom margin | 50 | 150.00 | 100.00 | — | — | — |
| **188** | **4¢ deep violet** | 50 | 10.00 | 5.00 | 3.00 | 1.50 | 2.00 |
| **189** | **4¢ rose lake** | 50 | 1.00 | .60 | .70 | .35 | 2.00 |
| | inscription blocks, plate 2, UL $30.00 | | | | | | |
| | inscription blocks, plate 3, UL $40.00 | | | | | | |
| a | imperf. pair, with gum | 50 | 75.00 | 50.00 | — | — | — |
| | as 'a', plate 2 UL $500.00 | | | | | | |
| ai | as "a", without gum | | 75.00 | 50.00 | — | — | — |
| | as 'ai', plate 2 UL $500.00 | | | | | | |
| | as 'ai', plate 4 UR $500.00 | | | | | | |
| b | vert. pair, imperf. between | 50 | 150.00 | 100.00 | — | — | — |
| c | horiz. pair, imperf. between | 50 | 150.00 | 100.00 | — | — | — |
| d | line perf. 14 | 50 | 7.50 | 5.00 | 6.00 | 4.00 | 8.00 |
| | inscription blocks, plate 2, UL $90.00 | | | | | | |
| iv | perf. 14, inverted watermark | 50 | 60.00 | 40.00 | | | |

**190 (Die I)**
Antlers even or equal height.
Grass above '5'.

**191 (Die II)**
Antler under 'T' is higher.
Grass above and to left of '5'.

| No. | | NH% | ★VF | ★F | ⊙VF | ⊙F | ✉ |
|---|---|---|---|---|---|---|---|
| **190** | **5¢ violet brown, Die I** | 50 | 15.00 | 7.50 | 3.00 | 1.50 | 4.00 |
| a | imperf. pair | 50 | 300.00 | 200.00 | — | — | — |
| **191** | **5¢ deep violet, Die II** | 50 | 2.00 | 1.00 | .50 | .25 | .50 |
| | inscription blocks, plate 2, UL $25.00 | | | | | | |
| | inscription blocks, plate 3, UL $30.00 | | | | | | |
| | inscription blocks, plate 4, UL $35.00 | | | | | | |
| | inscription blocks, plate 5, UR $40.00 | | | | | | |
| | inscription blocks, plates 6, 7, UR $50.00 | | | | | | |
| a | Die I, deep violet | 50 | 20.00 | 10.00 | 2.00 | 1.00 | 2.50 |
| b | imperf. pair, Die II | 50 | 100.00 | 50.00 | — | — | — |
| | as 'b', plate 3 UL (w/gum) $500.00 | | | | | | |
| | as 'b', plate 3 UL (w/o gum) $450.00 | | | | | | |
| c | horiz. pair, imperf. between, Die I | 50 | 300.00 | 200.00 | — | — | — |
| d | imperf. pair, Die I | 50 | 120.00 | 80.00 | — | — | — |
| e | perf. 14, Die I | 50 | 70.00 | 40.00 | 25.00 | 15.00 | 80.00 |
| f | perf. 14, Die II | 50 | 70.00 | 40.00 | 25.00 | 15.00 | 80.00 |
| g | horiz. pair, imperf. between, Die II, line perf. 14.4 | 50 | 300.00 | 200.00 | — | — | — |
| i | major re-entry | | | | | | |
| ii | lathework in left margin | 50 | 250.00 | 150.00 | | | |

Numerous re-entries exist, some strong.

**191i**
0.3mm shift to right, with doubling of inner left frameline, many letters of NEWFOUNDLAND POSTAGE, 5 FIVE CENTS 5, antler below ST, and profile of caribou's face

| No. | | NH% | ★VF | ★F | ⊙VF | ⊙F | ✉ |
|---|---|---|---|---|---|---|---|
| **192** | **6¢ dull blue** | 50 | 15.00 | 10.00 | 15.00 | 10.00 | 30.00 |
| a | imperf. pair (with or without gum) | 50 | 250.00 | 150.00 | — | — | — |
| **193** | **10¢ olive black** | 50 | 2.00 | 1.25 | 1.25 | .80 | 2.00 |
| a | imperf. pair (with or without gum) | 50 | 150.00 | 100.00 | — | — | — |
| i | inverted watermark | 50 | 12.00 | 8.00 | | | |
| ii | double perforated | 50 | 100.00 | 60.00 | | | |
| iii | imperf. pair., double printed | 50 | 1,250.00 | 1,000.00 | | | |
| **194** | **14¢ intense black** | 50 | 5.00 | 2.75 | 4.00 | 2.25 | 10.00 |
| a | imperf. pair | 50 | 200.00 | 140.00 | — | — | — |
| ii | imperf. horiz. pair | 50 | 300.00 | 200.00 | — | — | — |
| iii | vert. pair, imperf. between | 50 | 600.00 | 400.00 | | | |
| iv | imperf. bottom margin | 50 | | | | | |
| **195** | **15¢ magenta** | 50 | 4.00 | 2.75 | 3.00 | 2.25 | 10.00 |
| a | imperf. pair | 50 | 200.00 | 140.00 | — | — | — |
| b | line perf. 14 | 50 | 18.00 | 12.00 | 9.00 | 6.00 | 15.00 |
| **196** | **20¢ grey green** | 50 | 4.00 | 2.75 | 1.50 | .90 | 10.00 |
| a | imperf. pair (with or without gum) | 50 | 350.00 | 200.00 | — | — | — |
| b | line perf. 14 | 50 | 100.00 | 60.00 | 50.00 | 40.00 | |
| ii | inverted watermark | 50 | 50.00 | 30.00 | | | |
| **197** | **25¢ grey**, comb perf. 13½ | 50 | 4.50 | 3.00 | 3.50 | 2.00 | 10.00 |
| a | imperf. pair | 50 | 350.00 | 200.00 | — | — | — |
| b | horiz. pair, imperf. between | 50 | 750.00 | 500.00 | — | — | — |
| c | vert. pair, imperf. between, perf. 14.4 | 50 | 750.00 | 600.00 | — | — | — |
| d | line perf. 14 | 50 | 120.00 | 80.00 | 60.00 | 50.00 | |
| **198** | **30¢ ultramarine** | 50 | 50.00 | 25.00 | 35.00 | 25.00 | 70.00 |
| a | imperf. pair | 50 | 1,200.00 | 800.00 | — | — | — |
| b | vert. pair, imperf. between | 50 | 1,500.00 | 1,000.00 | — | — | — |
| c | line perf. 14 | 50 | 800.00 | 400.00 | | | |
| **199** | **48¢ red brown**, *1938* | 50 | 15.00 | 10.00 | 8.00 | 5.00 | 25.00 |
| a | imperf. pair | 50 | 180.00 | 120.00 | — | — | — |
| **Nos. 183–199** (17) Set | | 50 | 136.00 | 80.30 | 77.70 | 52.10 | |

See note after No. 182 regarding watermarked and unwatermarked pairs.

Nos. 200–207 are not assigned.

## ADDITIONAL VALUES

208
Duchess of York

209
Corner Brook Paper Mill

210
Loading Ore, Bell Island

**1932, Aug 15** **Engraved, Watermarked** **Perf. 13½**

| | | NH% | ★VF | ★F | ⊙VF | ⊙F | ✉ |
|---|---|---|---|---|---|---|---|
| **208** | **7¢ red brown** | 50 | 2.00 | 1.25 | 2.00 | 1.25 | 10.00 |
| a | imperf. pair (with or without gum) | 50 | 200.00 | 150.00 | — | — | — |
| b | horiz. pair, imperf. between, perf. 14 | 50 | 750.00 | 500.00 | — | — | — |
| **209** | **8¢ orange red** | 50 | 2.00 | 1.25 | 2.00 | .90 | 10.00 |
| a | imperf. pair | 50 | 200.00 | 150.00 | — | — | — |
| **210** | **24¢ light blue** | 50 | 4.00 | 3.00 | 5.00 | 3.00 | 15.00 |
| a | imperf. pair (with or without gum) | 50 | 250.00 | 150.00 | — | — | — |
| b | double impression | 50 | 3,000.00 | 2,000.00 | — | — | — |

First day covers: #208, 209 – $15.00 each; #210 – $25.00.

210b

## LAND & SEA POST OVERPRINT

211
Dog sled and airplane

**Overprinted bars and L. & S. Post. on C9**
**1933, Feb 9** **Engraved, Watermarked**
**Sheets of 25**

| NH +75% | | ★VF | ★F | ⊙VF | ⊙F | ✉ |
|---|---|---|---|---|---|---|
| **211** | **15¢ brown (C9)**, perf 13.8 | 15.00 | 9.00 | 13.00 | 9.00 | 25.00 |
| iii | perf 14.1 | 75.00 | 45.00 | 50.00 | 30.00 | 125.00 |
| a | vertical pair, one without overprint | 12,000.00 | 8,000.00 | | | |
| b | overprint reading up | 8,500.00 | 5,000.00 | | | |
| i | pair, one unwatermarked | 60.00 | 30.00 | 50.00 | 25.00 | |
| ii | overprint badly shifted | 100.00 | 60.00 | | | |

Qty: 70,000 (all sold out the first day they were on sale)

"L. & S." stands for "Land and Sea". E.R.D. is February 9, 1933.

211ii

## SIR HUMPHREY GILBERT ISSUE

212
Sir Humphrey Gilbert

213
Compton Castle

214
Gilbert Coat-of-Arms

215
Eton College

216
Token from Queen Elizabeth I

217
Gilbert Receiving Royal Patents

218
Fleet Leaving Plymouth

219
Fleet Arriving St. John's

220
Annexation of Newfoundland

221
England's Coat-of-Arms

222
Gilbert on the *Squirrel*

223
Map of Newfoundland, 1626

224
Queen Elizabeth I

225
Gilbert Statue at Truro

**1933, Aug 3** **Engraved, Watermarked**
**Perf 13.5 (comb), 14 (line)**

| NH +100% | | ★VF | ★F | ⊙VF | ⊙F | ✉ |
|---|---|---|---|---|---|---|
| **212** | **1¢ grey black** | 2.00 | 1.00 | 1.00 | .75 | 1.00 |
| a | imperf. pair (with and w/o gum) | 60.00 | 40.00 | — | — | — |
| i | reverse offset | 160.00 | 80.00 | — | — | — |
| ii | perforated SPECIMEN | 100.00 | 60.00 | | | |
| **213** | **2¢ green** | 2.00 | 1.00 | 1.00 | .75 | 1.00 |
| a | imperf. pair | 60.00 | 40.00 | — | — | — |
| b | double impression | 800.00 | 500.00 | — | — | — |
| iii | reverse offset | 200.00 | 100.00 | — | — | — |
| iv | perforated SPECIMEN | 100.00 | 60.00 | | | |

213b

| NH +100% | ★VF | ★F | ⊙VF | ⊙F | ✉ |
|---|---|---|---|---|---|
| **214 3¢ yellow brown** | 4.00 | 2.00 | 1.00 | .50 | 4.00 |
| a imperf. pair | 500.00 | 300.00 | — | — | — |
| i bisect used as 2¢ on cover | | | | | 50.00 |
| ii reverse offset | 300.00 | 150.00 | — | — | — |
| iii imperf. right margin | 250.00 | 150.00 | — | — | — |
| **215 4¢ carmine** | 3.00 | 1.50 | 1.00 | .50 | 4.00 |
| a imperf. pair (with or without gum) | 65.00 | 45.00 | — | — | — |
| **216 5¢ dull violet** | 5.00 | 2.50 | 1.50 | 1.25 | 3.00 |
| a imperf. pair | 500.00 | 300.00 | — | — | — |
| **217 7¢ blue** | 25.00 | 12.50 | 18.00 | 14.00 | 30.00 |
| b perf. 14 | 20.00 | 10.00 | 18.00 | 14.00 | 30.00 |
| **218 8¢ orange red** | 12.00 | 6.00 | 10.00 | 8.00 | 30.00 |
| a brownish red, error (200 thought to exist) | 750.00 | 375.00 | — | — | — |
| ii half used as 4¢ on cover | | | | | — |
| **219 9¢ ultramarine** | 14.00 | 7.00 | 11.00 | 9.00 | 30.00 |
| a imperf. pair | 700.00 | 350.00 | — | — | — |
| b perf. 14 | 120.00 | 60.00 | 100.00 | 70.00 | 150.00 |
| **220 10¢ red brown** | 12.00 | 6.00 | 9.00 | 7.00 | 20.00 |
| a imperf. pair | 750.00 | 400.00 | — | — | — |
| b perf. 14 | 160.00 | 80.00 | 150.00 | 100.00 | 200.00 |
| **221 14¢ black** | 25.00 | 12.50 | 20.00 | 17.50 | 35.00 |
| a imperf. pair | 600.00 | 400.00 | — | — | — |
| b perf. 14 | 30.00 | 15.00 | 25.00 | 22.50 | 37.50 |
| **222 15¢ claret** | 25.00 | 12.50 | 20.00 | 17.00 | 35.00 |
| a imperf. pair | 350.00 | 200.00 | — | — | — |
| i inverted watermark | 50.00 | 35.00 | | | |
| **223 20¢ deep green** | 20.00 | 10.00 | 14.00 | 10.00 | 25.00 |
| b perf. 14 | 25.00 | 12.50 | 18.00 | 14.00 | 30.00 |
| ii inverted watermark | 50.00 | 35.00 | | | |
| **224 24¢ violet brown** | 36.00 | 18.00 | 30.00 | 24.00 | 50.00 |
| a imperf. pair | 300.00 | 200.00 | — | — | — |
| b perf. 14 | 38.00 | 19.00 | 33.00 | 26.00 | 50.00 |
| ii inverted watermark | 65.00 | 40.00 | | | |
| **225 32¢ grey** | 36.00 | 18.00 | 30.00 | 24.00 | 50.00 |
| a perf. 14 | 38.00 | 19.00 | 33.00 | 26.00 | 50.00 |
| ii inverted watermark | 65.00 | 40.00 | | | |
| **Nos. 212–225** (14) Set | 221.00 | 110.50 | 167.50 | 134.25 | — |

Inverted watermarks exist on all values.

Issued to commemorate the 350th anniversary of the annexation of Newfoundland by England, 15 August 1583, by authority of Letters Patent issued by Queen Elizabeth I to Sir Humphrey Gilbert.

## SILVER JUBILEE ISSUE

226

227

228

229

Windsor Castle & King George V

**1935, May 6 — Engraved — Perf 11x12**
**Watermarked "Multiple Crown & Script CA"**

| NH +100% | ★VF | ★F | ⊙VF | ⊙F | ✉ |
|---|---|---|---|---|---|
| **226 4¢ bright rose** | 3.50 | 1.50 | 1.00 | .75 | 2.00 |
| **227 5¢ violet** | 3.50 | 1.50 | 1.35 | 1.00 | 2.00 |
| **228 7¢ dark blue** | 6.00 | 3.00 | 5.00 | 3.00 | 10.00 |
| **229 24¢ olive green** | 12.00 | 6.00 | 10.00 | 6.00 | 12.50 |
| a dark olive | 20.00 | 10.00 | 15.00 | 10.00 | 17.50 |
| **Nos. 226–229** (4) Set | 25.00 | 12.00 | 17.35 | 10.75 | |

The design features a portrait of King George V alongside Windsor Castle. This set is in honour of the 25th anniversary of the accession of King George V. Perforated "Specimen" sets at $450.00

## CORONATION "OMNIBUS" ISSUE

230

231

232

Queen Elizabeth & King George VI

**1937, May 12 — Engraved — Perf 11x11½**

| NH +100% | ★VF | ★F | ⊙VF | ⊙F | ✉ |
|---|---|---|---|---|---|
| **230 2¢ deep green** | 2.50 | 1.00 | 1.00 | .60 | 2.00 |
| **231 4¢ carmine rose** | 2.50 | 1.00 | 1.00 | .40 | 2.00 |
| **232 5¢ dark violet** | 5.00 | 2.00 | 2.00 | 1.00 | 4.00 |

Perforated "Specimen" sets at $350.00

Issued on the occasion of the Coronation of King George VI and Queen Elizabeth.

## LONG CORONATION ISSUE

233
Codfish

234
Newfoundland map

235
Caribou

236
Corner Brook Paper Mill

237
Salmon

238
Newfoundland Dog

239
Harp Seal Pup

240
Cape Race

241
Loading Ore, Bell Island

242
Sealing Fleet

243
Fishing Fleet

233iii

**1937, May 12 Engraved, Watermarked arms**
**Comb perf. 13.5, line perf. 13½ or 14**

Perforations: Two line perforations, perf. 13.7 and perf. 14.1 and one comb perforation, perf. 13.3 x 13.2 exist on all values.

| NH +100% | | ★VF | ★F | ⊙VF | ⊙F | ✉ |
|---|---|---|---|---|---|---|
| **233** | **1¢ grey black** | 1.00 | .50 | .50 | .25 | 1.25 |
| **a** | comb perf. 13.3 x 13.3 | 25.00 | 15.00 | 30.00 | 25.00 | 50.00 |
| **i** | "Fish Hook" variety (pos. 23) | 25.00 | 15.00 | 15.00 | 12.50 | 20.00 |
| **ii** | pair, 1 with watermark | 25.00 | 15.00 | — | — | — |
| **iii** | retouch of entire right inner frameline (pos. 11) | 50.00 | 30.00 | 30.00 | 20.00 | |

UL corner block of 9 with 233i on LR stamp and 233iii on centre left stamp: Mint values $100 (VF) and $60 (F).

A compound perf 13.7x14.1 has been reported.

**Die I**
No lines on bridge of nose

**Die II**
Lines on bridge of nose

| | | ★VF | ★F | ⊙VF | ⊙F | ✉ |
|---|---|---|---|---|---|---|
| **234** | **3¢ orange brown**, Die I, perf. 14 | 4.00 | 2.00 | 1.50 | 1.00 | 2.00 |
| **a** | Die II, line perf. 14 | 3.00 | 1.50 | 1.50 | 1.00 | 2.00 |
| **b** | vert. pair, imperf. between, Die I | 1,000.00 | 600.00 | — | — | — |
| **c** | as "b", Die II | 1,000.00 | 600.00 | — | — | — |
| **d** | horiz. pair, imperf. between, Die I | 800.00 | 500.00 | — | — | — |
| **e** | as "d", Die II | 800.00 | 500.00 | — | — | — |
| **f** | imperf. pair, Die II* | 300.00 | 200.00 | — | — | — |
| **g** | comb perf. 13.3 x 13.2, Die I | 2.50 | 1.50 | 1.25 | .75 | 1.25 |
| **h** | as "g", Die II | 3.00 | 2.00 | 1.50 | 1.00 | 2.00 |
| **i** | horiz. pair, imperf. vert., Die I (NH) | 1,800.00 | | | | |
| **j** | imperf. pair, Die I | 1,000.00 | 500.00 | — | — | — |
| **ii** | "Cigar Stub" variety, pos. 9 | 30.00 | 20.00 | 30.00 | 20.00 | 40.00 |
| **iii** | pair, 1 with watermark, Die I | 75.00 | 45.00 | — | — | — |
| **iv** | as "iii", Die II | 135.00 | 100.00 | — | — | — |
| **v** | Die I, major re-entry (pos. 35) | | | | | |
| **vi** | Die I, major re-entry (pos. 84) | | | | | |
| **vii** | Die I, major re-entry (pos. 98) | | | | | |

* 234f exists with and without gum.

**234ii**

**234v**
Entire design, especially at right side, including POSTAGE, lower right 3, LABRADOR and Corner (map)

**234vi**
In 3 THREE CENTS 3

**234vii**
Both 3's

Newfoundland

| NH +100% | | ★VF | ★F | ⊙VF | ⊙F | ✉ |
|---|---|---|---|---|---|---|
| **235** | **7¢ bright ultramarine**, line perf. 14 | 4.00 | 2.00 | 3.50 | 1.75 | 10.00 |
| a | comb perf. 13.3 x 13.2 | 650.00 | 350.00 | 600.00 | 400.00 | 800.00 |
| i | major re-entry (pos. 38) | 45.00 | 25.00 | 45.00 | 25.00 | 50.00 |
| ii | pair, 1 with watermark | 200.00 | 100.00 | | | |
| iii | major re-entry (pos. 23) | 45.00 | 25.00 | 45.00 | 25.00 | 50.00 |
| iv | re-entry (pos. 59) | 45.00 | 25.00 | 45.00 | 25.00 | 50.00 |
| v | re-entry (pos. 21) | 45.00 | 25.00 | 45.00 | 25.00 | 50.00 |

Numerous other frameline re-entries exist.

**235i**
Medallion, D, tree trunk next to oval and lower right 7

**235iii**
Medallion and inner frameline in upper right corner (often mistaken for pos. 38)

**235iv**
Complete inner frameline and partial outer frameline on the right, D, trunk of tree, and lower right 7

**235v**
Middle of right frameline

| | | ★VF | ★F | ⊙VF | ⊙F | ✉ |
|---|---|---|---|---|---|---|
| **236** | **8¢ scarlet** | 4.00 | 2.00 | 3.50 | 1.75 | 10.00 |
| i | pair, 1 with watermark | 150.00 | 100.00 | | | |
| a | imperf. pair | 600.00 | 300.00 | — | — | — |
| b | vert. pair, imperf. between | 2,500.00 | 1,500.00 | — | — | — |
| c | horiz. pair, imperf. vertically | 2,500.00 | 1,500.00 | — | — | — |
| d | comb perf. 13.3 x 13.2 | 6.00 | 3.00 | 5.00 | 3.50 | 12.00 |
| di | as d, pair, 1 with watermark | 200.00 | 125.00 | | | |
| **237** | **10¢ deep olive** | 6.00 | 3.00 | 6.00 | 3.50 | 10.00 |
| a | double impression | 350.00 | | | | |
| b | comb perf. 13.3 x 13.2 | 6.00 | 3.00 | 7.50 | 5.00 | 12.00 |
| i | pair, 1 with watermark | 200.00 | 120.00 | — | — | — |
| **238** | **14¢ black** | 6.00 | 3.00 | 5.00 | 3.00 | 10.00 |
| a | imperf. pair, w/o gum | 500.00 | 250.00 | — | — | — |
| b | comb perf. 13.3 x 13.2* | *20,000.00* | | *15,000.00* | | |
| i | major re-entry (pos. 40) | 40.00 | 25.00 | 45.00 | 25.00 | |
| iii | pair, 1 with watermark | 100.00 | 70.00 | — | — | — |
| v | "Male Dog" variety | 50.00 | 35.00 | 50.00 | 35.00 | |
| vi | major re-entry (pos. 20) | 40.00 | 25.00 | 45.00 | 25.00 | |
| vii | major re-entry (pos. 30) | 40.00 | 25.00 | 45.00 | 25.00 | |
| viii | major re-entry (pos. 50) | 40.00 | 25.00 | 45.00 | 25.00 | |
| ix | major re-entry (pos. 10) | 40.00 | 25.00 | 45.00 | 25.00 | |

* Certificate of authenticity recommended.

**238i**
NEWFOUNDLAND DOG and WF

**238viii**
WF, DLAND (of NEWFOUNDLAND DOG) and 12TH MAY

**238ix**
12TH MAY

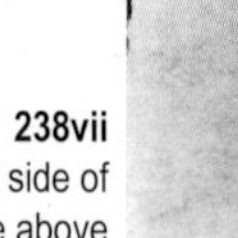

**238vi**
NDLAN, 12TH MAY 1937, left side of medallion and inner horizontal line above N CENTS

**238vii**
NDLAN, 12TH MAY 1937, left side of medallion and inner horizontal line above N CENTS (similar to pos. 20), and heavy frameline below CENTS

| NH +100% | | ★VF | ★F | ⊙VF | ⊙F | ✉ |
|---|---|---|---|---|---|---|
| **239** | **15¢ claret** | 6.00 | 3.00 | 5.00 | 3.00 | 10.00 |
| a | vert. pair, imperf. between | 2,500.00 | 1,500.00 | — | — | — |
| b | comb perf. 13.3 x 13.2 | 16.00 | 8.00 | 15.00 | 10.00 | 25.00 |
| i | pair, 1 with watermark | 50.00 | 35.00 | — | — | — |
| iii | as "b", pair, 1 with watermark | 120.00 | 80.00 | — | — | — |
| **240** | **20¢ green** | 6.00 | 3.00 | 4.00 | 2.25 | 10.00 |
| a | vert. pair, imperf. between | 4,000.00 | 2,500.00 | — | — | — |
| b | comb perf. 13.3 x 13.2 | 6.00 | 3.00 | 5.00 | 3.00 | 10.00 |
| ii | "Extra Smokestack" variety (pos. 55) | 75.00 | 50.00 | 60.00 | 40.00 | 60.00 |
| iii | pair, 1 with watermark | 200.00 | 100.00 | — | — | — |
| **241** | **24¢ light blue** | 6.00 | 3.00 | 5.00 | 3.50 | 10.00 |
| a | vert. pair, imperf. between | 6,000.00 | 4,000.00 | — | — | — |
| b | comb perf. 13.3 x 13.2 | 16.00 | 8.00 | 15.00 | 10.00 | 20.00 |
| i | pair, 1 with watermark | 200.00 | 125.00 | — | — | — |
| ii | re-entry of both inner and outer framelines on the right (pos. 61) | | | | | |
| iii | imperf. pair | 700.00 | | | | |

Numerous minor re-entries exist of framelines.

| | | ★VF | ★F | ⊙VF | ⊙F | ✉ |
|---|---|---|---|---|---|---|
| **242** | **25¢ slate** | 6.00 | 3.00 | 5.00 | 3.25 | 10.00 |
| a | imperf. pair (w/o gum) | 400.00 | 200.00 | — | — | — |
| b | comb perf. 13.3 x 13.2 | 16.00 | 8.00 | 15.00 | 10.00 | 20.00 |
| i | re-entry (pos. 97) | | | | | |
| ii | re-entry (pos. 40?) | | | | | |

**242ii**
Left side, including N and 2 of lower left 25 (similar to pos. 97 but not quite as strong)

**242i**
Left side, including upper left frameline, N, 2 of 25, and lower left frameline

**240ii**

| | | ★VF | ★F | ⊙VF | ⊙F | ✉ |
|---|---|---|---|---|---|---|
| **243** | **48¢ slate purple** | 10.00 | 5.00 | 6.00 | 3.75 | 15.00 |
| a | vert. pair, imperf. between | 5,000.00 | 3,500.00 | — | — | — |
| b | imperf. pair (with or w/o gum) | 400.00 | 200.00 | — | — | — |
| c | comb perf. 13.3 x 13.2 | 30.00 | 15.00 | 25.00 | 15.00 | 30.00 |
| i | major re-entry (pos. 60) | | | | | |
| ii | re-entry (pos. 65) | | | | | |

**243i**
Right side, with doubling of upper right edge of the medallion (portrait oval), extensions of horizontal lines into right inner frame, doubling of right frameline, and smudged inner frame on the left

**243ii**
Right frameline

| | | ★VF | ★F | ⊙VF | ⊙F |
|---|---|---|---|---|---|
| **Nos. 233–243** | (11) Set | 59.00 | 29.50 | 45.00 | 27.00 |

Issued as a complimentary set to the "Omnibus" Corontation issue.

Newfoundland

No. 244 is not assigned.

## ROYAL FAMILY ISSUE

245
King George VI

246
Queen Elizabeth

247
Princess Elizabeth

248
Queen Mary

**1938, May 12** — **Engraved, Watermarked Arms** — **Perf 13½**

| | | NH% | ★VF | ★F | ⊙VF | ⊙F | ✉ |
|---|---|---|---|---|---|---|---|
| **245** | **2¢ green** | 50 | 2.50 | 1.50 | .25 | .20 | 2.00 |
| | inscription blocks, plate 2, UR $350.00 | | | | | | |
| a | imperf. pair (with or without gum) | 50 | 200.00 | 100.00 | — | — | — |
| ii | pair, one with watermark | 50 | 200.00 | 125.00 | | | |
| **246** | **3¢ dark carmine** | 50 | 2.50 | 1.50 | .30 | .20 | 2.00 |
| | inscription blocks: plate 2, UR $350.00 | | | | | | |
| a | imperf. pair (with or without gum) | 50 | 200.00 | 100.00 | — | — | — |
| b | perf. 14, line perf. | 50 | 1,000.00 | 600.00 | 750.00 | 500.00 | 1,000 |
| iii | pair, one with watermark | 50 | 300.00 | 200.00 | | | |
| **247** | **4¢ light blue** | 50 | 3.25 | 2.00 | .25 | .20 | 2.00 |
| | inscription blocks: plate 2, UL $350.00 | | | | | | |
| a | imperf. pair (with or without gum) | 50 | 200.00 | 100.00 | — | — | — |
| ii | pair, one with watermark | 50 | 150.00 | 100.00 | | | |
| iii | inverted watermark | 50 | 100.00 | 60.00 | | | |
| **248** | **7¢ dark ultramarine** | 50 | 2.25 | 1.50 | 1.75 | 1.40 | 5.00 |
| a | imperf. pair (with or without gum) | 50 | 200.00 | 100.00 | — | — | — |
| b | vert. pair, imperf. between | 50 | 1,500.00 | | | | |
| ii | pair, one with watermark | 50 | 200.00 | 125.00 | | | |
| **Nos. 245–248** | (4) Set | 50 | 10.50 | 6.50 | 2.35 | 2.00 | |

First day covers: #246, 247, 248 – $5.00 each.

## ROYAL VISIT

249
Queen Elizabeth & King George VI

**1939, Jun 17** — **Engraved, Unwatermarked**

NH +50%

| | | ★VF | ★F | ⊙VF | ⊙F | ✉ |
|---|---|---|---|---|---|---|
| **249** | **5¢ violet blue** | 2.00 | 1.00 | 1.75 | 1.00 | 2.00 |
| | inscription blocks: plate 4 bottom $12.50 | | | | | |

## SURCHARGES on 249

250
Queen Elizabeth & King George VI

251
Queen Elizabeth & King George VI

**1939, Nov 20** — **Engraved, Unwatermarked**

NH +50%

| | | ★VF | ★F | ⊙VF | ⊙F | ✉ |
|---|---|---|---|---|---|---|
| **250** | **2¢ on 5¢ violet blue (249), surcharge in brown** | 2.00 | 1.25 | 1.50 | 1.25 | 3.00 |
| i | missing serif on '2' variety (pos. 28) | 24.00 | 12.00 | 20.00 | 10.00 | |
| | inscription blocks $15.00 each | | | | | |
| **251** | **4¢ on 5¢ violet blue (249), surcharge in red** | 1.50 | 1.00 | 1.50 | 1.00 | 3.00 |
| i | "CENTL" variety (pos. 43) | 30.00 | 15.00 | 25.00 | 12.00 | 40.00 |
| | inscription blocks $15.00 each | | | | | |

There are many varieties of broken letters and figures in the settings of these surcharges.

## GRENFELL ISSUE

252
Grenfell & "Strathcona II"

**1941, Dec 1** — **Engraved** — **Perf 12**

NH +50%

| | | ★VF | ★F | ⊙VF | ⊙F | ✉ |
|---|---|---|---|---|---|---|
| **252** | **5¢ dull blue** | .60 | .40 | .40 | .35 | 1.50 |
| i | imperf. between stamp and sheet margin at left | 350.00 | 250.00 | | | |
| | inscription blocks, $3.00 each | | | | | |

Issued to commemorate the 50th anniversary of the founding of the Grenfell Mission by Sir Wilfred Grenfell.

**First Day Covers**

| | | |
|---|---|---|
| 253 | Jul 25/42 | $10.00 |
| 254 | Nov 17/41 | $10.00 |
| 256 | Oct 1/41 | $10.00 |
| 257 | Jun 5/42 | $10.00 |
| 258 | Feb 8/43 | $10.00 |
| 259 | May 12/42 | $10.00 |
| 260 | Feb 8/43 | $10.00 |
| 262 | Feb 8/43 | $10.00 |

## DEFINITIVE RE-ISSUES
## WATERLOW PRINTINGS

See 183–210 for Perkins Bacon Printings

253
Codfish

254
King George VI

255
Queen Elizabeth

256
Princess Elizabeth

257
Caribou

258
Queen Mary

259
Corner Brook Paper Mill

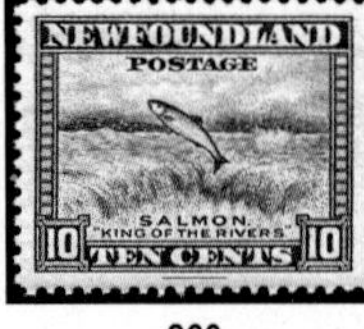

260
Salmon Leaping Falls

261
Newfoundland Dog

262
Harp Seal Pup

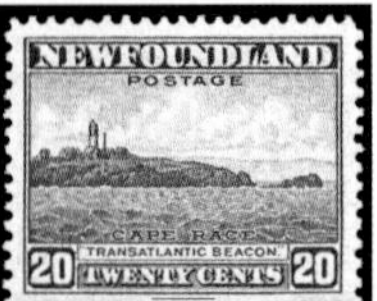

263
Cape Race

264
Loading Ore, Bell Island

265
Sealing Fleet

266
Fishing Fleet

**1941–1944** **Engraved, Watermarked Arms** **Perf 12½**

See also 183–210 for Perkins Bacon printings

The Waterlow printings (21.0 mm) are slightly larger than the Perkins printings (20.4 mm)

| | | NH% | ★VF | ★F | ⊙VF | ⊙F | ✉ |
|---|---|---|---|---|---|---|---|
| **253** | **1¢ dark grey** | 50 | .50 | .25 | .25 | .20 | |
| a | imperf. pair | 50 | 200.00 | 140.00 | — | — | |
| i | imperf. pair with security punch | 50 | 150.00 | 100.00 | | | |
| **254** | **2¢ deep green** | 50 | .50 | .30 | .25 | .20 | |
| i | inverted watermark | 50 | 20.00 | 10.00 | | | |
| ii | offset image on gum side | 50 | 250.00 | 200.00 | — | — | |
| iii | pair, one without watermark | 50 | 200.00 | 125.00 | | | |
| iv | imperf. pair with security punch | 50 | 150.00 | 100.00 | | | |
| **255** | **3¢ rose carmine** | 50 | .75 | .40 | .25 | .20 | |
| i | "broken A" in 'LAND' variety (pos. 49) | 50 | 60.00 | 30.00 | 60.00 | 30.00 | |
| ii | inverted watermark | 50 | 20.00 | 10.00 | | | |
| iii | pair, one without watermark | 50 | 100.00 | 70.00 | — | — | |
| iv | offset image on gum side (Qty: 200) | 50 | 175.00 | 125.00 | — | — | |
| v | background without cross-hatching | 50 | 200.00 | 120.00 | | | |
| vi | imperf. pair with security punch | 50 | 150.00 | 100.00 | | | |
| a | imperf. pair | 50 | 400.00 | 200.00 | | | |
| **256** | **4¢ blue** | 50 | 1.00 | .70 | .40 | .20 | |
| i | pair, one without watermark | 50 | 200.00 | 125.00 | — | — | |
| ii | imperf. pair with security punch | 50 | 150.00 | 100.00 | | | |
| iii | imperf. top margin | 50 | 900.00 | 750.00 | | | |
| **257** | **5¢ violet**, Die I | 50 | 1.25 | .70 | .25 | .20 | |
| a | imperf. pair | 50 | 300.00 | 150.00 | — | — | |
| b | horiz. pair, imperf. vert. | 50 | 600.00 | 400.00 | — | — | |
| c | double impression | 50 | 500.00 | 350.00 | | | |
| iv | gutter strip of 4, imperf. vert. | 50 | — | 1,000.00 | — | — | |
| v | pair, one without watermark | 50 | 175.00 | 120.00 | — | — | |
| vi | offset image on gum side | 50 | – | 250.00 | — | — | |
| vii | imperf. pair with security punch | 50 | 150.00 | 100.00 | | | |
| viii | major re-entry overall (Pl 42078, pos. 50) | | | | | | |
| ix | perf 13.5 | 50 | 150.00 | 75.00 | 10.00 | 5.00 | |

Numerous re-entries exist, some strong.

257viii

| | | NH% | ★VF | ★F | ⊙VF | ⊙F | ✉ |
|---|---|---|---|---|---|---|---|
| **258** | **7¢ violet blue**, *1942* | 50 | 1.75 | 1.10 | 1.25 | 1.10 | |
| i | pair, one without watermark | 50 | 300.00 | 200.00 | — | — | |
| ii | imperf. pair with security punch | 50 | 150.00 | 100.00 | | | |
| **259** | **8¢ red** | 50 | 2.00 | 1.25 | 1.00 | .70 | |
| i | pair, one without watermark | 50 | 200.00 | 125.00 | — | — | |
| ii | imperf. pair with security punch | 50 | 150.00 | 100.00 | | | |
| **260** | **10¢ brownish black** | 50 | 2.00 | 1.25 | 1.00 | .60 | |
| i | reverse offset on gum | 50 | 250.00 | 150.00 | — | — | |
| ii | imperf. pair with security punch | 50 | 150.00 | 100.00 | | | |
| **261** | **14¢ black** | 50 | 3.00 | 1.75 | 3.00 | 1.35 | |
| a | imperf. pair | 50 | 300.00 | 200.00 | — | — | |
| c | vert. pair, imperf. horiz. | 50 | 300.00 | 200.00 | — | — | |
| i | imperf. pair with security punch | 50 | 150.00 | 100.00 | | | |

| | | NH% | ★VF | ★F | ⊙VF | ⊙F | ✉ |
|---|---|---|---|---|---|---|---|
| **262** | **15¢ pale rose violet** | 50 | 3.00 | 1.75 | 2.00 | 1.50 | |
| i | offset image on gum side | 50 | 300.00 | 180.00 | — | — | |
| ii | imperf. pair with security punch | 50 | 150.00 | 100.00 | | | |
| **263** | **20¢ green** | 50 | 3.00 | 1.75 | 1.50 | 1.25 | |
| i | reverse offset | 50 | 300.00 | 180.00 | | | |
| ii | imperf. pair with security punch | 50 | 150.00 | 100.00 | | | |
| **264** | **24¢ deep blue** | 50 | 3.50 | 2.00 | 3.00 | 1.75 | |
| i | inverted watermark | 50 | 30.00 | 15.00 | | | |
| ii | offset image on gum side | 50 | 300.00 | 180.00 | — | — | |
| iii | imperf. pair with security punch | 50 | 150.00 | 100.00 | | | |
| **265** | **25¢ slate** | 50 | 3.50 | 2.00 | 3.00 | 1.75 | |
| i | imperf. pair with security punch | 50 | 150.00 | 100.00 | | | |
| **266** | **48¢ red brown**, *1944* | 50 | 4.75 | 3.00 | 2.50 | 2.00 | |
| i | offset image on gum side | 50 | 250.00 | 150.00 | — | — | |
| ii | imperf. pair with security punch | 50 | 150.00 | 100.00 | | | |
| **Nos. 253–266** | (14) Set | 50 | 30.00 | 17.90 | 19.00 | 12.50 | |

**1941–1944 DEFINITIVE RE-ISSUES INSCRIPTION BLOCKS**
**VF +50%, NH +50%**

| No. | Plate | Value | No. | Plate | Value |
|---|---|---|---|---|---|
| **253** | (41711) Centre Left | 50.00 | **260** | (41867) Centre Left | 40.00 |
| | (42430) each | 4.00 | | (43702) each | 8.00 |
| | (42430) Top Centre | 35.00 | | (43702) Centre Left | 35.00 |
| | (43965) each | 3.00 | | (43838) each | 8.00 |
| | | | | (43838) Centre Left | 35.00 |
| **254** | (43078) each | 4.00 | | | |
| | (43078) Top Centre | 40.00 | **261** | (41789) each | 20.00 |
| | (43968) each | 3.00 | | (41789) Centre | 45.00 |
| **255** | (41418) Centre Left | 55.00 | **262** | (41794) each | 20.00 |
| | (43066) each | 4.00 | | (41794) Centre Left | 45.00 |
| | (43066) Top Centre | 25.00 | | | |
| | (43967) each | 4.50 | **263** | (41796) each | 20.00 |
| | | | | (41796) Centre Left | 45.00 |
| **256** | (41420) Centre Left | 500.00 | | | |
| | others, blank corners | 6.00 | **264** | (41795) each | 20.00 |
| | | | | (41795) Centre Left | 45.00 |
| **257** | (43966) each | 6.00 | | | |
| **257iv** | | 2,250.00 | **265** | (41791) each | 20.00 |
| | | | | (41791) Centre Left | 45.00 |
| **259** | (41601) each | 8.00 | | | |
| | | | **266** | (41793) each | 25.00 |
| | | | | (41793) Centre Left | 60.00 |

## UNIVERSITY ISSUE

**267**
Memorial University College

**268**

**1943, Jan 1 — Engraved, Unwatermarked — Perf 12**

| NH +50% | | ★VF | ★F | ⊙VF | ⊙F | ✉ |
|---|---|---|---|---|---|---|
| **267** | **30¢ carmine** | 2.00 | 1.50 | 1.50 | 1.25 | 10.00 |
| | inscription blocks: plate 1 $10.00 each | | | | | |
| i | gutter pair | 25.00 | 15.00 | — | — | — |

## SURCHARGED

**1946, Mar 21 — Engraved, Unwatermarked**

| NH +50% | | ★VF | ★F | ⊙VF | ⊙F | ✉ |
|---|---|---|---|---|---|---|
| **268** | **2¢ on 30¢ carmine (267), surcharge in black** | .40 | .35 | .40 | .35 | 2.50 |
| | inscription blocks: plate 1 $4.00 each | | | | | |
| i | spacing variety in pair | 2.50 | 1.50 | | | |
| ii | surcharge doubled | 350.00 | 175.00 | | | |

## BIRTHDAY ISSUE

**269**
Princess Elizabeth

**1947, Apr 21 — Engraved, Watermarked Arms — Perf 12½**

| NH +50% | | ★VF | ★F | ⊙VF | ⊙F | ✉ |
|---|---|---|---|---|---|---|
| **269** | **4¢ light blue** | .40 | .35 | .25 | .20 | 1.00 |
| | inscription blocks, plate (43359): $3.00 each | | | | | |
| a | imperf. pair | 300.00 | 200.00 | | | |
| b | horiz. pair, imperf. vert. | 400.00 | 300.00 | | | |
| iii | as "b", gutter strip of 4 (all are off centre) | — | 1,000.00 | — | — | — |
| | inscription blocks $2,250 each | | | | | |
| iv | offset image on gum side | - | 350.00 | — | — | |
| v | imperf. pair with security punch | 150.00 | 100.00 | | | |

FDC: $10.00.

Issued on the occasion of the 21st birthday of Princess Elizabeth, heir presumptive to the throne.

## CABOT ISSUE

**270**
Cabot on the Matthew

**1947, Jun 24 — Engraved**

| NH +50% | | ★VF | ★F | ⊙VF | ⊙F | ✉ |
|---|---|---|---|---|---|---|
| **270** | **5¢ rose violet** | .40 | .35 | .30 | .25 | 1.50 |
| | inscription blocks, plate (43476) $3.50 each | | | | | |
| a | horiz. pair, imperf. between | 1,500.00 | 1,000.00 | | | |
| b | imperf. pair | 300.00 | 200.00 | | | |
| ii | reverse offset | 400.00 | 240.00 | | | |
| iii | imperf. pair with security punch | 150.00 | 100.00 | | | |
| iv | Aniline-type ink (blotchy print)* | 150.00 | 100.00 | | | |

* 100 copies reported.

Issued to commemorate the 450th anniversary of John Cabot's discovery of Newfoundland.

**Newfoundland joined Canada on April 1, 1949 and no further stamps were issued. The stamps remain valid for mail posted anywhere in Canada.**

Newfoundland

## NEWFOUNDLAND PLATE PROOFS

All Newfoundland proofs are on India paper unless noted otherwise. For items not on India paper, the approximate thickness is shown in parentheses.

| | | |
|---|---|---|
| **1P** | 1d black on thin card | 400.00 |
| **2P** | 2d black on thin card | 1,000.00 |
| **3P** | 3d black on thin card | 500.00 |
| **4P** | 4d black on thin card | 1,000.00 |
| **5P** | 5d black on thin card | 500.00 |
| **6P** | 6d black on thin card | 1,000.00 |
| **7P** | 6½d black on thin card | 1,000.00 |
| **8P** | 8d black on thin card | 1,000.00 |
| **9P** | 1/- black on thin card | 1,000.00 |
| **24P** | 2¢ green | 100.00 |
| **25P** | 5¢ dark brown | 100.00 |
| **i** | yellow brown | 90.00 |
| **ii** | olive brown | 90.00 |
| **iii** | brown, on card (.025") | 120.00 |
| **25TC** | claret brown | 100.00 |
| **i** | orange red | 150.00 |
| **ii** | dark bluish green | 200.00 |
| **iii** | blue green, on card (.012") | 200.00 |
| **iv** | black, on card (.012") | 200.00 |
| **27P** | 10¢ black | 75.00 |
| **i** | black, on card (.012") | 120.00 |
| **28P** | 12¢ red brown | 70.00 |
| **i** | red brown, on card (.012") | 100.00 |
| **28TC** | orange yellow | 90.00 |
| **30P** | 13¢ orange (shades) | 70.00 |
| **i** | yellow, on card (.012") | 100.00 |
| **30TC** | dark red violet | 120.00 |
| **31P** | 24¢ blue | 65.00 |
| **i** | blue, on card (.012") | 90.00 |

**Number 32 printed by National Bank Note Company**

Ribbon breaks oval at top. Vertical line shading between outer oval and ribbon along sides "N" and "F".

| | | |
|---|---|---|
| **32P** | 1¢ dull violet | 80.00 |
| **32TC** | dark red brown | 100.00 |
| **i** | carmine | 100.00 |
| **ii** | red | 100.00 |
| **iii** | purple red | 100.00 |
| **iv** | chestnut brown | 100.00 |
| **v** | yellow brown | 100.00 |
| **vi** | yellow orange | 100.00 |
| **vii** | blue green | 100.00 |
| **viii** | blue | 100.00 |
| **ix** | black | 150.00 |
| **x** | deep blue, thin transparent wove paper (gummed) | 250.00 |
| **xi** | orange red, thin wove paper, perf. 12 | 250.00 |
| **xii** | orange brown, paper as xi | 250.00 |
| **xiii** | blue green, paper as xi | 250.00 |
| **xiv** | deep blue, paper as xi | 250.00 |
| **xv** | dull dark violet, paper as xi | 250.00 |

**Number 32A printed by American Bank Note Company**

Solid shading between outer oval and ribbon along sides "N" and "F". Oval complete.

| | | |
|---|---|---|
| **32AP** | 1¢ violet brown (shades) | 100.00 |
| **i** | violet brown, on card (.015") | 80.00 |
| **32ATC** | dark red brown | 90.00 |
| **i** | sepia | 90.00 |
| **ii** | yellow brown (shades) | 90.00 |
| **iii** | orange | 90.00 |
| **iv** | blue green | 90.00 |
| **v** | dusky green (shades) | 90.00 |
| **vi** | dark violet | 90.00 |
| **vii** | orange yellow | 90.00 |
| **viii** | black | 125.00 |
| **ix** | light blue, on card (.015") | 150.00 |
| **x** | orange, on card (.015") | 150.00 |
| **33P** | 3¢ vermilion | 90.00 |
| **33TC** | dusky olive brown | 100.00 |
| **i** | green (shades) | 100.00 |
| **ii** | dusky blue green | 100.00 |
| **iii** | dark slate violet | 100.00 |
| **iv** | yellow brown | 100.00 |
| **v** | dark bluish grey (shades) | 100.00 |
| **vi** | brown | 100.00 |
| **vii** | green, on white wove paper (.003") | 100.00 |
| **35P** | 6¢ carmine rose | 90.00 |
| **i** | bright rose | 70.00 |
| **35TC** | deep orange | 100.00 |
| **i** | dusky olive brown | 100.00 |
| **ii** | green (shades) | 100.00 |
| **iii** | dark violet red | 100.00 |
| **iv** | brown (shades) | 100.00 |
| **v** | light red brown, on card (.015") | 100.00 |
| **47P** | 2¢ dull dusky green, on card (.015") | 450.00 |
| **i** | red orange, on yellowish wove paper (.003") | 400.00 |
| **49P** | 3¢ black (confirmation requested) | 400.00 |
| **56P** | ½¢ orange red, on wove paper (.003") | 500.00 |
| **56TC** | yellow brown, paper as 56P | 750.00 |
| **i** | red brown, paper as 56P | 750.00 |
| **ii** | dark brown, paper as 56P | 750.00 |
| **iii** | light green, paper as 56P | 750.00 |
| **iv** | dark green, paper as 56P | 750.00 |
| **v** | blue, paper as 56P | 750.00 |
| **58P** | ½¢ black, on wove paper (.003") | 500.00 |
| **58TC** | deep red, paper as 58P | 500.00 |
| **59P** | 10¢ black, on wove paper (.003") (confirmation requested) | 250.00 |
| **61P** | 1¢ deep green | 50.00 |
| **62P** | 2¢ carmine lake | 50.00 |
| **63P** | 3¢ ultramarine | 50.00 |
| **64P** | 4¢ olive green | 50.00 |
| **65P** | 5¢ violet | 50.00 |
| **66P** | 6¢ red brown | 50.00 |
| **67P** | 8¢ red orange | 50.00 |
| **68P** | 10¢ black brown | 50.00 |
| **69P** | 12¢ dark blue | 100.00 |
| **i** | 12¢ slate blue | 125.00 |
| **70P** | 15¢ scarlet | 50.00 |
| **71P** | 24¢ grey violet | 75.00 |
| **72P** | 30¢ slate | 50.00 |
| **73P** | 35¢ red | 50.00 |
| **74P** | 60¢ black | 50.00 |
| **61P–74P** | set of 14 | 775.00 |
| **78P** | ½¢ dark olive green | 75.00 |
| **79P** | 1¢ rose carmine | 75.00 |
| **81P** | 2¢ orange | 75.00 |
| **i** | brown orange | 75.00 |
| **83P** | 3¢ orange | 75.00 |
| **84P** | 4¢ violet | 75.00 |
| **i** | slate violet | 75.00 |
| **85P** | 5¢ blue | 75.00 |
| **86P** | 2¢ carmine | 100.00 |
| **i** | brown carmine | 200.00 |

Wove and card proofs are known on the Cabot (65–74) and Royal Family (79–83) issues.

Newfoundland

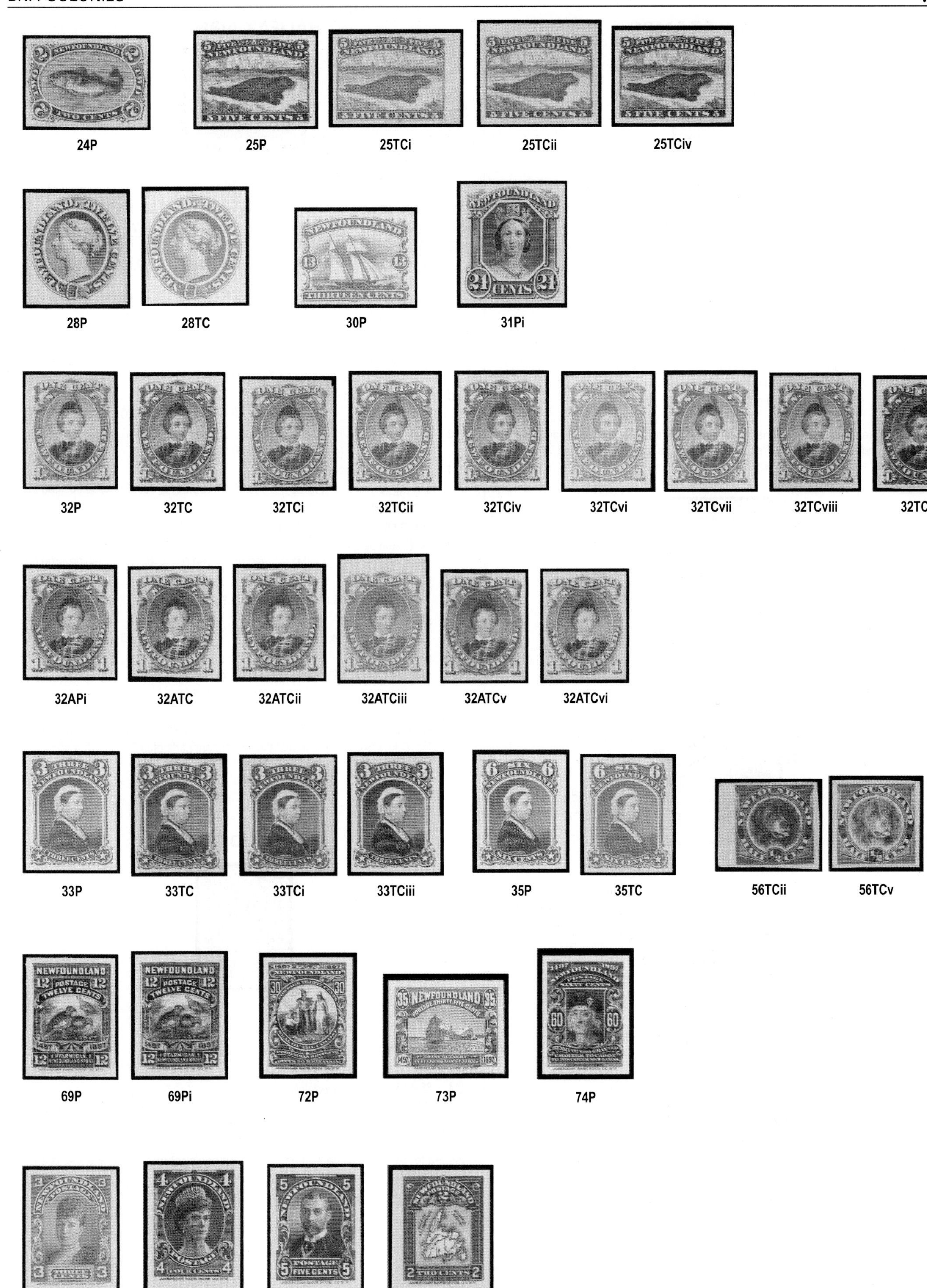

24P 25P 25TCi 25TCii 25TCiv

28P 28TC 30P 31Pi

32P 32TC 32TCi 32TCii 32TCiv 32TCvi 32TCvii 32TCviii 32TCix

32APi 32ATC 32ATCii 32ATCiii 32ATCv 32ATCvi

33P 33TC 33TCi 33TCiii 35P 35TC 56TCii 56TCv

69P 69Pi 72P 73P 74P

83P 84P 85P 86P

# AIR MAIL STAMPS

## HAWKER FLIGHT

C1
Caribou

| 1919, Apr 12 | Engraved, Unwatermarked | | | | | Perf 14 |
|---|---|---|---|---|---|---|
| NH +75% | Qty | ★VF | ★F | ⊙VF | ⊙F | ✉ |
| **C1 3¢ red brown (117)**, overprinted in black | (200) | 40,000 | 20,000 | 25,000 | 17,500 | 35,000 |
| a manuscript "Aerial Atlantic Mail JAR" † | | *88,000** | | *35,000* | | *50,000* |

* Unique unused. Sold in Baillie Sale May 5, 2006.
† similar manuscript also reported on 116 and 119.

Issued for use on Hawker's Trans-Atlantic flight. Fifteen copies were damaged and destroyed, 95 used on letters, 11 were given as presentations and 76 were sold in aid of the Marine Disasters Fund.

C1a

## ALCOCK AND BROWN FLIGHT

C2
Seals

| 1919, Jun 9 | Sheets of 25 | | | | | Perf 12 |
|---|---|---|---|---|---|---|
| NH +100% | Qty | ★VF | ★F | ⊙VF | ⊙F | ✉ |
| **C2 $1 on 15¢ scarlet (70)**, comma after "POST" | (6000) | 300.00 | 200.00 | 300.00 | 200.00 | 1,500 |
| a without comma after "POST" | (2800) | 330.00 | 220.00 | 380.00 | 240.00 | 1,500 |
| b as "a", without period after "1919", (pos.14) | (400) | 650.00 | 400.00 | 650.00 | 400.00 | 1,750 |
| c as "a", "A" of "AIR" under "a" of "Trans" (pos. 22) | (400) | 650.00 | 400.00 | 650.00 | 400.00 | 1,750 |
| ii small comma after "POST" | (400) | 650.00 | 400.00 | 650.00 | 400.00 | 1,750 |
| iii slanting surcharge | | 600.00 | 400.00 | 500.00 | 375.00 | |

Cover prices are for correct usage in period.

Issued for use on Alcock and Brown's and on other projected Trans-Atlantic flights.

## HALIFAX AIRMAIL

C3
Iceberg

| 1921, Nov 16 | Sheets of 25 | | | | | |
|---|---|---|---|---|---|---|
| NH +100% | Qty | ★VF | ★F | ⊙VF | ⊙F | ✉ |
| **C3 35¢ red (73)**, 2¾ mm between "AIR" and "MAIL" | (5560) | 200.00 | 140.00 | 250.00 | 150.00 | 250.00 |
| a inverted overprint, no period | (40 known) | 7,500.00 | 5,250.00 | — | — | — |
| b with period after "1921" | (3892) | 225.00 | 150.00 | 270.00 | 175.00 | 250.00 |
| c inverted overprint, with period | (28 known) | 10,000.00 | 7,500.00 | — | — | — |
| d "1" of "1921" below "f" of "Halifax" | (556) | 600.00 | 500.00 | 600.00 | 500.00 | 700.00 |
| e as "d", inverted overprint | (4 known) | 25,000.00 | 18,000.00 | — | — | — |
| f 1½ mm between "AIR" and "MAIL" | (1112) | 450.00 | 350.00 | 450.00 | 350.00 | 500.00 |
| g as "f", inverted overprint | (8 known) | 16,000.00 | 12,000.00 | — | — | — |
| h as "f", with period after "1921" | (2224) | 350.00 | 250.00 | 350.00 | 250.00 | 400.00 |
| i as "h", inverted overprint | (16 known) | 14,000.00 | 10,000.00 | — | — | — |
| j as "f", "1" of "1921" below "f" of "Halifax" | (556) | 600.00 | 500.00 | 600.00 | 500.00 | 700.00 |
| k as "j", inverted overprint | (4 known) | 25,000.00 | 18,000.00 | — | — | — |
| ix overprint badly slanted | | 800.00 | 400.00 | | | |

Blocks of 4, with 4 different types of overprint are possible (e.g., C3, C3b, C3f, C3h or C3a, C3c, C3g, C3i); value is sum of the component parts plus 25%.

## DE PINEDO FLIGHT

C4
King Henry VII

| 1927, May 18 | Engraved | | | | |
|---|---|---|---|---|---|
| NH +75% | ★VF | ★F | ⊙VF | ⊙F | ✉ |
| **C4 60¢ black (74)**, overprint in red | 70,000 | 40,000 | 25,000 | 15,000 | 30,000 |
| a short "7" in "1927" | 75,000 | 45,000 | 27,000 | 20,000 | 40,000 |

Issued for use on mail carried aboard De Pinedo's return flight to Europe. A total of 300 stamps were overprinted.

Newfoundland

## COLUMBIA FLIGHT

C5
Caribou

**1930, Sep 25** **Engraved** **Perf 14**

| NH +100% | | ★VF | ★F | ⊙VF | ⊙F | ✉ |
|---|---|---|---|---|---|---|
| **C5** | **50¢ on 36¢ olive green (126)**, surcharge in black | 12,000 | 6,000 | 12,000 | 6,000 | 16,000* |

A total of 300 stamps were overprinted; beware of forgeries.

* Cover price is for St. John's First Flight. For Harbour Grace add 20%.

## PICTORIAL ISSUE

See C9–C11 for watermarked issue

C6
Dog sled and airplane

C7
Airplane and packet ship

C8
Historic Transatlantic Flights

**1931, Jan 2** **Engraved, Unwatermarked**

| | | NH% | ★VF | ★F | ⊙VF | ⊙F | ✉ |
|---|---|---|---|---|---|---|---|
| **C6** | **15¢ brown** | 100 | 15.00 | 7.50 | 10.00 | 6.00 | 30.00 |
| a | horiz. pair, imperf. between | 50 | 1,500.00 | 1,000.00 | — | — | — |
| b | vert. pair, imperf. between | 50 | 1,800.00 | 1,200.00 | — | — | — |
| c | imperf. pair | 50 | 900.00 | 600.00 | — | — | — |
| i | block, horiz. perfs double | 50 | 750.00 | 500.00 | | | |
| **C7** | **50¢ green** | 100 | 45.00 | 22.50 | 35.00 | 20.00 | 80.00 |
| a | horiz. pair, imperf. between | 50 | 2,000.00 | 1,350.00 | 1,200.00 | 800.00 | |
| b | vert. pair, imperf. between | 50 | 2,500.00 | 1,650.00 | 1,200.00 | 800.00 | |
| c | imperf. pair | 50 | 1,200.00 | 800.00 | — | — | — |
| i | double perf. left margin | | 500.00 | 300.00 | — | — | — |
| **C8** | **$1 blue** | 100 | 90.00 | 45.00 | 80.00 | 55.00 | 150.00 |
| a | horiz. pair, imperf. between | 50 | 1,800.00 | 1,200.00 | — | — | — |
| b | vert. pair, imperf. between | 50 | 2,000.00 | 1,350.00 | — | — | — |
| c | imperf. pair | 50 | 1,000.00 | 800.00 | — | — | — |
| **Nos. C6–C8** | (3) Set | 100 | 150.00 | 75.00 | 125.00 | 81.00 | |

## PICTORIAL ISSUE

See C6–C8 for unwatermarked issue

C9
Dog sled and airplane

C10
Airplane and packet ship

C11
Historic Transatlantic Flights

**1931** **Engraved, Watermarked Coat-of-Arms**

| | | NH% | ★VF | ★F | ⊙VF | ⊙F | ✉ |
|---|---|---|---|---|---|---|---|
| **C9** | **15¢ brown** | 100 | 15.00 | 7.50 | 10.00 | 6.00 | 30.00 |
| a | horiz. pair, imperf. between | 50 | 1,500.00 | 1,000.00 | — | — | — |
| b | vert. pair, imperf. between | 50 | 1,800.00 | 1,400.00 | — | — | — |
| c | imperf. pair | 50 | 900.00 | 600.00 | — | — | — |
| i | block, cross watermark | 100 | 300.00 | 200.00 | — | — | — |
| ii | pair, 1 watermarked | 100 | 50.00 | 30.00 | 30.00 | 20.00 | — |
| iii | imperf. pair, 1 watermarked | 50 | 1,000.00 | 700.00 | — | — | — |
| **C10** | **50¢ green** | 100 | 50.00 | 27.50 | 50.00 | 30.00 | 100.00 |
| a | horiz. pair, imperf. between | 50 | 1,800.00 | 1,200.00 | — | — | — |
| b | vert. pair, imperf. between | 50 | 3,000.00 | 2,000.00 | — | — | — |
| c | horiz. pair, imperf. vert. | 50 | 1,500.00 | 1,000.00 | | | |
| **C11** | **$1 blue** | 100 | 130.00 | 65.00 | 125.00 | 75.00 | 250.00 |
| a | vert. pair, imperf. between | 50 | 1,800.00 | 1,200.00 | — | — | — |
| c | horiz. pair, imperf. between | 50 | 2,000.00 | 1,350.00 | — | — | — |
| d | vert, pair, imperf. horiz. | 50 | 1,250.00 | 900.00 | | | |
| e | imperf. pair | 50 | 1,200.00 | 800.00 | — | — | — |
| i | as "a" with imperf. lower sheet margin | 50 | 2,100.00 | 1,400.00 | — | — | — |
| **Nos. C9–C11** | (3) Set | 100 | 200.00 | 100.00 | 185.00 | 111.00 | |

## DORNIER DO-X FLIGHT

C12
Historic Transatlantic Flights

**1932, May 19** **Engraved, sheets of 4**
**Watermarked Coat-of-Arms**

| | | NH% | ★VF | ★F | ⊙VF | ⊙F | ✉ |
|---|---|---|---|---|---|---|---|
| **C12** | **$1.50 on $1.00 blue (C11)**, surcharge in red | 100 | 400.00 | 300.00 | 400.00 | 300.00 | 500.00 |
| **a** | inverted surcharge | 100 | 30,000.00 | 20,000.00 | | | |
| **i** | *dramatic* slanting surcharge** | 100 | 900.00 | 500.00 | 800.00 | 500.00 | 900.00 |

A total of 8,000 stamps (C12) were issued. Surcharge was applied to C11.
** Must be noticeably slanted (the VGG has quantified that as *more* than 1 (one) degree from horizontal).

## LABRADOR ISSUE

C13
"Put to Flight"

C14
"Land of Heart's Delight"

C15
"Spotting the herd"

C16
"News from Home"

C17
"Labrador, Land of Gold"

**1933, Jun 9** **Engraved**

| | | NH% | ★VF | ★F | ⊙VF | ⊙F | ✉ |
|---|---|---|---|---|---|---|---|
| **C13** | **5¢ light brown**, perf. 14.3 | 75 | 15.00 | 10.00 | 15.00 | 10.00 | 35.00 |
| **a** | imperf. pair | 60 | 350.00 | 300.00 | — | — | — |
| **b** | horiz. pair, imperf. between | 50 | 1,800.00 | 1,200.00 | — | — | — |
| **c** | vert. pair, imperf. between | 50 | 2,000.00 | 1,350.00 | — | — | — |
| **ii** | imperf. right margin (probably 10 exist) | 50 | 500.00 | 300.00 | | | |
| **iii** | perf. 13.8 | 75 | 40.00 | 25.00 | 30.00 | 20.00 | 50.00 |
| **iv** | as "c" with imperf. top margin | | 3,000.00 | 2,400.00 | — | — | — |
| **v** | imperf. bottom margin | 50 | 500.00 | 250.00 | | | |
| **vi** | imperf. left margin | 50 | 400.00 | 250.00 | | | |

| | | NH% | ★VF | ★F | ⊙VF | ⊙F | ✉ |
|---|---|---|---|---|---|---|---|
| **C14** | **10¢ yellow**, perf. 11.5 (shades) | 75 | 25.00 | 18.00 | 23.00 | 15.00 | 35.00 |
| **a** | imperf. pair, yellow orange shade | 60 | 250.00 | 200.00 | — | — | — |
| **i** | pale yellow shade** | 50 | 4,000.00 | 2,000.00 | | | * |
| **ii** | imperf. pair, brown orange shade | 60 | 250.00 | 200.00 | | | |

* a registered first flight cover has been reported.
** certificate recommended.

| | | NH% | ★VF | ★F | ⊙VF | ⊙F | ✉ |
|---|---|---|---|---|---|---|---|
| **C15** | **30¢ blue**, perf. 14.3 | 75 | 45.00 | 30.00 | 45.00 | 32.50 | 60.00 |
| **a** | imperf. pair | 60 | 900.00 | 600.00 | — | — | — |

No. C15 has been reported perf. 13.8; this has not been seen by the editors.

| | | NH% | ★VF | ★F | ⊙VF | ⊙F | ✉ |
|---|---|---|---|---|---|---|---|
| **C16** | **60¢ green**, perf. 11.5 | 75 | 90.00 | 60.00 | 80.00 | 60.00 | 100.00 |
| **a** | imperf. pair | 60 | 900.00 | 600.00 | — | — | — |
| **i** | pale green shade | 75 | 120.00 | 80.00 | | | |
| **ii** | imperf. top margin (5–10 exist) | | 750.00 | 500.00 | | | |

| | | NH% | ★VF | ★F | ⊙VF | ⊙F | ✉ |
|---|---|---|---|---|---|---|---|
| **C17** | **75¢ bistre**, perf. 14.3 | 75 | 85.00 | 60.00 | 80.00 | 60.00 | 100.00 |
| **a** | imperf. pair | 60 | 900.00 | 600.00 | — | — | — |
| **b** | horiz. pair, imperf. between | 50 | 7,500.00 | 4,500.00 | — | — | — |
| **c** | vert. pair, imperf. between | 50 | 7,500.00 | 4,500.00 | — | — | — |
| **iii** | perf. 13.8 | 75 | 100.00 | 75.00 | 100.00 | 75.00 | 150.00 |

Cover prices are for usage between 1933 and 1936

| | | NH% | ★VF | ★F | ⊙VF | ⊙F | ✉ |
|---|---|---|---|---|---|---|---|
| **Nos. C13–C17** (5) Set | | 75 | 255.00 | 153.00 | 243.00 | 177.50 | |
| **Nos. C13a–C17a** (5) Set of imperf. pairs | | 60 | 3,000.00 | 2,300.00 | | | |

C18
"Labrador, Land of Gold"

C19
View of St. John's

## BALBO FLIGHT

**1933, Jul 24** **Engraved, sheets of 4** **Perf 14.3**

| | | NH% | ★VF | ★F | ⊙VF | ⊙F | ✉ |
|---|---|---|---|---|---|---|---|
| **C18** | **$4.50 on 75¢ bistre (C17)**, surcharge in black | 100 | 450.00 | 350.00 | 550.00 | 400.00 | 1,100* |
| **a** | inverted surcharge | 30 | *150,000.00* | *50,000.00*† | — | — | — |
| **ii** | $4.50 on 10¢ yellow (C14) | 30 | *70,000.00* | *50,000.00* | — | — | — |
| **iii** | partially doubled surcharge | | | | | | 17,500 |
| **b** | perf. 13.8 | 100 | 500.00 | 400.00 | 600.00 | 450.00 | 1,200 |

Issued in connection with the return flight from Chicago to Rome of the squadron of Italian seaplanes under General Italo Balbo. No. C18ii is a proof. A total of 8,000 stamps were issued. **Beware of forged surcharges.**
*Official FDC dated July 26, 1933; a few are known on July 25, 1933.
† 4 sound singles exist; 4 repaired singles from a second pane of 4 exist.

## ST. JOHN'S

**1943, Jun 1** **Engraved, Unwatermarked** **Perf 12**

| | | NH% | ★VF | ★F | ⊙VF | ⊙F | ✉ |
|---|---|---|---|---|---|---|---|
| **C19** | **7¢ bright ultramarine** | 50 | .50 | .45 | .40 | .35 | 3.50 |

plate blocks, $5.00 each

The "Wayzata" airmail ($1 "First Transatlantic Air Mail and Passenger Flight", 1932) was never officially issued. Price for a F–VF NH copy is $50.00.

## POSTAGE DUE STAMPS

J1

J2

J3

J4

J5

J6

J7

**1939, May 1 Lithography, Unwatermarked Perf 10-10½**

| NH +100% | ★VF | ★F | ⊙VF | ⊙F | ✉ |
|---|---|---|---|---|---|
| **J1 1¢ yellow green,** | | | | | |
| perf. 11, *1949* | 6.00 | 3.00 | 8.00 | 4.00 | 125.00 |
| a perf. 10–10½ | 9.00 | 4.50 | 8.00 | 4.00 | 150.00 |
| **J2 2¢ vermilion** | 10.00 | 5.00 | 8.00 | 4.00 | 125.00 |
| a perf. 11 x 9, *1946* | 10.00 | 5.00 | 8.00 | 4.00 | 150.00 |
| **J3 3¢ ultramarine** | 10.00 | 5.00 | 8.00 | 4.00 | 125.00 |
| a perf. 11 x 9, *1949* | 10.00 | 5.00 | 10.00 | 5.00 | 150.00 |
| b perf. 9 (price for F-VF NH) | 5,000.00 | | | | |
| **J4 4¢ yellow orange,** | | | | | |
| perf. 11 x 9, *1949* | 14.00 | 7.00 | 14.00 | 7.00 | 150.00 |
| a perf. 10–10½ | 20.00 | 10.00 | 20.00 | 10.00 | 125.00 |
| **J5 5¢ pale brown** | 20.00 | 10.00 | 6.00 | 3.00 | 125.00 |
| i brown | 30.00 | 15.00 | 10.00 | 5.00 | 125.00 |
| **J6 10¢ dark violet** | 10.00 | 5.00 | 10.00 | 5.00 | 125.00 |

**1949 Lithography, Watermarked Arms Perf 11**

| | ★VF | ★F | ⊙VF | ⊙F | ✉ |
|---|---|---|---|---|---|
| **J7 10¢ dark violet** | 14.00 | 7.00 | 20.00 | 10.00 | 200.00 |
| a vert. pair, imperf. between (30 pairs known) | 1,200.00 | 800.00 | — | — | — |
| i 'POSTAGE LUE' variety (pos. 23 and 28) | 80.00 | 50.00 | 60.00 | 45.00 | |
| ii period after 'DUE' (pos. 91 and 96) | 80.00 | 50.00 | 60.00 | 45.00 | |

J7a, top margin vertical strip of 3, imperforate between top pair with "LUE" variety is known. At most six examples could possibly exist. Value $2,000.

Add 200% to used prices for cancels dated in-period.

| | ★VF | ★F | ⊙VF | ⊙F |
|---|---|---|---|---|
| **J1–J7 (7)** Set | 84.00 | 42.00 | 74.00 | 37.00 |

## OFFICIALLY SEALED

**OX1**
King Edward VII

**1905 Unwatermarked Engraved Perf 12**

| | NH% | ★VF | ★F | ⊙VF | ⊙F | ✉ |
|---|---|---|---|---|---|---|
| **OX1 black, blue paper** | 150 | 1,000.00 | 500.00 | 700.00 | 450.00 | 3,500 |
| i Watermarked | 150 | 1,500.00 | 750.00 | 900.00 | 600.00 | — |

One cover is known with two examples of OX1 sealing the end of an envelope, value $7,500.

| | NH% | ★VF | ★F | ⊙VF | ⊙F | ✉ |
|---|---|---|---|---|---|---|
| ii plate proof on india or card | | 1,000.00 | 600.00 | — | — | — |
| iii specimen overprint ‡ | 50 | 1,000.00 | 600.00 | — | — | — |
| iv specimen watermark ‡ | 50 | 1,500.00 | 900.00 | | | |

‡ All specimens have small 2mm punch hole.

## WATERMARKS

The first three illustrations represent watermarks as they appear from the back of a stamp. On 'vertical' stamps the normal appearance of WMK-2 from the back of the stamp is with the moose at the top facing left.

WMK-1

WMK-2
(see next page for different positions)

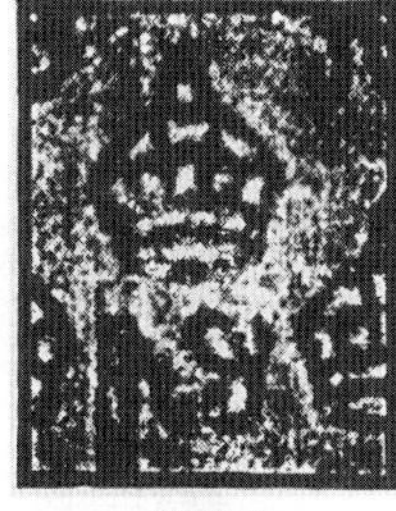
WMK-3

STACEY WISE
1858

WMK-5

# NEWFOUNDLAND WATERMARK-2

## HORIZONTAL FORMAT

*Watermark from the front of stamp.*

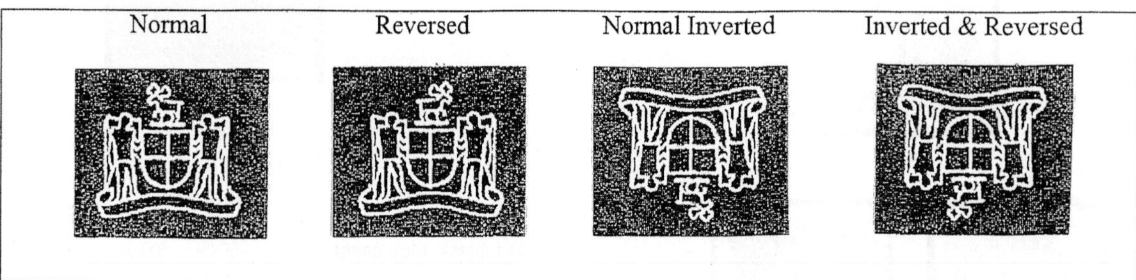


*Watermark from the back of stamp.*

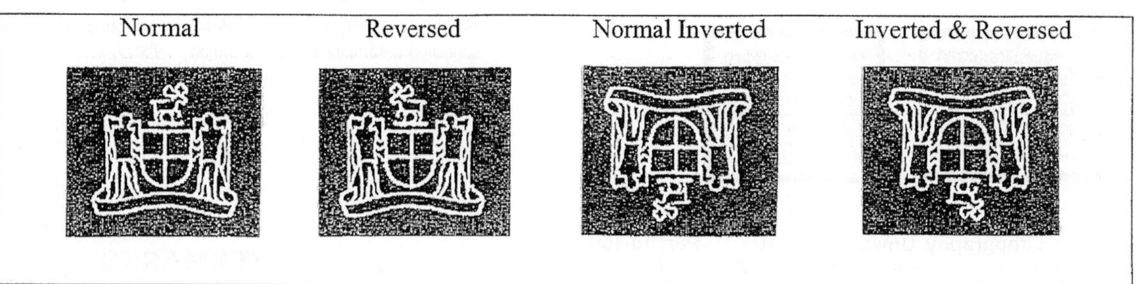


## VERTICAL FORMAT

*Watermark from the front of stamp.*

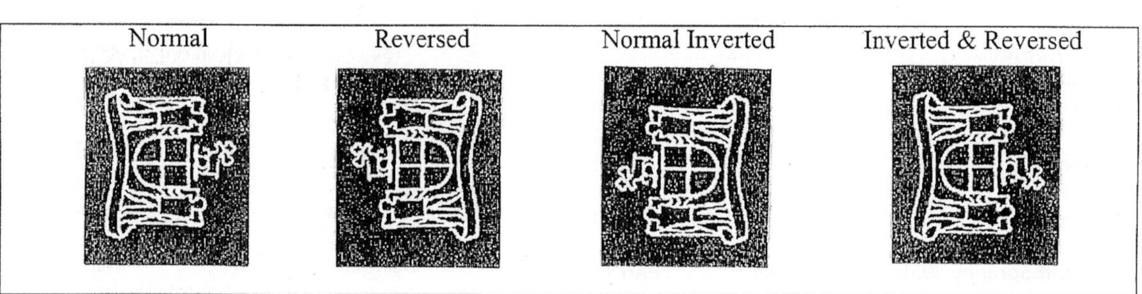


*Watermark from the back of stamp.*

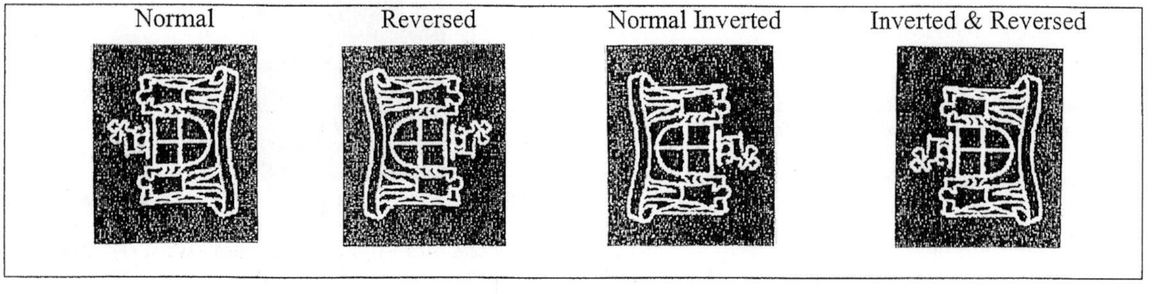

## COMPLETE BOOKLETS

BK2

BK4

| | | |
|---|---|---|
| **BK1** | 1¢ grey-green (131a) pane of 8, 2¢ carmine (132a) 2 panes of 8 | *3,500.00* |
| **BK2** | 1¢ green (183a) pane of 4, 2¢ rose (185a/perf 13½) 3 panes of 4 and 3¢ orange brown (187c) pane of 4 | 1,200.00 |
| **a** | 1¢ green (183a) pane of 4, 2¢ rose (185b) 3 panes of 4 and 3¢ orange brown (187c) pane of 4 *(all panes perf. 13.2)* | 1,200.00 |
| **BK3** | 1¢ grey black (184b) pane of 4, 2¢ green (186b) 3 panes of 4 and 3¢ orange brown (187b) pane of 4 *(all panes perf. 14)* | 900.00 |
| **BK4** | 1¢ grey black (184a) pane of 4, 2¢ green [Die I] (186a) 3 panes of 4 and 3¢ orange brown (187a) pane of 4 *(all panes perf. 13½)* | 700.00 |
| **a** | as BK4, but 2¢ green panes are Die II (186ai) | 750.00 |

## POSTAL STATIONERY

### ENVELOPES

**1899, printed by De La Rue & Company**

A number of distinct shades exist on all four varieties. Prices for used copies are for non-philatelic usage in period. The envelopes were made from white laid paper bearing the watermark "ORIGINAL/TURKEY MILL/KENT". Unused copies bearing the complete watermark are worth 10–15% premium. Unwatermarked copies are merely cutting varieties and no premium for such envelopes is justified.

U1

U2

| | | Unused | Used |
|---|---|---|---|
| **U1** | **3¢ violet**, 5½" x 3" (140 mm x 79 mm) | 15.00 | 90.00 |
| **a** | as above, 4¾" x 3¾" (120 mm x 95 mm) | 15.00 | 60.00 |
| **U2** | **5¢ blue**, 5½" x 3" (140 mm x 79 mm) | 15.00 | 80.00 |
| **a** | as above, 4¾" x 3¾" (120 mm x 95 mm) | 15.00 | 80.00 |

Used values are for non-philatelic use to pay the inland letter rate (3¢) or foreign letter rate (5¢).

### POST BANDS

**QUEEN VICTORIA**

**1889, printed by De La Rue & Company**

PB1

| | | Unused | Used |
|---|---|---|---|
| **PB1** | **1¢ green** | 7.00 | 35.00 |
| **PB2** | **2¢ carmine** | 7.00 | 50.00 |
| **PB3** | **3¢ brown** | 7.00 | 50.00 |

### REPLY LETTER CARD

**KING GEORGE V**

**1913, printed by De La Rue & Company.**

| | | Unused | Used |
|---|---|---|---|
| **ULY1** | **2¢ carmine + 2¢ carmine** | 150.00 | 500.00 |

Price for a used detached reply card is $500.

### POSTAL CARDS

**PRINCE OF WALES AND QUEEN VICTORIA**

**1874–1880, printed by the American Bank Note Company**

UX1

UX2

| | | Unused | Used |
|---|---|---|---|
| **UX1** | **1¢ green** | 7.50 | 120.00 |
| **UX2** | **2¢** | 7.50 | 450.00 |

Used prices are for copies used prior to 1881.

**PRINCE OF WALES AND QUEEN VICTORIA**

**1880, printed by British American Bank Note Company**

UX3

UX4

UX5

| | | Unused | Used |
|---|---|---|---|
| **UX3** | **1¢ green** | 4.00 | 7.50 |
| **UX4** | **2¢ vermilion** | 4.00 | 15.00 |

Several different varieties of stock were used for these cards.

### SURCHARGE

**1889**

| | | | |
|---|---|---|---|
| **UX5** | **2¢ on 1¢ green** (UX3) | 65.00 | 500.00 |

Several different fakes of this surcharge are known on unused copies. The price for UX5 used is for copies postmarked between May and July, 1889. Other copies are worth less.

## QUEEN VICTORIA

**1892**

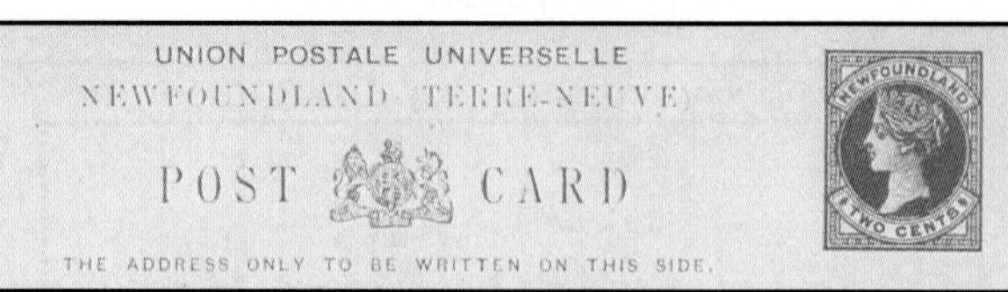


**UY6**

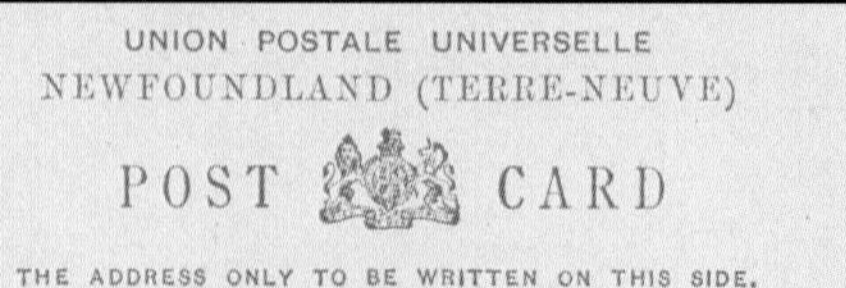

**UY6a**

| | | Unused | Used |
|---|---|---|---|
| **UY6** | 2¢ deep scarlet + 2¢ deep scarlet, last "E" of "UNIVERSELLE" to the right of "U" in "NEUVE" | 40.00 | 400.00 |

Some years after the cards were initially released, separated reply and message halves apparently were sold and used as single post cards. This seems to have occurred primarily in the 1920s. Used examples $125.00.

| | | | |
|---|---|---|---|
| **a** | 2¢ carmine red + 2¢ carmine red, last "E" of "UNIVERSELLE" to the left of "U" in "NEUVE" | 20.00 | 125.00 |

The widest part of the note at the lower left of the message half measures 34 mm on UY6, and 32 mm on UY6a.

### KING EDWARD VII AND QUEEN ALEXANDRA

**1903–1904**

**Printed by the American Bank Note Company**

**UX7**

**UX8**

| | | Unused | Used |
|---|---|---|---|
| **UX7** | **1¢ green** | 20.00 | 20.00 |
| **UX8** | **2¢ vermilion** | 20.00 | 35.00 |

Plate proofs on card mounted india paper are known for both values of UX7–UX8. Price $350.00 each.

## KING GEORGE V AND QUEEN MARY

**1911**

**UX9**

**UX10**

| | | Unused | Used |
|---|---|---|---|
| **UX9** | **1¢ green** | 30.00 | 45.00 |
| **UX10** | **2¢ red** | 10.00 | 25.00 |

## KING GEORGE V

**1913, printed by De La Rue & Company**

"POST CARD" in white on a green background.

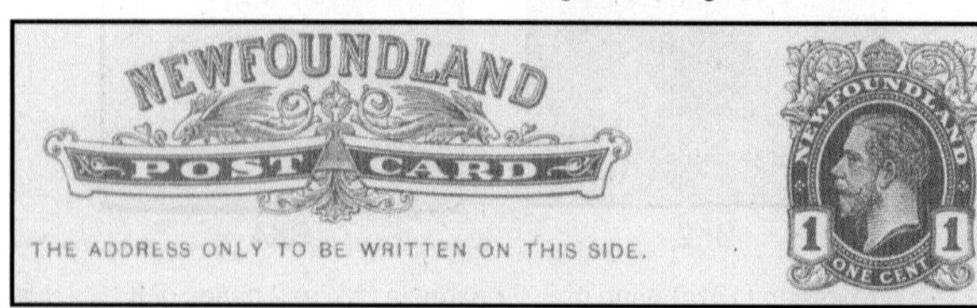


**UX11**

| | | Unused | Used |
|---|---|---|---|
| **UX11** | **1¢ green** | 20.00 | 40.00 |

## KING GEORGE V

**1915, printed by De La Rue & Company**

"POST CARD" in green on a white background. The shading between the legs of "A" in "CARD" is not connected to the shading below the word.

**UX12**

| | | Unused | Used |
|---|---|---|---|
| **UX12** | **1¢ green** | 8.00 | 12.00 |

## KING GEORGE V

**1930–1937**

**UX13a**

**UX13**

**UX13a**

"POST CARD" in green on a white background. The shading between the legs of "A" in "CARD" is connected by a diagonal line to the shading below the word.

| | | Unused | Used |
|---|---|---|---|
| **UX13** | **1¢ green**, weak right serif on "T" of "CENT" | 10.00 | 8.00 |
| **a** | as above, strong right serif on "T" of "CENT" | 10.00 | 15.00 |

**UX14**

| | | Unused | Used |
|---|---|---|---|
| **UX14** | **2¢ green** | 8.00 | 15.00 |

Newfoundland

## FORMULAR REGISTERED ENVELOPES

The charge (in parentheses) paid for the envelope, but prepaid neither the postage nor the registration fee. Envelopes are buff coloured with printing in blue.

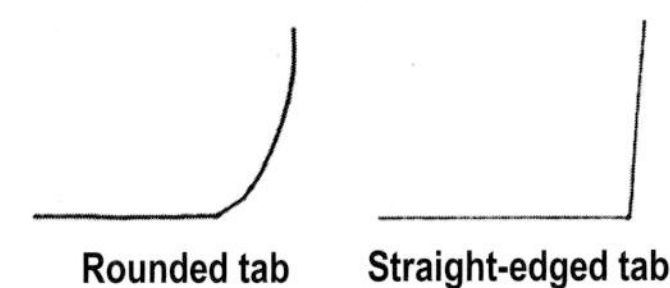

Rounded tab Straight-edged tab

| | | Unused | Used |
|---|---|---|---|
| URF1 | Size A – 155 mm x 95 mm (1¢), rounded tab | 20.00 | 25.00 |
| a | as above, straight edged tab | 25.00 | 25.00 |
| URF2 | Size B – 205 mm x 125 mm (2¢), rounded tab | 25.00 | 25.00 |
| a | as above, straight edged tab | 35.00 | 75.00 |
| URF3 | Size C – 228 mm x 105 mm (2¢) | 30.00 | 45.00 |
| URF4 | Size D – 290 mm x 150 mm (4¢) | 50.00 | 150.00 |

## FORMULAR AEROGRAMMES

| | | Unused | Used |
|---|---|---|---|

"CANADA" obliterated in dark blue at upper left of the folded form with "NEWFOUNDLAND" beside it. "AIR LETTER PAR AVION" in a box at the middle left.

| | | Unused | Used |
|---|---|---|---|
| UCF1 | light grey paper | 30.00 | 75.00 |

Similar to above, but words "CANADA" and "Newfoundland" are omitted. Watermarked 'Rolland/Croydon/Air Mail Canada".

| | | Unused | Used |
|---|---|---|---|
| UCF2 | light grey paper | 25.00 | 50.00 |

"NEWFOUNDLAND" at upper left of the folded form. "AIR LETTER" (only) in a box at the middle left. Watermarked as before.

| | | Unused | Used |
|---|---|---|---|
| UCF3 | light grey paper | 20.00 | 30.00 |

## REPLY COUPONS SOLD BY NEWFOUNDLAND

Reply coupons are purchased (or exchanged) at a post office to prepay (or receive) the minimum postage of a basic reply by surface mail.

London design

### INTERNATIONAL REPLY COUPONS

International Reply Coupons are issued by the Universal Postal Union.

**LONDON DESIGN**

**"UPU" (double-lined) watermark**

| | | | Value |
|---|---|---|---|
| 1 | 12¢ | Face: "...country of the Universal Postal Union..." Rev: German text in Gothic letters | 200.00 |

An uncut block of four is known of a 6¢ denomination.

## IMPERIAL REPLY COUPONS

Imperial design

**IMPERIAL**

**Multiple Crown and GVR (vertical) watermark**

| | | | Value |
|---|---|---|---|
| 1 | 5¢ | "This coupon ... It is valid for six months exclusive of the month of issue." (1927) | 100.00 |

**Multiple Crown and GVR (double-lined) watermark**

| | | | Value |
|---|---|---|---|
| 2 | 5¢ | "This coupon ... to a destination within the Empire" | 100.00 |

**Multiple Crown and GVIR (double-lined) watermark**

| | | | Value |
|---|---|---|---|
| 3 | 5¢ | as "2" | 100.00 |

# Topical Listing

Listed alphabetically are various topics. Within each topic is a numerical listing of stamps (by Scott number) that either features or includes in some way that particular topic within their stamp image. This list is a "work in progress" and is expected to be expanded in future editions.

### Aboriginal Indians
301, 553, 562-581, 764, 1091, 1108, 1199, 1233, 1238, 1494, 1511, 1736, 1755a, 1782, 1826a, 1826b, 1826c, 1826d, 1834a, 1915, 2214, 2226, 2269, 2279b, 2280b, 2380–2383, 2539, 2969

### Airplanes, helicopters
313, 351, 383, 414, 430, 436, 459-460, 468A, 468B, 494, 543, 549, 771, 779, 843-846, 873-876, 903-906, 969-972, 1101-1102, 1145, 1262-1263, 1330, 1333, 1404, 1449, 1455, 1504, 1525, 1528, 1539, 1577, 1596, 1737, 1807a, 1807b, 1807c, 1807d-1808, 1808b, 1808c, 1808d, 1808e, 1808f, 1808g, 1808h, 1808i, 1808j, 1808k, 1808l, 1808m, 1808n, 1808o, 1808p, 1832c, 1866, 2111a, 2111c, 2153b-2154, 2158-2159, 2317, 2418a, 2419, 2498a, 2499, C1, C3, C6-C8, CE1-CE4

### Alberta
177, 294, 355, 400, 426, 465B, 667, 757-761, 829, 864, 964, 981-982, 1021, 1054, 1077, 1111-1112, 1130-1131, 1152-1153, 1195-1198, 1428, 1468, 1477, 1553, 1709h, 1740, 1819a, 1854c, 1952b-1953, 2011, 2031, 2116, 2137, 2215-2216, 2224, 2228, 2263, 2267, 2335d, 2336d, 2470, 2520, 2546–2548, 2558b, 2558c, 2560, 2561, 2567c, 2567d, 270, 2571, 2642d, 2643e, 2661b, 2661e, 2663, 2666, 2669c, 2669e, 2672, 2674, 2718c, 2723, 2739a, 2741, 2778f, 2778g, 2784, 2785, 2838e, 2840, 2844a, 2845, 2844c–d, 2847–2848, 2857a, 2858, 2889d, 2894, 2903b, 2909, 2929b, 2931, 2963a, 2964

### Animals
1, 4, 12, 15, 256, 301, 314, 322-324, 335-336, 352, 360-361, 395, 398, 400, 562, 595, 597, 628, 698, 732, 813, 824-825, 827-828, 854, 883-884, 909, 1128, 1155-1161, 1170-1172, 1172A, 1174-1175, 1177-1178, 1180, 1205, 1325, 1335, 1452, 1500-1501, 1515, 1529-1532, 1574, 1614, 1630, 1630a, 1672, 1698, 1701-1702, 1708, 1708a, 1739, 1757, 1759, 1767-1768, 1781, 1800, 1818a, 1836-1837, 1850, 1852, 1879-1881, 1883-1884, 1900, 1933-1934, 1969-1970, 1990b, 2015-2016, 2057, 2059, 2083-2084, 2106, 2122-2123, 2153b-2154, 2167, 2173a, 2173d-2174, 2177, 2191, 2201-2202, 2326–2327, 2329–2330, 2387–2387d, 2388–2393, 2424–2432, 2461, 2504–2512, 2522, 2523b, 2525, 2602–2610, 2636–3641, 2642, 2709–2717, 2829–2834, 2879a–c, 2881–2883, 2959–2962, 3045, 3047–3049, 3052–3055, 3092a, 3093

### Arctic
412, 438, 847, 1574-1578, 2152, 2204-2205, 2326–2327, 2337, 2424–2426, 2498a, 2499, 2851–2856, 3056i, 3069, 3078

### Artifacts
563, 566, 571, 574, 578, 917-922, 927-930, 932-933, 1080-1083, 1755a, 1755b, 2724–2726

### Authors/poets/writers
438, 487, 504, 658-659, 695-696, 817-818, 978-979, 1090, 1243-1244, 1622-1626, 1761, 1828a, 1994-1997, 2276–2278, 2850

### Balloons
1921a, 1921b, 1921c, 1921d, 2146, 2418b, 2420

### Baseball
1221, 1901, 2434

### Bicentennials (200th anniversary)
283, 382, 388, 413, 499, 501, 540, 619, 1014, 1029, 1484, 1640, 2034, 2094, 2539, 2554–2555, 2650–2651, 2804

### Bicycles
631, 642, 1240, 1522, 1636, 1639, 1731, 1802, 1849, 1998, 2121c, 2225, 2757c, 2758

### Birds
320, 343, 353-354, 369, 415, 478, 496-498, 506, 532, 626, 752, 937, 1069, 1095-1098, 1204, 1288, 1321, 1412, 1514, 1564-1566, 1591-1594, 1627, 1631-1634, 1646, 1695, 1710-1713, 1770-1777, 1812-1814, 1839-1846, 1849, 1886-1893, 1979-1983, 2036-2040, 2095-2099, 2145a, 2163-2166, 2204, 2285a/2286, 2285c/2288, 2285d/2289, C9, 2388a, 2388d, 2388e, 2389, 2390, 2393, 2636b, 2638, 2929–2934, 2954c, 2958, 2959–2962, 3017–3022, B23–B24

### Black History
2315–2316, 2369, 2520–2521, 2619–2620, 2702–2703, 2805–2806, 2895, 2969, 3085-3086

### Bridges
156, 399, 737, 1237, 1485, 1524d, 1570-1573, 1645-1646, 1725, 1729, 1734, 1848, 1990a, 2076, 2100-2103, 2136, 2214, 2902c, 2907

### British Columbia
155, 226, 244, 272, 377, 400, 423, 509, 552, 599-600, 826, 883, 912, 965, 985, 1017, 1033, 1063, 1078-1079, 1092-1093, 1147, 1311, 1378, 1413, 1429, 1464, 1467, 1476, 1515, 1556, 1573, 1606c, 1613, 1650, 1709g, 1778, 1854a, 1903a, 1903c, 1904a, 1953b, 1989b-1990, 2029, 2078, 2152, 2190, 2264, 2283, 2324, 2335a, 2336a, 2366–2368, 2471a, 2472, 2558a, 2559, 2567b, 2569, 2642e, 2642h, 2643d, 2643h, 2661a, 2662, 2669a, 2670, 2718c, 2723, 2739c, 2741, 2778e, 2783, 2844e, 2849, 2860a, 2861, 2889c, 2891, 2902c, 2907, 2903b, 2909, 3056c, 3059, 3064, 3072

### Buildings
245, 283, 313, 321, 396, 414, 430-431, 436, 449, 465A, 469, 475, 484, 504, 581, 599-601, 633, 640, 651, 653, 659, 662-663, 682, 687-688, 690, 693, 723, 723C-725, 761, 780, 879-881, 954, 967, 1016, 1027, 1029, 1078, 1094, 1117, 1122-1125, 1181-1183, 1291, 1302-1305, 1314, 1334, 1338, 1361-1362, 1375-1376, 1378, 1404-1405, 1421, 1423-1424, 1426, 1448, 1453, 1467-1471, 1484, 1487, 1510, 1524b, 1524e, 1524f, 1524g, 1524i, 1524j, 1524k, 1553-1557, 1613, 1615a, 1617, 1640, 1731-1732, 1737, 1755a, 1755b, 1755c, 1755d, 1755e, 1755f, 1755g, 1755h, 1755i-1756, 1778, 1810, 1823a, 1827b, 1830a-1831, 1864-1865, 1874, 1903d, 1903e-1904, 1904b, 1904e, 1906, 1931, 1940-1944, 1952d, 1952e-1953, 1956, 1973-1977, 1989d, 1989e-1991, 2011, 2020, 2033-2034, 2056, 2070, 2076-2077, 2080, 2089, 2094, 2108, 2116-2117, 2135-2136, 2153b-2154, 2172, 2178-2182, 2209-2210, 2214, 2215-2218, 2241, 2249–2253B, 2263–2264, 2279c, 2280a, 2290, 2315, 2316, 2366b, 2368, 2471–2476, 2520, 2771, 2838c–d, 2841–2842, 2844c–d, 2846, 2848, 2889a–b, 2889d–e, 2890, 2892–2894, 2963c, 2963e, 2965–2966, 2970a, 2970e, 2971, 2975, 3056a, 3057, 3062, 3071

### Business
1103, 1145, 1636, 1833d-1834, 1834b, 1834c, 1834d, 1867, 1962, 2032, 2094, 2104, 2151

### Butterflies
1210-1213, 1563, 2045, 2145b, 2285b/2287

### CAPEX
311-314, 753-756, 1122-1125

### Castles
215

### Cats
732, 1170, 1708, 2058, 2122, 2123, 2636a, 2636e, 2637, 2641, 2829a, 2829c, 2829e, 2830, 2832, 2833

### Centennials (100th anniversary)
274, 311-314, 377, 392, 399, 431-432, 438, 448, 453, 471, 475, 505-506, 532, 534, 539, 542, 552, 612-614, 616-618, 622, 633-641, 643, 648-649, 654, 667, 669, 692-693, 767, 847, 857-858, 877, 897-899, 954, 967, 980, 996, 1003, 1049, 1214, 1343-1344, 1344b, 1344c, 1558, 1866, 1976, 2035, 2051-2052, 2104, 2116-2117, 2151, 2160, 2172, 2209-2210, 2224, 2225, 2227–2228, 2263–2264, 2274, 2282, 2331, 2332, 2337, 2339–2340, 2394, 2402, 2470, 2546–2548, 2531–2538, 2835–2836, 2981–2982, 3026–3038, 3042-3044, 3050, 3101

### Chemistry/chemicals
363, 2116, 2489

### Children
396, 476-477, 502-503, 519-530, 629, 631-632, 644-646, 651, 660, 674-679, 842, 871, 879, 1005, 1016, 1025, 1028, 1045, 1047, 1062, 1132, 1215, 1259, 1298, 1326, 1341, 1523a, 1523b, 1523c, 1523d, 1523e, 1578, 1627, 1629, 1784, 1813, 1815-1816, 1827b, 1833b, 1851, 1857, 1859-1862, 1917, 1923-1924, 1957, 1986, 2035, 2046, 2050, 2059-2060, 2120-2121, 2121b, 2121c, 2121d, 2157, 2184-2185, 2225, 2226, 2397d, 2401, 2402, 2404, 2498e, 2503, 2757c, 2758, 2815b, 2819, B21–B22

### Children's Stories
2541–2545, 2652–2654

### Christmas
519-530, 554-557, 606-609, 625-628, 650-651, 674-679, 697-699, 741-743, 773-775, 839-841, 870-872, 900-902, 973-975, 1004-1006, 1040-1042, 1067-1070, 1113-1116, 1148-1151, 1222-1224, 1256-1259, 1294-1297, 1339-1342, 1452-1455, 1499-1502, 1533-1536, 1585-1588, 1627-1629, 1669-1671, 1764-1766, 1815-1817, 1873-1875, 1922-1924, 1965-1967, 2004-2006, 2069-2071, 2124-2127, 2183-2186, 2239–2242, 2291–2295, 2343–2347, 2411–2415, 2490, 2492–2494, 2581–2585, 2687–2691, 2796–2800, 2879–2883, 2954–2958, 3045-3049

### Church (religious)
451-452, 502-503, 521, 524, 528-529, 609, 611, 628, 650, 653, 662-663, 687, 697-699, 768, 773-775, 870, 885-886, 973-975, 994, 998, 1004-1006, 1018, 1029-1031, 1040-1042, 1113-1116, 1129, 1222-1226, 1258, 1524c, 1669-1671, 1764-1766, 1823a, 1827d, 1858, 1874-1875, 1905, 1989c, 1992, 2079, 2125-2127, 2183, 2412, 2490, 2492–2494, 2582, 2688, 2797, 2880, 2955, 3046, 3051

### Coats-of-Arms
377, 400, 418-429, 429A, 1133, E10, E11

### Coins
2274, 2403

### Comics/cartoons
1579-1583, 2677a, 2677b, 2677c, 2677d, 2677e-2683

### Computer
1510, 1523d, 1597, 1737, 1818b, 2402

### Confederation
135, 141-145, 224, 275, 431-432, 448, 517

### Dance
565, 575, 1252-1255, 1562, 1819b, 1895

### Dinosaurs/prehistoric animals
1495-1498, 1740, 1818a, 2823–2828, 2923–2928

### Dogs
367, 454, 610, 772, 832, 1217-1220, 1576-1577, 1627, 1822a, 1952a, 2026-2027, 2048, 2060, 2111a, 2139-2141, 2266, 2397b, 2399, 2469, 2636c, 2636d, 2639–2640, 2829b, 2829d, 2831, 2834, 3052–3055, 3092c, 3094

### Dolls
841, 1274-1277

### Education/school/university
396, 640, 660, 1003, 1338, 1376, 1457, 1523d, 1756, 1778, 1810, 1823d, 1941-1944, 1961, 1973-1977, 2033-2034, 2089, 2172, 2209-2210, B13

### Emblems/logos
356, 389, 500, 505, 508-511, 517, 619, 635, 640, 648-649, 668, 680, 694, 735-736, 916, 971, 993, 1003, 1011, 1013, 1029-1031, 1062, 1103, 1272-1273, 1302-1305, 1341, 1347, 1443-1445, 1523b, 1539-1540, 1583-1584, 1589, 1640, 1656-1658, 1786, 1799, 1806, 1808a, 1808b, 1808c, 1808d, 1808e, 1808f, 1808g, 1808h, 1808i, 1808j, 1808k, 1808l, 1808m, 1808n, 1808o, 1808p-1809, 1819c, 1819d, 1834b, 1834c, 1834d-1835, 1857-1858, 1867, 1901-1902, 1917, 1925, 1940-1944, 1958, 1973-1977, 2028-2034, 2089, 2111a, 2111c-2112, 2158-2159, 2167, 2172, 2209-2210, 2225, 2228, 2265, 2275, 2281, 2282, 2284, 2299–2313, 2366–2368, 2371–2372, 2373–2375, 2384–2386, 2394, 2402, 2754–2755, 2757c, 2758, 2778–2793, 2837, 2866–2878, 2941–2953, 3009, 3023a–3025, 3026–3038, 3042, E7, E8, E9

### Errors of Design
50-65, 85-86, 96-98, 135, 142, 176, 194, 210, 247, 268, 272-273, 275, 282, 301-303, 311, 355, 359, 370, 376, 383, 388, 395-396, 411, 413, 417, 419, 429A, 431, 442, 453, 478, 490, 519-530, 541, 612, 619, 654, 658, 682, 688, 737, 746, 748-751, 821, 1018, 1025, 2844a, 2845, C1, C3, CE1, CE2, CE3, E3, J16B

### Explorers
7, 19, 97, 99-100, 102-103, 208, 227, 370, 378-379, 390, 397-398, 412, 438, 446, 512, 515-516, 540, 561, 738, 754, 763-764, 910, 995, 1011, 1104-1107, 1126-1129, 1199-1202, 1233-1236, 1406, 1649, 1779, 1988, 2026-2027, 2044, 2155, 2337, 2851–2856, 2969

### Fairy tales & Folklore
1289-1292, 1334-1337, 1432-1435, 1491-1494, 1665-1668

### Farming
157, 175, 203, 253, 256, 268, 271, 355, 395, 398, 405, 409, 456, 465A-466, 492, 596, 640, 863, 1207, 1215, 1300, 1329, 1422, 1425, 1524f, 1524g, 1552a, 1552d, 1552f, 1605h, 1605x, 1652-1653, 1810, 1824a, 1833a, 1833d, 1850-1851, 2110a, 2404

### Firefighting
364, 844, 1332, 1527d, 1605q, 1986

### Fish & marine life
302, 365, 395, 403, 407, 458, 468, 480, 814, 853, 1106, 1173, 1176, 1179, 1408, 1485, 1488, 1641-1644, 1676, 1715-1720, 1742, 1783, 1818a, 1833c, 1849, 1868-1871, 1948-1951, 1991D, 2087a, 2087b, 2087c, 2087d, 2088, 2088b, 2088c, 2088d, 2157, 2205, 2229a, 2229b, 2229c, 2229d, 2230, 2231, 2232, 2233, 2387–2387e, 2402, 2405

### Flags
257, 273, 277, 282, 423, 439, 453, 500, 614, 619, 688, 692-693, 700-703, 714-715, 729-730, 737, 740, 745-746, 776-779, 790, 797, 800, 806, 821-832, 851, 925-926, 947-948, 952-953, 968, 983-985, 991, 993, 1014, 1028, 1032, 1052, 1054, 1056, 1061, 1091, 1109, 1122-1124, 1133, 1139-1140, 1163, 1165-1166, 1169, 1184-1185, 1187-1194, 1194A, 1194B, 1194C, 1200, 1234, 1278, 1315, 1338, 1356, 1359, 1361-1362, 1388-1389, 1394-1396, 1423, 1467-1468, 1470, 1524e, 1546, 1572, 1606c, 1687, 1703, 1705, 1707, 1709a, 1709b, 1709c, 1709d, 1709e, 1709f, 1709g, 1709h, 1709i, 1709j, 1728-1730, 1736-1737, 1762-1763, 1809, 1859, 1904a, 1906, 1931, 1941, 1943, 1991, 2011, 2022, 2041-2042, 2076-2080, 2112, 2135-2139, 2155, 2159, 2161, 2189-2193, 2214, 2281, 2331, 2332, 2335–2336, 2350–2355, 2370, 2379, 2397–2401, 2484–2485, 2498–2503, 2531–2538, 2611–1616, 2693–2697, 2718–2723, 2739–2744, 2807–2808, 2844–2849, 2857–2858, 2889–2894, 2963–2968, 2970a, 2970e, 2971, 2975, 2981, 3086, E10, E11

### Flowers
399, 418-422, 424-429, 487, 509-511, 690, 705, 707-712, 781-787, 828, 855, 894-896, 961, 1148, 1311-1315, 1489, 1517-1522, 1575, 1598, 1638, 1787-1790, 1827c, 1850, 1856, 1882d, 1903a-1904, 1910a, 1910b, 1910c, 1910d-1914, 1918c, 1918d, 1941, 1946a, 1946b, 1946c, 1946d-1947, 1947b, 1947c, 1947d, 1975, 2047, 2072-2074, 2081-2082, 2091, 2091a, 2091b-2093, 2105, 2117, 2128-2134, 2142, 2145a, 2145b, 2145c, 2145d, 2150, 2179, 2187-2188, 2194a, 2194b, 2194c, 2194d-2200, 2206-2208, 2236, 2243–2247, 2254–2256, 2260–2262, 2298, 2318–2320, 2341–2342, 2356–2364, 2376–2378, 2440–2444, 2526–2530, 2621–2625, 2727–2731, 2809–2813, 2835–2836, 2896–2900, 2970b–d, 2972–2974, 2976–2980, 3087–3091

### Food (fruit, etc.)
608, 1069, 1349-1352, 1354-1355, 1363-1374, 1467, 1652, 1672, 1833a, 1833b, 1833c, 1833d-1834, 1834d, 2168-2171, 2211, 2402

### Football
2558–2576, 2598, 2754–2755

### Foreign (non-Canadian) subject or location
215, 440, 448, 486, 691, 1348, 1538, 1540, 1542–1544, 1584, 1590, 1606c, 1621, 1723-1724, 1960b, 1960c, 1960d, 1960e, 1960f, 1960g, 1960h, 1993, 2043, 2090, 2106, 2107, 2123, 2153b, 2154c, 2179–2182, 2271, 2272, 2273, 2325, 2327b, 2332, 2379, 2418a, 2418e, 2419, 2423, 2498c, 2501, 2618, 2732, 2805–2806, 2844d, 2848, 2981–2982

### Forts
243, 983-992, 1050-1059, 1109, 1547-1551, 2138

### Games and Toys
526, 627, 677, 839-840, 1151, 1816, 2006

### Ghosts
2748–2753, 2860–2865, 2935–2940

### Governor General
474, 491, 735, 914, 1447, 1509, 1940, 2024, 2370

### Health
380, 495, 560, 615, 856, 877, 980, 1060, 1132, 1209, 1264-1265, 1345, 1456, 1523e, 1603, 1639, 1735, 1823a-1824, 1824d-1825, 1917, 2035, 2056, 2120, 2275, 2488a, 2488d, 2557

### Hockey
359, 1111, 1401, 1443-1445, 1460, 1659-1660, 1819c, 1819d, 1838a, 1838b, 1838c, 1838d, 1838e, 1838f, 1885a, 1885b, 1885c, 1885d, 1885e, 1885f, 1935a, 1935b, 1935c, 1935d, 1935e, 1935f, 1939, 1971a, 1971b, 1971c, 1971d, 1971e, 1971f-1972, 1972b, 1972c, 1972d, 1972e, 1972f, 2017a, 2017b, 2017c, 2017d, 2017e, 2017f-2018, 2018b, 2018c, 2018d, 2018e, 2018f, 2085a, 2085b, 2085c, 2085d, 2085e, 2085f-2086, 2086b, 2086c, 2086d, 2086e, 2086f, 2265, 2339–2340, 2661–2676, 2778–2793, 2866–2878, 2935–2953, 3026–3044, 3079c, 3082, 3101

### Holograms & three-dimensional
1442, 1812

### Horses
157, 223, 268, 313, 504, 520, 562, 610, 614, 633, 643, 648-649, 652, 655, 667, 817, 840, 872, 911, 956, 1034, 1076, 1117, 1133, 1199, 1239, 1276, 1336, 1340, 1432, 1470, 1523e, 1616a, 1616e, 1653, 1672, 1736-1737, 1755b, 1758, 1791-1798, 1819a, 1823d, 1852, 1922, 1945, 1956, 1976, 2110a, 2151, 2329–2330, 2404, 2520, 2523b, 2525, 2546–2548, 2963c, 2965, 2970e, 2975, E3

### Insects, bugs
2145c, 2234–2238, 2328, 2388c, 2391, 2406–2410, 2708, 3087, 3099–3100

### Inuit/Eskimos
351, 454, 488-489, 748-751, 769-772, 835-838, 866-869, 1427, 1458, 2469, 2498e, 2503

### Inventors
274, 1832a, 1832b, 1832c, 1832d

### Joint issues
387, 691, 737, 1011, 1015, 1264-1265, 1413, 1649, 1779, 2000-2001, 2027, 2044, 2105-2106, 2122-2123, 2269, 2276–2278, 2379, 2387–2387d, 2981–2982, 3023–3025, 3039–3041

### Lighthouses
985, 1032-1035, 1058, 1063-1066, 1353, 1474, 1524l, 1645, 1779, 1827c, 1849, 1953e, 1990d, 2192, 2249–2253B, 2330, 2838d, 2841, 3061, 3066, 3073

### Living persons
373, 380, 630-631, 1736-1737, 1838a, 1838b, 1838c, 1838e, 1885a, 1885d, 1885e, 1935b, 1935d, 1935e, 1935f, 1940, 1971a-e, 1972a-e, 2017a-e, 2018a-e, 2085a-e, 2086a-e, 2118, 2178, 2180-2181, 2221–2222, 2225, 2333–2334, 2374, 2386, 2434, 2479–2483, 2549–2553, 2655a, 2655c, 2656, 2658, 2767–2770, 2773–2775, 2777, 2794–2795, 2837, 2850, 2866a–c, 2866e–f, 2867–2869, 2871–2875, 2877–2878, 2912a, 2917, 2922, 2935–2953, 2970b–c, 2972–2973, 2983a–e, 2986–2990, 3009, 3026, 3026d, 3026e, 3026f, 3030-3032, 3036-3038, 3079–3084, C7-C8

### Lunar New Year
1630, 1708, 1767-1768, 1836-1837, 1883-1884, 1933-1934, 1969-1970, 2015-2016, 2140-2141, 2201-2202, 2257–2258, 2296–2297, 2348–2349, 2416–2417, 2495–2497, 2599–2601, 2699–2701, 2801–2803, 2884–2887, 2959–2962, 3052–3055

### Manitoba
243, 397, 400, 422, 472, 505, 515, 633, 643, 723, 825, 856, 966, 987, 1020, 1050, 1312, 1426, 1478, 1487, 1562, 1635, 1709i, 1781, 1801-1804, 1854d, 1904a, 1941, 1990b, 1992, 2101, 2138, 2191, 2397b, 2399, 2539, 2558e, 2563, 2567f, 2573, 2611d, 2615, 2642c, 2643c, 2655d, 2661f, 2667, 2669f, 2675, 2659, 2696, 2771, 2778a, 2779, 2838a, 2839, 2860b, 2864, 2902d, 2906, 3017c, 3021, 3056f, 3070

### Maple Leaf
258-262, 314-315, 330, 354, 387, 417, 429A, 432, 437, 481, 500, 535-538, 635, 664-666, 680-682, 736, 873, 903, 906-908, 916, 923-924, 940, 943-946, 950-951, 1046, 1078, 1128, 1138, 1145, 1200, 1251, 1312, 1316, 1420-1431, 1444, 1446, 1582, 1607, 1614, 1692-1694, 1706, 1714, 1714B, 1723-1724, 1801-1804, 1807c-1808, 1808c, 1808e, 1808f, 1808j, 1808k, 1808m, 1808n, 1808o, 1808p, 1819c, 1825c-1827, 1835, 1861-1862, 1878, 1882b, 1901, 1904a, 1918b, 1926-1927, 1932, 1937, 1939, 1952b, 1984-1985, 1987, 2000, 2008-2010, 2013-2014, 2032, 2053-2055, 2063-2064, 2159-2161, 2331, 2332, 2350–2355, 2418–2423, 2718–2723, 2739–2744, 2807-2808, 2844–2849, 2857–2858, 2889–2894, 3042, C2, C4, C5, C7, C8

### Maps & Globes
85-86, 145, 194, 274, 336, 356, 370, 372, 376, 384, 387-388, 396, 411, 413, 416, 445-446, 453, 473, 479, 481, 493-494, 499, 540, 612, 691, 847, 890-893, 897, 977, 995, 1030-1031, 1061, 1077, 1103, 1110, 1126, 1145, 1202, 1235, 1251, 1406-1407, 1413, 1441-1442, 1563-1566, 1589, 1595, 1597, 1606e, 1649-1653, 1722, 1739-1742, 1755c, 1755g, 1780-1783, 1806, 1826b, 1831a, 1834b, 1861, 1902, 1962-1964, 1993, 2032, 2056, 2149, 2155, 2160, 2283, 2331, 2335–2336, 2337, 2397–2401, 2403, 2404, 2484–2485, 2531–2532, 2535–2538, 2852, 2855, C1, C2, C3, C4

### Medals/Medallions
1446-1447, 1609, 1877, 2065-2066, 2108, 2369, 2371–2372, 2373a, 2374, 2433–2434

### Medicine/medical/health
1302-1305, 1822a, 1822b, 1822c, 1822d, 1824c, 2557

### Minerals (gold, silver, copper)
373, 376-377, 401, 765-766, 864-865, 996, 1009, 1216, 1436-1440, 1606a, 1606b, 1606c, 1606d, 1606e, 1721, 2283

### Money
2274

### Mountains
155, 177, 595, 599-600, 632, 653, 727, 829, 912, 934, 936, 955, 1169, 1201, 1351, 1388, 1468, 1476, 1491, 1524h, 1524j, 1553, 1613-1614, 1650, 1739, 1830c, 1858, 1903c, 1952b, 1960a, 1960b, 1960c, 1960d, 1960e, 1960f, 1960g, 1960h, 1984, 1989b, 1991C, 1991D, 2087a-2088, 2105, 2116, 2137, 2162, 2224, 2279b, 2280b, 2366a, 2367, 2718c, 2723, 2844e, 2849, 2903b, 2909, 2970a, 2971, 3056h, 3068, 3077

### Movies & movie stars
1254, 1615a, 1615b, 1615c, 1615d, 1615e-1616, 1616b, 1616c, 1616d, 1616e, 1818a, 1821c, 2153a, 2153b, 2153c, 2153d-2154, 2154b, 2154c, 2154d, 2279a, 2279b, 2279c, 2279d, 2280a, 2280b, 2280c, 2280d, 2772–2777

### Mushrooms
1245-1248, 2461, 2463

### Music & instruments
396, 476-477, 680, 686, 780, 857-858, 860-861, 878, 1010, 1116, 1253, 1469, 1491-1494, 1526, 1533-1536, 1637, 1815, 1820a, 1820b, 1820c, 1820d-1821, 1968, 2021, 2118, 2178-2182, 2333–2334, 2479–2483, 2765–2770

### NATO
384, 1809

### New Brunswick
210, 400, 421, 824, 963, 992, 1014, 1016, 1182, 1423, 1465, 1471, 1481, 1489, 1554, 1572, 1709c, 1741, 1855c, 1952e, 2136, 2484a, 2485a, 2935b, 2937, 3050, 3056b, 3058, 3063, 3074

**Newfoundland**
282, 400, 427, 830, 957-958, 995, 1026, 1053, 1066, 1214, 1220, 1431, 1475, 1514, 1709e, 1783, 1855a, 1904e, 2077, 2173a, 2223, 2403, 2484d, 2485d, 2718a, 2719, 2838d, 2841, 2844c, 2846, 2929d, 2932, 2935a, 2936, 2963b–e, 2966–2968, 3056a, 3057, 3062, 3071

**Northwest Territories**
269, 429, 463, 506, 540, 831, 1009, 1018, 1027, 1427, 1483, 1513, 1782, 1953a, 2193, 2335c, 2336c, 2718d, 2720, 2844b, 2847, 3017b, 3019, 3056h, 3068, 3077

**Nova Scotia**
176, 242, 283, 382, 400, 420, 619, 823, 898, 960, 988, 1024, 1032, 1051, 1058, 1315, 1376, 1420, 1482, 1547-1551, 1558, 1651, 1709f, 1725, 1827b, 1827c, 1855e, 1903b, 1953e, 1975, 2089, 2102-2103, 2115, 2119, 2192, 2404, 2468, 2484b, 2485b, 2521, 2718b, 2721, 2739b, 2739c, 2740, 2742, 3017d, 3018

**Nunavut**
1784, 1904d, 1989a, 2189, 2838c, 2842, 2851–2856, 2929a, 2934, 3056h, 3056i, 3069, 3078

**Oil & petroleum**
55, 69-71, 73, 75, 95, 123, 294, 355, 381, 465B, 1721, 1867, 2116, 2267–2268

**Olympics (winter & summer)**
623-624, 629-632, 644-647, 656-657, 664-666, 681-689, 694, 848, 1077, 1111-1112, 1130-1131, 1152-1153, 1195-1198, 1399-1403, 1414-1418, 1608-1612, 2049-2050, 2143-2144, 2281, 2299–2313, 2366–2367, 2371–2372, 2373–2375, 2498c–2498d, 2501–2502, 2556, 3009, 3079–3084, B1-B12

**Ontario**
225, 400, 418, 442, 475, 511, 640-641, 723C, 767, 821, 897, 962, 983-984, 986, 996, 1027, 1035, 1052, 1055, 1059, 1064, 1122, 1181, 1313, 1411, 1421, 1462, 1469, 1472, 1484, 1488, 1512, 1555, 1571, 1652, 1672, 1709a, 1727-1729, 1732-1734, 1831d, 1854d, 1903e-1904, 1943, 1952c, 1974, 1976, 1989d-1990, 1998, 2023, 2028, 2080, 2161, 2214, 2217-2218, 2268, 2341–2342, 2397c, 2400, 2404, 2471c, 2471d, 2474–2475, 2558f, 2558g, 2564, 2565, 2567g, 2567h, 2574, 2575, 2598, 2642a, 2642f, 2642g, 2643a, 2643f, 2643g, 2661c, 2661g, 2664, 2668, 2669d, 2669g, 2673, 2676, 2724–2726, 2739e, 2744, 2754–2755, 2778b, 2778c, 2780, 2781, 2889b, 2893, 2902a, 2904, 2935c, 2939, 3017e, 3022, 3042-3044, 3056g, 3067, 3076

**Organizations**
354, 384, 493, 954, 980, 1215, 1657, 1769, 1786, 1799, 1821a, 1821b, 1821c, 1821d, 1824a, 1828c, 1828d, 1830d, 1834a, 1834b, 1834c, 1834d, 1857-1858, 1867, 1925, 1958, 1962, 1968, 1984-1985, 2032, 2094, 2104, 2282, 2394, 2402, 2645, 2718–2723, 2739–2744, B14–B19

**Paintings**
135, 142, 461-465, 465A, 465B, 492, 518, 532, 553, 562, 567, 570, 575, 579, 610, 617, 650-653, 732-734, 752, 763, 773-775, 813-814, 849-854, 883-884, 887-889, 955-966, 1016-1025, 1040-1042, 1076, 1203, 1227, 1241, 1271, 1294, 1296-1297, 1310, 1419-1431, 1466, 1516, 1545, 1559a, 1559b, 1559c-1560, 1560b, 1560c, 1560d-1561, 1561b, 1561c, 1602, 1635, 1743-1749, 1754, 1800, 1863, 1909, 1916, 1945, 1979-1983, 2002a, 2002b, 2002c, 2002d, 2002e, 2002f-2003, 2036-2040, 2067-2068, 2068a, 2095-2099, 2109-2110, 2110a, 2147-2148, 2148a, 2183, 2211-2212, 2223, 2276–2278, 2321–2322, 2395–2396, 2436–2439, 2644, 3046

**Paper, press, printing**
316, 334, 362, 375, 473, 484, 1044, 1136-1137, 1260, 1606d, 2104, 2151, 2167

**Parks**
726-727, 733, 934-937, 1084, 1472-1483, 1854a, 1854c, 1854e, 1855a, 1904d, 1952b, 1953b, 1989e, 2105, 2106, 2189, 2193, 2470, 2718a, 2718c, 2718d, 2718e, 2719–20, 2722–23, 2844–2849, 2857–2858, 2963a, 2964, 3056c, 3056d, 3056e, 3056f, 3056g, 3056h, 3059-3061, 3064-3068, 3070, 3072-3073, 3075-3077

**Parliament**
143, 159, 173, 202, 226, 241, 257, 277, 371, 399, 441-442, 450, 517, 544, 550, 714-715, 729-730, 740, 790, 797, 800, 806, 851, 925-926, 938-939, 941-942, 947-948, 952-953, 1061, 1163, 1165, 1186-1188, 1194, 1194A, 1260, 1293, 1904c, 2112, 2214, 2889b, 2893, 3086

**People**
261, 272, 275, 283, 302, 355, 362, 365-368, 373, 377, 380, 391, 394, 396, 410, 448, 475, 495, 517, 531, 542, 655, 661-663, 861, 894-895, 899, 915, 997, 1028, 1132, 1154, 1226, 1228, 1330-1332, 1423, 1444-1445, 1447-1448, 1510, 1576, 1590, 1606a, 1606b, 1606c, 1606e, 1608-1612, 1615a, 1615b, 1615d, 1615e-1616, 1616c, 1616d, 1616e-1617, 1636-1637, 1647-1648, 1655, 1657, 1672, 1709a, 1709b, 1709c, 1709d, 1709e, 1709f, 1709g, 1709h, 1709i, 1709j, 1722, 1727, 1736-1738, 1750-1753, 1761, 1818d, 1821d-1822, 1822b, 1822c, 1822d-1824, 1824c-1825, 1825b, 1825c, 1829a, 1829b, 1829c, 1829d-1830, 1830b, 1830c-1832, 1832b, 1832c, 1832d-1833, 1833c, 1867, 1876-1877, 1941-1943, 1993, 1999a, 1999b, 1999c, 1999d, 1999e, 1999f, 1999g, 1999h, 2019, 2021-2023, 2041-2042, 2061-2062, 2153a, 2153b, 2153c, 2153d-2154, 2154b, 2154c, 2154d-2155, 2158-2160, 2162, 2169, 2179-2182, 2219, 2220, 2221, 2222, 2225, 2226, 2227, 2228, 2240, 2267–2268, 2270–2273, 2275, 2276–2278, 2279–2280, 2282, 2284, 2315–2316, 2317, 2333–2334, 2373–2375, 2384–2386, 2418a, 2419, 2479–2483, 2489, 2498c, 2501, 2520–2521, 2549–2553, 2554–2555, 2567–2576, 2577–2580, 2618, 2619, 2620, 2635, 2650–2651, 2655–2659, 2660, 2684, 2702–2703, 2704–2707, 2732, 2755, 2765–2770, 2772–2777, 2786–2793, 2794–2795, 2804, 2805–2806, 2837, 2850, 2866–2878, 2895, 2902a–b, 2903b–c, 2904–2905, 2909–2910, 2912a–e, 2917–2922, 2935–2953, 2969, 3092b–e, 3094–3097

**Photography**
1237-1240, 2270, 2388–2393, 2404, 2626–2634, 2756–2764, 2814–2822, 2902–2910, 3016

**Politician**
484-485, 539, 558, 561, 616, 1293, 1661-1664, 1709a, 1709b, 1709c, 1709d, 1709e, 1709f, 1709g, 1709h, 1709i, 1709j, 1825a, 2112, 2557

**Postal service/mail delivery**
634-639, 815-816, 1094, 1122-1125, 1272-1273, 1657, 1900, 1956, 2041-2042, 2468–2469, 2649

**Power (electricity/gas)**
404, 408, 1411, 1562, 1831b

**Prime Ministers**
141, 144, 147, 303-304, 318-319, 349, 357-358, 393, 586-592, 859, 1584, 1825c, 1909, 2804

**Prince Edward Island**
224, 273, 400, 424, 431, 499, 618, 658, 827, 959, 1022, 1422, 1474, 1709j, 1742, 1855d, 1990e, 2034, 2135, 2276–2278, 2484c, 2485c, 2935e, 2940, 3017a, 3020, 3056d, 3061, 3066, 3073

**Quebec**
101, 156, 174, 201, 245, 379, 388, 400, 413, 419, 432, 464, 510, 601, 611, 642, 687-688, 780, 822, 956, 989-991, 1010, 1019, 1034, 1057, 1065, 1146, 1183, 1314, 1410, 1424, 1461, 1470, 1473, 1511, 1557, 1570, 1709b, 1730-1731, 1780, 1799, 1819b, 1831b, 1855b, 1902-1903, 1915, 1942, 1952d-1953, 1968, 1973, 1977, 1989e-1990, 2019-2022, 2030, 2033, 2035, 2079, 2100, 2209, 2269, 2290, 2397d, 2401, 2471b, 2473, 2558h, 2566, 2567i, 2576, 2642b, 2643b, 2661d, 2665, 2669b, 2671, 2718e, 2722, 2778d, 2782, 2838b, 2843, 2860d, 2862, 2935d, 2938, 2963c, 2965, 3000, 3056e, 3060, 3065, 3075

**R.C.M.P.**
223, 612-614, 777, 911, 1432, 1510, 1606c, 1736-1737, 1989c

**Radio**
541, 654, 1135, 1260, 1510, 1753, 1818c

**Red Cross**
317, 971, 1013, 1527a, 1605c

**Reptiles**
1309, 2145d, 2173b, 2173c, 2175-2176

**Rivers**
202, 269, 442, 465, 897, 1256, 1267-1268, 1321-1325, 1408-1412, 1484-1489, 1492, 1511-1515, 1540, 1570, 1572-1573, 1606a, 1606b, 1614, 1650, 1750, 1752, 1782-1783, 1854a, 1854b, 1854c, 1854d-1855, 1855b, 1855c, 1855d, 1855e, 1863, 1903c-1904, 1904c, 1952c, 1952d, 2011, 2076, 2087a, 2087b, 2087c, 2087d-2088, 2088b, 2088c, 2088d, 2101-2102, 2106, 2329, 2902d, 2906, C9

**Royalty**
2-3, 5, 8-11, 13-14, 16-18, 20-47, 50-54, 56-68, 72, 74, 76-84, 87-94, 96, 98, 104-120, 122, 124-134, 136-140, 149-154, 160-172, 178-184, 191-193, 195-200, 205-207, 211-214, 217-222, 228-240, 246, 248-252, 254-255, 263-267, 276-281, 284-293, 295-300, 305-306, 309-310, 315, 325-333, 337-341, 345, 347-348, 350, 374, 386, 401-409, 433, 454-460, 466-468, 468A, 468B, 471, 543-544, 549-550, 593, 593A, 604-605, 620-621, 704, 713, 716, 753, 755-756, 789, 791-792, 926, 926A, 1162, 1164, 1167-1168, 1357-1358, 1360, 1682-1683, 1722, 1856, 1932, 1987, 2012, 2075, 2142, 2150, 2188, 2248, 2298, 2464–2467, 2477–2478, 2513–2519, 2540, 2617, 2644, 2685–2686, 2698, 2859, 2888, 3098

**Santa Claus**
527, 627, 1067, 1339-1340, 1342, 1452, 1454-1455, 1500, 1502, 1628, 2069-2071, 2954a, 2956

**Saskatchewan**
355, 400, 425, 828, 863, 961, 967, 1023, 1056, 1375, 1412, 1425, 1463, 1480, 1653, 1709d, 1854b, 1989c, 2076, 2117, 2148a, 2210, 2227, 2397a, 2398, 2471e, 2476, 2558d, 2562, 2567e, 2572, 2929e, 2930, 3101

**Science**
396, 449, 507, 533-534, 582-585, 613, 865, 1099-1102, 1134-1138, 1206-1209, 1287, 1301, 1822b, 1830b, 2061-2062

**Scouting & Girl Guides**
356, 389, 993, 1062, 2225, 2402

**Ships & Boats**
158, 204, 208, 210, 216, 260, 262, 273, 282, 312, 351, 400, 412, 446, 457, 459-460, 464, 467-468, 468B, 482, 543, 549, 553, 567, 619, 670-673, 700-703, 738-739, 744-747, 764, 770, 776-779, 818, 824, 852, 910, 913, 1011-1012, 1014-1015, 1032, 1034-1035, 1106-1107, 1117, 1126, 1128, 1138-1144, 1200-1201, 1227-1232, 1234, 1236, 1261, 1266-1269, 1290, 1317-1320, 1322, 1324, 1333-1334, 1348, 1404, 1406, 1410, 1420, 1429, 1431, 1433, 1449, 1451, 1486, 1493, 1505, 1512-1513, 1524a, 1537, 1541, 1547, 1558, 1562, 1575, 1595, 1602, 1606b, 1614, 1635, 1639, 1649, 1726, 1728, 1730, 1733-1734, 1738, 1752, 1762-1763, 1779, 1803, 1823d, 1827a, 1827b, 1832c, 1834a, 1849, 1864-1866, 1904a, 1906, 1952d, 1963, 1990a, 2026-2027, 2041-2042, 2044, 2080, 2107, 2111b, 2155, 2214, 2219, 2225, 2226, 2269, 2279c, 2280a, 2290, 2337, 2369, 2384–2386, 2404, 2418c, 2421, 2486–2487, 2498a–b, 2499–2500, 2531–2538, 2611c, 2614, 2649, 2732, 2745–2747, 2748e, 2750, 2851–2856, 2889b, 2889e, 2892–2893, 2902d, 2906, 2969, 3050, 3056h, 3068, 3077, C6

**Space**
445, 681, 1046, 1079, 1100, 1441-1442, 1562, 1818a, 1831c, 1859, 1862, 1999a, 1999b, 1999c, 1999d, 1999e, 1999f, 1999g, 1999h, 2017a, 2017b, 2017c, 2017d, 2017e, 2017f-2018, 2018b, 2018c, 2018d, 2018e, 2018f, 2111a, 2111d, 2323–2325, 2418d, 2422, 2911–2922, 2983–2991

**Sports**
359, 365-368, 472, 483, 490, 500, 559, 629-632, 642, 644-647, 664-666, 757-762, 833-834, 848, 862, 968, 981-982, 1111-1112, 1130-1131, 1154, 1195-1198, 1221, 1343-1344, 1344b, 1344c, 1399-1403, 1414-1418, 1460, 1517-1522, 1553-1557, 1608-1612, 1650, 1659-1660, 1723-1724, 1753, 1801-1805, 1819c, 1819d, 1826b, 1838a, 1838b, 1838c, 1838d, 1838e, 1838f, 1885a, 1885b, 1885c, 1885d, 1885e, 1885f, 1894-1899, 1901, 1907-1908, 1935a, 1935b, 1935c, 1935d, 1935e, 1935f-1939, 1971a, 1971b, 1971c, 1971d, 1971e, 1971f-1972, 1972b, 1972c, 1972d, 1972e, 1972f, 1998, 2049-2052, 2085a, 2085b, 2085c, 2085d, 2085e, 2085f-2086, 2086b, 2086c, 2086d, 2086e, 2086f, 2113-2114, 2121a, 2121b, 2121c, 2121d, 2143-2144, 2161, 2220, 2265, 2281, 2299–2305, 2308–2313, 2338, 2339–2340, 2373–2375, 2556, 2558–2576, 2598, 2661–2676, 2704–2707, 2754–2755, 2778–2793, 2837, 2866–2878, 2935–2953, 3009, 3026–3044, 3079–3084, 3101, B4-B12

**Stamp-on-stamp & philately**
314, 399, 753-756, 909-913, 1722, 1738, 1900, 1956, 2119, 2468–2469, 2513–2517

**Statues/sculptures/carvings**
209, 227, 247, 378, 486, 488-489, 501, 656-657, 669, 748, 770, 836, 866, 1295, 1585-1587, 1778, 1823b, 1926, 1954-1955, 1967, 1975, 2335–2336, 2341–2342, 2349, 2397–2401, 2484–2485, 2981–2982

### Technology
641, 681, 1079, 1134-1138, 1206-1209, 1595-1598, 1654, 1834b, 1944, 1963-1964, 2488

### Television
1103, 1819c, 1819d, 1821d, 2153a-2154, 2733–2738, 2911–2922, 2991

### Totem pole
321, 455, 572, 1613, 1991C, 2152

### Trains, railroad
311, 400, 410, 459-460, 465, 468A, 468B, 531, 543, 549, 739, 839, 863, 901-902, 956, 964, 998-1002, 1023, 1036-1039, 1071-1074, 1093, 1099, 1117-1121, 1182, 1404, 1468, 1503, 1506, 1527e, 1579, 1605k, 1615a-1616, 1752, 1831a, 1903c, 1943, 1952c, 2028-2031, 2071, 2748b, 2751, 2757d, 2764, 2902c, 2907, E3

### Transportation
311-313, 447, 459-460, 468A, 468B, 543, 549, 635, 639, 723, 723C-725, 960, 1123, 1125, 1272-1273, 1331, 1451, 1490a, 1490b, 1490c, 1490d, 1490e, 1490f, 1524h, 1527a, 1527b, 1527c, 1527d, 1527e, 1527f, 1552a, 1552b, 1552c, 1552d, 1552e, 1552f, 1604a, 1604b, 1604c, 1604d, 1604e, 1604f-1605, 1605b, 1605c, 1605d, 1605e, 1605f, 1605g, 1605h, 1605i, 1605j, 1605k, 1605l, 1605m, 1605n, 1605o, 1605p, 1605q, 1605r, 1605s, 1605t, 1605u, 1605v, 1605w, 1605x, 1605y, 1639, 1739-1742, 1781, 1832d, 1851, 1860, 1944, 1952b, 2028-2031, 2070, 2284, 2498b, 2500, 2646–2648

### Trees
256, 269, 272, 301, 369, 385, 392, 395, 402, 406, 434-435, 455, 462, 516, 518, 523, 525, 530, 594, 610, 618, 626, 651-652, 659, 677, 679, 717-721, 732-734, 764, 780, 827, 842-844, 879, 900, 912, 925-926, 947-948, 952-953, 1069, 1122-1123, 1169, 1187-1188, 1191, 1194, 1194A, 1201, 1210-1213, 1217, 1244, 1257, 1271, 1283-1286, 1328, 1340, 1342, 1352, 1363-1374, 1405, 1408-1409, 1435, 1454, 1468, 1472, 1524a, 1524b, 1524c, 1524d, 1524e, 1524f, 1524g, 1524h, 1524i, 1524j, 1524k, 1524l, 1533, 1546, 1553-1555, 1557, 1593, 1613-1614, 1628, 1634, 1710-1712, 1756, 1770, 1774, 1785, 1854a, 1903b, 1903c, 1923, 1941-1944, 1952e, 1959, 1974, 2034, 2135, 2153c-2155, 2163, 2165, 2172-2173, 2186, 2190, 2209, 2223, 2225, 2241, 2250, 2276–2278, 2329, 2332, 2461, 2462, 2498b, 2500, 2838e, 2840, 2895, 2954, 2956–2958, 3045b, 3048, 3056b, 3056c, 3056f, 3056g, 3058–3059, 3063–3064, 3067, 3070, 3072, 3074, 3076

### United Nations
354, 372, 481, 507, 513-514, 560, 668, 690, 842, 976, 1045, 1110, 1288, 1523a, 1523b, 1523c, 1523d, 1523e, 1528, 1584, 1960a, 1960b, 1960c, 1960d, 1960e, 1960f, 1960g, 1960h-1961, 2718–2723, 2739–2744, 2844–2849, 2857–2858, 2889–2894, 2963–2968

### United States
691, 1413, 2332

### Universal Postal Union
371, 648-649, 1806

### War, military
247, 258-262, 283, 388, 486-487, 501, 680, 692-693, 819-820, 873-876, 1007-1008, 1043, 1049, 1075, 1094, 1249-1250, 1260-1263, 1298-1301, 1345-1348, 1448-1451, 1503-1506, 1525, 1527a, 1537-1544, 1546, 1558, 1590, 1605c, 1762-1763, 1808a, 1808b, 1808c, 1808d, 1808e, 1808f, 1808g, 1808h, 1808i, 1808j, 1808k, 1808l, 1808m, 1808n, 1808o, 1808p, 1825d, 1841, 1876-1877, 1906, 1926, 1993, 2025, 2043, 2065-2066, 2107-2108, 2190, 2384–2386, 2554–2555, 2578–2580, 2635, 2650–2651, 2684, 2748c, 2753, 2794–2795, 2835–2836, 2895, 2981–2982, C7, C8

### Water (ocean/sea/bay/river)
242, 244, 253, 262, 270, 273, 282, 312, 336, 351, 377, 387, 394-395, 412, 457-458, 463-464, 467, 480-481, 553, 567, 598-600, 629, 655, 726, 814, 833, 843, 845-846, 852, 862, 935-937, 968, 983-985, 991, 1012, 1015-1017, 1032-1035, 1084, 1139-1144, 1193, 1204-1205, 1214, 1217-1218, 1220, 1266, 1290, 1348-1349, 1351, 1353, 1389, 1404-1405, 1420, 1431, 1449, 1451, 1472, 1481-1482, 1493, 1524a, 1524b, 1524c, 1524d, 1524i, 1524k, 1524l, 1546, 1556, 1645-1646, 1649, 1651, 1687, 1695, 1705, 1721, 1725-1728, 1730, 1741-1742, 1762-1763, 1779-1780, 1803, 1845, 1855a, 1864-1865, 1867, 1904d, 1948-1951, 1953b, 1953d, 1988-1990, 1990d-1991, 1991D, 2022, 2043, 2046, 2079, 2136, 2155, 2157, 2163-2166, 2192-2193, 2204-2205, 2212a, 2219, 2223, 2229–2233, 2269, 2249, 2251, 2253–2253B, 2279c, 2280a, 2282, 2290, 2366b, 2368, 2369, 2397d, 2401, 2418a, 2419, 2468, 2486–2487, 2535, 2538, 2611a, 2611c, 2612, 2614, 2649, 2718–2723, 2889b, 2889e, 2892–2893, 2902c–d, 2906–2907, 2963b, 2967, 2969, 2981–2982, 3050, 3056b, 3056d, 3056e, 3056f, 3056g, 3056h, 3058, 3060-3061, 3063, 3065–3068, 3070, 3073–3077

### Waterfalls
225, 1854d, 1863, 1989a-1990, 2078, 2332, 2718d, 2720, 2935d, 2938, 3056f, 3070

### Women
385, 392, 470, 615, 622, 658, 659-660, 666, 668, 683, 768, 834, 860, 879-882, 1047-1048, 1075, 1209, 1227, 1260-1261, 1298-1300, 1302, 1326, 1345, 1434, 1453, 1456-1459, 1509, 1517, 1526, 1606d, 1608, 1610, 1622, 1624, 1661, 1663, 1823b-1825, 1895, 1939, 1942, 1944, 1994, 1997, 2035, 2112, 2153b, 2153d-2154, 2154c, 2171, 2178, 2180, 2226, 2315, 2333b, 2334c, 2373–2375, 2433, 2651, 2704–2707, 2733a, 2734, 2748a, 2749, 2765b, 2765c, 2765e, 2767, 2768, 2770, 2772c, 2775, 2814b, 2817, 2837, 2850, 2901, 3079–3085, 3092e, 3095

### Yukon
428, 461, 595, 727, 832, 955, 1025, 1413, 1430, 1438, 1479, 1486, 1606a, 1606b, 1606c, 1606d, 1606e, 1661, 1739, 1952a, 1960a, 2139, 2335b, 2336b, 2844e, 2849, 2860e, 2865, 2929c, 2933

### Zodiac
2445–2460

# People Listing

Listed alphabetically are individuals (other than Royalty) specifically being honoured and/or pictured

Abbott, Maude (1822d)
Abbott, Sir John (318)
Adams, Bryan (2333d, 2334a)
Alaimo, Marc (2983d, 2988)
Alarie, Pierrette (2180)
Albani, Emma (860)
Alexander, Lincoln M. (3086)
Allan, Sir Hugh (2042)
Anka, Paul (2221d, 2222d)
Apps, Syl (1885f)
Arbour, Louise (2549a, 2550)
Ashoona, Pitseolak (1458)
Baldwin, Robert (148)
Banting, Sir Frederic (1304, 1822a)
Bakula, Scott (2983b, 2990)
Barbeau, Marcel (1749)
Bartlett, Captain Robert A. (2337)
Béliveau, Jean (1885a, 2340b, 3026b, 3028, 3034)
Bell, Alexander Graham (274, 1832c)
Bennett, Richard B. (357, 590)
Bennett, W.A.C. (1709g)
Bernard, Warren "Whitey" (2794, 2795)
Bernier, Joseph E. (738)
Berthiaume, Trefflé (1044)
Best, Carrie (2433)
Bethune, Norman (1264–1265)
Bishop, William Avery (1525)
Black, Martha (1661)
Bombardier, Joseph-Armand (1832d)
Bondar, Roberta (1999b)
Boone, W. Hanson (1238)
Borduas, Paul-Émile (1747)
Borden, Sir Robert (303, 588)
Bossy, Mike (1971e, 1972e)
Bourassa, Henri (485)
Bourgeoys, Marguerite (660)
Bourque, Raymond (1971b, 1972b)
Bowell, Sir Mackenzie (350)
Bower, Johnny (2017d, 2018d, 2866c, 2869, 2875)
Bracken, John (1709i)
Brant, Molly (1091)
Brock, Sir Isaac (501, 2554)
Brodeur, Martin (2866f, 2872, 2878)
Brooks, Avery (2983d, 2988)
Brown, George (484)
Brown, Rosemary (2315)
Brown, Sir Isaac (501)
Brûlé (1126)
Buchanan, Kadeisha (2837)
Bucyk, John (2085f, 2086f)
Burke, Sarah (2704c, 2707)
Burr, Raymond (2279d, 2280d)
Butler, Édith (2333b, 2334c)
By, Colonel John (820)
Cabot, John (282, 1106, 1649)
Callaghan, Morley (1996)
Candy, John (2153a, 2154a)
Caouette, Réal (1664)
Captain Vancouver (2219)
Carr, Emily (532)
Carrey, Jim (2772e, 2777)
Cartier, George-Étienne (190)
Cartier, Jacques (7, 19, 97, 103, 208, 1011)
Casgrain, Thérèse (1047)
Catherwood, Ethel (1608)
Champlain (97, 99, 102, 379, 2155)
Chapdelaine, Maria (659)
Charlebois, Robert (2333a 2334d)
Chevrier, Lionel (1662)
Chown, Dr. S. D. (662)
Churchill, Sir Winston (440, 2271b, 2273)
Clarkson, Adrienne (1940)
Cockburn, Bruce (2480, 2480a, 2483a)
Colicos, John (2912b, 2919)
Comeau, Napoléon-Alexandre (1750)
Conan, Laure (978)
Connors, Stompin' Tom (2333c, 2334b)
Cook, Captain James (764, 765)

Cook, Dr. J. (663)
Creighton, Donald G. (1623)
Crosby, Sidney (2941a, 2942, 2948)
Crowfoot, Chief (1108)
Cunard, Sir Samuel (2041)
Da Costa, Mathieu (2969)
Dandurand, Raoul (1825a)
Davies, Robertson (2660)
Davies, Will (3092b, 3096)
de Gaspé, Philippe Aubert (1090)
de l'Incarnation, Marie (886)
de Mons, Pierre Dugua (2044)
de Salaberry, Colonel C.M. (819, 2650)
des Groseilliers, Médard Chouart (1127)
Desjardins, Alphonse (661, 1823c)
Desmarteau, Etienne (1609)
Desmond, Viola (2521)
Diefenbaker, John George (859)
Dionne, Marcel (2017b, 2018b)
Doohan, James (2912d, 2918)
Douglas, Tommy (1709d, 2557)
Drawson, Blair (3092c, 3094)
Dressler, Marie (2279c, 2280a)
Dryden, Ken (2866a, 2867, 2873)
Dubois, Gérard (3092d, 3097)
Dumont, Gabriel (1049)
Durnan, Bill (1971f, 1972f)
d'Youville, Marguerite (768)
Eaton, Timothy (1510)
Edwards, Henrietta (882)
Esposito, Phil (1935f, 2941b, 2943, 2949)
Esposito, Tony (2866b, 2868, 2874)
Fairclough, Ellen (2112)
Fenerty, C. (1136)
Ferron, Marcelle (1748)
Fessenden, R.A. (1135)
Finley, Gerald (2970b, 2972)
Firth, Sharon (3079b, 3081)
Firth, Shirley (3079b, 3081)
Fleming, Sir Sandford (739, 1963)
Forrester, Maureen (2178)
Fortes, Joe (2620)
Foster, Harry "Red" (1753)
Fox, Michael J. (2549d, 2553)
Fox, Terry (915, 1824c, 2999d, 3003)
Franklin, Benjamin (691, 2649)
Franklin, Sir John (1234)
Frappier, Dr. Armand (1822b)
Fraser, Simon (1201)
Fréchette, Louis-H. (1243)
Frobisher, Martin (412)
Frontenac (561)
Frum, Barbara (1821d)
Frye, Northrup (1829b)
Fuhr, Grant (2085b, 2086b)
Gadbois, Abbe Charles-Émile (1637)
Garneau, Hector de Saint-Denys (1995)
Garneau, Marc (1999a)
Gaudet, Sonja (3079e, 3084)
Gauvreau, Pierre (1746)
Gélinas, Gratien (1828b)
George, Chief Dan (2279b, 2280b)
Gérin-Lajoie, Marie-Joséphine (1457)
Gesner, Abraham (1832b)
Gilbert, Sir Humphrey (995)
Gisborne, F.N. (1138)
Gould, Glenn (1820b)
Goyette, Danielle (3079c, 3082)
Greene, Lorne (2153c, 2154d)
Greene, Nancy (3079a, 3080)
Grenfell, Sir Wilfred (438)
Gretzky, Wayne (1838a, 3026f, 3032, 3038)
Griffith, Harold R. (1305)
Grove, Frederick P. (817)
Guèvremont, Germaine (696)
Guimond, Olivier (2772d, 2776)
Guttman, Irving (2970d, 2974)
Gzowski, Sir Casimir Stanislaus (410)
Hadfield, Chris (1999d)
Haliburton, Thomas C. (1626)
Hall, Glenn (1935d)
Hall, William (2369)
Hamilton, Lewis (2992e, 2997)
Hanlan, Ned (862)
Hansen, Rick (2549b, 2551)
Harvey, Doug (1838d, 1786b, 2787b, 2789)
Harvie, Eric Lafferty (1830c)
Hayward, Bob (2486)
Hearne, Samuel (540)
Hébert, Anne (1994)
Hébert, Louis (1060)
Henday, Anthony (1199)
Henderson, Alexander (1239)
Henson, Josiah (997)
Hepburn, Audrey (2271a, 2272)
Herzberg, Dr. Gerhard (2061)
Hewitt, Foster (1819c)
Hill, James (3092e, 3095)
Hnatyshyn, Ramon (1940, 2024)
Hoodless, Adelaide Sophia (1456)
Hopkins, Frances Ann (1227)
Horton, Tim (1935a, 2786a, 2787a, 2788)
Howe, Gordie (1838b, 3026c, 3029, 3035)
Howe, Joseph (616)
Howell, Harry (2786d, 2787d, 2791)
Hudson, Henry (1107)
Hughes, Clara (3079d, 3083)
Hull, Bobby (1885e)
Humphrey, John Peters (1761)
Hunter, Tommy (2765d, 2769)
Huntsman, Dr. Archibald G. (1833c)
Inglis, Charles (1226)
Jackman, Capt. William (1433)
Jackson, Russ (2755)
Jenkins, Ferguson (2434)
Jobin, Raoul (2179)
Johnson, Edward (2182)
Johnson, Pauline (392)
Jolliet, Louis (1128)
Jones, J. Walter (1709j)
Jones, Oliver (2619)
Kaihori, Ayumi (2837)
Kane, Paul (553)
Karsh, Yousuf (2270)
Kelley, DeForest (2912c, 2921)
Kelly, Red (1935e, 2786f, 2787f, 2793)
Kelsey, Henry (512)
Killam, Dorothy and Isaac (1830b)
King, William Lyon Mackenzie (304, 589, 1584)
Kinnear, Helen Alice (1459)
Klein, George (1832a)
Krige, Alice (2983c, 2989)
Kunz, Anita (3092a, 3093)
La Salle (446)
La Vérendrye (378)
Labelle, Antoine (998)
Lafleur, Guy (1935b, 2340c, 2941c, 2944, 2950)
Lafontaine, Sir Louis (148)
LaMarsh, Judy (1663)
Lampman, Archibald (1244)
lang, k.d. (2765e, 2770)
Laporte, Pierre (558)
Laurence, Margaret (1622)
Laurier, Sir Wilfred (144, 147, 587)
Leacock, Stephen (504)
LeBlanc, Roméo (1940, 2370)
Lecavalier, René (1819d)
Leclerc, Félix (1820d)
Leduc, Fernand (1744)
Léger, Jules (735, 914, 1940)
Leggo, G.E. Desbarats W. (1137)
Lemelin, Roger (1829c)
Lemieux, Mario (3026e, 3031, 3037)
Lesage, Jean (1709b)
Lightfoot, Gordon (2221a, 2222a)
Lindsay, Ted (2017c, 2018c)
Livernois, Jules-Ernest (1240)
Livingstone, Kay (3085)
Lombardo, Guy (1820c)
MacDonald, Angus L. (1709f)
MacDonald, J.E.H. (617)
Macdonald, Sir John A. (141, 147, 586, 2804, 3010b, 3016)
Macdonald, Scott (2983b, 2990)
Mackenzie, Alexander (PM) (319)
Mackenzie, Sir Alexander (explorer) (516)
MacLean, Steve (1999c)
MacLeod, James F. (1109)
Macoun, John (895)
Macphail, Agnes (1293)
Mahovlich, Frank (1971a, 1972a)
Mance, Jeanne (615)
Mandela, Nelson (2805, 2806)
Manning, Ernest C. (1709h)
Marconi, Guglielmo (654, 1964)
Marie-Victorin, Frère (894)
Marquette, Father Jacques (1128)
Martel, Renée (2765b, 2767)
Mason, Bill (1752)
Massey, Hart (1830a)
Massey, Vincent (491, 735, 1940)
Matonabbee (1233)
McClung, Nellie (622)
McCrae, John (487)
McGarrigle, Kate & Anna (2482, 2482a, 2483b)
McGee, Thomas D'Arcy (146)
McKinney, Louise (880)
McLaughlin, Robert Samuel (2284)
McLuhan, Marshall (1829a)
McNair, John B. (1709c)
Meighen, Arthur (393)
Membertou (2226)
Merritt, William Hamilton (655)
Messier, Mark (2941e, 2946, 2952)
Michener, Daniel Roland (735, 1447, 1940)
Mikita, Stan (1971d, 1972d)
Mitchell, Joni (2221b, 2222b)
Mitchell, W.O. (1828a)
Molson, John (1117)
Montalban, Ricardo (2983a, 2986)
Montcalm, General (100)
Montferrand, Jos (1435)
Montgomery, Lucy Maud (658)
Montpetit, Édouard (1617)
Moodie, Susanna (1997)
Morenz, Howie (1935c)
Mosher, Aaron R. (899)
Mousseau, Jean-Paul (1745)
Mowat, Sir Oliver (517)
Mulgrew, Kate (2983c, 2989)
Mulock, Sir William (1722)
Munday, Phyllis (1751)
Munro, Alice (2850)
Murphy, Emily (1048)
Murray, Anne (2221c, 2222c)
Myers, Mike (2772a, 2773)
Neatby, Hilda Marion (1829d)
Nelligan, Émile (818)
Nimoy, Leonard (2912e, 2920)
Notman, William (1237)
O'Hara, Catherine (2772c, 2775)
Ormeaux, Dollard des (390)
Orr, Bobby (1838e, 2786c, 2787c, 2790, 3026d, 3030, 3036)
Osler, Sir William (495)
Ouellette, Gerald (1611)
Owl, Grey (2903c, 2910)
Palliser, John (1202)
Papineau, L.J. (539)
Parent, Bernie (2866e, 2871, 2877)
Park, Brad (2017e, 2018e)
Payette, Julie (1999h)
Pearson, Lester B. (591, 1825c)
Penfield, Wilder G. (1303)
Peterson, Oscar (2118)
Pickford, Mary (2153d, 2154b)
Pieczonka, Adrianne (2970c, 2973)
Pilote, Pierre (2085d, 2086d, 2786e, 2787e, 2792)
Plante, Jacques (1838f)
Polanyi, Dr. John Charles (2489)
Potts, Jerry (1432)
Potvin, Denis (1885d)
Pratt, E.J. (979)
Radisson, Pierre-Esprit (1127)
Reno, Ginette (2479, 2479a, 2483c)
Richard, Henri (2085a, 2086a)
Richard, Maurice (1838c, 2340a, 3026a, 3027, 3033)
Riel, Louis (515)
Riopelle, Jean-Paul (1743)
Robarts, John P. (1709a)
Robertson, Robbie (2481, 2481a, 2483d)
Robinson, Larry (2017a, 2018a)
Rogers, Ted (Sr.) (1818c)
Rosenfeld Fanny (1610)
Roué, WIlliam James (1738)
Roy, Gabrielle (1624)
Rutherford, Ernest (534)
Saint-Jean, Idola (881)
Saunders, Sir Charles (1833a)
Sauvé, Jeanne (1509, 1940)
Savard, Félix-Antoine (1625)
Savard, Serge (1971c, 1971d)
Sawchuck, Terry (1885b)
Schmidt, Milt (2017f, 2018f)
Schmirler, Sandra (2704b, 2706)
Schreyer, Edward (1940)
Schumacher, Michael (2992d, 2996)
Scott, Barbara Ann (2704a, 2705)
Secord, Laura (1434, 2651)
Selye, Dr. Hans (1822c)
Selkirk, Lord (397)
Senna, Ayrton (2992c, (2995)
Service, Robert W. (695)
Shadd, Abraham Doras (2316)
Shatner, William (2912a, 2917, 2983a, 2986)
Shearer, Norma (2279a, 2280c)
Shore, Eddie (1885c)
Short, Martin (2772b, 2774)
Simoneau, Léopold (2180)
Sinclair, Christine (2837)
Sittler, Darryl (2941f, 2947, 2953)
Smallwood, Joseph R. (1709e)
Smellie, Elizabeth (1825b)
Smith, Michael (2062)
Smith, Sir Donald Alexander (531)
Snow, Hank (2765a, 2766)
Spotton, John (1821c)
St. Laurent, Louis (592)
Stanley, Allan (2085c, 2086c)
Stefansson, Vilhjalmur (1236)
Stewart, Sir Jackie (2992a, 2993)
Stewart, Patrick (2983e, 2987)
Stowe, Emily (879)
Stephenson, Sir Wm. (1818d)
Sverdrup, Otto (2026)
Talon, Jean (398)
Tecumseh, War Chief (2555)
Teasdale, Dr. Louise (1824b)
Tekakwitha, Kateri (885)
Thirsk, Robert (1999e)
Thompson, David (370)
Thompson, Sir John (349)
Thomson, Tom (733, 734)
Traill, Catharine Parr (1997)
Travers, Mary (1526)
Tripp, Charles (2268)
Trottier, Bryan (2085e, 2086e)
Trout, Jennie K. (1302)
Trudeau, Pierre Elliott (1909)
Tryggvason, Bjarni (1999f)
Tupper, Sir Charles (358)
Tyrrell, Joseph Burr (1235)
Twain, Shania (2765c, 2768)
Vancouver, George (1200, 2219)
Vanier, George (474, 735, 1940)
Vanier, Pauline (1825b)
Vickers, Jon (2181)
Villeneuve, Gilles (1647, 1648, 2992b, 2994)
Wallenberg, Raoul (2618)
Walters, Angus (1228)
Ware, John (2520)
Watt-Cloutier, Sheila (2549c, 2552)
White, Portia (1820a)
Willan, Healey (861)
Williams, Dave (1999g)
Williams, James M. (2268)
Williams, Percy (1612)
Wolfe, General (100)
Worsley, Gump (2866d, 2870, 2876)
Wray, Fay (2153b, 2154c)
Yzerman, Steve (2941d, 2945, 2951)

# DEFINITIVE STAMP IDENTIFIER (1977–present)

Stamps are grouped by similar designs

## FLOWERS: 1977–1982

| | | Issued | Method | Printer | Perf |
|---|---|---|---|---|---|
| 705 | **1¢ lilac & multicoloured** | 1977 | Litho | CBN | 12.0x12.5 |
| xx | precancelled | | | | |
| 781 | **1¢ lilac & multicoloured** | 1979 | Photo | BABN | 13.0x13.3 |
| a | booklet single | 1977 | Photo | BABN | 12.0x12.5 |
| 707 | **2¢ pale brown & multicoloured** | 1977 | Litho | CBN | 12.0x12.5 |
| 782 | **2¢ pale brown & multicoloured** | 1979 | Photo | BABN | 13.0x13.3 |
| b | booklet single | 1978 | Photo | BABN | 12.0x12.5 |
| 708 | **3¢ dull green & multicoloured** | 1977 | Litho | CBN | 12.0x12.5 |
| xx | precancelled | | | | |
| 783 | **3¢ dull green & multicoloured** | 1979 | Photo | BABN | 13.0x13.3 |
| 709 | **4¢ dull lavender & multicoloured** | 1977 | Litho | CBN | 12.0x12.5 |
| 784 | **4¢ dull lavender & multicoloured** | 1979 | Photo | BABN | 13.0x13.3 |
| 710 | **5¢ dull brown & multicoloured** | 1977 | Litho | CBN | 12.0x12.5 |
| xx | precancelled | | | | |
| 785 | **5¢ dull brown & multicoloured** | 1979 | Photo | BABN | 13.0x13.3 |
| 711 | **10¢ ochre & multicoloured** | 1977 | Litho | CBN | 12.0x12.5 |
| a | perf change | 1978 | Litho | CBN | 13.0x13.3 |
| xx | precancelled | | | | |
| 786 | **10¢ ochre & multicoloured** | 1979 | Photo | BABN | 13.0x13.3 |
| 712 | **12¢ bright green & multicoloured** | 1978 | Photo | BABN | 13.0x13.3 |
| xx | precancelled (red lines) | | | | |
| 787 | **15¢ violet & multicoloured** | 1979 | Photo | BABN | 13.0x13.3 |
| xx | precancelled | | | | |

## TREES: 1977–1982

| | | Issued | Method | Printer | Perf |
|---|---|---|---|---|---|
| 717 | **15¢ sage green & multicoloured** | 1977 | Photo | BABN | 13.3 |
| 718 | **20¢ light blue & multicoloured** | 1977 | Photo | BABN | 13.3 |
| 719 | **25¢ stone & multicoloured** | 1977 | Photo | BABN | 13.3 |
| 720 | **30¢ grey-brown & multicoloured** | 1978 | Photo | BABN | 13.3 |
| 721 | **35¢ grey-brown & multicoloured** | 1979 | Photo | BABN | 13.3 |

## STREETS: 1977–1982

| | | Issued | Method | Printer | Perf |
|---|---|---|---|---|---|
| 723 | **50¢ multicoloured** | 1978 | Photo | BABN | 13.3 |
| 723A | **50¢ multicoloured** | 1978 | Litho | CBN | 13.3 |
| 723C | **60¢ multicoloured** | 1982 | Litho | CBN | 13.3 |
| 724 | **75¢ multicoloured** | 1978 | Photo | BABN | 13.3 |
| 725 | **80¢ multicoloured** | 1978 | Photo | BABN | 13.3 |

## NATIONAL PARK DEFINITIVES: 1979–1987

| | | Issued | Method | Printer | Perf |
|---|---|---|---|---|---|
| 726 | **$1 multicoloured**, tagged | 1979 | Litho | CBN | 13.3 |
| a | untagged | 1981 | Litho | CBN | 13.3 |
| 934 | **$1 multicoloured**, Clark paper | 1984 | Litho | CBN | 13.3 |
| iii | Harrison paper | 1985 | Litho | CBN | 13.3 |
| iv | Harrison paper, printer change | 1986 | Litho | BABN | 13.3 |
| 935 | **$1.50 multicoloured** | 1982 | Litho | CBN | 13.3 |

| | | Issued | Method | Printer | Perf |
|---|---|---|---|---|---|
| 727 | **$2 multicoloured**, APP | 1979 | Litho | CBN | 13.3 |
| iv | Clark paper | 1984 | Litho | CBN | 13.3 |
| v | Harrison paper | 1985 | Litho | CBN | 13.3 |
| 936 | **$2 multicoloured** | 1985 | Litho | CBN | 13.3 |
| i | printer change | 1986 | Litho | BABN | 13.3 |
| 937 | **$5 multicoloured**, Abitibi-Price Paper | 1983 | Litho | CBN | 13.3 |
| i | Clark paper | 1984 | Litho | CBN | 13.3 |
| ii | Harrison paper | 1985 | Litho | CBN | 13.3 |
| 1084 | **$5 multicoloured** | 1986 | Litho | CBN | 13.3 |
| ii | printer change | 1987 | Litho | BABN | 13.3 |

## QUEEN ELIZABETH II: 1977–1987

| | | Issued | Method | Printer | Perf |
|---|---|---|---|---|---|
| 713 | **12¢ bright blue & black** | 1977 | Photo | BABN | 13.0x13.3 |
| a | booklet single | 1977 | Photo | BABN | 12.0x12.5 |
| 716 | **14¢ red & black** | 1978 | Photo | BABN | 13.0x13.3 |
| a | booklet single | 1978 | Photo | BABN | 12.0x12.5 |
| 789 | **17¢ green & black** | 1979 | Photo | BABN | 13.0x13.3 |
| a | booklet single | 1979 | Photo | BABN | 12.0x12.5 |
| 791 | **30¢ deep magenta & black** | 1982 | Photo | BABN | 13.0x13.3 |
| 792 | **32¢ grey-blue & black**, APP | 1983 | Photo | BABN | 13.0x13.3 |
| i | Harrison paper | 1983 | Photo | BABN | 13.0x13.3 |
| 926 | **34¢ dark blue** | 1985 | Engr | BABN | 13.0x13.3 |
| 926A | **36¢ plum** | 1987 | Engr | BABN | 13.0x13.3 |

## HOUSES OF PARLIAMENT: 1977–1982

| | | Issued | Method | Printer | Perf |
|---|---|---|---|---|---|
| 797 | **1¢ grey blue**, booklet single | 1979 | Engr | BABN | 12.0x12.5 |
| 800 | **5¢ purple**, booklet single | 1979 | Engr | BABN | 12.0x12.5 |
| 714 | **12¢ blue**, coated paper | 1977 | Engr | BABN | 13.0x13.3 |
| iv | uncoated paper | 1978 | Engr | CBN | 13.0x13.3 |
| xx | precancelled | 1978 | Engr | CBN | 13.0x13.3 |
| 729 | **12¢ blue**, coil | 1977 | Engr | CBN | 10 vert |
| 715 | **14¢ red** | 1978 | Engr | CBN | 13.0x13.3 |
| 730 | **14¢ red**, coil | 1978 | Engr | CBN | 10 vert |
| 790 | **17¢ green** | 1979 | Engr | BABN | 13.0x13.3 |
| 806 | **17¢ green**, coil | 1979 | Engr | CBN | 10 vert |

## MAPLE LEAF: 1981–1984

| | | Issued | Method | Printer | Perf |
|---|---|---|---|---|---|
| 940 | **5¢ purple**, uncoated paper | 1982 | Engr | BABN | 12.0x12.5 |
| i | coated paper | 1982 | Engr | BABN | 12.0x12.5 |
| 943 | **8¢ dark blue** | 1983 | Engr | BABN | 12.0x12.5 |
| 944 | **10¢ dark green**, uncoated paper | 1982 | Engr | BABN | 12.0x12.5 |
| i | coated paper | 1982 | Engr | BABN | 12.0x12.5 |
| 907 | **(30¢) red**, coated paper | 1981 | Engr | BABN | 13.0x13.3 |
| ii | uncoated paper | 1981 | Engr | CBN | 13.0x13.3 |
| 908 | **(30¢) red**, coil | 1981 | Engr | CBN | 10 vert |
| 923 | **30¢ red on blue** | 1982 | Photo | BABN | 13.0x13.3 |
| b | booklet single | 1982 | Photo | BABN | 12.0x12.5 |
| 945 | **30¢ red**, uncoated paper | 1982 | Engr | BABN | 12.0x12.5 |
| i | coated paper | 1982 | Engr | BABN | 12.0x12.5 |
| 950 | **30¢ red**, coil | 1982 | Engr | CBN | 10 vert |
| 924 | **32¢ red on cream**, Abitibi-Price paper | 1983 | Photo | BABN | 13.0x13.3 |
| i | Harrison paper | 1983 | Photo | BABN | 13.0x13.3 |
| b | booklet single, APP | 1983 | Photo | BABN | 12.0x12.5 |
| bis | booklet single, Harrison | 1984 | Photo | BABN | 12.0x12.5 |
| 946 | **32¢ brown** | 1983 | Engr | BABN | 12.0x12.5 |
| 951 | **32¢ brown**, coil, Abitibi-Price paper | 1983 | Engr | CBN | 10 vert |
| iii | Clark paper | 1984 | Engr | CBN | 10 vert |

## ARTIFACTS: 1982–1987

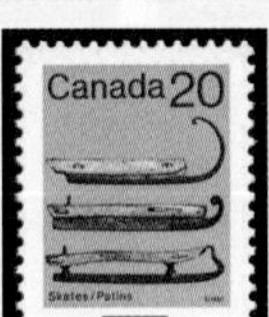

| | | Issued | Method | Printer | Perf |
|---|---|---|---|---|---|
| 917 | **1¢ light brown and multicoloured** Abitibi-Price paper | 1982 | Litho | AP | 14.0x13.3 |
| iii | Rolland paper | 1986 | Litho | AP | 14.0x13.3 |
| a | Harrison paper | 1985 | Litho | CBN | 13.0x13.3 |
| aii | Clark paper | 1985 | Litho | CBN | 13.0x13.3 |

| | | Issued | Method | Printer | Perf |
|---|---|---|---|---|---|
| 918 | **2¢ green and multicoloured**, | | | | |
| | Abitibi-Price paper | 1982 | Litho | AP | 14.0x13.3 |
| ii | Rolland paper | 1986 | Litho | AP | 14.0x13.3 |
| a | Clark paper | 1984 | Litho | CBN | 13.0x13.3 |
| ai | Harrison paper | 1986 | Litho | CBN | 13.0x13.3 |
| 919 | **3¢ purple and multicoloured**, | | | | |
| | Abitibi-Price paper | 1982 | Litho | AP | 14.0x13.3 |
| iii | Rolland paper | 1986 | Litho | AP | 14.0x13.3 |
| a | Harrison paper | 1985 | Litho | CBN | 13.0x13.3 |
| 920 | **5¢ flesh and multicoloured**, | | | | |
| | Abitibi-Price paper | 1982 | Litho | AP | 14.0x13.3 |
| i | Rolland paper | 1986 | Litho | AP | 14.0x13.3 |
| a | Clark paper | 1984 | Litho | CBN | 13.0x13.3 |
| ai | Harrison paper | 1985 | Litho | CBN | 13.0x13.3 |
| 921 | **10¢ blue and multicoloured**, | | | | |
| | Abitibi-Price paper | 1982 | Litho | AP | 14.0x13.3 |
| i | Rolland paper | 1986 | Litho | AP | 14.0x13.3 |
| a | Harrison paper, tagged | 1985 | Litho | CBN | 13.0x13.3 |
| 922 | **20¢ grey-brown and multicoloured**, | | | | |
| | Abitibi-Price paper | 1982 | Litho | CBN | 13.0x13.3 |
| ii | Rolland Paper | 1986 | Litho | CBN | 13.0x13.3 |
| 1080 | **25¢ yellow and multicoloured** | 1987 | Litho | AP | 14.0x13.3 |

| | | Issued | Method | Printer | Perf |
|---|---|---|---|---|---|
| 927 | **37¢ grey-green and multicoloured**, | | | | |
| | Abitibi-Price paper | 1983 | Litho | AP | 12.0x12.5 |
| i | Clark paper | 1984 | Litho | AP | 12.0x12.5 |
| 928 | **39¢ violet and multicoloured** | 1985 | Litho | AP | 12.0x12.5 |
| 1081 | **42¢ orange-brown and multicoloured** | 1987 | Litho | AP | 12.0x12.5 |
| 929 | **48¢ light brown and multicoloured**, | | | | |
| | Abitibi-Price paper | 1983 | Litho | AP | 12.0x12.5 |
| ii | Clark paper | 1983 | Litho | AP | 12.0x12.5 |
| 930 | **50¢ blue and multicoloured** | 1985 | Litho | AP | 12.0x12.5 |
| 1082 | **55¢ pink and multicoloured** | 1987 | Litho | AP | 12.0x12.5 |
| 932 | **64¢ grey and multicoloured**, | | | | |
| | Abitibi-Price paper | 1983 | Litho | AP | 12.0x12.5 |
| i | Clark paper | 1984 | Litho | AP | 12.0x12.5 |
| 933 | **68¢ tan and multicoloured** | 1985 | Litho | AP | 12.0x12.5 |
| 1083 | **72¢ apple green and multicoloured** | 1987 | Litho | AP | 12.0x12.5 |

## HOUSES OF PARLIAMENT: 1985–1990

| | | Issued | Method | Printer | Perf |
|---|---|---|---|---|---|
| 938 | **1¢ lime green**, Rolland paper, uncoated | 1987 | Engr | BABN | 12.5x12.0 |
| i | Harrison paper (coated) | 1987 | Engr | BABN | 12.5x12.0 |
| 939 | **2¢ deep green**, | | | | |
| | Abitibi-Price paper (uncoated) | 1985 | Engr | BABN | 12.5x12.0 |
| i | Rolland paper (uncoated) | 1985 | Engr | BABN | 12.5x12.0 |
| a | slate green, Harrison paper, (coated) | 1989 | Engr | BABN | 12.5x12.0 |
| 941 | **5¢ dark brown**, | | | | |
| | Abitibi-Price paper (uncoated) | 1985 | Engr | BABN | 12.5x12.0 |
| i | Rolland paper (uncoated) | 1985 | Engr | BABN | 12.5x12.0 |
| 942 | **6¢ henna brown**, | | | | |
| | Rolland paper (uncoated) | 1987 | Engr | BABN | 12.5x12.0 |
| i | Harrison paper (coated) | 1987 | Engr | BABN | 12.5x12.0 |
| 1186 | **6¢ purple** | 1989 | Engr | BABN | 12.5x12.0 |
| 925 | **34¢ multicoloured**, | | | | |
| | Harrison paper | 1985 | Litho | CBN | 13.3x13.0 |
| as | booklet single, Harrison paper | 1985 | Litho | BABN | 13.3x14.0 |
| b | booklet single, Rolland paper | 1986 | Litho | AP | 13.3x14.0 |
| 947 | **34¢ deep slate blue**, | | | | |
| | Abitibi-Price paper (uncoated) | 1985 | Engr | BABN | 12.5x12.0 |
| i | Rolland paper (uncoated) | 1985 | Engr | BABN | 12.5x12.0 |
| 952 | **34¢ dull red brown**, coil | 1985 | Engr | CBN | 10 horiz |
| 926B | **36¢ multicoloured**, Harrison paper | 1987 | Litho | CBN | 13.3x13.0 |
| e | booklet single, Rolland paper | 1987 | Litho | AP | 13.3x14.0 |
| 948 | **36¢ dark lilac rose**, | | | | |
| | Rolland paper (uncoated) | 1987 | Engr | BABN | 12.5x12.0 |
| i | Harrison paper (coated) | 1987 | Engr | BABN | 12.5x12.0 |
| 953 | **36¢ dark red**, coil | 1987 | Engr | CBN | 10 horiz |
| 1163 | **37¢ multicoloured** | 1987 | Litho | CBN | 13.3x13.0 |
| c | booklet single, HP | 1988 | Litho | AP | 13.3x14.0 |
| bs | booklet single, RP | 1988 | Litho | AP | 13.3x14.0 |
| 1187 | **37¢ blue** | 1988 | Engr | BABN | 12.5x12.0 |
| 1194 | **37¢ blue**, coil, Peterborough paper | 1988 | Engr | CBN | 10 horiz |
| i | coil, Rolland paper | 1988 | Engr | CBN | 10 horiz |
| 1165 | **38¢ multicoloured** | 1988 | Litho | CBN | 13.1x13.6 |
| ii | Peterborough paper | 1989 | Litho | CBN | 13.1x13.6 |
| 1188 | **38¢ blue** | 1989 | Engr | BABN | 12.5x12.0 |
| 1194A | **38¢ dark green**, coil | 1989 | Engr | CBN | 10 horiz |

## MAMMALS: 1987–1992

| | | Issued | Method | Printer | Perf |
|---|---|---|---|---|---|
| 1155 | **1¢ multicoloured**, Slater paper | 1988 | Litho | AP | 13.1x13.6 |
| ii | Coated Paper | 1991 | Litho | AP | 13.1x13.6 |
| a | perf change | 1991 | Litho | AP | 13.1x12.8 |
| 1156 | **2¢ multicoloured**, Slater paper | 1988 | Litho | AP | 13.1x13.6 |
| i | Coated Paper | 1991 | Litho | AP | 13.1x13.6 |
| 1157 | **3¢ multicoloured** | 1988 | Litho | AP | 13.1x13.6 |
| 1158 | **5¢ multicoloured** | 1988 | Litho | AP | 13.1x13.6 |
| 1159 | **6¢ multicoloured** | 1988 | Litho | AP | 13.1x13.6 |
| 1160 | **10¢ multicoloured**, tagged | 1988 | Litho | AP | 13.1x13.6 |
| ii | Coated Paper, untagged | 1991 | Litho | AP | 13.1x13.6 |
| a | perf change, Slater paper, tagged | 1991 | Litho | AP | 13.1x12.8 |
| 1161 | **25¢ multicoloured**, tagged | 1988 | Litho | AP | 13.1x13.6 |
| ii | Coated Paper, untagged | 1992 | Litho | AP | 13.1x13.6 |

| | | Issued | Method | Printer | Perf |
|---|---|---|---|---|---|
| 1170 | **43¢ multicoloured** | 1988 | Litho | AP | 12.0x12.5 |
| 1171 | **44¢ multicoloured** | 1989 | Litho | AP | 14.4x13.8 |
| i | Slater paper | 1989 | Litho | AP | 14.4x13.8 |
| c | perf change | 1989 | Litho | AP | 13.8 x 13.1 |
| a | booklet single | 1988 | Litho | AP | 12.5x13.1 |
| 1172 | **45¢ multicoloured** | 1990 | Litho | AP | 14.4x13.8 |
| d | perf change | 1990 | Litho | AP | 13.1 |
| f | booklet single | 1990 | Litho | AP | 12.5x13.1 |
| 1172A | **46¢ multicoloured** | 1990 | Litho | AP | 13.1 |
| g | perf change | 1990 | Litho | AP | 14.4x13.8 |
| c | booklet single | 1990 | Litho | AP | 12.5x13.1 |
| 1173 | **57¢ multicoloured** | 1988 | Litho | AP | 12.0x12.5 |
| i | Harrison paper | 1988 | Litho | AP | 12.0x12.5 |
| 1174 | **59¢ multicoloured** | 1989 | Litho | AP | 14.4x13.8 |
| i | Slater paper | 1989 | Litho | AP | 14.4x13.8 |
| a | perf change | 1989 | Litho | AP | 13.1 |
| 1175 | **61¢ multicoloured** | 1990 | Litho | AP | 14.4x13.8 |
| a | perf change | 1989 | Litho | AP | 13.1 |
| 1176 | **63¢ multicoloured** | 1990 | Litho | AP | 14.4x13.8 |
| a | perf change | 1990 | Litho | AP | 13.1 |
| 1177 | **74¢ multicoloured** | 1988 | Litho | AP | 12.0x12.5 |
| i | Rolland paper | 1988 | Litho | AP | 12.0x12.5 |
| 1178 | **76¢ multicoloured** | 1989 | Litho | AP | 14.4x13.8 |
| i | Slater paper | 1989 | Litho | AP | 14.4x13.8 |
| c | perf change | 1989 | Litho | AP | 13.1 |
| a | booklet single | 1989 | Litho | AP | 12.5x13.1 |
| 1179 | **78¢ multicoloured** | 1990 | Litho | AP | 14.4x13.8 |
| b | perf change | 1990 | Litho | AP | 13.1 |
| c | booklet single | 1990 | Litho | AP | 12.5x13.1 |
| 1180 | **80¢ multicoloured** | 1990 | Litho | AP | 13.1 |
| c | perf change | 1990 | Litho | AP | 14.4x13.8 |
| a | booklet single | 1990 | Litho | AP | 12.5x13.1 |

## QUEEN ELIZABETH II: 1987–2000

| | | Issued | Method | Printer | Perf |
|---|---|---|---|---|---|
| 1162 | **37¢ multicoloured (blue)** | 1987 | Litho | BABN | 13.3x13.0 |
| 1164 | **38¢ multicoloured (red)** | 1988 | Litho | BABN | 13.1x12.8 |
| a | booklet single | 1988 | Litho | AP | 13.1x13.6 |
| 1167 | **39¢ multicoloured (green)**, Harrison Paper | 1990 | Litho | BABN | 13.1x13.6 |
| b | perf change | 1990 | Litho | BABN | 13.1x12.8 |
| as | booklet single, Slater paper | 1990 | Litho | AP | 13.1x13.6 |
| 1168 | **40¢ multicoloured (brown)**, Peterborough Paper | 1990 | Litho | AP | 13.1x13.6 |
| i | Harrison paper | 1991 | Litho | AP | 13.1x13.6 |
| as | booklet single, Coated Paper | 1990 | Litho | AP | 13.1x13.6 |
| 1357 | **42¢ multicoloured** (purple) | 1991 | Litho | AP | 13.1x13.6 |
| 1358 | **43¢ multicoloured** (grey-black), Peterborough paper | 1992 | Litho | AP | 13.1x13.6 |
| as | booklet single, Coated paper | 1992 | Litho | AP | 13.1x13.6 |
| aivs | booklet single, Harrison paper | 1994 | Litho | CBN | 13.1x13.6 |
| avs | booklet single, Peterborough paper | 1994 | Litho | CBN | 13.1x13.6 |
| avis | booklet single, Coated paper | 1995 | Litho | APC | 13.1x13.6 |

| | | Issued | Method | Printer | Perf |
|---|---|---|---|---|---|
| 1360 | **45¢ multicoloured** (turquoise), Coated paper | 1995 | Litho | CBN | 13.1x13.6 |
| as | booklet single, Peterborough paper | 1995 | Litho | CBN | 13.1x13.6 |
| viii | printer change | 1995 | Litho | APC | 13.1x13.6 |
| 1681 | **46¢ multicoloured** (red) | 1998 | Litho | APC | 13.3x13.0 |
| 1683 | **47¢ multicoloured** (blue) | 2000 | Litho | CBN | 13.3x13.0 |

## FLAG OVER ... : 1989–2000

| | | Issued | Method | Printer | Perf |
|---|---|---|---|---|---|
| 1166 | **39¢ multicoloured** | 1989 | Litho | CBN | 13.6x13.1 |
| i | Ashton-Potter | 1990 | Litho | AP | 13.6x13.1 |
| c | AP, perf change | 1990 | Litho | AP | 12.8x13.1 |
| 1169 | **40¢ multicoloured** | 1990 | Litho | CBN | 13.6x13.1 |
| ai | booklet single | 1990 | Litho | AP | 13.6x13.1 |
| 1356 | **42¢ multicoloured** | 1991 | Litho | AP | 13.6x13.1 |
| 1359 | **43¢ multicoloured** | 1992 | Litho | AP | 13.6x13.1 |
| c | printer/perf change | 1994 | Litho | LM | 14.5x14.6 |
| x | printer change | 1995 | Litho | CBN | 13.6x13.1 |
| 1361 | **45¢ multicoloured** (large size) | 1995 | Litho | LM | 14.5x14.6 |
| c | printer/perf change, Coated Papers | 1995 | Litho | CBN | 13.6x13.1 |
| xiii | Peterborough Paper | 1996 | Litho | CBN | 13.6x13.1 |
| 1362 | **45¢ multicoloured** (small size) | 1998 | Litho | CBN | 13.0x13.3 |
| bs | booklet single, printer change | 1998 | Litho | APC | 13.0x13.3 |
| 1682 | **46¢ multicoloured** | 1998 | Litho | CBN | 13.0x13.3 |
| 1698 | **46¢ multicoloured** | 1998 | Litho | APC | Die cut |
| 1700 | **47¢ multicoloured** | 2000 | Litho | CBN | Die cut |

| | | Issued | Method | Printer | Perf |
|---|---|---|---|---|---|
| 1184 | **1¢ multicoloured (yellow)**, SP | 1990 | Litho | AP | 13.3x14.0 |
| i | Coated Paper | 1990 | Litho | AP | 13.3x14.0 |
| a | Slater Paper, perf change | 1990 | Litho | AP | 12.5x13.0 |
| 1185 | **5¢ multicoloured (pink)**, SP | 1990 | Litho | AP | 13.3x14.0 |
| i | Coated Paper | 1990 | Litho | AP | 13.3x14.0 |
| a | Slater Paper, perf change | 1990 | Litho | AP | 12.5x13.0 |
| 1189 | **39¢ multicoloured (blue)** | 1990 | Litho | AP | 13.3x14.0 |
| b | perf change | 1990 | Litho | AP | 12.5x13.0 |
| 1190 | **40¢ multicoloured (blue)** | 1990 | Litho | AP | 13.3x14.0 |

## FLAG OVER ... "QUICK STICK": 1989–1993

| | | Issued | Method | Printer | Perf |
|---|---|---|---|---|---|
| 1191 | **38¢ multicoloured** | 1989 | Litho | AP | Die cut |
| 1192 | **39¢ multicoloured** | 1990 | Litho | AP | Die cut |
| 1193 | **40¢ multicoloured** | 1991 | Litho | AP | Die cut |
| 1388 | **42¢ multicoloured** | 1992 | Litho | AP | Die cut |
| 1389 | **43¢ multicoloured** | 1993 | Litho | AP | Die cut |

## FLAG COILS: 1990–1998

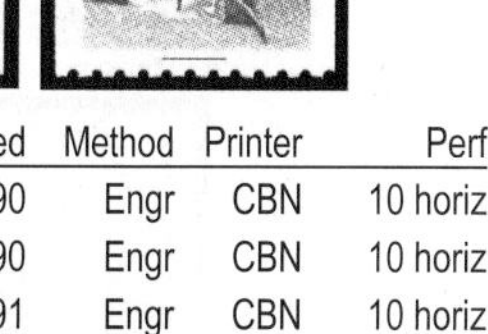


| | | Issued | Method | Printer | Perf |
|---|---|---|---|---|---|
| 1194B | **39¢ dark violet**, coil | 1990 | Engr | CBN | 10 horiz |
| 1194C | **40¢ blue grey**, coil | 1990 | Engr | CBN | 10 horiz |
| 1394 | **42¢ red**, coil | 1991 | Engr | CBN | 10 horiz |
| 1395 | **43¢ olive green**, coil | 1992 | Engr | CBN | 10 horiz |
| 1396 | **45¢ blue green**, coil | 1995 | Engr | CBN | 10 horiz |
| 1695 | **46¢ red**, coil | 1998 | Engr | CBN | 10 horiz |

## ARCHITECTURE: 1989–1992

| | | Issued | Method | Printer | Perf |
|---|---|---|---|---|---|
| 1181 | **$1 multicoloured (blue)**, Harrison paper | 1989 | Litho | BABN | 13.3 |
| ii | printer change, Coated Paper | 1992 | Litho | CBN | 13.3 |
| 1182 | **$2 multicoloured (orange)**, Harrison paper | 1989 | Litho | BABN | 13.3 |
| iii | printer change, Coated Paper | 1992 | Litho | CBN | 13.3 |
| 1183 | **$5 multicoloured (green)**, Peterborough Paper | 1990 | Litho | BABN | 13.3 |
| i | printer change, Coated Paper | 1992 | Litho | CBN | 13.3 |

## ARCHITECTURE: 1994–1998

| | | Issued | Method | Printer | Perf |
|---|---|---|---|---|---|
| 1375 | **$1 blue and multicoloured** | 1994 | Litho | LM | 14.6x14.0 |
| b | printer/perf change | 1995 | Litho | CBN | 13.3x13.0 |
| 1376 | **$2 brown and multicoloured**, | 1994 | Litho | LM | 14.6x14.0 |
| c | printer/perf change | 1995 | Litho | CBN | 13.3x13.0 |
| 1378 | **$5 blue green and multicoloured**, Type I | 1996 | Litho | CBN | 13.3x13.0 |
| a | reprint (Type II) | 1998 | Litho | CBN | 13.3x13.0 |

## EDIBLE BERRIES: 1992–1998

| | | Issued | Method | Printer | Perf |
|---|---|---|---|---|---|
| 1349 | **1¢ multicoloured** | 1992 | Litho | AP | 13.1x13.6 |
| i | printer change | 1994 | Litho | CBN | 13.1x13.6 |
| ii | printer change | 1995 | Litho | APC | 13.1x13.6 |
| 1350 | **2¢ multicoloured** | 1992 | Litho | AP | 13.1x13.6 |
| i | printer change, Harrison paper | 1994 | Litho | CBN | 13.1x13.6 |
| ii | Coated paper | 1994 | Litho | CBN | 13.1x13.6 |
| iii | printer change | 1995 | Litho | APC | 13.1x13.6 |

| | | Issued | Method | Printer | Perf |
|---|---|---|---|---|---|
| 1351 | **3¢ multicoloured** | 1992 | Litho | AP | 13.1x13.6 |
| i | printer change, Harrison paper | 1994 | Litho | CBN | 13.1x13.6 |
| ii | Coated paper | 1994 | Litho | CBN | 13.1x13.6 |
| iii | printer change | 1995 | Litho | APC | 13.1x13.6 |
| 1352 | **5¢ multicoloured** | 1992 | Litho | AP | 13.1x13.6 |
| i | printer change, Harrison paper | 1994 | Litho | CBN | 13.1x13.6 |
| ii | Coated paper | 1994 | Litho | CBN | 13.1x13.6 |
| iii | printer change | 1995 | Litho | APC | 13.1x13.6 |
| 1353 | **6¢ multicoloured** | 1992 | Litho | AP | 13.1x13.6 |
| i | printer change, Harrison paper | 1994 | Litho | CBN | 13.1x13.6 |
| ii | Coated paper | 1994 | Litho | CBN | 13.1x13.6 |
| 1354 | **10¢ multicoloured** | 1992 | Litho | AP | 13.1x13.6 |
| i | printer change, Harrison paper | 1994 | Litho | CBN | 13.1x13.6 |
| iii | Coated paper | 1994 | Litho | CBN | 13.1x13.6 |
| iv | printer change | 1995 | Litho | APC | 13.1x13.6 |
| 1355 | **25¢ multicoloured** | 1992 | Litho | AP | 13.1x13.6 |
| i | printer change, Harrison paper | 1994 | Litho | CBN | 13.1x13.6 |
| ii | Coated paper | 1994 | Litho | CBN | 13.1x13.6 |
| iii | printer change | 1995 | Litho | APC | 13.1x13.6 |

## FRUIT TREES: 1991–1996

| | | Issued | Method | Printer | Perf |
|---|---|---|---|---|---|
| 1363 | **48¢ multicoloured** | 1991 | Litho | AP | 13.1 |
| a | booklet single | 1991 | Litho | AP | 14.4x13.8 |
| 1364 | **49¢ multicoloured**, Coated Papers | 1992 | Litho | AP | 13.1 |
| a | booklet single | 1992 | Litho | AP | 14.4x13.8 |
| i | printer change, Harrison paper | 1994 | Litho | CBN | 13.1 |
| 1365 | **50¢ multicoloured**, Harrison paper | 1994 | Litho | CBN | 13.1 |
| as | booklet single, Peterborough paper | 1994 | Litho | CBN | 13.1 |
| i | printer change, Coated Papers | 1995 | Litho | APC | 13.1 |
| b | booklet single | 1995 | Litho | APC | 14.4x13.8 |
| 1366 | **52¢ multicoloured** | 1995 | Litho | CBN | 13.1 |
| b | printer/perf change | 1995 | Litho | APC | 14.4x13.8 |
| i | perf change | 1996 | Litho | APC | 13.1 |
| 1367 | **65¢ multicoloured** | 1991 | Litho | AP | 13.1 |
| 1368 | **67¢ multicoloured** | 1992 | Litho | AP | 13.1 |
| 1369 | **69¢ multicoloured**, Harrison paper | 1994 | Litho | CBN | 13.1 |
| i | Coated Papers | 1995 | Litho | AP | 13.1 |

| | | Issued | Method | Printer | Perf |
|---|---|---|---|---|---|
| 1370 | **71¢ multicoloured**, | | | | |
| | Peterborough paper | 1995 | Litho | CBN | 13.1 |
| i | Coated Papers | 1995 | Litho | APC | 13.1 |
| a | perf change | 1995 | Litho | APC | 14.4x13.8 |
| 1371 | **84¢ multicoloured** | 1991 | Litho | AP | 13.1 |
| a | booklet single | 1991 | Litho | AP | 14.4x13.8 |
| 1372 | **86¢ multicoloured** | 1992 | Litho | AP | 13.1 |
| a | booklet single | 1992 | Litho | AP | 14.4x13.8 |
| i | printer change | 1994 | Litho | CBN | 13.1 |
| 1373 | **88¢ multicoloured**, GT4 tag | 1994 | Litho | CBN | 13.1 |
| i | tag change, GT3 tag | 1994 | Litho | CBN | 13.1 |
| ii | printer change, GT3 tag | 1995 | Litho | APC | 13.1 |
| b | booklet single, GT3 tag | 1995 | Litho | APC | 14.4x13.8 |
| 1374 | **90¢ multicoloured** | 1995 | Litho | CBN | 13.1 |
| i | printer change | 1995 | Litho | APC | 13.1 |
| ii | perf change | 1996 | Litho | APC | 14.4x13.8 |

## STYLIZED MAPLE LEAF: 1998–1999

| | | Issued | Method | Printer | Perf |
|---|---|---|---|---|---|
| 1696 | **45¢ multicoloured** | 1998 | Photo | Avery | Die cut |
| 1697 | **45¢ multicoloured**, coil | 1998 | Flex | APC | 12.8x13.1 |
| 1699 | **46¢ multicoloured** | 1998 | Photo | Avery | Die cut |
| 1684 | **55¢ multicoloured** (orange leaf on blue background) | 1998 | Litho | APC | 13.0x13.3 |
| 1685 | **73¢ multicoloured** (yellow leaf on purple background) | 1998 | Litho | APC | 13.0x13.3 |
| 1686 | **95¢ multicoloured** (green leaf on peach background) | 1998 | Litho | APC | 13.0x13.3 |

## STYLIZED MAPLE LEAF: 2000–2002

| | | Issued | Method | Printer | Perf |
|---|---|---|---|---|---|
| 1878 | **47¢ multicoloured**, coil | 2000 | Litho | APC | 8.5 horiz |
| 1927 | **48¢ multicoloured**, coil | 2002 | Litho | AP | 8.5 horiz |

## WILDLIFE: 2000

| | | Issued | Method | Printer | Perf |
|---|---|---|---|---|---|
| 1879 | **60¢ multicoloured**, coil | 2000 | Litho | APC | 8.5 horiz |
| iv | booklet single | 2000 | Litho | APC | 8.5 horiz |
| 1880 | **75¢ multicoloured**, coil | 2000 | Litho | APC | 8.5 horiz |
| 1881 | **$1.05 multicoloured**, coil | 2000 | Litho | APC | 8.5 horiz |
| ii | booklet single | 2000 | Litho | APC | 8.5 horiz |

## WILDLIFE: 1997–2010

| | | Issued | Method | Printer | Perf |
|---|---|---|---|---|---|
| 1687 | **$1 multicoloured** (loon) | | | | |
| | Peterborough paper | 1998 | Engr | CBN | 13.3x13.0 |
| iv | Coated (TRC) paper | 2003 | Engr | CBN | 13.3x13.0 |
| 1688 | **$1 multicoloured** (deer) | 2005 | Engr | CBN | 12.5x13.1 |
| 1689 | **$1 multicoloured** (walrus) | 2005 | Engr | CBN | 12.5x13.1 |
| a | pair (1688, 1689) | | | | |
| b | souvenir sheet | | | | |
| 1690 | **$2 multicoloured** (bear) | | | | |
| | Peterborough paper | 1998 | Engr | CBN | 13.3x13.0 |
| i | Coated (TRC) paper | 2003 | Engr | CBN | 13.3x13.0 |
| 1691 | **$2 multicoloured** (falcons) | 2005 | Engr | CBN | 12.5x13.1 |
| 1692 | **$2 multicoloured** (horses) | 2005 | Engr | CBN | 12.5x13.1 |
| a | pair (1691, 1692) | | | | |
| b | souvenir sheet | | | | |
| 1693 | **$5 multicoloured** | 2003 | Engr | CBN | 12.5x13.1 |
| 1694 | **$8 multicoloured** | 1997 | Engr | CBN | 12.5x13.1 |
| 2405 | **$10 multicoloured** | 2010 | Engr | CBN | 12.5x13.1 |

## TRADITIONAL TRADES: 1999–2006

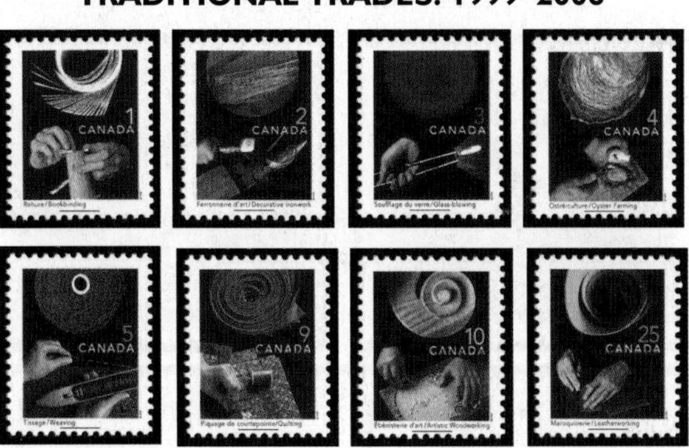

| | | Issued | Method | Printer | Perf |
|---|---|---|---|---|---|
| 1673 | **1¢ multicoloured** | 1999 | Litho | APC | 13.0x13.3 |
| i | printer change | 2000 | Litho | CBN | 13.0x13.3 |
| 1674 | **2¢ multicoloured** | 1999 | Litho | APC | 13.0x13.3 |
| i | printer change | 2001 | Litho | CBN | 13.0x13.3 |
| 1675 | **3¢ multicoloured** | 1999 | Litho | APC | 13.0x13.3 |
| 1676 | **4¢ multicoloured** | 1999 | Litho | APC | 13.0x13.3 |
| i | printer change | 2005 | Litho | CBN | 13.0x13.3 |
| 1677 | **5¢ multicoloured** | 1999 | Litho | APC | 13.0x13.3 |
| i | printer change | 2001 | Litho | CBN | 13.0x13.3 |
| 1678 | **9¢ multicoloured** | 1999 | Litho | APC | 13.0x13.3 |
| 1679 | **10¢ multicoloured** | 1999 | Litho | APC | 13.0x13.3 |
| i | printer change | 2001 | Litho | CBN | 13.0x13.3 |
| 1680 | **25¢ multicoloured** | 1999 | Litho | APC | 13.0x13.3 |
| i | printer change | 2001 | Litho | CBN | 13.0x13.3 |

| | | Issued | Method | Printer | Perf |
|---|---|---|---|---|---|
| 1928 | **65¢ multicoloured**, coil | 2002 | Litho | AP | 8.5 horiz |
| vii | booklet single | 2002 | Litho | AP | 8.5 horiz |
| 1929 | **77¢ multicoloured**, coil | 2002 | Litho | AP | 8.5 horiz |
| 1930 | **$1.25 multicoloured**, coil | 2002 | Litho | AP | 8.5 horiz |
| v | booklet single | 2002 | Litho | AP | 8.5 horiz |

## FLAG OVER ... : 2002–2004

| | | Issued | Method | Printer | Perf |
|---|---|---|---|---|---|
| 1931 | **48¢ multicoloured**, rounded corners | 2002 | Litho | AP | 8.5 |
| ii | square/pointed die cutting at corners | 2003 | Litho | AP | 8.5 |
| 1991 | **48¢ multicoloured** ('Vancouver/ 2010' imprint in red at lower right) | 2003 | Litho | AP | 8.5 |
| 2011 | **49¢ multicoloured**, C Paper | 2003 | Litho | AP | Die cut |
| i | printer change, F paper | 2004 | Litho | CBN | Die cut |

## QUEEN ELIZABETH II: 2003–2013

| | | Issued | Method | Printer | Perf |
|---|---|---|---|---|---|
| 2012 | **49¢ multicoloured**, C paper | 2003 | Litho | CBN | Die cut |
| i | F paper | 2004 | Litho | CBN | Die cut |
| 2075 | **50¢ multicoloured**, C paper | 2004 | Litho | CBN | Die cut |
| i | F paper | 2005 | Litho | CBN | Die cut |
| 2188 | **P multicoloured**, F paper | 2006 | Litho | CBN | Die cut |
| i | C paper | 2007 | Litho | CBN | Die cut |
| 2248 | **P multicoloured** | 2007 | Litho | CBN | 13.4 |
| 2298 | **P multicoloured** | 2009 | Litho | CBN | 13.4 |
| 2365 | **P multicoloured** | 2010 | Litho | CBN | 13.4 |
| 2617 | **P multicoloured** | 2013 | Litho | CBN | 13.4 |
| b | with repeating 'Canada' underprint | 2013 | Litho | CBN | 13.4 |
| 2698 | **63¢ multicoloured** | 2013 | -Litho | CBN | 13.4 |

## MAPLE LEAF: 2003–2004

| | | Issued | Method | Printer | Perf |
|---|---|---|---|---|---|
| 2008 | **49¢ multicoloured**, coil | 2003 | Litho | AP | 8.6 horiz |
| 2053 | **49¢ multicoloured**, coil | 2004 | Litho | CBN | Die cut |
| 2009 | **80¢ multicoloured**, coil | 2003 | Litho | AP | 8.6 vert |
| 2013 | **80¢ multicoloured**, C paper | 2003 | Litho | AP | Die cut |
| i | printer change, F paper | 2003 | Litho | LM | Die cut |
| 2054 | **80¢ multicoloured**, coil | 2004 | Litho | LM | 8.2 horiz |
| 2010 | **$1.40 multicoloured**, coil | 2003 | Litho | AP | 8.6 vert |
| 2014 | **$1.40 multicoloured**, C paper | 2003 | Litho | AP | Die cut |
| i | printer change, F paper | 2003 | Litho | LM | Die cut |
| 2055 | **$1.40 multicoloured**, coil | 2004 | Litho | LM | 8.2 horiz |

## FLOWERS: 2004–2010

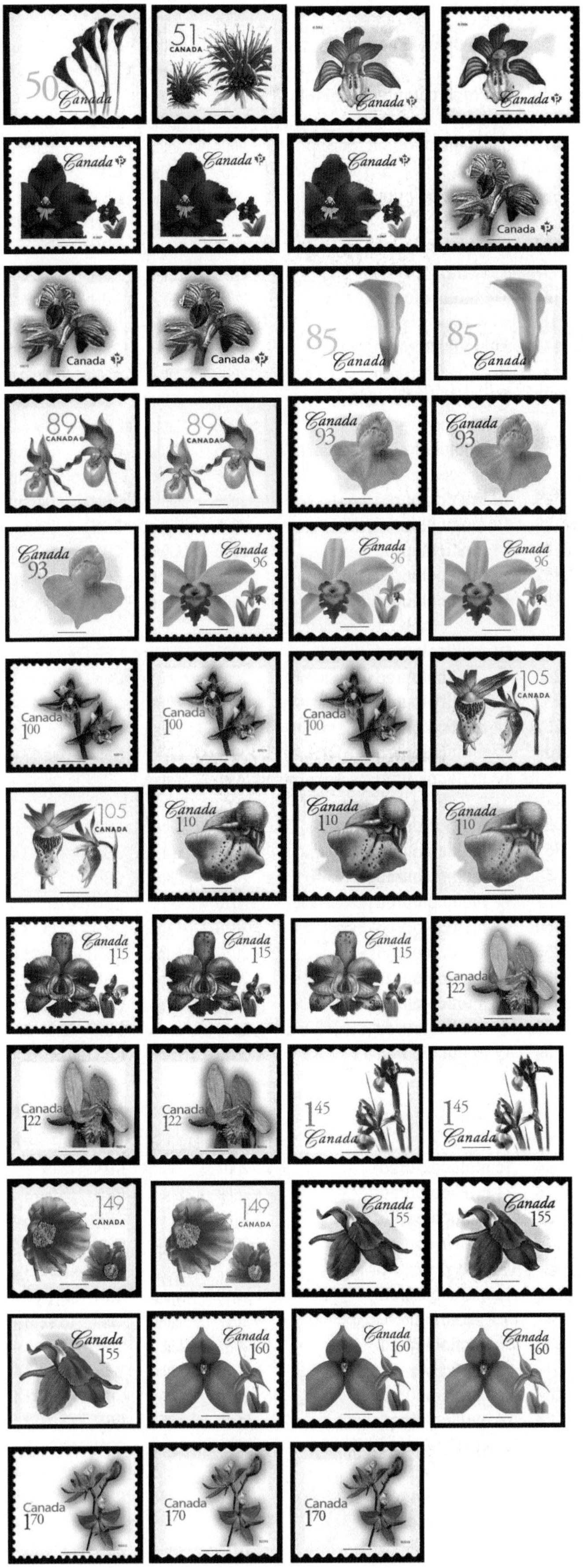

Coil serpentine die cut measurements are approximate on these stamps.

| | | Issued | Method | Printer | Perf |
|---|---|---|---|---|---|
| 2072 | **50¢ multicoloured**, coil | 2004 | Litho | LM | 8–9 horiz |
| a | perf change | 2005 | Litho | LM | 6–7 horiz |
| 2128 | **51¢ multicoloured**, coil, C paper | 2005 | Litho | LM | 7–8 horiz |
| iv | F paper | 2006 | Litho | LM | 7–8 horiz |
| vi | perf change | 2006 | Litho | LM | 7–9 horiz |
| 2187 | **(P) multicoloured**, coil | 2006 | Litho | LM | 7–9 horiz |
| iii | perf change | 2006 | Litho | LM | 8 horiz |
| 2194a | **(P) multicoloured**, s/s single | 2006 | Litho | LM | 13.4x13.1 |
| 2243a | **(P) multicoloured**, s/s single | 2007 | Litho | LM | 13.4x13.1 |
| 2244 | **(P) multicoloured**, coil | 2007 | Litho | LM | 8 horiz |
| 2244A | **(P) multicoloured**, 3,000/5,000 coil | 2007 | Litho | LM | 9.2 horiz |
| 2356a | **(P) multicoloured**, s/s single | 2010 | Litho | LM | 13.4x13.1 |
| 2357 | **(P) multicoloured**, coil | 2010 | Litho | LM | 8–9 horiz |
| 2361 | **(P) multicoloured**, 3,000/5,000 coil | 2010 | Litho | LM | 9.2 horiz |
| 2073 | **85¢ multicoloured**, coil | 2004 | Litho | LM | 8–9 horiz |
| a | perf change | 2005 | Litho | LM | 6–7 horiz |
| 2081 | **85¢ multicoloured**, booklet single | 2004 | Litho | LM | Die cut |
| 2129 | **89¢ multicoloured**, coil, F paper | 2005 | Litho | LM | 7–8 horiz |
| iv | C paper | 2006 | Litho | LM | 7–8 horiz |
| vii | perf change | 2006 | Litho | LM | 7–9 horiz |
| 2132 | **89¢ multicoloured**, booklet single | 2004 | Litho | LM | Die cut |
| 2194b | **93¢ multicoloured**, s/s single | 2006 | Litho | LM | 13.4x13.1 |
| 2195 | **93¢ multicoloured**, coil | 2006 | Litho | LM | 8 horiz |
| 2198 | **93¢ multicoloured**, booklet single | 2006 | Litho | LM | Die cut |
| 2243b | **96¢ multicoloured**, s/s single | 2007 | Litho | LM | 13.4x13.1 |
| 2245 | **96¢ multicoloured**, coil | 2007 | Litho | LM | 8 horiz |
| 2254 | **96¢ multicoloured**, booklet single | 2007 | Litho | LM | Die cut |
| 2356b | **$1.00 multicoloured**, s/s single | 2010 | Litho | LM | 13.4x13.1 |
| 2358 | **$1.00 multicoloured**, coil | 2010 | Litho | LM | 8–9 horiz |
| 2362 | **$1.00 multicoloured**, booklet single | 2010 | Litho | LM | 9.2 horiz |
| 2130 | **$1.05 multicoloured**, coil | 2005 | Litho | LM | 7–8 horiz |
| iv | perf change | 2006 | Litho | LM | 7–9 horiz |
| 2133 | **$1.05 multicoloured**, booklet single | 2004 | Litho | LM | Die cut |
| 2194c | **$1.10 multicoloured**, s/s single | 2006 | Litho | LM | 13.4x13.1 |
| 2196 | **$1.10 multicoloured**, coil | 2006 | Litho | LM | 8 horiz |
| 2199 | **$1.10 multicoloured**, booklet single | 2006 | Litho | LM | Die cut |
| 2243c | **$1.15 multicoloured**, s/s single | 2007 | Litho | LM | 13.4x13.1 |
| 2246 | **$1.15 multicoloured**, coil | 2007 | Litho | LM | 8 horiz |
| 2255 | **$1.15 multicoloured**, booklet single | 2007 | Litho | LM | Die cut |
| 2356c | **$1.22 multicoloured**, s/s single | 2010 | Litho | LM | 13.4x13.1 |
| 2359 | **$1.22 multicoloured**, coil | 2010 | Litho | LM | 8–9 horiz |
| 2363 | **$1.22 multicoloured**, booklet single | 2010 | Litho | LM | 9.2 horiz |
| 2074 | **$1.45 multicoloured**, coil | 2004 | Litho | LM | 8–9 horiz |
| a | perf change | 2005 | Litho | LM | 6–7 horiz |
| 2082 | **$1.45 multicoloured**, booklet single | 2004 | Litho | LM | Die cut |
| 2131 | **$1.49 multicoloured**, coil | 2005 | Litho | LM | 7–8 horiz |
| 2134 | **$1.49 multicoloured**, booklet single | 2004 | Litho | LM | Die cut |
| 2194d | **$1.55 multicoloured**, s/s single | 2006 | Litho | LM | 13.4x13.1 |
| 2197 | **$1.55 multicoloured**, coil | 2006 | Litho | LM | 8 horiz |
| 2200 | **$1.55 multicoloured**, booklet single | 2006 | Litho | LM | Die cut |
| 2243d | **$1.60 multicoloured**, s/s single | 2007 | Litho | LM | 13.4x13.1 |
| 2247 | **$1.60 multicoloured**, coil | 2007 | Litho | LM | 8 horiz |
| 2256 | **$1.60 multicoloured**, booklet single | 2007 | Litho | LM | Die cut |
| 2356d | **$1.70 multicoloured**, s/s single | 2010 | Litho | LM | 13.4x13.1 |
| 2360 | **$1.70 multicoloured**, coil | 2010 | Litho | LM | 8–9 horiz |
| 2364 | **$1.70 multicoloured**, booklet single | 2010 | Litho | LM | 9.2 horiz |

## FLAG OVER ... : 2004–2011

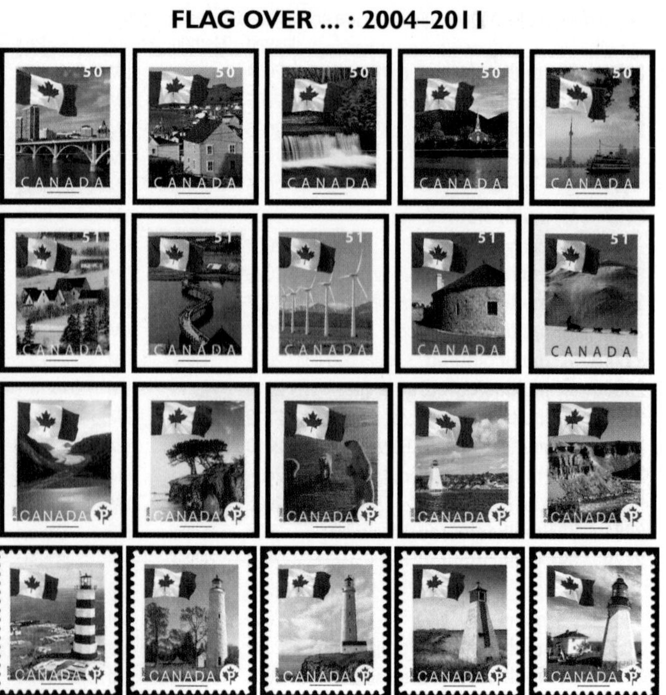

| | | Issued | Method | Printer | Perf |
|---|---|---|---|---|---|
| 2076 | **50¢ multicoloured** (bridge) | 2004 | Litho | CBN | Die cut |
| i | F paper | 2005 | Litho | CBN | Die cut |
| 2077 | **50¢ multicoloured** (town) | 2004 | Litho | CBN | Die cut |
| i | F paper | 2005 | Litho | CBN | Die cut |
| 2078 | **50¢ multicoloured** (waterfall) | 2004 | Litho | CBN | Die cut |
| i | F paper | 2005 | Litho | CBN | Die cut |
| 2079 | **50¢ multicoloured** (church) | 2004 | Litho | CBN | Die cut |
| i | F paper | 2005 | Litho | CBN | Die cut |
| 2080 | **50¢ multicoloured** (boat) | 2004 | Litho | CBN | Die cut |
| i | F paper | 2005 | Litho | CBN | Die cut |
| 2135 | **51¢ multicoloured** (houses) | 2005 | Litho | CBN | Die cut |
| i | printer/paper change | 2006 | Litho | LM | Die cut |
| 2136 | **51¢ multicoloured** (bridge) | 2005 | Litho | CBN | Die cut |
| i | printer/paper change | 2006 | Litho | LM | Die cut |
| 2137 | **51¢ multicoloured** (windmills) | 2005 | Litho | CBN | Die cut |
| i | printer/paper change | 2006 | Litho | LM | Die cut |
| 2138 | **51¢ multicoloured** (fort) | 2005 | Litho | CBN | Die cut |
| i | printer/paper change | 2006 | Litho | LM | Die cut |
| 2139 | **51¢ multicoloured** (dogsled) | 2005 | Litho | CBN | Die cut |
| i | printer/paper change | 2006 | Litho | LM | Die cut |
| 2189 | **P multicoloured** (lake) | 2006 | Litho | CBN | Die cut |
| 2190 | **P multicoloured** (cliff) | 2006 | Litho | CBN | Die cut |
| 2191 | **P multicoloured** (bears) | 2006 | Litho | CBN | Die cut |
| 2192 | **P multicoloured** (lighthouse) | 2006 | Litho | CBN | Die cut |
| 2193 | **P multicoloured** (river) | 2006 | Litho | CBN | Die cut |
| | Lighthouses: | | | | |
| 2249 | **P multicoloured** (striped) | 2007 | Litho | CBN | Die cut 13.4 |
| 2250 | **P multicoloured** (trees to left) | 2007 | Litho | CBN | Die cut 13.4 |
| 2251 | **P multicoloured** (water to left) | 2007 | Litho | CBN | Die cut 13.4 |
| 2252 | **P multicoloured** (field to left) | 2007 | Litho | CBN | Die cut 13.4 |
| 2253 | **P multicoloured** (house to left) | 2007 | Litho | CBN | Die cut 13.4 |
| 2253B | **P multicoloured** (house to right) | 2008 | Litho | CBN | Die cut 13.4 |
| | Mills: | | | | |
| 2350a | **P multicoloured** (Watson's), s/s | 2010 | Litho | CBN | 13.0x13.3 |
| 2351 | **P multicoloured** (Watson's) | 2010 | Litho | CBN | Die cut 13.4 |
| 2350b | **P multicoloured** (Keremeos), s/s | 2010 | Litho | CBN | 13.0x13.3 |
| 2352 | **P multicoloured** (Keremeos) | 2010 | Litho | CBN | Die cut 13.4 |
| 2350c | **P multicoloured** (Stone), s/s | 2010 | Litho | CBN | 13.0x13.3 |
| 2353 | **P multicoloured** (Stone) | 2010 | Litho | CBN | Die cut 13.4 |
| 2350d | **P multicoloured** (Riordon), s/s | 2010 | Litho | CBN | 13.0x13.3 |
| 2354 | **P multicoloured** (Riordon) | 2010 | Litho | CBN | Die cut 13.4 |
| 2350e | **P multicoloured** (Cornell), s/s | 2010 | Litho | CBN | 13.0x13.3 |
| 2355 | **P multicoloured** (Cornell) | 2010 | Litho | CBN | Die cut 13.4 |

## BENEFICIAL INSECTS: 2007–

| | | Issued | Method | Printer | Perf |
|---|---|---|---|---|---|
| 2234 | **1¢ multicoloured** | 2007 | Litho | CBN | 13.0x13.4 |
| 2328 | **2¢ multicoloured** | 2009 | Litho | CBN | 13.0x13.4 |
| 2235 | **3¢ multicoloured** | 2007 | Litho | CBN | 13.0x13.4 |
| i | transparent gum | 2014 | Litho | CBN | 13.0x13.4 |
| b | with added microprinting | 2012 | Litho | CBN | 13.0x13.4 |
| 2406 | **4¢ multicoloured** | 2010 | Litho | CBN | 13.0x13.4 |
| a | with added microprinting | 2012 | Litho | CBN | 13.0x13.4 |
| 2236 | **5¢ multicoloured** | 2007 | Litho | CBN | 13.0x13.4 |
| i | transparent gum | 2015 | Litho | CBN | 13.0x13.4 |
| 2407 | **6¢ multicoloured** | 2010 | Litho | CBN | 13.0x13.4 |
| 2408 | **7¢ multicoloured** | 2010 | Litho | CBN | 13.0x13.4 |
| 2409 | **8¢ multicoloured** | 2010 | Litho | CBN | 13.0x13.4 |
| a | with added microprinting | 2012 | Litho | CBN | 13.0x13.4 |
| 2410 | **9¢ multicoloured** | 2010 | Litho | CBN | 13.0x13.4 |
| 2237 | **10¢ multicoloured** | 2007 | Litho | CBN | 13.0x13.4 |
| i | transparent gum | 2014 | Litho | CBN | 13.0x13.4 |
| 2708 | **22¢ multicoloured** | 2014 | Litho | CBN | 13.0x13.4 |
| 2238 | **25¢ multicoloured** | 2007 | Litho | CBN | 13.0x13.4 |
| ii | transparent gum | 2012 | Litho | CBN | 13.0x13.4 |

## OLYMPIC SPORTS: 2009

| | | Issued | Method | Printer | Perf |
|---|---|---|---|---|---|
| 2299a | **curling**, s/s single | 2009 | Litho | CBN | 13.4x13.0 |
| 2303 | **curling**, booklet single | 2009 | Litho | CBN | 13.4 |
| 2299b | **bobsledding**, s/s single | 2009 | Litho | CBN | 13.4x13.0 |
| 2302 | **bobsledding**, booklet single | 2009 | Litho | CBN | 13.4 |
| 2299c | **snowboarding**, s/s single | 2009 | Litho | CBN | 13.4x13.0 |
| 2304 | **snowboarding**, booklet single | 2009 | Litho | CBN | 13.4 |
| 2299d | **skiing**, s/s single | 2009 | Litho | CBN | 13.4x13.0 |
| 2300 | **skiing**, booklet single | 2009 | Litho | CBN | 13.4 |
| 2299e | **hockey**, s/s single | 2009 | Litho | CBN | 13.4x13.0 |
| 2301 | **hockey**, booklet single | 2009 | Litho | CBN | 13.4 |

## OLYMPIC EMBLEMS and MASCOTS: 2009

| | | Issued | Method | Printer | Perf |
|---|---|---|---|---|---|
| 2305a | **Vancouver**, s/s single | 2009 | Litho | LM | 13.4x13.0 |
| 2307A | **Vancouver**, coil | 2009 | Litho | LM | 8–9 horiz |
| 2306 | **Vancouver**, 5,000 coil | 2009 | Litho | LM | 9.2 horiz |
| 2305b | **Paralympic**, s/s single | 2009 | Litho | LM | 13.4x13.0 |
| 2307B | **Paralympic**, coil | 2009 | Litho | LM | 8–9 horiz |
| 2307 | **Paralympic**, 5,000 coil | 2009 | Litho | LM | 9.2 horiz |
| 2305c | **98¢ Miga**, s/s single | 2009 | Litho | LM | 13.4x13.0 |
| 2308 | **98¢ Miga**, coil | 2009 | Litho | LM | 8–9 horiz |
| 2311 | **98¢ Miga**, booklet single | 2009 | Litho | LM | 9.2 horiz |
| 2305d | **$1.18 Sumi**, s/s single | 2009 | Litho | LM | 13.4x13.0 |
| 2309 | **$1.18 Sumi**, coil | 2009 | Litho | LM | 8–9 horiz |
| 2312 | **$1.18 Sumi**, booklet single | 2009 | Litho | LM | 9.2 horiz |
| 2305e | **$1.65 Quatchi**, s/s single | 2009 | Litho | LM | 13.4x13.0 |
| 2310 | **$1.65 Quatchi**, coil | 2009 | Litho | LM | 8–9 horiz |
| 2313 | **$1.65 Quatchi**, booklet single | 2009 | Litho | LM | 9.2 horiz |

## CANADIAN PRIDE (O CANADA): 2011

| | | Issued | Method | Printer | Perf |
|---|---|---|---|---|---|
| 2418a | **soldier's uniform**, s/s single | 2011 | Litho | CBN | 13.0x13.3 |
| 2419 | **soldier's uniform**, booklet single | 2011 | Litho | CBN | 13.4 |
| 2418b | **hot-air balloon**, s/s single | 2011 | Litho | CBN | 13.0x13.3 |
| 2420 | **hot-air balloon**, booklet single | 2011 | Litho | CBN | 13.4 |
| 2418c | **search/rescue**, s/s single | 2011 | Litho | CBN | 13.0x13.3 |
| 2421 | **search/rescue**, booklet single | 2011 | Litho | CBN | 13.4 |
| 2418d | **Canadarm**, s/s single | 2011 | Litho | CBN | 13.0x13.3 |
| 2422 | **Canadarm**, booklet single | 2011 | Litho | CBN | 13.4 |
| 2418e | **backpack**, s/s single | 2011 | Litho | CBN | 13.0x13.3 |
| 2423 | **backpack**, booklet single | 2011 | Litho | CBN | 13.4 |

## CANADIAN PRIDE: 2012

| | | Issued | Method | Printer | Perf |
|---|---|---|---|---|---|
| 2498a | **coast guard ship**, s/s single | 2012 | Litho | CBN | 13.0x13.4 |
| 2499 | **coast guard ship**, booklet single | 2012 | Litho | CBN | 13.4 |
| a | with repeating 'Canada' underprint | 2012 | Litho | CBN | 13.4 |
| 2498b | **van window**, s/s single | 2012 | Litho | CBN | 13.0x13.4 |
| 2500 | **van window**, booklet single | 2012 | Litho | CBN | 13.4 |
| a | with repeating 'Canada' underprint | 2012 | Litho | CBN | 13.4 |
| 2498c | **olympic athlete**, s/s single | 2012 | Litho | CBN | 13.0x13.4 |
| 2501 | **olympic athlete**, booklet single | 2012 | Litho | CBN | 13.4 |
| a | with repeating 'Canada' underprint | 2012 | Litho | CBN | 13.4 |
| 2498d | **bobsled**, s/s single | 2012 | Litho | CBN | 13.0x13.4 |
| 2502 | **bobsled**, booklet single | 2012 | Litho | CBN | 13.4 |
| a | corrected spelling of "Lueders" | 2012 | Litho | CBN | 13.4 |
| b | with repeating 'Canada' underprint | 2012 | Litho | CBN | 13.4 |
| 2498e | **inuit child**, s/s single | 2012 | Litho | CBN | 13.0x13.4 |
| 2503 | **inuit child**, booklet single | 2012 | Litho | CBN | 13.4 |
| d | with repeating 'Canada' underprint | 2012 | Litho | CBN | 13.4 |

## BABY WILDLIFE: 2012–2016

| | | Issued | Method | Printer | Perf |
|---|---|---|---|---|---|
| 2424a | P **Arctic hare**, s/s single | 2011 | Litho | LM | 13.4x13.1 |
| 2426 | P **Arctic hare**, coil | 2011 | Litho | LM | 8.2 horiz |
| 2425 | P **Arctic hare**, 5,000 coil | 2011 | Litho | LM | 9.2 horiz |
| 2504a | P **Racoons**, s/s single | 2012 | Litho | LM | 13.4x13.1 |
| 2506 | P **Racoons**, coil | 2012 | Litho | LM | 8.2 horiz |
| 2505 | P **Racoons**, 5,000 coil | 2012 | Litho | LM | 9.2 horiz |
| 2602a | P **Woodchucks**, s/s single | 2013 | Litho | LM | 13.4x13.1 |
| 2604 | P **Woodchucks**, coil | 2013 | Litho | LM | 8.2 horiz |
| 2603 | P **Woodchucks**, 5,000 coil | 2013 | Litho | LM | 9.2 horiz |
| 2709a | P **Beavers**, s/s single | 2014 | Litho | LM | 13.4x13.1 |
| 2711 | P **Beavers**, coil | 2014 | Litho | LM | 8.2 horiz |
| 2710A | P **Beavers**, 5,000 coil | 2014 | Litho | LM | 9.2 horiz |
| 2692 | **63¢ Woodchucks**, coil | 2013 | Litho | LM | 8.2 horiz |
| 2692A | **63¢ Woodchucks**, 5,000 coil | 2013 | Litho | LM | 9.2 horiz |
| 2709b | **$1.00 Burrowing owl**, s/s single | 2014 | Litho | LM | 13.4x13.1 |
| 2710 | **$1.00 Burrowing owl**, coil | 2014 | Litho | LM | 13.5 |
| 2424b | **$1.03 Red fox**, s/s single | 2011 | Litho | LM | 13.4x13.1 |
| 2427 | **$1.03 Red fox**, coil | 2011 | Litho | LM | 8.2 horiz |
| 2430 | **$1.03 Red fox**, booklet single | 2011 | Litho | LM | 9.2 horiz |
| 2504b | **$1.05 Caribou**, s/s single | 2012 | Litho | LM | 13.4x13.1 |
| 2507 | **$1.05 Caribou**, coil | 2012 | Litho | LM | 8.2 horiz |
| 2510 | **$1.05 Caribou**, booklet single | 2012 | Litho | LM | 9.2 horiz |
| 2602b | **$1.10 Porcupine**, s/s single | 2013 | Litho | LM | 13.4x13.1 |
| 2605 | **$1.10 Porcupine**, coil | 2013 | Litho | LM | 8.2 horiz |
| 2608 | **$1.10 Porcupine**, booklet single | 2013 | Litho | LM | 9.2 horiz |
| 2709c | **$1.20 Mountain goat**, s/s single | 2014 | Litho | LM | 13.4x13.1 |
| 2712 | **$1.20 Mountain goat**, coil | 2014 | Litho | LM | 8.2 horiz |
| 2715 | **$1.20 Mountain goat**, booklet single | 2014 | Litho | LM | 9.2 horiz |
| 2424c | **$1.25 Canada geese**, s/s single | 2011 | Litho | LM | 13.4x13.1 |
| 2428 | **$1.25 Canada geese**, coil | 2011 | Litho | LM | 8.2 horiz |
| 2431 | **$1.25 Canada geese**, booklet single | 2011 | Litho | LM | 9.2 horiz |
| 2504c | **$1.29 Loons**, s/s single | 2012 | Litho | LM | 13.4x13.1 |
| 2508 | **$1.29 Loons**, coil | 2012 | Litho | LM | 8.2 horiz |
| 2511 | **$1.29 Loons**, booklet single | 2012 | Litho | LM | 9.2 horiz |
| 2602c | **$1.34 Fawn**, s/s single | 2013 | Litho | LM | 13.4x13.1 |
| 2606 | **$1.34 Fawn**, coil | 2013 | Litho | LM | 8.2 horiz |
| 2609 | **$1.34 Fawn**, booklet single | 2013 | Litho | LM | 9.2 horiz |
| 2424d | **$1.75 Polar bear**, s/s single | 2011 | Litho | LM | 13.4x13.1 |
| 2429 | **$1.75 Polar bear**, coil | 2011 | Litho | LM | 8.2 horiz |
| 2432 | **$1.75 Polar bear**, booklet single | 2011 | Litho | LM | 9.2 horiz |
| 2504d | **$1.80 Moose**, s/s single | 2012 | Litho | LM | 13.4x13.1 |
| 2509 | **$1.80 Moose**, coil | 2012 | Litho | LM | 8.2 horiz |
| 2512 | **$1.80 Moose**, booklet single | 2012 | Litho | LM | 9.2 horiz |
| 2709d | **$1.80 Puffin**, s/s single | 2014 | Litho | LM | 13.4x13.1 |
| 2713 | **$1.80 Puffin**, coil | 2014 | Litho | LM | 8.2 horiz |
| 2716 | **$1.80 Puffin**, booklet single | 2014 | Litho | LM | 9.2 horiz |
| 2602d | **$1.85 Black bear**, s/s single | 2013 | Litho | LM | 13.4x13.1 |
| 2607 | **$1.85 Black bear**, coil | 2013 | Litho | LM | 8.2 horiz |
| 2610 | **$1.85 Black bear**, booklet single | 2013 | Litho | LM | 9.2 horiz |
| 2709e | **$2.50 Wapiti**, s/s single | 2014 | Litho | LM | 13.4x13.1 |
| 2714 | **$2.50 Wapiti**, coil | 2014 | Litho | LM | 8.2 horiz |
| 2717 | **$2.50 Wapiti**, booklet single | 2014 | Litho | LM | 9.2 horiz |

## QUEEN ELIZABETH II: 2016

| | | Issued | Method | Printer | Perf |
|---|---|---|---|---|---|
| 2888 | P **multicoloured** | 2016 | Litho | LM | 13.4x13.7 |

## CANADIAN PRIDE: 2013

| | | Issued | Method | Printer | Perf |
|---|---|---|---|---|---|
| 2611a | **chairs on dock**, s/s single | 2013 | Litho | CBN | 13.0x13.4 |
| 2612 | **chairs on dock**, booklet single | 2013 | Litho | CBN | 13.4 |
| a | with repeating 'Canada' underprint | 2013 | Litho | CBN | 13.4 |
| 2693 | **63¢ chairs on dock**, booklet single | 2013 | Litho | CBN | 13.4 |
| 2611b | **hay bale**, s/s single | 2013 | Litho | CBN | 13.0x13.4 |
| 2613 | **hay bale**, booklet single | 2013 | Litho | CBN | 13.4 |
| a | with repeating 'Canada' underprint | 2013 | Litho | CBN | 13.4 |
| 2694 | **63¢ hay bale**, booklet single | 2013 | Litho | CBN | 13.4 |
| 2611c | **sailboat**, s/s single | 2013 | Litho | CBN | 13.0x13.4 |
| 2614 | **sailboat**, booklet single | 2013 | Litho | CBN | 13.4 |
| a | with repeating 'Canada' underprint | 2013 | Litho | CBN | 13.4 |
| 2695 | **63¢ sailboat**, booklet single | 2013 | Litho | CBN | 13.4 |
| 2611d | **'living flag'**, s/s single | 2013 | Litho | CBN | 13.0x13.4 |
| 2615 | **'living flag'**, booklet single | 2013 | Litho | CBN | 13.4 |
| a | with repeating 'Canada' underprint | 2013 | Litho | CBN | 13.4 |
| 2696 | **63¢ 'living flag'**, booklet single | 2013 | Litho | CBN | 13.4 |
| 2611e | **fishing hut**, s/s single | 2013 | Litho | CBN | 13.0x13.4 |
| 2616 | **fishing hut**, booklet single | 2013 | Litho | CBN | 13.4 |
| a | with repeating 'Canada' underprint | 2013 | Litho | CBN | 13.4 |
| 2697 | **63¢ fishing hut**, booklet single | 2013 | Litho | CBN | 13.4 |

## UNESCO WORLD HERITAGE SITES: 2014–2017

| | | Issued | Method | Printer | Perf |
|---|---|---|---|---|---|
| 2718a | **Gros Morne**, s/s single | 2014 | Litho | CBN | 13.3x13.0 |
| 2719 | **Gros Morne**, booklet single | 2014 | Litho | CBN | 13.4 |
| 2718b | **Joggins**, s/s single | 2014 | Litho | CBN | 13.3x13.0 |
| 2721 | **Joggins**, booklet single | 2014 | Litho | CBN | 13.4 |
| 2718c | **Rocky mtns**, s/s single | 2014 | Litho | CBN | 13.3x13.0 |
| 2723 | **Rocky mtns**, booklet single | 2014 | Litho | CBN | 13.4 |
| 2718d | **Nahanni**, s/s single | 2014 | Litho | CBN | 13.3x13.0 |
| 2720 | **Nahanni**, booklet single | 2014 | Litho | CBN | 13.4 |
| 2718e | **Miguasha**, s/s single | 2014 | Litho | CBN | 13.3x13.0 |
| 2722 | **Miguasha**, booklet single | 2014 | Litho | CBN | 13.4 |
| 2889a | **Grand Pré**, s/s single | 2016 | Litho | LM | 13.3x13.0 |
| 2890 | **Grand Pré**, booklet single | 2016 | Litho | LM | 13.8x13.6 |
| 2889b | **Rideau Canal**, s/s single | 2016 | Litho | LM | 13.3x13.0 |
| 2893 | **Rideau Canal**, booklet single | 2016 | Litho | LM | 13.8x13.6 |
| 2889c | **Sgang Gwaay**, s/s single | 2016 | Litho | LM | 13.3x13.0 |
| 2891 | **Sgang Gwaay**, booklet single | 2016 | Litho | LM | 13.8x13.6 |
| 2889d | **Buffalo Jump**, s/s single | 2016 | Litho | LM | 13.3x13.0 |
| 2894 | **Buffalo Jump**, booklet single | 2016 | Litho | LM | 13.8x13.6 |
| 2889e | **Lunenburg**, s/s single | 2016 | Litho | LM | 13.3x13.0 |
| 2892 | **Lunenburg**, booklet single | 2016 | Litho | LM | 13.8x13.6 |
| 2963a | **Dinosaur Park**, s/s single | 2017 | Litho | CBN | 13.4x13.0 |
| 2964 | **Dinosaur Park**, booklet single | 2017 | Litho | CBN | 13.0 |
| 2963b | **Mistaken Point**, s/s single | 2017 | Litho | CBN | 13.4x13.0 |
| 2967 | **Mistaken Point**, booklet single | 2017 | Litho | CBN | 13.0 |
| 2963c | **Old Québec**, s/s single | 2017 | Litho | CBN | 13.4x13.0 |
| 2965 | **Old Québec**, booklet single | 2017 | Litho | CBN | 13.0 |
| 2963d | **L'Anse aux Meadows**, s/s single | 2017 | Litho | CBN | 13.4x13.0 |
| 2968 | **L'Anse aux Meadows**, bklt single | 2017 | Litho | CBN | 13.0 |
| 2963e | **Red Bay Basque**, s/s single | 2017 | Litho | CBN | 13.4x13.0 |
| 2966 | **Red Bay Basque**, booklet single | 2017 | Litho | CBN | 13.0 |

## FROM FAR and WIDE

| | | Issued | Method | Printer | Perf |
|---|---|---|---|---|---|
| 3056a | **St. John's**, s/s single | 2018 | Litho | LM | 13.4x13.0 |
| 3057 | **St. John's**, 5,000 coil | 2018 | Litho | LM | 9.2 horiz |
| 3062 | **St. John's**, coil | 2018 | Litho | LM | 8.2 horiz |
| 3071 | **St. John's**, booklet single | 2018 | Litho | LM | 13.8x13.6 |
| 3056b | **Hopewell Rocks**, s/s single | 2018 | Litho | LM | 13.4x13.0 |
| 3058 | **Hopewell Rocks**, 5,000 coil | 2018 | Litho | LM | 9.2 horiz |
| 3063 | **Hopewell Rocks**, coil | 2018 | Litho | LM | 8.2 horiz |
| 3074 | **Hopewell Rocks**, booklet single | 2018 | Litho | LM | 13.8x13.6 |
| 3056c | **MacMillan Park**, s/s single | 2018 | Litho | LM | 13.4x13.0 |
| 3059 | **MacMillan Park**, 5,000 coil | 2018 | Litho | LM | 9.2 horiz |
| 3064 | **MacMillan Park**, coil | 2018 | Litho | LM | 8.2 horiz |
| 3072 | **MacMillan Park**, booklet single | 2018 | Litho | LM | 13.8x13.6 |
| 3056d | **PEI Park**, s/s single | 2018 | Litho | LM | 13.4x13.0 |
| 3061 | **PEI Park**, 5,000 coil | 2018 | Litho | LM | 9.2 horiz |
| 3066 | **PEI Park**, coil | 2018 | Litho | LM | 8.2 horiz |
| 3073 | **PEI Park**, booklet single | 2018 | Litho | LM | 13.8x13.6 |
| 3056e | **Rocher-Percé Park**, s/s single | 2018 | Litho | LM | 13.4x13.0 |
| 3060 | **Rocher-Percé Park**, 5,000 coil | 2018 | Litho | LM | 9.2 horiz |
| 3065 | **Rocher-Percé Park**, coil | 2018 | Litho | LM | 8.2 horiz |
| 3075 | **Rocher-Percé Park**, bklt single | 2018 | Litho | LM | 13.8x13.6 |
| 3056f | **$1.00 Pisew Falls**, s/s single | 2018 | Litho | LM | 13.4x13.0 |
| 3070 | **$1.00 Pisew Falls**, coil | 2018 | Litho | LM | 13.5 |
| 3056g | **$1.20 Point Pelee Park**, s/s single | 2018 | Litho | LM | 13.4x13.0 |
| 3067 | **$1.20 Point Pelee Park**, coil | 2018 | Litho | LM | 8.2 horiz |
| 3076 | **$1.20 Point Pelee Park**, bklt single | 2018 | Litho | LM | 9.2 horiz |
| 3056h | **$1.80 Náátsʼįhchʼoh Park**, s/s single | 2018 | Litho | LM | 13.4x13.0 |
| 3068 | **$1.80 Náátsʼįhchʼoh Park**, coil | 2018 | Litho | LM | 8.2 horiz |
| 3077 | **$1.80 Náátsʼįhchʼoh Park**, bklt single | 2018 | Litho | LM | 9.2 horiz |
| 3056i | **$2.50 Arctic Bay**, s/s single | 2018 | Litho | LM | 13.4x13.0 |
| 3069 | **$2.50 Arctic Bay**, coil | 2018 | Litho | LM | 8.2 horiz |
| 3078 | **$2.50 Arctic Bay**, booklet single | 2018 | Litho | LM | 9.2 horiz |

# NUMBER CHANGES / ADDITIONS

## New numbers assigned by Scott

| Canada | |
|---|---|
| New Scott # | Was Unitrade # |
| 338b | 338aii |
| 760b | 760ai |
| 1181c | 1181iii |
| 1341b | 1341i |
| 1357b | 1357i |
| 1679c | — |
| 2070c | 2070ii |
| 2206c | 2206ii |
| 2710b | 2710ii |

| Newfoundland | |
|---|---|
| New Scott # | Was Unitrade # |
| 234j | 234viii |
| 248b | 248iii |

## New Unitrade numbers

146i
463pviii
590xxi
766aii
1167di
1394ii
1395vi
1395vii
2052ii
2188aii
BK340i
CL21ai
CL21bii

Newfoundland:
BK2a

Newfoundland:
15iii

New paper fluorescence varieties:

1394iii
1394iv

## Unitrade number changes

Over the course of editing the Unitrade catalogue, various catalogue numbers may have been found to be inconsistent. These have been changed for better clarification.

1164aii has been changed to 1164di

## Unitrade description changes

The following listings have had a "significant" change in their description.

**195d** "flat plate printing" changed to "rotary press, dry printing"

## Unitrade numbers deleted

New Brunswick
7iii not known to exist

### Index to Advertisers

Arpin Philately Inc., 4
Canada Stamp Finder, 33
Century Stamp Co. Ltd, 8
City Stamp Montreal, 5
CK Stamps, 34
Davo (Unitrade), 589
Deveney Stamps, 12
Hugo Deshaye (Philatelist) Inc., 9
Eastern Auctions, 705
F.v.H. Stamps, 12
Greenwood Stamp Company, 31
Longley Auctions, 663
Gary J. Lyon (Philatelist) Ltd., 38
R. Maresch & Son, 36, 37
Medallion Stamps, 563
Rousseau Stamps and Coins, 10
Roy's Stamps, 4
Saskatoon Stamp Centre, 11
Sparks Auctions, 35
TPM, 6, 7
Unitrade Associates, 32 (Harris album), 33 (Deluxe mint sheet album), 34 (stockbooks), 589 (Davo), 589 (block stockbooks), 621 (stockbooks), 667 (S mounts), 668, 674 (Flexo-grip), 675, 676 (G mounts)
E.S.J. van Dam Ltd., 601
Vance Auctions Ltd., 9
Weeda Stamps Ltd., 590

# Symbols and Abbreviations

To conserve space, many symbols and abbreviations are used throughout the catalogue.
Those with which the reader may not be familiar are listed here.

| | |
|---|---|
| ✉ | single stamp on cover |
| ★ | single mint |
| ⊙ | single used |
| *EP* | 'every pane' (constant variety appears on *every* pane of noted plate/cylinder) |
| [Permanent symbol] | Permanent™ (domestic rate face value of stamp) |
| — | not known in the grade indicated |
| ABN | American Bank Note Company |
| AD | Avery Dennison Canada Inc., printer |
| AP | Ashton-Potter Ltd. |
| APC | Ashton-Potter Canada Ltd. |
| BAB | BA Banknote |
| BABN | British American Bank Note Company |
| BK | booklet (number) |
| bklt. | booklet |
| blk. | block |
| BP | booklet pane |
| BPO | British Post Office |
| CBN | Canadian Bank Note Company |
| CPC | Canada Post Corporation |
| CP | coated paper |
| (D) | diagonal specimen overprint |
| DEX | dextrine gum |
| DF | dull fluorescence (uncoated, non-fluorescent paper) |
| ERD | earliest recorded date |
| F | fluorescent paper |
| FCP | Fluorescent-coated paper (instead of tagging) |
| FDC | First Day Cover |
| FK | fluorescent ink |
| /fl | flecked paper (fluorescent fibres) |
| G | good condition (grade) |
| GT | General (Ottawa) Tagging |
| GT2 | General Tagging on two opposite edges |
| GT3 | General Tagging on two opposite edges with one parallel bar through the middle of stamp |
| GT4 | General Tagging along all edges of stamp |
| GTX | Special General Tagging for the 'Greet-More' Christmas stamps: tagging on all white areas except within the illustration |
| (H) | horizontal specimen overprint |
| HB | hibrite paper |
| HF | high fluorescence |
| imperf. | imperforate(d) |
| L | left (pane, etc.) |
| LC | lower centre (pane, etc.) |
| LF | low fluorescence |
| LL | lower left |
| LM | Leigh-Mardon Pty Ltd. (Australia) |
| LR | lower right |
| LMG | The Lowe–Martin Group |
| med. | medium |
| MF | medium fluorescence |
| NF | no fluorescence (dead) (coated, non-fluorescent paper) |
| NH | never-hinged mint stamp |
| NH% | premium for NH mint stamp |
| OFDC | Official First Day Cover |
| O.G. | original gum |
| OP2 | General tagging (stable) |
| OP4 | General tagging (migratory) used only by BABN prior to October 1972 |
| ovpt | overprint(ed) |
| P | Proof |
| PB | plate or inscription block |
| PE | number of perforated edges |
| perf. | perforated, perforations |
| PL | uncoated non-fluorescent paper (also DF) |
| Pl. | plate |
| pos. | position |
| ptg. | printing |
| PVA | polyvinyl alcohol gum |
| R | right (pane, etc.) |
| RF | rarity factor |
| Sc. | Scott (number) |
| s/a | self-adhesive |
| s/e | straight edge |
| SF | speckled fluorescence (see /fl ) |
| TC | Trial Colour Proof |
| TI | tab inscription |
| UN | untagged |
| UC | upper centre |
| UL | upper left |
| UPU | Universal Postal Union |
| UR | upper right |
| (V) | vertical specimen overprint |
| w/gum | with original gum |
| w/o gum | without gum (as issued) |
| wag | water-activated gum |
| wmk. | watermark |
| wmkd. | watermarked |
| W1B | Winnipeg 1-bar tagging |
| W2B | Winnipeg 2-bar tagging |
| WCB | Winnipeg centre-bar tagging |
| Wpg. | Winnipeg |

**Calendar Notations**

Dates are shown in Month, Day, Year sequence whether spelled out or represented by digital notation (MM/DD/YY)

Hence: 01/30/89 can represent
January 30, 1889
OR
January 30, 1989.

Also: 01/—/89 can represent
January, 1889
OR
January, 1989.

**Quantity Notations**

The Roman numeral M is used to represent one thousand times the quantity indicated.

Hence: 5M is the same as 5,000
and: 5MM is the same as 5,000,000

**Paper Manufacturers**

| | |
|---|---|
| APP | Abitibi-Price Inc. paper |
| AVP | Avery paper |
| CLP | Clark paper |
| CP/FP | Coated Papers/Fasson paper |
| CPP | Coated Papers Limited paper |
| FP | Fasson Canada Inc. paper |
| HP | Harrison and Sons Inc. paper (greenish gum) |
| JAC | JAC Paper |
| PP | Peterborough Paper Converters Inc. paper (greenish gum) |
| RP | Rolland paper (white gum) |
| SP | Slater paper (cream-coloured gum) |
| S/FP | Slater/Fasson paper (coated paper) |
| SR | Spicer paper |
| TRC | Tullis Russell Coatings (coated paper) |